LITERARY MARKET PLACE™

LMP
2022

WITHDRAWN

FROM COLLECTION

Literary Market Place™
82nd Edition

Publisher
Thomas H. Hogan

Senior Director, ITI Reference Group
Owen O'Donnell

Managing Editor
Karen Hallard

Assistant Editor
Karen DiDario

Tampa Operations:

Manager, Tampa Editorial Operations
Debra James

Project Coordinator, Tampa Editorial
Carolyn Victor

Graphics & Production:

Production Manager
Tiffany Chamenko

Production
Dana Stevenson
Jackie Crawford

LITERARY MARKET PLACE™

LMP 2022

THE DIRECTORY OF THE AMERICAN BOOK PUBLISHING INDUSTRY WITH INDUSTRY INDEXES

Volume

Published by

Information Today, Inc.
143 Old Marlton Pike
Medford, NJ 08055-8750
Phone: (609) 654-6266
Fax: (609) 654-4309
E-mail (Orders): custserv@infotoday.com
Web site: www.infotoday.com

ISSN 0000-1155
ISBN 978-1-57387-576-9 (set)
Library of Congress Catalog Card Number 41-51571

Information Today, Inc.
143 Old Marlton Pike
Medford, NJ 08055-8750
Phone: 800-300-9868 (Customer Service)
              800-409-4929 (Editorial)
Fax: 609-654-4309
E-mail (orders): custserv@infotoday.com
Web Site: www.infotoday.com

Printed in the United States of America

US $469.50
ISBN 13:978-1-57387-576-9

CONTENTS

VOLUME 2

ADVERTISING, MARKETING & PUBLICITY

BOOK MANUFACTURING

SALES & DISTRIBUTION

SERVICES & SUPPLIERS

INDEXES

Preface

The 2022 edition marks the 82nd annual publication of *Literary Market Place*™—the leading directory of the American and Canadian book publishing industry. Covering publishers and literary agents to manufacturers and shipping services, *LMP* is the most comprehensive directory of its kind. The revised 2022 edition contains almost 8,000 entries. Of these listings 2,158 are publishers—including Canadian houses and small presses. Together with its companion publication, *International Literary Market Place*™, these directories cover the global book publishing industry.

Organization & Content
Volume 1 covers core publishing industry information: Book Publishers; Editorial Services and Agents; Associations, Events, Courses and Awards; and Books and Magazines for the Trade.

Volume 2 contains information on service providers and suppliers to the publishing industry. Advertising, Marketing and Publicity; Book Manufacturing; Sales and Distribution; and Services and Suppliers can be found in this volume.

Entries generally contain name, address, telephone and other telecommunications data, key personnel, company reportage, branch offices, brief statistics and descriptive annotations. Where applicable, Standard Address Numbers (SANs) have been included. SANs are unique numbers assigned to the addresses of publishers, wholesalers and booksellers. Publishers' entries also contain their assigned ISBN prefixes. Both the SAN and ISBN systems are administered by R.R. Bowker LLC.

Indexes
In addition to the numerous section-specific indexes appearing throughout, each volume of *LMP* contains four indexes that reference listings appearing in that volume. The Industry Indexes cover two distinct areas of data: a Company Index that includes the name, address, communications information and page reference for company listings and a separate Personnel Index that includes the main personnel associated with each entry as well as the page reference. Other indexes include the Index to Sections for quickly finding specific categories of information and the Index to Advertisers.

A Note to Authors
Prospective authors seeking a publisher should be aware that there are publishers who, as a condition for publishing and marketing an individual's work, may require a significant sum of money be paid to the publisher. This practice is known by a number of terms including author subsidized publishing, author investment, and co-operative publishing. Before entering an agreement involving such a payment, the author is advised to make a careful investigation to determine the standing of the publisher's imprint in the industry.

Similarly, authors seeking literary representation are advised that some agents request a nominal reading fee that may be applied to the agent's commission upon representation. Other agencies may charge substantially higher fees which may not be applicable to a future commission and which are not refundable. The recommended course is to first send a query letter with an outline, sample chapter, and a self-addressed stamped envelope (SASE). Should an agent express interest in handling the manuscript, full details of fees and commissions should be obtained in writing before the complete manuscript is sent. Should an agency require significant advance payment from an author, the author is cautioned to make a careful investigation to determine the agency's standing in the industry before entering an agreement. The author should always retain a copy of the manuscript in his or her possession.

Occasionally, the editors of *LMP* will receive complaints against publishers or agents listed in the work. If, after investigation and review, the editors determine that the complaints are significant and justified, we may exclude the company or individual in question. However, the absence of a listing in *LMP* for any particular publisher or agent should not be construed as a judgment on the legitimacy or integrity of that organization or individual.

Compilation
LMP is updated throughout the year via a number of methods. A request for updated information is sent to current entrants to corroborate and update the information contained on our database. All updates received are edited for the next product release. Those entrants who do not respond to our request may be verified through telephone interviews or online research. Entrants who cannot be verified or who fall short of entry criteria are dropped from the current edition.

Information for new listings is gathered in a similar method. Possible new listings are identified through ongoing research, or when a listing request is received either from the organization itself or from a third party. If sufficient information is not initially gathered to create a listing, a data collection form is provided to the organization to submit essential listing information.

Updated information or suggestions for new listings can be submitted by mail to:

Literary Market Place
Information Today, Inc.
121 Chanlon Rd, Suite G-20
New Providence, NJ 07974-2195

An updating method using the Internet is also available for *LMP* listings:

Visit the *Literary Market Place* web site to update an *LMP* listing. **Literarymarketplace.com** allows you the opportunity to provide new information for a listing by clicking on the "Update or Correct Your Entry" option. The Feedback option on the home page of the web site can be used to suggest new entries as well.

Related Services

Literary Market Place, along with its companion volume *International Literary Market Place*, is available through the Internet at **www.literarymarketplace.com**. Designed to give users simple, logical access to the information they require, the site offers users the choice of searching for data alphabetically, geographically, by type, or by subject. Continuously updated by Information Today's team of editors, this is a truly enhanced version of the *LMP* and *ILMP* databases, incorporating features that make "must-have" information easily available.

Arrangements for placing advertisements in *LMP* can be coordinated through Lauri Rimler by telephone at 800-409-4929 (press 1) or 908-219-0088, or by e-mail at lwrimler@infotoday.com.

Your feedback is important to us. We strongly encourage you to contact us with suggestions or comments on the print edition of *LMP*, or its web site. Our editorial office can be reached by telephone at 800-409-4929 (press 3) or 908-219-0277, or by e-mail at khallard@infotoday.com.

The editors would like to thank those entrants who took the time to respond to our requests for current information.

Abbreviations & Acronyms

The following is a list of acronyms & abbreviations used throughout *LMP*.

AALA - Association of American Literary Agents
AB - Alberta
Acct(s) - Account(s)
Acctg - Accounting
Acq(s) - Acquisition(s)
Ad - Advertising
Admin - Administrative, Administration, Administrator
Aff - Affairs
AK - Alaska
AL - Alabama
appt - appointment
Apt - Apartment
AR - Arkansas
Assoc - Associate
Asst - Assistant
AV - Audiovisual
Ave - Avenue
AZ - Arizona

B&W - Black & White
BC - British Columbia
Bd - Board
bio - biography
BISAC - Book Industry Standards and Communications
Bldg - Building
Blvd - Boulevard
Br - Branch
Busn - Business

CA - California
CEO - Chief Executive Officer
CFO - Chief Financial Officer
Chmn - Chairman
Chpn - Chairperson
CIO - Chief Information Officer
Circ - Circulation
CN - Canada
CO - Colorado
Co(s) - Company(-ies)
Co-edns - Co-editions
Coll(s) - College(s)
Comm - Committee
Commun(s) - Communication(s)
Comp - Compiler
Compt - Comptroller
Cont - Controller
Contrib - Contributing
COO - Chief Operating Officer
Coord - Coordinator
Corp - Corporate, Corporation
Coun - Counsel
CT - Connecticut
Ct - Court
CTO - Chief Technical / Technology Officer

Ctr - Center
Curr - Current
Cust - Customer
CZ - Canal Zone

DC - District of Columbia
DE - Delaware
Dept - Department
Devt - Development
Dir(s) - Director(s)
Dist - Distributed, Distribution, Distributor
Div - Division
Dom - Domestic
Dr - Drive

ed - edition
Ed(s) - Editor(s)
Edit - Editorial
Educ - Education, Educational
El-hi - Elementary-High School
Elem - Elementary
Ency - Encyclopedia
Eng - English
Engg - Engineering
Engr - Engineer
Equip - Equipment
ESL - English as a Second Language
Est - Established
EVP - Executive Vice President
exc - except
Exec - Executive
Expwy - Expressway
ext - extension

Fed - Federal
Fin - Finance, Financial
fl - floor
FL - Florida
Freq - Frequency
Fwy - Freeway

GA - Georgia
Gen - General
Govt - Government
GU - Guam

HD - High-definition
HI - Hawaii
HR - Human Resources
HS - High School
Hwy - Highway

IA - Iowa
ID - Idaho
IL - Illinois
Illus - Illustrator
IN - Indiana
Inc - Incorporated

indiv(s) - individual(s)
Indus - Industrial, Industry
Info - Information
Instl - Institutional
Instn(s) - Institution(s)
Instrl - Instructional
Intl - International
ISBN - International Standard Book Number
ISSN - International Standard Serial Number
IT - Information Technology

Jr - Junior
Jt - Joint
Juv - Juvenile

K - Kindergarten
KS - Kansas
KY - Kentucky

LA - Louisiana
Lang(s) - Language(s)
Lib(s) - Library(-ies)
Libn - Librarian
Lit - Literature

MA - Massachusetts
MB - Manitoba
MD - Maryland
Mdse - Merchandise
Mdsg - Merchandising
ME - Maine
Med - Medical
memb(s) - member(s)
Metro - Metropolitan
Mfg - Manufacturing
Mgmt - Management
Mgr - Manager
MI - Michigan
Mkt(s) - Market(s)
Mktg - Marketing
MN - Minnesota
Mng - Managing
MO - Missouri
mo - month
MS - Mississippi
ms(s) - manuscript(s)
MT - Montana

Natl - National
NB - New Brunswick
NC - North Carolina
ND - North Dakota
NE - Nebraska
NH - New Hampshire
NJ - New Jersey
NL - Newfoundland and Labrador
NM - New Mexico
No - Number

NS - Nova Scotia
NT - Northwest Territories
NU - Nunavut
NV - Nevada
NY - New York

Off(s) - Office(s)
Offr - Officer
OH - Ohio
OK - Oklahoma
ON - Ontario
Oper(s) - Operation(s)
OR - Oregon

PA - Pennsylvania
Pbk(s) - Paperback(s)
PE - Prince Edward Island
Perms - Permissions
Photo - Photograph
Photog - Photographer, Photography
Pkwy - Parkway
pp - pages
PR - Public Relations
PR - Puerto Rico
Pres - President
Proc - Processing
Prod(s) - Product(s)
Prodn - Production
Prodr - Producer
Prof - Professional, Professor
Prog(s) - Program(s)
Proj(s) - Project(s)
Promo(s) - Promotion(s)
Prop - Proprietor
Pub Aff - Public Affairs

Publg - Publishing
Publr - Publisher
Pubn(s) - Publication(s)
Purch - Purchasing

QC - Quebec

R&D - Research & Development
Rd - Road
Ref - Reference
Reg - Region
Regl - Regional
Rel - Relations
Rep(s) - Representative(s)
Res - Research
RI - Rhode Island
Rm - Room
Rte - Route
Rts - Rights

SAN - Standard Address Number
SASE - Self-Addressed Stamped Envelope
SC - South Carolina
Sci - Science
SD - South Dakota
Secy - Secretary
Serv(s) - Service(s)
SK - Saskatchewan
Soc - Social, Sociology
Spec - Special
Sq - Square
Sr - Senior
St - Saint, Street
Sta - Station
Ste - Sainte

Subn(s) - Subscription(s)
Subs - Subsidiary
Supv - Supervisor
SVP - Senior Vice President
Synd - Syndicated, Syndication

Tech - Technical
Technol - Technology
Tel - Telephone
Terr - Terrace
TN - Tennessee
Tpke - Turnpike
Treas - Treasurer
TX - Texas

UK - United Kingdom
Univ - University
unsol - unsolicited
UT - Utah

V - Vice
VA - Virginia
VChmn - Vice Chairman
VI - Virgin Islands
vol(s) - volume(s)
VP - Vice President
VT - Vermont

WA - Washington
WI - Wisconsin
WV - West Virginia
WY - Wyoming

yr - year
YT - Yukon Territory

Advertising, Marketing & Publicity

Advertising Agencies

Listed here are the principal agencies for book industry advertising.

Accurate Writing & More
16 Barstow Lane, Hadley, MA 01035
Tel: 413-586-2388
Web Site: frugalmarketing.com
Key Personnel
Owner & Dir: Shel Horowitz *E-mail:* shel@
principledprofit.com
Dir: Dina Friedman
Founded: 1981
Copywriting of book covers, print & radio
ads, direct mail pieces, press releases, fliers,
brochures, catalog & web page copy, newsletters, other promotional materials. Marketing
strategy development emphasizing low cost,
high return strategies.
Book Publishing Account(s): All Books; Arts &
Farces; Asalako Press; Author House; Autodidactic Press; AWM Books; Bialkin Books;
BJB Publishing; bookbrowse.com; Construction Trades Press; CS Publishing; Dr Ivan Delman; Emerald Wave; Enterprise Publishing;
Equestrian Press; Equilibrium Press; Firstbooks; ForeWord Magazine; Freedom Publishing; Golden Healing Publishing; Gropen
Associates; Gwent Press; Hope Springs Press;
Humble Press; Images from the Past; Inmark
Associates; Kitchen Cupboard Press; Liam
Works; Life Words; Love Gifts Publishing;
Marketing Sherpa; Mindfulness Press; Nehemia
& Solomon; Persolog GmbH; Pineapplesoft;
Prism Publishing; sitesell.com; Six Strings
Press; Space Link Books; United Graphics;
Walking Tree Press; John Wiley & Sons;
WordMate
Magazine Account(s): Cooperative Life; Related
Matters
Other Account(s): adjunction.com; Asian Arts &
Antiques; Bart's Homemade; Blue Ridge Office
Products; The Body Works; Cate Cummings
Book Publicist; Dependable Business Alternatives; Energy Management Consultants; FinancialPlanningforNurses.com; 1stBooks.com; Dr
Dan Garfield; Gray Panthers of Brooklyn; Image Marketing; Independent Consultants Network; The Informer; Jones Town & Country
Realty; Lorna Kepes; MASSAID; Dr Jonathan
Miller; M2 Presswire.net; Naturally First; People Speak; prowebguide.com; Quest Group;
Radwell Communications; Ragan Communications; Real Estate Org.com; Rhode Island
Folk Music Society; Tom Russell & Associates; Roger Salloom; The Tea House; Hollis
Thomases Publicist; Turning Tide Productions;
U Mass Family Business Center; Union Car
Wash; White Lotus Home
Membership(s): Connecticut Authors & Publishers Association; Independent Book Publishers
Association (IBPA); Independent Publishers of
New England (IPNE); National Writers Union
(NWU); Western New England Editorial Freelancers Network

Backe Communications
Radnor Corporate Ctr, Bldg 3, Suite 101, 100
Matson Ford Rd, Radnor, PA 19087
Tel: 610-947-6900
Web Site: www.backemarketing.com
Key Personnel
Pres & CEO: John E Backe *Tel:* 610-947-6900
ext 6901 *E-mail:* jebacke@backemarketing.com
SVP, Client Servs & Strategy: Malcolm Brown
Tel: 610-947-6900 ext 6904
Full service agency serving the advertising, public
relations & corporate communications needs of
clients in publishing, healthcare, pharmaceutical, education, high-tech, travel, insurance &
other fields. Services include direct mail programs from concept development through list
purchases & printing, college adoption programs, journal ads & outserts, complete campaigns & publicity.
Book Publishing Account(s): Dorchester Publishing; McGraw-Hill; Turner White Communications; John Wiley & Sons Inc
Magazine Account(s): Philadelphia Magazine
Other Account(s): Aegis Therapies (Beverly
Enterprises); Airgas; Amplifier Research
Corp; Alfred Angelo; Arcadia University;
Avalon Carpet Tile and Flooring; Berwick Offray LLC; The Bryn Mawr Trust Company;
C&D Technologies; Harriet Carter; Charming Shoppes/Fashion Bug; Christiana Care
Health System; Civil War Trust; M Cohen &
Sons; Comcast; Community Energy; Conrail;
Crozer-Keystone Health System; CSS Industries Inc; CVM Engineers; DIA-Drug Information Association; EMC Technology Inc; Eureka Educational Products; Exelon Enterprises;
Five Below; Fresh Finds; Gesu School; GlaxoSmithKline; Gloucester County; Haverford
Trust; Hill's Main Line Seafood; Independence
Visitor Center; Industry Sales Tax Solutions;
The Iron Shop; Johnson & Johnson; KidsPeace;
The Kirschner Center; Luggage Online; Lutron;
Montgomery County Community College; New
Wind Energy; Norfolk Southern Corp; Novartis; Omnicare CR; PECO; Peirce-Phelps Viking
Culinary Arts Center; Pennsylvania College of
Optometry; Philadelphia Zoo; Pizza Hut; The
PMA Insurance Group; PNC Asset Management; Portescap; PQ Corp; Robinson Luggage;
Rossi Shoe Service; SCA Personal Care; SCP
Private Equity Partners; SunGard Data Systems; Susquehanna International Group LLP;
TEMEX; Tredegar Performance Films; Triton
PCS/SunCom; University of New Haven; Wissahickon Mountain Spring Water; Wyeth

Ted Barkus Co Inc
8017 Anderson St, Philadelphia, PA 19118
Key Personnel
Pres: Allen E Barkus *E-mail:* a.barkus-tbc@att.
net
Founded: 1958
Advertising & promotion, public relations.
Magazine Account(s): Travelore Report
Other Account(s): Amana; Bulova; Eureka;
Toshiba; Unilever

Benoit & Associates
744 Stockton Heights Ct, Bourbonnais, IL 60914
Tel: 815-932-2582 *Fax:* 815-932-2594
Web Site: www.benoit-associates.com
Key Personnel
Pres: Michael J Benoit *E-mail:* mbenoit@benoit-
associates.com
Full service design & advertising studio. Specialize in technical & color airbrush illustration &
computer generated art (Mac & IBM) design,
art direction, in-house photography, elementary
through college textbook cover & newsletters,
brochures, letterheads & annual reports. High
volume, high quality, quick turnaround & satisfaction guaranteed.

Blitz Media-Direct
Subsidiary of The Linick Group Inc
Linick Bldg, 7 Putter Lane, Middle Island, NY
11953
Mailing Address: PO Box 102, Middle Island,
NY 11953-0102
Tel: 631-924-3888; 631-924-8555; 630-604-8599
E-mail: blitz4pr@gmail.com; linickgroup@gmail.
com
Key Personnel
Pres: Andrew S Linick, PhD
EVP: Roger Dextor
VP: Gaylen Andrews
Founded: 1969
Full service interactive digital marketing agency
serves publishers, independent presses, authors,
startup enterprises, direct marketing/direct response advertisers; association, club, membership organizations; catalog (consumer &
business-to-business) +/or retail outlets; educational firms, seminars, schools, colleges; financial, bank, insurance, investment; non-financial
services, healthcare, personal service, utilities;
fundraising; office equipment, electronics, publisher/subscription & travel & tourism direct
marketers; moneyback guarantee on consulta-

tion by phone. Provides comprehensive graphic redesign/new web site content development, interactive services with web site marketing makeover advice for first-time authors, self-publishers, professionals & entrepreneurs. Specializes in flash, animation, online advertising/PR, links to top search engines, consulting on a 100% satisfaction guarantee. Free site evaluation marketing checklist (a $250 value) for LMP readers.

Book Publishing Account(s): Epic Publishing; Internet Publishing; Liberty Books; MacLean Authors.com; Millennium Publishing Inc; myKidsdeservebetter.com; Quality Publishing Inc; Vision Quest Publishing; Word Publishing Inc

Magazine Account(s): Body in Motion; Chef's Life; Cross Trainer; Epicurean Traveler & Epicurean.com; Karate International & Fitness; Muscular Development; Original Ninja; Practical Gourmet; Time Magazine; Total Fitness; Travel Agent

Other Account(s): Aloe Products Center; American Express; Book Club for the Martial Arts; chikaradojo.com; Citicorp; Consumer Aid Publishers; Festa Chiropractic/Optilux Wellness Center; garrisonweapons.com; Gourmet Traveler; Huntington Press; joinmagi.com; Lasting Love Productions Inc; Louis Publications Inc; loweapons.com; Modern Bu-Jutsu Inc; National Association of Photo Sellers (NAPS); Okinawan Kobujutsu Kyokai Assn; Dr Craig Rubenstein, DC, DACBN, CCN; The Direct Marketing Mail Order Guild; World Dating Consultants Inc

Branch Office(s)
7 Lincoln Ave, Smithtown, NY 11787

Copywriters' Council of America™ (CCA)
Division of The Linick Group Inc
CCA Bldg, 7 Putter Lane, Middle Island, NY 11953-1920
Mailing Address: PO Box 102, Middle Island, NY 11953-0102
Tel: 631-924-3888; 631-924-8555; 631-604-8599
Key Personnel
Founder: Andrew S Linick, PhD
 E-mail: cca4dmcopy@gmail.com
EVP: Roger Dextor
Art Dir: Barbara Lande
Mktg Dir: Shane Clarke
Edit Dir: Kelly Boyles
35,000+ freelance direct response advertising/marketing copywriters & consultants. Specialize in writing convincing selling copy, layout & design, circulars & more. All types of digital advertising, interactive media, B2B e-mail campaigns, marketing & sales promotion, collateral materials. Phone consultation available, second opinion critique service by mail, media plans & schedules. E-campaigns, TV & telemarketing scripts/infomericals, video news releases/production, mailing lists, printing, ghostwritten articles, online advertising services, keynote speeches & in-house training seminars. Direct mail packages & ads evaluated. Work accepted on a retainer, per project basis; discounts available for multiple assignments. Provides comprehensive graphic redesign/new web site content development, interactive services with web site marketing makeover advice for first-time authors, self-publishers, professionals & entrepreneurs. Specializes in online advertising/PR, links to top search engines, consulting on a 100% satisfaction guarantee. Free site evaluation marketing checklist (a $250 value) for LMP readers.

Book Publishing Account(s): Advertising/Marketing/Sales Promotion Book Club; American Health Institute; American Publishing Co; Colony Publishing Ltd; Culbert Productions of Canada Inc; Epic Publishing; Get Rich Book Club; Millennium Publishing; New Horizon Publishing; New World Press; Safe Harbor

Press; Strategic Innovations International; Time Inc; Warner Publishing

Magazine Account(s): The Affluent Traveler™; Epicurean; Epicurean Traveler & Epicurean.com; Interior Designers; Martial Arts World; Official Karate; The Practical Gourmet®; Prentice-Hall; State University of New York; Time Inc; Total Fitness; Travelscape; Trippin Out; Who's Who in the Martial Arts; Z Publications

Other Account(s): Action Video Inc; Best Publishing Co; Brave Pay TV; British Airways; Deca Aloe Inc; First-time Author's & Publisher's Advisory Advice-Line™; First Time Homebuyers Helpline™; Independent Presses Alliance Ltd; International Gourmet Magazine; Lincoln Savings Bank; Mail-order Entrepreneurs Society; MNC Retail Services Corp; The Mortgage Store of RI; National Association of Photo Sellers (NAPS); National Learning Corp; Newsletter Association of America; Reliable Finance Corp; SamuraiSupply.com; Small Dog Adventures; South River R A L Design; WatchMeDad.com

Branch Office(s)
7 Lincoln Ave, Smithtown, NY 11787
Membership(s): ADA; American Association of Advertising Agencies (4A's); The Imaging Alliance

DJD/Golden Advertising
145 W 28 St, 12th fl, New York, NY 10001
Tel: 212-366-5033 *Fax:* 212-243-5044
E-mail: call@djdgolden.com
Web Site: www.djdgolden.com
Key Personnel
Partner: Marcia Golden *E-mail:* mgolden@djdgolden.com; Dominique Pasqua; Malcolm Petrook; Courtney St Clement
Want to improve sales? Our cost-effective, high response public relations, direct mail & print advertising for campaigns or projects generate business. Just ask our clients. Full service agency with clients nationwide. Also collateral, sales tools, media kits, incentive programs & sales meeting/trade show presentations.
Book Publishing Account(s): Crain Communications Inc; R R Bowker
Magazine Account(s): Business Insurance
Other Account(s): Standard Rate & Data Service

Franklin Advertising Associates Inc
441 Main St, Yarmouth Port, MA 02675
Mailing Address: PO Box 161, Yarmouth Port, MA 02675
Tel: 508-362-7472
E-mail: contact@franklinad.com
Web Site: www.franklinad.com
Key Personnel
Pres: Martin A Summerfield
Founded: 1970
Full service advertising agency.
Book Mfg Account(s): Bound-to-Stay-Bound Books Inc

The Gate Worldwide
71 Fifth Ave, 8th fl, New York, NY 10003
Tel: 212-508-3400 *Fax:* 212-508-3402 (cgi)
E-mail: contact@thegateworldwide.com
Web Site: thegateworldwide.com
Key Personnel
Chief Creative Offr: David Bernstein *Tel:* 212-508-3445 *E-mail:* david.bernstein@thegateworldwide.com
Pres: Beau Fraser *E-mail:* beau.fraser@thegateworldwide.com
Financial advertising.
Book Publishing Account(s): Executive Reports Corp; Parker Publishing Company; Prentice-Hall

Henry Holmes Literary Agent/Book Publicist/Marketing Consultant
Mitchell Heights, Apt 205, 2100 S Main St, Fall River, MA 02724
Tel: 508-672-2258; 508-415-4062 (cell)
Key Personnel
Pres & Literary Agent: Henry Holmes
Book jacket copywriting, copy-editing for advertising, direct-mail copywriting, event promotions/publicity, press kits, press news release, public relations for organizations & nonprofits & speech writing/editing (general), proofreading, substantive editing, ms evaluation & critique & mentoring.

JVW Direct
309 W Hutchinson Ave, Pittsburgh, PA 15218
Key Personnel
Pres: Jay Van Wagenen
Creative agency for publishers in all areas of direct marketing: book clubs, continuity programs, periodicals, professional & reference books, software, video cassettes. Complete range of services available: direct mail & space advertising concepts; e-mails & online ads, broadcast concepts & scripts; finished copy & comp; electronic mechanicals.

Book Publishing Account(s): Boardroom; Bonnier; Bookspan; Conde-Nast; Dennis Publishing; Disney Publishing; Healthy Directions; Hearst Corp; House of White Birches; Meredith Publishing; Oxmoor House; Rapaport Publishing; Scholastic; Martha Stewart Living

Magazine Account(s): Architectural Design; Better Homes & Gardens; Bon Appetit; Chance; Click Magazine; Cross Stitch & Needlework; Do It Yourself; Esquire; Family Fun; Family Life; Florida Travel & Life; Glamour; Golf; Golf Digest; Golf for Women; GQ; Harper's Bazaar; Horticulture; House Beautiful; Lucky; Men's Health; More; New Yorker; Nick Jr; Oprah; Outside; Popular Science; Redbook; Saveur; Scholastic Choice; Science Illustrated; Southern Living; Time International; Traditional Home

Other Account(s): AIG Private Client Group; Colonial Penn; Columbia House; HCI; Healthy Directions; People's Benefit Life Insurance Co; Providian
Membership(s): ECHO Academy of Direct Marketing Arts & Sciences

Julie A Laitin Enterprises Inc
160 West End Ave, Suite 23N, New York, NY 10023
Tel: 917-841-8566
E-mail: info@julielaitin.com
Web Site: www.julielaitin.com
Key Personnel
Pres: Julie A Laitin *E-mail:* jlaitin@julielaitin.com
SVP: Cynthia Amorese
Sr Writer: Ravelle Brickman
Acct Mgr: Martha Hall
Founded: 1982
Full service public relations & marketing. Specialize in healthcare.
Other Account(s): AbelsonTaylor Inc; Closerlook; Flashpoint Medica; HCB Health; MicroMass Communications; Strikeforce; Triple Threat Communications

LK Advertising Agency
Subsidiary of The Linick Group Inc
Linick Bldg, 7 Putter Lane, Middle Island, NY 11953
Mailing Address: PO Box 102, Middle Island, NY 11953-0102
Tel: 631-924-3888; 631-924-8555; 631-604-8599
E-mail: topmarketingadvisor@gmail.com
Web Site: topmarketingadvisor.com

Key Personnel
Pres: Andrew S Linick, PhD
  E-mail: linickgroup@gmail.com
EVP & Mktg Res Mgr: Roger Dextor
Dir, Spec Projs: Barbara Deal
Copy Chief: Kelly Boyles
Full service creative services: Internet & brand development, consulting, advertising, marketing from initial idea & design through complete fulfillment in the areas of consumer, business & trade. Planning, design, copy & production. Complete art, design & graphics. 12-month direct marketing action/business plans; innovative copy, layout & design through production; business/consumer/trade launch packages for all publishers (newsletters, magazines, books); specialize in circulation promotion, club & continuity plans, mail order selling, creative copy for two-step inquiry/lead generation & conversion packages, trial subscriptions, soft & hard offers, printed premiums, bouncebacks & package inserts & more. Interactive e-direct mail campaigns. Provides comprehensive graphic redesign/new web site content development, interactive services with web site marketing makeover advice for first-time authors, self-publishers, professionals & entrepreneurs. Specializes in online advertising/PR, links to top search engines, consulting on a 100% satisfaction guarantee. Free site evaluation marketing checklist (a $250 value) for LMP readers.
Book Publishing Account(s): American Health Institute; Casino Digest; Copywriter's Council of America; Creative Management Resources Inc; Epic Publishing LLC; Gruman Data Systems Inc; International Hair Research Center; Maclean Authors.com; National Learning Corp; New World Press Books.com; Newsletter Communications Corp; Northern Mortgage Funding Inc; Passport International of New York; Pharmco Inc; The Practical Gourmet
Book Mfg Account(s): B P Publishing Inc; Kroma Lithographers; LK Litho
Magazine Account(s): American Karate; The American Traveler; Combat Karate; Epicurean-Traveler.com; Food & Wine; Karate International; Ninja; Official Karate Magazine; The Practical Gourmet; Total Fitness; Travel International
Other Account(s): All Recipes.com; AloeProductsCenter.com; Ambrosia Catering; Casino Digest; Creative Management Resources Inc; The Direct Mail/Mail Order Guild; First-Time Home Buyers Helpline™; Grumman Corp; International Hair Research Center; National Association of Photo Sellers (NAPS); Newsletter Communications Corp; Northern Mortgage Funding Inc; officialkaratemag.com; Passport International of New York; Pharmco Inc; Rand Group Inc; Travel, Tourism, Transportation & Hospitality Advice Line™; whistlekick.com

Mail Order Media & Marketing Inc
5500 Linkside Ct, Suite 2-A, Fuquay Varina, NC 27526-8499
Tel: 203-254-9390 *Fax:* 203-254-3253
E-mail: mailordermedia2000@yahoo.com
Key Personnel
Pres: Toni Menoudakos
Founded: 1987
Media services.
Magazine Account(s): Botanic Choice; Discount Diabetic; Indiana Botanic Gardens
Other Account(s): SunHeat; T&R Distributing

Donya Melanson Associates
5 Bisson Lane, Merrimac, MA 01860
Tel: 978-346-9240 *Fax:* 978-346-8345
E-mail: dmelanson@dmelanson.com
Web Site: www.dmelanson.com
Key Personnel
Principal: Donya Melanson
Corporate communications, graphic design, advertising, image building.
Book Publishing Account(s): Copley Custom Publishing Group; TechMark; US Department of Agriculture (USDA); US Geological Survey (USGS)
Other Account(s): Cambridge College; The Commonwealth of Massachusetts; Federal Geographic Data Committee (FGDC)

Preston Kelly
222 First Ave NE, Minneapolis, MN 55413
Tel: 612-843-4000 *Fax:* 612-843-3900
E-mail: iconicideas@prestonkelly.com
Web Site: prestonkelly.com
Key Personnel
Pres: Chuck Kelly *Tel:* 612-843-3999
  E-mail: chuck@prestonkelly.com
EVP & Creative Dir: Chris Preston
Full service advertising & public relations agency.
Other Account(s): Be The Match; HealthPartners; Mall of America; Minnesota Zoo; Physicians Mutual; Piper Jaffray; Roundy's Supermarkets Inc; STAGG Chili; Taco John's; Valley Fresh; Wipfli CPAs and Consultants; YMCA

Roth Advertising Inc
PO Box 96, Sea Cliff, NY 11579
Tel: 516-674-8603 *Fax:* 516-368-3885
Web Site: www.rothadvertising.com
Key Personnel
Founder: Charles A Roth *E-mail:* charles@rothadvertising.com
Pres: Daniel J Roth *E-mail:* dan@rothadvertising.com
Founded: 1971
An advertising & marketing services agency for book publishers with special emphasis on the trade, institutional & consumer religious markets.
Book Publishing Account(s): Association of Theological Booksellers; Baylor University Press; BlueBridge; Chicken Soup for the Soul; The Christophers; Convivium Press; Fortress Press; HarperOne; New City Press; Orbis Books; Pauline Books & Media; Paulist Press; Westminster John Knox Press
Magazine Account(s): Commonwealth; Harvard Divinity Bulletin; The Tablet Publishing Co Ltd
Other Account(s): Association of Catholic Publishers; Catholic Media Association (CMA)
Membership(s): Association of Catholic Publishers Inc

The Souza Agency Inc
PO Box 128, Annapolis, MD 21401-0128
Tel: 410-573-1300 *Fax:* 410-573-1305
E-mail: info@souza.com
Web Site: www.souza.com
Key Personnel
Founder: Anthony Souza
Mng Dir: Roseanne Souza
Founded: 1982
Strategic spirit solutions, advertising, marketing & publishing.

Tri-Media Integrated Marketing Technologies Inc
1027 Pelham St, Unit 2, Fonthill, ON L0S 1E0, Canada
Mailing Address: 1027 S Pelham Rd, Unit 2, Welland, ON L3C 3E2, Canada
E-mail: think@tri-media.com
Web Site: tri-media.com
Key Personnel
Founder & CEO: Albert Iannantuono
  E-mail: alberti@tri-media.com
Dir, Creative & Strategy: Nader Ashway
  E-mail: nader@tri-media.com
Dir, Sales: Jim Durkee *E-mail:* jimd@tri-media.com
Dir, Solutions Architect: Rob Martinelli
  E-mail: robm@tri-media.com
Founded: 1986
Integrated marketing communications.

Verso Advertising Inc
50 W 17 St, 5th fl, New York, NY 10011
Tel: 212-292-2990 *Fax:* 212-557-2592
Web Site: www.versoadvertising.com
Key Personnel
Pres: Denise Berthiaume
EVP & Mng Dir: Michael Kazan *Tel:* 212-292-2901 *E-mail:* michael@versoadvertising.com
VP & Group Dir: Jennifer Pasanen
Founded: 1989
Full service advertising agency specializing in book publishing.
Book Publishing Account(s): Avon; Basic Books; Berkley Publishing Group; Crown Publishing Group; Da Capo Press; Dutton; Ecco; Egmont USA; Farrar, Straus & Giroux, LLC; Anne Geddes; HarperCollins; HarperCollins Children's Books; HarperOne; HarperPerennial; Henry Holt; Houghton Mifflin Harcourt; It Books; Kensington; Macmillan Children's; William Morrow; W W Norton & Company Inc; Penguin Academic; Penguin Young Readers Group; Public Affairs; Putnam; Readers Digest Books; Riverhead; Thames & Hudson; Tor Books; Vintage/Anchor; Workman; Yale University Press
Other Account(s): AAP; Books for a Better Life; Jerusalem Book Fair

Wunderman
Member of WPP Group
3 Columbus Circle, New York, NY 10019
Tel: 212-941-3000
Web Site: www.wunderman.com
Key Personnel
Pres: Jamie Gallo
Chief Creative Offr: Sami Thessman
Integrated marketing services firm with particular emphasis on customer relationship management; direct mail promotion, strong analytics around managing customer data; deliver Internet services, not only web design but e-business strategies; teleservices & database marketing.
Other Account(s): AARP; AT&T; Burger King®; Chevron Corporation; Citigroup Inc; Claro; Colgate-Palmolive Company; Cox Communications Inc; Diageo; EA; Ford; Jaguar Cars; Kraft Foods Inc; L'Oreal; Land Rover; Lufthansa; Microsoft Corporation; Morgan Stanley; MSN; Nationwide; Natura; Nike Inc; Nintendo®; Nokia; Novartis; Novo Nordisk®; Rogers Communications, Inc; Southern California Edison; Telefonica SA; Time Warner; Xerox

Promotional Printing & Allied Services — Activity Index

Promotional Printing & Allied Services

The following firms are active in the production of promotional material–direct mail pieces, posters, displays, etc. For lists of book compositors, printers and binders, see the sections entitled **Prepress Services** and **Printing, Binding & Book Finishing**.

AP Images
Division of Associated Press (AP)
200 Liberty St, New York, NY 10281
Tel: 212-621-1930 *Fax:* 212-621-1955
E-mail: info@ap.org
Web Site: www.ap.org
News & historical photographs. Assignment photography, domestic & foreign. Digital photo transmission to & from most locations; online photo archive.

appatura™, A Broadridge Company
Division of Broadridge Financial Solutions Inc
65 Challenger Rd, Suite 400, Ridgefield Park, NJ 07660
Tel: 201-508-6000 *Toll Free Tel:* 800-277-2155
E-mail: contactus@appatura.com
Web Site: www.appatura.com
Key Personnel
CEO: Richard Plotka
CIO: Faisal Fareed
Chief Prod Offr: Harsh Choudhary
Chief Strategy Offr: John Closson
Head, Fin: Alpha Diarra
Full services direct marketing company including: desktop publishing/electronic prepress, digital-on-demand print, offset print, automated mailing & literature fulfillment from data to distribution.

Arrow Graphics Inc
PO Box 380291, Cambridge, MA 02238
E-mail: info@arrow1.com
Web Site: www.arrow1.com
Key Personnel
Pres: Alvart Badalian
Sr Graphic/Pubn Designer: Aramais Andonian
Founded: 1988
Complete book production services with state-of-the-art electronic design & publishing capabilities: copy-editing; indexing; typesetting & composition; typography; design & art direction from concept to finished product; printing; consultation; project management. Novels, poetry, monographs, self-help, how-to, guides, ebooks & children's picture books. From ms to camera-ready to bound book, serving the publishing industry & self-publishing community. Call or write for free information, or visit our web site.

Bolger Vision Beyond Print
3301 Como Ave SE, Minneapolis, MN 55414-2809
Tel: 651-645-6311 *Toll Free Tel:* 866-264-3287
E-mail: contact@bolgerinc.com
Web Site: www.bolgerinc.com
Key Personnel
CEO: Dik Bolger *E-mail:* dbolger@bolgerinc.com
Mktg Mgr: Kristen Stradinger
  E-mail: kstradinger@bolgerinc.com
Founded: 1934
Full service commercial printer, digital printing, print on demand, variable print, technology solutions, mailing, fulfillment & distribution. Specialty products include college publications, catalogs, marketing product brochures, direct mail, luxury print.

BR Printers
665 Lenfest Rd, San Jose, CA 95133
Tel: 408-278-7711 *Fax:* 408-929-8062
E-mail: info@brprinters.com
Web Site: www.brprinters.com
Key Personnel
Pres: Adam DeMaestri *E-mail:* adam@brprinters.com
VP & Chief Strategy Offr: David Gall
SVP, Sales: Derek Giulianelli *Tel:* 303-916-5346 (cell) *E-mail:* derek@brprinters.com
VP, Fin: Carina Follante
VP, KY Off: Chris Gerhold
Dir, HR: Kathryn Torre
Gen Mgr, CA Off: James Barrios
Founded: 1992
Leading provider of digital printing products. Based in San Jose, CA, with a production facility in Independence, KY & mailing & fulfillment operation in Denver, CO. The company's product portfolio includes self-publishing solutions, print-on-demand, short run publications, web-to-print, rebinds, wide format, promotional products, direct e-mail, fulfillment & other digital printing solutions.
Branch Office(s)
10154 Toebben Dr, Independence, KY 41051

Century Direct LLC
15 Enter Lane, Islandia, NY 11749
Tel: 212-763-0600
E-mail: contact@centurydirect.net
Web Site: www.centurydirect.net
Key Personnel
VP, Sales & Busn Devt: Martin A Rego
  E-mail: regom@centurydirect.net
Founded: 1932
Direct mail, newsletters, publications & catalogs are our specialty; electronic prepress, full binding, in-house lettershop.
Membership(s): Direct Mail Fundraisers Association (DMFA); Greater Hudson Valley Postal Customers Council; Greater New York Postal Customers Council; Hudson Valley Direct Marketing Association; National Association of College & University Mail Services (NACUMS); National Catholic Development Conference Council

CG Book Printers
Division of Corporate Graphics Commercial (CGC)
1750 Northway Dr, North Mankato, MN 56003
Tel: 507-388-3300 *Toll Free Tel:* 800-729-7575
  Fax: 507-386-6350
E-mail: cgbooks@corpgraph.com
Web Site: www.corpgraph.com
Key Personnel
Pres: Dan Kvasnicka *Tel:* 507-386-6340
  Fax: 507-344-5548 *E-mail:* dekvasnicka@corpgraph.com
Sales Exec, Book Mfg Sales: Mike Schmitt
  Tel: 507-386-6349 *E-mail:* mjschmitt@corpgraph.com
Founded: 1989
CG Book Printers currently provides book manufacturing services for publishers who sell product to school library & trade markets. In addition, we offer fulfillment services for those publishers wishing to maintain their inventories in the same location where their books are manufactured.
We bind books in hard case & paperback formats. We use Smyth sewn, side sew & adhesive bound for hard case trade or library bound books & section sew, or adhesive bind for paperback books.

Champion Printing Inc
Division of BCS Ventures
3422 Misty Creek Dr, Erlanger, KY 41018
Tel: 859-727-5501 *Toll Free Tel:* 800-543-1957 (US) *Fax:* 859-727-5507
E-mail: sales@championprintinginc.com
Web Site: www.championprintinginc.com
Key Personnel
Pres: Brian Sass
Sales Mgr: Bill Kopp *E-mail:* bkopp@championprintinginc.com
Founded: 1964
Commercial printer; specialize in bind-in & blow-in response envelopes & self-mailers.

City Diecutting
Affiliate of Bookdisplays LLC
One Cory Rd, Morristown, NJ 07960
Tel: 973-270-0370 *Fax:* 973-270-0369
E-mail: sales@bookdisplays.com
Web Site: www.bookdisplays.com
Key Personnel
CEO: Eric De Vos *Tel:* 973-270-0370 ext 11
  E-mail: edevos@bookdisplays.com
Pres: Robert Dembowski *Tel:* 973-270-0370 ext 17 *E-mail:* rdembowski@bookdisplays.com
Founded: 1989
Retail point of purchase cardboard & corrugated displays for merchandising books. In-stock displays for most standard trim sizes. 4/C branding on headers/risers. Custom displays for national rollouts. Sturdy displays designed for books. Proudly made in the USA using American materials & labor.
Membership(s): American Booksellers Association (ABA); The Association of Publishers for Special Sales (APSS); Independent Book Publishers Association (IBPA)

Cliff Digital
14700 S Main St, Gardena, CA 90248
Tel: 310-323-5600 *Toll Free Tel:* 866-429-2242
  Fax: 310-400-3090
E-mail: cliff@cliffdigital.com
Web Site: www.cliffdigital.com
Key Personnel
Owner: Dave Thomas
Prodn Mgr: Paolo Johnson
Large format printer, banners, murals, vinyl decals, prototype products, backdrops, t-shirts, movie props, screen printing & design.

The Colad Group LLC
693 Seneca St, 5th fl, Buffalo, NY 14210
Tel: 716-961-1776 *Toll Free Tel:* 800-950-1755
  Fax: 716-961-1753
E-mail: info@colad.com
Web Site: www.colad.com
Key Personnel
Pres: Todd Anson
Founded: 1947
Printer of film laminated paperboard products; also specializes in turned edge binders.

Corporate Graphics Book Printers, see CG Book Printers

CRW Graphics Communications
9100 Pennsauken Hwy, Pennsauken, NJ 08110
Tel: 856-662-9111 *Toll Free Tel:* 800-820-3000
Fax: 856-665-1789
E-mail: info@crwgraphics.com
Web Site: www.crwgraphics.com
Key Personnel
Pres: David Carpenter
EVP: George Slater
VP, Sales & Mktg: Will Glassman
E-mail: wglassman@crwgraphics.com
Cust Serv Mgr: Rich Quigley *E-mail:* rquigley@
crwgraphics.com
High quality, multicolor sheetfed printing for promotional materials & short-medium run books, journals, magazines & book covers/jackets. In-house bindery with hand assembly, die-cutting & Ultra-Kote UV coating. Prepress services include extensive electronic & conventional capabilities: type, comp, color separations, DTP service bureau, with digitally imposed output. Three shift conventional make-up & stripping, Opticopy & Misomex imposing. Full range of direct digital & film based proofing. Specialize in getting you from desktop to press with all your book & book promotional projects. Expert technical support & customer service.

Cypress House
Imprint of Comp-Type Inc
155 Cypress St, Fort Bragg, CA 95437
Tel: 707-964-9520 *Toll Free Tel:* 800-773-7782
Fax: 707-964-7531
Web Site: www.cypresshouse.com
Key Personnel
Pres: Cynthia Frank *E-mail:* cynthia@
cypresshouse.com
Mng Ed: Joe Shaw *E-mail:* joeshaw@
cypresshouse.com
Complete editorial, design, production, marketing & promotion services to independent publishers. Promotional services offered are typography, print brokering, editorial, copywriting, copy-editing & publicity.

RR Donnelley Marketing Solutions
35 W Wacker Dr, Chicago, IL 60601
Toll Free Tel: 800-742-4455
Web Site: www.rrd.com/services/marketing
Key Personnel
Pres, Mktg Solutions: Doug Ryan
A premier provider of sophisticated direct mail programs. We specialize in highly customized 1-to-1 communications, advanced production technology, project management & direct marketing services. RR Donnelley can help you break out of everyday direct mail to produce results beyond expected. From strategy & design to execution, RR Donnelley offers the knowledge that delivers.

Fairfield Marketing Group Inc
Subsidiary of FMG Inc
The Direct Mail Ctr, 830 Sport Hill Rd, Easton, CT 06112-1241
Tel: 203-261-5585 *Fax:* 203-261-0884
E-mail: info@fairfieldmarketing.com
Web Site: www.fairfieldmarketing.com
Key Personnel
Pres & CEO: Edward P Washchilla, Jr
VP, Cust Serv: Mike Lozada *Tel:* 203-261-5585 ext 204
VP, Fulfillment: Jason Paul Miller *Tel:* 203-261-5585 ext 203 *E-mail:* jason@fairfieldmarketing.com
Founded: 1986
Specialists in mailing list brokerage & list management services. FMG clients rely on us for annual direct marketing programs. We are customer driven & accommodate. Specialty services: custom designed account management; expedient list rental approval; monthly usage reports; market & account analyses; fulfillment, mailing & mail response services; freelance art work; graphic design; advertising & promotional copywriting; binding services; lettershop services; computer services. FMG is a full service direct mail marketing firm.
Membership(s): American Booksellers Association (ABA); Bridgeport Regional Business Council (BRBC); Education Market Association; United States Chamber of Commerce (USCC)

Stephen Gould Corp
35 S Jefferson Rd, Whippany, NJ 07981
Tel: 973-428-1500; 973-428-1510
E-mail: info@stephengould.com
Web Site: www.stephengould.com
Key Personnel
CEO: Michael Golden
CFO: Anthony Lupo
Pres: Justin Golden
EVP: John Golden
Cont: Kim Ings
Dir, Info Systems: Nanette Rosenbaum
Dir, Opers: Jason Rosario
Founded: 1939
Manufacturers & designers of corrugated & chipboard displays. Die-cutting, letterpress, offset, posters, silk screen, decorative foam.

Graphic Litho
Division of High Speed Process Printing Corp
130 Shepard St, Lawrence, MA 01843
Tel: 978-683-2766 *Fax:* 978-681-7588
E-mail: sales@graphiclitho.com
Web Site: www.graphiclitho.com
Key Personnel
Pres: Ralph E Wilbur
Founded: 1960
Services provided include printing & mailing of promotional literature, POP, book stands & displays, backlit displays, large store & window signage, life-size standees. Our products are produced on presses & equipment capable of printing sheet sizes up to 54 x 77 inches & folding sheet sizes up to 44 x 76 inches.
Membership(s): Print Services & Distribution Association (PSDA); Printing Industries of New England (PINE); PRINTING United Alliance

Hannecke Display Systems Inc
210 Grove St, Franklin, MA 02038
Tel: 774-235-2329
E-mail: info@hannecke.com
Web Site: www.hannecke.com
Key Personnel
Owner & CEO: Cuno Von Olenhusen
Design & manufacture patented point of purchase & in-store display systems for books & magazines, audio & video cassettes, CD & boxed software & other packaged products.

Harty Integrated Solutions
Division of The Harty Press Inc
25 James St, New Haven, CT 06513
Mailing Address: PO Box 324, New Haven, CT 06513
Tel: 203-562-5112 *Toll Free Tel:* 800-654-0562
Fax: 203-782-9168
Web Site: www.hartynet.com
Key Personnel
Pres: George R Platt *E-mail:* gplatt@hartynet.com
VP: Kevin Platt *E-mail:* kplatt@hartynet.com
Founded: 1900
Commercial printers & direct mail services.

The Hibbert Group
400 Pennington Ave, Trenton, NJ 08650
Tel: 609-394-7500 *Toll Free Tel:* 888-HIBBERT (442-2378)
E-mail: info@hibbertgroup.com
Web Site: hibbert.com
Key Personnel
Co-Chmn & CEO: Timothy J Moonan
Co-Chmn: Thomas J Moonan
SVP: Michelle Spedding
SVP, IT: Kenneth J Swiatkowski
SVP, Opers: Ron Arellano; Rosemary Mengel Hober
SVP, Sales: Paul A Zukowski
In-house digital & offset print applications; product fulfillment.
Branch Office(s)
1100 US Hwy 130, Robbinsville, NJ 08691 (dist ctr)
19521 E 32 Pkwy, Aurora, CO 80011-8141 (dist ctr)
890 Ships Landing Way, New Castle, DE 19720 (dist ctr)

The Horah Group
Subsidiary of Personalized Mobile LLC
351 Manville Rd, Suite 105, Pleasantville, NY 10570
Tel: 914-495-3200 *Fax:* 914-769-8802
Web Site: www.horah.com
Key Personnel
Pres: Richard Goldsmith *E-mail:* dgoldsmith@
horah.com
Founded: 1981
Direct marketing production agency; full service lettershop.

Inland Press
Subsidiary of Detroit Legal News
2001 W Lafayette Blvd, Detroit, MI 48216
Tel: 313-961-6000
Web Site: www.inlandpress.com
Key Personnel
Pres & CEO: Bradley L Thompson, II
E-mail: bthompson@inlandpress.com
CFO: Steve Fowler *E-mail:* sfowler@inlandpress.com
Founded: 1895
Commercial printing & publisher.
Membership(s): Book Manufacturers' Institute (BMI); Great Lakes Graphics Association (GLGA); PRINTING United Alliance

Intellicor Communications LLC
330 Eden Rd, Lancaster, PA 17601
Toll Free Tel: 800-233-0107
Web Site: www.intellicor.com
Commercial printing, mailing & marketing.

Interprint Web Printing
Subsidiary of Morten Inc
12350 US 19 N, Clearwater, FL 33764
Tel: 727-531-8957 *Toll Free Tel:* 800-749-5152
Fax: 727-536-0647
E-mail: info@interprintwebprinting.com
Web Site: www.interprintwebprinting.com
Key Personnel
CEO: Scott J Morten
Founded: 1965
Commercial printing: sheetfed & heat-set, web offset; magazine printing, catalog & direct mail.
Membership(s): Printing Industries of Florida (PIF)

Linda Kittlitz & Associates
193 Coleridge St, San Francisco, CA 94110-5112
Tel: 415-550-8898 *Toll Free Tel:* 800-550-8898
Fax: 415-550-7975
Web Site: www.lkandassociates.com
Key Personnel
Owner: Linda G Kittlitz *E-mail:* linda@
lkandassociates.com
Founded: 1990
Promotional products distributor, packaging, printing, embroidery & graphic design. Products include T-shirts, caps, pens, key tags, sports balls & embroidery.

Membership(s): Promotional Marketing Association of California (PMANC); Promotional Products Association International (PPAI); Visual Media Alliance (VMA)

OneTouchPoint
1225 Walnut Ridge Dr, Hartland, WI 53029
Tel: 262-369-6000 *Toll Free Tel:* 800-332-2348
Fax: 262-369-5647
E-mail: info@1touchpoint.com
Web Site: www.1touchpoint.com
Key Personnel
CEO: Dave Holland
Dir, Mktg & Sales Opers: Carey Howard
Founded: 1982
Online & offline marketing execution capabilities combined with an adaptive technology interface & a national tem of solution innovators & domain experts to help companies across industry sectors create consistent & meaningful engagements with end consumers regardless of channel, medium or location. We produce & distribute beautifully crafted print, point of purchase, campaign & promotional materials, as easily as we can create targeted, personalized outreach based on customer value or lifecycle stage.
Branch Office(s)
5241 Voges Rd, Madison, WI 53718 *Tel:* 608-838-9147
525 W Alameda Dr, Suite 101, Tempe, AZ 85282, Contact: James Parker *Tel:* 480-966-4003 *Fax:* 480-966-4016
5280 Joliet St, Denver, CO 80239 *Tel:* 303-227-1400
1441 Western Ave, Cincinnati, OH 45214
Tel: 513-421-1600
8410-B Tuscany Way, Austin, TX 78754
Tel: 512-454-6874

Presskits
Subsidiary of Ardmore Graphic Services Inc
PO Box 71, East Walpole, MA 02032
Toll Free Tel: 800-472-3497
E-mail: files@presskits.com; team@presskits.com
Web Site: presskits.com
Key Personnel
Owner & Pres: Tom Spiegel
Founded: 1986
Manufacturer of pocket folders, video sleeves, CD & disk mailers, packaging, portfolios, three-ring binders & sales kits for solutions to your packaging & folder needs.

The Printer
2810 Cowell Blvd, Davis, CA 95618
Tel: 530-753-2519 *Fax:* 530-753-2528
E-mail: info@the-printer.net
Web Site: the-printer.net
Key Personnel
Owner & Estimator: Howard Galbreath
Founded: 1966
Offset sheetfed & digital printing.
Membership(s): National Foundation of Independent Businesses (NFIB)

Progress Printing Plus
2677 Waterlick Rd, Lynchburg, VA 24502
Tel: 434-239-9213 *Toll Free Tel:* 800-572-7804
Fax: 434-832-7573
E-mail: info@progressprintplus.com
Web Site: www.progressprintplus.com
Key Personnel
Pres: Michael Thornton *E-mail:* mthornton@progressprintplus.com
Dir, Busn Devt: Gerald Bowles
E-mail: gbowles@progressprintplus.com
Founded: 1962
Brochures, catalogs, publications, pamphlets, die-cutting & general commerical printing.

V G Reed & Sons Inc
1002 S 12 St, Louisville, KY 40210-1302
Toll Free Tel: 800-635-9788 *Fax:* 502-560-0197
Web Site: www.vgreed.com
Key Personnel
Pres: Bobby Reed, Sr
VP, Natl Sales: Scott W Reed
Founded: 1938
Full service provider of print & fulfillment for the pharmaceutical, manufacturing, consumer products, financial services & healthcare industries. ISO 9001-2015 certified & cGMP compliant.

Regal Press
79 Astor Ave, Norwood, MA 02062
Tel: 781-769-3900 *Toll Free Tel:* 800-447-3425
Fax: 781-769-7361
E-mail: info@regalpress.com
Web Site: www.regalpress.com
Key Personnel
VP, Sales: Mike Simone *E-mail:* msimone@regalpress.com
Commercial printer. Offset printing, digital printing, thermography, foil stamping, embossing, engraving & custom products.

The John Roberts Company
9687 East River Rd NW, Minneapolis, MN 55433
Tel: 763-755-5500 *Toll Free Tel:* 800-551-1534
Fax: 763-755-0394
E-mail: success@johnroberts.com
Web Site: www.johnroberts.com; www.facebook.com/TheJohnRobertsCompany
Key Personnel
CEO: Michael Keene *Tel:* 763-754-4401
E-mail: mrk@johnroberts.com
CFO: Mike Thews *Tel:* 763-754-4303
E-mail: thews@johnroberts.com
Pres: Marnie Janezich *Tel:* 763-754-4327
E-mail: marnie.keene@johnroberts.com
Cont: Chantelle Butcher *Tel:* 763-754-4333
E-mail: chantelle.butcher@johnroberts.com
EVP, Sales: Mark Carlson *Tel:* 763-754-4404
E-mail: mark.carlson@johnroberts.com
VP, Opers: Scott Zorn *Tel:* 763-754-4416
E-mail: scott.zorn@johnroberts.com
Dir, Client Servs: Emily Schultz *Tel:* 763-754-4445 *E-mail:* emily.schultz@johnroberts.com
Dir, HR: Debby Boyd *Tel:* 763-754-4366
E-mail: dboyd@johnroberts.com
Dir, Mktg: Kyle Kennedy *Tel:* 763-754-4364
E-mail: kyle.kennedy@johnroberts.com
Founded: 1951
Full service commercial, catalog & direct response printing company. Specialize in inserts, catalogs, corporate collateral annual reports, brochures & direct mail, direct to plate, 6-color sheetfed & web printing, die-cutting, full bindery, mailing services, fulfillment services.

RRD Manchester
151 Red Stone Rd, Manchester, CT 06042
Tel: 860-649-5570 *Fax:* 860-649-7800
Web Site: www.rrdonnelley.com/commercial-print/location/rr-donnelley-manchester
Printing & typography.

St Joseph Communications-Print Group
50 Macintosh Blvd, Concord, ON L4K 4P3, Canada
Tel: 905-660-3111
E-mail: marketing@stjoseph.com
Web Site: stjoseph.com
Key Personnel
Pres: John Gagliano
EVP, Sales & Mktg: Ray D'Antonio
VP & Gen Mgr: Ryan Anderson
Camera, film stripping, saddlestitch & perfect binding, shrink wrapping & mailing. Involved in the production of magazines, booklets, catalogs & advertising material; creative market research.

Branch Office(s)
119 Snow Blvd, Concord, ON L4K 4N9, Canada
Tel: 905-695-8544
1165 Kenaston St, Ottawa, ON K1G 6S1, Canada
Tel: 613-729-4303

Scott Publications Inc
2145 W Sherman Blvd, Norton Shores, MI 49441
Tel: 231-755-2200 *Toll Free Tel:* 866-733-9382
Fax: 231-755-1003
E-mail: contactus@scottpublications.com
Web Site: scottpublications.com
Key Personnel
Pres: Robert H Keessen *E-mail:* rkeessen@scottpublications.com
Publr: Ruth M Keessen
Ed: Kelly Herrold *E-mail:* kherrold@scottpublications.com
Founded: 2001
Publish craft magazines & books.

Separa Color
6951 Oran Circle, Buena Park, CA 90621
Tel: 818-988-2882 *Toll Free Tel:* 800-859-0629
Fax: 818-988-3882
E-mail: sales@separacolor.com
Web Site: www.separacolor.com; www.simplybrochures.com; www.simplycatalogs.com; www.simplypostcards.com
Key Personnel
Pres: David C Field

Tribal Print Source
Division of Southern California Tribal Chairman's Association
36146 Pala Temecula Rd, Bldg J, Pala, CA 92059
Mailing Address: 35008 Pala Temecula Rd, PMB 436, Pala, CA 92059
Tel: 760-597-2650
E-mail: sales@tribalprintsource.com
Web Site: www.tribalprintsource.com
Founded: 2003

TWIG One Stop
10444 White Pinto Ct, Lake Worth, FL 33449
Tel: 561-588-0244 *Toll Free Tel:* 855-894-4178
E-mail: info@twigonestop.com
Web Site: www.twigonestop.com
Key Personnel
Owner: Ike Thaler *E-mail:* ike@twigonestop.com
Founded: 1997
Full service promotional company specializing in: full color printing, graphic design, direct mail services & promotional items.

Universal Bindery (Sask) Ltd
516-A Duchess St, Saskatoon, SK S7K 0R1, Canada
Tel: 306-652-8313 *Toll Free Tel:* 888-JOE-MENU (563-6368) *Fax:* 306-244-2994
E-mail: gib@unibindery.com
Key Personnel
Pres: Gilbert Davis
Founded: 1966

Universal|Wilde
26 Dartmouth St, Westwood, MA 02090
Tel: 781-251-2700 *Fax:* 781-251-2613
Web Site: www.universalwilde.com
Key Personnel
Pres & CEO: Stephen Flood
COO: Christopher Armstrong
CFO: Joe Musanti
VP, HR: Jennifer MacAskill
VP, Sales: Jim Bailey
Mktg Mgr: Ryan Collins
Founded: 1958
Full service marketing communications company that can deliver end-to-end solutions: creative services. integrated print, lettershop/direct mail services, fulfillment & distribution services. Also premiums & incentives for trade show

giveaways, gift with purchase, direct mail programs & advertising specialties.
Branch Office(s)
403 VFW Dr, Rockland, MA 02370 *Tel:* 781-871-7744 *Fax:* 781-878-2967
48 Third Ave, Somerville, MA 02143 *Tel:* 617-591-3000 *Fax:* 617-591-3091

Viridiam LLC
3030 Lowell Dr, Green Bay, WI 54311
Tel: 920-465-3030 *Toll Free Tel:* 800-829-6555

Web Site: www.viridiam.com
Key Personnel
VP, Sales: Rob Butler
Filing products, custom index tabs, print services & marketing services.

Whitman Printing & Creative Services LLC
PO Box 1681, Batavia, NY 14020
Tel: 516-294-5350 *Fax:* 516-294-5239
E-mail: info@whitmanprinting.com
Web Site: www.whitmanprinting.com

Key Personnel
Owner: Rebecca L Almeter *E-mail:* becky@ whitmanprinting.com
Founded: 1996
Print services company that specializes in direct mail & printing solutions.
Membership(s): Direct Marketing Club of New York (DMCNY); Mailing & Fulfillment Service Association (MFSA); Print Services & Distribution Association (PSDA)

Public Relations Services

The public relations firms listed below handle book and library accounts and can undertake special campaigns for publishers and authors.

Accurate Writing & More
16 Barstow Lane, Hadley, MA 01035
Tel: 413-586-2388
Web Site: frugalmarketing.com; www.
accuratewriting.com
Key Personnel
Owner & Dir: Shel Horowitz *E-mail:* shel@
principledprofit.com
Dir: Dina Friedman
Founded: 1981
Press releases, public service announcements,
public relations strategy, online public relations,
client biographies, backgrounders, media kits,
pitch letters, web page content & newsletters &
marketing plans.
Publishing Account(s): All Books; Arts & Farces;
Asalako Press; Author House; Autodidactic
Press; AWM Books; Bialkin Books; BJB Publishing; Construction Trades Press; CS Publishing; Dr Ivan Delman; Emerald Wave; Enterprise Publishing; Equestrian Press; Equilibrium Press; 1stBooks.com; Freedom Publishing; Golden Healing Publishing; Green Island Audio Books; Gropen Associates; Gwent
Press; Hope Springs Press; Humble Press; Images from the Past; Inmark Associates; Jenkins Group; Kitchen Cupboard Press; Liam
Works; Life Tools Press; Life Words; Market-
ingSherpa.com; Maverick Spirit Press; Mind-
blazer.com; Mindfulness Press; Nehemia &
Solomon; Peanut Butter & Jelly Press; Persolog GmbH; Pineapplesoft; Prism Publishing;
Publishinggame.com; Related Matters Newsletter; Six Strings Press; Space Link Books;
United Graphics; Walking Tree Press; John
Wiley & Sons; WordMate
Membership(s): Connecticut Authors & Publish-
ers Association; Independent Book Publishers
Association (IBPA); Independent Publishers of
New England (IPNE); National Writers Union
(NWU); Western New England Editorial Free-
lancers Network

Alice B Acheson
Unit of Acheson-Greub Inc
PO Box 735, Friday Harbor, WA 98250
Tel: 360-378-2815 *Fax:* 360-378-2815
E-mail: aliceba7@gmail.com
Founded: 1981
Consulting on national & local publicity, market-
ing & publishing; media tours, public relations
campaigns & subsidiary rights for publishers &
authors of fiction & nonfiction.
Publishing Account(s): Mountain Dog Books;
New Libri Press; Thoughtcatcher Publishing
Membership(s): Book Promotion Forum; Inde-
pendent Book Publishers Association (IBPA);
Pacific Northwest Booksellers Association
(PNBA); Pacific Northwest Writers Associa-
tion; Publishers' Publicity Association

Antonia Hall Communications
9663 Santa Monica Blvd, No 1128, Beverly Hills,
CA 90210
Tel: 707-234-9738
E-mail: ahcassociates@gmail.com
Web Site: www.antoniahallcommunications.com
Key Personnel
Founder & Principal: Antonia Hall
Founded: 1996
Provides services for authors, filmmakers, politi-
cians, philanthropists & other visionaries. We
have garnered media attention on top radio

& television shows & in the most influential
newspapers, magazines & blogs. We also offer
event planning & product launches. We successfully blend creative strategies & knowledgeable expertise for all of your promotional
needs: publicity services, social media campaigns, search engine optimization (SEO) enhanced copywriting, marketing materials &
superior customer service.
Publishing Account(s): Berrett-Koehler Publishers; CreateSpace; DVG Publishing; Estrella
Catarina; Findhorn Press; Quest Books; Winter
Goose Publications
Membership(s): Book Promotion Forum

Ascend Public Relations
2629 Second Ave N, Seattle, WA 98109
Key Personnel
Pres: Tom Wolf
Founded: 1999
Publicity services for authors.

Ascot Media Group Inc
PO Box 2394, Friendswood, TX 77549
Tel: 832-334-2733 *Toll Free Tel:* 800-854-1134
Toll Free Fax: 800-854-2207
Web Site: www.ascotmedia.com
Key Personnel
CEO: Trish Stevens *E-mail:* tstevens@
ascotmediagroup.com
Mgmt: Monica Foster *E-mail:* mfoster@
ascotmediagroup.com; Kim McCall
E-mail: kmccall@ascotmediagroup.com
Founded: 2003
PR services for authors & publishers include TV
& radio interviews; reviews & articles in news-
papers & magazines; Internet viral campaigns.

Stephanie Barko Literary Publicist
16100 Crystal Hills, Austin, TX 78737
Tel: 512-291-6188
E-mail: stephanie@stephaniebarko.com
Web Site: www.stephaniebarko.com; www.
diybookplatform.com
Key Personnel
Principal: Stephanie Barko
Founded: 2006
Custom book publicity for adult nonfiction & historical fiction publishers & authors. Debut authors welcome. Specializations in history, memoir, career, 19th century historicals & western
themes & spiritual subjects: platform development, pre-publication endorsement acquisition,
pre- & post-publication review requests, virtual
tours, media pitching, event scheduling, press
release creation & launch, electronic press kits
& integrated online campaigns. Traditional, hybrid & Indie publication tracks accepted.
Publishing Account(s): CreateSpace; Ingram
Membership(s): Independent Book Publishers Association (IBPA); PEN America; Story Circle
Network; Writer's League of Texas

Ted Barkus Co Inc
8017 Anderson St, Philadelphia, PA 19118
Key Personnel
Pres: Allen E Barkus *E-mail:* a.barkus-tbc@att.
net
Founded: 1958
Write & distribute press releases, write & edit
newsletters; offer creative & production services for promotional brochures & mailers;

direct response formats; arrange media interviews, newspaper, magazine, radio & television
ads.

The Barnabas Agency
Division of The B&B Media Group Inc
PO Box 3113, Corsicana, TX 75151-3113
Tel: 903-654-1319
E-mail: info@barnabasagency.com
Web Site: www.barnabasagency.com
Key Personnel
Pres & CEO: Tina Jacobson *E-mail:* tina@
barnabasagency.com
VP & COO: Rick Roberson *E-mail:* rick@
barnabasagency.com
VP, PR: Diane Morrow *E-mail:* diane@
barnabasagency.com
Founded: 2002
Formed to come alongside ministries, organiza-
tions & individuals needing assistance & guid-
ance with their overall public platform, strat-
egy, branding & communications needs.
Membership(s): Public Relations Society of
America Inc (PRSA)

The Blaine Group Inc
8665 Wilshire Blvd, No 301, Beverly Hills, CA
90211
Tel: 310-360-1499 *Fax:* 310-360-1498
Web Site: www.blainegroupinc.com
Key Personnel
Pres & CEO: Devon Blaine *E-mail:* devon@
blainegroupinc.com
Founded: 1975
National, regional & local promotional campaigns
& tours for authors & publishers, involving all
media outlets. Includes publicity, advertising &
marketing.
Publishing Account(s): Burma: An Enlightened
Spirit; From the Trench to the Bench: Navi-
gating the Legal System & Finding Your Spir-
itual Path Along the Way; Get the Most Out
of Motherhood: A Hot Mess to Mindful Mom
Parenting Guide; Hot Mess to Mindful Mom:
40 Ways to Find Balance & Joy in Your Every
Day; Managing Like a Boss: Develop Yourself into a Leader; Urgent Care: 10 Cures for
America's Ailing Healthcare System

Blitz Media-Direct
Subsidiary of The Linick Group Inc
Linick Bldg, 7 Putter Lane, Middle Island, NY
11953
Mailing Address: PO Box 102, Middle Island,
NY 11953-0102
Tel: 631-924-3888; 631-924-8555; 630-604-8599
E-mail: blitz4pr@gmail.com; linickgroup@gmail.
com
Key Personnel
Pres: Andrew S Linick, PhD
EVP: Roger Dextor
VP: Gaylen Andrews
Representatives for publishers & authors: free
publicity, creation of news releases & articles for national distribution online & offline
in Sunday supplements, newspapers, magazines, co-ops, trade & business journals. Trade
shows, direct mail, radio & TV interviews ar-
ranged. Promotional tours in all major & secondary markets; advertising & sales promotion consultants. Job planning, implementation, open house, media representatives, press

conferences, development of mailing lists for new product information sheets. Specialize in "blitzing" the media. Consultation by phone: second opinion critique services available per hour/diem/project. Provides comprehensive graphic redesign/new web site content development, interactive services with web site marketing makeover advice for first-time authors, self-publishers, professionals & entrepreneurs. Specializes in online advertising/PR, links to top search engines, consulting on a 100% satisfaction guarantee. Free site evaluation marketing checklist (a $250 value) for LMP readers.
Publishing Account(s): American Health Institute; Best Publishing Inc; Culbert Productions, Canada; Dr Rubenstein Wellness Group; Epic Publishing LLC; Epicurean.com; Epicurean-Traveler.com; Hearst Group; High Score Publishing; International Hair Research Institute; Isshin-Ryu Productions Inc; MAGI® (Martial Arts Grandmasters International®); Mail Order Trade Publishers of America; Med-Health Publications; Medical Health Publications, St Thomas, VI; National Associations of Photo Sellers (NAPS); National Learning Corp; New World Press; Nu-chem Laboratories; Okinawan Kobujutsu Kyokai Association; Passbook Publishing; The Rhode Island Mortgage Store
Branch Office(s)
7 Lincoln Ave, Smithtown, NY 11787

C Blohm & Associates Inc
5999 Monona Dr, Monona, WI 53716-3531
Tel: 608-216-7300
E-mail: hello@cblohm.com
Web Site: www.cblohm.com
Key Personnel
Pres & CEO: Charlene Blohm *Tel:* 608-216-7300 ext 17 *E-mail:* charlene@cblohm.com
VP: Emily Embury
Strategy Dir: Saul Hafenbredl
Acct Mgr: Chloe Dechow
Founded: 1991
Public relations & digital marketing agency for education & special needs industries. With extensive experience in marketing, sales, advertising & public relations, the firm handles both print & electronic educational publishers that produce content for preschool through college. Client services include media & public relations, market positioning & planning, advertising & sales collateral development, case studies, visibility campaigns, conference presentations & awards consultation.

Book Publishers Network
817 238 St SE, Suite G, Bothell, WA 98021
Mailing Address: PO Box 2256, Bothell, WA 98041
Tel: 425-483-3040 *Fax:* 425-483-3098
Web Site: www.bookpublishersnetwork.com
Key Personnel
Pres: Sheryn Hara *E-mail:* sheryn@bookpublishersnetwork.com
Founded: 1984
Publishing consultant in the areas of: editing, cover design, book design & layout, reviews, distribution, literary agent referral, media, publicity, book tours, etc.
Membership(s): Book Publishers of the Northwest (BPNW); Independent Book Publishers Association (IBPA)

Brickman Marketing
395 Del Monte Ctr, No 250, Monterey, CA 93940
Tel: 831-594-1500
E-mail: brickman@brickmanmarketing.com
Web Site: www.brickmanmarketing.com
Key Personnel
Owner & Pres: Wendy Brickman

Founded: 1990
Award-winning firm providing cost-effective public relations & marketing services.

Brody Public Relations
145 Kingwood Stockton Rd, Stockton, NJ 08559-1711
Tel: 908-295-0600
Web Site: www.brodypr.com
Key Personnel
Pres: Beth Brody *E-mail:* beth@brodypr.com
Founded: 1988
Full service national & local publicity for publishers, authors, speakers, products & services. Specialize in self-help, healthcare, consumer, music, arts, entertainment & business fields. Offer cost-effective placement, author tours & use of continually updated media list, including TV, radio, cable, online syndicated columnists, wire services, newspapers & magazines. Develop special events, contests & in-store appearances.
Publishing Account(s): Bantam Doubleday Dell; Berkley Publishing; Full Moon Publishing; Marquis Who's Who; Martindale-Hubbell®; Peterson's Publishing; Random House; Rock Hill Press; Thunders Mouth Press; Tower Hill Press; Villard Books; Wiley

Rosalie Brody
360 E 72 St, New York, NY 10021
Tel: 212-988-8951
Key Personnel
Owner & Pres: Rosalie Brody Feder *E-mail:* roz360b@yahoo.com
Full service national & local publicity, public relations & promotion campaigns for publishers, authors, associations & foundations. Complete author tours, preparation of press materials for print media, radio & TV interviews, press conferences, bookstore promotion, convention planning & special events.

Casemate | IPM
Division of Casemate Group
1950 Lawrence Rd, Havertown, PA 19083
Tel: 610-853-9131 *Fax:* 610-853-9146
E-mail: casemate@casematepublishers.com
Web Site: www.casemateipm.com
Key Personnel
VP, Busn Devt: Simone Drinkwater
Sales Dir: Jane R Graf *E-mail:* jane.graf@casematepublishers.com
Founded: 1995
Full service sales & marketing for publishers: overall market planning, advertising, publicity, direct mail, trade representation.
Publishing Account(s): Allison & Busby; Artvoices Art Books; Ayebia Clarke Publishing; Big Sky Publishing; Black Knight Books; Briza Publications; Capital Books; Carnegie Publishing; Choc Lit; Classics Illustrated; CP Press; Enodare; Grub Street Cookery; Historika; Jackson Westgate Publishing Group; JJ Books; Kashi House; Kolibri Languages; Leading Authorities Press; Liberties Press; Litera Publications; Medina Publishing; New Africa Books; Penguin Random House South Africa; Protea Boekhuis; Publishing 451; Real Reads; Struik Inspirational Gifts; George F Thompson; Tilde Publishing & Distribution; UCT Publications; University of Buckingham Press; Waverly Lee Media; White Owl

Clear Concepts
1329 Federal Ave, Suite 6, Los Angeles, CA 90025
Tel: 323-285-0325
Key Personnel
Owner: Karen Kleiner

Founded: 1986
Research, media planning, writing & distribution of press releases.

Communication Matters
48 Aylmer Ave, Ottawa, ON K1S 2X1, Canada
Tel: 613-233-5423
Web Site: www.communicationmatters.ca
Key Personnel
Pres: Elaine Kenney *E-mail:* ekenney@communicationmatters.ca
Founded: 1991
Publicity, publishing, writing/editing & marketing; arranging publicity through radio, TV & print media; preparing people for interviews; publishing services include editing & design, print & project management; press releases, business & personal profiles & human interest stories.
Membership(s): Book Promoters Association of Canada; National Press Club; Saskatchewan Writers Guild

Cook Public Relations
3251 Spear Ave, Arcata, CA 95521
Tel: 707-630-3597; 415-302-1752 (cell)
Web Site: www.cookpr.com
Key Personnel
Owner & Pres: Sharon Cook *Tel:* 415-302-1752 (cell) *E-mail:* sharon@cookpr.com
Founded: 1986
Book publicity.
Publishing Account(s): Defy Your DNA/Dr Stephan Shrewsbury; Anne Geddes Collection; McGraw-Hill "The Wine Lovers Healthy Weight Loss Plan"; Media Arts Group Inc/Thomas Kinkade; Miramax/Hyperion/The Lightning Thief; Salt Kills/Dr Surender Neravetla; Sterling Publishing Co Inc, NY/"New Testament Code"; Watkins Publishing/London "Civilization One"

Copywriters' Council of America™ (CCA)
Division of The Linick Group Inc
CCA Bldg, 7 Putter Lane, Middle Island, NY 11953-1920
Mailing Address: PO Box 102, Middle Island, NY 11953-0102
Tel: 631-924-3888; 631-604-8599; 631-924-8555
Key Personnel
Chmn, Consulting Group: Andrew S Linick, PhD *E-mail:* cca4dmcopy@gmail.com
Sr Consultant: Gaylen Andrews
EVP: Roger Dextor
VP: Kelly Boyles
Measurable response publicity, press releases & public relations campaigns for writers, authors, publishers, self-publishers, independent presses, direct marketers, Internet & digital entrepreneurs. Clientele worldwide. A database of 35,500 plus professional member publicists, book promotion & direct response/Internet marketing specialists. Desktop publishing experts with online database system. Creative copywriting & graphic design, printing, photo reproduction & lettershop services, PR Feature Newswire Services: efficient targeting reaching 12,500 newspapers-58 million circulation. Get direct access to the editors interested specifically in your news. Free creative referral service. Provides comprehensive graphic redesign/new web site content development, Internet services with web site marketing makeover advice for first-time authors, self-publishers, professionals & entrepreneurs. Specializes in online free publicity, building newsworthy newsrooms, links to top search engines, consulting on a 100% satisfaction guarantee. Free site evaluation marketing checklist (a $250 value) for LMP readers.
Publishing Account(s): Advanced Health Institute Inc; The Affluent Gourmet Traveler; B P Publishing Inc; Best Publishing Inc;

Cross Trainer Magazine; Epic Publishing Co Inc; Epicurean.com; Epicurean-Traveler.com; Fairchild Publications; Hearst Magazines; Med-Health Publications; NAPS; National Learning Corp; New World Press; The Practical Gourmet; Time Inc; Total Fitness
Branch Office(s)
7 Lincoln Ave, Smithtown, NY 11787

Dougherty and Associates Public Relations
1303 Caldwell Mountain Rd, Hot Springs, NC 28743
Tel: 828-622-3285 *Fax:* 828-622-3285
E-mail: dougherty1515@gmail.com
Web Site: doughertyandassociatespr.com
Key Personnel
Pres: Michael J Dougherty
Founded: 2002 (reestablished)
Specializing in literary PR (publishing, authors, corporate & personal representation), Michael Dougherty has 35+ years experience in the publishing industry. He is formerly Exec Dir of Publicity at Jeremy P Tarcher & Dir of Mktg-Sales-Publicity at Renaissance Media Inc/Audio Renaissance.
Publishing accounts include major houses as well as smaller niche publishers. Worked with authors including Maya Angelou, Tom Wolfe, Gore Vidal, M Scott Peck, Arianna Huffington, Joseph Wambaugh, Nancy Reagan, Dick Morris, Ben Stein, Morley Winograd/Mike Hais, Tracey A Benson, Daniel Beunza, Ken Follett, Larry King, & dozens of others.
Publishing Account(s): Arcadia Books Ltd; Harvard Education Press; Kube Publishing/London; Princeton University Press; Rutgers University Press

Eileen Duhne Public Relations
203-B Picnic Ave, San Rafael, CA 94901
Tel: 415-459-2573 *Fax:* 415-459-2573
E-mail: eduhne@comcast.net
Web Site: eduhne.com
Founded: 1993
Public relations, marketing & publishing services for authors & publishers. Services include advertising, national publicity, author tours. Specialize in general trade, pop culture, environmental, photography & health/spirituality.

The Lisa Ekus Group LLC
57 North St, Hatfield, MA 01038
Tel: 413-247-9325 *Fax:* 413-247-9873
E-mail: info@lisaekus.com
Web Site: lisaekus.com
Key Personnel
Principal & Pres: Lisa Ekus *E-mail:* lisaekus@lisaekus.com
Co-Owner & Agent: Sally Ekus *E-mail:* sally@lisaekus.com
Founded: 1982
Represents a diversified selection of cookbooks, restaurants, food personalities & food products. Full service culinary agency specializing in talent & literary representation. Support & advance the careers of culinary professionals around the globe. Identify high profile publishing, media & endorsement opportunities for clients. Offer specialized media training programs for authors. Offer personalized, detail-oriented literary services (for cookbooks, health & women's nonfiction topics only) to more than 150 authors, many of whom have published multiple books.
Publishing Account(s): Abrams; Artisan; Chronicle Books; Grand Central; Houghton Mifflin Harcourt; William Morrow; Penguin Group USA, A Penguin Random House Company; Quirk; Regan Books; Robert Rose; Running Press; Simon & Schuster; Stewart, Tabori & Chang; Ten Speed Press; University of Florida

Press; University of North Carolina Press; Workman Publishing
Membership(s): Chefs Collaborative; International Association of Culinary Professionals (IACP); Women Presidents' Organization

Fairfield Marketing Group Inc
Subsidiary of FMG Inc
The Direct Mail Ctr, 830 Sport Hill Rd, Easton, CT 06112-1241
Tel: 203-261-5585 *Fax:* 203-261-0884
E-mail: info@fairfieldmarketing.com
Web Site: www.fairfieldmarketing.com
Key Personnel
Pres & CEO: Edward P Washchilla, Jr
VP, Cust Serv: Mike Lozada *Tel:* 203-261-5585 ext 204
VP, Fulfillment: Jason Paul Miller *Tel:* 203-261-5585 ext 203 *E-mail:* jason@fairfieldmarketing.com
Founded: 1986
Specialists in mailing list brokerage & list management services. FMG clients rely on us for annual direct marketing programs. We are customer driven & accommodate. Specialty services: custom designed account management; expedient list rental approval; monthly usage reports; market & account analyses; fulfillment, mailing & mail response services; freelance art work; graphic design; advertising & promotional copywriting; binding services; lettershop services; computer services. FMG is a full service direct mail marketing firm.
Membership(s): American Booksellers Association (ABA); Bridgeport Regional Business Council (BRBC); Education Market Association; United States Chamber of Commerce (USCC)

Bryan Farrish Marketing
1828 Broadway, 2nd fl, Santa Monica, CA 90404
Tel: 310-998-8305
E-mail: airplay@radio-media.com
Web Site: www.radio-media.com
Key Personnel
Owner: Bryan Farrish
Promoter: Nerry Berry
Founded: 1998
Radio publicity (radio interview) booking.

Flynn Media
1233 Fitzwater St, Philadelphia, PA 19147
Tel: 215-772-3048
Web Site: www.flynnmedia.com
Key Personnel
Founder: Erin Flynn Jay *E-mail:* erin@flynnmedia.com
Founded: 2001
Offer writing, editing & public relations services representing authors & speakers.
Membership(s): Women's Business Enterprise Network (WBENC)

The Frank Promotion Corp
10860 Green Valley Walk, Boynton Beach, FL 33437
Tel: 561-737-2325
E-mail: frankpromo@aol.com
Key Personnel
Pres: Ben G Frank
Print Media Dir: R Frank
Founded: 1976
Obtain radio & TV talk shows & newspaper & magazine stories for publishers, authors & medical health practitioners & businesses who want to promote their books, ideas, stories & new products; public relations & advertising.

Gail Leondar Public Relations
21 Belknap St, Arlington, MA 02474
Tel: 781-648-1658

E-mail: gail@glprbooks.com
Web Site: www.glprbooks.com
Key Personnel
Pres: Gail Leondar-Wright
Founded: 1992
Publicity for books & authors. Specialize in progressive books.

Goldberg McDuffie Communications
250 Park Ave, 7th fl, New York, NY 10177
Tel: 212-705-4211
E-mail: bookpr@goldbergmcduffie.com
Web Site: www.goldbergmcduffie.com
Key Personnel
CEO: Lynn C Goldberg *E-mail:* lgoldberg@goldbergmcduffie.com
Founded: 1981
A strategic communications public relations & marketing firm for publishers of books, authors, awards & institutions. Over 25 years of strategic publicity & marketing campaigns across all platforms. National broadcast publicity, print media, tours, digital marketing & social media outreach, special events, lectures & consulting. Represents literary & commercial fiction, politics & current affairs, business, pop culture/lifestyle, health & science, art/photography & travel.

Sandra Goroff & Associates
42 Waterfall Dr, Suite L, Canton, MA 02021
Tel: 617-750-0555
E-mail: sgma@aol.com
Web Site: www.sandragoroff.com
Key Personnel
Founder & Pres: Sandra Goroff
National & local public relations, publicity campaigns & promotional marketing for publishers, books, authors & personalities. Brand & new product launches for publishers. Radio & television placement, print interviews, book review coverage, special events & consulting services.

Susannah Greenberg Public Relations
41 Old Brook Rd, Dix Hills, NY 11746
Tel: 646-801-7477
E-mail: publicity@bookbuzz.com
Web Site: bookbuzz.com; linkedin.com/in/susannahgreenberg; www.facebook.com/SusannahGreenbergPublicRelations; twitter.com/SueGreenbergPR
Key Personnel
Founder & Pres: Susannah Greenberg
Represents publishers, authors & book industry organizations throughout North America. Susannah works with clients to secure media placements (features, interviews, reviews & mentions) in TV, radio, print & Internet. She researches media outlets, writes press releases & pitch letters, creates online press kits & works to optimize her clients' social media presence by advising them on platforms & content strategy.
Publishing Account(s): Albert Whitman & Co.; Book Industry Study Group; Chronicle Books; Hazelden Publishing; hoopla; Women's National Book Association
Membership(s): Women's Media Group; Women's National Book Association (WNBA)

Gulotta Communications Inc
321 Walnut St, Newton, MA 02460
Tel: 617-630-9286 *Fax:* 978-733-6162
Web Site: www.booktours.com
Key Personnel
Pres: Victor Gulotta *E-mail:* victor@booktours.com
Founded: 1993
Offers full service book promotion & publicity for authors & publishers seeking online, broadcast & print media exposure. In addition a full array of powerful marketing services are avail-

able including direct mail, print & broadcast advertising & web marketing. Founder & president Victor Gulotta has been publicizing books for more than three decades & has worked with such authors as Isaac Asimov, Jonathan Kozol, Margaret Thatcher, Richard Brodie, Thomas Szasz, James Randi, Martin Gardner, Gloria Nagy, Ken Fisher, Baxter Black, Nicholas Basbanes, Henry David Abraham, Karen Kondazian & Stewart E Weisberg.
Publishing Account(s): Atlantic Monthly Press; Avon; Columbia University Press; Crown; HarperCollins; Harvard University Press; Little, Brown; M E Sharpe; Oxford University Press; Simon & Schuster; Ten Speed Press; University of Massachusetts Press; Wiley; William Morrow

Kathryn Hall, Publicist
PO Box 1486, Ukiah, CA 95482
Tel: 707-468-8201
E-mail: khpbooks@gmail.com
Web Site: www.kathrynhallpublicist.com; estrellacatarina.com
Founded: 1980
Kathryn Hall, Publicist is a longstanding boutique firm that specializes in working primarily with innovative thought leaders & grounded early adopters who are authors of nonfiction books, particularly business titles. Media placement is secured across platforms including print, broadcast & social media. All socially responsible projects considered. Larger projects requiring other publishing services available. Contact for further information.
Publishing Account(s): Berrett-Koehler Publishers Inc; Marshall Goldsmith; HarperCollins; Jossey-Bass; Rich Karlgaard; Harvey Mackay; Viking Penguin

Anita Halton Associates
559 Alta Vista Way, Laguna Beach, CA 92651
Tel: 415-640-5486 (cell)
E-mail: ahapub@aol.com
Web Site: anitahaltonassociates.com
Key Personnel
Pres: Anita Halton
Founded: 1985
Publicity & marketing services for authors & publishers. National & local campaigns.
Membership(s): Independent Book Publishers Association (IBPA)

The Hendra Agency Inc
142 Sterling Place, Brooklyn, NY 11217-3307
Tel: 718-622-3232; 212-947-9898 *Fax:* 718-622-3322
Key Personnel
Pres: Barbara J Hendra
Acct Exec: Jan Andrew; Jeanne Taylor; Stephen Will
Founded: 1979
Full service national & local publicity, public relations & promotion campaigns for book & computer publishers & authors. TV, radio, online & newspaper interviews & reviews, advertising, press kits & materials, parties & specialized promotions & complete marketing services. Major trade & business publisher & author accounts.
Membership(s): Publishers' Publicity Association

Hill+Knowlton Strategies
237 Park Ave, 4th fl, New York, NY 10017
Tel: 212-885-0300
Web Site: www.hkstrategies.com
Key Personnel
Global Chmn & CEO: Jack Martin *Tel:* 212-885-0372
Global COO & VChmn: Mark Thorne
Chief Global Strategist, CEO & Group SJR: Alexander Jutkowitz *Tel:* 212-885-0606

Global Gen Coun: Meredith Marks
Chief Content & Communs Offr: Leslie Cauley
Global Busn Devt & Client Servs: Scott Pollard *Tel:* 212-885-0315 *E-mail:* scott.pollard@hkstrategies.com
Global Head, Talent: Kate Augustine
Global public relations & integrated communications agency.
Branch Office(s)
3200 Bristol St, Suite 300, Costa Mesa, CA 92626 *Tel:* 949-223-2300
6300 Wilshire Blvd, 10th fl, Los Angeles, CA 90048 *Tel:* 310-633-9400
60 Green St, San Francisco, CA 94111 *Tel:* 415-281-7120
607 14 St NW, Suite 300, Washington, DC 20005 *Tel:* 202-333-7400
255 Alhambra Circle, Suite 330, Miami, FL 33134 *Tel:* 305-443-5454
215 S Monroe St, Suite 703, Tallahassee, FL 32301 *Tel:* 850-222-4100
201 E Kennedy Blvd, Suite 1611, Tampa, FL 33602 *Tel:* 813-221-0030
222 Merchandise Mart Plaza, Suite 275, Chicago, IL 60654 *Tel:* 312-255-1200
500 W Fifth St, Suite 1000, Austin, TX 78701 *Tel:* 512-474-8848
500 N Akard St, Suite 2125, Dallas, TX 75201 *Tel:* 214-363-3990
708 S Main St, Suite 200, Houston, TX 77002 *Tel:* 713-752-1900
Julia Industrial Park, 791 "C" St, San Juan, PR 00920 *Tel:* 787-474-2525

Hilsinger-Mendelson West Inc
8916 Ashcroft Ave, Los Angeles, CA 90048
Tel: 310-659-7930
E-mail: hmiwest@aol.com
Web Site: www.hilsingermendelson.com
Key Personnel
CEO: Judy Hilsinger
Pres & COO: Sandi Mendelson *Tel:* 212-725-7707 *Fax:* 212-725-7708 *E-mail:* smendelson@hmieast.com
VP & Exec Dir, Publicity: David Kass
Sr Publicist: Margaret Rogalski
Digital Media Mgr: Amrit Judge
Off Mgr: Renee Gulotta
Publicity Mgr: Emily Willette
Founded: 1983
Preeminent bi-coastal, full service public relations & publicity (national & regional), providing authors, publishers & corporations with press kit materials; national & local media tours; brand-building strategies & campaigns; organization of events. More than 25 years experience with an unprecedented track record of more than 100 national bestsellers in the past decade.
Branch Office(s)
Hilsinger-Mendelson East, 226 Fifth Ave, 4th fl, New York, NY 10001 *Tel:* 212-725-7707 *Fax:* 212-725-7708 *E-mail:* hmi@hmieast.com

HJMT Public Relations Inc
78 E Park Ave, Long Beach, NY 11561
Tel: 347-696-0220
E-mail: info@hjmt.com
Web Site: www.hjmt.com
Key Personnel
Pres & CEO: Hilary Topper *E-mail:* hilary@hjmt.com
EVP: Lisa Gordon *E-mail:* lisa@hjmt.com
Founded: 1992
Boutique public relations, event planning, social media & graphic design agency.

Henry Holmes Literary Agent/Book Publicist/Marketing Consultant
Mitchell Heights, Apt 205, 2100 S Main St, Fall River, MA 02724
Tel: 508-672-2258; 508-415-4062 (cell)

Key Personnel
Pres & Literary Agent: Henry Holmes
Book jacket copywriting, copy-editing for advertising, direct mail copywriting, event promotions/publicity, press kits, press news release, public relations for organizations & nonprofits & speech writing/editing (general).

HurleyMedia LLC
1477 Canyon Rd, Santa Fe, NM 87501
Tel: 505-603-6392
Web Site: www.hurleymedia.com
Key Personnel
Owner: Joanna Thorne Hurley *E-mail:* jth@hurleymedia.com
Founded: 1994
We offer full service packaging for photography & art books from concept through publication, including editorial, design, production, as well as placement with a suitable publisher/distributor, marketing & publicity as needed to supplement publisher's efforts.

Integrated PR Agency (IPR)
Penthouse, 9025 Wilshire Blvd, Suite 500, Beverly Hills, CA 90211
Tel: 310-858-8230
Web Site: www.integrated-pr.com
Key Personnel
Owner & Founder: Monique Moss *E-mail:* monique@integrated-pr.com
Founded: 2010
Leading full service PR agency.

Jane Wesman Public Relations Inc
322 Eighth Ave, Suite 1702, New York, NY 10001
Tel: 212-620-4080 *Fax:* 212-620-0370
Web Site: www.wesmanpr.com
Key Personnel
Pres: Jane Wesman *Tel:* 212-620-4080 ext 11 *E-mail:* jane@wesmanpr.com
Dir, Publicity: Andrea J Stein *Tel:* 212-620-4080 ext 15
Soc Media Mgr: Sarah Kelley
Graphic Design Coord: Victoria Lau
Create high impact book publicity campaigns that build name recognition & generates sales. Specialize in obtaining national media coverage on TV & radio, in newspapers & magazines including author interviews, feature stories & book reviews. Also generate in-depth Internet publicity including online video interviews & podcasts & produce television & radio satellite tours. Other services include the creation of written press materials, author media training & interview preparation & the dissemination of publicity information to booksellers.
Publishing Account(s): Barricade Books; Center Street/Hachette; Crown Business; Free Press; Grand Central Publishing; HarperCollins; Jossey-Bass; Lifetree Media; McGraw-Hill; Thomas Nelson Inc; Palgrave; Portfolio; St Martin's Press; Select Books; Simon & Schuster; Waterside Productions; Wiley
Membership(s): ArtTable; National Association of Women Business Owners (NAWBO); Publishers' Publicity Association; Women's Media Group

K H Marketing Communications
16205 NE Sixth St, Bellevue, WA 98008
Tel: 425-269-7411 (cell)
Key Personnel
Owner & Pres: Kathy D Hoggan *E-mail:* kdhoggan@aol.com
Founded: 1991
Marketing select titles to the book trade & to niche markets outside the book trade; creating catalogs; writing back cover & promo copy; generating publicity for titles, authors & publishers; securing rights for compilation publications & sourcing content.

Publishing Account(s): Current Inc; Martingale Publishers; NTC/Contemporary Publishing; Palmer/Pletsch Publishers; Portland Press; Reading A-Z; Sea Hill Press; Washington State University; West 175 Publishers; The Wright Group Inc

Kelley & Hall Book Publicity

5 Briar Lane, Marblehead, MA 01945
Tel: 617-680-1976 *Fax:* 781-631-5959
Web Site: www.kelleyandhall.com
Key Personnel
Partner: Jocelyn Kelley *E-mail:* jocelyn@kelleyandhall.com; Megan Kelley Hall; Gloria Kelley
Founded: 2004
Full service agency providing public relations & promotional services for the publishing industry including authors, publishers, independent book producers, self-published authors & author associations for fiction & nonfiction titles. Produce creative & comprehensive online & print media kits which will secure timely news stories & book review coverage. Specialize in creating innovative article ideas. Publicity campaigns include national & local media coverage, features in newspaper & magazines as well as Internet promotion, publicity & social networking. Custom proposals will be sent upon request.

Kreab

House of Sweden, Suite 504, 2900 "K" St NW, Washington, DC 20007
Tel: 202-536-1590
E-mail: washingtondc@kreab.com
Web Site: www.kreab.com/washington-dc
Key Personnel
Mng Partner: Tapio Christiansen *Tel:* 202-536-1591 *E-mail:* tchristiansen@kreabgavinanderson.com
Sr Advisor: Richard J Wolff *Tel:* 646-283-3423
E-mail: rwolff@kreabgavinanderson.com
Corporate, financial, public relations, public affairs, crisis management, special events, health care & other key areas of public relations. Owned by Magnora, Omnicom/DAS & multiple other partners. Offices located worldwide.

KT Public Relations & Literary Services

1905 Cricklewood Cove, Fogelsville, PA 18051
Tel: 610-395-6298
Web Site: www.ktpublicrelations.com
Key Personnel
Founder & Owner: Kae Tienstra *E-mail:* kae@ktpublicrelations.com
Agent: Jon Tienstra *E-mail:* jon@ktpublicrelations.com
Founded: 1993
Offer publicity services to publishers & authors. Act as literary agents, separate from our publicity business.
Publishing Account(s): Central Recovery Press; Visable Ink Press

The Literary Media & Publishing Consultants

1815 Wynnewood Rd, Philadelphia, PA 19151
Tel: 215-877-2012
Key Personnel
CEO: Vanesse Lloyd-Sgambati
E-mail: vlloydsgam@aol.com
Founded: 1992
Specialize in publishing ventures as well as promotion of African American & women authors; consultant to publishers, authors & corporate entities that are interested in literacy; development of children's book fairs.
Publishing Account(s): Doubleday Basic Books; Perseus Books; Running Press; Smiley Group

Susan Magrino Agency

352 Park Ave S, 6th fl, New York, NY 10010

Tel: 212-957-3005 *Fax:* 212-957-4071
E-mail: info@smapr.com
Web Site: www.smapr.com
Key Personnel
Pres: Ms Allyn Magrino
EVP: Leigh Ann Ambrosi
Acct Dir: Mary Blanton Ogushwitz
Full service public relations; specialize in television, magazines, travel, beauty & fitness, lifestyle & design, foods & restaurant.

Scott Manning & Associates

433 Broadway, Suite 433, New York, NY 10013
Tel: 646-661-6665
Web Site: www.scottmanningpr.com
Key Personnel
Owner: Scott Manning *E-mail:* scott@scottmanningpr.com
Publicity Mgr: Abigail Welhouse
Founded: 1995
Public relations & marketing consulting for authors & literary organizations.
Publishing Account(s): Grove Atlantic
Branch Office(s)
20 Main St, Box 417, Hancock, NH 03449
  Tel: 603-525-4767
Membership(s): Publishers' Publicity Association

Media Connect

Division of Finn Partners
301 E 57 St, 4th fl, New York, NY 10022
Tel: 212-583-2718
Web Site: www.media-connect.com
Key Personnel
Mng Dir: David Hahn *Tel:* 212-593-5847
Chief Mktg Offr: Brian Feinblum *E-mail:* brian.feinblum@finnpartners.com
VP & Dir, PTA en Espanol: Deborah Kohan
Founded: 1962
Full service national & local publicity campaigns for authors & publishers. Nonfiction & fiction, hardcover, trade, ebooks, audiobooks & paperback; TV, radio, digital media, social media & newspaper interviews in person or by phone, syndicate radio & TV interviews to newsrooms nationwide. Arrange press conferences; train authors & write their press kits. All work done on a pay-for-success basis. Specialize in media, radio & print promotions & arranging satellite media tours & TV production worldwide. Morning Drive Radio Tours®; blogging, podcasts & college media tours.
Publishing Account(s): BenBella Books; Grand Central Publishing; Greenleaf Book Group; HarperBusiness; HarperCollins; HarperSanFrancisco; Harvard University Press; Hay House; Houghton Mifflin Harcourt Publishing Company; Knopf; Little, Brown; McGraw-Hill; Milkweed Editions; Morgan James Publishers; National Geographic; W W Norton & Company Inc; Pantheon; Pocket; Random House; St Martin's; Scribners; Simon & Schuster; Sports Illustrated; Thomas Nelson; TOR/Forge; Touchstone; John Wiley; Zondervan

Media Masters Publicity

61 Depot St, Tryon, NC 28782
Tel: 828-859-9456
E-mail: info@mmpublicity.com
Web Site: www.mmpublicity.com
Key Personnel
Sr Partner: Tracey Daniels *E-mail:* tracey@mmpublicity.com
Founded: 1998
Full service literary publicity agency. Specialize in publicity for children's & teen books, cookbooks & lifestyle titles. Personalized service for every client with emphasis on procuring quality media results. Services: implementing & executing national & local media campaigns, author tours & appearances, TV & radio satellite tours, press kit design & consulting. Per-

project or retainer services. Client list includes large & small publishing houses.
Branch Office(s)
6106 Majestic Pines Dr, Kingwood, TX 77345, Partner: Karen Wadsworth *Tel:* 617-869-5854
  E-mail: karen@mmpublicity.com
Membership(s): The American Library Association (ALA); Society of Children's Book Writers & Illustrators (SCBWI); Young Adult Library Services Association (YALSA)

Media Relations Agency

Division of Kocina Marketing Cos
350 W Burnsville Pkwy, Suite 350, Burnsville, MN 55337
Tel: 952-697-5220 *Fax:* 952-697-3256
Web Site: www.publicity.com
Key Personnel
Founder & CEO: Lonny Kocina
Partner & COO: Heather Champine
  E-mail: heather@mediarelations.com
Founded: 1988
Traditional print, online print, TV & radio broadcasting. Electronic & print media placements on a performance basis; charge is per placement secured. Also develop web sites & handle sports marketing projects.

S J Miller Communications

PO Box 834, Randolph, MA 02368-0834
Tel: 781-986-0732
E-mail: bookpromotion@gmail.com
Web Site: bookpr.com
Key Personnel
Founder & Publicist: Stacey J Miller
  E-mail: staceyjmiller@bookpr.com
Online promotion as well as traditional, full-service public relations for trade books. Represent authors & publishers. Create & distribute story pitches to producers, editors & reviewers. All nonfiction & fiction books welcome. Customized proposals are available upon request. Now offering blog tours.

Monteiro & Co Inc

301 E 57 St, 4th fl, New York, NY 10022
Tel: 212-832-8183
Web Site: www.monteiroandco.com
Key Personnel
Pres: Barbara Monteiro *E-mail:* bam@monteiroandco.com
Publicist: Connie Perry
Publicity & marketing services for nonfiction books, authors & magazines. Specialize in political books, business publications, biographies & economics books.
Publishing Account(s): Bill Janeway/Cambridge; Barbara Kahn/Norton; Paul Krugman/NY Times; Ian Mitroff/Palgrave
Membership(s): Publishers' Publicity Association

Multicultural Marketing Resources Inc

720 Greenwich St, No 7T, New York, NY 10014
Tel: 212-242-3351
Web Site: www.multicultural.com
Key Personnel
Pres: Lisa Skriloff *E-mail:* lisa@multicultural.com
Founded: 1994
Public relations & marketing services for diversity experts/authors in marketing to multicultural customers.
Publishing Account(s): Multicultural Marketing News; Multicultural Speakers Showcase; Multicultural Travel News; The Source Book of Multicultural Experts

Music City Arts Network

PO Box 843, Brentwood, TN 37024
Toll Free Tel: 888-80-SHINE (807-4463)
E-mail: info@musiccityarts.net
Web Site: www.musiccityartsupdate.com; www.shinetimebooks.com

Key Personnel
Owner & Pres: Chuck Whiting
  E-mail: chucwhit@usit.net
Founded: 1993
Full service communications firm offering services such as writing, editing, media placement, on-air interview placements, research, public relations plan development, song & jingle selection, book development, digital marketing, photography, event planning, etc.
Publishing Account(s): The Littlest Star: A Musical Story; Music City Arts Update; The Ryman Diaries; Shine Time Records & Books; John & Lillie Spreckels: Diaries, Desserts & San Diego Dreams; Wordabulous!: Celebrating the Positive Power of Words
Membership(s): The American Society of Composers, Authors and Publishers (ASCAP); Association for Education in Journalism and Mass Communication (AEJMC); Broadcast Music Inc (BMI); Country Music Association (CMA); National Songwriters Association International (NSAI); The Recording Academy (NARAS)

News & Experts LLC
18 Broad St, Charleston, SC 29401
Toll Free Tel: 800-204-7115
E-mail: info@newsandexperts.com
Web Site: newsandexperts.com
Guaranteed publicity for authors & publishers. National radio & TV shows, print & author tours.
Publishing Account(s): Advantage Media Group; Da Capo; Dearborn; HarperCollins; Human Kenetics; Prentice Hall; Soho Press

Nissen Public Relations LLC
18 Bank St, Suite 101, Summit, NJ 07901
Tel: 908-376-6470
E-mail: info@nissenpr.com
Web Site: www.nissenpr.com
Key Personnel
Founder & Book Publicist: Rob Nissen
Founded: 2000
Full service book publicity & book marketing firm that specializes in nonfiction categories with an emphasis on business, politics, history, biography, health, current affairs, lifestyle & science. Work with a variety of trade publishers & authors, managing everything from multi-city tours to online campaigns, creating a customized publicity strategy for each title. Our campaigns generate coverage in a wide variety of mainstream & niche media sources. Also offer professional copywriting services, press release distribution, online promotion & arrange speaking tours, lectures & book signing events.
Membership(s): Publishers' Publicity Association

The Nolan/Lehr Group Inc
214 W 29 St, Suite 1002, New York, NY 10001
Tel: 212-967-8200
E-mail: dblehr@cs.com
Web Site: www.nolanlehrgroup.com
Key Personnel
Pres: Donald B Lehr *Tel:* 917-304-4058
  E-mail: donald@nolanlehrgroup.com
Off Mgr: Jennifer Alperen
Founded: 1972
Full service national public relations office for authors, publishers, trade associations, foundations, organizations & services. Specialize in general nonfiction, reference & religion. Creation & production of press releases, press kits & other collateral materials. Interviews booked in all national & local print & broadcast media, live, satellite, online & telephone. Offer press conferences, in-city promotions, special events, publication day parties & events, consultation services, photography. Work closely with the author & publisher.

Caroline O'Connell Communications
11275 La Maida St, Suite 200, North Hollywood, CA 91601-4514
E-mail: oconnellpr@aol.com
Web Site: www.oconnellcommunications.com
Key Personnel
Owner & Pres: Caroline O'Connell
Founded: 1990
Full service public relations firm for publishers & authors since 1990, that conducts national & local tours with an emphasis on the West Coast. Arrange press conferences, train authors & prepare media kits. Specialize in business, beauty, education & political books.

One Potata Productions Inc
80 E 11 St, Suite 301-A, New York, NY 10003
Tel: 212-353-3478 *Fax:* 212-353-9667
E-mail: onepotata@gmail.com
Web Site: onepotata.com
Key Personnel
Pres: Diane Mancher
Founded: 1992
Experienced independent public relations firm. Specialize in books & authors. Custom designed publicity campaigns developed for publishers & authors. National radio, TV & print placements, local media tours, radio satellite tours & monthly magazine placements. Write & design targeted press materials. Areas of interest include current events, personalities, pop culture, cookbooks, health/fitness, gay & lesbian & African-American titles.

Over the River Public Relations LLC
116 Gladwin Ave, Leonia, NJ 07605
Tel: 201-503-1321 *Fax:* 201-503-0952
E-mail: info@otrpr.com
Web Site: www.otrpr.com
Key Personnel
Founder & Pres: Rachel Tarlow Gul
  E-mail: rachel@otrpr.com; Jennifer Richards
  E-mail: jen@otrpr.com
Founded: 2000
Full service national & local publicity campaigns for publishers & authors of fiction, nonfiction, hardcover trade & mass market. Services include press kit development, radio, TV, print & Internet media tours, book signings. Work with many publishers, big & small.
Publishing Account(s): Applause; The Audio Publishers Association; Harcourt; HarperCollins; Simon & Schuster; Three Rooms Press; Viking

PadillaCRT
1101 W River Pkwy, Suite 400, Minneapolis, MN 55415
Tel: 612-455-1700 *Fax:* 612-455-1060
Web Site: www.padillacrt.com
Key Personnel
Chair & CEO: Lynn Casey
Chief Creative Offr: Heath Ruddick
EVP: Marian Briggs; Matt Kucharski
SVP: Kathy Burnham; Riff Yeager
VP, Creative Opers: Jennifer Iwanicki
Founded: 1961
Full service public relations firm with expertise in national media placement, author tours & special event planning & promotion. Specialize in business book promotion.
Branch Office(s)
4 World Trade Center, 150 Greenwich St, 48th fl, New York, NY 10007, EVP & Mng Dir: Greg Tarmin *Tel:* 212-229-0500 *Fax:* 212-229-2925
101 W Commerce Rd, Richmond, VA 22314, Pres: Mark Raper *Tel:* 804-675-8100

Page Turner Publicity
8785 SW 28 St, Miami, FL 33165
Tel: 949-254-3214
E-mail: pgturnerpub@aol.com
Web Site: www.pageturnerpublicity.com

Key Personnel
Owner & Pres: Javier Perez
Founded: 2003
A full service literary publicity firm that handles both English & Spanish language clients. We provide personalized hands-on public relations services to the publishing industry. Our experienced staff works closely with both individual authors & publishers to create optimal media campaigns for books of all genres. Listens closely to a client's goals & expectations & then plan & execute tailored, strategic publicity plans to meet them. Services include designing creative & well-produced hard-copy & Internet press kits, planning author tours, arranging book signings, speaking engagements & literary events, securing book reviews from newspapers & magazines across the country scheduling both national & local television, radio, Internet, print interviews & Internet/social media publicity.
Membership(s): Florida Authors & Publishers Association Inc (FAPA); Publishers Association of Los Angeles; South Florida Writers Association

Parkhurst Communications Inc
11 Riverside Dr, Suite 1-TW, New York, NY 10023
Tel: 212-362-9722
Web Site: www.parkhurstcommunications.com
Key Personnel
Pres: William Parkhurst *E-mail:* billparkhurst@parkhurstcommunications.com
Collaborative Partnership & Sr Trainer: Nanette DeWester
Founded: 1981
Communications & media training, presentation skills programs, business writing & leadership workshops. Clients include legendary authors, corporate & nonprofit organizations & major publishers.
Membership(s): Association for Talent Development (ATD); National Speakers Association (NSA); Publishers' Publicity Association

Phoenix Media
29 Miriam Dr, Matawan, NJ 07747
Tel: 732-441-1519 *Fax:* 732-566-1913
Web Site: www.phoenixmediapr.com
Key Personnel
Pres: Donna Gould *E-mail:* donnagould@sprintmail.com
Founded: 1997
Full service publicity & public relations company. Specialize in radio campaigns, publicity campaigns, national interview campaigns for authors, products & corporations.
Publishing Account(s): Atria Books (div of Simon & Schuster); Avery Books; Broadway Books; Element Books; The Free Press; Gotham Books; HarperCollins; Hylas Publishing; McGraw-Hill Publishers; Penguin Group USA, A Penguin Random House Company; Prentice Hall; Putnam Publishing; Random House; Rutgers University Press; St Martin's Press; Simon & Schuster; Warner Books; Workman Publishing
Membership(s): Publishers' Publicity Association

Porter Novelli
Division of Omnicom Group Inc
195 Broadway, 17th fl, New York, NY 10007
Tel: 212-601-8000
Web Site: www.porternovelli.com
Key Personnel
CFO & Pres, Global Busn Opers: Patrick Resk
Chief Mktg Offr: Kate Cusick
Mng Dir: Kyle Farnham
Founded: 1972

PR by the Book LLC
PO Box 6226, Round Rock, TX 78683

Tel: 512-501-4399 Fax: 512-501-4399
E-mail: info@prbythebook.com
Web Site: www.prbythebook.com
Key Personnel
CEO/Chief Publicity Strategist: Marika Flatt
   E-mail: marika@prbythebook.com
COO: Doug Flatt
Sr Publicist: Judy McDonough
Publicist: Leslie Barrett
Founded: 2002
Media relations & social media services for authors, publishers & small businesses. Provide services including full scale publicity campaigns, tour city campaigns, radio or online only blog tours & various other a la carte publicity projects.
Publishing Account(s): B&H Publishing Group; DK Books; Insight Editions; Patagonia Books; Wiley
Membership(s): Independent Book Publishers Association (IBPA); Writer's League of Texas

PR Newswire
Subsidiary of Cision Ltd
350 Hudson St, Suite 300, New York, NY 10014-4504
Toll Free Tel: 888-776-0942; 800-776-8090
   Toll Free Fax: 800-793-9313
E-mail: mediainquiries@prnewswire.com
Web Site: www.prnewswire.com
Key Personnel
CIO: Robert Coppola
Chief HR Offr: Whitney Benner
Pres, Americas: Jason Edelboim
Founded: 1954
Transmits the full texts of press releases simultaneously & within minutes to more than 2,000 news media across the country; News Lines provide national, regional, state or local coverage & international distribution to any country in the world. Also can be ordered. Newswire offers a number of special services: The Feature News Line, for next-day delivery of feature news; PR/TV News Line, reaching editors at 600 TV stations nationwide; EntertaiNET, a wire directly to the desks of entertainment editors & PRN Facsimile Services, for simultaneous fax transmissions to clients' proprietary lists; Fax-on-Demand Service allows clients to store a document of any length for automatic retrieval by any caller & deliverable to any fax machine worldwide. Financial news is transmitted directly to the investment community via the Investors Research Wire & through various specialized databases. A range of Internet-based audio & video services are also available.
Branch Office(s)
303 Second St, 9th fl, San Francisco, CA 94107
   Toll Free Tel: 866-732-1382
2901 28 St, Suite 100, Santa Monica, CA 90405
   Toll Free Tel: 866-732-1382
1515 Wynkoop St, Denver, CO 80202 Toll Free Tel: 866-732-1382
180 N Stetson Ave, Suite 1350, Chicago, IL 60601 Toll Free Tel: 866-732-1382
12051 Indian Creek Ct, Beltsville, MD 20705
   Toll Free Tel: 800-378-7112
4041 Jefferson Plaza NE, Suite 100, Albuquerque, NM 87109 Toll Free Tel: 866-732-1382 Fax: 201-942-7020
1300 E Ninth St, Suite 700, Cleveland, OH 44114
   Toll Free Tel: 800-826-3133

PR/PR Public Relations
2301 Hickory Lane, Orlando, FL 32803
Tel: 407-895-8800
Web Site: www.prpr.net
Key Personnel
Pres & Owner: Russell Trahan E-mail: russell@prpr.net
Specialize in nonfiction authors.

Press Box Publicity
3920 Duncan Dr, Boca Raton, FL 33434
Tel: 912-658-7860
E-mail: sportspr@smithpublicity.com
Web Site: pressboxpublicity-smithpublicity.com
Key Personnel
Pres: Adam Rifenberick
Founded: 2004
Sports media book publicist & public relations services for print & broadcast media.

Promotion in Motion
714 Crescent Dr, Beverly Hills, CA 90210
Tel: 323-461-3921; 310-497-4001 (cell) Fax: 323-461-0917
E-mail: irwinzuckerpr@aol.com
Web Site: www.promotioninmotion.net; www.bookpublicists.org
Key Personnel
Pres: Irwin Zucker E-mail: irwin@promotioninmotion.net
VP: Devra Hill
Acct Exec: Barry Benson; Max Kilstofte; Judi Shari; Taryn Tanner; Lori Zee
Local, regional & national promotional campaigns for authors: radio, TV & press. Specialize in setting phone interviews nationally with radio stations & authors.

Jennifer Prost Public Relations
51 Christopher St, Montclair, NJ 07042
Tel: 973-746-8723
E-mail: jprostpr@comcast.net
Web Site: www.jenniferprost.com
Founded: 1998
Publicity services for authors & publishers.

Publicis North America
1675 Broadway, New York, NY 10009
Tel: 212-474-5000
Web Site: www.publicisna.com
Key Personnel
CEO: Carla Serrano E-mail: carla.serrano@publicisna.com
Chief Creative Offr: Andy Bird
Chief Digital Offr: Dawn Winchester
Chief Mktg Offr: Jamie Rosen E-mail: jamie.rosen@publicisna.com
Founded: 1993
Full service public relations firm.
Branch Office(s)
500 Corporate Pkwy, Suite 140, Buffalo, NY 14226 Tel: 716-626-4433
2001 The Embarcadero, San Francisco, CA 94133, Mng Dir: Julie Liss Tel: 415-293-2001 E-mail: julie.liss@riney.com
168 N Ninth, Suite 250, Boise, ID 83702, Mng Dir: Christal Gammill Tel: 208-395-8300 E-mail: christal.gammill@publicisna.com
2909 Hennepin Ave S, Minneapolis, MN 55408 Tel: 612-822-2960
325 Arlington Ave, Suite 700, Charlotte, NC 28203 Tel: 704-344-7900
2828 Routh St, Suite 300, Dallas, TX 75201 Tel: 214-749-0080
7300 Lone Star Dr, No 200, Plano, TX 75024 Tel: 469-366-2550
424 Second Ave W, Seattle, WA 98119, Pres: Melissa Nelson Tel: 206-285-2222 E-mail: melissa.nelson@publicisna.com
111 Queen St E, Suite 200, Toronto, ON M5C 1S2, Canada, Chief Mktg Offr: Brett McIntosh Tel: 416-925-7733
One Riverside Dr W, Windsor, ON N9A 5K3, Canada Tel: 519-252-9479
3530 Blvd St-Laurent, Montreal, QC H2X 2V1, Canada, Pres: Rachelle Claveau Tel: 514-285-1414 E-mail: rachelle.claveau@publicisna.com

Raab Associates Inc
730 Yale Ave, Swarthmore, PA 19081
Tel: 914-241-2117

E-mail: info@raabassociates.com
Web Site: www.raabassociates.com
Key Personnel
Pres: Susan Salzman Raab
Founded: 1986
Full service agency. Specialize in marketing consulting & children's & parenting book publicity & promotion. Services include arranging author tours, national & local media campaigns, author appearances, in-store promotions, Internet publicity, marketing & consulting.

Renaissance Consultations
PO Box 561, Auburn, CA 95604
Tel: 530-362-1339
E-mail: info@marketingandpr.com
Web Site: www.MarketingAndPR.com
Key Personnel
Owner & Dir, Media Rel: Ms S A "Sam" Jernigan E-mail: sam@marketingandpr.com
Founded: 1998
With over a decade of experience in the publishing trenches, we offer a menu of writing, book development & marketing strategies for authors wanting to pursue traditional or self-publishing routes. With a comprehensive array of services & a customized approach to each project we accept, authors can choose precisely the type of assistance they need in advancing the journey of getting their book to its intended audience.
Publishing Account(s): Author's Publishing Cooperative; Next Hat Press; Zumaya Publishing
Membership(s): National Writers Union (NWU)

Rivendell Media Inc
1248 Rte 22 W, Mountainside, NJ 07092
Tel: 908-232-2021 ext 200 Fax: 908-232-0521
E-mail: info@rivendellmedia.com; sales@rivendellmedia.com
Web Site: www.rivendellmedia.com
Key Personnel
Pres & CEO: Todd Evans Tel: 908-232-2021 ext 210 E-mail: todd@rivendellmedia.com
Specialize in LGBT media placement.

Sherri Rosen Publicity Intl NYC
454 Manhattan Ave, Suite 3-J, New York, NY 10026
Tel: 212-222-1183
E-mail: sherri@sherrirosen.com
Web Site: www.sherrirosen.com
Key Personnel
Pres: Sherri Rosen
Founded: 1999
Specialize in literary publicity with emphasis on sex, inspirational, spirituality & relationships - science fiction, published or self-published works. Work with authors in US & globally on their mss, podcasts & videos. Also do ghostwriting, web sites & work on mss, proposals & videos. Author of Publicity from the Trenches: For Published & Self-Published Authors.
Publishing Account(s): Inspirational Publicity
Membership(s): International Women's Writing Guild (IWWG); National Writers Union (NWU)

Ruder Finn Inc
425 E 53 St, New York, NY 10022
Tel: 212-593-6400
E-mail: info@ruderfinn.com
Web Site: www.ruderfinn.com
Key Personnel
CEO: Kathy Bloomgarden, PhD
Chief Innovation Offr: Michael Schubert
EVP, Storytelling & Media: Rachel Spielman
Dir, Mktg & Communs: Sarah Coles
   E-mail: coless@ruderfinn.com
Promote books, especially mass market, cultural & art books & have media tours as well as a division that designs art books.

Branch Office(s)

600 California St, 11th fl, San Francisco, CA 94108, Global Head, Technol: Robin Kim *Tel:* 628-235-2101 *E-mail:* kimr@ruderfinn.com

East Lake Villas, E-101, 35 Dongzhimenwai Main St, 100027 Dongcheng District, Beijing, China, SVP & Gen Mgr: Judy Guo *Tel:* (010) 6462 7321 *Fax:* (010) 6462 7327 *E-mail:* judy.guo@rfcomms.com

Overseas Chinese Village, 3 Peace Rd, Guangzhou 510095, China, VP & Gen Mgr: Grace Liang *Tel:* (020) 8349 5783 *Fax:* (020) 8359 9685 *E-mail:* liangg@ruderfinnasia.com

Base Bldg, 9th fl, No 45, N Caoxi Rd, Xuhui District, Shanghai, China, SVP & Gen Mgr: Tony Dong *Tel:* (021) 5383 1188 *Fax:* (021) 6248 3176 *E-mail:* dongt@ruderfinnasia.com

24/F Neich Tower, 128 Gloucester Rd, Hong Kong, Hong Kong, SVP & Gen Mgr: Paul Yang *Tel:* 2521 0800 *Fax:* 2521 7088 *E-mail:* yangp@ruderfinnasia.com

Unit 001A, Tower B, Ground fl, Global Business Park, MG Rd, Gurgaon, Haryana 122 002, India, SVP & Gen Mgr: Jefferson Hou *Tel:* (0124) 4264343 *E-mail:* houj@ruderfinnasia.com

114 Lavender St, No 14-01 CT Hub 2, Singapore 338729, Singapore, SVP & Gen Mgr: Poh Leng Yu *Tel:* 6235 4495 *Fax:* 6235 7796 *E-mail:* yupl@ruderfinnasia.com

The Salisbury, 29 Finsbury Circus, London EC2M 7AQ, United Kingdom, Mng Dir: Nick Leonard *Tel:* (020) 7438 3050 *Fax:* (020) 7438 3083 *E-mail:* nleonard@ruderfinn.co.uk

Susan Schwartzman Public Relations

88 Kings Way, Pawling, NY 12564
Toll Free Tel: 877-833-4276 *Toll Free Fax:* 877-833-4276
E-mail: susan@susanschwartzmanpublicity.com
Web Site: www.susanschwartzmanpublicity.com
Founded: 1992
Full service publicity firm for publishers & authors. Publicity campaigns include national & local television & radio, author tours, feature stories in newspapers & magazines, review coverage, Online publicity, press kits & consulting. Represent literary & commercial fiction as well as nonfiction titles covering a broad range of subjects: memoirs, self-help, dating, baby boomer topics, social issues, parenting, current affairs, politics, environmental, history, food, sports & business. Extensive experience promoting award-winning cookbooks.
Membership(s): Publishers' Publicity Association

SSPR LLC

One Northfield Plaza, Suite 400, Northfield, IL 60093
Toll Free Tel: 800-287-2279
Web Site: www.sspr.com
Key Personnel
CEO: Heather Kelly
Founded: 1978
Create press releases, arrange national newspaper, magazine, radio & TV, newsletter interviews. Contacts with approximately 100 radio stations for phone interviews; trade shows.
Branch Office(s)
20 N Wacker Dr, Suite 4100, Chicago, IL 60606, Contact: Mellony Vasquez *Tel:* 847-955-0700
715 Bryant St, Suite 201, San Francisco, CA 94107, Contact: Kasey Thomas
105 E Moreno Ave, Suite 101, Colorado Springs, CO 80903, Contact: Kristen Broyles
1880 JFK Blvd, Suite 404, Philadelphia, PA 19103, Contact: Nicole Paleologus

StarGroup International Inc

1194 Old Dixie Hwy, Suite 201, West Palm Beach, FL 33413
Tel: 561-547-0667
E-mail: info@stargroupinternational.com
Web Site: stargroupinternational.com
Key Personnel
Pres & CEO: Brenda Star *E-mail:* brenda@stargroupinternational.com
Creative Dir: Mel Abfier
Internet Mktg Coord: Butch Butler
Mktg, Media & Website Devt: Rusty Durham
Media Specialist: Sam Smyth
Founded: 1993
Book Production: concept development, ghostwriting, editing, illustration, design, print promotion & distribution (all projects, fee based).
Membership(s): The Association of Publishers for Special Sales (APSS); Florida Authors & Publishers Association Inc (FAPA); Independent Book Publishers Association (IBPA)

Story Monsters LLC

4696 W Tyson St, Chandler, AZ 85226-2903
Tel: 480-940-8182 *Fax:* 480-940-8787
Web Site: www.StoryMonsters.com; www.AuthorsandExperts.com; www.SchoolBookings.com; www.partnershippublishing.com; www.fivestarpublishingsecrets.com; www.eStarPublish.com; www.DragonflyBookAwards.com
Key Personnel
Pres: Linda F Radke *E-mail:* Linda@StoryMonsters.com
Founded: 1985
Offer comprehensive e-book & printed book publishing-related support to publishers, authors, corporations, small presses & university presses. Services include marketing, national publicity, media kit production, book trailers, print brokering & web sites. Work with authors & publishers to promote a variety of genres. In addition to providing basic marketing services, the company also provides co-opportunities in advertising, catalogues, bookmarks & workshops. Call or e-mail for more information. Awarded Book Marketers of the Year Award by Book Publicists of Southern California.
Publishing Account(s): Dr Nicolas Bazan; Jana Bommersbach; Alex Cord; Carol Hageman; Dr Rick Niece; Kathy Peach; Sharon Ritt; Conrad J Storad; Sharon Wozny
Membership(s): Arizona Professional Writers (APW); Book Publicists of Southern California (BPSC); The Children's Book Council (CBC); Independent Book Publishers Association (IBPA); Local First Arizona; National Federation of Press Women; Society of Children's Book Writers & Illustrators (SCBWI)

T C Public Relations

One N La Salle St, Suite 600, Chicago, IL 60602
Tel: 312-422-1333
Web Site: www.tcpr.net
Key Personnel
Pres: Thomas Ciesielka *E-mail:* tc@tcpr.net
Publicist: Lori Solyom
Specialize in business, legal & book public relations.

Tandem Literary

28 Clinton Rd, Glen Ridge, NJ 07028
Tel: 212-629-1990 *Fax:* 212-629-1990
Web Site: tandemliterary.com
Key Personnel
Pres & Dir, Mktg: Meg Walker *E-mail:* meg@tandemliterary.com
Pres & Dir, Publicity: Gretchen Koss *E-mail:* gretchenkoss@tandemliterary.com
Founded: 2009
Author tours, pitch book review & features editors, national & local broadcast media, arrange radio interviews, press materials & pitch online media including blogs, social networking & online marketing.

To Press & Beyond

825 E Pedregosa St, Suite 2, Santa Barbara, CA 93103
Tel: 805-898-2263
E-mail: info@topressandbeyond.com
Web Site: www.topressandbeyond.com
Key Personnel
Owner & Pres: Gail M Kearns *E-mail:* gail@topressandbeyond.com
Partner: Penelope C Paine *E-mail:* pennypaine@aol.com
Founded: 2001
Book publishing consulting & support services. We shepherd your print +/or ebook through writing, editing, design & layout, printing, distribution, sales & marketing & promotion, both in trade & niche markets & on the Web. We have worked with over 400 authors & independent publishers worldwide. You can contact Gail Kearns for a half-hour gratis phone consult about your project.
Membership(s): The Association of Publishers for Special Sales (APSS); Independent Book Publishers Association (IBPA)

Toni Werbell Public Relations

5900 Arlington Ave, 9P, Riverdale, NY 10471
Tel: 929-222-4209
E-mail: twprbooks@aol.com
Key Personnel
Principal: Toni Werbell
Founded: 1986
Creation of attention-grabbing press material, including releases, client bios, Q&As, talking points & background material for books, public policy organizations & cultural institutions. Creation of book club Reader's Guides for literary fiction.

Upper Access Inc

87 Upper Access Rd, Hinesburg, VT 05461
SAN: 667-1195
Tel: 802-482-2988
E-mail: upperaccessbooks@gmail.com
Web Site: www.upperaccess.com
Key Personnel
VP & Publr: Stephen T Carlson *E-mail:* steve@upperaccess.com
Publicist: Kristen Lewis
Founded: 1986
Publisher of books & software. Also consult with other publishers on book production, publicity & business operation.
Membership(s): The Association of Publishers for Special Sales (APSS); Independent Book Publishers Association (IBPA); Independent Publishers of New England (IPNE); Publishers North (PubNorth)

Warwick Associates

18340 Sonoma Hwy, Sonoma, CA 95476
Tel: 707-939-9212 *Fax:* 707-938-3515
E-mail: warwick@vom.com
Web Site: www.warwickassociates.com
Key Personnel
Pres: Simon Warwick-Smith
Founded: 1985
Full service television, radio, print & web publicity service for publishers & authors, nationally, regionally & locally. Services include developing & implementing strategic advertising & publicity campaigns; coaching authors on presentation; arranging book signings & lectures; creating press kits, newsletters & feature oriented articles; eliciting pre-publication & post-publication reviews; keeping book distribution reps informed of publisher & author activities. Conference organization available. Specialize in spirituality & celebrity publicity.
Publishing Account(s): Associated Publishers Group; Blake Publishing (UK); Brad Blanton, PhD; Nicholas Brealey Publishing (UK); Business Outreach; Call Sign Press; Career

Press; Celebrity Placement Services; Center for Conscious Evolution; Claremont Publishing; Daimon Verlag (Switzerland); C W Daniels Pty Ltd (UK); Dunhill Publishing; Earth Heart Publishing; Eckankar; Feterson Press; Flaming Rose Press; W Foulsham Pty Ltd (UK); Gateway Books (UK); Global Pacific Records; Grail Foundation Press (Germany); Hawk Press; Barbara Marx Hubbard; Inner Traditions, International; Investment Publishing House; Learning & Integration Inc; Lindesfarne; Barry Long Books (Australia); Mandeville Press/John-Roger; Mashiyach Ministries; Ralph Metzner PhD; Midpoint Trade Books; New Knowledge Library; New Page Books; Noetic Sciences; Origin Press; Phoenix Rising; Pluto Project; Power Press; St Lynn's Press; Seekers Press; Seti Institute; Silver Light Publications; Soka Gakkai International; Tharpa Publishing (UK); Torchlight Publishing; Unity School of Christianity; Valhalla Press; Vorco Publishing; Waveside Press

Weber Shandwick
909 Third Ave, New York, NY 10022
Tel: 212-445-8000 *Fax:* 212-445-8001
Web Site: www.webershandwick.com
Key Personnel
Chmn: Jack Leslie *E-mail:* jleslie@
  webershandwick.com
CEO: Andy Polansky *E-mail:* apolansky@
  webershandwick.com
Pres: Gail Heimann *E-mail:* gheimann@
  webershandwick.com
Founded: 1921
Full service public relations firm with additional expertise in high tech broadcast communications, promotions & healthcare.

Skye Wentworth Public Relations
19 Boardman St, Newburyport, MA 01950
Tel: 978-462-4453
E-mail: skyewentworth@gmail.com
Web Site: www.skyewentworth.org/wordpress;
  www.skyewentworth.org

Key Personnel
Book Publicist: Skye Wentworth
Founded: 2000
Book publicity.

Meryl Zegarek Public Relations Inc
255 W 108 St, Suite 9D1, New York, NY 10025
Tel: 917-493-3601
Web Site: www.mzpr.com
Key Personnel
Pres: Meryl Zegarek *E-mail:* mz@mzpr.com
Founded: 2000
A full service public relations & publicity company with specialties in books, authors, publishing, comprehensive campaigns for traditionally published & self-published authors, media tours, web promotions, as well as consulting on publicity book proposals & marketing.

Irwin Zucker, see Promotion in Motion

Direct Mail Specialists

Listed below are selected firms that are experienced in handling various aspects of direct mail promotion of books.

A B Data Ltd
600 A B Data Dr, Milwaukee, WI 53217
Tel: 414-961-6400 *Toll Free Tel:* 866-217-4470
Fax: 414-961-6410
E-mail: consulting@abdata.com
Web Site: www.abdata.com
Key Personnel
Pres: Thomas R Glenn
Co-Mng Dir: Bruce Arbit; Charles Pruitt
Branch Office(s)
1808 Swann St NW, Washington, DC 20009
Tel: 202-618-2900 *Fax:* 202-462-2085
3507 Kyoto Gardens Dr, Palm Beach Gardens, FL 33410 *Tel:* 561-336-1801
One Battery Park, 32nd fl, New York, NY 10004
Tel: 646-290-9137
19 Weissburg St, Tel Aviv 69358, Israel *Tel:* (03) 720-8782
Membership(s): Association of National Advertisers Inc (ANA)

AllMedia Inc
1400 Preston Rd, No 400, Plano, TX 75093
Tel: 469-467-9100 *Fax:* 214-291-5431
Web Site: www.allmediainc.com
Key Personnel
Pres: Laura McClendon Bogush
E-mail: lmcclendon@allmediainc.com
VP: Rick Becker *E-mail:* rbecker@allmediainc.com
Founded: 1981
Provides full service response media brokerage & management, customized research, planning, presentation & analysis to direct mailers in the US & worldwide. Industries served include business & consumer magazines, catalogs, financial services & retailers.

American International Distribution Corp (AIDC)
82 Winter Sport Lane, Williston, VT 05495
Mailing Address: PO Box 80, Williston, VT 05495-0080
Tel: 802-862-0095 *Toll Free Tel:* 800-678-2432
Fax: 802-864-7749
Web Site: www.aidcvt.com
Key Personnel
Pres & CEO: Marilyn McConnell
Dir, Opers: Michael Pelland
Founded: 1986
Complete direct mail specialists, call center, subscription, continuity, list maintenance, order fulfillment, credit/collections, data management, online capable, Pubnet, Advantis, Internet, web site hosting & development, subscription standing order, periodicals.
Membership(s): Book Industry Study Group (BISG); Independent Publisher's Guild (IPG)

appatura™, A Broadridge Company
Division of Broadridge Financial Solutions Inc
65 Challenger Rd, Suite 400, Ridgefield Park, NJ 07660
Tel: 201-508-6000 *Toll Free Tel:* 800-277-2155
E-mail: contactus@appatura.com
Web Site: www.appatura.com
Key Personnel
CEO: Richard Plotka
CIO: Faisal Fareed
Chief Prod Offr: Harsh Choudhary
Chief Strategy Offr: John Closson
Head, Fin: Alpha Diarra

From data to distribution; overall market plan: copy, design, art, list consultation, printing, literature distribution, computer services, personalized communication, all mailing services.

BMI Global-OMS
100 Beard Sawmill Rd, Suite 360, Shelton, CT 06484-6150
Tel: 203-546-5581 *Fax:* 203-546-5575
E-mail: info@BMIGlobalOMS.com
Web Site: www.BMIGlobalOMS.com
Key Personnel
CEO: Barry Blumenfield

Casemate | IPM
Division of Casemate Group
1950 Lawrence Rd, Havertown, PA 19083
Tel: 610-853-9131 *Fax:* 610-853-9146
E-mail: casemate@casematepublishers.com
Web Site: www.casemateipm.com
Key Personnel
VP, Busn Devt: Simone Drinkwater
Sales Dir: Jane R Graf *E-mail:* jane.graf@casematepublishers.com
Founded: 1995
Full service marketing for book publishers, including: complete direct mail campaigns from concept through production & monitoring results, catalog production, publicity campaigns, trade sales distribution & special sales, web site print-on-demand.

Century Direct LLC
15 Enter Lane, Islandia, NY 11749
Tel: 212-763-0600
E-mail: contact@centurydirect.net
Web Site: www.centurydirect.net
Key Personnel
VP, Sales & Busn Devt: Martin A Rego
E-mail: regom@centurydirect.net
Founded: 1932
Direct mail, newsletters, publications & catalogs, in-house lettershop. Electronic prepress; sheetfed offset printing in 2- & 4-colors; complete bindery; envelope printing, data processing, inkjet & laser imaging, warehousing, shipping & fulfillment.
Membership(s): Direct Mail Fundraisers Association (DMFA); Greater Hudson Valley Postal Customers Council; Greater New York Postal Customers Council; Hudson Valley Direct Marketing Association; National Association of College & University Mail Services (NACUMS); National Catholic Development Conference Council

CG Book Printers
Division of Corporate Graphics Commercial (CGC)
1750 Northway Dr, North Mankato, MN 56003
Tel: 507-388-3300 *Toll Free Tel:* 800-729-7575
Fax: 507-386-6350
E-mail: cgbooks@corpgraph.com
Web Site: www.corpgraph.com
Key Personnel
Pres: Dan Kvasnicka *Tel:* 507-386-6340
Fax: 507-344-5548 *E-mail:* dekvasnicka@corpgraph.com
Sales Exec, Book Mfg Sales: Mike Schmitt
Tel: 507-386-6349 *E-mail:* mjschmitt@corpgraph.com
Founded: 1989

CG Book Printers currently provides book manufacturing services for publishers who sell product to school library & trade markets. In addition, we offer fulfillment services for those publishers wishing to maintain their inventories in the same location where their books are manufactured.
We bind books in hard case & paperback formats. We use Smyth sewn, side sew & adhesive bound for hard case trade or library bound books & section sew, or adhesive bind for paperback books.

Champion Printing Inc
Division of BCS Ventures
3422 Misty Creek Dr, Erlanger, KY 41018
Tel: 859-727-5501 *Toll Free Tel:* 800-543-1957 (US) *Fax:* 859-727-5507
E-mail: sales@championprintinginc.com
Web Site: www.championprintinginc.com
Key Personnel
Pres: Brian Sass
Sales Mgr: Bill Kopp *E-mail:* bkopp@championprintinginc.com
Founded: 1964
Blow-ins, bind-in order form response envelopes in catalog & self-mailers.

Conrad Direct Inc
300 Knickerbocker Rd, Cresskill, NJ 07626
Tel: 201-567-3200 *Fax:* 201-567-1530
E-mail: listinfo@conraddirect.com
Web Site: www.conraddirect.com
Key Personnel
CEO: Barbara Schonwald *E-mail:* bschonwald@conraddirect.com
COO: Steve Maier
Pres: Tom Colwell; Sharon Traina
Founded: 1982
Mailing list brokers & marketing consultants to book publishers & cataloguers who advertise via direct mail also to consumer & business magazine publishers & nonprofit organizations.
Membership(s): Association of National Advertisers Inc (ANA); Direct Marketing Association of Washington; Direct Marketing Club of New York (DMCNY)

Content Critical Solutions
121 Moonachi Ave, Moonachi, NJ 07074
Tel: 201-528-2777
E-mail: sales_info@contentcritical.com
Web Site: www.contentcritical.com
Key Personnel
Pres & CEO: Fred Van Alstyne
CTO: John Slaney
Provides creation, production, digital & conventional printing, fulfillment & electronic delivery of customized & personalized communications.
Branch Office(s)
25000 Industrial Blvd, Hayward, CA 94545

Copywriters' Council of America™ (CCA)
Division of The Linick Group Inc
CCA Bldg, 7 Putter Lane, Middle Island, NY 11953-1920
Mailing Address: PO Box 102, Middle Island, NY 11953-0102
Tel: 631-924-3888; 631-924-8555; 631-604-8599
Key Personnel
Chmn, Consulting Group: Andrew S Linick, PhD
E-mail: cca4dmcopy@gmail.com

Sr Consultant: Gaylen Andrews
EVP: Roger Dextor
Dir, Spec Projs: Barbara Deal
Copy Chief: Kelly Boyles
Professional organization of 35,500 freelance Internet & digital marketing direct response advertising copywriters & consultants in over 1,500 fields that specializes in business, consumer & industrial markets. Create ad copy, design & layouts for the trade; direct mail packages, brochures, catalogs, booklets, circulars. Premiums, customer surveys, package inserts, postcard decks, e-mail campaigns, newsletters, articles, reports, sales manuals, sales letters, how-to books & all types of promotional literature. Phone consultation, second opinion critique service by e-mail. Media schedules, mailing lists, printing, ghostwritten articles, speeches, in-house training seminars, press releases, lead generation, mail advertising & marketing plans. Mailing evaluated & programs reviewed before mailing costs incurred. Also, renewal & billing series. Work accepted on per diem, per project or retainer basis & client satisfaction is guaranteed. Provides comprehensive graphic redesign/new web site content development, interactive services with web site marketing makeover advice for first-time authors, self-publishers, professionals & entrepreneurs. Specializes in online advertising/PR, links to top search engines, consulting on a 100% satisfaction guarantee. Free site evaluation marketing checklist (a $250 value) for LMP readers.
Branch Office(s)
7 Lincoln Ave, Smithtown, NY 11787

The Corporate Communications Group (CCG)
14 Henderson Dr, West Caldwell, NJ 07006
Tel: 973-808-0009 *Fax:* 973-808-9740
E-mail: info@corpcomm.com
Web Site: home.corpcomm.com
Key Personnel
EVP, Sales & Busn: Jeff Pinkin *Tel:* 973-808-0009 ext 2193 *E-mail:* je_pinkin@corpcomm.com
Founded: 1964
Full service marketing support company offering creative services, printing, lettershop/direct mail services & fulfillment.
Branch Office(s)
54 Indian Lane E, Towaco, NJ 07082

Corporate Graphics Book Printers, see CG Book Printers

Demand Marketing
377 Fisher Rd, Suite D, Grosse Pointe, MI 48230
Tel: 313-823-8598 *Toll Free Tel:* 888-977-2256
Fax: 313-823-8598
E-mail: info@create-demand.com
Web Site: www.create-demand.com
Key Personnel
Pres: William Patterson *E-mail:* wpatterson@create-demand.com
Founded: 2003
Direct & database marketing agency. DM strategy, data analytics, database development & creative execution (mail, e-mail, web, telemarketing), outbound business-to-business telemarketing/call center.
Membership(s): Direct Marketing Agency Council; Direct Marketing Association of Detroit

Direct Marketing Solutions Inc
1275 Fairfax Ave, San Francisco, CA 94124
Tel: 415-642-8600 *Fax:* 415-642-8640
E-mail: dmsi@directmailing.com
Web Site: www.directmailing.com
Key Personnel
Principal: Glenn Chase *Tel:* 415-642-8600 ext 128

Planning & development of mail order programs & direct response advertising. Prospect list research, testing, response analysis & database management.

Fairfield Marketing Group Inc
Subsidiary of FMG Inc
The Direct Mail Ctr, 830 Sport Hill Rd, Easton, CT 06112-1241
Tel: 203-261-5585 *Fax:* 203-261-0884
E-mail: info@fairfieldmarketing.com
Web Site: www.fairfieldmarketing.com
Key Personnel
Pres & CEO: Edward P Washchilla, Jr
VP, Cust Serv: Mike Lozada *Tel:* 203-261-5585 ext 204
VP, Fulfillment: Jason Paul Miller *Tel:* 203-261-5585 ext 203 *E-mail:* jason@fairfieldmarketing.com
Founded: 1986
Mailing list brokerage & list management services. FMG clients rely on us for annual direct marketing programs. We are customer driven & accomodate. Specialty services: custom designed account management; expedient list rental approval; monthly usage reports; market & account analyses; fulfillment, mailing & mail response services; freelance art work; graphic design; advertising & promotional copywriting; binding services; lettershop services; computer services. FMG is a full service direct mail marketing firm.
Membership(s): American Booksellers Association (ABA); Bridgeport Regional Business Council (BRBC); Education Market Association; United States Chamber of Commerce (USCC)

The Hibbert Group
400 Pennington Ave, Trenton, NJ 08650
Tel: 609-394-7500 *Toll Free Tel:* 888-HIBBERT (442-2378)
E-mail: info@hibbertgroup.com
Web Site: hibbert.com
Key Personnel
Co-Chmn & CEO: Timothy J Moonan
Co-Chmn: Thomas J Moonan
SVP: Michelle Spedding
SVP, IT: Kenneth J Swiatkowski
SVP, Opers: Ron Arellano; Rosemary Mengel Hober
SVP, Sales: Paul A Zukowski
Personalized laser letters, inquiry programs, rebate programs, mailing list maintenance, collating, inserting, shrink packaging, assembling & mailing, warehousing, fulfillment, distribution, inventory control & inkjet imaging.
Branch Office(s)
1100 US Hwy 130, Robbinsville, NJ 08691 (dist ctr)
19521 E 32 Pkwy, Aurora, CO 80011-8141 (dist ctr)
890 Ships Landing Way, New Castle, DE 19720 (dist ctr)

The Independent Book Publishers Association (IBPA)
1020 Manhattan Beach Blvd, Suite 204, Manhattan Beach, CA 90266
Tel: 310-546-1818
E-mail: info@ibpa-online.org
Web Site: www.ibpa-online.org
Key Personnel
CEO: Angela Bole *E-mail:* angela@ibpa-online.org
COO: Terry Nathan *E-mail:* terry@ibpa-online.org
Vendor Rel, Mktg & Ad: Kathy Sveen *E-mail:* kathy@ibpa-online.org
Founded: 1983 (as Publishers Association of Southern California)

Nonprofit association of independent book publishers offering marketing, education & advocacy.
Membership(s): American Booksellers Association (ABA); The American Library Association (ALA); Book Industry Study Group (BISG)

Lazarus Marketing Inc
50 Charles Lindbergh Blvd, Suite 504, Uniondale, NY 11553-3650
Tel: 516-678-5107; 212-431-3337 *Fax:* 516-766-3160
Web Site: www.lazarusmarketing.com
Key Personnel
Pres: Donna Garda *E-mail:* donnag@lazmkt.com
Full service direct marketing production. Execution of major projects with an emphasis on retail, banking & cable. In-house services include automatic inserting & labeling, laser personalized letters & cards, data processing, data entry, print production & fulfillment.

Andrew S Linick PhD, The Copyologist®
Subsidiary of The Linick Group Inc
Linick Bldg, 7 Putter Lane, Middle Island, NY 11953
Mailing Address: PO Box 102, Middle Island, NY 11953-0102
Tel: 631-924-3888; 631-924-8555; 631-604-8599
E-mail: linickgroup@gmail.com
Web Site: topmarketingadvisor.com
Key Personnel
CEO & Creative Dir: Andrew S Linick, PhD
E-mail: topmarketingadvisor@gmail.com
EVP: Roger Dextor
List Mgr: John Kelty
Copy Chief: Kelly Boyles
Founded: 1969
Complete services in Internet direct response marketing, including mail order, direct mail marketing, complete copy & finished artwork, consulting, brochures, e-commerce campaigns. Internet direct mail, catalogs, lead generating conversion programs, mailing lists, media schedules, interactive media, self-mailers, broadsides, price lists, customer profile questionnaires, premiums & package inserts. Circulation promotion, renewals & collection series, direct mail & mail order copy & design critique service for existing packages & promotions. Direct marketing advice critique service by phone, fax & e-mail for authors, entrepreneurs, first time publishers, small to medium size publishers, marketers of all information products handbooks through interactive programs. Provides comprehensive graphic redesign/new web site content development, interactive services with web site marketing makeover advice for first-time authors, self-publishers, professionals & entrepreneurs. Specializes in flash, animation, online advertising/PR, links to top search engines, consulting on a 100% satisfaction guarantee. Free site evaluation marketing checklist (a $250 value) for LMP readers.
Membership(s): ADA

LK Advertising Agency
Subsidiary of The Linick Group Inc
Linick Bldg, 7 Putter Lane, Middle Island, NY 11953
Mailing Address: PO Box 102, Middle Island, NY 11953-0102
Tel: 631-924-3888; 631-924-8555; 631-604-8599
E-mail: topmarketingadvisor@gmail.com
Web Site: topmarketingadvisor.com
Key Personnel
Pres: Andrew S Linick, PhD
E-mail: linickgroup@gmail.com
EVP & Mktg Res Mgr: Roger Dextor
EVP: Shane Clarke
Dir, Spec Projs: Barbara Deal

Copy Chief: Kelly Boyles
Founded: 1968
Specialize in direct response/direct mail marketing, Internet, mail order, sales & multimedia new product promotions. Development of products for national syndication, money back guarantee on consultation by phone (no charge for initial consultation - password LMP), direct marketing analysis/market research; complete fulfillment & back-end marketing programs; 12-month direct marketing action/business plans; business/consumer/trade launch packages; specialize in circulation promotion, club & continuity plans, mail order selling, creative copy for two-step inquiry/lead generation & conversion packages, trial subscriptions, e-mail & e-commerce campaigns, targeted e-public relations, opt-in mailing lists. Provides comprehensive graphic redesign/new web site content development, interactive services with web site marketing makeover advice for first-time authors, self-publishers, professionals & entrepreneurs. Specializes in online advertising/PR, links to top search engines, consulting on a 100% satisfaction guarantee. Free site evaluation marketing checklist (a $250 value) for LMP readers.
Membership(s): The Association of Publishers for Special Sales (APSS); Direct Mail Marketing Association (DMMA); The Imaging Alliance

MDR, A D&B Co
Division of The Dun & Bradstreet Corp
6 Armstrong Rd, Suite 301, Shelton, CT 06484
Tel: 203-926-4800 *Toll Free Tel:* 800-333-8802
Fax: 203-225-4603 *Toll Free Fax:* 866-532-7097
E-mail: mdrinfo@dnb.com
Web Site: mdreducation.com
Founded: 1969
Marketing information & services for the K-12, higher education, library, early childhood & related education markets. Powered by the most complete, current & accurate education databases available in the industry, MDR provides e-mail contacts & deployment, direct mail lists, sales contact & lead solutions, along with web & social media marketing services.
Branch Office(s)
20 S Clark St, Suite 2100, Chicago, IL 60603, VP, Clients: Steve Gatland *Toll Free Tel:* 800-333-8802 *Fax:* 312-345-4360

Donya Melanson Associates
5 Bisson Lane, Merrimac, MA 01860
Tel: 978-346-9240 *Fax:* 978-346-8345
E-mail: dmelanson@dmelanson.com
Web Site: www.dmelanson.com
Key Personnel
Principal: Donya Melanson
Advertising & design services, web site development, copywriting, mail list research & purchase, production, printing & mailing.

Premier Graphics
860 Honeyspot Rd, Stratford, CT 06615
Tel: 203-378-6200 *Toll Free Tel:* 800-414-1624
Fax: 203-386-1624
E-mail: info@premieruplink.com
Web Site: www.premieruplink.com
Key Personnel
CFO: Cesar Garcia
Founded: 1984
Payment processing, transaction processing, Internet inquiry handling & fulfillment, managed database services, letter, statement, imaging & mailing services.

Swan Packaging Fulfillment Inc
415 Hamburg Tpke, Wayne, NJ 07470
Tel: 973-790-8417 *Fax:* 973-790-0216
Web Site: www.swanpackaging.com
Key Personnel
Pres: Timothy S Werkley *E-mail:* tim@swanpackaging.com
Founded: 1986
Provides third party order fulfillment (pick & pack) & contract packaging services (kit assembly, automated book cartoning & shrink-wrapping). Specialize in book packaging & fulfillment & ship via all carriers, including USPS bulk mail. Operate from a 125,000 sq ft facility located approximately 20 miles west of New York City.
Membership(s): Direct Marketing Club of New York (DMCNY); FMA

Tribal Print Source
Division of Southern California Tribal Chairman's Association
36146 Pala Temecula Rd, Bldg J, Pala, CA 92059
Mailing Address: 35008 Pala Temecula Rd, PMB 436, Pala, CA 92059
Tel: 760-597-2650

E-mail: sales@tribalprintsource.com
Web Site: www.tribalprintsource.com
Founded: 2003
Print pieces are customized by our powerful variable data software engine, enabling each individual piece to be custom tailored in both image & text for each recipient.

Universal|Wilde
26 Dartmouth St, Westwood, MA 02090
Tel: 781-251-2700 *Fax:* 781-251-2613
Web Site: www.universalwilde.com
Key Personnel
Pres & CEO: Stephen Flood
COO: Christopher Armstrong
CFO: Joe Musanti
VP, HR: Jennifer MacAskill
VP, Sales: Jim Bailey
Mktg Mgr: Ryan Collins
Founded: 1958
Communications platform Xccelerate™ for distribution & fulfillment. 15,000 orders fulfilled per week, each with multiple components, as well as on demand output. At peak capacity, we handle more than 50,000 orders, including bulk orders, pick/pack kits, on demand enrollment kits & booklets. Our distribution team processes up to 3 million pieces per day, using multi-list handling, perfect matching systems, read & print capabilities, Intelligent Mail® barcode, commingling & entry point deliver & on-site postal verification.
Branch Office(s)
403 VFW Dr, Rockland, MA 02370 *Tel:* 781-871-7744 *Fax:* 781-878-2967
48 Third Ave, Somerville, MA 02143 *Tel:* 617-591-3000 *Fax:* 617-591-3091

Yeck Brothers Co
2222 Arbor Blvd, Dayton, OH 45439
Tel: 937-294-4000 *Toll Free Tel:* 800-417-2767
Fax: 937-294-6985
Web Site: www.yeck.com
Key Personnel
Pres: Bob Yeck *Tel:* 937-294-4000 ext 205
E-mail: byeck@yeck.com
Founded: 1938
Mailing, database & fulfillment services/plastic cards.
Membership(s): Epicomm

Mailing, Duplicating & Fax Services

ABDI Inc
16 Avenue "A", Leetsdale, PA 15056
Toll Free Tel: 800-796-6471 *Fax:* 412-741-4161
E-mail: e-fulfillment@abdintl.com
Web Site: www.abdi-ecommerce10.com/abdintl;
www.abdintl.com/abdintl
Key Personnel
CEO: Michael D Cheteyan, II
Pres: Judy G Cheteyan *E-mail:* j.cheteyan@
abdintl.com
VP, Fin & IT: Bryan A Cox
Gen Opers Mgr: Ericka D Giles
Produce high quality, efficient & cost-effective
B&W article reprints & standards printing
with a turnaround time of 5 days or less for
associations & the publishing community. Our
services contribute to your success by enhanc-
ing your total quality service to your mem-
bers/customers while drastically reducing your
overall printing costs.

**American International Distribution Corp
(AIDC)**
82 Winter Sport Lane, Williston, VT 05495
Mailing Address: PO Box 80, Williston, VT
05495-0080
Tel: 802-862-0095 *Toll Free Tel:* 800-678-2432
Fax: 802-864-7749
Web Site: www.aidcvt.com
Key Personnel
Pres & CEO: Marilyn McConnell
Dir, Opers: Michael Pelland
Founded: 1986
Lettershop, call center, telemarketing, computer
services, online ordering, subscription, conti-
nuity; direct marketing service, distribution &
fulfillment, web hosting & development.
Membership(s): Book Industry Study Group
(BISG); Independent Publisher's Guild (IPG)

appatura™, A Broadridge Company
Division of Broadridge Financial Solutions Inc
65 Challenger Rd, Suite 400, Ridgefield Park, NJ
07660
Tel: 201-508-6000 *Toll Free Tel:* 800-277-2155
E-mail: contactus@appatura.com
Web Site: www.appatura.com
Key Personnel
CEO: Richard Plotka
CIO: Faisal Fareed
Chief Prod Offr: Harsh Choudhary
Chief Strategy Offr: John Closson
Head, Fin: Alpha Diarra
Founded: 1949
Document management; from data to distribution,
on demand printing. Personalized computer let-
ters, mailing list enhancement, offset printing;
literature distribution & fulfillment; manual &
machine inserting, all mailing services.

CDS Global
Subsidiary of Hearst Corp
1901 Bell Ave, Des Moines, IA 50315-1099
Tel: 515-247-7500 *Toll Free Tel:* 866-897-7987
E-mail: salesinfo@cds-global.com
Web Site: www.cds-global.com
Key Personnel
Chmn & CEO: Malcolm Netburn
CFO: Paul Polus
SVP, Global Opers: Nancy Gessmann
Subscription fulfillment, merge/purge, list main-
tenance & management, demographic segmen-
tation, product fulfillment, printing services,
lettershop, telemarketing.

Branch Office(s)
1550 E Washington Ave, Des Moines, IA 50036
2005 Lakewood Dr, Boone, IA 50036
25 Main Place, Suite 125, Council Bluffs, IA
51503
3107 Shelby St, Harlan, IA 51537
411 E South St, Tipton, IA 52772
1600 36 St, West Des Moines, IA 50266
1419 W Fifth St, Wilton, IA 52778
2286 Crosswind Dr, Suite A, Prescott, AZ 86301
Hearst Tower, 300 W 57 St, 10th fl, New York,
NY 10019
12401 Research Blvd, Bldg 1, Suite 420, Austin,
TX 78759
261-265 Chalmers St, Suite 401, Level 4, Redfern, NSW 2016, Australia *Tel:* (02) 8296 5400
E-mail: sales@cdsglobal.com.au
Tower House, Sovereign Park, Lathkill St, Market
Harborough, Leics LE16 9EF, United Kingdom
Tel: (01858) 468811 *E-mail:* sales@cdsglobal.
co.uk *Web Site:* www.cdsglobal.co.uk

Century Direct LLC
15 Enter Lane, Islandia, NY 11749
Tel: 212-763-0600
E-mail: contact@centurydirect.net
Web Site: www.centurydirect.net
Key Personnel
VP, Sales & Busn Devt: Martin A Rego
E-mail: regom@centurydirect.net
Founded: 1932
Completely automated lettershop, including
inkjetting, data processing, laser imaging, au-
tomatic insertion, line-stamp affixing, comput-
erized enhancement for maximum postal dis-
counts, fulfillment; also 2- & 4-color sheetfed
printing, envelope printing & electronic pre-
press.
Membership(s): Direct Mail Fundraisers As-
sociation (DMFA); Greater Hudson Valley
Postal Customers Council; Greater New York
Postal Customers Council; Hudson Valley Direct Marketing Association; National Association of College & University Mail Services
(NACUMS); National Catholic Development
Conference Council

Fairfield Marketing Group Inc
Subsidiary of FMG Inc
The Direct Mail Ctr, 830 Sport Hill Rd, Easton,
CT 06112-1241
Tel: 203-261-5585 *Fax:* 203-261-0884
E-mail: info@fairfieldmarketing.com
Web Site: www.fairfieldmarketing.com
Key Personnel
Pres & CEO: Edward P Washchilla, Jr
VP, Cust Serv: Mike Lozada *Tel:* 203-261-5585
ext 204
VP, Fulfillment: Jason Paul Miller *Tel:* 203-261-
5585 ext 203 *E-mail:* jason@fairfieldmarketing.
com
Founded: 1986
Mailing list brokerage & list management services. FMG clients rely on us for annual direct
marketing programs. We are customer driven
& accomodate. Specialty services: custom
designed account management; expedient list
rental approval; monthly usage reports; market
& account analyses; fulfillment, mailing & mail
response services; freelance art work; graphic
design; advertising & promotional copywriting;
binding services; lettershop services; computer
services. FMG is a full service direct mail marketing firm.

Membership(s): American Booksellers Association (ABA); Bridgeport Regional Business
Council (BRBC); Education Market Association; United States Chamber of Commerce
(USCC)

First Choice Copy
5208 Grand Ave, Maspeth, NY 11378
Tel: 718-381-1480 (ext 200) *Toll Free Tel:* 800-
222-COPY (222-2679)
Web Site: www.firstchoice-copy.com
Key Personnel
Owner & Pres: Joe Meisner *Tel:* 718-381-1480
ext 212 *E-mail:* jmeisner@nyc.rr.com
Short run perfect-bound books. Full 600 DPI resolution & full cover covers. Serving the publishing industry for reprints & short run book
printing, all electronically printed. Nation's
leading service bureau for on demand printing
utilizing state-of-the-art equipment including
a fully networked Xerox Docutech, 9 5090s,
color equipment - 2 Canon 800s & 500, networked to the Fiery & full in-house bindery.
Most electronic media accepted. Postscript file
preferred, but will accept source applications
too. Shop runs 24/7. Free pick up & delivery
for jobs over $300. Average turnaround 3-5
days.

Global Order Fulfillment, see ABDI Inc

The Hibbert Group
400 Pennington Ave, Trenton, NJ 08650
Tel: 609-394-7500 *Toll Free Tel:* 888-HIBBERT
(442-2378)
E-mail: info@hibbertgroup.com
Web Site: hibbert.com
Key Personnel
Co-Chmn & CEO: Timothy J Moonan
Co-Chmn: Thomas J Moonan
SVP: Michelle Spedding
SVP, IT: Kenneth J Swiatkowski
SVP, Opers: Ron Arellano; Rosemary Mengel
Hober
SVP, Sales: Paul A Zukowski
Complete database management, CRM, multi-
channel engagement, direct mail, promotion &
mailing services, printing & fulfillment.
Branch Office(s)
1100 US Hwy 130, Robbinsville, NJ 08691 (dist
ctr)
19521 E 32 Pkwy, Aurora, CO 80011-8141 (dist
ctr)
890 Ships Landing Way, New Castle, DE 19720
(dist ctr)

PMSI Direct
242 Old New Brunswick Rd, Suite 350, Piscat-
away, NJ 08854
Tel: 732-465-1570 *Toll Free Tel:* 800-238-1316
Web Site: www.pmsidirect.com
Key Personnel
COO: Mark Corsi
Founded: 1984
Complete lettershop & direct marketing support
services.

Premier Graphics
860 Honeyspot Rd, Stratford, CT 06615
Tel: 203-378-6200 *Toll Free Tel:* 800-414-1624
Fax: 203-386-1624
E-mail: info@premieruplink.com
Web Site: www.premieruplink.com

Key Personnel
CFO: Cesar Garcia
Founded: 1984
Payment processing, transaction processing, Internet inquiry handling & fulfillment, managed database services, letter, statement, imaging & mailing services.

PremierIMS Inc
11101 Ella Blvd, Houston, TX 77067
Tel: 832-608-6400 *Fax:* 832-608-6420
E-mail: info@premier-ims.com
Web Site: www.premier-ims.com
Key Personnel
Founder & CEO: Norm Pegram
Pres: Geno Baiamonte
VP, Sales: Max Noble
Founded: 2008
Digital & offset printing, direct mailing services, fulfillment & distribution.

ProFAX Inc
20 Max Ave, Hicksville, NY 11801-1419
Toll Free Tel: 877-942-8100

E-mail: sales@profax.com
Web Site: www.profax.com
Key Personnel
Pres: Ralph Potente
Founded: 1989
Provides fax broadcasting services.

SGW Integrated Marketing Communications Inc
219 Changebridge Rd, Montville, NJ 07045
Tel: 973-299-8000
E-mail: info@sgw.com
Web Site: www.sgw.com
Key Personnel
CEO: Dave Scelba
Pres & COO: Frank Giarratano
Founded: 1986
Branding, advertising, PR & social media design, video, web site design, search engine optimization (SEO), media planning.

Streem Communications LLC
Division of Cleo Communications
4949 Harrison Ave, Rockford, IL 61107

Mailing Address: PO Box 15835, Loves Park, IL 61132-5835
Tel: 815-282-7695 *Toll Free Tel:* 800-325-7732
Fax: 815-639-8931 *Toll Free Fax:* 888-435-2348
E-mail: streemsales@cleo.com; sales@cleo.com
Web Site: www.streem.net
Key Personnel
CEO: Mahesh Rajasekharan, PhD
Fax on demand & fax broadcasting services.

Valid USA
1011 Warrenville Rd, Suite 450, Lisle, IL 60532
Tel: 630-852-8200 *Toll Free Tel:* 800-773-1588 (cust serv); 855-825-4387 (sales)
Web Site: www.valid.com
Services to direct database marketing organizations, including: address & data hygiene such as NCOA, DSF, DPV, LACS, SuiteLink; merge/purge (consumer, business & Canadian); business intelligence; database design, development & support; marketing automation solutions; direct mail printing; personalization (up to 600 dpi); finishing, mailing & commingling; plastic card manufacturing & personalization.

Mailing List Brokers & Services

Mailing list brokers have lists of almost every conceivable type. Names in all trades and professions can be purchased for circulation at a wide range of prices. These firms often handle mailing services as well.

ACT ONE Mailing List Services Inc
237 Washington St, 2nd fl, Marblehead, MA 01945-3334
Tel: 781-639-1919 *Toll Free Tel:* 800-ACT-LIST (228-5478) *Fax:* 781-639-2733
E-mail: info@act1lists.com
Web Site: www.act1lists.com
Key Personnel
Pres & CEO: Steven M Cushinsky
 E-mail: stevec@act1lists.com
Full service mailing, telemarketing, fax & e-mail list compiler, broker & manager.

Acxiom
301 E Dave Ward Dr, Conway, AR 72032
Toll Free Tel: 888-322-9466
Web Site: www.acxiom.com
Key Personnel
CEO: Dennis Self
CIO: Janet Cinfio
Founded: 1969
Provides a comprehensive global suite of consumer insights in the market, allowing you to build premier data lists for powerful digital & offline acquisition campaigns & strategies.
Branch Office(s)
1901 Butterfield Rd, Suite 900, Downers Grove, IL 60515
100 W 33 St, 10th fl, New York, NY 10001
River Place Corporate Park 3, 6500 River Place Blvd, Bldg 3, Suite 300, Austin, TX 78730

ALC Inc
750 College Rd E, Suite 201, Princeton, NJ 08540
Tel: 609-580-2800 *Toll Free Tel:* 800-252-5478
 Fax: 609-580-2888
E-mail: info@alc.com
Web Site: www.alc.com
Key Personnel
Chmn & CEO: Donn Rappaport *Tel:* 609-580-2800 ext 2505 *E-mail:* donn.rappaport@alc.com
Pres & COO: Susan Rice Rappaport
 E-mail: susan.rice.rappaport@alc.com
CFO: Peter Derosa *E-mail:* peter.derosa@alc.com
Pres, ALC Digital: Gregg Galletta *E-mail:* gregg.galletta@alc.com
Pres, Data Mgmt: Britt Vatne *E-mail:* britt.vatne@alc.com
Pres, Smart Data Solutions: Fran Green
 E-mail: fran.green@alc.com
EVP, Info Technol: Patricia Stecher *E-mail:* pat.stecher@alc.com
EVP, Strategic Planning: Bryan MacDonald
 E-mail: bryan.macdonald@alc.com
SVP, Data Acq: Tom Fleming *E-mail:* tom.fleming@alc.com; Rachel Mercer
 E-mail: rachel.mercer@alc.com
VP, Database Servs: Michael Reckinger
 E-mail: michael.reckinger@alc.com
Mng Partner, Data Acq: David Dotson
 E-mail: david.dotson@alc.com
Mailing list manager, broker, compiler.
Branch Office(s)
770 Tamalpais Dr, Suite 204, Corte Madera, CA 94925, Contact: Laurie Cole *Tel:* 415-886-6107
 E-mail: laurie.cole@alc.com
11670 Fountains Dr, Suite 200, Maple Grove, MN 55369, Contact: Tom Fleming *Tel:* 763-400-7665 *E-mail:* tom.fleming@alc.com

539 Bielenberg Dr, Suite 200, Woodbury, MN 55125, Contact: Michael Reckinger *Tel:* 651-264-3052 *E-mail:* michael.reckinger@alc.com
120 White Plains Rd, Suite 205, Tarrytown, NY 10591, Contact: Britt Vatne *Tel:* 914-524-5400 *Fax:* 914-524-5290 *E-mail:* britt.vatne@alc.com
1125 S Ball St, Suite 104, Grapevine, TX 76051, Contact: Holly Hammond *Tel:* 972-871-2828 *Fax:* 972-871-2929 *E-mail:* holly.hammond@alc.com
99 Trophy Club Dr, Trophy Club, TX 76262, Contact: David Dotson *Tel:* 817-742-0758 *Fax:* 817-887-2444 *E-mail:* david.dotson@alc.com

AllMedia Inc
1400 Preston Rd, No 400, Plano, TX 75093
Tel: 469-467-9100 *Fax:* 214-291-5431
Web Site: www.allmediainc.com
Key Personnel
Pres: Laura McClendon Bogush
 E-mail: lmcclendon@allmediainc.com
VP: Rick Becker *E-mail:* rbecker@allmediainc.com
Founded: 1981
Assists clients in building their businesses by identifying new prospects via direct mail & e-mail. List management department helps turn customer housefiles into profit centers & our list & alternate media brokerage department helps plan successful direct marketing campaigns targeted to any offer.

American List Counsel Inc, see ALC Inc

Best Mailing Lists Inc
7507 E Tanque Verde Rd, Tucson, AZ 85715
Toll Free Tel: 800-692-2378 *Fax:* 520-885-3100
E-mail: best@bestmailing.com
Web Site: www.bestmailing.com
Key Personnel
Founder & CEO: Karen J Kirsch
EVP: Herbert Kirsch
Founded: 1984
Direct marketing, e-mail marketing, printing & telemarketing.

CDS Global
Subsidiary of Hearst Corp
1901 Bell Ave, Des Moines, IA 50315-1099
Tel: 515-247-7500 *Toll Free Tel:* 866-897-7987
E-mail: salesinfo@cds-global.com
Web Site: www.cds-global.com
Key Personnel
Chmn & CEO: Malcolm Netburn
CFO: Paul Polus
SVP, Global Opers: Nancy Gessmann
Subscription fulfillment, merge/purge, list maintenance & management, demographic segmentation, product fulfillment, printing services, lettershop, telemarketing.
Branch Office(s)
1550 E Washington Ave, Des Moines, IA 50036
2005 Lakewood Dr, Boone, IA 50036
25 Main Place, Suite 125, Council Bluffs, IA 51503
3107 Shelby St, Harlan, IA 51537
411 E South St, Tipton, IA 52772
1600 36 St, West Des Moines, IA 50266
1419 W Fifth St, Wilton, IA 52778
2286 Crosswind Dr, Suite A, Prescott, AZ 86301

Hearst Tower, 300 W 57 St, 10th fl, New York, NY 10019
12401 Research Blvd, Bldg 1, Suite 420, Austin, TX 78759
261-265 Chalmers St, Suite 401, Level 4, Redfern, NSW 2016, Australia *Tel:* (02) 8296 5400
 E-mail: sales@cdsglobal.com.au
Tower House, Sovereign Park, Lathkill St, Market Harborough, Leics LE16 9EF, United Kingdom *Tel:* (01858) 468811 *E-mail:* sales@cdsglobal.co.uk *Web Site:* www.cdsglobal.co.uk

Cross Country Computer Corp
250 Carleton Ave, East Islip, NY 11730-1240
Tel: 631-334-1810
E-mail: inquiry@crosscountrycomputer.com
Web Site: www.crosscountrycomputer.com
Key Personnel
Founder: Dick Berger *E-mail:* dberger@crosscountrycomputer.com
Principal/Pres & CEO: Thomas Berger
 E-mail: tberger@crosscountrycomputer.com
Principal/EVP: Elisa Berger, PhD
 E-mail: eberger@crosscountrycomputer.com
EVP & Chief Security Offr: Dave Love
 E-mail: dlove@crosscountrycomputer.com
VP, Client Servs: Joan Redwood
 E-mail: jredwood@crosscountrycomputer.com
VP, Fin & HR: Irene Lory *E-mail:* ilory@crosscountrycomputer.com
Dir, Database Architecture: Harvey Cooper
 E-mail: hcooper@crosscountrycomputer.com
Dir, IT: Anita Inkles *E-mail:* ainkles@crosscountrycomputer.com
Mgr, Prodn: Nick Mattina *E-mail:* nmattina@crosscountrycomputer.com
Founded: 1975
Service bureau specializing in database design & maintenance, desktop database systems, data enhancement, profiling, response analysis, modeling, merge/purge, CASS certification, postal presorting, NCOA, list rental fulfillment, data entry & e-mail broadcasting.
Membership(s): Association of National Advertisers Inc (ANA); Direct Marketing Club of New York (DMCNY)

Data Axle
Formerly Infogroup
13155 Noel Rd, Suite 1750, Dallas, TX 75240
Toll Free Tel: 866-DATAXLE (328-2953)
E-mail: sales@data-axle.com; corporate.communications@data-axle.com
Web Site: www.data-axle.com
Founded: 1917
Mailing list selection, compilation & brokerage for direct mail & telemarketing campaigns. Lists include businesses, S&P Big Business companies & their executives, professional offices, institutions, key executives, families by age & income, mail order buyers, association members & publication subscription lists. Free catalog. On-site data processing services.
Branch Office(s)
125 S Wacker, Suite 1700, Chicago, IL 60606
1523 S Bell Ave, Ames, IA 50010
20 Burlington Mall Rd, Suite 300, Burlington, MA 01803
1550 Utica Ave S, No 500, Minneapolis, MN 55416
1020 E First St, Papillion, NE 68046
10 Vose Farm Rd, Peterbough, NH 03458

155 W 23 St, New York, NY 10011

2 Blue Hill Plaza, 3rd fl, Pearl River, NY 10956

4 International Dr, Suite 210, Rye Brook, NY 10573

421 SW Sixth Ave, Suite 400, Portland, OR 97204

2930 Westlake Ave N, Seattle, WA 98109

4001 S Business Park Ave, Marshfield, WI 54449

1290 Central Pkwy W, No 500, Mississauga, ON L5C 4R3, Canada

Dunhill International List Co Inc

6400 Congress Ave, Suite 1750, Boca Raton, FL 33487-2898

Tel: 561-998-7800 *Toll Free Tel:* 800-DUNHILL (386-4455) *Fax:* 561-998-7880

E-mail: dunhill@dunhillintl.com

Web Site: www.dunhills.com

Key Personnel

Owner & Pres: Robert Dunhill *E-mail:* robert@dunhillintl.com

VP, Opers: Cindy Dunhill *Tel:* 561-998-7800 ext 6422 *E-mail:* cindy@dunhillintl.com

VP, Sales: Candy Dunhill *Tel:* 561-998-7800 ext 6424 *E-mail:* candy@dunhillintl.com

Mktg Dir: Lisa Martino *Tel:* 561-998-7800 ext 6421 *E-mail:* lisa@dunhillintl.com

Sr Acct Exec: Greg D'Aquila *Tel:* 561-998-7800 ext 6436 *E-mail:* gdaquila@dunhillintl.com; Chrissi Milano *Tel:* 561-998-7800 ext 6434 *E-mail:* chrissi@dunhillintl.com

Prodn Mgr: Mary Reed *E-mail:* mary@dunhillintl.com

Founded: 1938

Mailing, phone & e-mail lists of domestic & international business firms & executives in all SIC categories including retailers, wholesalers, manufacturers, science & engineering. 120 million families by age, income, etc. Choose from 20,000 categories. Other services provided include: e-mail broadcasting, printing & mailing, e-mail & phone appending & digital display advertising.

Membership(s): Florida Direct Marketing Association

Fairfield Marketing Group Inc

Subsidiary of FMG Inc

The Direct Mail Ctr, 830 Sport Hill Rd, Easton, CT 06112-1241

Tel: 203-261-5585 *Fax:* 203-261-0884

E-mail: info@fairfieldmarketing.com

Web Site: www.fairfieldmarketing.com

Key Personnel

Pres & CEO: Edward P Washchilla, Jr

VP, Cust Serv: Mike Lozada *Tel:* 203-261-5585 ext 204

VP, Fulfillment: Jason Paul Miller *Tel:* 203-261-5585 ext 203 *E-mail:* jason@fairfieldmarketing.com

Founded: 1986

Mailing list brokerage & list management services. FMG clients rely on us for annual direct marketing programs. We are customer driven & accommodate. Specialty services: custom designed account management; expedient list rental approval; monthly usage reports; market & account analyses; fulfillment, mailing & mail response services; freelance art work; graphic design; advertising & promotional copywriting; binding services; lettershop services; computer services. FMG is a full service direct mail marketing firm.

Membership(s): American Booksellers Association (ABA); Bridgeport Regional Business Council (BRBC); Education Market Association; United States Chamber of Commerce (USCC)

Infogroup, see Data Axle

Lake Group Media Inc

One Byram Brook Place, Armonk, NY 10504

Tel: 914-925-2400 *Fax:* 914-925-2499

Web Site: www.lakegroupmedia.com

Key Personnel

CEO: Ryan Lake *E-mail:* ryan.lake@lakegroupmedia.com

COO: Karen Lake *E-mail:* karen.lake@lakegroupmedia.com

SVP: Joe Robinson *E-mail:* joe.robinson@lakegroupmedia.com

Mng Dir: Heather Maylander *E-mail:* heather.maylander@lakegroupmedia.com

Mailing list brokers & managers, database marketing consultants, interactive marketing.

Lawyers & Judges Publishing Co Inc

917 N Swan Rd, Suite 300, Tucson, AZ 85711

Mailing Address: PO Box 30040, Tucson, AZ 85751-0040

Tel: 520-323-1500 *Fax:* 520-323-0055

E-mail: sales@lawyersandjudges.com

Web Site: www.lawyersandjudges.com

Key Personnel

Pres & Publr: Steve Weintraub

Founded: 1963

Lists of mail order buyers of products & publications. Response lists of personal injury attorneys, accountants & financial institutions & insurance claims adjusters, police, accident reconstructionists.

Listco Direct Marketing

1276 46 St, Brooklyn, NY 11219

Tel: 718-871-8400 *Fax:* 718-871-7692

E-mail: info@listcodirect.com

Web Site: www.listcodirect.com

Key Personnel

Pres: Meyer Eckstein

VP: Shlomo Eckstein

Acct Exec: Blima Salczer

List Broker: Simon Winkler

Bookkeeping: Devoiry Horowitz

Full service direct marketing, creative concepts, copy, design, typesetting, full service printing, binding, computer & database services, list marketing & maintenance, merge/purge, list brokerage & management, complete lettershop services.

Marketry Inc

1420 NW Gilman Blvd, No 2558, Issaquah, WA 98027

Tel: 425-451-1262 *Toll Free Tel:* 800-346-2013

Web Site: www.marketry.com

Key Personnel

Pres: Greg Swent *E-mail:* greg@marketry.com

Founded: 1980

Direct mailing lists, opt-in e-mail lists, online media brokerage, database creation & consulting.

MCH Strategic Data

Division of MCH Inc

601 E Marshall St, Sweet Springs, MO 65351

Mailing Address: PO Box 295, Sweet Springs, MO 65351

Toll Free Tel: 800-776-6373

E-mail: sales@mchdata.com

Web Site: www.mchdata.com

Key Personnel

Pres: Amy Rambo

CEO: Peter Long

CIO: Kelly Holder

VP, Mktg: Angela Ridpath

Founded: 1928

Leading provider of data & technology solutions. MCH's commitment to providing superior solutions is evidenced by ongoing investment & development in people, data, technology & services. Those services range from purchasing

or leasing data, database integration & development, custom analytics & data technology solutions.

MDR, A D&B Co

Division of The Dun & Bradstreet Corp

6 Armstrong Rd, Suite 301, Shelton, CT 06484

Tel: 203-926-4800 *Toll Free Tel:* 800-333-8802 *Fax:* 203-225-4603 *Toll Free Fax:* 866-532-7097

E-mail: mdrinfo@dnb.com

Web Site: mdreducation.com

Founded: 1969

Marketing information & services for the K-12, higher education, library, early childhood & related education markets. Powered by the most complete, current & accurate education databases available in the industry, MDR provides e-mail contacts & deployment, direct mail lists, sales contact & lead solutions, along with web & social media marketing services.

Branch Office(s)

20 S Clark St, Suite 2100, Chicago, IL 60603 *Toll Free Tel:* 800-333-8802 *Fax:* 312-345-4360

MSC Lists

PO Box 32510, Minneapolis, MN 55432

Tel: 763-502-8819 *Fax:* 763-571-8292

Key Personnel

Contact: Ann Herrin; Jim Lance

List broker & manager.

Special Libraries Association (SLA)

7918 Jones Branch Dr, Suite 300, McLean, VA 22102

Tel: 703-647-4900 *Fax:* 703-506-3266

E-mail: sla@sla.org

Web Site: www.sla.org

Key Personnel

Deputy CEO: Doug Newcomb *Tel:* 703-647-4923 *E-mail:* dnewcomb1@sla.org

CFO: Linda N Broussard *Tel:* 703-647-4938 *E-mail:* lbroussard@sla.org

Exec Dir: Amy Burke *E-mail:* aburke@sla.org

Founded: 1909

Addresses of SLA member librarians provided for the promotion of products & services used by specialized libraries & information centers & their clients. Subject interests as well as geographic selections are available.

Specialist Marketing Services Inc

777 Terrace Ave, Suite 401, Hasbrouck Heights, NJ 07604

Tel: 201-865-5800

E-mail: info@sms-inc.com

Web Site: www.sms-inc.com

Key Personnel

Chmn: Lon Mandell *E-mail:* lonman@sms-inc.com

CFO: Nora Bush

CTO: Bruce Sherman

EVP, Cust Acq & Strategic Devt: Susan Giampietro

EVP, Data Div: Joanne Adams

VP, Sales: Kathy Hermann *Tel:* 201-865-5800 ext 2230 *E-mail:* kathyher@sms-inc.com

Founded: 1987

List broker of identified mail order buyers of books, magazines & merchandise. Specialize in general merchandise, culture, executive, health, garden & gifts, self-improvement & juvenile. Custom compilations in all fields including business, professional, cultural & consumer markets. Professional list management of direct mail & mail order buyer lists. Computerization, marketing & maintenance of direct mail lists & mail order buyers & subscribers.

Branch Office(s)

2000 Glades Rd, Suite 406, Boca Raton, FL 33431 *Tel:* 561-416-2888 *E-mail:* fl@sms-inc.com

80 South St, Milford, NH 03055, Contact: Jeremy Johnson *Tel:* 201-865-5800 *E-mail:* milford@sms-inc.com

640 Johnson Ave, Suite GL-001, Bohemia, NY 11716 *Tel:* 631-787-3007 *E-mail:* li@sms-inc.com

520 Columbia Dr, Suite 206, Johnson City, NY 13790 *Tel:* 607-770-1985 *E-mail:* ny@sms-inc.com

Philadelphia Technology Park, 4775 League Island Blvd, Philadelphia, PA 19112 *Toll Free Tel:* 888-656-1689 *E-mail:* philly@sms-inc.com

Women's Publications
Imprint of Consumer Press
13326 SW 28 St, Suite 102, Fort Lauderdale, FL 33330-1102
Tel: 954-370-9153 *Fax:* 954-472-1008 (orders only)
E-mail: info@consumerpress.com
Web Site: www.consumerpress.com

Key Personnel
Pres & Publr: Diana Gonzalez
List Mgr & Mktg Dir: Linda Muzzarelli
Founded: 1988
Consumer, homeowner, women's, home business, newspaper, radio, TV, lender, library lists.
Membership(s): Independent Book Publishers Association (IBPA)

Fred Woolf List Co Inc
60 Newtown Rd, PMB 132, Danbury, CT 06810
Tel: 203-456-6239 *Toll Free Tel:* 800-431-1557
Fax: 914-694-1710
E-mail: info@woolflist.com
Web Site: www.woolflist.com
Key Personnel
Pres: Fred Woolf
SVP: Sheila Woolf *E-mail:* sheila@woolflist.com
Founded: 1972
Compilers & brokers of all types of lists; national coverage.

Worldata
3000 N Military Trail, Boca Raton, FL 33431-6321
Tel: 561-393-8200 *Toll Free Tel:* 800-331-8102
E-mail: hello@worldata.com
Web Site: www.worldata.com
Key Personnel
Pres & CEO: Jay Schwedelson *E-mail:* jays@worldata.com
Founded: 1975
The leader in information marketing services, providing postal, e-mail & telemarketing database services & interactive marketing solutions all housed under one roof, with a client base that reads like a who's who in the direct/interactive marketing community.
Membership(s): Association of National Advertisers Inc (ANA); NEPA

Columnists & Commentators — Subject Index

COLUMNISTS & COMMENTATORS — SUBJECT INDEX

Columnists & Commentators

Prior to this section is a list of columnists and commentators classified by their special interests. For related information, see **Radio Programs Featuring Books, TV Programs Featuring Books** and **Book Review Syndicates**.

Letters in parentheses indicate type(s) of media:

(P)–Press   (R)–Radio   (TV)–Television

Publishers, authors and other correspondents are advised that only the U.S. Postal Service can deliver to Post Office Boxes.

Diane Abrams (P)
Whitegate Features Syndicate
Division of Whitegate International Corp
71 Faunce Dr, Providence, RI 02906
Tel: 401-274-2149
Web Site: www.whitegatefeatures.com
Key Personnel
Pres: Ed Isaac
Mgr: Mari Howard
Founded: 1988
Health, beauty, fashion, reviews, beauty products, clothing, spas, exercise equipment, interviews.

Adler, Corey, Issac (P-TV)
Whitegate Features Syndicate
Division of Whitegate International Corp
71 Faunce Dr, Providence, RI 02906
Tel: 401-274-2149
Web Site: www.whitegatefeatures.com
Key Personnel
Pres: Ed Isaac
Mgr: Mari Howard
Founded: 1988
Anything anyone would ever do when they travel.

Jane Adler (P-TV)
Whitegate Features Syndicate
Division of Whitegate International Corp
71 Faunce Dr, Providence, RI 02906
Tel: 401-274-2149
Web Site: www.whitegatefeatures.com
Key Personnel
Pres: Ed Isaac
Mgr: Mari Howard
Founded: 1988
Three columns; indoor gardening, relationships/self-help, medical, health & travel, writes & reviews products & interviews.

Diana Barth (P)
535 W 51 St, Suite 3-A, New York, NY 10019
Tel: 212-307-5465
E-mail: diabarth@juno.com; diabarth99@gmail.com
Columns on performing arts, TV, film & personalities. Book, theatre & film reviews.

David Bouchier (R)
David Bouchier's Commentary on WSHU
PO Box 763, Stony Brook, NY 11790
Tel: 631-751-2660
E-mail: bouchier@wshu.org
Web Site: wshu.org/people/david-bouchier; davidbouchier.com
Founded: 1992
WSHU, Public Radio, Fairfield, CT (weekly/humor).

Wilson Casey, "Trivia" Guinness World Record Holder (P)
TrivGuy Wilson Casey
282 Spring Dr, Spartanburg, SC 29302
Tel: 864-621-7129
E-mail: trivguy@bellsouth.net; wc@triviaguy.com

Web Site: triviaguy.com
Founded: 2000
"Trivia" Guiness World Record holder's "TrivGuy" column, provides trivia columns to newspapers & other media; 6 multiple choice questions with answers syndicated daily (7x/week); Also have a weekly version. King Features Syndicate nationally distributes Wilson Casey's "Bible Trivia" column once a week. Columns run the gamut of category appeal & are available 365 days per year in over 500 papers. Nationwide references. Free trial available.

Leon Collins (P)
Whitegate Features Syndicate
Division of Whitegate International Corp
71 Faunce Dr, Providence, RI 02906
Tel: 401-274-2149
Web Site: www.whitegatefeatures.com
Key Personnel
Pres: Ed Isaac
Mgr: Mari Howard
Founded: 1988
Science.

Steve Corey (P)
Whitegate Features Syndicate
Division of Whitegate International Corp
71 Faunce Dr, Providence, RI 02906
Tel: 401-274-2149
Web Site: www.whitegatefeatures.com
Key Personnel
Pres: Ed Isaac
Mgr: Mari Howard
Founded: 1988
Computer software review; everything in computers: software, hardware, books, gadgets, etc. Also travel column.

Dr Mildred L Culp (P)
WorkWise™
24541 S Wildwood Trail, Crete, IL 60417-3735
E-mail: workwise@comcast.net
Web Site: knoxne.ws/mildred-culp
Founded: 1982
Print & online commentary showcasing emerging trends in the workplace for business & recruitment sections in print & online. Focuses on job hunting, recruitment & careers. Statistics & scholarly findings always welcome.

Carla Demers (P)
Whitegate Features Syndicate
Division of Whitegate International Corp
71 Faunce Dr, Providence, RI 02906
Tel: 401-274-2149
Web Site: www.whitegatefeatures.com
Key Personnel
Pres: Ed Isaac
Mgr: Mari Howard
Founded: 1988
Art review, crafts & craft materials, photography.

Amy E Farrar (P)
Farrar Writing & Editing
4638 Manchester Rd, Mound, MN 55364
Tel: 952-451-5982 *Fax:* 952-472-6874 (call first)
E-mail: amyfarrar@mchsi.com
Web Site: www.writeandedit.net
Founded: 1999
Independent freelance writer & editor for book publishers & individuals. Author of *Global Warming: Essential Viewpoints*, *The Indispensable Field Guide to Freelance Writing* & *ADHD*. Primary topics are environment, health, medical & travel.

Karen Feld (P-R-TV)
Capital Connections®
Division of Capital Connections
304 E 65 St, Unit 26-C, New York, NY 10065-6785
Tel: 212-327-1067; 202-236-0047
E-mail: news@karenfeld.com; karen@karenfeld.com
Web Site: www.karenfeld.com
Founded: 2005
Column runs once a week, political & Hollywood personalities, events, inside gossip, anecdotes, covers arts/business/politics/entertainment. Also contributes to various online columns.

Gayle Feldman (P)
The Bookseller
131 E 74 St, New York, NY 10021
Tel: 212-772-8265 *Fax:* 212-517-4020
E-mail: feldmangayle@gmail.com
Web Site: www.gaylefeldman.com; www.thebookseller.com
New York correspondent for *The Bookseller*; features & reviews for other print & online publications.

Foster Travel Publishing (P)
1623 Martin Luther King Jr Way, Berkeley, CA 94709
Tel: 510-549-2202
Web Site: www.fostertravel.com
Key Personnel
Owner & Pres: Lee Foster *E-mail:* lee@fostertravel.com
Founded: 1972
Travel column available from web site. Full text travel writing photography on 200 destinations worldwide. Reports on essence-of-the destination. Weekly travel commentary blog.
Membership(s): American Society of Media Photographers (ASMP); Bay Area Independent Publishers Association (BAIPA); Bay Area Travel Writers; Society of American Travel Writers (SATW)

Rita Berman Frischer (P)
450 NE 100 St, Suite 426, Seattle, WA 98125
Tel: 206-361-9772; 818-469-0535 (cell) *Fax:* 206-361-9772
E-mail: rcfrischer@aol.com

Book reviewer for Seattle Jewish Transcript-JT News; Los Angeles Jewish Journal; Reform Judaism; Your Child, Jewish Book World; other Jewish interest publications; children's book reviews for various library & Judaic publications; lecturer on librarianship & children. All topics related to Judaism, children's issues & literature.

Joseph C Goulden (P)
1534 29 St NW, Washington, DC 20007
Tel: 202-965-4757
E-mail: josephg894@aol.com
Military & law; intelligence & espionage book reviews for the Washington Times & Washington Lawyer.

Joe & Teresa Graedon (P-R)
King Features Syndicate
Division of Hearst Corp
300 W 57 St, 41st fl, New York, NY 10019
Tel: 212-969-7550 *Toll Free Tel:* 800-526-5464; 800-708-7311 (FL edit) *Fax:* 646-280-1550
Web Site: www.kingfeatures.com; www. peoplespharmacy.org
Syndicated; "The People's Pharmacy", pharmacology column; provides health, pharmaceutical & nutrition information; alternative therapies including herbs & home remedies.

Polly Guerin (P-R)
Pollytalk from New York
15 Park Ave, No 14A, New York, NY 10016-4348
Tel: 212-725-0977
E-mail: pollytalknyc@gmail.com
Web Site: www.pollytalk.com
Writer/commentator on fashion, beauty, house & home, personalities, travel, animals, consumerism, health, inspirational, color theory, Art Deco, Victorian, antiques, decorative arts, collectibles. Several online blogs.

Bruce Hoffman (P)
Whitegate Features Syndicate
Division of Whitegate International Corp
71 Faunce Dr, Providence, RI 02906
Tel: 401-274-2149
Web Site: www.whitegatefeatures.com
Key Personnel
Pres: Ed Isaac
Mgr: Mari Howard
Founded: 1988
Everything to do with business & finance: books & interviews.

Alice Hornbaker (P-R-TV)
Life After 50 & The Alice Hornbaker Show
11050 Springfield Pike, No F-508, Cincinnati, OH 45246
Tel: 513-772-3506 *Fax:* 513-772-3506
E-mail: ajhornbaker@yahoo.com
Web Site: www.wmkvfm.org
"Life After 50", radio column & blog, broadcast on air 3 times weekly WMKV 89.3 FM, Mon 5pm, Fri 2pm & Sun 2pm, aging issues & profiles. "Around the World" on the Internet, Mon 10am at www.wmkvfm.org. "The Alice Hornbaker Show" airs Mon 10-11am, Mon on public radio WMKV 89.3 FM & on the Internet as the "Over-the-Hill" disc jockey playing big band era music, commentary & stories. Author of *WOLD in Cincinnati*, a novel (available on Amazon.com).

Shirley Horner (P)
New York Times
535 Mountain Ave, New Providence, NJ 07974
Tel: 908-795-2512
E-mail: sjhorner@comcast.net

Founded: 1979
Reviewer.

Linda King (P)
Whitegate Features Syndicate
Division of Whitegate International Corp
71 Faunce Dr, Providence, RI 02906
Tel: 401-274-2149
Web Site: www.whitegatefeatures.com
Key Personnel
Pres: Ed Isaac
Mgr: Mari Howard
Founded: 1988
Interviews, current events, senior topics & book reviews.

Jill Kramer - Best of Books (P)
Whitegate Features Syndicate
Division of Whitegate International Corp
71 Faunce Dr, Providence, RI 02906
Tel: 401-274-2149
Web Site: www.whitegatefeatures.com
Key Personnel
Pres: Ed Isaac
Mgr: Mari Howard
Best of books.

Anthony Lane (P)
The New Yorker
One World Trade Center, New York, NY 10007
Tel: 212-286-2860
Web Site: www.newyorker.com
Current cinema reviews; art reviews.

Maria Liberati (P-R-TV)
The Basic Art of Italian Cooking
1250 Bethlehem Pike, Unit 241, Hatfield, PA 19440
Tel: 215-436-9524
E-mail: maria@marialiberati.com
Web Site: www.marialiberati.com
"Maria & Co" & "Maria Liberati's The Basic Art of Italian Cooking™".

Judith Martin (P)
Andrews McMeel Syndication
Division of Andrews McMeel Universal
1130 Walnut St, Kansas City, MO 64106-2109
Tel: 816-581-7300 *Toll Free Tel:* 800-255-6734
Web Site: syndication.andrewsmcmeel.com
"Miss Manners" advice & etiquette column.

Connie Martinson Talks Books (P-TV)
2288 Coldwater Canyon, Beverly Hills, CA 90210
Tel: 310-271-4127
E-mail: talksbks@aol.com
Web Site: www.conniemartinson.com
Key Personnel
Prodr & Host: Connie Martinson
Founded: 1979
Interviews with authors. Streaming video online.

Michael J McManus (P)
9311 Harrington Dr, Potomac, MD 20854
Tel: 301-978-3105
E-mail: mike@marriagesavers.com
Web Site: www.ethicsandreligion.com
Founded: 1981
Writes "Ethics & Religion" for 20 newspapers. Accepts story suggestions.

Vick Mickunas (R)
The Book Nook
4805 Meredith Rd, Yellow Springs, OH 45387
Tel: 937-767-1396
E-mail: vick@vickmickunas.com
Web Site: www.wyso.org/programs/book-nook
Founded: 1994

Independent radio producer & author interviewer. Airs Sat 7-8 AM, Sun 10:30-11 AM (ET) on WYSO public radio. WYSO is a 50,000 watt National Public Radio affiliate that serves southwest Ohio.

Mary Mueller (P)
516 Bartram Rd, Moorestown, NJ 08057
Tel: 856-778-4769
E-mail: mamam49@aol.com
"Soup's On!" & "Letters to a Friend." More topics: marriage enrichment, spiritual, parenting-keeping teenagers off drugs. Also provides freelance proofreading services.
Please send free review copies for possible review in small local media outlets.

The People's Pharmacy, see Joe & Teresa Graedon

Ruth & Robert Reld (P)
Whitegate Features Syndicate
Division of Whitegate International Corp
71 Faunce Dr, Providence, RI 02906
Tel: 401-274-2149
Web Site: www.whitegatefeatures.com
Key Personnel
Pres: Ed Isaac
Mgr: Mari Howard
Founded: 1990
Fine dining, restaurant reviews & food & wine ratings. Also review cooking products, cooking equipment, recipes & recipe books.

Jan Riggenbach (P)
Jandon Features
2319 S 105 Ave, Omaha, NE 68124
Tel: 402-502-4367
Web Site: midwestgardening.com
Midwest Gardening, gardening newspaper. *Garden Idea File*, newspaper.

Alex Ross (P)
The New Yorker
One World Trade Center, New York, NY 10007
Tel: 212-286-2860
Web Site: www.newyorker.com; www. therestisnoise.com
Reviews & analyses of musical events, classical & opera.

Bruce E Southworth Reviews (P-TV)
1621 Lafond Ave, St Paul, MN 55104-2212
Tel: 651-808-1099
E-mail: mnbookcritic@yahoo.com
Key Personnel
Owner & Principal: Bruce E Southworth
Freelance for several newspapers, magazines & Internet sites. Co-produced a cable television program "Speaking of Mysteries", featuring interviews.

Matt Stewart (P)
Whitegate Features Syndicate
Division of Whitegate International Corp
71 Faunce Dr, Providence, RI 02906
Tel: 401-274-2149
Web Site: www.whitegatefeatures.com
Key Personnel
Pres: Ed Isaac
Mgr: Mari Howard
Founded: 1988
Music (including classical music), CD & equipment reviews.

Hope Strong (P)
Whitegate Features Syndicate
Division of Whitegate International Corp
71 Faunce Dr, Providence, RI 02906
Tel: 401-274-2149

Web Site: www.whitegatefeatures.com
Key Personnel
Pres: Ed Isaac
Mgr: Mari Howard
Founded: 1988
"Strong Style"- anything with new ways to live.
  Lifestyles & decorating.

Margaret Swaine (P)
2 Hawthorn Gardens, Unit 4, Toronto, ON M4W
  1P3, Canada

Tel: 416-961-5328
E-mail: m.swaine@rogers.com
Web Site: www.margaretswaine.com
Founded: 1979
Restaurants & travel, ski, golf & spa. Online
  column appears on web sites for Best Health
  Magazine, Ensemble Travel Magazine, National
  Post, Ottawa Citizen, Travel Industry Today &
  Zoomer Magazine. Online column appears on
  the web sites for Air Canada Vacations, Global
  Gourmet & WestJet Vacations.

Eric Tyson (P)
King Features Syndicate
300 W 57 St, 15th fl, New York, NY 10019-5238
Tel: 212-969-7550 *Toll Free Tel:* 800-526-5464
  Fax: 646-280-1550
E mail: eric@erictyson.com
Web Site: www.erictyson.com
Key Personnel
Pres: T R Shephard, III
VP & Gen Mgr: Keith McCloat
Gen Mgr, Syndication: Brendan Burford
Investor's Guide.

Book Review Syndicates

Publishers, authors and other correspondents are advised that only the U.S. Postal Service can deliver to Post Office Boxes.

BookPage®
2143 Belcourt Ave, Nashville, TN 37212
Tel: 615-292-8926 *Fax:* 615-292-8249
Web Site: bookpage.com
Key Personnel
Pres & Publr: Michael A Zibart
  E-mail: michael@bookpage.com
Publr & Ed-in-Chief: Trisha Ping
Assoc Publr: Julia Steele
Deputy Ed: Cat Acree
Mktg Mgr: Mary Claire Zibart *E-mail:* mary@
  bookpage.com
Prodn Mgr: Penny Childress
Founded: 1988
Monthly book review publication distributed
  through subscribing bookstores & public li-
  braries.
Books Reviewed: 1,000

Catholic News Service (CNS)
Division of US Conference of Catholic Bishops
3211 Fourth St NE, Washington, DC 20017-1100
Tel: 202-541-3250 *Fax:* 202-541-3117
E-mail: cns@catholicnews.com
Web Site: www.catholicnews.com

Key Personnel
Natl Ed: Julie Asher *Tel:* 202-541-3266
Book Review Ed: Nancy O'Brien
Founded: 1920
Distribute news stories on books & book reviews
  to Catholic newspaper clients throughout the
  US & more than 60 countries.
Books Reviewed: 75-80

Literary Features Syndicate
88 Briarcliff Rd, Larchmont, NY 10538
Tel: 914-834-7480
Key Personnel
Ed: Barbara Basbanes Richter *E-mail:* barbara.
  basbanes@gmail.com
Reviewer: Nicholas A Basbanes
Young Adult Book Reviewer: Nicole Basbanes
  Claire
Founded: 1991
Reviews of the best new books, author reviews &
  news in the world of books.
Books Reviewed: 200

Rainbo Electronic Reviews
5405 Cumberland Rd, Minneapolis, MN 55410

Tel: 612-408-4057
Web Site: www.rainboreviews.com
Key Personnel
Ed: Richard Trethewey *E-mail:* editor@
  rainboreviews.com
Founded: 1980
Reviews are seen on web site; books (computer,
  mysteries, nonfiction, fiction, children's &
  cookbooks); video & audiobooks.
Books Reviewed: 350

United Press International (UPI)
Subsidiary of News World Communications
1133 19 St NW, Suite 800, Washington, DC
  20036
Tel: 202-898-8000
E-mail: media@upi.com
Web Site: www.upi.com
Key Personnel
Pres: Nicholas Chiaia
Founded: 1907
News, TV, radio, sports & features.
Branch Office(s)
1200 N Federal Hwy, Suite 200, Boca Raton, FL
  33432

Book Review & Index Journals & Services

In order to obtain copyright registration, two copies of every book published in the United States must be sent to the Library of Congress, U.S. Copyright Office, 101 Independence Avenue SE, Washington, DC 20559-6000. All copyrighted materials are then reviewed for eligibility for Library of Congress (LC) cataloging and subsequent listings in the National Union Catalog, the Library's MARC system and other cataloging aids.

In addition to the review sources listed here, one will find reviewers listed in the sections **Magazines for the Trade** (volume 1), **Serials Featuring Books, Radio Programs Featuring Books** and **TV Programs Featuring Books**.

Publishers, authors and other correspondents are advised that only the U.S. Postal Service can deliver to Post Office Boxes.

Abridged Readers' Guide to Periodical Literature
Grey House Publishing Inc™
4919 Rte 22, Amenia, NY 12501
Mailing Address: PO Box 56, Amenia, NY 12501-0056
Tel: 518-789-8700 *Toll Free Tel:* 800-562-2139
Fax: 518-789-0556
E-mail: books@greyhouse.com
Web Site: greyhouse.com
Smaller subset of *Readers' Guide to Periodical Literature*. Comprehensive indexing of 72 of the most popular general-interest periodicals published in the US & Canada.
Frequency: 2 paperback issues, March & Sept plus library-bound annual cumulation in Jan
$295
ISSN: 0001-334X

Academic Reviews
1-A Glenwood Ave, Lynbrook, NY 11563
Tel: 516-593-1275
E-mail: info@academicreviews.com
Web Site: www.academicreviews.com
Key Personnel
Publr: Barbara Fiegas; Preston Treiber
Exec Ed: Carol Hoffman
Ed, Art & Architecture: Douglas Madison
   E-mail: artarch@academicreviews.com
Ed, Busn: Seth Brockman *E-mail:* busbooks@academicreviews.com
Ed, Engg: Robert W Townsend
   E-mail: engbooks@academicreviews.com
Ed, Environment & Energy: Hans G Eckmair
   E-mail: envenergy@academicreviews.com
Ed, Humanities: Helene M Tobin
   E-mail: humanities@academicreviews.com
Ed, Life Sci: Morgen Anne Hoving
   E-mail: lifesci@academicreviews.com
Ed, Lib Sci & Ref: Albert Stahl
   E-mail: libsciref@academicreviews.com
Ed, Physical Sci: Jason Duncan Stonebridge
   E-mail: physicalsci@academicreviews.com
Ed, Security & Terrorism: Peter August Never
   E-mail: secterror@academicreviews.com
Ed, Soc & Behavorial Sci: Cheyenne Page
   E-mail: socbehsci@academicreviews.com
Review titles in undergraduate & graduate fields.
First published 1979
Frequency: Monthly (exc Aug)
Circulation: 5,000
$36/yr US, $44/yr foreign
ISSN: 0894-993X
Books Reviewed: 650/issue

African American Review (AAR)
Modern Language Association (MLA) Division on Black American Literature & Culture
St Louis University, 317 Adorjan Hall, 3800 Lindell Blvd, St Louis, MO 63108
Tel: 314-977-3688 *Fax:* 314-977-1514
Web Site: aar.slu.edu
Subscription Address: Johns Hopkins University Press, Journals Div, PO Box 19966, Baltimore, MD 21211-0966 *Tel:* 410-516-6987

Toll Free Tel: 800-548-1784 *Fax:* 410-516-3866
E-mail: jrnlcirc@press.jhu.edu *Web Site:* www.press.jhu.edu
Key Personnel
Mng Ed: Aileen M Keenan *E-mail:* keenanam@slu.edu
Ed: Nathan L Grant
AAR journal includes essays on African-American literature, theatre, film, art & culture generally; interviews; poetry; fiction & book reviews.
First published 1967
Frequency: Quarterly
Number of pages: 215
Circulation: 1,750
$40/yr indivs US, $48/yr (online), $110/yr instns US (print)
ISSN: 1062-4783
Books Reviewed: 50/yr

American Book Publishing Record® Monthly
Grey House Publishing Inc™
4919 Rte 22, Amenia, NY 12501
Mailing Address: PO Box 56, Amenia, NY 12501-0056
Tel: 518-789-8700 *Toll Free Tel:* 800-562-2139
Fax: 518-789-0556
E-mail: books@greyhouse.com
Web Site: greyhouse.com
Access to the newest cataloging records from the Library of Congress.
Frequency: Monthly
Number of pages: 3,500
$660/yr
ISSN: 0002-7707

American Book Review
University of Houston-Victoria, School of Arts & Sciences, 3007 N Ben Wilson St, Victoria, TX 77901
Tel: 361-570-4848 *Fax:* 361-580-5507
E-mail: americanbookreview@uhv.org
Web Site: americanbookreview.org
Key Personnel
Publr & Ed: Jeffrey R Di Leo
Mng Ed: Jeff Sartain
Asst Ed: Lauren Pirosko *Tel:* 361-570-4139
Literary book reviews.
First published 1977
Frequency: 6 issues/yr
Number of pages: 32
Circulation: 5,000
$5/issue, $24/yr indivs, $30/yr instns
ISSN: 0149-9408
Books Reviewed: 240/yr

American Journal of Philology
Johns Hopkins University Press
2715 N Charles St, Baltimore, MD 21218-4363
SAN: 202-7348
Toll Free Tel: 800-548-1784 (journal orders)
   Fax: 410-516-6968
E-mail: jrnlcirc@press.jhu.edu (journal orders)
Web Site: www.press.jhu.edu/journals/american_journal_of_philology/index.html

Key Personnel
Ed: David H J Larmour
The journal that has helped shape American classical scholarship since 1880, it has achieved worldwide recognition as a forum for international exchange among classicists & philologists.
First published 1880
Frequency: Quarterly
Number of pages: 176
Circulation: 332
$50/yr indivs, $205/yr instns, $45/yr students
ISSN: 0002-9475
Books Reviewed: 10

American Quarterly
Johns Hopkins University Press
2715 N Charles St, Baltimore, MD 21218-4363
SAN: 202-7348
Toll Free Tel: 800-548-1784 (journal orders)
   Fax: 410-516-6968
E-mail: jrnlcirc@press.jhu.edu (journal orders)
Web Site: www.press.jhu.edu/journals/american_quarterly/index.html
Key Personnel
Dir, Mktg & Online Book Publg: Becky Brasington Clark *E-mail:* rbc@press.jhu.edu
Mng Ed: Jeannette Hall
Ed: Mari Yoshihara
Mgr, Info Systems: Stacey L Armstead
   E-mail: sla@press.jhu.edu
The official publication of the American Studies Association, serving as a guide to studies in the culture of the US. Available to members only.
First published 1949
Frequency: Quarterly
Number of pages: 252
Circulation: 4,513
$200/yr instns, $45/yr indivs, $40/yr students
ISSN: 0003-0678

The Annals of The American Academy of Political & Social Science
SAGE Publishing
2455 Teller Rd, Thousand Oaks, CA 91320
Toll Free Tel: 800-818-7243 *Toll Free Fax:* 800-583-2665
E-mail: journals@sagepub.com
Web Site: www.sagepub.com
Key Personnel
Exec Ed: Thomas A Kecskemethy
Mng Ed: Emily Babson
Organized Dec 14, 1889 to promote the progress of political & social science, especially through publications & meetings. The Academy seeks to gather & present reliable information to assist the public in forming an intelligent & accurate judgment.
Also available online (ISSN: 1552-3349).
First published 1889
Frequency: 6 issues/yr
Circulation: 4,800
Instl: $963/$851 (hard/soft), single issue $176/$156 (hard/soft), print & electronic $980/$868 (hard/soft), electronic only $781; Indiv:

$217/$109 (hard/soft), single issue $49/$38 (hard/soft)
ISSN: 0002-7162

ATLA Catholic Periodical & Literature Index (CPLI)
American Theological Library Association
300 S Wacker Dr, Suite 2100, Chicago, IL 60606-6701
Tel: 312-454-5100 *Toll Free Tel:* 888-665-ATLA (665-2852) *Fax:* 312-454-5505
E-mail: products@atla.com
Web Site: www.atla.com
Key Personnel
Exec Dir: Brenda Bailey-Hainer *Tel:* 312-454-5100 ext 4429
Dir, Prodn: Maria Stanton *Tel:* 312-454-5100 ext 4420
Author & subject index to selected list of Catholic periodicals & books: Title bibliography of books, for adults, by Catholic authors & publishers with selection of Catholic-interest books by other authors & publishers; index of book reviews by reviewer. Updated monthly & available online through EBSCO Publishing (www.ebscohost.com).
First published 1930
Frequency: Quarterly; 4th issue is annual cumulated vol
Circulation: 500
ISSN: 0008-8285

AudioFile®
AudioFile® Publications Inc
37 Silver St, Portland, ME 04101
Tel: 207-774-7563 *Toll Free Tel:* 800-506-1212 *Fax:* 207-775-3744
E-mail: info@audiofilemagazine.com
Web Site: www.audiofilemagazine.com
Key Personnel
Founder & Ed: Robin F Whitten *E-mail:* robin@audiofilemagazine.com
Publr: Michele L Cobb *E-mail:* michele@audiofilemagazine.com
Art Dir: Jennifer Steele
Mng Ed: Jennifer M Dowell *E-mail:* jennifer@audiofilemagazine.com
Review Ed: Elizabeth K Dodge
Edit Asst: Alisha Langerman; Joanne Simonean
Audiobook reviews & recommendations. Focus on the listening experience & the unique aspects of the audio performance. Reviews published weekly on web site. Also narrator & author profiles. Award exceptional performances with AudioFile's Earphone Awards.
First published 1992
Frequency: 6 issues/yr
Number of pages: 72
Circulation: 20,000
$19.95/yr, $26.95/2 yrs, $60/yr (prof subn with annual "Audiobook Reference Guide"); $10/issue
ISSN: 1063-0244
Books Reviewed: 2,500/yr

The Barnhart Dictionary Companion
Lexik House Publishers
PO Box 2018, Hyde Park, NY 12538
Tel: 845-489-0333
E-mail: info@lexikhouse.com
Web Site: www.lexikhouse.com
Key Personnel
Publr & Ed: David K Barnhart
Review dictionaries & other books about language; fully document 1,500 new words, new meanings & changes in usage annually.
First published 1982
Frequency: Quarterly
Number of pages: 103
$98/yr US, $116 foreign
ISSN: 0736-1122
Books Reviewed: 4/issue, 16/yr

BC BookWorld
Subsidiary of A R T Bookworld Productions Ltd
3516 W 13 Ave, Vancouver, BC V6R 2S3, Canada
Tel: 604-736-4011 *Fax:* 604-736-4011
E-mail: bookworld@telus.net
Web Site: www.bcbookworld.com
Key Personnel
Publr: Alan Twigg
News & photos of BC books & authors.
First published 1987
Frequency: Quarterly
Circulation: 45,000
$25/yr, $40/2 yrs
ISSN: 1701-5405
Books Reviewed: 100/issue, 400/yr

Bellevue Literary Review
NYU School of Medicine, Dept of Medicine, 550 First Ave, OBV-A612, New York, NY 10016
Tel: 212-263-3973
E-mail: info@BLReview.org
Web Site: www.BLReview.org
Key Personnel
Publr: David Oshinsky
Ed-in-Chief: Dr Danielle Ofri
Mng Ed: Stacy Bodziak
Sr Nonfiction Ed: Dr Jerome Lowenstein
Sr Fiction Ed: Ronna Wineberg
Poetry Ed: Jason Schneiderman
Fiction Ed: Suzanne McConnell
Asst Poetry Ed: Jen Hyde
Editors invite submissions of previously unpublished works of fiction, creative nonfiction, poetry & critical essays that touch upon relationships to the human body, illness, health & healing. We encourage creative interpretations of these themes. Interested in high-quality literary writing.
First published 2001
Frequency: Semiannual
Number of pages: 192
Circulation: 3,000
$20/yr
ISSN: 1537-5048
Books Reviewed: 1/issue

Henry Berry
293 Ellsworth St, No 8D, Bridgeport, CT 06605
Mailing Address: PO Box 176, Southport, CT 06890
Tel: 203-332-7629
E-mail: henryberryinct@gmail.com
Independent book reviewer (formerly Editor/Publisher of *The Small Press Book Review*) of nonfiction & university press works mainly in the areas of cultural history, history, social history, regional studies, literary criticism, biography, minority studies & political philosophy posted at academia.com, Amazon & Goodreads with links to Facebook & Twitter.
Books Reviewed: 30-50/yr

Book Review Index
Gale
Division of Cengage Learning
27500 Drake Rd, Farmington Hills, MI 48331-3535
SAN: 213-4373
Tel: 248-699-4253 *Toll Free Tel:* 800-877-4253 *Fax:* 248-699-8074 *Toll Free Fax:* 800-414-5043 (orders); 800-414-5045
E-mail: gale.galeord@cengage.com
Web Site: www.gale.com
Key Personnel
PR Mgr, Corp Communs: Kristina Massari
Provides access to reviews of books, periodicals, books on tape & electronic media representing a wide range of popular, academic & professional interests.
First published 1965
Frequency: Annual

$685/yr
ISSN: 0524-0581
Books Reviewed: more than 600 publications are indexed including journals & national general interest publications & newspapers

Bookforum
350 Seventh Ave, New York, NY 10001
Tel: 212-475-4000 *Fax:* 212-529-1257
E-mail: info@bookforum.com; editors@bookforum.com
Web Site: www.bookforum.com
Key Personnel
Exec Publr: Danielle McConnell
Mktg Dir: Kate Koza *E-mail:* kate@bookforum.com
The preeminent review of literary fiction, scholarly nonfiction & arts criticism.
First published 1994
Frequency: 5 issues/yr
Circulation: 38,500
$4.95/newsstand, $18/1 yr subn, $32/2 yr subn

Booklist
The American Library Association (ALA)
225 N Michigan Ave, Suite 1300, Chicago, IL 60601
SAN: 201-0062
Tel: 312-944-6780 *Toll Free Tel:* 800-545-2433 *Fax:* 312-440-9374
E-mail: info@booklistonline.com; ala@ala.org
Web Site: www.booklistonline.com; www.ala.org
Subscription Address: PO Box 421027, Palm Coast, FL 32142 *Toll Free Tel:* 888-350-0949
E-mail: blst@kable.com
Key Personnel
Ed & Publr: Bill Ott *E-mail:* bott@ala.org
Adult Books Ed: Donna Seaman *E-mail:* dseaman@ala.org
Video Ed: Sue-Ellen Beauregard *E-mail:* sbeaureg@ala.org
Off Mgr: Michael Ruzicka
Review adult, young adult & juvenile books (most before publication); media, including videos, DVDs, audios & audiobooks, encyclopedias, dictionaries & other reference works including online databases.
Frequency: Semimonthly (exc monthly July & Aug); 22 issues/yr
Circulation: 24,000
$9/issue, $165.50/yr, $279.50/2 yrs, $389.50/3 yrs, $184/yr foreign
ISSN: 0006-7385
Books Reviewed: 4,500/yr (adult), 3,700/yr (youth), 900/yr (media), 600/yr (reference)

Boston Review
Boston Critic Inc
PO Box 425786, Cambridge, MA 02142
Mailing Address: 30 Wadsworth St, E53-70, Cambridge, MA 02142
Tel: 617-324-1360 *Toll Free Tel:* 877-406-2443 (cust serv) *Fax:* 617-452-3356
E-mail: review@bostonreview.net
Web Site: bostonreview.net
Key Personnel
Publr: Louisa Daniels Kearney
Mng Ed: Adam McGee *E-mail:* adam@bostonreview.net
Ed-in-Chief: Deborah Chasman *E-mail:* deb@bostonreview.net; Joshua Cohen *E-mail:* jcohen57@stanford.edu
Mktg Mgr: Anne Boylan
Sr Ed: Chloe Fox *E-mail:* chloe@bostonreview.net
Magazine of culture & politics. Books reviewed bimonthly in print & online.
First published 1975
Frequency: 6 issues/yr
Number of pages: 64
Circulation: 10,000
$39.95/yr, $59.95/2 yrs
ISSN: 0734-2306

Bulletin of the American Schools of Oriental Research (BASOR)
American Schools of Oriental Research (ASOR)
Boston University, 656 Beacon St, 5th fl, Boston, MA 02215
Tel: 617-353-6570 *Fax:* 617-353-6575
E-mail: asor@bu.edu; asorpubs@bu.edu
Web Site: www.asor.org (print only subns); www.jstor.org (electronic only & print plus electronic subns)
Key Personnel
Co-Ed: Eric H Cline; Christopher A Rollston
Pubns & Fulfillment Mgr: Inda Omerefendic
Tel: 617-358-4376
First published 1919
Frequency: 2 issues/yr
Number of pages: 120
Circulation: 1,700
$290/yr instns (print), $322 foreign
ISSN: 0003-097X
Books Reviewed: 9

Bulletin of the History of Medicine
Johns Hopkins University Press
2715 N Charles St, Baltimore, MD 21218-4363
SAN: 202-7348
Toll Free Tel: 800-548-1784 (journal orders)
Fax: 410-516-6968
E-mail: jrnlcirc@press.jhu.edu (journal orders)
Web Site: www.press.jhu.edu/journals/bulletin_of_the_history_of_medicine/index.html
Key Personnel
Ed: Mary Fissell; Randall M Packard
Assoc Ed: Carolyn McLaughlin
Official publication of the Association for the History of Medicine & Johns Hopkins Institute of the History of Medicine.
Frequency: Quarterly
Number of pages: 255
Circulation: 1,573
$50/yr indivs, $195/yr instns, $45/yr students
ISSN: 0007-5140
Books Reviewed: 100

Callaloo
Johns Hopkins University Press
2715 N Charles St, Baltimore, MD 21218-4363
SAN: 202-7348
Toll Free Tel: 800-548-1784 (journal orders)
Fax: 410-516-6968
E-mail: jrnlcirc@press.jhu.edu (journal orders)
Web Site: www.press.jhu.edu/journals/callaloo/index.html
Key Personnel
Ed: Charles Rowell
A journal of African-American & African arts & letters.
Frequency: Quarterly
Number of pages: 300
Circulation: 600
$65/yr indivs, $225/yr instns
ISSN: 0161-2492
Books Reviewed: 12

The Bulletin of the Center for Children's Books
Johns Hopkins University Press
2715 N Charles St, Baltimore, MD 21218-4363
SAN: 202-7348
Tel: 410-516-6900; 410-516-6987 (journal orders outside US & CN); 217-244-0324 (bulletin info) *Toll Free Tel:* 800-548-1784 (journal orders) *Fax:* 410-516-6968; 410-516-3866 (journal orders)
E-mail: bccb@illinois.edu; jlorder@jhupress.jhu.edu
Web Site: www.press.jhu.edu/journals/bulletin-center-childrens-books
Key Personnel
Ed: Deborah Stevenson
Review juvenile books.
First published 1947

Frequency: 11 issues/yr
Number of pages: 40
Circulation: 1,000
$55/yr indivs, $120/yr instns (print or online)
ISSN: 0008-9036
Books Reviewed: 900/yr

Children's Bookwatch
Midwest Book Review
278 Orchard Dr, Oregon, WI 53575-1129
Tel: 608-835-7937
E-mail: mbr@execpc.com
Web Site: www.midwestbookreview.com
Key Personnel
Ed-in-Chief: James A Cox
Review large & small press publications: audio cassettes, videos, young adult/children's books, fiction, general interest nonfiction, CD music & children's educational CD-ROMs.
First published 1990
Frequency: Monthly
Number of pages: 8
Circulation: 50,000
Free online
ISSN: 0896-4521
Books Reviewed: 70/issue

CHOICE
Association of College & Research Libraries (ACRL)
Division of The American Library Association (ALA)
575 Main St, Suite 300, Middletown, CT 06457
Tel: 860-347-6933; 860-347-1387 (ad); 240-646-7027 (subn); 818-487-4555
E-mail: acrlsubscriptions@pubservice.com; support@acrlchoice.freshdesk.com
Web Site: www.ala.org/acrl/choice; www.choice360.org
Subscription Address: PO Box 15995, North Hollywood, CA 91615 *Tel:* 818-487-4555 *Toll Free Tel:* 844-291-0455 *Fax:* 818-487-4550 *E-mail:* acrlsubscriptions@pubservice.com
Key Personnel
Publr & Ed: Mark Cummings *Tel:* 860-347-6933 ext 119 *E-mail:* mcummings@ala-choice.org
Edit Dir: Bill Mickey *E-mail:* bmickey@ala-choice.org
Dir, Info & Prodn Servs: Lisa Gross
Dir, Opers: Rachel Hendrick
Ad Sales Mgr: Pamela Marino *E-mail:* pmarino@ala-choice.org
Humanities Ed: Becky Bartlett
Math & Natural Sci Ed: Melissa Ceraso
Political Sci Ed: John Stoehr
Ref Ed: Pamela Sandstrom
Soc Sciences Ed: Lisa Mitten
Sr Web Developer: Jason Simon
Current, comparative reviews of nonfiction & reference books & electronic resources of importance to universities, 2- & 4-year colleges, public & special libraries & the informed public. Serves national libraries in Europe, Asia & Australia. Available online as *Choice Reviews Online.*
Frequency: Monthly
Circulation: 2,400
$469/yr US, $499/yr CN & Mexico, $599/yr foreign
ISSN: 0009-4978
Books Reviewed: 7,000+/yr

Chronicles: A Magazine of American Culture
The Charlemagne Institute
8011 34 Ave S, Suite C11, Bloomington, MN 55425
Web Site: www.chroniclesmagazine.org
Subscription Address: PO Box 3247, Northbrook, IL 60065-9968 *Toll Free Tel:* 800-877-5459
Key Personnel
Exec Ed: Edward Welsch

Book reviews, political, economic & social criticism.
First published 1977
Frequency: Monthly
Number of pages: 52
Circulation: 7,500
$44.99/yr, $79.99/2 yrs, $104.99/3 yrs
ISSN: 0887-5731
Books Reviewed: 7/issue (3 in-depth, 4 in-brief)

Communication Abstracts
EBSCO Publishing
10 Estes St, Ipswich, MA 01938
Tel: 978-356-6500 *Toll Free Tel:* 800-653-2726 *Fax:* 978-356-6565
E-mail: information@ebscohost.com
Web Site: www.ebscohost.com
Key Personnel
Pres & CEO: Tim Collins *E-mail:* tcollins@ebscohost.com
EVP, Mktg, Sales, PR & Strategic Partnerships: Sam Brooks *E-mail:* sbrooks@ebscohost.com
VP, Communs: Kathleen McEvoy *Tel:* 800-653-2726 ext 2594 *E-mail:* kmcevoy@ebsco.com
Provides coverage of recent literature in all areas of communication studies (both mass & interpersonal). Includes expanded coverage of new communications technologies.
First published 1978
Frequency: 6 issues/yr
Circulation: 1,300

Current Biography
Grey House Publishing Inc™
4919 Rte 22, Amenia, NY 12501
Mailing Address: PO Box 56, Amenia, NY 12501-0056
Tel: 518-789-8700 *Toll Free Tel:* 800-562-2139 *Fax:* 518-789-0556
E-mail: books@greyhouse.com
Web Site: greyhouse.com
Offers 19-20 biographical, up-to-date profiles of accomplished & rising stars of politics, industry, entertainment & the arts from the US & around the world.
First published 1940
Frequency: 11 issues/yr
$199/yr, $370/2 yrs, $495/3 yrs
ISSN: 0011-3344

Dayton Daily News
Cox Media Group Ohio
Unit of Cox Media (Atlanta)
4805 Meredith Rd, Yellow Springs, OH 45387
Tel: 937-767-1396
Key Personnel
Book Reviewer: Vick Mickunas *E-mail:* vick@vickmickunas.com
Vick Mickunas is the author of regular reviews in the print version of the *Dayton Daily News* & other Cox Ohio newspapers. His reviews are also published on the Cox Ohio web sites.
First published 2004
Circulation: 192,000 (Sun)
ISSN: 0890-8931

Diacritics
Johns Hopkins University Press
2715 N Charles St, Baltimore, MD 21218-4363
SAN: 202-7348
Toll Free Tel: 800-548-1784 (journal orders)
Fax: 410-516-6968
E-mail: jrnlcirc@press.jhu.edu (journal orders)
Web Site: www.press.jhu.edu/journals/diacritics/index.html
Key Personnel
Mng Ed: Diane Brown
Ed: Laurent Dubreuil
A preeminent forum for exchange among literary theorists, critics & philosophers. Each issue features articles in which contributors compare & analyze books on particular theoretical

works & develop their own positions on the theses, methods & theoretical implications of these works.
Frequency: Quarterly
Number of pages: 80
Circulation: 205
$40/yr indivs, $133/yr instns
ISSN: 0300-7162
Books Reviewed: 5

District Administration Magazine
Professional Media Group
35 Nutmeg Dr, Suite 205, Trumbull, CT 06611
Tel: 203-663-0100
E-mail: circulation@promediagrp.com
Web Site: www.districtadministration.com
Key Personnel
Publr: Daniel E Kinnaman *Tel:* 203-663-0106
 Fax: 203-663-0149 *E-mail:* dkinnaman@
 promediagrp.com
Edit Dir: J D Solomon
Educational ideas & leadership for district-level decision makers. Each issue investigates how trends in curriculum development & breakthroughs in technology are transforming America's schools. From profiles of successful school programs & provocative opinion pieces, to product info, research summaries & the most important education news. Written to help school district leaders improve their schools & communities.
Frequency: 10 issues/yr
Circulation: 200,000 print & digital
Free to district level administrators, school bd chmn & district level busn offrs; $72/yr for all others
ISSN: 1537-5749
Books Reviewed: 10/issue

E L H (English Literary History)
Johns Hopkins University Press
2715 N Charles St, Baltimore, MD 21218-4363
SAN: 202-7348
Toll Free Tel: 800-548-1784 (journal orders)
 Fax: 410-516-3866 (journal orders)
E-mail: jrnlcirc@press.jhu.edu (journal orders)
Web Site: www.press.jhu.edu/journals/
 english_literary_history/index.html
Key Personnel
Mng Ed: Sarah Ross
Ed: Douglas Mao
Frequency: Quarterly
Number of pages: 256
Circulation: 999
$50/yr indivs, $240/yr instns, $40/yr students
ISSN: 0013-8304

Film Quarterly
University of California Press
Journals & Digital Publishing, 155 Grand Ave, Suite 400, Oakland, CA 94612-3758
Tel: 510-883-8326 (fulfillment) *Fax:* 510-836-8910 (fulfillment)
E-mail: customerservice@ucpress.edu
Web Site: www.filmquarterly.org; fq.ucpress.edu
Key Personnel
Ed: B Ruby Rich
Assoc Ed: Regina Longo *E-mail:* regina@
 filmquarterly.org
Book Review Ed: Noah Isenberg
Edit Asst: Marc Francis
Academic journal of film, television & video, theory & criticism. Also includes reviews of current & recent books.
First published 1945
Frequency: Quarterly
Number of pages: 125
Circulation: 1,000
$60/yr indiv (print & online), $46/yr indiv (online), $26/yr student (online)
ISSN: 0015-1386
Books Reviewed: 30/yr

First Things: A Journal of Religion, Culture & Public Life
Institute on Religion & Public Life
35 E 21 St, 6th fl, New York, NY 10010
Tel: 212-627-1985 *Fax:* 212-627-2184
E-mail: ft@firstthings.com
Web Site: www.firstthings.com
Subscription Address: PO Box 8509, Big Sandy, TX 75755-9955 *Toll Free Tel:* 877-905-9920
Key Personnel
Ed: R R Reno
A monthly journal of religion & public life.
First published 1991
Frequency: Monthly (10/yr; 2 double issues, June/July & Aug/Sept)
Circulation: 30,000
$4.95/issue, $39/yr
ISSN: 1047-5141
Books Reviewed: 5-6 major reviews/issue (50-60/yr)

Forecast
Baker & Taylor LLC
2550 W Tyvola Rd, Suite 300, Charlotte, NC 28217
Mailing Address: PO Box 6885, Bridgewater, NJ 08807-0855
Tel: 704-998-3100 *Toll Free Tel:* 800-775-1800 (info servs); 800-775-1700 (cust serv)
 Toll Free Fax: 866-557-3396 (cust serv)
E-mail: btinfo@baker-taylor.com
Web Site: www.baker-taylor.com
Key Personnel
Dir, Mdsg, Ad Sales & Edit: Lynn Bond
Ed: Charles Pizar
Mktg Specialist: Donna Heffner
Promotes new & forthcoming adult hardcover, paperback & spoken word audio titles. Digital only.
First published 1969
Frequency: Monthly
Number of pages: 87
Free

Foreword Reviews
Division of Foreword Magazine Inc
413 E Eighth St, Traverse City, MI 49686
Tel: 231-933-3699
Web Site: www.forewordreviews.com
Key Personnel
Publr: Victoria Sutherland *E-mail:* victoria@
 forewordreviews.com
Assoc Publr: Bill Harper *E-mail:* bill@
 forewordreviews.com
Ed-in-Chief: Matt Sutherland *E-mail:* matt@
 forewordreviews.com
Mng Ed: Michelle Anne Schingler
 E-mail: mschingler@forewordreviews.com
Review source covering independent & university presses only. Sent to booksellers & librarians across the country. Also available online & major newsstands.
First published 1998
Frequency: 6 issues/yr
Number of pages: 95
Circulation: 30,000
$5.99 each, $29.95/yr, $59.95/yr intl
ISSN: 1099-2642
Books Reviewed: 40/issue

Forthcoming Books™
Grey House Publishing Inc™
4919 Rte 22, Amenia, NY 12501
Mailing Address: PO Box 56, Amenia, NY 12501-0056
Tel: 518-789-8700 *Toll Free Tel:* 800-562-2139
 Fax: 518-789-0556
E-mail: books@greyhouse.com
Web Site: greyhouse.com
Lists just-published & to-be-published books, with ISBNs & US Library of Congress numbers.

First published 1966
Frequency: Quarterly
Number of pages: 4,500
$550/yr
ISSN: 0015-8119

Harvard Educational Review
Harvard Education Publishing Group
Division of Harvard Graduate School of Education
8 Story St, 1st fl, Cambridge, MA 02138
Tel: 617-495-3432 *Toll Free Tel:* 888-437-1437 (orders) *Fax:* 617-496-3584; 978-348-1233 (orders)
Web Site: hepg.org/her-home/home
Key Personnel
Assoc Dir & Ed-in-Chief: Caroline Chauncey
 E-mail: caroline_chauncey@harvard.edu
Dir, Sales & Mktg: Christina DeYoung
 E-mail: christina_deyoung@gse.harvard.edu
Ms Subns & Rts & Perms: Laura Clos
 E-mail: laura_clos@harvard.edu
Scholarly opinion & research in the field of education. Readers include professional educators & researchers, school & college administrators; college, university, school & public libraries. Also available online (ISSN: 1943-5045).
First published 1931
Frequency: Quarterly
Circulation: 2,700 paid
Individuals (print & online): $61/yr US, $84/yr CN, $102/yr intl; Individuals (online only): $41/yr; Institutions (print & online): $435/yr US, $450/yr CN, $508/yr intl; Institutions (online only): $397/yr
ISSN: 0017-8055
Books Reviewed: 12/yr

The Henry James Review
Johns Hopkins University Press
2715 N Charles St, Baltimore, MD 21218-4363
SAN: 202-7348
Tel: 410-516-6987 (journal orders outside US & CN) *Toll Free Tel:* 800-548-1784 (journal orders) *Fax:* 410-516-6968
E-mail: jrnlcirc@press.jhu.edu (journal orders)
Web Site: www.press.jhu.edu/journals/
 henry_james_review/index.html
Key Personnel
Mng Ed: B Joanne Webb
Ed: Susan M Griffin
Publishes spirited critical essays & reviews of this major American writer by noted critics, bringing together contemporary scholarly, critical & theoretical work.
Frequency: 3 issues/yr
Number of pages: 108
Circulation: 343
$40/yr indivs, $128/yr instns, $35/yr students
ISSN: 0273-0340
Books Reviewed: 5

The Historical Novels Review
Historical Novel Society
400 Dark Star Ct, Fairbanks, AK 99709
Tel: 217-581-7538 *Fax:* 217-581-7534
E-mail: reviews@historicalnovelsociety.org
Web Site: historicalnovelsociety.org
Key Personnel
Publisher: Richard Lee *E-mail:* richard@
 historicalnovelsociety.org
Mng Ed: Bethany Latham *E-mail:* blatham@jsu.edu
Book Review Ed: Sarah Johnson
 E-mail: sljohnson2@eiu.edu
Features Editor: Lucinda Byatt
 E-mail: textline13@gmail.com
US Membership Secy: Georgine Olson
 E-mail: georgine@mosquitonet.com
Reviews currently published historical fiction from the US & Great Britain.
First published 1997
Frequency: Quarterly

Number of pages: 64
Circulation: 1,400
$50/yr
ISSN: 1471-7492
Books Reviewed: 1,200/yr

History: Reviews of New Books
Taylor & Francis Inc
530 Walnut St, Suite 850, Philadelphia, PA 19106
Tel: 215-625-8900 (ext 4) *Toll Free Tel:* 800-354-1420 *Fax:* 215-207-0050; 215-207-0046 (cust serv)
E-mail: historyreviews@taylorandfrancis.com; support@tandfonline.com
Web Site: www.tandfonline.com
Lets readers know what's new in current scholarship on historical topics. Covers all geographic areas & time periods, from ancient times to present. The reviews outline & evaluate the author's arguments, describe the sources used in the research & place the book in the context of other scholarship.
Also available online (ISSN: 1930-8280).
First published 1972
Frequency: 6 issues/yr
Number of pages: 40
Circulation: 400
$144/yr indivs (print & online), $441/yr instns (print & online), $386/yr instns (online only)
ISSN: 0361-2759
Books Reviewed: 150/yr

The Horn Book Guide
Horn Book Inc
300 The Fenway, Suite P-311, Palace Road Bldg, Boston, MA 02115
Tel: 617-278-0225 *Toll Free Tel:* 888-628-0225
  Fax: 617-278-6062
E-mail: info@hbook.com
Web Site: www.hbook.com
Subscription Address: 7585 Industrial Pkwy, Plain City, OH 43064 *Toll Free Tel:* 877-523-6072 *Fax:* 760-317-2335 *E-mail:* hbgsubs@pcspublink.com
Key Personnel
Group Publr: Rebecca T Miller *Tel:* 646-380-0738 *E-mail:* rmiller@mediasourceinc.com
Ed-in-Chief: Roger Sutton
Creative Dir: Lolly Robinson *Tel:* 617-628-0225 ext 226 *E-mail:* lrobinson@hbook.com
Mng Ed: Katrina Hedeen *E-mail:* khedeen@hbook.com
Assoc Ed: Cynthia K Ritter *E-mail:* critter@hbook.com
Edit Asst: Russell Perry *E-mail:* rperry@hbook.com
Brief critical reviews of virtually every hardcover trade children's & young adult books published in the US. Publishers should submit 2 copies of appropriate new titles preferably 3 months in advance of publication date. Publisher must be included in *Literary Market Place* to be considered.
First published 1990
Frequency: Semiannual
Number of pages: 288
Circulation: 2,600
$35/issue, $60/yr
ISSN: 1044-405X
Books Reviewed: 2,200/issue, 4,400/yr

The Horn Book Magazine
Horn Book Inc
300 The Fenway, Suite P-311, Palace Road Bldg, Boston, MA 02115
Tel: 617-278-0225 *Toll Free Tel:* 888-628-0225
  Fax: 617-278-6062
E-mail: info@hbook.com
Web Site: www.hbook.com
Subscription Address: 7585 Industrial Pkwy, Plain City, OH 43064 *Toll Free Tel:* 877-523-

6072 *Fax:* 760-317-2335 *E-mail:* hbmsubs@pcspublink.com
Key Personnel
Group Publr: Rebecca T Miller *Tel:* 646-380-0738 *E-mail:* rmiller@mediasourceinc.com
Ed-in-Chief: Roger Sutton
Exec Ed: Elissa Gershowitz
  E-mail: egershowitz@hbook.com
Creative Dir: Lolly Robinson *Tel:* 617-628-0225 ext 226 *E-mail:* lrobinson@hbook.com
Book Review Ed: Martha V Parravano
  E-mail: mvp@hbook.com
Asst Ed: Shoshana Flax *E-mail:* sflax@hbook.com
Children's literature journal featuring reviews, essays, columns, interviews with authors, illustrators & current announcements.
First published 1924
Frequency: 6 issues/yr
Number of pages: 128
Circulation: 8,500
$72/yr
ISSN: 0018-5078
Books Reviewed: Approximately 600/yr

Human Rights Quarterly
Johns Hopkins University Press
2715 N Charles St, Baltimore, MD 21218-4363
SAN: 202-7348
Tel: 410-516-6987 (journal orders outside US & CN) *Toll Free Tel:* 800-548-1784 (journal orders) *Fax:* 410-516-3866 (journal orders)
E-mail: jrnlcirc@press.jhu.edu (journal orders)
Web Site: www.press.jhu.edu/journals/human_rights_quarterly
Key Personnel
Ed-in-Chief: Bert Lockwood
Mng Ed: Verjine Adanalian
Provides insight into complex human rights issues through current research policy, analysis & philosophical essays.
Frequency: Quarterly
Number of pages: 232
Circulation: 1,010
$15/issue; Indivs: $50/yr print, $60/yr online; Instns: $230/yr print, $250/yr online, $322/yr print & online
ISSN: 0275-0392
Books Reviewed: 12

ICSID Review: Foreign Investment Law Journal
Oxford University Press USA
2001 Evans Rd, Cary, NC 27513
Tel: 919-677-0977 *Toll Free Tel:* 800-852-7323
  Fax: 919-677-1714
Web Site: academic.oup.org
Key Personnel
Ed-in-Chief: Meg Kinnear; Campbell McLachlan
Lead Prodn Ed: Victoria Bache *E-mail:* victoria.bache@oup.com
Prodn Ed: Laura Jose *E-mail:* ljose@oup.com
The only journal devoted exclusively to foreign investment law for legal & business professionals.
Frequency: 3 issues/subn
Number of pages: 248
Circulation: 707
$92/yr indivs (print), $243/yr instns (print), $286/yr instns (print & online)
ISSN: 0258-3690
Books Reviewed: 5

International Leads (IL)
International Relations Round Table (IRRT)
Unit of The American Library Association (ALA)
225 N Michigan Ave, Suite 1300, Chicago, IL 60601
Tel: 312-944-6780 *Toll Free Tel:* 800-545-2433
  Fax: 312-440-9374
E-mail: ala.intl.leads@gmail.com; ala@ala.org

Web Site: www.ala.org/rt/irrt/intlleads/internationalleads; www.ala.org/rt/irrt; www.ala.org
Key Personnel
Ed: Rebecca Miller; Florence Mugambi
Reviews works dealing with librarianship in countries other than the US, with international library & information science agencies & activities.
Frequency: Quarterly
Circulation: 850
ISSN: 0892-4546

Internet Bookwatch
Midwest Book Review
278 Orchard Dr, Oregon, WI 53575-1129
Tel: 608-835-7937
E-mail: mbr@execpc.com
Web Site: www.midwestbookreview.com
Key Personnel
Ed-in-Chief: James A Cox
Review large & small press publications: audio cassettes, videos, books, fiction, general interest nonfiction, CD music & children's educational CD-ROMs.
First published 1995
Frequency: Monthly
Number of pages: 80
Circulation: 50,000
Free online
Books Reviewed: 200

James, Henry Review, see The Henry James Review

Jeunesse: Young People, Texts, Cultures
University of Winnipeg, Centre for Research in Young People's Texts & Cultures, 515 Portage Ave, Winnipeg, MB R3B 2E9, Canada
Tel: 204-786-9351 *Fax:* 204-774-4134
E-mail: jeunesse@uwinnipeg.ca
Web Site: www.jeunessejournal.ca
Key Personnel
Mng Ed: Larissa Wodtke *E-mail:* l.wodtke@uwinnipeg.ca
Ed: Heather Snell
Journal offering in-depth criticism of texts for, by & about young people, with a special interest in Canada. Scholarly articles & reviews are supplemented by illustrations, photos & interviews with authors of children's books. An important source for academics, parents, teachers & librarians. Recent issues have focused on censorship, picture-book illustration, psychoanalytic readings of children's literature & the retelling of fairy tales & myths. Articles may be submitted directly to our web site or as attachments in Word or RTF format. Alternately, submit three copies, along with a SASE. Author's name should be removed from all submissions & appear on a separate page along with contact infomation & a 100-word abstract.
Also available online (ISSN: 1920-261X).
First published 2009
Frequency: 2 issues/yr
Circulation: 300
$50/yr CN, $60/yr US, $70/yr outside US & CN (indivs/school print & online); $35/yr (indivs/school online only)
ISSN: 1920-2601
Books Reviewed: 30-40/issue

Journal of Cuneiform Studies (JCS)
American Schools of Oriental Research (ASOR)
Boston University, 656 Beacon St, 5th fl, Boston, MA 02215
Tel: 617-353-6570 *Fax:* 617-353-6575
E-mail: asor@bu.edu; asorpubs@bu.edu
Web Site: www.asor.org (print only subns); www.jstor.org (electronic only & print plus electronic subns)

Key Personnel
Mng Ed: Billie Jean Collins
Ed: Piotr Michalowski *E-mail:* piotrm@umich.edu
Pubns & Fulfillment Mgr: Inda Omerefendic
  Tel: 617-358-4376
First published 1947
Frequency: Annual
Number of pages: 144
Circulation: 650
Indivs: $75/yr, $96 foreign; Instns: $117/yr, $138 foreign
ISSN: 0022-0256
Books Reviewed: 3

Journal of Modern Greek Studies
Johns Hopkins University Press
2715 N Charles St, Baltimore, MD 21218-4363
SAN: 202-7348
Toll Free Tel: 800-548-1784 (journal orders)
  Fax: 410-516-6968
E-mail: jrnlcirc@press.jhu.edu (journal orders)
Web Site: www.press.jhu.edu/journals/
  journal_of_modern_greek_studies/index.html
Key Personnel
Ed: Thomas W Gallant; Artemis Leontis
Only scholarly journal to focus exclusively on
  Greek culture, literature & politics from the
  late Byzantine period to the present.
Frequency: Semiannual
Circulation: 443
$50/yr indivs, $140/yr instns, $45/yr students
ISSN: 0738-1727
Books Reviewed: 5

Kirkus
Kirkus Media LLC
65 W 36 St, Suite 700, New York, NY 10018
E-mail: customercare@kirkus.com
Web Site: www.kirkusreviews.com
Subscription Address: 2600 Via Fortuna, Suite
  130, Austin, TX 78746 *Toll Free Tel:* 800-316-
  9361 *E-mail:* customercare@kirkus.com *Web
  Site:* www.kirkusreviews.com
Key Personnel
CEO: Meg LaBorde Kuehn
Pres & Publr: Mark Winkleman
Ed-in-Chief: Tom Beer
Mng Ed & Nonfiction Ed: Eric Liebetrau
  Tel: 843-754-3784 *E-mail:* eliebetrau@kirkus.com
Children's & Young Adult Ed: Vicky Smith
  Tel: 207-671-6846 *E-mail:* vsmith@kirkus.com
Fiction Ed: Laurie Muchnick *Tel:* 212-209-1531
  ext 25 *E-mail:* lmuchnick@kirkus.com
Young Adult Ed: Laura Simeon
Asst Ed: Chelsea Langford *Tel:* 212-209-1531 ext
  20 *E-mail:* clangford@kirkus.com
Critical prepublication reviews of fiction, nonfic-
  tion, children's, young adult & self-published
  books. Issued to libraries, producers, periodicals, publishers, agents, booksellers & individ-
  uals. For all review submissions of traditionally
  published nonfiction, send 2 galleys to Kirkus
  Reviews: adult nonfiction, 479 Old Carolina Ct,
  Mount Pleasant, SC 29464; adult traditionally
  published fiction: 65 W 36 St, Suite 700, New
  York, NY 10018; traditionally published chil-
  dren's & teen: 108 Stillman St, South Portland,
  ME 04106. All inquiries about self-published
  books can be answered by calling 212-209-
  1531 or through the Kirkus web site.
First published 1933
Frequency: Semimonthly
Number of pages: 136
Circulation: 5,200
Rates upon request
ISSN: 0042-6598
Books Reviewed: 8,000/yr

Lambda Literary
PO Box 20186, New York, NY 10014

Tel: 213-277-5755 *Fax:* 323-643-4281
E-mail: admin@lambdaliterary.org
Web Site: www.lambdaliterary.org
Key Personnel
Exec Dir: Sue Landers
Mng Ed: William Johnson *E-mail:* wjohnson@
  lambdaliterary.org
Online journal, review of contemporary LGBTQ
  literature.
First published 1979
Frequency: Daily
Circulation: 63,000
ISSN: 1048-9487
Books Reviewed: Reviews posted daily

LARB Quarterly Journal
Los Angeles Review of Books
6671 Sunset Blvd, Suite 1521, Los Angeles, CA
  90028
Tel: 323-952-3950
E-mail: info@lareviewofbooks.org; editorial@
  lareviewofbooks.org
Web Site: lareviewofbooks.org
Key Personnel
Publr & Ed-in-Chief: Tom Lutz *E-mail:* tom@
  lareviewofbooks.org
Mng Dir: Jessica Kubinec *E-mail:* jessica@
  lareviewofbooks.org
Exec Ed: Boris Dralyuk *E-mail:* boris@
  lareviewofbooks.org
Mng Ed: Medaya Ocher *E-mail:* medaya@
  lareviewofbooks.org
Literary journal featuring original art, essays, po-
  etry & fiction.
First published 2013
Frequency: Quarterly
Number of pages: 144
Circulation: 1,250
$10/mo or $100/yr (LARB membership)

Leading Edge Review
3651 Robin Lane, Minnetonka, MN 55503
Tel: 952-217-4665
Web Site: www.leadingedgereview.com
Key Personnel
Founder & Publr: Sheila K Andersen
  E-mail: sheila@leadingedgereview.com
A quarterly consumer-oriented bookstore catalog
  that features body/mind/spirit titles. Distributed
  to bookstores, expos & trade shows. Advertis-
  ing available.
First published 1988
Frequency: Quarterly
Number of pages: 24
Circulation: 25,000/issue
Free to bookstore customer
Books Reviewed: 60-70/issue

Library Bookwatch
Midwest Book Review
278 Orchard Dr, Oregon, WI 53575-1129
Tel: 608-835-7937
E-mail: mbr@execpc.com
Web Site: www.midwestbookreview.com
Key Personnel
Ed-in-Chief: James A Cox
Review large & small press publications: audio-
  cassettes, videos, books, fiction, general interest
  nonfiction, CD music & children's educational
  CD-ROMs.
First published 1992
Frequency: Monthly
Number of pages: 12
Circulation: 50,000
Free online
Books Reviewed: 75

Library Journal
Media Source Inc
123 William St, Suite 802, New York, NY 10038
Tel: 646-380-0700 *Toll Free Tel:* 800-588-1030
  Fax: 646-380-0756

E-mail: ljinfo@mediasourceinc.com
Web Site: www.libraryjournal.com
Key Personnel
Pres & CEO: Steve Zales *Tel:* 614-873-7940
  E-mail: szales@mediasourceinc.com
Group Publr: Rebecca T Miller *Tel:* 646-380-
  0738 *E-mail:* rmiller@mediasourceinc.com
Ed-in-Chief: Meredith Schwartz *Tel:* 646-380-
  0745 *E-mail:* mschwartz@mediasourceinc.com
Mng Ed: Bette-Lee Fox *Tel:* 646-380-0717
  E-mail: blfox@mediasourceinc.com
Reviews Ed: Neal Wyatt
Reviews over 8,000 books, audiobooks, DVDs,
  databases & web sites annually & provides
  coverage of technology, management, policy &
  other professional concerns through our print
  journal, weekly newsletters, online reporting &
  digital & live events. Over 75,000 library direc-
  tors, administrators & staff in public, academic
  & special libraries read *Library Journal.*
First published 1876
Frequency: Semimonthly (exc monthly during
  Jan, July, Aug & Dec)
Number of pages: 104
Circulation: 12,000
$157.99/yr US, $199.99/yr CN & Mexico,
  $219.99/yr foreign
ISSN: 0363-0277
Books Reviewed: 5,000

The Lion and the Unicorn
Johns Hopkins University Press
2715 N Charles St, Baltimore, MD 21218-4363
SAN: 202-7348
Toll Free Tel: 800-548-1784 (journal orders)
  Fax: 410-516-6968
E-mail: jrnlcirc@press.jhu.edu (journal orders)
Web Site: www.press.jhu.edu/journals/
  lion_and_the_unicorn/index.html
Key Personnel
Ed: David Russell; Karin E Westman; Naomi J
  Wood
Theme & genre-centered journal of international
  scope, committed to a serious discussion of
  literature for children.
Frequency: 3 issues/yr
Number of pages: 160
Circulation: 457
$40/yr indivs, $135/yr instns, $35/yr students
ISSN: 0147-2593
Books Reviewed: 6

Literature & Medicine
Johns Hopkins University Press
2715 N Charles St, Baltimore, MD 21218-4363
SAN: 202-7348
Toll Free Tel: 800-548-1784 (journal orders)
  Fax: 410-516-6968
E-mail: jrnlcirc@press.jhu.edu (journal orders)
Web Site: www.press.jhu.edu/journals/
  literature_and_medicine/index.html
Key Personnel
Mng Ed: Anna Fenton-Hathaway
Ed: Catherine Belling
Showcase for the creative & critical work of
  renowned physician-writers, leading literary
  scholars & medical humanists.
Frequency: Semiannual
Number of pages: 164
Circulation: 262
$40/yr indivs, $115/yr instns, $35/yr students
ISSN: 0278-9671
Books Reviewed: 5

M L N (Modern Language Notes)
Johns Hopkins University Press
2715 N Charles St, Baltimore, MD 21218-4363
SAN: 202-7348
Toll Free Tel: 800-548-1784 (journal orders)
  Fax: 410-516-6968
E-mail: jrnlcirc@press.jhu.edu (journal orders)
Web Site: www.press.jhu.edu/journals/
  modern_language_notes/index.html

Key Personnel
Ed: James Coleman; Pier Massimo Forni; Walter
  Stephens; Bernadette Wegenstein
Contemporary continental criticism in Italian,
  Hispanic, German, French & comparative lit-
  erature.
Frequency: 5 issues/yr
Number of pages: 256
Circulation: 727
$50/yr indivs, $238/yr instns, $45/yr students
ISSN: 0026-7910
Books Reviewed: 12

Management Communication Quarterly: An International Journal

SAGE Publishing
2455 Teller Rd, Thousand Oaks, CA 91320
Toll Free Tel: 800-818-7243 *Toll Free Fax:* 800-
  583-2665
E-mail: journals@sagepub.com
Web Site: www.sagepub.com
Key Personnel
Ed: Patricia Sias
Brings together communication research from a
  wide variety of fields, with a focus on man-
  agerial & organizational effectiveness. Includes
  book reviews & notes from professionals in the
  field. Online only.
Frequency: Quarterly
Circulation: 1,200
$793/yr instns, $150/yr indivs
ISSN: 1552-6798
Books Reviewed: 2/yr

MBR Bookwatch

Midwest Book Review
278 Orchard Dr, Oregon, WI 53575-1129
Tel: 608-835-7937
E-mail: mbr@execpc.com
Web Site: www.midwestbookreview.com
Key Personnel
Ed-in-Chief: James A Cox
Review large & small press publications: audio-
  cassettes, videos, books, fiction, general inter-
  est nonfiction, CD music & educational CD-
  ROMs.
First published 1997
Frequency: Monthly
Number of pages: 50
Circulation: 50,000
Free online
Books Reviewed: 200

Medievalia et Humanistica: Studies in Medieval & Renaissance Culture

Rowman & Littlefield
4501 Forbes Blvd, Suite 200, Lanham, MD
  20706
SAN: 208-5143
Tel: 301-459-3366; 717-794-3800 (cust serv)
  Toll Free Tel: 800-462-6420 (ext 3024, cust
  serv) *Fax:* 301-429-5748; 717-794-3803 (cust
  serv) *Toll Free Fax:* 800-338-4550 (cust serv)
E-mail: customercare@rowman.com
Web Site: rowman.com
Key Personnel
Sales Dir: Sheila Burnett *Tel:* 301-459-3366 ext
  5606 *E-mail:* sburnett@rowman.com
Reviews new, critical & scholarly books in all
  areas of Medieval & Renaissance studies. In-
  cludes annual list of outstanding books.
First published 1943
Frequency: Annual
Number of pages: 168
Circulation: 2,000
$90 hardcover, $85 ebook
ISSN: 0076-6127
Books Reviewed: 35/yr

The Midwest Book Review

Midwest Book Review
278 Orchard Dr, Oregon, WI 53575-1129

Tel: 608-835-7937
E-mail: mbr@execpc.com; mwbookrevw@aol.
  com
Web Site: www.midwestbookreview.com
Key Personnel
Ed-in-Chief: James A Cox
Book review publisher.
First published 1980
Frequency: Monthly
Circulation: 50,000
Free online
Books Reviewed: 700

Mystery Readers Journal

Mystery Readers International
7155 Marlborough Terr, Berkeley, CA 94705
Tel: 510-845-3600
Web Site: www.mysteryreaders.org
Key Personnel
Ed: Janet A Rudolph *E-mail:* janet@
  mysteryreaders.org
Assoc Ed: Kate Derie
Thematic mystery review periodical. Each issue
  contains articles, reviews & author essays on
  a specific theme (i.e. art mysteries, historical
  mysteries & sports mysteries).
First published 1983
Frequency: Quarterly
Number of pages: 88
Circulation: 2,000
$39/yr, $50/yr overseas airmail, $15/pdf download
ISSN: 1043-3473
Books Reviewed: 2,000

Near Eastern Archaeology

American Schools of Oriental Research (ASOR)
Boston University, 656 Beacon St, 5th fl, Boston,
  MA 02215
Tel: 617-353-6570 *Fax:* 617-353-6575
E-mail: asor@bu.edu; asorpubs@bu.edu
Web Site: www.asor.org (print only subns); www.
  jstor.org (electronic only & print plus electronic
  subns)
Key Personnel
Pubns & Fulfillment Mgr: Inda Omerefendic
  Tel: 617-358-4376
Ed: Thomas Schneider
First published 1938
Frequency: Quarterly
Circulation: 3,700
Indivs: $40/yr (print or online), $72/yr foreign
  (print); Instns: $191/yr (print), $223/yr foreign
  (print)
ISSN: 1094-2076
Books Reviewed: 2

New Haven Review

The Institute Library
55 Elmwood Rd, New Haven, CT 06515
Tel: 203-494-7018
Web Site: www.newhavenreview.com
Key Personnel
Publr: Nichole Gleisner *E-mail:* nichole.
  gleisner@gmail.com
Publishes reviews, essays, poems, fiction & oc-
  casional pieces by writers who live in the New
  Haven area & elsewhere. Solicits contributions
  but welcomes unsol submissions. Pay for full
  story or article $500 & $25 per poem. Fa-
  vor will be shown to articles & book reviews
  that, in form, subject matter, or authorial back-
  ground, can claim a credible connection to
  New Haven & its broader environs, but not
  an absolute necessity.
First published 2007
Frequency: 2 issues/yr
Number of pages: 160
Circulation: 500
$20/yr, $30/2 yrs
ISSN: 1940-8714
Books Reviewed: 2/issue

New Literary History: A Journal of Theory & Interpretation

Johns Hopkins University Press
2715 N Charles St, Baltimore, MD 21218-4363
SAN: 202-7348
Tel: 410-516-6987 (journal orders outside US &
  CN) *Toll Free Tel:* 800-548-1784 (journal or-
  ders) *Fax:* 410-516-6968
E-mail: jrnlcirc@press.jhu.edu (journal orders)
Web Site: www.press.jhu.edu/journals/
  new_literary_history/index.html
Key Personnel
Founding Ed: Ralph Cohen
Mng Ed: Mollie H Washburne
Ed: Rita Felski
Focuses on theory & interpretation of literary
  change, definition of literary periods & the evo-
  lution of styles, conventions & genres.
Frequency: Quarterly
Number of pages: 220
Circulation: 789
$48/yr indivs, $225/yr instns, $40/yr students
ISSN: 0028-6087

The New York Review of Science Fiction

Subsidiary of Burrowing Wombat Press
206 Valentine St, Yonkers, NY 10704-1814
Tel: 914-965-4861
Web Site: www.nyrsf.com
Key Personnel
Publr: Kevin Maroney *E-mail:* kjm@panix.com
Review journal devoted to speculative fiction.
First published 1988
Frequency: Monthly
Number of pages: 32
Circulation: 300
$3/issue; $30/yr (bulk) US
ISSN: 1052-9438
Books Reviewed: 5/issue; 60/yr

The New York Times Book Review

The New York Times Co
620 Eighth Ave, 5th fl, New York, NY 10018
Tel: 212-556-1234 *Toll Free Tel:* 800-631-2580
  (subns)
E-mail: bookreview@nytimes.com; books@
  nytimes.com
Web Site: www.nytimes.com
Key Personnel
Mng Ed: David Kelly
Deputy Ed: Tina Jordan
Sr Ed: Gregory Cowles
Ed: Pamela Paul
Preview Ed: Dave Kim; Emily Eakin; Elisabeth
  Egan
Asst Preview Ed: MJ Franklin
Review books & essays related to publishing &
  published in the US & available through gen-
  eral interest bookstores. By subscription only.
$4/wk US, $4.95/wk CN, $5.50/wk foreign
ISSN: 0028-7806

North Carolina Literary Review (NCLR)

East Carolina University/North Carolina Literary
  & Historical Association/University of North
  Carolina Press
East Carolina University, English Dept, ECU
  Mailstop 555 English, Greenville, NC 27858-
  4353
Tel: 252-328-1537 *Fax:* 252-328-4889
E-mail: ncluser@ecu.edu
Web Site: www.nclr.ecu.edu
Key Personnel
Ed: Margaret Bauer *E-mail:* bauerm@ecu.edu
Articles, essays, interviews, fiction/poetry by &
  about North Carolina writers & literature, cul-
  ture & history. Essay reviews only; excerpts
  from forthcoming books when relevant & ap-
  propriate.
First published 1992
Frequency: Annual
Number of pages: 200
Circulation: 750

$15/yr indiv, $25/2 yrs indiv, $25/yr instl, $50/yr
   foreign
ISSN: 1063-0724
Books Reviewed: 8-12/yr

Paper Brigade
Jewish Book Council
520 Eighth Ave, 4th fl, New York, NY 10018
Tel: 212-201-2920 *Fax:* 212-532-4952
E-mail: info@jewishbooks.org
Web Site: www.jewishbookcouncil.org
Key Personnel
Exec Dir: Naomi Firestone-Teeter
Edit Dir: Carol E Kaufman
Mng Ed: Becca Kantor *E-mail:* becca@
   jewishbooks.org
Children's & Young Adult Ed: Ms Michal
   Hoschander Malen
Articles, interviews, personal essays, fiction, po-
   etry, photography & illustrations that, together,
   highlight the breadth & diversity of Jewish
   books today.
Frequency: Annual
Number of pages: 200
$25 US, $36 foreign

Pennsylvania Literary Journal (PLJ)
Anaphora Literary Press
1108 W Third St, Quanah, TX 79252
Tel: 470-289-6395
Web Site: anaphoraliterary.com
Key Personnel
Dir & Ed-in-Chief: Dr Anna Faktorovich
   E-mail: director@anaphoraliterary.com
Peer-reviewed, academic & creative journal,
   which publishes scholarly essays, fiction (short
   stories & poems), nonfiction, personal essays,
   interviews, book reviews & other works. A
   member of the Council of Literary Magazines
   & Presses & the Independent Book Publishers
   Association, with an editorial board of estab-
   lished academics, editors & best-selling writers.
   Special issues range from Popular Arts to In-
   terviews with Best-Selling Young Adult Writ-
   ers, British Literature, New Historicism, New
   Formalism, editing technique & film studies.
   It is cataloged in the *MLA International Bib-
   liography*, the *MLA Directory of Periodicals*,
   Genamics JournalSeek & *Duotrope's Digest*.
   PLJ has published works by & interviews with
   New York Times bestselling writers like Larry
   Niven & Cinda Williams Chima. Only e-mailed
   submissions accepted.
First published 2009
Frequency: 3 issues/yr
Number of pages: 150
Circulation: 20 copies/issue, plus EBSCO & Pro-
   Quest online viewing
$45/yr US, $60/yr elsewhere
ISSN: 2151-3066
Books Reviewed: 4 books/issue, 12 books/yr

Philosophy & Literature
Johns Hopkins University Press
2715 N Charles St, Baltimore, MD 21218-4363
SAN: 202-7348
Toll Free Tel: 800-548-1784 (journal orders)
   Fax: 410-516-6968
E-mail: jrnlcirc@press.jhu.edu (journal orders)
Web Site: www.press.jhu.edu/journals/
   philosophy_and_literature/index.html
Key Personnel
Founding Ed: Denis Dutton
Ed: Garry Hagberg
Explores the dialogue between literary & theoret-
   ical studies & philosophy. A constant source
   of fresh, stimulating ideas in aesthetics, theory
   of criticism & more in an assortment of lively
   essays & reviews written in clear, jargon-free
   prose. Home to the annual Bad Writing Contest.
Frequency: Semiannual

Number of pages: 224
Circulation: 450
$40/yr indivs, $135/yr instns, $35/yr students
ISSN: 0190-0013
Books Reviewed: 60

Poetry Flash
1450 Fourth St, Suite 4, Berkeley, CA 94710
Tel: 510-525-5476 *Fax:* 510-525-6752
E-mail: info@poetryflash.org
Web Site: www.poetryflash.org
Key Personnel
Publr & Ed: Joyce Jenkins *E-mail:* editor@
   poetryflash.org
Bd Chair & Devt Dir: Mark Baldridge
Assoc Ed: Richard Silberg
Publishes online quality reviews, poems, inter-
   views, essays & book trade & submission &
   award information for all creative writers. Al-
   though poetry is the editorial focus, interviews
   with prose writers & reviews of fiction & liter-
   ary nonfiction are featured. Sponsors the annual
   Northern California Book Awards.
First published 1972
Distributed free primarily on the West Coast

ProtoView
Ringgold Inc
7515 NE Ambassador Place, Suite A, Portland,
   OR 97220
Tel: 503-281-9230
E-mail: info@protoview.com
Web Site: www.protoview.com
Key Personnel
Ed: Eithne O'Leyne *E-mail:* eithne.oleyne@
   ringgold.com
Subscription database incorporating Reference &
   Research & *SciTech Book News*. Abstracts, bib-
   liographic & expanded metadata on scholary
   works in all media. ProtoView content licensed
   to discovery channels, including vendors &
   related products owned by Baker & Taylor,
   ProQuest, Gale/Cengage & others.
ISSN: 2372-3424

PsycCRITIQUES™
American Psychological Association
750 First St NE, Washington, DC 20002-4242
Tel: 202-336-5500 *Fax:* 202-336-5502
E-mail: subscriptions@apa.org
Web Site: www.apa.org
Key Personnel
Ed: Dr Danny Wedding *E-mail:* psyccritiques@
   mimh.edu
Ms Coord: Allison Jillens
Full-text database with tens of thousands of inci-
   sive book & film reviews from 1956 to present.
   It provides users with insight on publications
   from a psychological perspective allowing them
   to choose relevant reading material, to select
   appropriate course materials & more.
$65/yr APA membs, $130/yr nonmembs
ISSN: 1554-0138

Publishers Weekly
PWxyz LLC
71 W 23 St, Suite 1608, New York, NY 10010
Tel: 212-377-5500 *Fax:* 212-377-2733
Web Site: www.publishersweekly.com
Key Personnel
Pres: George Slowik, Jr *E-mail:* george@
   publishersweekly.com
Publr: Cevin Bryerman *Tel:* 212-377-5703
   E-mail: cbryerman@publishersweekly.com
VP, Busn Devt: Carl Pritzkat *E-mail:* cpritzkat@
   publishersweekly.com
VP, Opers: Patrick Turner *E-mail:* patrick@
   publishersweekly.com
Adult Book Dir: Louisa Ermelino
   E-mail: lermelino@publishersweekly.com
Art Dir: Clive Chiu *E-mail:* cchiu@
   publishersweekly.com

Edit Dir: Jim Milliot *Tel:* 212-377-5705
   E-mail: jmilliot@publishersweekly.com
News Dir: Rachel Deahl *E-mail:* rdeahl@
   publishersweekly.com
Exec Ed: Jonathan Segura *E-mail:* jsegura@
   publishersweekly.com
Mng Ed: Dan Berchenko *E-mail:* dberchenko@
   publishersweekly.com
Sr Writer: Andrew R Albanese
   E-mail: aalbanese@publishersweekly.com
Sr Ed: Mark Rotella *E-mail:* mrotella@
   publishersweekly.com
Sr News Ed: Calvin Reid *E-mail:* creid@
   publishersweekly.com
Children's Book Ed: Diane Roback
   E-mail: roback@publishersweekly.com
Digital Ed & Assoc News Ed: John Maher
   E-mail: jmaher@publishersweekly.com
Fiction Reviews Ed: David Varno
Assoc Ed, Children's Books: Emma Kantor
   E-mail: ekantor@publishersweekly.com
Assoc Reviews Ed: Phoebe Cramer
Asst Ed, Children's Books: Matia Burnett
   E-mail: mburnett@publishersweekly.com
Features Ed: Carolyn Juris *E-mail:* cjuris@
   publishersweekly.com
Sr Religion Ed: Lynn Garrett *E-mail:* lgarrett@
   publishersweekly.com
Religion News Ed: Emma Koonse
   E-mail: ekoonse@publishersweekly.com
Religion Reviews Ed: Seth Satterlee
   E-mail: ssatterlee@publishersweekly.com
Sr Reviews Ed: Peter Cannon; Rose Fox
Reviews Ed: Alex Crowley; Annie Coreno; Ev-
   erett Jones
BookLife Ed: Adam Boretz *E-mail:* aboretz@
   publishersweekly.com
Bookselling & Intl News Ed: Ed Nawotka
   E-mail: enawotka@publishersweekly.com
Copy Ed: Hannah Kushnick *E-mail:* hkushnick@
   publishersweekly.com
Mktg/Licensing Mgr: Christi Cassidy
   E-mail: ccassidy@publishersweekly.com
International news magazine of book publishing
   & bookselling.
Digital ISSN: 2150-4000.
First published 1872
Frequency: Weekly (51 issues/yr)
Circulation: 68,000 print; 1,000,000 online
Print, digital & online: $289.99/yr US, $339.99/yr
   CN; Digital & online: $229.99/yr US & CN
ISSN: 0000-0019
Books Reviewed: 9,000/yr

Publishing Trends
Market Partners International Inc
232 Madison Ave, Suite 1400, New York, NY
   10016
Tel: 212-447-0855 *Fax:* 212-447-0785
E-mail: info@publishingtrends.com
Web Site: www.marketpartnersinternational.com;
   www.publishingtrends.com
Key Personnel
Dir: Amy Rhodes; Lorraine W Shanley
Web site on news & opinion on the changing
   world of publishing.
Frequency: Weekly
Free online

QBR The Black Book Review
QBR
591 Warburton Ave, Unit 170, Hastings-on-
   Hudson, NY 10706
Tel: 914-231-6778
Web Site: www.qbr.com
Key Personnel
Dir: Max Rodriguez *E-mail:* mrod@qbr.com
Online review of African-American books & pro-
   ducer of the Harlem Book Fair.

Readers' Guide to Periodical Literature
Grey House Publishing Inc™
4919 Rte 22, Amenia, NY 12501

Mailing Address: PO Box 56, Amenia, NY
12501-0056
Tel: 518-789-8700 *Toll Free Tel:* 800-562-2139
Fax: 518-789-0556
E-mail: books@greyhouse.com
Web Site: greyhouse.com
Index to the 300 most popular general-interest
periodicals published in the US & Canada.
First published 1900
Frequency: 3 paperback issues, March-Sept plus
library-bound annual cumulation in Jan
Number of pages: 300
$495
ISSN: 0034-0464

Reference & User Services Quarterly (RUSQ)
Reference & User Services Association (RUSA)
Division of The American Library Association
(ALA)
225 N Michigan Ave, Suite 1300, Chicago, IL
60601
SAN: 201-0062
Tel: 312-280-4395 *Toll Free Tel:* 800-545-2433
Fax: 312-280-5273
E-mail: rusa@ala.org
Web Site: www.ala.org/rusa
Key Personnel
Contact: Leighann Wood
Column Ed: Neal Wyatt
Open access journal.
Frequency: Quarterly
Circulation: 3,825
$25/issue, $65/yr CN & Mexico, $75/yr all other
foreign
ISSN: 2163-5242
Books Reviewed: 35-40

Retailing Insight
Continuity Publishing Inc
119 N Commercial St, Suite 560, Bellingham,
WA 98225
Tel: 360-676-0789 *Toll Free Tel:* 800-463-9243
E-mail: info@retailinginsight.com
Web Site: retailinginsight.com
Key Personnel
Assoc Ed: Maggie Feeney
Trade magazine for retail stores selling books,
music & giftware for the body, mind & spirit.
Frequency: 7 issues/yr
Circulation: 17,000
$42/yr US, $55/yr CN, free to qualified retailers
ISSN: 2166-0638
Books Reviewed: 15/issue, 105/yr

Reviewer Bookwatch
Midwest Book Review
278 Orchard Dr, Oregon, WI 53575-1129
Tel: 608-835-7937
E-mail: mbr@execpc.com
Web Site: www.midwestbookreview.com
Key Personnel
Ed-in-Chief: James A Cox
Review large & small press publications: audio-
cassettes, videos, books, fiction, general interest
nonfiction, CD music & children's educational
CD-ROMs.
First published 1992
Frequency: Monthly
Number of pages: 50
Circulation: 50,000
Free online
Books Reviewed: 200

Reviews in American History
Johns Hopkins University Press
2715 N Charles St, Baltimore, MD 21218-4363
SAN: 202-7348
Toll Free Tel: 800-548-1784 (journal orders)
Fax: 410-516-6968
E-mail: jrnlcirc@press.jhu.edu (journal orders)
Web Site: www.press.jhu.edu/journals/
reviews_in_american_history/index.html

Key Personnel
Ed: Thomas Slaughter
Mng Ed: Denise Thompson-Slaughter
Comprehensive evaluations of important new
books in all areas of American history.
Frequency: Quarterly
Number of pages: 192
Circulation: 1662
$45/yr indivs, $185/yr instns, $37/yr students
ISSN: 0048-7511
Books Reviewed: 120/yr

School Library Journal
Media Source Inc
123 William St, Suite 802, New York, NY 10038
Tel: 646-380-0752 *Toll Free Tel:* 800-595-1066
Fax: 646-380-0756
E-mail: slj@mediasourceinc.com; sljsubs@
pcspublink.com
Web Site: www.slj.com; www.facebook.com/
schoollibraryjournal; twitter.com/sljournal
Subscription Address: PO Box 461119, Escon-
dido, CA 92046
Key Personnel
Group Publr: Rebecca T Miller *Tel:* 646-380-
0738 *E-mail:* rmiller@mediasourceinc.com
Reviews Dir: Kiera Parrott *E-mail:* kparrott@
mediasourceinc.com
Ed-in-Chief: Kathy Ishizuka *E-mail:* kishizuka@
mediasourceinc.com
Mng Ed, SLJ Reviews: Luann Toth *Tel:* 646-380-
0749 *E-mail:* ltoth@mediasourceinc.com
Articles about library service to children & young
adults; reviews of new books & multimedia
products for children & young adults by school
& public librarians.
Frequency: Monthly
Number of pages: 115
Circulation: 38,000
$15/issue newsstand; Indivs: $136.99/yr (print or
digital), $159.99/yr (print & digital); Instns:
$136.99/yr (print only), $249.99/yr (digital
only), $349.99/yr (print & digital)
ISSN: 0362-8930
Books Reviewed: 4,500/yr, including 360 for
young adults & 1,000 reviews for multimedia
products

Science Books & Films
American Association for the Advancement of
Science (AAAS)
1200 New York Ave NW, Washington, DC 20005
Tel: 202-326-6400 *Fax:* 202-371-9526
E-mail: media@aaas.org
Web Site: www.aaas.org
Subscription Address: Box 3000, Dept SBF,
Denville, NJ 07834
Key Personnel
Ed-in-Chief: Maria Sosa *Tel:* 202-326-6453
E-mail: msosa@aaas.org
Reviews new books, AV materials & software in
all the sciences for all ages. Reviews are writ-
ten by experts in the respective fields. SB&F
online provides searchable database of reviews.
First published 1965
Frequency: 6 issues/yr
Circulation: 4,500
$45/yr, $85/2 yrs
ISSN: 0098-342X
Books Reviewed: 850/yr

Small Press Bookwatch
Midwest Book Review
278 Orchard Dr, Oregon, WI 53575-1129
Tel: 608-835-7937
E-mail: mbr@execpc.com
Web Site: www.midwestbookreview.com
Key Personnel
Ed-in-Chief: James A Cox
Review small press publications: audiocassettes,
videos, books, fiction, general interest nonfic-
tion & CD music.

First published 1997
Frequency: Monthly
Number of pages: 20
Circulation: 50,000
Free online
Books Reviewed: 70

Sunday San Francisco Chronicle Book Review
San Francisco Chronicle
Subsidiary of Hearst Communications Inc
901 Mission St, San Francisco, CA 94103
Tel: 415-777-1111 *Toll Free Tel:* 866-732-4766
Web Site: www.sfgate.com
Key Personnel
Book Ed: John McMurtrie *E-mail:* jmcmurtrie@
sfchronicle.com
Broad-based daily newspaper with daily book re-
view column & Sunday book review section;
reviews of hardcover, softcover, nonfiction, fic-
tion, poetry, children's books, literary guide;
interviews; best sellers list; industry news; es-
says.
Frequency: Weekly

Theatre Journal
Johns Hopkins University Press
2715 N Charles St, Baltimore, MD 21218-4363
SAN: 202-7348
Toll Free Tel: 800-548-1784 (journal orders)
Fax: 410-516-6968
E-mail: jrnlcirc@press.jhu.edu (journal orders)
Web Site: www.press.jhu.edu/journals/
theatre_journal/index.html
Key Personnel
Ed: Joanne Tompkins
Mng Ed: Bob Kowkabany
One of the most authoritative & useful publica-
tions in theatre studies. Features social & his-
torical studies, production reviews & analysis
of dramatic texts & production.
Frequency: Quarterly
Number of pages: 152
Circulation: 2263
$48/yr indivs, $175/yr instns, $40/yr students
ISSN: 0192-2882
Books Reviewed: 12

Voice of Youth Advocates
Voice of Youth Advocates (VOYA)
Division of E L Kurdyla Publishing LLC
16211 Oxford Ct, Bowie, MD 20715
Mailing Address: PO Box 958, Bowie, MD
20718-0958
Tel: 301-805-2191 *Fax:* 301-805-2192
Web Site: www.voyamagazine.com
Key Personnel
Owner & Publr: Edward Kurdyla
E-mail: publisher@kurdylapublishing.com
Ed-in-Chief: RoseMary Ludt *E-mail:* rmludt@
voyamagazine.com
Review Ed: Lisa Kurdyla *E-mail:* reviews@
voyamagazine.com
Articles & reviews; library materials & services
for, about & by adolescents.
First published 1978
Frequency: 6 issues/yr
Number of pages: 104
Circulation: 6,500
$10/issue, $62/yr
ISSN: 0160-4201
Books Reviewed: 240/issue, 1,440/yr

Washington Monthly
Washington Monthly Corp
1200 18 St NW, Suite 330, Washington, DC
20036
Tel: 202-955-9010 *Fax:* 202-955-9011
E-mail: editors@washingtonmonthly.com
Web Site: www.washingtonmonthly.com
Key Personnel
VP: Edwin Grosvenor *E-mail:* egrosvenor@
washingtonmonthly.com

VP, Circ & Busn: Claire Iseli *E-mail:* claire@washingtonmonthly.com
Publr: Diane Straus
Ed-in-Chief: Paul Glastris *E-mail:* pglastris@washingtonmonthly.com
Review political & public policy books.
First published 1969
Frequency: 5 issues/yr
Number of pages: 64
Circulation: 15,000 paid, 3,000 controlled
$5.95/issue, $19.95/yr indiv, $29.95/yr instl
ISSN: 0043-0633
Books Reviewed: 50/yr

Wisconsin Bookwatch
Midwest Book Review
278 Orchard Dr, Oregon, WI 53575-1129
Tel: 608-835-7937
E-mail: mbr@execpc.com
Web Site: www.midwestbookreview.com
Key Personnel
Ed-in-Chief: James A Cox

Review large & small press publications: audio-cassettes, videos, books, fiction, general interest nonfiction, CD music & children's educational CD-ROMs.
First published 1990
Frequency: Monthly
Number of pages: 12
Circulation: 50,000
Free online
Books Reviewed: 70

World Literature Today
University of Oklahoma
630 Parrington Oval, Suite 110, Norman, OK 73019-4033
Tel: 405-325-4531
E-mail: wlt@ou.edu
Web Site: www.worldliteraturetoday.org
Key Personnel
Exec Dir: Robert Con Davis-Undiano
Asst Dir & Ed-in-Chief: Daniel Simon
  E-mail: dsimon@ou.edu

Art Dir: Jennifer Blair
Mktg Dir, Progs & Devt: Terry D Stubblefield
  E-mail: tdstubb@ou.edu
Mng Ed: Michelle Johnson *E-mail:* lmjohnson@ou.edu
Book Reviews Ed: Robert Vollmar
Circ & Accts Specialist: Kay Blunck
  E-mail: kblunck@ou.edu
Critical essays & reviews covering all the major & most of the smaller languages & literatures of the world.
Also available online (ISSN: 1945-8134).
First published 1927
Frequency: 6 issues/yr
Number of pages: 96
Circulation: 300,000
$8.95/issue, $35/yr indivs, $60/yr foreign indivs, $135/yr instns, $205/yr foreign instns
ISSN: 0196-3570
Books Reviewed: 1,200

Book Exhibits

AIGA, the professional association for design
222 Broadway, New York, NY 10038
Tel: 212-807-1990 *Fax:* 212-807-1799
E-mail: general@aiga.org
Web Site: www.aiga.org
Key Personnel
Exec Dir: Bennie F Johnson
Sr Dir, Admin: Amy Chapman *Tel:* 212-710-3137
National nonprofit membership organization for graphic design professionals that sponsors competitions & major exhibits annually, including book shows & communication graphics. Exhibits & the work of two award recipients are published in *Graphic Design USA* (annual). Exhibits circulate for small rental fee.

The American Collective Stand®
277 White St, Buchanan, NY 10511
Tel: 914-739-7500 *Toll Free Tel:* 800-462-7687
    Fax: 914-739-7575
Web Site: www.americancollectivestand.com
Key Personnel
Pres: Janet Fritsch *Tel:* 734-677-0955
    E-mail: janet@americancollectivestand.com
EVP: Jon Malinowski *E-mail:* jon@
    americancollectivestand.com
A US collective of individual stands representing all segments of publishing, book trade & electronic sectors for selling & buying rights & making strategic distribution alliances. Check out our database of Participant Profiles including key contact people, e-mails, available rights & other important information on our web site (www.americancollectivestand.com) to the right person & do business at International Book Fairs such as Frankfurt, London & Beijing.

American Institute of Graphic Arts, see AIGA, the professional association for design

Children's Books USA Inc
Subsidiary of Foreword Magazine Inc

425 Boardman Ave, Traverse City, MI 49684
Tel: 231-933-3699
E-mail: info@childrensbooksusa.com
Web Site: www.childrensbooksusa.com
Key Personnel
Mng Dir: Matt Sutherland; Victoria Sutherland
Organize & manage American collective exhibit at Bologna Children's Book Fair. An all-inclusive turnkey service. We arrange for space, signage, decoration, shipping, customs, loading & unloading.

The Combined Book Exhibit®
277 White St, Buchanan, NY 10511
Tel: 914-739-7500 *Toll Free Tel:* 800-462-7687
    Fax: 914-739-7575
E-mail: info@combinedbook.com
Web Site: www.combinedbook.com; www.
    cbedatabase.com
Key Personnel
Pres: Jon Malinowski *E-mail:* jon@
    combinedbook.com
Dir, Busn Devt: Chris Malinowski *E-mail:* chris@
    combinedbook.com
Mktg Coord: Claribel Ortega *E-mail:* claribel@
    combinedbook.com
Founded: 1933
Organize combined book & multimedia exhibits for publishers worldwide covering books, periodicals, audio, video & ebooks. Areas covered include library, academic education, trade & international markets. Upwards of 20 major conferences & trade shows scheduled.

Exhibit Promotions Plus Inc
11620 Vixens Path, Ellicott City, MD 21042-1539
Tel: 410-997-0763 *Fax:* 410-997-0764
E-mail: exhibit@epponline.com
Web Site: www.epponline.com
Key Personnel
Founder & Pres: Harve C Horowitz, Esq
CFO: Eileen S Horowitz

Sr Mgr, Cust Rel: Kelly K Marshall
Founded: 1969
Scholarly association representation; Generate program & journal advertising in conjunction with international, national, regional & state exhibits in subject-arranged collections. Catalog for each meeting with emphasis on titles authored by members of sponsoring association. Marketing & managing trade shows for nonprofit associations. Total convention management company including site selection/hotel contracting.

National Association of Book Entrepreneurs (NABE)
PO Box 606, Cottage Grove, OR 97424
Tel: 541-942-7455 *Fax:* 541-942-7455
E-mail: nabe@bookmarketingprofits.com
Web Site: www.bookmarketingprofits.com
Key Personnel
Exec Dir: Al Galasso
Founded: 1980
Combined book displays, North American Bookdealers Exchange Book Showcase, at various regional & national trade shows including mail order, business, gift shop, premium & school product shows.

The Scholar's Choice
6300 W Port Bay Rd, Suite 101, Wolcott, NY 14590
Tel: 315-905-4208
E-mail: information@scholarschoice.com
Web Site: www.scholarschoice.com
Key Personnel
Owner: Thomas Prins *E-mail:* tom@
    scholarschoice.com
Promote & market scholarly books through exhibits. More than 100 academic conferences scheduled in the humanities & human sciences.

Book Clubs

Included below are a variety of book clubs. Letters in parenthesis indicate the type of club.

(A)–Adult   (J)–Juvenile   (A-J)–Adult & Juvenile

The Advertising, Marketing & Sales Promotion Book Club (A)
Division of LKA Inc
Book Club Bldg, 7 Putter Lane, Middle Island, NY 11953
Mailing Address: PO Box 102, Middle Island, NY 11953-0102
Tel: 631-924-3888 (ext 100)
E-mail: amspbookclub@gmail.com; linickgroup@gmail.com
Key Personnel
Pres: Howard J Jones, Sr
Mktg Dir: James A Douglas
Edit Dir: Gary R Alexander
E-books, streaming videos, Podcasts, Webinars, DVDs, business self-improvement, continuity programs, how-to correspondence courses, manuals, guides, handbooks, teaching aids, training; desktop publishing software programs, integrated systems; workshops/seminars for members owning Macintosh & PC compatible products on Internet marketing, e-learning direct response advertising, direct mail, e-mail, consulting, telecommunications, mail order selling; marketing/sales promotion & related subjects of interest to corporate decision makers, AMS-consultants, directors, agency executives, account supervisors; advertising, marketing & sales promotion leading-edge executives & other direct marketers of products & services. Areas: business-to-business, consumer, industrial digital marketing & trade & technical advertising/promotion, e-commerce, Internet web site marketing makeovers. Geared toward the 25-65 age bracket.
Number of Members: 85,275
Publication(s): *Ideas & Trends* (monthly)

Arrow (grades 4-6) (J)
Scholastic Inc
557 Broadway, New York, NY 10012
Tel: 212-343-6100 *Toll Free Tel:* 800-724-6527 (press 1) *Toll Free Fax:* 800-223-4011
E-mail: bookclubs@scholastic.com
Web Site: scholastic.com/bookclubs
Key Personnel
EVP, Pres, Book Clubs & e-Commerce: Judy Newman
Since 1948, Scholastic Book Clubs has inspired kids to love reading by making it easy & affordable for them to choose their very own books. The Scholastic Book Clubs flyers, both in print & digitally, offer a wide range of age-appropriate books handpicked by our editors. At prices starting as low as just $1, these flyers make it possible for kids of all income levels & from every part of the country to have access to great books & build their own home collections.
Publication(s): Monthly book catalogs for early childhood to middle school (sold exclusively in the school market).

Book Club for the Martial Arts Inc (A)
The Karate & Self Defense Book Club Inc
Subsidiary of LKA Inc
7 Putter Lane, Middle Island, NY 11953
Mailing Address: PO Box 102, Middle Island, NY 11953-0102
Tel: 631-924-3888
E-mail: bcma@gmail.com; okmagads@gmail.com

Key Personnel
Pres: Andrew S Linick, PhD
  E-mail: linickgroup@gmail.com
Ed: Chuck Reeves
Mktg Dir: Shane Clarke
Oper Mgr: Barbara Deal
Instructional/educational/recreational/inspirational books, ebooks, training & entertainment videos, DVDs, PC & Macintosh compatible products, software, games, accessories, equipment, supplies, seminars, workshops, tournaments worldwide/domestic, correspondence courses, home-study training techniques/manuals/guides/handbook/aides covering practically all aspects, origins, styles & systems, schools, associations, organizations on the martial arts. Also related subjects, such as health, nutrition, physical fitness, weightlifting, philosophy/religion, healing therapies, sports photography & martial arts travel & tours. Geared toward the 18-65 age bracket.
Number of Members: 90,450
Publication(s): *Satori* (monthly)

Children's Braille Book Club (J)
National Braille Press
88 Saint Stephen St, Boston, MA 02115-4312
Tel: 617-266-6160 *Toll Free Tel:* 800-548-7323 (cust serv) *Fax:* 617-437-0456
E-mail: contact@nbp.org
Web Site: www.nbp.org
Key Personnel
Pres: Brian A MacDonald *E-mail:* bmacdonald@nbp.org
VP, Braille Pubns: Tony Grima *Tel:* 617-266-6160 ext 429 *E-mail:* agrima@nbp.org
Children's print-braille books, PreK-3rd grade.
Number of Members: 2,951

Classics of Golf (A)
120 Research Dr, Stratford, CT 06615
Tel: 845-765-6050 *Toll Free Tel:* 800-483-6449
E-mail: info@classicsofgolf.com; customerservice@classicsofgolf.com
Web Site: www.classicsofgolf.com
Key Personnel
Publr: Michael P Beckerich *E-mail:* mpb@classicsofgolf.com
Publish classic books on golf.

Club Leo (Spanish & bilingual books for all grades) (J)
Scholastic Inc
557 Broadway, New York, NY 10012
Tel: 212-343-6100 *Toll Free Tel:* 800-724-6527 (press 1) *Toll Free Fax:* 800-223-4011
E-mail: bookclubs@scholastic.com
Web Site: scholastic.com/bookclubs
Key Personnel
EVP, Pres, Book Clubs & e-Commerce: Judy Newman
Since 1948, Scholastic Book Clubs has inspired kids to love reading by making it easy & affordable for them to choose their very own books. The Scholastic Book Clubs flyers, both in print & digitally, offer a wide range of age-appropriate books handpicked by our editors. At prices starting as low as just $1, these flyers make it possible for kids of all income levels & from every part of the country to have access to great books & build their own home collections.
Publication(s): Monthly book catalogs for early childhood to middle school (sold exclusively in the school market).

Compassion Books (A-J)
Compassion Books Inc
7036 Hwy 80 S, Burnsville, NC 28714
SAN: 200-9277
Tel: 828-675-5909 *Toll Free Tel:* 800-970-4220
  Fax: 828-675-9687
E-mail: orders@compassionbooks.com
Web Site: www.compassionbooks.com
Key Personnel
Dir: Bruce Greene *E-mail:* bruce@compassionbooks.com
Established: 1981
Comprehensive distribution of books & videos for children & adults on death, dying & loss, bereavement, comfort & hope. Over 400 titles chosen through professional reviewers.

Conservative Book Club (A)
Eagle Publishing Inc
300 New Jersey Ave NW, Suite 500, Washington, DC 20001
Tel: 202-216-0601 *Fax:* 202-216-0614
Web Site: www.conservativebookclub.com
Key Personnel
Ed-in-Chief: Christopher N Malagisi
  E-mail: cmalagisi@conservativebookclub.com
Mng Ed: Bradley Matthews
Lead Ad Mgr: Anne H Pelczar *E-mail:* anne.pelczar@conservativebookclub.com
Mktg & Ad Mgr: Laura Falcon
Conservative books on politics, economics, defense, religion, social issues, home school, history & entertainment. Selections may be returned to Conservative Book Club, 6121 Greenwood Dr, Dept 0800, Louisville, KY 40258.
Number of Members: 50,000
Publication(s): *Conservative Book Club* (16 times/yr, bulletin)

Crafter's Choice® (A)
Bookspan LLC
34 W 27 St, 10th fl, New York, NY 10001
Tel: 716-250-5700 (cust serv)
E-mail: customer.service@crafterschoice.com
Web Site: www.crafterschoice.com
The number one crafting club in America featuring a variety of crafts such as quilting, knitting, scrapbooking & more.
Publication(s): *Crafter's Choice*

Doubleday Book Club® (A)
Bookspan LLC
34 W 27 St, 10th fl, New York, NY 10001
Tel: 716-250-5700 (cust serv) *Toll Free Tel:* 866-250-3166
E-mail: customer.service@doubledaybookclub.com; member.services@doubledaybookclub.com
Web Site: www.doubledaybookclub.com
Established: 1930
The best in women's fiction, suspense & romance at great prices.

Doubleday Large Print Book Club® (A)
Bookspan LLC
34 W 27 St, 10th fl, New York, NY 10001
Tel: 716-250-5700 (cust serv)
E-mail: customer.service@doubledaylargeprint.
com
Web Site: www.doubledaylargeprint.com
Established: 1985
Bestsellers, nonfiction, reference, Christian titles, etc all in fine large print editions. Most books are NAVH compliant.
Publication(s): *The Doubleday Large Print Monthly Magazine*

5th Grade Book Club (J)
Scholastic Inc
557 Broadway, New York, NY 10012
Tel: 212-343-6100 *Toll Free Tel:* 800-724-6527
(press 1) *Toll Free Fax:* 800-223-4011
E-mail: bookclubs@scholastic.com
Web Site: scholastic.com/bookclubs
Key Personnel
EVP, Pres, Book Clubs & e-Commerce: Judy Newman
Since 1948, Scholastic Book Clubs has inspired kids to love reading by making it easy & affordable for them to choose their very own books. The Scholastic Book Clubs flyers, both in print & digitally, offer a wide range of age-appropriate books handpicked by our editors. At prices starting as low as just $1, these flyers make it possible for kids of all income levels & from every part of the country to have access to great books & build their own home collections.
Publication(s): Monthly book catalogs for early childhood to middle school (sold exclusively in the school market).

Firefly (PreK-K) (J)
Scholastic Inc
557 Broadway, New York, NY 10012
Tel: 212-343-6100 *Toll Free Tel:* 800-724-6527
(press 1) *Toll Free Fax:* 800-223-4011
E-mail: bookclubs@scholastic.com
Web Site: scholastic.com/bookclubs
Key Personnel
EVP, Pres, Book Clubs & e-Commerce: Judy Newman
Since 1948, Scholastic Book Clubs has inspired kids to love reading by making it easy & affordable for them to choose their very own books. The Scholastic Book Clubs flyers, both in print & digitally, offer a wide range of age-appropriate books handpicked by our editors. At prices starting as low as just $1, these flyers make it possible for kids of all income levels & from every part of the country to have access to great books & build their own home collections.
Publication(s): Monthly book catalogs for early childhood to middle school (sold exclusively in the school market).

1st Grade Book Club (J)
Scholastic Inc
557 Broadway, New York, NY 10012
Tel: 212-343-6100 *Toll Free Tel:* 800-724-6527
(press 1) *Toll Free Fax:* 800-223-4011
E-mail: bookclubs@scholastic.com
Web Site: scholastic.com/bookclubs
Key Personnel
EVP, Pres, Book Clubs & e-Commerce: Judy Newman
Since 1948, Scholastic Book Clubs has inspired kids to love reading by making it easy & affordable for them to choose their very own books. The Scholastic Book Clubs flyers, both in print & digitally, offer a wide range of age-appropriate books handpicked by our editors. At prices starting as low as just $1, these flyers make it possible for kids of all income levels

& from every part of the country to have access to great books & build their own home collections.
Publication(s): Monthly book catalogs for early childhood to middle school (sold exclusively in the school market).

4th Grade Book Club (J)
Scholastic Inc
557 Broadway, New York, NY 10012
Tel: 212-343-6100 *Toll Free Tel:* 800-724-6527
(press 1) *Toll Free Fax:* 800-223-4011
E-mail: bookclubs@scholastic.com
Web Site: scholastic.com/bookclubs
Key Personnel
EVP, Pres, Book Clubs & e-Commerce: Judy Newman
Since 1948, Scholastic Book Clubs has inspired kids to love reading by making it easy & affordable for them to choose their very own books. The Scholastic Book Clubs flyers, both in print & digitally, offer a wide range of age-appropriate books handpicked by our editors. At prices starting as low as just $1, these flyers make it possible for kids of all income levels & from every part of the country to have access to great books & build their own home collections.
Publication(s): Monthly book catalogs for early childhood to middle school (sold exclusively in the school market).

Get Rich Book Club (A)
Division of LKA Inc
7 Putter Lane, Middle Island, NY 11953
Mailing Address: PO Box 102, Middle Island, NY 11953-0102
Tel: 631-924-3888 (ext 202)
E-mail: grbookclub@gmail.com; linickgroup@gmail.com
Key Personnel
Pres: Andrew S Linick, PhD
Ed: Gayle Geisert
Mktg Dir: Rogue Savage
Oper Mgr: Luanne Ray
How-to books, Podcasts, Webinars, ebooks, e-classes, e-commerce, home-study, DVDs, educational, instructional, training courses; desktop publishing programs; Internet marketing, search engine optimization (SEO), web site promotion, PC & Macintosh compatible products-business & personal software, accessories, aids, training & supplies-concerned with how to make, save, borrow & invest wisely for financial freedom, wealth & happiness. Business management, business opportunity communication, consulting, direct response marketing, education, financial planning, investments, mail order, office management, personal development, real estate, retirement, self-improvement, success, travel, wealth, sports, photography, Internet, web site marketing, promotion & web site makeovers. Age group targeted 25-65+.
Number of Members: 50,325
Publication(s): *Financial Independence* (Monthly)

The Good Cook® (A)
Bookspan LLC
34 W 27 St, 10th fl, New York, NY 10001
Tel: 716-250-5700 (cust serv)
E-mail: customer.service@thegoodcook.com
Web Site: www.thegoodcook.com
Established: 1971
Cookbook club.
Publication(s): *The Good Cook*

History Book Club® (A)
Bookspan LLC
34 W 27 St, 10th fl, New York, NY 10001
Tel: 716-250-5700 (cust serv)
E-mail: customer.service@historybookclub.com
Web Site: www.historybookclub.com

Established: 1947
Adult nonfiction; history, world affairs, biography.
Publication(s): *History Book Club Catalogue* (every 3 weeks)

Honeybee (ages 2-4) (J)
Scholastic Inc
557 Broadway, New York, NY 10012
Tel: 212-343-6100 *Toll Free Tel:* 800-724-6527
(press 1) *Toll Free Fax:* 800-223-4011
E-mail: bookclubs@scholastic.com
Web Site: scholastic.com/bookclubs
Key Personnel
EVP, Pres, Book Clubs & e-Commerce: Judy Newman
Since 1948, Scholastic Book Clubs has inspired kids to love reading by making it easy & affordable for them to choose their very own books. The Scholastic Book Clubs flyers, both in print & digitally, offer a wide range of age-appropriate books handpicked by our editors. At prices starting as low as just $1, these flyers make it possible for kids of all income levels & from every part of the country to have access to great books & build their own home collections.
Publication(s): Monthly book catalogs for early childhood to middle school (sold exclusively in the school market).

Inchworm (ages 3-5) (J)
Scholastic Inc
557 Broadway, New York, NY 10012
Tel: 212-343-6100 *Toll Free Tel:* 800-724-6527
(press 1) *Toll Free Fax:* 800-223-4011
E-mail: bookclubs@scholastic.com
Web Site: scholastic.com/bookclubs
Key Personnel
EVP, Pres, Book Clubs & e-Commerce: Judy Newman
Since 1948, Scholastic Book Clubs has inspired kids to love reading by making it easy & affordable for them to choose their very own books. The Scholastic Book Clubs flyers, both in print & digitally, offer a wide range of age-appropriate books handpicked by our editors. At prices starting as low as just $1, these flyers make it possible for kids of all income levels & from every part of the country to have access to great books & build their own home collections.
Publication(s): Monthly book catalogs for early childhood to middle school (sold exclusively in the school market).

Junior Library Guild (J)
7858 Industrial Pkwy, Plain City, OH 43064
Tel: 614-733-0312 *Toll Free Tel:* 800-491-0174
Fax: 614-733-0501 *Toll Free Fax:* 800-827-3080
E-mail: editorial@juniorlibraryguild.com
Web Site: www.juniorlibraryguild.com
Key Personnel
Edit Dir: Susan Marston *Tel:* 646-380-0701
Established: 1929
Children's book service for libraries featuring new hardcover books for PreK-12. Thirty monthly selections. Monthly catalogue with authors'/illustrators' bios & reviews curriculum indications.
Branch Office(s)
123 William St, Suite 802, New York, NY 10038

Kindergarten Book Club (J)
Scholastic Inc
557 Broadway, New York, NY 10012
Tel: 212-343-6100 *Toll Free Tel:* 800-724-6527
(press 1) *Toll Free Fax:* 800-223-4011
E-mail: bookclubs@scholastic.com
Web Site: scholastic.com/bookclubs
Key Personnel
EVP, Pres, Book Clubs & e-Commerce: Judy Newman

Since 1948, Scholastic Book Clubs has inspired kids to love reading by making it easy & affordable for them to choose their very own books. The Scholastic Book Clubs flyers, both in print & digitally, offer a wide range of age-appropriate books handpicked by our editors. At prices starting as low as just $1, these flyers make it possible for kids of all income levels & from every part of the country to have access to great books & build their own home collections.
Publication(s): Monthly book catalogs for early childhood to middle school (sold exclusively in the school market).

Laissez Faire Club (A)
Laissez Faire Books
Division of Agora Financial
808 St Paul St, Baltimore, MD 21202
Toll Free Tel: 877-453-1177
E-mail: contact@lfb.org; feedback@lfb.org
Web Site: www.lfb.org
Key Personnel
Exec Ed: Jeffrey Tucker *E-mail:* tucker@lfb.org
Free market, objectivist, libertarian selections & free thought/skeptic.
Number of Members: 4,000
Publication(s): *Jason Hanson Spy Survival Briefing* (monthly, newsletter); *Laissez Faire* (monthly, newsletter)

Library of Science® Book Club (A)
Bookspan LLC
34 W 27 St, 10th fl, New York, NY 10001
Tel: 716-250-5700 (cust serv)
E-mail: customer.service@libraryofscience.net
Web Site: www.libraryofscience.net
Books for the professional scientist & the informed layperson on the mathematical, physical, life & earth sciences.

The Literary Guild® (A)
Bookspan LLC
34 W 27 St, 10th fl, New York, NY 10001
Toll Free Tel: 866-284-3202
E-mail: member.services@literaryguild.com
Web Site: www.literaryguild.com
Established: 1927
Offer a variety of genres including fiction, nonfiction, history, biography, self-help & cookbooks.

Lucky (grades 2-3) (J)
Scholastic Inc
557 Broadway, New York, NY 10012
Tel: 212-343-6100 *Toll Free Tel:* 800-724-6527 (press 1) *Toll Free Fax:* 800-223-4011
E-mail: bookclubs@scholastic.com
Web Site: scholastic.com/bookclubs
Key Personnel
EVP, Pres, Book Clubs & e-Commerce: Judy Newman
Since 1948, Scholastic Book Clubs has inspired kids to love reading by making it easy & affordable for them to choose their very own books. The Scholastic Book Clubs flyers, both in print & digitally, offer a wide range of age-appropriate books handpicked by our editors. At prices starting as low as just $1, these flyers make it possible for kids of all income levels & from every part of the country to have access to great books & build their own home collections.
Publication(s): Monthly book catalogs for early childhood to middle school (sold exclusively in the school market).

Maryheart Crusaders Inc (A)
531 W Main St, Meriden, CT 06451-2707
Tel: 203-238-9735 *Toll Free Tel:* 800-879-1957 (orders only) *Fax:* 203-235-0059
E-mail: maryheart@msn.com

Web Site: www.maryheartcrusaders.com
Key Personnel
Pres: Louise D'Angelo *Tel:* 203-235-5979
Mgr, Book Dept: Theresa Perrotti
Mgr, Candle Dept: Michael D'Angelo
Catholic religious goods store.
Number of Members: 2,222
Publication(s): *The Catholic Answer to the Jehovah's Witnesses*; *The Catholic Answer to the Jehovah's Witnesses (Spanish ed)*; *Come Climb the Ladder & Rejoice Vol I*; *Come Climb the Ladder & Rejoice Vol II*; *Come Home the Door Is Open*; *The Triumph of the Immaculate Heart of Mary: Visions of the Golden Lady of Happiness*

Metaphysical Book Club (A)
Warwick Press
18340 Sonoma Hwy, Sonoma, CA 95476
Tel: 707-939-9212 *Fax:* 707-938-3515
E-mail: warwick@vom.com
Web Site: www.warwickassociates.com
Key Personnel
Pres: Simon Warwick-Smith
Established: 1985

The Military Book Club® (A)
Bookspan LLC
34 W 27 St, 10th fl, New York, NY 10001
Tel: 716-250-5700 (cust serv)
E-mail: customer.service@militarybookclub.com
Web Site: www.militarybookclub.com
Established: 1990
Book club for military, history & warfare enthusiasts.

Mystery Guild® (A)
Bookspan LLC
34 W 27 St, 10th fl, New York, NY 10001
Tel: 716-250-5700 (cust serv)
E-mail: customer.service@mysteryguild.com
Web Site: www.mysteryguild.com
Established: 1948
Serving the needs of mystery fans & the mystery community.

Next Chapter Book Club (NCBC) (A-J)
125 Woodside Park Dr, Amelia, OH 45102
Tel: 614-404-6060
Web Site: nextchapterbookclub.org
Key Personnel
Founder: Thomas Fish, PhD *E-mail:* tfish@nextchapterbookclub.org
Exec Dir: Susan M Berg *E-mail:* sberg@nextchapterbookclub.org
Prog Mgr: Rachel Staley *E-mail:* rstaley@nextchapterbookclub.org
Established: 2002
Community-based reading program for adolescents & adults with intellectual & developmental disabilities. Network includes 300 book clubs in 31 states, 4 Canadian provinces & 3 European countries.
Number of Members: 2,000

One Spirit® (A)
Bookspan LLC
34 W 27 St, 10th fl, New York, NY 10001
Tel: 716-250-5700 (cust serv)
E-mail: customer.service@onespirit.com
Web Site: www.onespirit.com
Established: 1995
Resource for spirit, mind & body.
Publication(s): *The One Spirit Review*

Roots & Rhythm Inc (A)
PO Box 837, El Cerrito, CA 94530
Tel: 510-965-9503 *Toll Free Tel:* 888-ROOTS-66 (766-8766) *Fax:* 510-526-9001
E-mail: roots@toast.net
Web Site: www.rootsandrhythm.com

Key Personnel
Owner: Frank Scott; Nancy Scott-Noennig
Mail order: records, cassettes, CDs, discs, books & videos.
Publication(s): *Roots & Rhythm Newsletter* (5-7 issues/yr)

Science Fiction Book Club® (A)
Bookspan LLC
34 W 27 St, 10th fl, New York, NY 10001
Tel: 716-250-5700 (cust serv)
E-mail: customer.service@sfbc.com
Web Site: www.sfbc.com
Established: 1953

2nd Grade Book Club (J)
Scholastic Inc
557 Broadway, New York, NY 10012
Tel: 212-343-6100 *Toll Free Tel:* 800-724-6527 (press 1) *Toll Free Fax:* 800-223-4011
E-mail: bookclubs@scholastic.com
Web Site: scholastic.com/bookclubs
Key Personnel
EVP, Pres, Book Clubs & e-Commerce: Judy Newman
Since 1948, Scholastic Book Clubs has inspired kids to love reading by making it easy & affordable for them to choose their very own books. The Scholastic Book Clubs flyers, both in print & digitally, offer a wide range of age-appropriate books handpicked by our editors. At prices starting as low as just $1, these flyers make it possible for kids of all income levels & from every part of the country to have access to great books & build their own home collections.
Publication(s): Monthly book catalogs for early childhood to middle school (sold exclusively in the school market).

SeeSaw (K-1) (J)
Scholastic Inc
557 Broadway, New York, NY 10012
Tel: 212-343-6100 *Toll Free Tel:* 800-724-6527 (press 1) *Toll Free Fax:* 800-223-4011
E-mail: bookclubs@scholastic.com
Web Site: scholastic.com/bookclubs
Key Personnel
EVP, Pres, Book Clubs & e-Commerce: Judy Newman
Since 1948, Scholastic Book Clubs has inspired kids to love reading by making it easy & affordable for them to choose their very own books. The Scholastic Book Clubs flyers, both printed & online, offer a wide range of age-appropriate books handpicked by our editors. At prices starting as low as just $1, these flyers make it possible for kids of all income levels & from every part of the country to have access to great books & build their own home library.

Simply Audiobooks (A)
935 Sheldon Ct, Burlington, ON L7L 5K6, Canada
Tel: 905-634-3035 *Toll Free Tel:* 877-554-4332 *Fax:* 905-847-9310
E-mail: customerservice@simplyaudiobooks.com
Web Site: www.simplyaudiobooks.com
Key Personnel
CEO: Ian Small
Established: 2003
Online audiobook retailer offering unlimited rentals, sales & downloads to anywhere in North America.
Branch Office(s)
2225 Kenmore Ave, Suite 122, Buffalo, NY 14207-1359

TAB (grades 6 & up) (J)
Scholastic Inc
557 Broadway, New York, NY 10012

Tel: 212-343-6100 *Toll Free Tel:* 800-724-6527
  (press 1) *Toll Free Fax:* 800-223-4011
E-mail: bookclubs@scholastic.com
Web Site: scholastic.com/bookclubs
Key Personnel
EVP, Pres, Book Clubs & e-Commerce: Judy
  Newman
Since 1948, Scholastic Book Clubs has inspired
  kids to love reading by making it easy & affordable for them to choose their very own
  books. The Scholastic Book Clubs flyers, both
  in print & digitally, offer a wide range of age-
  appropriate books handpicked by our editors.
  At prices starting as low as just $1, these flyers
  make it possible for kids of all income levels
  & from every part of the country to have access to great books & build their own home
  collections.
Publication(s): Monthly book catalogs for early
  childhood to middle school (sold exclusively in
  the school market).

TEENS (grades 7 & up) (J)
Scholastic Inc
557 Broadway, New York, NY 10012
Tel: 212-343-6100 *Toll Free Tel:* 800-724-6527
  (press 1) *Toll Free Fax:* 800-223-4011
E-mail: bookclubs@scholastic.com
Web Site: scholastic.com/bookclubs
Key Personnel
EVP, Pres, Book Clubs & e-Commerce: Judy
  Newman
Since 1948, Scholastic Book Clubs has inspired
  kids to love reading by making it easy & affordable for them to choose their very own
  books. The Scholastic Book Clubs flyers, both
  in print & digitally, offer a wide range of age-
  appropriate books handpicked by our editors.
  At prices starting as low as just $1, these flyers
  make it possible for kids of all income levels
  & from every part of the country to have ac-

cess to great books & build their own home
  collections.
Publication(s): Monthly book catalogs for early
  childhood to middle school (sold exclusively in
  the school market).

3rd Grade Book Club (J)
Scholastic Inc
557 Broadway, New York, NY 10012
Tel: 212-343-6100 *Toll Free Tel:* 800-724-6527
  (press 1) *Toll Free Fax:* 800-223-4011
E-mail: bookclubs@scholastic.com
Web Site: scholastic.com/bookclubs
Key Personnel
EVP, Pres, Book Clubs & e-Commerce: Judy
  Newman
Established: 1948
Since 1948, Scholastic Book Clubs has inspired
  kids to love reading by making it easy & affordable for them to choose their very own
  books. The Scholastic Book Clubs flyers, both
  in print & digitally, offer a wide range of age-
  appropriate books handpicked by our editors.
  At prices starting as low as just $1, these flyers
  make it possible for kids of all income levels
  & from every part of the country to have access to great books & build their own home
  collections.
Publication(s): Monthly book catalogs for early
  childhood to middle school (sold exclusively in
  the school market).

We Need Diverse Books Older (grades 3-6) (J)
Scholastic Inc
557 Broadway, New York, NY 10012
Tel: 212-343-6100 *Toll Free Tel:* 800-724-6527
  (press 1) *Toll Free Fax:* 800-223-4011
E-mail: bookclubs@scholastic.com
Web Site: scholastic.com/bookclubs
Key Personnel
EVP, Pres, Book Clubs & e-Commerce: Judy
  Newman

Since 1948, Scholastic Book Clubs has inspired
  kids to love reading by making it easy & affordable for them to choose their very own
  books. The Scholastic Book Clubs flyers, both
  in print & digitally, offer a wide range of age-
  appropriate books handpicked by our editors.
  At prices starting as low as just $1, these flyers
  make it possible for kids of all income levels
  & from every part of the country to have access to great books & build their own home
  collections.
Publication(s): Monthly book catalogs for early
  childhood to middle school (sold exclusively in
  the school market).

**We Need Diverse Books Younger
(Kindergarten-grade 2)** (J)
Scholastic Inc
557 Broadway, New York, NY 10012
Tel: 212-343-6100 *Toll Free Tel:* 800-724-6527
  (press 1) *Toll Free Fax:* 800-223-4011
E-mail: bookclubs@scholastic.com
Web Site: scholastic.com/bookclubs
Key Personnel
EVP, Pres, Book Clubs & e-Commerce: Judy
  Newman
Since 1948, Scholastic Book Clubs has inspired
  kids to love reading by making it easy & affordable for them to choose their very own
  books. The Scholastic Book Clubs flyers, both
  in print & digitally, offer a wide range of age-
  appropriate books handpicked by our editors.
  At prices starting as low as just $1, these flyers
  make it possible for kids of all income levels
  & from every part of the country to have access to great books & build their own home
  collections.
Publication(s): Monthly book catalogs for early
  childhood to middle school (sold exclusively in
  the school market).

Book Lists & Catalogs

Many organizations compile book lists and catalogs throughout the year, including lists of religious books, juvenile books, bestsellers, international topics, etc. This is not an inclusive list, but it is representative of the various fields. The lists outlined below vary greatly in format and scope.

Letters in parenthesis indicate type of book list:

(A)–Adult   (J)–Juvenile   (A-J)–Adult & Juvenile

Further information concerning children's book lists may be obtained from The Children's Book Council, 54 West 39th Street, 14th floor, New York, NY 10018; The American Library Association, 225 N Michigan Avenue, Suite 1300, Chicago, IL 60601; and The Center for Children's Books, 501 East Daniel Street, Champaign, IL 61820.

Adoption Book Catalog (A-J)
Affiliate of Tapestry Books
131 John Muir Dr, Amherst, NY 14228
Tel: 716-639-3900 *Toll Free Tel:* 866-691-3300
E-mail: info@tapestrybooks.com
Web Site: www.tapestrybooks.com
Key Personnel
Contact: Chris Fancher *E-mail:* chris@adoptionstar.com
Mail order catalog containing books for children & adults about adoption, infertility & related subjects.

American Association for the Advancement of Science (AAAS) (A-J)
1200 New York Ave NW, Washington, DC 20005
Tel: 202-326-6400 *Fax:* 202-371-9526
E-mail: media@aaas.org
Web Site: www.aaas.org
Key Personnel
CEO: Sudip Parikh
Chief Communs Offr & Dir, Off Public Progs: Tiffany Lohwater
Founded: 1848
Science Books & Films (journal); SB&F Online; Inquiry in the Library; SB&F, Best Books for Children printed annually. Healthy People 2010 Library Initiative.

Anti-Defamation League (A-J)
605 Third Ave, New York, NY 10158-3560
Tel: 212-885-7700
Web Site: www.adl.org
Key Personnel
CEO: Jonathan Greenblatt
General & specialized books, pamphlets, reports, children's plays & stories, ethnic studies, posters, bibliographies & audio-visual materials dealing with human relations. Specialize in prejudice & discrimination, Jewish-Christian relations, Jews & Judaism, multicultural education, Israel & the Middle East, anti-Semitism, the Holocaust.

Association for Childhood Education International (A)
1875 Connecticut Ave NW, 10th fl, Washington, DC 20009
Tel: 202-372-9986 *Toll Free Tel:* 800-423-3563
E-mail: headquarters@acei.org
Web Site: acei.org
Key Personnel
Exec Dir: Diane Whitehead
Dir, Pubns & Webmaster: Anne Watson Bauer
Founded: 1892
Association of professionals concerned with the health, education & well being of children, infancy through early adolescence.
Publish *Childhood Education: Innovations* bi-monthly journal.

Association for Library Service to Children (ALSC) (J)
Division of The American Library Association (ALA)
225 N Michigan Ave, Suite 1300, Chicago, IL 60601
Tel: 312-280-2163 *Toll Free Tel:* 800-545-2433
Fax: 312-280-5271
E-mail: alsc@ala.org
Web Site: www.ala.org/alsc
Key Personnel
Exec Dir: Aimee Strittmatter
E-mail: astrittmatter@ala.org
Deputy Dir: Alena Rivers *Tel:* 800-545-2433 ext 5866 *E-mail:* arivers@ala.org
Awards Coord: Jordan Dubin *Tel:* 800-545-2433 ext 5839 *E-mail:* jdubin@ala.org
Prog Coord: Ann Michaud *Tel:* 800-545-2433 ext 2166 *E-mail:* amichaud@ala.org
Membership/Mktg Specialist: Elizabeth Serrano *Tel:* 800-545-2433 ext 2164 *E-mail:* eserrano@ala.org
Caldecott Medal Books: complete list of medal-winning picture books.
Newbery Medal Books: complete list of books awarded this medal for literature. Notable books, software, videos & recordings for children.

Baker & Taylor LLC (A)
Division of Follett Corporation
2550 W Tyvola Rd, Suite 300, Charlotte, NC 28217
Tel: 704-998-3100 *Toll Free Tel:* 800-775-1800 (info servs) *Fax:* 704-998-3319
Toll Free Fax: 800-775-2600
E-mail: btinfo@baker-taylor.com
Web Site: www.baker-taylor.com
Key Personnel
EVP & Gen Mgr: Amandeep Kochar
EVP, Opers: Gary Dayton
Founded: 1828
Baker & Taylor Inc (www.baker-taylor.com) is an aggregator & distributor of books, digital content & entertainment products. The company leverages its unsurpassed worldwide distribution network to deliver rich content in multiple formats, anytime & anywhere. Baker & Taylor offers cutting-edge digital media services & innovative technology platforms to thousands of publishers & libraries worldwide. Baker & Taylor also offers industry-leading customized library services. Baker & Taylor is proud to power Blio (blioreader.com), a flexible engaging & revolutionary e-reading application.
Branch Office(s)
Commerce Service Center, 251 Mount Olive Church Rd, Dept R, Commerce, GA 30599
Tel: 706-335-5000 *Toll Free Tel:* 800-775-1200
Momence Service Center, 501 S Gladiolus St, Momence, IL 60954, VP, Opers/Gen Mgr: Terrell Osborne *Tel:* 815-802-2444 *Toll Free Tel:* 800-775-2300

Pittsburgh Service Center, 875 Greentree Rd, Suite 678, Pittsburgh, PA 15220 *Tel:* 412-787-8890 *Toll Free Tel:* 800-775-2600
Membership(s): The American Library Association (ALA); Book Industry Study Group (BISG)

Bank Street Book Store (J)
Division of Bank Street College of Education
2780 Broadway, New York, NY 10025
Tel: 212-678-1654 *Fax:* 212-316-7026
E-mail: books@bankstreet.edu
Web Site: www.bankstreetbooks.com
Key Personnel
Mgr: Caitlyn Morrissey *E-mail:* cmorrissey@bankstreet.edu
Founded: 1970
Juvenile books, educational games, audio & videocassettes, early childhood education & CD-ROMs.

The Children's Book Council (CBC) (J)
54 W 39 St, 14th fl, New York, NY 10018
Tel: 212-966-1990
E-mail: cbc.info@cbcbooks.org
Web Site: www.cbcbooks.org
Key Personnel
Exec Dir: Carl Lennertz *E-mail:* carl.lennertz@cbcbooks.org
Annual Bibliographies: *Children's Choices*, a child-selected bibliography; *Notable Social Studies Trade Books for Young People*; *Outstanding Science Trade Books for Students K-12*; *Best STEM Books*, recommendations to educators, librarians, parents & guardians for the best children's books with STEM content; *Beyond: Advanced Reader List*, helps adults recommend age appropriate titles that will challenge advanced readers; *Building a Home Library*, guidance to parents, grandparents & others interested in assembling an at-home library for the kids in their care.
Catalog: Reading encouragement materials & select publications & products for library & education professionals.

DeVorss & Co (A)
553 Constitution Ave, Camarillo, CA 93012-8510
Mailing Address: PO Box 1389, Camarillo, CA 93011-1389
Tel: 805-322-9010 *Toll Free Tel:* 800-843-5743
Fax: 805-322-9011
E-mail: service@devorss.com
Web Site: www.devorss.com
Key Personnel
Pres: Gary R Peattie *Tel:* 805-322-9010 ext 14 *E-mail:* gpeattie@devorss.com
Founded: 1929
Metaphysical, spiritual, inspirational, self-help, body/mind/spirit, New Thought. Annual *De Vorss Publications Catalog* & *Wholesale Distributors Catalog* (for bookstores). Announcements of new books as available.

Horn Book Inc (A)
300 The Fenway, Suite P-311, Palace Road Bldg,
  Boston, MA 02115
Tel: 617-278-0225 *Toll Free Tel:* 888-628-0225
  Fax: 617-278-6062
E-mail: info@hbook.com
Web Site: www.hbook.com
Key Personnel
Group Publr: Rebecca T Miller *Tel:* 646-380-
  0738 *E-mail:* rmiller@mediasourceinc.com
Ed-in-Chief: Roger Sutton
Founded: 1924
Review publications: *The Horn Book Magazine &
  The Horn Book Guide to Children's & Young
  Adult Books.*

Jewish Book Council (A)
520 Eighth Ave, 4th fl, New York, NY 10018
Tel: 212-201-2920 *Fax:* 212-532-4952
E-mail: info@jewishbooks.org
Web Site: www.jewishbookcouncil.org
Key Personnel
Exec Dir: Naomi Firestone-Teeter
Prog Dir: Evie Saphire-Bernstein *E-mail:* evie@
  jewishbooks.org
Building Your Home Jewish Library: A Begin-
  ner's List; *Jewish Book Annual Vol 53*; *Jew-
  ish Book Fair List 1997*; *Jewish Book Month
  Kit*, Nov 14-Dec 14, 1998; National Jewish
  Book Awards: A List of Books That Received
  Awards from 1949-1996; A Selected Bibliog-
  raphy; annotated bibliographies: *Anti-Semitism*;
  *Guide to Books on Death & Bereavement for
  Adults & Children*; *How To Organize A Jewish
  Library*; *Israel*; *The Reality*; *Jerusalem 3000*;
  Jewish History; *Jewish Life Cycle Events*; *Jew-
  ish Story Collections*; *Jewish Women.*

NameBank International (A)
1001 Cathedral St, Baltimore, MD 21201
Tel: 410-864-0854 *Fax:* 410-864-0837

E-mail: lists@namebank.com
Web Site: www.namebank.com
Key Personnel
Dir: Jenelle Ketcham *Tel:* 410-864-0840
  E-mail: jketcham@namebank.com
Founded: 1980
Health, investments & travel, mailing lists. Caters
  mainly to senior citizens.

**National Council of Teachers of English
  (NCTE)** (A-J)
340 N Neil St, Suite 104, Champaign, IL 61820
Tel: 217-328-3870 *Toll Free Tel:* 877-369-6283
  (cust serv) *Fax:* 217-328-9645
E-mail: customerservice@ncte.org; permissions@
  ncte.org
Web Site: ncte.org
Key Personnel
Exec Dir: Emily Kirkpatrick
Div Dir, Pubns & Perms Coord: Kurt Austin
  Tel: 217-278-3619
Media Sales: Liz Barrett *E-mail:* ebarrett@
  townsend-group.com
Founded: 1911
Professional learning books for teachers; college,
  el-hi lists; lists of teachers by name; publish-
  ers of 11 periodicals, a national newspaper &
  national standards for teachers of English &
  language arts.

ProtoView (A)
Division of Ringgold Inc
7515 NE Ambassador Place, Suite A, Portland,
  OR 97220
Tel: 503-281-9230
E-mail: info@protoview.com
Web Site: www.protoview.com
Key Personnel
Pres, Ringgold Inc: Laura Cox
Chief Mktg Offr, Ringgold Inc: Jay Henry
Ed: Eithne O'Leyne

Founded: 1975 (as Book News Inc)
Ringgold's ProtoView service is centered around
  professionally-written abstracts & metadata of
  new titles, content which is supplied back to
  the publisher & sent to the discovery services
  used in academic settings. ProtoView abstracts
  & metadata are used in librarian- & public-
  facing resources offered by ProQuest, EBSCO,
  GOBI® Library Solutions from EBSCO, Baker
  & Taylor & Gale/Cengage. ProtoView author
  affiliations incorporate the Ringgold ID & institutional records from Ringgold's Identify
  database, expanding the data applications possible for any publisher using both services.

**Trade Commission in Miami, Embassy of
  Spain in the US** (A-J)
2655 Le Juene Rd, Suite 1114, Miami, FL 33134
Tel: 305-446-4387 *Fax:* 305-446-2602
E-mail: info@newspanishbooks.com
Web Site: www.newspanishbooks.us
Produces *New Spanish Books*, an annual online
  compilation/guide to current Spanish titles, selected by a panel of experts from the US, with
  rights available for translation in the US. Includes up-to-date information about the Spanish
  publishing scene, translation grants, Spanish literary prizes, recent translations, news & events
  in the US & more.

Upstart Books™ (A-J)
Division of Demco Inc
PO Box 7488, Madison, WI 53707
Tel: 608-241-1201 *Toll Free Tel:* 800-356-
  1200 (orders); 800-962-4463 (cust serv)
  Toll Free Fax: 800-245-1329 (orders)
E-mail: custserv@demco.com; order@demco.com
Web Site: www.demco.com/upstart
Key Personnel
Prod Devt Mgr, Lib Mkts: Heidi Green

Serials Featuring Books

The listings below outline a selected list of general interest and specialty periodicals that feature book reviews and/or articles on books and authors. The list also includes periodicals used for book-related advertising and reference purposes. The types of periodicals included are magazines, newspapers, newspaper magazine sections, newsletters & online publications.

Newspaper editions in this section are indicated as follows: (d) daily; (m) morning; (e) evening; (Sat) Saturday; (Sun) Sunday.

Magazines for the book publishing trade may be found in **Magazines for the Trade** (volume 1). Additionally, journals and services involved in book reviews can be found in **Book Review and Index Journals & Services**.

For a comprehensive international directory of periodicals, see *Ulrich's Periodicals Directory* (online only, compiled by ProQuest LLC, 630 Central Avenue, New Providence, NJ 07974), which lists magazines by subject and includes notations indicating those that carry book reviews.

Abilene Reporter-News
Published by Gannett Co Inc
101 Cypress St, Abilene, TX 79601
Mailing Address: PO Box 30, Abilene, TX 79604
Tel: 325-673-4271 *Toll Free Tel:* 844-900-7098 (sales)
E-mail: publishme@reporternews.com
Web Site: www.reporternews.com
Key Personnel
News Dir/Ed: Greg Jaklewicz *Tel:* 325-676-6764
   E-mail: greg.jaklewicz@reporternews.com
Sunday page, syndicated.
First published 1881
Frequency: Daily
Circulation: 40,000 (d); 50,000 (Sun)
$1.50/daily, $2/Sun

Academe: Magazine of the AAUP
Published by American Association of University Professors (AAUP)
1133 19 St NW, Suite 200, Washington, DC 20036
Tel: 202-737-5900 *Toll Free Tel:* 800-424-2973
   Fax: 202-737-5526
E-mail: academe@aaup.org
Web Site: www.aaup.org
Key Personnel
Dir, External Rel: Gwendolyn Bradley
   E-mail: gbradley@aaup.org
Mng Ed: Michael Ferguson *E-mail:* mferguson@aaup.org
Book Review Ed: Michael DeCesare
   E-mail: mdecesare@aaup.org
Journal of higher education from a faculty perspective. No unsol mss, query first.
First published 1915
Book Use: Reviews
Frequency: 6 issues/yr
Avg pages per issue: 56
Circulation: 44,000
Free to membs, $92/yr domestic nonmembs, $97/yr foreign nonmembs
ISSN: 0190-2946
Sell back issues
Avg reviews per issue: 3
Trim Size: 8 1/4 x 10 7/8
Ad Rates: Full page $3,075, 1/2 page $1,880
Ad Closing Date(s): 1 1/2 months before cover date

The Ada News
Published by CNHI LLC
116 N Broadway, Ada, OK 74820
Tel: 580-332-4433 *Fax:* 580-332-8734
E-mail: news@theadanews.com
Web Site: www.theadanews.com
Key Personnel
Publr: Mark Millsap *E-mail:* mark@normantranscript.com
Local community newspaper. Occasional book reviews & author interviews.
Circulation: 5,000 (Tues-Sat)

Advisor Today
Published by National Association of Insurance & Financial Advisors (NAIFA)
2901 Telestar Ct, Falls Church, VA 22042-1205
Tel: 703-770-8100 *Toll Free Tel:* 877-TO-NAIFA (866-2432)
E-mail: membersupport@naifa.org
Web Site: www.advisortoday.com
Key Personnel
Ed-in-Chief: Ayo Mseka *Tel:* 703-770-8204
   E-mail: amseka@naifa.org
Pubn & Circ Coord: Tara Heuser *Tel:* 703-770-8207 *E-mail:* theuser@naifa.org
News & how-to articles for the professional life & health insurance agent & financial planner. No unsol mss, query first.
First published 1906
Frequency: 6 issues/yr
Avg pages per issue: 100
Circulation: 40,000
Free to membs, $50/yr indivs, $60/yr instns, $100/yr intl
ISSN: 1529-823X
Buy illustrations & photographs; Sell back issues

The Advocate
Published by Capital City Press LLC
10705 Rieger Rd, Baton Rouge, LA 70809
Tel: 225-388-0200 (circ); 225-388-0315 (newsroom) *Toll Free Tel:* 800-960-6397 (in Louisiana)
E-mail: newstips@theadvocate.com
Web Site: theadvocate.com
Key Personnel
Publr: Dan Shea
Features Ed: Karen Martin *Tel:* 225-388-0378
   E-mail: kmartin@theadvocate.com
Travel, puzzles, hobbies, art reviews, books & authors, entertainment, history & features.
Frequency: Daily
Digital & print: $14.95/mo (Sat & Sun), $24.95/mo (Mon-Sun); digital only: $9.99/mo

Afro-American Newspaper
1531 S Edgewood St, Baltimore, MD 21227
Tel: 410-554-8277 (edit); 410-554-8200 (subns)
   Toll Free Fax: 877-570-9297
E-mail: editor@afro.com; subs@afro.com
Web Site: www.afro.com
Key Personnel
Pres: Benjamin Murphy Phillips, IV
VP, Mktg & Technol: Kevin Peck
Publr: Frances Murphy Draper
Dir, Opers: Andre R Draper
Mng Ed: Tiffany Ginyard
Ed: Sean Yoes *E-mail:* syoes@afro.com
General interest newspaper targeted for African-American audience. Reviews done in-house, occasional author interviews.
First published 1892
Frequency: Monthly
$20/yr digital only, $70/yr print & digital

AGNI Magazine
Published by Boston University
236 Bay State Rd, Boston, MA 02215
E-mail: agni@bu.edu
Web Site: www.bu.edu/agni
Key Personnel
Ed: Sven Birkerts
Sr Ed: William Pierce
New literary fiction, poetry & essays by emerging & established writers. Accept unsol mss. For submission policy, see www.agnionline.bu.edu/submit.
First published 1972
Frequency: Semiannual
Avg pages per issue: 240
Circulation: 4,000
$23/yr
ISSN: 0191-3352
Trim Size: 8 1/2 x 5 3/8
Ad Rates: Full page $500, 1/2 page $350
Ad Closing Date(s): Feb 5 & Aug 1

Akron Beacon Journal
Published by GateHouse Media LLC
44 E Exchange St, Akron, OH 44328
Tel: 330-996-3000
Web Site: www.ohio.com
Key Personnel
Pres & Publr: Bill Albrecht *Tel:* 330-996-3782
   E-mail: balbrecht@gatehousemedia.com
Ed: Michael Shearer *Tel:* 330-996-3750
   E-mail: mshearer@thebeaconjournal.com
Book reviews in-house, through syndication & other outside sources; occasional author interviews. Sunday pages.
Circulation: 70,000 (m); 100,000 (Sun)
Digital & print: $9.99/mo (Sat & Sun), $19.50/mo (Mon-Sun); digital only: $9.99/mo

Albuquerque Journal
Published by Albuquerque Publishing Co
7777 Jefferson NE, Albuquerque, NM 87109
Tel: 505-823-3800; 505-823-4400 (circ)
   Toll Free Tel: 800-990-5765; 800-577-8683 (subscriber servs)
Web Site: www.abqjournal.com
Key Personnel
Ed-in-Chief: Karen Moses *Tel:* 505-823-3803
   E-mail: kmoses@abqjournal.com
Mng Ed: Dan Herrera *Tel:* 505-823-3810
   E-mail: dherrera@abqjournal.com
Occasional book reviews.
Circulation: 304,224 (d); 379,315 (Sun)
Digital & print: $12/mo (Sun only), $15.50/mo (Fri-Sun), $20.50/mo (Mon-Sun); digital only: $10/mo

Alexandria Daily Town Talk
Published by Gannett Co Inc
PO Box 7558, Alexandria, LA 71306
Tel: 318-487-6397
E-mail: editor@thetowntalk.com

Web Site: www.thetowntalk.com
Weekly page book reviews, author interviews; in-house & syndicated reviews.
First published 1883
Circulation: 41,000 (d)

Alfred Hitchcock's Mystery Magazine
Published by Dell Magazines
Division of Penny Publications LLC
44 Wall St, Suite 904, New York, NY 10005-2401
Tel: 212-686-7188 *Toll Free Tel:* 800-220-7443 (corp sales) *Fax:* 212-480-5751
E-mail: alfredhitchcockmm@dellmagazines.com
Web Site: www.alfredhitchcockmysterymagazine.com
Subscription Address: Dell Magazines Direct, 6 Prowitt St, Norwalk, CT 06855-1220
Key Personnel
Ed: Linda Landrigan
Asst Mktg Mgr: Monique St Paul
Short stories of mystery, crime & detection, short-short contest, puzzle & book reviews.
First published 1956
Frequency: 6 issues/yr
Avg pages per issue: 192
Circulation: 90,000
$34.97/yr, $63.97/2 yrs, $59.94/yr intl, $35.88/yr digital
ISSN: 0002-5224
Avg reviews per issue: 4
Trim Size: 5 7/8 x 8 1/2
Ad Rates: 4-color back cover $1,800, B&W page $1,000, B&W 1/2 page-horizontal $600
Ad Closing Date(s): 3 months before sale date

Amarillo Globe News
Published by GateHouse Media LLC
600 S Tyler, Suite 103, Amarillo, TX 79101
Tel: 806-376-4488
Web Site: www.amarillo.com
Key Personnel
Regl Exec Ed: Jill Nevels-Haun *E-mail:* jnevels-haun@lubbockonline.com
One page weekly, in-house & through syndication; occasional author interviews.
Circulation: Globe: 55,000 (e); Sun Globe News: 65,000
Digital & print: $14.25/4 wks (Sun only), $19.09/4 wks (Fri-Sun), $22.50/4 wks (Mon-Sat), $23.45/4 wks (Mon-Sun); digital only: $9.99/mo

American Educator
Published by American Federation of Teachers
555 New Jersey Ave NW, Washington, DC 20001
Tel: 202-879-4420
E-mail: ae@aft.org
Web Site: www.aft.org/ae
Key Personnel
Art Dir: Jennifer Chang
Mng Ed: Jennifer Dubin
Graphic Designer: Jennifer Barney
Articles on education, labor, politics & social commentary. Includes news, book reviews & features for teachers at all grade levels, preschool through college & university.
First published 1977
Frequency: Quarterly
Avg pages per issue: 40
Circulation: 900,000
$10/yr nonmembs
ISSN: 0148-432X
Trim Size: 8 1/4 x 10 7/8

The American Legion Magazine
Published by The American Legion
700 N Pennsylvania St, Indianapolis, IN 46204
Mailing Address: PO Box 1055, Indianapolis, IN 46206
Tel: 317-630-1298; 317-630-1200 (cust serv)
Fax: 317-630-1223

E-mail: magazine@legion.org
Web Site: www.legion.org
Subscription Address: Box 1954, Indianapolis, IN 46206
Key Personnel
Commns Dir: Jeff Stoffer *Tel:* 317-630-1298
Mktg: Diane M Andretti *E-mail:* dandretti@legion.org
Contains feature articles that address a compelling issue in American society. Issues relating to veterans affairs, the US military, national security, foreign affairs, American values & patriotism often are preferred. Also publish selected general-interest articles & question & answer interviews with prominent national & world figures. Articles are not required to have a military angle. We make all assignments based on a 300-word query letter. Prefer to work with published/established writers.
First published 1919
Book Use: Occasional excerpts
Frequency: Monthly
Avg pages per issue: 72
Circulation: 2,400,000 paid
Free to membs, $6/yr membs of Sons & Auxiliary, $15/yr nonmembs, $21/yr foreign
ISSN: 0002-9734
Buy nonfiction, cartoons; Sell back issues
Trim Size: 7 3/4 x 10 1/2
Ad Rates: B&W page $51,415, 4-color page $69,790
Ad Closing Date(s): 1st day of 2nd month preceding issue date

American Letters & Commentary (AL&C)
Subsidiary of University of Texas at San Antonio, Dept of English
One UTSA Circle, San Antonio, TX 78249-0643
E-mail: amerletters@satx.rr.com
Web Site: www.amletters.org
Key Personnel
Co-Ed: Catherine Kasper; David Ray Vance
For submission policy, see guidelines on our web site.

American Press
4900 Hwy 90 E, Lake Charles, LA 70615
Mailing Address: PO Box 2893, Lake Charles, LA 70602
Tel: 337-433-3000 *Fax:* 337-494-4070
E-mail: news@americanpress.com
Web Site: www.americanpress.com
Key Personnel
Book Review Ed: Donna Price
Sunday book reviews; occasional local author interviews.
Circulation: 29,000 (d); 32,000 (Sun)
$.50/daily, $1.25/Sun

American Scientist
Published by Sigma Xi, The Scientific Research Society
Cape Fear Bldg, Suite 300, 3200 Chapel Hill Nelson Hwy, Research Triangle Park, NC 27709-0013
Tel: 919-549-4691 *Toll Free Tel:* 800-282-0444 *Fax:* 919-549-0090
E-mail: editors@amscionline.org
Web Site: www.americanscientist.org
Key Personnel
Art Dir: Barbara Aulicino
Dir, Digital Features: Katie L Burke
Ed-in-Chief: Fenella Saunders
Mng Ed: Stacey Lutkoski
Reports on recent research in pure & applied sciences; written for scientists in all disciplines.
First published 1913
Frequency: 6 issues/yr
Circulation: 55,000 paid
Print only: $30/yr, $54/2 yrs; print & digital: $36/yr, $66/2 yrs
ISSN: 0003-0996

Buy art & cartoons; Sell back issues
Trim Size: 8 3/16 x 10 7/8
Ad Rates: B&W page $2,900, 4-color page $4,000
Ad Closing Date(s): 1st of month, 2 months prior to publication

American Songwriter
Published by ForASong Media LLC
PO Box 330249, Nashville, TN 37203
Tel: 615-321-6096
Web Site: americansongwriter.com
Subscription Address: PO Box 90187, Long Beach, CA 90809 *Toll Free Tel:* 888-881-5861
E-mail: americansongwriter@pfsmag.com
Key Personnel
Publr: Albie Del Favero *Tel:* 615-321-6096 ext 105 *E-mail:* adelfavero@americansongwriter.com
Ed-in-Chief: Caine O'Rear
Asst Ed: Brittney McKenna *E-mail:* bmckenna@americansongwriter.com
American Songwriter Magazine covers every aspect of the craft & art of songwriting, from how & why writers give birth to their songs, to engaging & informative assessments of our songwriting culture as a whole. The magazine provides in-depth interviews with up-&-coming, established & legendary songwriters; discussions on performance rights organizations & copyright law; & interviews with publishers, producers, A&R executives & other industry representatives who have something of interest to say to our readers. American Songwriter strives to serve as the unparalleled source of inspiration for passionate music fans & songwriters alike, by exploring all genres of music. Also available online.
First published 1984
Book Use: Reviews, might excerpt if appropriate
Frequency: 6 issues/yr
Circulation: 30,000
$2.49/mo, $24.95/yr
ISSN: 0896-8993
Sell articles, ad reprints & back issues

The American Spectator
Published by The American Spectator Foundation
122 S Royal St, Suite 1, Alexandria, VA 22314
Tel: 703-807-2011
E-mail: editor@spectator.org
Web Site: spectator.org
Key Personnel
Publr: Melissa Mackenzie
Edit Dir: Wladyslaw Pleszczynski
Ed-in-Chief: R Emmett Tyrrell, Jr
Occasional book reviews & articles featuring books. Online only.
First published 1924

AMG/Parade
Published by Athlon Media Group
60 E 42 St, Suite 820, New York, NY 10165
Tel: 212-478-1910
E-mail: info@amgparade.com
Web Site: athlonmediagroup.com
Key Personnel
Pres & CEO: Chuck Allen
CFO: Mary Lee Vanderkooi
Chief Revenue Offr Brand Sales: Amy Chernoff
EVP, New Ventures & Busn Devt: Tracey Altman
SVP & Chief Content Offr: Lisa Delaney
SVP & Chief Digital Offr: Michael McCracken
SVP & Chief Mktg Offr, Digital: Monique Kakar
General interest publication for a mass audience with editorial content on people, education, Washington & Hollywood, science & medicine & changing tastes & trends.
First published 1941
Frequency: Weekly
Circulation: 18,000,000

Trim Size: 8.250 x 9.375
Ad Rates: B&W page $584,800, 4-color page
  $722,800

The Amherst News
Published by SaltWire Network
2717 Joseph Howe Dr, Halifax, NS B3J 2T2,
  Canada
Mailing Address: PO Box 610, Halifax, NS B3J
  2T2, Canada
Tel: 902-664-1260
Web Site: www.thecumberlandnewsnow.com
Key Personnel
Mng Ed: Darrell Cole *E-mail:* darrell.cole@
  amherstnews.ca
In-house, syndicated, author interviews.
First published 1893
$1.85/wk

Analog Science Fiction & Fact
Published by Dell Magazines
Division of Penny Publications LLC
44 Wall St, Suite 904, New York, NY 10005
Toll Free Tel: 800-220-7443 (corp sales)
E-mail: analogsf@dellmagazines.com
Web Site: www.analogsf.com
Subscription Address: Dell Magazines Direct, 6
  Prowitt St, Norwalk, CT 06855-1220, Con-
  tact: Lisa Begley *Tel:* 203-866-6688 ext
  204 *Fax:* 203-854-5962 *E-mail:* lbegley@
  pennypublications.net
Key Personnel
Ed: Trevor Quachri
Publishes 7-9 science fiction stories per issue, fact
  articles & book review.
First published 1930
Book Use: Reviews, excerpts & serializations
Frequency: 6 double issues/yr
Avg pages per issue: 144
Circulation: 32,900
$34.97/yr, $46.97/yr intl, $63.97/2 yrs, $87.97/2
  yrs intl, $35.88/yr digital
ISSN: 1059-2113
Buy freelance fiction, poetry & cartoons; Sell
  back issues
Trim Size: 5 7/8 x 8 1/2
Ad Rates: B&W page $1,000, 4-color back cover
  $1,800
Ad Closing Date(s): 3 months before sale date

Anchorage Daily News
Published by Alaska Daily News LLC
300 W 31 Ave, Anchorage, AK 99503
Tel: 907-257-4200; 907-257-4400 (subns)
  Toll Free Tel: 800-478-4200 (AK only); 866-
  528-0236 (subns)
E-mail: letters@adn.com
Web Site: www.adn.com
Key Personnel
Pres & CEO: Ryan Binkley *E-mail:* ryan@adn.
  com
Publr: Andy Pennington *Tel:* 907-257-4210
  E-mail: apennington@adn.com
Ed: David Hulen *Tel:* 907-257-4596
  E-mail: dhulen@adn.com
Reviews books by Alaskan authors or on topics
  of specific interest to Alaskans.
First published 1946
Frequency: Daily (Mon-Fri & Sun)
Digital & print: $11.49/mo (Sun only), $16.95/mo
  (Thurs, Fri & Sun), $24.95/mo (Mon-Fri &
  Sun); digital only: $11.99/mo, $119.90/yr

Anniston Star
Published by Consolidated Publishing Co
4305 McClellan Blvd, Anniston, AL 36206
Tel: 256-236-1551 *Fax:* 256-241-1970
E-mail: news@annistonstar.com
Web Site: www.annistonstar.com
Key Personnel
Publr: Josephine Ayers
Exec Ed: Anthony Cook

Mng Ed: Ben Cunningham
  E-mail: bcunningham@annistonstar.com
Every Sunday, Life & Arts section, occasional au-
  thor interviews; book reviews every Sunday in
  Coffee Break section.
Circulation: 30,000
$.75/daily, $2/Sun; digital & print: $9.25/mo
  (Sun only), $9.50/mo (Wed-Sat), $11.25/mo
  (Fri-Sun), $16.25/mo (Wed-Sun); digital only:
  $7.99/mo, $69.99/yr

The Antigonish Review
Published by St Francis Xavier University
PO Box 5000, Antigonish, NS B2G 2W5, Canada
Tel: 902-867-3962 *Fax:* 902-867-5563
E-mail: tar@stfx.ca
Web Site: www.antigonishreview.com
Key Personnel
Mng Ed: Thomas Hodd
Book Reviews Ed: Leo Furey
Literary journal.
First published 1970
Frequency: Quarterly
Avg pages per issue: 144
Circulation: 1,000
$75/yr print, $140/2 yrs, $20/back issue; $30/yr
  digital, $45/2 yrs, $10/back issue (if available)
ISSN: 0003-5662
Avg reviews per issue: 4
Ad Rates: Full page $300, 1/2 page $150

Archaeology
Published by Archaeological Institute of America
36-36 33 St, Long Island City, NY 11106
Tel: 718-472-3050 *Toll Free Tel:* 877-275-9782
  (subns) *Fax:* 718-472-3051
E-mail: editorial@archaeology.org; general@
  archaeology.org
Web Site: www.archaeology.org; www.
  archaeological.org
Subscription Address: PO Box 433091, Palm
  Coast, FL 32164 *Tel:* 386-246-0414 *Toll
  Free Tel:* 877-ARKY-SUB (275-9782)
  E-mail: subscription@archaeology.org
Key Personnel
Publr: Kevin Quinlan *Tel:* 857-305-9354
  E-mail: kquinlan@archaeological.org
Ed-in-Chief: Jarrett A Lobell *Tel:* 718-472-3050
  ext 4908 *E-mail:* jarrett@archaeology.org
Deputy Ed: Eric A Powell *E-mail:* eric@
  archaeology.org
Sr Ed: Benjamin Leonard *E-mail:* ben@
  archaeology.org; Daniel Weiss *E-mail:* daniel@
  archaeology.org
Contains articles written by freelance science
  writers & professionals edited to meet the
  needs of the general reader; excavation reports,
  recent discoveries & special studies of ancient
  cultures. No unsol mss, query first.
First published 1948
Book Use: Review new titles
Frequency: 6 issues/yr
Avg pages per issue: 72
Circulation: 225,000 paid
$14.97/yr US or digital only, $29.97/yr CN & intl
ISSN: 0003-8113
Sell articles, ad reprints & back issues
Trim Size: 8 x 10 1/2
Ad Closing Date(s): 30 days prior to sale date

Argus Leader
Published by Gannett Co Inc
200 S Minnesota Ave, Sioux Falls, SD 57104
Tel: 605-331-2200; 605-331-2222; 605-331-2300
  (newsroom) *Toll Free Tel:* 800-952-0127 (cust
  serv)
Web Site: www.argusleader.com
Key Personnel
News Dir: Cory Myers *E-mail:* ctmyers@
  argusleader.com
Occasionally local, in-house & other sources.
  Occasional author interviews. Weekly book
  section-Sunday.

The Arizona Daily Star
Published by Lee Enterprises Inc
4850 S Park Ave, Tucson, AZ 85714
Tel: 520-573-4142 *Toll Free Tel:* 800-695-4492
  (cust serv)
E-mail: metro@tucson.com; circulation@tucson.
  com
Web Site: tucson.com
Key Personnel
Pres & Publr: John D'Orlando *Tel:* 520-573-4215
  E-mail: jdorlando@tucson.com
Sunday page reviews, in-house & through syndi-
  cation; occasional author interviews.
Circulation: 160,587 (d); 234,163 (Sun)
Digital & print: $14.99/mo (Sun only, Sat & Sun,
  Wed & Sun or Wed, Sat & Sun), $23.99/mo
  (Wed-Sun), $24.99/mo (Mon-Sun)

The Arizona Republic
Published by Gannett Co Inc
200 E Van Buren St, Phoenix, AZ 85004
Tel: 602-444-8000 *Toll Free Tel:* 800-331-9303
  (delivery); 800-332-6733 (subns)
E-mail: azrepubliccustomerservice@gannett.com;
  newsubs@azcentral.com
Web Site: www.azcentral.com
Key Personnel
Edit Dir: Philip Boas *E-mail:* phil.boas@
  arizonarepublic.com
Features Dir: Rebecca Bartkowski
  E-mail: rebecca.bartkowski@gannett.com
Exec Ed: Greg Burton *E-mail:* greg.burton@
  azcentral.com
Pages produced in-house, through syndication &
  by other sources. Author interviews & book
  reviews.
Circulation: 488,000 (m); 603,500 (Sun)
Digital & print: $18/mo (Wed & Sun), $27/mo
  (Wed & Fri-Sun), $32/mo (Mon-Sun); digital
  only: $9.99/mo

Arkansas Democrat-Gazette
Published by Arkansas Democrat-Gazette Inc
Subsidiary of Wehco Media
121 E Capitol Ave, Little Rock, AR 72201
Mailing Address: PO Box 2221, Little Rock, AR
  72203
Tel: 501-378-3400 *Toll Free Tel:* 800-482-1121
  (subns) *Fax:* 501-372-4765
Web Site: www.arkansasonline.com
Key Personnel
Publr: Walter E Hussman, Jr
Mng Ed: David Baily *Tel:* 501-378-3594
Moviestyle Ed/Columnist: Phillip Martin
  Tel: 501-378-3473 *E-mail:* pmartin@
  arkansasonline.com
Book reviews & occasional author interviews.
Frequency: Daily
Circulation: 182,212 (d); 274,494 (Sun)
$34/mo
ISSN: 1060-4332

Army Magazine
Published by Association of the US Army
2425 Wilson Blvd, Arlington, VA 22201
Tel: 703-841-4300 *Toll Free Tel:* 800-336-4570
Web Site: www.ausa.org
Key Personnel
Art Dir: Sam Votsis *E-mail:* svotsis@ausa.org
Ed-in-Chief: Rick Maze *E-mail:* rmaze@ausa.org
Mng Ed: Elizabeth Rathbun *E-mail:* lrathbun@
  ausa.org
Military-oriented.
First published 1904
Book Use: Reviews
Frequency: Monthly
Avg pages per issue: 64
Circulation: 100,000 paid
Free to membs
ISSN: 0004-2455

Buy freelance, nonfiction, art, cartoons; Sell back issues
Trim Size: 8 1/8 x 10 7/8
Ad Rates: B&W page $9,950 (1x), 4-color page $11,485 (1x)
Ad Closing Date(s): 1st of month preceding publication

Art in America
Published by ArtNews Media/Penske Media Corp
475 Fifth Ave, New York, NY 10017
Tel: 212-398-1690 *Toll Free Tel:* 800-925-8059 (subns)
E-mail: ads@artmediaholdings.com
Web Site: www.artinamericamagazine.com
Key Personnel
Dir, Mktg: Vajra Kingsley *E-mail:* vkingsley@ artmediaholdings.com
Ed: William S Smith
Comprehensive reporting & commentary on major achievements & events throughout the art world, particularly in painting, sculpture, photos & prints; includes numerous reproductions.
First published 1913
Book Use: Departmentalized book reviews, exhibition reviews & news columns
Frequency: Monthly
Avg pages per issue: 120
Circulation: 45,000
$79/yr, $110/yr CN, $127/yr intl
ISSN: 0004-3214
Buy freelance nonfiction; Sell articles & ad reprints, back issues
Trim Size: 9 x 10 7/8
Ad Rates: B&W page $6,409, 4-color page $8,236
Ad Closing Date(s): see Media Kit on web site

Artesia Daily Press
503 W Main St, Artesia, NM 88210
Mailing Address: PO Box 190, Artesia, NM 88211-0190
Tel: 575-746-3524 *Fax:* 575-746-8795
Web Site: www.artesianews.com
Key Personnel
Publr: Danny Scott *E-mail:* danny@artesianews. com
Local news in print & online.
Frequency: Daily (Tues-Fri & Sun)
Circulation: 3,200 (Tues-Fri); 3,500 (Sun)
$.50/issue (Tues-Fri), $1/issue (Sun), $6.75/mo local print, $8/mo electronic

Asbury Park Press
Published by Gannett Co Inc
3600 Hwy 66, Neptune, NJ 07754
Mailing Address: PO Box 1550, Neptune, NJ 07754
Tel: 732-922-6000 *Toll Free Tel:* 800-822-9770
E-mail: newstips@app.com
Web Site: www.app.com
Key Personnel
VP, News: Hollis R Towns
Exec Ed: Paul D'Ambrosio
Regl Features Planner: Bill Canacci
Sunday edition includes books page; occasional author interviews.
Circulation: 159,705 (e); 223,833 (Sun)
Digital & print: $16/mo (Fri & Sun), $19/mo (Fri-Sun), $28/mo (Mon-Sun)

The Asheville Citizen-Times
Published by Gannett Co Inc
14 O Henry Ave, Asheville, NC 28801
Mailing Address: PO Box 2090, Asheville, NC 28802-2090
Tel: 828-252-5611 *Toll Free Tel:* 800-672-2472
E-mail: news@citizen-times.com
Web Site: www.citizen-times.com
Key Personnel
News Dir: Katie Wadington *Tel:* 828-232-5829
E-mail: kwadington@citizen-times.com

Sunday in *Leisure* section; frequent author interviews.
First published 1870
Circulation: 75,000 (d); 82,000 (Sun)
$1/daily, $2/Sun
Avg reviews per issue: 2

Asimov's Science Fiction
Published by Dell Magazines
Division of Penny Publications LLC
44 Wall St, Suite 904, New York, NY 10005-2401
Tel: 212-686-7188 *Toll Free Tel:* 800-220-7443 (corp sales) *Fax:* 212-480-5751
E-mail: asimovs@dellmagazines.com; customerservice@pennypublications.com
Web Site: www.asimovs.com
Subscription Address: Dell Magazines Direct, 6 Prowitt St, Norwalk, CT 06855-1220
Key Personnel
Pres: Peter Kanter
SVP: Bruce W Sherbow
Dir, Mktg, E-Commerce & Brand Licensing: Abigail Browning
Sr Art Dir: Victoria Green
Ed: Sheila Williams *Tel:* 212-686-7188 ext 2323
E-mail: swilliams@dellmagazines.net
Circ Servs & Subns: Sandy Marlowe
Features science fiction & fantasy.
First published 1977
Book Use: Short stories
Frequency: 6 double issues/yr
Avg pages per issue: 208
Circulation: 62,600
$34.97/yr, $46.97/yr intl, $63.97/2 yrs, $87.97/2 yrs intl, $35.88/yr digital only
ISSN: 1055-2146
Buy freelance fiction & poetry; Sell back issues
Trim Size: 8 1/2 x 5 3/8
Ad Rates: B&W page $1,800, 4-color back cover $3,240 (rates include ads in both Asimov's Science Fiction & Analog Science Fiction & Fact)
Ad Closing Date(s): 3 months before sale date

Athens Messenger
Published by Adams Publishing Group
9300 Johnson Rd, Athens, OH 45701
Tel: 740-592-6612
E-mail: info@athensmessenger.com; subscriptions@athensmessenger.com
Web Site: www.athensmessenger.com
Key Personnel
Publr: Mark Cohen *E-mail:* mark.cohen@ adamspg.com
Ad Dir: Amanda Montgomery
E-mail: amontgomery@adamspg.com
Ed: Tyler Buchanan *E-mail:* tbuchanan@ athensmessenger.com
In-house reviews with authors with a local connection & those with Ohio interests. Monthly local author interviews.
First published 1904
Circulation: 10,000 (d); 12,000 (Sun)

Atlanta Journal-Constitution
Subsidiary of Cox Media Group LLC
223 Perimeter Center Pkwy, Atlanta, GA 30346-1301
Tel: 404-526-5151 *Fax:* 404-526-5746
E-mail: customercare@ajc.com
Web Site: www.ajc.com
Key Personnel
Publr: Donna B Hall
Sr Features Ed: Nicole D Smith *E-mail:* nicole. smith@ajc.com
Ed: Kevin Riley *Tel:* 404-526-2161
E-mail: kriley@ajc.com
Weekly column, in-house & through syndication, with frequent author interviews.
First published 1868

Circulation: 427,300 (Mon-Thurs); 485,300 (Fri); 515,700 (Sat); 693,500 (Sun)
Digital & print: $12.99/mo (Sun only), $24.99/mo (Mon-Sun); digital only: $4.99/mo

The Atlantic
Published by Atlantic Monthly Group LLC
600 New Hampshire Ave NW, Washington, DC 20037
Tel: 202-266-6000
Web Site: www.theatlantic.com
Subscription Address: PO Box 37564, Boone, IA 50037-0564 *Tel:* 515-237-3670 (intl) *Toll Free Tel:* 800-234-2411 *E-mail:* theatlantic@ cdsfulfillment.com
Key Personnel
Chmn: David G Bradley
VChmn: Peter Lattman
Pres: Bob Cohn
Sr Art Dir: Oliver Munday
Creative Dir: Peter Mendelsund
Ed-in-Chief: Jeffrey Goldberg
Exec Ed: Adrienne LaFrance
Literary Ed: Ann Hulbert
Public affairs, politics & the arts. Considers unsol mss, either fiction or nonfiction & poetry. Ad closing date & trim sizes information available at advertising.theatlantic.com.
First published 1857
Frequency: 10 issues/yr
Avg pages per issue: 130
Circulation: 496,000
$24.50/yr print or digital, $34.50/yr print & digital
ISSN: 0276-9077
Buy freelance fiction, nonfiction & poetry

Augusta Chronicle
Published by GateHouse Media LLC
725 Broad St, Augusta, GA 30901
Tel: 706-724-0851 *Toll Free Tel:* 866-249-8223
Web Site: www.augustachronicle.com
Key Personnel
News Ed: Mike Wynn *Tel:* 706-823-3218
E-mail: mike.wynn@augustachronicle.com
Sunday book page.
Digital & print: $18.42/mo (Sun only), $19.37/mo (Fri-Sun), $31.43/mo (Mon-Sun); digital only: $9.95/mo, $99.50/yr

Austin American-Statesman
Published by GateHouse Media LLC
305 S Congress Ave, Austin, TX 78704
Mailing Address: PO Box 670, Austin, TX 78767
Tel: 512-445-4040 *Toll Free Tel:* 800-445-9898 (cust serv) *Fax:* 512-445-3679
E-mail: customercare@statesman.com
Web Site: www.statesman.com
Key Personnel
Exec Features Ed: Sharon Chapman *Tel:* 512-445-3647 *E-mail:* schapman@statesman.com
Weekly book page, in-house & through syndication. Occasional author interviews.
First published 1871
Circulation: 130,000 (d); 191,000 (Sun)
Digital & print: $29.99/mo (Sun only), $70.99/mo (Mon-Sun); digital only: $19.99/mo

The Baltimore Sun
Published by Baltimore Sun Media Group
Subsidiary of Tribune Publishing Co
300 E Cromwell St, Baltimore, MD 21230
Tel: 410-332-6000 *Toll Free Tel:* 800-829-8000 *Fax:* 410-332-6455
E-mail: newstips@baltimoresun.com
Web Site: www.baltimoresun.com
Key Personnel
Publr & Ed-in-Chief: Trif Alatzas *E-mail:* trif. alatzas@baltsun.com
Mng Ed: Sam Davis *E-mail:* sdavis@baltsun.com
Sunday, 2 pages, 4-5 reviews per week in-house & freelance. Occasional author interviews.

First published 1837
Circulation: 270,000 (d); 420,000 (Sun)
$6.93/wk digital

Bangor Daily News
Published by Bangor Publishing Co
One Merchants Plaza, Bangor, ME 04401
Mailing Address: PO Box 1329, Bangor, ME 04402
Tel: 207-990-8000 *Toll Free Tel:* 800-432-7964 (ME only)
Web Site: www.bangordailynews.com
Key Personnel
Publr: Richard J Warren
Mng Ed: Dan MacLeod *Tel:* 207-990-8260 *E-mail:* dmacleod@bangordailynews.com
Sr Ed, Features: Sarah Walker Caron *Tel:* 207-990-8120 *E-mail:* scaron@bangordailynews.com
First published 1889
Circulation: 35,000 (m); 45,000 (Sat)
Digital & print: $24.25/mo (Mon-Sat); digital only: $8.43/mo, $93.90/yr

Barrow News-Journal
Published by MainStreet Newspapers Inc
33 Lee St, Jefferson, GA 30549
Mailing Address: PO Box 908, Jefferson, GA 30549
Tel: 706-367-5233 *Fax:* 706-367-8056
E-mail: news@barrowjournal.com
Web Site: www.barrowjournal.com
Key Personnel
Co-Publr: Mike Buffington; Scott Buffington
Ed: Chris Bridges *E-mail:* editor@barrowjournal.com
First published 1893
Frequency: Wed & Sun
Circulation: 15,800 (Wed); 4,400 (Sun)
$45/yr print & digital
Ad Rates: $9.20/retail, $9.45/classified

Battle Creek Enquirer
Published by Gannett Co Inc
77 E Michigan Ave, Suite 101, Battle Creek, MI 49017-3093
Tel: 269-964-7161; 269-966-0672 *Toll Free Tel:* 800-333-4139
E-mail: battlecreekenquirer@gannett.com; bceeditors@battlecreekenquirer.com
Web Site: www.battlecreekenquirer.com
Weekly (2-3 reviews); Sunday page, syndicated reviews.
Circulation: 30,000 (e); 38,000 (Sun)
$1/daily, $2/Sun
New York Rep(s): Gannett Media Sales

The Bay City Times
Published by MLive Media Group
810 N Water St, Bay City, MI 48708
Tel: 989-895-8551; 989-671-1201 *Toll Free Tel:* 800-878-1400 *Fax:* 989-895-5910
E-mail: bcnews@mlive.com
Web Site: www.mlive.com/bay-city
Key Personnel
Ed: Clark Hughes *E-mail:* chughes3@mlive.com
Weekly page. Book reviews through syndication; author interviews from AP.
Circulation: 35,000 (e); 44,000 (Sun)
$11.52/4 wks (Sun only, home delivery)
Avg reviews per issue: 4

The Beachcomber
Published by The SandPaper Inc
1816 Long Beach Blvd, Surf City, NJ 08008
Tel: 609-494-5900 *Fax:* 609-494-1437
E-mail: beachcomberlbi@gmail.com
Web Site: thesandpaper.net
Key Personnel
Publr: Curt Travers
Off Mgr: Lee Little

Occasional book reviews.
Frequency: 6 issues/yr
Avg pages per issue: 48
Free

Beaufort Gazette
Published by The McClatchy Co
10 Buck Island Rd, Bluffton, SC 29910
Mailing Address: PO Box 5727, Hilton Head Island, SC 29938
Tel: 843-706-8140 *Toll Free Tel:* 877-706-8100
Web Site: www.islandpacket.com
Key Personnel
Publr: Rodney Mahone *E-mail:* rmahone@mcclatchy.com
Sr Ed: Liz Farrell *E-mail:* lfarrell@islandpacket.com
First published 1897
$12.99/mo digital, $129.99/yr

The Beaumont Enterprise
Published by Hearst Newspapers
Division of Hearst Corp
380 Main St, Beaumont, TX 77701
Mailing Address: PO Box 3071, Beaumont, TX 77704-3071
Tel: 409-833-3311
E-mail: localnews@beaumontenterprise.com
Web Site: www.beaumontenterprise.com
Key Personnel
Publr: Mark Adkins *Tel:* 409-838-2898 *E-mail:* madkins@beaumontenterprise.com
Mng Ed: Ashley Sanders *Tel:* 409-838-2860 *E-mail:* arsanders@beaumontenterprise.com
Ed: Timothy M Kelly *Tel:* 409-838-2801 *E-mail:* tkelly@hearstnp.com
Sunday, books page & reviews.
Circulation: 65,000 (d); 75,000 (Sun)
$3.88/wk (Sun print & electronic)

Birmingham News
Published by Alabama Media Group
1731 First Ave N, Birmingham, AL 35203
Tel: 205-325-4444 *Toll Free Tel:* 800-568-4123
E-mail: customercare@bhamnews.com; life@al.com
Web Site: www.al.com/birmingham
Books & Alabama author info.
Print & digital: $18.07/mo (Sun), $24.09/mo (Wed & Sun), $30.12/mo (Wed, Fri & Sun); unlimited digital only $19.99/mo

The Bismarck Tribune
Published by Lee Enterprises Inc
707 E Front Ave, Bismarck, ND 58504
Mailing Address: PO Box 5516, Bismarck, ND 58506-5516
Tel: 701-223-2500 *Fax:* 701-223-2063
E-mail: news@bismarcktribune.com
Web Site: bismarcktribune.com
Key Personnel
Publr: Gary Adkisson *Tel:* 701-250-8299 *E-mail:* gary.adkisson@bismarcktribune.com
Ad Dir: Lisa Weisz *Tel:* 701-250-8232 *E-mail:* lisa.weisz@bismarcktribune.com
Circ Dir: Bural Coffey *Tel:* 701-250-8203 *E-mail:* bural.coffey@bismarcktribune.com
Ed: Amy Dalrymple *Tel:* 701-250-8267 *E-mail:* amy.dalrymple@bismarcktribune.com
Occasional, local author interviews & book reviews.
First published 1873
Circulation: 30,100
$5/mo digital basic, $9.99/mo digital plus, $22/mo silver, $37/mo gold, $46/mo platinum

The Blade
Published by Block Communications Inc
541 N Superior St, Toledo, OH 43660
Tel: 419-724-6000
Web Site: www.toledoblade.com

Key Personnel
Publr & Ed-in-Chief: John R Block
Dir, Mktg: Luann Sharp
Exec Ed: Kurt Franck
Mng Ed: Dave Murray
Frequency: Daily
Avg pages per issue: 40
Circulation: 52,000 (d); 80,000 (Sun)
$1/daily, $3/Sun

Borrow County News, see Barrow News-Journal

The Boston Globe Sunday Magazine
Published by Boston Globe Media Partners LLC
One Exchange Place, 2nd fl, Boston, MA 02109
Tel: 617-929-2955 *Toll Free Tel:* 888-MY-GLOBE (694-5623, subns)
E-mail: magazine@globe.com
Web Site: www.bostonglobe.com/magazine
Key Personnel
Ed: Veronica Chao *E-mail:* veronica.chao@globe.com
General interest; excerpts.
First published 1872
Book Use: Excerpts
Frequency: Weekly
Circulation: 754,000
$5/wk print (Sun only), $27.72/mo digital

The Boston Globe/The Boston Sunday Globe
Published by Boston Globe Media Partners LLC
One Exchange Place, 2nd fl, Boston, MA 02109
Mailing Address: PO Box 55819, Boston, MA 02205-5819
Tel: 617-929-7400 *Toll Free Tel:* 888-MY-GLOBE (694-5623, subns)
E-mail: customerservice@globe.com
Web Site: www.bostonglobe.com
Key Personnel
Publr: John Henry
Mng Ed: Jennifer Peter *Tel:* 617-929-3148 *E-mail:* jennifer.peter@globe.com
Ed: Brian McGrory *Tel:* 617-929-3059 *E-mail:* mcgrory@globe.com
Sr Deputy Mng Ed: Mark S Morrow *Tel:* 617-929-7129 *E-mail:* mark.morrow@globe.com
Deputy Mng Ed, Local News & Features: Felice Belman *Tel:* 617-929-7496 *E-mail:* felice.belman@globe.com
Deputy Mng Ed, Print & Opers: David Dahl *Tel:* 617-929-2809 *E-mail:* dahl@globe.com
Daily & Sunday, in-house & other sources, frequent author interviews, book excerpts.
First published 1872
Digital & print: $9.50/wk (Sat & Sun), $14.34/wk (Mon-Sun); print only: $5/wk (Sun only), $7.50/wk (Sat & Sun)

Boston Herald
Published by MediaNews Group Inc
100 Grossman Dr, 4th fl, Braintree, MA 02184
Tel: 617-426-3000 *Toll Free Tel:* 800-882-1211 (subns)
Web Site: www.bostonherald.com
Key Personnel
Ed-in-Chief: Joe Sciacca
In-house & freelance, daily, Sunday section; frequent author interviews.
Circulation: 108,548 (d); 85,398 (Sat); 81,925 (Sun)
Digital & print: $18/4 wks (Sun only), $63/4 wks (Mon-Sun); digital only: $9.98/4 wks
ISSN: 0738-5854

Boston Magazine
Published by Metro Corp
300 Massachusetts Ave, Boston, MA 02115
Tel: 617-262-9700 *Fax:* 617-262-4925; 617-267-1774 (edit)
E-mail: editor@bostonmagazine.com
Web Site: www.bostonmagazine.com

Key Personnel
Publr: Lynne Montesanto *Tel:* 617-275-2006
  E-mail: lmontesanto@bostonmagazine.com
Assoc Publr: Christina Miller *Tel:* 617-974-8431
  E-mail: cmiller@bostonmagazine.com
Ed-in-Chief: Chris Bogel
Exec Ed: Brittany Jasnoff
Mng Ed: Angela Mats
Covers issues confronting Boston metropolitan
  area, including politics, lifestyles, business
  trends, youth scene & sociological currents;
  culture, sports, entertainment reviews, fashion,
  dining & travel.
First published 1962
Book Use: Reviews
Frequency: Monthly
Avg pages per issue: 190
Circulation: 75,000
$15/yr, $25/2 yrs
Buy nonfiction; Sell article & ad reprints, back
  issues
Trim Size: 8 x 10 1/2

Bostonia
Published by Boston University
985 Commonwealth Ave, Boston, MA 02215
Tel: 617-353-3081 *Fax:* 617-353-6488
E-mail: bostonia@bu.edu
Web Site: www.bu.edu/bostonia
Key Personnel
Asst VP & Exec Ed: Doug Most *Tel:* 617-353-
  6190 *E-mail:* dmost@bu.edu
Mng Ed: Cynthia Buccini *Tel:* 617-353-5840
  E-mail: cbuccini@bu.edu
Alumni magazine of Boston University.
First published 1900
Book Use: Reviews, excerpts
Frequency: 3 issues/yr
Avg pages per issue: 88
Circulation: 240,000
Free to alumni
ISSN: 0164-1441
Trim Size: 8 1/8 x 10 7/8

Boys' Life
Published by Boy Scouts of America
1325 W Walnut Hill Lane, Irving, TX 95015
Toll Free Tel: 866-584-6589 (subns)
Web Site: www.boyslife.org
Subscription Address: PO Box 152401, Irving,
  TX 75015-2401 *Tel:* 972-580-2366
Key Personnel
Natl Sales Dir: Jay Stuart *Tel:* 877-929-5433 ext
  12006 *E-mail:* jay.stuart@scouting.org
Mktg Specialist: Jillian Foley *Tel:* 877-929-5433
  ext 12005 *E-mail:* jillian.foley@scouting.org
Ad Prodn Mgr: Lisa Hott
Mng Ed: Mike Goldman
Premiere magazine for kids, tweens & teens with
  active lifestyles, featuring award-winning ed-
  itorial, pictorials, comics, games & movie re-
  views, buying guides, fiction & more.
First published 1911
Book Use: Reviews & excerpts
Frequency: Monthly
Avg pages per issue: 60
Circulation: 1,000,000 paid
$3.95/issue, $24/yr
ISSN: 0006-8608
Sell articles & ad reprints, back issues
Trim Size: 8 x 10 1/2
Ad Rates: Full page 4-color bleed $52,765 (open
  gross rate)
Ad Closing Date(s): 1 1/2 months prior to issue
  date

Bozeman Daily Chronicle
Published by Big Sky Publishing
Division of Pioneer News Group
2820 W College St, Bozeman, MT 59718
Mailing Address: PO Box 1190, Bozeman, MT
  59771-1190

Tel: 406-587-4491 *Fax:* 406-587-7995
E-mail: citydesk@dailychronicle.com
Web Site: www.bozemandailychronicle.com
Key Personnel
Publr: Mark Dobie *Tel:* 406-582-2626
  E-mail: mdobie@dailychronicle.com
Mng Ed: Nick Ehli *Tel:* 406-582-2647
  E-mail: nehli@dailychronicle.com
Asst Mng Ed: Ted Sullivan *Tel:* 406-582-2659
  E-mail: tsullivan@dailychronicle.com
City Ed: Michael Wright *Tel:* 406-582-2638
  E-mail: mwright@dailychronicle.com
In-house & through syndication; occasional au-
  thor interviews.
Avg pages per issue: 90
Circulation: 15,000
Digital & print: $11.70/mo (Sun only), $14.30/mo
  (Fri-Sun), $16.90/mo (Tues-Sun)

Brandon Sun
Division of FP Canadian Newspapers
501 Rosser Ave, Brandon, MB R7A 0K4, Canada
Tel: 204-727-2451 *Toll Free Tel:* 877-786-2472
  (rural); 866-438-8186 *Fax:* 204-571-7430 (edit)
E-mail: opinion@brandonsun.com; circ@
  brandonsun.com
Web Site: www.brandonsun.com
Key Personnel
Publr: Jim Mihaly *Tel:* 204-571-7401
  E-mail: jmihaly@brandonsun.com
Sales & Mktg Dir: Glen Parker *Tel:* 204-571-
  7424 *E-mail:* gparker@brandonsun.com
Ed: Matt Goerzen *Tel:* 204-571-7445
  E-mail: mgoerzen@brandonsun.com
Kids book reviews biweekly, in-house & through
  syndication; occasional author interviews.
First published 1882
Frequency: Daily (Mon-Sat)
Circulation: 18,027
Digital & print: $56.21/3 mos, $108.19/6 mos,
  $214.57/yr plus tax; digital only: $11.83/mo
  plus tax

Brick - A Literary Journal
Box 609, Sta P, Toronto, ON M5S 2Y4, Canada
Tel: 416-593-9684
E-mail: info@brickmag.com
Web Site: www.brickmag.com
Key Personnel
Publr: Laurie D Graham
Mng Ed: Allison LaSorda
Ed: Dionne Brand; David Chariandy; Michael
  Helm; Liz Johnston; Martha Sharpe; Rebecca
  Silver Slayter; Madeleine Thien
A twice yearly feast of the best literary nonfiction
  in English. Nonfiction submissions only. See
  web site for details.
First published 1977
Frequency: Semiannual
Avg pages per issue: 168
Circulation: 5,500
$25/yr CN, $26/yr US, $30/yr intl
ISSN: 0382-8565
Trim Size: 8 x 8 1/2
Ad Rates: B&W full page $800, 1/2 page $550,
  1/4 page $325
Ad Closing Date(s): April 2 for May release, Oct
  2 for Nov release

BRIDES
Published by Dotdash
1500 Broadway, 6th fl, New York, NY 10036
Tel: 212-204-4000 *Toll Free Tel:* 800-456-6162
  (subns)
E-mail: editors@brides.com; bricustserv@
  cdsfulfillment.com
Web Site: www.brides.com; www.dotdash.com/
  our-brands
Key Personnel
Exec Dir: Lisa Harman Gooder
Services magazine for brides-to-be, grooms, fam-
  ilies & friends. Information on planning wed-

dings, relationships, trousseau, honeymoons &
  new homes.
First published 1934
Book Use: Reviews

British Heritage Travel
Published by Kliger Heritage Media
201 E 87 St, Suite 23C, New York, NY 10128
Toll Free Tel: 877-843-8862
E-mail: info@britishheritage.com;
  memberservices@britishheritage.com
Web Site: britishheritage.com
Subscription Address: PO Box 579, Palm Coast,
  FL 32142-0579
Key Personnel
CEO: Jack Kliger
British travel, history, life & culture. Includes
  book reviews & information on British literary
  figures.
First published 1976
Book Use: Reviews & videos
Frequency: 6 issues/yr
Avg pages per issue: 68
Circulation: 20,000
$29.95/yr US, $41.95/yr CN & intl
ISSN: 0195-2633
Trim Size: 9 x 10.875
Ad Rates: 4-color full page $3,000

Brockville Recorder & Times
Published by Postmedia Network Inc
2479 Parkedale Ave, Brockville, ON K6V 3H2,
  Canada
Tel: 613-342-4441
Web Site: www.recorder.ca
Key Personnel
Media Sales Dir: Kerry Sammon *Tel:* 613-
  342-4441 ext 500267 *E-mail:* ksammon@
  postmedia.com
Edit: Ron Zajac *Tel:* 613-342-4441 ext 500245
  E-mail: rzajac@postmedia.com
Daily syndication & occasional author interviews.
First published 1821
Circulation: 15,100 (e)
$14.99/4 wks, $3.99/mo digital

Buffalo News
One News Plaza, Buffalo, NY 14203
Mailing Address: PO Box 100, Buffalo, NY
  14240
Tel: 716-849-4444; 716-842-1111
  Toll Free Tel: 800-777-8640 *Fax:* 716-856-5150
E-mail: subscriberservices@buffnews.com
Web Site: www.buffalonews.com
Key Personnel
Arts & Books Ed: Jeff Simon *Tel:* 716-849-4438
  E-mail: jsimon@buffnews.com
In-house reviews weekly, multiple pages, occa-
  sional author interviews.
Circulation: 250,300 (d), 338,800 (Sun)
$13/mo digital, $11.75/mo print & digital (Sun
  only)

The Burlington Free Press
Published by Gannett Co Inc
100 Bank St, Suite 700, Burlington, VT 05401
Tel: 802-863-3441 *Toll Free Tel:* 800-427-3126
  Fax: 802-660-1802
E-mail: metro@burlingtonfreepress.com
Web Site: www.burlingtonfreepress.com
Key Personnel
Pres: Jim Fogler *Tel:* 802-660-1800
Exec Ed: Emilie Stigliani *Tel:* 802-660-1897
  E-mail: estigliani@freepressmedia.com
In-house & through syndication; biweekly author
  interviews.
Circulation: 41,901 (d); 47,566 (Sun)
New York Rep(s): Gannett Media Sales

Calgary Herald
Published by Postmedia Network Inc
215 16 St SE, Calgary, AB T2E 7P5, Canada
Tel: 403-235-7100 *Toll Free Tel:* 800-372-9219

E-mail: mysubscription@calgaryherald.com
Web Site: calgaryherald.com
Key Personnel
Mng Dir: Martin Hudson *Tel:* 403-235-7257
   E-mail: mhudson@postmedia.com
Ed (Arts & Life, Travel, Features): Michele Jarvie
   E-mail: mjarvie@postmedia.com
Book reviews in "Arts" section.
First published 1883
Circulation: 223,000 (e); 247,000 (Sat)
Digital & print: $39/mo (Mon-Sat), $21.67/mo
   (Sat only); e-paper: $9.99/mo; digital only:
   $9.95/mo, $99.99/yr

Campus Technology
Published by 1105 Media Inc
6300 Canoga Ave, Suite 1150, Woodland Hills,
   CA 91367
Tel: 818-734-1520 *Fax:* 818-734-1522
Web Site: campustechnology.com
Key Personnel
Pres & Group Publr: Kevin O'Grady
   E-mail: kogrady@1105media.com
Edit Dir, Educ: David Nagel *E-mail:* dnagel@
   1105media.com
Exec Ed: Rhea Kelly *Tel:* 818-814-5347
   E-mail: rkelly@1105media.com
Focused exclusively on the use of technology
   across all areas of higher education.
First published 2004
Frequency: 6 issues/yr digital, 3 issues/yr print
Avg pages per issue: 72
Circulation: 40,709
Free for those who qualify
ISSN: 1553-7544
Buy freelance, nonfiction, art & cartoons; Sell
   articles & ad reprints, back issues
Trim Size: 8 1/4 x 11
Ad Closing Date(s): 4 weeks prior to publication
   date

Cape Cod Times
Published by GateHouse Media LLC
319 Main St, Hyannis, MA 02601
Tel: 508-775-1200 *Fax:* 508-771-3292
Web Site: www.capecodonline.com; capecodtimes.
   com
Key Personnel
Books Ed: Gwenn Friss *Tel:* 508-862-1155
   E-mail: gfriss@capecodonline.com
Sunday page; book reviews in-house, through
   syndication, wire service; biweekly author in-
   terviews. Tend to concentrate on bestsellers &
   general audience books; of particular interest:
   nature (especially nonfiction) & science, environment, self-help, quality fiction.
Circulation: 49,850 (m); 60,600 (Sun)

The Capital Gazette
Published by Baltimore Sun Media Group
Subsidiary of Tribune Publishing Co
PO Box 6727, Annapolis, MD 21401
Tel: 410-268-5000; 410-268-7000 (classified);
   410-268-4800 (circ) *Fax:* 410-280-5953 (news-
   room); 410-268-4643
Web Site: www.capitalgazette.com
Key Personnel
Ed: Rick Hutzell *Tel:* 410-280-5938
   E-mail: rhutzell@capgaznews.com
Sunday paper, in-house & through syndication.
   Local author interviews only.
Circulation: 50,000
$2.99/wk print & digital, $1.99/wk digital

Catholic Digest
Published by Bayard Inc
One Montauk Ave, Suite 200, New London, CT
   06320
Tel: 860-437-3012
E-mail: queries@catholicdigest.com
Web Site: www.catholicdigest.com

Subscription Address: PO Box 291826, Kettering,
   OH 45429 *Toll Free Tel:* 800-678-2836
Key Personnel
Mng Ed: Paul McKibben *E-mail:* pmckibben@
   bayard-inc.com
General interest Catholic family magazine. No
   unsol mss.
First published 1936
Book Use: Excerpts & reviews
Frequency: 9 issues/yr
Avg pages per issue: 128
Circulation: 150,000
$19.95/yr, $35.95/2 yrs, $51/3 yrs
ISSN: 0008-7998
Buy freelance nonfiction, art
Trim Size: 6 x 9
Ad Rates: 4-color page $3,700

The Cedar Rapids Gazette
Published by The Gazette Co
500 Third Ave SE, Cedar Rapids, IA 52401
Tel: 319-398-8211; 319-398-8333
   Toll Free Tel: 800-397-8333 (subns)
E-mail: customercare@thegazette.com
Web Site: thegazette.com
Key Personnel
Exec Ed: Zack Kucharski *Tel:* 319-398-8219
   E-mail: zack.kucharski@thegazette.com
Occasional section cover story, with color art-
   work, weekly page review, in-house & through
   syndication; occasional author interviews.
Circulation: 140,000 (d); 150,000 (Sun)
Digital & print: $35.40/13 wks (Sun only),
   $80.50/13 wks (Mon-Sun); print only: $22.10/
   13 wks (Sun only); digital only: $9.97/mo

Charleston Gazette-Mail
Published by HD Media Company LLC
1001 Virginia St E, Charleston, WV 25301
Tel: 304-348-5140; 304-348-4800 (subns)
   Toll Free Tel: 888-259-8867 (subns)
E-mail: support@wvgazettemail.com
Web Site: www.wvgazettemail.com
Key Personnel
Publr: Jim Heady
Features Ed: Maria Young *Tel:* 304-348-5115
   E-mail: maria.young@wvgazettemail.com
Occasional column, in-house & through syndica-
   tion.
Circulation: 54,554 (m); 107,903 (Sun)
$1/daily, $2/Sun

The Charlotte Observer
Published by The McClatchy Co
550 S Caldwell St, Charlotte, NC 28202
Tel: 704-358-5000 *Toll Free Tel:* 800-532-5350
   (cust serv)
Web Site: www.charlotteobserver.com/
   entertainment/books
Key Personnel
Publr: Rodney Mahone *E-mail:* rmahone@
   mcclatchy.com
Exec Ed: Sherry Chisenhall *E-mail:* schisenhall@
   charlotteobserver.com
Mng Ed: Taylor Batten *Tel:* 704-358-5934
   E-mail: tbatten@charlotteobserver.com
Book reviews & author interviews.
First published 1886
Digital & print: $55.77/13 wks (Sun only),
   $83.66/13 wks (Wed & Fri-Sun), $111.54/13
   wks (Mon-Sun); digital only: $12.99/mo
Avg reviews per issue: 4-5

Chattanooga Times Free Press
Published by Chattanooga Publishing Co Inc
400 E 11 St, Chattanooga, TN 37403
Tel: 423-756-6900
Web Site: www.timesfreepress.com
Key Personnel
Pres: Jeff DeLoach
Ed & Dir, Content: Allison Gerber
   E-mail: agerber@timesfreepress.com

Occasional author interviews & book reviews.
Digital & print: $20/mo (Sun), $34/mo (Mon-
   Sun)

The Chicago Magazine
Published by Tribune Publishing Co
160 N Stetson Ave, 4th fl, Chicago, IL 60601
Tel: 312-222-8999 *Toll Free Tel:* 800-999-0879
E-mail: letters@chicagomag.com; chicago@
   emailcustomerservice.com
Web Site: www.chicagomag.com; www.
   chicagotribune.com
Key Personnel
Publr & Ed-in-Chief: Susanna Homan
   E-mail: susanna@chicagomag.com
Exec Ed: Terrance Noland *E-mail:* tnoland@
   chicagomag.com
Culture Ed: Tal Rosenberg *E-mail:* trosenberg@
   chicagomag.com
General interest newspaper magazine with
   Chicago & Midwest focus. Books & readings
   info in "Arts & Culture" section.
Book Use: Excerpts & photo essays
Frequency: 11 issues/yr
Circulation: 1,167,000
$19.90/yr, $28/2 yrs, $36/3 yrs, $9.99/yr digital
Trim Size: 7 x 10 1/2

Chicago Reader
Published by Sun-Times Media LLC
30 N Racine Ave, Suite 300, Chicago, IL 60607
Tel: 312-222-6920
E-mail: mail@chicagoreader.com
Web Site: www.chicagoreader.com
Key Personnel
Creative Dir: Vince Cerasani
Ed: Jake Malooley *E-mail:* kmalooley@
   chicagoreader.com
Freelance source; occasional book reviews, long
   essays, occasional local author. Also available
   online.
First published 1971
Frequency: Weekly
Circulation: 90,000
Free
ISSN: 1096-6919

Chicago Tribune
Published by Chicago Tribune Media Group
   (CTMG)
Subsidiary of Tribune Publishing Co
160 N Stetson Ave, Chicago, IL 60601
Toll Free Tel: 800-974-7520
E-mail: editor@chicagotribune.com
Web Site: www.chicagotribune.com
Key Personnel
Publr & Ed-in-Chief: R Bruce Dold
Mng Ed, Content: Peter Kendall
   E-mail: pkendall@chicagotribune.com
One review daily, Sunday 8-10 reviews. In-house
   & freelance reviewers.
First published 1847
Circulation: 740,154 (d); 675,065 (Sat); 1,137,447
   (Sun)
Digital & print: $64.87/13 wks (Mon-Sun),
   $19.92/8 wks (Sun only); digital only: $7.96/4
   wks

The Chippewa Herald
Published by Lee Enterprises Inc
321 Frenette Dr, Chippewa Falls, WI 54729
Mailing Address: PO Box 69, Chippewa Falls,
   WI 54729
Tel: 715-723-5515 *Toll Free Tel:* 800-236-5515;
   866-477-0648 (classifieds) *Fax:* 715-723-9644
Web Site: www.chippewa.com
Key Personnel
Publr: Josh Trust *E-mail:* josh.trust@lee.net
Ed: John Casper *E-mail:* john.casper@lee.net
Infrequent & in-house reviews.

Circulation: 4,000
$5/mo digital basic, $3/13 wks digital plus, $29/
26 wks digital plus, $24/mo full access (silver),
$39.75/mo full access (platinum)

Christian New Age Quarterly
PO Box 276, Clifton, NJ 07015-0276
E-mail: info@christiannewage.com
Web Site: www.christiannewage.com
Key Personnel
Ed: Catherine Groves
Dir, Communs: Frederick Moe
Reviewer, Christian Focus: Daniel Hahn
Reviewer, New Age View: Joanne Winetzki
Authentic dialogue between Christians & New
Agers. Content examines Christianity & the
New Age movement with special regard to
contrasts & similarities. No simultaneous sub-
missions. Writers' guidelines: send SASE or
visit www.christiannewage.com.
First published 1989
Book Use: Reviews; request reviewers address
before sending review copies
Frequency: Quarterly
Avg pages per issue: 20
$3.50/issue, $5/issue foreign, $12.50/yr, $18.50/yr
foreign
ISSN: 0899-7292
Buy nonfiction; Sell back issues ($3.50)
Trim Size: 7 x 8 1/2
Ad Rates: B&W/color page $45
Ad Closing Date(s): Jan 1, April 1, July 1, Oct 1

The Christian Science Monitor
210 Massachusetts Ave, Boston, MA 02115
Tel: 617-450-2300 *Toll Free Tel:* 800-288-7090
E-mail: customerservice@csmonitor.com
Web Site: www.csmonitor.com
Subscription Address: PO Box 6074, Harlan, IA
51593 *Toll Free Tel:* 800-456-2220 (US); 800-
333-2777 (CN) *E-mail:* csmonitorcustserv@
cdsfulfillment.com
Key Personnel
Mng Ed: Amelia Newcomb
Books Ed: April Austin
Ed: Mark Sappenfield
Reviews of hardcover fiction & nonfiction. Best-
seller lists for fiction & nonfiction, children's
books, poetry & religion throughout the year.
First published 1908
Frequency: Daily
$11/mo digital, $15/mo print & digital

The Chronicle-Herald
Published by SaltWire Network
2717 Joseph Howe Dr, Halifax, NS B3J 2T2,
Canada
Tel: 902-426-2811 *Toll Free Tel:* 800-563-1187
Fax: 902-426-1158
E-mail: reception@herald.ca
Web Site: www.thechronicleherald.ca
Key Personnel
Contact: Allison Lawlor
Sunday, books page; in-house, freelance & oc-
casionally syndicated column; frequent author
interviews.
Frequency: Daily (Mon-Sat)
Circulation: 100,000 (d)
Digital & print: $4.20/wk (Sat only), $6.30/wk
(Mon-Sat); digital only: $14.99/mo

Chronicle-Journal
Subsidiary of Continental Newspapers (Canada)
Ltd
75 S Cumberland St, Thunder Bay, ON P7B 1A3,
Canada
Tel: 807-343-6200
E-mail: circulation@chroniclejournal.com
Web Site: www.chroniclejournal.com
Key Personnel
Publr & Gen Mgr: Clint Harris *E-mail:* charris@
chroniclejournal.com

Mng Ed: Greg Giddens *E-mail:* ggiddens@
chroniclejournal.com
Book page, one per week, in-house & by syndica-
tion; frequent author interviews; book reviews.
Avg pages per issue: 28
Circulation: 24,600 (d); 24,400 (Sat); 21,500
(Sun)
$1/daily, $1.50/Sat

Chronicles: A Magazine of American Culture
Published by The Charlemagne Institute
8011 34 Ave S, Suite C11, Bloomington, MN
55425
Web Site: www.chroniclesmagazine.org
Subscription Address: PO Box 3247, Northbrook,
IL 60065-9968 *Toll Free Tel:* 800-877-5459
Key Personnel
Exec Ed: Edward Welsch
Essays & reviews on various aspects of American
Culture including literature, popular culture, ed-
ucation & social issues. No unsol mss, query
first.
First published 1977
Frequency: Monthly
Avg pages per issue: 52
Circulation: 7,500
$44.99/yr, $79.99/2 yrs, $104.99/3 yrs
ISSN: 0887-5731
Buy freelance fiction, nonfiction, poetry, art &
cartoons; Sell articles & ad reprints, back is-
sues
Avg reviews per issue: 3 in-depth, 4 in-brief
Trim Size: 8 3/8 x 10 7/8
Ad Rates: B&W page $650, 4-color page $1,134
Ad Closing Date(s): 8 weeks prior to release date

Cincinnati Enquirer
Published by Gannett Co Inc
312 Elm St, Cincinnati, OH 45202
Tel: 513-721-2700 *Toll Free Tel:* 800-876-4500
(subns); 877-513-7355 (cust serv)
Web Site: www.cincinnati.com
Key Personnel
Pres: Eddie Tyner *Tel:* 513-768-8500
E-mail: president@enquirer.com
Exec Ed: Beryl Love *Tel:* 513-768-8551
E-mail: blove@enquirer.com
Use wire reviews & no longer write reviews
in-house. Pitches must have a local/greater
Cincinnati connection, which would include
authors coming here on tour.
Circulation: 201,200 (d); 330,000 (Sun)

Civil Engineering
Published by American Society of Civil Engi-
neers (ASCE)
1801 Alexander Bell Dr, Reston, VA 20191
Tel: 703-295-6300 *Toll Free Tel:* 800-548-ASCE
(548-2723)
E-mail: ascelibrary@asce.org
Web Site: www.asce.org/cemagazine
Key Personnel
Ed-in-Chief: Laurie Shuster *E-mail:* lshuster@
asce.org
Ad Dir: Dianne Vance *E-mail:* dvance@asce.org
Art Dir: Jeff Roth *E-mail:* jroth@asce.org
Mng Ed: Margaret Mitchell *E-mail:* mmitchell@
asce.org
Sr Ed/Features Mgr: Robert L Reid
E-mail: rreid@asce.org
Sr Ed: Catherine A Cardno, PhD
E-mail: ccardno@asce.org
Prodn Mgr: Sean Richardson
E-mail: srichardson@asce.org
Directed toward the civil, structural & environ-
mental design engineers in the engineering con-
struction market. No unsol mss, query first.
First published 1930
Book Use: Book listings, occasional reviews; gen-
eral interest engineering/design/planning books
Frequency: Monthly
Avg pages per issue: 120

Circulation: 140,000
Free to membs
ISSN: 0885-7024
Sell articles & ad reprints, back issues
Trim Size: 7 7/8 x 10 7/8
Ad Rates: B&W page $11,650, 4-color page
$14,395

Clarion-Ledger
Published by Gannett Co Inc
201 S Congress St, Jackson, MS 39201
Tel: 601-961-7000 *Toll Free Tel:* 877-850-5343
E-mail: letters@jackson.gannett.com
Web Site: www.clarionledger.com
Key Personnel
Exec Ed: Sam R Hall *Tel:* 601-961-7163
E-mail: srhall@jackson.gannett.com
Features Ed: Stephen Ward *E-mail:* sward2@
jackson.gannett.com
Sunday in *Artist Leisure* section. Reviews in-
house/freelance, occasional author interviews.
First published 1837
Circulation: 39,133 (d & Sat)

Cleveland Daily Banner
Published by Cleveland Newspapers Inc
1505 25 St NW, Cleveland, TN 37311
Mailing Address: PO Box 3600, Cleveland, TN
37320-3600
Tel: 423-472-5041 *Fax:* 423-476-1046; 423-614-
6529 (newsroom)
E-mail: news@clevelandbanner.com
Web Site: www.clevelandbanner.com
Key Personnel
Publr & Ed: Ralph C Baldwin, Jr
Daily book reviews, in-house & through syndica-
tion; author interviews.
Circulation: 11,000 (e); 13,000 (Sun)
$75/yr

College Spotlight
Published by College & Career Press LLC
PO Box 300484, Chicago, IL 60630
Tel: 773-718-0366 *Fax:* 773-718-0366
Web Site: www.ccpnewsletters.com/college-
spotlight
Key Personnel
Publr & Mng Ed: Andrew Morkes
E-mail: amorkes@chicagopa.com
College, high school & career guidance librarian.
Books on college & career exploration.
First published 2002
Frequency: 9 issues/yr
Avg pages per issue: 10
$29.99/yr, $54.99/2 yrs, $79.99/3 yrs
ISSN: 1525-4313
Trim Size: 8 1/2 x 11

Colorado Springs Gazette
Published by Clarity Media
30 E Pikes Peak Ave, Suite 100, Colorado
Springs, CO 80903
Tel: 719-632-5511 (advert) *Toll Free Tel:* 866-
632-6397 (cust serv) *Fax:* 719-636-0202
E-mail: customercare@gazette.com
Web Site: www.gazette.com
Key Personnel
Publr: Dan Steever *Tel:* 719-636-0104
E-mail: dan.steever@gazette.com
Mng Ed: Jim Trotter *Tel:* 719-636-0251
E-mail: jim.trotter@gazette.com
Ed: Vince Bzdek *Tel:* 719-636-0273
E-mail: vince.bzdek@gazette.com
Weekly author interviews on Sunday books page.
Circulation: 89,000 (d); 138,900 (Sun)
$1.50/Sun

Columbia Missourian
Published by Missourian Publishing Association
Subsidiary of University of Missouri
Lee Hills Hall, 221 S Eighth St, Columbia, MO
65201

Mailing Address: PO Box 917, Columbia, MO
65205
Tel: 573-882-5700; 573-882-5720 (newsroom)
E-mail: news@columbiamissourian.com
Web Site: www.columbiamissourian.com
Key Personnel
Exec Ed: Ruby L Bailey *Tel:* 573-882-6695
E-mail: baileyru@missouri.edu
Mng Ed: Jeanne Abbott *Tel:* 573-882-5741
E-mail: abbottjm@missouri.edu
First published 1908
Frequency: Daily (exc Mon & Sat)
Circulation: 5,574
$5.95/mo digital, $7.95/mo print & digital

The Columbus Dispatch
Published by GateHouse Media LLC
62 E Broad St, Columbus, OH 43216
Tel: 614-461-5200 *Toll Free Tel:* 877-734-7728
(cust serv)
Web Site: www.dispatch.com
Key Personnel
Ed: Alan D Miller *E-mail:* amiller@dispatch.com
Book Ed: Becky Kover *E-mail:* bkover@dispatch.
com
Asst Features Ed: Ryan E Smith *E-mail:* rsmith@
dispatch.com
Book news & reviews, author interviews.
Circulation: 248,200 (m); 385,200 (Sun)
Digital & print: $71.37/13 wks (Sat & Sun),
$94.77/13 wks (Mon-Sun); digital only:
$7.99/mo

The Columbus Ledger Enquirer Newspapers
Published by The McClatchy Co
945 Broadway, Suite 102, Columbus, GA 31901
Tel: 706-324-5526 *Toll Free Tel:* 800-282-7859
Web Site: www.ledger-enquirer.com
Key Personnel
Gen Mgr & VP, Ad: Ross McDuffie *Tel:* 706-
571-8615 *E-mail:* rmcduffie@ledgerenquirer.
com
Reviews appear sporadically.
Circulation: 25,750 (d); 33,600 (Sun)
Digital & print: $42.12/13 wks (Wed & Sun),
$63.18/13 wks (Thurs-Sun), $84.24/13 wks
(Mon-Sun); digital only: $8.99/mo, $129.99/yr

Commentary
Published by Commentary Inc
561 Seventh Ave, 16th fl, New York, NY 10018
Tel: 212-891-1400 *Toll Free Tel:* 800-829-6270
(subns) *Fax:* 212-891-6700
E-mail: service@commentarymagazine.com;
ads@commentarymagazine.com; submissions@
commentarymagazine.com
Web Site: www.commentarymagazine.com
Key Personnel
Publr: Carol Moskot
Opers Dir: Stephanie Roberts *E-mail:* sroberts@
commentarymagazine.com
Sr Ed: Abe Greenwald
Ed: John Podhoretz
Analyses of current events with an emphasis on
politics, social policy & culture, with special
interest in Jewish affairs.
First published 1945
Book Use: Reviews & excerpts
Frequency: Monthly
Avg pages per issue: 72
Circulation: 26,000 paid
$5.95/issue, $29.99/yr print US, $19.99/yr digital
US, CN & intl
ISSN: 0010-2601
Buy fiction, nonfiction, no poetry, art, cartoons;
Sell articles
Avg reviews per issue: 6
Ad Rates: B&W page $3,430, 4-color page
$5,100
Ad Closing Date(s): 20th of the 2nd month pre-
ceding month of issue

The Commercial Appeal
Published by Gannett Co Inc
495 Union Ave, Memphis, TN 38103
Tel: 901-529-2345 *Toll Free Tel:* 844-900-7099
(subns)
Web Site: www.commercialappeal.com
Key Personnel
Exec Ed: Mark Russell *E-mail:* mark.russell@
commercialappeal.com
Pop Culture Ed: John Beifuss *E-mail:* john.
beifuss@commercialappeal.com
Sunday, one page, in-house, through syndication
& other sources. Occasional author interviews.

Concord Monitor
Published by Newspapers of New England (NNE)
One Monitor Dr, Concord, NH 03302
Mailing Address: PO Box 1177, Concord, NH
03302-1177
Tel: 603-224-5301 *Fax:* 603-228-5856
Web Site: www.concordmonitor.com
Key Personnel
Ed-in-Chief: Steve Leone
Mng Ed: Jonathan Van Fleet
Gen Mgr: Ernesto Burden
Book page on Sundays; occasional regional au-
thor interviews; in-house book reviews; fea-
tures.
Circulation: 22,000 (e)
Digital & print: $22/4 wks, $260/yr (Mon-Sun),
$156/yr (Sun only); digital only: $10.99/mo,
$104/yr

Conde Nast Traveler
Published by Conde Nast
One World Trade Center, 26th fl, New York, NY
10007-0090
Tel: 212-286-2860 *Toll Free Tel:* 800-777-0700
(subns)
E-mail: letters@condenasttraveler.com
Web Site: www.cntraveler.com; www.condenast.
com
Key Personnel
Ed-in-Chief: Melinda Stevens
Mng Ed: Paula Maynard
Contains travel, dining, entertainment, fashion,
business articles of interest to affluent travelers.
First published 1987
Book Use: Excerpts
Frequency: Monthly
Avg pages per issue: 125
Circulation: 814,833
$10/yr, $15/2 yrs (print & digital)
Sell article & ad reprints, back issues
Ad Rates: 4-color full page $154,353, 1/2 page
$100,303, 1/3 page $61,709

The Connecticut Post
Published by Hearst Newspapers
Division of Hearst Corp
1057 Broad St, Bridgeport, CT 06604
Tel: 203-330-6248; 203-333-6688 (cust serv)
Fax: 203-738-1230 (edit)
Web Site: www.ctpost.com
Key Personnel
Edit Page Ed: Hugh Bailey *Tel:* 203-842-2546
Asst Mng Ed: Ralph Hohman
Arts & Entertainment Ed: Patrick Quinn *Tel:* 203-
842-2553 *E-mail:* pquinn@ctpost.com
Sunday column; frequent author interviews; area
authors.
Circulation: 77,239 (d); 88,583 (Sun)
Digital & print: $2.99/wk (Sun only), $7.99/wk
(Mon-Sun); digital only: $3.50/wk

Cornwall Standard-Freeholder
Published by Postmedia Network Inc
1150 Montreal Rd, Cornwall, ON K6H 1E2,
Canada
Tel: 613-933-3160
Web Site: www.standard-freeholder.com

Key Personnel
Ad Dir: Kerry Sammon *Tel:* 613-933-3160 ext
508246 *E-mail:* ksammon@postmedia.com
Regl Mng Ed: Hugo Rodrigues *Tel:* 613-
933-3160 ext 508225 *E-mail:* hrodrigues@
postmedia.com
First published 1846
Frequency: Daily
Circulation: 5,780 (d); EMC-Thurs non-
subscribers 20,000
$1.25
Trim Size: Broadsheet

Corpus Christi Caller-Times
Published by Gannett Co Inc
820 N Lower Broadway, Corpus Christi, TX
78401
Mailing Address: PO Box 9136, Corpus Christi,
TX 78468-9136
Tel: 361-884-2011 *Toll Free Tel:* 800-827-2011;
844-900-7096
E-mail: caller-times@gannett.com
Web Site: www.caller.com
Key Personnel
News Dir: Mary Ann Beckett *Tel:* 361-886-3623
E-mail: maryann.beckett@caller.com
Ed: Tim Archuleta *E-mail:* tim.archuleta@caller.
com
Sunday page produced in-house, by syndication
& through various wire services. Occasional
author interviews.
First published 1883
Circulation: 68,028 (d); 94,415 (Sun)

Cosmopolitan
Published by Hearst Communications Inc
Division of Hearst Magazines
300 W 57 St, New York, NY 10019-3787
Tel: 212-649-2000; 212-649-3570 (edit off)
E-mail: cosmo_letters@hearst.com
Web Site: www.cosmopolitan.com; www.hearst.
com
Subscription Address: PO Box 6000, Harlan, IA
51593
Key Personnel
SVP & Publg Dir: Nancy Berger *Tel:* 212-841-
8495 *E-mail:* nberger@hearst.com
Assoc Publr & Ad: Stacy Nathan *Tel:* 212-649-
3984 *E-mail:* snathan@hearst.com
Ed-in-Chief: Jessica Pels
Edited for young women interested in self-
improvement with articles on careers, clothes,
beauty, travel, entertainment, the arts, relation-
ships, men & sex.
First published 1886
Book Use: Reviews of books periodically
Frequency: Monthly
Avg pages per issue: 344
Circulation: 2,700,000
$4.99/issue, $12/yr, $22/2 yrs, $6/6 mos (digital)
ISSN: 0010-9541
Buy fiction & nonfiction; Sell articles & ad
reprints, back issues
Trim Size: 7 3/4 x 10 7/8
Ad Rates: B&W page $251,000, 4-color page
$313,750

Courier-Journal
Published by Gannett Co Inc
525 W Broadway, Louisville, KY 40202
Mailing Address: PO Box 740031, Louisville, KY
40201-7431
Tel: 502-582-4011 *Toll Free Tel:* 800-866-2211
(cust serv)
Web Site: www.courier-journal.com
Key Personnel
News Dir: Mike Trautmann *Tel:* 502-582-4295
E-mail: mtrautmann@courier-journal.com
Ed: Richard A Green *Tel:* 502-582-4642
E-mail: rgreen@gannett.com
Sunday book section.
First published 1867

Courier-Post

Published by Gannett Co Inc
301 Cuthbert Blvd, Cherry Hill, NJ 08002
Mailing Address: PO Box 5300, Cherry Hill, NJ 08034
Tel: 856-663-6000
E-mail: cpfeat@courierpostonline.com
Web Site: www.courierpostonline.com
Key Personnel
Audience Engagement/Features Ed: Tammy Paolino *Tel:* 856-486-2477 *E-mail:* tpaolino@gannettnj.com
Saturday, in-house & Gannett News Service. Occasional author interviews.
First published 1875
Circulation: 104,565 (e); 100,755 (Sat); 105,000 (Sun)
$12/mo (Sun only), $16/mo (Thurs-Sun), $23/mo (Mon-Sun)

CRA Today

Published by Christian Retail Association Inc (CRA)
200 West Bay Dr, Largo, FL 33770
Tel: 727-596-7625 *Fax:* 727-593-3523
E-mail: service@munce.com
Web Site: www.christianretailassociation.org/cra-today
Key Personnel
Pres: Bob Munce
Ad & Content Dir: Sue Brewer
Creative Dir: Mike Solava
Ed: Andrea Stock
Educate retailers & inform them of upcoming Christian products.
First published 2019
Frequency: Quarterly
Avg pages per issue: 52
Free to membs

Cricket

Published by The Cricket Magazine Group
Subsidiary of Cricket Media (Carus Publishing Co)
70 E Lake St, Suite 800, Chicago, IL 60601
Tel: 312-701-1720 *Toll Free Tel:* 800-852-0790
Web Site: www.cricketmag.com; www.cricketmagkids.com
Key Personnel
Art Dir: Anna Lender
Ed: Lonnie Plecha
Publish *CRICKET* for young people ages 9-14, *SPIDER*, ages 6-9, *LADYBUG* for children ages 3-6 & *BABYBUG* 6 mos-2 yrs; prints stories, poems & articles written & illustrated by international authors & artists.
See submission guidelines at cricket-mag.submittable.com.
First published 1973
Book Use: We consider previously published children's books for possible reprint or excerption in our magazines
Frequency: Monthly (exc combined issues May/June, July/Aug & Nov/Dec)
Avg pages per issue: 48
Circulation: 50,000
$33.95/9 issues
ISSN: 0090-6034
Buy freelance fiction, nonfiction, poetry, puzzles, recipes, activities; Sell back issues
Avg reviews per issue: 4

Cruising World

Published by Bonnier Corp
460 N Orlando Ave, Suite 200, Winter Park, FL 32789
Tel: 407-571-4914 *Toll Free Tel:* 866-436-2461 *Fax:* 401-845-5180
E-mail: editor@cruisingworld.com
Web Site: www.cruisingworld.com
Subscription Address: PO Box 420235, Palm Coast, FL 32142-0235
Key Personnel
Group Publr: Sally Helme *E-mail:* sally.helme@bonniercorp.com
Ed-in-Chief: Mark Pillsbury *E-mail:* mark.pillsbury@cruisingworld.com
Deals with cruising in mid-sized sailboats; readership is upper middle class professionals. See submission policies & guidelines on web site.
First published 1974
Book Use: Reviews & excerpts
Frequency: Monthly
Circulation: 130,000 paid
$7/issue, $28/yr, $44/yr CN, $60/yr intl
ISSN: 0098-3519
Buy nonfiction; Sell articles, ad reprints & back issues
Trim Size: 8 x 10 3/4
Ad Rates: B&W page $23,000, 4-color page $28,180
Ad Closing Date(s): see web site

The Daily Gleaner

Published by Brunswick News Inc (BNI)
71 Alison Blvd, Fredericton, NB E3C 2N5, Canada
Tel: 506-452-6671 *Toll Free Tel:* 800-222-9710
E-mail: customerservice@brunswicknews.com
Web Site: tj.news/dailygleaner
Book reviews in-house; occasional author interviews.
First published 1881
Frequency: Daily
Circulation: 29,000 (d)
$25.99/mo print & digital

Daily Hampshire Gazette

Published by Newspapers of New England (NNE)
115 Conz St, Northampton, MA 01060
Tel: 413-584-5000
E-mail: circulation@gazettenet.com; newsroom@gazettenet.com (news & press releases)
Web Site: www.gazettenet.com
Key Personnel
Publr: Michael Moses *Tel:* 413-585-3462
  E-mail: mmoses@gazettenet.com
Arts Ed: Steve Pfarrer *Tel:* 413-584-5000 ext 262
  E-mail: spfarrer@gazettenet.com
Wednesday page, in-house & through syndication. Occasional Saturday reviews. Weekly author interviews.
Circulation: 20,500 (d)
$19.60/4 wks print & digital, $8.25/mo digital only
Avg reviews per issue: 2

Daily Inter Lake

Published by Hagadone Corp
727 E Idaho St, Kalispell, MT 59901
Mailing Address: PO Box 7610, Kalispell, MT 59904
Tel: 406-755-7000 *Fax:* 406-758-4481 (news); 406-752-6114
E-mail: newsed@dailyinterlake.com
Web Site: www.dailyinterlake.com
Key Personnel
Publr: Rick Weaver *Tel:* 406-758-4444
  E-mail: rvweaver@dailyinterlake.com
Mng Ed: Matt Baldwin *Tel:* 406-758-4447
  E-mail: mbaldwin@dailyinterlake.com
Occasional in-house book reviews & author interviews in the Arts, etc section.
Circulation: 14,500 (d); 15,000 (Sun)
$22.68/4 wks print & digital, $12.80/4 wks digital only

Daily News

813 College St, Bowling Green, KY 42102
Mailing Address: PO Box 90012, Bowling Green, KY 42102-9012
Tel: 270-783-3200 (circ); 270-781-1700
E-mail: editor@bgdailynews.com
Web Site: www.bgdailynews.com
Key Personnel
Co-Publr & Pres: Pipe Gaines
Co-Publr: Scott Gaines
Gen Mgr: Kent O'Toole *E-mail:* kotoole@bgdailynews.com
Mng Ed: Daniel Pike *Tel:* 270-783-3235
  E-mail: dpike@bgdailynews.com
Ed: Steve Gaines *E-mail:* sgaines@bgdailynews.com
In-house book reviews every Sunday, one page.
Digital & print: $8.99/mo (Sun only), $15/mo (Sun only postal), $17.99/mo (Mon-Sun), $29/mo (Mon-Sun postal); digital only: $8.99/mo

Daily News

Published by Tribune Publishing Co
4 New York Plaza, New York, NY 10004
Tel: 212-210-2100
E-mail: customerservice@nydailynews.com
Web Site: www.nydailynews.com
Key Personnel
Ed-in-Chief: Robert York *E-mail:* ryork@nydailynews.com
Sunday in "Now" section, in-house; frequent book features.
Frequency: Daily
Circulation: 602,857 (d); 644,766 (Sun)
Digital & print: $2.49/wk (Fri-Sun), $4.99/wk (Mon-Sun); digital only: $1.99/wk

The Daily Post-Athenian

Published by Adams Publishing Group
320 S Jackson St, Athens, TN 37303
Mailing Address: PO Box 340, Athens, TN 37371-0340
Tel: 423-745-5664 *Fax:* 423-745-8295
E-mail: news@dailypostathenian.com; circulation@dailypostathenian.com
Web Site: www.dailypostathenian.com
Key Personnel
Publr/Ad Dir: Jeff Schumacher *E-mail:* jeff.schumacher@dailypostathenian.com
Ed: Dewey Morgan *E-mail:* dewey.morgan@dailypostathenian.com
In-house book reviews biweekly in entertainment section; occasional author interviews.
First published 1848
Frequency: 5 days/wk
Circulation: 7,265 (d); 7,671 (weekend)
$130/yr print & online, $9.50/mo digital

Daily Press

Published by Daily Press Media Group
Subsidiary of Tribune Publishing Co
703 Mariners Row, Newport News, VA 23606
Tel: 757-247-4600; 757-247-4800 (circ)
  Toll Free Tel: 800-543-8908
E-mail: customerservice@dailypress.com
Web Site: www.dailypress.com
Key Personnel
Mng Ed: Ryan Gilchrest *Tel:* 757-247-4673
  E-mail: rgilchrest@dailypress.com
Features Ed: Andi Petrini *Tel:* 757-247-4643
  E-mail: apetrini@dailypress.com
In-house, Sunday page; occasional author interviews.
First published 1896
Circulation: 40,000 (d); 82,509 (Sun)

The Daily Sentinel

Subsidiary of Southern News Inc
4920 Colonial Dr, Nacogdoches, TX 75961
Mailing Address: PO Box 630068, Nacogdoches, TX 75693-0068
Tel: 936-564-8361 *Fax:* 936-560-4267
E-mail: news@dailysentinel.com
Web Site: dailysentinel.com
Key Personnel
Publr & Ed: Debi Ryan *Tel:* 936-558-3206
  E-mail: dryan@dailysentinel.com
In-house & syndicated book reviews weekly on Sunday; frequent author interviews.
Avg pages per issue: 32

Circulation: 6,000 (d); 6,200 (Sun)
$1/daily; $2/Sun

The Daily Times
Published by Adams Publishing Group
307 E Harper Ave, Maryville, TN 37803
Tel: 865-981-1100; 865-981-1140 (newsroom)
  Fax: 865-981-1175 (newsroom)
E-mail: editor@thedailytimes.com
Web Site: www.thedailytimes.com
Key Personnel
Publr: Carl Esposito *Tel:* 865-981-1137
Ed: J Todd Foster *Tel:* 865-981-1139
  E-mail: todd.foster@thedailytimes.com
Occasional author interviews; book reviews.
First published 1883
Circulation: 13,000 (d)
$1.50/daily, $2/Sun

The Dallas Morning News
Published by A H Belo Corp
1954 Commerce St, Dallas, TX 75201
Tel: 214-977-8222 *Toll Free Tel:* 800-925-1500
E-mail: customercare@dallasnews.com
Web Site: www.dallasnews.com
Key Personnel
VP & Ed: Mike Wilson *E-mail:* mikewilson@
  dallasnews.com
Mng Ed: Keith Campbell *E-mail:* kcampbell@
  dallasnews.com
Publish book reviews from established network
  of freelance critics. We do not accept unsol
  reviews.
Circulation: 200,000 (d); 300,000 (Sun)
$2.49/daily, $3.79/Sun; digital only: $6.89/wk;
  digital & print (Sun only): $64.87/13 wks,
  $103.74/26 wks, $155.48/yr; digital & print
  (Wed-Sun): $77.87/13 wks, $129.74/26 wks,
  $207.48/yr; digital & print (Mon-Sun): $90.87/
  13 wks, $155.74/26 wks, $259.48/yr
ISSN: 1553-846X

Dayton Daily News
Published by Cox Media Group Ohio
1611 S Main St, Dayton, OH 45409-2547
Tel: 937-222-5700; 937-225-2000 (Cox)
  Toll Free Tel: 888-397-6397 *Fax:* 937-225-2241
E-mail: customercare@daytondailynews.com
Web Site: www.daytondailynews.com
Key Personnel
Ed-in-Chief: Rob Rohr
Sr Ed: Ron Rollins *Tel:* 937-225-2165
  E-mail: rollins@coxinc.com
Books featured in Sunday weekly section, in-
  house, through syndication & other sources,
  feature author interviews.
Circulation: 180,000 (e); 230,000 (Sun)
$10.62/wk (Mon-Sun), $7.87/wk (Thurs-Sun),
  $3.99/wk (Sun only)
ISSN: 0897-0920

Decatur Daily
Published by Tennessee Valley Printing
201 First Ave SE, Decatur, AL 35609
Mailing Address: PO Box 2213, Decatur, AL
  35609-2213
Tel: 256-353-4612; 256-340-2410 (circ)
  Toll Free Tel: 888-353-4612 *Fax:* 256-340-2392
E-mail: news@decaturdaily.com
Web Site: www.decaturdaily.com
Key Personnel
Publr: Clint Shelton *Tel:* 256-340-2465
  E-mail: clint.shelton@decaturdaily.com
Online Mng Ed: Bruce McLellan *Tel:* 256-340-
  2431 *E-mail:* bruce.mclellan@decaturdaily.com
In-house & other; book reviews, "Sunday Book-
  page".
First published 1912
Circulation: 25,000

Delaware State News
Subsidiary of Independent Newsmedia Inc USA

110 Galaxy Dr, Dover, DE 19901
Tel: 302-674-3600; 302-741-8298 (cust serv)
E-mail: readerservices@newszap.com;
  newsroom@newszap.com
Web Site: delawarestatenews.net
Key Personnel
Publr: Darel La Prade *E-mail:* dlaprade@
  newszap.com
Ed: Andrew West
Occasional local author interviews.
First published 1953
Frequency: Daily
Circulation: 12,000 (Mon & Sat); 17,000 (Tues,
  Thurs & Fri); 35,000 (Wed); 23,600 (Sun)
Digital & print: $7.99/mo (Sun only), $17.99/mo
  (Mon-Sun); digital only: $5.99/mo
Trim Size: 10 3/4 x 12 1/4
Ad Rates: $2,386 per page/Wed & Sun; $1,988
  per page/weekday

Delta Democrat Times
Division of Emmerich Newspapers
988 N Broadway, Greenville, MS 38701
Mailing Address: PO Box 1618, Greenville, MS
  38701
Tel: 662-335-1155 *Fax:* 662-335-2860
E-mail: ddtnews@ddtonline.com
Web Site: www.ddtonline.com
Key Personnel
Publr & Ed: Jon Alverson *Tel:* 662-378-0761
  E-mail: jalverson@ddtonline.com
Occasional column & author interviews; in-house.
First published 1868
Frequency: Daily (Tues-Sat)
Circulation: 3,500
$78/6 mos, $156/yr

Democrat & Chronicle
Published by Gannett Co Inc
245 E Main St, Rochester, NY 14604
Tel: 585-232-7100 *Toll Free Tel:* 800-790-9565
  (cust serv)
Web Site: www.democratandchronicle.com
Key Personnel
Ed: Mike Kilian *Tel:* 585-258-2220
  E-mail: mkilian@gannett.com
Exec Admin Asst: Tamra Springer *Tel:* 585-258-
  2221 *E-mail:* tspringer@gannett.com
Daily, in-house, through syndication & other
  sources; occasional author interviews.
Frequency: Daily
Circulation: 177,000 (d); 207,600 (Sat); 245,800
  (Sun)
$1.50/daily, $3/Sun

The Denver Post
Published by MediaNews Group Inc
101 W Colfax Ave, Denver, CO 80202-5177
Tel: 303-954-1000; 303-954-1010; 303-832-3232
  (cust serv) *Toll Free Tel:* 800-336-7678
E-mail: memberservices@denverpost.com;
  newsroom@denverpost.com
Web Site: www.denverpost.com
Key Personnel
Ed: Lee Ann Colacioppo *Tel:* 303-954-1754
  E-mail: lcolacioppo@denverpost.com
Features Ed: Barbara Ellis *Tel:* 303-954-1751
  E-mail: bellis@denverpost.com
Eight-page tabloid pull-out, "Books & Authors"
  each Sunday, occasional reviews daily; weekly
  author interview/feature; up to 6 feature reviews; columnists cover mysteries, children's
  books, regional interest/local history & science fiction/fantasy each month; occasional reviews of current audiobooks; "Footnotes", also
  weekly, brief reviews of 3-5 books; in-house &
  wire services; book review through syndication
  & by freelancers.
Circulation: 518,000 (d); 858,000 (Sun)
Digital & print: $7.58/mo (Sun & holidays),
  $8.67/mo (Wed & Sun), $30.33/mo (Mon-Sun);
  digital only: $11.99/mo

**The Des Moines Register & The Des Moines
Sunday Register**
Published by Gannett Co Inc
400 Locust St, Suite 500, Des Moines, IA 50309
Tel: 515-284-8000 *Toll Free Tel:* 877-424-0225
  (delivery cust serv) *Fax:* 515-286-2504
E-mail: metroiowa@dmreg.com
Web Site: www.desmoinesregister.com
Key Personnel
Exec Ed: Carol Hunter *Tel:* 515-284-8545
  E-mail: chunter@dmreg.com
Occasional author interviews. Book review in-
  house, through syndication & freelance.
Circulation: 84,500 (d); 146,500 (Sun)

The Desert Sun
Published by Gannett Co Inc
750 N Gene Autry Trail, Palm Springs, CA
  92262
Tel: 760-322-8889 *Toll Free Tel:* 800-834-6052
  (circ)
E-mail: thedesertsun@gannett.com
Web Site: www.mydesert.com
Key Personnel
Exec Ed: Julie Makinen *Tel:* 760-778-4511
  E-mail: julie.makinen@desertsun.com
Mng Ed: Kate Franco *Tel:* 760-778-4688
  E-mail: kate.franco@desertsun.com
Book reviews in-house & through syndication;
  some author interviews.
First published 1927
Circulation: 60,000 (d & Sat); 72,000 (Sun)

Detroit Free Press
Published by Gannett Co Inc
160 W Fort St, Detroit, MI 48226
Tel: 313-222-6400; 313-222-6610 (features)
  Toll Free Tel: 800-395-3300 (cust serv)
  Fax: 313-223-4726 (features)
E-mail: features@freepress.com; cserv@michigan.
  com
Web Site: www.freep.com
Key Personnel
Ed & VP: Peter Bhatia *E-mail:* pbhatia@
  freepress.com
Arts & Entertainment Ed: Steve Byrne
  E-mail: spbyrne@freepress.com
Weekly, in-house; frequent author interviews;
  book review special section annually.
Circulation: 380,000 (m); 750,000 (Sun)

The Detroit News
Published by Michigan.com
160 W Fort St, Detroit, MI 48226
Tel: 313-222-2480 *Fax:* 313-496-5249
Web Site: www.detroitnews.com
Key Personnel
Publr & Ed: Jonathan Wolman *Tel:* 313-222-2110
  E-mail: jon.wolman@detroitnews.com
Mng Ed: Gary Miles *Tel:* 313-222-2594
  E-mail: gmiles@detroitnews.com
Asst Mng Ed, Features: Felecia Henderson
  Tel: 313-222-2557 *E-mail:* fhenderson@
  detroitnews.com
Edit Page Ed: Nolan Finley *Tel:* 313-222-2064
  E-mail: nolan.finley@detroitnews.com
Book reviews, author interviews.
Circulation: 300,000 (d); 700,000 (Sun)

Le Devoir
Published by Le Devoir Inc
Subsidiary of L'Imprimerie Populaire Inc
1265 Berri St, 8th fl, Montreal, QC H2L 4X4,
  Canada
Tel: 514-985-3333 *Fax:* 514-985-3340
E-mail: redaction@ledevoir.com
Web Site: www.ledevoir.com
Key Personnel
VP, Devt: Christianne Benjamin
Publr & Ed: Brian Myles

Saturday book review section; in-house & through syndication; weekly author interviews.
Frequency: Weekly
Avg pages per issue: 20
Circulation: 29,000 (d); 45,000 (Sat)
$2.83 (Sat)

Down East Magazine
Published by Down East Enterprise Inc
680 Commercial St (US Rte 1), Rockport, ME 04856
SAN: 208-6301
Mailing Address: PO Box 679, Camden, ME 04843
Tel: 207-594-9544 *Toll Free Tel:* 800-766-1670
E-mail: editorial@downeast.com
Web Site: www.downeast.com
Key Personnel
Ed-in-Chief: Brian Kevin *E-mail:* bkevin@downeast.com
Features articles & columns which concentrate on Maine's heritage, contemporary events & newsmakers. Occasional features on Maine authors.
First published 1954
Book Use: Reviews, occasional excerpts
Frequency: Monthly
Avg pages per issue: 180
Circulation: 100,000 paid
$19.99/yr digital, $34/yr print, $39/yr digital & print
ISSN: 0012-5776
Buy freelance nonfiction; Sell articles, ad reprints & back issues

Duluth News Tribune
Published by Forum Communications Co
424 W First St, Duluth, MN 55802
Tel: 218-723-5281 *Fax:* 218-723-5295
E-mail: news@duluthnews.com
Web Site: www.duluthnewstribune.com
Key Personnel
Publr: Neal Ronquist *Tel:* 218-723-5235
Mng Ed: Andrew Krueger *Tel:* 218-720-4102
Arts & Entertainment Reporter: Christa Lawler *Tel:* 218-879-5536
No reviews; short synopses (2-4) on Sundays of books on regional interest.
Book Use: Local author reviews
Circulation: 40,106 (d); 60,480 (Sun)
$1.25/daily, $2/Sun

Duncan Banner
1001 W Elm Ave, Duncan, OK 73534
Mailing Address: PO Box 1268, Duncan, OK 73534-1268
Tel: 580-255-5354 *Fax:* 580-255-8889
E-mail: editor@duncanbanner.com
Web Site: www.duncanbanner.com
Key Personnel
Publr: Mark Millsap *E-mail:* mark@normantranscript.com
Ad Mgr: Crystal Childers *E-mail:* addirector@duncanbanner.com
Two each Sunday-Education section; in-house or syndicated; infrequent local author interviews.
First published 1892
Frequency: Daily exc Mon & Sat
Circulation: 10,000 (e)
$14.99/mo print & digital, $11.99/mo digital only

East Valley Tribune
Division of 10/13 Communications
1620 W Fountainhead Pkwy, Suite 219, Tempe, AZ 85282
Tel: 480-898-6500; 480-898-5641 *Fax:* 480-898-5606
E-mail: customercare@evtrib.com
Web Site: www.eastvalleytribune.com
Key Personnel
Publr: Steve Strickbine
Opers Mgr: Chuck Morales *Tel:* 480-898-5690 *E-mail:* chuck@timespublications.com

Weekly one page, through syndication & other sources. Author interviews.
First published 1891
Frequency: Weekly (Sun print)
Circulation: 140,000 (Sun)
Free

Edmonton Journal
Published by Postmedia Network Inc
10006 101 St, Edmonton, AB T5J 0S1, Canada
Tel: 780-429-5100 *Toll Free Tel:* 800-249-4695 (subns)
E-mail: city@edmontonjournal.com
Web Site: www.edmontonjournal.com
Key Personnel
Features Ed: Liane Faulder *Tel:* 780-429-5294 *E-mail:* lfaulder@postmedia.com
Book reviews in-house & through freelancers; frequent author interviews.
First published 1903
Frequency: Daily (Mon-Sat)
Circulation: 172,078 (e); 212,923 (Sat)
Digital & print: $21.67/mo (Sat only), $39/mo (Mon-Sat); digital only: $9.95/mo, $99.99/yr; e-paper: $9.99/mo

The El Paso Times
Published by Gannett Co Inc
500 W Overland Dr, Suite 150, El Paso, TX 79901
Tel: 915-546-6100; 915-546-6119 (newsroom) *Toll Free Tel:* 800-351-1677 (cust serv) *Fax:* 915-546-6284; 915-546-6415 (newsroom)
E-mail: elpasotimes@gannett.com
Web Site: www.elpasotimes.com
Key Personnel
Ed: Zahira Torres *Tel:* 915-546-6155 *E-mail:* ztorres@elpasotimes.com
Prodn Gen Mgr: Patsy Hernandez *Tel:* 915-546-6182 *E-mail:* phernandez@elpasotimes.com
Sunday reviews & columns; occasional author interviews; book reviews in-house & by syndication.
First published 1881
Circulation: 45,000 (d); 50,000 (Sun)

Ellery Queen's Mystery Magazine
Published by Dell Magazines
Division of Penny Publications LLC
44 Wall St, Suite 904, New York, NY 10005-2401
Tel: 212-686-7188 *Toll Free Tel:* 800-220-7443 (corp sales) *Fax:* 212-480-5751
E-mail: elleryqueenmm@dellmagazines.com; advertising@pennypublications.com
Web Site: www.elleryqueenmysterymagazine.com
Subscription Address: Dell Magazines Direct, 6 Prowitt St, Norwalk, CT 06855-1220
Tel: 203-866-6688 *Toll Free Tel:* 800-220-7443 *Fax:* 203-854-5962
Key Personnel
Pres: Peter Kanter
Sr Art Dir: Victoria Green
Dir, Mktg, E-Commerce & Brand Licensing: Abigail Browning
Ed: Janet Hutchings
Sr Asst Ed: Jackie Sherbow
Asst Mktg Mgr: Monique St Paul
Book Reviewer: Steve Steinbock
Contains 18-20 short stories of mystery, crime & detection, most never published before. No e-mail submissions. Only submit by online submission manager.
First published 1941
Book Use: Book Reviews
Frequency: 6 issues/yr
Avg pages per issue: 192
Circulation: 100,000
$34.97/yr, $63.97/2 yrs, $59.94/yr intl, $35.88/yr digital
ISSN: 0013-6328

Buy freelance fiction, short humorous verse & mystery/crime related cartoons; Sell back issues
Avg reviews per issue: 10
Trim Size: 5 7/8 x 8 1/2
Ad Rates: 4-color back cover $1,800, B&W page $1,000, B&W 1/2 page-horizontal $600
Ad Closing Date(s): 3 months before sale date

The Emporia Gazette
Published by White Corp Media Inc
517 Merchant St, Emporia, KS 66801
Tel: 620-342-4800 *Fax:* 620-342-8108
E-mail: news@emporia.com
Web Site: www.emporiagazette.com
Subscription Address: PO Drawer C, Emporia, KS 66801
Key Personnel
Publr & Ed: Christopher Walker *E-mail:* walker@emporia.com
Features/Edit Ed: Regina Murphy *E-mail:* regina@emporia.com
Weekly, in-house; occasional author interviews.
First published 1895
Circulation: 10,000 (e)
$9.50/mo, $28.48/3 mos, $54.11/6 mos, $108.23/yr

English Journal
Published by National Council of Teachers of English (NCTE)
340 N Neil St, Suite 104, Champaign, IL 61820
Tel: 217-328-3870 *Toll Free Tel:* 877-369-6283 (cust serv) *Fax:* 217-328-9645
E-mail: englishjournal@ncte.org
Web Site: ncte.org
Key Personnel
Ed: Toby Emert; R Joseph Rodriguez
Prodn Ed: Rona Smith
Journal of ideas for English language arts teachers in junior & senior high schools & middle schools. Presents information on the teaching of writing & reading, literature & language. Includes information on how teachers are applying practices, research & multimodal literacies in their classrooms.
First published 1912
Book Use: Reviews of young adult literature & professional books
Frequency: 6 issues/yr
Avg pages per issue: 128
Circulation: 9,000 paid
$12.50/yr student & emeritus, $25/yr membs, $75/yr nonmembs & instns, add $8 foreign, membership is required for indiv subns
ISSN: 0013-8274
Trim Size: 8 1/4 x 10 7/8
Ad Rates: B&W page $2,140, 4-color page $2,750
Ad Closing Date(s): 1st of 2nd month prior to publication

The Enterprise
Published by GateHouse Media LLC
5 Cohannet St, Taunton, MA 02780
Tel: 508-427-4000
E-mail: newsroom@enterprisenews.com
Web Site: www.enterprisenews.com
Key Personnel
VP, News: Lisa Strattan *E-mail:* pub@wickedlocal.com
City Ed: Rebecca Hyman *E-mail:* rhyman@gatehousemedia.com
Sunday; in-house, syndicated.
Frequency: Daily
Circulation: 47,000 (e & Sat); 58,000 (Sun)
Digital & print: $24/12 wks (Sun only), $48/12 wks (Mon-Sun); digital only: $9.95/mo, $99.95/yr
ISSN: 0744-2114

Entertainment Weekly
Published by Meredith Corporation
11766 Wilshire Blvd, Los Angeles, CA 90025

Web Site: ew.com; www.meredith.com/brand/
    entertainmentweekly
Key Personnel
Ed-in-Chief: J D Heyman
Brand Sales Dir: Ellie Duque *Tel:* 310-268-7206
    E-mail: ellie.duque@meredith.com
Book reviews, author interviews & in-depth enter-
    tainment coverage.
First published 1990
Frequency: Monthly
$6.99 newstand

The Erie Times-News
Published by GateHouse Media LLC
205 W 12 St, Erie, PA 16534
Tel: 814-870-1600
Web Site: goerie.com
Key Personnel
Pres & Publr: Terry Cascioli *Tel:* 814-870-1612
    E-mail: tcascioli@timesnews.com
Exec Ed: Matt Martin *Tel:* 814-870-1704
    E-mail: matt.martin@timesnews.com
Three days per week on Op-Ed page; Sunday
    page & column. In-house. Occasionally syn-
    dicated column. Galleys & review copies of
    books are encouraged; especially interested in
    books with a connection to the Erie, PA region.
Circulation: 39,935 (d); 54,329 (Sun)
Digital & print: $27.30/13 wks (Sun only),
    $48.10/13 wks (Mon-Sun); digital only:
    $4.99/mo, $29.99/yr

Esquire Magazine
Published by Hearst Communications Inc
Division of Hearst Magazines
300 W 57 St, New York, NY 10019-3787
Tel: 212-649-4020 (edit off); 212-649-2000
E-mail: editor@esquire.com
Web Site: www.esquire.com; www.hearst.com
Subscription Address: PO Box 6000, Harlan, IA
    51593-1500
Key Personnel
Exec Dir, Mktg: Jason Graham
Ed-in-Chief: Michael Sebastian
Articles of information & counsel for men on a
    broad range of subjects including politics, busi-
    ness, sports & the arts. Features include fiction,
    fashion, personal finance & health.
First published 1933
Book Use: Reviews
Frequency: 8 issues/yr
Avg pages per issue: 200
Circulation: 750,000 paid
$6.99/issue US, $15/yr, $25/2 yrs
ISSN: 0014-0791
Buy freelance fiction, nonfiction & art; Sell arti-
    cles & ad reprints, back issues
Trim Size: 9 x 10 3/4
Ad Rates: B&W page $97,495, 4-color page
    $144,860
Ad Closing Date(s): 45 days prior to sale date

ESSENCE Magazine
Published by ESSENCE Communications Inc
241 37 St, 4th fl, Brooklyn, NY 11232
Toll Free Tel: 800-274-9398 (subns)
Web Site: www.essence.com
Key Personnel
Chief Content & Creative Offr: Moana Luu
How-to information directed toward Black
    women. Covers health, beauty, fashion, food,
    business, parenting, the arts & travel. Feature
    articles include celebrity interviews, current
    events & fitness. Also available online. No un-
    sol mss, query first.
First published 1970
Book Use: Reviews & excerpts
Frequency: Monthly
Avg pages per issue: 130
Circulation: 1,078,000 paid
$4.99/issue, $10/yr print & digital
ISSN: 0014-0880

Buy freelance fiction, nonfiction, art; Sell articles
    & ad reprints, back issues
Trim Size: 8 x 10 1/2

The Express-Times
Published by PennLive LLC
18 Centre Sq, Easton, PA 18042
Tel: 610-258-7171 *Fax:* 610-258-7130
E-mail: news@lehighvalleylive.com
Web Site: www.lehighvalleylive.com/expresstimes
Key Personnel
Mng Prodr: Nick Falsone *Tel:* 610-553-3312
    E-mail: nfalsone@lehighvalleylive.com
Produced in-house & from other sources. Focus is
    on local authors (Lehigh Valley, PA & Western
    NJ).
Circulation: 50,000

The Fairfield Chronicle
Subsidiary of Reboli Newspapers Inc
PO Box 6123, West Caldwell, NJ 07007-6123
Tel: 973-227-4433
Key Personnel
Publr: John A Reboli
Ed-in-Chief: Kelly J Kilborn
Local news & book reviews. Book submissions
    accepted for review.

Farm Journal
Published by Farm Journal Media
30 S 15 St, Suite 900, Philadelphia, PA 19102
Mailing Address: PO Box 958, Mexico, MO
    65265
Tel: 573-581-9641 (edit requests)
Toll Free Tel: 800-331-9310 (subns) *Fax:* 573-
    581-9646
E-mail: editors@farmjournal.com;
    customerservice@farmjournal.com
Web Site: www.agweb.com/farmjournal; www.
    farmjournal.com
Key Personnel
CEO: Andy Weber
Pres & COO: Steve Custer
Mng Ed: Katie Humphreys *E-mail:* khumphreys@
    farmjournal.com
Ed: Rhond Brooks *E-mail:* rbrooks@farmjournal.
    com
Practical information on crops & livestock. Em-
    phasis on agricultural production, technology &
    policy.
First published 1877
Book Use: Occasional reviews
Frequency: 14 issues/yr
Avg pages per issue: 80
Circulation: 345,085
$29.95/yr, $60/yr intl
ISSN: 0014-8008
Trim Size: 7 3/4 x 10 1/2
Ad Closing Date(s): 5 to 6 weeks prior to mailing

Fayetteville Observer
Published by GateHouse Media LLC
458 Whitfield St, Fayetteville, NC 28306
Mailing Address: PO Box 849, Fayetteville, NC
    28302
Tel: 910-323-4848 *Toll Free Tel:* 800-682-3476
E-mail: customerservice@fayobserver.com
Web Site: www.fayobserver.com
Key Personnel
Publr: Robert Gruber *Tel:* 910-486-3501
    E-mail: bgruber@fayobserver.com
Exec Ed: Matt Leclercq *Tel:* 910-486-3551
    E-mail: mleclercq@fayobserver.com
Lifestyle & Sports Ed: Monica Holland *Tel:* 910-
    486-3518 *E-mail:* mholland@fayobserver.com
Sunday page, column & occasional author inter-
    views; book reviews in-house & syndicated.
Circulation: 88,000 (m); 92,000 (Sun)
Digital & print: $9.40/mo (Mon-Sun); digital
    only: $12.95/mo, $79.95/yr

Field & Stream®
Published by Bonnier Corp
Division of The Bonnier Group
2 Park Ave, New York, NY 10016
Tel: 386-447-6355
E-mail: fsletters@bonniercorp.com
Web Site: www.fieldandstream.com
Subscription Address: PO Box 420235, Palm
    Coast, FL 32142-0235 *Toll Free Tel:* 800-289-
    0639
Key Personnel
CEO: David Ritchie
Ed-in-Chief: Colin Kearns
Mng Ed: Jean McKenna *Tel:* 212-779-5000 ext
    5290
Deputy Ed: Slaton L White
Articles on hunting & fishing, including humor,
    profiles, how-to, gear reviews, news & essays.
    Unsol mss accepted, but prefer queries.
First published 1895
Frequency: 6 issues/yr
Avg pages per issue: 100
Circulation: 1,250,000 paid
$7.99/issue, $10/yr US, $26/yr CN, $40/yr foreign
ISSN: 8755-8599
Buy freelance, nonfiction, art, cartoons, pho-
    tographs
Trim Size: 8 x 10 1/2
Ad Rates: B&W full page $105,200, 4-color full
    page $131,500
Ad Closing Date(s): 1st of 2nd month preceding
    issue

The Flint Journal
Published by MLive Media Group
540 Saginaw St, Suite 101, Flint, MI 48502
Tel: 810-766-6280; 810-766-6100
    Toll Free Tel: 800-878-1400
E-mail: customercare@mlive.com; flnews@mlive.
    com; advertise@mlive.com
Web Site: www.mlive.com/flint
Sunday page, in-house; occasional author inter-
    views on Lifestyle page.
Frequency: 4 issues/wk
$4.99/wk (print & digital)

Florida Sportsman
Published by Outdoor Sportsman Group
3725 SE Ocean Blvd, Suite 202, Stuart, FL
    34996
Tel: 772-219-7400 *Toll Free Tel:* 800-274-6386
    (subn only)
Web Site: www.floridasportsman.com
Key Personnel
Publr: Blair Wickstrom *E-mail:* blair@
    floridasportsman.com
Ed: Jeff Weakley *E-mail:* jeff@floridasportsman.
    com
How-to & where-to about fishing, boating & out-
    door activity in Florida & the islands.
First published 1969
Frequency: Monthly
Avg pages per issue: 120
Circulation: 77,058
$15/yr
ISSN: 0015-3885
Buy nonfiction, occasional fiction; Sell articles, ad
    reprints & back issues
Trim Size: 8 x 10 7/8
Ad Rates: 4-color page $6,500
Ad Closing Date(s): 45 days prior to cover month

The Florida Times-Union
Published by GateHouse Media LLC
One Independent Dr, Suite 200, Jacksonville, FL
    32202
Tel: 904-359-4111
E-mail: newstips@jacksonville.com
Web Site: jacksonville.com
Key Personnel
Sales Dir: Liz Borten *Tel:* 904-359-4099
    E-mail: lborten@jacksonville.com

Ed: Mary Kelli Palka *Tel:* 904-359-4107
  E-mail: mpalka@jacksonville.com
Jack (Fri weekend magazine).
First published 1883
Circulation: 96,968 (d); 155,087 (Sun)
Digital only: $9.99/mo, $59.99/yr; see web site
  for print subn rates

Florida Today
Published by Gannett Co Inc
One Gannett Plaza, PO Box 419000, Melbourne,
  FL 32940-9000
Tel: 321-242-3500 *Fax:* 321-242-6601
E-mail: letters@floridatoday.com
Web Site: www.floridatoday.com
Key Personnel
Exec Ed: Mara Bellaby *Tel:* 321-242-3573
  E-mail: mbellaby@floridatoday.com
Highlights local authors online.
Circulation: 100,000

Fort Worth Star-Telegram
Published by The McClatchy Co
808 Throckmorton St, Fort Worth, TX 76102
Mailing Address: PO Box 1870, Fort Worth, TX
  76101
Tel: 817-390-7400 *Toll Free Tel:* 800-776-7827
  (cust serv)
E-mail: paper@star-telegram.com
Web Site: www.star-telegram.com
Key Personnel
Publr: Ryan Mote *Tel:* 817-390-7454
  E-mail: rmote@star-telegram.com
Exec Ed: Steve Coffman *Tel:* 817-390-7704
  E-mail: scoffman@star-telegram.com
Two or three pages in Sunday newspaper & daily
  book reviews; in-house & through syndication;
  news feature on authors; regular author inter-
  views.
First published 1909
Digital & print: $52/13 wks (Wed & Sun),
  $79.30/13 wks (Wed-Sun), $92.30/13 wks
  (Mon-Sun); digital only: $9.99/mo

The Forum
Published by Forum Communications Co
101 Fifth St N, Fargo, ND 58102
Mailing Address: PO Box 2020, Fargo, ND
  58107-2020
Tel: 701-235-7311 *Fax:* 701-241-5406
E-mail: letters@forumcomm.com; news@
  forumcomm.com; inforum@fccinteractive.com
Web Site: www.inforum.com
Key Personnel
Ed: Matthew Von Pinnon *Tel:* 701-241-5579
  E-mail: mvonpinnon@forumcomm.com
Deputy Ed: Danielle Teigen *Tel:* 701-451-5709
  E-mail: danielle.teigen@forumcomm.com
Sunday in *Entertainment* section; in-house & by
  AP; through syndication.
Frequency: Daily
Circulation: 53,000 (d); 67,000 (Sun)
Digital & print: $15.64/mo (weekend), $21.97/mo
  (Mon-Sun); digital only: $9.99/mo

The Free Lance-Star
1340 Central Park Blvd, Suite 100, Fredericks-
  burg, VA 22401-4940
Tel: 540-374-5400
Web Site: www.fredericksburg.com
Key Personnel
Ed: Phil Jenkins *Tel:* 540-374-5422
  E-mail: pjenkins@freelancestar.com
In-house & other weekly one-page reviews, style
  section does author interviews.
Circulation: 27,000
$2/daily, $3/Sun, $21.67/mo digital & print (Mon-
  Sun)

The Fresno Bee
Published by The McClatchy Co

1626 "E" St, Fresno, CA 93786
Tel: 559-441-6111 *Toll Free Tel:* 800-877-3400
Web Site: www.fresnobee.com
Key Personnel
Pres & Publr: Ken Riddick *Tel:* 559-441-6060
  E-mail: kriddick@fresnobee.com
SVP & Exec Ed: Jim Boren *Tel:* 559-441-6307
  E-mail: jboren@fresnobee.com
SVP, Sales & Strategic Mktg: John Coak-
  ley *Tel:* 559-441-6143 *E-mail:* jcoakley@
  fresnobee.com
Mng Ed: John Rich *Tel:* 559-441-6663
  E-mail: jrich@fresnobee.com
Sunday Page, plus 2-3 wire reviews per week;
  in-house & through syndication, mostly local
  author interviews.
First published 1922
Circulation: 110,167 (d); 162,989 (Sun)

Gaffney Ledger
1604 W Floyd Baker Blvd, Gaffney, SC 29341
Mailing Address: PO Box 670, Gaffney, SC
  29342
Tel: 864-489-1131 *Fax:* 864-487-7667
Web Site: www.gaffneyledger.com
Key Personnel
Publr: Cody Sossamon *E-mail:* cody@
  gaffneyledger.com
Ed: Klonie Jordan *E-mail:* editor@gaffneyledger.
  com
Lifestyles/Features: Abbie Sossamon
  E-mail: abbie@gaffneyledger.com
In-house, syndicated & other book reviews peri-
  odically; occasional author interviews.
First published 1894
Frequency: 3 issues/wk (Mon, Wed & Fri)
Circulation: 9,200
$2/single issue online only, $65/yr print or online,
  $77/yr print & online

The Georgia Review
Published by University of Georgia
c/o The University of Georgia, 706 A Main Li-
  brary, Athens, GA 30602
Tel: 706-542-3481 *Toll Free Tel:* 800-542-3481
  Fax: 706-542-0047
E-mail: garev@uga.edu
Web Site: thegeorgiareview.com
Key Personnel
Ed: Stephen Corey
National Magazine Award-winning literary jour-
  nal that publishes short stories, poems, essays,
  reviews & art. No simultaneous submissions.
  No submissions between May 1 & Aug 15.
  Submission guidelines are on web site.
Membership(s): Community of Literary Maga-
  zines & Presses (CLMP).
First published 1947
Frequency: Quarterly
Avg pages per issue: 200
Circulation: 3,000
$15/issue, $40/yr, $70/2 yrs
ISSN: 0016-8386
Avg reviews per issue: 3-4
Trim Size: 7 x 10
Ad Rates: Inside cover $750, full page $500, 1/2
  page $350
Ad Closing Date(s): Jan 15, April 15, July 15,
  Oct 15

Glamour
Published by Conde Nast
One World Trade Center, 26th fl, New York, NY
  10007-0090
Tel: 212-286-2860; 515-243-3273 (subns)
  Toll Free Tel: 800-274-7410 (subns)
E-mail: glamourpublicity@condenast.com
Web Site: www.glamour.com; www.condenast.
  com
Key Personnel
Chief Busn Offr: Susan Plagemann
Creative Dir: Nathalie Kirsheh

Ed-in-Chief: Samantha Barry
Contains articles & features on fashion, beauty,
  health, travel, lifestyle, entertainment, auto, diet
  & fitness, careers for young women, ages 18-
  34. Digital only.
First published 1939
Free

Glendale News-Press
Published by Times Community News
Subsidiary of Los Angeles Times
453 S Spring St, 3rd fl, Los Angeles, CA 90013
Tel: 818-637-3200 *Fax:* 818-790-5690 (news-
  room)
E-mail: gnp@latimes.com
Web Site: www.latimes.com/socal/glendale-news-
  press
Key Personnel
Exec Ed: John Canalis *Tel:* 717-966-4607
  E-mail: john.canalis@latimes.com
Mng Ed: Carol Cormaci *Tel:* 818-495-4156
  E-mail: carol.cormaci@latimes.com
Book reviews, local author interviews only. Sat-
  urday entertainment tabloid, the *Living* section;
  in-house & through syndication. Occasional
  cover story (page 1) on books & authors; also
  excerpts. Only run news happening in Glen-
  dale, CA.
First published 1905
Frequency: Daily
Circulation: 20,000 (d)
Digital & print: $2.49/wk (Sun only), $4.99/wk
  (Mon-Sun); digital only: $1.99/wk

The Globe & Mail
351 King St, E, Toronto, ON M5A 0N1, Canada
Tel: 416-585-5000
E-mail: books@globeandmail.com
Web Site: www.globeandmail.com
Key Personnel
Publr & CEO: Phillip Crawley
Ed-in-Chief: David Walmsley *Tel:* 416-585-5000
  ext 5300
Books Ed: Mark Medley *E-mail:* mmedley@
  globeandmail.com
Saturday, 24 pages, freelance review. Frequent au-
  thor interviews; produce a separate book review
  section every week.
Circulation: 330,600 (d)
$9.44/wk, $5.24/Sat only

Golf Digest
Published by Discovery Inc
One World Trade Center, 27th fl, New York, NY
  10007-0090
Toll Free Tel: 800-313-0337 (cust serv)
E-mail: editors@golfdigest.com
Web Site: golfdigest.com
Subscription Address: PO Box 37065, Boone,
  IA 50037-0065 *Toll Free Tel:* 800-PAR-GOLF
  (727-4653)
Key Personnel
Publr: Dan Robertson
Ed-in-Chief: Jerry Tarde
Ed, Golf Digest Resource Ctr: Cliff Schrock
Devoted to special interest service articles helping
  readers to play better golf & enjoy the sport
  more. No unsol mss, query first.
First published 1950
Book Use: Reviews in annual roundup; excerpts
Frequency: Monthly
Avg pages per issue: 150
Circulation: 1,200,000
$19.99/yr print or digital, $29.99/yr print & digi-
  tal
ISSN: 0017-176X
Buy freelance fiction, poetry, photos, art & car-
  toons; Sell articles, ad reprints & back issues
Trim Size: 9 x 10.875
Ad Rates: B&W page $84,000, 1/2 page $54,600,
  4-color page $120,000, 1/2 page $78,000

Good Housekeeping
Published by Hearst Communications Inc
Division of Hearst Magazines
300 W 57 St, New York, NY 10019-3787
Tel: 212-649-2200; 212-649-2000
E-mail: feedback@goodhousekeeping.com
Web Site: www.goodhousekeeping.com; www.
hearst.com
Subscription Address: PO Box 6000, Harlan, IA
51593 *E-mail:* ghkcustserv@cdsfulfillment.com
Key Personnel
SVP & Group Publg Dir: Patricia Haegele
Digital Dir: Lauren Matthews
Ed-in-Chief: Jane Francisco
Contains articles of interest to homemakers, half
of whom also work outside the home. Topics
include food, fashion, decorating, beauty, diet,
health, interpersonal relations, social problems,
personalities, fiction, current affairs.
First published 1885
Frequency: Monthly
Avg pages per issue: 220
Circulation: 4,951,240
$3.99/issue, $7.97/yr, $15/2 yrs, $20/3 yrs
ISSN: 0017-209X

Grand Forks Herald
Published by Forum Communications Co
375 Second Ave N, Grand Forks, ND 58203
Tel: 701-780-1100 *Toll Free Tel:* 800-477-6572
(ND, SD, MN & MT) *Fax:* 701-780-1123
Web Site: www.grandforksherald.com
Key Personnel
Publr: Korrie Wenzel *Tel:* 701-780-1103
E-mail: kwenzel@gfherald.com
Weekly book page produced through various
sources. Author interviews, in-house & through
syndication, appear sporadically.
$17.25/mo (Mon-Sun print & digital all-access),
$11.50/mo (Fri-Sun print), $6.95/mo (digital
all-access)
Avg reviews per issue: 7

The Grand Rapids Press
Published by MLive Media Group
169 Monroe NW, Suite 100, Grand Rapids, MI
49503
Tel: 616-222-5400 *Toll Free Tel:* 800-878-1411
(subns)
E-mail: grnews@mlive.com; advertise@mlive.
com
Web Site: www.mlive.com/grand-rapids
Subscription Address: Advance Central Services,
3102 Walker Ridge Dr, Walker, MI 48544
Key Personnel
VP, Content: John Hiner
Sunday page, in-house & through syndication;
occasional author interviews.
Circulation: 133,107 (d); 182,252 (Sun)
Digital & print: $3.99/wk (Sun only), $4.49/wk
(Thurs & Sun), $4.99/wk (Tues, Thurs & Sun);
digital only: $4.99/wk

The Graphic Leader
Published by Postmedia Network Inc
c/o Postmedia Network, 365 Bloor St E, Toronto,
ON M4W 3L4, Canada
Tel: 204-857-3427
Web Site: thegraphicleader.com
Key Personnel
Ed: Brian Oliver *E-mail:* boliver@postmedia.com
Occasional column; author interviews.
First published 1895
Frequency: Weekly
Avg pages per issue: 32
Circulation: 10,000

The Greenville News
Published by Gannett Co Inc
32 E Broad St, Greenville, SC 29601
Mailing Address: PO Box 1688, Greenville, SC
29602-1688

Toll Free Tel: 800-736-7136
E-mail: customercare@greenvillenews.com
Web Site: www.greenvilleonline.com
Key Personnel
Exec Ed: Katrice Hardy *Tel:* 864-298-4165
E-mail: khardy1@greenvillenews.com
Weekly through syndication; author interviews.
Circulation: 95,008 (d); 128,784 (Sun)
$15/mo (Sun only), $29/mo (Mon-Sun)

GROUP Magazine
Published by Group Publishing Inc
1515 Cascade Ave, Loveland, CO 80538
Tel: 970-669-3836 *Toll Free Tel:* 800-447-1070
Fax: 970-292-4373
E-mail: info@group.com
Web Site: www.group.com
Key Personnel
Exec Ed: Rick Lawrence *E-mail:* rlawrence@
group.com
Youth ministry, youth ministers.
First published 1974
Book Use: Reviews of youth ministry resources
Frequency: Quarterly
Avg pages per issue: 100
Free
ISSN: 0163-8971
Buy nonfiction & cartoons
Trim Size: 8 x 10 3/4; live area 7 x 10

Hadassah Magazine
Published by Hadassah, The Women's Zionist
Organization of America Inc
40 Wall St, 8th fl, New York, NY 10005
Tel: 212-451-6289 *Toll Free Tel:* 800-664-5646
(subns) *Fax:* 212-451-6257
E-mail: magazine@hadassah.org
Web Site: www.hadassahmagazine.org
Key Personnel
Exec Ed: Lisa Hostein *Tel:* 212-451-6292
Mng Ed: Zelda Shluker *Tel:* 212-451-6288
Ad Mgr: Celia Weintrob *Tel:* 212-451-6283
E-mail: cweintrob@hadassah.org
Deals with social, economic, political & cultural
issues in the US & the spiritual & economic
development of Israel. Articles, stories, reviews
& interviews with an appeal to an educated
Jewish reader.
First published 1914
Frequency: 6 issues/yr
Avg pages per issue: 76
Circulation: 255,000 paid
$4/issue, $36/yr, $39/yr foreign
ISSN: 0017-6516
Buy freelance fiction, nonfiction, art & cartoons;
Sell back issues up to one year if available. Do
not provide reprints
Trim Size: 7 7/8 x 10 1/2; 1/8 bleed for all sides
Ad Rates: B&W page $7,750; 4-color page
$9,900
Ad Closing Date(s): 1st of the month, 2 months
prior to issue date

The Hamilton Spectator
Published by Metroland Media Group Ltd
Division of Torstar Corp
44 Frid St, Hamilton, ON L8N 3G3, Canada
Tel: 905-526-3333 *Fax:* 905-526-0147 (busn off);
905-526-1395 (news); 905-521-8986 (entertain-
ment/edit)
Web Site: www.thespec.com/hamilton-whatson/
books
Key Personnel
Publr: Neil Oliver *E-mail:* noliver@metroland.
com
Mng Ed: Howard Elliott *E-mail:* helliott@
thespec.com; Jim Poling *E-mail:* jpoling@
thespec.com
Features book reviews, news & releases from the
writing community in Hamilton & worldwide.
Circulation: 120,000
$9.03/mo digital

Harper's Bazaar
Published by Hearst Communications Inc
Division of Hearst Magazines
300 W 57 St, New York, NY 10019-3787
Tel: 212-903-5000; 212-903-5061 (edit); 212-903-
5398 (publg)
Web Site: www.harpersbazaar.com; www.hearst.
com
Subscription Address: PO Box 6000, Harlan, IA
51593
Key Personnel
VP, Publr & Chief Revenue Offr: Carol A Smith
Ed-in-Chief: Glenda Bailey
Edited for women interested in fashion & beauty;
also for the professional fashion designer &
retailer. Includes travel articles, profiles & in-
terviews.
First published 1867
Book Use: Fashion
Frequency: Monthly
Avg pages per issue: 325
Circulation: 734,504
$4.99/issue, $10/yr, $15/2 yrs, $20/3 yrs
ISSN: 0017-7873
Trim Size: 8 1/4 x 11 1/8
Ad Rates: 4-color page $134,270
Ad Closing Date(s): 5th of the 2nd month of pre-
ceding issue

Harper's Magazine
Published by Harper's Magazine Foundation
666 Broadway, 11th fl, New York, NY 10012
Tel: 212-420-5720 *Toll Free Tel:* 800-444-4653
Fax: 212-228-5889
E-mail: harpers@harpers.org
Web Site: www.harpers.org
Subscription Address: PO Box 6237, Harlan, IA
51593-1737
Key Personnel
Pres & Publr: John R MacArthur
VP & Gen Mgr: Lynn Carlson *E-mail:* lynn@
harpers.org
VP, PR: Giulia Melucci
Edit Dir: Ellen Rosenbush
Art Dir: Stacey Clarkson
Deputy Ed: Emily Cooke
Sr Ed: Katia Bachko; Giles Harvey
Ed: Christopher Beha
Contains short fiction as well as articles on lit-
erature, politics, science, education, the arts,
entertainment & business for an informed au-
dience. Accept very few unsol mss. Submit in
writing. Send queries with a SASE to editorial
department.
First published 1850
Book Use: Excerpts & essay-reviews
Frequency: Monthly
Avg pages per issue: 96
Circulation: 105,000 paid
$6.99/issue, $30/yr, $33/yr CN, $50/yr foreign
ISSN: 0017-789X
Buy freelance fiction, nonfiction, poetry, art &
cartoons; Sell articles & ad reprints, back is-
sues
Avg reviews per issue: 6-8
Trim Size: 8 x 10.75
Ad Rates: B&W page $8,795, 4-color page
$13,645
Ad Closing Date(s): 12th of 2nd month preceding
issue date

The Hartford Courant
Published by Tribune Publishing Co
285 Broad St, Hartford, CT 06115
Tel: 860-525-5555 (cust serv); 860-241-6200
E-mail: custserv@courant.com
Web Site: www.courant.com; www.ctnow.com
Key Personnel
Publr & Ed-in-Chief: Andrew Julien
E-mail: ajulien@courant.com
Dir, Content: Richard Green *E-mail:* rgreen@
courant.com

Features Ed: Cindy Kuse *E-mail:* ckuse@courant.
com
Digital & print: $2.49/wk (Sun only), $4.99/wk
(Mon-Sun); digital only: $1.99/wk
ISSN: 1047-4153

Harvard Magazine
Published by Harvard Magazine Inc
7 Ware St, Cambridge, MA 02138-4037
Tel: 617-495-5746; 617-496-9780 *Fax:* 617-495-
0324
E-mail: customerservice@harvardmag.com
Web Site: www.harvardmagazine.com
Key Personnel
Publr: Irina Kuksin *E-mail:* irina_kuksin@
harvard.edu
Dir, Fundraising & Circ: Felecia Carter
E-mail: felecia_carter@harvard.edu
Mng Ed: Jonathan S Shaw *E-mail:* jon_shaw@
harvard.edu
Sr Ed: Jean Martin *E-mail:* jean_martin@harvard.
edu
Ed: John S Rosenberg *E-mail:* john_rosenberg@
harvard.edu
General interest material devoted to Harvard-
related subjects & aimed at sharing the wealth
of Harvard; contains articles about the Har-
vard community, its intellectual life & people.
Books must be by Harvard students, gradu-
ates (any Harvard school) or faculty, or about
Harvard-related subjects, higher education, Har-
vard graduates.
First published 1898
Book Use: Reviews, listings & occasional author
profiles; excerpts-all require some Harvard con-
nection
Frequency: 6 issues/yr
Avg pages per issue: 116
Circulation: 258,000
$27/yr US, $35/yr CN, $45/yr Mexico, $55/yr intl
Buy freelance, nonfiction; Sell back issues
Trim Size: 8 3/8 x 10 1/2
Ad Rates: See media kit for national & regional
rates
Ad Closing Date(s): 15th of 2nd month preceding
publication

Herald-Dispatch
Published by HD Media Company LLC
946 Fifth Ave, Huntington, WV 25701
Mailing Address: PO Box 2017, Huntington, WV
25720
Tel: 304-526-4000 (operator) *Toll Free Tel:* 800-
444-2446 (newsroom); 800-955-6110 (display
& retail ad)
Web Site: www.herald-dispatch.com
Key Personnel
Ed & Publr: Ed Dawson *Tel:* 304-526-2787
E-mail: editor@herald-dispatch.com
Ad Dir: Charles Jessup *Tel:* 304-526-2820
E-mail: cjessup@herald-dispatch.com
Circ & Mktg Specialist: Jill Briggs *Tel:* 304-526-
2806 *E-mail:* jbriggs@herald-dispatch.com
In-house & through syndication; occasional inter-
views with local authors.
Circulation: 23,700 (m); 24,700 (Sun)

Herald News
Published by North Jersey Media Group
One Garret Mountain Plaza, Woodland Park, NJ
07424
Mailing Address: PO Box 471, Woodland Park,
NJ 07424-0471
Tel: 973-569-7000 *Toll Free Tel:* 888-282-3422
Fax: 973-569-7037
E-mail: northjerseymediagroup@gannett.com
Web Site: www.northjersey.com
Occasional column; in-house, syndicated &
through wire services; occasional author in-
terviews.

Circulation: 50,000 (m)
Digital & print: $18/mo (Thurs & Sun), $32/mo
(Mon-Sun); digital only: $9.99/mo

Herald News
Published by GateHouse Media LLC
207 Pocasset St, Fall River, MA 02722
Tel: 508-676-8211 *Fax:* 508-324-4047
E-mail: news@heraldnews.com
Web Site: www.heraldnews.com
Key Personnel
Pres & Group Publr: Peter Mayer
Dir, Content & Interactive: Jon Root
E-mail: jroot@heraldnews.com
Ed-in-Chief: Lynne Sullivan *Tel:* 508-676-2534
E-mail: lsullivan@heraldnews.com
Occasional column; in-house & through syndi-
cation, occasional author interviews & book
reviews; Sunday book review page.
Circulation: 38,000 (d); 38,100 (Sun)
Digital & print: $24/12 wks (Sun only), $48/12
wks (Mon-Sun); digital only: $9.95/mo,
$99.95/yr

The Herald-Sun Newspapers
Published by Durham Herald Co Inc
1530 N Gregson St, Suite 2A, Durham, NC
27701
Tel: 919-419-6500 *Toll Free Tel:* 800-522-4205
E-mail: news@heraldsun.com
Web Site: www.heraldsun.com
Key Personnel
Exec Ed: Robyn Tomlin *Tel:* 919-829-4806
Mng Ed: Jane Elizabeth *Tel:* 919-836-5909
Author interviews & book reviews.
Circulation: 40,000 (m); 55,000 (Sun)
Digital & print: $34.94/13 wks (Wed & Sun),
$69.88/13 wks (Mon-Fri & Sun); digital only:
$8.99/mo, $129.99/yr

The Hibbing Daily Tribune
Published by Adams Publishing Group
2142 First Ave, Hibbing, MN 55746
Mailing Address: PO Box 38, Hibbing, MN
55746-0038
Tel: 218-262-1011 *Fax:* 218-262-4318
E-mail: news@hibbingdailytribune.net
Web Site: hibbingmn.com
Key Personnel
News Asst: Connie Dickson; Hannah White
In-house, syndicated & other book reviews in
space available in Accent section, reviews with
excerpts, reproduction of jacket cover or author
photo, occasional author interviews.
First published 1893
Frequency: Daily (Tues-Sun print & Mon e-
edition)
Circulation: 10,000
$3.45/wk carrier, $3.61/wk mail, $3.95/wk motor
route

The High Point Enterprise
Published by HP Enterprise Inc
213 Woodbine St, High Point, NC 27260
Tel: 336-888-3500 *Fax:* 336-888-0809
Web Site: www.hpenews.com; www.facebook.
com/hpenterprise
Key Personnel
Publr: Nancy Baker *E-mail:* nbaker@hpenews.
com
Ad Dir: David Jones *E-mail:* djones@hpenews.
com
Ed: Megan Ward *E-mail:* mward@hpenews.com
Weekly, wire copy, syndicated; occasional local
author interviews.
Circulation: 50,000 (d)
Print & e-edition: $16.24/mo (Mon-Sun); full dig-
ital access (no print): $10/mo

The Hollywood Reporter
Published by Prometheus Global Media LLC

5700 Wilshire Blvd, Suite 500, Los Angeles, CA
90036
Tel: 323-525-2000; 323-525-2150 (subns);
323-525-2130 (edit); 323-525-2013 (ad)
Toll Free Tel: 866-525-2150 (subns)
E-mail: thrnews@thr.com
Web Site: www.hollywoodreporter.com
Key Personnel
EVP/Group Publr, Entertainment Group: Lynne
Segall
Exec Creative Dir: Shanti Marlar
News Dir: Erik Hayden
Exec Mng Ed: Sudie Redmond
Edit Dir: Matthew Belloni
Exec Ed, Features: Stephen Galloway
The oldest weekly entertainment trade publica-
tion, delivers the business of entertainment,
including motion pictures, TV, home video,
music, convergence, the crafts & production fa-
cilities servicing those media to over 100,000
readers in 64 countries.
First published 1930
Print & iPad: $99/yr, $249/yr intl; digital all
access: $129/yr; print & digital all access:
$199/yr, $299/yr intl
ISSN: 0018-3660

The Honolulu Star-Advertiser
Published by Oahu Publications Inc
Subsidiary of Black Press Ltd
7 Waterfront Plaza, Suite 210, 500 Ala Moana
Blvd, Honolulu, HI 96813
Tel: 808-529-4747 *Fax:* 808-529-4750
E-mail: citydesk@staradvertiser.com
Web Site: www.staradvertiser.com
Key Personnel
Pres & Publr: Dennis Francis *Tel:* 808-529-4700
VP & Ed: Frank Bridgewater *Tel:* 808-529-4791
E-mail: fbridgewater@staradvertiser.com
Mng Ed, Spec Sections: Clarke Reilly *Tel:* 808-
529-4742 *E-mail:* creilly@staradvertiser.com
Book reviews.
First published 2010
Frequency: Daily
Circulation: 130,000 (e)
Digital & print: $28.15/mo (Wed-Sun), $42.25/mo
(Mon-Sun); digital only: $21.95/mo

House Beautiful
Published by Hearst Communications Inc
Division of Hearst Magazines
300 W 57 St, 27th fl, New York, NY 10019-3787
Tel: 212-903-5206; 212-903-5005 (publg)
Web Site: www.housebeautiful.com; www.hearst.
com
Subscription Address: PO Box 6000, Harlan, IA
51593
Key Personnel
Edit Dir: Joanna Saltz
Sr Features Ed: Emma Bazilian
Articles on architecture, decorating, home fur-
nishings, design, practical home planning &
maintenance. Also covers travel, entertainment,
gardening & food.
First published 1896
Frequency: 10 issues/yr
Avg pages per issue: 176
Circulation: 804,917
$4.99/issue, $10/yr, $15/2 yrs
ISSN: 0018-6422
Trim Size: 8 1/4 x 10 7/8
Ad Rates: 4-color full page $182,590, 1/2 page
$118,685

Houston Chronicle
Published by Houston Chronicle Publishing Co
Division of Hearst Newspapers
4747 Southwest Fwy, Houston, TX 77027
Mailing Address: PO Box 4260, Houston, TX
77210-4260
Tel: 713-220-7171 *Fax:* 713-362-3575
Web Site: www.houstonchronicle.com

Key Personnel
Chmn: Jack Sweeney
Pres & Publr: John McKeon
Ed & EVP: Nancy Barnes
Exec Ed, Opinions & Editorials: Jeff Cohen
Books Ed: Alyson Ward *Tel:* 713-362-7128
   E-mail: alyson.ward@chron.com
Entertainment Ed: Robert Morast
News Ed: Lisa Gray
Sunday in *Zest* magazine; book reviews in-house,
  freelancers & academic sources. Frequent au-
  thor interviews Sunday.
First published 1901

Huntsville Times
Published by Alabama Media Group
200 Westside Sq, Suite 100, Huntsville, AL
  35801
Tel: 256-532-4000 *Toll Free Tel:* 800-239-5271
E-mail: advertise@al.com; marketing@al.com
Web Site: www.al.com/huntsville; www.
  alabamamediagroup.com
Subscription Address: PO Box 1487, West Sta,
  Huntsville, AL 35807
Key Personnel
Pres: Tom Bates *E-mail:* tbates@al.com
In-house & through syndication; author inter-
  views.
Circulation: 40,000 (Wed/Fri); 60,433 (Sun)
Digital & print: $4.17/wk (Sun only), $5.56/wk
  (Wed & Sun), $6.95/wk (Wed, Fri & Sun); dig-
  ital only: $4.61/wk

Idaho State Journal
Published by Adams Publishing Group
305 S Arthur St, Pocatello, ID 83204
Mailing Address: PO Box 431, Pocatello, ID
  83204-0431
Tel: 208-232-4161 *Fax:* 208-233-8007
E-mail: newsroom@journalnet.com
Web Site: www.idahostatejournal.com
Key Personnel
Mng Ed: Ian Fennell *Tel:* 208-239-3121
  E-mail: ifennell@journalnet.com
Occasional author interviews; in-house & by syn-
  dicate; occasional reviews & excerpts.
Circulation: 17,000 (e); 18,500 (Sun)
Digital & print: $9.10/mo (Sun only), $12.39/mo
  (Thurs, Fri & Sun), $14.77/mo (Tues-Fri &
  Sun); digital only: $9.10/mo

The Independent Record
Published by Lee Enterprises Inc
PO Box 4249, Helena, MT 59604
Tel: 406-447-4000 *Toll Free Tel:* 800-523-2272
  Fax: 406-447-4052
Web Site: helenair.com
Key Personnel
Publr: Anita Fasbender *Tel:* 406-447-4012
  E-mail: anita.fasbender@helenair.com
Ed: Jesse Chaney *Tel:* 406-447-4074
  E-mail: jesse.chaney@helenair.com
Weekly book page-wire & reviews.
Circulation: 14,500 (m); 15,000 (Sun)
$5/mo digital basic, $9.99/mo digital plus

Indianapolis Star/News
Published by Gannett Co Inc
130 S Meridian St, Indianapolis, IN 46225
Mailing Address: PO Box 145, Indianapolis, IN
  46206-0145
Tel: 317-444-4000 (call ctr) *Toll Free Tel:* 888-
  357-7827
E-mail: indianapolisstar@gannett.com
Web Site: www.indystar.com
Key Personnel
VP, Sales: David Hakanson
Sr News Dir: Ginger Rough
Exec Ed: Ronnie Ramos *Tel:* 317-444-6166
  E-mail: ronnie.ramos@indystar.com
Weekly book reviews; 200 reviews/yr, in-house;
  occasional author interviews.

Circulation: 557,990
ISSN: 1930-2533

Inland Valley Daily Bulletin
Published by Southern California News Group
9616 Archibald Ave, Suite 100, Rancho Cuca-
  monga, CA 91730
Tel: 909-987-6397
E-mail: service@langnews.com
Web Site: www.dailybulletin.com
Key Personnel
Pres & Publr: Ron Hasse *Tel:* 818-713-3883
  E-mail: publisher@scng.com
Exec Ed: Frank Pine *Tel:* 909-483-9360
  E-mail: editor@scng.com
Author interviews if local.
First published 1882
Circulation: 49,899 (d); 54,401 (Sun)
Digital & print: $12.50/4 wks (Sun only), $15/4
  wks (Thurs-Sun, $25/4 wks (Mon-Sun))

Iowa City Press-Citizen
Published by Gannett Co Inc
123 N Linn St, Suite 2-E, Iowa City, IA 52245
Mailing Address: PO Box 2480, Iowa City, IA
  52244-2480
Tel: 319-337-3181 *Toll Free Tel:* 877-424-0071
E-mail: customerservice@press-citizen.com
Web Site: www.press-citizen.com
Key Personnel
Sales Mgr: Michael Vitti *Tel:* 319-339-7350
  E-mail: mvitti@press-citizen.com
Reviews books in-house & through syndication.
Circulation: 14,000; 10,000 paid

Island Packet
Published by The McClatchy Co
10 Buck Island Rd, Bluffton, SC 29910
Mailing Address: PO Box 5727, Hilton Head Is-
  land, SC 29938
Tel: 843-706-8140 *Toll Free Tel:* 877-706-8100
Web Site: www.islandpacket.com
Key Personnel
Publr: Rodney Mahone *E-mail:* rmahone@
  mcclatchy.com
Gen Mgr & Exec Ed: Brian Tolley
  E-mail: btolley@islandpacket.com
Sr Ed: Liz Farrell *E-mail:* lfarrell@islandpacket.
  com
Weekly in-house, syndicated & wire service book
  reviews, "Book Page" author interviews.
First published 1897
$12.99/mo digital, $129.99/yr

The Jackson Sun
Published by Gannett Co Inc
245 W Lafayette St, Jackson, TN 38301
Tel: 731-427-3333 *Toll Free Tel:* 800-372-3922
Web Site: www.jacksonsun.com
In-house, through syndication & other outside
  sources, book signings & previews.
Circulation: 30,000 (weekly); 35,000 (Sun)
Digital & print: $16/mo (Wed & Sun), $26/mo
  (Mon-Sun); digital only: $10/mo

The Jersey Journal
Published by The Evening Journal Association
One Harmon Plaza, Suite 1010, Secaucus, NJ
  07094
Tel: 201-653-1000
Web Site: www.jjournal.com
Key Personnel
Publr: David Blomquist *E-mail:* dblomquist@
  jjournal.com
VP & Ed: Margaret Schmidt *Tel:* 201-217-2480
  E-mail: margaret.schmidt@jjournal.com
Mng Ed: Ron Zeitlinger *Tel:* 201-217-2429
  E-mail: ron.zeitlinger@jjournal.com
Occasional story; occasional local book review.
Circulation: 20,000 (d)
$1/day

Johnson City Press
Published by Sandusky Newspaper Group
204 W Main St, Johnson City, TN 37604
Mailing Address: PO Box 1717, Johnson City,
  TN 37605-1717
Tel: 423-929-3111 *Fax:* 423-929-7484
E-mail: circulation@johnsoncitypress.com
Web Site: www.johnsoncitypress.com
Key Personnel
Publr: Rick Thomason *Tel:* 423-722-0501
  E-mail: rthomason@johnsoncitypress.com
Daily, in-house & syndicated; AP wire & *The
  New York Times.* Occasional author interviews.
Circulation: 32,000 (m); 35,000 (Sun)
Print: $11.70/mo (Wed & Sun), $10.83/mo (Fri-
  Sun); digital only $13.55/mo; digital & print:
  $14.30/mo (Mon-Sun)

Journal & Courier
Published by Gannett Co Inc
823 Park East Blvd, Suite C, Lafayette, IN 47905
Tel: 765-423-5511 *Toll Free Tel:* 800-456-3223
Web Site: www.jconline.com
Key Personnel
Ed & News Dir: Carol Bangert
  E-mail: cbangert@gannett.com
Prodr: Joseph Mutascio *E-mail:* jmutascio@
  gannett.com
Daily newspaper; infrequent book reviews, in-
  house; infrequent author interviews.
Circulation: 37,000 (d); 44,000 (Sun)
$.75/daily, $1.75/Sun

The Journal Gazette
Published by Fort Wayne Newspapers
Affiliate of Ogden Newspapers
600 W Main St, Fort Wayne, IN 46802-1498
Tel: 260-461-8773 (newsroom); 260-461-8519
  (subscriber info) *Toll Free Tel:* 800-324-0505
  (circ) *Fax:* 260-461-8648 (newsroom)
E-mail: jgnews@jg.net
Web Site: www.journalgazette.net
Key Personnel
Publr: Julie Inskeep *Tel:* 260-461-8490
  E-mail: jinskeep@jg.net
Mng Ed: Jim Touvell *Tel:* 260-461-8629
  E-mail: jtouvell@jg.net
Ed: Sherry Skufca *Tel:* 260-461-8201
  E-mail: sskufca@jg.net
Edit Page Ed: Karen Francisco *Tel:* 260-461-8206
  E-mail: kfrancisco@jg.net
Book reviews.
Circulation: 41,000 (m); 71,000 (Sun)
$22.95/mo (daily print), $16.70/mo (Fri-Sun
  print), $10.85/mo (Sun only print), $20/mo
  (digital)

The Journal News
Published by Gannett Co Inc
1133 Westchester Ave, Suite N-110, White Plains,
  NY 10604
Tel: 914-694-9300 *Toll Free Tel:* 800-942-1010
  (subns)
E-mail: westchesterthejournalnews@gannett.com
Web Site: www.lohud.com
Key Personnel
News Dir: Mary Dolan *E-mail:* mdolan@lohud.
  com
Community Content Ed: Karen Croke
  E-mail: kcroke1@lohud.com
Sunday page in Leisure section "Living Section"
  in-house & through syndication & wire ser-
  vices. Print-on-demand or self-published books
  are not reviewed.
Circulation: 87,205 (d); 104,652 (Sun)

Journal of Marketing
Published by American Marketing Association
130 E Randolph St, 22nd fl, Chicago, IL 60601
Tel: 312-542-9000 *Toll Free Tel:* 800-AMA-1150
  (262-1150)

E-mail: jom@ama.org; amasubs@
subscriptionoffice.com
Web Site: www.ama.org/journal-of-marketing
Key Personnel
VP, Pubns: David W Stewart
Ed-in-Chief: Christine Moorman
Develops & disseminates knowledge about real-
world marketing questions useful to scholars,
educators, managers, policy makers, consumers
& other societal stakeholders around the world.
It is the premier outlet for substantive research
in marketing.
First published 1936
Frequency: 6 times/yr
Avg pages per issue: 144
Circulation: 8,200
Indivs: $41/issue, $171/yr online only, $186/yr
print only, $190/yr print & online; Instns:
$82/issue, $449/yr print or online only, $540/yr
print & online
ISSN: 0022-2429 (print); 1547-7185 (online)
Sell articles, ad reprints & back issues

Journal of Marketing Research
Published by American Marketing Association
130 E Randolph St, 22nd fl, Chicago, IL 60601
Tel: 312-542-9000 Toll Free Tel: 800-AMA-1150
(262-1150)
E-mail: jmr@ama.org; amasubs@
subscriptionoffice.com
Web Site: www.ama.org
Key Personnel
VP, Pubns: David W Stewart
Ed: Rajdeep Grewal
Articles representing the entire spectrum of topics in marketing. It welcomes diverse theoretical perspectives & a wide variety of data &
methodological approaches. Seeks papers that
make methodological, substantive +/or theoretical contributions. Empirical studies in papers
that seek to make a theoretical +/or substantive contribution may involve experimental +/or
observational designs & rely on primary data
(including qualitative date) +/or secondary data
(including meta-analytic data sets).
First published 1964
Frequency: 6 times/yr
Avg pages per issue: 128
Circulation: 4,400
Indivs: $41/issue, $171/yr online only, $186/yr
print only, $190/yr print & online; Instns:
$82/issue, $449/yr print or online only, $540/yr
print & online
ISSN: 0022-2437 (print); 1547-7193 (online)
Sell articles, ad reprints & back issues

Journal Star
Published by GateHouse Media LLC
One News Plaza, Peoria, IL 61643
Tel: 309-686-3000 Toll Free Tel: 800-322-0804
(cust serv) Fax: 309-686-3296
E-mail: news@pjstar.com
Web Site: www.pjstar.com
Key Personnel
Pres & Publr: Paul Gaier Tel: 309-686-3005
E-mail: pgaier@gatehousemedia.com
Exec Ed: Dennis Anderson Tel: 309-686-3159
E-mail: danderson@pjstar.com
Occasional author interviews; in-house & syndi-
cated.
First published 1855
Circulation: 70,000 (d); 90,000 (Sun)
Digital & print: $32.50/13 wks (Sun only),
$41.60/13 wks (weekend), $78/13 wks (Mon-
Sun); digital only: $4.99/mo, $34.99/yr

The Kansas City Star
Published by The McClatchy Co
1601 McGee St, Kansas City, MO 64108
Tel: 816-234-4636 Toll Free Tel: 877-962-7827
(subns)
Web Site: www.kansascity.com

Key Personnel
VP & Ed: Mike Fannin Tel: 816-234-4345
E-mail: mfannin@kcstar.com
Mng Ed: Greg Farmer Tel: 816-234-4321
E-mail: gfarmer@kcstar.com
Weekly books page, daily features page; staff
freelance & wire sources; reviews & author in-
terviews. Self-published print & ebooks rarely
considered for review or mention.
Circulation: 216,000 (m); 275,000 (Sat); 325,000
(Sun)
Digital & print: $8.91/wk (Mon-Sun), $7.81/wk
(Wed-Sun), $5.61/wk (Wed & Sun); digital
only: $12.99/mo

Kentucky Living
Published by Kentucky Association of Electric
Cooperatives
PO Box 32170, Louisville, KY 40232-2170
Tel: 502-815-6339 Toll Free Tel: 800-595-4846
Fax: 502-459-1611
E-mail: e-mail@kentuckyliving.com
Web Site: www.kentuckyliving.com
Key Personnel
Ed: Anita Travis Richter
Kentucky feature magazine.
First published 1948
Book Use: Notice of new Kentucky books, Ken-
tucky authors & excerpts
Frequency: Monthly
Avg pages per issue: 64
Circulation: 475,000
$15/yr, $25/3 yrs
ISSN: 1043-853X
Buy nonfiction; Sell back issues
Trim Size: 8 1/8 x 10 7/8
Ad Closing Date(s): 22nd of the month, 5 weeks
preceding publication; Jan & Feb, 16th of the
month, 6 weeks preceding publication

Kentucky New Era
Published by New Era
1618 E Ninth St, Hopkinsville, KY 44240
Mailing Address: PO Box 729, Hopkinsville, KY
42241
Tel: 270-886-4444 Fax: 270-887-3222
E-mail: editor@kentuckynewera.com
Web Site: www.kentuckynewera.com
Key Personnel
Pres: Chuck Henderson E-mail: chenderson@
kentuckynewera.com
Publr: Taylor Wood Hayes E-mail: twhayes@
kentuckynewera.com
Dir, Sales & Mktg: Ted Jatczak
E-mail: tjatczak@kentuckynewera.com
In-house occasional, syndicated; occasional local
author interviews.
First published 1869
Frequency: Daily (Mon-Sat)
Circulation: 14,000 (d)
Print: $14/mo, $40/3 mos, $76/6 mos, $296/yr;
online: $14/mo, $42/3 mos, $84/6 mos,
$164.85/yr

The Kingston Whig-Standard
Published by Postmedia Network Inc
6 Cataraqui St, Kingston, ON K7L 4Z7, Canada
Tel: 613-544-5000
Web Site: www.thewhig.com
Key Personnel
Ed-in-Chief: Steve Serviss E-mail: steve.serviss@
postmedia.com
Weekly book reviews tabloid; syndicated & free-
lance in-house. Occasional author interviews &
freelance.
Frequency: Daily (Tues-Sat)
Circulation: 23,686 (d)
$22/4 wks, $3.99/mo digital
ISSN: 1197-4397
Avg reviews per issue: 3

Kiplinger's Personal Finance Magazine
Published by The Kiplinger Washington Editors
Inc
1100 13 St NW, Suite 750, Washington, DC
20005
Tel: 202-887-6400 Toll Free Tel: 800-544-0155
(subn servs) Toll Free Fax: 888-547-5464 (spec
issues)
E-mail: sub.services@kiplinger.com
Web Site: www.kiplinger.com
Key Personnel
Exec Ed: Anne Kates Smith
Mng Ed: Barbara Hoch Marcus
Sr Ed: Eileen Ambrose; Jane Bennett Clark; San-
dra Block; Jeffrey R Kosnett
Ed-at-Large: Janet Bodnar
For general, adult audience interested in personal
finance topics, especially investing & money
management.
First published 1947
Frequency: Monthly
Avg pages per issue: 100
Circulation: 600,000
$7/issue, $12/yr print & digital
Sell article & ad reprints, back issues
Trim Size: 7.875 x 10.5
Ad Rates: 4-color page $66,801, 2/3 page
$53,123, 1/2 page $46,788, 1/3 page $33,422
Ad Closing Date(s): 5-6 weeks preceding publica-
tion

Kitsap Sun
Published by Gannett Co Inc
545 Fifth St, Bremerton, WA 98337
Mailing Address: PO Box 259, Bremerton, WA
98337
Tel: 360-792-8558; 360-792-9222 (circ)
Toll Free Tel: 844-900-7106
E-mail: sunnews@kitsapsun.com
Web Site: www.kitsapsun.com
Key Personnel
Ed: David Nelson Tel: 360-415-2679
E-mail: david.nelson@kitsapsun.com
Weekly book reviews.
Circulation: 20,000
Digital & print: $14/mo (Sun only), $23/mo
(Mon-Sun); digital only: $10/mo

The Knoxville News-Sentinel
Published by Gannett Co Inc
2332 News Sentinel Dr, Knoxville, TN 37921-
5761
Tel: 865-523-3131 Toll Free Tel: 844-900-7097
(cust serv)
E-mail: features@knoxnews.com
Web Site: www.knoxnews.com
Key Personnel
Exec Ed: Joel Christopher Tel: 865-342-6300
E-mail: jchristo@gannett.com
Book reviews & occasional author interviews.
$9.99/mo

LA Times, see Los Angeles Times

The Lakeville Journal
Published by The Lakeville Journal Co LLC
64 Rte 7 N, Falls Village, CT 06039
Mailing Address: PO Box 1688, Lakeville, CT
06039
Tel: 860-435-9873
E-mail: editor@lakevillejournal.com; compass@
lakevillejournal.com
Web Site: www.tricornernews.com/
lakevillagejournal
Key Personnel
Publr & Ed-in-Chief: Janet Manko
E-mail: publisher@lakevillejournal.com
Exec Ed, Spec Sections: Cynthia Hochswender
E-mail: cynthiah@lakevillejournal.com
Art & entertainment section with book reviews.
First published 1897
Frequency: Weekly

Circulation: 4,800 paid
$28/yr web only, $53/yr print inside Litchfield County, $38/yr digital

Lansing State Journal
Published by Gannett Co Inc
300 S Washington Sq, Suite 300, Lansing, MI 48933
Tel: 517-377-1000 *Toll Free Tel:* 800-234-1719
E-mail: lansingstatejournal@gannett.com (cust serv)
Web Site: www.lsj.com
Key Personnel
Exec Ed: Stephanie Angel *Tel:* 517-377-1076
  E-mail: sangel@lsj.com
Circulation: 75,000 (d); 94,000 (Sun)

Las Vegas Magazine
Published by Greenspun Media Group
2275 Corporate Circle, Suite 300, Henderson, NV 89074
Tel: 702-383-7185; 702-990-2550 (corp)
E-mail: gmginfo@gmgvegas.com
Web Site: www.lasvegasmagazine.com
Key Personnel
Publr: Jamal Parker *E-mail:* jamal.parker@ gmgvegas.com
Mng Ed: Nina King
Ed: Ken Miller
Assoc Ed: Kiko Miyasato
Entertainment/TV-Tour Guide & in-room hotel resort publication.
Frequency: Weekly
Circulation: 139,047
Free
Trim Size: 8 1/4 x 10 3/4
Ad Rates: Full page $5,256, 1/2 page horizontal $3,055, 1/3 page square $2,472
Ad Closing Date(s): 3rd Wednesday before issue date

Las Vegas Review-Journal
Published by Las Vegas Review-Journal Inc
1111 W Bonanza Rd, Las Vegas, NV 89106
Mailing Address: PO Box 70, Las Vegas, NV 89125-0070
Tel: 702-383-0211; 702-383-0264 (newsroom)
Web Site: www.lvrj.com
Key Personnel
Publr & Ed: J Keith Moyer *Tel:* 707-477-3829
  E-mail: kmoyer@reviewjournal.com
Exec Ed: Glenn Cook *Tel:* 702-387-2906
  E-mail: gcook@reviewjournal.com
Mng Ed: Anastasia Hendrix *Tel:* 702-383-0232
  E-mail: ahendrix@reviewjournal.com
Sunday column on Southwestern books, reviews; through syndication.
Circulation: 174,127 (d); 200,955 (Sun)
Digital & print: $5.99/mo (Sun only), $8.99/mo (Thurs-Sun), $9.99/mo (Mon-Sun); digital only: $8.99/mo, $89/yr

Las Vegas Weekly
Published by Greenspun Media Group
2275 Corporate Circle, Suite 300, Henderson, NV 89074
Tel: 702-990-2550 *Fax:* 702-383-7264
E-mail: letters@lasvegassun.com
Web Site: www.lasvegasweekly.com
Key Personnel
Pres & Ed, Las Vegas Sun: Brian Greenspun
Ed: Spencer Patterson
Thursday in-house & through syndication; occasional author interviews.
Circulation: 45,000 (e); 235,000 (Sun)
First copy free, additional copies $2
Avg reviews per issue: 4
Trim Size: 10 1/2 x 13 1/2
Ad Rates: Full page $4,056, 1/2 page $2,108

The Lewiston Tribune
Published by Tribune Publishing Co

505 Capital St, Lewiston, ID 83501
Mailing Address: PO Box 957, Lewiston, ID 83501
Tel: 208-743-9411 *Toll Free Tel:* 800-745-9411 (ID & WA only) *Fax:* 208-746-1185
E-mail: city@lmtribune.com
Web Site: lmtribune.com
Key Personnel
Mktg Dir: Doug Bauer *Tel:* 208-848-2269
  E-mail: dbauer@lmtribune.com
Mng Ed: Craig Clohessy *Tel:* 208-848-2251
  E-mail: cclohessy@lmtribune.com
Friday page; occasional author interviews; in-house, through syndication & other sources.
First published 1892
Frequency: Daily
Circulation: 21,000 (m); 24,000 (Sun)

The Lexington Herald-Leader
Published by The McClatchy Co
100 Midland Ave, Lexington, KY 40508-1943
Tel: 859-231-3100
Web Site: www.kentucky.com
Key Personnel
Exec Ed & Gen Mgr: Peter Baniak *Tel:* 859-231-3446 *E-mail:* pbaniak@herald-leader.com
Sunday, one page syndicated in-house books of regional & local interest.
Circulation: 159,826 (d); 190,057 (Sun)
Digital & print: $55.12/13 wks (Sat & Sun), $96.46/13 wks (Mon-Sun); digital only: $12.99/mo, $129.99/yr

Liguorian
Published by Liguori Publications
One Liguori Dr, Liguori, MO 63057-1000
Tel: 636-464-2500 *Toll Free Tel:* 866-848-2492
E-mail: liguorian@sfsdayton.com (cust serv)
Web Site: www.liguorian.org
Key Personnel
Pres & Publr: Fr Byron Miller
Mng Ed: Elizabeth Herzing-Gebhart *Tel:* 636-223-1538 *E-mail:* eherzing@liguori.org
Religious publication for people of all ages with Catholic (Christian) convictions; advertising accepted; do not consider previously published material or simultaneous submissions. Contact editor for submission guidelines at liguorianeditor@liguori.org.
First published 1913
Book Use: Reviews
Frequency: 10 issues/yr
Avg pages per issue: 44
Circulation: 50,000 paid
$25/yr print & digital
Buy freelance fiction & nonfiction
Avg reviews per issue: 3-4
Ad Rates: See web site for media kit or contact adsales@liguori.org

The Literary Review
Published by Fairleigh Dickinson University
285 Madison Ave, Madison, NJ 07940
Tel: 973-443-8564
E-mail: info@theliteraryreview.org
Web Site: www.theliteraryreview.org
Key Personnel
Ed-in-Chief: Minna Proctor
Prodn Ed: Kate Munning
Edit Coord: Louise D Stahl
Literary journal.
First published 1957
Frequency: Quarterly
Avg pages per issue: 180
Circulation: 2,000
$10/issue
ISSN: 0024-4589
Trim Size: 6 x 9

Living Lutheran
Published by Augsburg Fortress Publishers

8765 W Higgins Rd, 5th fl, Chicago, IL 60631-4183
Tel: 773-380-2540 *Toll Free Tel:* 800-638-3522
  Fax: 773-380-2409
E-mail: livinglutheran@elca.org
Web Site: www.livinglutheran.org
Subscription Address: PO Box 1209, Minneapolis, MN 55440-1209 *Toll Free Tel:* 800-328-4648 *E-mail:* subscriptions@1517.media
Key Personnel
Ed: Jennifer Younker
Content Ed: Megan Brandsrud; John Potter; Erin Strybis
Ad: Ben Bitner
General interest magazine of the Evangelical Lutheran Church in America. No unsol mss, query first.
First published 1987
Book Use: Books column & reviews, articles
Frequency: Monthly
Avg pages per issue: 60
Circulation: 135,802
$1.66/issue, $19.95/yr, $31.95/2 yrs, $41.95/3 yrs
ISSN: 0024-743X
Buy nonfiction, art & cartoons; Sell back issues
Trim Size: 8 x 10 1/2
Ad Rates: Full page $4,050, 2-page spread $8,100
Ad Closing Date(s): 8 weeks before cover date

The London Free Press
Published by Postmedia Network Inc
210 Dundas St, Suite 201, London, ON N6A 5J3, Canada
Tel: 519-679-1111 *Fax:* 519-667-4523
Web Site: www.lfpress.com
Key Personnel
Entertainment, Travel, Life Ed: Barbara Taylor
  Tel: 519-667-5468 *E-mail:* btaylor@postmedia.com
Saturday pages, in-house & by freelancers, occasional author interviews.
First published 1849
Frequency: Daily (Mon-Sat)
Circulation: 105,000 (d); 135,000 (Sat)
Print: $14/4 wks (Sat only), $24/4 wks (Mon-Sat); digital: $9.99/mo

Long Beach Press-Telegram, see Press-Telegram

Los Angeles Magazine
Published by Emmis Publishing LP
5900 Wilshire Blvd, 10th fl, Los Angeles, CA 90036
Tel: 323-801-0100 *Toll Free Tel:* 800-876-5222 (cust serv) *Fax:* 323-801-0105
E-mail: letters@lamag.com
Web Site: www.lamag.com
Key Personnel
Assoc Publr: Michael J Petruncola
Design Dir: Steven E Banks
Prodn Dir: Julia St Pierre
Exec Ed: Matthew Segal
Ed-in-Chief: Mary Melton
Mng Ed: Ann Herold
Sr Ed: Linda Immediato
Arts & Culture Ed: Marielle Wakim
Covers life in the Los Angeles metropolitan & suburban area. Features on cultural happenings, new ideas & trends, interviews with controversial figures, politics, business, travel & entertainment.
First published 1961
Book Use: Monthly reviews & occasional excerpts
Frequency: Monthly
Avg pages per issue: 350
Circulation: 140,000 paid
$14.99/yr, $28/2 yrs, $40/3 yrs print only; $9.99/yr, $18/2 yrs, $27/3 yrs digital only; $19.99/yr, $32/2 yrs, $43/3 yrs print & digital
Trim Size: 8 x 10 1/2

Los Angeles Times
2300 E Imperial Hwy, El Segundo, CA 90245
Tel: 213-237-5000 *Fax:* 213-237-3535
E-mail: customerservice@latimes.com
Web Site: www.latimes.com
Key Personnel
Exec Chmn: Patrick Soon-Shiong, MD
Publr & CEO: Chris Argentieri
Exec Ed: Norman Pearlstine
Mng Ed: Scott Kraft
Deputy Mng Ed: Julia Turner
Book Club Ed: Donna Wares
Books Ed: Boris Kachka
Daily newspaper with reviews daily & Sunday.
Reviews in-house, by freelancers & by syndication.
First published 1881
Frequency: Daily
Circulation: 1,253,849 (Sun); 907,997 (Mon-Sat)
Digital & print: $4/wk (Sun only), $15/wk (Mon-Sun); digital only: $6.93/wk

Lubbock Avalanche-Journal
Published by GateHouse Media LLC
710 Avenue "J", Lubbock, TX 79401
Tel: 806-762-8844
Web Site: www.lubbockonline.com
Key Personnel
Mng Ed: Adam Young *Tel:* 806-766-8717
E-mail: ayoung@lubbockonline.com
Daily in Arts Section; book reviews; in-house & through syndication; occasional author interviews.
Circulation: 68,000 (d); 79,000 (Sun)
Digital & print: $12.95/4 wks (Sun only), $14.95/4 wks (Fri-Sun), $22.75/4 wks (Mon-Sun); digital only: $9.99/mo, $78.87/yr

The Magazine Antiques
Published by Brant Publications Inc
315 W 36 St, New York, NY 10018
Tel: 646-992-3840 *Toll Free Tel:* 800-925-9271 (subns)
E-mail: tmacustserv@cdsfulfillment.com; tmaedit@themagazineantiques.com
Web Site: www.themagazineantiques.com
Key Personnel
Publr: Don Sparacin *Tel:* 646-992-3857
E-mail: don@themagazineantiques.com
Mng Ed: Katherine Lanza
Sr Ed: Sammy Dalati
Ed: Gregory Cerio
Features furniture, painting, sculpture, prints, glass & textiles. Columns discuss current exhibitions, recent museum acquisitions & book reviews.
First published 1922
Book Use: Book reviews
Frequency: 6 issues/yr
Avg pages per issue: 151
Circulation: 30,000
$24.95/yr, $58.80/yr CN, $69.95/yr intl
ISSN: 0161-9284
Buy freelance nonfiction; Sell articles, ad reprints & back issues
Trim Size: 8 1/2 x 10 7/8
Ad Rates: 4-color page $4,230
Ad Closing Date(s): 25th of month 2 months previous to publishing date

The Magazine of Fantasy & Science Fiction
Published by Spilogale Inc
PO Box 3447, Hoboken, NJ 07030
Tel: 201-876-2551 *Fax:* 201-876-2551
E-mail: fandsf@aol.com
Web Site: www.fandsf.com
Key Personnel
Publr: Gordon Van Gelder
Asst Publr: Barbara J Norton
Ed: C C Finlay
Fantasy & science fiction; regular departments on science, film, television, cartoons, short stories.

Accepted unsol mss typed on clean white bond, double-spaced, with 1-inch margins. Put your name on each page & include SASE or submit online at submissions.ccfinlay.com/fsf. Do not accept simultaneous submissions.
First published 1949
Book Use: Reviews & serialized novels
Frequency: 6 issues/yr
Avg pages per issue: 260
Circulation: 30,000 paid
$8.99/issue, $53.94/yr, $67.94/yr foreign
ISSN: 0024-984X
Buy freelance fiction, nonfiction, poetry, art & cartoons; Sell back issues
Avg reviews per issue: 2 book review columns/issue
Trim Size: 5 1/4 x 7 5/8
Ad Rates: B&W page $1,310, 4-color back cover (no 4 only) $3,575
Ad Closing Date(s): 20th of 3rd month preceding publication. Nov/Dec issue published Nov 1, closes Aug 20

Mansfield News Journal
Published by Gannett Co Inc
70 W Fourth St, Mansfield, OH 44903
Tel: 419-522-3311 *Toll Free Tel:* 877-424-0216 (cust serv)
Web Site: www.mansfieldnewsjournal.com
Key Personnel
Ed: David Yonke *E-mail:* dyonke@gannett.com
Syndicate & in-house; weekly column; occasional rare author interviews.
Circulation: 36,000 (d); 48,700 (Sun)
Digital & print: $15/mo (Thurs-Sun), $23/mo (Mon-Sun); digital only: $9.99/mo

Marietta Daily Journal
Published by Times-Journal Inc
47 Waddell St SE, Marietta, GA 30060
Mailing Address: PO Box 449, Marietta, GA 30061
Tel: 770-428-9411; 770-795-5000 *Fax:* 770-422-9533
E-mail: mdjnews@mdjonline.com; customerservice@mdjonline.com
Web Site: www.mdjonline.com
Key Personnel
Publr: Otis Brumby, III *E-mail:* otis@mdjonline.com
VP, Content: J K Murphy *Tel:* 770-428-9411 ext 207 *E-mail:* jkmurphy@mdjonline.com
Gen Mgr: Lee B Garrett *Tel:* 770-428-9411 ext 301 *E-mail:* lgarrett@mdjonline.com
Sr Ed: Jon Gillooly *Tel:* 770-428-9411 ext 211 *E-mail:* jgillooly@mdjonline.com
Features Ed: Katy Ruth Camp *Tel:* 770-428-9411 ext 222 *E-mail:* krcamp@mdjonline.com
Occasional book reviews.
Circulation: 20,000 (d); 21,000 (Sun)
$9.99/mo

Marin Independent Journal
Published by MediaNews Group Inc
4000 Civic Center Dr, Suite 301, San Raphael, CA 94903
Tel: 415-883-8600 *Fax:* 415-382-7209
E-mail: calendar@marinij.com
Web Site: www.marinij.com
Key Personnel
Lifestyles Ed: Vicki Larson *Tel:* 415-382-7286
E-mail: lifestyles@marinij.com
In-house & through syndication. Frequent Marin author interviews.
First published 1861
Circulation: 40,000 (e)
Digital & print: $52/13 wks (Sun only), $96/8 wks (Thurs-Sun), $112/8 wks (Mon-Sun); digital only: $9.95/mo

Medford Mail Tribune
Published by Rosebud Media LLC

111 N Fir St, Medford, OR 97501
Mailing Address: PO Box 1108, Medford, OR 97501-0229
Tel: 541-776-4411 *Fax:* 541-776-4376
E-mail: news@mailtribune.com
Web Site: www.mailtribune.com
Key Personnel
Ed-in-Chief: Cathy Noah *Tel:* 541-776-4464
E-mail: cnoah@mailtribune.com
Occasional local author interviews.

Men's Journal
Published by American Media Inc
4 New York Plaza, New York, NY 10004
Tel: 212-484-1616 *Toll Free Tel:* 800-677-6367 (cust serv) *Fax:* 212-484-3429
Web Site: www.mensjournal.com
Key Personnel
Chief Content Offr: Greg Emmanuel
Chief Revenue Offr: Jay Gallagher *Tel:* 212-484-1799 *E-mail:* jay.gallagher@mensjournal.com
Men's magazine for sports, travel, fitness & adventure.
First published 1992
Frequency: Monthly
Circulation: 1,000,000
$24.95/2 yrs print or digital
ISSN: 1063-4657
Trim Size: 8 1/4 x 10 7/8
Ad Rates: B&W full page $183,465, 1/2 page $110,090; 4-color full page $204,685, 1/2 page $122,325

The Miami Herald
Published by The McClatchy Co
3511 NW 91 Ave, Miami, FL 33172
Tel: 305-350-2111 *Toll Free Tel:* 800-843-4372 (subns)
Web Site: www.miamiherald.com
Key Personnel
Pres & Publr: Aminda "Mindy" Marques Gonzales *Tel:* 305-376-3429
Mng Ed: Rick Hirsch *Tel:* 305-376-3504
Features Ed: Kendall Hamersly *Tel:* 305-376-3667
E-mail: khamersly@miamiherald.com
Book pages in "Sunday in South Florida" section; in-house, syndicate & other sources, frequent author interviews & book features; Friday children's book feature.
First published 1903
Circulation: 450,000 (d); 550,000 (Sun)
Digital & print: $83.46/13 wks (Thurs-Sun), $111.28/13 wks (Mon-Sun); digital only: $12.99/mo, $129.99/yr

Michigan Quarterly Review
Published by University of Michigan
0576 Rackham Bldg, 915 E Washington St, Ann Arbor, MI 48109-1070
Tel: 734-764-9265
E-mail: mqr@umich.edu
Web Site: www.michiganquarterlyreview.com
Key Personnel
Mng Ed: Vicki Lawrence
Ed: Jonathan Freedman
Journal of literature & the humanities.
First published 1962
Frequency: Quarterly
Avg pages per issue: 200
Circulation: 1,000
$7/issue, $9/spec issue
ISSN: 0026-2420 (print); 1558-7266 (online)
Avg reviews per issue: 1
Trim Size: 6 x 9
Ad Rates: Full page $200, 1/2 page $100, inside cover $300, back cover $350
Ad Closing Date(s): Nov 15, March 15, May 15 & Aug 15

The Middletown Press
Published by Hearst Newspapers
Division of Hearst Corp
100 Gando Dr, New Haven, CT 06513

Tel: 860-347-3331
E-mail: editor@middletownpress.com
Web Site: www.middletownpress.com
Key Personnel
Mng Ed: Cassandra Day *Tel:* 860-685-9125
 E-mail: cassandra.day@hearstmediact.com
Daily, in-house syndication; locally oriented book
 reviews in Weekend section.
Frequency: Daily
Circulation: 8,500 (d); 21,038 (Sun)
$3/wk digital

Milwaukee Journal/Sentinel
Published by Gannett Co Inc
PO Box 371, Milwaukee, WI 53201
Tel: 414-224-2000 *Toll Free Tel:* 844-900-7103
 (cust serv) *Fax:* 414-224-2133
E-mail: jsfeat@journalsentinel.com;
 milwaukeejournalsentinel@gannett.com
Web Site: www.jsonline.com
Key Personnel
SVP & Ed: George Stanley *Tel:* 414-224-2248
 E-mail: george.stanley@jrn.com
Book reviews & occasional author interviews.
Circulation: 220,000 (e); 490,000 (Sun)
$9.99/mo digital

Moberly Monitor-Index
218 N Williams St, Moberly, MO 65270
Tel: 660-263-4123 *Fax:* 660-263-3626
Web Site: www.moberlymonitor.com
Key Personnel
Publr: Mike Murphy
First published 1869
Frequency: Daily
Avg pages per issue: 14
Circulation: 3,000 (d)
$14.73/mo
Ad Closing Date(s): 9 AM 2 days before publica-
 tion

The Modesto Bee
Published by The McClatchy Co
948 11 St, 3rd fl, Modesto, CA 95354
Tel: 209-578-2000 *Toll Free Tel:* 800-776-4233
E-mail: customerservice@modbee.com
Web Site: modbee.com
Key Personnel
Gen Mgr & VP, Ad: Tim Ritchey *Tel:* 209-578-
 2040 *E-mail:* tritchey@modbee.com
Ed: Brian Clark *Tel:* 209-578-2362
 E-mail: bclark@modbee.com
Infrequently, Sundays. In-house & through syndi-
 cation. Occasional author interviews.
First published 1884
Circulation: 60,595 (d); 72,680 (Sun)
Digital & print: $49.10/13 wks (Wed & Sun),
 $63.13/13 wks (Fri-Sun), $84.17/13 wks (Mon-
 Sun); digital only: $12.99/mo, $129.99/yr

Moment Magazine
Published by The Center for Creative Change
4115 Wisconsin Ave NW, Suite LL10, Washing-
 ton, DC 20016
Tel: 202-363-6422 *Toll Free Tel:* 800-777-1005
 (cust serv) *Fax:* 202-362-2514
E-mail: editor@momentmag.com
Web Site: www.momentmag.com
Key Personnel
Ed-in-Chief & CEO: Nadine Epstein
Focuses on Jewish life, including social, religion,
 political science, history, arts & lifestyle. No
 unsol mss, query first.
First published 1975
Book Use: Reviews; author interviews
Frequency: 6 issues/yr
Avg pages per issue: 80
Circulation: 90,000 print/mo
$17.97/yr, $29.97/2 yrs
ISSN: 0099-0280
Sell back issues
Trim Size: 8 1/8 x 10 1/2

Ad Rates: Full page $3,640. Discounts for univer-
 sity presses
Ad Closing Date(s): 5th of month preceding issue

Monadnock Ledger-Transcript
Published by Newspapers of New England (NNE)
20 Grove St, Peterborough, NH 03458
Mailing Address: PO Box 36, Peterborough, NH
 03458-0036
Tel: 603-924-7172 *Fax:* 603-924-3681
E-mail: news@ledgertranscript.com
Web Site: www.ledgertranscript.com
Key Personnel
Publr: Heather McKernan *Tel:* 603-924-7172 ext
 222 *E-mail:* hmckernan@ledgertranscript.com
Ed: Ben Conant *Tel:* 603-924-7172 ext 226
 E-mail: bconant@ledgertranscript.com
Reviews for weekly paper. Book reviews in-
 house. Occasionally author interviews; only
 review books with a local connection (i.e. local
 authors, books about the local area or writing
 authors involved in a local reading).
Frequency: 2 issues/wk (Tues & Thurs)
Digital & print: $8.04/mo (in state mail), $11.49/
 mo (out of state mail); digital only: $5.99/mo

The Montgomery Advertiser
Published by Gannett Co Inc
425 Molton St, Montgomery, AL 36104
Tel: 334-262-1611 *Toll Free Tel:* 877-424-0007
 (subns)
E-mail: newstips@montgomeryadvertiser.com
Web Site: www.montgomeryadvertiser.com
Key Personnel
Exec Ed: Bro Krift *E-mail:* bkrift@
 montgomeryadvertiser.com
Sunday page, in-house, syndicated & by other
 sources; occasional author interviews.
First published 1829
Full access $20/mo (Mon-Sun), $18/mo (Wed-
 Sun), $10/mo (Sun & Wed) or digital only

Montreal Gazette
Published by Postmedia Network Inc
1010 Sainte-Catherine St W, Suite 200, Montreal,
 QC H3B 5L1, Canada
Tel: 514-987-2222; 514-987-2400 (reader sales &
 serv) *Toll Free Tel:* 800-361-8478 (ext 2400,
 reader sales & serv) *Fax:* 514-987-2640
E-mail: letters@thegazette.canwest.com
Web Site: montrealgazette.com
Key Personnel
Mng Ed: Basem Boshra *Tel:* 514-987-2628
 E-mail: bboshra@postmedia.com
Deputy Mng Ed: Jeff Blond *Tel:* 514-987-2486
 E-mail: jblond@postmedia.com
Ed: Lucinda Chodan *Tel:* 514-987-2508
 E-mail: lchodan@postmedia.com
Monthly tabloid, in-house, syndication & free-
 lancers, author interviews.
First published 1778
Frequency: Daily (Mon-Sat)
Avg pages per issue: 16
Circulation: 140,000 (m); 170,000 (Sat); 135,000
 (Sun)
Digital only: $9.95/mo; e-paper: $9.99/mo; digital
 & print: $18/mo (Sat only), $30/mo (Mon-Sat)

The Morning Call
Published by The Morning Call Inc
Subsidiary of Tribune Publishing Co
101 N Sixth St, Allentown, PA 18101
Mailing Address: PO Box 1260, Allentown, PA
 18105
Tel: 610-820-6566 *Fax:* 610-820-6693
E-mail: news@mcall.com
Web Site: www.mcall.com
Key Personnel
Ed-in-Chief: Theresa Rang *E-mail:* terry.rang@
 mcall.com
Content Ed, Entertainment & Life: Craig Larimer
 E-mail: clarimer@mcall.com

Sunday, in-house & by freelancers, feature occa-
 sional local author interviews.
First published 1883
Frequency: Daily
Circulation: 79,726 (d); 127,517 (Sat); 187,000
 (Sun)
Digital & print: $2.49/wk (Sun only), $4.99/wk
 (Mon-Sun); digital only: $1.99/wk
Avg reviews per issue: 3

Morning Times
Published by Morning Times Inc
201 N Lehigh Ave, Sayre, PA 18840
Tel: 570-888-9643 *Fax:* 570-888-6463
E-mail: editor@morning-times.com
Web Site: www.morning-times.com
Key Personnel
Publr: Kelly Luvison *E-mail:* kluvison@morning-
 times.com
Mng Ed: Pat McDonald
Daily newspaper, book reviews weekly, in-house
 syndicated & other sources.
First published 1891
Frequency: Daily
Circulation: 10,000
Online only: $2/day, $15/mo, $24/3 mos, $79/yr;
 home delivery: $40/13 wks, $79/26 wks,
 $142/yr; mail delivery: $50/13 wks, $100/26
 wks, $195/yr

Mother Earth News
Published by Ogden Publications Inc
1503 SW 42 St, Topeka, KS 66609-1265
Tel: 785-274-4300 *Toll Free Tel:* 800-234-3368
 Fax: 785-274-4305
E-mail: letters@motherearthnews.com
Web Site: www.motherearthnews.com
Key Personnel
Publr: Bill Uhler
Sustainable living magazine containing articles
 of interest to active, educated people inter-
 ested in self-sufficiency through renewable
 energy sources & lifestyles, with articles on
 ecology, do-it-yourself projects, gardening, nat-
 ural health, green transportation, modern home-
 steading, sustainable farming & real food.
First published 1970
Frequency: Semimonthly
Circulation: 500,000 paid
$4.95/issue, $17/yr, $27/yr CN, $32/yr foreign
ISSN: 0027-1535
Buy freelance nonfiction & art; Sell articles,
 reprints & back issues
Trim Size: 8 x 10 1/2
Ad Rates: B&W page $24,500, 4-color page
 $35,000
Ad Closing Date(s): Jan 22, March 19, May 21,
 July 23, Sept 17

Mother Jones
Published by Foundation for National Progress
222 Sutter St, Suite 600, San Francisco, CA
 94108
Mailing Address: PO Box 584, San Francisco,
 CA 94104-0584
Tel: 415-321-1700 *Toll Free Tel:* 800-438-6656
E-mail: backtalk@motherjones.com (comments to
 ed)
Web Site: www.motherjones.com
Key Personnel
CEO: Monika Bauerlein
Publr: Steven Katz
Ed-in-Chief: Clara Jeffery
Investigative reporting, national political news,
 features on important contemporary issues &
 commentary.
First published 1976
Book Use: Reviews & excerpts for a well-
 educated, affluent, politically liberal audience
Frequency: 6 issues/yr
Avg pages per issue: 100
Circulation: 200,000 paid

Print only: $12/yr US, $27/yr CN, $32/yr intl; print & digital: $18/yr US, $33/yr CN, $38/yr intl; digital only: $12/yr
ISSN: 0362-8841
Buy nonfiction, art & cartoons; Sell articles & reprints, back issues
Trim Size: 8 x 10 1/2
Ad Rates: B&W page $10,595, 4-color page $14,125

The Nation
Published by The Nation Co LP
520 Eighth Ave, 21st fl, New York, NY 10018
Tel: 212-209-5400 *Toll Free Tel:* 800-333-8536 (cust serv) *Fax:* 212-982-9000
E-mail: thenation@email.customerservice.com
Web Site: www.thenation.com
Subscription Address: PO Box 433308, Palm Coast, FL 32143-9537
Key Personnel
Pres: Erin O'Mara
Publr & Edit Dir: Katrina Vanden Heuvel
Assoc Publr, Consumer Mktg: Katelyn Belyus
Assoc Publr, Ad: Tim Johnson
Ed: D D Guttenplan
Literary Ed: David Marcus
Ed-at-Large: John Palatella
Circ: Vivian Gomez
Politics, arts, foreign affairs, education & law.
First published 1865
Book Use: Reviews (John Palatella)
Frequency: Weekly & semiweekly during summer - 34 issues/yr
Avg pages per issue: 40
Circulation: 141,375
$4.99/issue, $89/yr, $139/2 yrs, add $26 postage CN, add $59 other
ISSN: 0027-8378
Buy nonfiction, poetry & art (no fiction); Sell back issues
Trim Size: 8 1/4 x 10 7/8
Ad Rates: B&W page $8,640, 4-color page $12,100
Ad Closing Date(s): Call for schedule or visit www.thenation.com/mediakit

National Defense Magazine
Published by National Defense Industrial Association (NDIA)
2101 Wilson Blvd, Suite 700, Arlington, VA 22201-3061
Tel: 703-522-1820
Web Site: www.nationaldefensemagazine.org
Key Personnel
Ed-in-Chief: Stew Magnuson *Tel:* 703-247-2545
E-mail: smagnuson@ndia.org
Mng Ed: Jon Harper *Tel:* 703-247-2542
E-mail: jharper@ndia.org
Creative Dir: Brian Taylor *Tel:* 703-247-2546
E-mail: btaylor@ndia.org
Sales Dir: Kathleen Kenney *Tel:* 703-247-2576
E-mail: kkenney@ndia.org
Technical, military & management articles & departments for military & industrial audience, including those in federal government. North American industrial base, acquisition officers in industry & military. No unsol mss, query first.
First published 1920
Frequency: Monthly
Circulation: total qualified 83,768; qualified paid 56,412
$5/issue, $40/yr, $45/yr foreign
ISSN: 0092-1491
Sell articles, ad reprints & back issues
Ad Rates: B&W page $6,665, 4-color page $8,580
Ad Closing Date(s): 8th of month preceding cover date

National Post
Published by Postmedia Network Inc

365 Bloor St E, 3rd fl, Toronto, ON M4W 3L4, Canada
Tel: 416-383-2300 *Toll Free Tel:* 800-267-6568
Fax: 416-383-2305
Web Site: nationalpost.com
Key Personnel
SVP, Content (Natl Post): Gerry Nott
Exec Prod, Features: Dustin Parks
E-mail: dparks@postmedia.com
Ed-in-Chief: Anne Marie Owens
Books Ed: Paul Taunton *Tel:* 416-645-8816
E-mail: ptaunton@postmedia.com

National Review
Published by National Review Inc
19 W 44 St, Suite 1701, New York, NY 10036
Tel: 212-679-7330 *Toll Free Tel:* 800-464-5526 (cust serv)
E-mail: letters@nationalreview.com
Web Site: www.nationalreview.com
Subscription Address: PO Box 433015, Palm Coast, FL 32143-3015
Key Personnel
Publr: E Garrett Bewkes, IV
Sales Dir: Jim Fowler *Tel:* 212-849-2843
E-mail: jfowler@nationalreview.com
Mng Ed: Jason Lee Steorts
Ed: Richard Lowry
Literary Ed: Katherine Howell
Conservative opinion; reports & analyzes national & international developments; includes: articles, editorials, social commentary, book & movie reviews & arts & manners.
First published 1955
Book Use: Reviews, commentary
Frequency: 24 issues/yr
Avg pages per issue: 64
Circulation: 160,000 paid
$59.99/yr print, $99/yr digital, $130/yr print & digital
ISSN: 0028-0038
Buy freelance fiction, nonfiction, poetry, art & cartoons; Sell back issues & reprints
Trim Size: 8 1/4 x 10 3/4
Ad Rates: B&W page $8,640, 4-color page $12,100
Ad Closing Date(s): 4 weeks preceding cover date

National Wildlife
Published by National Wildlife Federation
11100 Wildlife Center Dr, Reston, VA 20190-5362
Tel: 703-438-6000 *Toll Free Tel:* 800-822-9919 (membership); 800-611-1599 (children's)
Fax: 703-438-6544
E-mail: moore@nwf.org
Web Site: www.nwf.org
Key Personnel
Edit Dir & Ed: Lisa Moore
Dir, Communs: Miles Grant *E-mail:* grantm@nwf.org
Nature & environment for a general audience.
First published 1962
Book Use: Occasional excerpts
Frequency: 6 issues/yr
Avg pages per issue: 52
Circulation: 450,000 paid
Donation basis
ISSN: 0028-0402
Buy freelance, art & nonfiction; Sell back issues
Trim Size: 8 5/8 x 10 7/8

Nature
Published by Springer Nature
One New York Plaza, Suite 4500, New York, NY 10004-1562
Tel: 212-726-9200 *Toll Free Tel:* 888-331-6288
Fax: 212-696-9006
E-mail: feedback@nature.com
Web Site: www.nature.com

Subscription Address: Hampshire Intl Busn Park, Cromwell Place, Lime Tree Way, Basingstoke, Hants RG24 8YJ, United Kingdom
E-mail: subscriptions@nature.com
Key Personnel
VP, Magazines & Edit: Stephen Pincock
Ed-in-Chief: Magdalena Skipper
Mng Dir: Dean Sanderson
Sr Ed, Biology: Noah Gray
Books & Arts Ed: Barbara Kiser
Journal of original scientific research articles & letters, review articles, news of science in universities, industry & government; book reviews, correspondence & opinion. Available in print & online.
First published 1869
Book Use: Weekly review section
Frequency: 51 issues/yr
Circulation: 65,500 paid
Print & online: $199/yr indivs, $119/yr students
ISSN: 0028-0836 (print); 1476-4687 (online)
Sell articles, ad reprints & back issues
Trim Size: 8 1/4 x 11
Ad Rates: B&W page $12,015, 4-color page $14,410
Ad Closing Date(s): Film & camera ready material - 17 days prior to cover date

Nevada Magazine
Division of Nevada Department of Tourism & Cultural Affairs
401 N Carson St, Carson City, NV 89701
Tel: 775-687-0610 *Toll Free Tel:* 855-729-7117
Fax: 775-687-6159
E-mail: editor@nevadamagazine.com
Web Site: nevadamagazine.com
Key Personnel
Publr: Janet M Geary *Tel:* 775-687-0603
E-mail: jmgeary@nevadamagazine.com
Art Dir: Kippy Spilker *Tel:* 775-687-0606
E-mail: kspilker@nevadamagazine.com
Ed: Megg Mueller *Tel:* 775-687-0602
E-mail: mmueller@nevadamagazine.com
Ad & Mktg Mgr: Adele Hoppe *Tel:* 775-687-0605 *E-mail:* ahoppe@nevadamagazine.com
Circ Mgr: Carrie Roussel *Tel:* 775-687-0610
E-mail: carrie@nevadamagazine.com
For Nevada tourists & residents. Focuses on travel, recreation, Nevada dining, nature & entertainment.
First published 1936
Book Use: Reviews & excerpts on Nevada topics
Frequency: 6 issues/yr
Avg pages per issue: 80
Circulation: 20,000 paid
$9.95/yr digital, $21.95/yr print, $26.95/yr print & digital
ISSN: 0199-1248
Buy nonfiction; Sell back issues
Trim Size: 8 3/8 x 10 7/8
Ad Rates: 4-color page $4,000
Ad Closing Date(s): 1-2 months prior to issue

The New Criterion
Published by The Foundation for Cultural Review Inc
900 Broadway, Suite 602, New York, NY 10003
Tel: 212-247-6980 *Fax:* 212-247-3127
Web Site: www.newcriterion.com
Subscription Address: PO Box 3000, Denville, NJ 07834 *Toll Free Tel:* 800-783-4903
Key Personnel
Publr & Ed: Roger Kimball
Exec Ed: James Panero
Contains literary & cultural essays & poetry.
First published 1982
Book Use: Reviews
Frequency: Monthly (exc July & Aug)
Avg pages per issue: 80
Circulation: 7,000 paid
$7.75/issue, $48/yr, $62/yr CN, $70/yr foreign
ISSN: 0734-0222

Sell back issues ($12)
Ad Closing Date(s): 10th of each month prior to issue date

New Hampshire Sunday News & Union Leader
Published by Union Leader Corp
100 William Loeb Dr, Manchester, NH 03108-9555
Mailing Address: PO Box 9555, Manchester, NH 03108-9555
Tel: 603-668-4321
E-mail: news@unionleader.com
Web Site: www.unionleader.com
Key Personnel
Publr: Joe McQuaid *Tel:* 603-668-4321 ext 554
    E-mail: publisher@unionleader.com
Mng Ed: Matt Sartwell *E-mail:* msartwell@unionleader.com
Exec Ed: Trent Spiner *E-mail:* tspiner@unionleader.com
HR Mgr: Sarah Neveu *Tel:* 603-668-4321 ext 296
    E-mail: sneveu@unionleader.com
PR Mgr: Stephanie Baxter *Tel:* 603-668-4321 ext 506 *E-mail:* sbaxter@unionleader.com
Travel articles, building & repair sections; book reviews, arts & entertainment all in separate sections on Sunday. Looking for freelance articles.
First published 1863
Circulation: 90,000 (Sun)
$14.95/mo

New Haven Register
Published by Hearst Newspapers
Division of Hearst Corp
100 Gando Dr, New Haven, CT 06513
Tel: 203-789-5200 *Toll Free Tel:* 888-969-0949
    Fax: 203-789-5705
E-mail: subscriptions@nhregister.com
Web Site: www.nhregister.com
Key Personnel
Exec Ed: Helen Bennett Harvey *Tel:* 203-789-5730 *E-mail:* helen.bennett@hearstmediact.com
Asst Mng Ed: Viktoria Sundqvist *Tel:* 860-685-9130 *E-mail:* viktoria.sundqvist@hearstmediact.com
Syndicated Sunday in *Arts & Leisure* section; in-house & weekly author interviews.
Circulation: 80,000 (m); 110,000 (Sun)
Digital & print: $2.99/wk (Sun only), $7.99/wk (Mon-Sun); digital only: $3/wk

New Living
PO Box 1001, Patchogue, NY 11772
Tel: 631-751-8819
Web Site: www.newliving.com
Key Personnel
Publr & Ed-in-Chief: Christine Lynn Harvey
    E-mail: charvey@newliving.com
Holistic health & fitness.
In-house, syndicated, feature author bylined articles promoting author's book (only health & fitness related topics).
First published 1991
Frequency: Monthly
Avg pages per issue: 24
Circulation: 100,000
Ad Rates: B&W page $1,195l 4-color $1,295 (for additional ad rates, see web site)
Ad Closing Date(s): 15th of month prior to issue date

New Mexico Magazine
Published by State of New Mexico
Lew Wallace Bldg, 495 Old Santa Fe Trail, Santa Fe, NM 87501
Tel: 505-827-7447 *Toll Free Tel:* 800-898-6639
    (subns only)
E-mail: ask@nmmagazine.com; nm.magazine@state.nm.us
Web Site: www.newmexico.com/nmmagazine

Subscription Address: PO Box 12002, Sante Fe, NM 87504-9794
Key Personnel
Mng Ed & Soc Media Dir: Kate Nelson *Tel:* 505-476-0203 *E-mail:* kate.nelson@state.nm.us
Exec Ed: John Clary Davies *Tel:* 505-231-3759
    E-mail: john.davies@state.nm.us
Sr Ed: Alicia Ines Guzman *Tel:* 505-490-0284
    E-mail: alicia.guzman@state.nm.us
Circ Mgr: Kurt Coey *Tel:* 505-827-6387
    E-mail: kurt.coey@state.nm.us
Stories & color photography on people, places, events, history, prehistory, art, architecture & food of interest to residents, visitors & students of the Southwest & New Mexico. No unsol mss, query first.
First published 1923
Frequency: Monthly
Avg pages per issue: 78
Circulation: 70,000
$25.95/yr, $45.95/yr CN & foreign
ISSN: 0028-6249
Buy fiction, nonfiction; Sell back issues
Trim Size: 8 1/4 x 10 3/4
Ad Closing Date(s): 2 months preceding publication

The New Orleans Advocate, see The Times-Picayune | The New Orleans Advocate

The New Republic
Published by Lake Avenue Publishing
One Union Sq W, New York, NY 10003
Tel: 646-779-8000 *Toll Free Tel:* 800-827-1289
    (cust serv)
E-mail: letters@tnr.com (ms & letters to ed submissions); poetry@tnr.com (poetry submissions)
Web Site: newrepublic.com
Key Personnel
Publr: Kerrie Gillis *E-mail:* kgillis@newrepublic.com
Edit Dir: Emily Cooke *E-mail:* emily@newrepublic.com
Ed-in-Chief: Win McCormack
Mng Ed: Lorraine Cademartori
    E-mail: lcademartori@newrepublic.com
Ed: Chris Lehmann *E-mail:* clehmann@newrepublic.com
Journal of opinion which includes literary criticism as well as arts & culture.
First published 1914
Book Use: Reviews
Frequency: 10 issues/yr
Avg pages per issue: 44
Circulation: 40,000 paid
$20/yr digital, $30/yr print & digital
ISSN: 0028-6583
Buy nonfiction, poetry & art; Sell articles & ad reprints, back issues (syndicated)
Trim Size: 8 x 10 1/2
Ad Rates: B&W full page $6,340, 4-color full page $9,060
Ad Closing Date(s): 4 weeks preceding cover dates, see web site

New Spanish Books
Published by Trade Commission in Miami, Embassy of Spain in the US
2655 Le Juene Rd, Suite 1114, Miami, FL 33134
Tel: 305-446-4387 *Fax:* 305-446-2602
E-mail: info@newspanishbooks.com
Web Site: www.newspanishbooks.us
Annual online compilation/guide to current Spanish titles, selected by a panel of experts from the US, with rights available for translation in the US. Includes up-to-date information about the Spanish publishing scene, translation grants, Spanish literary prizes, recent translations, news & events in the US & more.

New York Daily News, see Daily News

New York Magazine
Published by New York Media LLC
75 Varick St, 4th fl, New York, NY 10013
Tel: 212-508-0700 *Toll Free Tel:* 800-678-0900
    (subns)
E-mail: contactus@nymag.com
Web Site: nymag.com
Key Personnel
Mng Ed: Anne Clarke
Prodn Coord: Gail Smith *E-mail:* gail.smith@nymag.com
Book Critic: Christian Lorentzen
Literary Critic: Molly Young
Biweekly. Deals with contemporary lifestyles & personalities in the New York metropolitan area. Covers politics, business, fine arts, entertainment, home furnishings, food, wine & fashion.
First published 1968
Frequency: 29 issues/yr
Avg pages per issue: 140
Circulation: 378,757
$5/mo digital, $70/yr print & digital
ISSN: 0028-7369
Buy art, nonfiction; Sell articles & back issues
Trim Size: 7 7/8 x 10 1/2
Ad Rates: See web site
Ad Closing Date(s): 2 weeks prior to on sale date

New York Post Inc
Published by NYP Holdings Inc
Division of Newscorp
1211 Avenue of the Americas, New York, NY 10036-8790
Tel: 212-930-8000 *Toll Free Tel:* 800-552-7678
    (cust serv)
E-mail: slareau@nypost.com
Web Site: www.nypost.com
Key Personnel
Group VP, Ad: Patrick Judge
Natl Ad: Scott Lareau *E-mail:* slareau@nypost.com
Reviews in-house, through syndication & other outside sources.
Circulation: 428,238 (d)
$2.50/wk (Sat & Sun or Fri-Sun), $4.99/wk (Mon-Fri or Mon-Sun)

The New York Review of Books
Published by NYREV Inc
435 Hudson St, Suite 300, New York, NY 10014-3994
Tel: 212-757-8070 *Fax:* 212-333-5374
E-mail: mail@nybooks.com
Web Site: www.nybooks.com
Subscription Address: PO Box 9310, Big Sandy, TX 75755-9310 *Toll Free Tel:* 800-354-0050
    E-mail: nyrsub@nybooks.info *Web Site:* www.nybooks.com
Key Personnel
Publr: Mr Rea S Hederman
Exec Ed: Jana Prikryl
Sr Ed: Hugh Eakin; Gabriel Winslow-Yost
Ed: Emily Greenhouse
Prodn Ed: Daniel Drake
Ed-at-Large: Daniel Mendelsohn
Assoc Ed: Maya Chung
Off Mgr: Diane Seltzer *E-mail:* dseltzer@nybooks.com
Literary journal. Articles by American & European writers.
First published 1963
Book Use: Essay-length book reviews
Frequency: 20 issues/yr
Avg pages per issue: 64
Circulation: 134,503
$8.95/issue, $74.95/yr
ISSN: 0028-7504
Sell $15/back issue within the US, $25/back issue outside the US
Trim Size: 10 3/4 x 14 5/8

Ad Rates: B&W page $13,775, 4-color page $15,841
Ad Closing Date(s): 37 days prior to cover date

The New York Times
Published by The New York Times Co
620 Eighth Ave, New York, NY 10018
Tel: 212-556-1234 *Toll Free Tel:* 800-698-4637 (cust serv)
E-mail: books@nytimes.com
Web Site: www.nytimes.com
Key Personnel
Exec Ed: Dean Baquet
Deputy Ed, News & Features: Andrew LaVallee
Sr Staff Ed: Lauren Christensen
Children's Book Ed: Jennifer Krauss
Op-Ed Ed: Jim Dao
Asst Ed: John Williams
Nonfiction Critic: Jennifer Ildiko Szalai
Daily column; Sunday section.
Circulation: 1,718,400 (Sun)
Digital & print: $10/wk (Sat & Sun), $11/wk (Fri-Sun), $12/wk (Mon-Fri), $18/wk (Mon-Sun); digital only: $4/mo

The New York Times Book Review
Published by The New York Times Co
620 Eighth Ave, 5th fl, New York, NY 10018
Tel: 212-556-1234 *Toll Free Tel:* 800-631-2580 (subns)
E-mail: bookreview@nytimes.com; books@nytimes.com
Web Site: www.nytimes.com
Key Personnel
Mng Ed: David Kelly
Deputy Ed: Tina Jordan
Sr Ed: Gregory Cowles
Ed: Pamela Paul
Preview Ed: Dave Kim; Emily Eakin; Elisabeth Egan
Asst Preview Ed: MJ Franklin
Review books & essays related to publishing & published in the US & available through general interest bookstores. By subscription only.
$4/wk US, $4.95/wk CN, $5.50/wk foreign
ISSN: 0028-7806

The New Yorker
Published by Conde Nast
One World Trade Center, 38th fl, New York, NY 10007-0090
Tel: 212-286-2860; 515-243-3273 (subns)
Toll Free Tel: 800-444-7570
E-mail: fiction@newyorker.com (fiction submissions); TNY_shouts@advancemags.com (Shouts & Murmurs submissions)
Web Site: www.newyorker.com; www.condenast.com
Key Personnel
Ed: David Remnick
Poetry Ed: Kevin Young
Staff Writer: Kathryn Schulz; Parul Sehgal; Katy Waldman
Discusses current ideas & events, combining domestic & international news analysis with cartoons, criticism of sports, fashion & arts, biographical profiles, short fiction & poetry. Carries entertainment guide for New York. Send fiction & Shouts & Murmurs submissions by e-mail as noted above. Poetry submissions via Submittable only, see web site. No unsol Talk of the Town stories or other nonfiction. No unsol submissions by fax accepted.
First published 1925
Book Use: Reviews
Frequency: Weekly
Avg pages per issue: 112
Circulation: 1,035,428
$1/wk
ISSN: 0028-792X

Trim Size: 7 7/8 x 10 3/4
Ad Rates: 4-color full page $180,343, 1/2 page $108,169

The News & Observer
Published by The News & Observer Publishing Co
421 Fayetteville St, Suite 104, Raleigh, NC 27601
Tel: 919-829-4500 *Toll Free Tel:* 800-522-4205 (cust serv)
E-mail: customerservice@newsobserver.com
Web Site: www.newsobserver.com
Key Personnel
Mng Ed: Jane Elizabeth *Tel:* 919-836-5909
E-mail: jelizabeth@newsobserver.com
Features Ed: Jessica Banov *Tel:* 919-829-4831
E-mail: jbanov@newsobserver.com
Sunday, two-page review section; column by J Peder Zane; occasional author interviews.
Circulation: 165,000 (m); 205,000 (Sun)
Digital: $12.99/mo, $129.99/yr

News & Record
Published by BH Media Group Inc
200 E Market St, Greensboro, NC 27401
Tel: 336-373-7000; 336-274-5476 (subns)
Toll Free Tel: 800-553-6880
E-mail: feedback@greensboro.com; subscriberservices@greensboro.com
Web Site: www.greensboro.com
Key Personnel
Publr: Alton Brown *Tel:* 336-727-7349
E-mail: abrown@wsjournal.com
Mng Ed: Cindy Loman *Tel:* 336-373-7212
E-mail: cindy.lowman@greensboro.com
Edit Page Ed: Allen Johnson *Tel:* 336-373-7010
E-mail: allen.johnson@greensboro.com
Once a week; occasional author interviews, separate book page. Book reviews in-house, syndicated & through other outside sources.
Circulation: 60,000 (m); 70,000 (Sun)
Digital & print: $11.10/mo (Wed-Sun), $13.23/mo (Sun only), $27.89/mo (Mon-Sun); digital only: $8.95/mo

The News-Star
Published by Gannett Co Inc
411 N Fourth St, Monroe, LA 71201
Tel: 318-322-5161 *Toll Free Tel:* 800-259-7788; 877-424-0036 (cust serv)
Web Site: www.thenewsstar.com
Key Personnel
Ed: Barbara Leader *Tel:* 318-362-0262
Occasional weekly column.
Frequency: Daily
Circulation: 22,000 (d); 26,000 (Sun)
Digital & print: $12/mo (Sun only), $24/mo (Mon-Sun); digital only: $9.99/mo

The News-Times
Published by Hearst Newspapers
Division of Hearst Corp
333 Main St, Danbury, CT 06810
Tel: 203-744-5100 *Fax:* 203-792-8730 (edit)
Web Site: www.newstimes.com
Key Personnel
Features Ed: Linda Tuccio-Koonz *Tel:* 203-731-3330 *E-mail:* lkoonz@newstimes.com
Especially interested in Connecticut authors & women's issues in general. Food trends, local arts, local pop culture, music, theater, home decor & fashion (need Connecticut angle).
Book Use: Book reviews, author interviews; Sunday features, travel, trends, food, cooking
Frequency: Daily
Circulation: 38,000
$3.50/wk digital

The News Tribune
Published by The McClatchy Co
1950 S State St, Tacoma, WA 98405

Tel: 253-597-8742 *Fax:* 253-597-8274
Web Site: www.thenewstribune.com
Key Personnel
Pres & Publr: Rebecca Poynter *Tel:* 253-597-8554
E-mail: rebecca.poynter@thenewstribune.com
Ed & VP, News: Dale Phelps *Tel:* 253-597-8681
E-mail: dale.phelps@thenewstribune.com
Local Sales Dir: Rob White *Tel:* 253-597-8407
E-mail: rob.white@thenewstribune.com
Sunday; book review off the wire & freelance; local columnist who writes book reviews with a national & local focus; literary calendar of book signings; bestseller lists featured.
Circulation: 38,762 (d); 87,332 (Sun)
Digital & print: $26/13 wks (Sun only), $45.50/13 wks (Fri-Sun), $71.50/13 wks (Mon-Sun); digital only: $12.99/mo, $129.99/yr

News Tribune
Published by Central Missouri Newspapers Inc
210 Monroe St, Jefferson City, MO 65101
Tel: 573-636-3131
E-mail: editor@newstribune.com
Web Site: www.newstribune.com
Key Personnel
Mng Ed: Gary Castor *Tel:* 573-761-0255
E-mail: gary@newstribune.com
Frequency: Daily
Circulation: 2,700 (m); 17,000 (e); 24,300 (Sun)
$21/mo print & digital

Newsday
Published by Newsday Media Group
235 Pinelawn Rd, Melville, NY 11747
Tel: 631-843-2700 *Toll Free Tel:* 800-639-7329 (cust care)
Web Site: www.newsday.com
Key Personnel
Ed: Deborah Henley *E-mail:* editor@newsday.com
Sunday review section; weekly author interviews; in-house & freelance.
Circulation: 404,542 (d); 476,723 (Sun)
Digital & print: $1.99 wk (Sun only), $5.99/wk (Mon-Sun); digital only: $3.49/wk

Newsweek
Published by Newsweek Media Group
33 Whitehall St, New York, NY 10004
Tel: 646-867-7100
E-mail: enquiries@newsweek.com; support@newsweek.com
Web Site: www.newsweek.com
Key Personnel
Global Ed-in-Chief: Nancy Cooper
Edit Dir: Hank Gilman
Mng Ed: Melissa Jewsbury
Weekly news magazine, (in print, online & on mobile devices), features news & commentary on the week's developments in the nation & the world. Articles cover national & international affairs, science, sports, business, medicine, religion, entertainment & the arts. International editions also available.
First published 1933
Book Use: Reviews, excerpts
Frequency: Weekly
Avg pages per issue: 105
$99/yr print or digital, $129/yr print & digital
ISSN: 0028-9604
Buy nonfiction, poetry, art, cartoons; Sell articles, ad reprints & back issues
Trim Size: 8 1/8 x 10 1/2

The North Platte Telegraph
Published by BH Media Group Inc
621 N Chestnut St, North Platte, NE 69101
Mailing Address: PO Box 370, North Platte, NE 69103-0370
Tel: 308-532-6000 *Toll Free Tel:* 800-753-7092
Fax: 308-532-9268
E-mail: editor@nptelegraph.com

Web Site: www.nptelegraph.com
Key Personnel
Publr: Dee Klein *Tel:* 308-535-4708
  E-mail: dklein@nptelegraph.com
Mng Ed: Joan von Kampen *Tel:* 308-535-4707
  E-mail: joan.vonkampen@nptelegraph.com
Frequent Western author interviews & book reviews.
Circulation: 8,100
$6.50/mo digital, $22.94/mo digital & print, $35.97/mo digital & print (mail delivery)

Nutrition Health Review
Published by Matrix Medical Communications
1595 Paoli Pike, Suite 201, West Chester, PA 19380
Tel: 464-266-0702 *Toll Free Tel:* 866-325-9975; 866-325-9907 *Fax:* 464-266-0726
E-mail: info@matrixmedcom.com
Web Site: matrixmedicalcommunications.com
Key Personnel
Pres/Group Publr: Robert L Dougherty
VP/Exec Ed: Elizabeth A Klumpff
  E-mail: eklumpp@matrixmedcom.com
Assoc Ed: Angela M Saba
Asst Ed: Frank Hosking, III
Vegetarianism, psychiatry, medicine & health-oriented articles, medical news, nutrition, psychology & food preparation info. No advertising included.
First published 1975
Book Use: Reviews, excerpts
Frequency: Quarterly
Avg pages per issue: 28
Circulation: 265,000 paid
$3/issue, $12/yr, $24/2 yrs, $46/2 yrs foreign
ISSN: 0164-7202
Buy nonfiction, art & cartoons; Sell articles
Trim Size: 11 x 17

Ocala Star-Banner
Published by GateHouse Media LLC
2121 SW 19 Avenue Rd, Ocala, FL 34471
Tel: 352-867-4010 *Toll Free Tel:* 800-541-2172
E-mail: osbletters@starbanner.com
Web Site: www.ocala.com
Key Personnel
Publr: Robin Quillon
Mng Ed: Jim Ross *E-mail:* jim.ross@starbanner.com
Circulation: 45,000
Digital & print: $78/13 wks (Sun only), $143/13 wks (Thurs-Sun), $169/13 wks (Mon-Sun); digital only: $12.95/mo

Ohio Magazine
Published by Great Lakes Publishing
1422 Euclid Ave, Suite 730, Cleveland, OH 44115
Tel: 614-461-5083 (sales); 216-771-2833
  Toll Free Tel: 800-210-7293 (cust care)
E-mail: editorial@ohiomagazine.com
Web Site: www.ohiomagazine.com
Key Personnel
Pres: Lute Harmon, Jr
Assoc Publr & Ad Dir: Karen Matusoff
Dir, Prodn: Steven A Zemanek
Sr Ed: Linda Feagler
Ed: Jim Vickers
Covers general Ohio topics for upscale audience. Occasional stories about Ohio authors.
First published 1978
Book Use: Reviews & excerpts
Frequency: Monthly
Avg pages per issue: 132
Circulation: 52,424
$17.98/yr, $29.97/2 yrs, $38.83/3 yrs
ISSN: 0279-3504
Buy Ohio-related nonfiction, essays & art; Sell articles & back issues

The Oklahoman
Published by Oklahoma Publishing Co
100 W Main, Suite 100, Oklahoma City, OK 73102
Mailing Address: PO Box 25125, Oklahoma City, OK 73125
Tel: 405-475-3311; 405-478-7171 (cust serv)
  Toll Free Tel: 877-987-2737
Web Site: oklahoman.com
Key Personnel
Publr & Ed: Kelly Dyer Fry *E-mail:* kfry@oklahoman.com
Features Ed: Matthew Price *E-mail:* mprice@oklahoman.com
Sunday column & review page; in-house; occasional author interviews.
Circulation: 226,059 (m); 214,746 (Sat); 333,000 (Sun)
Digital & print: $2.77/wk (Wed & Sun), $4.50/wk (Mon-Sun); digital only: $9.99/mo
Avg reviews per issue: 6-8

The Olympian
Published by The McClatchy Co
522 Franklin St SE, Olympia, WA 98501
Tel: 360-754-5400 *Fax:* 360-357-0202
E-mail: news@theolympian.com
Web Site: www.theolympian.com
Key Personnel
Exec Ed: Dusti Demarest *Tel:* 360-357-0206
  E-mail: ddemarest@theolympian.com
Sunday page, new book review.
Circulation: 25,455 (m); 30,007 (Sun)
Digital & print: $26/13 wks (Sun only), $45.50/13 wks (Fri-Sun), $71.50/13 wks (Mon-Sun); digital only: $12.99/mo, $129.99/yr

Omaha World-Herald Sunday Arts Section
Published by BH Media Group Inc
1314 Douglas St, Suite 700, Omaha, NE 68102
Tel: 402-444-1000 *Toll Free Tel:* 800-BUG-NEWS (284-6397)
E-mail: news@owh.com
Web Site: www.omaha.com
Key Personnel
Pres & Publr: Todd Sears *Tel:* 402-444-1179
  E-mail: todd.sears@owh.com
Exec Ed: Melissa Matczak *Tel:* 402-444-1088
  E-mail: melissa.matczak@owh.com
Sunday, 1 page, reviews by syndication & in-house, frequent author interviews.
Circulation: 95,616 paid
Digital & print: $19.50/mo (Sun only), $23.84/mo (Fri-Sun), $49.95/mo (Mon-Sun); digital only: $9.95/mo, $99.95/yr

The Orange County Register
Published by MediaNews Group Inc
2190 S Towne Centre Place, Anaheim, CA 92806
Tel: 714-796-7000
Web Site: www.ocregister.com
Subscription Address: Box 11626, Santa Ana, CA 92701
Key Personnel
Pres & Publr: Ron Hasse *Tel:* 818-713-3883
  E-mail: publisher@scng.com
VP, Opers: John Merendino *E-mail:* jmerendino@scng.com
Exec Ed: Frank Pine *Tel:* 909-483-9360
  E-mail: editor@scng.com
Dir, Circ: Kat Wang *E-mail:* kwang@scng.com
Sunday, 2 pages; book reviews in-house, through syndication & freelance; author interviews 4-5 times per month.
Frequency: Daily
Circulation: 236,770 (d); 299,339 (Sun)
Digital & print: $12.50/4 wks (Sun only), $15/4 wks (Thurs-Sun), $25/4 wks (Mon-Sun); digital only: $10/4 wks

The Oregonian
Published by Oregonian Media Group

1500 SW First Ave, Portland, OR 97201
Tel: 503-221-8240 (subns); 503-221-8481 (ad)
  Toll Free Tel: 800-452-1420 (outside OR)
Web Site: oregonlive.com
Key Personnel
Ed & VP, Content: Therese Bottomly *Tel:* 503-221-8434 *E-mail:* tbottomly@oregonian.com
Mng Prodr: Kjerstin Gabrielson *Tel:* 503-412-7012 *E-mail:* kgabrielson@oregonian.com
In-house & freelance, Sunday book section; frequent author interviews & book reviews.
First published 1850
Circulation: 354,000 (d); 440,000 (Sun)
Digital & print: $4.99/wk (Wed & Sun), $6/wk (Wed & Fri-Sun); digital only: $6/wk

The Orlando Sentinel
Published by Tribune Publishing Co
633 N Orange Ave, Orlando, FL 32801
Tel: 407-420-5000
Web Site: www.orlandosentinel.com
Key Personnel
Publr & Gen Mgr: Nancy A Meyer
  E-mail: nmeyer@tribpub.com
Ed-in-Chief: Julie Anderson *E-mail:* janderson@sun-sentinel.com
Mng Ed: Roger Simmons *E-mail:* rsimmons@orlandosentinel.com
Syndicated; in-house. Frequent author interviews & book blog.
First published 1876
Circulation: 300,000 (d & Sat); 400,000 (Sun)
Digital & print: $2.49/wk (Thurs & Sun), $4.99/wk (Mon-Sun); digital only: $1.99/wk

Ottawa Citizen
Published by Postmedia Network Inc
1101 Baxter Rd, Box 5020, Ottawa, ON K2C 3M4, Canada
Tel: 613-829-9100; 613-596-3664 (newsroom); 613-596-3590 (ad); 613-596-1950 (reader sales & serv) *Toll Free Tel:* 800-267-6100 (reader sales & serv); 888-744-3725 (classified)
E-mail: subscriberservices@ottawacitizen.com (reader sales & serv)
Web Site: ottawacitizen.com
Key Personnel
Ed: Michelle Richardson *Tel:* 613-726-5960
  E-mail: mirichardson@postmedia.com
Deputy Ed: Chris Aung-Thwin *Tel:* 343-998-6066
  E-mail: caungthwin@postmedia.com
Edit Pages Ed: Christina Spencer *Tel:* 613-596-3559 *E-mail:* cspencer@postmedia.com
Dir, Fin: Shirley Tam *Tel:* 613-596-3597
  E-mail: stam@ottawacitizen.com
Weekly hardcover & paperback reviews, with in-house & freelance children's book column & weekly author interviews. Pre-Christmas book review section, extra pages Spring & Fall.
Print, digital & e-paper: $26/mo (Fri & Sat), $39/mo (Mon-Sat); digital only: $9.95/mo; e-paper only: $9.99/mo
ISSN: 0839-3222

Outdoor Life®
Published by Bonnier Corp
Division of The Bonnier Group
2 Park Ave, New York, NY 10016
Tel: 212-779-5000
Web Site: www.outdoorlife.com
Subscription Address: PO Box 6364, Harlan, IA 51593-1864 *Tel:* 515-237-3697 *Toll Free Tel:* 800-365-1580 *E-mail:* odlcustserv@cdsfulfillment.com *Web Site:* www.outdoorlife.com/cs
Key Personnel
Group Edit Dir: Anthony Licata
Mng Ed: Jean McKenna *Tel:* 212-779-5000 ext 5290
Articles on hunting, fishing, conservation, gun dogs, humor; for the outdoor sports person & family. No unsol mss, query first.

First published 1898
Frequency: 10 issues/yr
Circulation: 750,000
$12/yr US, $26/yr CN, $40/yr intl
Buy freelance, nonfiction, art, photos & illustrations
Trim Size: 7 7/8 x 10 1/2
Ad Rates: B&W full page $53,200, 4-color full page $66,150
Ad Closing Date(s): See www.outdoorlife.com/advertising

Outside Magazine
Published by Outside Integrated Media LLC
Outside Plaza, 400 Market St, Santa Fe, NM 87501
Tel: 505-989-7100 *Fax:* 505-989-4700
Web Site: www.outsideonline.com
Subscription Address: PO Box 6228, Harlan, IA 51593-1728 *Toll Free Tel:* 800-678-1131
E-mail: oumcustserv@cdsfulfillment.com
Key Personnel
Ed-in-Chief: Lawrence J Burke
Ed: Christopher Keyes *E-mail:* ckeyes@outsideim.com
Contemporary lifestyles for active adults; features sports, fitness, photography, adventure, travel & portraits of men & women adventurers; reviews wildlife, outdoor sports gear & clothing, product news, destination/travel options & environmental & political issues.
First published 1976
Book Use: Reviews & excerpts
Frequency: Monthly
Circulation: 675,000 paid
$24/yr, $36/2 yrs print & digital
ISSN: 0278-1433
Buy freelance nonfiction & art; Sell back issues
Trim Size: 8 x 10 7/8
Ad Rates: B&W page $98,190, full color page $101,750
Ad Closing Date(s): Last week in the month

Pacific Northwest Magazine
Published by The Seattle Times
1000 Denny Way, Seattle, WA 98109
Mailing Address: PO Box 70, Seattle, WA 98111
Tel: 206-464-2111 *Toll Free Tel:* 800-542-0820 (cust serv)
E-mail: customerservice@seattletimes.com
Web Site: www.seattletimes.com/pacific-nw-magazine
Key Personnel
Magazine Ed: Bill Reader *Tel:* 206-464-2416
  E-mail: breader@seattletimes.com
Assoc Ed: Sandy Dunham *Tel:* 206-464-2252
  E-mail: sdunham@seattletimes.com
Sunday general interest regional magazine, 1-2 book sections per year; author profiles.
Circulation: 821,800
Digital & print: $3.99/wk (Sun only), $8.70/wk (Mon-Sun); digital only: $4.99/wk
Ad Rates: Full page $6,880, 1/2 page $3,665
Ad Closing Date(s): 20 days prior to publication date

The Palm Beach Post
Published by GateHouse Media LLC
2751 S Dixie Hwy, West Palm Beach, FL 33405
Tel: 561-820-4663 *Toll Free Tel:* 800-926-7678
E-mail: breakingnews@pbpost.com
Web Site: www.palmbeachpost.com
Key Personnel
Mng Ed: Nicholas Moschella *Tel:* 561-820-4441
  E-mail: nmoschella@pbpost.com
Culture Ed: Larry Aydlette *Tel:* 561-820-4436
  E-mail: laydlette@pbpost.com
In-house & through syndication. Author interviews.
First published 1916
Circulation: 220,000

Digital & print: $3.45/wk (Sun only), $7.38/wk (Mon-Sun)
ISSN: 1528-5758

Palo Alto Weekly
Published by Embarcadero Media
450 Cambridge Ave, Palo Alto, CA 94306
Tel: 650-326-8210 *Fax:* 650-326-3928
E-mail: editor@paweekly.com
Web Site: www.paloaltoonline.com
Key Personnel
Pres & Publr: William S Johnson *Tel:* 650-223-6505 *E-mail:* bjohnson@paweekly.com
Arts & Entertainment Ed: Karla Kane *Tel:* 650-223-6517
News weekly serving Palo Alto, Stanford University, Menlo Park, Los Altos Hills, Portola Valley, CA; monthly book section.
First published 1979
Frequency: Weekly (Fri)
Circulation: 37,000

Parade Magazine, see AMG/Parade

Parents Magazine
Published by Meredith Corporation
225 Liberty St, New York, NY 10281
Toll Free Tel: 800-727-3682 (subns)
E-mail: pmmcustserv@cdsfulfillment.com (subns)
Web Site: www.parents.com
Key Personnel
Exec Ed: Julia Dennison
Deputy Ed: Melissa Bykofsky
Features Ed: Anna Halkidis
Contains articles on family formation & growth for young mothers, with features on food, home, beauty, fashion, child development, marriage, work, money, health, fathers, education.
First published 1926
Book Use: Reviews of adult & juvenile fiction
Frequency: Monthly
Avg pages per issue: 225
Circulation: 2,200,000
$9.98/yr
ISSN: 0161-4193
Buy nonfiction & art; no unsol mss, query first
Trim Size: 7 7/8 x 10 1/2
Ad Rates: B&W full page $198,700, 4-color full page $254,400
Ad Closing Date(s): 15th of month, 2 months prior to issue date

The Paris Review
Published by The Paris Review Foundation
544 W 27 St, New York, NY 10001
Tel: 212-343-1333
E-mail: queries@theparisreview.org
Web Site: www.theparisreview.org
Subscription Address: PO Box 8524, Big Sandy, TX 75755-8524 *Tel:* 903-636-1118 *Toll Free Tel:* 866-354-0212 *E-mail:* subscriptions@theparisreview.org
Key Personnel
Publr: Mona Simpson
Publg Dir: Lori Dorr *E-mail:* ldorr@theparisreview.org
Digital Dir: Craig Teicher
Mng Ed: Hasan Altaf
Ed: Emily Stokes
Poetry Ed: Vijay Seshadri
Literary quarterly dedicated to bringing the works of new & established writers to the critical attention of an educated audience. See web site for submission policy.
First published 1953
Book Use: Excerpts
Frequency: Quarterly
Avg pages per issue: 200
Circulation: 23,000
$49/yr US, $54/yr CN, $64/yr foreign
ISSN: 0031-2037
Sell back issues

Trim Size: 9 1/4 x 6 1/8
Ad Rates: B&W full page $3,000, 4-color full page $4,500

The Pasadena Citizen
Published by Hearst Newspapers
c/o Houston Chronicle, PO Box 4260, Houston, TX 77210
Tel: 713-362-7211
E-mail: help@chron.com
Web Site: www.chron.com/neighborhood/pasadena
Key Personnel
Ed: Greg May *Tel:* 713-362-4013 *E-mail:* greg.may@chron.com
Division of the *Houston Chronicle*.

Pasatiempo, The Santa Fe New Mexican
Published by The New Mexican Inc
202 E Marcy St, Santa Fe, NM 87501
Mailing Address: PO Box 2048, Santa Fe, NM 87504-2021
Tel: 505-983-3303
Web Site: www.santafenewmexican.com/pasatiempo/
Key Personnel
Arts & Pasatiempo Ed: Kristina Melcher
  E-mail: kmelcher@sfnewmexican.com
Arts & entertainment magazine included with Friday edition of The Santa Fe New Mexican. 1-2 author interviews per week, in-house book reviews.
Frequency: Weekly
Circulation: 27,000
$1/daily, $1.25/Sun & Fri
Avg reviews per issue: 3

The Patriot Ledger
Published by GateHouse Media LLC
400 Crown Colony Dr, Quincy, MA 02169-0916
Mailing Address: PO Box 699159, Quincy, MA 02269-9159
Tel: 617-786-7000; 617-786-7026 *Fax:* 617-786-7335
E-mail: features@ledger.com
Web Site: www.patriotledger.com
Key Personnel
Mng Ed: Ken Johnson *Tel:* 617-786-7052
  E-mail: kenjohnson@patriotledger.com
Features Ed: Dana Barbuto *Tel:* 617-786-7074
  E-mail: dbarbuto@ledger.com
Weekly, in-house & through syndication. Weekly author interviews occasionally.
Circulation: 50,000 (e); 60,000 (Sat)
Digital & print: $24/12 wks (Sat only), $48/12 wks (Mon-Sat); e-paper: $95/yr; digital only: $9.95/mo

Pennsylvania Literary Journal (PLJ)
Published by Anaphora Literary Press
1108 W Third St, Quanah, TX 79252
Tel: 470-289-6395
Web Site: anaphoraliterary.com/journals/plj
Key Personnel
Dir & Ed-in-Chief: Dr Anna Faktorovich
  E-mail: director@anaphoraliterary.com
Peer-reviewed journal that publishes critical essays, book reviews, short stories, interviews, photographs, art & poetry. It is cataloged in the *MLA International Bibliography*, the *MLA Directory of Periodicals, Genamics JournalSeek & Duotrope's Digest*. PLJ has published works by & interviews with *New York Times* best-selling writers like Larry Niven & Cinda Williams Chima. Only e-mailed submissions accepted.
First published 2009
Frequency: 3 issues/yr
Avg pages per issue: 150
Circulation: 20 copies/issue, plus EBSCO & ProQuest online viewing
$45/yr US, $60/yr elsewhere
ISSN: 2151-3066
Avg reviews per issue: 4 books/issue

Trim Size: 6 x 9
Ad Rates: Full page $15, 1/2 page $10

Pensacola News Journal
Published by Gannett Co Inc
2 N Palasox St, Pensacola, FL 32502
Tel: 850-435-8500 *Toll Free Tel:* 877-424-0028
(cust serv)
E-mail: online@pnj.com
Web Site: www.pnj.com
Key Personnel
Publr: Lisa Reese *Tel:* 850-435-8565
Exec Ed: Lisa Nellessen Savage *Tel:* 850-435-
8514 *E-mail:* lnelless@gannett.com
Produced in-house with occasional author inter-
views. Local weekend entertainment in *Week-
ender* magazine inserted in Friday daily paper.
Circulation: 42,000 (d); 52,000 (Sun)

Penthouse
Published by Penthouse World Digital LLC
8944 Mason Ave, Chatsworth, CA 91311
E-mail: letters@penthouse.com; support@
penthouse.zendesk.com
Web Site: www.penthousemagazine.com
Articles range from contemporary comment to
photographic essays on beautiful women. Fea-
tures interviews, sports, humor, politics, na-
tional & international issues.
First published 1965
Frequency: 6 issues/yr
Print: $13.99/newsstand issue, $24.95/yr, $36.95/
yr intl, $42.95/2 yrs, $66.95/2 yrs intl; digital:
$9.99/issue, $24.99/yr, $39.99/2 yrs
ISSN: 0090-2020
Sell reprints & back issues

People
Published by Meredith Corporation
225 Liberty St, New York, NY 10281
Tel: 212-522-1212 *Toll Free Tel:* 877-604-6512
(cust serv)
Web Site: www.people.com
Subscription Address: PO Box 60001, Tampa, FL
33660-0001 *Toll Free Tel:* 800-541-9000
Key Personnel
SVP & Publr: Cece Ryan *Tel:* 212-522-7130
E-mail: cece.ryan@meredith.com
VP & Assoc Publr: Lana Lorusso *Tel:* 212-522-
7130 *E-mail:* cece.ryan@meredith.com
Personality journalism, focusing on the paceset-
ters of the news, film & TV, the arts & sci-
ences, as well as ordinary people in extraordi-
nary circumstances.
First published 1974
Frequency: Weekly
Avg pages per issue: 126
Circulation: 3,400,000
$5.99/issue
ISSN: 0093-7673
Sell articles & ad reprints, back issues
Trim Size: 7 7/8 x 10 1/2
Ad Rates: B&W page $282,100, 4-color page
$402,900 (non-bleed)
Ad Closing Date(s): 5 weeks before issue date

The Peterborough Examiner
Published by Metroland Media Group Ltd
60 Hunter St E, Peterborough, ON K9H 1G5,
Canada
Tel: 705-745-4641
Web Site: www.peterboroughexaminer.com
Key Personnel
Ad Dir: Michael Everson *Tel:* 705-745-
4641 ext 2431 *E-mail:* michael.everson@
peterboroughdaily.com
Mng Ed: Kennedy Gordon *Tel:* 705-745-
4641 ext 2438 *E-mail:* kennedy.gordon@
peterboroughdaily.com
Occasional interviews with local authors, wire
service-Canadian Press.
Circulation: 23,000 (e)

Phi Delta Kappan
Published by Phi Delta Kappa International®
1820 N Fort Myer Dr, Suite 320, Arlington, VA
22209
Mailing Address: PO Box 13090, Arlington, VA
22219
Tel: 812-339-1156 *Toll Free Tel:* 800-766-1156
Fax: 812-339-0018
E-mail: memberservices@pdkintl.org; kappan@
pdkintl.org
Web Site: www.pdkintl.org; journals.sagepub.com/
home/pdk
Key Personnel
Exec Dir, Phi Delta Kappa International: Joshua
Starr
Ed-in-Chief: Joan Richardson *Tel:* 313-824-5061
E-mail: jrichardson@pdkintl.org
Design Dir: Carol Bucheri *Tel:* 812-269-6618
E-mail: cbucheri@pdkintl.org
Contains articles on current events & issues in
education.
First published 1915
Book Use: Occasional excerpts
Frequency: 8 issues/yr
Avg pages per issue: 80
Circulation: 18,000
For pricing, please see pdk.sagepub.com/site/sub-
scriptions
ISSN: 0031-7217 (print); 1940-6487 (online)
Buy nonfiction, art & cartoons; Sell ad, full-text
electronic versions of articles, back issues
Trim Size: 8 3/8 x 10 7/8
Ad Rates: B&W page $2,200, 4-color page
$3,045
Ad Closing Date(s): 15th of each month, 2
months prior to publication

Physics Today
Published by American Institute of Physics
One Physics Ellipse, College Park, MD 20740-
3843
Tel: 301-209-3040; 516-576-2270 (circ) *Fax:* 301-
209-0842; 516-349-9704 (circ)
E-mail: help@aip.org; pteditors@aip.org (subns)
Web Site: www.aip.org; www.physicstoday.org
Key Personnel
Art Dir: Donna Padian
Ed-in-Chief: Charles Day *E-mail:* cday@aip.org
Mng Ed: Richard J Fitzgerald *E-mail:* rjf@aip.org
Articles & news of interest to professional physi-
cists, astrophysicists, geophysicists & those
with a general interest in physical science.
First published 1948
Book Use: Regular reviews & books received
lists; occasional excerpts
Frequency: Monthly
Avg pages per issue: 80
Circulation: 123,000 paid
$25/yr nonmembs, free to membs
ISSN: 0031-9228
Buy cartoons; Sell articles & back issues
Trim Size: 8 x 10 1/2
Ad Rates: B&W page $10,970, 4-color per page
add $1,600
Ad Closing Date(s): 1st of month preceding pub-
lication

Pittsburgh Post-Gazette
Published by PG Publishing Co
Division of Block Communications Inc
358 North Shore Dr, Pittsburgh, PA 15212
Tel: 412-263-1100 *Toll Free Tel:* 800-228-6397
(cust serv); 855-743-6763 (subns)
Web Site: www.post-gazette.com
Key Personnel
Publr & Ed-in-Chief: John Robinson Block
Exec Ed: Keith C Burris
Columnist/Book Review Ed: Tony Norman
Column weekly, in-house reviewers; syndicated &
author interviews on a regular basis.
Circulation: 244,000 (d); 430,000 (Sun)

$2/issue, $4/issue (Sun); digital & print: $5.50/wk
(Sun only), $6/wk (Thurs, Fri & Sun); digital
only: $11.96/4 wks
Avg reviews per issue: 1 (Tues), 3 (Sun)

The Plain Dealer
Published by Advance Ohio
4800 Tiedeman Rd, Brooklyn, OH 44144
Tel: 216-999-5000 *Toll Free Tel:* 800-362-0727
E-mail: marketing@advance-ohio.com
Web Site: www.advance-ohio.com; www.
plaindealer.com
Key Personnel
Pres & Ed: George Rodrigue *Tel:* 216-999-4373
E-mail: grodrigue@plaind.com
Daily review & 2 pages Sunday, in-house. Fre-
quent author interviews; Christmas book review
incorporated in gift-giving section; children's &
adults; bestseller list on Sunday.
Circulation: 900,000

Playboy
Published by Playboy Enterprises Inc
10960 Wilshire Blvd, Suite 2200, Los Angeles,
CA 90024
Tel: 310-424-1800 *Toll Free Tel:* 800-511-2457
(cust serv)
E-mail: playboy@netbillingsupport.com
Web Site: www.playboy.com; www.
playboyenterprises.com
Key Personnel
CEO: Ben Kohn
Chief Creative Offr: Cooper Hefner
CFO & COO: David Isreal
Chief Mktg Offr: Jared Dougherty
Entertainment magazine for men, offering fiction,
serious & satirical articles, sports, interviews,
cartoons, picture stories of attractive women &
reviews of features on fashion, food, merchan-
dise & travel.
First published 1953
Frequency: Quarterly
Avg pages per issue: 220
$24.99/issue print, $7.99/issue digital, $24.99/yr
digital only, $39.99/yr print & digital
ISSN: 0032-1478
Trim Size: 9 x 10 3/8
Ad Rates: B&W full page $64,660, 1/2 page
$38,770; 4-color full page $90,540, 1/2 page
$58,840

Plays, The Drama Magazine for Young People
Published by Sterling Partners Inc
897 Washington St, No 600160, Newton, MA
02460
Tel: 617-630-9100 *Toll Free Tel:* 800-630-5755
Fax: 617-630-9101
E-mail: customerservice@playsmagazine.com
Web Site: www.playsmagazine.com
Key Personnel
Ed: Elizabeth Preston *E-mail:* lpreston@
playsmagazine.com
One-act plays & programs for school age actors
& audiences.
First published 1941
Frequency: Monthly (Oct-May, with Jan/Feb
combined)
Avg pages per issue: 48
Circulation: 2,000
$59/yr, $71/yr CN, $84/yr foreign
ISSN: 0032-1540
Buy freelance play scripts; Sell play reprints,
back issues (subscribers only)

Popular Mechanics
Published by Hearst Communications Inc
Division of Hearst Magazines
300 W 57 St, New York, NY 10019-3787
Tel: 212-649-2000; 212-649-2859 (edit); 212-
649-2853 (publg) *Toll Free Tel:* 800-333-4948
(subns)
E-mail: popularmechanics@hearst.com

Web Site: www.popularmechanics.com; www.
hearst.com
Subscription Address: PO Box 6000, Harlan, IA
51593-1500
Key Personnel
Publr: Cameron Connors
SVP & CFO: Michael Scherzer
Ed-in-Chief: Ryan D'Agostino
Contains ideas & information on automobiles,
home building & maintenance, boating & out-
door recreation, science, hi-fi & electronics,
computer, telecommunications, sports.
First published 1902
Book Use: Occasional reviews
Frequency: 10 issues/yr
Avg pages per issue: 191
Circulation: 1,200,000 paid; 21,281 controlled
$4.99/issue, $12/yr print or digital, $13/yr print &
digital
ISSN: 0032-4558
Trim Size: 7 3/4 x 10 1/2
Ad Rates: 4-color page $172,790
Ad Closing Date(s): 7-8 weeks before issue date

Popular Science®
Published by Bonnier Corp
Division of The Bonnier Group
2 Park Ave, 9th fl, New York, NY 10016
Tel: 212-779-5000 *Fax:* 212-779-5108
E-mail: letters@popsci.com
Web Site: www.popsci.com
Subscription Address: PO Box 6364, Harlan, IA
51593-1864
Key Personnel
Exec Dir, Brand Mktg: Beth Hetrick
Group Edit Dir: Anthony Licata
Creative Dir: Pete Sucheski
Ed-in-Chief: Joe Brown
Exec Ed: Kevin Gray
Mng Ed: Corinne Iozzio
Sr Ed: Sophie Brushwick
Assoc Ed: Mary Beth Griggs
Feature articles on science & technology includ-
ing space & aviation, electronics products,
computer, automotive products, car tests &
housing products. No unsol mss, query first.
First published 1872
Book Use: Occasional reviews, excerpts
Frequency: Quarterly
Avg pages per issue: 100
Circulation: 1,250,000
$7.99/issue, $10/yr US, $18/yr CN, $24/yr intl
ISSN: 0161-7370
Buy nonfiction, art, cartoons; Sell article & ad
reprints, back issues
Trim Size: 7 3/8 x 10 1/2
Ad Rates: B&W page $63,450, 4-color page
$89,820 + 10% (for a bleed)
Ad Closing Date(s): 45 days prior to sale date

Port Arthur News
Published by Carpenter Newsmedia
2349 Memorial Blvd, Port Arthur, TX 77640
Tel: 409-721-2400; 409-729-6397
E-mail: panews@panews.com (edit)
Web Site: www.panews.com
Key Personnel
Publr: Rich Macke *E-mail:* rich.macke@panews.
com
Ed: Ken Stickney *E-mail:* ken.stickney@panews.
com
In-house reviews & occasional author interviews.
First published 1897
Digital & print: $52/yr (Sat only), $131.88/yr
(Tues-Sat); digital only: $9.99/mo, $29.97/3
mos, $119.88/yr

The Portland Press Herald/Maine Sunday Telegram
Published by Maine Today Media Inc
One City Ctr, 5th fl, Portland, ME 04101

Mailing Address: PO Box 1460, Portland, ME
04104-5009
Tel: 207-791-6000 (subns); 207-791-6650
Toll Free Tel: 800-442-6036 (within ME)
Fax: 207-791-6920
E-mail: online@mainetoday.com; circulation@
mainetoday.com
Web Site: www.pressherald.com
Key Personnel
Publr & CEO: Lisa DeSisto *Tel:* 207-791-6630
E-mail: lisa@mainetoday.com
Exec Ed: Cliff Schechtman *Tel:* 207-791-6693
E-mail: cschechtman@mainetoday.com
Mng Ed: Steve Greenlee *Tel:* 207-791-6301
E-mail: sgreenlee@pressherald.com
Sunday, book reviews through syndication &
other sources.
Circulation: 46,751 (d); 56,756 (Sun)
$11.99/mo digital

The Post & Courier
Published by Evening Post Industries
134 Columbus St, Charleston, SC 29403-4800
Tel: 843-577-7111; 843-853-POST (853-7678)
Fax: 843-937-5579
E-mail: features@postandcourier.com
Web Site: www.postandcourier.com
Key Personnel
Publr: P J Browning *E-mail:* pbrowning@
postandcourier.com
Ad Pres: Scott Embry *Tel:* 843-937-5405
E-mail: sembry@postandcourier.com
Edit Page Ed: Rick Nelson *Tel:* 843-937-5701
E-mail: rnelson@postandcourier.com
Features Ed: Lauren Sausser *Tel:* 843-937-5598
E-mail: lsausser@postandcourier.com
Sunday page *Post & Courier*, in-house & syndi-
cated column; occasional author interviews.
First published 1803
Circulation: 1,800,000/mo
$12.95/mo digital, $27.50/mo digital & print

The Post-Standard
Published by Advance Media New York
220 S Warren St, Syracuse, NY 13202
Tel: 315-470-0011; 315-470-2265 (newsroom);
315-470-6397 (cust serv)
Web Site: www.syracuse.com
Key Personnel
Features Ed: Steve Carlic
Periodic, in-house & through syndication. Fre-
quent regional interviews. Book review page-
previews of books written by or directed to
Central New Yorkers.
Circulation: 95,000 (m)
$1.25/Mon-Sat, $2.50/Sun

The Press & Sun Bulletin
Published by Gannett Co Inc
33 Lewis Rd, Suite 9, Binghamton, NY 13905
Mailing Address: PO Box 1270, Binghamton, NY
13902-1270
Tel: 607-798-1234 *Toll Free Tel:* 800-253-5343
(subns)
E-mail: pressandsun@gannett.com
Web Site: www.pressconnects.com
Key Personnel
Exec Ed: Kevin Hogan *E-mail:* khogan@gannett.
com
Daily community in-house & by syndication. Oc-
casional author interviews.
Frequency: Daily
Circulation: 38,234 (m); 53,944 (Sun)

The Press Democrat
Division of Sonoma Media Investments LLC
427 Mendocino Ave, Santa Rosa, CA 95401
Tel: 707-521-5235; 707-526-8585 (newsroom)
Toll Free Tel: 800-675-5056 (newsroom)
Fax: 707-521-5330 (newsroom)
E-mail: info@pressdemocrat.com
Web Site: www.pressdemocrat.com

Key Personnel
Features Ed: Corinne Asturias *E-mail:* corinne.
asturias@pressdemocrat.com
Sunday page; in-house, through syndication & by
other sources; semimonthly author interviews.
First published 1857
Circulation: 97,000 (m); 103,000 (Sun)
Digital & print: $17/mo (Sun only), $28/mo
(Mon-Sun); digital only: $12/mo

The Press of Atlantic City
Published by BH Media Group Inc
1000 W Washington Ave, Pleasantville, NJ 08232
Tel: 609-272-7000 *Toll Free Tel:* 877-773-7724
Fax: 609-272-7224
E-mail: spage@pressofac.com
Web Site: www.pressofatlanticcity.com
Key Personnel
Exec Ed & VP, News: Kris Worrell *Tel:* 609-272-
7277 *E-mail:* kworrell@pressofac.com
Mng Ed: Buzz Keough *Tel:* 609-272-7238
E-mail: bkeough@pressofac.com
Sunday page, in-house & through syndication;
occasional author interviews.
Circulation: 90,000 (m); 105,000 (Sun)
Digital & print: $9.50/mo (Sun only), $16.25/mo
(Thurs-Sun or Mon-Sun); digital only: $6.95/
mo
Avg reviews per issue: 6

Press-Register
Published by Alabama Media Group
Unit of Advance Local Media LLC
18 S Royal St, Mobile, AL 36602
Tel: 251-219-5400 *Toll Free Tel:* 800-239-1340
E-mail: circulationcs@press-register.com
Web Site: www.al.com
Sunday page. In-house & through syndication;
author interviews.
First published 1813
$18.07/mo digital & Sun print, $19.99/mo digital
only

Press-Telegram
Published by Digital First Media
727 Pine Ave, Long Beach, CA 90813
Tel: 562-435-1161; 562-499-1222 (subns); 562-
499-1382 (ad sales)
E-mail: ptnews@presstelegram.com
Web Site: www.presstelegram.com
Key Personnel
Group Pres & Publr: Ron Hasse *E-mail:* ron.
hasse@socalnewsgroup.com
Exec Ed: Frank Pine *Tel:* 909-483-9360
E-mail: frank.pine@socalnewsgroup.com
City Ed: Melissa Evans *Tel:* 562-499-1280
E-mail: mevans@scng.com
Columnist: Tim Grobaty *Tel:* 562-714-2116
E-mail: tgrobaty@scng.com
Weekly page, in-house & by syndication. Occa-
sional author interviews.
First published 1897
Circulation: 20,432 (d); 34,605 (Sun)
$20/8 wks

The Progressive
Published by The Progressive Inc
30 W Mifflin, Suite 703, Madison, WI 53703
Tel: 608-257-4626 *Toll Free Tel:* 800-827-0555
E-mail: editorial@progressive.org
Web Site: www.progressive.org
Subscription Address: PO Box 392, Oregon, IL
61061
Key Personnel
Publr: Norman Stockwell
Mng Ed: Bill Lueders
Ed: Ruth Conniff
Web Ed: Mrill Ingram
Contains investigative reporting, analysis & com-
mentary on major issues of political, economic
& social concern.
First published 1909

Book Use: Reviews
Frequency: 6 issues/yr
Avg pages per issue: 72
Circulation: 40,000 paid
$4.95/issue, $29.70/yr, $50/yr instns, $42/yr CN, $48/yr foreign
ISSN: 0033-0736
Buy nonfiction, poetry & art; Sell articles, ad reprints, back issues
Trim Size: 7 1/4 x 9 5/8
Ad Rates: $3,000 color full page, $3,500 color cover
Ad Closing Date(s): 20th of each published month

Psychology Today
Published by Sussex Publishers LLC
115 E 23 St, 9th fl, New York, NY 10010
Tel: 212-260-7210 *Toll Free Tel:* 800-234-8361 (subns) *Fax:* 212-260-7566
E-mail: sales@psychologytoday.com; subscriptions@psychologytoday.com
Web Site: www.psychologytoday.com
Key Personnel
CEO: Jo Colman
EVP & Publr: John Thomas
    E-mail: johnthomas@psychologytoday.com
Ed-in-Chief: Kaja Perina
Deputy Ed: Lybi Ma
Psychological information & media insight for the general audience. Covers personal relations, family issues, human behavior, pop culture, media, neuropsychology. Includes editorials, queries for writers, interviews, research news; extensive news & feature articles, very little fiction or poetry. No unsol mss, query first.
First published 1967
Frequency: 6 issues/yr
Avg pages per issue: 92
Circulation: 250,000
$29.97/yr, $37.97/yr CN, $49.99/yr foreign
ISSN: 0033-3107
Buy freelance nonfiction, art & fiction; Sell articles & back issues
Trim Size: 8 x 10 1/2
Ad Rates: B&W full page $13,755, 1/2 page $7,875, 4-color full page $20,055, 1/2 page $11,550
Ad Closing Date(s): 2 months before issue date, beginning of month

Queen's Quarterly
Published by Queen's University
Douglas Library, Rm 402D, 93 University Ave, Kingston, ON K7L 5C4, Canada
Tel: 613-533-2667
E-mail: queens.quarterly@queensu.ca
Web Site: www.queensu.ca/quarterly
Key Personnel
Busn Mgr: Penny Roantree
Ed: Boris Castel
Literary Ed: Joan Harcourt
First published 1893
Frequency: Quarterly
Avg pages per issue: 160
Circulation: 3,000
$6.50/issue, $20/yr CN, $25/yr US & foreign
ISSN: 0033-6041
Trim Size: 6 x 9

Rain Taxi Review of Books
Published by Rain Taxi
PO Box 3840, Minneapolis, MN 55403
E-mail: info@raintaxi.com
Web Site: www.raintaxi.com
Key Personnel
Art Dir: Kelly Everding
Ed: Eric Lorberer
Publishes original work by writers in all stages of their careers. Books are considered in the categories of poetry, fiction, literary nonfiction, art & graphic novels. Occasional reviews of

children's & young adult books, audio books & chapbooks. No electronic files. Only printed books (finished books or bound galleys) are accepted for consideration.
Frequency: Quarterly
$16/yr, $28/2 yrs domestic; $25/yr, $45/2 yrs CN & Mexico; $45/yr, $80/2 yrs overseas

Reader's Digest
Published by Trusted Media Brands Inc
750 Third Ave, 3rd fl, New York, NY 10017
SAN: 212-4416
Tel: 914-238-1000 *Toll Free Tel:* 877-732-4438 (cust serv)
E-mail: customercare@trustedmediabrands.com
Web Site: www.rd.com; www.trustedmediabrands.com/brands/readers-digest
Key Personnel
Chief Admin Offr: Dean Durbin
Chief Content Offr: Bruce Kelley
SVP, Sales & Mktg: John Boland *Tel:* 646-518-4252 *E-mail:* john.boland@trustedmediabrands.com
Dir, PR: Becky Wisdom *E-mail:* becky.wisdom@trustedmediabrands.com
Sr Prodn Mgr: Leslie Kogan *Tel:* 914-244-5433 *E-mail:* leslie.kogan@trustedmediabrands.com
Contains general interest, nonfiction reading for the entire family. The balance are articles condensed from other publications; a condensation of a current book is carried in each issue.
First published 1922
Book Use: Excerpts
Frequency: 10 issues/yr
Avg pages per issue: 214
Circulation: 3,000,000
$3.99/issue, $10/yr, $15/2 yrs (includes digital)
ISSN: 0034-0375
Buy freelance, nonfiction, art & cartoons; Sell article & reprints, back issues
Trim Size: 5.187 x 7.25
Ad Rates: 4-color full page $77,660, 1/2 page $46,650; B&W full page $68,170, 1/2 page $40,920

The Record
Published by Metroland Media Group Ltd
Subsidiary of Torstar Corp
160 King St E, Kitchener, ON N2G 4E5, Canada
Tel: 519-894-2250; 519-894-3000 (cust serv)
    Toll Free Tel: 800-265-8261; 800-210-5210 (cust serv)
Web Site: www.therecord.com
Key Personnel
Publr: Donna Luelo *Tel:* 519-895-5500
Ed-in-Chief: Jim Poling *Tel:* 519-895-5600
City Ed: Neil Ballantyne *Tel:* 519-895-5633
    E-mail: nballantyne@therecord.com
Saturday page; in-house & syndicated, in-house book reviewers, plus occasional outside book reviews.
Circulation: 60,000
Digital, print & e-edition: $2.52/wk (Fri & Sat), $3.84/wk (Mon-Sat); digital only: $7.99/mo; e-edition (Mon-Sat): $9.99/mo

The Record
Published by Glacier Ventures International
6 Mallory, Sherbrooke, QC J1M 2E2, Canada
Tel: 819-569-9525 *Fax:* 819-569-6345
Web Site: www.sherbrookerecord.com
Key Personnel
Publr & Mng Ed: Sharon McCully
    E-mail: outletjournal@sympatico.ca
First published 1897
Frequency: Daily (Mon-Fri)
Circulation: 4,100 (e)
Digital only: $11.25/mo, $125/yr; print only: $50.59/3 mos, $97.73/6 mos, $178.21/yr; digital & print: $55.59/3 mos, $102.73/6 mos, $183.21/yr

The Record
Published by North Jersey Media Group
Subsidiary of Gannett Co Inc
One Garret Mountain Plaza, Woodland Park, NJ 07424
Mailing Address: PO Box 471, Woodland Park, NJ 07424-0471
Tel: 973-569-7000; 973-585-5633 (cust serv)
    Toll Free Tel: 888-282-3422 *Fax:* 973-569-7037
E-mail: northjerseymediagroup@gannett.com
Web Site: www.northjersey.com
Key Personnel
Ed: Daniel Sforza *E-mail:* dsforza@northjersey.com
Magazines & Features Writer: Kimberly Wilson *E-mail:* wilsonk@northjersey.com
In-house & through syndication; author interviews when warranted.
Circulation: 177,969 (d); 192,817 (Sun)

The Record
Published by MediaNews Group Inc
7 Wells St, Suite 103, Saratoga Springs, NY 12866
Tel: 518-270-1200 *Fax:* 518-583-8014
E-mail: newsroom@troyrecord.com
Web Site: www.troyrecord.com
Key Personnel
Publr: Kevin Corrado *E-mail:* kcorrado@medianewsgroup.com
City Ed: Nicholas Buonanno
    E-mail: nbuonanno@digitalfirstmedia.com
Irregular book reviews in-house.
First published 1896
Circulation: 20,000
Digital & print: $59.15/13 wks (Thurs, Fri & Sun), $91.55/13 wks (Mon-Sun); digital only: $12/mo

Record-Journal
Published by The Record-Journal Publishing Co
500 S Broad St, 2nd fl, Meriden, CT 06450
Tel: 203-235-1661; 203-634-3933 (cust serv)
    Fax: 203-639-0210 (edit); 203-235-4048 (ad)
E-mail: newsroom@record-journal.com
Web Site: www.myrecordjournal.com
Key Personnel
Pres & Publr: Eliot C White *Tel:* 203-317-2350
    E-mail: ewhite@thewesterlysun.com
EVP & Asst Publr: Elizabeth White *Tel:* 203-317-2226 *E-mail:* lwhite@record-journal.com
SVP & Ed: Ralph Tomaselli *Tel:* 203-317-2220
    E-mail: rtomaselli@record-journal.com
Mng Ed: Eric Cotton *Tel:* 203-317-2344
    E-mail: ecotton@record-journal.com
Frequency: Daily
Circulation: 30,855 (d); 30,961 (Sun)
$37/mo print & digital, $15.99/mo digital only

The Recorder & Times (Brockville), see
    Brockville Recorder & Times

Red Deer Advocate
Published by Black Press Group Ltd
2950 Bremner Ave, Red Deer, AB T4R 1M9, Canada
Tel: 403-343-2400
E-mail: editorial@reddeeradvocate.com
Web Site: www.reddeeradvocate.com
Key Personnel
Publr: Mary Kemmis *Tel:* 403-314-4311
    E-mail: mkemmis@reddeeradvocate.com
Mng Ed: David Marsden *Tel:* 403-314-4324
    E-mail: david.marsden@reddeeradvocate.com
Occasional local & visiting author interviews. Book reviews in-house & syndicated. Sunday edition "Red Deer Life" distributed free to households in Red Deer.
Circulation: 23,300 (d)
$15/mo

Redbook
Published by Hearst Communications Inc

Division of Hearst Magazines
300 W 57 St, 22nd fl, New York, NY 10019-3787
Tel: 212-649-3463 (edit); 212-649-3330 (publg/ad)
E-mail: redbook@hearst.com
Web Site: www.redbookmag.com; www.hearst.com
Key Personnel
Edit Dir: Jane Francisco
Articles on beauty, parenting, relationships, health & fitness. Online presence only.
First published 1903
ISSN: 0034-2106

Regina Leader-Post
Published by Postmedia Network Inc
PO Box 2020, Regina, SK S4P 3G4, Canada
Tel: 306-781-5211 *Toll Free Tel:* 800-667-8751 (subns) *Fax:* 306-657-6438
Web Site: www.leaderpost.com
Key Personnel
Mng Ed: Tim Switzer *Tel:* 306-781-5223
  E-mail: tswitzer@postmedia.com
Ed: Heather Persson *Tel:* 306-657-6315
  E-mail: hpersson@postmedia.com
Weekly half-page; in-house & through syndication. Occasional author interviews.
Circulation: 62,000
Digital & print: $15/mo (Sat only), $28/mo (Mon-Sat); digital only: $9.95/mo

The Register-Guard
Published by GateHouse Media LLC
3500 Chad Dr, Suite 600, Eugene, OR 97408
Tel: 541-485-1234
Web Site: www.registerguard.com
Key Personnel
Publr: Shanna Cannon *Tel:* 541-338-2525
  E-mail: scannon@registerguard.com
First published 1867
Frequency: Daily
Digital & print: $32/mo (Fri-Sun), $48/mo (Mon-Sun); digital only: $12.95/mo
ISSN: 0739-8557
Avg reviews per issue: 60

The Register-Mail
Published by GateHouse Media LLC
140 S Prairie St, No 539, Galesburg, IL 61401
Tel: 309-343-7181 *Toll Free Tel:* 800-747-7181
E-mail: news@register-mail.com
Web Site: www.galesburg.com
Key Personnel
Publr: David Adams *Tel:* 309-343-7181 ext 286
  E-mail: dadams@gatehousemedia.com
Features Ed: Robyn Gautschy *Tel:* 309-343-7181 ext 265 *E-mail:* rgautschy@gatehousemedia.com
Occasional column, books & travel.
Circulation: 10,000 (e)
Digital & print: $24.91/mo; digital only: $6.99/mo, $69.99/yr

The Republican
Published by MassLive LLC
1350 Main St, Springfield, MA 01103
Tel: 413-788-1000; 413-788-1200 (newsroom)
  Fax: 413-788-1301 (newsroom)
E-mail: masslivesales@masslive.com
Web Site: www.masslivemedia.com/republican
Key Personnel
Publr & CEO: George Arwady *Tel:* 413-788-1312
  E-mail: garwady@repub.com
Pres: David Starr *Tel:* 413-788-1040
  E-mail: dstarr@repub.com
VP & Asst to Publr: Robyn A Newhouse
  Tel: 413-788-1021 *E-mail:* rnewhouse@repub.com
Opers Dir: Tom Sewall *E-mail:* tsewall@repub.com

Ad Dir: Mark A French *Tel:* 413-788-1108
  E-mail: mfrench@repub.com
Exec Ed: Wayne E Phaneuf *Tel:* 413-788-1315
  E-mail: wphaneuf@repub.com
Mng Ed: Cynthia Simison *Tel:* 413-788-1214
  E-mail: csimison@repub.com
Book page in Sunday edition. Occasional author interviews.
$10.90/wk print & digital (Mon-Sun), $3.90/wk (Thurs & Sun); $40/mo digital

Richmond Times-Dispatch
Published by BH Media Group Inc
300 E Franklin St, Richmond, VA 23219
Tel: 804-649-6000 *Toll Free Tel:* 800-468-3382
Web Site: www.richmond.com
Key Personnel
Mng Ed: Mike Szvetitz *E-mail:* mszvetitz@timesdispatch.com
Sunday (Times-Dispatch); in-house, freelance & occasional author interviews.
Circulation: 89,401 (d); 120,280 (Sun)
Digital & print: $44/mo (Sun only), $50/mo (Thurs-Sun), $70/mo (Mon-Sun); digital only: $11.99/mo, $144/yr

The Roanoke Times
Published by BH Media Group Inc
201 Campbell Ave SW, Roanoke, VA 24011
Mailing Address: PO Box 2491, Roanoke, VA 24010-2491
Tel: 540-981-3211 (cust serv); 540-981-3340 (newsroom) *Toll Free Tel:* 800-346-1234 (cust serv)
E-mail: letters@roanoke.com
Web Site: www.roanoke.com
Key Personnel
Publr: Terry Jamerson *E-mail:* terry.jamerson@roanoke.com
Newsroom Mgr: Karen Belcher *E-mail:* karen.belcher@roanoke.com
Weekly page in-house.
First published 1886
Circulation: 163,000 (d); 230,000 (Sun)
Digital & print: $8.88/mo (Sun only), $13.31/mo (Fri-Sun), $16.90/mo (Mon-Sun); digital & e-edition: $8.95/mo, $100/yr

Rocky Mount Telegram
Division of Cook Communications
1151 Falls Rd, Suite 2008, Rocky Mount, NC 27804
Mailing Address: PO Box 1080, Rocky Mount, NC 27802
Tel: 252-366-8190; 252-329-9505 (cust care)
Web Site: www.rockymounttelegram.com
Key Personnel
Publr: Kyle Stephens *Tel:* 252-366-8146
  E-mail: kstephens@rmtelegram.com
Ed: Gene Metrick *Tel:* 252-366-8141
  E-mail: gmetrick@rmtelegram.com
Daily page, syndicated & in-house; occasional author interviews.
Circulation: 10,047 (e); 12,664 (Sun)
$5/mo digital, $16/mo print (home delivery), $25/mo print (mail delivery)

Rolling Stone
Published by Penske Media Corp
Subsidiary of Penske Business Media LLC
475 Fifth Ave, New York, NY 10017
Tel: 212-484-1616
E-mail: rseditors@rollingstone.com
Web Site: www.rollingstone.com
Subscription Address: PO Box 62230, Tampa, FL 33662
Key Personnel
Pres: Gus Wenner
Ed: Jason Fine
Sr Writer: David Fricke
General interest magazine covering modern American culture, politics & art with special

interest in music. Review rock history books & rock biographies.
First published 1967
Book Use: Some reviews, some excerpts
Frequency: 12 issues/yr
Avg pages per issue: 92
Circulation: 670,671 paid
$9.99/issue, $49.95/yr print, $59.95/yr print & digital
ISSN: 0035-791X
Buy freelance, nonfiction & art
Trim Size: 9.6875 x 11.75
Ad Rates: B&W full page $209,945, 1/2 page $125,965, 4-color full page $233,270, 1/2 page $139,965
Ad Closing Date(s): Varies

Ruralite
Published by Ruralite Services Inc
5605 NE Elam Young Pkwy, Hillsboro, OR 97124
Tel: 503-357-2105
E-mail: info@ruralite.org
Web Site: www.ruralite.org
Key Personnel
Mng Ed: Leon Espinoza *E-mail:* editor@ruralite.org
First published 1954
Frequency: Monthly
Avg pages per issue: 32
Circulation: 326,050
$15/yr, $20/yr foreign
Buy freelance nonfiction
Trim Size: 8 3/8 x 10 3/4
Ad Rates: B&W page $7,090, 4-color page $8,150
Ad Closing Date(s): 20th of month, 2 months prior to issue date

Rutland Online Herald
Published by Brunswick Publishing LLC
77 Grove St, Suite 102, Rutland, VT 05701
Mailing Address: PO Box 668, Rutland, VT 05702-0668
Tel: 802-747-6121; 802-747-6131 (cust serv)
  Toll Free Tel: 800-498-4296 (VT); 800-776-5512 (outside VT)
E-mail: customerservices@rutlandherald.com
Web Site: www.rutlandherald.com
Key Personnel
Gen Mgr: Rob Mitchell *Tel:* 802-774-3028
  E-mail: rob.mitchell@rutlandherald.com
Author interviews.
First published 1794
Frequency: Daily (Tues-Sat)
$22.92/mo digital & print, $9/2 wks digital only

The Sacramento Bee
Published by The McClatchy Co
2100 "Q" St, Sacramento, CA 95816
Mailing Address: PO Box 15779, Sacramento, CA 95852
Tel: 916-321-1000 *Toll Free Tel:* 800-284-3233
Web Site: www.sacbee.com
Key Personnel
Mng Ed: Scott Lebar *Tel:* 916-321-1182
  E-mail: slebar@sacbee.com
4-6 reviews; reviews & features about authors also run during the week in the scene section; book reviews in-house & through syndication; author interviews; books & media published in Monday's paper, highlights 4 new books each week (hardcover & paperback).
First published 1857
Circulation: 163,482 (d); 177,626 (Sun)
Digital & print: $56.39/13 wks (Sun only), $84.59/13 wks (Fri-Sun), $112.79/13 wks (Mon-Sun); digital only: $12.99/mo, $129.99/yr

SAIL Magazine
Published by Cruz Bay Publishing Inc
Subsidiary of Active Interest Media (AIM)
10 Bokum Rd, Essex, CT 06426-1185

Mailing Address: 23a Glendale St, Salem, MA 01970
Tel: 860-767-3200 *Fax:* 860-767-1048
E-mail: sailmail@sailmagazine.com
Web Site: www.sailmagazine.com
Subscription Address: PO Box 37274, Boone, IA 50037-0274 *Tel:* 386-447-6318 *Toll Free Tel:* 800-745-7245 *E-mail:* salcustserv@cdsfulfillment.com
Key Personnel
Group Publr: Bob Bauer *E-mail:* bbauer@aimmedia.com
Art Dir: Steve Jylkka *E-mail:* sjylkka@aimmedia.com
Ed-in-Chief: Peter Nielsen *E-mail:* pnielsen@sailmagazine.com
Exec Ed: Adam Cort *E-mail:* acort@sailmagazine.com
Information on all aspects of recreational sailing including cruising, racing & equipment.
First published 1970
Book Use: Reviews, excerpts
Frequency: Monthly
Avg pages per issue: 100
Circulation: 68,000
$15/yr plus postage US, $30/yr CN, $42/yr foreign
ISSN: 0036-2700
Sell articles, ad reprints, back issues
Trim Size: 9 x 10 7/8
Ad Rates: B&W full page $10,970, 4-color full page $15,675

St Anthony Messenger
Published by Franciscan Friars of St John the Baptist Province
28 W Liberty St, Cincinnati, OH 45202-6498
Tel: 513-241-5615 *Toll Free Tel:* 800-488-0488
E-mail: sam@cambeywest.com
Web Site: info.franciscanmedia.org/st-anthony-messenger
Key Personnel
Publr: Daniel Kroger, OFM
Art Dir: Mary Catherine Kozusko
Mng Ed: Daniel Imwalle
Franciscan Ed: Pat McCloskey
For Catholic families; written to help people live a Christian life.
First published 1893
Book Use: 60-72 reviews & 2 excerpts per year
Frequency: Monthly
Avg pages per issue: 60
Circulation: 55,000
$39/yr US, $69/yr CN & foreign
ISSN: 0036-276X
Buy freelance fiction, nonfiction, poetry, art & cartoons & photos; Sell articles & ad reprints, back issues
Trim Size: 8.125 x 10.75
Ad Rates: Full page $3,500, 1/2 page $2,100

St Louis Post-Dispatch
Published by Lee Enterprises Inc
900 N Tucker Blvd, St Louis, MO 63101
Tel: 314-340-8000; 314-340-8888 (cust serv)
Toll Free Tel: 800-365-0820
E-mail: service@stltoday.com
Web Site: www.stltoday.com
Key Personnel
Dir, PR: Tracy Rouch *Tel:* 314-340-8903
   E-mail: trouch@post-dispatch.com
Ed-in-Chief: Gilbert Bailon *Tel:* 314-340-8387
   E-mail: gbailon@post-dispatch.com
Book Ed: Jane Henderson *Tel:* 314-340-8107
   E-mail: jhenderson@post-dispatch.com
Go! Entertainment section with book reviews & book blog.
Circulation: 394,900 (d); 485,800 (Sun)
Digital & print: $23.75/mo (Sun only), $51/mo (Thurs-Sun), $61.75/mo (Mon-Sun); digital only: $9.99/mo

St Paul Pioneer Press
Published by Digital First Media
10 River Park Plaza, Suite 700, St Paul, MN 55107
Toll Free Tel: 800-950-9080
E-mail: letters@pioneerpress.com; customerservice@pioneerpress.com
Web Site: www.twincities.com
Key Personnel
Books Ed: Mary Ann Grossmann *Tel:* 651-228-5574 *E-mail:* mgrossmann@pioneerpress.com
Ed: Mike Burbach *Tel:* 651-228-5544
   E-mail: mburbach@pioneerpress.com
Sunday pages, in-house & through syndication & outside sources. Author interviews conducted by staff several times monthly.
Circulation: 191,155 (d); 248,660 (Sun)
Digital & print: $8/mo (Sun only), $10/mo (Thurs & Sun), $18/mo (Mon-Sun); digital only: $10/mo
ISSN: 0892-1083

St Thomas Times-Journal
Published by Postmedia Network Inc
PO Box 82, St Thomas, ON N5P 3T5, Canada
Tel: 519-631-2790
Web Site: www.stthomastimesjournal.com
Key Personnel
Publr & Ad Sales Mgr: Linda LeBlanc
   E-mail: linda.leblanc@sunmedia.ca
In-house book reviews that appear irregularly.
Frequency: Daily (Tues-Fri)
Circulation: 1,550 (e)
$22.99/mo

The Salem News
Published by North of Boston Media Group
Subsidiary of CNHI LLC
32 Dunham Rd, Beverly, MA 01915
Tel: 978-922-1234 *Fax:* 978-927-4524
E-mail: sn@salemnews.com
Web Site: www.salemnews.com
Key Personnel
Publr: Karen Andreas *Tel:* 978-946-2241
   E-mail: kandreas@salemnews.com
Mng Ed: Cheryl Richardson *Tel:* 978-338-2664
   E-mail: crichardson@salemnews.com
Ed: David Olson *Tel:* 978-338-2531
   E-mail: dolson@salemnews.com
News Ed: Helen Gifford *Tel:* 978-338-2508
   E-mail: hgifford@salemnews.com
Edit Asst: Joann Mackenzie *Tel:* 978-338-2670
   E-mail: jomackenzie@salemnews.com
Frequency: Daily (Mon-Sat)
Circulation: 31,077 (e)
$54/8 wks print & digital, $36/8 wks digital only

Salisbury Post
131 W Innes St, Salisbury, NC 28144
Mailing Address: PO Box 4639, Salisbury, NC 28145-4639
Tel: 704-633-8950 *Fax:* 704-639-0003
E-mail: news@salisburypost.com
Web Site: www.salisburypost.com
Key Personnel
Book Review Ed: Deirdre Parker Smith
   E-mail: deirdre.smith@salisburypost.com
In-house, syndicated & freelance book reviews, one-page, weekly, occasional author interviews.
Circulation: 17,000 (d)
$.75/daily; $1.25/Sun

The Salt Lake Tribune
90 S 400 W, Suite 700, Salt Lake City, UT 84101
Tel: 801-257-8742 *Fax:* 801-257-8800
E-mail: newsroom@sltrib.com; features@sltrib.com
Web Site: www.sltrib.com
Key Personnel
Owner & Publr: Paul Huntsman
Ed: Jennifer Napier-Pearce

Arts & Living Ed: Anna Cekola *Tel:* 801-257-8769
Sunday arts section; produced in-house & through syndication, author interviews twice a month.
First published 1871
Circulation: 79,998 (d); 81,262 (Sat); 98,232 (Sun)
Print only: $66/12 wks (Sun only), $73.20/12 wks (Fri-Sun), $90/12 wks (Mon-Sun); digital & print: $71.04/12 wks (Sun only), $78.24/12 wks (Fri-Sun), $95.04/12 wks (Mon-Sun); digital only: $7.99/mo
ISSN: 0746-3502
Avg reviews per issue: 1-2

The San Angelo Standard Times
Published by Gannett Co Inc
34 W Harris Ave, San Angelo, TX 76903
Mailing Address: PO Box 5111, San Angelo, TX 76902-5111
Toll Free Tel: 800-588-1884
E-mail: standard@gosanangelo.com
Web Site: www.gosanangelo.com
Key Personnel
Ed & News Dir: Jen Killin-Guadarrama *Tel:* 325-659-8249 *E-mail:* jennifer.killin@gosanangelo.com
Occasionally in-house & by syndication; author interviews.
Circulation: 35,612 (m); 38,512 (Sat); 41,578 (Sun)
Digital & print: $17/mo (Wed & Sun), $23/mo (Mon-Sun); digital only: $9.99/mo

San Antonio Express-News
Published by Hearst Newspapers
Division of Hearst Corp
301 Avenue "E", San Antonio, TX 78205
Mailing Address: PO Box 2171, San Antonio, TX 78297-2171
Tel: 210-250-3000 *Toll Free Tel:* 800-456-7411
E-mail: citydesk@express-news.net
Web Site: www.expressnews.com; www.mysanantonio.com
Key Personnel
COO: Susan Pape
VP & Ed: Marc Duvoisin *E-mail:* marc.duvoisin@express-news.net
Features Ed: Emily Spicer *E-mail:* espicer@express-news.net
Sunday Insight.
Circulation: 296,000 (d); 200,000 (Sat); 420,000 (Sun)
Digital & print: $3.99/wk (Sun only), $9.99/wk (Mon-Sun); digital only: $9.99/mo

The San Diego Union-Tribune
Published by The San Diego Union-Tribune LLC
600 B St, No 1201, San Diego, CA 92101
Mailing Address: PO Box 120191, San Diego, CA 92112-0191
Tel: 619-293-1211
E-mail: local@sduniontribune.com
Web Site: www.sandiegouniontribune.com/entertainment/books
Key Personnel
Publr & Ed-in-Chief: Jeff Light *Tel:* 619-293-1201 *E-mail:* jeff.light@sduniontribune.com
Mng Ed: Lora Cicalo *Tel:* 619-293-1376
   E-mail: lora.cicalo@sduniontribune.com
Online book reviews & bestselling books.
Frequency: Daily
Circulation: 183,000 (d); 268,000 (Sun)
Digital & print: $2.49/wk (Sun only), $4.99/wk (Mon-Sun); digital only: $1.99/wk

San Francisco Chronicle
Published by Hearst Newspapers
Division of Hearst Corp
901 Mission St, San Francisco, CA 94103
Tel: 415-777-1111 *Toll Free Tel:* 800-499-5700

E-mail: books@sfchronicle.com; feedback@
sfchronicle.com
Web Site: www.sfchronicle.com; www.sfgate.com
Subscription Address: PO Box 80083, Prescott,
AZ 86304-8083
Key Personnel
Deputy Mng Ed, Features: Kitty Morgan
E-mail: kmorgan@sfchronicle.com
Sr Arts & Entertainment Ed: Robert Morast
E-mail: robert.morast@sfchronicle.com
In-house & freelance reviews & occasional author
interviews.
First published 1865
Circulation: 167,602 (d); 252,088 (Sun)
Print only: $5.65/wk (Sun only), $8.70/wk (Mon-
Sun); digital & print: $6.50/wk (Sun only),
$14.60/wk (Mon-Sun); digital only: $12.60/wk
ISSN: 1932-8672

San Francisco Examiner
835 Market St, Suite 550, San Francisco, CA
94103
Tel: 415-359-2600 *Fax:* 415-359-2766
E-mail: info@sfexaminer.com
Web Site: www.sfexaminer.com
Key Personnel
Arts & Entertainment Ed: Leslie Katz *Tel:* 415-
359-2727 *E-mail:* lkatz@sfexaminer.com
San Francisco local author interviews.
First published 1865
Frequency: 3 issues/wk (print ed Sun, Wed &
Thurs)
Circulation: 255,000
Free
Ad Rates: See media kit online

The SandPaper
Published by The SandPaper Inc
1816 Long Beach Blvd, Surf City, NJ 08008
Tel: 609-494-5900 *Fax:* 609-494-1437
E-mail: beachcomberlbi@gmail.com
Web Site: thesandpaper.net
Key Personnel
Publr: Curt Travers
Off Mgr: Lee Little
Regular book reviews of Jersey Shore books.
Tabloid newspaper format.
Frequency: Weekly
Avg pages per issue: 80
Circulation: 30,000
Free

Santa Barbara News-Press
Published by Ampersand Publishing LLC
715 Anacapa St, Santa Barbara, CA 93101
Mailing Address: PO Box 1359, Santa Barbara,
CA 93102-1359
Tel: 805-564-5200; 805-966-7171 (subns)
Fax: 805-966-6258
E-mail: news@newspress.com
Web Site: www.newspress.com
Key Personnel
Co-Publr: Wendy McCaw *Tel:* 805-564-5165
E-mail: wmccaw@newspress.com; Arthur von
Wisenberger *E-mail:* avw@newspress.com
Weekly page, in-house, through syndication &
wire services; very occasional author inter-
views.
First published 1855
Circulation: 55,000 (d); 57,608 (Sun)
Digital & print: $4.50/wk (Fri-Sun), $8.50/wk
(Mon-Sun); digital only: $60/yr

Santa Cruz County Sentinel
Published by Santa Cruz Sentinel Publishers Co
Affiliate of Media News Group
324 Encinal St, Santa Cruz, CA 95060
Tel: 831-423-4242
E-mail: newsroom@santacruzsentinel.com
Web Site: www.santacruzsentinel.com

Key Personnel
Publr & Ed: Gary Omernick *Tel:* 831-706-3228
E-mail: gomernick@santacruzsentinel.com
Mng Ed: Melissa Murphy *Tel:* 831-706-3252
E-mail: mmurphy@santacruzsentinel.com
Lifestyles Ed: Anthony Solis *Tel:* 831-706-3259
E-mail: tsolis@santacruzsentinel.com
No local book reviews; author interviews in fea-
tures section & weekly entertainment book col-
umn; through syndication.
Circulation: 20,000 (e); 24,500 (Sun)
Digital & print: $2.30/wk (Sun only), $3.80/wk
(Thurs, Fri & Sun), $5.50/wk (Mon-Sun)

Santa Maria Times
Published by Lee Enterprises Inc
3200 Skyway Dr, Santa Maria, CA 93455
Tel: 805-925-2691 *Toll Free Tel:* 888-422-8822
Fax: 805-928-5657
Web Site: santamariatimes.com
Key Personnel
Publr: Cynthia Schur *Tel:* 805-739-2154
E-mail: cschur@leecentralcoastnews.com
Mng Ed: Marga Cooley *Tel:* 805-739-2143
E-mail: mcooley@leecentralcoastnews.com
Ed: Emily Slater *Tel:* 805-739-2217
E-mail: eslater@leecentralcoastnews.com
Reviews appear online; local author interviews;
in-house syndicated.
First published 1882
Circulation: 22,000 (d & Sun)
Digital & print: $21.25/mo silver option, $38/mo
platinum option; digital only: $5/mo basic,
$9.99/mo plus

Saskatoon StarPhoenix
Published by Postmedia Network Inc
204 Fifth Ave N, Saskatoon, SK S7K 2P1,
Canada
Tel: 306-657-6231 *Toll Free Tel:* 800-667-2002
Fax: 306-657-6437
E-mail: citydesk@thestarphoenix.com
Web Site: www.thestarphoenix.com
Key Personnel
Ed: Heather Persson *Tel:* 306-657-6315
E-mail: hpersson@postmedia.com
Mktg: Hilary Klassen *Tel:* 306-657-6322
E-mail: hiklassen@postmedia.com
One Saturday page, in-house & by outside
sources; author interviews weekly.
First published 1902
Frequency: Daily (Mon-Sat)
Circulation: 63,000 (m)
Digital & print: $18/mo (Sat only), $30/mo
(Mon-Sat); digital only: $9.95/mo; e-paper:
$9.99/mo
ISSN: 0832-4174

Savannah Morning News
Published by GateHouse Media LLC
1375 Chatham Pkwy, Savannah, GA 31405
Mailing Address: PO Box 1088, Savannah, GA
31402-1088
Tel: 912-236-9511 *Toll Free Tel:* 888-348-3309
(cust care)
E-mail: news@savannahnow.com
Web Site: savannahnow.com
Key Personnel
Publr: Michael C Traynor *Tel:* 912-652-0268
Mktg & Events Dir: Megan Miller *Tel:* 912-652-
0445 *E-mail:* megan.miller@savannahnow.com
Exec Ed: Susan Catron
Sunday page, in-house & other sources. Occa-
sional author interviews.
First published 1850
Frequency: Daily
Digital & print: $14.92/mo (Sun only), $14.96/mo
(Fri-Sun), $17.66/mo (Mon-Sun); digital only:
$12.95/mo, $99.50/yr

SchoolArts Magazine
Published by Davis Publications Inc

50 Portland St, Worcester, MA 01608
Tel: 508-754-7201 *Toll Free Tel:* 800-533-2847
(ext 220, cust serv); 800-533-2847 (ext 219,
ad) *Fax:* 508-753-3834; 508-791-0779 (edit)
E-mail: contactus@schoolartsmagazine.com
Web Site: www.davisart.com
Key Personnel
Pres: Julian Wade *E-mail:* jwade@davisart.com
Art Dir: Julia Wade *E-mail:* juliawade@davisart.
com
Dir, Mktg: Toni Henneman *E-mail:* thenneman@
davisart.com
Sr Ed: Missy Nicholson *E-mail:* mnicholson@
davisart.com
Ed: Nancy Walkup *E-mail:* nwalkup@davisart.
com
Natl Sales Mgr: Scott Benson *E-mail:* sbenson@
davisart.com
Art education lesson plans for all levels, from ele-
mentary through post-secondary & college.
First published 1901
Frequency: 10 issues/yr (Sept-June)
Avg pages per issue: 72
Circulation: 24,000 paid; 700 controlled
$24.95/yr, $39.95/2 yrs, $49.95/3 yrs
ISSN: 0036-6463
Trim Size: 8 1/8 x 10 7/8
Ad Rates: B&W page $1,813, 4-color page addi-
tional $550
Ad Closing Date(s): 5-6 weeks before issue date

Science of Mind Magazine
Published by Centers for Spiritual Living
573 Park Point Dr, Golden, CO 80401-7042
Tel: 720-279-1643 *Toll Free Tel:* 800-247-6463
(US & CN)
Web Site: www.scienceofmind.com
Subscription Address: ESP Computer Services,
PO Box 15368, North Hollywood, CA 91615,
Contact: Michael Jordan *Toll Free Tel:* 800-
247-6463 *Fax:* 818-487-4500
Key Personnel
Publr & Ed: David Goldberg
Publg Busn Mgr: Dennise Simone
E-mail: dsimone@csl.org
Spirituality, metaphysics, philosophy, self-help &
inspirational.
First published 1927
Book Use: Reviews
Frequency: Monthly
Avg pages per issue: 112
Circulation: 60,000
$3.95/issue US, $4.95/issue CN
ISSN: 0036-8458
Buy nonfiction; Sell back issues/books
Trim Size: 5 1/2 x 8
Ad Rates: B&W page $1,580, 4-color page
$2,800
Ad Closing Date(s): 60 days prior to publication
date

ScienceNews
Published by Society for Science & the Public
1719 "N" St NW, Washington, DC 20036
Tel: 202-785-2255 *Toll Free Tel:* 800-552-4412
(subns)
E-mail: editors@sciencenews.org
Web Site: www.sciencenews.org
Subscription Address: PO Box 292255, Kettering,
OH 45429-0255
Key Personnel
Publr: Maya Ajmera
Ed-in-Chief: Nancy Shute
Mng Ed, Magazine: Erin Wayman
E-mail: ewayman@sciencenews.org
For scientists & those interested in the latest de-
velopments in science, medicine & technology.
No unsol mss.
First published 1922
Book Use: Listings with brief reviews
Frequency: 26 issues/yr
Avg pages per issue: 36
Circulation: 113,629 paid

$50/yr membs print & digital, $25/yr digital only
ISSN: 0036-8423
Sell article & ad reprints; sell back issues at $5/
issue
Trim Size: 8 1/4 x 10 1/2
Ad Rates: 4-color page $4,000
Ad Closing Date(s): 5 weeks advance of issue
date

Scientific American™
Published by Scientific American Inc
Division of Springer Nature America Inc
One New York Plaza, 46th fl, New York, NY
10004
Tel: 212-451-8200 *Toll Free Tel:* 800-333-1199
(cust serv)
E-mail: editors@sciam.com
Web Site: www.scientificamerican.com
Subscription Address: PO Box 3187, Har-
lan, IA 51537 *Toll Free Tel:* 800-333-1199
E-mail: scacustserv@cdsfulfillment.com
Key Personnel
SVP & Ed-in-Chief: Mariette DiChristina
VP, Magazines & Edit: Stephen Pincock
Head, Communs: Rachel Scheer
Mng Ed: Curtis Brainard
Chief Features Ed: Seth Fletcher
Magazine of discovery & innovation for decision-
makers in industry, government & universi-
ties. Available in print & online. No unsol mss,
query first.
First published 1845
Book Use: One major review, 3-4 brief reviews
Frequency: Monthly
Avg pages per issue: 120
Circulation: 350,000 paid worldwide
$34.99/yr print & digital, $39.99/yr digital & 4
yr archive, $99/yr print, digital & full archive,
$199.99/yr unlimited
ISSN: 0036-8733
Sell articles, ad reprints & back issues
Trim Size: 8 1/8 x 10 3/4
Ad Rates: B&W full page $34,200, 4-color full
page $51,266; see web site for complete list of
ad rates

The Seattle Times
Published by Seattle Times Co
1000 Denny Way, Seattle, WA 98109
Mailing Address: PO Box 70, Seattle, WA 98111
Tel: 206-464-2111; 206-464-2121 (cust serv);
206-464-2200 (newsroom) *Toll Free Tel:* 800-
542-0820 (cust serv)
Web Site: www.seattletimes.com
Key Personnel
Mng Ed: Ray Rivera *Tel:* 206-652-6521
Features Ed: Stefanie Loh *Tel:* 206-464-8994
Sunday, in-house, syndicate & freelancers. Fre-
quent author interviews.
Frequency: Daily
Circulation: 236,563 (d); 232,580 (Sat); 504,993
(Sun)

Seattle Weekly
Published by Sound Publishing Inc
11630 Slater Ave NE, Suite 8/9, Kirkland, WA
98034
Tel: 206-623-0500
E-mail: info@seattleweekly.com
Web Site: www.seattleweekly.com
Key Personnel
Ed: Andy Hobbs *E-mail:* ahobbs@
soundpublishing.com
Digital only. Book reviews & author interviews &
stories.
First published 1976
$39.99/yr

Self
Published by Conde Nast
One World Trade Center, 26th fl, New York, NY
10007-0090

Tel: 212-286-2860; 515-243-3273 (subns)
Toll Free Tel: 800-274-6111 (subns)
E-mail: letters@self.com; slfcustserv@
cdsfulfillment.com
Web Site: www.self.com
Key Personnel
Chief Revenue & Mktg Offr: Pamela Drucker
Mann
Ed-in-Chief: Carolyn Kylstra
Chief Busn Offr: Eric Gillin
Articles pertaining to the physical, emotional, cul-
tural, financial & sexual well-being of women.
Digital only format.
First published 1979
Book Use: Excerpts
Frequency: Monthly
Circulation: 1,420,858

Seventeen Magazine
Published by Hearst Communications Inc
Division of Hearst Magazines
300 W 57 St, 17th fl, New York, NY 10019-3787
Tel: 212-649-2000
E-mail: mail@seventeen.com
Web Site: www.seventeen.com; www.hearst.com
Key Personnel
Exec Dir: Kristin Koch
Articles on fashion, beauty, food & issues, fiction
for female teenage audience. Digital only.
First published 1944

Sierra
Published by Sierra Club
2101 Webster St, Suite 1300, Oakland, CA 94612
Tel: 415-977-5691
E-mail: sierra.magazine@sierraclub.org
Web Site: www.sierraclub.org/sierra
Key Personnel
Ed-in-Chief: Jason Mark
Sr Ed: Paul Rauber
Contains articles on conservation, natural his-
tory, outdoor recreation & the environmental
movement for Sierra Club members & others.
Accepts clips if available. No e-mail queries.
First published 1893
Book Use: Reviews & excerpts
Frequency: 6 issues/yr
Avg pages per issue: 100
Circulation: 517,000 paid
ISSN: 0161-7362
Buy freelance nonfiction; Sell back issues
Avg reviews per issue: 3
Trim Size: 8 x 10 3/4

Simcoe Reformer
Published by Postmedia Network Inc
50 Gilbertson Dr, Simcoe, ON N3Y 4L2, Canada
Tel: 519-426-5710
E-mail: reformer.newsroom@sunmedia.ca
Web Site: www.simcoereformer.ca
Key Personnel
Mng Ed: Kim Novak *E-mail:* knovak@postmedia.
com
Daily newspaper.
Circulation: 9,800
$14.99/4 wks print, $3.99/mo digital

Sioux City Journal
Published by Sioux City Newspapers Inc
Division of Lee Enterprises Inc
515 Pavonia St, Sioux City, IA 51101
Tel: 712-293-4250 *Toll Free Tel:* 800-397-9820
Fax: 712-293-4211
Web Site: siouxcityjournal.com
Subscription Address: PO Box 118, Sioux City,
IA 51102
Key Personnel
Ed: Bruce Miller *E-mail:* bmiller@
siouxcityjournal.com
Includes weekly entertainment section. Author
interviews weekly.
Frequency: Daily

Circulation: 58,000 (d); 57,000 (Sat); 60,000
(Sun)
$5/mo digital basic, $9.99/mo digital plus

Ski®
Published by Active Interest Media (AIM)
5720 Flatiron Pkwy, Boulder, CO 80301
Tel: 303-253-6300 *Toll Free Tel:* 800-678-0817
(subns)
E-mail: editor@skimag.com
Web Site: www.skimag.com
Key Personnel
Dir, Mktg & Busn Devt: Amy Lewis
E-mail: alewis@aimmedia.com
Industry Sales Dir: Ginna Larson
E-mail: glarson@aimmedia.com
Western Sales Dir: Al Crolius *E-mail:* acrolius@
aimmedia.com
Gen Mgr: David Perry
Contains articles on technique, equipment, resorts
& experiences of interest to skiers, real estate,
kids gear & reviews. No unsol mss, query first.
First published 1936
Frequency: 6 issues/yr
Avg pages per issue: 150
Circulation: 300,000
$10/yr US, $20/yr CN, $30/yr intl
ISSN: 0037-6159
Buy nonfiction; Sell articles, ad reprints & back
issues
Trim Size: 8 1/2 x 10 7/8
Ad Rates: 4-color page $24,500

Sky & Telescope
Published by American Astronomical Society
90 Sherman St, Suite A, Cambridge, MA 02140
Tel: 617-864-7360 *Toll Free Tel:* 866-644-1377
Fax: 617-864-6117
E-mail: info@skyandtelescope.com
Web Site: www.skyandtelescope.com
Key Personnel
Ed-in-Chief: Peter Tyson
Sr Ed: Kelly Beatty; Alan M MacRobert
Assoc Ed: S N "Jr" Johnson-Roehr; Sean Walker
News Ed: Monica Young
Observing Ed: Diana Hannikainen
Sci Ed: Camille Carlile
Written for those interested in astronomy, space
science, observatories, planetariums, telescope
making & celestial events.
First published 1941
Book Use: Reviews & advertisements
Frequency: Monthy
Avg pages per issue: 84
Circulation: 71,017
$5.99/issue, $37.95/yr, $49.95/yr CN, $61.95/yr
foreign
ISSN: 0037-6604
Buy nonfiction, art & cartoons; Sell articles, ad
reprints & back issues
Trim Size: 8 3/8 x 10 1/2
Ad Rates: 4-color page $6,000

Smithsonian
Published by Smithsonian Institution
PO Box 37012, MRC 513, Washington, DC
20013-7012
Tel: 202-633-6090
E-mail: smithsonianmagazine@si.edu
Web Site: www.smithsonianmag.com; www.
facebook.com/smithsonianmagazine
Subscription Address: PO Box 62060, Tampa,
FL 33662-0608 *Tel:* 810-910-3609 *Toll Free
Tel:* 800-766-2149 *E-mail:* smithsonian@
customersvc.com
Key Personnel
Dir, Edit Opers: Debra Rosenberg
Art Dir: Maria G Keehan
Ed-in-Chief: Michael Caruso
Deputy Ed: Terence Monmaney
Sr Ed: Kathleen M Burke; T A Frail; Arik Gab-
bai; Jenni Rothenberg-Gritz; April White

Examines the quality of modern life in terms of the cultural, intellectual, social & physical environment. All web-based submission process - must submit via web site, www.smithsonian.mag.com/contact-us. Also available electronically.
First published 1970
Book Use: Nonfiction reviews & excerpts & first serial excerpts only
Frequency: 10 issues/yr
Avg pages per issue: 104
Circulation: 1,800,000 paid
$12/yr US, $25/yr CN, $38/yr foreign
ISSN: 0037-7333
Buy nonfiction; Sell back issues
Trim Size: 7 7/8 x 10 1/2 x 10 7/8
Ad Rates: B&W full page $108,979, 2-color full page $134,900, 4-color full page $159,600
Ad Closing Date(s): 10th of the month, 2 months preceding issue date

Sojourners Magazine
Published by Sojourners
408 "C" St NE, Washington, DC 20002
Tel: 202-328-8842 *Toll Free Tel:* 800-714-7474 (ad sales) *Fax:* 202-328-8757
E-mail: sojourners@sojo.net; sojourners@cambeywest.com (subns)
Web Site: www.sojo.net
Key Personnel
Ed: Jim Rice
Sr Assoc Ed: Rose Marie Berger; Julie Polter
Assoc Ed: Betsy Shirley
Ecumenical Christian magazine offering an alternative perspective on matters of faith, politics & culture today. For writers guidelines see submission policy at www.sojo.net/writers.
First published 1971
Book Use: Reviews
Frequency: 11 issues/yr
Avg pages per issue: 52
Circulation: 29,000
$2.95/issue digital, $4.95/issue print, $19.95/yr digital, $39.95/yr US, $49.95/yr CN, $59.95/yr foreign print & digital
ISSN: 1550-1140
Buy nonfiction, poetry, art & cartoons; Sell article & ad reprints, back issues, resource guides, books
Trim Size: 8 3/16 x 10 7/8
Ad Rates: 4-color page $2,160, 1/2 page $1,530
Ad Closing Date(s): Approximately 10th of 3rd month prior to issue date

South Bend Tribune
Published by Schurz Communications Inc
225 W Colfax Ave, South Bend, IN 46626
Tel: 574-235-6161 *Fax:* 574-236-1765
E-mail: sbtnews@sbtinfo.com; sbtcustserv@press-one.com
Web Site: www.southbendtribune.com
Key Personnel
Publr: Sally Brown
VP, Publg: Cory Bollinger
VP, Ad: Shelley Chakan
Exec Ed: Alan Achkar *E-mail:* aachkar@sbtinfo.com
Sunday page, in-house & wire service; author interviews several times a month - mainly wire service interviews - local angle preferred, but not required for in-house interviews.
Circulation: 65,000 (e); 90,000 (Sun)
$24.70/mo (Mon-Sun print & digital), $13/mo (Sat & Sun print & digital), $11.27/mo (Sun only print & digital), $.99/wk (digital only)

Southern Living
Published by Meredith Corporation
4100 Old Montgomery Hwy, Birmingham, AL 35209-5713
Tel: 205-445-6000
Web Site: www.southernliving.com

Subscription Address: PO Box 37508, Boone, IA 50037-0508 *Toll Free Tel:* 800-272-4101
E-mail: slvcustserv@cdsfulfillment.com
Key Personnel
Publr: Deirdre Finnegan *Tel:* 212-455-1276
E-mail: deirdre.finnegan@meredith.com
Service publication about the American South. Reviews & author interviews are all staff-written. No unsol mss, query first.
First published 1966
Book Use: Reviews & interviews with authors of southern books
Frequency: Monthly
Avg pages per issue: 200
Circulation: 2,800,000
$4.99/issue, $14.95/yr
Buy nonfiction; Sell articles & back issues
Trim Size: 8 x 10 1/2
Ad Rates: 4-color full page $277,800, 2/3 page $213,000, 1/2 page $173,700, 1/3 page $125,100

The Spokesman-Review
Published by Cowles Publishing Co
999 W Riverside Ave, Spokane, WA 99201
Mailing Address: PO Box 2160, Spokane, WA 99210-2160
Tel: 509-459-5400 (newsroom); 509-747-4422 (cust serv) *Fax:* 509-459-5098
E-mail: features@spokesman.com
Web Site: www.spokesman.com
Key Personnel
Ed: Rob Curley *Tel:* 509-459-5030
E-mail: robc@spokesman.com
Features Ed: Carolyn Lamberson *Tel:* 509-459-5068
Sunday page; in-house & through syndication. Author interviews, 3 or more a month.
First published 1883
Circulation: 110,000 (d); 140,000 (Sun)
Digital & print: $12.99/mo (Mon-Sun); digital only: $9.99/mo

Sports Afield
Published by Field Sports Publishing
15621 Chemical Lane, Suite B, Huntington Beach, CA 92649
Tel: 714-373-4910 *Toll Free Tel:* 800-451-4788 *Fax:* 714-894-4949
E-mail: letters@sportsafield.com
Web Site: www.sportsafield.com
Key Personnel
Ed-in-Chief: Diana Rupp
Big-game hunting adventure stories & hunting destinations. Submission guidelines available web site.
First published 1887
Book Use: Reviews in monthly almanac section; occasional excerpts
Frequency: 6 issues/yr
Avg pages per issue: 90
Circulation: 50,000 paid
$7.99/issue, $27.97/yr, $49.97/2 yrs
ISSN: 0038-8149
Buy freelance, nonfiction, art & photography; Sell back issues
Trim Size: 8 1/4 x 10 7/8
Ad Rates: 4-color page $4,650, 1/2 page $2,820, 1/4 page $1,645

The Springfield News-Leader
Published by Gannett Co Inc
651 Boonville Ave, Springfield, MO 65806
Tel: 417-836-1100
Web Site: www.news-leader.com
Key Personnel
News Dir: Cheryl Whitsitt *E-mail:* cwhitsitt@gannett.com
Weekly page, in-house & through syndication; rare author interviews.
First published 1867
Circulation: 35,000 (Mon-Sat); 45,000 (Sun)

Standard-Examiner
Published by The Ogden Newspapers Inc
332 Standard Way, Ogden, UT 84404
Mailing Address: PO Box 12790, Ogden, UT 84412-2790
Tel: 801-625-4200; 801-625-4400
Toll Free Tel: 800-651-2105
E-mail: customerservice@standard.net
Web Site: www.standard.net
Key Personnel
Exec Ed: Jordan Carroll *Tel:* 801-625-4210
E-mail: jcarroll@standard.net
City Ed: Jessica Kokesh *Tel:* 801-625-4229
E-mail: jkokesh@standard.net
Columnist: Mark Saal *Tel:* 801-625-4272
E-mail: msaal@standard.net
Author interviews (local writers & well known writers visiting the area).
First published 1888
Circulation: 280,000/wk
Print: $6.50/mo (Sun only), $9.75/mo (Fri-Sun), $15.16/mo (Mon-Sun); digital: $9.99/mo

The Standard Times
Published by South Coast Media Group
Subsidiary of GateHouse Media LLC
25 Elm St, New Bedford, MA 02740
Tel: 508-997-7411 *Toll Free Tel:* 800-445-7482 (subns) *Fax:* 508-997-7491
Web Site: www.southcoasttoday.com
Key Personnel
Circ Serv Dir: Chad Campbell
Circ Serv Mgr: Mark Foisy *Tel:* 508-979-4400
E-mail: mfoisy@s-t.com
News Ed: Jennifer Driscoll *Tel:* 508-979-4466
E-mail: jdriscoll@s-t.com
Frequency: Daily
Circulation: 24,000 (d & Sat); 30,000 (Sun)
Digital & print: $26/13 wks (Sun only), $52/13 wks (Mon-Sun); digital only: $12/mo

Standard-Freeholder, see Cornwall Standard-Freeholder

The Star-Ledger
Published by NJ Advance Media
One Star Ledger Plaza, Newark, NJ 07102
Tel: 973-392-4040 (edit) *Toll Free Tel:* 888-STAR-LEDGER (782-7533 cust serv)
E-mail: custserv@starledger.com
Web Site: www.nj.com/starledger
Key Personnel
VP, Opers: Stephen Leotsakos
E-mail: sleotsakos@starledger.com
Publr & Ed: Richard Vezza *Tel:* 973-836-4906
E-mail: rvezza@starledger.com
Gen Mgr: John F Dennan *E-mail:* jdennan@starledger.com
Weekly, in-house book reviews & features.
$19.99/mo (7-day digital only), $3.95/wk (Sun & Thurs print & digital), $5.25/wk (Thurs-Sun print & digital), $7.95/wk (7-day print & digital)

Star Magazine
Published by American Media Inc
4 New York Plaza, New York, NY 10004
Tel: 212-545-4800
Web Site: starmagazine.com
Key Personnel
SVP & Group Publr: Neil Goldstein
E-mail: ngoldstein@amilink.com
Ed-in-Chief: James Heidenry
Assoc Publr, Mktg: Pamela Madden
E-mail: pmadden@amilink.com
Weekly book reviews, in-house & syndicated, local author interviews, local bestseller list & calendar of book-related events.
Frequency: Weekly

Circulation: 165,000 (Sun)
Ad Rates: B&W 2/3 page $98,770, 1/3 page
$49,390; 4-color full page $137,155, 1/2 page
$82,310

Star Tribune
Published by StarTribune Media Co LLC
650 Third Ave S, Suite 1300, Minneapolis, MN
55402
Tel: 612-673-4000
Web Site: www.startribune.com/variety/books
Key Personnel
Publr & CEO: Michael Klingensmith
Sr Books Ed: Laurie Hertzel *E-mail:* laurie.
hertzel@startribune.com
Sunday section, in-house. 2 page book review
section every Sunday. Reviews on Mondays &
1 book review on Tuesday.
First published 1867
Frequency: Daily
Circulation: 297,478 (d); 504,616 (Sun)
Digital & print: $5.83/wk (Sun only), $9.72/wk
(Mon-Sun); print only: $4.34/wk; digital only:
$3.79/wk
ISSN: 0895-2825

The State
Published by The State Media Co
Subsidiary of The McClatchy Co
1401 Shop Rd, Columbia, SC 29201-4843
Tel: 803-771-6161 *Toll Free Tel:* 800-888-5353;
800-888-3566 (cust serv)
E-mail: state@thestate.com
Web Site: www.thestate.com
Key Personnel
Publr: Rodney Mahone *E-mail:* rmahone@
mcclatchy.com
Exec Ed: Brian Tolley *E-mail:* btolley@thestate.
com
Sr Ed: Paul Osmundson *E-mail:* posmundson@
thestate.com
Sunday page, in-house; frequent author inter-
views.
First published 1891
Frequency: Daily
Circulation: 115,000 (d); 130,000 (Sun)
$16.99/mo digital

The State Journal
Published by Frankfort Newsmedia LLC
1216 Wilkinson Blvd, Frankfort, KY 40601
Tel: 502-227-4556 *Fax:* 502-227-2831
E-mail: news@state-journal.com
Web Site: www.state-journal.com
Key Personnel
Publr: Steve Stewart *Tel:* 502-209-6994
E-mail: steve.stewart@state-journal.com
News Ed: Chanda Veno *Tel:* 502-209-6299
E-mail: chanda.veno@state-journal.com
First published 1902
Circulation: 10,000 (d); 12,000 (Sun)

The State Journal-Register
Published by GateHouse Media LLC
PO Box 219, Springfield, IL 62705-0219
Tel: 217-788-1300
E-mail: sjr@sj-r.com
Web Site: www.sj-r.com
Key Personnel
Gen Mgr & Ad Dir: Eugene Jackson
E-mail: ejackson@sj-r.com
Sunday page, in-house & by syndication. Infre-
quent author interviews.
Frequency: Daily
Circulation: 50,000 (Sun)
Digital & print: $9.13/mo (Sun only), $19.12/mo
(Mon-Sun); digital only: $5.99/mo, $39.99/yr

Staten Island Advance
Published by SILive.com
950 W Fingerboard Rd, Staten Island, NY 10305

Tel: 718-981-1234; 718-816-3900 (cust serv)
E-mail: editor@siadvance.com
Web Site: www.silive.com
Key Personnel
Publr: Caroline Diamond Harrison
Exec Ed: Brian J Laline *E-mail:* laline@
siadvance.com
Edit Page Ed: Mark Hanley *E-mail:* hanley@
siadvance.com
Circ Mgr: Richard Salerno *E-mail:* salerno@
siadvance.com
Sunday in "Arts & Ideas" section; in-house & by
syndication.
Digital & print: $18/mo (Thurs-Sun), $25.78/mo
(Mon-Sun); digital only: $19.99/mo

Statesville Record & Landmark
Published by BH Media Group Inc
222 E Broad St, Statesville, NC 28677
Tel: 704-873-1451 *Fax:* 704-872-3150
E-mail: news@statesville.com; circulation@
statesville.com
Web Site: www.statesville.com
Key Personnel
Publr: Eric Millsap
Daily page.
Circulation: 15,600 (d); 14,900 (Sat); 16,600
(Sun)
Digital & print: $5.32/mo (Sun only), $9.62/mo
(Mon-Sat), $16.50/mo (Mon-Sun); digital only:
$7.95/mo, $79.95/yr

Sun Journal
Published by The Lewiston Sun Journal
Division of Sun Media Group
104 Park St, Lewiston, ME 04240
Mailing Address: PO Box 4400, Lewiston, ME
04243-4400
Tel: 207-784-5411 *Toll Free Tel:* 800-482-0753
Fax: 207-777-3436
E-mail: circulation@sunjournal.com
Web Site: www.sunjournal.com
Key Personnel
Exec Ed: Judith Meyer *Tel:* 207-689-2902
E-mail: jmeyer@sunjournal.com
Reviews of books about the state of Maine.
Circulation: 31,422 (d); 31,505 (Sun)
Digital & print: $10.60/4 wks (Sun only), $14.60/
4 wks (Thurs-Sun), $19.60/4 wks (Mon-Sun);
digital only: $11.96/4 wks

Sun-Sentinel
Published by Sun-Sentinel Co
Division of Tribune Co
333 SW 12 Ave, Deerfield Beach, FL 33442
Tel: 954-356-4000 *Fax:* 954-356-4559
E-mail: feedback@sun-sentinel.com (cust serv)
Web Site: www.sun-sentinel.com
Key Personnel
News Ed: David Hayes *Tel:* 954-356-4831
E-mail: dthayes@sun-sentinel.com
Sunday page. Feature author interviews fre-
quently; book reviews in-house, through syn-
dication & freelance.

Sunset
Published by Sunset Publishing Corp
Subsidiary of Regent LLC
9720 Wilshire Blvd, Suite 600, Beverly Hills, CA
90212
Tel: 510-858-3400 *Toll Free Tel:* 800-777-0117
(subns); 877-297-7138 (cust serv)
E-mail: customerservice@sunset.com
Web Site: www.sunset.com
Subscription Address: PO Box 3228, Harlan, IA
51593 *Toll Free Tel:* 800-777-0117
Key Personnel
Ed-in-Chief: Matt Bean
Exec Ed: Hugh Garvey
Guide to the Western states; covers travel, food
& entertaining, home & building, gardening,
outdoor living.

First published 1898
Book Use: Occasional reviews
Frequency: Monthly
Avg pages per issue: 120
Circulation: 1,000,000
$20/yr all access print & digital (US only)
ISSN: 0039-5404
Sell back issues
Trim Size: 8 3/8 x 10 1/2
Ad Closing Date(s): 7 weeks preceding issue date

Tallahassee Democrat
Published by Gannett Co Inc
277 N Magnolia Dr, Tallahassee, FL 32301
Tel: 850-599-2100 *Toll Free Tel:* 800-999-2271
(subns)
E-mail: letters@tallahassee.com
Web Site: www.tallahassee.com
Key Personnel
Pres & Publr: Skip Foster *Tel:* 850-599-2126
Exec Ed: William Hatfield *Tel:* 850-599-2177
Sunday weekly, in-house, through syndicated wire
service & other sources.
Circulation: 56,000 (m); 78,000 (Sun)
Digital & print: $4.30/mo (Sun only), $13/mo
(Mon-Sun)

Tampa Bay Times
Published by Times Publishing Co
490 First Ave S, St Petersburg, FL 33701
Mailing Address: PO Box 1121, St Petersburg,
FL 33731-1121
Tel: 727-893-8111 *Toll Free Tel:* 800-888-7012
Fax: 727-893-8675
E-mail: custserv@tampabay.com
Web Site: www.tampabay.com
Key Personnel
Chmn & CEO: Paul Tash *Tel:* 727-893-8887
Fax: 727-892-2328 *E-mail:* ptash@tampabay.
com
EVP & Gen Mgr: Joe De Luca *Tel:* 813-226-
3307 *E-mail:* jdeluca@tampabay.com
VP & CFO: Andy Corty *Tel:* 727-893-8204
Fax: 727-822-5083 *E-mail:* acorty@tampabay.
com
VP & Ed: Neil Brown *Tel:* 727-893-8441
E-mail: nbrown@tampabay.com
VP, Ad & Mktg: Bruce Faulmann *Tel:* 727-893-
8984 *Fax:* 727-892-2328 *E-mail:* bfaulmann@
tampabay.com
Exec Ed: Mark Katches *Tel:* 727-893-8441
E-mail: markkatches@tampabay.com
Sunday, in-house; occasional author interviews.
Circulation: 181,280 (d); 294,483 (Sun)
Digital & print: $7.75/mo (Sun only), $14.75/mo
(Mon-Sun); digital only: $7.75/mo

Technology Review
Published by MIT
One Main St, 13th fl, Cambridge, MA 02142
Tel: 617-475-8000 *Toll Free Tel:* 800-877-5230
(subns)
E-mail: customer-service@technologyreview.com
Web Site: www.technologyreview.com
Subscription Address: 235 Pine St, San Francisco,
CA 94104 *Tel:* 415-659-2980
Key Personnel
Publr & CEO: Elizabeth Bransom-Boudreau
Ed-in-Chief: Gideon Lichfield
Deputy Ed: Michael Reilly
Mng Ed: Timothy Maher
Ed-at-Large: David Rotman
MIT's national magazine on emerging technology.
No unsol mss, query first.
First published 1899
Book Use: Reviews & excerpts
Frequency: 6 issues/yr
Avg pages per issue: 80
Circulation: 177,436 paid
$35.95/yr digital, $55.95/yr print, $79.95/yr print
& digital
ISSN: 0040-1692

Buy freelance fiction, nonfiction; Sell articles &
ad reprints, back issues
Trim Size: 8 3/16 x 10 1/2
Ad Rates: B&W full page $21,056, 4-color full
page $28,075
Ad Closing Date(s): 5 weeks prior to cover date

The Telegram
Published by SaltWire Network
36 Austin St, St John's, NL A1B 4C2, Canada
Mailing Address: PO Box 8660, Sta A, St John's,
NL A1B 3T7, Canada
Tel: 709-364-6300 *Toll Free Tel:* 888-333-8840
(circ) *Fax:* 709-364-3939
E-mail: telegram@thetelegram.com; circ@
thetelegram.com
Web Site: www.thetelegram.com
Key Personnel
Sr Mng Ed: Steve Bartlett *E-mail:* steve.bartlett@
thetelegram.com
Night Ed: Mark Vaughan-Jackson *E-mail:* mark.
vaughan-jackson@thetelegram.com
Atlantic Regl Columnist: Russell Wangersky
E-mail: russell.wangersky@thetelegram.com
Daily, in-house & through wire services; occa-
sional author interviews; book reviews; publish
book lists from public library.
First published 1879
Circulation: 40,000 (e); 60,000 (weekend)
Digital & print: $19.99/mo (Fri & Sat), $26.07/
mo (Mon-Sat); digital only: $14.99/mo

Telegram & Gazette/Sunday Telegram
Published by GateHouse Media LLC
100 Front St, Worcester, MA 01615
Mailing Address: PO Box 15012, Worcester, MA
01615-0012
Tel: 508-793-9200 *Toll Free Tel:* 800-922-8200
Fax: 508-793-9281
E-mail: newstips@telegram.com
Web Site: www.telegram.com
Key Personnel
Pres: Paul Provost *Tel:* 508-793-9111
E-mail: paul.provost@telegram.com
Exec Ed: Dave Nordman *Tel:* 508-793-9375
E-mail: david.nordman@telegram.com
Syndicated book reviews; holiday roundups.
Digital & print: $26/13 wks (Sun only), $39/13
wks (Thurs-Sun), $52/13 wks (Mon-Sun); digi-
tal only: $39.99/yr

The Telegraph
Published by The McClatchy Co
1675 Montpelier Ave, Macon, GA 31201
Tel: 478-744-4200 *Toll Free Tel:* 800-342-5845
(GA only) *Fax:* 478-744-4385
Web Site: www.macon.com
Key Personnel
Sr Ed: Sundra Hominik *Tel:* 478-744-4345
E-mail: shominik@macon.com
Deputy Ed: Lauren Gorla *Tel:* 478-744-4292
E-mail: lgorla@macon.com
Sunday full-page reviews written in-house, by
freelancers & wire service. Occasional author
interviews.
First published 1826
Circulation: 60,000 (m); 75,000 (Sun)
Digital & print: $42.12/13 wks (Wed & Sun),
$56.16/13 wks (Thurs-Sun), $84.24/13 wks
(Mon-Sun); digital only: $8.99/mo, $129.99/yr

The Telegraph Journal
Published by Brunswick News Inc (BNI)
210 Crown St, St John, NB E2L 2X7, Canada
Mailing Address: PO Box 2350, St John, NB
E2L 3V8, Canada
Tel: 506-859-4900 *Toll Free Tel:* 800-295-8665
Fax: 506-633-6758
Web Site: tj.news
Key Personnel
Publr: James Irving
Ed-in-Chief: Wendy Metcalfe

Mng Ed: Jack Poirier
Sr Ed: Marie Sutherland
Weekly reviews (Sat), local author interviews.
First published 1862
Circulation: 40,000
$1/daily, $1.70/Sat, $25.99/mo
Avg reviews per issue: 5

The Tennessean
Published by Gannett Co Inc
1801 West End, 17th fl, Nashville, TN 37203
Tel: 612-259-8300 *Toll Free Tel:* 800-342-8237
E-mail: customer@tennessean.com
Web Site: www.tennessean.com
Key Personnel
Exec Ed: Maria DeVarenne
E-mail: mdevarenne@tennessean.com
General news/info, profiles, occasional reviews.
Circulation: 190,000 (d); 234,000 (Sat); 285,000
(Sun)

Texas Monthly
Published by Genesis Park
PO Box 1569, Austin, TX 78767-1569
Tel: 512-320-6900 *Toll Free Tel:* 800-759-2000
(orders) *Fax:* 512-476-9007
Web Site: www.texasmonthly.com
Key Personnel
CEO: Paul Hobby
Pres & Chief Creative Offr: Scott Brown
VP, Prodn: Roy Leamon *Tel:* 512-320-6990
E-mail: rleamon@texasmonthly.com
Ed-in-Chief: Tim Taliaferro
Deputy Ed: Jeff Salamon
Mng Ed: Christiane Wartell
Features Ed: Dave Mann
Sales Resource Mgr: Hannah Vickers
Covers politics & law, sports, culture, entertain-
ment & business for Texans.
First published 1973
Frequency: Monthly
Circulation: 300,000
$19.99/yr US print only, $24.99/yr US print &
digital; $14.99/yr US, CN & intl digital only
ISSN: 0148-7736
Sell articles, ad reprints & back issues
Trim Size: 8 1/8 x 10 1/2
Ad Closing Date(s): 4 weeks preceding cover
date

Time Magazine
Published by Time USA LLC
225 Liberty St, New York, NY 10281
E-mail: editors@time.com
Web Site: time.com
Key Personnel
Ed-in-Chief & CEO: Edward Felsenthal
Deputy Ed: Sam Jacobs; Eben Shapiro
Assoc Audience Engagement Ed: Annabel Gutter-
man *E-mail:* annabel.gutterman@time.com
Covers national & international news organized
by departments including art, behavior, books,
business, cinema, design, education, environ-
ment, law, modern living, music, nation, press,
religion, theater, video & world.
First published 1923
Book Use: Reviews
Frequency: Weekly
Avg pages per issue: 82
Circulation: 2,000,000
$5.99/issue, $12/yr
ISSN: 0040-781X
Ad Rates: B&W page $172,400, 4-color page
$265,100

Time Out!
Published by Daily Herald
Subsidiary of Paddock Publications Inc
95 W Algonquin Rd, Arlington Heights, IL 60005
Mailing Address: PO Box 280, Arlington Heights,
IL 60006-0280
Tel: 847-427-4300

E-mail: news@dailyherald.com
Web Site: www.dailyherald.com
Key Personnel
Chmn, Publr & CEO: Douglas K Ray *Tel:* 847-
427-4510 *E-mail:* dray@dailyherald.com
Metro Ed: Lisa Miner *Tel:* 847-427-4516
E-mail: lminer@dailyherald.com
Tabloid section in the *Daily Herald* print news-
paper & e-edition. Reviews, in-house & syndi-
cated, author interviews.
Frequency: Weekly (Fri)
Avg reviews per issue: 1 or 2
Ad Closing Date(s): Mon-Sat issues 5 pm 3 days
prior, Sun 5 pm Tues prior

The Times
Published by Gannett Co Inc
401 Market St, Suite 1500, Shreveport, LA
71101-6911
Tel: 318-459-3200 *Toll Free Tel:* 866-979-6397
(cust serv)
Web Site: www.shreveporttimes.com
Key Personnel
Circ Dir: Kevin Welsh *E-mail:* kwelsh@gannett.
com
Ed: Scott Ferrell *E-mail:* scott.ferrell@
shreveporttimes.com
Book reviews; author news.
Circulation: 139,000 (m); 169,000 (Sun)

The Times Argus
Published by Vermont Community Media LLC
47 N Main St, Suite 200, Barre, VT 05641
Tel: 802-479-0191 *Toll Free Tel:* 800-776-5512
Fax: 802-479-4096
E-mail: news@timesargus.com;
customerservices@timesargus.com
Web Site: www.timesargus.com
First published 1897
Frequency: Daily (Tues-Sat)
Circulation: 10,000 (e)

Times Colonist
Division of Glacier Community Media
2621 Douglas St, Victoria, BC V8T 4M2, Canada
Tel: 250-380-5211
E-mail: customerservice@timescolonist.com
Web Site: www.timescolonist.com
Key Personnel
Publr & Ed: Dave Obee *Tel:* 250-380-5201
E-mail: dobee@timescolonist.com
Book Columnist: Adrian Chamberlin
Monitor (Sun), Arts section (Fri); in-house &
through syndication. Occasional author inter-
views.
Frequency: Daily (Tues-Sun)
Circulation: 55,000 (d); 70,000 (Sun)
Digital & print: $22.50/mo (Fri-Sun), $26/mo
(Tues-Sun)

**The Times-Picayune | The New Orleans
Advocate**
Published by NOLA Media Group
840 St Charles Ave, New Orleans, LA 70130
Tel: 504-636-7400 *Toll Free Tel:* 800-960-6397
E-mail: newstips@theadvocate.com;
subscriberservices@theadvocate.com
Web Site: www.nola.com
Key Personnel
Mng Ed: Fred Kalmbach *Tel:* 225-388-0313
E-mail: fkalmbach@theadvocate.com
Ed: Peter Kovacs *Tel:* 225-388-0277
E-mail: pkovacs@theadvocate.com
Digital & print: $14.95/mo (Sat & Sun), $24.95/
mo (Mon-Sun); digital only: $9.99/mo

The Times Union
Published by Hearst Newspapers
Division of Hearst Corp
645 Albany Shaker Rd, Albany, NY 12211
Mailing Address: PO Box 15000, Albany, NY
12212

Tel: 518-454-5694 *Fax:* 515-454-5628
E-mail: tucitydesk@timesunion.com
Web Site: www.timesunion.com
Key Personnel
Publr & CEO: George R Hearst, III
  E-mail: ghearst@timesunion.com
VP & Ed: Rex Smith *E-mail:* rsmith@timesunion.
  com
VP, Ad: Tom Eason *E-mail:* teason@timesunion.
  com
Sr Ed, Features: Gary Hahn *E-mail:* ghahn@
  timesunion.com
Sr Ed, Local News: Casey Seiler
  E-mail: cseiler@timesunion.com
Sr Ed, News: Lisa Robert Lewis *E-mail:* llewis@
  timesunion.com
Features Ed: Sara Tracey *E-mail:* stracey@
  timesunion.com
Occasional author interviews.
$2/wk Sun print & digital, $1.50/wk digital only

Today's Christian Woman
Published by Christianity Today International
465 Gundersen Dr, Carol Stream, IL 60188-2498
Tel: 630-260-6200 *Toll Free Tel:* 877-247-4787
  (cust serv)
E-mail: tcw@christianitytoday.com
Web Site: www.todayschristianwoman.com
Key Personnel
Ed: Kelli B Trujillo
Mission: To challenge & equip women to love
  God more deeply & live fearlessly for his king-
  dom. Online only.
First published 2012
Book Use: Reviews published online
Free
Buy freelance nonfiction; Sell back issues, down-
  loadable PDFs

Topeka Capital-Journal
Published by GateHouse Media LLC
100 SE Ninth St, Suite 500, Topeka, KS 66612-
  1213
Tel: 785-295-1111 *Toll Free Tel:* 800-291-3914
Web Site: cjonline.com
Key Personnel
Publr: Stephen Wade *Tel:* 785-295-1115
  E-mail: stephen.wade@cjonline.com
Ed & VP, Audience Devt: Tomari Quinn
  E-mail: tomari.quinn@cjonline.com
Dir, Digital Sales: Terri Benson *E-mail:* terri.
  benson@cjonline.com
Sunday column, occasional author interviews.
First published 1879
Frequency: Daily
Circulation: 31,950 (d)
Digital & print: $17.90/mo (Sun only), $25.39/mo
  (Fri-Sun), $32.95/mo (Mon-Sun); digital only:
  $9.95/mo, $99.50/yr

The Toronto Star
Published by Toronto Star Newspapers Ltd
One Yonge St, Toronto, ON M5E 1E6, Canada
Tel: 416-367-2000 *Fax:* 416-869-4328
E-mail: city@thestar.ca
Web Site: www.thestar.com
Key Personnel
Publr: John Boynton
Ed: Irene Gentle
Edit Writer: Dianne Rinehart
Weekend section, reviews & column in "Book"
  section; in-house & other sources. Frequent
  author interviews.
Circulation: 193,050 (d); 290,153 (Sat); 185,159
  (Sun)
Digital & e-paper: $5.30/wk; digital, e-paper &
  print: $5.49/wk (weekend), $6.90/wk (Mon-
  Sun); digital only: $19.99/mo

Toronto Sun
Published by Postmedia Network Inc

365 Bloor St E, 6th fl, Toronto, ON M4W 3L4,
  Canada
Tel: 416-947-2222; 416-383-2300 *Fax:* 416-947-
  1664 (newsroom)
E-mail: torsun.citydesk@sunmedia.ca
Web Site: www.torontosun.com
Key Personnel
Deputy Ed: Kevin Hann *E-mail:* khann@
  postmedia.com
Entertainment Ed: Mark Daniell
  E-mail: mdaniell@postmedia.com
One page; in-house; frequent author interviews.
Circulation: 250,000 (d); 450,000 (Sun)
Digital, e-paper & print: $16/4 wks (Sun only),
  $30/4 wks (Mon-Sun); digital or e-paper:
  $9.99/mo, $99.99/yr

Town & Country
Published by Hearst Communications Inc
Division of Hearst Magazines
300 W 57 St, New York, NY 10019-3787
Tel: 212-903-5000; 212-649-2000
  Toll Free Tel: 800-289-8696 (subns)
E-mail: tnc@hearst.com
Web Site: www.townandcountrymag.com; www.
  hearst.com
Subscription Address: PO Box 6000, Harlan, IA
  51593
Key Personnel
Publr & Chief Revenue Offr: Jennifer Leven
  Bruno
Ed-in-Chief: Stellene Volandes
For the affluent; covers travel, the home, person-
  alities, fashion, beauty, food & other subjects.
First published 1846
Book Use: Reviews & excerpts, author profiles
Frequency: Monthly
Avg pages per issue: 230
Circulation: 464,330 paid & verified
$6.99/issue, $10/yr, $20/2 yrs, $25/3 yrs
ISSN: 0040-9952
Sell articles & ad reprints, back issues
Trim Size: 8.75 x 10.875
Ad Rates: B&W page $97,360, 4-color page
  $125,270
Ad Closing Date(s): 20th of 2nd month preceding
  issue date

The Town Talk, see Alexandria Daily Town Talk

Travel + Leisure
Published by Time Inc Affluent Media Group
225 Liberty St, New York, NY 10281
Tel: 212-522-1212 *Toll Free Tel:* 800-888-8728
  (cust serv)
Web Site: www.travelandleisure.com
Subscription Address: Box 62160, Tampa, FL
  33662 *Tel:* 813-979-6625
Key Personnel
Ed-in-Chief: Nathan Lump
Exec Ed: Jesse Ashlock
Mng Ed: Laura Teusink *E-mail:* laura.teusink@
  travelandleisure.com
Offers insider access to destination around the
  globe with a signature mix of smart advice,
  immersive photography & expert reporting on
  hotels, food, design, style, culture & trends.
First published 1971
Book Use: Reviews
Frequency: Monthly
Avg pages per issue: 200
Circulation: 953,484 paid & verified
$5.99/issue, $45/yr US, $57/yr CN
ISSN: 0041-2007
Buy freelance nonfiction & art; Sell articles, ad
  reprints & back issues
Trim Size: 8 x 10 1/2
Ad Rates: B&W page $111,100, 4-color page
  $163,300
Ad Closing Date(s): 2 months preceding issue
  date

Traverse, Northern Michigan's Magazine
Published by MyNorth Media
125 Park St, Suite 155, Traverse City, MI 49684
Tel: 231-941-8174 *Toll Free Tel:* 800-678-3416
E-mail: sales@traversemagazine.com
Web Site: mynorth.com
Key Personnel
Mktg Dir: Erin Lutke *Tel:* 231-941-5976
Sales Dir: Julie Parker *E-mail:* jparker@mynorth.
  com
Ed: Emily Tyra
Regional, highlighting the history, culture, people
  & natural beauty of northern Michigan.
First published 1981
Book Use: Excerpts
Frequency: Monthly
Avg pages per issue: 110
Circulation: 24,000
$24/yr
ISSN: 0746-2735
Buy fiction, nonfiction, poetry, art & cartoons;
  Sell ad reprints & back issues
Trim Size: 8 1/4 x 10 7/8
Ad Rates: 4-color full page $3,230
Ad Closing Date(s): 6 weeks prior to cover date

Tribune-Review
Published by Trib Total Media
622 Cabin Hill Dr, Greensburg, PA 15601
Tel: 724-836-6675 (newsroom) *Toll Free Tel:* 800-
  909-8742 (cust serv)
E-mail: gtrcity@tribweb.com
Web Site: www.triblive.com
Key Personnel
Exec Mng Ed: Jerry DeFlitch *E-mail:* jdeflitch@
  tribweb.com
Exec Ed: Susan K McFarland
  E-mail: smcfarland@tribweb.com
Features Ed: Jonna Miller *E-mail:* jonnamiller@
  tribweb.com
Sunday page in style section; in-house author.
First published 1974
Circulation: 120,000
Print & digital: $5/mo, $60/yr (Sun only), $6/mo,
  $72.80/yr (Thurs & Sun), $12/mo, $144/yr
  (Mon-Sun); digital only: $8/mo, $96/yr

Tricycle: The Buddhist Review
Published by The Tricycle Foundation
89 Fifth Ave, Suite 301, New York, NY 10003
Tel: 212-929-0320 *Toll Free Tel:* 800-873-9871
  (cust serv & subns)
E-mail: editorial@tricycle.org; tricycle@gpr4ads.
  com (ad rates)
Web Site: www.tricycle.org
Key Personnel
Publr & Ed: James Shaheen
Features Ed: Andrew Cooper
Explores the intersection of Buddhism & western
  culture. All subscriptions are payable through
  company web site. No unsol mss, query first
  via web site only. No e-mail queries accepted.
First published 1991
Frequency: Quarterly
Avg pages per issue: 120
Circulation: 30,000
$49/yr digital, $59/yr print & digital
ISSN: 1055-484X
Avg reviews per issue: 1-2
Trim Size: 8 1/4 x 10 7/8
Ad Closing Date(s): Nov (Winter), Feb (Spring),
  May (Summer), Aug (Fall)

Tulsa World
Published by BH Media Group Inc
315 S Boulder Ave, Tulsa, OK 74103
Mailing Address: PO Box 1770, Tulsa, OK 74102
Tel: 918-581-8400
E-mail: letters@tulsaworld.com
Web Site: www.tulsaworld.com
Subscription Address: PO Box 85048, Richmond,
  VA 23261-5048

Key Personnel
Pres & Publr: Gloria Fletcher
Exec Ed: Susan Ellerbach *E-mail:* susan.
ellerbach@tulsaworld.com
Sunday, publishing notes on paperbacks, weekly
books column page of reviews, page of book
news; in-house & syndicated book reviews.
Frequent author interviews.
Circulation: 144,000 (d); 207,000 (Sun)
Digital & print: $21.67/mo (Wed & Sun), $34.67/
mo (Wed & Fri-Sun), $43.45/mo (Mon-Sun);
digital only: $5.95/mo, $59.95/yr

TV Guide Magazine
Published by TV Guide Magazine LLC
Subsidiary of NTVB Media
50 Rockefeller Plaza, 14th fl, New York, NY
10020
Mailing Address: PO Box 37360, Boone, IA
50099-0360
Toll Free Tel: 800-866-1400 (cust serv)
E-mail: letters@tvgm.com
Web Site: www.tvguidemagazine.com; www.
tvinsider.com
TV, cable & pay-TV reporting. No unsol mss,
query first.
First published 1953
Book Use: Excerpts of TV-related material
Frequency: 26 issues/yr
Avg pages per issue: 88
Circulation: 1,100,000
$4.99/issue
Buy nonfiction; Sell articles & ad reprints
Trim Size: 7 x 10
Ad Rates: B&W full page $97,700, 4-color full
page $119,100

**Tyler Morning Telegraph -
Courier-Times-Telegraph**
Published by M Roberts Media
410 W Erwin St, Tyler, TX 75702
Tel: 903-597-8111
E-mail: opinion@tylerpaper.com; news@
tylerpaper.com
Web Site: tylerpaper.com
Key Personnel
Publr & Chief Revenue Offr: Justin Wilcox
Tel: 903-596-6299
Ed: Emily Guevara *Tel:* 903-596-6281
E-mail: eguevara@tylerpaper.com
Sunday, in-house; occasional local author inter-
views.
First published 1929
Circulation: 22,556 (m); 47,568 (Sun)

Unity Magazine
Published by Unity Worldwide Ministries
1901 NW Blue Pkwy, Unity Village, MO 64065-
0001
Tel: 816-524-3550 *Toll Free Tel:* 800-248-6489
(cust serv)
E-mail: unity@unityonline.org
Web Site: www.unity.org/publications/unity-
magazine
Key Personnel
Ed: Katy Koontz *E-mail:* umageditor@
unityonline.org
Contains articles on healing, metaphysics, pros-
perity, prayer & spirituality; advertising in-
cluded. First published as *Modern Thought*.
First published 1889
Frequency: 6 issues/yr
Avg pages per issue: 44
Circulation: 16,000 paid
$6.95/issue, $21.95/yr, $36.95/yr foreign
ISSN: 0162-3567
Buy nonfiction
Avg reviews per issue: 4
Trim Size: 8 1/2 x 11
Ad Rates: See media kit on web site

US Catholic
Published by Claretian Publications
205 W Monroe St, 9th fl, Chicago, IL 60606
Tel: 312-544-8191
E-mail: editors@uscatholic.org
Web Site: www.uscatholic.org; claretians.org
Subscription Address: PO Box 1201, Skogie, IL
60076-1021 *Toll Free Tel:* 800-328-6515
Key Personnel
Ed-in-Chief: Fr John J Molyneux
Mng Ed: Emily Sanna
General interest publication about Catholic faith
& life.
First published 1963
Book Use: Reviews
Frequency: Monthly
Avg pages per issue: 52
Circulation: 13,000 paid
US: $30/yr, $50/2 yrs, $70/3 yrs; CN & foreign:
$40/yr, $60/2 yrs, $80/3 yrs (print & digital)
ISSN: 0041-7548
Buy freelance fiction, nonfiction, art & cartoons,
poetry; Sell back issues & reprints
Avg reviews per issue: 3
Trim Size: 8 1/4 x 10 3/8
Ad Rates: 4-color full page $1,900, 1/2 page
$1,325
Ad Closing Date(s): 60 days preceding issue date

US News & World Report Magazine
Published by US News & World Report
1050 Thomas Jefferson St NW, 4th fl, Washing-
ton, DC 20007
Tel: 202-955-2225
Web Site: www.usnews.com
Key Personnel
Ed & Chief Content Offr: Brian Kelly
E-mail: bkelly@usnews.com
Analysis of important national & world news for
an affluent, well-educated audience. Digital
only.
First published 1933

Us Weekly
Published by American Media Inc
4 New York Plaza, New York, NY 10004
Tel: 212-545-4800
E-mail: letters@usmagazine.com
Web Site: www.usmagazine.com
Key Personnel
EVP & Chief Revenue Offr: Victoria Lasdon
Rose *Tel:* 212-484-3424 *E-mail:* victoria.rose@
usmagazine.com
Head, Integrated Sales: Brian Kennedy
E-mail: brian.kennedy@usmagazine.com
Brief articles on entertainment personalities;
heavy photographic content; all color.
First published 1977
Frequency: Weekly
Avg pages per issue: 80
Circulation: 1,950,000
$5.99/issue print or digital, $72/yr digital, $81/yr
print
ISSN: 0147-510X
Avg reviews per issue: 2-4
Trim Size: 7 3/4 x 10 1/2
Ad Rates: B&W full page $260,640, 1/2 page
$156,384, 4-color full page $289,595, 1/2 page
$173,757
Ad Closing Date(s): Mon closing 4 weeks prior
to issue date

USA Today
Published by Gannett Co Inc
7950 Jones Branch Dr, McLean, VA 22108-0605
Tel: 703-854-3400 *Toll Free Tel:* 800-872-0001
Web Site: www.usatoday.com
Key Personnel
Pres & Publr: Maribel Perez Wadsworth
Ed-in-Chief: Nicole Carroll
Friday page; in-house & freelance. Occasional
author interviews.

First published 1982
Circulation: 2,300,000 (d); 2,600,000 (Fri)
$9.99/mo e-newspaper, $4.99/mo digital

Utne Reader
Published by Ogden Publications
Subsidiary of Ogden News
1503 SW 42 St, Topeka, KS 66609-1265
Toll Free Tel: 800-736-8863 (cust serv); 800-678-
5779; 800-736-8863 (utne reader) *Fax:* 785-
274-4305
E-mail: editor@utne.com; customerservice@
ogdenpubs.com (subns)
Web Site: www.utne.com
Key Personnel
Publr: Bill Uhler
Ed: Chris Williams
Reprints the best articles from some 1,300 al-
ternative publications. The magazine provides
coverage missing from the mainstream, includ-
ing emerging trends & alternative views on
everything from politics & pop culture to the
environment & economy. The magazine edu-
cates & activates & is aimed at people passion-
ate about living at the forefront of progressive
culture. For submissions policy, see guidelines
on web site. No phone queries.
First published 1984
Book Use: Reviews, excerpts
Frequency: Quarterly
Avg pages per issue: 100
Circulation: 127,500
$6.99/issue, $39.96/yr US print & digital, $50/yr
CN, prepaid in US funds, $55/yr (air mail) for-
eign prepaid in US funds
ISSN: 1544-2225
Buy freelance art; Sell back issues
Trim Size: 8 x 10 1/2

The Valley Advocate
Published by Newspapers of New England (NNE)
115 Conz St, Northampton, MA 01060
Mailing Address: PO Box 477, Northampton, MA
01061
Tel: 413-584-5000
E-mail: editor@valleyadvocate.com
Web Site: www.valleyadvocate.com
Key Personnel
Ed: Dave Eisenstadter *E-mail:* deisen@
valleyadvocate.com
Syndicated book reviews once or twice a month,
occasional author interviews.
Frequency: Weekly
Circulation: 55,000
Free

Vancouver Sun
Published by Postmedia Network Inc
400-2985 Virtual Way, Vancouver, BC V5M 4X7,
Canada
Tel: 604-605-2000 *Fax:* 604-605-2323
E-mail: subscribe@vancouversun.com
Web Site: www.vancouversun.com
Key Personnel
Ed-in-Chief: Harold Munro *Tel:* 604-605-2185
E-mail: hmunro@postmedia.com
Mng Ed: Valerie Casselton *Tel:* 604-605-2125
E-mail: vcasselton@postmedia.com
Features Ed: Hardip Johal *Tel:* 604-605-2047
E-mail: hjohal@postmedia.com
Book reviews & author interviews.
First published 1912
Frequency: Daily (Mon-Sat)
Circulation: 208,675 (Sat)
$39/mo

Vanity Fair
Published by Conde Nast
One World Trade Center, 41st fl, New York, NY
10007-0090
Tel: 212-286-2860; 515-243-3273 (subns)
Toll Free Tel: 800-365-0635 (subns)
E-mail: letters@vf.com

Web Site: www.vanityfair.com; www.condenast.
  com
Key Personnel
CEO, Conde Nast: Roger Lynch
Chief Busn Offr: Chris Mitchell
Chief Revenue & Mktg Offr: Pamela Drucker
  Mann
Ed-in-Chief: Radhika Jones
Literature, the arts, politics & popular culture.
First published 1983
Book Use: Excerpts
Frequency: Monthly
Avg pages per issue: 125
Circulation: 1,197,922
Digital & print: $49.99/yr US, $59.99/yr CN,
  $68/yr foreign; digital only: $29.99/yr
Trim Size: 8 x 10 7/8
Ad Rates: 4-color full page $235,652, 1/2 page
  $149,471

Variety
Published by Penske Media Corp
11175 Santa Monica Blvd, Los Angeles, CA
  90025
Tel: 323-617-9100 *Toll Free Tel:* 800-552-3632
E-mail: variety@pubservice.com; news@variety.
  com
Web Site: www.variety.com
Key Personnel
Chief Mktg Offr: Dea Lawrence
Group Publr & Chief Revenue Offr: Michelle
  Sobrino-Sterns
SVP: Timothy M Gray
VP & Exec Ed: Steven Gaydos
Assoc Publr: Donna Pennestri
Exec Ed: Ramin Setoodeh
Mng Ed: Joe Bel Bruno
Co Ed-in-Chief: Claudia Eller; Andrew Wallen-
  stein
Mng Ed, Television: Cynthia Littleton
B2B publication for the entertainment industry.
First published 1905
Frequency: 48 issues/yr
Circulation: 40,000
$109/yr print, $129/yr print +/or digital US, $299/
  yr print & digital CN, $129/yr digital only CN
  & intl, $349/yr print & digital intl
ISSN: 0042-2738

VFW Magazine
Published by Veterans of Foreign Wars of the US
406 W 34 St, Suite 523, Kansas City, MO 64111
Tel: 816-756-3390 *Fax:* 816-968-1169
E-mail: magazine@vfw.org
Web Site: www.vfw.org/media-and-events/vfw-
  magazine
Key Personnel
Publr & Ed-in-Chief: Timothy K Dyhouse
  E-mail: tdyhouse@vfw.org
Art Dir: Lauren Goldman *E-mail:* lgoldman@vfw.
  org
Sr Ed: Janie Dyhouse *E-mail:* jdyhouse@vfw.org
Assoc Ed: Kari Williams *E-mail:* kwilliams@vfw.
  org
Sr Writer: Dave Spiva *E-mail:* dspiva@vfw.org
Articles of current interest to veterans; for VFW
  members. Includes book reviews. No unsol
  mss, query first.
First published 1904
Book Use: Excerpts
Frequency: 10 issues/yr
Avg pages per issue: 56
Circulation: 1,300,000 paid
Free to VFW membs, $15/yr nonmembs, $20/yr
  foreign
ISSN: 0161-8598
Buy freelance nonfiction, art; Sell articles & ad
  reprints, back issues
Ad Rates: B&W full page $29,830, 4-color full
  page $37,755
Ad Closing Date(s): see web site for dates

Victoria Advocate
311 E Constitution St, Victoria, TX 77901
Mailing Address: PO Box 1518, Victoria, TX
  77902
Tel: 361-574-1222 (newsroom); 361-575-1451
  Toll Free Tel: 800-365-5779 (cust serv)
  Fax: 361-574-1220 (newsroom); 361-574-1225
E-mail: feedback@vicad.com
Web Site: www.victoriaadvocate.com
Key Personnel
Publr & Ed: Chris Cobler *Tel:* 361-574-1271
  E-mail: ccobler@vicad.com
Mng Ed: Becky Cooper *Tel:* 361-574-1285
  E-mail: bcooper@vicad.com
Features Ed: Elena Watts *Tel:* 361-580-6585
  E-mail: ewatts@vicad.com
Sunday, book reviews in-house & through syndi-
  cation.
First published 1846
Circulation: 40,100 (d); 42,300 (Sun)
Digital & print: $8.99/4 wks (Sun only), $15/4
  wks (Mon-Sun); digital only: $15/4 wks; print
  only: $24.25/4 wks (Mon-Sat)

The Virginian-Pilot
Published by Tribune Publishing Co
150 W Brambleton Ave, Norfolk, VA 23510
Tel: 757-446-9000
Web Site: pilotonline.com
Key Personnel
Mng Ed: Ryan Gilchrest *E-mail:* rgilchrest@
  dailypress.com
Books Ed: Erica Smith *Tel:* 757-446-2354
  E-mail: erica.smith@pilotonline.com
Sundays, 1 1/2 pages. Rare feature stories on
  writers. Often carry syndicated reviews. Re-
  views written by freelancers. Columns weekly,
  by alternating freelancers - one on children's &
  young adult, the other on adult titles.
First published 1865
Circulation: 199,800 (m); 228,600 (Sat); 238,600
  (Sun)
$1.50/Sun; digital only: $1.99/wk; digital & print:
  $4.99/wk (Mon-Sun)

Vogue
Published by Conde Nast
One World Trade Center, 26th fl, New York, NY
  10007-0090
Tel: 212-286-2860; 515-243-3273 (subns)
  Toll Free Tel: 800-234-2347 (subns); 800-405-
  8085 (intl subns)
E-mail: contact@vogue.com
Web Site: www.vogue.com; www.condenast.com
Key Personnel
Chief Busn Offr: Susan Plagemann
  E-mail: susan_plagemann@condenast.com
Ed-in-Chief: Anna Wintour
Mgr, Sales Opers: Nina Capaccione
  E-mail: nina_capaccione@condenast.com
Covers fashion, beauty, health, fitness, travel, en-
  tertainment & other areas of interest to women.
First published 1892
Book Use: Monthly book reviews
Frequency: Monthly
Avg pages per issue: 428
Circulation: 1,267,754
$21.99/yr US, $50/yr CN, $70/yr intl
ISSN: 0042-8000
Trim Size: 8 x 10 7/8
Ad Rates: 4-color full page $196,535, 1/2 page
  $132,687

The Wall Street Journal, A News Corp Co
Published by Dow Jones & Company
1211 Avenue of the Americas, 8th fl, New York,
  NY 10036
Tel: 212-416-3000; 609-514-0870
  Toll Free Tel: 800-369-2834; 800-568-7625
  (cust support)
E-mail: wsjsupport@wsj.com
Web Site: www.wsj.com; www.dowjones.com

Subscription Address: 200 Burnett Rd, Chicopee,
  MA 01020
Key Personnel
Publr: William Lewis
Ed-in-Chief: Matt Murray
Features: Michael W Miller
In-house & other sources; rare author interviews.
First published 1889
Frequency: 6 days/wk (Mon-Fri & combined Sat/
  Sun weekend ed)
Circulation: 1,011,200
$43/mo classic print, $39/mo all access digital,
  $45/mo print & digital
Avg reviews per issue: 1
Ad Rates: B&W page $277,200, 1/2 page
  $138,600, color page $354,823.27, 1/2 page
  $198,709.39 (natl rates)

Walla Walla Union-Bulletin
112 S First Ave, Walla Walla, WA 99362
Mailing Address: PO Box 1358, Walla Walla, WA
  99362-0306
Tel: 509-525-3300; 509-525-3301 (cust serv)
  Toll Free Tel: 800-423-5617
E-mail: news@wwub.com
Web Site: www.union-bulletin.com
Key Personnel
Publr: Brian Hunt *Tel:* 509-526-8331
Ed: Dian Ver Valen *Tel:* 509-526-8320
  E-mail: dianvervalen@wwub.com
Ed, Marquee: Annie Charnley Eveland *Tel:* 509-
  526-8313 *E-mail:* annieeveland@wwub.com
Arts & Entertainment (Thursday) distributed
  weekly in the area. Reviews (freelancers), syn-
  dicated, occasional local author interviews.
First published 1934
Frequency: Daily (Mon-Fri & Sun)
Avg pages per issue: 16
Circulation: 10,000
Print only: $6.50/mo (Sun only), $14.30/mo
  (Mon-Fri), $15.60/mo (Mon-Fri & Sun); dig-
  ital only: $15.60/mo
Avg reviews per issue: 1

Washington Monthly
Published by Washington Monthly Corp
1200 18 St NW, Suite 330, Washington, DC
  20036
Tel: 202-955-9010 *Fax:* 202-955-9011
E-mail: editors@washingtonmonthly.com
Web Site: www.washingtonmonthly.com
Key Personnel
VP: Edwin Grosvenor *E-mail:* egrosvenor@
  washingtonmonthly.com
VP, Circ & Busn: Claire Iseli *E-mail:* claire@
  washingtonmonthly.com
Publr: Diane Straus
Ed-in-Chief: Paul Glastris *E-mail:* pglastris@
  washingtonmonthly.com
Fresh look at government, public policy, current
  news, cultural issues.
First published 1969
Book Use: Reviews & excerpts
Frequency: 5 issues/yr
Avg pages per issue: 64
Circulation: 15,000 paid; 3,000 controlled
$5.95/issue, $19.95/yr
ISSN: 0043-0633
Sell articles, back issues & college guide
Avg reviews per issue: 10
Trim Size: 8 3/8 x 10 7/8
Ad Rates: 4-color full page $2,700, cover 2
  $4,000, cover 3 $3,500, cover 4 $4,000

The Washington Post Magazine
Published by The Washington Post Co
One Franklin Sq, 1301 "K" St NW, Washington,
  DC 20071
Tel: 202-334-7585 *Toll Free Tel:* 800-477-4679
E-mail: wpmagazine@washpost.com
Web Site: www.washingtonpost.com/lifestyle/
  magazine

Key Personnel
Exec Features Ed: Liz Seymour
Deputy Features Ed: Mitch Rubin
Ed: Richard Just
Deputy Ed: David Rowell
Aims to tell stories about the Washington area through long-form narrative journalism.
First published 1986
Book Use: Excerpts & adaptations
Frequency: Weekly (Sun)
Circulation: 1,267,759

The Washington Times
Published by The Washington Times Corp
3600 New York Ave NE, Washington, DC 20002
Tel: 202-636-3000
E-mail: circulation@washingtontimes.com
Web Site: www.washingtontimes.com
Key Personnel
Pres & Exec Ed: Christopher Dolan *Tel:* 202-636-3183 *E-mail:* cdolan@washingtontimes.com
Books Ed: Carol Herman
In-house, freelance & other sources. Book section Mon-Fri. Occasional author interviews.
Circulation: 100,000 (d)
$99.95/yr print or digital, $12.95/mo digital only
Avg reviews per issue: 12

Washingtonian
Published by Washingtonian Media Inc
1828 "L" St NW, Suite 200, Washington, DC 20036
Tel: 202-296-3600 (edit & busn); 202-296-1246 (print & online ad); 202-296-7580 (classified); 202-296-0715 (subns)
E-mail: editorial@washingtonian.com; subscriptions@washingtonian.com
Web Site: www.washingtonian.com
Subscription Address: The Washingtonian Subscription Service, PO Box 5530, Harlan, IA 51593-1030
Key Personnel
Pres & CEO: Catherine Merrill Williams
COO: Michael Johnson
Publr: Susan Farkas *E-mail:* sfarkas@washingtonian.com
Ad Dir: Kristen Anderson *E-mail:* kanderson@washingtonian.com
Prodn Dir: Cathy Dobos *E-mail:* cdobos@washingtonian.com
Exec Ed: Sherri Dalphonse *E-mail:* sdalphonse@washingtonian.com
Sr Mng Ed: William O'Sullivan *E-mail:* bosullivan@washingtonian.com
Articles Ed: Kristen Hinman
Ed: Michael Schaffer
Prodn Mgr: Sarah Rina Huang
Features matters of general interest for residents of the DC area.
First published 1965
Book Use: Washington-related excerpts
Frequency: Monthly
Avg pages per issue: 160
Circulation: 113,009 paid
$18/yr print & digital, $9.99/yr digital only
ISSN: 0043-0897
Buy freelance nonfiction & art; Sell back issues
Ad Rates: 4-color page $22,400
Ad Closing Date(s): 2 months preceding publication date

Watertown Daily Times
Published by Johnson Newspaper Corp
260 Washington St, Watertown, NY 13601
Tel: 315-782-1000 *Toll Free Tel:* 800-642-6222
Fax: 315-661-2523 (newsroom); 315-661-2520 (busn off)
E-mail: news@wdt.net
Web Site: www.nny360.com
Key Personnel
Mng Ed: Alec Johnson *Tel:* 315-661-2351
E-mail: aej@wdt.net

Features Ed: Christina Knott *Tel:* 315-661-2397
E-mail: cknott@wdt.net
Weekly half-page devoted to books, through syndication & weekly author interviews; produce own magazine section.
First published 1861
Frequency: Daily (Tues-Sun)
Circulation: 37,000 (d); 40,000 (Sun)
Digital & print: $20.35/mo (Fri-Sun), $25.11/mo (Tues-Sat), $26.85/mo (Tues-Sun); digital only: $9.99/mo, $119.88/yr

Welland Tribune
Published by Metroland Media Group Ltd
55 King St, Suite 600, St Catharines, ON L2R 3H5, Canada
Tel: 905-440-2516
E-mail: tribunecirc@niagaradailies.com (cust serv)
Web Site: www.wellandtribune.ca
Key Personnel
Group Dir, Media Sales: Jay Allin *Tel:* 905-225-1614 *E-mail:* jallin@starmetrolandmedia.com
Ed-in-Chief: Angus Scott *Tel:* 905-225-1625
E-mail: angus.scott@niagaradailies.com
Occasionally, in-house; local author interviews covering the Niagara area; also syndicated.
Circulation: 16,500 (m)
$3.25/wk (Thurs-Sat), $5.21/wk (Mon-Sat), $5.99/4 wks e-paper

The Whitehorse Star
Published by Whitehorse Star Ltd
2149 Second Ave, Whitehorse, YT Y1A 1C5, Canada
Tel: 867-667-4481 *Fax:* 867-668-7130
E-mail: letters@whitehorsestar.com
Web Site: www.whitehorsestar.com
Key Personnel
Publr: Ms Jackie Pierce
Ed: Jim Butler
One column every Friday edition; author interviews.
Circulation: 5,100 (e)
$1/issue (Mon & Wed), $1.25/issue (Fri), $15/mo full digital & archives

The Wichita Eagle
Published by The McClatchy Co
330 N Mead St, Wichita, KS 67202
Tel: 316-268-6000 *Toll Free Tel:* 800-200-6627 (subns)
Web Site: www.kansas.com
Key Personnel
Exec Ed: Michael Roehrman *Tel:* 316-269-6753
One Sunday page, syndicated.
Circulation: 70,000 (d); 110,000 (Sun)
Digital & print: $41.93/13 wks (Sun only), $102.02/13 wks (Mon-Fri & Sun); digital only: $12.99/mo, $129.99/yr
Avg reviews per issue: 4

Wichita Falls Times Record News
Published by Gannett Co Inc
1301 Lamar St, Wichita Falls, TX 76301
Mailing Address: PO Box 120, Wichita Falls, TX 76307-0120
Tel: 940-767-8341 *Toll Free Tel:* 800-627-1646
Web Site: www.timesrecordnews.com
Key Personnel
Ed: Deanna Watson *E-mail:* deanna.watson@timesrecordnews.com
Weekly broadsheet, in-house & through syndication; occasional author interviews; Sunday books page.
Circulation: 16,000 (d); 18,000 (Sun)

Willamette Week
Published by City of Roses Newspaper Co
2220 NW Quimby St, Portland, OR 97210
Tel: 503-243-2122

Web Site: www.wweek.com
Key Personnel
Publr & Ed: Mark Zusman *E-mail:* mzusman@wweek.com
Arts & Culture Ed: Matthew Singer
E-mail: msinger@wweek.com
First published 1974
Frequency: Weekly
Circulation: 70,000
Free

The Wilson Quarterly
Published by Woodrow Wilson International Center for Scholars
One Woodrow Wilson Plaza, 1300 Pennsylvania Ave NW, Washington, DC 20004-3027
Tel: 202-691-4000
E-mail: wq@wilsoncenter.org
Web Site: wilsonquarterly.com
Key Personnel
Mng Ed: Richard Solash *E-mail:* richard.solash@wilsoncenter.org
Busn Dir: Suzanne Napper *E-mail:* suzanne.napper@wilsoncenter.org
Online magazine which provides unique insight, deep dives & fresh takes on developments in politics, culture, foreign affairs, history, the environment & more. Selected e-mail submissions will be considered.
First published 1976
Frequency: Quarterly
ISSN: 0363-3276
Buy nonfiction, multimedia

Windsor Star
Published by Postmedia Network Inc
300 Oulette Ave, Windsor, ON N9A 7B4, Canada
Tel: 519-225-5711 *Toll Free Tel:* 800-265-5647 (CN only) *Fax:* 519-255-5515
Web Site: www.windsorstar.com
Key Personnel
Mng Ed: Craig Pearson *Tel:* 519-255-5767
E-mail: cpearson@postmedia.com
Saturday page, in-house; monthly author interviews.
First published 1918
Circulation: 81,000 (d); 95,700 (Sat)
$30/mo (Tues-Sat); digital & print: $18/mo (Sat only); digital only: $9.95/mo, $99.99/yr; e-paper: $1.99/issue, $9.99/mo, $99.99/yr
ISSN: 0839-2277

Winnipeg Free Press
Published by FP Newspapers Inc
1355 Mountain Ave, Winnipeg, MB R2X 3B6, Canada
Tel: 204-697-7000 *Toll Free Tel:* 800-542-8900
Fax: 204-697-7412
E-mail: letters@freepress.mb.ca
Web Site: www.winnipegfreepress.com
Key Personnel
Publr: Bob Cox *Tel:* 204-697-7547 *E-mail:* bob.cox@freepress.mb.ca
Literary Ed: Ben MacPhee-Sigurdson *Tel:* 204-697-7307 *E-mail:* ben.macphee-sigurdson@freepress.mb.ca
Feature author interviews; in-house book & freelance reviews. Books section runs every Saturday in the Weekend Review section.
Circulation: 125,000 (d); 162,000 (Sat)
Digital & print: $4.96/wk (Sat only), $8.72/wk (Mon-Sat); digital only: $3.92/wk
Avg reviews per issue: 8-9

Winston-Salem Journal
Published by BH Media Group Inc
418 N Marshall St, Winston-Salem, NC 27102
Mailing Address: PO Box 3159, Winston-Salem, NC 27102
Tel: 336-727-7211 *Toll Free Tel:* 800-642-0925
E-mail: contact@wsjournal.com
Web Site: www.journalnow.com

Key Personnel
Weekend Ed: Jon Jimison *Tel:* 336-727-7287
  E-mail: jjimison@wsjournal.com
Sunday book review, in-house & by freelancers.
  Several author interviews per year via features.
First published 1897
Circulation: 95,992 (m); 102,000 (Sun)
Digital & print: $19.15/mo (Sun only), $23.50/mo
  (Mon, Sat & Sun), $38.48/mo (Mon-Sun); digital only: $8.95/mo

Wisconsin State Journal
Published by Capital Newspapers
Division of Lee Enterprises Inc
1901 Fish Hatchery Rd, Madison, WI 53713
Mailing Address: PO Box 8056, Madison, WI
  53708
Tel: 608-252-6100; 608-252-6200
  Toll Free Tel: 800-362-8333 (cust serv & circ)
E-mail: wsjcity@madison.com
Web Site: madison.com/wsj
Key Personnel
Publr: Tom Wiley *E-mail:* twiley@madison.com
Ed: John Smalley *Tel:* 608-252-6104
  E-mail: jsmalley@madison.com
Sunday page, features, columns; in-house & other
  book reviews. Author interviews.
Circulation: 108,000 (d); 114,000 (Sat); 161,000
  (Sun)
$5/mo digital access
ISSN: 0749-405X

Working Mother
Published by Working Mother Network
Division of Bonnier Corp
2 Park Ave, 9th fl, New York, NY 10016
Tel: 212-779-5000
Web Site: www.workingmother.com
Key Personnel
Editor-in-Chief: Meredith Bodgas
  E-mail: meredith.bodgas@workingmother.com
Creative Dir: Cara Reynoso *E-mail:* cara.
  reynoso@workingmother.com
Sr Ed: Audrey Goodson Kingo *E-mail:* audrey.
  kingo@workingmother.com
Assoc Publr: Olivia Kopchik *E-mail:* olivia.
  kopchik@workingmother.com
Contains articles & information for working
  mothers with children at home. Features articles & columns on money management, family
  relationships, health care, personal fulfillment,
  cooking & entertainment, business & careers,
  child development & humor. No unsol mss,
  query first.
First published 1979

Book Use: Reviews & excerpts
Frequency: Quarterly
Avg pages per issue: 53
Circulation: 750,000 paid
$3.99/issue, $9.97/yr, $12.97/3 yrs, $19.97/yr
  (USD) CN, $29.97/yr foreign
Buy nonfiction; Sell back issues $7 includes shipping & handling
Trim Size: 7 7/8 x 10 1/2
Ad Rates: B&W full page $61,010; 4-color full
  page $71,870

Wyoming Tribune-Eagle
Published by Adams Publishing Group
702 W Lincolnway, Cheyenne, WY 82001
Tel: 307-634-3361 *Toll Free Tel:* 800-561-6268
  Fax: 307-633-3189 (newsroom); 307-633-3191
E-mail: customerservice@wyomingnews.com
Web Site: www.wyomingnews.com
Key Personnel
Mng Ed: Brian Martin *Tel:* 307-633-3120
  E-mail: bmartin@wyomingnews.com
Asst Mng Ed: Erica Klimt *Tel:* 307-633-3129
  E-mail: eklimt@wyomingnews.com
Features Ed: Ellen Fike *Tel:* 307-633-3135
  E-mail: efike@wyomingnews.com
In-house & through syndication: "To Do" entertainment section, Fri-Sun; occasional author
  interviews.
Frequency: Daily (Tues-Sun)
Circulation: 14,000 (d); 14,750 (Sun)
$100/6 mos, $182/yr, $95/yr digital

Yachting®
Published by Bonnier Corp
Division of The Bonnier Group
460 N Orlando Ave, Suite 200, Winter Park, FL
  32789
Tel: 407-571-4914
Web Site: www.yachtingmagazine.com
Subscription Address: PO Box 6364, Harlan,
  IA 51593 *Tel:* 515-237-3697 (intl) *Toll Free
  Tel:* 800-999-0869
Key Personnel
Publr: David Carr *Tel:* 954-594-7655
  E-mail: david.carr@bonniercorp.com
Ed-in-Chief: Patrick Sciacca *E-mail:* editor@
  yachtingmagazine.com
Mktg & Events Mgr: Deborah Velez *Tel:* 407-
  571-4839 *E-mail:* deborah.velez@bonniercorp.
  com
For those interested in pleasure boats & luxury
  yachts; articles on large power & sailing vessels, yachting events & marine equipment.
First published 1907

Frequency: Monthly
Avg pages per issue: 250
Circulation: 93,736 paid
$7/issue, $16/yr, $39/yr CN, $62/yr intl
Buy nonfiction & photos of interest to yachtsmen;
  Sell article & ad reprints, back issues
Trim Size: 8 3/8 x 10 7/8
Ad Rates: B&W page $36,410, 4-color page
  $40,010
Ad Closing Date(s): 45 days prior to sale date

Yankee Magazine
Published by Yankee Publishing Inc
1121 Main St, Dublin, NH 03444
Mailing Address: PO Box 520, Dublin, NH
  03444
Tel: 603-563-8111
Web Site: newengland.com
Subscription Address: PO Box 420235, Palm
  Coast, FL 32142-0235 *Toll Free Tel:* 800-288-
  4284
Key Personnel
Pres: Jamie Trowbridge
VP & Publr: Brook Holmberg
VP, Sales: J D Hale, Jr
Ed-in-Chief: Judson Hale
Ed: Mel Allen
New England's magazine with regional stories
  covering food, travel, home, garden & other
  topics.
First published 1935
Book Use: Reviews & excerpts of titles that deal
  with New England
Frequency: 6 issues/yr
Avg pages per issue: 128
Circulation: 282,000 paid
$4.99/issue, $24/yr
ISSN: 0044-0191
Buy freelance fiction, nonfiction, photography
Trim Size: 7 3/4 x 10 1/2

Zest Magazine
Published by Houston Chronicle Publishing Co
Subsidiary of Hearst Corp
4747 Southwest Fwy, Houston, TX 77027
Mailing Address: PO Box 4260, Houston, TX
  77210-4260
Tel: 713-220-7171 *Fax:* 713-362-3575
Web Site: www.houstonchronicle.com
Key Personnel
Chmn: Jack Sweeney
Books Ed: Alyson Ward *Tel:* 713-362-7128
  E-mail: alyson.ward@chron.com
Circulation: 825,000

News Services & Feature Syndicates

A & A
Division of Abramson & Abramson
PO Box 543, Hazelwood, MO 63042-0543
Tel: 314-786-5046
E-mail: aaartwork@aol.com; aaauthor@aol.com
Web Site: www.elaineabramson.com
Key Personnel
Pres: Elaine Sandra Abramson
EVP: Martin Stanley Abramson
Founded: 1967
Syndicate *Appraisals by Abramson*, an appraisal
column; *Pattern Craft by A & A*, craft &
sewing patterns with instructions; *The Golden
Gourmets*, cartoons & stories; *Those Char-
acters From Cowtown*, cartoons; *The Ro-
mantiCats*, cartoons; *COW-TOWN*, cartoons;
Party Gators, cartoons; *The Frisky Investiga-
tors*, cartoons; *The Star Staples*, cartoons; *The
Collegiate Crunchies*, cartoons; *The Culinary
Court*, cartoons; *The Artists' World*, column
dealing with problems the artist faces such as
health insurance, copyrights, etc. *The Collegiate Crunchies, The RomantiCats & COW-
TOWN* appearing on the Pixelon Network; *Ru-
fus & Mary*, cartoons; *Kaya, the Lucky Lab*;
Myschevious Animals; *Tummy Ticklers*, cartoons; *From Fat to Fabulous: A Lifestyle Guide
for Restaurant Lovers*. All submissions must
be through a recognized agent. All unagented
submissions are returned unopened. No unsol
submissions. Author or artist must have creden-
tials in subject applying to write or illustrate.
We license our work out & also provide art &
author services.
Membership(s): Best of Missouri Hands; Chesterfield Writers Guild; Composers, Authors &
Artists of America; Creative Coalition; Croak
& Dagger New Mexico; Electronically Published Internet Connection (EPIC); Graphic
Artists Guild; Greater St Louis Art Association (GSLAA); Greater St Louis Artists Guild;
Maryland Art League; Midwest Independent
Booksellers Association (MIBA); Mystery
Writers of America (MWA); National Associ-
ation of Memoir Writers (NAMW); National
Association of Television Program Execu-
tives Inc (NATPE); National League of Amer-
ican Pen Women; National Writers Associa-
tion (NWA); National Writers Union (NWU);
New Mexico Book Co-op; North Texas Writ-
ers Group; Publishers Association of the West
(PubWest); Romance Writers of America
(RWA); Romance Writers of America (RWA),
Kiss of Death Chapter; St Louis Writers Guild;
Sisters in Crime; Society of Children's Book
Writers & Illustrators (SCBWI); Southern In-
dependent Booksellers Alliance (SIBA); South-
West Writers; Texas Association of Motion
Media Professionals (TAMMP); Thriller Writ-
ers of America; Writers Under the Arch

American Press Service & Features Syndicate
PO Box 854, Van Nuys, CA 91408
Tel: 818-997-6496
E-mail: iscs3assoc@aol.com
Key Personnel
Pres: Andrew K Wellworth
VP & Gen Mgr: Israel I Bick
Founded: 1971
300 members. Query first.
Membership(s): Los Angeles Press Club

American Urban Radio Networks (AURN)
938 Penn Ave, Suite 701, Pittsburgh, PA 15222-
3811

Tel: 412-456-4099 *Fax:* 412-456-4077
Web Site: www.aurn.com
Key Personnel
SVP, Prog Opers & Affiliations: Lenore Williams
Tel: 412-456-4098 *E-mail:* lwilliams@aurn.com
Founded: 1972
Entertainment, sports, news; 450 subscribers;
movie reviews.
Branch Office(s)
932 W Madison, Chicago, IL 60607, Exec Sales
Dir, Western Reg: Stephen Bates *Tel:* 312-558-
1906 *E-mail:* sbates@aurn.com
112 W 34 St, Suite 2110, New York, NY 10120,
Pres, Sales: Andy Anderson *Tel:* 212-883-2117
Fax: 212-687-3792 *E-mail:* aanderson@aurn.
com

Andrews McMeel Syndication
1130 Walnut St, Kansas City, MO 64106-2109
Tel: 816-581-7300 *Toll Free Tel:* 800-255-6734
Web Site: syndication.andrewsmcmeel.com
Key Personnel
Pres & CEO: Andy Sareyan *E-mail:* asareyan@
amuniversal.com
VP & Mng Ed: Sue Roush *Tel:* 816-581-7320
E-mail: sroush@amuniversal.com
VP, Sales: John Vivona *Tel:* 816-581-7350
E-mail: salesdirector@amuniversal.com
Founded: 1970
Newspaper syndication (columnists, cartoons,
comic strips).

Associated Press (AP)
200 Liberty St, New York, NY 10281
Tel: 212-621-1500
E-mail: info@ap.org
Web Site: www.ap.org
Key Personnel
Pres & CEO: Gary Pruitt
Ed-at-Large: Jerry Schwartz
Multimedia news service.
Number of Subscribers: 10,000

BGHT News
Division of Master Associates
Townsend, 4 Gabriel St, Livingston Manor, NY
12758
Mailing Address: PO Box 116, Livingston Manor,
NY 12758-0116
Tel: 845-439-8177 *Fax:* 845-205-4474
Web Site: bght.blogspot.com
Key Personnel
Pres & CEO: E C Townsend
E-mail: edwardctownsend@hotmail.com
Syndicated bowling & golf columns & feature
stories in newspapers & Internet news outlets.
Syndicated "Here and There" travel column.

Ashleigh Brilliant Enterprises
117 W Valerio St, Santa Barbara, CA 93101
Tel: 805-682-0531
Web Site: www.ashleighbrilliant.com
Key Personnel
Pres: Ashleigh Brilliant
VP: Dorothy Brilliant
Founded: 1967
Panel feature; send $5 with SASE for samples &
catalog; accept unsol mss.

Broadcast Wire & Audio
Subsidiary of The Canadian Press/La Presse
Canadienne
c/o The Canadian Press, 36 King St E, Toronto,
ON M5C 2L9, Canada

Tel: 416-507-2126 *Toll Free Tel:* 800-434-7578
(CN only) *Fax:* 416-364-1325
E-mail: broadcast@thecanadianpress.com
Web Site: www.thecanadianpress.com
Key Personnel
Dir, Broadcasting: Rose Kingdon
Data & audio news agency serving Canadian
broadcasters providing regional, national &
international news, weather, sports & features
& alphanumeric cable TV information displays
to Canada's major CATV operators.
Number of Subscribers: 400

Business Wire
Division of Berkshire Hathaway Co
101 California St, 20th fl, San Francisco, CA
94111
Tel: 415-986-4422 *Toll Free Tel:* 800-227-0845
E-mail: info@businesswire.com
Web Site: www.businesswire.com
Key Personnel
SVP, Global Media: Neil Hershberg
VP, Digital Strategy: Michael Toner
VP, Prod Mgmt: Galina Patil
Dir, Prod Mktg Mgmt: Serena Ehrlich
Dir, Tradeshow & Event Servs: Jim Liebenau
Founded: 1961
Business Wire electronically disseminates some
1,000 full-text news releases daily to the media, the Internet, online services & databases &
the global investment community in 150 countries in 45 languages. The company's multi-
channel delivery network, with access to some
60 international & national news agencies, financial information providers & web-based
news services throughout North America, Europe, Asia, Latin America, the Middle East
& Africa, provides real-time, simultaneous
access to key audiences – the news media,
trade publications, institutional & individual
investors, business-to-business decision-makers
& consumers. Business Wire has 24 US offices,
Paris, Frankfurt, London, Brussels, Tokyo &
Sydney offices & reciprocal offices throughout
the world.
Branch Office(s)
40 E 52 St, 14th fl, New York, NY 10022
Tel: 212-752-9600 *Toll Free Tel:* 800-221-2462

California Focus, see Southern California Focus

The Canadian Press/La Presse Canadienne
36 King St E, Toronto, ON M5C 2L9, Canada
Tel: 416-364-0321 *Fax:* 416-364-0207 (news-
room)
E-mail: sales@thecanadianpress.com
Web Site: www.thecanadianpress.com
Key Personnel
CEO: Malcolm Kirk
Ed-in-Chief: Stephen Meurice
Founded: 1917
News-gathering agency. Provides content licens-
ing services, custom content production ser-
vices, real-time & archival database services,
media monitoring services, newsfeed syndica-
tion services & publishes *The Canadian Press
Stylebook & Caps & Spelling*.
Number of Subscribers: 600

Capitol News Service
Division of Metropolitan News
530 Bercut Dr, Suite E, Sacramento, CA 95811
Tel: 916-445-6336
E-mail: sacramentobulletin@gmail.com

Web Site: www.mnc.net/capitol.htm
Key Personnel
Ed: Dan Gougherty
Government & politics.

Catholic News Service (CNS)
Division of US Conference of Catholic Bishops
3211 Fourth St NE, Washington, DC 20017-1100
Tel: 202-541-3250 *Fax:* 202-541-3117
E-mail: cns@catholicnews.com
Web Site: www.catholicnews.com
Key Personnel
Digital Ed: Jim Lackey
Intl Ed: Barb Fraze
Natl Ed: Julie Asher *Tel:* 202-541-3266
Founded: 1920
Distribute news stories & photos to Catholic
  newspaper clients throughout the US & in 40
  other countries. Branch offices in New York,
  NY & Rome, Italy. No unsol mss, query first.
  Publishes in English & Spanish.
Number of Subscribers: 400
Membership(s): Catholic Media Association
  (CMA); SIGNIS (World Catholic Association
  for Communication)

Congressional Quarterly Roll Call, see CQ Roll
  Call

Continental Features/Continental News Service
501 W Broadway, Plaza A, PMB 265, San Diego,
  CA 92101
Tel: 858-492-8696
E-mail: info@continentalnewsservice.com;
  continentalnewstime@gmail.com
Web Site: www.continentalnewsservice.com
Key Personnel
Pres & Ed-in-Chief: Gary P Salamone
Founded: 1981
Captioned photos on the *News Story of the Day*;
  country/background profiles; interview articles
  with national officials & international figures:
  News Tip of the Month. Market editorial com-
  mentary/analysis produced in-house. Publish
  children's newspaper, *Kids Newstime* & periodic national news magazine *Continental Newstime*, specializing in covering the unreported
  & under-reported world & national news, with
  238,000 multimedia, biweekly advertising circulation. Publishes a Northern California community newspaper & special complimentary,
  online Washington, DC, Chicago, Miami, Seattle, Boston, Anchorage, Atlanta, Honolulu, San
  Diego, Rochester (NY), Minneapolis & Houston news editions, on a rotational basis. Accept
  submissions with SASE; no unsol mss, query
  first; photos should be screened or half-toned
  (no negatives). CF/CNS is interested in adding
  substantially to our group of sponsored feature
  writers & feature cartoonists.

CQ Roll Call
Subsidiary of FiscalNote
1201 Pennsylvania Ave NW, Suite 600, Washing-
  ton, DC 20004
Tel: 202-650-6500; 202-650-6511 (subns); 202-
  650-6621 (cust serv) *Toll Free Tel:* 800-432-
  2250; 800-678-8511 (subns)
E-mail: customerservice@cqrollcall.com
Web Site: cqrollcall.com; www.rollcall.com
Key Personnel
Publr: Josh Resnik
VP & Ed: Ed Timms
Mng Ed, Audience: John Helton
Asst Mng Ed, Prodn: George LeVines
Sr Staff Ed: Andrew Menezes
Design Ed: Chris Hale
Deputy Ed, News: Jason Dick
Deputy Ed, Visual Reporting: Gillian Roberts
Founded: 1955
Journals & newsletters on Congress, legislation,
  politics & national affairs; online products.

Crain Communications Inc
1155 Gratiot Ave, Detroit, MI 48207-2732
Tel: 313-446-6000 *Fax:* 313-446-0383
E-mail: info@crain.com
Web Site: crain.com
Key Personnel
Chmn: Keith Crain
Chief HR Offr: Nikki Kallek
CFO: Bob Recchia
CIO: Anthony Diponio
Pres & COO: K C Crain
SVP: Christopher Crain
VP & Gen Coun: Peter Grantz
Mng Dir, Audience, Prod & Mktg: Bonnie Roche
Dir, Procurement & Facilities: Eric Walters
Founded: 1916
Business media company with 56 business, trade
  & consumer brands in North America, Europe
  & Asia. Print publications, web sites, digital
  newsletters, webinars, direct mail, mobile apps,
  research, white papers & more.
Branch Office(s)
400 Continental Blvd, 6th fl, El Segundo, CA
  90245-5074 *Tel:* 310-426-2470
1975 W El Camino Real, Suite 304, Mountain
  View, CA 94040-2218 *Tel:* 650-390-6200
601 13 St NW, Suite 9000 S, Washington, DC
  20005-6714
150 N Michigan Ave, Chicago, IL 60601
  Tel: 312-649-5200
685 Third Ave, New York, NY 10017-4024
  Tel: 212-210-0100
1725 Merriman Rd, Suite 300, Akron, OH 44313-
  9006 *Tel:* 330-836-9180
700 W St Clair Ave, Suite 310, Cleveland, OH
  44113-1256 *Tel:* 216-522-1383
Crain Communications GmbH, Technopark
  Oberpfaffenhofen, Argelsrieder Feld 13, 82234
  Oberpfaffenhofen, Germany *Tel:* (0815) 390
  7400
11 Ironmonger Lane, London EC2Y 8EY, United
  Kingdom *Tel:* (020) 7194 7530

Creators Syndicate
737 Third St, Hermosa Beach, CA 90254
Tel: 310-337-7003
E-mail: info@creators.com
Web Site: www.creators.com
Key Personnel
Founder & CEO: Rick Newcombe
Pres & COO: Jack Newcombe
Newspaper columns, comics, editorial cartoons &
  puzzles, all daily & weekly newspapers. Accept
  unsol mss.

The Cricket Letter Inc
Subsidiary of Cricket Communications Inc
PO Box 527, Ardmore, PA 19003-0527
Tel: 610-924-9158 *Fax:* 610-924-9159
E-mail: crcktinc@aol.com
Key Personnel
VP, Cricket Communications Inc & Publr/Ed-
  in-Chief, The Cricket Letter: Mark E Bat-
  tersby *Tel:* 610-924-9157 *E-mail:* mebatt12@
  earthlink.net
Publr, Cricket Communications Inc: J D Krickett
Tax, financial, real estate, business editorial of in-
  terest to foreign investors. No unsol mss, query
  first.
Number of Subscribers: 7,325

Entertainment News Service
Subsidiary of Reboli Publishing Co
PO Box 6123, West Caldwell, NJ 07007-6123
Tel: 973-227-4433
Key Personnel
Publr: John A Reboli
PR Mgr: Kim Kulick
TV/movie entertainment, book reviews. Accept
  submissions. Subscribers & members include
  127 newspapers, 23 radio & 8 TV stations.

The Fairfield Chronicle
Subsidiary of Reboli Newspapers Inc
PO Box 6123, West Caldwell, NJ 07007-6123
Tel: 973-227-4433
Key Personnel
Publr: John A Reboli
Ed-in-Chief: Kelly J Kilborn
Local news & book reviews. Book submissions
  accepted for review.

Gannett News Service
Unit of Gannett Co Inc
7950 Jones Branch Dr, McLean, VA 22107-0150
Tel: 703-854-6000
E-mail: pr@gannett.com
Web Site: www.gannett.com
Key Personnel
Pres & CEO: Bob Dickey
Newswire to newspapers.

Global Horizons
1330 New Hampshire Ave NW, Unit 609, Washington, DC 20036
Key Personnel
Pres & Columnist: Ed Flattau *E-mail:* edflattau@
  msn.com
Founded: 1985
Environment & ecology material syndicated. Does
  not accept submissions.

Global Information Network Ltd
Affiliate of IDN-InDepthNews
6040 Boulevard E, No 21-H, West New York, NJ
  07093
Tel: 212-244-3123
E-mail: newsdesk@mindspring.com
Web Site: www.indepthnews.net
Key Personnel
Exec Dir: Lisa Vives
Founded: 1981
Newswire covering political, economic & social
  issues in Africa & other developing nations,
  as well as US news on minority issues: hu-
  man rights, labor, the environment, population,
  health & habitat. No unsol mss, query first.
Number of Subscribers: 1,000

Dave Goodwin & Associates
721 86 St, Miami Beach, FL 33141-1115
Tel: 305-865-0158
E-mail: davegoodwi@aol.com
Web Site: davegoodwin.weebly.com
Key Personnel
Owner: Dave Goodwin
Insurance, business & finance, management, con-
  sumer education, travel & resorts. May query
  first with samples but does not accept unsol
  mss.
Membership(s): South Florida International Press
  Club (SFIPC)

Gracenote, a Nielsen Company
2000 Powell St, Suite 1500, Emeryville, CA
  94608
Tel: 510-428-7200
Web Site: www.gracenote.com
Key Personnel
Chief Content Offr: Atul Phadnis
Chief Prod Offr: Simon Adams
Chief Revenue Offr: Amilcar Perez
CTO: Kay Johansson
Pres: Karthik Rao
SVP, Busn Devt & Strategy: Ginger Bushell
SVP, Mktg & Communs: Graham McKenna
Electronic data & technology company power-
  ing music services, consumer electronics com-
  panies, automakers, media companies & ca-
  ble/satellite operators.
Branch Office(s)
6255 Sunset Blvd, Los Angeles, CA 90028
  Tel: 323-817-3505

40 Media Dr, Queensbury, NY 12804 *Tel:* 518-792-9914

211 Horseshoe Lake Dr, Halifax, NS B3S 0B9, Canada *Tel:* 902-835-3320

Av del Libertador 6350, Piso 6, C1428ART Buenos Aires, Argentina

Macquarie Park, Level 1, Bldg B, 11 Talavera Rd, Sydney, NSW 2113, Australia *Tel:* (02) 8397 7014

Rua George Ohm, 230-Torre A, 20° andar, Brooklin, 04576-020 Sao Paulo-SP, Brazil *Tel:* (011) 4420 9000 ext 9091

Gracenote GmbH, St-Martin-Str 61, 81669 Munich, Germany *Tel:* (089) 961183-0

Todi Estate, 2nd fl, B Wing, Lower Parel (W), Mumbai, Maharashtra 400 013, India

Gracenote KK, Shibuya Place 8F, 1-10-5 Dogenzaka, Shibuya-ku, Tokyo 150-0043, Japan *Tel:* (03) 3464-7785

Plot No 885, Amman, Wadi Sagra, Block 7, Bldg No 106, Off No 182, 8th fl, City Plazza, Amman 05047, Jordan

Millenium Tower, 13th fl, Radarweg 29, 1043 NX Amsterdam, Netherlands *Tel:* (020) 680 2560

Binnenwal 2, 3432 GH Nieuwegein, Netherlands *Tel:* (030) 600-71-71 *Fax:* (030) 600-71-77

Gracenote Korea Ltd, Seoul City Tower, Bldg 22F, 110, Huam-ro, Jung-gu, Seoul 04637, South Korea *Tel:* (02) 598-5857 *Fax:* (02) 798-5854

Hearst Newspapers
Division of Hearst Corp
300 W 57 St, New York, NY 10019
Tel: 212-649-2000
Web Site: www.hearst.com/newspapers
Key Personnel
Pres: Jeffrey M Johnson
Pres, Digital Media: Robertson Barrett
SVP & CFO: Barnabas Kui
SVP, Circ: Paul Barbetta
EVP: John C McKeon
EVP, Ad Sales: Mike DeLuca
Publishes 24 daily & 60 weekly newspapers.

Inman
Division of Inman Group Inc
75 N Woodward Ave, Suite 80368, Tallahassee, FL 32313
Tel: 510-658-9252
E-mail: customerservice@inman.com
Web Site: www.inman.com
Key Personnel
Founder & Owner: Brad Inman
COO: Morgan Brown
Real estate features; 10 or 12 columns; electronic newspaper for real estate professionals.

Jandon Features
2319 S 105 Ave, Omaha, NE 68124
Tel: 402-502-4367
Web Site: midwestgardening.com
Key Personnel
Columnist & Garden Book Reviewer: Jan Riggenbach *E-mail:* jan@riggenbach.info
Seasonal garden articles & weekly garden column; garden book reviews.

Jewish Telegraphic Agency
24 W 30 St, 4th fl, New York, NY 10001
Tel: 646-778-5520
E-mail: info@70facesmedia.org
Web Site: www.jta.org; www.70facesmedia.org
Key Personnel
VP, Fin: Lee Silverstein
Ed-in-Chief: Andy Silow-Carroll
Founded: 1917
Jewish news & features.

Keister-Williams Newspaper Services Inc
PO Box 8187, Charlottesville, VA 22906

Tel: 434-293-4709 *Toll Free Tel:* 800-293-4709
E-mail: kw@kwnews.com
Web Site: www.kwnews.com
Key Personnel
Pres: Ky Lindsay
VP, Mktg: Meta L Nay
Busn Mgr: Carol Lindsay
Founded: 1984
Religion feature provided to newspapers.

Keystone Press Agency Inc
Subsidiary of Zuma Press
412 N El Camino Real, San Clemente, CA 92672
Tel: 949-481-3747 *Fax:* 949-481-3941
E-mail: info@keystonepictures.com
Web Site: www.keystonepictures.com
Key Personnel
Owner: Scott McKiernan *E-mail:* scott@keystonepictures.com
Founded: 1892
Picture archive.

King Features Syndicate
Subsidiary of Hearst Corp
300 W 57 St, New York, NY 10019-5238
Tel: 212-969-7550 *Toll Free Tel:* 800-526-5464
Web Site: www.kingfeatures.com
Key Personnel
Pres: C J Kettler
VP & Gen Mgr: Keith McCloat
Dir, Ad & PR: Beth Nock
Pubns Dir & Ed: Chris Rithcreek
Gen Mgr: Carla Silva
Founded: 1915
Columns, comic strips, cartoon panels, puzzles for newspaper use. Accept unsol column samples with cover letter, send to submissions editor in New York. Send copies as original material will not be returned. Visit web site for further information.

Kiplinger's Personal Finance/The Kiplinger Washington Editors Inc
1100 13 St NW, Suite 750, Washington, DC 20005-4364
Tel: 202-887-6400 *Toll Free Tel:* 800-544-0155 (cust serv)
E-mail: feedback@kiplinger.com
Web Site: www.kiplinger.com
Key Personnel
Ed: Mark Solherm
Off Mgr: Glen Mayers
Founded: 1947
Monthly personal finance/consumer magazine. No unsol mss, query first.
Number of Subscribers: 600,000

Merrell Enterprises
3542 E State Rte 73, Waynesville, OH 45068
Tel: 202-265-1925 *Fax:* 513-855-4277
Web Site: www.merrellenterprises.com
Key Personnel
Pres: Jesse H Merrell *E-mail:* jesse@jessehmerrell.com
Religious & political columns.

Metro Editorial Services
Division of Metro Creative Graphics Inc
519 Eighth Ave, New York, NY 10018
Tel: 212-947-5100 (ext 253, outside US & CN)
Toll Free Tel: 800-223-1600
E-mail: service@metro-email.com
Web Site: www.mcg.metrocreativeconnection.com
Key Personnel
Mng Ed: Andrew Griffin *E-mail:* agriffin@metro-email.com
Founded: 1903
Consumer editorial features distributed to 10,000 newspapers nationwide.

Military Update
PO Box 231111, Centreville, VA 20120-1111
Tel: 703-830-6863
E-mail: milupdate@aol.com
Web Site: www.militaryupdate.com
Key Personnel
News Columnist: Tom Philpott
Founded: 1994
Weekly military news column; 40 daily newspapers near military bases.

The Morristown News
Subsidiary of Reboli Newspapers Inc
PO Box 6123, West Caldwell, NJ 07007-6123
Tel: 973-227-4433
Key Personnel
Publr: John A Reboli
Ed: Samuel Miller
Local news for NJ. Book submissions accepted for review.

Motor News Media Corp
3710 Capitol Circle, Suite F, Grimes, IA 50111-5046
Tel: 515-986-1155
E-mail: motornewsmedia@live.com
Web Site: www.motornewsmedia.com
Key Personnel
Pres & CEO: Kenneth J Chester, Jr
Founded: 1989
Automotive news, features & photography; approximately 30 newspapers; interested writers should query first.
Number of Subscribers: 30

New Dimensions Radio
Subsidiary of New Dimensions Foundation
PO Box 7847, Santa Rosa, CA 95407
Tel: 707-468-5215
E-mail: info@newdimensions.org
Web Site: www.newdimensions.org
Key Personnel
Exec Dir, Host & Mng Prodr: Justine Toms
Founded: 1973
Positive options & solutions for the future & personal growth. Topics include social changes & the arts & humanities as applied to everyday life; 40,000 subscribers; accept submissions; no unsol mss; query first. Heard in 300 communities in the US by over 1.5 million listeners.

The New York Times Licensing Group
Division of The New York Times Co
620 Eighth Ave, 20th fl, New York, NY 10018
Tel: 212-556-1927
E-mail: nytlg-sales@nytimes.com
Web Site: nytlicensing.com
Key Personnel
VP, Global Sales: Alice Ting *Tel:* 212-556-5967 *E-mail:* alicet@nytimes.com
Exec Dir, US/CN & Global Mktg: Aidan McNutty *Tel:* 212-556-4015 *E-mail:* mcnulaj@nytimes.com
Mng Ed, News Serv: Ray Krueger *E-mail:* krueger@nytimes.com
Deliver Times journalism & curated content for publications & organizations of all sizes. Offers access to current & archival material across an extensive range of subjects. Content types include text, photo journalism, dynamic infographics, podcasts & video. All packages are rights-cleared & integrated with features to make them instantly available to global audiences.

NYT Licensing, see The New York Times Licensing Group

The Parsippany News
Subsidiary of Reboli Newspapers Inc
PO Box 6123, West Caldwell, NJ 07007-6123
Tel: 973-227-4433

Key Personnel
Publr: John A Reboli
Mng Ed: Susan Rothchild
Local news for NJ. Book submissions accepted for review.

Post Bulletin Co LLC
Subsidiary of Small Newspaper Group
18 First Ave SE, Rochester, MN 55903
Tel: 507-285-7600 *Toll Free Tel:* 800-562-1758
E-mail: news@postbulletin.com
Web Site: www.postbulletin.com
Key Personnel
News Ed: Brian Sander *Tel:* 507-281-7420
    E-mail: sander@postbulletin.com
News & Life Ed: Jeff Pieters *Tel:* 507-285-7748
    E-mail: jpieters@postbulletin.com
One-panel cartoons, editorial cartoons, columns & approximately 500 various newspapers/publications. Send resume with 12 clippings of work, either columns or cartoons & send SASE for reply.
Number of Subscribers: 43,000

Press Associates Union News Service
4000 Cathedral Ave NW, No 535B, Washington, DC 20016
Tel: 312-806-4825
E-mail: paiunionnews@gmail.com
Key Personnel
Pres & Ed: Mark Gruenberg
Founded: 1955
Legislative, economic, political & social issues, job safety & health. No unsol mss, query first.
Number of Subscribers: 110
Membership(s): International Labor Communications Association (ILCA)

Publishers' Feature Service
Subsidiary of NPR Services
4013 Coyte Ct, Marietta, GA 30062
Tel: 561-247-5533
E-mail: pfssyndicate@gmail.com
Web Site: publishersfeatureservice.com
Key Personnel
Contact: Robert J Heller
Founded: 1996
Independent feature service bureau: travel & the arts.
Number of Subscribers: 14,840

Quiz Features
PO Box 42222, Northwest Sta, Washington, DC 20015-0822
Tel: 202-966-0025 *Fax:* 202-966-0025
Key Personnel
Author & Gen Mgr: Donald Saltz
Founded: 1966
Daily Trivia Quiz: "Check Your Knowledge" & "Why That Expression?". Also theme quizzes & weekly "News Quiz".

Religion News Service
Subsidiary of Religion News Foundation
c/o University of Missouri's Journalism School, 30 Neff Annex, Columbia, MO 65211

Tel: 573-884-1327
E-mail: info@religionnews.com
Web Site: www.religionnews.com
Key Personnel
Publr & CEO: Thomas L Gallagher
Ed-in-Chief: Bob Smietana *E-mail:* bob. smietana@religionnews.com
Mng Ed: Paul O'Donnell *E-mail:* paul.odonnell@religionnews.com
Founded: 1934
Worldwide coverage of domestic & foreign religious news & photos; features. Uses news stories & news features; query first; prefer experienced journalists. Dist by Universal Press Syndicate & Canadian Press.

70 Faces Media, see Jewish Telegraphic Agency

Southern California Focus
1720 Oak St, Santa Monica, CA 90405
Tel: 310-452-3918
Web Site: www.californiafocus.net
Key Personnel
Owner & Author: Thomas D Elias
    E-mail: tdelias@aol.com
Founded: 1972
California public affairs column.
Number of Subscribers: 93
Membership(s): Los Angeles Press Club

Thomson Reuters
3 Times Sq, New York, NY 10036
Tel: 646-223-4000; 646-223-6100 (edit); 646-223-6000 (newsroom)
Web Site: www.thomsonreuters.com
Key Personnel
Pres & CEO: Steve Hasker
COO, Cust Mkts: Brian Peccarelli
COO, Opers & Enablement: Neil Masterson
Chief of Staff: Carla Jones
Pres, Reuters News: Michael Friedenberg
EVP & Chief People Offr: Mary Alice Vuicic
EVP & Gen Coun: Deirdre Stanley
SVP & Head, Corp Fin: Mike Eastwood
Ed-in-Chief, Reuters News: Stephen J Adler
Founded: 1851
Global news service.

The Tribune News Service
Division of Tribune Content Agency
160 N Stetson Ave, Chicago, IL 60601
Tel: 312-222-4131
E-mail: tcanews@trbpub.com
Web Site: www.mctdirect.com; tribunecontentagency.com/tribune-news-service
Key Personnel
VP, Opers: Jack Barry *Tel:* 312-222-2193
    E-mail: jbarry@tribpub.com
Sales Dir: Rick DeChantal *Tel:* 312-222-4544
    E-mail: rdechantal@tribpub.com
Assoc Ed: Zach Finken *Tel:* 312-527-8756
    E-mail: zfinken@tribpub.com; Emily Rosenbaum *Tel:* 312-222-4423 *E-mail:* erosenbaum@tribpub.com
Founded: 1973
Insightful coverage of politics & breaking news; lifestyle & entertainment reports; sports &

business; compelling photography & useful graphics. Experienced editors deliver material from 70 leading companies, including the Los Angeles Times, Chicago Tribune, Miami Herald, The Dallas Morning News, Seattle Times & the Philadelphia Inquirer.

United Press International (UPI)
Subsidiary of News World Communications
1133 19 St NW, Suite 800, Washington, DC 20036
Tel: 202-898-8000
E-mail: media@upi.com
Web Site: www.upi.com
Key Personnel
Pres: Nicholas Chiaia
Founded: 1907
News, news picture & feature service.
Branch Office(s)
1200 N Federal Hwy, Suite 200, Boca Raton, FL 33432

Washington Post News Service with Bloomberg News
1301 "K" St NW, Washington, DC 20071
Tel: 202-334-7666
E-mail: syndication@washpost.com
Web Site: www.washingtonpost.com/syndication
Key Personnel
Dir, Mktg & Technol: Robert S Cleland
Edit Dir: Richard Aldacushion
Mng Ed: Effie Dawson
Founded: 1962
Supplemental news service (subscribers only); no unsol mss.
Number of Subscribers: 644

Whitegate Features Syndicate
Division of Whitegate International Corp
71 Faunce Dr, Providence, RI 02906
Tel: 401-274-2149
Web Site: www.whitegatefeatures.com
Key Personnel
Pres: Ed Isaac
VP: Steve Corey
Talent Dir & Mgr of Spec Projs: Eve Green
Mgr: Mari Howard
Newspaper features & cartoons. Subscribers all around world. Every newspaper submitted; each columnist has own set number of newspapers. Accept unsol mss, but do not return submissions, do not send SASE.

Wingo LLC
Subsidiary of AmeriMarketing/Wingo LLC
12161 Ken Adams Way, Wellington, FL 33414
Tel: 561-379-2635
E-mail: sat@amerimarketing.com
Web Site: www.wingopromo.com; www.amerimarketing.com
Key Personnel
Owner & VP: Scott Thompson
VP: Daryl Thompson
Founded: 1981
Promote market games to increase newspaper circulation; 40 subscribers, promotional printing service, direct response printing.

Radio, TV & Cable Networks

A+E Networks®
235 E 45 St, New York, NY 10017
Tel: 212-210-1400 *Fax:* 212-210-9755
Web Site: www.aenetworks.com; twitter.com/
    aenetworks; www.facebook.com/AENetworks
Key Personnel
Pres: Paul Buccieri
EVP, Corp Communs: Michael Feeney
    E-mail: michael.feeney@aenetworks.com
Exec Asst: Mark Silverman *E-mail:* mark.
    silverman@aenetworks.com
Founded: 1984
Global content company comprised of some of
    the most popular & culturally relevant brands
    in media including A&E®, BIOGRAPHY®,
    Blaze™, Crime+Investigation®, FYI™, HIS-
    TORY®, HISTORY2™, Lifetime®, LMN™
    & VICE TV®. A+E Networks' portfolio ex-
    tends across platforms & genres, with a long-
    form production division, A+E Studios™; un-
    scripted production unit, A+E Originals™; film
    division, A&E IndieFilms®; full service digi-
    tal storytelling hub, 45th & Dean™; strategic
    investment division, A+E Ventures™; A+E
    Digital®, encompassing watch apps, games
    & SVOD initiatives including Lifetime Movie
    Club & HISTORY Vault. A+E Networks' chan-
    nels & branded programming reach more than
    335 million households in over 200 territories
    in 42 languages. A+E Networks has offices in
    the US, UK, Germany, Italy, Japan, Korea &
    Singapore. A+E Networks is a joint venture
    With Hearst Communications & Disney–ABC
    Television Group, a unit of The Walt Disney
    Company.

ABC Television Network
Subsidiary of The Walt Disney Co
47 W 66 St, New York, NY 10023
Tel: 818-460-7477
Web Site: abc.go.com
Key Personnel
Chmn & CEO, The Walt Disney Co: Robert A
    Iger
Pres, ABC: Karey Burke
Sr EVP & Corp Communs Offr, The Walt Disney
    Co: Zenia Mucha
Sr EVP & Gen Coun: Alan N Braverman
Network programming.

AMC
Subsidiary of AMC Networks Inc
11 Penn Plaza, 18th fl, New York, NY 10001
Tel: 212-324-8500
E-mail: amccustomerservice@amc.com
Web Site: www.amc.com
Key Personnel
Pres: Sarah Barnett
EVP, PR: Marnie Black *Tel:* 917-542-6361
Founded: 1984
Twenty-four hour movie based network dedicated
    to the American movie fan. A network that
    reaches 86 million homes, offers a comprehen-
    sive library of popular movies & a critically
    acclaimed slate of movie based original pro-
    gramming.

Bonneville International Corp
Subsidiary of Deseret Management Corp
Broadcast House, 55 N 300 W, Salt Lake City,
    UT 84101-3502
Tel: 801-575-5555
Web Site: bonneville.com
Key Personnel
Pres: Darrell Brown

CFO & SVP: Kent Nate
Founded: 1964
Broadcasting company consisting of 21 radio sta-
    tions & an NBC affiliate TV station.

Cable One
210 E Earll Dr, Phoenix, AZ 85012
Tel: 602-364-6000
Web Site: www.cableone.net
Key Personnel
Pres & CEO: Julie M Laulis
CFO & SVP: Steven S Cochran
COO: Michael E Bowker
VP, Fin & Treas: Raymond L Storck, Jr
Founded: 1986
Leading broadband communications provider
    serving more than 800,000 residential & busi-
    ness customers in 21 states. Cable One pro-
    vides customers with a wide array of connec-
    tivity & entertainment services, including high-
    speed Internet & advanced Wi-Fi solutions,
    cable television & phone service. Cable One
    Business provides scalable & cost-effective
    products for businesses ranging in size from
    small to mid-market, in addition to enterprise,
    wholesale & carrier customers.

The California Channel
1121 "L" St, Suite 110, Sacramento, CA 95814
Tel: 916-444-9792 *Fax:* 916-444-9812
E-mail: contact_us@calchannel.com
Web Site: www.calchannel.com
Key Personnel
Pres: John Hancock
Founded: 1989
Independent public affairs cable network for the
    state of California, modeled after the national
    C-SPAN network. 5.8 million subscribers. The
    network's core programming is gavel-to-gavel
    coverage of California Senate & Assembly
    floor sessions, committee hearings, state press
    conferences & other special events. California
    broadcast area only.

Canal SUR
Unit of SUR LLC
2105 NW 102 Ave, 3rd fl, Miami, FL 33172-
    2217
Tel: 305-227-6000 *Fax:* 305-554-6776
E-mail: info@condista.com
Web Site: www.canalsur.com
Key Personnel
Pres: Arturo Delgado
Founded: 1992
Live daily newscasts from the leading Latin
    American broadcasting networks. Journalis-
    tic & public opinion programs with in-depth
    coverage of current affairs from each coun-
    try. The most popular game, comedy, variety
    show, sports & children programming from
    Latin America. 4,500,000 subscribers; 4 affili-
    ates. Broadcast nationwide within the US.

CBS Television Network
Subsidiary of ViacomCBS Inc
51 W 52 St, New York, NY 10019-6188
Tel: 212-975-4321
Web Site: www.cbs.com
Key Personnel
Pres, CBS Corporation: Joseph Ianniello
EVP & Chief Communs Offr, CBS Corporation:
    Dana McClintock *E-mail:* dlmcclintock@cbs.
    com

EVP, Chief Res & Analytics Offr: Radha Subra-
    manyam
Founded: 1928
Radio, cable & TV broadcasting.

City University Television (CUNY TV)
365 Fifth Ave, Suite 1400, New York, NY 10016
Tel: 212-817-7575 *Fax:* 212-251-0826
Web Site: www.cuny.tv
Key Personnel
Exec Dir: Gail Yancosek
Founded: 1985
University cable television channel serving over
    7.3 million subscribers with educational, cul-
    tural, international & university based program-
    ming. Broadcasting in the 5 boroughs of New
    York City.

Comcast Cable Communications LLC
Division of Comcast Corp
Comcast Ctr, 1701 John F Kennedy Blvd,
    Philadelphia, PA 19103
Tel: 215-286-1700
E-mail: comcast_communications@comcast.com
Web Site: www.xfinity.com
Key Personnel
Sr EVP, Comcast Corp: Stephen B Burke
Founded: 1963
Operates cable television systems which serve ap-
    proximately 22 million subscribers nationwide.

Cox Communications Inc
Subsidiary of Cox Enterprises Inc
6205-B Peachtree Dunwoody Rd, Atlanta, GA
    30328
Tel: 404-843-5897 *Toll Free Tel:* 888-566-7751
E-mail: coxcorp.customerrelations@cox.com
Web Site: www.cox.com
Key Personnel
Exec Dir, Media Rel: Todd Smith *Tel:* 404-269-
    3124 *E-mail:* todd.smith@cox.com
Provider of digital cable television, telecommu-
    nications & home automation services. Cox
    serves approximately 6 million residences &
    businesses in the US.

The Crime Channel
310 N Indian Hills Blvd, Suite 214, Claremont,
    CA 91711
Tel: 760-360-9986
E-mail: crimechannel@dc.rr.com
Web Site: www.thecrimechannel.com
Key Personnel
Pres: Arnie Frank
Entertaining, informational & educational pro-
    grams, all crime related. Series, documentaries
    & motion pictures. Broadcast throughout the
    US.

E! Entertainment Television Inc
Division of NBCUniversal
100 Universal City Plaza, Universal City, CA
    91608
Tel: 323-954-2400
Web Site: www.eonline.com
Twenty-four hour coverage of entertainment news
    & events; 55 million subscribers; long-form
    programming; telecast nationwide; program-
    ming seen in 120 countries internationally.

ESPN Inc
ESPN Plaza, Bristol, CT 06010
Tel: 860-766-2000

E-mail: hello@espn.com
Web Site: www.espn.com
Key Personnel
EVP & CFO: Bryan Castellani
Pres: Jimmy Pitaro
SVP, Sales & Mktg: Patricia S Betron
VP, Communs: Katina Arnold
VP, Sales Communs: Cindy Freed
Founded: 1979
One of the most widely distributed cable networks, reaching more than 90 million homes. ESPN is America's #1 source for sports programming, airing more that 5,100 live +/or original hours of programming annually, including Monday Night Football, MLB, NBA, WNBA, college football, men's & women's college basketball, the X Games, the Great Outdoor Games. Its programming philosophy is to present a wide variety of exclusive, high-quality, innovative & in-depth sports events including both the marquee & narrow-interest; sports news, most notably the Emmy Award-winning SportsCenter & Outside the Lines.

In Touch Ministries
PO Box 7900, Atlanta, GA 30357
Tel: 770-451-1001 *Toll Free Tel:* 800-789-1473
Web Site: www.intouch.org
Key Personnel
Host: Dr Charles Stanley
Founded: 1988
Dr Charles Stanley can be heard on SiriusXM FamilyTalk (Christian teaching & talk) channel 161.

INSP LLC
PO Box 7750, Charlotte, NC 28241-7750
Tel: 803-578-1000 *Fax:* 803-578-1735
E-mail: info@insp.com
Web Site: www.insp.com
Key Personnel
Chmn & CEO: David Cerullo
COO: Dale S Ardizzone
CFO: Robert Brace
EVP, Corp Communs & Res: John E Roos
EVP, Worldwide Sales: Marc Favaro
SVP, Programming: Doug Butts
VP, Opers-Media Communs: Brack Rogers
Founded: 1990
24/7 general entertainment to 80 million US households via 2,800 cable systems; Dish Network, CVS, DirectTV & telcos.

KTTV-Fox 11
Division of Fox Television Stations LLC
1999 S Bundy Dr, Los Angeles, CA 90025
Tel: 310-584-2000
Web Site: foxla.com
Key Personnel
VP, News Dir: Kris Knutsen
Broadcast television station.

Minnesota Public Radio
480 Cedar St, St Paul, MN 55101
Tel: 651-290-1500 *Toll Free Tel:* 800-228-7123
(membs) *Fax:* 651-290-1188
E-mail: mail@mpr.org
Web Site: www.mpr.org
Key Personnel
CEO: Jon McTaggart
SVP & Chief Busn Devt Offr: Timothy T Roesler
E-mail: troesler@americanpublicmedia.org
Founded: 1967
Regional public radio network of 45 stations in Minnesota, North & South Dakota, Wisconsin & Michigan. Three services: news, classical, The Current. More than 900,000 listeners, almost 100,000 members.

National Broadcasting Co (NBC)
Division of NBCUniversal

30 Rockefeller Plaza, New York, NY 10112
Tel: 212-664-4444
Web Site: www.nbc.com
Key Personnel
CEO, NBCUniversal: Stephen B Burke

National Public Radio
1111 N Capitol St NE, Washington, DC 20002
Tel: 202-513-2000 *Fax:* 202-513-3329
E-mail: mediarelations@npr.org
Web Site: www.npr.org
Key Personnel
Pres & CEO: Jarl Mohn
SVP, News & Edit Dir: Nancy Barnes
Exec Dir, Media Rel: Isabel Lara *Tel:* 202-513-2300
Program producer & distributor, as well as a membership organization with more than 770 member stations; news & information & cultural programming, broadcast nationwide.

NBCUniversal Telemundo Enterprises
Division of NBCUniversal
Telemundo Ctr, One Telemundo Way, Miami, FL 33182
Tel: 786-585-7000
Web Site: www.telemundo.com
Key Personnel
CFO: Amanda Calpin
VP, Ad Sales: Gian Pablo Kates
VP, Network Partnerships: Gerry Rojas
World-class media company leading the industry in production & distribution of high-quality Spanish language content to US Hispanics & audiences around the world. Telemundo Network features original Spanish language entertainment, news & sports content reaching 94% of US Hispanic TV households in 210 markets through 30 local stations, 51 affiliates & its national feed. Telemundo also owns WKAQ, a television station that serves viewers in Puerto Rico.

New England Sports Network (NESN)
480 Arsenal St, Bldg 1, Watertown, MA 02472
Tel: 617-536-9233 *Fax:* 617-536-7814
E-mail: sports@nesn.com
Web Site: www.nesn.com
Key Personnel
PR Mgr: Gary Roy
Founded: 1984
Most watched regional sports network in New England with 4 million subscribers. NESN is owned by the Boston Red Sox & Boston Bruins.

Premiere Networks Inc
Subsidiary of iHeartMedia Inc
15260 Ventura Blvd, Sherman Oaks, CA 91403
Tel: 818-377-5300
E-mail: feedback@premierenetworks.com
Web Site: www.premierenetworks.com
Key Personnel
Dir, Busn Opers: Michael Kindhart
PR Dir: Rachel Nelson *Tel:* 818-461-8057
Founded: 1987
Syndicated talk radio with over 6,000 affiliates reaching 245 million people monthly. Broadcast area, around the world via satellite & Internet. *Coast to Coast AM* is hosted by Art Bell & George Noory. Monthly, 4-color magazine *After Dark* uses freelance material from writers.
Branch Office(s)
3495 Piedmont Rd, Bldg 12, Suite 300, Atlanta, GA 30305 *Tel:* 404-365-4387
233 N Michigan Ave, Suite 2800, Chicago, IL 60611 *Tel:* 312-540-2921
27675 Halsted Rd, Farmington Hills, MI 48331 *Tel:* 248-324-5444
1270 Avenue of the Americas, New York, NY 10020 *Tel:* 212-445-3900

125 W 55 St, 4th fl, New York, NY 10019
801 Woodridge Center Dr, Charlotte, NC 28217
Tel: 704-714-9444
14001 N Dallas Pkwy, Suite 300, Dallas, TX 75240 *Tel:* 972-239-6220

Public Broadcasting Service
2100 Crystal Dr, Arlington, VA 22202-3785
Tel: 703-739-5000
E-mail: corporatesecretary@pbs.org
Web Site: www.pbs.org
Key Personnel
Pres & CEO: Paula Kerger
Founded: 1969
There are 350 member stations nationally.

The EW Scripps Co
2800 Scripps Ctr, 312 Walnut St, Cincinnati, OH 45202
Tel: 513-977-3000 *Toll Free Tel:* 800-888-3000
Web Site: www.scripps.com
Key Personnel
Pres & CEO: Adam Symson
Pres, Local Media: Brian Lawlor
EVP & CFO: Lisa Knutson
EVP & Gen Coun: Bill Appleton
Deputy Gen Coun & Chief Ethics Offr: David Giles
SVP, Cont & Treas: Doug Lyons
SVP, Natl Media: Laura Tomlin
VP & Chief Diversity Offr: Danyelle ST Wright
VP & CIO: Bob Carson
VP & Corp Secy: Julie McGehee
VP, Audit & Compliance: Mark Koors
VP, Corp Communs & Investor Rel: Carolyn Micheli
VP, Strategy & Corp Devt: Robin Davis
VP, Strategy, New Busn & Corp Dev: Robert Kalutkiewicz
Television broadcasting.

Service Electric Cable TV Inc
2260 Avenue "A", Bethlehem, PA 18017
Tel: 610-865-9100 *Toll Free Tel:* 800-232-9100 (PA)
E-mail: office@sectv.com
Web Site: www.sectv.com
Key Personnel
Pres: John M Walson
VP & Cont: Joe Macus
Gen Mgr: John Capparell
Founded: 1948
Cable TV systems, phone & Internet.

Spectrum
Division of Charter Communications
400 Atlantic St, 10th fl, Stamford, CT 06901
Tel: 203-905-7800
Web Site: www.spectrum.com; www.facebook.com/Spectrum
TV, Internet & voice services to residential & business customers.

Superadio Networks
Division of Access.1 Communications Corp
112 W 34 St, Suite 2110, New York, NY 10120
Tel: 212-714-1000 *Fax:* 212-643-3871
Web Site: www.superadio.com
Key Personnel
CEO: Chelsey Maddox-Dorsey
Pres: Eric Faison *Tel:* 212-609-1168
E-mail: eric@superadio.com
Network Affiliate Coord: Shawnjua Kelley *Tel:* 212-714-1000 ext 265
E-mail: affiliaterelations@superadio.com
Founded: 1988
Produce & distribute marquee radio programs including shows in the urban, urban adult, mainstream top 40, rhythmic, talk, country, hot AC, rock, dance, alternative, gospel & oldies format.
Branch Office(s)
241 Boston Post Rd W, Marlborough, MA 01752,

Dist Mgr: Dianne Cook *Tel:* 508-620-0006
Fax: 952-556-9375 *E-mail:* dianne@superadio.
com

Syfy
Division of NBCUniversal
30 Rockefeller Plaza, New York, NY 10112
Tel: 212-664-4444
E-mail: feedback@syfy.com
Web Site: www.syfy.com
Key Personnel
EVP, Mktg & Digital, USA Network & Syfy:
Alexandra Shapiro
Founded: 1992
Science fiction, science fact, fantasy & horror. 94
million subscribers in US; broadcasts interna-
tionally.

TBS Inc, see Turner Broadcasting System Inc, A
WarnerMedia Company

TCM, see Turner Classic Movies (TCM)

Telemundo, see NBCUniversal Telemundo
Enterprises

**Turner Broadcasting System Inc, A
WarnerMedia Company**
One CNN Center, Atlanta, GA 30303-2720
Tel: 404-827-1700
E-mail: turner.info@turner.com
Web Site: www.turner.com
Key Personnel
Pres: David Levy
EVP, Global Chief Communs Offr & Corp Mktg
Offr: Molly Battin
EVP & Gen Coun: Louise Sams
EVP & Global Chief HR Offr: Angela Santone
Admin Offr: Pascal Descroches
Founded: 1976
Global entertainment, sports & news company.
Turner owns & operates brands including Adult
Swim, Bleacher Report, Boomerang, Cartoon
Network, CNN, ELEAGUE, FilmStruck, Great
Big Story, HLN, iStreamPlanet, Super Deluxe,
TBS, Turner Classic Movies (TCM), TNT,
truTV & Turner Sports.

Turner Classic Movies (TCM)
Division of Turner Broadcasting System Inc, A
Time Warner Company
1050 Techwood Dr NW, Atlanta, GA 30318
Tel: 404-885-5535
E-mail: tcm@emailcustomerservice.com
Web Site: www.tcm.com
Founded: 1994
Classic movie network from 1920s-1990s, 24
hours a day, commercial-free, uninterrupted
to 80 million households in the US.

Univision Networks
Division of Univision Communications Inc
605 Third Ave, 12th fl, New York, NY 10158-
5200
Tel: 212-455-5200
Web Site: www.univision.com
Key Personnel
CEO: Vincent Sadusky
CFO: Peter H Lori
Pres & COO: Jessica Rodriguez
Pres, Ad Sales & Mktg: Steve Mandala
US Hispanic cable network delivering broad-
based, family oriented programming (including
sports, music, classic movies, novelas, variety
& news, children's programming & bilingual
block) in Spanish language; 1,866 affiliates,
nationwide.
Branch Office(s)
2323 Bryan St, Suite 1900, Dallas, TX 75201
Tel: 214-758-2300

USA Network
Division of NBCUniversal
30 Rockefeller Plaza, 21st fl, New York, NY
10112
Tel: 212-413-5000
Web Site: www.usanetwork.com
Founded: 1971
Cable television leader in original series & home
to blockbuster theatrical films, acquired televi-
sion series & entertainment events.

**The Weather Channel (TWC) Television
Network**
Subsidiary of Weather Group Television LLC
300 Interstate N Pkwy, Atlanta, GA 30339
Tel: 770-226-0000
Web Site: weathergroup.com
Key Personnel
Communs Mgr: Katie Shuford *E-mail:* katie.
shuford@weathergroup.com
Founded: 1982
24-hour all-weather satellite television program-
ming service with 100 million subscribers. In-
ternational, national, regional & local weather
conditions & forecasts, shown nationwide.

**WKTX AM830 & NBN-Radio/TV (Nationality
Broadcasting Network)**
Division of NBN Productions
11906 Madison Ave, Lakewood, OH 44107
Tel: 216-221-0330 *Fax:* 216-221-3638
Key Personnel
Prog Dir: Jack Cory
Opers Mgr: Jim Georgiades
International programming with affiliates of Scola
Satellite & Cox Cable broadcast in Northeast-
ern Ohio; 18 million subscribers, North Ameri-
can continent; news & entertainment.
Branch Office(s)
178 N Mecca, Cortland, OH 44410

Xfinity, see Comcast Cable Communications
LLC

Radio Programs Featuring Books

Listed here are radio programs that deal with books & authors. Programs are listed alphabetically by program name. Some are hosted by established critics who devote their entire program to reviews of current books; others feature books only occasionally. Also see the sections **Columnists & Commentators** and **TV Programs Featuring Books**.

AirTalk with Larry Mantle
KPCC-FM
Division of Southern California Public Radio
(SCPR)
474 S Raymond Ave, Pasadena, CA 91105
Tel: 626-583-5100 *Fax:* 626-583-5101
E-mail: airtalk@kpcc.org
Web Site: www.kpcc.org
Key Personnel
Sr Prodr: Fiona Ng
Host: Larry Mantle
Newstalk, interviews, call-ins.
Air Time: Mon-Fri 10 AM-noon

All About Books
KUCV-FM - NET Radio
1800 N 33 St, Lincoln, NE 68503
Tel: 402-472-6141 *Toll Free Tel:* 888-638-7346
Fax: 402-472-1785
E-mail: radio@netnebraska.org
Web Site: www.netnebraska.org/radio
Key Personnel
Prodr: Jeff Smith *Tel:* 402-470-6370
E-mail: jsmith@netnebraska.org
Weekly program about books.
Air Time: Wed 10 AM

All Sides
WOSU-FM
Division of Ohio State University
2400 Olentangy River Rd, Columbus, OH 43210-1027
Tel: 614-292-9678 (ext 49784)
E-mail: allsides@wosu.org
Web Site: www.wosu.org
Key Personnel
Host: Ann Fisher
Call in; National Public Radio affiliate, politics, history, English language, science. Books featured are primarily nonfiction.
Air Time: Mon-Fri 10 AM-noon (ET)

All Things Considered
National Public Radio
1111 N Capitol St NE, Washington, DC 20002
Tel: 202-513-2000
Web Site: www.npr.org
Key Personnel
Host: Audie Cornish; Ailsa Chang; Ari Shapiro; Mary Louise Kelly
Debut Date: 1971
News & information, current issues, book reviews & author interviews broadcast on stations nationwide at various times. See web site for list of stations & times.
Air Time: Daily

Amazon Country
WXPN-FM 88.5
Division of University of Pennsylvania
3025 Walnut St, Philadelphia, PA 19104
Tel: 215-898-6677 *Fax:* 215-898-0707
E-mail: wxpndesk@xpn.org; amazon@xpn.org
Web Site: www.xpn.org
Key Personnel
Host & Prodr: Debra D'Alessandro
Gen Mgr: Roger La May
Debut Date: 1974
Lesbian & feminist music & public affairs.
Air Time: Sun 11 AM-noon

Background Briefing
KPFK-FM (Pacifica)
Member of Pacifica Foundation
3729 Cahuenga Blvd W, North Hollywood, CA 91604
Tel: 818-985-2711 *Fax:* 818-763-7526
E-mail: comments@kpfk.org
Web Site: www.kpfk.org
Key Personnel
Host & Prodr: Ian Masters *E-mail:* icmasters@gmail.com
Interviews on world affairs.
Air Time: Mon-Thurs 5-6 PM, Sun 11 AM-noon

Beneath the Surface
KPFK-FM (Pacifica)
Member of Pacifica Foundation
3729 Cahuenga Blvd W, North Hollywood, CA 91604
Tel: 818-985-2711 *Fax:* 818-763-7526
E-mail: comments@kpfk.org
Web Site: www.kpfk.org
Key Personnel
Exec Prodr: Robert Brenner
Host: Suzi Weissman
Current issues, news & author interviews.
Air Time: Sun 10-11 AM

Between the Covers
KBOO-FM
20 SE Eighth Ave, Portland, OR 97214
Tel: 503-231-8032 *Fax:* 503-231-7145
E-mail: amnews@kboo.org
Web Site: www.kboo.fm/program/between-covers
Interviews with locally & nationally known fiction & nonfiction authors. Numerous hosts.
Air Time: 1st, 2nd & 4th Thurs 11-11:30 AM, 3rd & 5th Thurs 11 AM-noon

Book Bits
WTBF-AM/FM
Division of Troy Broadcasting Corp
67 W Court Sq, Troy, AL 36081
Tel: 334-566-0300 *Toll Free Tel:* 888-970-8769 (public use only) *Fax:* 334-566-5689
E-mail: wtbfdoc@yahoo.com
Key Personnel
Opers & Prog Mgr: Dave Kirby
Debut Date: 1985
Daily 3-minute book reviews.

The Book Nook
WYSO
Affiliate of National Public Radio
150 E South College St, Yellow Springs, OH 45387
Mailing Address: 4805 Meredith Rd, Yellow Springs, OH 45387
Tel: 937-767-6420 *Fax:* 937-769-1382
Web Site: wyso.org/programs/book-nook
Key Personnel
Prodr & Host: Vick Mickunas *E-mail:* vick@vickmickunas.com
Debut Date: 1994
Author interviews on a wide range of topics. The program covers fiction & nonfiction book titles.
Do not send any mail to WYSO. All book submissions must be sent to the mailing address.

WYSO is a 50,000 watt National Public Radio affiliate that serves southwest Ohio.
Air Time: Sat 7-8 AM, Sun 10:30-11 AM (ET)

The Book Show
WAMC Northeast Public Radio
318 Central Ave, Albany, NY 12206
Mailing Address: PO Box 66600, Albany, NY 12206
Tel: 518-465-5233 *Toll Free Tel:* 800-323-9262
E-mail: book@wamc.org; mail@wamc.org
Web Site: www.wamc.org
Key Personnel
Host: Joe Donahue
Author/host interviews regarding their books, lives & their craft. A celebration of both reading & writers.
Air Time: Syndicated by National Productions (WAMC) & varies by station

Boston Sunday Review
WBZ-FM
Subsidiary of Beasley Media Group
55 Morissey Blvd, Boston, MA 02125
Tel: 617-746-1400 *Fax:* 617-746-1402
Web Site: www.985thesportshub.com
Key Personnel
Prodr: Tracy Clements *E-mail:* tclements@985thesportshub.com
Host: Mat Schaffer
General interest talk show & author interviews.
Air Time: Sun 6-8 AM

Charlie Brennan Show
KMOX-AM
Division of Entercom Communications Corp
1220 Olive St, 3rd fl, St Louis, MO 63103-2301
Tel: 314-621-2345 *Fax:* 314-588-1234
E-mail: kmoxnews@kmox.com
Web Site: kmox.radio.com/shows/charlie-brennan-show
Key Personnel
Host: Charles Brennan *E-mail:* charles.brennan@entercom.com
Interviews, phone-ins, issues of the day.
Air Time: Mon-Fri 8:30-11 AM

Chuck & Kelly in the Morning
WGY-AM
Division of iHeartMedia Inc
Riverhill Ctr, 1203 Troy-Schenectady Rd, Latham, NY 12110-1046
Tel: 518-452-4800
Web Site: www.wgy.com
Key Personnel
Host: Chuck Custer *E-mail:* chuck@wgy.com; Kelly Stevens *E-mail:* kelly@wgy.com
Book reviews, interviews & entertainment.
Air Time: Mon-Fri 5:30-9 AM

Cityscape
WFUV-FM
Affiliate of Fordham University
Fordham University, 441 E Fordham Rd, Keating Hall, Rm B-12, Bronx, NY 10458-9993
Tel: 718-817-4550
E-mail: thefolks@wfuv.org; cityscapewfuv@gmail.com
Web Site: www.wfuv.org

Key Personnel
Prodr, News & Pub Aff Dir: George Bodarky
    E-mail: gbodarky@wfuv.org
Urban issues, environment, literature, arts, human
    rights.
Air Time: Sun 6:30-7 AM

Community Spotlight
WESB-107.5 FM
Division of WESB Inc
1490 Saint Francis Dr, Bradford, PA 16701
Tel: 814-368-4141 *Fax:* 814-368-3180
E-mail: 1490@wesb.com
Web Site: www.wesb.com
Key Personnel
Pres & Gen Mgr: Don Fredeen
    E-mail: dfredeen@wesb.com
Host & Prodr: Anne Holliday
Talk show featuring community leaders, best-
    selling authors, actors & politicians.
Air Time: Fri 9:30 AM

Cover to Cover Open Book
KPFA-FM
Affiliate of Pacifica Foundation
1929 Martin Luther King Jr Way, Berkeley, CA
    94704
Tel: 510-848-6767 *Fax:* 510-848-3812
E-mail: comments@kpfa.org
Web Site: www.kpfa.org
Key Personnel
Coord: Richard Wolinsky *E-mail:* richwol@well.
    com
Host: Reyna Cowan *E-mail:* reynacowan@gmail.
    com; Jack Foley *E-mail:* jandafoley@sbcglobal.
    net; Jovelyn Richards *E-mail:* jovelynrichards@
    aol.com; Nina Serrano *E-mail:* ninaserrano34@
    gmail.com
Weekly interviews with poets, performance artist,
    film-makers, novelists & storytellers. The first
    week of every month is a combined one-hour
    program featuring Jack Foley & Nina Serrano.
    The second week is hosted by Nina Serrano,
    Poet 2 Poet. The third week is hosted by Jove-
    lyn Richards, Jovelyn's Bistro. The fourth week
    is hosted by Reyna Cowan, Frame to Frame.
    The fifth week (if there is one) is hosted again
    by Jovelyn Richards, Jovelyn's Bistro.
Air Time: Wed 3:30 PM, first Wed of the month
    3-4 PM

Extension 720 with Justin Kaufmann
WGN-AM
Division of Tribune Co Broadcasting Inc
303 E Wacker Dr, 18th fl, Chicago, IL 60601
Tel: 312-222-4700
E-mail: comments@wgnradio.com
Web Site: www.wgnradio.com
Key Personnel
Host: Justin Kaufmann
General interest talk & interviews.
Air Time: Mon-Fri 7-10 PM

Gwin Faulconer-Lippert Show
KTOK-AM
Subsidiary of iHeartMedia Inc
1900 Northwest Expwy, Suite 1000, Oklahoma
    City, OK 73118
Tel: 405-840-5271; 405-841-0200
Web Site: ktok.iheart.com
Various topics.
Air Time: Sun 8 PM

Forum
KQED-FM
Affiliate of National Public Radio
2601 Mariposa St, San Francisco, CA 94110
Tel: 415-553-2135 *Toll Free Tel:* 866-733-6786
    (call-in) *Fax:* 415-553-2174
E-mail: forum@kqed.org
Web Site: www.kqed.org/forum

Key Personnel
Prodr: Judy Campbell
Host: Mina Kim; Michael Krasny
Community concerns, consumer issues & inter-
    views.
Air Time: Mon-Fri 9-10 AM & 10-11 AM (two
    segments)

Fresh Air
WHYY-FM
Affiliate of National Public Radio
Independence Mall West, 150 N Sixth St,
    Philadelphia, PA 19106
Tel: 215-351-1200
E-mail: talkback@whyy.org
Web Site: www.whyy.org/programs/fresh-air
Key Personnel
Host & Exec Prodr: Terry Gross
Exec Prodr: Danny Miller
Prodr: Sam Briger; Amy Salit
Talk show; arts, popular culture & entertainment.
    Author interviews & book material. Broadcast
    nationally via National Public Radio.
Air Time: Check newspaper listing or web site

Lewis Burke Frumkes Show
WPAT-AM
Affiliate of Multicultural Radio Broadcasting Inc
27 Williams St, 11th fl, New York, NY 10005
Tel: 212-966-1059
Web Site: www.wpat930am.com
Key Personnel
Host & Prodr: Lewis Burke Frumkes
    E-mail: lewisfrumkes@gmail.com
Interviews with high profile people in arts & sci-
    ences.
Air Time: Sun 8-8:30 PM

Garage Logic
Hubbard Interactive
3415 University Ave SE, St Paul, MN 55114
Tel: 651-632-6646 *Fax:* 651-647-2932
Web Site: garagelogic.com/authors-corner
Key Personnel
Host: Joe Soucheray
Current topics podcast. Author's Corner feature
    on web site.

Steve Gruber
WAAM Talk 1600
4230 Packard Rd, Ann Arbor, MI 48108-1597
Tel: 734-971-1600 *Fax:* 734-973-2916
Web Site: www.waamradio.com
Key Personnel
News & Opers Dir: Dan Martin *Tel:* 734-971-
    1600 ext 15 *E-mail:* dan@waamradio.com
Gen Mgr & Sales Mgr: Theron Hughes *Tel:* 734-
    971-1600 ext 14 *E-mail:* x@waamradio.com
News, interviews, political talk show.
Air Time: Mon-Fri 6-9 AM

Roger Hedgecock Report
KFMB-760 AM
Division of TEGNA Media
7677 Engineer Rd, San Diego, CA 92111
Tel: 858-292-7600
E-mail: rogerhedgecock@gmail.com
Web Site: 760kfmb.com
Key Personnel
Host: Roger Hedgecock
Talk show. Politics, current events, occasional au-
    thor interviews.
Air Time: Mon-Fri 7:30 AM, 12:30 PM, 3:30 PM
    & 5 PM

The Tom Kearney Show
WPTF-680 AM
Division of Curtis Media Group
3012 Highwoods Blvd, Suite 201, Raleigh, NC
    27604
Tel: 919-790-9392 (busn); 919-860-9783 (studio)

Web Site: wptf.com/tom-kearney
Key Personnel
Host: Tom Kearney
Debut Date: 1988
General interest, various topics.
Air Time: Mon-Fri 9-10 PM

KOMO-1000 News
KOMO-AM Radio
Division of Sinclair Broadcast Group Inc
140 Fourth Ave N, Seattle, WA 98109
Tel: 206-404-5666
E-mail: editor@komoradio.com
Web Site: www.komonews.com
Key Personnel
Prog Dir: Rick Van Cise
News, current events.
Air Time: Mon-Sun all day

Mark Levin Show
WTVN-AM 610
Division of iHeartMedia Inc
2323 W Fifth Ave, Suite 200, Columbus, OH
    43204
Tel: 614-486-6101
Web Site: 610wtvn.iheart.com; www.
    marklevinshow.com
Key Personnel
Host: Mark Levin
Talk show; includes interviews & call-ins.
Air Time: Mon-Fri 10 PM-midnight

LNK Today
KLIN-AM
Division of NRG Media
4343 "O" St, Lincoln, NE 68510
Tel: 402-475-4567 *Fax:* 402-479-1411
E-mail: news@klin.com
Web Site: www.klin.com
Key Personnel
Host: Jack Mitchell *E-mail:* jackm@klin.com
Local news, talk & interviews.
Air Time: Mon-Fri 6-9 AM

Maryland Today
WPOC-FM
Subsidiary of iHeartMedia Inc
711 W 40 St, Suite 350, Baltimore, MD 21211
Tel: 410-366-7600
Web Site: www.wpoc.com
Public affairs program, including author inter-
    views.
Air Time: Sun 6-6:30 AM

Metroscope
KGON-FM, KFXX-1080-AM
Division of Entercom Communications Corp
0700 SW Bancroft St, Portland, OR 97239
Tel: 503-223-1441 *Fax:* 503-223-6909
E-mail: metroscope@entercom.com
Web Site: www.metroscopepdx.com
Key Personnel
Pub Aff Dir/Host: Preston Hiefield
Public affairs & news program; local concerns &
    issues. Also features authors & artists.
Air Time: Sun 6 AM (KGON-FM); Sun 10 PM
    (KFXX-1080-AM)

Dori Monson Show
KIRO-FM
Division of Bonneville International Corp
1820 Eastlake Ave E, Seattle, WA 98102
Tel: 206-726-7000 *Toll Free Tel:* 800-756-5476
Web Site: www.mynorthwest.com/category/the-
    dori-monson-show
Key Personnel
Prog Dir: Ryan Maguire *E-mail:* rmaguire@
    bonneville.com
Host: Dori Monson *E-mail:* dmonson@
    bonneville.com

Pop culture, politics & sports, talk show; author interviews.
Air Time: Mon-Fri noon-3 PM

Morning Edition
National Public Radio
1111 N Capitol St NE, Washington, DC 20002
Tel: 202-513-2000 *Fax:* 202-513-3329
Web Site: www.npr.org
Key Personnel
Host/Correspondent: David Greene
Host: Steve Inskeep; Noel King; Rachel Martin
Debut Date: 1979
News & information, used live or rebroadcast by over 600 National Public Radio stations; author interviews & book talk when relevant.
Air Time: Mon-Fri 5-9 AM (ET)

Morning Edition
KUHF-FM
Affiliate of National Public Radio
University of Houston, 4343 Elgin St, Houston, TX 77204-0887
Tel: 713-748-8888
E-mail: news@houstonpublicmedia.org
Web Site: www.npr.org/programs/morning-edition
Key Personnel
Dir, News & Pub Aff: Dave Fehling
  E-mail: dfehling@houstonpublicmedia.org
Debut Date: 1979
Local news inserts.
Air Time: Mon-Fri 5-9 AM

Morning News with Larry Richert & John Shumway
KDKA-Radio AM 1020
Division of Entercom Communications Corp
Foster Plaza, Bldg 5, 651 Holiday Dr, Pittsburgh, PA 15220
Tel: 412-920-9400
E-mail: newsdesk@kdka.com
Web Site: kdkaradio.radio.com
Key Personnel
Prog Dir: Jim Graci
Host: Larry Richert; John Shumway
Current events & news.
Air Time: Mon-Fri 6-10 AM

The Morning Show with Dave Lee
WCCO-AM
Division of Entercom Communications Corp
625 Second Ave S, Minneapolis, MN 55402
Tel: 612-370-0611; 651-989-9226 (studio/contest)
E-mail: newstips@wccoradio.com
Web Site: wccoradio.radio.com
Key Personnel
Host: Dave Lee
Air Time: Mon-Fri 5-9 AM

New Letters on the Air
New Letters Quarterly Magazine
Division of University of Missouri-Kansas City
UMKC, University House, 5101 Rockhill Rd, Kansas City, MO 64110-2499
Tel: 816-235-1159 *Toll Free Tel:* 888-LIT-AIRS (548-2477)
E-mail: radio@newletters.org
Web Site: www.newletters.org
Key Personnel
Ed-in-Chief: Robert Stewart *E-mail:* stewartr@umkc.edu
Prodr & Host: Angela Elam *E-mail:* elama@umkc.edu
Asst Prodr: Jamie Walsh *E-mail:* walshjm@umkc.edu
Debut Date: 1977
29-minute public radio program featuring interviews with or public readings by creative writers-poets, novelists, essayists, dramatists-talking about the creative process & their work. Available to any public radio station;

recent programs can be heard free online at www.newletters.org or older archive interviews can be purchased through the web site. New Letters on the Air has been on the public airwaves since 1977, making it public radio's longest continuously-running literary program.
Air Time: Public Radio Satellite Service (PRSS) feed on Content Depot 1 PM (ET). Selected programs available at www.prx.org. Digital download available for stations not connected to the satellite (e-mail Jamie Welsh for details)

Nightside with Dan Rea
WBZ-AM
Subsidiary of iHeartMedia
1170 Soldiers Field Rd, Boston, MA 02134
Tel: 617-787-7000
Web Site: www.wbz.com
Key Personnel
Prog Dir: Peter Casey
General interest talk & political issues.
Air Time: Mon-Fri 8 PM-midnight

On My Mind
WAMU-FM
Affiliate of American University Radio
4401 Connecticut Ave NW, Washington, DC 20008
Mailing Address: 4400 Massachusetts Ave NW, Washington, DC 20016-8082
Tel: 202-854-8851
E-mail: drpodcast@wamu.org
Web Site: dianerehm.org
Key Personnel
Prodr: Sandra Baker; Alison Brody; Rebecca Kaufman
Host: Diane Rehm
Debut Date: 1984
Conversations with newsmakers, writers, artists & thinkers on a variety of issues.

On The Bookshelf
WTBF-AM/FM
Division of Troy Broadcasting Corp
67 W Court Sq, Troy, AL 36081
Tel: 334-566-0300 *Toll Free Tel:* 888-970-8769 (public use only) *Fax:* 334-566-5689
E-mail: wtbfdoc@yahoo.com
Key Personnel
Opers & Prog Mgr: Dave "Doc" Kirby
Debut Date: 1992
Interviews with book authors (30 minutes).
Air Time: Sun 11:30 AM-noon (970 AM); Sun 9:30-10 AM (94.7 FM)

On-the-Go
KGO810
Division of Cumulus Media Inc
750 Battery St, 2nd fl, San Francisco, CA 94111
Tel: 415-808-0810 (call-in show hotline); 415-995-5735 (mktg/promo) *Fax:* 415-954-8700
Web Site: www.kgoradio.com
Key Personnel
Host: John Hamilton *E-mail:* johnhamiltonotg@gmail.com
Travel & leisure.
Air Time: Sun 9-10 AM

Penny for Your Thoughts
WDWS-AM
15 Main St, Champaign, IL 61820
Tel: 217-351-5300
E-mail: talk@wdws.com; newsroom@wdws.com
Web Site: www.wdws.com
Key Personnel
Host: Brian Barnhart
Talk, call-ins & entertainment. Also as podcast.
Air Time: Mon-Fri 9-11 AM

Radio Times
WHYY-FM

Affiliate of National Public Radio
Independence Mall West, 150 N Sixth St, Philadelphia, PA 19106
Tel: 215-351-1200
E-mail: talkback@whyy.org
Web Site: www.whyy.org/programs/radio-times
Key Personnel
Host & Exec Prodr: Marty Moss-Coane
Talk & interviews; general interest.
Air Time: Mon-Fri 10-11 AM

The Mark Reardon Show
KMOX-AM
Division of Entercom Communications Corp
1220 Olive St, 3rd fl, St Louis, MO 63103-2301
Tel: 314-621-2345 *Fax:* 314-588-1234
E-mail: kmoxnews@kmox.com
Web Site: kmox.radio.com/shows/mark-reardon-show
Key Personnel
Host: Mark Reardon *E-mail:* mark.reardon@entercom.com
Interviews, phone-ins & issues of the day.
Air Time: Mon-Fri 2-4 PM

Joel Riley Show
WTVN-AM 610
Division of iHeartMedia Inc
2323 W Fifth Ave, Suite 200, Columbus, OH 43204
Tel: 614-486-6101
Web Site: 610wtvn.iheart.com
Key Personnel
Host: Joel Riley *E-mail:* joelriley@iheartmedia.com
Talk show, includes interviews.
Air Time: Mon-Fri 5:35-9 AM

Ross Files
KIRO-FM
Division of Bonneville International Corp
1820 Eastlake Ave E, Seattle, WA 98102
Tel: 206-726-7000 *Toll Free Tel:* 800-756-5476
Web Site: www.mynorthwest.com/category/dave-ross-blog
Key Personnel
Prog Dir: Ryan Maguire *E-mail:* rmaguire@bonneville.com
Host: Dave Ross
News/issues talk show, author interviews.
Air Time: Mon-Fri 5 AM-noon

St Louis on the Air
KWMU-FM/St Louis Public Radio
Affiliate of National Public Radio
St Louis Public Radio, 3651 Olive St, St Louis, MO 63108
Tel: 314-516-5968 *Fax:* 314-516-5993
E-mail: news@stlpublicradio.org
Web Site: www.stlpublicradio.org
Key Personnel
Prodr: Alex Heuer *E-mail:* heueral@umsl.edu
News, talk & information.
Air Time: Mon-Fri noon-1 PM; rebroadcast 10-11 PM

Sports to the Max
WCCO-AM
Division of Entercom Communications Corp
625 Second Ave S, Minneapolis, MN 55402
Tel: 612-370-0611; 651-989-9226 (studio/contest)
Web Site: wccoradio.radio.com
Key Personnel
Host: Mike Max
Sports talk & interviews.
Air Time: Mon-Fri 6:30-9 PM

Street Soldiers
KMEL-FM
Subsidiary of iHeartMedia Inc
340 Townsend St, San Francisco, CA 94107
Tel: 415-538-1061

Web Site: www.kmel.com
Key Personnel
Prog Dir: Don Parker *E-mail:* donparker@
   iheartmedia.com
Host: Dr Joe Marshall
Interview format; public interest & public affairs.
   Live.
Air Time: Sun 8-10 PM

The Sunday Journal
KOST-103.5 FM
Subsidiary of iHeartMedia Inc
3400 W Olive Ave, Suite 550, Burbank, CA
   91505
Tel: 818-559-2252
E-mail: info@kost1035.com
Web Site: kost1035.iheart.com
Key Personnel
Dir, Mktg & Promos: Ilene Woodbury
Host: Kari Steele *E-mail:* karisteele@iheartmedia.
   com
Public affairs show.
Air Time: Sun 6-7 AM

Sunday Morning Magazine
WKRQ-FM
Division of Hubbard Radio LLC
2060 Redding Rd, Cincinnati, OH 45202
Tel: 513-699-5102 *Fax:* 513-699-5000
Web Site: www.wkrq.com
Key Personnel
Host: Rodney Lear *E-mail:* rlear@
   hubbardinteractive.com
Varies; news & talk, current events & features;
   relevant author interviews.
Air Time: Sun 7-8 AM

That's Life
PMPNetwork Inc
4 Cabot Pl, 3rd fl, Suite 9, Stoughton, MA 02072
Tel: 781-341-8332 *Fax:* 781-344-7207
E-mail: info@pmpnetwork.com
Web Site: www.pmpnetwork.com
Key Personnel
CEO, PMPNetwork.com & Interviewer: Mark
   Snyder *E-mail:* mark@pmpnetwork.com
Prodr: Rod Belmont *E-mail:* rod@pmpnetwork.
   com; Irwin Marx *E-mail:* irwin@pmpnetwork.
   com
Internet celebrity interview show.
Air Time: Varies

Think
KERA-FM
Affiliate of National Public Radio
3000 Harry Hines Blvd, Dallas, TX 75201
Tel: 214-871-1390 *Toll Free Tel:* 800-933-5372
   Fax: 214-754-0635
E-mail: think@kera.org
Web Site: think.kera.org
Key Personnel
Sr Prodr: Stephen Becker *E-mail:* sbecker@kera.
   org
Host: Krys Boyd
Debut Date: 2006
General interest topics; politics, current events,
   historical nonfiction, science, language, society
   & culture; authors interviewed. Live, call-in.
Air Time: Mon-Thurs noon-1 PM

Today's Black Woman (TBW)
1720 Mars Hill Rd, Suite 8-253, Acworth, GA
   30101
Tel: 404-697-0104
E-mail: tbwradioshow@gmail.com

Web Site: www.jenniferkeitt.com
Key Personnel
Host: Jennifer Keitt
Issues & information of interest to Black women.

Tolbert & Lund
KNBR-AM
Division of Cumulus Media Inc
750 Battery St, 3rd fl, San Francisco, CA 94111
Tel: 415-995-6800 *Fax:* 415-995-6867
Web Site: www.knbr.com/shows/tom-tolbert
Key Personnel
Radio Prodr: Brian Smith
Prog Dir: Jeremiah Crowe *E-mail:* jeremiah.
   crowe@cumulus.com
Promos Dir: Jennifer Violet Kennedy
Host: John Lund; Tom "Mr T" Tolbert
   E-mail: mrt@knbr.com
Sports talk show; interviews.
Air Time: Mon-Fri 3-7 PM

Total Information AM
KMOX-AM
Division of Entercom Communications Corp
1220 Olive St, 3rd fl, St Louis, MO 63103-2301
Tel: 314-621-2345 *Fax:* 314-588-1234
E-mail: kmoxnews@kmox.com
Web Site: kmox.radio.com/shows/total-
   information-am
Key Personnel
Host: Tom Ackerman; Michael Calhoun; Deb-
   bie Monterrey *E-mail:* debbie.monterrey@
   entercom.com
Early day rise & shine, news, features, interviews,
   sports, traffic & weather.
Air Time: Mon-Fri 5-8:30 AM

Twin Cities News Talk
KTLK-1130 AM
Division of iHeartMedia Inc
1600 Utica Ave S, Suite 500, Minneapolis, MN
   55416
Tel: 952-417-3000
Web Site: twincitiesnewstalk.iheart.com
Author interviews relevant to news on regular
   daily newscasts.

WBAL News Now
WBAL-AM
Division of Hearst Corp
3800 Hooper Ave, Baltimore, MD 21211
Tel: 410-467-3000
E-mail: mdnewsnow@wbal.com
Web Site: www.wbal.com
Key Personnel
Host: Bryan Nehman
Prodr: Malarie Pinkard *E-mail:* mpinkard@hearst.
   com; Jacob Young *E-mail:* jlyoung@hearst.com
Telephone interviews on a variety of subjects.
Air Time: Mon-Fri 5-9 AM

Weekend All Things Considered
National Public Radio
1111 N Capitol St NE, Washington, DC 20002
Tel: 202-513-2000 *Fax:* 202-513-3329
Web Site: www.npr.org
Key Personnel
Host: Michel Martin
News & information, current issues.
Air Time: Sat & Sun 5-6 PM

Weekend Edition Saturday
National Public Radio
1111 N Capitol St NE, Washington, DC 20002
Tel: 202-513-2000 *Fax:* 202-513-3329

Web Site: www.npr.org
Key Personnel
Host: Scott Simon
Debut Date: 1986
News & information, authors & writers.
Air Time: Sat 8-10 AM (ET)

Weekend Edition Sunday
National Public Radio
1111 N Capitol St NE, Washington, DC 20002
Tel: 202-513-2000 *Fax:* 202-513-3329
Web Site: www.npr.org
Key Personnel
Host: Lulu Garcia-Navarro
Debut Date: 1987
News & information, author & writer interviews.
Air Time: Sun 8-10 AM (ET)

The John Williams Show
WGN-AM
Division of Tribune Co Broadcasting Inc
303 E Wacker Dr, 18th fl, Chicago, IL 60601
Tel: 312-222-4700
E-mail: comments@wgnradio.com
Web Site: www.wgnradio.com
Key Personnel
Prodr: Griffin Fillipitch
Host: John Williams *Tel:* 312-222-5478
General talk show.
Air Time: Mon-Fri 1-3 PM, Sat 10 AM-noon

Worldview
WBEZ-FM
Affiliate of Chicago Public Media Inc
848 E Grand Ave, Chicago, IL 60611
Tel: 312-948-4600
E-mail: worldview@wbez.org; news@wbez.org
Web Site: www.wbez.org
Key Personnel
Sr Prodr: Steve Bynum
Host: Jerome McDonnell
Focus on international news & international af-
   fairs interviews. Also features art, activism &
   social movements in Chicago.
Air Time: Mon-Fri noon-1 PM

WTOP News
WTOP-AM/FM
Division of Hubbard Radio LLC
5425 Wisconsin Ave, Chevy Chase, MD 20815
Tel: 202-895-5000
E-mail: newsroom@wtopnews.com
Web Site: wtop.com
Key Personnel
Dir, News & Programming: Mike McMearty
   Tel: 202-895-5039 *E-mail:* mmcmearty@wtop.
   com
Gen Mgr: Joel Oxley *Tel:* 202-895-5012
   E-mail: joxley@wtop.com
All news format.

Your Legal Rights
KALW-FM
Affiliate of National Public Radio
500 Mansell St, San Francisco, CA 94134
Tel: 415-841-4121 *Fax:* 415-841-4125
E-mail: kalw@kalw.org
Web Site: www.kalw.org/programs/your-legal-
   rights
Key Personnel
Host: Jeff Hayden
Practical information on legal & consumer affairs;
   interview authors of relevant books. Live in
   Bay Area; call-in show.
Air Time: Wed 7-8 PM

TV Programs Featuring Books

Listed here are adult & juvenile TV programs that deal with books & authors. Programs are listed alphabetically by program name. Some are hosted by established critics who devote their entire program to reviews of current books; others mention books only occasionally. Also see the sections **Columnists & Commentators** and **Radio Programs Featuring Books**.

ABC2 News: Good Morning Maryland
WMAR-TV (ABC)
Member of Scripps TV Station Group
6400 York Rd, Baltimore, MD 21212
Tel: 410-377-2222
Web Site: www.wmar2news.com
Key Personnel
Morning Prodr: Calvin Johnson
Host: Jamie Costello; Christian Schaffer
News, author interviews.
Air Time: 4:30 AM & 7 AM

Action News 5
WMC-TV (NBC)
Division of Gray Television
1960 Union Ave, Memphis, TN 38104
Tel: 901-726-0416 (newsroom); 901-726-0555
    Fax: 901-278-7633
E-mail: news@wmctv.com; desk@wmctv.com
Web Site: www.wmctv.com
Key Personnel
News Dir: Gregg Phillips *E-mail:* gphillips@
    wmctv.com
Opers Mgr: Brent Green *E-mail:* bgreen@wmctv.
    com
Anchor: Joe Birch; Kym Clark
News & information.
Air Time: Mon-Sun 4-7 AM, noon-1 PM, 3-3:30
    PM, 6-6:30 PM, 10-10:30 PM

After Words
Cable-Satellite Public Affairs Network (C-SPAN2
    Book TV)
400 N Capitol St NW, Suite 650, Washington,
    DC 20001
Tel: 202-737-3220 *Fax:* 202-737-0580
E-mail: booktv@c-span.org
Web Site: www.c-span.org; booktv.org
Key Personnel
Sr Exec Prodr: Peter Slen
After Words is Book TV's newest author inter-
    view series. Each week nonfiction writers are
    interviewed by a guest host.
Air Time: Sat 10 PM (ET), Sun 9 PM (ET), Mon
    midnight (ET) on Book TV on C-SPAN2

AM Northwest
KATU-TV (ABC)
Division of Sinclair Broadcast Group Inc
2153 NE Sandy Blvd, Portland, OR 97232
Tel: 503-231-4610; 503-231-4222 *Fax:* 503-231-
    4626
E-mail: amnw@katu.com
Web Site: katu.com
Key Personnel
Host: Helen Raptis
Debut Date: 1976
Live author & entertainment interviews.
Air Time: Mon-Fri 9-10 AM

Awareness
WIS-TV (NBC)
Division of Gray Television
1111 Bull St, Columbia, SC 29201
Tel: 803-799-1010 *Fax:* 803-758-1278
Web Site: www.wistv.com
Key Personnel
Host: Leland Pinder
Minority issues.
Air Time: Sun 11-11:30 PM

Bay Area Focus
KBCW-TV
855 Battery St, San Francisco, CA 94111
Tel: 415-765-8144
Web Site: sanfrancisco.cbslocal.com/category/
    bayareafocus
Key Personnel
Host: Michelle Griego
Public affairs-news/talk, Bay Area issues, politics,
    authors, celebrities, national issues.
Air Time: Sun 8 AM

Black Renaissance
KBCW-TV
855 Battery St, San Francisco, CA 94111
Tel: 415-765-8144
Web Site: cwsanfrancisco.cbslocal.com/category/
    black-renaissance
Key Personnel
Prodr: Jan Mabry
News/interview show focused on arts & culture,
    race relations, politics & all other issues of in-
    terest to African Americans.
Air Time: Sun 11 AM (every 3rd week)

The Black Voice
KRIV-TV
Subsidiary of Fox Television Stations LLC
4261 Southwest Fwy, Houston, TX 77027
Tel: 713-479-2600; 713-479-2801 (newsroom)
    Fax: 713-479-2859 (newsroom)
Web Site: www.fox26houston.com
Key Personnel
Host: Jose Grinan *E-mail:* jose.grinan@foxtv.com
Public affairs program focusing on issues facing
    the Black community.

Books & The World
Cape Cod Writers Center
919 Main St, Osterville, MA 02655
Mailing Address: PO Box 408, Osterville, MA
    02655
Tel: 508-420-0200
E-mail: writers@capecodwriterscenter.org
Web Site: capecodwriterscenter.org
Key Personnel
Exec Dir: Nancy Rubin Stuart
Host: Madeline Holt
Debut Date: 1978
One of the longest running, cable access, author
    interview TV programs in New England & on
    YouTube. Two authors, including locally, na-
    tionally & internationally known writers, are
    recorded at the Cape Cod Community Me-
    dia Center in Dennis Port. Recordings appear
    on local access stations on Cape Cod, Mas-
    sachusetts & in the region & available for au-
    thors to have shown everywhere in the US.
Air Time: Locally controlled

CBS News Sunday Morning
CBS News
Division of ViacomCBS Inc
Box O, 524 W 57 St, New York, NY 10019
Tel: 212-975-3247
E-mail: sundays@cbsnews.com
Web Site: www.cbsnews.com/sunday-morning
Key Personnel
Exec Prodr: Rand Morrison
Sr Prodr: Gavin Boyle; Amy Rosner; Jason Sacca

90 minute news program highlighting the arts.
Air Time: Sun 9-10:30 AM

CBS 6 News at Noon
WTVR-TV (CBS)
Division of Local TV LLC
3301 W Broad St, Richmond, VA 23230
Tel: 804-254-3600 *Fax:* 804-254-3697
E-mail: newstips@wtvr.com
Web Site: www.wtvr.com
Key Personnel
Gen Mgr: Stephen Hayes *E-mail:* shayes@wtvr.
    com
Anchor: Cheryl Miller *E-mail:* cmiller@wtvr.com
Debut Date: 1948
Talk show; news & interviews.
Air Time: Mon-Fri noon-12:30 PM

CBS13 News at Noon
KOVR-TV
Subsidiary of CBS Television Stations
2713 KOVR Dr, West Sacramento, CA 95605
Tel: 916-374-1313 *Fax:* 916-374-1304
E-mail: news@kovr.com
Web Site: www.kovr.com
Key Personnel
News Dir: Mike Dello Stritto
News, features, inserts & general interest inter-
    views.
Air Time: Mon-Fri noon-12:30 PM

Channel 9 News
WCPO-TV (ABC)
Subsidiary of EW Scripps Co
1720 Gilbert Ave, Cincinnati, OH 45202
Tel: 513-721-9900 *Fax:* 513-721-6032
E-mail: newsdesk@wcpo.com
Web Site: www.wcpo.com
Key Personnel
Anchor/Host: Timyka Artist *E-mail:* timyka.
    artist@wcpo.com
Air Time: Sun 8-9 AM

Daybreak
WFAA-TV
Subsidiary of TEGNA Media
606 Young St, Dallas, TX 75202-4810
Tel: 214-748-9631 *Fax:* 214-977-6585
E-mail: news8@wfaa.com
Web Site: www.wfaa.com
Key Personnel
Exec Prodr: Sheena Autin
Anchor: Ron Corning *E-mail:* rcorning@wfaa.
    com
News.
Air Time: Mon-Fri 5-7 AM

Eyewitness Morning News
WWL-TV (CBS)
Subsidiary of TEGNA Media
1024 N Rampart St, New Orleans, LA 70116
Tel: 504-529-6298 *Fax:* 504-529-6472
E-mail: pressrelease@wwltv.com
Web Site: www.wwltv.com
Key Personnel
Prodr: Haleigh Wolfe *E-mail:* hwolfe@wwltv.com
Host: Eric Paulsen *E-mail:* epaulsen@wwltv.com;
    Sheba Turk *E-mail:* sturk@wwltv.com

Live morning news/interviews, entertainment, health & medical.
Air Time: Mon-Fri 4:30-9 AM

Eyewitness News at Noon
WCHS-TV (ABC)
Division of Sinclair Broadcast Group Inc
1301 Piedmont Rd, Charleston, WV 25301
Tel: 304-346-5358 *Fax:* 304-346-4765
E-mail: news@wchstv.com
Web Site: www.wchstv.com
Key Personnel
Dir: Matt Sampson
Prodr: Rachel Tarr
News & interviews.
Air Time: Mon-Fri noon-1 PM

Face the Nation
CBS News
Division of ViacomCBS Inc
2020 "M" St NW, Washington, DC 20036
Tel: 202-457-4481
E-mail: facethenation@cbsnews.com
Web Site: www.cbsnews.com/face-the-nation
Key Personnel
Exec Prodr: Mary Hager
Anchor & Moderator: Margaret Brennan
Debut Date: 1954
Interview & discussion broadcast with topics determined by events of the week.
Live from Washington, DC.
Air Time: Sun 10:30-11 AM

Fox In The Morning
WJW-TV (Fox)
Subsidiary of Fox Broadcasting
5800 S Marginal Rd, Cleveland, OH 44103
Tel: 216-432-4077
Web Site: www.fox8cleveland.com
Key Personnel
Planning Prodr: Margaret Daykin
  E-mail: margaret.daykin@fox8.com
Anchor: Kristi Capel; Wayne Dawson; Stefani Schaefer
News interviews.
Air Time: Mon-Fri 4-10 AM

Fox 13 News
WTVT (FOX)
Division of Fox Television Stations LLC
3213 W Kennedy Blvd, Tampa, FL 33609
Mailing Address: PO Box 31113, Tampa, FL 33631-3113
Tel: 813-870-9630 (newsroom); 813-876-1313
  Fax: 813-871-3135 (news & sports)
E-mail: fox13tampanews@wtvt.com
Web Site: www.fox13news.com
Key Personnel
VP & News Dir: John Hoffman
VP & Gen Mgr: Jeff Maloney
Asst News Dir: Scott Jones
Anchor: Chris Cato; Linda Hurtado; Kelly Ring; Cynthia Smoot; Mark Wilson
Air Time: Mon-Fri 4-10 AM, noon-1 PM, 4-7 PM, 10 PM-midnight

FOX 26 Morning News
KRIV-TV
Subsidiary of Fox Television Stations LLC
4261 Southwest Fwy, Houston, TX 77027
Tel: 713-479-2600; 713-479-2801 (newsroom)
  Fax: 713-479-2859 (newsroom)
Web Site: www.fox26houston.com
Key Personnel
VP, Creative Servs & Programming: Ralph Rendon *E-mail:* ralph.rendon@foxtv.com
Sr Anchor: Jose Grinan *E-mail:* jose.grinan@foxtv.com
News format. Live.
Air Time: Mon-Fri 6-10 AM, Sat 5-8 AM, Sun 5-7 AM

FOX 26 News at Noon
KRIV-TV
Subsidiary of Fox Television Stations LLC
4261 Southwest Fwy, Houston, TX 77027
Tel: 713-479-2600; 713-479-2801 (newsroom)
  Fax: 713-479-2859 (newsroom)
Web Site: www.fox26houston.com
Key Personnel
Sr Anchor: Jose Grinan *E-mail:* jose.grinan@foxtv.com
News format. Live.
Air Time: Mon-Fri noon-12:30 PM

Fox 2 News-Live at 11
WJBK-TV
16550 W Nine Mile, Southfield, MI 48075
Mailing Address: PO Box 2000, Southfield, MI 48037-0200
Tel: 248-552-5103 *Fax:* 248-557-1199
E-mail: fox2newsdesk@foxtv.com
Web Site: www.fox2detroit.com
News & interviews with authors & others.
Air Time: Mon-Fri 11 AM-noon

Good Day Atlanta
WAGA-TV (Fox)
Subsidiary of Fox Television Stations LLC
1551 Briarcliff Rd NE, Atlanta, GA 30306
Tel: 404-875-5555
E-mail: gooddayatlanta@foxtv.com
Web Site: www.fox5atlanta.com
Key Personnel
Exec Prodr: Amy Oates Ranel
Anchor: Alyse Eady; Ron Gant; Buck Lanford; Sharon Lawson
News & interviews.
Air Time: Mon-Fri 4:30-10 AM

Good Day Tampa Bay
WTVT (FOX)
Division of Fox Television Stations LLC
3213 W Kennedy Blvd, Tampa, FL 33609
Mailing Address: PO Box 31113, Tampa, FL 33631-3113
Tel: 813-870-9630 (newsroom); 813-876-1313
  Fax: 813-871-3135 (news & sports)
E-mail: fox13tampanews@wtvt.com
Web Site: www.fox13news.com/good-day
Key Personnel
Exec Prodr: Laura Cross
News, entertainment, features, medical format, personal financial, women's issues, nutrition, retirement & parenting.
Air Time: Mon-Fri 4-10 AM, Sat & Sun 6-10 AM

Good Morning America
ABC News
Division of The Walt Disney Co
47 W 66 St, New York, NY 10023
Tel: 818-460-7477
Web Site: abc.go.com/shows/good-morning-america
Key Personnel
Sr Exec Prodr: Tom Cibrowski
Host: Robin Roberts; George Stephanopoulis
Interviews, features.
Air Time: Mon-Fri 7-9 AM

Good Morning Oklahoma
KTUL-TV (ABC)
Subsidiary of Sinclair Broadcast Group Inc
3333 S 29 West Ave, Tulsa, OK 74101
Tel: 918-445-8888 *Fax:* 918-445-9354
E-mail: news@ktul.com
Web Site: ktul.com/station/good-morning-oklahoma; www.ktul.com
Key Personnel
Dir, Broadcasting Opers: Roger Herring
  E-mail: rbherring@sbgtv.com

Wide range of topics & author interviews.
Air Time: Mon-Fri 5-7 AM

Good Morning Texas
WFAA-TV
Subsidiary of TEGNA Media
606 Young St, Dallas, TX 75202-4810
Tel: 214-748-9631 *Fax:* 214-977-6585
E-mail: news8@wfaa.com
Web Site: www.wfaa.com
Key Personnel
Prodr: Paige McCoy Smith
Host: Jane McGarry
Interviews talk show with various people.
Air Time: Mon-Fri 9-10 AM

Lynne Hayes-Freeland Show
KDKA-TV
Division of ViacomCBS Inc
420 Fort Duquesne Blvd, Suite 100, Pittsburgh, PA 15222
Tel: 412-575-2200
E-mail: newsdesk@kdka.com
Web Site: pittsburgh.cbslocal.com
Key Personnel
Prodr & Host: Lynne Hayes-Freeland
  E-mail: lhfreeland@kdka.com
Minority issues, general interest with minority angle. Taped Wednesday mornings.
Air Time: Sat 6:30 AM, Sun 6 AM

Herman & Sharron Show
WCLF-TV
Division of Christian Television Network
6922 142 Ave, Largo, FL 33771
Mailing Address: PO Box 6922, Clearwater, FL 33758
Tel: 727-535-5622 *Fax:* 727-531-2497
Web Site: www.ctnonline.com
Key Personnel
Host: Herman Bailey; Sharron Bailey
Talk show interviews.
Air Time: Mon-Fri 10 AM & 5 PM

Hola Houston
KRIV-TV
Subsidiary of Fox Television Stations LLC
4261 Southwest Fwy, Houston, TX 77027
Tel: 713-479-2600; 713-479-2801 (newsroom)
  Fax: 713-479-2859 (newsroom)
Web Site: www.fox26houston.com
Public affairs program focusing on issues facing the Hispanic community.

Homekeepers
WCLF-TV
Division of Christian Television Network
6922 142 Ave, Largo, FL 33771
Mailing Address: PO Box 6922, Clearwater, FL 33758
Tel: 727-535-5622 *Fax:* 727-531-2497
Web Site: www.ctnonline.com
Key Personnel
Host: Arthelene Rippy *E-mail:* arthelenerippy@gmail.com
Talk show for homemakers, cooking segment, some music.
Air Time: Mon-Fri 5:30 AM & 1 PM (ET)

In Depth
Cable-Satellite Public Affairs Network (C-SPAN2 Book TV)
400 N Capitol St NW, Suite 650, Washington, DC 20001
Tel: 202-737-3220 *Fax:* 202-737-0580
E-mail: booktv@c-span.org
Web Site: www.c-span.org; booktv.org
Key Personnel
Sr Exec Prodr: Peter Slen

Comprehensive, live 3 hour look at one authors work, with questions from viewers via phone & e-mail.
Air Time: First Sun of the month noon & 10 PM on Book TV on C-SPAN2

KRON 4 News at 5
KRON-TV
Subsidiary of Nextstar Broadcasting
900 Front St, 3rd fl, San Francisco, CA 94111
Tel: 415-441-4444; 415-561-8905 (news dept)
E-mail: 4listens@kron4.com
Web Site: www.kron4.com
Key Personnel
Anchor: Vicki Liviakis; Pam Moore
Assignment Ed: Tamara Berry *E-mail:* berry@kron.com
News & features.
Air Time: Mon-Fri 5-6 PM

KRON 4 News at 6
KRON-TV
Subsidiary of Nextstar Broadcasting
900 Front St, 3rd fl, San Francisco, CA 94111
Tel: 415-441-4444; 415-561-8905 (news dept)
E-mail: 4listens@kron4.com
Web Site: www.kron4.com
Key Personnel
Anchor: Pam Moore; Ken Wayne
Assignment Ed: Tamara Berry *E-mail:* berry@kron.com
Hard news.
Air Time: Mon-Fri 6-7 PM

KRON 4 News at 10
KRON-TV
Subsidiary of Nextstar Broadcasting
900 Front St, 3rd fl, San Francisco, CA 94111
Tel: 415-441-4444; 415-561-8905 (news dept)
E-mail: 4listens@kron4.com
Web Site: www.kron4.com
Key Personnel
Anchor: Pam Moore; Ken Wayne
Assignment Ed: Tamara Berry *E-mail:* berry@kron.com
Local news.
Air Time: Mon-Fri 10-11 PM

KTVU Channel 2 News at Noon
KTVU Partnership
Affiliate of Fox Television Stations Inc
2 Jack London Sq, Oakland, CA 94607
Tel: 510-834-1212 *Fax:* 510-451-2610
E-mail: newstips@foxtv.com
Web Site: www.ktvu.com
Key Personnel
Anchor: Gasia Mikaelian
Assignment Mgr: Jay Martinez *E-mail:* jay.martinez@foxtv.com
News.
Air Time: Mon-Fri noon-12:30 PM

KTVU Channel 2 News at 6
KTVU Partnership
Affiliate of Fox Television Stations Inc
2 Jack London Sq, Oakland, CA 94607
Tel: 510-834-1212 *Fax:* 510-451-2610
E-mail: newstips@foxtv.com
Web Site: www.ktvu.com
Key Personnel
Host: Julie Haener; Frank Somerville
Assignment Mgr: Jay Martinez *E-mail:* jay.martinez@foxtv.com
Air Time: Mon-Fri 6-6:30 PM

Local 4 News at 5
WDIV-TV (NBC)
Subsidiary of Graham Media Group
550 W Lafayette Blvd, Detroit, MI 48226
Tel: 313-222-0500
E-mail: news@wdiv.com

Web Site: www.clickondetroit.com
Key Personnel
Prodr: Tim French
News, weather & sports.
Air Time: Mon-Fri 5-6:30 PM

Local 4 News at Noon
WDIV-TV (NBC)
Subsidiary of Graham Media Group
550 W Lafayette Blvd, Detroit, MI 48226
Tel: 313-222-0500
E-mail: news@wdiv.com
Web Site: www.clickondetroit.com
Key Personnel
Host: Errod Kasney; Rhonda Walker
News, weather, sports & interviews.
Air Time: Mon-Fri noon-12:30 PM

Connie Martinson Talks Books
2288 Coldwater Canyon, Beverly Hills, CA 90210
Tel: 310-271-4127
E-mail: talksbks@aol.com
Web Site: www.conniemartinson.com
Key Personnel
Prodr & Host: Connie Martinson
Debut Date: 1981
Interviews with authors; recommends books. Cox Cable, Southwestern Cable & American Cable (San Diego, CA), PCTV-San Francisco, represents Los Angeles Public Library twice daily on channel 35 (LA City view), channel 16 (S M, CA), CPCCTV Cablevision of Ohio (City of Retton, WA, Charlotte, NC), channel 2 (Las Vegas, NV), channel 26 (San Francisco, CA, Vail, CO, Coral Gables, FL) program streamed from San Francisco government TV, Los Angeles CityView, channel 35, Las Vegas, channel 2 on Internet, UCTV-satellite youtube/user. Connie Martinson's channel, Claremont College Digital Library 640 digital archives.
Air Time: Varies

Meet the Press
NBC-TV
Division of NBCUniversal
4001 Nebraska Ave NW, Washington, DC 20016
Tel: 202-885-4598
E-mail: mtpnewsreleases@msnbc.com
Web Site: www.meetthepressnbc.com
Key Personnel
Exec Prodr: John Reiss
Host: Chuck Todd
Interviews with newsmakers; direct discussion & report.
Air Time: Sun 10:30 AM in Washington, DC & NY (check local listings elsewhere)

Midday News
WKYC-TV (NBC)
Subsidiary of TEGNA Media
1333 Lakeside Ave, Cleveland, OH 44114
Tel: 216-344-3333 *Fax:* 216-344-3314
E-mail: news@wkyc.com
Web Site: www.wkyc.com
Key Personnel
Anchor: Maureen Kyle *Tel:* 216-344-7444
News & interviews.
Air Time: Mon-Fri noon-12:30 PM

Midday News
WFAA-TV
Subsidiary of TEGNA Media
606 Young St, Dallas, TX 75202-4810
Tel: 214-748-9631 *Fax:* 214-977-6585
E-mail: news8@wfaa.com
Web Site: www.wfaa.com
Key Personnel
Anchor: Demetria Obilor; Kara Sewell
Air Time: Mon-Fri 11 AM-noon

Midday on 5
WPTV-NBC
Affiliate of Scripps Howard Broadcasting
1100 Banyan Blvd, West Palm Beach, FL 33401
Tel: 561-655-5455
E-mail: newstips@wptv.com
Web Site: www.wptv.com
News segment.
Air Time: Mon-Fri 11 AM-noon

Mornings on Two
KTVU Partnership
Affiliate of Fox Television Stations Inc
2 Jack London Sq, Oakland, CA 94607
Tel: 510-834-1212 *Fax:* 510-451-2610
E-mail: newstips@foxtv.com
Web Site: www.ktvu.com
Key Personnel
Anchor: Gasia Mikaelian; Dave Clark
Assignment Mgr: Jay Martinez *E-mail:* jay.martinez@foxtv.com
News & interviews.
Air Time: Mon-Fri 7-10 AM

News at 5
WCCO-TV
Division of ViacomCBS Inc
90 S 11 St, Minneapolis, MN 55403
Tel: 612-339-4444 *Fax:* 612-330-2767
E-mail: wcconewstips@cbs.com
Web Site: minnesota.cbslocal.com
Key Personnel
News Dir: Kari Patey
Newscasts.
Air Time: Mon-Fri 5-5:30 PM

News at 5, 6, 10 & 11 PM
WSVN-TV
Division of Sunbeam Television Corp
1401 79 Street Causeway, Miami, FL 33141
Tel: 305-751-6692 *Toll Free Tel:* 800-845-7777 (FL only)
E-mail: newsdesk@wsvn.com
Web Site: www.wsvn.com
Key Personnel
Anchor: Belkys Nerey; Craig Stevens
News, information & entertainment.
Air Time: Mon-Fri 5-11:30 PM

News at Noon
WSVN-TV
Division of Sunbeam Television Corp
1401 79 Street Causeway, Miami, FL 33141
Tel: 305-751-6692 *Toll Free Tel:* 800-845-7777 (FL only)
E-mail: newsdesk@wsvn.com
Web Site: www.wsvn.com
Key Personnel
Anchor: Christine Cruz
News.
Air Time: Mon-Fri noon-1 PM

News at Noon
WCCO-TV
Division of ViacomCBS Inc
90 S 11 St, Minneapolis, MN 55403
Tel: 612-339-4444 *Fax:* 612-330-2767
E-mail: wcconewstips@cbs.com
Web Site: minnesota.cbslocal.com
Key Personnel
News Dir: Kari Patey
Newscasts & interviews.
Air Time: Mon-Fri noon-12:30 PM

News Channel 8 at Noon
WTNH-8TV (ABC)
Subsidiary of Nexstar Media Group Inc
8 Elm St, New Haven, CT 06510
Tel: 203-784-8888 *Fax:* 203-787-9698
E-mail: news8@wtnh.com
Web Site: www.wtnh.com

Key Personnel
Anchor: Keith Kountz
News, features & interviews.
Air Time: Mon-Fri noon-12:30 PM

News Channel 5 Live on 5
WEWS-TV (ABC)
Member of Scripps TV Station Group
3001 Euclid Ave, Cleveland, OH 44115
Tel: 216-431-3700; 216-431-5555 *Fax:* 216-431-3666
E-mail: newsdesk@wews.com
Web Site: www.news5cleveland.com
News, information, entertainment. Live.
Air Time: Mon-Fri 5-6 PM

News Channel 7 at Noon
WSPA-TV (CBS)
Subsidiary of Nexstar Media Group Inc
250 International Dr, Spartanburg, SC 29303
Tel: 864-576-7777
E-mail: assignmentdesk@wspa.com
Web Site: wspa.com
Key Personnel
Anchor: Fred Cunningham
News-oriented.
Air Time: Mon-Fri noon-12:30 PM

News 5 at Noon
KCTV5
4500 Shawnee Mission Pkwy, Fairway, KS 66205
Tel: 913-677-5555 *Fax:* 913-677-7243
E-mail: kctv5@kctv5.com; newsdesk@kctv5.com
Web Site: www.kctv5.com
Key Personnel
Host: Carolyn Long
News & interviews.
Air Time: Mon-Fri noon-12:30 PM

News 4 at Noon
WBZ-TV
Division of CBS Television Stations
1170 Soldiers Field Rd, Boston, MA 02134
Tel: 617-787-7000 *Fax:* 617-787-7346
E-mail: newstips@wbzty.com
Web Site: www.wbztv.com; boston.cbslocal.com
Key Personnel
News Dir: Johnny Green
News & talk format.
Air Time: Mon-Fri noon-12:30 PM

News Six at Noon
WKMG-TV
Division of Graham Media Group
4466 John Young Pkwy, Orlando, FL 32804
Tel: 407-291-6000 *Fax:* 407-298-2122
E-mail: desk@wkmg.com
Web Site: www.clickorlando.com
Key Personnel
Anchor: Bridgett Ellison; Kirstin O'Connor; Justin Warmoth
Air Time: Mon-Fri noon-12:30 PM

Nightline
ABC News
Division of The Walt Disney Co
47 W 66 St, New York, NY 10023
Tel: 202-222-7777
Web Site: abcnews.go.com/nightline
Key Personnel
Exec Prodr: Steven Baker
Co-Anchor: Juju Chang; Dan Harris; Byron Pitts
In-depth coverage of topical news issues/events of the day.
Air Time: Mon-Fri 12:35 AM (ET) (check local listings in other time zones)

Noon News
KCRA-TV (NBC)
3 Television Circle, Sacramento, CA 95814-0794

Tel: 916-446-3333 *Fax:* 916-441-4050 (news); 916-325-3731 (gen)
Web Site: www.kcra.com
News & guest segments featuring authors, chefs & personalities in the public eye. Live.
Air Time: Mon-Fri noon-1 PM

Noon News
WRAL-TV (NBC)
Subsidiary of Capitol Broadcasting Co Inc
2619 Western Blvd, Raleigh, NC 27606
Mailing Address: PO Box 12000, Raleigh, NC 27605-2000
Tel: 919-821-8555 *Fax:* 919-821-8541
E-mail: assignmentdesk@wral.com
Web Site: www.wral.com
Key Personnel
Anchor: Jeff Hogan
News.
Air Time: Mon-Fri noon-1 PM

Noon News
WISH-TV
Subsidiary of Nexstar Media Group Inc
1950 N Meridian St, Indianapolis, IN 46202
Tel: 317-923-8888; 317-921-NEWS (921-6397, news hotline) *Fax:* 317-931-2242 (news); 317-926-1144 (sales)
E-mail: newsdesk@wishtv.com
Web Site: www.wishtv.com
Air Time: Mon-Fri 11 AM-noon

Noon Newscast
KSAT-TV (ABC)
Division of Graham Media Group
1408 N Saint Mary St, San Antonio, TX 78215
Tel: 210-351-1200
E-mail: news@ksat.com
Web Site: www.ksat.com
Key Personnel
News Dir: Bernice Kearney *E-mail:* bkearney@ksat.com
Assignment Mgr: Sean Talbot
News & interviews.
Air Time: Mon-Fri noon-1 PM

PBS News Hour
PBS-TV
3939 Campbell Ave, Arlington, VA 22206
Tel: 703-998-2150 *Fax:* 703-998-4151
E-mail: newsdesk@newshour.org
Web Site: www.pbs.org/newshour
Key Personnel
Exec Prodr: Sarah Just
Anchor & Mng Ed: Judy Woodruff
Nightly newscast including regular book reviews.
Air Time: Consult local PBS listings, time varies

The 700 Club
Division of The Christian Broadcasting Network
977 Centerville Tpke, Virginia Beach, VA 23463
Tel: 757-226-7000 *Fax:* 757-226-2017
Web Site: www.cbn.com; www.700club.com
Key Personnel
CEO: Gordon Robertson
Guest Booking: Molly Young
Host: Terry Meeuwsen; Pat Robertson
News, talk, inspiration.
Air Time: Mon-Fri 10-11 AM, 11 PM-midnight, 3-4 AM (ET) (ABC Family Channel) or check local listing

7 News at 11 AM
KMGH-TV (ABC)
123 Speer Blvd, Denver, CO 80203
Tel: 303-832-7777
E-mail: 7newsdesk@kmgh.com
Web Site: www.thedenverchannel.com
Key Personnel
Gen Mgr: Dean Littleton

News program with occasional author interviews.
Air Time: Mon-Fri 11 AM-noon

7 News at Noon
WHDH-TV
Subsidiary of Sunbeam Television Corp
7 Bulfinch Place, Boston, MA 02114
Tel: 617-725-0777
E-mail: newstips@whdh.com
Web Site: www.whdh.com
News.
Air Time: Mon-Fri noon-1 PM

7 News at 6
WHDH-TV
Subsidiary of Sunbeam Television Corp
7 Bulfinch Place, Boston, MA 02114
Tel: 617-725-0777
E-mail: newstips@whdh.com
Web Site: www.whdh.com
News.
Air Time: Mon-Fri 6-6:30 PM

Show Me St Louis
KSDK-TV (NBC)
Division of TEGNA Media
1000 Market St, St Louis, MO 63101
Tel: 314-421-5055 *Fax:* 314-444-5164
E-mail: smsl@ksdk.com
Web Site: www.ksdk.com
Key Personnel
Sr Prodr: Melissa Spears
Anchor: Dana Dean
Local news & interviews.
Air Time: Mon-Fri 10 PM

60 Minutes
CBS News
Division of ViacomCBS Inc
524 W 57 St, New York, NY 10019
Tel: 212-975-3247
E-mail: 60m@cbsnews.com
Web Site: www.cbsnews.com
Key Personnel
Exec Prodr: Bill Owens
Exec Ed: Tanya Simon
Correspondent: Steve Kroft; Scott Pelley; Lesley Stahl; L Jon Wertheim; Bill Whitaker
Debut Date: 1968
Television news magazine focusing on people & events in news & behind headlines.
Air Time: Sun 7-8 PM (ET)

Street Beat
CW50 (CBS)
26905 W Eleven Mile Rd, Southfield, MI 48033
Tel: 248-355-7000
E-mail: streetbeat@wkbdtv.com
Web Site: www.cw50detroit.com
Key Personnel
Dir, Programming & Community Affairs: Paul Prange *Tel:* 248-355-7012 *E-mail:* paprange@cbs.com
Current affairs featuring community & organization events. Books featured are of local interest to those living in Detroit area & throughout Michigan. Taped.
Air Time: Sat 8:30 AM

The Sunday Business Page
KDKA-TV
Division of ViacomCBS Inc
420 Fort Duquesne Blvd, Suite 100, Pittsburgh, PA 15222
Tel: 412-575-2200
E-mail: newsdesk@kdka.com
Web Site: pittsburgh.cbslocal.com
Key Personnel
Host: Jon Delano *E-mail:* jdelano@kdka.com
Business issues, computer news & programs. Taped.
Air Time: Sun 6:30 AM

Talk of the Town
WTVF-TV
474 James Robertson Pkwy, Nashville, TN 37219
Tel: 615-248-5214
Web Site: www.newschannel5.com
Key Personnel
Prodr & Host: Merryll Rose *E-mail:* meryll.
rose@newschannel5.com
Host: Leland Statom
Topical interest, interviews & lifestyle entertainment.
Air Time: Mon-Fri 11-11:30 AM

Talkin' Pittsburgh
WPXI-TV (NBC)
4145 Evergreen Rd, Pittsburgh, PA 15214
Tel: 412-237-1100 *Fax:* 412-323-8097
Web Site: www.wpxi.com
Key Personnel
Prodr & Pub Aff Dir: Jonas Chaney *Tel:* 412-237-
1491 *E-mail:* jchaney@wpxi.com
Talk show; public affairs, interviews.
Air Time: Wed 12:55 PM

The Ten O'Clock News
KTVU Partnership
Affiliate of Fox Television Stations Inc
2 Jack London Sq, Oakland, CA 94607
Tel: 510-834-1212 *Fax:* 510-451-2610
E-mail: newstips@foxtv.com
Web Site: www.ktvu.com
Key Personnel
Host: Julie Haener; Frank Somerville
Assignment Mgr: Jay Martinez *E-mail:* jay.
martinez@foxtv.com
News.
Air Time: Mon-Fri 10-11 PM

Today
NBC-TV
Division of NBCUniversal
30 Rockefeller Plaza, New York, NY 10112
Tel: 212-664-4602
E-mail: todaystories@nbcuni.com
Web Site: www.today.com
Key Personnel
Exec Prodr: Libby Leist
Anchor: Savannah Guthrie; Hoda Kotb
Anchor, Weather & Features: Al Roker
News & features.
Air Time: Mon-Fri 7-11 AM

Today in St Louis
KSDK-TV (NBC)
Division of TEGNA Media
1000 Market St, St Louis, MO 63101
Tel: 314-421-5055 *Fax:* 314-444-5164
E-mail: newstips@ksdk.com
Web Site: www.ksdk.com
Key Personnel
Anchor: Allie Corey; Rene Knott

Local & national news & interviews.
Air Time: Mon-Fri 4-7 AM, Sat & Sun 6-7 AM
& 9-10 AM

The Tonight Show Starring Jimmy Fallon
NBC-TV
Division of NBCUniversal
Studio 6B, 30 Rockefeller Plaza, New York, NY
10112
Tel: 212-664-4444
Web Site: www.nbc.com/the-tonight-show
Key Personnel
Host: Jimmy Fallon
Guest appearances & interviews, including authors.
Air Time: Mon-Fri 11:35 PM-12:35 AM (ET)
(check local listings elsewhere)

12 About Town
WWBT-TV (NBC)
Division of Gray Television
5710 Midlothian Tpke, Richmond, VA 23225
Mailing Address: PO Box 12, Richmond, VA
23218-0012
Tel: 804-230-1212 *Fax:* 804-230-2789
E-mail: newsroom@nbc12.com
Web Site: www.nbc12.com
Key Personnel
VP & Gen Mgr: Mr Kym Grinnage
Entertainment topics for viewers in the area. Air
time varies. A segment of 12 News at Noon.

12 News at Noon
WWBT-TV (NBC)
Division of Gray Television
5710 Midlothian Tpke, Richmond, VA 23225
Mailing Address: PO Box 12, Richmond, VA
23218-0012
Tel: 804-230-1212 *Fax:* 804-230-2789
E-mail: newsroom@nbc12.com
Web Site: www.nbc12.com
Key Personnel
VP & Gen Mgr: Mr Kym Grinnage
News, special features & interviews.
Air Time: Mon-Fri noon-12:30 PM

20/20
ABC News
Division of The Walt Disney Co
47 W 66 St, New York, NY 10023
Tel: 818-460-7477
Web Site: abcnews.go.com/2020
Key Personnel
Sr Exec Prodr: David Sloan
Anchor: David Muir; Amy Robach
News magazine, features & investigative reporting.
Air Time: Fri 9-10 PM (ET) (check local listings
in other areas)

WAVY News 10 Midday
WAVY-TV (NBC)
Subsidiary of Nexstar Media Group Inc
300 Wavy St, Portsmouth, VA 23704
Tel: 757-393-1010
E-mail: newsdesk@wavy.com
Web Site: www.wavy.com
Key Personnel
VP & Gen Mgr: Carol Ward
Host: Katie Collett; Don Roberts
News, weather & sports.
Air Time: Mon-Fri noon-1 PM

WAVY News 10 Today
WAVY-TV (NBC)
Subsidiary of Nexstar Media Group Inc
300 Wavy St, Portsmouth, VA 23704
Tel: 757-393-1010
E-mail: newsdesk@wavy.com
Web Site: www.wavy.com
Key Personnel
VP & Gen Mgr: Carol Ward
Host: Katie Collett; Don Roberts
Live interviews, news & weather.
Air Time: Mon-Fri 4:30-7 AM

WIS News Midday
WIS-TV (NBC)
Division of Gray Television
1111 Bull St, Columbia, SC 29201
Tel: 803-799-1010 *Fax:* 803-758-1278
Web Site: www.wistv.com
Key Personnel
Host: Emily Scarlett; Greg Adaline
Talk show, news oriented; public affairs & interviews.
Air Time: Mon-Fri noon-12:30 PM

A Word on Words
WNPT-TV
161 Raines Ave, Nashville, TN 37203-5330
Tel: 615-259-9325
E-mail: tv8@wnpt.org
Web Site: awordonwords.org
Key Personnel
Host: J T Ellison; Mary Laura Philpott
Debut Date: 2015
Books & authors.
Air Time: Sun 10:26 AM & alternates on Thurs
7:26 PM

World News Tonight with David Muir
ABC News
Division of The Walt Disney Co
47 W 66 St, New York, NY 10023
Tel: 212-456-4040
Web Site: abc.go.com/shows/world-news-tonight
Key Personnel
Exec Prodr: Almin Karamehmedovic
Anchor: David Muir
Hard news program.
Air Time: Mon-Fri 6:30-7 PM (ET)

Book Manufacturing

Complete Book Manufacturing

This section includes companies offering complete book manufacturing services. The descriptions of the services provided are paid components.

Many of the companies listed here have been recommended by the manufacturing departments of book publishers as being active and experienced in the production of books.

A-R Editions Inc
1600 Aspen Commons, Suite 100, Middleton, WI 53562
Tel: 608-836-9000 *Fax:* 608-831-8200
E-mail: info@areditions.com
Web Site: www.areditions.com
Key Personnel
Pres & CEO: Patrick Wall *Tel:* 608-203-2575
  E-mail: patrick.wall@areditions.com
Dir, Spec Projs: James Zychowicz *Tel:* 608-203-2580 *E-mail:* james.zychowicz@areditions.com
Founded: 1962
Membership(s): American Musicological Society (AMS); Audio Engineering Society (AES); Music Library Association; Music Publishers Association (MPA)

ABDI Inc
16 Avenue "A", Leetsdale, PA 15056
Toll Free Tel: 800-796-6471 *Fax:* 412-741-4161
E-mail: e-fulfillment@abdintl.com
Web Site: www.abdi-ecommerce10.com/abdintl;
  www.abdintl.com/abdintl
Key Personnel
CEO: Michael D Cheteyan, II
Pres: Judy G Cheteyan *E-mail:* j.cheteyan@abdintl.com
VP, Fin & IT: Bryan A Cox
Gen Opers Mgr: Ericka D Giles
Founded: 1985
Turnaround: 8 Workdays
Print Runs: 50 min - 50,000 max

Adair Graphic Communications
Division of Printwell
26975 Northline Rd, Taylor, MI 48180
Tel: 734-941-6300 *Fax:* 734-942-0920
E-mail: adair@printwell.com
Web Site: www.adairgraphic.com
Key Personnel
Pres & CEO: Paul Borg
VP: Dennis Adair *E-mail:* dennis@adairgraphic.com
Founded: 1931
Turnaround: 10 Workdays
Print Runs: 500 min - 500,000 max

Adams Press
1712 Oakton St, Evanston, IL 60202
E-mail: info@adamspress.com
Key Personnel
Pres: James A Kepler *E-mail:* jkepler@adamspress.com
Founded: 1942
Turnaround: 20-25 Workdays
Print Runs: 100 min - 15,000 max (print; publish on demand available)

Membership(s): The Association of Publishers for Special Sales (APSS); Independent Book Publishers Association (IBPA); Independent Writers of Chicago (IWOC); Midwest Writers Association

AGS
Subsidiary of RR Donnelley
4590 Graphics Dr, White Plains, MD 20695
Tel: 301-843-1800 *Fax:* 301-843-6339
E-mail: info@ags.com
Web Site: www.ags.com
Key Personnel
Pres: Mike Donohue *E-mail:* mike.donohue@rrd.com
VP, Sales & Mktg: Alan Flint *E-mail:* aflint@ags.com
Founded: 1975
Print Runs: 50 min - 1,000,000 max
Membership(s): American Society of Association Executives (ASAE)

American Mathematical Society (AMS)
201 Charles St, Providence, RI 02904-2213
SAN: 201-1654
Tel: 401-455-4000 *Toll Free Tel:* 800-321-4267
  Fax: 401-331-3842; 401-455-4046 (cust serv)
E-mail: cust-serv@ams.org; ams@ams.org
Web Site: www.ams.org
Key Personnel
Exec Dir: Dr Catherine A Roberts
Publr: Dr Sergei Gelfand
Assoc Exec Dir: Dr Robert M Harrington
Assoc Exec Dir, Washington, DC: Dr Karen Saxe
Founded: 1888
Print Runs: 100 min - 10,000 max
Branch Office(s)
1527 18 St NW, Washington, DC 20036-1358
  (govt rel & sci policy) *Tel:* 202-588-1100
  Fax: 202-588-1853 *E-mail:* amsdc@ams.org
Mathematical Reviews®, 416 Fourth St, Ann Arbor, MI 48103-4820 (edit) *Tel:* 734-996-5250
  Fax: 734-996-2916 *E-mail:* mathrev@ams.org
Secretary of the AMS - Society Governance, Dept of Computer Science, North Carolina State University, Box 8206, Raleigh, NC 27695-8206 *Tel:* 919-515-7863 *Fax:* 919-515-7896
  E-mail: secretary@ams.org
Membership(s): Society for Scholarly Publishing (SSP)

appatura™, A Broadridge Company
Division of Broadridge Financial Solutions Inc
65 Challenger Rd, Suite 400, Ridgefield Park, NJ 07660
Tel: 201-508-6000 *Toll Free Tel:* 800-277-2155
E-mail: contactus@appatura.com
Web Site: www.appatura.com

Key Personnel
CEO: Richard Plotka
CIO: Faisal Fareed
Chief Prod Offr: Harsh Choudhary
Chief Strategy Offr: John Closson
Head, Fin: Alpha Diarra
Founded: 1949
Print Runs: 1,000 min - 250,000 max

Aptara Inc
Subsidiary of iEnergizer
2901 Telestar Ct, Suite 522, Falls Church, VA 22042
Tel: 703-352-0001
E-mail: moreinfo@aptaracorp.com
Web Site: www.aptaracorp.com
Key Personnel
Pres: Samir Kakar
EVP, Fin & Cont: Prashant Kapoor
SVP, Busn & Contact Ctr Opers: Ashish Madan
Busn Devt: Michael Scott *E-mail:* michael.scott@aptaracorp.com
Founded: 1988
Branch Office(s)
150 California St, Suite 301, Newton, MA 02458
  Tel: 617-423-7755
11009 Metric Blvd, Bldg J, Suite 150, Austin, TX 78758 *Tel:* 512-876-5997
299 Elizabeth St, Level 1, Sydney 2000, Australia
  Tel: (02) 8251 0070
Tower 1 & 2, 8/100, Acharya Thulasi Rd (Shandy Rd), Pallavaram, Chennai 600 043, India
  Tel: (044) 22640676
No 2310, Doon Express Business Park, Saharanpur Rd, Bldg 2000, Dehradun 248 002, India
  Tel: (0135) 2644055
7B, Leela Infopark, Technopark, Trivandrum, Kerala 695 581, India *Tel:* (0471) 14063370
A-37, Sector-60, Noida 201 301, India
  Tel: (0120) 7182424
D-10, Sector-2, Noida 201 301, India *Tel:* (0120) 24423678
SEZ Bldg 4A, 1st fl, S P Infocity, Pune Saswad Rd, Phursungi, Pune 412 308, India *Tel:* (020) 66728000

Arbor Books
244 Madison Ave, Box 254, New York, NY 10016
Tel: 212-956-0950 *Toll Free Tel:* 877-822-2500
  Fax: 914-401-9385
E-mail: info@arborbooks.com; editorial@arborbooks.net
Web Site: www.arborbooks.com; www.arborservices.co
Key Personnel
Owner: Joel Hochman *Tel:* 877-822-2502 *E-mail:* arborbooksjoel@aol.com;

Larry Leichman *Tel:* 877-822-2504
E-mail: arborbookslarry@aol.com
Mktg Dir: Olga Vladi
Founded: 1992
Turnaround: 21 Workdays; 1-7 Workdays for art
Print Runs: 1 min - 1,000,000 max

Arbor Services, see Arbor Books

Arrow Graphics Inc
PO Box 380291, Cambridge, MA 02238
E-mail: info@arrow1.com
Web Site: www.arrow1.com
Key Personnel
Pres: Alvart Badalian
Sr Graphic/Pubn Designer: Aramais Andonian
Founded: 1988
Print Runs: 300 min - 25,000 max

Asia Pacific Offset Inc
1312 "Q" St NW, Suite B, Washington, DC
  20009
Tel: 202-462-5436 *Toll Free Tel:* 800-756-4344
  Fax: 202-986-4030
Web Site: www.asiapacificoffset.com
Key Personnel
Pres: Andrew Clarke *E-mail:* andrew@
  asiapacificoffset.com
Founded: 1997
Turnaround: 104 Workdays including color separation & shipping
Print Runs: 2,000 min
Branch Office(s)
870 Market St, Suite 801, San Francisco, CA
  94102, Dir, Sales: Amy Armstrong *Tel:* 415-
  433-3488 *Fax:* 415-433-3489 *E-mail:* amy@
  asiapacificoffset.com
1768 Oakmont Ct, Ann Arbor, MI 48108, Dir,
  Sales: Dean Sherman *Tel:* 734-223-6218
  E-mail: dean@asiapacificoffset.com
62 Rivington St, Suite 2B, New York, NY 10002,
  Dir, Sales & Mktg: Simona Jansons *Tel:* 212-
  941-8300 *Fax:* 212-941-9810 *E-mail:* simona@
  asiapacificoffset.com
16 Clements Dr, Avoca Beach, NSW 2251, Australia, Dir, Sales: Penny Crocker *Tel:* (02) 4832
  6174 *E-mail:* penny@asiapacificoffset.com
57 Norfolk St, Ponsonby, Auckland 1021, New
  Zealand, Consultant: Barbara Nielsen *Tel:* (09)
  378-4971 *E-mail:* barbara@asiapacificoffset.
  com
C/ Tamarit 104, esc D, entrance 2, 08015
  Barcelona, Spain, Dir, Sales: Carlos
  Blavia *Tel:* 933278837 *Fax:* 933254826
  E-mail: carlos@asiapacificoffset.com
20 Mortlake High St, London SW14 8JN, United
  Kingdom, Dir, Sales: Adrian Gatheroole
  Tel: (020) 3170 8700 *Fax:* (020) 3170 8704
  E-mail: adrian@asiapacificoffset.com

Automated Graphic Systems, see AGS

B & Z Printing Inc
1300 E Wakeham Ave, Unit B, Santa Ana, CA
  92705
Tel: 714-892-2000
Web Site: www.bandzprinting.com
Key Personnel
Pres: Frank Buono *E-mail:* frank@bandzprinting.
  com
Founded: 1984
Turnaround: 7-10 Workdays
Print Runs: 3,000 min

Bang Printing Co Inc
Division of CJK Group Inc
3323 Oak St, Brainerd, MN 56401
Tel: 218-829-2877 *Toll Free Tel:* 800-328-0450
  Fax: 218-829-7145
E-mail: info@bangprinting.com
Web Site: www.bangprinting.com

Key Personnel
Pres: Todd Vanek *E-mail:* toddv@bangprinting.
  com
VP, Opers: Joe Saiko *E-mail:* joes@bangprinting.
  com
VP, Sales: Doug Walters *E-mail:* dougw@
  bangprinting.com
Founded: 1899
Turnaround: 10-25 Workdays
Print Runs: 1,000 min - 500,000 max

BBC, see Brown Book Co Ltd

Berryville Graphics
Member of Bertelsmann Printing Group
25 Jack Enders Blvd, Berryville, VA 22611
Tel: 540-955-2750 *Fax:* 540-955-2633
E-mail: info@bvgraphics.com
Web Site: www.bpg-usa.com
Key Personnel
CEO: Christof Ludwig
COO: Jorge Velasco
CFO: Christoph Mittendorf
CTO: Yannic Schroeder
Founded: 1956
Turnaround: 15 Workdays (initial orders); 6
  Workdays (reprint orders); 4 Workdays (out
  of stock)
Print Runs: 1,500 min
Branch Office(s)
100 N Miller St, Fairfield, PA 17320 *Tel:* 414-
  208-2800
871 Baker St, Martinsburg, VA 25405 *Tel:* 304-
  267-3600

Blue Note Books, see Blue Note Publications Inc

Blue Note Publications Inc
721 North Dr, Suite D, Melbourne, FL 32934
Tel: 321-799-2583; 321-622-6289
  Toll Free Tel: 800-624-0401 (orders) *Fax:* 321-
  799-1942; 321-622-6830
E-mail: bluenotebooks@gmail.com
Web Site: bluenotepublications.com
Key Personnel
Pres: Paul Maluccio
Founded: 1988
Turnaround: 20 Workdays
Print Runs: 25 min - 10,000 max (short run digi-
  tal print-on-demand available)

BookLogix
1264 Old Alpharetta Rd, Alpharetta, GA 30005
SAN: 860-0376
Tel: 470-239-8547 *Toll Free Fax:* 888-564-7890
E-mail: publishing@booklogix.com
Web Site: www.booklogix.com
Key Personnel
CEO: Angela DeCaires
Founded: 2009

Bookmasters
Division of Baker & Taylor Publisher Services
30 Amberwood Pkwy, Ashland, OH 44805
Tel: 419-281-5100 *Toll Free Tel:* 800-537-6727
  Fax: 419-281-0200
E-mail: info@btpubservices.com
Web Site: www.btpubservices.com
Key Personnel
Dir of Mfg: Brad Sharp *E-mail:* bsharp@
  bookmasters.com
Founded: 1972

Bradford & Bigelow Inc
3 Perkins Way, Newburyport, MA 01950-4007
Tel: 978-904-3100
E-mail: sales@bradford-bigelow.com
Web Site: www.bradford-bigelow.com
Key Personnel
CFO: Carmen Frederico
Pres: John Galligan

VP, Sales & Busn Devt: Bob Bradley *Tel:* 978-
  904-3108 *E-mail:* bbradley@bradford-bigelow.
  com
Founded: 1970
Turnaround: 10 Workdays
Print Runs: 50 min - 250,000 max
Membership(s): Book Manufacturers' Institute
  (BMI); PRINTING United Alliance

Brown Book Co Ltd
65 Crockford Blvd, Toronto, ON M1R 3B7,
  Canada
Tel: 416-504-9696 *Fax:* 416-504-9393
E-mail: bbc@brownbook.ca
Web Site: www.brownbook.ca
Key Personnel
Owner & Pres: Robert Brown
Opers Supv: Sharon Endugesick
Prodn Coord: Melissa Brown

C & C Offset Printing Co USA Inc
Subsidiary of C & C Joint Printing Co (HK) Ltd
70 W 36 St, Unit 10C, New York, NY 10018
Tel: 212-431-4210 *Toll Free Fax:* 866-540-4134
Web Site: www.ccoffset.com
Key Personnel
Dir & EVP, C & C Offset Printing Co (USA)
  Inc & C & C Offset Printing Co (NY) Inc,
  New York, NY: Simon Chan *E-mail:* schan@
  ccoffset.com
Sales Mgr, C & C Offset Printing Co (NY)
  Inc, New York, NY: Frances Harkness
  E-mail: fharkness@ccoffset.com; Timothy Mc-
  Nulty
CEO, C & C Joint Printing Co (HK) Ltd, Hong
  Kong: Jackson Leung
Deputy Gen Mgr, C & C Joint Printing Co (HK)
  Ltd, Hong Kong: Francis Ho; Kit Wong
Dir, C & C Offset Printing Co (France) Ltd:
  Michele Olson Niel *E-mail:* michele@
  candcoffset.fr
Pres, C & C Printing Japan Co Ltd, Tokyo,
  Japan: Yamamoto Masaaki
Dir, C & C Offset Printing Co (UK) Ltd: Tracy
  Broderick *E-mail:* tracy@candcoffset.co.uk
Sales Rep, Australian Off: Lena Frew
  E-mail: lena.frew@candcprinting.com
Founded: 1980
Turnaround: Varies
Print Runs: 2,000 min - 3,000,000 max (average
  book runs: 7,500-50,000)
Branch Office(s)
C & C Offset Printing Co Ltd (Australia Off),
  Lithocraft Graphics, 3-7 Permas Way, Trugan-
  ina, Victoria 3029, Australia *Tel:* (0613) 8366
  0200 *Fax:* (0613) 8366 0299
C & C Joint Printing Co (Beijing) Ltd, Bei-
  jing Economic & Technological Development
  Area (BDA), Donghuan North Rd, No 3, Bei-
  jing 100176, China (plant) *Tel:* (010) 6787
  6655 *Fax:* (010) 6787 8255 *E-mail:* ccbj@
  candcprinting.cn
C & C Joint Printing Co (Guangdong) Ltd, Hua
  Xin Bldg E Block, Rm 1511, 2 Shuiyin Rd,
  Huanshi East, Guangzhou 510075, China
  Tel: (020) 3760 0979; (020) 3760 0980
  Fax: (020) 3760 0977 *E-mail:* guangzhou@
  candcprinting.com
C & C Joint Printing (Shanghai) Co Ltd,
  3333 Cao Ying Rd, Qingpu Industrial
  Zone, Shanghai 201712, China (plant)
  Tel: (021) 5922 6000 *Fax:* (021) 5922 6111
  E-mail: shanghai@candcprinting.com *Web
  Site:* www.candcprinting.com
C & C Joint Printing Co (Guangdong) Ltd,
  Chunhu Industrial Estate, Pinghu, Long
  Gang, Shenzhen 518111, China (plant)
  Tel: (0755) 3360 9988 *Fax:* (0755) 3360 9998
  E-mail: guangdong@candcprinting.com *Web
  Site:* www.candcprinting.com
C & C Offset Printing Co (France) Ltd, 15, rue
  d'Aboukir, 75002 Paris, France *Tel:* 01 40 26
  21 07 *Fax:* 01 44 76 08 96

C & C Offset Printing Co Ltd, C & C Bldg, 36
Ting Lai Rd, Tai Po, New Territories, Hong
Kong (corp headquarters) *Tel:* 2666 4988
Fax: 2666 4938 *E-mail:* info@candcprinting.
com *Web Site:* www.candcprinting.com
C & C Printing Japan Co Ltd, Tozaido Bldg, 3F,
2-6-12 Hitotsubashi, Chiyoda-ku, Tokyo 101-
0003, Japan *Tel:* (03) 5216 4580 *Fax:* (03)
5216 4610 *E-mail:* mail@candcprinting.co.jp
Web Site: www.candcprinting.co.jp
C & C Offset Printing Co (UK) Ltd, 75 Newman
St, 3rd fl, London W1T 3EN, United Kingdom
Tel: (020) 7637 5033 *Fax:* (020) 7637 5044
E-mail: info@candcoffset.co.uk

C-M Books, see Cushing-Malloy Inc

Cenveo Inc
200 First Stamford Place, 2nd fl, Stamford, CT
06902
Tel: 203-595-3000 *Fax:* 203-595-3070
E-mail: info@cenveo.com
Web Site: www.cenveo.com
Key Personnel
CEO: Robert G Burton, Jr
CFO: Mark Hiltwein
Pres: Michael Burton
Founded: 1830
Turnaround: 10 Workdays
Print Runs: 1,500 min - 1,000,000 max

Cenveo Publisher Services
555 Virginia Dr, Fort Washington, PA 19034
Tel: 267-470-1590 *Fax:* 215-591-9093
E-mail: info.psg@cenveo.com
Web Site: www.cenveopublisherservices.com
Key Personnel
CFO: John Pennie
Pres: Atul Goel
VP, Journal Publg Servs: Debbie McClanahan
VP, Learning Solutions: Waseem Andrabi
VP, Media & Intl Delivery Ctr: Dwayne Reed
Dir, Mktg: Mike Groth *E-mail:* mike.groth@
cenveo.com
Founded: 1998
Branch Office(s)
3575 Hempland Rd, Lancaster, PA 17601
Tel: 717-285-9095
5457 Twin Knolls Rd, Suite 200, Columbia, MD
21045 *Tel:* 410-850-0500 *Toll Free Tel:* 800-
257-5529
2905 Byrdhill Rd, Richmond, VA 23228
No 31 Kempapura, Hebbal, Bangalore 560 024,
India *Tel:* (080) 4000 4888
36 Barnaby Rd, Kilpauk, Chennai, Tamil Nadu
600 010, India *Tel:* (044) 4205 8888
Marwah Ctr, 5th fl, Krishanlal Marwah Marg,
Andheri East, Mumbai 400 072, India
Tel: (022) 4098 5200
Steller IT Park, Tower I, 3rd fl, C 25, Sector 62,
Noida 201 301, India *Tel:* (0120) 461 3700
One Mulgrave Chambers, 26-28 Mulgrave Rd,
Sutton, Surrey SM2 6LE, United Kingdom

Cenveo St Louis
101 Workman Ct, Eureka, MO 63025
Tel: 314-966-2000 *Toll Free Tel:* 800-800-8845
Fax: 314-966-4725
Web Site: www.cenveo.com

CG Book Printers
Division of Corporate Graphics Commercial
(CGC)
1750 Northway Dr, North Mankato, MN 56003
Tel: 507-388-3300 *Toll Free Tel:* 800-729-7575
Fax: 507-386-6350
E-mail: cgbooks@corpgraph.com
Web Site: www.corpgraph.com
Key Personnel
Pres: Dan Kvasnicka *Tel:* 507-386-6340

Fax: 507-344-5548 *E-mail:* dekvasnicka@
corpgraph.com
Sales Exec, Book Mfg Sales: Mike Schmitt
Tel: 507-386-6349 *E-mail:* mjschmitt@
corpgraph.com
Founded: 1989
Print Runs: 50 min - 100,000 max

Codra Enterprises Inc
17692 Cowan, Suite 200, Irvine, CA 92614
Tel: 949-756-8400 *Toll Free Tel:* 888-992-6372
Fax: 949-756-8484
E-mail: codra@codra.com; sales@codra.com
Web Site: www.codra.com
Key Personnel
Pres: Gary Kim
Sales: Chris Scotti *Tel:* 949-322-5639
E-mail: chris@codra.com
Founded: 1985
Turnaround: 30-40 Workdays
Print Runs: 3,000 min - 3,000,000 max
Membership(s): Independent Publishers Associa-
tion; Pacific Northwest Booksellers Association
(PNBA); Publishers Association of the West
(PubWest)

Color House Graphics Inc
3505 Eastern Ave SE, Grand Rapids, MI 49508
Toll Free Tel: 800-454-1916 *Fax:* 616-245-5494
Web Site: www.colorhousegraphics.com
Key Personnel
Pres: Steve Landheer
Gen Mgr: Phil Knight *E-mail:* pknight@
colorhousegraphics.com
Founded: 1987
Turnaround: 5-20 Workdays
Print Runs: 1 min - 50,000 max (1-500 digital
short-run, 500+ offset)
Membership(s): The Association of Publishers
for Special Sales (APSS); Colorado Indepen-
dent Publishers Association (CIPA); Evangel-
ical Christian Publishers Association (ECPA);
Florida Authors & Publishers Association Inc
(FAPA); Independent Book Publishers Associa-
tion (IBPA); Printing Industries of Michigan
Inc (PIM); Publishers Association of the West
(PubWest)

ColorPage
Division of Tri-State Associated Services Inc
81 Ten Broeck Ave, Kingston, NY 12401
Tel: 845-331-7581 *Toll Free Tel:* 800-836-7581
Fax: 845-331-1571
E-mail: sales@colorpageonline.com
Web Site: www.colorpageonline.com
Key Personnel
Pres & Mktg Strategist/Consultant: Frank J Cam-
pagna, II *E-mail:* fcampagna@colorpageonline.
com
Acct Mgr & Cont: Kathy Riggins
E-mail: kriggins@colorpageonline.com
Prodn Mgr: Randy Delanoy
Cust Serv Supv: Debbie Downes
E-mail: ddownes@colorpageonline.com
Founded: 1976
Turnaround: 10-15 Workdays
Print Runs: 25 min - 20,000 max

C Harrison Conroy Co Inc
501 Penman St, Charlotte, NC 28203
Tel: 704-358-0459 *Toll Free Tel:* 800-242-2789
Fax: 704-358-0459
E-mail: chcphoto@charrisonconroy.com
Web Site: www.charrisonconroy.com
Key Personnel
Pres: Hal Conroy
Founded: 1936

Consolidated Printers Inc
2630 Eighth St, Berkeley, CA 94710
Tel: 510-495-3113 (sales); 510-843-8565 (admin)

Web Site: www.consoprinters.com
Key Personnel
CEO: Lawrence A Hawkins
Founded: 1952
Turnaround: 2-20 Workdays
Print Runs: 2,000 min - 500,000 max

Corporate Graphics Book Printers, see CG
Book Printers

The Country Press Inc
One Commercial Dr, Lakeville, MA 02347
Mailing Address: PO Box 489, Middleborough,
MA 02346
Tel: 508-947-4485 *Toll Free Tel:* 888-343-2227
Fax: 508-947-8989
E-mail: info@countrypressinc.com
Web Site: www.countrypressprinting.com
Key Personnel
Pres: Mike Pinto
VP & Gen Mgr: George Medeiros
VP, Cust Opers: David Brooks
Founded: 1967
Turnaround: 3-7 Workdays
Print Runs: 11 min - 5,000 max

Crane Duplicating Service Inc
4915 Rattlesnake Hammock Rd, Suite 207,
Naples, FL 34113
Tel: 305-280-6742 (help desk) *Fax:* 239-732-8415
E-mail: info@craneduplicating.com
Web Site: www.craneduplicating.com
Key Personnel
Pres & CEO: Richard W Price
Mgr, Cust Serv: Jean Fahr
Founded: 1955
Turnaround: 5-7 Workdays, Same day; 3 or 4
Workdays available at extra cost
Print Runs: 11 min - 50,000 max (5-7 Days for
short runs)

Crown Connect
250 W Rialto Ave, San Bernadino, CA 92408
Tel: 909-888-7531 *Fax:* 909-889-1639
E-mail: sales@crownconnect.com
Web Site: www.crownconnect.com
Key Personnel
CFO: Nicole Albright *Tel:* 909-888-7531 ext 204
Pres: Denny Shorett *Tel:* 909-888-7531 ext 225
VP, Opers: Ken Martin *Tel:* 909-888-7531 ext
206
Mgr, Busn Devt: Erin Warren *Tel:* 909-888-7531
ext 228
Prodn Mgr: Chris McPhate *Tel:* 909-888-7531 ext
214
Founded: 1970

Cushing-Malloy Inc
1350 N Main St, Ann Arbor, MI 48104-1045
Tel: 734-663-8554 *Fax:* 734-663-5731
Web Site: www.cushing-malloy.com; www.c-
mbooks.com
Key Personnel
Chmn of the Bd: Connie M Cushing
E-mail: ccushing@cushing-malloy.com
VP of Sales: Tedd Litty *E-mail:* tlitty@cushing-
malloy.com
Cust Serv/Sales: Adam Hieber *E-mail:* ahieber@
cushing-malloy.com
Founded: 1948
Turnaround: 15-30 Workdays
Print Runs: 150 min - 50,000 max
Membership(s): Independent Book Publishers As-
sociation (IBPA); Publishers Association of the
West (PubWest)

Data Reproductions Corp
4545 Glenmeade Lane, Auburn Hills, MI 48326
Tel: 248-371-3700 *Toll Free Tel:* 800-242-3114
Fax: 248-371-3710
Web Site: datarepro.com

Key Personnel
Pres: Dennis Kavanagh
Gen Mgr: Steve Olko
Acct Mgr: Kimberly Kavanagh *Tel:* 248-881-6518
(cell) *E-mail:* kkavanagh@datarepro.com
Sales Exec: Nick Janosi *Tel:* 734-426-1229
E-mail: njanosi@datarepro.com
Founded: 1967
Turnaround: 15 Workdays
Print Runs: 250 min - 100,000 max

Desktop Miracles Inc
112 S Main St, Suite 294, Stowe, VT 05672
Tel: 802-253-7900 *Toll Free Fax:* 888-293-2676
E-mail: info@desktopmiracles.com
Web Site: www.desktopmiracles.com
Key Personnel
Pres & CEO: Barry T Kerrigan *E-mail:* barry@
desktopmiracles.com
VP: Virginia Kerrigan *E-mail:* virginia@
desktopmiracles.com
Founded: 1994
Turnaround: 10-15 Workdays
Print Runs: 500 min

DNP America LLC
Subsidiary of Dai Nippon Printing Co Ltd
335 Madison Ave, 3rd fl, New York, NY 10017
Tel: 212-503-1060
E-mail: gps@dnp-g.com
Web Site: www.dnpamerica.com
Key Personnel
VP & Gen Mgr: Norikatsu Nakamura
Founded: 1976
Print Runs: 1,000 min
Branch Office(s)
2099 Gateway Place, Suite 490, San Jose, CA
95110 *Tel:* 408-735-8880
3858 Carson St, Suite 300, Torrance, CA 90503
Tel: 310-540-5123

RR Donnelley
35 W Wacker Dr, Chicago, IL 60601
Toll Free Tel: 800-742-4455
Web Site: www.rrd.com
Key Personnel
Pres & CEO: Daniel L Knotts
Pres, Busn Servs: John Pecaric
Pres, Mktg Solutions: Doug Ryan
EVP & CFO: Terry D Peterson
EVP & CIO: Ken O'Brien
EVP & Chief HR Offr: Sheila Rutt
EVP & Chief Strategy & Transformation Offr:
Elif Sagsen-Ercel
EVP, Gen Coun, Chief Compliance Offr & Corp
Secy: Deborah Steiner
EVP, Dom Opers & Chief Supply Chain Offr:
Glynn Perry
SVP & Chief Acctg Offr: Michael J Sharp
Founded: 1864
Turnaround: 3-6 Weeks
Print Runs: 3,000 min - 500,000 max
Branch Office(s)
955 Gateway Center Way, San Diego, CA 92102
Tel: 619-527-4600
40610 County Center Dr, Temecula, CA 92591
Tel: 951-296-2890
151 Red Stone Rd, Manchester, CT 06042
Tel: 860-649-5570
9125 Bachman Rd, Orlando, FL 32824 *Tel:* 407-
859-2030
5800 Peachtree Rd, Atlanta, GA 30341 *Tel:* 770-
458-6351
825 Riverside Pkwy, Suite 300, Austell, GA
30168 *Tel:* 770-948-1330
1750 Wallace Ave, St Charles, IL 60174 *Tel:* 630-
313-7000
609 S Kirk Rd, St Charles, IL 60174 *Tel:* 630-
762-7600
One Poplar Ave, Thurmont, MD 21788 *Tel:* 301-
271-7171

65 Sprague St, Hyde Park, MA 02136 *Tel:* 617-
360-2000
18780 W 78 St, Chanhassen, MN 55317
Tel: 952-937-9764
5500 12 Ave E, Shakopee, MN 55379 *Tel:* 952-
941-7546
6305 Sunset Corporate Dr, Las Vegas, NV 89120
Tel: 702-949-8500
5 Henderson Dr, West Caldwell, NJ 07006
Tel: 973-882-7000
12301 Vance Davis Dr, Charlotte, NC 28269
Tel: 704-949-3568
One Litho Way, Durham, NC 27703 *Tel:* 919-
596-3660
3801 Gantz Rd, Grove City, OH 43123 *Tel:* 614-
539-5527
700 Nestle Way, Suite 200, Breinigsville, PA
18031 *Tel:* 610-391-3900
9985 Gantry Rd, Philadelphia, PA 19115
Tel: 215-671-9500
218 N Braddock Ave, Pittsburgh, PA 15208
Tel: 412-241-8200
1210 Key Rd, Columbia, SC 29201 *Tel:* 803-799-
9550
1645 W Sam Houston Pkwy N, Houston, TX
77043 *Tel:* 713-468-7175
1550 Lakeway Dr, Suite 600, Lewisville, TX
75057 *Tel:* 972-353-7500
630 W 1000 N, Logan, UT 84321 *Tel:* 435-755-
4000
201 E Progress Dr, West Bend, WI 53095
Tel: 262-338-6101
Membership(s): Association of American Publishers (AAP); Book Industry Study Group
(BISG); Book Manufacturers' Institute (BMI)

W R Draper Co
Division of The Arthur Press (1978) Ltd
162 Norfinch Dr, Toronto, ON M3N 1X6, Canada
Tel: 416-663-6001 *Fax:* 416-663-6043
E-mail: info@arthurpress.com
Web Site: www.arthurpress.com
Key Personnel
Pres: Jeremy Thorn
Founded: 1954
Turnaround: 10 Workdays
Print Runs: 1,000 min - 75,000 max

Dunn & Co Inc
Affiliate of Legacy Publishing Group
75 Green St, Clinton, MA 01510
Mailing Address: PO Box 1185, Clinton, MA
01510
Tel: 978-368-8505 *Fax:* 978-368-7867
E-mail: info@booktrauma.com
Web Site: www.booktrauma.com
Key Personnel
Chmn: David M Dunn
Pres: Peter R Heelan
VP: Rocco Windover
Founded: 1976
Turnaround: 3-10 Workdays
Print Runs: 100 min

Ecological Fibers Inc
40 Pioneer Dr, Lunenburg, MA 01462
Tel: 978-537-0003 *Fax:* 978-537-2238
E-mail: info@ecofibers.com
Web Site: www.ecofibers.com
Key Personnel
Pres: John A Quill
VP, Sales: Dave Robbins *E-mail:* drobbins@
ecofibers.com
Dir, Book Group Sales: Jim McCafferty
E-mail: jmccafferty@ecofibers.com
Dir, Busn Opers: Joyce Hardell *E-mail:* joyce@
ecofibers.com
Founded: 1972
Branch Office(s)
730 York Ave, Pawtucket, RI 02861 *Tel:* 401-725-
9700 *Fax:* 401-724-4970

Membership(s): Book Industry Guild of New
York; Book Manufacturers' Institute (BMI);
Bookbuilders of Boston; Publishing Profession-
als Network (PPN)

Emprint®
5425 Florida Blvd, Baton Rouge, LA 70806
Tel: 225-923-2550 *Toll Free Tel:* 800-211-8335
Web Site: emprint.com
Key Personnel
CEO: Mr Courtney Westbrook
Pres & COO: Becky Vance *E-mail:* beckyv@
emprint.com
Turnaround: 5 Workdays
Print Runs: 2 min - 125,000 max
Branch Office(s)
109 Research Dr, Harahan, LA 70123 *Tel:* 504-
733-9654 *Toll Free Tel:* 877-568-1555
Fax: 504-733-8506
151 Southpark Rd, Suite 100, Lafayette, LA
70508 *Tel:* 337-839-9761 *Toll Free Tel:* 888-
874-9761
2830 Breard St, Monroe, LA 71201 *Tel:* 318-387-
1725 *Toll Free Tel:* 800-256-2259

Ferry Associates Inc
49 Fostertown Rd, Medford, NJ 08055
Tel: 609-953-1233 *Toll Free Tel:* 800-257-5258
Fax: 609-953-8637
Web Site: www.ferryassociates.com
Key Personnel
Pres: Kevin Ferry *E-mail:* kferry@ferryassociates.
com
Founded: 1982
Turnaround: Standard 2 week delivery
Print Runs: 1,000 min - 10,000,000 max

First Choice Copy
5208 Grand Ave, Maspeth, NY 11378
Tel: 718-381-1480 (ext 200) *Toll Free Tel:* 800-
222-COPY (222-2679)
Web Site: www.firstchoice-copy.com
Key Personnel
Owner & Pres: Joe Meisner *Tel:* 718-381-1480
ext 212 *E-mail:* jmeisner@nyc.rr.com
Turnaround: 3-5 Workdays

Flottman Co Inc
720 Centre View Blvd, Crestview Hills, KY
41017
Tel: 859-331-6636 *Fax:* 859-344-7085
E-mail: info@flottmanco.com
Web Site: www.flottmanco.com
Key Personnel
CEO: Sue F Steller *E-mail:* ssteller@flottmanco.
com
VP & CFO: Peter Flottman
Founded: 1921

Four Colour Print Group
2410 Frankfort Ave, Louisville, KY 40206
Tel: 502-896-9644 *Fax:* 502-896-9594
E-mail: sales@fourcolour.com
Web Site: www.fourcolour.com
Key Personnel
Pres & CEO: George C Dick *Tel:* 502-896-9644
ext 303 *E-mail:* gdick@fourcolour.com
Prodn Dir: Amy Martin *Tel:* 502-896-9644 ext
315 *E-mail:* amartin@fourcolour.com
Prodn Mgr: Cindy Jones *Tel:* 502-896-9644 ext
310 *E-mail:* cjones@fourcolour.com
Founded: 1985
Turnaround: 90 Workdays
Print Runs: 1,000 min - 100,000 max
Branch Office(s)
FCI Digital, 2032 S Alex Rd, Suite A, West
Carrollton, OH 45449 *Tel:* 931-859-9701
Fax: 931-859-9709 *E-mail:* sales@fcidigital.
com *Web Site:* www.fcidigital.com

FRIESENS
EST. 1907
— EMPLOYEE-OWNED —

Friesens Corp
One Printers Way, Altona, MB R0G 0B0, Canada
Tel: 204-324-6401 *Fax:* 204-324-1333
E-mail: book_info@friesens.com
Web Site: www.friesens.com
Key Personnel
Pres & CEO: Chad Friesen
Gen Sales Mgr: Doug Symington
   E-mail: dougs@friesens.com
Founded: 1907
Friesens is North America's premier book & book packaging manufacturer, providing publishers with quality, all in-house services at our 250,000 sq ft state-of-the-art & eco-friendly book production facility. Friesens customers include Penguin Random House, HarperCollins, Gallup Press, Orca Books, Hachette Publishing (Avalon Travel), Art Institute of Chicago, Smithsonian, DK Publishing, ECW Publishing, & many more. Whatever your book publishing needs, Friesens is committed to ensuring your experience is as satisfying as the products we produce.
Turnaround: 3-4 Weeks
Print Runs: 250 min - 250,000 max (& more)
Membership(s): Book Manufacturers' Institute (BMI)
See Ad in this Section

Fry Communications Inc
800 W Church Rd, Mechanicsburg, PA 17055
Tel: 717-766-0211 *Toll Free Tel:* 800-334-1429
   Fax: 717-691-0341
E-mail: info@frycomm.com
Web Site: www.frycomm.com
Key Personnel
Chmn of the Bd: Henry Fry
CEO: Mike Lukas
CFO: Chris Wawrzyniak
CTO: David S Fry
VP, Sales: Kevin Quinn
Founded: 1934
Turnaround: 7-12 Workdays
Print Runs: 10,000 min - 2,000,000 max

Fundcraft Publishing
410 Hwy 72 W, Collierville, TN 38017
Mailing Address: PO Box 340, Collierville, TN 38027
Tel: 901-853-7070 *Toll Free Tel:* 800-853-1363
   Fax: 901-853-6196
E-mail: info@fundcraft.com
Web Site: www.fundcraft.com
Key Personnel
Pres: Chris Bradley *E-mail:* cbradley@cookbooks.com
Publr: David Bradley
Turnaround: 40-60 Workdays
Print Runs: 100 min

G & H Soho Inc
413 Market St, Elmwood Park, NJ 07407
Tel: 201-216-9400 *Fax:* 201-216-1778
E-mail: print@ghsoho.com
Web Site: www.ghsoho.com
Key Personnel
Pres: Gerry Burstein
Prodn Mgr: Jason Burstein

Founded: 1985
Turnaround: 3-40 Workdays
Print Runs: 5 min - 10,000 max
Membership(s): Association of Graphic Communications; Book Industry Guild of New York; Digital Printing Council; PRINTING United Alliance

GEX Inc
2 Industrial Way, Atkinson, NH 03811
Tel: 603-870-9292
Web Site: www.gexinc.com
Key Personnel
Pres: Gary Russell
VP: Jim LaPierre; Karla Russell
Founded: 1986

Giant Horse Printing Inc
1336 San Mateo Ave, South San Francisco, CA 94080
Tel: 650-875-7137 *Fax:* 650-875-7194
E-mail: info@gianthorse.com
Web Site: www.gianthorse.com
Key Personnel
Pres: Chiu Bing Ma
Founded: 1970
Turnaround: 7-10 Workdays
Print Runs: 1 min - 50,000 max

Global Order Fulfillment, see ABDI Inc

Graphic Connections Group LLC
174 Chesterfield Industrial Blvd, Chesterfield, MO 63005
Tel: 636-519-8320 *Toll Free Tel:* 800-378-0378
   Fax: 636-519-8310
Web Site: www.gcfrog.com

Key Personnel
Owner & Pres: Jeff Charlton
VP, Mktg: Michael Hecht *E-mail:* mhecht@gcfrog.com
Turnaround: 5-7 Workdays from final proof authorization
Print Runs: 25 min - 2,500 max

Graphic Litho
Division of High Speed Process Printing Corp
130 Shepard St, Lawrence, MA 01843
Tel: 978-683-2766 *Fax:* 978-681-7588
E-mail: sales@graphiclitho.com
Web Site: www.graphiclitho.com
Key Personnel
Pres: Ralph E Wilbur
Founded: 1960
Print Runs: 1,000 min
Membership(s): Print Services & Distribution Association (PSDA); Printing Industries of New England (PINE); PRINTING United Alliance

Hess Print Solutions
Division of CJK Group Inc
3765 Sunnybrook Rd, Brimfield, OH 44240
Toll Free Tel: 800-678-1222
E-mail: info@hessprintsolutions.com
Web Site: www.hessprintsolutions.com
Key Personnel
Dir & VP: Burt Phillips
VP, IT: Douglas Holzschuh
Founded: 2006
Print Runs: 1,000 min
Membership(s): Book Manufacturers' Institute (BMI)

Hignell Book Printing Ltd
Division of Unigraphics Ltd
488 Burnell St, Winnipeg, MB R3G 2B4, Canada
Tel: 204-784-1030 *Toll Free Tel:* 800-304-5553
   Fax: 204-774-4053
E-mail: books@hignell.mb.ca
Web Site: www.hignell.mb.ca
Key Personnel
Pres: Kevin Polley *E-mail:* kevin@unigraphics.mb.ca
VP & Gen Mgr: David Morcom *E-mail:* davem@unigraphics.mb.ca
Founded: 1908
Turnaround: 15 Workdays
Print Runs: 100 min - 10,000 max

The P A Hutchison Co
400 Penn Ave, Mayfield, PA 18433
SAN: 991-5559
Tel: 570-876-4560 *Toll Free Tel:* 800-USA-PRNT
   (872-7768) *Fax:* 570-876-4561
E-mail: sales@pahutch.com
Web Site: www.pahutch.com
Key Personnel
Pres & CEO: Chris Hutchison
Dir, Sales & Admin: Erin Jones
Founded: 1911
Turnaround: 3-20 Workdays
Print Runs: 10 min - 200,000 max (digital & conventional)

Imago
110 W 40 St, New York, NY 10018
Tel: 212-921-4411 *Fax:* 212-921-8226
E-mail: sales@imagousa.com
Web Site: www.imagousa.com
Key Personnel
Pres & CEO: Howard Musk *E-mail:* howardm@imagogroup.com
Founded: 1985
Turnaround: 5-10 Workdays for color separations; 4-6 Weeks for printing & binding
Print Runs: 3,000 min
Branch Office(s)
Imago West Coast, 23412 Moulton Pkwy, Suite

250, Laguna Hills, CA 92653 (sales), Contact: Tammy Simms *Tel:* 949-367-1635 *Fax:* 949-367-1639
Imago Australia, 10 Help St, Suite 27, Level 6, Chatswood, NSW 2067, Australia (sales) *Tel:* (04) 3753 3351 (cell); (04) 4806 8704 (cell) *E-mail:* sales@imagaoaus.com
Imago Brazil, Domiciano Rossi, 340 unid 154, 09726-121 Sao Bernardo do Campo, Brazil (sales) *Tel:* (011) 2306 8546; (011) 2306 8547 *E-mail:* imagobra@gmail.com
Imago Shenzhen, Rm 2511-2512, Block A, United Plaza No 5022, Bin He Rd, Fu Tian Centre District, Shenzhen 518033, China (prodn), Contact: Kendrick Cheung *Tel:* (0755) 8304 8899 *Fax:* (0755) 8251 4073 *E-mail:* enquiries@imago.com.hk
Imago France, 23 rue Lavoisier, 75008 Paris, France (sales) *Tel:* 01 45 26 47 74 *Fax:* 01 78 94 14 44 *E-mail:* sales@imagogroup.com
Imago Services (HK) Ltd, Unit B309, 1/F, New East Sun Industrial Bldg, 18 Shing Yip St, Kwun Tong, Hong Kong (prodn), Contact: Kendrick Cheung *Tel:* 2811 3316 *E-mail:* enquiries@imago.com.hk
Imago Productions (Malaysia) Pte Ltd, No 43, Taman Emas, Jl Utama 31, Telok Panglima Garang, 42500 Kuala Langot, Selangor, Malaysia (prodn, incorporating South Africa sales) *Tel:* (017) 4288771 (cell) *E-mail:* enquiries@imago.com.sg
Imago Publishing, Albury Ct, Albury Thame, Oxon OX9 2LP, United Kingdom (sales), Dir: Simon Rosenheim *Tel:* (01844) 337000 *Fax:* (01844) 339935 *E-mail:* sales@imago.co.uk *Web Site:* imagogroup.com

InfinitPrint Solutions Inc
14 N Tenth St, Richmond, IN 47374
Tel: 765-962-1507 *Toll Free Tel:* 800-478-4885
   Fax: 765-962-4997
E-mail: info@infinitprint.com
Web Site: infinitprint.com
Key Personnel
Pres: Michael D Gibbs *E-mail:* mike@infinitprint.com
Founded: 1972
Turnaround: 30 Workdays
Print Runs: 100 min - 5,000 max
Branch Office(s)
211 NW Seventh St, Richmond, IN 47374
   Tel: 765-966-7130 *Fax:* 765-966-7131

Ironmark
9040 Junction Dr, Annapolis Junction, MD 20701
Toll Free Tel: 888-775-3737
E-mail: marketing@ironmarkusa.com
Web Site: ironmarkusa.com
Key Personnel
CEO: Scott Hargest *E-mail:* scott@ironmarkusa.com; Jeff Ostenso *E-mail:* jeff@ironmarkusa.com
Pres: Matt Marzullo *E-mail:* mmarzullo@ironmarkusa.com
SVP, Sales: Scott Kravitz *E-mail:* skravitz@ironmarkusa.com
VP, Opers: Chris Marzullo *E-mail:* cmarzullo@ironmarkusa.com
Sr Sales Exec: Larry Davis *E-mail:* ldavis@ironmarkusa.com
Founded: 1955
Turnaround: 20 Workdays, case bound; 10 Workdays, paperback; 15 Workdays, mechanically bound
Print Runs: 500 min - 500,000 max

Itzhack Shelomi Design
25 Cushman Rd, Scarsdale, NY 10583
Tel: 212-689-7469
E-mail: studio@ishelomi.com; studio@serifes.com
Web Site: www.ishelomi.com

Key Personnel
Owner & Creative Dir: Itzhack Shelomi
Founded: 1987

JP Graphics Inc
3001 E Venture Dr, Appleton, WI 54911
Tel: 920-733-4483 *Fax:* 920-733-1700
E-mail: support@jpinc.com
Web Site: www.jpinc.com; www.print.jpinc.com
Key Personnel
Pres: Rod Stoffel
Sales Mgr: Randy Hearley
Founded: 1969

Kelmscott, a Fuse LLC company
5656 McDermott Dr, Berkeley, IL 60163
Tel: 630-898-4261
Web Site: www.kelmscott.com
Key Personnel
Principal: Bill Barta
Pres: Scott Voris
EVP: Jason Tews *E-mail:* jtews@kelmscott.com
VP, Strategy & Client Servs: Jennifer Cox
Dir, Opers: Ketan Shah
Founded: 1936

King Printing
181 Industrial Ave E, Lowell, MA 01852-5147
Tel: 978-458-2345 *Fax:* 978-458-1441
E-mail: inquiries@kingprinting.com
Web Site: www.kingprinting.com; www.adibooks.com
Founded: 1978
Print Runs: 1 min - 10,000 max
Membership(s): Independent Book Publishers Association (IBPA); Printing Industries of New England (PINE); PRINTING United Alliance

Knepper Press Corp
2251 Sweeney Dr, Clinton, PA 15026
Tel: 724-899-4200 *Fax:* 724-899-1331
Web Site: www.knepperpress.com
Key Personnel
Chmn: Ted Ford *E-mail:* tedford@knepperpress.com
CFO: Jerry Sales *E-mail:* jerry.sales@knepperpress.com
Cont: Dawn Bates *E-mail:* dawn.bates@knepperpress.com
Pres: Bob Hreha *E-mail:* bobhreha@knepperpress.com
Founded: 1873
Turnaround: 10-20 Workdays
Print Runs: 500 min - 25,000 max

Kromar Printing Ltd
725 Portage Ave, Winnipeg, MB R3G 0M8, Canada
Tel: 204-775-8721 *Fax:* 204-783-8985
E-mail: info@kromar.com
Web Site: www.kromar.com
Key Personnel
CEO: Jack Cohen
COO: Joseph Cohen *E-mail:* josephcohen@kromar.com
Founded: 1945
Turnaround: 15 Workdays
Print Runs: 500 min - 50,000 max
Branch Office(s)
130 Slater St, Ottawa, ON K1P 6E2, Canada
   Tel: 613-563-7577 *Fax:* 613-594-8705
   E-mail: kromar@kromar.com

Lake Book Manufacturing Inc
2085 N Cornell Ave, Melrose Park, IL 60160
Tel: 708-345-7000
E-mail: info@lakebook.com
Web Site: www.lakebook.com
Key Personnel
Pres & COO: Dan Genovese
VP, Fin & CFO: Bob Flatow

VP & Gen Mgr: Bill Richards
VP, Mfg: Steve Quagliato
VP, Opers: Bill Flavin
VP, Sales & Mktg: Nick Vergoth
VP, Technol: Paul Genovese

Leo Paper USA
Division of Leo Paper Group
1180 NW Maple St, Suite 102, Issaquah, WA 98027
Tel: 425-646-8801 *Fax:* 425-646-8805
E-mail: info@leousa.com
Web Site: www.leopaper.com
Key Personnel
Pres: Behzad Pakzad
Founded: 1982
Turnaround: 30-40 Workdays
Print Runs: 3,500 min - 2,000,000 max
Branch Office(s)
286 Fifth Ave, 6th fl, New York, NY 10001, Contact: John DiMasi *Tel:* 917-305-0708 *Fax:* 917-305-0709 *E-mail:* info@leousanewyork.com

Lidec Inc
800, blvd Industriel, bureau 202, Saint-Jean-sur-Richlieu, QC J3B 8G4, Canada
Tel: 514-843-5991 *Toll Free Tel:* 800-350-5991 (CN only) *Fax:* 514-843-5252
E-mail: lidec@lidec.qc.ca
Web Site: www.lidec.qc.ca
Founded: 1965

Lightning Source LLC
Subsidiary of Ingram Content Group LLC
1246 Heil Quaker Blvd, La Vergne, TN 37086
Tel: 615-793-5000 (Ingram) *Toll Free Tel:* 800-378-5508; 800-509-4156 (cust serv)
E-mail: lsicustomersupport@ingramcontent.com; contentacquisitioninquiries@ingramcontent.com
Web Site: www.ingramcontent.com/publishers/print
Key Personnel
Chief Content Offr: Phil Ollila
CFO: Brian Dauphin
Chief Logistics Offr, Global Opers: John F Secrest
Supv, Content Acq Sales: Bailey Davis
Founded: 1997

Lo Gatto Bookbinding
390 Paterson Ave, East Rutherford, NJ 07073
Tel: 201-438-4344 *Fax:* 201-438-1775
E-mail: bookbindin@aol.com
Web Site: www.logattobookbinding.com
Key Personnel
Contact: Michael Lo Gatto
Founded: 1967
Turnaround: 7-10 Workdays

Lumina Datamatics Inc
Affiliate of Datamatics Global Services (Mumbai)
4 Collins Ave, Plymouth, MA 02360
Tel: 508-746-0300 *Fax:* 508-746-3233
Web Site: luminadatamatics.com
Key Personnel
SVP: Jack Mitchell *Tel:* 508-746-0300 ext 203
    E-mail: jack.mitchell@luminad.com
SVP, Content Technol: John Wheeler
    E-mail: john.wheeler@luminad.com
SVP, Prod Devt: Gordon Laws *E-mail:* gordon.laws@luminad.com
SVP, Sales: Prashant Prabhu *E-mail:* prashant.prabhu@luminad.com
VP, Fin & Acctg: John Chappell *E-mail:* john.chappell@luminad.com
Founded: 1974
Branch Office(s)
31572 Industrial Rd, Suite 400, Livonia, MI 48150 *Toll Free Tel:* 800-717-9153 *Fax:* 734-525-4455

510 Thornall St Metropark, Suite 100, Edison, NJ 08837 (sales) *Toll Free Tel:* 888-772-5532 *Fax:* 732-635-0600
345 Seventh Ave, 4th fl, New York, NY 10001 *Tel:* 646-453-1000 *Fax:* 212-564-8255
1797 Seddon Ct, Ashland, OH 44805 *Tel:* 419-289-0558 *Fax:* 419-289-8923
3265 Farmtrail Rd, York, PA 17406 *Tel:* 717-764-4000
Datamatics Global Services GmbH doo, Gunduliceva br 33, 78000 Banja Luka, Bosnia and Herzegovina *Tel:* 51304120
Im Leuschner, Park 3, 64347 Griesheim, Germany *Tel:* (06155) 862 99-0 *Fax:* (06155) 862 99-19
Ascendas International Tech Park, Taramani Rd, 12th fl, Phase II, Chennai 600 113, India *Tel:* (044) 6604 6000; (044) 6604 6001; (044) 6604 6002 *Fax:* (044) 6604 6098
Knowledge Ctr, St No 17, MIDC, Andheri (E), Mumbai 400 093, India *Tel:* (022) 6102 0000 *Fax:* (022) 2834 3669
Suyojit Datamatics Knowledge Center, Suyojit IT Park, Survey No 804, Unit No S1-S3, Nashik-Mumbai Hwy, Nashik 422 002, India *Tel:* (0253) 610 2222 *Fax:* (0253) 610 2271
Off No 5, 2nd fl, Tower 1, Stellar IT Park, C-25, Sector 62, Noida 201 301, India *Tel:* (0120) 494 0999
Plot No 29-34, East Coast Rd, Saram Revenue Village, Oulgaret Municipality, Lawspet Post, Puducherry 605 008, India *Tel:* (0413) 660 4500; (0413) 660 4501

Maple Press
480 Willow Springs Lane, York, PA 17406
Mailing Address: PO Box 2695, York, PA 17405-2695
Tel: 717-764-5911 *Toll Free Tel:* 800-999-5911 *Fax:* 717-764-4702
E-mail: sales@maplepress.com
Web Site: www.maplepress.com
Key Personnel
Pres: James S Wisotzkey
VP, Opers: Chris Benyovszky
VP, Sales: Bob Bethune
VP, Sales & Mktg: Andrew J Van Sprang
    E-mail: vansprang@maplepress.com
Founded: 1901
Print Runs: 25 min - 200,000 max
Branch Office(s)
92 Rockvale Rd, Tewksbury, MA 01876, VP, Sales: Bob Bethune *Tel:* 978-858-0900 *Fax:* 978-858-0920 *E-mail:* bethune@maplepress.com
Membership(s): Book Industry Study Group (BISG); Book Manufacturers' Institute (BMI)

Maracle Inc
1156 King St E, Oshawa, ON L1H 1H8, Canada
Tel: 905-723-3438 *Toll Free Tel:* 800-558-8604 *Fax:* 905-723-1759
E-mail: hello@maracleinc.com
Web Site: www.maracleinc.com
Key Personnel
Pres: George Sittlinger *Tel:* 905-723-3438 ext 236
Dir, Opers: Nadene D Aldred
Sales & Busn Devt Mgr: Brian Ostrander *Tel:* 905-723-3438 ext 272
    E-mail: bostrander@maracleinc.com
Founded: 1920
Turnaround: 10 Workdays
Print Runs: 500 min - 500,000 max
Membership(s): Book Manufacturers' Institute (BMI); Canadian Book Manufacturer Association; Canadian Society of Association Executives (CSAE); Ontario Printing & Imaging Association; PRINTING United Alliance

Marrakech Express Inc
720 Wesley Ave, No 10, Tarpon Springs, FL 34689

Tel: 727-942-2218 *Toll Free Tel:* 800-940-6566 *Fax:* 727-937-4758
E-mail: print@marrak.com
Web Site: www.marrak.com
Key Personnel
CEO: Peter Henzell
Prodn Mgr: Steen Sigmund
Sales/Estimator: Shirley Copperman
Founded: 1976
Turnaround: 7-10 Workdays
Print Runs: 500 min - 1,000,000 max

Maverick Publications Inc
63324 Nels Anderson Rd, Bend, OR 97701
Mailing Address: PO Box 5007, Bend, OR 97708
Tel: 541-382-6978
E-mail: moreinfo@maverickbooks.com
Web Site: www.maverickbooks.com; www.mavbooks.com
Key Personnel
Owner: Gary Asher
Founded: 1967
Turnaround: 25 Workdays
Print Runs: 100 min - 20,000 max

McClain Printing Co
212 Main St, Parsons, WV 26287-1033
Mailing Address: PO Box 403, Parsons, WV 26287-0403
Tel: 304-478-2881 *Toll Free Tel:* 800-654-7179 *Fax:* 304-478-4658
E-mail: mcclain@mcclainprinting.com
Web Site: www.mcclainprinting.com
Key Personnel
Pres: Kenneth E Smith
VP, Publg: Michelle McKinnie
Founded: 1958
Turnaround: 90-120 Workdays
Print Runs: 250 min - 10,000 max

McNaughton & Gunn Inc
Plant: 960 Woodland Dr, Saline, MI 48176
Mailing Address: PO Box 10, Saline, MI 48176-0010
Tel: 734-429-5411 *Toll Free Fax:* 800-677-BOOK (677-2665)
Web Site: www.bookprinters.com
Key Personnel
Pres: Julie McFarland
Exec Dir, Mktg/Sales: Jonnie Bryant
Midwest Regl Sales Mgr: David Hilberer
    Tel: 734-429-8757 *Fax:* 800-677-2665
    E-mail: davidh@mcnaughton-gunn.com
North Central/Greater Chicago Regl Sales Mgr: Marc Moore *Tel:* 734-429-8758 *Fax:* 800-677-2665 *E-mail:* marcm@mcnaughton-gunn.com
Founded: 1975
McNaughton & Gunn builds lasting client relationships through our customer-focused book printing process. M&G team members will work with you step-by-step to provide flexible solutions & a customizable experience, insuring your satisfaction whether you are a large publisher or a self-publisher. *Creating Books. Making History.*
Print Runs: 24 min - 100,000 max
Branch Office(s)
395 W Napa St, Suite 2, Sonoma, CA 95476, West Coast Regl Mgr: Frank Gaynor
    Tel: 707-939-9343 *Fax:* 707-939-9346
    E-mail: fwgaynor@bookprinterswest.com

Meadows Design Office
3800 Yuma St NW, Washington, DC 20016
Tel: 202-966-6007
E-mail: mdo@mdomedia.com
Key Personnel
Pres & Creative Dir: Marc Meadows
E-mail: marc@mdomedia.com
Curator & Image Res: Amy Meadows
Founded: 1981
Print Runs: 100 min - 100,000 max
Membership(s): AIGA, the professional associa-
tion for design; Type Directors Club

Moran Printing Inc, see Emprint®

Morris Press Cookbooks®
Division of Morris Printing Group Inc
3212 E Hwy 30, Kearney, NE 68847
Mailing Address: PO Box 2110, Kearney, NE
68848-2110
Tel: 308-236-7888; 308-234-1385
Toll Free Tel: 800-445-6621 *Fax:* 308-234-3969
E-mail: cookbook@morriscookbooks.com
Web Site: www.morriscookbooks.com
Founded: 1933
Print Runs: 200 min - 50,000 max

Nissha USA Inc
Division of Nissha Co Ltd
1051 Perimeter Dr, Suite 600, Schaumburg, IL
60173
Tel: 847-413-2665 *Fax:* 847-413-4085
Web Site: www.nissha.com
Key Personnel
Chmn: Junya Suzuki
Dir & CEO: Hiroyuki Uenishi
Founded: 1993

Offset Paperback Manufacturers Inc
Member of Bertelsmann Printing Group
2211 Memorial Hwy, Dallas, PA 18612
Tel: 570-675-5261 *Fax:* 570-675-8714
Web Site: www.bpg-usa.com
Key Personnel
CEO: Christof Ludwig
COO: Jorge Velasco
CFO: Christoph Mittendorf
CTO: Yannic Schroeder
Founded: 1965
Turnaround: Offset 3-25 Workdays, digital 24 hrs-
5 Workdays
Print Runs: 2,500 min

OGM USA
4333 46 St, Suite F2, Sunnyside, NY 11104
Tel: 212-964-2430
Web Site: www.ogm.it
Key Personnel
Chmn, CEO & Sales Rep: Rino Varrasso
E-mail: rvarrasso@ogm-usa.com
Founded: 1974
Turnaround: 30 Workdays
Print Runs: 1,000 min - 3,000,000 max

Omnipress
2600 Anderson St, Madison, WI 53704
Tel: 608-246-2600 *Toll Free Tel:* 800-828-0305
E-mail: justask@omnipress.com
Web Site: www.omnipress.com
Key Personnel
VP, Prodn: Greg Hubbard *Tel:* 608-778-6863
Dir, Mkt Devt: Dan Loomis
Dir, Mktg: Tracy Grzybowski
Dir, Servs: Rob Bossingham
Gen Mgr: Jonny Popp *Tel:* 608-215-9650
Founded: 1977
Turnaround: 5 Workdays
Print Runs: 1 min - 5,000 max

OneTouchPoint
1225 Walnut Ridge Dr, Hartland, WI 53029

Tel: 262-369-6000 *Toll Free Tel:* 800-332-2348
Fax: 262-369-5647
E-mail: info@1touchpoint.com
Web Site: www.1touchpoint.com
Key Personnel
CEO: Dave Holland
Dir, Mktg & Sales Opers: Carey Howard
Founded: 1982
Turnaround: order processing: within 8 hours;
digital printing: 24-48 hours after proof ap-
proval; press: 7 days after proof approval
Print Runs: 1 min - 500,000 max
Branch Office(s)
5241 Voges Rd, Madison, WI 53718 *Tel:* 608-
838-9147
525 W Alameda Dr, Suite 101, Tempe, AZ
85282, Contact: James Parker *Tel:* 480-966-
4003 *Fax:* 480-966-4016
5280 Joliet St, Denver, CO 80239 *Tel:* 303-227-
1400
1441 Western Ave, Cincinnati, OH 45214
Tel: 513-421-1600
8410-B Tuscany Way, Austin, TX 78754
Tel: 512-454-6874

Overseas Printing Corporation
Division of InnerWorkings Inc
4040 Civic Center Dr, Suite 200, San Rafael, CA
94903
Tel: 415-500-8331 *Fax:* 415-835-9899
Web Site: www.overseasprinting.com
Key Personnel
Sr Prodn Mgr: Shaun Garrett *E-mail:* sgarrett@
inwk.com
Founded: 1972
Turnaround: 8-12 Weeks

Paraclete Press Inc
36 Southern Eagle Cartway, Brewster, MA 02631
SAN: 282-1508
Mailing Address: PO Box 1568, Orleans, MA
02653-1568
Tel: 508-255-4685 *Toll Free Tel:* 800-451-5006
Fax: 508-255-5705
E-mail: customerservice@paracletepress.com
Web Site: www.paracletepress.com
Key Personnel
Design & Web Site Servs: Paul Tingley
E-mail: pault@paracletepress.com
Founded: 1981
Turnaround: 20 Workdays
Print Runs: 500 min - 15,000 max
Membership(s): Association of Catholic Publish-
ers Inc; Evangelical Christian Publishers Asso-
ciation (ECPA)

Patterson Printing Co
1550 Territorial Rd, Benton Harbor, MI 49022
Tel: 269-925-2177 *Toll Free Tel:* 800-848-8826
Fax: 269-925-6057
E-mail: sales@patterson-printing.com
Web Site: www.patterson-printing.com
Key Personnel
Pres: Leroy Patterson
Plant Mgr: Pamela Thames *Tel:* 269-925-2177 ext
542
Founded: 1956
Print Runs: 250 min

PCA Printing, see Printing Corporation of the
Americas Inc

POD Print
2012 E Northern St, Wichita, KS 67216
Tel: 316-522-5599 *Toll Free Tel:* 800-767-6066
E-mail: info@podprint.com
Web Site: www.podprint.com
Key Personnel
Owner: Grace Rishel; Jim Rishel
Prodn Opers Mgr: Traci Grote *E-mail:* tgrote@
podprint.com

Founded: 1978
Print Runs: 1 min - 25,000 max (every service
offered on-demand)
Membership(s): Print Services & Distribution Association (PSDA); PRINTING United Alliance

Printing Corporation of the Americas Inc
620 SW 12 Ave, Pompano Beach, FL 33069
Tel: 954-781-8100 *Toll Free Tel:* 866-721-1PCA
(721-1722)
Web Site: pcaprintingplus.com
Key Personnel
Pres: Buddy Tuchman
Sales Mgr: Steven Konecky *E-mail:* steven@
pcaprinting.com
Founded: 1980
Turnaround: 5-10 Workdays
Print Runs: 500 min - 100,000 max

PrintWest
1111 Eighth Ave, Regina, SK S4R 1C9, Canada
Tel: 306-525-2304 *Toll Free Tel:* 800-236-6438
Fax: 306-757-2439
E-mail: general@printwest.com
Web Site: www.printwest.com
Key Personnel
Pres & Dir, Opers: Corie Triffo
VP, Sales & Mktg: Ken Benson
Founded: 1992
Turnaround: 15 Workdays
Print Runs: 1,000 min - 100,000 max

Progress Printing Plus
2677 Waterlick Rd, Lynchburg, VA 24502
Tel: 434-239-9213 *Toll Free Tel:* 800-572-7804
Fax: 434-832-7573
E-mail: info@progressprintplus.com
Web Site: www.progressprintplus.com
Key Personnel
Pres: Michael Thornton *E-mail:* mthornton@
progressprintplus.com
Dir, Busn Devt: Gerald Bowles
E-mail: gbowles@progressprintplus.com
Founded: 1962
Turnaround: 7-9 Workdays after final proof ap-
proval
Print Runs: 5,000 min - 500,000 max

Publishers Book Bindery (NY)
250 W 16 St, 4th fl, New York, NY 10011
Tel: 917-497-2950
Key Personnel
Pres: Ed Goldman
Founded: 1946
Print Runs: 100 min - 50,000 max

Publishers' Graphics LLC
131 Fremont St, Chicago, IL 60185
Tel: 630-221-1850
E-mail: contactpg@pubgraphics.com
Web Site: pubgraphics.com
Key Personnel
Pres: Nick A Lewis *E-mail:* nlewis@pubgraphics.
com
VP: Kathleen Lewis *E-mail:* kmlewis@
pubgraphics.com
Founded: 1996
Turnaround: 2-8 Workdays
Print Runs: 1 min - 20,000 max
Branch Office(s)
3777 Rider Trail S, St Louis, MO 63045
Tel: 314-739-3777 *Fax:* 314-739-1436
Sales Office(s): Louisville, KY, VP, Sales: Cara
Lahey *Tel:* 630-291-4867 *E-mail:* clahey@
pubgraphics.com

Sheridan GR
Division of CJK Group Inc
5100 33 St SE, Grand Rapids, MI 49512
Tel: 616-957-5100
Web Site: www.sheridan.com

Key Personnel
VP, Sales: Joe Thomson *E-mail:* joe.thomson@ sheridan.com
Cust Serv Mgr: Tanya Eldred *E-mail:* tanya. eldred@sheridan.com
Estimating & Purch Mgr: Steve DeWeerd *E-mail:* steve.deweerd@sheridan.com
Plant Mgr: Jason Nelson *E-mail:* jason.nelson@ sheridan.com
Founded: 1884
Print Runs: 1 min - 100,000 max

Sheridan MI
Division of CJK Group Inc
613 E Industrial Dr, Chelsea, MI 48118
Tel: 734-475-9145
Web Site: www.sheridan.com
Key Personnel
Pres: Paul Bozuwa *E-mail:* paul.bozuwa@ sheridan.com
VP, Book Sales: Joe Thomson *E-mail:* joe. thomson@sheridan.com
VP, Fin: Nicole Mummert *E-mail:* nicole. mummert@sheridan.com
VP, HR: Ken Rapp *E-mail:* ken.rapp@sheridan. com
VP, Opers: Paul Loy *E-mail:* paul.loy@sheridan. com
Cust Serv Mgr: Ed Blissick *E-mail:* ed.blissick@ sheridan.com
Direct Sales Rep: Jessica Ansorge *Tel:* 734-385-1544 *E-mail:* jessica.ansorge@sheridan. com; Kathy Brown *Tel:* 734-385-1540 *E-mail:* kathy.brown@sheridan.com; Rebecca Humrich *Tel:* 734-385-1543 *E-mail:* rebecca. humrich@sheridan.com; Jennifer Riemen-schneider *Tel:* 734-385-1533 *E-mail:* jennifer. riemenschneider@sheridan.com
Founded: 1950

Signature Book Printing Inc
8041 Cessna Ave, Gaithersburg, MD 20879
Tel: **301-258-8353** *Fax:* **301-670-4147**
E-mail: **book@sbpbooks.com**
Web Site: **sbpbooks.com**
Key Personnel
Pres: Phil Nanzetta
Off Mgr: Linda Wood
Founded: 1986
We produce hard cover & soft cover, full color & B&W books of (virtually) any type, including children's, coffee table, travel & cookbooks. Everything is produced by offset lithography. We print runs from 500 to 20,000 copies & can do as few as 500 copies competitively for hard cover & full color books. We are nationally recognized for excellent quality, top value & smooth, easy customer service.
Visit our web site at sbpbooks.com for extensive information on book printing & for a large range of examples of our work. For pricing, visit sbpbooks.com or call us at 301-258-8353.
Print Runs: 500 min - 20,000 max

Smith & Sons Printers Inc
6403 Rutledge Pike, Knoxville, TN 37924
Tel: 865-523-1419
Web Site: www.ssprintinc.com
Key Personnel
Owner: Stephen Ownby *E-mail:* stephen@ssprint. com
Founded: 1979
Print Runs: 250 min - 100,000 max

Spectrum PrintGroup Inc
1535 Farmer's Lane, Suite 254, Santa Rosa, CA 95405
Tel: 707-542-6044 *Toll Free Tel:* 888-340-6049
Fax: 707-542-6045
E-mail: sales@spectrumprintgroup.com

Web Site: www.spectrumprintgroup.com
Key Personnel
Pres: Duncan McCallum *Tel:* 707-542-6044 ext 102 *E-mail:* duncan@spectrumprintgroup.com
Busn Devt Mgr: Elise Gochberg *Tel:* 415-461-1130 *E-mail:* elise@spectrumprintgroup.com
Founded: 1985
Print Runs: 500 min - 100,000 max

Sterling Pierce Co Inc
395 Atlantic Ave, East Rockaway, NY 11518
Tel: 516-593-1170 *Fax:* 516-593-1401
Web Site: www.sterlingpierce.com
Key Personnel
Owner & Pres: William Burke
Mgr: Steven Cieslicki *E-mail:* scieslicki@ sterlingpierce.com
Founded: 1980
Turnaround: 5-7 Workdays
Print Runs: 5 min - 5,000 max

Sun Graphics LLC
1818 Broadway, Parsons, KS 67357
Toll Free Tel: 800-835-0588 *Fax:* 620-421-2089
E-mail: info@sun-graphics.com
Web Site: www.sun-graphics.com
Key Personnel
VP, Mktg: John Hammett *Tel:* 918-695-2267 *E-mail:* jhammett@sun-graphics.com
VP, Sales: John Hohenshell *Tel:* 913-257-9420 *E-mail:* jhohenshell@sun-graphics.com
Commercial Sales & Book Div Sales: Melody Morris *Tel:* 620-660-0614 *E-mail:* mmorris@ sun-graphics.com
Founded: 1998
Turnaround: 10-15 Workdays
Print Runs: 500 min - 50,000 max
Membership(s): Independent Book Publishers Association (IBPA); Publishers Association of the West (PubWest)

John S Swift Co Inc
999 Commerce Ct, Buffalo Grove, IL 60089
Tel: 847-465-3300 *Fax:* 847-465-3309
Web Site: www.johnswiftprint.com
Key Personnel
Pres: John S Swift *E-mail:* jss@johnswiftprint. com
Founded: 1912
Turnaround: 5 Workdays & up
Print Runs: 10 min - 100,000 max
Branch Office(s)
John S Swift Print of NJ Inc, 375 North St, Unit N, Teterboro, NJ 07608, Contact: Rick Frydrych *Tel:* 201-678-3232 *Fax:* 201-378-3001 *E-mail:* rickfry@johnswiftprint.com

Taylor Specialty Books
Division of Balfour/Taylor
1550 W Mockingbird Lane, Dallas, TX 75235
Tel: 214-819-8588 (cust serv) *Fax:* 214-819-5051 (cust serv) *Toll Free Fax:* 800-203-9778
E-mail: rfq@taylorpub.com (estimates)
Web Site: www.taylorspecialtybooks.com
Key Personnel
VP, Sales & Mktg, Specialty Books: Rick Parra *Tel:* 214-819-5027 *E-mail:* rick.parra@balfour. com
Sales Rep: Kim Hawley *E-mail:* khawley@ taylorpub.com; George Levesque *E-mail:* glevesque@taylorpub.com; Mark Mc-Combs *E-mail:* mmcombs@taylorpub.com
Founded: 1939
Turnaround: 25-30 Workdays
Print Runs: 250 min - 25,000 max

Toof American Digital
4222 Pilot Dr, Memphis, TN 38118
Tel: 901-274-3632 *Toll Free Tel:* 800-722-4772
Web Site: www.toofamericandigital.com

Key Personnel
Pres: Stillman McFadden
Founded: 1864
Turnaround: 60 Workdays
Print Runs: 2,000 min - 500,000 max

Versa Press Inc
1465 Spring Bay Rd, East Peoria, IL 61611-9788
Tel: 309-822-8272 *Toll Free Tel:* 800-447-7829
Fax: 309-822-8141
Web Site: www.versapress.com
Key Personnel
Chmn: Joseph F Kennell
Pres: Steven J Kennell
Sales Mgr: Darold D Frerichs *E-mail:* dfrerichs@ versapress.com
Founded: 1937
Turnaround: 20 Workdays
Print Runs: 500 min - 50,000 max
Membership(s): Book Manufacturers' Institute (BMI)

Vicks Lithograph & Printing Corp
5166 Commercial Dr, Yorkville, NY 13495
Tel: 315-736-9344
E-mail: info@vicks.biz
Web Site: www.vicks.biz
Key Personnel
CEO: Dwight E Vicks, III
Founded: 1918
Turnaround: 10 Workdays
Print Runs: 1 min - 100,000 max
Membership(s): Book Manufacturers' Institute (BMI); PRINTING United Alliance

Walker360
2501 Fifth Ave E, Montgomery, AL 36107
Tel: 334-832-4975
E-mail: info@walker360.com
Web Site: walker360.com
Key Personnel
Pres: Taylor Blackwell *E-mail:* taylor@ walker360.com
Cont: Estella Riley *E-mail:* estella@walker360. com
IT Dir: Connie Manoliu *E-mail:* connie@ walker360.com

Walsworth
306 N Kansas Ave, Marceline, MO 64658
Toll Free Tel: 800-265-6795
Web Site: www.walsworth.com; www. walsworthhistorybooks.com
Key Personnel
CEO: Don O Walsworth
COO: Jim Mead
Pres: Don Walsworth, Jr
VP, Mktg & Communs: Kristin Mateski *E-mail:* kristin.mateski@walsworth.com
Founded: 1937
Turnaround: 4 Weeks
Print Runs: 1,000 min - 500,000 max
Branch Office(s)
803 S Missouri Ave, Marceline, MO 64658 (printing & bindery facility)
Donning Co Publishers, 731 S Brunswick St, Brookfield, MO 64628 *Tel:* 660-675-5570 *Web Site:* www.donning.com
The Ovid Bell Press, 1201 Bluff St, Fulton, MO 65251-0370 *Toll Free Tel:* 800-835-8919 *Web Site:* www.ovidbell.com
903 E 104 St, Suite 700, Kansas City, MO 64131 (yearbook sales & mktg facility) *Toll Free Tel:* 800-369-2965
7300 W 110 St, Suite 600, Overland Park, KS 66210 (sales & mktg)
2180 Maiden Lane, St Joseph, MI 49085 (printing & bindery facility) *Toll Free Tel:* 888-563-3220
656 S Douglas St, Ripon, WI 54971 (printing & bindery facility)

Walter's Publishing
Division of Taylor Corp
1750 Northway Dr, North Mankato, MN 56003
Toll Free Tel: 800-447-3274
E-mail: info@walterspublishing.com
Web Site: www.walterspublishing.com
Key Personnel
Pres: Carolynn McCourtney
VP, Mktg: Jennifer Stein
Founded: 1939

Webcom Inc
Division of Marquis Book Printing Inc
3480 Pharmacy Ave, Toronto, ON M1W 2S7,
  Canada
Tel: 416-496-1000 *Toll Free Tel:* 800-665-9322
  Fax: 416-496-1537
E-mail: webcom@webcomlink.com
Web Site: www.webcomlink.com
Key Personnel
Pres & CEO: Mike Collinge
Dir of HR & Cust Serv: Rhonda Suurd
Dir of Sales: Marc Doucet
Founded: 1975
Turnaround: 15 Workdays
Print Runs: 50 min - 100,000 max
Sales Office(s): 65 Spring Valley Ave, River
  Edge, NJ 07661, Sales: Susan Ginch *Tel:* 201-
  262-4301 *Fax:* 201-262-6375 *E-mail:* susan.
  ginch@webcomlink.com
Membership(s): Book Manufacturers' Institute
  (BMI); Canadian Book & Periodical Council;
  PRINTING United Alliance

Webcrafters Inc
2211 Fordem Ave, Madison, WI 53704
Tel: 608-244-3561 *Toll Free Tel:* 800-356-8200
  Fax: 608-244-5120

E-mail: info@webcrafters-inc.com
Web Site: www.webcrafters-inc.com
Key Personnel
CEO: Chris Kurtzman
VP, Div Dir: Brad Koch
Membership(s): Book Manufacturers' Institute
  (BMI)

Whitehall Printing Co
4244 Corporate Sq, Naples, FL 34104
Tel: 239-643-6464 *Toll Free Tel:* 800-321-9290
  Fax: 239-643-6439
E-mail: info@whitehallprinting.com
Web Site: www.whitehallprinting.com
Key Personnel
Chmn: Mike Hirsch
Pres: Jeff Hirsch
VP: Emil G Hirsch
Founded: 1959
Turnaround: 10-15 Business days
Print Runs: 250 min - 50,000 max

Wimmer Cookbooks
Division of Mercury Printing, an RR Donnelley
  Co
4650 Shelby Air Dr, Memphis, TN 38118
Toll Free Tel: 800-548-2537 *Fax:* 901-363-1771
Web Site: www.wimmerco.com
Key Personnel
Acct Coord: Robyn Hite
Sales & Mktg: Terry Rayner
Founded: 1946
Turnaround: 49 Workdays
Print Runs: 1,000 min

Worzalla
3535 Jefferson St, Stevens Point, WI 54481
Tel: 715-344-9608 *Fax:* 715-344-2578

Web Site: www.worzalla.com
Key Personnel
Chmn of the Bd: Charles Nason
Pres: James Fetherston
VP, Fin: Samuel Crockett
VP, Opers: Brian McManus
VP, Sales: Richard Letchinger
Cust Serv Mgr: Kim Deuel
Field Sales: Rodger Beyer
Founded: 1892
Turnaround: 20 Workdays
Print Runs: 50 min - 1,000,000 max
Sales Office(s): 4819 W Berteau Ave, Chicago, IL
  60641, Contact: Tim Taylor *Tel:* 773-383-7892
  E-mail: ttaylor@worzalla.com
2231 Morris Ave, Suite 3, Union, NJ 07083, Con-
  tact: Edmund Corvelli, III *Tel:* 201-749-7995
  E-mail: ecorvelli@worzalla.com
222 W 37 St, 10th fl, New York, NY 10018,
  Contact: Sam Gallucci *Tel:* 201-851-3292
  E-mail: sgallucci@worzalla.com
Membership(s): Book Manufacturers' Institute
  (BMI)

Yurchak Printing Inc
920 Links Ave, Landisville, PA 17538
Tel: 717-399-0209
E-mail: ypi.info@yurchak.com
Web Site: www.yurchak.com
Key Personnel
Founder & CEO: John Yurchak, Jr
Pres: John W Yurchak
VP, Opers: Jason Yurchak
Dir, Busn Devt: Randy Boyer
Founded: 1998
Turnaround: 5-20 Workdays
Print Runs: 1 min - 1,500 max
Membership(s): International Printers' Network
  (IPN)

Prepress Services Index

DATA PROCESSING SERVICES

FOREIGN LANGUAGE COMPOSITION

INDEXING

MATHEMATICS & CHEMISTRY COMPOSITION

MUSIC COMPOSITION

NON-ROMAN ALPHABETS

Prepress Services

The list below includes companies offering a variety of prepress services, including indexing, data processing, color separations, art and design, word processing interface, proofreading, production and various composition and typesetting services. The descriptions of the services provided are paid components.

For additional companies and individuals providing indexing and/or proofing services, see **Editorial Services** (volume 1). Additionally, companies and individuals providing art and design services can be found in **Artists & Art Services**.

A-R Editions Inc
1600 Aspen Commons, Suite 100, Middleton, WI 53562
Tel: 608-836-9000 *Fax:* 608-831-8200
E-mail: info@areditions.com
Web Site: www.areditions.com
Key Personnel
Pres & CEO: Patrick Wall *Tel:* 608-203-2575
   E-mail: patrick.wall@areditions.com
Dir, Publg Servs: Lance Ottman *E-mail:* lance.
   ottman@areditions.com
Dir, Spec Projs: James Zychowicz *Tel:* 608-203-
   2580 *E-mail:* james.zychowicz@areditions.com
Founded: 1962

A to Z Indexing & Bibliographic Services
20 St James Rd, Shrewsbury, MA 01545
Tel: 508-842-5602
Web Site: sites.google.com/site/atozindexing
Key Personnel
Owner: Kathleen Rocheleau *E-mail:* kathleen.
   rocheleau@gmail.com
Founded: 1994

Access Points Indexing
PO Box 1155, Hood River, OR 97031
Tel: 541-806-5436
Web Site: www.accesspointsindexing.com
Key Personnel
Owner: Mary Harper *E-mail:* mary@
   accesspointsindexing.com
Founded: 2005
Membership(s): American Society for Indexing
   (ASI)

Ace Pro Inc, see Progressive Publishing Services
(PPS)

Adair Graphic Communications
Division of Printwell
26975 Northline Rd, Taylor, MI 48180
Tel: 734-941-6300 *Fax:* 734-942-0920
E-mail: adair@printwell.com
Web Site: www.adairgraphic.com
Key Personnel
Pres & CEO: Paul Borg
VP: Dennis Adair *E-mail:* dennis@adairgraphic.
   com
Founded: 1931
Turnaround: 15 Workdays

Adams Design
4493 Horseshoe Bend, Murrells Inlet, SC 29576
Tel: 843-655-7097
E-mail: sa@stephenadamsdesign.com
Web Site: www.stephenadamsdesign.com
Key Personnel
Pres: Stephen Adams *E-mail:* sa@rof.net
Founded: 1990
Turnaround: 7 Workdays

Adams Press
1712 Oakton St, Evanston, IL 60202
E-mail: info@adamspress.com
Key Personnel
Pres: James A Kepler *E-mail:* jkepler@
   adamspress.com

Founded: 1942
Turnaround: 20-25 Workdays
Membership(s): The Association of Publishers
   for Special Sales (APSS); Independent Book
   Publishers Association (IBPA); Independent
   Writers of Chicago (IWOC); Midwest Writers
   Association

AJP Communications Inc
95 Macdonald Ave, Burnaby, BC V5C 4M4,
   Canada
Tel: 604-879-5880
E-mail: info@ajpcommunications.com
Web Site: www.ajpcommunications.com
Key Personnel
Creative Dir: Amy Pon
Founded: 1998

All Craft Digital Inc
289-C Skidmores Rd, Deer Park, NY 11729
Tel: 631-254-8495 *Fax:* 631-254-8496
Key Personnel
Pres: Jason Buser
Founded: 1970
Turnaround: 1 Workday

Allard Inc
4601 50 St, Suite 204, Lubbock, TX 79414
Tel: 214-736-4983
E-mail: info@allardinc.com
Web Site: www.allardinc.com
Key Personnel
Pres: Mike Bean
Founded: 1978

Allex Indexing
6039 Sunshine Dr, Ferndale, WA 98248-9234
Tel: 360-778-1308
Web Site: www.indexpert.com
Key Personnel
Indexer: Wendy Allex *E-mail:* wendy@indexpert.
   com
Founded: 2000
Membership(s): American Society for Indexing
   (ASI)

amb™, see Ambassador Press Inc

Ambassador Press Inc
1400 Washington Ave N, Minneapolis, MN 55411
Tel: 612-521-0123
E-mail: info@ambpress.com
Web Site: www.ambpress.com
Key Personnel
Co-Owner, Pres & CEO: Candice Engle-Fieldman
Co-Owner & EVP: Harold Engle
Founded: 1960
Turnaround: 3 Workdays

American International Distribution Corp
(AIDC)
82 Winter Sport Lane, Williston, VT 05495
Mailing Address: PO Box 80, Williston, VT
   05495-0080
Tel: 802-862-0095 *Toll Free Tel:* 800-678-2432
   Fax: 802-864-7749

Web Site: www.aidcvt.com
Key Personnel
Pres & CEO: Marilyn McConnell
Dir, Opers: Michael Pelland
Founded: 1986
BISAC compatible software
Membership(s): Book Industry Study Group
   (BISG); Independent Publisher's Guild (IPG)

American Mathematical Society (AMS)
201 Charles St, Providence, RI 02904-2213
SAN: 201-1654
Tel: 401-455-4000 *Toll Free Tel:* 800-321-4267
   Fax: 401-331-3842; 401-455-4046 (cust serv)
E-mail: cust-serv@ams.org; ams@ams.org
Web Site: www.ams.org
Key Personnel
Exec Dir: Dr Catherine A Roberts
Publr: Dr Sergei Gelfand
Assoc Exec Dir: Dr Robert M Harrington
Assoc Exec Dir, Washington, DC: Dr Karen Saxe
Founded: 1888
Turnaround: 7 Workdays
Branch Office(s)
1527 18 St NW, Washington, DC 20036-1358
   (govt rel & sci policy) *Tel:* 202-588-1100
   Fax: 202-588-1853 *E-mail:* amsdc@ams.org
Mathematical Reviews®, 416 Fourth St, Ann Ar-
   bor, MI 48103-4820 (edit) *Tel:* 734-996-5250
   Fax: 734-996-2916 *E-mail:* mathrev@ams.org
Secretary of the AMS - Society Governance, Dept
   of Computer Science, North Carolina State
   University, Box 8206, Raleigh, NC 27695-
   8206 *Tel:* 919-515-7863 *Fax:* 919-515-7896
   E-mail: secretary@ams.org
Membership(s): Society for Scholarly Publishing
   (SSP)

Apex CoVantage
4045 Sheridan Ave, No 266, Miami Beach, FL
   33140
Tel: 703-709-3000 *Fax:* 703-709-8242
E-mail: info@apexcovantage.com
Web Site: www.apexcovantage.com
Key Personnel
Co-Founder & CEO: Dr Shashikant Gupta
Co-Founder & COO: Margaret Gupta
Pres, Content Solutions: Pardha Karamsetty
Founded: 1988
Membership(s): Society for Scholarly Publishing
   (SSP); Software & Information Industry Asso-
   ciation (SIIA)

appatura™, A Broadridge Company
Division of Broadridge Financial Solutions Inc
65 Challenger Rd, Suite 400, Ridgefield Park, NJ
   07660
Tel: 201-508-6000 *Toll Free Tel:* 800-277-2155
E-mail: contactus@appatura.com
Web Site: www.appatura.com
Key Personnel
CEO: Richard Plotka
CIO: Faisal Fareed
Chief Prod Offr: Harsh Choudhary
Chief Strategy Offr: John Closson
Head, Fin: Alpha Diarra
Founded: 1949

Aptara Inc
Subsidiary of iEnergizer
2901 Telestar Ct, Suite 522, Falls Church, VA
  22042
Tel: 703-352-0001
E-mail: moreinfo@aptaracorp.com
Web Site: www.aptaracorp.com
Key Personnel
Pres: Samir Kakar
EVP, Fin & Cont: Prashant Kapoor
SVP, Busn & Contact Ctr Opers: Ashish Madan
Busn Devt: Michael Scott *E-mail:* michael.scott@
  aptaracorp.com
Founded: 1988
Branch Office(s)
150 California St, Suite 301, Newton, MA 02458
  Tel: 617-423-7755
11009 Metric Blvd, Bldg J, Suite 150, Austin,
  TX 78758 *Tel:* 512-876-5997
299 Elizabeth St, Level 1, Sydney 2000, Australia
  Tel: (02) 8251 0070
Tower 1 & 2, 8/100, Acharya Thulasi Rd (Shandy
  Rd), Pallavaram, Chennai 600 043, India
  Tel: (044) 22640676
No 2310, Doon Express Business Park, Saharan-
  pur Rd, Bldg 2000, Dehradun 248 002, India
  Tel: (0135) 2644055
7B, Leela Infopark, Technopark, Trivandrum,
  Kerala 695 581, India *Tel:* (047) 14063370
A-37, Sector-60, Noida 201 301, India
  Tel: (0120) 7182424
D-10, Sector-2, Noida 201 301, India *Tel:* (0120)
  24423678
SEZ Bldg 4A, 1st fl, S P Infocity, Pune Saswad
  Rd, Phursungi, Pune 412 308, India *Tel:* (020)
  66728000

Aquent LLC
101 W Elm St, Suite 300, Conshohocken, PA
  19428-2075
Tel: 610-828-0900 *Toll Free Fax:* 877-303-5224
E-mail: questions@aquent.com
Web Site: aquentstudios.com; aquent.com
Key Personnel
Mgr: Kelly Griffin
Founded: 1986

Arbor Books
244 Madison Ave, Box 254, New York, NY
  10016
Tel: 212-956-0950 *Toll Free Tel:* 877-822-2500
  Fax: 914-401-9385
E-mail: info@arborbooks.com; editorial@
  arborbooks.net
Web Site: www.arborbooks.com; www.
  arborservices.co
Key Personnel
Owner: Joel Hochman *Tel:* 877-822-
  2502 *E-mail:* arborbooksjoel@aol.com;
  Larry Leichman *Tel:* 877-822-2504
  E-mail: arborbookslarry@aol.com
Mktg Dir: Olga Vladi
Founded: 1992
BISAC compatible software
Turnaround: 21 Workdays; 1-7 Workdays for art

Arbor Services, see Arbor Books

Arrow Graphics Inc
PO Box 380291, Cambridge, MA 02238
E-mail: info@arrow1.com
Web Site: www.arrow1.com
Key Personnel
Pres: Alvart Badalian
Sr Graphic/Pubn Designer: Aramais Andonian
Founded: 1988

Art Related Technology Inc
4 Brattle St, Rm 305, Cambridge, MA 02138
Tel: 617-661-1225 *Fax:* 617-491-0618
E-mail: artinc@artrelated.com

Web Site: www.artrelated.com
Key Personnel
Art Dir: Marvin Mortee
Founded: 1983

Asia Pacific Offset Inc
1312 "Q" St NW, Suite B, Washington, DC
  20009
Tel: 202-462-5436 *Toll Free Tel:* 800-756-4344
  Fax: 202-986-4030
Web Site: www.asiapacificoffset.com
Key Personnel
Pres: Andrew Clarke *E-mail:* andrew@
  asiapacificoffset.com
Founded: 1997
Turnaround: 105 Workdays including color separation & shipping
Branch Office(s)
870 Market St, Suite 801, San Francisco, CA
  94102, Dir, Sales: Amy Armstrong *Tel:* 415-
  433-3488 *Fax:* 415-433-3489 *E-mail:* amy@
  asiapacificoffset.com
1768 Oakmont Ct, Ann Arbor, MI 48108, Dir,
  Sales: Dean Sherman *Tel:* 734-223-6218
  E-mail: dean@asiapacificoffset.com
62 Rivington St, Suite 2B, New York, NY 10002,
  Dir, Sales & Mktg: Simona Jansons *Tel:* 212-
  941-8300 *Fax:* 212-941-9810 *E-mail:* simona@
  asiapacificoffset.com
16 Clements Dr, Avoca Beach, NSW 2251, Australia, Dir, Sales: Penny Crocker *Tel:* (02) 4382
  6174 *E-mail:* penny@asiapacificoffset.com
57 Norfolk St, Ponsonby, Auckland 1021, New
  Zealand, Consultant: Barbara Nielsen *Tel:* (09)
  378-4971 *E-mail:* barbara@asiapacificoffset.
  com
C/ Tamarit 104, esc D, entrance 2, 08015
  Barcelona, Spain, Dir, Sales: Carlos
  Blavia *Tel:* 933278837 *Fax:* 933254826
  E-mail: carlos@asiapacificoffset.com
20 Mortlake High St, London SW14 8JN, United
  Kingdom, Dir, Sales: Adrian Gatheroole
  Tel: (020) 3170 8700 *Fax:* (020) 3170 8704
  E-mail: adrian@asiapacificoffset.com

Bang Printing Co Inc
Division of CJK Group Inc
3323 Oak St, Brainerd, MN 56401
Tel: 218-829-2877 *Toll Free Tel:* 800-328-0450
  Fax: 218-829-7145
E-mail: info@bangprinting.com
Web Site: www.bangprinting.com
Key Personnel
Pres: Todd Vanek *E-mail:* toddv@bangprinting.
  com
VP, Opers: Joe Saiko *E-mail:* joes@bangprinting.
  com
VP, Sales: Doug Walters *E-mail:* dougw@
  bangprinting.com
Founded: 1899
Turnaround: 10-25 Workdays

Barcode Graphics Inc
25 Brodie Dr, Unit 5, Richmond Hill, ON L4B
  3K7, Canada
Tel: 905-770-1154 *Toll Free Tel:* 800-263-3669
  (orders) *Fax:* 905-787-1575
E-mail: info@barcodegraphics.com
Web Site: www.barcodegraphics.com
Key Personnel
Pres: John Herzig *E-mail:* jherzig@
  barcodegraphics.com
Founded: 1982

The Bear Wallow Publishing Co
809 S 12 St, La Grande, OR 97850
Tel: 541-962-7864
Web Site: www.bear-wallow.com
Key Personnel
Co-Owner: Cathy Gildemeister; Jerry Gildemeis-
  ter *E-mail:* j-c@bear-wallow.com
Founded: 1976

Benoit & Associates
744 Stockton Heights Ct, Bourbonnais, IL 60914
Tel: 815-932-2582 *Fax:* 815-932-2594
Web Site: www.benoit-associates.com
Key Personnel
Pres: Michael J Benoit *E-mail:* mbenoit@benoit-
  associates.com

David Berman Communications
340 Selby Ave, Ottawa, ON K2A 3X6, Canada
Tel: 613-728-6777 *Toll Free Tel:* 800-665-1809
E-mail: info@davidberman.com
Web Site: www.wcag2.com
Key Personnel
Pres: David Berman
Founded: 1984
Branch Office(s)
182 Pearson Ave, Toronto, ON, Canada *Fax:* 416-
  532-7786
969 Second St SE, Charlottesville, VA 22902
6 Jl 14/7, Petaling Jaya Selangor, 46100 Kuala
  Lumpur, Malaysia

Berryville Graphics
Member of Bertelsmann Printing Group
25 Jack Enders Blvd, Berryville, VA 22611
Tel: 540-955-2750 *Fax:* 540-955-2633
E-mail: info@bvgraphics.com
Web Site: www.bpg-usa.com
Key Personnel
CEO: Christof Ludwig
COO: Jorge Velasco
CFO: Christoph Mittendorf
CTO: Yannic Schroeder
Founded: 1956
Turnaround: 15 Workdays (initial orders); 6
  Workdays (reprint orders); 4 Workdays (out
  of stock)
Branch Office(s)
100 N Miller St, Fairfield, PA 17320 *Tel:* 414-
  208-2800
871 Baker St, Martinsburg, VA 25405 *Tel:* 304-
  267-3600

Bindagraphics Inc
2701 Wilmarco Ave, Baltimore, MD 21223-9922
Tel: 410-362-7200 *Toll Free Tel:* 800-326-0300
  Fax: 410-362-7233
E-mail: info@bindagraphics.com
Web Site: www.bindagraphics.com
Key Personnel
Owner & Pres: Matt Anson
Founded: 1974
Turnaround: Same day & longer
Branch Office(s)
Bindagraphics South Inc, 100 N Pendleton S,
  High Point, NC 27260 *Tel:* 336-431-6200
  Fax: 410-431-6232
Membership(s): Binding Industries Association
  (BIA); PRINTING United Alliance

Blanks Printing & Imaging Inc
2343 N Beckley Ave, Dallas, TX 75208
Tel: 214-741-3905 *Toll Free Tel:* 800-325-7651
E-mail: sales@blanks.com
Web Site: www.blanks.com
Key Personnel
CFO: Doug Heyerdahl *E-mail:* cfo@blanks.com
Pres: Leron Blanks *E-mail:* lblanks@blanks.com
VP: Jeff Blanks *E-mail:* jblanks@blanks.com
VP, Sales & Mktg: Mark Connor
  E-mail: mconnor@blanks.com
Opers Mgr: Jan Thornton *E-mail:* jthornton@
  blanks.com
Founded: 1941

Blue Note Books, see Blue Note Publications Inc

Blue Note Publications Inc
721 North Dr, Suite D, Melbourne, FL 32934

Tel: 321-799-2583; 321-622-6289
  Toll Free Tel: 800-624-0401 (orders) Fax: 321-799-1942; 321-622-6830
E-mail: bluenotebooks@gmail.com
Web Site: bluenotepublications.com
Key Personnel
Pres: Paul Maluccio
Founded: 1988
Turnaround: 20 Workdays

BookComp Inc
6124 Belmont Ave NE, Belmont, MI 49306
Tel: 616-774-9700
E-mail: production@bookcomp.com
Web Site: www.bookcomp.com
Key Personnel
Pres: Jon F Dertien E-mail: jd@bookcomp.com
Prodn Mgr: JoAnn Sikkes
Edit: Nicholle Robertson E-mail: nicholle@bookcomp.com
Founded: 1989
Turnaround: 10 Workdays
Membership(s): American Association of University Presses (AAUP)

Bookmasters
Division of Baker & Taylor Publisher Services
30 Amberwood Pkwy, Ashland, OH 44805
Tel: 419-281-5100 Toll Free Tel: 800-537-6727
  Fax: 419-281-0200
E-mail: info@btpubservices.com
Web Site: www.btpubservices.com
Key Personnel
Dir of Mfg: Brad Sharp E-mail: bsharp@bookmasters.com
Founded: 1972
BISAC compatible software

BookWise Design
29089 SW Costa Circle W, Wilsonville, OR 97070
Tel: 503-542-3551 Toll Free Tel: 800-697-9833
Web Site: bookwisedesign.com
Key Personnel
Partner & Art Dir: Shannon Bodie
  E-mail: shannon@bookwisedesign.com
Partner & Creative Consultant: Bob Swingle
  Tel: 503-542-3550
Proj Mgr: Jann Armstrong Tel: 509-675-3440
  E-mail: jann@bookwisedesign.com
Founded: 1985

The Bureau
Division of The Vomela Companies
2354 English St, Maplewood, MN 55109
Tel: 612-788-1000; 612-432-3516 (sales)
  Toll Free Tel: 800-788-9536 Fax: 612-788-7792
E-mail: sales@thebureau.com
Web Site: www.thebureau.com
Key Personnel
Pres & CEO: Mark Auth
VP, Sales & Busn Devt: Tim Dobratz
  E-mail: tim.dobratz@vomela.com
Gen Mgr: John Henderson
Natl Acct Sales Rep: Mike Schreiner
Turnaround: 3-5 Workdays

Burmar Technical Corp
106 Ransom Ave, Sea Cliff, NY 11579
Tel: 516-484-6000 Fax: 516-484-6356
Web Site: burmar.net
Key Personnel
Pres: Norma Novotny E-mail: norma.novotny@burmar.net
VP: Christine Jensen E-mail: christine.jensen@burmar.net
Founded: 1954

BW&A Books Inc
112 W McClanahan St, Oxford, NC 27565
Tel: 919-956-9111 Fax: 919-956-9112

E-mail: bwa@bwabooks.com
Web Site: www.bwabooks.com
Key Personnel
Pres & Designer: Chris Crochetiere
  E-mail: chris@bwabooks.com
VP & Designer: Julie Allred E-mail: julie@bwabooks.com
Founded: 1988
Turnaround: Varies

C & C Offset Printing Co USA Inc
Subsidiary of C & C Joint Printing Co (HK) Ltd
70 W 36 St, Unit 10C, New York, NY 10018
Tel: 212-431-4210 Toll Free Fax: 866-540-4134
Web Site: www.ccoffset.com
Key Personnel
Dir & EVP, C & C Offset Printing Co (USA) Inc & C & C Offset Printing Co (NY) Inc, New York, NY: Simon Chan E-mail: schan@ccoffset.com
Sales Mgr, C & C Offset Printing Co (NY) Inc, New York, NY: Frances Harkness
  E-mail: fharkness@ccoffset.com; Timothy McNulty
CEO, C & C Joint Printing Co (HK) Ltd, Hong Kong: Jackson Leung
Deputy Gen Mgr, C & C Joint Printing Co (HK) Ltd, Hong Kong: Francis Ho; Kit Wong
Dir, C & C Offset Printing Co (France) Ltd: Michele Olson Niel E-mail: michele@candcoffset.fr
Pres, C & C Printing Japan Co Ltd, Tokyo, Japan: Yamamoto Masaaki
Dir, C & C Offset Printing Co (UK) Ltd: Tracy Broderick E-mail: tracy@candcoffset.co.uk
Sales Rep, Australian Off: Lena Frew
  E-mail: lena.frew@candcprinting.com
Founded: 1980
Turnaround: Varies
Branch Office(s)
C & C Offset Printing Co Ltd (Australia Off), Lithocraft Graphics, 3-7 Permas Way, Truganina, Victoria 3029, Australia Tel: (613) 8366 0200 Fax: (613) 8366 0299
C & C Joint Printing Co (Beijing) Ltd, Beijing Economic & Technological Development Area (BDA), Donghuan North Rd, No 3, Beijing 100176, China (plant) Tel: (010) 6787 6655 Fax: (010) 6787 8255 E-mail: ccbj@candcprinting.cn
C & C Joint Printing Co (Guangdong) Ltd, Hua Xin Bldg E Block, Rm 1511, 2 Shuiyin Rd, Huanshi East, Guangzhou 510075, China Tel: (020) 3760 0979; (020) 3760 0980 Fax: (020) 3760 0977 E-mail: guangzhou@candcprinting.com
C & C Joint Printing (Shanghai) Co Ltd, 3333 Cao Ying Rd, Qingpu Industrial Zone, Shanghai 201712, China (plant) Tel: (021) 5922 6000 Fax: (021) 5922 6111 E-mail: shanghai@candcprinting.com Web Site: www.candcprinting.com
C & C Joint Printing Co (Guangdong) Ltd, Chunhu Industrial Estate, Pinghu, Long Gang, Shenzhen 518111, China (plant) Tel: (0755) 3360 9988 Fax: (0755) 3360 9998 E-mail: guangdong@candcprinting.com Web Site: www.candcprinting.com
C & C Offset Printing Co (France) Ltd, 15, rue d'Aboukir, 75002 Paris, France Tel: 01 40 26 21 07 Fax: 01 44 76 08 96
C & C Offset Printing Co Ltd, C & C Bldg, 36 Ting Lai Rd, Tai Po, New Territories, Hong Kong (corp headquarters) Tel: 2666 4988 Fax: 2666 4938 E-mail: info@candcprinting.com Web Site: www.candcprinting.com
C & C Printing Japan Co Ltd, Tozaido Bldg, 3F, 2-6-12 Hitotsubashi, Chiyoda-ku, Tokyo 101-0003, Japan Tel: (03) 5216 4580 Fax: (03) 5216 4610 E-mail: mail@candcprinting.co.jp Web Site: www.candcprinting.co.jp

C & C Offset Printing Co (UK) Ltd, 75 Newman St, 3rd fl, London W1T 3EN, United Kingdom
Tel: (020) 7637 5033 Fax: (020) 7637 5044
E-mail: info@candcoffset.co.uk

Cape Cod Compositors Inc
811 Washington St, Suite 2, Pembroke, MA 02359-2333
Tel: 781-826-2100
Key Personnel
Pres: Missy Garnett E-mail: mg@capecodcompositors.com
Sr Assoc: Joanne Jesse
Cust Serv: Tami Trask
Founded: 1986

Cenveo Publisher Services
555 Virginia Dr, Fort Washington, PA 19034
Tel: 267-470-1590 Fax: 215-591-9093
E-mail: info.psg@cenveo.com
Web Site: www.cenveopublisherservices.com
Key Personnel
CFO: John Pennie
Pres: Atul Goel
VP, Journal Publg Servs: Debbie McClanahan
VP, Learning Solutions: Waseem Andrabi
VP, Media & Intl Delivery Ctr: Dwayne Reed
Dir, Mktg: Mike Groth E-mail: mike.groth@cenveo.com
Founded: 1998
Branch Office(s)
3575 Hempland Rd, Lancaster, PA 17601
  Tel: 717-285-9095
5457 Twin Knolls Rd, Suite 200, Columbia, MD 21045 Tel: 410-850-0500 Toll Free Tel: 800-257-5529
2905 Byrdhill Rd, Richmond, VA 23228
No 31 Kempapura, Hebbal, Bangalore 560 024, India Tel: (080) 4000 4888
36 Barnaby Rd, Kilpauk, Chennai, Tamil Nadu 600 010, India Tel: (044) 4205 8888
Marwah Ctr, 5th fl, Krishanlal Marwah Marg, Andheri East, Mumbai 400 072, India
  Tel: (022) 4098 5200
Steller IT Park, Tower I, 3rd fl, C 25, Sector 62, Noida 201 301, India Tel: (0120) 461 3700
One Mulgrave Chambers, 26-28 Mulgrave Rd, Sutton, Surrey SM2 6LE, United Kingdom

Cenveo St Louis
101 Workman Ct, Eureka, MO 63025
Tel: 314-966-2000 Toll Free Tel: 800-800-8845
  Fax: 314-966-4725
Web Site: www.cenveo.com

CG Book Printers
Division of Corporate Graphics Commercial (CGC)
1750 Northway Dr, North Mankato, MN 56003
Tel: 507-388-3300 Toll Free Tel: 800-729-7575
  Fax: 507-386-6350
E-mail: cgbooks@corpgraph.com
Web Site: www.corpgraph.com
Key Personnel
Pres: Dan Kvasnicka Tel: 507-386-6340
  Fax: 507-344-5548 E-mail: dekvasnicka@corpgraph.com
Sales Exec, Book Mfg Sales: Mike Schmitt
  Tel: 507-386-6349 E-mail: mjschmitt@corpgraph.com
Founded: 1989

Cimarron Design
8285 Kincross Dr, Boulder, CO 80301-4228
Tel: 303-530-1785
Web Site: www.cimarrondesign.com
Key Personnel
Owner: Troy Scott Parker E-mail: tsparker@cimarrondesign.com
Founded: 1989
Turnaround: 5-15 Workdays

Circle Graphics Inc
316 Main St, Suite 1C, Reisters Town, MD 21136
Tel: 410-833-2200
E-mail: production@circleusa.com
Web Site: www.circleusa.com
Key Personnel
Pres: Richard Berkowitz
Consultant: Jay Berkowitz; Frank Dunn
Founded: 1974

Clare Printing
206 S Keystone Ave, Sayre, PA 18840
Tel: 570-888-2244
E-mail: hr@clareprint.com
Web Site: www.clareprint.com
Key Personnel
Pres: Ian Clare
Prodn Mgr: Alicia Blokzyl
Founded: 1903

Coach House Printing
80 bpNichol Lane, Toronto, ON M5S 3J4,
Canada
Tel: 416-979-2217 *Toll Free Tel:* 800-367-6360
(outside Toronto) *Fax:* 416-977-1158
E-mail: mail@chbooks.com
Web Site: www.chbooks.com
Key Personnel
Publr: Stan Bevington *E-mail:* stan@chbooks.com
Edit Dir: Alana Wilcox *E-mail:* alana@chbooks.com
Prodn Mgr: John De Jesus *E-mail:* john@chbooks.com
Founded: 1965
Turnaround: 14 Workdays

ColorPage
Division of Tri-State Associated Services Inc
81 Ten Broeck Ave, Kingston, NY 12401
Tel: 845-331-7581 *Toll Free Tel:* 800-836-7581
Fax: 845-331-1571
E-mail: sales@colorpageonline.com
Web Site: www.colorpageonline.com
Key Personnel
Pres & Mktg Strategist/Consultant: Frank J Campagna, II *E-mail:* fcampagna@colorpageonline.com
Acct Mgr & Cont: Kathy Riggins
E-mail: kriggins@colorpageonline.com
Prodn Mgr: Randy Delanoy
Cust Serv Supv: Debbie Downes
E-mail: ddownes@colorpageonline.com
Founded: 1976
Turnaround: 10-15 Workdays

Communicorp Inc
Subsidiary of Aflac Inc
1001 Lockwood Ave, Columbus, GA 31999
Tel: 706-324-1182
E-mail: mktech@communicorp.com
Web Site: www.communicorp.com
Key Personnel
Pres & CEO: Eric Seldon
VP: Mike Thomas
Sr Mgr, Prodn Servs: Jason Lansdon
Sr Mgr, Sales & Mktg Servs: John Shutter *Tel:* 706-763-2912 *E-mail:* jshutter@communicorp.com
Founded: 1981
Branch Office(s)
100 Galleria Pkwy, Suite 450, Atlanta, GA 30339
Tel: 770-541-4515 *Toll Free Tel:* 800-775-7998

Concord Editorial & Design LLC
9450 SW Gemini Dr, Suite 68669, Beaverton, OR 97008
Tel: 616-827-7537 *Fax:* 616-825-6048
E-mail: info@concordeditorial.com
Web Site: www.concordeditorial.com
Key Personnel
Pres & Proj Dir: David Fideler, PhD

Founded: 2005
Turnaround: 10 Workdays

Cookbook Publishers Inc
11633 W 83 Terr, Lenexa, KS 66285
Mailing Address: PO Box 15920, Lenexa, KS 66285-5920
Tel: 913-492-5900 *Toll Free Tel:* 800-227-7282
Fax: 913-492-5947
E-mail: info@cookbookpublishers.com
Web Site: www.cookbookpublishers.com
Key Personnel
Pres: Kevin Naughton
New Busn Devt: Stephanie Jones
Founded: 1947
Turnaround: 5-30 Workdays

Coral Graphic Services Inc
Member of Bertelsmann Printing Group
840 S Broadway, Hicksville, NY 11801
Tel: 516-576-2100 *Fax:* 516-576-2168
E-mail: info@coralgraphics.com
Web Site: www.bpg-usa.com
Key Personnel
CEO: Christof Ludwig
COO: Jorge Velasco
CFO: Christoph Mittendorf
CTO: Yannic Schroeder
Founded: 1982
Branch Office(s)
4700 Commerce Crossing Dr, Louisville, KY 40229 *Tel:* 502-962-5466 *Fax:* 502-962-9023
25 Jack Enders Blvd, Berryville, VA 22611
Tel: 540-955-2750 *Fax:* 540-955-9164
Membership(s): Association of the Graphic Arts (AGA); Book Industry Guild of New York; PRINTING United Alliance

Corporate Disk Co
4610 Prime Pkwy, McHenry, IL 60050-7005
Tel: 815-331-6000 *Toll Free Tel:* 800-634-3475
Fax: 815-331-6030
E-mail: info@disk.com
Web Site: www.disk.com
Key Personnel
Owner & VP, Sales: Joe D Foley *Tel:* 815-331-6000 ext 233 *E-mail:* jfoley@disk.com
Founded: 1984

Corporate Graphics Book Printers, see CG Book Printers

Courier Printing
Division of RR Donnelley
One Courier Place, Smyrna, TN 37167
Tel: 615-355-4000 *Toll Free Tel:* 800-467-0444
Fax: 615-355-4088
Web Site: www.courierprinting.com
Key Personnel
Pres: Michelle Yun
Turnaround: 5-15 Workdays

Crown Connect
250 W Rialto Ave, San Bernadino, CA 92408
Tel: 909-888-7531 *Fax:* 909-889-1639
E-mail: sales@crownconnect.com
Web Site: www.crownconnect.com
Key Personnel
CFO: Nicole Albright *Tel:* 909-888-7531 ext 204
Pres: Denny Shorett *Tel:* 909-888-7531 ext 225
VP, Opers: Ken Martin *Tel:* 909-888-7531 ext 206
Mgr, Busn Devt: Erin Warren *Tel:* 909-888-7531 ext 228
Prodn Mgr: Chris McPhate *Tel:* 909-888-7531 ext 214
Founded: 1970

Custom Studios
Subsidiary of Nationwide Custom Services Inc
77 Main St, Tappan, NY 10983

Tel: 845-365-0414 *Toll Free Tel:* 800-631-1362
Fax: 845-365-0864
E-mail: customusa@aol.com
Web Site: customstudios.com
Key Personnel
Owner & Pres: Norman Shaifer
VP: Helen Newman; Harry Title
Founded: 1960

Cypress House
Imprint of Comp-Type Inc
155 Cypress St, Fort Bragg, CA 95437
Tel: 707-964-9520 *Toll Free Tel:* 800-773-7782
Fax: 707-964-7531
Web Site: www.cypresshouse.com
Key Personnel
Pres: Cynthia Frank *E-mail:* cynthia@cypresshouse.com
Mng Ed: Joe Shaw *E-mail:* joeshaw@cypresshouse.com
Founded: 1986
Turnaround: 60 Workdays
Membership(s): American Booksellers Association (ABA); Bay Area Independent Publishers Association (BAIPA); California Independent Booksellers Alliance (CALIBA); Independent Book Publishers Association (IBPA); Pacific Northwest Booksellers Association (PNBA)

Darwill
11900 W Roosevelt Rd, Hillside, IL 60162
Tel: 708-236-4900 *Fax:* 708-236-5820
E-mail: info@darwill.com
Web Site: www.darwill.com
Key Personnel
Pres & Co-CEO: Brandon Van Dyke; Troy Van Dyke
Founded: 1951

Data Conversion Laboratory Inc (DCL)
61-18 190 St, Suite 205, Fresh Meadows, NY 11365
Tel: 718-357-8700 *Toll Free Tel:* 800-321-2816 (provider problems)
E-mail: info@dclab.com
Web Site: www.dataconversionlaboratory.com
Key Personnel
Pres: Mark Gross
COO: Amy Williams
CFO: Judy Gross
CIO: Tammy Bilitzky
Chief Revenue Offr: Jeff Wood
CTO & Dir, Res: Mike Gross
Natl Sales Dir: Brian Trombley
Sales Dir, Publg: Amber Watson
Founded: 1981
Membership(s): American Institute of Architects; Association for Enterprise Integration (AFEI/CALS); Association of American Publishers (AAP); Graphic Communications Association (GCA); Society for Scholarly Publishing (SSP)

Data Index Inc
13713 NW Indian Springs Dr, Vancouver, WA 98685
Tel: 425-760-9193
Web Site: www.dataindex.com
Key Personnel
Pres: John Oglesby *E-mail:* joglesby@dataindex.com
Gen Mgr: Michelle Dufour
Founded: 1985
Turnaround: Quote specific for pressure sensitive labels; 1 Workday for ISBN or UPC digital files
Membership(s): American Society for Quality (ASQ)

Datacolor
5 Princess Rd, Lawrenceville, NJ 08648

Tel: 609-924-2189 *Toll Free Tel:* 800-982-6496
(support) *Fax:* 609-895-7414
E-mail: marketing@datacolor.com
Web Site: www.datacolor.com
Key Personnel
Sr Mktg Mgr: Patricia Shenk *E-mail:* pshenk@
datacolor.com
Founded: 1970

DataStream Content Solutions LLC, see DSCS
LLC

Delmas Typesetting Inc
461 Hilldale Dr, Ann Arbor, MI 48105
Tel: 734-662-8899
E-mail: delmastype@comcast.net
Web Site: www.delmastype.com
Key Personnel
Pres: William Kalvin
Founded: 1979

Desktop Miracles Inc
112 S Main St, Suite 294, Stowe, VT 05672
Tel: 802-253-7900 *Toll Free Fax:* 888-293-2676
E-mail: info@desktopmiracles.com
Web Site: www.desktopmiracles.com
Key Personnel
Pres & CEO: Barry T Kerrigan *E-mail:* barry@
desktopmiracles.com
VP: Virginia Kerrigan *E-mail:* virginia@
desktopmiracles.com
Founded: 1994
Turnaround: 10-15 Workdays

diacriTech Inc
4 S Market St, 4th fl, Boston, MA 02109
Tel: 617-600-3366 *Fax:* 617-848-2938
Web Site: www.diacritech.com
Key Personnel
EVP: Madhu Rajamani *E-mail:* madhu@
diacritech.com
Dir, Prodn & Edit Servs: Maureen Ross
E-mail: m.ross@diacritech.com
Founded: 1997

Didona Design
160 Grandview Rd, Ardmore, PA 19003
Tel: 610-649-3110
E-mail: didona@didonadesign.com
Web Site: www.didonadesign.com
Key Personnel
Pres: Lawrence R Didona
Mktg Mgr: Cathy Didona
Founded: 1986

dix! Digital Prepress Inc
8462 Wayfarer Dr, Cicero, NY 13039
Tel: 315-288-5888 *Fax:* 315-288-5898
E-mail: info@dixtype.com
Web Site: www.dixtype.com
Key Personnel
Pres: Scott Wenger *E-mail:* swenger@dixtype.
com
Acct Exec, Sales & Mktg: Kelly Farley
E-mail: kfarley@dixtype.com
Founded: 1923

DNP America LLC
Subsidiary of Dai Nippon Printing Co Ltd
335 Madison Ave, 3rd fl, New York, NY 10017
Tel: 212-503-1060
E-mail: gps@dnp-g.com
Web Site: www.dnpamerica.com
Key Personnel
VP & Gen Mgr: Norikatsu Nakamura
Founded: 1976
Turnaround: 30-60 Workdays

Branch Office(s)
2099 Gateway Place, Suite 490, San Jose, CA
95110 *Tel:* 408-735-8880
3858 Carson St, Suite 300, Torrance, CA 90503
Tel: 310-540-5123

RR Donnelley
35 W Wacker Dr, Chicago, IL 60601
Toll Free Tel: 800-742-4455
Web Site: www.rrd.com
Key Personnel
Pres & CEO: Daniel L Knotts
Pres, Busn Servs: John Pecaric
Pres, Mktg Solutions: Doug Ryan
EVP & CFO: Terry D Peterson
EVP & CIO: Ken O'Brien
EVP & Chief HR Offr: Sheila Rutt
EVP & Chief Strategy & Transformation Offr:
Elif Sagsen-Ercel
EVP, Gen Coun, Chief Compliance Offr & Corp
Secy: Deborah Steiner
EVP, Dom Opers & Chief Supply Chain Offr:
Glynn Perry
SVP & Chief Acctg Offr: Michael J Sharp
Founded: 1864
Turnaround: 3-6 Weeks
Branch Office(s)
955 Gateway Center Way, San Diego, CA 92102
Tel: 619-527-4600
40610 County Center Dr, Temecula, CA 92591
Tel: 951-296-2890
151 Red Stone Rd, Manchester, CT 06042
Tel: 860-649-5570
9125 Bachman Rd, Orlando, FL 32824 *Tel:* 407-
859-2030
5800 Peachtree Rd, Atlanta, GA 30341 *Tel:* 770-
458-6351
825 Riverside Pkwy, Suite 300, Austell, GA
30168 *Tel:* 770-948-1330
1750 Wallace Ave, St Charles, IL 60174 *Tel:* 630-
313-7000
609 S Kirk Rd, St Charles, IL 60174 *Tel:* 630-
762-7600
One Poplar Ave, Thurmont, MD 21788 *Tel:* 301-
271-7171
65 Sprague St, Hyde Park, MA 02136 *Tel:* 617-
360-2000
18780 W 78 St, Chanhassen, MN 55317
Tel: 952-937-9764
5500 12 Ave E, Shakopee, MN 55379 *Tel:* 952-
941-7546
6305 Sunset Corporate Dr, Las Vegas, NV 89120
Tel: 702-949-8500
5 Henderson Dr, West Caldwell, NJ 07006
Tel: 973-882-7000
12301 Vance Davis Dr, Charlotte, NC 28269
Tel: 704-949-3568
One Litho Way, Durham, NC 27703 *Tel:* 919-
596-3660
3801 Gantz Rd, Grove City, OH 43123 *Tel:* 614-
539-5527
700 Nestle Way, Suite 200, Breinigsville, PA
18031 *Tel:* 610-391-3900
9985 Gantry Rd, Philadelphia, PA 19115
Tel: 215-671-9500
218 N Braddock Ave, Pittsburgh, PA 15208
Tel: 412-241-8200
1210 Key Rd, Columbia, SC 29201 *Tel:* 803-799-
9550
1645 W Sam Houston Pkwy N, Houston, TX
77043 *Tel:* 713-468-7175
1550 Lakeway Dr, Suite 600, Lewisville, TX
75057 *Tel:* 972-353-7500
630 W 1000 N, Logan, UT 84321 *Tel:* 435-755-
4000
201 E Progress Dr, West Bend, WI 53095
Tel: 262-338-6101
Membership(s): Association of American Publishers (AAP); Book Industry Study Group
(BISG); Book Manufacturers' Institute (BMI)

W R Draper Co
Division of The Arthur Press (1978) Ltd

162 Norfinch Dr, Toronto, ON M3N 1X6, Canada
Tel: 416-663-6001 *Fax:* 416-663-6043
E-mail: info@arthurpress.com
Web Site: www.arthurpress.com
Key Personnel
Pres: Jeremy Thorn
Founded: 1954
Turnaround: 10 Workdays

DSCS LLC
5000 College Ave, Suite 4100, College Park, MD
20742
Tel: 301-405-2883 *Fax:* 301-314-2799
E-mail: info@dscs.com
Web Site: www.dscs.com
Key Personnel
Pres: Jason Myers
Founded: 1994
BISAC compatible software
Turnaround: 10 Workdays

Dual Graphics
370 Cliffwood Park, Brea, CA 92821
Tel: 714-990-3700 *Fax:* 714-990-6818
Web Site: www.dualgraphics.com
Key Personnel
Pres & CEO: Jim Joyce
Cont: Jamie Bengard
VP, Opers: Tom Dupuis
Sales Mgr: Craig Evans
Founded: 1906

East Mountain Editing Services
PO Box 1895, Tijeras, NM 87059-1895
Tel: 505-281-8422
Web Site: www.spanishindexing.com
Key Personnel
Mgr: Francine Cronshaw *E-mail:* cronshaw@
nmia.com
Founded: 1992
Turnaround: 9 Workdays
Membership(s): American Society for Indexing
(ASI)

Edison Lithograph & Printing Corp
3725 Tonnelle Ave, North Bergen, NJ 07047-
2421
Tel: 201-902-9191 *Fax:* 201-902-0475
E-mail: info@edisonlitho.com
Web Site: www.edisonlitho.com
Key Personnel
COO: Joseph Ostreicher
Founded: 1958

Emprint®
5425 Florida Blvd, Baton Rouge, LA 70806
Tel: 225-923-2550 *Toll Free Tel:* 800-211-8335
Web Site: emprint.com
Key Personnel
CEO: Mr Courtney Westbrook
Pres & COO: Becky Vance *E-mail:* beckyv@
emprint.com
Turnaround: 5 Workdays
Branch Office(s)
109 Research Dr, Harahan, LA 70123 *Tel:* 504-
733-9654 *Toll Free Tel:* 877-568-1555
Fax: 504-733-8506
151 Southpark Rd, Suite 100, Lafayette, LA
70508 *Tel:* 337-839-9761 *Toll Free Tel:* 888-
874-9761
2830 Breard St, Monroe, LA 71201 *Tel:* 318-387-
1725 *Toll Free Tel:* 800-256-2259

Fairfield Marketing Group Inc
Subsidiary of FMG Inc
The Direct Mail Ctr, 830 Sport Hill Rd, Easton,
CT 06112-1241
Tel: 203-261-5585 *Fax:* 203-261-0884
E-mail: info@fairfieldmarketing.com
Web Site: www.fairfieldmarketing.com

Key Personnel
Pres & CEO: Edward P Washchilla, Jr
VP, Cust Serv: Mike Lozada *Tel:* 203-261-5585 ext 204
VP, Fulfillment: Jason Paul Miller *Tel:* 203-261-5585 ext 203 *E-mail:* jason@fairfieldmarketing. com
Founded: 1986
Turnaround: 5-10 Workdays
Membership(s): American Booksellers Association (ABA); Bridgeport Regional Business Council (BRBC); Education Market Association; United States Chamber of Commerce (USCC)

FCI Digital
Subsidiary of Four Colour Print Group
2032 S Alex Rd, Suite A, West Carrollton, OH 45449
Tel: 937-859-9701
Web Site: www.fcidigital.com
Key Personnel
Gen Mgr: Steve Orf *E-mail:* steveo@fcidigital. com
Founded: 1989
Turnaround: 2 Workdays

Ferry Associates Inc
49 Fostertown Rd, Medford, NJ 08055
Tel: 609-953-1233 *Toll Free Tel:* 800-257-5258 *Fax:* 609-953-8637
Web Site: www.ferryassociates.com
Key Personnel
Pres: Kevin Ferry *E-mail:* kferry@ferryassociates. com
Founded: 1982
Turnaround: Standard 2 week delivery

Filmet Inc
1051 Russellton Rd, Cheswick, PA 15024-1045
Toll Free Tel: 800-255-9000 *Fax:* 724-275-1704
Web Site: www.filmet.com; www.profilmet.com
Key Personnel
Pres: Rick Bachelder *E-mail:* rbachelder@filmet. com
Founded: 1977
Branch Office(s)
103 W Third Ave, Lititz, PA 17543 *Tel:* 717-517-7174

The Font Bureau Inc
Affiliate of Type Network
151 Beach Rd, Vineyard Haven, MA 02568
E-mail: info@fontbureau.com
Web Site: fontbureau.typenetwork.com
Key Personnel
Founder: David Berlow; Roger Black
Gen Mgr: Sam Berlow
Founded: 1989
Turnaround: 1 Workday

Leanne Franson
4 Poplar Ave, Martensville, SK S0K 2T0, Canada
Mailing Address: PO Box 1327, Martensville, SK S0K 2T0, Canada
Tel: 306-382-1696
E-mail: leanne@leannefranson.com
Web Site: www.leannefranson.com
Founded: 1991
Turnaround: 3-7+ Workdays
Membership(s): Communication-Jeunesse; Illustration Quebec; Picture Book Artists Association (PBAA)

Frederic Printing
Subsidiary of RR Donnelley
14701 E 38 Ave, Aurora, CO 80011-1215
Tel: 303-371-7990 *Fax:* 303-371-7959
Web Site: www.fredericprinting.com

Key Personnel
Pres: Kurt Hamlin *Tel:* 303-418-6208
Founded: 1878

Fry Communications Inc
800 W Church Rd, Mechanicsburg, PA 17055
Tel: 717-766-0211 *Toll Free Tel:* 800-334-1429 *Fax:* 717-691-0341
E-mail: info@frycomm.com
Web Site: www.frycomm.com
Key Personnel
Chmn of the Bd: Henry Fry
CEO: Mike Lukas
CFO: Chris Wawrzyniak
CTO: David S Fry
VP, Sales: Kevin Quinn
Founded: 1934
Turnaround: 7-12 Workdays

G & H Soho Inc
413 Market St, Elmwood Park, NJ 07407
Tel: 201-216-9400 *Fax:* 201-216-1778
E-mail: print@ghsoho.com
Web Site: www.ghsoho.com
Key Personnel
Pres: Gerry Burstein
Prodn Mgr: Jason Burstein
Founded: 1985
Turnaround: 3-40 Workdays
Membership(s): Association of Graphic Communications; Book Industry Guild of New York; Digital Printing Council; PRINTING United Alliance

GEX Inc
2 Industrial Way, Atkinson, NH 03811
Tel: 603-870-9292
Web Site: www.gexinc.com
Key Personnel
Pres: Gary Russell
VP: Jim LaPierre; Karla Russell
Founded: 1986

GHP
475 Heffernan Dr, West Haven, CT 06516
Tel: 203-479-7500 *Fax:* 203-479-7575
Web Site: www.ghpmedia.com
Key Personnel
CEO: John Robinson *E-mail:* john.robinson@ghpmedia.com
Partner: Fred Hoxsie *E-mail:* fred.hoxsie@ghpmedia.com
VP, Sales: Steve Bortner *E-mail:* steve.bortner@ghpmedia.com
Founded: 1991
Turnaround: 2-3 Workdays

GLS Companies
1280 Energy Park Dr, St Paul, MN 55108-5106
Tel: 651-644-3000 *Toll Free Tel:* 800-655-9405
Web Site: www.glsmn.com
Key Personnel
Chmn: Gary Garner
CFO: Scott Richardson
CTO: Frank Powell
VP, Opers: Steve Kirk
VP, Sales: Todd Matuska
Mktg Dir: Jim Benedict *E-mail:* jim.benedict@glsmn.com
Founded: 1947
Branch Office(s)
6845 Winnetka Circle, Brooklyn Park, MN 55428-1537 *Tel:* 763-535-7277 *Toll Free Tel:* 888-646-7277

Celia Godkin
Mod 6, Comp 12, 10 James St, Frankville, ON K0E 1H0, Canada
Tel: 613-275-7204
E-mail: celia@godkin.ca
Web Site: www.celiagodkin.com

Founded: 1983
Membership(s): The Botanical Artists of Canada; Canadian Society of Children's Authors Illustrators & Performers (CANSCAIP); The Writers' Union of Canada

Goose River Press
3400 Friendship Rd, Waldoboro, ME 04572-6337
Tel: 207-832-6665
E-mail: gooseriverpress@gmail.com
Web Site: gooseriverpress.com
Key Personnel
Owner & Ed: Deborah J Benner
Founded: 1999
Turnaround: 20-40 Workdays
Membership(s): Maine Writers & Publishers Alliance (MWPA); Waldoboro Business Association

Graphic World Inc, see GW Inc

GraphiColor Corp
Division of Allegra Princeton
3490 N Mill Rd, Vineland, NJ 08360
Tel: 856-691-2507 *Toll Free Tel:* 800-552-2507 *Fax:* 856-696-3229
Web Site: www.graphicolorcorp.com
Key Personnel
Pres: Robert W Stenger, Jr *Tel:* 856-691-2507 ext 111 *E-mail:* bob@graphicolorcorp.com
Founded: 1919

Graphics Two
819 S Main St, Burbank, CA 91506
Tel: 818-841-4922
Key Personnel
Owner: Bert Johnson *E-mail:* cabert@aol.com; Jeanne Vlazny
Founded: 1973

GW Inc
2290 Ball Dr, St Louis, MO 63146
Tel: 314-567-9854
Web Site: www.gwinc.com
Key Personnel
CEO: Kevin Arrow
EVP: Andy Vosburgh; Mike Loomis
VP, Content Opers: Suzanne Kastner
Branch Office(s)
GW Tech Pvt Ltd, Atrium Bldg, Plot No A-45, Zone C, 2nd fl, Industrial Area Phase-VIII B, Mohali, Punjab 160 059, India *Tel:* (0172) 3006100 *Fax:* (0172) 3006128

Molly Hall
4338 Mitchell St, Philadelphia, PA 19128
Tel: 215-970-1837
E-mail: mollyhallindexer@hotmail.com
Founded: 1995
Turnaround: 5 Workdays

HBP Inc
952 Frederick St, Hagerstown, MD 21740
Tel: 301-733-2000 *Toll Free Tel:* 800-638-3508 *Fax:* 301-733-6586
E-mail: contactus@hbp.com
Web Site: www.hbp.com
Key Personnel
Owner & Pres: John Snyder
VP, Busn Devt & Mktg: Ilene Lerner *Tel:* 703-289-9038 *E-mail:* ilerner@hbp.com
Founded: 1903
Turnaround: 4-7 Workdays
Sales Office(s): 2818 Fallfax Dr, Falls Church, VA 22042 *Tel:* 703-289-9000
Membership(s): CUA; Printing & Graphics Association MidAtlantic (PGAMA); Printing Industries of Virginia (PIVA); PRINTING United Alliance

Heidelberg Graphics
2 Stansbury Ct, Chico, CA 95928
SAN: 211-5654
Tel: 530-342-6582 *Fax:* 530-342-6582
E-mail: heidelberggraphics@gmail.com; service@
heidelberggraphics.com
Web Site: www.heidelberggraphics.com
Key Personnel
Owner & Pres: Larry S Jackson
Founded: 1972
Turnaround: 15-30 Workdays

Hennegan Co
Division of RR Donnelley
7455 Empire Dr, Florence, KY 41042
Tel: 859-282-3600 *Fax:* 859-282-3601
Web Site: www.hennegan.com
Founded: 1885

Herr's Indexing Service
76-340 Kealoha St, Kailua Kona, HI 96740-2915
Tel: 808-365-4348
Web Site: www.herrsindexing.com
Key Personnel
Owner: Linda Herr Hallinger
  E-mail: lindahallinger@gmail.com
Founded: 1944
Membership(s): American Society for Indexing
  (ASI); Editorial Freelancers Association (EFA)

Worth Higgins & Associates Inc
8770 Park Central Dr, Richmond, VA 23227-1146
Tel: 804-264-2304 *Toll Free Tel:* 800-883-7768
  Fax: 804-264-5733
E-mail: contact@whaprint.com
Web Site: www.worthhiggins.com
Key Personnel
CEO: Rick La Reau
Pres & COO: Benny Bowman *E-mail:* b.
  bowman@whaprint.com
VP, Sales: Brian Losch *E-mail:* blosch@whaprint.
  com
Dir, Corp Communs: Scott Hudson
  E-mail: shudson@whaprint.com
Founded: 1970

The P A Hutchison Co
400 Penn Ave, Mayfield, PA 18433
SAN: 991-5559
Tel: 570-876-4560 *Toll Free Tel:* 800-USA-PRNT
  (872-7768) *Fax:* 570-876-4561
E-mail: sales@pahutch.com
Web Site: www.pahutch.com
Key Personnel
Pres & CEO: Chris Hutchison
Dir, Sales & Admin: Erin Jones
Founded: 1911
Turnaround: 3-20 Workdays

Imago
110 W 40 St, New York, NY 10018
Tel: 212-921-4411 *Fax:* 212-921-8226
E-mail: sales@imagousa.com
Web Site: www.imagousa.com
Key Personnel
Pres & CEO: Howard Musk *E-mail:* howardm@
  imagogroup.com
Founded: 1985
Turnaround: 5-10 Workdays for color separations;
  4-6 Weeks for printing & binding
Branch Office(s)
Imago West Coast, 23412 Moulton Pkwy, Suite
  250, Laguna Hills, CA 92653 (sales), Contact:
  Tammy Simms *Tel:* 949-367-1635 *Fax:* 949-
  367-1639
Imago Australia, 10 Help St, Suite 27, Level
  6, Chatswood, NSW 2067, Australia (sales)
  Tel: (04) 3753 3351 (cell); (04) 4806 8704
  (cell) *E-mail:* sales@imagoaus.com
Imago Brazil, Domiciano Rossi, 340 unid 154,
  09726-121 Sao Bernardo do Campo, Brazil

  (sales) *Tel:* (011) 2306 8546; (011) 2306 8547
  E-mail: imagobra@gmail.com
Imago Shenzhen, Rm 2511-2512, Block A,
  United Plaza No 5022, Bin He Rd, Fu
  Tian Centre District, Shenzhen 518033,
  China (prodn), Contact: Kendrick Cheung
  Tel: (0755) 8304 8899 *Fax:* (0755) 8251 4073
  E-mail: enquiries@imago.com.hk
Imago France, 23 rue Lavoisier, 75008 Paris,
  France (sales) *Tel:* 01 45 26 47 74 *Fax:* 01 78
  94 14 44 *E-mail:* sales@imagogroup.com
Imago Services (HK) Ltd, Unit B309, 1/F,
  New East Sun Industrial Bldg, 18 Shing
  Yip St, Kwun Tong, Hong Kong (prodn),
  Contact: Kendrick Cheung *Tel:* 2811 3316
  E-mail: enquiries@imago.com.hk
Imago Productions (Malaysia) Pte Ltd, No
  43, Taman Emas, Jl Utama 31, Telok Pan-
  glima Garang, 42500 Kuala Langot, Selan-
  gor, Malaysia (prodn, incorporating South
  Africa sales) *Tel:* (017) 4288771 (cell)
  E-mail: enquiries@imago.com.sg
Imago Publishing, Albury Ct, Albury Thame,
  Oxon OX9 2LP, United Kingdom (sales),
  Dir: Simon Rosenheim *Tel:* (01844) 337000
  Fax: (01844) 339935 *E-mail:* sales@imago.co.
  uk *Web Site:* imagogroup.com

Infinity Graphics
2277 Science Pkwy, Suite 5, Okemos, MI 48864
Tel: 517-349-4635 *Toll Free Tel:* 800-292-2633
  Fax: 517-349-7608
E-mail: barcode@infinitygraphics.com
Web Site: www.infinitygraphics.com
Key Personnel
Owner & Partner: Brian Perry
Owner, Partner & Bar Code Specialist: Suzette
  Perry
Founded: 1972
Turnaround: Same day for bar codes, 1-2 weeks
  book design, 4-6 weeks books
Membership(s): Independent Book Publishers As-
  sociation (IBPA)

Innodata Inc
55 Challenger Rd, Suite 202, Ridgefield Park, NJ
  07660
Tel: 201-371-8000 *Toll Free Tel:* 877-454-8400
E-mail: info@innodata.com; marketing@innodata.
  com
Web Site: innodata.com
Key Personnel
Pres & CEO: Jack S Abuhoff
EVP & COO: Ashok Kumar Mishra
SVP & Gen Coun: Amy Agress
SVP, Prod Innovation: R Douglas Kemp
Founded: 1988
Turnaround: As little as 12 hours
Membership(s): The Association for Work Pro-
  cess Improvement; Association of American
  Publishers Professional & Scholarly Publish-
  ing Division; Center for Information Devel-
  opment & Content Management Strategies
  (CIDM); International Association of Out-
  sourcing Professionals (IAOP); National Fed-
  eration of Abstracting and Information Services
  (NFAIS); Society for Technical Communica-
  tion (STC); Society of Knowledge Based Publishers (SKBP); Software & Information Industry
  Association (SIIA)

Innovative Design & Graphics
1327 Greenleaf St, Evanston, IL 60202
Tel: 847-475-7772 *Fax:* 847-475-7784
E-mail: info@idgevanston.com
Web Site: www.idgevanston.com
Key Personnel
Owner: Tim Sonder *E-mail:* tim@idgevanston.
  com
Founded: 1981
Membership(s): Chicago Creative Coalition; Pro-
  motional Products Association International
  (PPAI)

International Press Publication Inc
Spadina Rd, Richmond Hill, ON L4B 3C5,
  Canada
Tel: 905-883-0343
E-mail: sales@ippbooks.com
Web Site: www.ippbooks.com; www.facebook.
  com/ippbooks; twitter.com/ippbooks2
Key Personnel
Pres: Bali Sethi
Founded: 1976
Membership(s): The American Library Associa-
  tion (ALA); Children's Literature Association
  (ChLA); Ontario Library Association

Interstate Printing Co
2002 N 16 St, Omaha, NE 68110
Tel: 402-341-8028 *Toll Free Tel:* 800-788-4177
Web Site: www.interstateprinting.com
Founded: 1917
Turnaround: 7 Workdays

Ironmark
9040 Junction Dr, Annapolis Junction, MD 20701
Toll Free Tel: 888-775-3737
E-mail: marketing@ironmarkusa.com
Web Site: ironmarkusa.com
Key Personnel
CEO: Scott Hargest *E-mail:* scott@ironmarkusa.
  com; Jeff Ostenso *E-mail:* jeff@ironmarkusa.
  com
Pres: Matt Marzullo *E-mail:* mmarzullo@
  ironmarkusa.com
SVP, Sales: Scott Kravitz *E-mail:* skravitz@
  ironmarkusa.com
VP, Opers: Chris Marzullo *E-mail:* cmarzullo@
  ironmarkusa.com
Sr Sales Exec: Larry Davis *E-mail:* ldavis@
  ironmarkusa.com
Founded: 1955
Turnaround: 20 Workdays, case bound; 10 Work-
  days, paperback; 15 Workdays, mechanically
  bound

Itzhack Shelomi Design
25 Cushman Rd, Scarsdale, NY 10583
Tel: 212-689-7469
E-mail: studio@ishelomi.com; studio@serifes.
  com
Web Site: www.ishelomi.com
Key Personnel
Owner & Creative Dir: Itzhack Shelomi
Founded: 1987

James Enterprises Graphic Services Inc
4925 W Grand Ave, Chicago, IL 60639-4412
Key Personnel
Pres: Barbara James
Founded: 1983
Turnaround: 1 Workday

Jenkins Group Inc
1129 Woodmere Ave, Suite B, Traverse City, MI
  49686
Tel: 231-933-0445 *Toll Free Tel:* 800-706-4636
  Fax: 231-933-0448
E-mail: info@bookpublishing.com
Web Site: www.bookpublishing.com
Key Personnel
CEO: Jerrold R Jenkins *Tel:* 231-933-0445 ext
  1008 *E-mail:* jrj@bookpublishing.com
Pres & COO: James Kalajian *Tel:* 231-933-0445
  ext 1006 *E-mail:* jjk@bookpublishing.com
Book Prodn Mgr: Leah Nicholson *Tel:* 231-
  933-0445 ext 1015 *E-mail:* lnicholson@
  bookpublishing.com
Mng Ed, Independent Publisher Online: Jim
  Barnes *E-mail:* jimb@bookpublishing.com
Founded: 1989

JP Graphics Inc
3001 E Venture Dr, Appleton, WI 54911
Tel: 920-733-4483 *Fax:* 920-733-1700
E-mail: support@jpinc.com
Web Site: www.jpinc.com; www.print.jpinc.com
Key Personnel
Pres: Rod Stoffel
Sales Mgr: Randy Hearley
Founded: 1969

Kachergis Book Design Inc
14 Small St N, Pittsboro, NC 27312
Tel: 919-542-3507
E-mail: goodbooks@kachergisbookdesign.com
Web Site: www.kachergisbookdesign.com
Key Personnel
Pres: Anne Kachergis
Founded: 1980

Kappa Graphics LLP
Division of Kappa Printing Management Associates LLC (KPMA)
50 Rock St, Hughestown, PA 18640
Tel: 570-655-9681 *Toll Free Tel:* 800-236-4396 (sales)
E-mail: weborders@kappapma.com
Web Site: www.kappapma.com/kappagraphics; kappapuzzles.com
Key Personnel
CEO: Nick Karabots
Pres: Thomas Simunek
Founded: 1906

Kelmscott, a Fuse LLC company
5656 McDermott Dr, Berkeley, IL 60163
Tel: 630-898-4261
Web Site: www.kelmscott.com
Key Personnel
Principal: Bill Barta
Pres: Scott Voris
EVP: Jason Tews *E-mail:* jtews@kelmscott.com
VP, Strategy & Client Servs: Jennifer Cox
Dir, Opers: Ketan Shah
Founded: 1936

Knepper Press Corp
2251 Sweeney Dr, Clinton, PA 15026
Tel: 724-899-4200 *Fax:* 724-899-1331
Web Site: www.knepperpress.com
Key Personnel
Chmn: Ted Ford *E-mail:* tedford@knepperpress.com
CFO: Jerry Sales *E-mail:* jerry.sales@knepperpress.com
Cont: Dawn Bates *E-mail:* dawn.bates@knepperpress.com
Pres: Bob Hreha *E-mail:* bobhreha@knepperpress.com
Founded: 1873
Turnaround: 10-20 Workdays

Lachina Precision Graphics Services
3791 S Green Rd, Cleveland, OH 44122
Tel: 216-292-7959
E-mail: info@lachina.com
Web Site: www.lachina.com
Key Personnel
Pres: Jeff Lachina *E-mail:* jeff@lachina.com
Dir, Prodn Servs: Whitney Philipp *E-mail:* wphilipp@lachina.com
Dir, Proj Mgmt Off: Shawn Vazinski *E-mail:* svazinski@lachina.com
Founded: 1978

Lake Book Manufacturing Inc
2085 N Cornell Ave, Melrose Park, IL 60160
Tel: 708-345-7000
E-mail: info@lakebook.com
Web Site: www.lakebook.com
Key Personnel
Pres & COO: Dan Genovese

VP, Fin & CFO: Bob Flatow
VP & Gen Mgr: Bill Richards
VP, Mfg: Steve Quagliato
VP, Opers: Bill Flavin
VP, Sales & Mktg: Nick Vergoth
VP, Technol: Paul Genovese

The Lane Press Inc
87 Meadowland Dr, South Burlington, VT 05403
Mailing Address: PO Box 130, Burlington, VT 05402
Tel: 802-863-5555 *Toll Free Tel:* 877-300-5933
Fax: 802-264-1485
E-mail: sales@lanepress.com
Web Site: www.lanepress.com
Key Personnel
Edit Dir: Beth Renaud
Founded: 1904

Larson Texts Inc
1762 Norcross Rd, Erie, PA 16510
Tel: 814-824-6365 *Toll Free Tel:* 800-530-2355
Fax: 814-824-6377
Web Site: www.larsontexts.com
Key Personnel
CEO: Matt Totske
IT Mgr: Kathleen Williams
Sr Researcher: Tim Larson
Founded: 1983

Leo Paper USA
Division of Leo Paper Group
1180 NW Maple St, Suite 102, Issaquah, WA 98027
Tel: 425-646-8801 *Fax:* 425-646-8805
E-mail: info@leousa.com
Web Site: www.leopaper.com
Key Personnel
Pres: Behzad Pakzad
Founded: 1982
Turnaround: 30-40 Workdays
Branch Office(s)
286 Fifth Ave, 6th fl, New York, NY 10001, Contact: John DiMasi *Tel:* 917-305-0708 *Fax:* 917-305-0709 *E-mail:* info@leousanewyork.com

The Lexington Press Inc
15 Meriam St, Lexington, MA 02420
Mailing Address: PO Box 51, Lexington, MA 02420-0001
Tel: 781-862-8900 *Fax:* 781-861-0375
Web Site: www.lexingtonpress.com
Key Personnel
Pres: Robert F Sacco *E-mail:* bob@lexingtonpress.com
Founded: 1955

Linguistic Systems Inc (LSI)
260 Franklin St, Suite 230, Boston, MA 02110
Tel: 617-528-7410 *Toll Free Tel:* 800-654-5006
E-mail: clientservice@linguist.com
Web Site: www.linguist.com
Key Personnel
Founder & Pres: Martin Roberts *Tel:* 617-528-7412 *E-mail:* mroberts@linguist.com
VP: Mark Ettinger
VP, Engg: Boris Katsevman
VP, Lang Serv Progs: Jean-Paul Fandel
Founded: 1967

Linick International Inc
Division of The Linick Group Inc
Linick Bldg, 7 Putter Lane, Middle Island, NY 11953
Mailing Address: PO Box 102, Middle Island, NY 11953-0102
Tel: 631-924-3888; 631-924-8555; 631-604-8599
E-mail: topmarketingadvisor@gmail.com
Web Site: topmarketingadvisor.com

Key Personnel
Chmn & CEO: Andrew S Linick, PhD
E-mail: linickgroup@gmail.com
Treas: Marvin Glickman
EVP: Roger Dextor
Founded: 1972
BISAC compatible software
Turnaround: 3-7 Workdays
Branch Office(s)
7 Lincoln Ave, Smithtown, NY 11787

LK Litho
Division of The Linick Group Inc
Linick Bldg, 7 Putter Lane, Middle Island, NY 11953
Mailing Address: PO Box 102, Middle Island, NY 11953-0102
Tel: 631-924-3888; 631-924-8555; 631-604-8599
E-mail: lklitho@mail.com; linickgroup@gmail.com
Web Site: topmarketingadvisor.com
Key Personnel
EVP: Roger Dextor
Founded: 1968
BISAC compatible software
Turnaround: 5-10 Workdays depending on job

Lowe Graphics & Printing
Division of E T Lowe Publishing Co
220 Great Circle Rd, Suite 122, Nashville, TN 37228
Tel: 615-242-6649 *Fax:* 615-254-8867
Web Site: www.etlowe.com
Key Personnel
Pres: Albert E Ambrose, Jr *E-mail:* albert@etlowe.com
VP, Prodn: Charles Sutherland *E-mail:* charles@etlowe.com
Founded: 1906

Lumina Datamatics Inc
Affiliate of Datamatics Global Services (Mumbai)
4 Collins Ave, Plymouth, MA 02360
Tel: 508-746-0300 *Fax:* 508-746-3233
Web Site: luminadatamatics.com
Key Personnel
SVP: Jack Mitchell *Tel:* 508-746-0300 ext 203
E-mail: jack.mitchell@luminad.com
SVP, Content Technol: John Wheeler
E-mail: john.wheeler@luminad.com
SVP, Prod Devt: Gordon Laws *E-mail:* gordon.laws@luminad.com
SVP, Sales: Prashant Prabhu *E-mail:* prashant.prabhu@luminad.com
VP, Fin & Acctg: John Chappell *E-mail:* john.chappell@luminad.com
Founded: 1974
Branch Office(s)
31572 Industrial Rd, Suite 400, Livonia, MI 48150 *Toll Free Tel:* 800-717-9153 *Fax:* 734-525-4455
510 Thornall St Metropark, Suite 100, Edison, NJ 08837 (sales) *Toll Free Tel:* 888-772-5532 *Fax:* 732-635-0600
345 Seventh Ave, 4th fl, New York, NY 10001 *Tel:* 646-453-1000 *Fax:* 212-564-8285
1797 Seddon Ct, Ashland, OH 44805 *Tel:* 419-289-0558 *Fax:* 419-289-8923
3265 Farmtrail Rd, York, PA 17406 *Tel:* 717-764-4000
Datamatics Global Services GmbH doo, Gunduliceva br 33, 78000 Banja Luka, Bosnia and Herzegovina *Tel:* 51304120
Im Leuschner, Park 3, 64347 Griesheim, Germany *Tel:* (06155) 862 99-0 *Fax:* (06155) 862 99-19
Ascendas International Tech Park, Taramani Rd, 12th fl, Phase II, Chennai 600 113, India *Tel:* (044) 6604 6000; (044) 6604 6001; (044) 6604 6002 *Fax:* (044) 6604 6098

Knowledge Ctr, St No 17, MIDC, Andheri (E), Mumbai 400 093, India *Tel:* (022) 6102 0000 *Fax:* (022) 2834 3669

Suyojit Datamatics Knowledge Center, Suyojit IT Park, Survey No 804, Unit No S1-S3, Nashik-Mumbai Hwy, Nashik 422 002, India *Tel:* (0253) 610 2222 *Fax:* (0253) 610 2271

Off No 5, 2nd fl, Tower 1, Stellar IT Park, C-25, Sector 62, Noida 201 301, India *Tel:* (0120) 494 0999

Plot No 29-34, East Coast Rd, Saram Revenue Village, Oulgaret Municipality, Lawspet Post, Puducherry 605 008, India *Tel:* (0413) 660 4500; (0413) 660 4501

Mandel Graphic Solution
727 W Glendale Ave, Suite 100, Milwaukee, WI 53209
Tel: 414-271-6970 *Fax:* 414-386-4660
E-mail: info@mandelcompany.com
Web Site: www.mandelcompany.com
Key Personnel
Pres: Rick Mandel *E-mail:* rick.mandel@mandelcompany.com
Founded: 1892

Maracle Inc
1156 King St E, Oshawa, ON L1H 1H8, Canada
Tel: 905-723-3438 *Toll Free Tel:* 800-558-8604
Fax: 905-723-1759
E-mail: hello@maracleinc.com
Web Site: www.maracleinc.com
Key Personnel
Pres: George Sittlinger *Tel:* 905-723-3438 ext 236
Dir, Opers: Nadene D Aldred
Sales & Busn Devt Mgr: Brian Ostrander *Tel:* 905-723-3438 ext 272
E-mail: bostrander@maracleinc.com
Founded: 1920
Turnaround: 10 Workdays
Membership(s): Book Manufacturers' Institute (BMI); Canadian Book Manufacturer Association; Canadian Society of Association Executives (CSAE); Ontario Printing & Imaging Association; PRINTING United Alliance

MBA Computer Service
1920 Lookout Dr, North Mankato, MN 56003
Tel: 507-625-3797
Key Personnel
Pres: DeMar Borth *E-mail:* demar@abdobooks.com

McClain Printing Co
212 Main St, Parsons, WV 26287-1033
Mailing Address: PO Box 403, Parsons, WV 26287-0403
Tel: 304-478-2881 *Toll Free Tel:* 800-654-7179
Fax: 304-478-4658
E-mail: mcclain@mcclainprinting.com
Web Site: www.mcclainprinting.com
Key Personnel
Pres: Kenneth E Smith
VP, Publg: Michelle McKinnie
Founded: 1958
Turnaround: 90-120 Workdays

Meadows Design Office
3800 Yuma St NW, Washington, DC 20016
Tel: 202-966-6007
E-mail: mdo@mdomedia.com
Key Personnel
Pres & Creative Dir: Marc Meadows *E-mail:* marc@mdomedia.com
Curator & Image Res: Amy Meadows
Founded: 1981

Melissa Data Corp
22382 Avenida Empresa, Rancho Santa Margarita, CA 92688-2112
Tel: 949-858-3000 *Toll Free Tel:* 800-800-6245

E-mail: info@melissadata.com
Web Site: www.melissadata.com
Key Personnel
Founder & Pres: Raymond F Melissa *E-mail:* raymond@melissadata.com
Founded: 1985
Turnaround: 2 Workdays
Branch Office(s)
150 Grossman Dr, Suite 208, Braintree, MA 02184-4902
29100 SW Town Center Loop W, Suite 250, Wilsonville, OR 97070-9315

Miles 33 International LLC
Subsidiary of Miles 33 Ltd
40 Richards Ave, Norwalk, CT 06854
Tel: 203-838-2333 *Fax:* 203-838-4473
E-mail: info@miles33.com
Web Site: www.miles33.com
Key Personnel
VP, US Opers: Jeff Malik

Moran Printing Inc, see Emprint®

MPS North America LLC
Subsidiary of MPS Ltd
5728 Major Blvd, Suite 528, Orlando, FL 32819
Tel: 407-472-1280 *Toll Free Tel:* 866-978-1008
Fax: 212-981-2983
E-mail: marketing@mpslimited.com
Web Site: www.mpslimited.com
Founded: 1973
Branch Office(s)
1901 S Fourth St, Suite 222, Effingham, IL 62401
477 Madison Ave, 6th fl, New York, NY 10022
1822 E NC Hwy 54, Suite 120, Durham, NC 27713-3210
MPS Ltd, HMG Ambassador, 137 Residency Rd, Bangalore 560 025, India *Tel:* (080) 4178 4242 *Fax:* (080) 4178 4222
MPS Ltd, RR Towers, Super A, 16/17 TVK Industrial Estate, Guindy, Chennai 600 032, India *Tel:* (044) 4916 2222 *Fax:* (044) 4916 2225
MPS Ltd, 33 IT Park, Sahastradhara Rd, Dehradun 248 001, India *Tel:* (0135) 6677 954
MPS Ltd, 709 DLI Corporate Greens, Sector 74A, Narsinghpur, Gurugram 122 004, India *Tel:* (0124) 661 3134
MPS Interactive Systems, GRM Tech Bldg, 2nd fl, Plot No DH-6/29, Action Area-1, Rajarhat, New Town, Kolkata, West Bengal 700 156, India *Tel:* (033) 66111500
MPS Interactive Systems, The Great Oasis, D-13, 2nd fl, Marol Industrial Estate, Andheri (E), Mumbai 400 093, India *Tel:* (022) 6643 8100 *Fax:* (022) 6643 8800
MPS Ltd, C35, Sector 62, Noida 201 307, India (corp off) *Tel:* (0120) 4599750 *Fax:* (0120) 4021280
Membership(s): Publishing Professionals Network (PPN)

NAC, see North American Color Inc

NETS
Division of Newgen North America Inc
2714 Bee Caves Rd, Suite 201, Austin, TX 78746-5682
Web Site: www.netype.com
Founded: 1940
Branch Office(s)
60/3 Lattice Bridge Rd, Thiruvanmiyur, Chennai, India *Tel:* (044) 4348 0800 *Fax:* (044) 2443 0740

New England Typographic Service, see NETS

Newgen North America Inc
Subsidiary of Newgen KnowledgeWorks
2714 Bee Cave Rd, Suite 201, Austin, TX 78746
Tel: 512-478-5341 *Fax:* 512-476-4756

E-mail: sales@newgen.co
Web Site: www.newgen.co
Key Personnel
Pres: Maran Elancheran *E-mail:* maran@newgen.co
EVP: Tej PS Sood *E-mail:* tej@newgen.co
Founded: 1955

Nissha USA Inc
Subsidiary of Nissha Co Ltd
1051 Perimeter Dr, Suite 600, Schaumburg, IL 60173
Tel: 847-413-2665 *Fax:* 847-413-4085
Web Site: www.nissha.com
Key Personnel
Chmn: Junya Suzuki
Dir & CEO: Hiroyuki Uenishi
Founded: 1993

North American Color Inc
5960 S Sprinkle Rd, Portage, MI 49002
Tel: 269-323-0552 *Toll Free Tel:* 800-537-8296
Fax: 269-323-0190
E-mail: info@nac-mi.com
Web Site: www.nac-mi.com
Key Personnel
VP, Accts: Susan Blesch *E-mail:* sblesch@nac-mi.com
Opers Mgr: Tim Leto
Founded: 1981
Turnaround: 1-3 Workdays
Membership(s): Epicomm; Graphic Artists Guild; International Publishers Association (IPA); PRINTING United Alliance

North Market Street Graphics (NMSG)
Affiliate of Archetype Inc
317 N Market St, Lancaster, PA 17603
Tel: 717-392-7438 *Fax:* 717-397-8037
E-mail: mail@nmsgbooks.com
Web Site: www.nmsgbooks.com
Key Personnel
Owner: Elizabeth Andes; LeRoy R Stipe, Jr
VP of Opers: Vicky Dawes
Dir of Prepress Opers: Dennis Bicksler
Prepress Mgr: Dean Brian
Founded: 1988

OEC Graphics Inc
555 W Waukau Ave, Oshkosh, WI 54902
Tel: 920-235-7770 *Fax:* 920-235-2252
Web Site: www.oecgraphics.com
Key Personnel
CEO: Jack Schloesser *E-mail:* jack.schloesser@oecgraphics.com
Pres: Jeff Schloesser *E-mail:* jeff.schloesser@oecgraphics.com
VP, Mktg & Communs: Jennifer Navin *E-mail:* jennifer.navin@oecgraphics.com
Founded: 1912
Branch Office(s)
909 S Perkins St, Appleton, WI 54914 *Tel:* 920-832-4044 *Fax:* 920-832-4080
33288 Central Ave, Union City, CA 94587 *Tel:* 510-240-6970
7630 S Quincy St, Willowbrook, IL 60527 *Tel:* 630-455-6700 *Fax:* 630-455-6703
Membership(s): Flexographic Technical Association (FTA)

Offset Paperback Manufacturers Inc
Member of Bertelsmann Printing Group
2211 Memorial Hwy, Dallas, PA 18612
Tel: 570-675-5261 *Fax:* 570-675-8714
Web Site: www.bpg-usa.com
Key Personnel
CEO: Christof Ludwig
COO: Jorge Velasco
CFO: Christoph Mittendorf
CTO: Yannic Schroeder
Founded: 1965
Turnaround: 3 Workdays

OGM USA
4333 46 St, Suite F2, Sunnyside, NY 11104
Tel: 212-964-2430
Web Site: www.ogm.it
Key Personnel
Chmn, CEO & Sales Rep: Rino Varrasso
E-mail: rvarrasso@ogm-usa.com
Founded: 1974
Turnaround: 30 Workdays

O'Neil Digital Solutions LLC
12655 Beatrice St, Los Angeles, CA 90066
Tel: 310-448-6400
E-mail: sales@oneildata.com
Web Site: www.oneildata.com
Key Personnel
Pres & COO: Terry Chan
EVP, Sales & Mktg: Mark Rosson
Dir, HR: LaDonna Wise
Founded: 1973
Turnaround: 3-10 Workdays

Overseas Printing Corporation
Division of InnerWorkings Inc
4040 Civic Center Dr, Suite 200, San Rafael, CA 94903
Tel: 415-500-8331 *Fax:* 415-835-9899
Web Site: www.overseasprinting.com
Key Personnel
Sr Prodn Mgr: Shaun Garrett *E-mail:* sgarrett@inwk.com
Founded: 1972
Turnaround: 8-12 Weeks

The Ovid Bell Press Inc
Subsidiary of Walsworth Publishing Co
1201 Bluff St, Fulton, MO 65251
Mailing Address: PO Box 370, Fulton, MO 65251-0370
Tel: 573-642-2256 *Toll Free Tel:* 800-835-8919
E-mail: sales@ovidbell.com
Web Site: ovidbell.com
Key Personnel
CFO: Jill Custard *E-mail:* jillcustard@ovidbell.com
Pres: Troy Williams *Tel:* 573-310-2599
E-mail: troywilliams@ovidbell.com
VP, Sales & Mktg: David O'Donley *Tel:* 573-310-2630 *E-mail:* david@ovidbell.com
Plant Mgr: Kevin Werdehausen *Tel:* 573-310-2598
E-mail: kevin.werdehausen@ovidbell.com
Founded: 1927
Turnaround: 5 Workdays

Pantagraph Printing
217 W Jefferson St, Bloomington, IL 61701
Mailing Address: PO Box 1406, Bloomington, IL 61702-1406
Tel: 309-829-1071
E-mail: queries1@pantagraphprinting.com
Web Site: www.pantagraphprinting.com
Key Personnel
Pres: Mike Dolan
Founded: 1889

Paraclete Press Inc
36 Southern Eagle Cartway, Brewster, MA 02631
SAN: 282-1508
Mailing Address: PO Box 1568, Orleans, MA 02653-1568
Tel: 508-255-4685 *Toll Free Tel:* 800-451-5006
Fax: 508-255-5705
E-mail: customerservice@paracletepress.com
Web Site: www.paracletepress.com
Key Personnel
Design & Web Site Servs: Paul Tingley
E-mail: pault@paracletepress.com
Founded: 1981
Turnaround: 5 Workdays or more
Membership(s): Association of Catholic Publishers Inc; Evangelical Christian Publishers Association (ECPA)

PCA Printing, see Printing Corporation of the Americas Inc

PIPS Inc, see Product Identification & Processing Systems Inc

POD Print
2012 E Northern St, Wichita, KS 67216
Tel: 316-522-5599 *Toll Free Tel:* 800-767-6066
E-mail: info@podprint.com
Web Site: www.podprint.com
Key Personnel
Owner: Grace Rishel; Jim Rishel
Prodn Opers Mgr: Traci Grote *E-mail:* tgrote@podprint.com
Founded: 1978
Turnaround: 1-5 days
Membership(s): Print Services & Distribution Association (PSDA); PRINTING United Alliance

PrairieView Press
625 Seventh St, Gretna, MB R0G 0V0, Canada
Mailing Address: PO Box 460, Gretna, MB R0G 0V0, Canada
Tel: 204-327-6543 *Toll Free Tel:* 800-477-7377
Toll Free Fax: 866-480-0253
Web Site: prairieviewpress.com
Key Personnel
Owner & Pres: Chester Goossen
Founded: 1968

Printing Corporation of the Americas Inc
620 SW 12 Ave, Pompano Beach, FL 33069
Tel: 954-781-8100 *Toll Free Tel:* 866-721-1PCA (721-1722)
Web Site: pcaprintingplus.com
Key Personnel
Pres: Buddy Tuchman
Sales Mgr: Steven Konecky *E-mail:* steven@pcaprinting.com
Founded: 1980
Turnaround: 5-10 Workdays

PrintWest
1111 Eighth Ave, Regina, SK S4R 1C9, Canada
Tel: 306-525-2304 *Toll Free Tel:* 800-236-6438
Fax: 306-757-2439
E-mail: general@printwest.com
Web Site: www.printwest.com
Key Personnel
Pres & Dir, Opers: Corie Triffo
VP, Sales & Mktg: Ken Benson
Founded: 1992
Turnaround: 15 Workdays

Pro-Composition Inc
2501 Catherine St, Suite 3, York, PA 17408
Tel: 717-965-9872
Web Site: www.pro-composition.com
Key Personnel
Pres: Jodi Brenner *E-mail:* jbrenner@pro-composition.com
Founded: 1979
Turnaround: 5-10 Workdays

Product Identification & Processing Systems Inc
10 Midland Ave, Suite M-02, Port Chester, NY 10573-5911
Tel: 212-996-6000 *Toll Free Tel:* 888-783-7439
Fax: 212-410-7477 *Toll Free Fax:* 800-241-PIPS (241-7477)
E-mail: info@pips.com
Web Site: www.pips.com
Key Personnel
VP: Randy Wright
Founded: 1978
BISAC compatible software
Turnaround: Same day
Branch Office(s)
8532 Sanford Dr, Richmond, VA 23228-2813

Tel: 804-264-4434 *Toll Free Tel:* 888-373-0028
E-mail: infova@pips.com
Membership(s): Book Industry Study Group (BISG)

Progress Printing Plus
2677 Waterlick Rd, Lynchburg, VA 24502
Tel: 434-239-9213 *Toll Free Tel:* 800-572-7804
Fax: 434-832-7573
E-mail: info@progressprintplus.com
Web Site: www.progressprintplus.com
Key Personnel
Pres: Michael Thornton *E-mail:* mthornton@progressprintplus.com
Dir, Busn Devt: Gerald Bowles
E-mail: gbowles@progressprintplus.com
Prepress Coord: Clay Atkins *E-mail:* catkins@progressprintplus.com; David Shelton
E-mail: dshelton@progressprintplus.com; Stacy Wilson *E-mail:* swilson@progressprintplus.com
Founded: 1962
Turnaround: 7-9 Workdays after final proof approval

Progressive Publishing Services (PPS)
555 Ryan Run Rd, Suite B, York, PA 17404
Tel: 717-764-5908 *Fax:* 717-764-5530
E-mail: info@pps-ace.com
Web Site: www.pps-ace.com
Key Personnel
VP: Darby Jo Campbell *E-mail:* dcampbell@pps-ace.com
Dir: Crystal Clifton *E-mail:* cclifton@pps-ace.com
Founded: 2015

Pronk Media Inc
PO Box 340, Beaverton, ON L0K 1A0, Canada
Tel: 416-441-3760
E-mail: info@pronk.com
Web Site: www.pronk.com
Key Personnel
Pres: Gord Pronk *Tel:* 416-441-3760 ext 203
E-mail: gord@pronk.com

Publication Identification & Processing Systems
Division of Product Identification & Processing Systems Inc
10 Midland Ave, Suite M-02, Port Chester, NY 10573
Tel: 212-996-6000 *Toll Free Tel:* 888-783-7439
Fax: 212-410-7477 *Toll Free Fax:* 800-241-7477
E-mail: info@pips.com
Web Site: www.pips.com
Key Personnel
VP: George Wright, IV *Tel:* 212-996-6000 ext 110 *E-mail:* gw4@pips.com
Founded: 1978
BISAC compatible software
Turnaround: Same day
Branch Office(s)
8532 Sanford Dr, Richmond, VA 23228 *Tel:* 804-264-4434 *Toll Free Tel:* 888-373-0028
E-mail: infova@pips.com
Membership(s): Book Industry Study Group (BISG)

Publishing Data Management Inc
39 Broadway, 28th fl, New York, NY 10006
Tel: 212-673-3210 *Fax:* 212-673-3390
E-mail: info@pubdata.com
Web Site: www.pubdata.com
Key Personnel
Pres: Addison Roverano *E-mail:* addison@pubdata.com
Founded: 1970
Turnaround: 1 hour-3 Workdays

Publishing Resources Inc
425 Carr 693, PMB 160, Dorado, PR 00646
Tel: 787-647-9342
E-mail: pri@chevako.net
Key Personnel
Pres: Ronald J Chevako
EVP & Ed: Anne W Chevako
Founded: 1976

Reno Typographers
1020 S Rock Blvd, Suite C, Reno, NV 89502
Tel: 775-852-8800
E-mail: info@renotype.com; work@renotype.com
Web Site: www.renotype.com
Key Personnel
Owner & Pres: Kurt Hoge
Founded: 1979

The Renton Printery Inc
315 S Third St, Renton, WA 98057-2028
Tel: 425-235-1776
E-mail: info@rentonprintery.com
Web Site: www.rentonprintery.com
Key Personnel
Pres & CEO: Richard Sweeney
Founded: 1959

The Roberts Group
12803 Eastview Curve, Apple Valley, MN 55124
Tel: 952-322-4005
E-mail: info@editorialservice.com
Web Site: www.editorialservice.com
Key Personnel
Owner: Sherry Roberts; Tony Roberts
Founded: 1990

Ross Gage Inc
8502 Brookville Rd, Indianapolis, IN 46239
Tel: 317-283-2323 *Toll Free Tel:* 800-799-2323
   Fax: 317-931-2108
E-mail: info@rossgage.com
Web Site: www.rossgage.com
Key Personnel
Pres: Thomas W Ross *E-mail:* tomross@rossgage.
   com
VP: Bill Main *E-mail:* bmain@rossgage.com
Opers Coord/Cust Serv: Carol Eads
   E-mail: ceads@rossgage.com
Founded: 1972

Schoolhouse Indexing
10-B Parade Ground Rd, Etna, NH 03750
Tel: 603-643-1617
Web Site: schoolhouseindexing.com
Key Personnel
Owner & Indexer: Christine Hoskin
   E-mail: christine@schoolhousefarm.net
Membership(s): American Society for Indexing
(ASI)

Schroeder Indexing Services
23 Camilla Pink Ct, Bluffton, SC 29909
Tel: 843-705-9779; 843-415-3900 (cell)
E-mail: sanindex@schroederindexing.com
Web Site: www.schroederindexing.com
Key Personnel
Owner & CEO: Sandi Schroeder
Membership(s): American Society for Indexing
(ASI)

Scribe Inc
842 S Second St, Philadelphia, PA 19147
Tel: 215-336-5094 *Fax:* 215-336-5092
E-mail: contact@scribenet.com
Web Site: www.scribenet.com
Key Personnel
Pres: David Alan Rech *E-mail:* drech@scribenet.
   com
Founded: 1993
BISAC compatible software
Turnaround: 2 days-2 weeks

Branch Office(s)
7540 Windsor Dr, Suite 200B, Allentown, PA
18195
3758 SW 30 Ave, Fort Lauderdale, FL 33312

SGS International LLC
Division of Sgsco
626 W Main St, Suite 500, Louisville, KY 40202
Tel: 502-637-5443
E-mail: info@sgsco.com
Web Site: www.sgsintl.com
Key Personnel
CEO: Piyush Chaudhari
COO: Hoyoung Pak
Chief HR Offr: Andrew Tidwell
Pres, Design & Digital: Rob McCarthy
Pres, Global Accts: Julien Tessier
VP, Gen Coun & Secy: Justin Schauer
Founded: 1946
Branch Office(s)
7435 Empire Dr, Florence, KY 41042 *Tel:* 859-
   525-1190 *Fax:* 859-647-8205
3449 Technology Dr, Suite 311, Nokomis, FL
   34275 *Tel:* 941-932-2177
3045 Chastain Meadows Pkwy, Suite 200, Marietta, GA 30066 *Tel:* 678-354-4800
1032 W Fulton Market, Suite 100, Chicago, IL
   60607 *Tel:* 312-575-0700
150 Corporate Dr, Elgin, IL 60123 *Tel:* 847-695-
   9515
1720 W Detweiller Dr, Peoria, IL 61615
   Tel: 309-692-1530
607 Jonesboro Rd, West Monroe, LA 71292
   Tel: 318-322-0518
2125 E Lincoln St, Birmingham, MI 48009
   Tel: 248-594-1818
2006 Cole St, Birmingham, MI 48009 *Tel:* 248-
   594-1818
9300 Winnetka Ave N, Brooklyn Park, MN
   55445 *Tel:* 763-488-5700
2130 Kratky Rd, St Louis, MO 63114 *Tel:* 314-
   968-6800
252 W 37 St, 8th fl, New York, NY 10018
   Tel: 646-561-0100
33 E 17 St, New York, NY 10003 *Tel:* 212-242-
   8787
333 Westchester Ave, Suite W1100, White Plains,
   NY 10604 *Tel:* 914-750-4217
4322 Piedmont Pkwy, Greensboro, NC 27410
   Tel: 336-369-4700
535 Wilmer Ave, Cincinnati, OH 45226 *Tel:* 513-
   321-7500
1108 Broadway St, Cincinnati, OH 45202
3091 Mayfield Rd, Suite 210, Cleveland Heights,
   OH 44118
2781 Roberts Ave, Philadelphia, PA 19129
   Tel: 215-843-2243
1000 Cliff Mine, Suite 360, Pittsburgh, PA 15275
   Tel: 412-787-1283
68 Cumberland St, Suite 200, Woonsocket, RI
   02895 *Tel:* 401-531-2300
1101 E Arapaho Rd, Suite 220, Richardson, TX
   75081 *Tel:* 214-565-9000
5301 Lewis Rd, Sandston, VA 23150 *Tel:* 804-
   226-2490
1518 First Ave S, Suite 601, Seattle, WA 98134
   Tel: 206-305-7366
119 N McCarthy Rd, Suite A, Appleton, WI
   54913 *Tel:* 920-996-9055
W234 N2091 Ridgeview Pkwy Ct, Suite 400,
   Waukesha, WI 53188 *Tel:* 262-549-6890
521 Nottinghill Rd, Suite 5, London, ON N6K
   4L4, Canada *Tel:* 519-668-0520
2620 Slough St, Mississauga, ON L4T 3T2,
   Canada *Tel:* 905-405-1555
7687 Bath Rd, Mississauga, ON L4T 3T1,
   Canada *Tel:* 905-364-3200
2 Dorchester Ave, Toronto, ON M8Z 4W3,
   Canada *Tel:* 416-252-9331
14 Dorchester Ave, Toronto, ON M8Z 4W3,
   Canada *Tel:* 416-622-1005
559 College St, Suite 301, Toronto, ON M6G
   1A9, Canada *Tel:* 416-535-4131

18 Dorchester Ave, Toronto, ON M8Z 4W3,
   Canada *Tel:* 416-252-9503
6300 Avenue du Parc, Suite 300, Montreal, QC
   H2V 4H8, Canada *Tel:* 514-426-5608
Juan F Segui 4646, 6º piso, C1425ADF Buenos
   Aires, Argentina *Tel:* (0114) 776-4847
Av Brigadeiro Faria Lima, 1478 CJ 513, Jardim
   Paulistano, 01451-001 Sao Paulo-SP, Brazil
   Tel: (011) 3032-1260
Rua do Rocio 423, Suite 212, Vila Olimpia, Sao
   Paulo-SP, Brazil *Tel:* (011) 3842-8687
1055 W Zhonshan Rd 302, Bldg A, Shanghai,
   China
Suite 601, Bldg 7, Bridge 8, 10 Jianguo Middle
   Rd, Shanghai 200025, China *Tel:* (021) 6135-
   5960
Zhuoyue Times Plaza, Units 02-04, 14th fl, 4068
   Yitian Rd, Futian CBD, Shenzhen 518048,
   China *Tel:* (0755) 8371-7701
Oficentro Trilogia Edificio 1, Oficina 114, Escazu
   San Jose, Costa Rica *Tel:* 2228-0242
49 Blvd du General Martial Valin, 75015 Paris,
   France *Tel:* 01 45 58 80 00
Pier F, Franziusstr 6, 60314 Frankfurt am Main,
   Germany *Tel:* (0160) 5396246
Ginza Plaza, Rm 2015, Level 21, 2A-2H Sai Ye-
   ung Choi St S, Mong Kok, Kowloon, Hong
   Kong *Tel:* 3767 9700
1st fl, Om Sadan, Mehra Estate, LBS Marg
   Vikhroli (West), Mumbai 400 079, India
   Tel: (022) 42008585
Allahabad Bank Bldg, 2nd fl, 98 Mecricar Rd,
   Puram Coimbatore, Tamil Nadu 641 002, India
10, Sangothipalayam, Arasur Coimbatore, Tamil
   Nadu 641 407, India *Tel:* 9003825891
Victoria House, 8e etage, St Louis St, Port Louis,
   Mauritius *Tel:* 211 6360
125, route Menagerie, Port Louis, Mauritius
   Tel: 230 211 90 15
Km 8 letra C Carretera Libre a Celaya, Frac-
   cionamiento Industrial Balvanera, 76900 Cor-
   regidora, QRO, Mexico *Tel:* (01442) 245-2525
Andres Bello No 45 Piso 8, Colonia Polanco
   Chapultepec, 11560 Mexico, CDMX, Mexico
   Tel: (0155) 250-2121
Herengracht 598-600, 1017 CJ Amsterdam,
   Netherlands *Tel:* (020) 3034-589
Citynet Bldg 1, 183 Epifanio de los Santos Ave,
   1555 Mandaluyong, Metro Manila, Philippines
   Tel: (02) 910-5058
59 New Bridge Rd, Singapore 059405, Singapore
34 Petain Rd, Singapore 208101, Singapore
   Tel: 6513 9689
77 Kampong Bahru Rd, No 02-01, Singapore
   169376, Singapore *Tel:* 6224 2152
Carrer Laurea Miro, 153, 2º1a, 08950 Esplugues
   de Llobregat, Barcelona, Spain *Tel:* 934 809
   841
Place Saint-Francois 2, 1003 Lausanne, Switzerland *Tel:* (021) 552 22 00
Fort Dunlop, Unit 101, Birmingham, West Mid-
   lands B24 9FD, United Kingdom *Tel:* (0121)
   740-0247
Off 9, Orchid Rd, Hessle, East Riding, Yorks
   HU13 0DH, United Kingdom *Tel:* (01482)
   225835
Brewery House, The Maltings, Silvester St, Hull
   HU1 3HA, United Kingdom *Tel:* (01482)
   973000
Citadel Trading Park, Citadel Way, Garrison Rd,
   Hull HU9 1TQ, United Kingdom *Tel:* (01482)
   225835
91-94 Lower Marsh, London SE1 7AB, United
   Kingdom *Tel:* (020) 7202 4720
Morley House, 6 Nottingham St, London W1U
   5EJ, United Kingdom *Tel:* (020) 7224 0874
South Suffolk Business Ctr, Unit 9, Alexandra
   Rd, Sudbury CO10 2ZX, United Kingdom
   Tel: (01787) 464234
Salterbeck Trading Estate, Harrington, Working-
   ton, Cumbria CA14 5BX, United Kingdom
   Tel: (01946) 833600

Shepherd Inc
2223 Key Way Dr, Suite B, Dubuque, IA 52002
Tel: 563-584-0500
Web Site: www.shepherd-inc.com
Key Personnel
Prodn Mgr: Deb Leibfried
Founded: 1989

Signature Book Printing Inc
8041 Cessna Ave, Gaithersburg, MD 20879
Tel: **301-258-8353** *Fax:* **301-670-4147**
E-mail: **book@sbpbooks.com**
Web Site: **sbpbooks.com**
Key Personnel
Pres: Phil Nanzetta
Off Mgr: Linda Wood
Founded: 1986
**We produce hard cover & soft cover, full color
& B&W books of (virtually) any type, including children's, coffee table, travel &
cookbooks. Everything is produced by offset lithography. We print runs from 500 to
20,000 copies & can do as few as 500 copies
competitively for hard cover & full color
books. We are nationally recognized for
excellent quality, top value & smooth, easy
customer service.**
**Visit our web site at sbpbooks.com for exten-
sive information on book printing & for a
large range of examples of our work. For
pricing, visit sbpbooks.com or call us at 301-
258-8353.**

Six Red Marbles LLC
101 Station Landing, Medford, MA 02155
Tel: 857-588-9000
E-mail: info@sixredmarbles.com
Web Site: www.sixredmarbles.com
Key Personnel
CEO: David Goodman
Chief Mktg & Admin Offr: Robin Zaccardo
EVP, Busn Devt: John Kenney
EVP, Opers: Michele Baird
SVP, Fin: Meg Trant
SVP, Prodn: Alexandre Vallette
SVP, Technol: Chris Kaefer
VP, Busn Devt: Cary Drake
VP, Learning Strategy: Kelvin Bentley
Exec Dir, Humanities: Bill Scroggie
Exec Dir, STEM: Joyce Spangler
Founded: 1996
Branch Office(s)
4030 W Braker Lane, Bldg 3, Suite 350, Austin,
TX 78759 *Tel:* 512-372-4800
209 Austine Dr, Suite 115, Brattleboro, VT 05301
Tel: 410-527-1606
Jouve India Pvt Ltd, 1st fl, No 1415, No 283/
1B2, Old Mahabalipuram Rd, Kottivakkam,
Chennai 600 041, India *Tel:* (044) 40205300
The Great Eastern Ctr, 2nd fl, 70, Nehru Place,
Delhi 110 019, India *Tel:* (011) 42636116

Smith & Sons Printers Inc
6403 Rutledge Pike, Knoxville, TN 37924
Tel: 865-523-1419
Web Site: www.ssprintinc.com
Key Personnel
Owner: Stephen Ownby *E-mail:* stephen@ssprint.
com
Founded: 1979

Smith-Edwards-Dunlap Co
2867 E Allegheny Ave, Philadelphia, PA 19134
Tel: 215-425-8800 *Toll Free Tel:* 800-829-0020
Fax: 215-425-9715
E-mail: sales@sed.com
Web Site: www.sed.com
Key Personnel
Pres: Jonathan Shapiro
Sales Mgr: Fred Binder
Founded: 1880

Southeastern Printing Co
3601 SE Dixie Hwy, Stuart, FL 34997
Tel: 772-287-2141 *Toll Free Tel:* 800-226-8221
Fax: 772-288-3988
E-mail: sales@seprint.com
Web Site: www.seprint.com
Key Personnel
Pres: Don Mader
Founded: 1924
Turnaround: 20-40 Workdays
Branch Office(s)
950 SE Eighth St, Hialeah, FL 33010 *Tel:* 305-
885-8707 *Fax:* 305-888-9903 *E-mail:* info@
seprint.com
Sales Office(s): 6001 Park of Commerce Blvd,
Suite 200, Boca Raton, FL 33487 *Tel:* 561-
998-0870

Southern Graphic Systems LLC, see SGS
International LLC

Barbara Spurll Illustration
160 Browning Ave, Toronto, ON M4K 1W5,
Canada
Tel: 416-594-6594 *Toll Free Tel:* 800-989-3123
Web Site: www.barbaraspurll.com
Key Personnel
Prop: Barbara Spurll *E-mail:* barbara@
barbaraspurll.com
Founded: 1975
Membership(s): Canadian Association of Pro-
fessional Image Creators (CAPIC); Canadian
Society of Children's Authors Illustrators &
Performers (CANSCAIP)

Square Two Design Inc
2325 Third St, Suite 213, San Francisco, CA
94107
Tel: 415-437-3888
E-mail: info@square2.com
Web Site: www.square2.com
Key Personnel
Pres & Creative Dir: Eddie Lee *Tel:* 415-437-
3888 ext 101
Founded: 1991
Branch Office(s)
No 8 Hua Jia Di Nan Jie, Chao Yang District,
Beijing 100102, China, Pres: Min Wang
Tel: (01350) 1084-543 *E-mail:* mwang@
square2.com

Studio 31 Inc
2740 SW Martin Downs Blvd, Suite 358, Palm
City, FL 34990
Tel: 772-781-7195 *Fax:* 772-781-6044
Web Site: www.studio31.com
Key Personnel
Founder & Pres: James Wasserman *E-mail:* jim@
studio31.com
Partner: Bill Corsa
Founded: 1977

Sun Graphics LLC
1818 Broadway, Parsons, KS 67357
Toll Free Tel: 800-835-0588 *Fax:* 620-421-2089
E-mail: info@sun-graphics.com
Web Site: www.sun-graphics.com
Key Personnel
VP, Mktg: John Hammett *Tel:* 918-695-2267
E-mail: jhammett@sun-graphics.com
VP, Sales: John Hohenshell *Tel:* 913-257-9420
E-mail: jhohenshell@sun-graphics.com
Commercial Sales & Book Div Sales: Melody
Morris *Tel:* 620-660-0614 *E-mail:* mmorris@
sun-graphics.com
Founded: 1998
Turnaround: 15-20 Workdays
Membership(s): Independent Book Publishers As-
sociation (IBPA); Publishers Association of the
West (PubWest)

John S Swift Co Inc
999 Commerce Ct, Buffalo Grove, IL 60089
Tel: 847-465-3300 *Fax:* 847-465-3309
Web Site: www.johnswiftprint.com
Key Personnel
Pres: John S Swift *E-mail:* jss@johnswiftprint.
com
Founded: 1912
Turnaround: 5 Workdays
Branch Office(s)
John S Swift Print of NJ Inc, 375 North St,
Unit N, Teterboro, NJ 07608, Contact: Rick
Frydrych *Tel:* 201-678-3232 *Fax:* 201-378-3001
E-mail: rickfry@johnswiftprint.com

Swordsmith Productions
PO Box 242, Pomfret, CT 06258
Tel: 860-208-4829
E-mail: information@swordsmith.com
Web Site: www.swordsmith.com
Key Personnel
Pres: Leigh Grossman
Founded: 1994
Turnaround: 3-6 Workdays for coding & tagging;
10-15 Workdays for other editorial production

Symbology Inc
7351 Kirkwood Lane N, Suite 126, Maple Grove,
MN 55369
Tel: 763-315-8080 *Toll Free Tel:* 800-328-2612
Fax: 763-315-8088
E-mail: clientservices@symbology.com; sales@
symbology.com
Web Site: www.symbology.com
Key Personnel
Pres: Jeff Gossen *E-mail:* jgossen@symbology.
com
VP, Sales & Mktg: John Gorowsky
E-mail: jgorowsky@symbology.com
Founded: 1980
Membership(s): The American Library Associa-
tion (ALA)

Symmetry Creative Production
1300 S Grove Ave, Suite 103, Barrington, IL
60010
Tel: 847-382-8750
E-mail: information@symmetrycp.com
Web Site: www.symmetrycp.com
Key Personnel
Owner & Partner: Roger Tillander *Tel:* 847-382-
7530
Owner & Exec Dir, Edit: Mary Beth Gasiorowski
Tel: 847-382-7550
Owner & Prodn: John F Deady *Tel:* 847-382-
7577
Dir, Art, Design & Photog: Beth Morrison
Tel: 847-382-7540
Acct Exec: Mike Tambellini *Tel:* 847-382-7610
Founded: 2002

Taylor Specialty Books
Division of Balfour/Taylor
1550 W Mockingbird Lane, Dallas, TX 75235
Tel: 214-819-8588 (cust serv) *Fax:* 214-819-5051
(cust serv) *Toll Free Fax:* 800-203-9778
E-mail: rfq@taylorpub.com (estimates)
Web Site: www.taylorspecialtybooks.com
Key Personnel
VP, Sales & Mktg, Specialty Books: Rick Parra
Tel: 214-819-5027 *E-mail:* rick.parra@balfour.
com
Sales Rep: Kim Hawley *E-mail:* khawley@
taylorpub.com; George Levesque
E-mail: glevesque@taylorpub.com; Mark Mc-
Combs *E-mail:* mmcombs@taylorpub.com
Founded: 1939
Turnaround: 25-30 Workdays

Texas Graphic Resource Inc
1234 Round Table Dr, Dallas, TX 75247
Tel: 214-630-2800 *Fax:* 214-630-0713

E-mail: info@texasgraphics.com
Web Site: www.texasgraphics.com
Founded: 1907

Thistle Printing Ltd
Division of DATA Communications Management Corp
35 Mobile Dr, Toronto, ON M4A 2P6, Canada
Tel: 416-288-1288 *Fax:* 416-288-0737
E-mail: sales@thistleprinting.com
Web Site: www.thistleprinting.com
Key Personnel
Gen Mgr: Mike Branov
Founded: 1931

Times Citizen Communication Inc
Division of Spokesman Press
406 Stevens St, Iowa Falls, IA 50126
Tel: 641-648-2521 *Toll Free Tel:* 800-798-2691
Fax: 641-648-4765
E-mail: tcc@iafalls.com
Web Site: timescitizen.com
Key Personnel
Dir, Local Media: Tony Baranowski
Founded: 1974

Times Printing LLC
Division of Kappa Printing Management Associates LLC (KPMA)
100 Industrial Dr, Random Lake, WI 53075
Tel: 920-994-4396 *Toll Free Tel:* 800-236-4396
(sales)
E-mail: info@kappapma.com
Web Site: www.kappapma.com
Founded: 1918
Turnaround: 5-10 Workdays

Toof American Digital
4222 Pilot Dr, Memphis, TN 38118
Tel: 901-274-3632 *Toll Free Tel:* 800-722-4772
Web Site: www.toofamericandigital.com
Key Personnel
Pres: Stillman McFadden
Founded: 1864
Turnaround: 80 Workdays

TotalWorks™ Inc
420 W Huron St, Chicago, IL 60654
Tel: 773-489-4313
E-mail: production@totalworks.net
Web Site: www.totalworks.net
Key Personnel
Principal, Pres & CEO: Gail Ludewig
Principal & EVP: Bruce Jensen
VP, Sales & Mktg: Louise Pauly
Founded: 1927
Turnaround: 2 Workdays
Membership(s): American Marketing Association; BMA; Chicago Association of Direct Marketing (CADM); Women's Business Enterprise Network (WBENC)

Townsend Communications Inc
20 E Gregory Blvd, Kansas City, MO 64114
Tel: 816-361-0616
Web Site: www.townsendcommunications.com; www.townsendprint.com
Key Personnel
Pres: Guy Townsend, III
VP: Joe Chambers
Founded: 1964

Tukaiz LLC
2917 N Latoria Lane, Franklin Park, IL 60131
Tel: 847-455-1588; 847-288-4968 (sales)
Toll Free Tel: 800-543-2674
E-mail: contacttukaiz@tukaiz.com
Web Site: www.tukaiz.com
Key Personnel
Founder & Mng Dir: Frank Defino, Sr
VP, Mng Dir & CFO: Christopher Calabra

VP & Mng Dir: Daniel Defino; Frank Defino, Jr
Founded: 1963

Universal|Wilde
26 Dartmouth St, Westwood, MA 02090
Tel: 781-251-2700 *Fax:* 781-251-2613
Web Site: www.universalwilde.com
Key Personnel
Pres & CEO: Stephen Flood
COO: Christopher Armstrong
CFO: Joe Musanti
VP, HR: Jennifer MacAskill
VP, Sales: Jim Bailey
Mktg Mgr: Ryan Collins
Founded: 1958
Branch Office(s)
403 VFW Dr, Rockland, MA 02370 *Tel:* 781-871-7744 *Fax:* 781-878-2967
48 Third Ave, Somerville, MA 02143 *Tel:* 617-591-3000 *Fax:* 617-591-3091

Versa Press Inc
1465 Spring Bay Rd, East Peoria, IL 61611-9788
Tel: 309-822-8272 *Toll Free Tel:* 800-447-7829
Fax: 309-822-8141
Web Site: www.versapress.com
Key Personnel
Chmn: Joseph F Kennell
Pres: Steven J Kennell
Sales Mgr: Darold D Frerichs *E-mail:* dfrerichs@versapress.com
Founded: 1937
Turnaround: 20 Workdays
Membership(s): Book Manufacturers' Institute (BMI)

ViaTech Publishing Solutions Inc
11935 N Stemmons Fwy, Dallas, TX 75234
Tel: 214-827-8151
E-mail: marketing@viatechpub.com
Web Site: www.viatech.io
Key Personnel
CEO: Michael Bertuch
VP, Global Sales: Tom Bergenholtz
Founded: 1928
Turnaround: 5-20 Workdays
Branch Office(s)
8857 Alexander Rd, Batavia, NY 14020
5668 E 61 St, Commerce, CA 90040
5021 Old Dixie Rd, Forest Park, GA 30297
Kingston Business Park, Kingston Bagpuize, Abingdon, Oxon OX13 5FE, United Kingdom *Tel:* (01865) 822170
Membership(s): Book Manufacturers' Institute (BMI)

Viridiam LLC
3030 Lowell Dr, Green Bay, WI 54311
Tel: 920-465-3030 *Toll Free Tel:* 800-829-6555
Web Site: www.viridiam.com
Key Personnel
VP, Sales: Rob Butler
Founded: 1888
Turnaround: 15 Workdays
Membership(s): Book Manufacturers' Institute (BMI)

Walsworth
306 N Kansas Ave, Marceline, MO 64658
Toll Free Tel: 800-265-6795
Web Site: www.walsworth.com; www.walsworthhistorybooks.com
Key Personnel
CEO: Don O Walsworth
COO: Jim Mead
Pres: Don Walsworth, Jr
VP, Mktg & Communs: Kristin Mateski *E-mail:* kristin.mateski@walsworth.com
Founded: 1937
Branch Office(s)
803 S Missouri Ave, Marceline, MO 64658 (printing & bindery facility)

Donning Co Publishers, 731 S Brunswick St, Brookfield, MO 64628 *Tel:* 660-675-5570 *Web Site:* www.donning.com
The Ovid Bell Press, 1201 Bluff St, Fulton, MO 65251-0370 *Toll Free Tel:* 800-835-8919 *Web Site:* www.ovidbell.com
7300 W 110 St, Suite 600, Overland Park, KS 66210 (sales & mktg)
2180 Maiden Lane, St Joseph, MI 49085 (printing & bindery facility)
656 S Douglas St, Ripon, WI 54971 (printing & bindery facility)

Fred Weidner & Daughter Printers
99 Hudson St, 5th fl, New York, NY 10013
Tel: 646-706-5180
E-mail: info@fwdprinters.com
Web Site: www.fwdprinters.com
Key Personnel
Pres: Cynthia Weidner *E-mail:* cynthia@fwdprinters.com
Creative Dir: Carol Mittelsdorf *E-mail:* carol@fwdprinters.com
Founded: 1860
Turnaround: 5-10 Workdays

WeMakeBooks.ca
Division of Heidy Lawrance Associates
238 Willowdale Ave, North York, ON M2N 4Z5, Canada
Tel: 416-733-1827 *Fax:* 416-733-7663
Web Site: www.wemakebooks.ca
Key Personnel
Owner: Heidy Lawrance *E-mail:* heidy@wemakebooks.ca
Founded: 1988

Westchester Publishing Services
4 Old Newtown Rd, Danbury, CT 06810
Tel: 203-791-0080 *Fax:* 203-791-9286
E-mail: info@westchesterpubsvcs.com
Web Site: www.westchesterpublishingservices.com
Key Personnel
Founder & Chmn: Dennis Pistone
Pres & CEO: Paul J Crecca *E-mail:* paul.crecca@westchesterpubsvcs.com
Chief Revenue Offr: Tyler M Carey *Tel:* 203-658-6581 *E-mail:* tyler.carey@westchesterpubsvcs.com
Dir, Edit Servs: Susan Baker *Tel:* 203-791-0080 ext 103 *E-mail:* susan.baker@westchesterpubsvcs.com
Dir, Opers: Terry Colosimo *E-mail:* terry.colosimo@westchesterpubsvcs.com
Dir, Technol: Michael Jon Jensen *E-mail:* michael.jensen@westchesterpubsvcs.com
Busn Devt Mgr: Tim Cross *E-mail:* tim.cross@westchesterpubsvcs.com
Key Accts Mgr: William Foley *Tel:* 203-791-0080 ext 104 *E-mail:* bill.foley@westchesterpubsvcs.com
Prodn Mgr, Journals Servs: Celeste Bilyard *E-mail:* celeste.bilyard@westchesterpubsvcs.com
Founded: 1969
Turnaround: 5 Workdays

Whitehall Printing Co
4244 Corporate Sq, Naples, FL 34104
Tel: 239-643-6464 *Toll Free Tel:* 800-321-9290
Fax: 239-643-6439
E-mail: info@whitehallprinting.com
Web Site: www.whitehallprinting.com
Key Personnel
Chmn: Mike Hirsch
Pres: Jeff Hirsch
VP: Emil G Hirsch
Founded: 1959
Turnaround: 10-15 Business days

Widen Enterprises Inc
6911 Mangrove Lane, Madison, WI 53713
Tel: 608-222-1296 *Toll Free Tel:* 800-444-2828
E-mail: marketing@widen.com
Web Site: www.widen.com
Key Personnel
CEO: Matthew Gonnering
CFO: Michael Kiesler
VP, Cust Devt: Brian Becker
VP, Mktg & Cust Experience: Jake Athey
VP, Prod Mgmt: Deanna Ballew
Dir, Creative & Brand Strategy: Nina Brakel-Schutt
Dir, Premedia Opers: Debby Leisner
Founded: 1948
Branch Office(s)
Aldgate Tower, 2 Leman St, London E1 8FA, United Kingdom *Tel:* (020) 3890 6777

B Williams & Associates, see BW&A Books Inc

Windhaven®
466 Rte 10, Orford, NH 03777
Tel: 603-512-9251 (cell)
E-mail: info@windhavenpress.com
Web Site: www.windhavenpress.com
Key Personnel
Dir & Ed: Nancy C Hanger *E-mail:* nhanger@windhavenpress.com
Ed & Consultant: Andrew V Phillips
   E-mail: andrew@windhavenpress.com
Founded: 1985

Turnaround: 3-5 days book design; 5-7 days typesetting; 7-14 days proofing; 2-4 weeks full production
Membership(s): Editorial Freelancers Association (EFA); National Writers Union (NWU)

WordCo Indexing Services Inc
66 Franklin St, Norwich, CT 06360
E-mail: office@wordco.com
Web Site: www.wordco.com
Key Personnel
Founder & CEO: Stephen Ingle *E-mail:* sringle@wordco.com
Proj Coord: Amy Moriarty *E-mail:* amoriarty@wordco.com
Founded: 1988
Turnaround: 5-15 Workdays
Membership(s): American Society for Indexing (ASI)

Worzalla
3535 Jefferson St, Stevens Point, WI 54481
Tel: 715-344-9608 *Fax:* 715-344-2578
Web Site: www.worzalla.com
Key Personnel
Chmn of the Bd: Charles Nason
Pres: James Fetherston
VP, Fin: Samuel Crockett
VP, Opers: Brian McManus
VP, Sales: Richard Letchinger
Cust Serv Mgr: Kim Deuel
Field Sales: Rodger Beyer
Founded: 1892
Turnaround: 20 Workdays

Sales Office(s): 4819 W Berteau Ave, Chicago, IL 60641, Contact: Tim Taylor *Tel:* 773-383-7892
   E-mail: ttaylor@worzalla.com
2231 Morris Ave, Suite 3, Union, NJ 07083, Contact: Edmund Corvelli, III *Tel:* 201-749-7995
   E-mail: ecorvelli@worzalla.com
222 W 37 St, 10th fl, New York, NY 10018, Contact: Sam Gallucci *Tel:* 201-851-3292
   E-mail: sgallucci@worzalla.com
Membership(s): Book Manufacturers' Institute (BMI)

Writer's Relief, Inc
18766 John J Williams Hwy, Unit 4, Box 335, Rehoboth Beach, DE 19971
Toll Free Tel: 866-405-3003 *Fax:* 201-641-1253
E-mail: info@writersrelief.com
Web Site: www.WritersRelief.com
Key Personnel
Pres: Ronnie L Smith *E-mail:* ronnie@wrelief.com

X-Height Studio
83 High St, Milford, MA 01757
Tel: 508-478-3897 *Toll Free Tel:* 888-474-8973
E-mail: info@x-heightstudio.com
Web Site: www.x-heightstudio.com
Key Personnel
Founder & Owner: Cecile Kaufman
Founded: 1999
Membership(s): Bookbuilders of Boston; Editorial Freelancers Association (EFA); Graphic Artists Guild

Printing, Binding & Book Finishing Index

COMIC BOOK PRINTING

DIE-CUTTING

DIGITAL PRINTING

EDITION (HARDCOVER) BINDING

EMBOSSING

SHORT RUN PRINTING

SIDE STITCH BINDING

Printing, Binding & Book Finishing

This section includes companies offering printing, binding and/or book finishing services. The descriptions of the services provided are paid components.

Many of the companies listed have been recommended by the manufacturing departments of book publishers as being active and experienced in the production of books.

Absolut Color
109 W 27 St, New York, NY 10001
Tel: 212-868-0404
E-mail: info@absolutcolor.com
Web Site: www.absolutcolor.com
Key Personnel
Pres: Dan Shill
VP: Peter Gordon
Founded: 1960
Turnaround: 1 Workday

AcmeBinding
Division of HF Group LLC
8844 Mayfield Rd, Chesterland, OH 44026
Tel: 440-729-9411 *Toll Free Tel:* 888-485-5415
    Fax: 440-729-9415
Web Site: www.acmebinding.com
Key Personnel
VP & Gen Mgr: Jim Bratton *E-mail:* jbratton@
    hfgroup.com
Plant Mgr: Dave Lair *E-mail:* dlair@hfgroup.com
Off Mgr/Cust Serv: Rick Burkhart
    E-mail: rburkhart@hfgroup.com
Founded: 1821
Turnaround: 20 Workdays
Print Runs: 1 min - 100,000 max (max for printing, not binding - binding, no limits for quantity)
Branch Office(s)
1010 N Sycamore St, North Manchester, IN
    46962, Pres: Jim Heckman *Tel:* 260-982-2107
    Toll Free Tel: 800-334-3628 *Fax:* 260-982-1130
    E-mail: jheckman@hfgroup.com
92 Cambridge St, Charlestown, MA 02129-0212,
    Pres & COO: Paul Parisi *Tel:* 617-242-1100
    Toll Free Tel: 800-242-1821 *Fax:* 617-242-3764
    E-mail: pparisi@hfgroup.com
6204 Corporate Park Dr, Browns Summit, NC
    27214-9745, VP & Gen Mgr: Scott May
    Tel: 336-931-0800 *Toll Free Tel:* 800-444-7534
    Fax: 336-931-0711 *E-mail:* smay@hfgroup.
    com
340 First St, Utica, NE 68456, Gen Mgr:
    Damon Osborne *Tel:* 402-534-2261 *Toll
    Free Tel:* 800-869-0420 *Fax:* 402-534-2761
    E-mail: dosborne@hfgroup.com
45 N Main St, Unit 528, Hatfield, PA 19440
    (transportation hub), Off Mgr: Andy Selheimer *Tel:* 215-855-2293 *E-mail:* aselheimer@
    hfgroup.com
105 W Thomas St, Atlanta, TX 75551-2736
    (transportation hub) *Tel:* 260-982-2107
    Fax: 260-982-1130
Membership(s): The American Library Association (ALA); Book Manufacturers' Institute
    (BMI); Printing Industries of New England
    (PINE); PRINTING United Alliance

Action Printing
Division of Gannett Corp
N6637 Rolling Meadows Dr, Fond du Lac, WI
    54937
Mailing Address: PO Box 1955, Fond du Lac, WI
    54936-1955
Tel: 920-907-7820
E-mail: info@actionprinting.com
Web Site: www.actionprinting.com
Key Personnel
Gen Mgr: Darwin Bethke *E-mail:* dbethke@
    actionprinting.com

Natl Acct Mgr: Adam Kempf *E-mail:* akempf@
    actionprinting.com
Press & Bindery Mgr: Brian Thiede
    E-mail: bthiede@actionprinting.com
Founded: 1970
Turnaround: 10 Workdays
Print Runs: 500 min - 250,000 max
Membership(s): Great Lakes Graphics Association
    (GLGA); PRINTING United Alliance

Adair Graphic Communications
Division of Printwell
26975 Northline Rd, Taylor, MI 48180
Tel: 734-941-6300 *Fax:* 734-942-0920
E-mail: adair@printwell.com
Web Site: www.adairgraphic.com
Key Personnel
Pres & CEO: Paul Borg
VP: Dennis Adair *E-mail:* dennis@adairgraphic.
    com
Founded: 1931
Turnaround: 10 Workdays
Print Runs: 500 min - 500,000 max

Adams Press
1712 Oakton St, Evanston, IL 60202
E-mail: info@adamspress.com
Key Personnel
Pres: James A Kepler *E-mail:* jkepler@
    adamspress.com
Founded: 1942
Turnaround: 30-45 Workdays
Print Runs: 100 min
Membership(s): The Association of Publishers
    for Special Sales (APSS); Independent Book
    Publishers Association (IBPA); Independent
    Writers of Chicago (IWOC); Midwest Writers
    Association

AGS
Subsidiary of RR Donnelley
4590 Graphics Dr, White Plains, MD 20695
Tel: 301-843-1800 *Fax:* 301-843-6339
E-mail: info@ags.com
Web Site: www.ags.com
Key Personnel
Pres: Mike Donohue *E-mail:* mike.donohue@rrd.
    com
VP, Sales & Mktg: Alan Flint *E-mail:* aflint@ags.
    com
Founded: 1975
Print Runs: 50 min - 1,000,000 max
Membership(s): American Society of Association
    Executives (ASAE)

amb™, see Ambassador Press Inc

Ambassador Press Inc
1400 Washington Ave N, Minneapolis, MN 55411
Tel: 612-521-0123
E-mail: info@ambpress.com
Web Site: www.ambpress.com
Key Personnel
Co-Owner, Pres & CEO: Candice Engle-Fieldman
Co-Owner & EVP: Harold Engle
Founded: 1960
Turnaround: 3 Workdays
Print Runs: 100 min - 500,000 max

American Mathematical Society (AMS)
201 Charles St, Providence, RI 02904-2213
SAN: 201-1654
Tel: 401-455-4000 *Toll Free Tel:* 800-321-4267
    Fax: 401-331-3842; 401-455-4046 (cust serv)
E-mail: cust-serv@ams.org; ams@ams.org
Web Site: www.ams.org
Key Personnel
Exec Dir: Dr Catherine A Roberts
Publr: Dr Sergei Gelfand
Assoc Exec Dir: Dr Robert M Harrington
Assoc Exec Dir, Washington, DC: Dr Karen Saxe
Founded: 1888
Print Runs: 100 min - 10,000 max
Branch Office(s)
1527 18 St NW, Washington, DC 20036-1358
    (govt rel & sci policy) *Tel:* 202-588-1100
    Fax: 202-588-1853 *E-mail:* amsdc@ams.org
Mathematical Reviews®, 416 Fourth St, Ann Arbor, MI 48103-4820 (edit) *Tel:* 734-996-5250
    Fax: 734-996-2916 *E-mail:* mathrev@ams.org
Secretary of the AMS - Society Governance, Dept
    of Computer Science, North Carolina State
    University, Box 8206, Raleigh, NC 27695-
    8206 *Tel:* 919-515-7863 *Fax:* 919-515-7896
    E-mail: secretary@ams.org
Membership(s): Society for Scholarly Publishing
    (SSP)

an ICON Company LLC
401 Harper Ave SW, Lenoir, NC 28645
Tel: 828-758-7260 *Fax:* 828-754-6353
E-mail: info@lenoirprinting.com
Web Site: lenoirprinting.com
Key Personnel
Pres: Jeffrey R Chrisman
Turnaround: 8-10 Workdays

Anderberg Innovative Print Solutions
6999 Oxford St, St Louis Park, MN 55426
Tel: 952-848-7300 *Toll Free Tel:* 800-231-9777
    Fax: 952-920-1103
E-mail: sales@anderbergprint.com
Web Site: www.anderbergprint.com
Key Personnel
Owner: Greg Anderberg; Paul Anderberg
Founded: 1971

Angstrom Graphics Print
Division of Angstrom Group
4437 E 49 St, Cleveland, OH 44125
Tel: 216-271-5300 *Toll Free Tel:* 800-634-1262
E-mail: info@angstromgraphics.com
Web Site: www.angstromgraphics.com
Key Personnel
Chmn & CEO: Wayne Angstrom
Mng Dir: Mark Angstrom
Founded: 1918
Branch Office(s)
7060 W State Rd 84, Suite 1, Davie, FL 33317
    Tel: 954-926-5000

Any Laminating Service
13214 Crenshaw Blvd, Gardena, CA 90249
Tel: 310-464-8885 *Toll Free Tel:* 800-400-3105
E-mail: quoterequest@anylam.com
Web Site: anylam.com
Key Personnel
Owner & Pres: Jim Rosenberger

Founded: 1977
Turnaround: 2-3 Workdays
Print Runs: 100 min - 30,000 max
Membership(s): Digital Print Industry Association; PRINTING United Alliance

Apex Die Corp
840 Cherry Lane, San Carlos, CA 94070
Tel: 650-592-6350 *Fax:* 650-592-5315
E-mail: info@apexdie.com
Web Site: www.apexdie.com
Key Personnel
VP, Fin & CFO: Eva Cummings *Tel:* 650-592-6350 ext 231 *E-mail:* ecummings@apexdie.com
Pres & Prod Mgr: Teddee Cullen *Tel:* 650-592-6350 ext 262 *E-mail:* tedcullen@apexdie.com
Founded: 1956
Membership(s): Foil & Specialty Effects Association (FSEA); PRINTING United Alliance

APG Group
235 Homestead Place, Suite 1A, Park Ridge, NJ 07656
Tel: 201-420-8501
Web Site: www.apggroupinc.com
Key Personnel
Owner: Arlene Packles *E-mail:* arlene@apggroupinc.com
Founded: 1994

appatura™, A Broadridge Company
Division of Broadridge Financial Solutions Inc
65 Challenger Rd, Suite 400, Ridgefield Park, NJ 07660
Tel: 201-508-6000 *Toll Free Tel:* 800-277-2155
E-mail: contactus@appatura.com
Web Site: www.appatura.com
Key Personnel
CEO: Richard Plotka
CIO: Faisal Fareed
Chief Prod Offr: Harsh Choudhary
Chief Strategy Offr: John Closson
Head, Fin: Alpha Diarra
Founded: 1949
Print Runs: 1,000 min - 250,000 max

Arbor Books
244 Madison Ave, Box 254, New York, NY 10016
Tel: 212-956-0950 *Toll Free Tel:* 877-822-2500
Fax: 914-401-9385
E-mail: info@arborbooks.com; editorial@arborbooks.net
Web Site: www.arborbooks.com; www.arborservices.co
Key Personnel
Owner: Joel Hochman *Tel:* 877-822-2502 *E-mail:* arborbooksjoel@aol.com; Larry Leichman *Tel:* 877-822-2504 *E-mail:* arborbookslarry@aol.com
Mktg Dir: Olga Vladi
Founded: 1992
Turnaround: 21 Workdays; 1-7 Workdays for art
Print Runs: 1 min - 1,000,000 max

Arbor Services, see Arbor Books

Asia Pacific Offset Inc
1312 "Q" St NW, Suite B, Washington, DC 20009
Tel: 202-462-5436 *Toll Free Tel:* 800-756-4344
Fax: 202-986-4030
Web Site: www.asiapacificoffset.com
Key Personnel
Pres: Andrew Clarke *E-mail:* andrew@asiapacificoffset.com
Founded: 1997
Turnaround: 105 Workdays including color separation & shipping
Print Runs: 2,000 min

Branch Office(s)
870 Market St, Suite 801, San Francisco, CA 94102, Dir, Sales: Amy Armstrong *Tel:* 415-433-3488 *Fax:* 415-433-3489 *E-mail:* amy@asiapacificoffset.com
1768 Oakmont Ct, Ann Arbor, MI 48108, Dir, Sales: Dean Sherman *Tel:* 734-223-6218 *E-mail:* dean@asiapacificoffset.com
62 Rivington St, Suite 2B, New York, NY 10002, Dir, Sales & Mktg: Simona Jansons *Tel:* 212-941-8300 *Fax:* 212-941-9810 *E-mail:* simona@asiapacificoffset.com
16 Clements Dr, Avoca Beach, NSW 2251, Australia, Dir, Sales: Penny Crocker *Tel:* (02) 4382 6174 *E-mail:* penny@asiapacificoffset.com
57 Norfolk St, Ponsonby, Auckland 1021, New Zealand, Consultant: Barbara Nielsen *Tel:* (09) 378-4971 *E-mail:* barbara@asiapacificoffset.com
C/ Tamarit 104, esc D, entrance 2, 08015 Barcelona, Spain, Dir, Sales: Carlos Blavia *Tel:* 933278837 *Fax:* 933254826 *E-mail:* carlos@asiapacificoffset.com
20 Mortlake High St, London SW14 8JN, United Kingdom, Dir, Sales: Adrian Gatheroole *Tel:* (020) 3170 8700 *Fax:* (020) 3170 8704 *E-mail:* adrian@asiapacificoffset.com

Automated Graphic Systems, see AGS

B & Z Printing Inc
1300 E Wakeham Ave, Unit B, Santa Ana, CA 92705
Tel: 714-892-2000
Web Site: www.bandzprinting.com
Key Personnel
Pres: Frank Buono *E-mail:* frank@bandzprinting.com
Founded: 1984
Turnaround: 7-10 Workdays
Print Runs: 3,000 min

Bamboo Ink
807 Oliver Hill Way, Richmond, VA 23219
Mailing Address: PO Box 398, Richmond, VA 23218-0398
Tel: 804-230-4515
E-mail: info@bambooink.com
Web Site: www.bambooink.com
Key Personnel
Owner & Sales: Robert Rhodes *E-mail:* bob@bambooink.com
Cust Serv: Brooke Rhodes *E-mail:* brooke@bambooink.com

Bang Printing Co Inc
Division of CJK Group Inc
3323 Oak St, Brainerd, MN 56401
Tel: 218-829-2877 *Toll Free Tel:* 800-328-0450
Fax: 218-829-7145
E-mail: info@bangprinting.com
Web Site: www.bangprinting.com
Key Personnel
Pres: Todd Vanek *E-mail:* toddv@bangprinting.com
VP, Opers: Joe Saiko *E-mail:* joes@bangprinting.com
VP, Sales: Doug Walters *E-mail:* dougw@bangprinting.com
Founded: 1899
Turnaround: 10-25 Workdays
Print Runs: 1,000 min - 500,000 max

Bedford Printing Co
1501 S Blount St, Raleigh, NC 27603
Mailing Address: PO Box 28617, Raleigh, NC 27611
Tel: 919-832-3973 *Fax:* 919-755-0204
Web Site: www.bedfordprinting.com
Key Personnel
Owner & Pres: Roger L Jones *E-mail:* rjones@bedfordprinting.com

Founded: 1975
Print Runs: 1 min - 1,000,000 max
Membership(s): PICA

Beidel Printing House Inc
Division of White Mane Publishing Co Inc
225 S Fayette St, Shippensburg, PA 17257
Mailing Address: PO Box 708, Shippensburg, PA 17257-0708
Tel: 717-532-5063 *Fax:* 717-532-2502
E-mail: customerservice@dreamprint.com
Web Site: dreamprint.com
Key Personnel
VP & Ed: Harold Collier
VP, Opers: Thomas M Fritz
Founded: 1917

Berryville Graphics
Member of Bertelsmann Printing Group
25 Jack Enders Blvd, Berryville, VA 22611
Tel: 540-955-2750 *Fax:* 540-955-2633
E-mail: info@bvgraphics.com
Web Site: www.bpg-usa.com
Key Personnel
CEO: Christof Ludwig
COO: Jorge Velasco
CFO: Christoph Mittendorf
CTO: Yannic Schroeder
Founded: 1956
Turnaround: 15 Workdays (initial orders); 6 Workdays (reprint orders); 4 Workdays (out of stock)
Print Runs: 1,500 min
Branch Office(s)
100 N Miller St, Fairfield, PA 17320 *Tel:* 414-208-2800
871 Baker St, Martinsburg, VA 25405 *Tel:* 304-267-3600

Bethany Press International Inc
6820 W 115 St, Bloomington, MN 55438
Tel: 952-914-7400 *Toll Free Tel:* 888-717-7400
Fax: 952-914-7410
E-mail: info@bethanypress.com
Web Site: www.bethanypress.com
Key Personnel
Pres & CEO: Pete Larson
Founded: 1997

Bindagraphics Inc
2701 Wilmarco Ave, Baltimore, MD 21223-9922
Tel: 410-362-7200 *Toll Free Tel:* 800-326-0300
Fax: 410-362-7233
E-mail: info@bindagraphics.com
Web Site: www.bindagraphics.com
Key Personnel
Owner & Pres: Matt Anson
Founded: 1974
Turnaround: Same day & longer
Branch Office(s)
Bindagraphics South Inc, 100 N Pendleton S, High Point, NC 27260 *Tel:* 336-431-6200 *Fax:* 410-431-6232
Membership(s): Binding Industries Association (BIA); PRINTING United Alliance

The Bindery Inc
8201 Brooklyn Blvd, Brooklyn Park, MN 55445
Tel: 763-201-2800 *Toll Free Tel:* 800-851-6598
Fax: 763-201-2790
E-mail: info@thebinderymn.com
Web Site: www.thebinderymn.com
Key Personnel
Pres & CEO: Rob Stire *E-mail:* rstire@thebinderymn.com
VP, Opers: Mat Browne *Tel:* 763-201-2723 *E-mail:* mbrowne@thebinderymn.com
VP, Sales: Jim Helmer *Tel:* 763-201-2731 *E-mail:* jhelmer@thebinderymn.com
Founded: 1974
Membership(s): Binding Industries Association (BIA); Epicomm; PRINTING United Alliance

Birmingham Printing & Publishing Inc
3101 Sixth Ave S, Birmingham, AL 35233
Mailing Address: PO Box 131298, Birmingham,
AL 35213-6298
Tel: 205-251-5113 *Toll Free Tel:* 888-276-1192
Fax: 205-251-2222
E-mail: sales@bhamprinting.com
Web Site: bhamprinting.com
Founded: 1910

Blanks Printing & Imaging Inc
2343 N Beckley Ave, Dallas, TX 75208
Tel: 214-741-3905 *Toll Free Tel:* 800-325-7651
E-mail: sales@blanks.com
Web Site: www.blanks.com
Key Personnel
CFO: Doug Heyerdahl *E-mail:* cfo@blanks.com
Pres: Leron Blanks *E-mail:* lblanks@blanks.com
VP: Jeff Blanks *E-mail:* jblanks@blanks.com
VP, Sales & Mktg: Mark Connor
    E-mail: mconnor@blanks.com
Opers Mgr: Jan Thornton *E-mail:* jthornton@
    blanks.com
Founded: 1941

Blitzprint Inc
1235 64 Ave SE, Suite 1, Calgary, AB T2H 2J7,
Canada
Toll Free Tel: 866-479-3248 *Fax:* 403-253-5642
E-mail: books@blitzprint.com
Web Site: www.blitzprint.com
Key Personnel
Pres: Kevin Lanuke
Founded: 1999
Turnaround: 15-20 business days
Print Runs: 25 min - 1,000 max
Membership(s): Association of Book Publishers
    of British Columbia

Blue Note Books, see Blue Note Publications Inc

Blue Note Publications Inc
721 North Dr, Suite D, Melbourne, FL 32934
Tel: 321-799-2583; 321-622-6289
    Toll Free Tel: 800-624-0401 (orders) *Fax:* 321-
    799-1942; 321-622-6830
E-mail: bluenotebooks@gmail.com
Web Site: bluenotepublications.com
Key Personnel
Pres: Paul Maluccio
Founded: 1988
Turnaround: 20 Workdays
Print Runs: 25 min - 10,000 max

Blue Ridge Printing Co
544 Haywood Rd, Asheville, NC 28806
Tel: 828-254-1000 *Toll Free Tel:* 800-633-4298
    Fax: 828-252-6455
E-mail: info@brprinting.com
Web Site: www.brprinting.com
Key Personnel
Pres: Bruce Fowler *Tel:* 828-254-1000 ext 238
    E-mail: bruce_f@brprinting.com
Dir, Sustainability & Sr Buyer: Allen Fowler
    Tel: 828-254-1000 ext 249 *E-mail:* allen_f@
    brprinting.com
Founded: 1974
Turnaround: 10 Workdays
Print Runs: 1,000 min

BookFactory
2302 S Edwin C Moses Blvd, Dayton, OH 45417
Tel: 937-226-7100 *Toll Free Tel:* 877-431-2665
    Fax: 614-388-5635
E-mail: sales@bookfactory.com
Web Site: www.bookfactory.com
Key Personnel
Sales Mgr: Tessin Farmer
Founded: 2002
Turnaround: 20 Workdays after approval
Print Runs: 25 min - 3,000 max

Bookmasters
Division of Baker & Taylor Publisher Services
30 Amberwood Pkwy, Ashland, OH 44805
Tel: 419-281-5100 *Toll Free Tel:* 800-537-6727
    Fax: 419-281-0200
E-mail: info@btpubservices.com
Web Site: www.btpubservices.com
Key Personnel
Dir of Mfg: Brad Sharp *E-mail:* bsharp@
    bookmasters.com
Founded: 1972

BookMobile
5120 Cedar Lake Rd, Minneapolis, MN 55416
Tel: 763-398-0030 *Toll Free Tel:* 844-488-4477
    Fax: 763-398-0198
Web Site: www.bookmobile.com
Key Personnel
Founder & CEO: Don Leeper
Dir, Sales & Mktg: Nicole Baxter *Tel:* 763-398-
    0030 ext 126 *E-mail:* nbaxter@bookmobile.
    com
Founded: 1982
Turnaround: 10 Workdays or less
Print Runs: 25 min - 3,000 max

Bookshelf Bindery Ltd
22 Secord Dr, Unit 16, St Catharines, ON L2N
1K8, Canada
Tel: 905-934-2801
E-mail: bookshelfbindery@bellnet.ca
Key Personnel
Pres: Cam Gregory
Founded: 1914
Turnaround: 15 Workdays
Print Runs: 1 min - 5,000 max

BR Printers
665 Lenfest Rd, San Jose, CA 95133
Tel: 408-278-7711 *Fax:* 408-929-8062
E-mail: info@brprinters.com
Web Site: www.brprinters.com
Key Personnel
Pres: Adam DeMaestri *E-mail:* adam@brprinters.
    com
VP & Chief Strategy Offr: David Gall
SVP, Sales: Derek Giulianelli *Tel:* 303-916-5346
    (cell) *E-mail:* derek@brprinters.com
VP, Fin: Carina Follante
VP, KY Off: Chris Gerhold
Dir, HR: Kathryn Torre
Gen Mgr, CA Off: James Barrios
Founded: 1992
Turnaround: 3-5 Workdays
Print Runs: 1 min - 10,000 max
Branch Office(s)
10154 Toebben Dr, Independence, KY 41051
    Tel: 859-292-1700 *Fax:* 859-292-1710

Bradford & Bigelow Inc
3 Perkins Way, Newburyport, MA 01950-4007
Tel: 978-904-3100
E-mail: sales@bradford-bigelow.com
Web Site: www.bradford-bigelow.com
Key Personnel
CFO: Carmen Frederico
Pres: John Galligan
VP, Sales & Busn Devt: Bob Bradley *Tel:* 978-
    904-3108 *E-mail:* bbradley@bradford-bigelow.
    com
Founded: 1970
Turnaround: 10 Workdays
Print Runs: 50 min - 250,000 max
Membership(s): Book Manufacturers' Institute
    (BMI); PRINTING United Alliance

Bridgeport National Bindery Inc
662 Silver St, Agawam, MA 01001
Mailing Address: PO Box 289, Agawam, MA
    01001-0289
Tel: 413-789-1981 *Toll Free Tel:* 800-223-5083
E-mail: info@bnbindery.com
Web Site: www.bnbindery.com
Key Personnel
Pres: James M Larsen
EVP: Bruce F Jacobsen
VP, Print on Demand Div: Kent Larson
Founded: 1947
Turnaround: 2-5 Workdays
Print Runs: 1 min - 1,000 max
Membership(s): Book Manufacturers' Institute
    (BMI)

The Bureau
Division of The Vomela Companies
2354 English St, Maplewood, MN 55109
Tel: 612-788-1000; 612-432-3516 (sales)
    Toll Free Tel: 800-788-9536 *Fax:* 612-788-7792
E-mail: sales@thebureau.com
Web Site: www.thebureau.com
Key Personnel
Pres & CEO: Mark Auth
VP, Sales & Busn Devt: Tim Dobratz
    E-mail: tim.dobratz@vomela.com
Gen Mgr: John Henderson
Natl Acct Sales Rep: Mike Schreiner

C & C Offset Printing Co USA Inc
Subsidiary of C & C Joint Printing Co (HK) Ltd
70 W 36 St, Unit 10C, New York, NY 10018
Tel: 212-431-4210 *Toll Free Fax:* 866-540-4134
Web Site: www.ccoffset.com
Key Personnel
Dir & EVP, C & C Offset Printing Co (USA)
    Inc & C & C Offset Printing Co (NY) Inc,
    New York, NY: Simon Chan *E-mail:* schan@
    ccoffset.com
Sales Mgr, C & C Offset Printing Co (NY)
    Inc, New York, NY: Frances Harkness
    E-mail: fharkness@ccoffset.com; Timothy Mc-
    Nulty
CEO, C & C Joint Printing Co (HK) Ltd, Hong
    Kong: Jackson Leung
Deputy Gen Mgr, C & C Joint Printing Co (HK)
    Ltd, Hong Kong: Francis Ho; Kit Wong
Dir, C & C Offset Printing Co (France) Ltd:
    Michele Olson Niel *E-mail:* michele@
    candcoffset.fr
Pres, C & C Printing Japan Co Ltd, Tokyo,
    Japan: Yamamoto Masaaki
Dir, C & C Offset Printing Co (UK) Ltd: Tracy
    Broderick *E-mail:* tracy@candcoffset.co.uk
Sales Rep, Australian Off: Lena Frew
    E-mail: lena.frew@candcprinting.com
Founded: 1980
Turnaround: Varies
Print Runs: 2,000 min - 3,000,000 max (average
    book runs: 7,500-50,000)
Branch Office(s)
C & C Offset Printing Co Ltd (Australia Off),
    Lithocraft Graphics, 3-7 Permas Way, Trugan-
    ina, Victoria 3029, Australia *Tel:* (0613) 8366
    0200 *Fax:* (0613) 8366 0299
C & C Joint Printing Co (Beijing) Ltd, Bei-
    jing Economic & Technological Development
    Area (BDA), Donghuan North Rd, No 3, Bei-
    jing 100176, China (plant) *Tel:* (010) 6787
    6655 *Fax:* (010) 6787 8255 *E-mail:* ccbj@
    candcprinting.cn
C & C Joint Printing Co (Guangdong) Ltd, Hua
    Xin Bldg E Block, Rm 1511, 2 Shuiyin Rd,
    Huanshi East, Guangzhou 510075, China
    Tel: (020) 3760 0979; (020) 3760 0980
    Fax: (020) 3760 0977 *E-mail:* guangzhou@
    candcprinting.com
C & C Joint Printing (Shanghai) Co Ltd,
    3333 Cao Ying Rd, Qingpu Industrial
    Zone, Shanghai 201712, China (plant)
    Tel: (021) 5922 6000 *Fax:* (021) 5922 6111
    E-mail: shanghai@candcprinting.com *Web
    Site:* www.candcprinting.com
C & C Joint Printing Co (Guangdong) Ltd,
    Chunhu Industrial Estate, Pinghu, Long
    Gang, Shenzhen 518111, China (plant)

Tel: (0755) 3360 9988 *Fax:* (0755) 3360 9998
E-mail: guangdong@candcprinting.com *Web Site:* www.candcprinting.com
C & C Offset Printing Co (France) Ltd, 15, rue d'Aboukir, 75002 Paris, France *Tel:* 01 40 26 21 07 *Fax:* 01 44 76 08 96
C & C Offset Printing Co Ltd, C & C Bldg, 36 Ting Lai Rd, Tai Po, New Territories, Hong Kong (corp headquarters) *Tel:* 2666 4988 *Fax:* 2666 4938 *E-mail:* info@candcprinting. com *Web Site:* www.candcprinting.com
C & C Printing Japan Co Ltd, Tozaido Bldg, 3F, 2-6-12 Hitotsubashi, Chiyoda-ku, Tokyo 101-0003, Japan *Tel:* (03) 5216 4580 *Fax:* (03) 5216 4610 *E-mail:* mail@candcprinting.co.jp *Web Site:* www.candcprinting.co.jp
C & C Offset Printing Co (UK) Ltd, 75 Newman St, 3rd fl, London W1T 3EN, United Kingdom *Tel:* (020) 7637 5033 *Fax:* (020) 7637 5044 *E-mail:* info@candcoffset.co.uk

C-M Books, see Cushing-Malloy Inc

California Offset Printers Inc
Division of COP Communications
620 W Elk Ave, Glendale, CA 91204
Tel: 818-291-1100 *Toll Free Tel:* 800-280-6446
Fax: 818-291-1192
E-mail: info@copcomms.com
Web Site: www.copprints.com
Key Personnel
Pres & CEO: William Rittwage
E-mail: brittwage@copprints.com
Founded: 1963
Turnaround: 5 Workdays
Print Runs: 10,000 min - 250,000 max
Membership(s): APALA; Epicomm; Printing Industries of Southern California (PIASC); Western Fulfillment Management Association (WFMA); Western Publishing Association (WPA)

Canterbury Press
120 Interstate N Pkwy E, Suite 200, Atlanta, GA 30339
Tel: 770-952-8309 *Fax:* 770-952-4623
E-mail: sales@canterburypress.net
Web Site: canterburypress.net
Key Personnel
Contact: Jim Solmson *E-mail:* jsolmson@ canterburypress.net
Founded: 1950
Membership(s): Printing & Imaging Association of Georgia (PIAG); PRINTING United Alliance

Cenveo Inc
200 First Stamford Place, 2nd fl, Stamford, CT 06902
Tel: 203-595-3000 *Fax:* 203-595-3070
E-mail: info@cenveo.com
Web Site: www.cenveo.com
Key Personnel
CEO: Robert G Burton, Jr
CFO: Mark Hiltwein
Pres: Michael Burton
Founded: 1830
Turnaround: 10 Workdays
Print Runs: 1,500 min - 1,000,000 max

Cenveo St Louis
101 Workman Ct, Eureka, MO 63025
Tel: 314-966-2000 *Toll Free Tel:* 800-800-8845
Fax: 314-966-4725
Web Site: www.cenveo.com

CG Book Printers
Division of Corporate Graphics Commercial (CGC)
1750 Northway Dr, North Mankato, MN 56003

Tel: 507-388-3300 *Toll Free Tel:* 800-729-7575
Fax: 507-386-6350
E-mail: cgbooks@corpgraph.com
Web Site: www.corpgraph.com
Key Personnel
Pres: Dan Kvasnicka *Tel:* 507-386-6340
Fax: 507-344-5548 *E-mail:* dekvasnicka@ corpgraph.com
Sales Exec, Book Mfg Sales: Mike Schmitt
Tel: 507-386-6349 *E-mail:* mjschmitt@ corpgraph.com
Founded: 1989
Print Runs: 50 min - 100,000 max

CJK
3962 Virginia Ave, Cincinnati, OH 45227
Tel: 513-271-6035 *Toll Free Tel:* 800-598-7808
Fax: 513-271-6082
E-mail: info@cjkusa.com
Web Site: www.cjkusa.com
Key Personnel
CEO: Tim Ruppert *E-mail:* truppert@cjkusa.com
Founded: 1872
Turnaround: 10-20 Workdays
Print Runs: 1,000 min - 500,000 max
Sales Office(s): Gulf Coast Sales, Tallahassee, FL
Tel: 850-668-6788 *Fax:* 850-681-6778
Cincinnati (OH) Sales, Contact: Chris Casey
Tel: 513-271-6035 ext 277 *Toll Free Tel:* 800-598-7808 *Fax:* 513-271-6082 *E-mail:* ccasey@ cjkusa.com
Dayton (OH)/Northern OH/Michigan Sales, Contact: Patrick Latham *Tel:* 513-271-6035 ext 241 *Toll Free Tel:* 800-598-7808 *Fax:* 513-271-6082 *E-mail:* platham@cjkusa.com
Tennessee/Carolinas Sales, Morristown, TN, Contact: Bill White *Tel:* 423-748-0201 *Fax:* 423-585-0915 *E-mail:* bwhite@cjkusa.com
Membership(s): PRINTING United Alliance

CJK Print Possibilities, see CJK

Clare Printing
206 S Keystone Ave, Sayre, PA 18840
Tel: 570-888-2244
E-mail: hr@clareprint.com
Web Site: www.clareprint.com
Key Personnel
Pres: Ian Clare
Prodn Mgr: Alicia Blokzyl
Founded: 1903
Print Runs: 50 min - 10,000 max

Clear Print
9025 Fullbright Ave, Chatsworth, CA 91311
Tel: 818-709-1220 *Fax:* 818-709-1320
E-mail: info@clearprint.com; sales@clearprint. com
Web Site: www.clearprint.com
Key Personnel
Pres: Geoffrey Pick *E-mail:* geoff@clearprint.com
Founded: 1980

Coach House Printing
80 bpNichol Lane, Toronto, ON M5S 3J4, Canada
Tel: 416-979-2217 *Toll Free Tel:* 800-367-6360
(outside Toronto) *Fax:* 416-977-1158
E-mail: mail@chbooks.com
Web Site: www.chbooks.com
Key Personnel
Publr: Stan Bevington *E-mail:* stan@chbooks.com
Edit Dir: Alana Wilcox *E-mail:* alana@chbooks. com
Prodn Mgr: John De Jesus *E-mail:* john@ chbooks.com
Founded: 1965
Turnaround: 14 Workdays
Print Runs: 200 min - 2,000 max

Codra Enterprises Inc
17692 Cowan, Suite 200, Irvine, CA 92614
Tel: 949-756-8400 *Toll Free Tel:* 888-992-6372
Fax: 949-756-8484
E-mail: codra@codra.com; sales@codra.com
Web Site: www.codra.com
Key Personnel
Pres: Gary Kim
Sales: Chris Scotti *Tel:* 949-322-5639
E-mail: chris@codra.com
Founded: 1985
Turnaround: 30-40 Workdays
Print Runs: 3,000 min - 3,000,000 max
Membership(s): Independent Publishers Association; Pacific Northwest Booksellers Association (PNBA); Publishers Association of the West (PubWest)

Color Graphic Press Inc
42 Main St, Nyack, NY 10960
Tel: 845-535-3444 *Fax:* 845-535-3446
E-mail: info@cgpny.com
Web Site: www.cgpny.com
Key Personnel
Pres: Paul Rochman
Founded: 1969

Color House Graphics Inc
3505 Eastern Ave SE, Grand Rapids, MI 49508
Toll Free Tel: 800-454-1916 *Fax:* 616-245-5494
Web Site: www.colorhousegraphics.com
Key Personnel
Pres: Steve Landheer
Gen Mgr: Phil Knight *E-mail:* pknight@ colorhousegraphics.com
Founded: 1987
Turnaround: 5-20 Workdays
Print Runs: 1 min - 50,000 max (10-500 digital short-run, 500+ offset)
Membership(s): The Association of Publishers for Special Sales (APSS); Colorado Independent Publishers Association (CIPA); Evangelical Christian Publishers Association (ECPA); Florida Authors & Publishers Association Inc (FAPA); Independent Book Publishers Association (IBPA); Printing Industries of Michigan Inc (PIM); Publishers Association of the West (PubWest)

ColorPage
Division of Tri-State Associated Services Inc
81 Ten Broeck Ave, Kingston, NY 12401
Tel: 845-331-7581 *Toll Free Tel:* 800-836-7581
Fax: 845-331-1571
E-mail: sales@colorpageonline.com
Web Site: www.colorpageonline.com
Key Personnel
Pres & Mktg Strategist/Consultant: Frank J Campagna, II *E-mail:* fcampagna@colorpageonline. com
Acct Mgr & Cont: Kathy Riggins
E-mail: kriggins@colorpageonline.com
Prodn Mgr: Randy Delanoy
Cust Serv Supv: Debbie Downes
E-mail: ddownes@colorpageonline.com
Founded: 1976
Turnaround: 10-15 Workdays
Print Runs: 25 min - 20,000 max

Communicorp Inc
Subsidiary of Aflac Inc
1001 Lockwood Ave, Columbus, GA 31999
Tel: 706-324-1182
E-mail: mktech@communicorp.com
Web Site: www.communicorp.com
Key Personnel
Pres & CEO: Eric Seldon
VP: Mike Thomas
Sr Mgr, Prodn Servs: Jason Lansdon
Sr Mgr, Sales & Mktg Servs: John Shutter *Tel:* 706-763-2912 *E-mail:* jshutter@ communicorp.com

Founded: 1981
Branch Office(s)
100 Galleria Pkwy, Suite 450, Atlanta, GA 30339
Tel: 770-541-4515 *Toll Free Tel:* 800-775-7998

C Harrison Conroy Co Inc
501 Penman St, Charlotte, NC 28203
Tel: 704-358-0459 *Toll Free Tel:* 800-242-2789
Fax: 704-358-0459
E-mail: chcphoto@charrisonconroy.com
Web Site: www.charrisonconroy.com
Key Personnel
Pres: Hal Conroy
Founded: 1936

Consolidated Printers Inc
2630 Eighth St, Berkeley, CA 94710
Tel: 510-495-3113 (sales); 510-843-8565 (admin)
Web Site: www.consoprinters.com
Key Personnel
CEO: Lawrence A Hawkins
Founded: 1952
Turnaround: 2-20 Workdays
Print Runs: 2,000 min - 500,000 max

Continental Web Press Inc
1430 Industrial Dr, Itasca, IL 60143-1858
Tel: 630-773-1903
E-mail: inquiries@continentalweb.com
Web Site: www.continentalweb.com
Key Personnel
Pres & CEO: Diane Field
VP: Ken Field, Sr
VP, Busn Devt: Ken Field, Jr
Founded: 1973

Cookbook Publishers Inc
11633 W 83 Terr, Lenexa, KS 66285
Mailing Address: PO Box 15920, Lenexa, KS 66285-5920
Tel: 913-492-5900 *Toll Free Tel:* 800-227-7282
Fax: 913-492-5947
E-mail: info@cookbookpublishers.com
Web Site: www.cookbookpublishers.com
Key Personnel
Pres: Kevin Naughton
New Busn Devt: Stephanie Jones
Founded: 1947
Turnaround: 30-60 Workdays
Print Runs: 100 min - 50,000 max

Copycats
216 E 45 St, 10th fl, New York, NY 10017
Tel: 212-557-2111 *Toll Free Tel:* 800-404-2679
Fax: 212-557-2039
E-mail: client@copycats.com
Web Site: www.copycats.com
Key Personnel
COO: Robert Stor *E-mail:* rstor@copycats.com
Founded: 1984
Turnaround: 3 Workdays
Print Runs: 1 min - 5,000 max
Membership(s): Epicomm

Coral Graphic Services Inc
Member of Bertelsmann Printing Group
840 S Broadway, Hicksville, NY 11801
Tel: 516-576-2100 *Fax:* 516-576-2168
E-mail: info@coralgraphics.com
Web Site: www.bpg-usa.com
Key Personnel
CEO: Christof Ludwig
COO: Jorge Velasco
CFO: Christoph Mittendorf
CTO: Yannic Schroeder
Founded: 1982
Branch Office(s)
4700 Commerce Crossing Dr, Louisville, KY 40229 *Tel:* 502-962-5466 *Fax:* 502-962-9023

25 Jack Enders Blvd, Berryville, VA 22611
Tel: 540-955-2750 *Fax:* 540-955-9164
Membership(s): Association of the Graphic Arts (AGA); Book Industry Guild of New York; PRINTING United Alliance

Corporate Disk Co
4610 Prime Pkwy, McHenry, IL 60050-7005
Tel: 815-331-6000 *Toll Free Tel:* 800-634-3475
Fax: 815-331-6030
E-mail: info@disk.com
Web Site: www.disk.com
Key Personnel
Owner & VP, Sales: Joe D Foley *Tel:* 815-331-6000 ext 233 *E-mail:* jfoley@disk.com
Founded: 1984
Turnaround: 24 hours-3 weeks

Corporate Graphics Book Printers, see CG Book Printers

The Country Press Inc
One Commercial Dr, Lakeville, MA 02347
Mailing Address: PO Box 489, Middleborough, MA 02346
Tel: 508-947-4485 *Toll Free Tel:* 888-343-2227
Fax: 508-947-8989
E-mail: info@countrypressinc.com
Web Site: www.countrypressprinting.com
Key Personnel
Pres: Mike Pinto
VP & Gen Mgr: George Medeiros
VP, Cust Opers: David Brooks
Founded: 1967
Print Runs: 11 min - 5,000 max

Courier Printing
Division of RR Donnelley
One Courier Place, Smyrna, TN 37167
Tel: 615-355-4000 *Toll Free Tel:* 800-467-0444
Fax: 615-355-4088
Web Site: www.courierprinting.com
Key Personnel
Pres: Michelle Yun
Turnaround: 5-15 Workdays
Print Runs: 2,500 min - 500,000 max

Crane Duplicating Service Inc
4915 Rattlesnake Hammock Rd, Suite 207, Naples, FL 34113
Tel: 305-280-6742 (help desk) *Fax:* 239-732-8415
E-mail: info@craneduplicating.com
Web Site: www.craneduplicating.com
Key Personnel
Pres & CEO: Richard W Price
Mgr, Cust Serv: Jean Fahr
Founded: 1955
Turnaround: 5-7 Workdays; Same day, 3 or 4 Workdays available at extra cost depending upon book
Print Runs: 11 min - 50,000 max

Crown Roll Leaf Inc
91 Illinois Ave, Paterson, NJ 07503
Tel: 973-742-4000 *Toll Free Tel:* 800-631-3831
Fax: 973-742-0219
Web Site: www.crownrollleaf.com
Key Personnel
CEO: George Waitts
Founded: 1971

Cushing-Malloy Inc
1350 N Main St, Ann Arbor, MI 48104-1045
Tel: 734-663-8554 *Fax:* 734-663-5731
Web Site: www.cushing-malloy.com; www.c-mbooks.com
Key Personnel
Chmn of the Bd: Connie M Cushing *E-mail:* ccushing@cushing-malloy.com
VP of Sales: Tedd Litty *E-mail:* tlitty@cushing-malloy.com

Cust Serv/Sales: Adam Hieber *E-mail:* ahieber@cushing-malloy.com
Founded: 1948
Turnaround: 15-30 Workdays
Print Runs: 150 min - 50,000 max
Membership(s): Independent Book Publishers Association (IBPA); Publishers Association of the West (PubWest)

D C Graphics Inc
59 Central Ave, Suite 15, Farmingdale, NY 11735
Tel: 631-777-3100 *Fax:* 631-777-7899
E-mail: prepress@dcgraphicsinc.com
Web Site: www.dcgraphicsinc.com
Key Personnel
Pres: Eugene Prohaske
VP: Christine Brandon
Founded: 1994
Turnaround: 1 Workday
Membership(s): Association of Graphic Solutions Providers

D&K Group Inc
1795 Commerce Dr, Elk Grove Village, IL 60007
Tel: 847-956-0160; 847-956-4757 (tech support)
Toll Free Tel: 800-632-2314 *Fax:* 847-956-8214
E-mail: info@dkgroup.net
Web Site: www.dkgroup.com
Key Personnel
Pres: Karl Singer
VP, Sales & Mktg: Tom Pidgeon *E-mail:* tom.pidgeon@dkgroup.net
Mktg Communs Specialist: Brian Biegel *E-mail:* brian.biegel@dkgroup.net
Founded: 1979

Data Reproductions Corp
4545 Glenmeade Lane, Auburn Hills, MI 48326
Tel: 248-371-3700 *Toll Free Tel:* 800-242-3114
Fax: 248-371-3710
Web Site: datarepro.com
Key Personnel
Pres: Dennis Kavanagh
Gen Mgr: Steve Olko
Acct Mgr: Kimberly Kavanagh *Tel:* 248-881-6518 (cell) *E-mail:* kkavanagh@datarepro.com
Sales Exec: Nick Janosi *Tel:* 734-426-1229 *E-mail:* njanosi@datarepro.com
Founded: 1967
Turnaround: 15 Workdays
Print Runs: 250 min - 100,000 max

Jerilyn Glenn Davis
Cathedral Sta, Box 1712, New York, NY 10025
Tel: 212-889-2239
E-mail: jdavisbook@gmail.com

DeHART's Media Services Inc
6586 Whitbourne Dr, San Jose, CA 95120
Tel: 408-768-1575
Web Site: www.deharts.com
Key Personnel
Pres: Don DeHart *E-mail:* don@deharts.com
Founded: 1972
Turnaround: 7-15 Workdays (short run); 30 Workdays (over 1,000)
Print Runs: 25 min - 10,000 max
Membership(s): Independent Book Publishers Association (IBPA); PRINTING United Alliance

Dekker Bookbinding Inc
2941 Clydon Ave SW, Grand Rapids, MI 49519
Tel: 616-538-5160 *Toll Free Tel:* 800-299-BIND (299-2463)
E-mail: hello@dekkerbook.com
Web Site: www.dekkerbook.com
Key Personnel
Pres: Chris Dekker
VP: Corbin Dekker
Founded: 1928
Turnaround: 14 Workdays

Print Runs: 100 min - 100,000 max
Membership(s): Binding Industries Association (BIA); FSC Forest Stewardship Council; PRINTING United Alliance

Democrat Printing & Lithographing Co
6401 Lindsey Rd, Little Rock, AR 72206
Toll Free Tel: 800-622-2216 *Fax:* 501-907-7953
Web Site: democratprinting.com
Key Personnel
Chmn of the Bd: Frank Parke, III
CEO: Haynes Whitney
Pres: Thomas Whitney
Founded: 1871
Turnaround: 6 Workdays
Print Runs: 10,000 min - 250,000 max

Diecrafters Inc
1349 S 55 Ct, Cicero, IL 60804-1211
Tel: 708-656-3336 *Fax:* 708-656-3386
E-mail: info@diecrafters.com
Web Site: www.diecrafters.com
Key Personnel
Pres: Robert Windler
Founded: 1947

The Dingley Press
119 Lisbon St, Lisbon, ME 04250
Tel: 207-353-4151 *Toll Free Tel:* 800-317-4574
Fax: 207-353-9886
E-mail: info@dingley.com
Web Site: www.dingley.com
Key Personnel
Pres & CEO: Eric Lane *E-mail:* elane@dingley.com
VP, Fin: Neal Poston *E-mail:* nposton@dingley.com
VP, Sales & Mktg: Jim Gibbs *E-mail:* jgibbs@dingley.com
Founded: 1928
Print Runs: 300,000 min - 5,000,000 max

Diversified Printing Services Inc
3425 Cherokee Ave, Columbus, GA 31906
Tel: 706-323-2759 *Toll Free Fax:* 888-410-5502
Web Site: www.1dps.com
Key Personnel
Owner: Brad Wheeler *E-mail:* bw@1dps.com
Founded: 1969
Turnaround: 24 hours

dix! Digital Prepress Inc
8462 Wayfarer Dr, Cicero, NY 13039
Tel: 315-288-5888 *Fax:* 315-288-5898
E-mail: info@dixtype.com
Web Site: www.dixtype.com
Key Personnel
Pres: Scott Wenger *E-mail:* swenger@dixtype.com
Acct Exec, Sales & Mktg: Kelly Farley *E-mail:* kfarley@dixtype.com
Founded: 1923
Turnaround: 2-10 Workdays

DNP America LLC
Subsidiary of Dai Nippon Printing Co Ltd
335 Madison Ave, 3rd fl, New York, NY 10017
Tel: 212-503-1060
E-mail: gps@dnp-g.com
Web Site: www.dnpamerica.com
Key Personnel
VP & Gen Mgr: Norikatsu Nakamura
Founded: 1976
Turnaround: 30-60 Workdays
Branch Office(s)
2099 Gateway Place, Suite 490, San Jose, CA 95110 *Tel:* 408-735-8880
3858 Carson St, Suite 300, Torrance, CA 90503 *Tel:* 310-540-5123

Docunet Corp
2435 Xenium Lane N, Plymouth, MN 55441
Tel: 763-475-9600 *Toll Free Tel:* 800-936-2863
Fax: 763-475-1516
E-mail: print@docunetworks.com
Web Site: www.docunetworks.com
Key Personnel
Partner: Wendy Morical *E-mail:* wnm@docunetworks.com; Brant Nelson
Founded: 1991
Print Runs: 1 min - 5,000 max
Membership(s): Print Industry of Minnesota (PIMN); Women's Business Enterprise Network (WBENC)

RR Donnelley
35 W Wacker Dr, Chicago, IL 60601
Toll Free Tel: 800-742-4455
Web Site: www.rrd.com
Key Personnel
Pres & CEO: Daniel L Knotts
Pres, Busn Servs: John Pecaric
Pres, Mktg Solutions: Doug Ryan
EVP & CFO: Terry D Peterson
EVP & CIO: Ken O'Brien
EVP & Chief HR Offr: Sheila Rutt
EVP & Chief Strategy & Transformation Offr: Elif Sagsen-Ercel
EVP, Gen Coun, Chief Compliance Offr & Corp Secy: Deborah Steiner
EVP, Dom Opers & Chief Supply Chain Offr: Glynn Perry
SVP & Chief Acctg Offr: Michael J Sharp
Founded: 1864
Turnaround: 3-6 Weeks
Print Runs: 3,000 min - 500,000 max
Branch Office(s)
955 Gateway Center Way, San Diego, CA 92102 *Tel:* 619-527-4600
40610 County Center Dr, Temecula, CA 92591 *Tel:* 951-296-2890
151 Red Stone Rd, Manchester, CT 06042 *Tel:* 860-649-5570
9125 Bachman Rd, Orlando, FL 32824 *Tel:* 407-859-2030
5800 Peachtree Rd, Atlanta, GA 30341 *Tel:* 770-458-6351
825 Riverside Pkwy, Suite 300, Austell, GA 30168 *Tel:* 770-948-1330
1750 Wallace Ave, St Charles, IL 60174 *Tel:* 630-313-7000
609 S Kirk Rd, St Charles, IL 60174 *Tel:* 630-762-7600
One Poplar Ave, Thurmont, MD 21788 *Tel:* 301-271-7171
65 Sprague St, Hyde Park, MA 02136 *Tel:* 617-360-2000
18780 W 78 St, Chanhassen, MN 55317 *Tel:* 952-937-9764
5500 12 Ave E, Shakopee, MN 55379 *Tel:* 952-941-7546
6305 Sunset Corporate Dr, Las Vegas, NV 89120 *Tel:* 702-949-8500
5 Henderson Dr, West Caldwell, NJ 07006 *Tel:* 973-882-7000
12301 Vance Davis Dr, Charlotte, NC 28269 *Tel:* 704-949-3568
One Litho Way, Durham, NC 27703 *Tel:* 919-596-3660
3801 Gantz Rd, Grove City, OH 43123 *Tel:* 614-539-5527
700 Nestle Way, Suite 200, Breinigsville, PA 18031 *Tel:* 610-391-3900
9985 Gantry Rd, Philadelphia, PA 19115 *Tel:* 215-671-9500
218 N Braddock Ave, Pittsburgh, PA 15208 *Tel:* 412-241-8200
1210 Key Rd, Columbia, SC 29201 *Tel:* 803-799-9550
1645 W Sam Houston Pkwy N, Houston, TX 77043 *Tel:* 713-468-7175
1550 Lakeway Dr, Suite 600, Lewisville, TX 75057 *Tel:* 972-353-7500

630 W 1000 N, Logan, UT 84321 *Tel:* 435-755-4000
201 E Progress Dr, West Bend, WI 53095 *Tel:* 262-338-6101
Membership(s): Association of American Publishers (AAP); Book Industry Study Group (BISG); Book Manufacturers' Institute (BMI)

W R Draper Co
Division of The Arthur Press (1978) Ltd
162 Norfinch Dr, Toronto, ON M3N 1X6, Canada
Tel: 416-663-6001 *Fax:* 416-663-6043
E-mail: info@arthurpress.com
Web Site: www.arthurpress.com
Key Personnel
Pres: Jeremy Thorn
Founded: 1954
Turnaround: 10 Workdays
Print Runs: 1,000 min - 75,000 max

Drummond
5664 New Peachtree Rd, Atlanta, GA 30341
Tel: 678-597-1050 *Fax:* 678-597-1051
E-mail: info@drummond.com
Web Site: pgc-atl.com
Key Personnel
Pres, Atlanta Div: Gene Hindman

D3Logic Inc
89 Commercial Way, East Providence, RI 02915
Tel: 401-435-4300 *Toll Free Tel:* 844-385-5388
E-mail: contact@d3-inc.com
Web Site: www.d3-inc.com
Key Personnel
Pres: Ralph R Delmonico, Jr
Branch Office(s)
D3 Synergy LLC, 399 River Rd, Hudson, MA 01749 *Tel:* 508-281-7800

Dual Graphics
370 Cliffwood Park, Brea, CA 92821
Tel: 714-990-3700 *Fax:* 714-990-6818
Web Site: www.dualgraphics.com
Key Personnel
Pres & CEO: Jim Joyce
Cont: Jamie Bengard
VP, Opers: Tom Dupuis
Sales Mgr: Craig Evans
Founded: 1906

Dunn & Co Inc
Affiliate of Legacy Publishing Group
75 Green St, Clinton, MA 01510
Mailing Address: PO Box 1185, Clinton, MA 01510
Tel: 978-368-8505 *Fax:* 978-368-7867
E-mail: info@booktrauma.com
Web Site: www.booktrauma.com
Key Personnel
Chmn: David M Dunn
Pres: Peter R Heelan
VP: Rocco Windover
Turnaround: 3-10 Workdays
Print Runs: 100 min

Dupli Envelope & Graphics Corp
6761 Thompson Rd N, Syracuse, NY 13211
Tel: 315-472-1316 *Toll Free Tel:* 800-724-2477
E-mail: sales@duplionline.com; orders@duplionline.com
Web Site: www.duplionline.com
Key Personnel
Pres: J Kemper Matt, Jr *Tel:* 315-234-7241 *E-mail:* kemper@duplionline.com
NY Regl Sales Mgr: Matthew J Oliver *Tel:* 315-234-7246 *E-mail:* moliver@duplionline.com
Founded: 1965
Print Runs: 1,000 min - 1,000,000 max

Branch Office(s)
124 Francis Ave, Newington, CT 06111 *Toll Free Tel:* 800-666-6847
2533 Yellow Springs Rd, Malvern, PA 19355 *Toll Free Tel:* 800-726-7599

Dynamic Graphic Finishing
Member of Bertelsmann Printing Group
945 Horsham Rd, Horsham, PA 19044
Tel: 215-441-8880
E-mail: info@dgfinc.com
Web Site: www.bpg-usa.com
Key Personnel
CEO: Christof Ludwig
COO: Jorge Velasco
CFO: Christoph Mittendorf
CTO: Yannic Schroeder
Founded: 1986
Turnaround: 3 Workdays
Branch Office(s)
c/o Berryville Graphics, 25 Jack Enders Blvd, Berryville, VA 22611 *Tel:* 540-955-2750
Fax: 540-955-9164

Eckhart & Co Inc
4011 W 54 St, Indianapolis, IN 46254
Tel: 317-347-2665 *Toll Free Tel:* 800-443-3791
Fax: 317-347-2666
E-mail: info@eckhartandco.com
Web Site: www.eckhartandco.com
Key Personnel
Pres: Chris Eckhart *Tel:* 317-347-2660
E-mail: chriseckhart@eckhartandco.com
Sales Rep: Mike Reynolds *Tel:* 317-347-2667
E-mail: mikereynolds@eckhartandco.com
Founded: 1918
Turnaround: 10-15 Workdays
Membership(s): Binding Industries Association (BIA); Print Image International

Edison Lithograph & Printing Corp
3725 Tonnelle Ave, North Bergen, NJ 07047-2421
Tel: 201-902-9191 *Fax:* 201-902-0475
E-mail: info@edisonlitho.com
Web Site: www.edisonlitho.com
Key Personnel
COO: Joseph Ostreicher
Founded: 1958

Emprint®
5425 Florida Blvd, Baton Rouge, LA 70806
Tel: 225-923-2550 *Toll Free Tel:* 800-211-8335
Web Site: emprint.com
Key Personnel
CEO: Mr Courtney Westbrook
Pres & COO: Becky Vance *E-mail:* beckyv@emprint.com
Turnaround: 5 Workdays
Print Runs: 2 min - 125,000 max
Branch Office(s)
109 Research Dr, Harahan, LA 70123 *Tel:* 504-733-9654 *Toll Free Tel:* 877-568-1555
Fax: 504-733-8506
151 Southpark Rd, Suite 100, Lafayette, LA 70508 *Tel:* 337-839-9761 *Toll Free Tel:* 888-874-9761
2830 Breard St, Monroe, LA 71201 *Tel:* 318-387-1725 *Toll Free Tel:* 800-256-2259

EP Graphics
Division of Dynamic Resource Group
169 S Jefferson St, Berne, IN 46711
Tel: 260-589-2145 *Toll Free Tel:* 877-589-2145
Fax: 260-589-2810
Web Site: www.epgraphics.com
Key Personnel
CEO: Tyler Kitt
Founded: 1925
Turnaround: 15 Workdays
Print Runs: 25,000 min - 500,000 max

Fairfield Marketing Group Inc
Subsidiary of FMG Inc
The Direct Mail Ctr, 830 Sport Hill Rd, Easton, CT 06112-1241
Tel: 203-261-5585 *Fax:* 203-261-0884
E-mail: info@fairfieldmarketing.com
Web Site: www.fairfieldmarketing.com
Key Personnel
Pres & CEO: Edward P Washchilla, Jr
VP, Cust Serv: Mike Lozada *Tel:* 203-261-5585 ext 204
VP, Fulfillment: Jason Paul Miller *Tel:* 203-261-5585 ext 203 *E-mail:* jason@fairfieldmarketing.com
Founded: 1986
Turnaround: 1-7 Workdays
Print Runs: 2,500 min - 10,000,000 max
Membership(s): American Booksellers Association (ABA); Bridgeport Regional Business Council (BRBC); Education Market Association; United States Chamber of Commerce (USCC)

Fenway Group
870 Commonwealth Ave, Boston, MA 02215
Tel: 617-226-1900 *Fax:* 617-226-1901
E-mail: info@fenwaycommunications.com
Web Site: www.fenway-group.com
Key Personnel
Founder, Pres & Creative Dir: Rick Sands
E-mail: rsands@sandscreativegroup.com
Founded: 1993
Print Runs: 1 min (no max)
Membership(s): Printing Industries of New England (PINE); PRINTING United Alliance

Ferry Associates Inc
49 Fostertown Rd, Medford, NJ 08055
Tel: 609-953-1233 *Toll Free Tel:* 800-257-5258
Fax: 609-953-8637
Web Site: www.ferryassociates.com
Key Personnel
Pres: Kevin Ferry *E-mail:* kferry@ferryassociates.com
Founded: 1982
Turnaround: Standard 2 week delivery
Print Runs: 1,000 min - 10,000,000 max

Filmet Inc
1051 Russellton Rd, Cheswick, PA 15024-1045
Toll Free Tel: 800-255-9000 *Fax:* 724-275-1704
Web Site: www.filmet.com; www.profilmet.com
Key Personnel
Pres: Rick Bachelder *E-mail:* rbachelder@filmet.com
Founded: 1977
Branch Office(s)
103 W Third Ave, Lititz, PA 17543 *Tel:* 717-517-7174

First Choice Copy
5208 Grand Ave, Maspeth, NY 11378
Tel: 718-381-1480 (ext 200) *Toll Free Tel:* 800-222-COPY (222-2679)
Web Site: www.firstchoice-copy.com
Key Personnel
Owner & Pres: Joe Meisner *Tel:* 718-381-1480 ext 212 *E-mail:* jmeisner@nyc.rr.com
Turnaround: 3-5 Workdays

Four Colour Print Group
2410 Frankfort Ave, Louisville, KY 40206
Tel: 502-896-9644 *Fax:* 502-896-9594
E-mail: sales@fourcolour.com
Web Site: www.fourcolour.com
Key Personnel
Pres & CEO: George C Dick *Tel:* 502-896-9644 ext 303 *E-mail:* gdick@fourcolour.com
Prodn Dir: Amy Martin *Tel:* 502-896-9644 ext 315 *E-mail:* amartin@fourcolour.com

Prodn Mgr: Cindy Jones *Tel:* 502-896-9644 ext 310 *E-mail:* cjones@fourcolour.com
Founded: 1985
Turnaround: 90 Workdays
Print Runs: 25 min - 100,000 max (digital printing 25-250 copies; offset printing 250-25,000 copies; web printing 25,000-100,000 copies)
Branch Office(s)
FCI Digital, 2032 S Alex Rd, Suite A, West Carrollton, OH 45449 *Tel:* 931-859-9701
Fax: 931-859-9709 *E-mail:* sales@fcidigital.com *Web Site:* www.fcidigital.com

Frederic Printing
Subsidiary of RR Donnelley
14701 E 38 Ave, Aurora, CO 80011-1215
Tel: 303-371-7990 *Fax:* 303-371-7959
Web Site: www.fredericprinting.com
Key Personnel
Pres: Kurt Hamlin *Tel:* 303-418-6208
Founded: 1878

EST. ◆ 1907
FRIESENS
—— **EMPLOYEE-OWNED** ——

Friesens Corp
One Printers Way, Altona, MB R0G 0B0, Canada
Tel: 204-324-6401 *Fax:* 204-324-1333
E-mail: book_info@friesens.com
Web Site: www.friesens.com
Key Personnel
Pres & CEO: Chad Friesen
Gen Sales Mgr: Doug Symington
E-mail: dougs@friesens.com
Founded: 1907
Friesens is North America's premier book & book packaging manufacturer, providing publishers with quality, all in-house services at our 250,000 sq ft state-of-the-art & eco-friendly book production facility. Friesens customers include Penguin Random House, HarperCollins, Gallup Press, Orca Books, Hachette Publishing (Avalon Travel), Art Institute of Chicago, Smithsonian, DK Publishing, ECW Publishing, & many more. Whatever your book publishing needs, Friesens is committed to ensuring your experience is as satisfying as the products we produce.
Turnaround: 3-4 Weeks
Print Runs: 250 min - 250,000 max (& more)
Membership(s): Book Manufacturers' Institute (BMI); PRINTING United Alliance
See Ad in Complete Book Manufacturing section

Fry Communications Inc
800 W Church Rd, Mechanicsburg, PA 17055
Tel: 717-766-0211 *Toll Free Tel:* 800-334-1429
Fax: 717-691-0341
E-mail: info@frycomm.com
Web Site: www.frycomm.com
Key Personnel
Chmn of the Bd: Henry Fry
CEO: Mike Lukas
CFO: Chris Wawrzyniak
CTO: David S Fry
VP, Sales: Kevin Quinn
Founded: 1934
Turnaround: 7-12 Workdays
Print Runs: 10,000 min - 2,000,000 max

Fuse Graphics
1800 Sandy Plains Pkwy, Suite 124, Marietta, GA 30066

Tel: 770-499-7777 *Fax:* 770-499-7778
E-mail: info@fusegraphicsatlanta.com
Web Site: www.fusegraphicsatlanta.com
Key Personnel
Owner & CEO: Kelly Carlin
Owner & Pres: James J Carlin
Founded: 1988
Turnaround: 5-7 Workdays

G & H Soho Inc
413 Market St, Elmwood Park, NJ 07407
Tel: 201-216-9400 *Fax:* 201-216-1778
E-mail: print@ghsoho.com
Web Site: www.ghsoho.com
Key Personnel
Pres: Gerry Burstein
Prodn Mgr: Jason Burstein
Founded: 1985
Turnaround: 3-40 Workdays
Print Runs: 25 min - 10,000 max
Membership(s): Association of Graphic Communications; Book Industry Guild of New York; Digital Printing Council; PRINTING United Alliance

Garlich Printing Co
525 Rudder Rd, St Louis, MO 63026
Tel: 636-349-8000 *Toll Free Tel:* 844-449-4752
Fax: 636-349-8080
E-mail: customerservice@garlich.com
Web Site: www.garlich.com
Key Personnel
Pres: Brad Garlich *E-mail:* bgarlich@garlich.com
VP, Fin & Admin: Greg Garlich
E-mail: ggarlich@garlich.com
VP, Prodn: Don Hockenbury
E-mail: dhockenbury@garlich.com
Founded: 1928

GHP
475 Heffernan Dr, West Haven, CT 06516
Tel: 203-479-7500 *Fax:* 203-479-7575
Web Site: www.ghpmedia.com
Key Personnel
CEO: John Robinson *E-mail:* john.robinson@ghpmedia.com
Partner: Fred Hoxsie *E-mail:* fred.hoxsie@ghpmedia.com
VP, Sales: Steve Bortner *E-mail:* steve.bortner@ghpmedia.com
Founded: 1991
Turnaround: 5-7 Workdays

Global Interprint Inc
800 Warrington Rd, Santa Rosa, CA 95403
Tel: 707-545-1220 *Fax:* 707-545-1210
Web Site: www.globalinterprint.com
Key Personnel
Gen Mgr: Augusta Cobar *E-mail:* augusta@globalinterprint.com
Founded: 1979

GLS Companies
1280 Energy Park Dr, St Paul, MN 55108-5106
Tel: 651-644-3000 *Toll Free Tel:* 800-655-9405
Web Site: www.glsmn.com
Key Personnel
Chmn: Gary Garner
CFO: Scott Richardson
CTO: Frank Powell
VP, Opers: Steve Kirk
VP, Sales: Todd Matuska
Mktg Dir: Jim Benedict *E-mail:* jim.benedict@glsmn.com
Founded: 1947
Print Runs: 1,000 min
Branch Office(s)
6845 Winnetka Circle, Brooklyn Park, MN 55428-1537 *Tel:* 763-535-7277 *Toll Free Tel:* 888-646-7277 *Fax:* 763-535-7322

Goose River Press
3400 Friendship Rd, Waldoboro, ME 04572-6337
Tel: 207-832-6665
E-mail: gooseriverpress@gmail.com
Web Site: gooseriverpress.com
Key Personnel
Owner & Ed: Deborah J Benner
Founded: 1999
Turnaround: 7-28 Workdays
Print Runs: 50 min - 10,000 max
Membership(s): Maine Writers & Publishers Alliance (MWPA); Waldoboro Business Association

Gorham Printing
3718 Mahoney Dr, Centralia, WA 98531
Tel: 360-623-1323 *Toll Free Tel:* 800-837-0970
E-mail: info@gorhamprinting.com
Web Site: www.gorhamprinting.com
Key Personnel
Owner: Kurt Gorham
Co-Owner: Norma Gorham
Gen Mgr: Garrett Borden
Book Designer: Kathy Campbell
Founded: 1977
Turnaround: 2-3 weeks softbound, 6-7 weeks hardbound
Print Runs: 25 min - 2,000 max
Membership(s): Association of Personal Historians

Graphic Composition Inc
N1246 Technical Dr, Greenville, WI 54942
Tel: 920-757-6977 *Toll Free Tel:* 800-262-8973
Fax: 920-757-9266
E-mail: socialmedia@graphiccomp.com
Web Site: www.graphiccomp.com
Key Personnel
Pres: Mark Jungen
Founded: 1946

Graphic Litho
Division of High Speed Process Printing Corp
130 Shepard St, Lawrence, MA 01843
Tel: 978-683-2766 *Fax:* 978-681-7588
E-mail: sales@graphiclitho.com
Web Site: www.graphiclitho.com
Key Personnel
Pres: Ralph E Wilbur
Founded: 1960
Print Runs: 1,000 min
Membership(s): Print Services & Distribution Association (PSDA); Printing Industries of New England (PINE); PRINTING United Alliance

GraphiColor Corp
Division of Allegra Princeton
3490 N Mill Rd, Vineland, NJ 08360
Tel: 856-691-2507 *Toll Free Tel:* 800-552-2507
Fax: 856-696-3229
Web Site: www.graphicolorcorp.com
Key Personnel
Pres: Robert W Stenger, Jr *Tel:* 856-691-2507 ext 111 *E-mail:* bob@graphicolorcorp.com
Founded: 1919

Great Lakes Bindery Inc
3741 Linden Ave SE, Wyoming, MI 49548
Tel: 616-245-5264 *Fax:* 616-245-5883
E-mail: jeremy@greatlakesbindery.com
Web Site: www.greatlakesbindery.com
Key Personnel
Pres: Steve Landheer
Gen Mgr & Sales Rep: Matt Landheer
E-mail: matt@greatlakesbindery.com
Plant Mgr: Brian Willemstyn
Founded: 1978
Print Runs: (call for information)

HBP Inc
952 Frederick St, Hagerstown, MD 21740

Tel: 301-733-2000 *Toll Free Tel:* 800-638-3508
Fax: 301-733-6586
E-mail: contactus@hbp.com
Web Site: www.hbp.com
Key Personnel
Owner & Pres: John Snyder
VP, Busn Devt & Mktg: Ilene Lerner *Tel:* 703-289-9038 *E-mail:* ilerner@hbp.com
Founded: 1903
Turnaround: 4-7 Workdays
Print Runs: 1 min - 250,000 max
Sales Office(s): 2818 Fallfax Dr, Falls Church, VA 22042 *Tel:* 703-894-3700
Membership(s): CUA; Printing & Graphics Association MidAtlantic (PGAMA); Printing Industries of Virginia (PIVA); PRINTING United Alliance

Heidelberg Graphics
2 Stansbury Ct, Chico, CA 95928
SAN: 211-5654
Tel: 530-342-6582 *Fax:* 530-342-6582
E-mail: heidelberggraphics@gmail.com; service@heidelberggraphics.com
Web Site: www.heidelberggraphics.com
Key Personnel
Owner & Pres: Larry S Jackson
Founded: 1972
Turnaround: 15-60 Workdays
Print Runs: 5 min - 50,000 max

Hennegan Co
Division of RR Donnelley
7455 Empire Dr, Florence, KY 41042
Tel: 859-282-3600 *Fax:* 859-282-3601
Web Site: www.hennegan.com
Founded: 1885

Hess Print Solutions
Division of CJK Group Inc
3765 Sunnybrook Rd, Brimfield, OH 44240
Toll Free Tel: 800-678-1222
E-mail: info@hessprintsolutions.com
Web Site: www.hessprintsolutions.com
Key Personnel
Dir & VP: Burt Phillips
VP, IT: Douglas Holzschuh
Founded: 2006
Membership(s): Book Manufacturers' Institute (BMI)

HF Group LLC
8844 Mayfield Rd, Chesterland, OH 44026
Tel: 440-729-2445; 440-729-9411 (bindery)
E-mail: custservice-oh@hfgroup.com
Web Site: www.hfgroup.com
Key Personnel
CEO: Jay Fairfield *Tel:* 440-729-2445 ext 4 *E-mail:* jayfairfield@hfgroup.com
VP & Gen Mgr: Jim Bratton *E-mail:* jbratton@hfgroup.com
Founded: 1821
Turnaround: 14-28 Workdays
Branch Office(s)
1010 N Sycamore St, North Manchester, IN 46962, Pres: Jim Heckman *Tel:* 260-982-2107 *E-mail:* jheckman@hfgroup.com
92 Cambridge St, Charlestown, MA 02129-0212, VP: John Parisi *Tel:* 617-242-1100 *E-mail:* jparisi@hfgroup.com
340 First St, Utica, NE 68456, Gen Mgr: Damon Osborne *Tel:* 402-534-2261 *E-mail:* dosborne@hfgroup.com
6204 Corporate Park Dr, Browns Summit, NC 27214-9745, Contact: Eric Fairfield *Tel:* 336-931-0800 *E-mail:* efairfield@hfgroup.com
45 N Main St, Unit 528, Hatfield, PA 19440 (transportation hub) *Tel:* 215-855-2293
105 W Thomas St, Atlanta, TX 75551-2736 (transportation hub) *Tel:* 260-982-2107 *Fax:* 260-982-1130

Worth Higgins & Associates Inc

8770 Park Central Dr, Richmond, VA 23227-1146
Tel: 804-264-2304 *Toll Free Tel:* 800-883-7768
Fax: 804-264-5733
E-mail: contact@whaprint.com
Web Site: www.worthhiggins.com
Key Personnel
Pres & COO: Benny Bowman *E-mail:* b.
  bowman@whaprint.com
VP, Sales: Brian Losch *E-mail:* blosch@whaprint.
  com
Dir, Corp Communs: Scott Hudson
  E-mail: shudson@whaprint.com
Founded: 1970
Print Runs: 500 min - 10,000 max

Hignell Book Printing Ltd

Division of Unigraphics Ltd
488 Burnell St, Winnipeg, MB R3G 2B4, Canada
Tel: 204-784-1030 *Toll Free Tel:* 800-304-5553
  Fax: 204-774-4053
E-mail: books@hignell.mb.ca
Web Site: www.hignell.mb.ca
Key Personnel
Pres: Kevin Polley *E-mail:* kevin@unigraphics.
  mb.ca
VP & Gen Mgr: David Morcom *E-mail:* davem@
  unigraphics.mb.ca
Founded: 1908
Turnaround: 15 Workdays
Print Runs: 100 min - 10,000 max

Holmberg Co Inc

4155 Berkshire Lane N, Minneapolis, MN 55446-
  3814
Tel: 763-559-4155 *Toll Free Tel:* 800-328-5101
E-mail: customerservice@holmberg.com
Web Site: www.holmberg.com
Key Personnel
Natl Acct Mgr: Lynnette Hawkinson *Tel:* 800-
  328-5101 ext 2020 *E-mail:* lhawkinson@
  holmberg.com
Founded: 1958

The P A Hutchison Co

400 Penn Ave, Mayfield, PA 18433
SAN: 991-5559
Tel: 570-876-4560 *Toll Free Tel:* 800-USA-PRNT
  (872-7768) *Fax:* 570-876-4561
E-mail: sales@pahutch.com
Web Site: www.pahutch.com
Key Personnel
Pres & CEO: Chris Hutchison
Dir, Sales & Admin: Erin Jones
Founded: 1911
Turnaround: 3-20 Workdays
Print Runs: 10 min - 500,000 max (digital & con-
  ventional)

Imago

110 W 40 St, New York, NY 10018
Tel: 212-921-4411 *Fax:* 212-921-8226
E-mail: sales@imagousa.com
Web Site: www.imagousa.com
Key Personnel
Pres & CEO: Howard Musk *E-mail:* howardm@
  imagogroup.com
Founded: 1985
Turnaround: 5-10 Workdays for color separations;
  4-6 Weeks for printing & binding
Print Runs: 3,000 min
Branch Office(s)
Imago West Coast, 23412 Moulton Pkwy, Suite
  250, Laguna Hills, CA 92653 (sales), Contact:
  Tammy Simms *Tel:* 949-367-1635 *Fax:* 949-
  367-1639
Imago Australia, 10 Help St, Suite 27, Level
  6, Chatswood, NSW 2067, Australia (sales)
  Tel: (04) 3753 3351 (cell); (04) 4806 8704
  (cell) *E-mail:* sales@imagaoaus.com
Imago Brazil, Domiciano Rossi, 340 unid 154,
  09726-121 Sao Bernardo do Campo, Brazil

(sales) *Tel:* (011) 2306 8546; (011) 2306 8547
  E-mail: imagobra@gmail.com
Imago Shenzhen, Rm 2511-2512, Block A,
  United Plaza No 5022, Bin He Rd, Fu
  Tian Centre District, Shenzhen 518033,
  China (prodn), Contact: Kendrick Cheung
  Tel: (0755) 8304 8899 *Fax:* (0755) 8251 4073
  E-mail: enquiries@imago.com.hk
Imago France, 23 rue Lavoisier, 75008 Paris,
  France (sales) *Tel:* 01 45 26 47 74 *Fax:* 01 78
  94 14 44 *E-mail:* sales@imagogroup.com
Imago Services (HK) Ltd, Unit B309, 1/F,
  New East Sun Industrial Bldg, 18 Shing
  Yip St, Kwun Tong, Hong Kong (prodn),
  Contact: Kendrick Cheung *Tel:* 2811 3316
  E-mail: enquiries@imago.com.hk
Imago Productions (Malaysia) Pte Ltd, No
  43, Taman Emas, Jl Utama 31, Telok Pan-
  glima Garang, 42500 Kuala Langot, Selan-
  gor, Malaysia (prodn, incorporating South
  Africa sales) *Tel:* (017) 4288771 (cell)
  E-mail: enquiries@imago.com.sg
Imago Publishing, Albury Ct, Albury Thame,
  Oxon OX9 2LP, United Kingdom (sales),
  Dir: Simon Rosenheim *Tel:* (01844) 337000
  Fax: (01844) 339935 *E-mail:* sales@imago.co.
  uk *Web Site:* imagogroup.com

Impressions Inc

1050 Westgate Dr, St Paul, MN 55114
Tel: 651-646-1050 *Toll Free Tel:* 800-251-4285
  Fax: 651-646-7228
E-mail: info@i-i.com
Web Site: www.i-i.com
Key Personnel
CEO: Mike Jorgensen
VP, Packaging: Dave Bade
Sales & Mktg Mgr: Jenna Hazaert *Tel:* 651-917-
  1394
Founded: 1967
Turnaround: 7-10 Workdays
Branch Office(s)
235 Eastgate Dr SE, Hutchinson, MN 55350
Membership(s): Advertising Federation of Min-
  nesota; Advertising Specialty Institute; Ameri-
  can Marketing Association; Institute of Packag-
  ing Professionals; ISO; Private Label Manufac-
  turers Association

InfinitPrint Solutions Inc

14 N Tenth St, Richmond, IN 47374
Tel: 765-962-1507 *Toll Free Tel:* 800-478-4885
  Fax: 765-962-4997
E-mail: info@infinitprint.com
Web Site: infinitprint.com
Key Personnel
Pres: Michael D Gibbs *E-mail:* mike@infinitprint.
  com
Founded: 1972
Turnaround: 30 Workdays
Print Runs: 50 min - 5,000 max
Branch Office(s)
211 NW Seventh St, Richmond, IN 47374
  Tel: 765-966-7130 *Fax:* 765-966-7131

Infinity Graphics

2277 Science Pkwy, Suite 5, Okemos, MI 48864
Tel: 517-349-4635 *Toll Free Tel:* 800-292-2633
  Fax: 517-349-7608
E-mail: barcode@infinitygraphics.com
Web Site: www.infinitygraphics.com
Key Personnel
Owner & Partner: Brian Perry
Owner, Partner & Bar Code Specialist: Suzette
  Perry
Founded: 1972
Turnaround: 3-4 Weeks
Print Runs: 1 min - 10,000 max
Membership(s): Independent Book Publishers As-
  sociation (IBPA)

Interstate Printing Co

2002 N 16 St, Omaha, NE 68110
Tel: 402-341-8028 *Toll Free Tel:* 800-788-4177
Web Site: www.interstateprinting.com
Founded: 1917
Turnaround: 7 Workdays
Print Runs: 500 min

Ironmark

9040 Junction Dr, Annapolis Junction, MD 20701
Toll Free Tel: 888-775-3737
E-mail: marketing@ironmarkusa.com
Web Site: ironmarkusa.com
Key Personnel
CEO: Scott Hargest *E-mail:* scott@ironmarkusa.
  com; Jeff Ostenso *E-mail:* jeff@ironmarkusa.
  com
Pres: Matt Marzullo *E-mail:* mmarzullo@
  ironmarkusa.com
SVP, Sales: Scott Kravitz *E-mail:* skravitz@
  ironmarkusa.com
VP, Opers: Chris Marzullo *E-mail:* cmarzullo@
  ironmarkusa.com
Sr Sales Exec: Larry Davis *E-mail:* ldavis@
  ironmarkusa.com
Founded: 1955
Turnaround: 20 Workdays, case bound; 10 Work-
  days, paperback; 15 Workdays, mechanically
  bound
Print Runs: 500 min - 500,000 max

ITW Foils

Division of Illinois Tool Works
5 Malcolm Hoyt Dr, Newburyport, MA 01950
Tel: 978-225-8200 *Toll Free Tel:* 800-942-9995
  Fax: 978-462-0831
E-mail: info@itwsf.com
Web Site: www.itwfoils.com
Founded: 1926

JP Graphics Inc

3001 E Venture Dr, Appleton, WI 54911
Tel: 920-733-4483 *Fax:* 920-733-1700
E-mail: support@jpinc.com
Web Site: www.jpinc.com; www.print.jpinc.com
Key Personnel
Pres: Rod Stoffel
Sales Mgr: Randy Hearley
Founded: 1969

Kappa Graphics LLP

Division of Kappa Printing Management Asso-
  ciates LLC (KPMA)
50 Rock St, Hughestown, PA 18640
Tel: 570-655-9681 *Toll Free Tel:* 800-236-4396
  (sales)
E-mail: weborders@kappapma.com
Web Site: www.kappapma.com/kappagraphics;
  kappapuzzles.com
Key Personnel
CEO: Nick Karabots
Pres: Thomas Simunek
Founded: 1906
Print Runs: 30,000 min - 500,000 max

Knepper Press Corp

2251 Sweeney Dr, Clinton, PA 15026
Tel: 724-899-4200 *Fax:* 724-899-1331
Web Site: www.knepperpress.com
Key Personnel
Chmn: Ted Ford *E-mail:* tedford@knepperpress.
  com
CFO: Jerry Sales *E-mail:* jerry.sales@
  knepperpress.com
Cont: Dawn Bates *E-mail:* dawn.bates@
  knepperpress.com
Pres: Bob Hreha *E-mail:* bobhreha@knepperpress.
  com
Founded: 1873
Turnaround: 10-20 Workdays
Print Runs: 500 min - 50,000 max

The C J Krehbiel Company, see CJK

Kromar Printing Ltd
725 Portage Ave, Winnipeg, MB R3G 0M8, Canada
Tel: 204-775-8721 *Fax:* 204-783-8985
E-mail: info@kromar.com
Web Site: www.kromar.com
Key Personnel
CEO: Jack Cohen
COO: Joseph Cohen *E-mail:* josephcohen@kromar.com
Founded: 1945
Turnaround: 15 Workdays
Print Runs: 500 min - 50,000 max
Branch Office(s)
130 Slater St, Ottawa, ON K1P 6E2, Canada
    Tel: 613-563-7577 *Fax:* 613-594-8705
    E-mail: kromar@kromar.com

La Crosse Graphics Inc
3025 East Ave S, La Crosse, WI 54601
Tel: 608-788-2500 *Toll Free Tel:* 800-832-2503
    Fax: 608-788-2660
Web Site: www.lacrossegraphics.com
Key Personnel
Pres: Tim Morgan
VP, Opers: Dianna Clements *Tel:* 608-788-2500 ext 202 *E-mail:* dclements@lacrossegraphics.com
VP, Sales: Heath Tschumper *Tel:* 608-788-2500 ext 203 *E-mail:* htschumper@lacrossegraphics.com
Purchasing Mgr: Shawn Wortman *Tel:* 608-788-2500 ext 206 *E-mail:* swortman@lacrossegraphics.com
Founded: 1987

Labels Inc
10 Merrill Industrial Dr, Hampton, NH 03842
Tel: 603-929-3088 *Toll Free Tel:* 800-852-2357
    Fax: 603-929-7305
E-mail: sales@labelsinc.com
Web Site: www.labelsinc.com
Key Personnel
VP, Sales & Mktg: Chris Snow
Founded: 1975

Lake Book Manufacturing Inc
2085 N Cornell Ave, Melrose Park, IL 60160
Tel: 708-345-7000
E-mail: info@lakebook.com
Web Site: www.lakebook.com
Key Personnel
Pres & COO: Dan Genovese
VP, Fin & CFO: Bob Flatow
VP & Gen Mgr: Bill Richards
VP, Mfg: Steve Quagliato
VP, Opers: Bill Flavin
VP, Sales & Mktg: Nick Vergoth
VP, Technol: Paul Genovese

L+L Printers
6200 Yarrow Dr, Carlsbad, CA 92011
Tel: 760-438-3456; 760-477-0321 *Fax:* 760-929-0853
E-mail: info@llprinters.com
Web Site: www.llprinters.com
Key Personnel
Partner & CEO: Bill Anderson
Partner & Pres, Mktg & Sales: Joel Green
Partner & VP, Sales: Alan Peel; Dirk Williams
COO: Frank Scorzelli
Founded: 1959
Branch Office(s)
8221 Arjons Dr, Suite E, San Diego, CA 92126
    Tel: 858-859-9044 *Fax:* 858-571-7352

The Lane Press Inc
87 Meadowland Dr, South Burlington, VT 05403

Mailing Address: PO Box 130, Burlington, VT 05402
Tel: 802-863-5555 *Toll Free Tel:* 877-300-5933
    Fax: 802-264-1485
E-mail: sales@lanepress.com
Web Site: www.lanepress.com
Key Personnel
Edit Dir: Beth Renaud
Founded: 1904

Lawton Connect
649 Triumph Ct, Orlando, FL 32805
Tel: 407-260-0400 *Toll Free Tel:* 877-330-1900
    Fax: 407-260-1321
E-mail: hello@lawtonconnect.com
Web Site: www.lawtonconnect.com
Key Personnel
Pres & CEO: Kimberly Lawton-Koon
    E-mail: kimberly@lawtonconnect.com
VP: Tyler Koon *E-mail:* ty@lawtonconnect.com
Founded: 1900
Turnaround: 3-5 Workdays

Lee Publications
Division of Stry-Lenkoff Co LLC
1100 W Broadway, Louisville, KY 40203
Mailing Address: PO Box 32120, Louisville, KY 40232-2120
Tel: 502-587-6804 *Toll Free Tel:* 800-626-8247
    Fax: 502-587-6822
E-mail: info@leemagicpen.com
Web Site: www.leemagicpen.com
Key Personnel
CEO: Rick Herndon

Lenoir Printing Solutions, see an ICON Company LLC

Leo Paper USA
Division of Leo Paper Group
1180 NW Maple St, Suite 102, Issaquah, WA 98027
Tel: 425-646-8801 *Fax:* 425-646-8805
E-mail: info@leousa.com
Web Site: www.leopaper.com
Key Personnel
Pres: Behzad Pakzad
Founded: 1982
Turnaround: 40 Workdays
Print Runs: 3,500 min - 2,000,000 max
Branch Office(s)
286 Fifth Ave, 6th fl, New York, NY 10001, Contact: John DiMasi *Tel:* 917-305-0708 *Fax:* 917-305-0709 *E-mail:* info@leousanewyork.com

Letterhead Press Inc (LPI)
16800 W Ryerson Rd, New Berlin, WI 53151
Tel: 262-787-1717 *Fax:* 262-787-1710; 262-787-7315 (estimating)
E-mail: contact@letterhead-press.com
Web Site: www.letterheadpress.com
Key Personnel
Pres: Michael Graf
VP, Sales & Mktg: Dick Reindl *E-mail:* dick@letterhead-press.com
Founded: 1984
Print Runs: 1 min - 10,000,000 max
Membership(s): Foil & Specialty Effects Association (FSEA); Great Lakes Graphics Association (GLGA); PRINTING United Alliance

The Lexington Press Inc
15 Meriam St, Lexington, MA 02420
Mailing Address: PO Box 51, Lexington, MA 02420-0001
Tel: 781-862-8900 *Fax:* 781-861-0375
Web Site: www.lexingtonpress.com
Key Personnel
Pres: Robert F Sacco *E-mail:* bob@lexingtonpress.com

Founded: 1955
Print Runs: 50 min - 1,000 max

Lightning Source LLC
Subsidiary of Ingram Content Group LLC
1246 Heil Quaker Blvd, La Vergne, TN 37086
Tel: 615-793-5000 (Ingram) *Toll Free Tel:* 800-378-5508; 800-509-4156 (cust serv)
E-mail: lsicustomersupport@ingramcontent.com
Web Site: www.ingramcontent.com/publishers/print
Key Personnel
Chief Content Offr: Phil Ollila
CFO: Brian Dauphin
Chief Logistics Offr, Global Opers: John F Secrest
Supv, Content Acq Sales: Bailey Davis
Founded: 1997

Lo Gatto Bookbinding
390 Paterson Ave, East Rutherford, NJ 07073
Tel: 201-438-4344 *Fax:* 201-438-1775
E-mail: bookbindin@aol.com
Web Site: www.logattobookbinding.com
Key Personnel
Contact: Michael Lo Gatto
Founded: 1967
Turnaround: 10 Workdays

Long's Roullet Bookbinders Inc
2800 Monticello Ave, Norfolk, VA 23504
Tel: 757-623-4244 *Fax:* 757-627-1404
E-mail: bindlrbi@gmail.com
Web Site: longs-roullet.com
Key Personnel
Pres: Alain Roullet
VP: Eileen Roullet
Founded: 1975

Mandel Graphic Solution
727 W Glendale Ave, Suite 100, Milwaukee, WI 53209
Tel: 414-271-6970 *Fax:* 414-386-4660
E-mail: info@mandelcompany.com
Web Site: www.mandelcompany.com
Key Personnel
Pres: Rick Mandel *E-mail:* rick.mandel@mandelcompany.com
Founded: 1892

Manroland Inc
Subsidiary of Manroland Sheetfed GmbH
800 E Oak Hill Dr, Westmont, IL 60559
Tel: 630-920-2000
E-mail: info.us@manrolandsheetfed.com
Web Site: manrolandsheetfed.com
Key Personnel
CEO: Sean Springett

Maple Press
480 Willow Springs Lane, York, PA 17406
Mailing Address: PO Box 2695, York, PA 17405-2695
Tel: 717-764-5911 *Toll Free Tel:* 800-999-5911
    Fax: 717-764-4702
E-mail: sales@maplepress.com
Web Site: www.maplepress.com
Key Personnel
Pres: James S Wisotzkey
VP, Opers: Chris Benyovszky
VP, Sales: Bob Bethune
VP, Sales & Mktg: Andrew J Van Sprang
    E-mail: vansprang@maplepress.com
Founded: 1901
Print Runs: 25 min - 200,000 max
Branch Office(s)
92 Rockvale Rd, Tewksbury, MA 01876, VP, Sales: Bob Bethune *Tel:* 978-858-0900
    Fax: 978-858-0920 *E-mail:* bethune@maplepress.com
Membership(s): Book Industry Study Group (BISG); Book Manufacturers' Institute (BMI)

Maps.com
120 Cremona Dr, Suite 260, Santa Barbara, CA 93117
Tel: 805-685-3100 *Toll Free Tel:* 800-430-7532
    Fax: 805-699-7550
E-mail: info@maps.com
Web Site: www.maps.com
Key Personnel
Pres & CEO: John Glanville
Dir, Busn Devt: Eric Sanborn
Dir, Opers: Bryan Wilby
Founded: 1991
Print Runs: 1,000 min (no max)
Membership(s): Association of American Publishers PreK-12 Learning Group; Association of Directory Publishers (ADP); Better Business Bureau (BBB); International Map Industry Association (IMIA); National Council for the Social Studies (NCSS); News Media Alliance; North American Cartography Information Society (NACIS); Yellow Pages Publishers Association (YPPA)

Maracle Inc
1156 King St E, Oshawa, ON L1H 1H8, Canada
Tel: 905-723-3438 *Toll Free Tel:* 800-558-8604
    Fax: 905-723-1759
E-mail: hello@maracleinc.com
Web Site: www.maracleinc.com
Key Personnel
Pres: George Sittlinger *Tel:* 905-723-3438 ext 236
Dir, Opers: Nadene D Aldred
Sales & Busn Devt Mgr: Brian Ostrander *Tel:* 905-723-3438 ext 272
    E-mail: bostrander@maracleinc.com
Founded: 1920
Turnaround: 10 Workdays
Print Runs: 500 min - 500,000 max
Membership(s): Book Manufacturers' Institute (BMI); Canadian Book Manufacturer Association; Canadian Society of Association Executives (CSAE); Ontario Printing & Imaging Association; PRINTING United Alliance

Marquis Book Printing Inc
350, rue des Entrepreneurs, Montmagny, QC G5V 4T1, Canada
Tel: 418-246-5666 *Toll Free Tel:* 855-566-1937; 800-246-2468
E-mail: marquis@marquisbook.com
Web Site: www.marquislivre.com; www.marquisbook.com
Key Personnel
Pres & CEO: Serge Loubier
VP, Sales: Pierre Frechette
Founded: 1937
Turnaround: 5-10 Workdays
Print Runs: 1 min - 1,000,000 max (1/1, 2/2 + 4/4)
Sales Office(s): 2700 rue Rachel E, No 100, Montreal, QC H2H 1S7, Canada *Tel:* 514-954-1131
    Toll Free Tel: 877-594-1364

Marrakech Express Inc
720 Wesley Ave, No 10, Tarpon Springs, FL 34689
Tel: 727-942-2218 *Toll Free Tel:* 800-940-6566
    Fax: 727-937-4758
E-mail: print@marrak.com
Web Site: www.marrak.com
Key Personnel
CEO: Peter Henzell
Prodn Mgr: Steen Sigmund
Sales/Estimator: Shirley Copperman
Founded: 1976
Turnaround: 7-10 Workdays
Print Runs: 500 min - 1,000,000 max

Martin Printing Co Inc
1765 Powdersville Rd, Easley, SC 29642
Mailing Address: PO Box 69, Easley, SC 29641
Toll Free Tel: 888-985-7330 *Fax:* 864-859-8620
E-mail: info@martinprinting.com
Web Site: www.martinprinting.com
Key Personnel
Pres: William Ragsdale
VP, Sales & Mktg: Craig Ragsdale
    E-mail: craig@martinprinting.com
Founded: 1902
Turnaround: 5-7 Workdays
Print Runs: 500 min - 1,000,000 max
Branch Office(s)
1743 Powdersville Rd, Easley, SC 29642 (prodn facility)
Membership(s): PICA

The Master's Press
14550 Midway Rd, Dallas, TX 75244
Tel: 972-387-0046 *Fax:* 972-404-0317
Web Site: www.themasterspress.com
Key Personnel
Pres: Charlene Sims *E-mail:* char@themasterspress.com
Gen Mgr: Aaron Cottle *E-mail:* aaron@themasterspress.com
Founded: 1976
Turnaround: 1-3 Workdays
Print Runs: 25 min - 25,000 max
Membership(s): National Foundation of Independent Businesses (NFIB); Print Image International; PRINTING United Alliance

McClain Printing Co
212 Main St, Parsons, WV 26287-1033
Mailing Address: PO Box 403, Parsons, WV 26287-0403
Tel: 304-478-2881 *Toll Free Tel:* 800-654-7179
    Fax: 304-478-4658
E-mail: mcclain@mcclainprinting.com
Web Site: www.mcclainprinting.com
Key Personnel
Pres: Kenneth E Smith
VP, Publg: Michelle McKinnie
Founded: 1958
Turnaround: 90-120 Workdays
Print Runs: 250 min - 10,000 max

McNaughton & Gunn Inc
Plant: 960 Woodland Dr, Saline, MI 48176
Mailing Address: PO Box 10, Saline, MI 48176-0010
Tel: 734-429-5411 *Toll Free Fax:* 800-677-BOOK (677-2665)
Web Site: www.bookprinters.com
Key Personnel
Pres: Julie McFarland
Exec Dir, Mktg/Sales: Jonnie Bryant
Midwest Regl Sales Mgr: David Hilberer
    Tel: 734-429-8757 *Fax:* 800-677-2665
    E-mail: davidh@mcnaughton-gunn.com
North Central/Greater Chicago Regl Sales
    Mgr: Marc Moore *Tel:* 734-429-8758
    Fax: 800-677-2665 *E-mail:* marcm@mcnaughton-gunn.com
Founded: 1975
McNaughton & Gunn builds lasting client relationships through our customer-focused book printing process. M&G team members will work with you step-by-step to provide flexible solutions & a customizable experience, insuring your satisfaction whether you are a large publisher or a self-publisher. *Creating Books. Making History.*
Print Runs: 24 min - 100,000 max

Branch Office(s)
395 W Napa St, Suite 2, Sonoma, CA 95476,
    West Coast Regl Mgr: Frank Gaynor
    Tel: 707-939-9343 *Fax:* 707-939-9346
    E-mail: fwgaynor@bookprinterswest.com

Moran Printing Inc, see Emprint®

Morris Printing Group Inc
3212 E Hwy 30, Kearney, NE 68847
Mailing Address: PO Box 2110, Kearney, NE 68848-2110
Tel: 308-236-7888 *Toll Free Tel:* 800-650-7888
    Fax: 308-237-0263
Web Site: www.morrisprintinggroup.com
Key Personnel
Owner: Scott Morris
VP, Opers: Ryan Morris
Founded: 1933
Turnaround: 5-15 Workdays
Print Runs: 25 min - 5,000 max

Morris Publishing®
Division of Morris Printing Group Inc
3212 E Hwy 30, Kearney, NE 68847
Mailing Address: PO Box 2110, Kearney, NE 68848-2110
Tel: 308-236-7888 *Toll Free Tel:* 800-650-7888
    Fax: 308-237-0263
E-mail: publish@morrispublishing.com
Web Site: www.morrispublishing.com
Key Personnel
Mgr: Gerald Bergstrom
Founded: 1994
Turnaround: 20-30 Workdays
Print Runs: 25 min - 5,000 max

Multi-Reliure
2112 Ave de la Transmission, Shawinigan, QC G9N 8N8, Canada
Tel: 819-537-6008 *Toll Free Tel:* 888-735-4873
    Fax: 819-537-4598
E-mail: info@multi-reliure.com; administration@multi-reliure.com
Web Site: www.multireliure.com
Key Personnel
Gen Mgr: Yvon Sauvageau *Tel:* 888-735-4873 ext 28 *E-mail:* ysauvageau@multi-reliure.com
Prodn Dir: Patrick Paquet *Tel:* 888-735-4873 ext 22 *E-mail:* ppaquet@multi-reliure.com
Prodn Coord: Sonia Paquet *Tel:* 888-735-4873 ext 23 *E-mail:* spaquet@multi-reliure.com
Admin & HR: Melanie Ethier *Tel:* 888-735-4873 ext 21
Founded: 1988

NAPCO Inc
120 Trojan Ave, Sparta, NC 28675
Mailing Address: PO Box 1029, Sparta, NC 28675-1029
Tel: 336-372-5228 *Toll Free Tel:* 800-854-8621
    Fax: 336-372-8602
E-mail: info@napcousa.com
Web Site: www.napcousa.com
Key Personnel
Cont: Kathy Royal
Pres & CEO: James R Proffit
EVP: Jerry Pearce
Founded: 1977

Nissha USA Inc
Subsidiary of Nissha Co Ltd
1051 Perimeter Dr, Suite 600, Schaumburg, IL 60173
Tel: 847-413-2665 *Fax:* 847-413-4085
Web Site: www.nissha.com
Key Personnel
Chmn: Junya Suzuki
Dir & CEO: Hiroyuki Uenishi
Founded: 1993

Noble Book Press Corp
211 Ditmas Ave, Brooklyn, NY 11218
Tel: 718-435-9321 *Fax:* 718-435-0464
Key Personnel
Pres: Philip B Weinreich *E-mail:* pwnoble@aol.
  com
Founded: 1981
Turnaround: 12-17 Workdays
Print Runs: 500 min - 100,000 max

Offset Paperback Manufacturers Inc
Member of Bertelsmann Printing Group
2211 Memorial Hwy, Dallas, PA 18612
Tel: 570-675-5261 *Fax:* 570-675-8714
Web Site: www.bpg-usa.com
Key Personnel
CEO: Christof Ludwig
COO: Jorge Velasco
CFO: Christoph Mittendorf
CTO: Yannic Schroeder
Founded: 1965
Turnaround: 3 Workdays, digital 24 hrs
Print Runs: 2,500 min

OGM USA
4333 46 St, Suite F2, Sunnyside, NY 11104
Tel: 212-964-2430
Web Site: www.ogm.it
Key Personnel
Chmn, CEO & Sales Rep: Rino Varrasso
  E-mail: rvarrasso@ogm-usa.com
Founded: 1974
Turnaround: 30 Workdays
Print Runs: 75 min - 300,000 max

Omnipress
2600 Anderson St, Madison, WI 53704
Tel: 608-246-2600 *Toll Free Tel:* 800-828-0305
E-mail: justask@omnipress.com
Web Site: www.omnipress.com
Key Personnel
VP, Prodn: Greg Hubbard *Tel:* 608-778-6863
Dir, Mkt Devt: Dan Loomis
Dir, Mktg: Tracy Grzybowski
Dir, Servs: Rob Bossingham
Gen Mgr: Jonny Popp *Tel:* 608-215-9650
Founded: 1977
Turnaround: 5 Workdays
Print Runs: 1 min - 5,000 max

O'Neil Digital Solutions LLC
12655 Beatrice St, Los Angeles, CA 90066
Tel: 310-448-6400
E-mail: sales@oneildata.com
Web Site: www.oneildata.com
Key Personnel
Pres & COO: Terry Chan
EVP, Sales & Mktg: Mark Rosson
Dir, HR: LaDonna Wise
Founded: 1973
Turnaround: 3-10 Workdays
Print Runs: 500 min

OneTouchPoint
1225 Walnut Ridge Dr, Hartland, WI 53029
Tel: 262-369-6000 *Toll Free Tel:* 800-332-2348
  Fax: 262-369-5647
E-mail: info@1touchpoint.com
Web Site: www.1touchpoint.com
Key Personnel
CEO: Dave Holland
Dir, Mktg & Sales Opers: Carey Howard
Founded: 1982
Turnaround: order processing: within 8 hours;
  digital printing: 24-48 hours after proof ap-
  proval; press: 7-10 days after proof approval
Print Runs: 1 min - 500,000 max
Branch Office(s)
5241 Voges Rd, Madison, WI 53718 *Tel:* 608-
838-9147

525 W Alameda Dr, Suite 101, Tempe, AZ
  85282, Contact: James Parker *Tel:* 480-966-
  4003 *Fax:* 480-966-4016
5280 Joliet St, Denver, CO 80239 *Tel:* 303-227-
  1400
1441 Western Ave, Cincinnati, OH 45214
  Tel: 513-421-1600
8410-B Tuscany Way, Austin, TX 78754
  Tel: 512-454-6874

Outskirts Press Inc
10940 S Parker Rd, Suite 515, Parker, CO 80134
Toll Free Tel: 888-OP-BOOKS (672-6657)
  Toll Free Fax: 888-208-8601
E-mail: info@outskirtspress.com
Web Site: www.outskirtspress.com
Key Personnel
CEO: Jeanine Sampson
CFO & CTO: Lynn Sampson
Pres & Chief Mktg Offr: Brent Sampson
Founded: 2003
Turnaround: 35 Workdays
Print Runs: 1 min (no max)

Overseas Printing Corporation
Division of InnerWorkings Inc
4040 Civic Center Dr, Suite 200, San Rafael, CA
  94903
Tel: 415-500-8331 *Fax:* 415-835-9899
Web Site: www.overseasprinting.com
Key Personnel
Sr Prodn Mgr: Shaun Garrett *E-mail:* sgarrett@
  inwk.com
Founded: 1972
Turnaround: 8-12 Weeks
Print Runs: 1,000 min

The Ovid Bell Press Inc
Subsidiary of Walsworth Publishing Co
1201 Bluff St, Fulton, MO 65251
Mailing Address: PO Box 370, Fulton, MO
  65251-0370
Tel: 573-642-2256 *Toll Free Tel:* 800-835-8919
E-mail: sales@ovidbell.com
Web Site: ovidbell.com
Key Personnel
CFO: Jill Custard *E-mail:* jillcustard@ovidbell.
  com
Pres: Troy Williams *Tel:* 573-310-2599
  E-mail: troywilliams@ovidbell.com
VP, Sales & Mktg: David O'Donley *Tel:* 573-
  310-2630 *E-mail:* david@ovidbell.com
Plant Mgr: Kevin Werdehausen *Tel:* 573-310-2598
  E-mail: kevin.werdehausen@ovidbell.com
Founded: 1927
Turnaround: 5 Workdays
Print Runs: 5,000 min - 150,000 max

Pacific Publishing Co Inc
636 Alaska St S, Seattle, WA 98108
Mailing Address: PO Box 80156, Seattle, WA
  98108
Tel: 206-461-1300
E-mail: ppcprint@nwlink.com; ppccirc@nwlink.
  com; ppcbind@nwlink.com
Web Site: pacificpublishingcompany.com
Key Personnel
Pres & CEO: Peter Bernard
Dir, Opers: Richard Fazakerley *Tel:* 206-461-1282
  E-mail: opsmanager@nwlink.com
Dir, Sales & Mktg: Tammy Knaggs *Tel:* 206-461-
  1322 *E-mail:* ppcadmanager@nwlink.com
Gen Mgr: Robert Munford *Tel:* 206-461-1304
Opers Supv: Steve Yip *Tel:* 206-461-1287
Print Runs: 3,000 min - 100,000 max

Panaprint Inc
7979 NE Industrial Blvd, Macon, GA 31216
Tel: 478-788-0676 *Toll Free Tel:* 800-622-0676
  Fax: 478-788-4276
Web Site: www.panaprint.com

Key Personnel
Pres: Wanzie Collins *E-mail:* wcollins@panaprint.
  com
Sales: Byron Prickett *E-mail:* bprickett@
  panaprint.com
Founded: 1973
Turnaround: 10-20 Workdays
Membership(s): Epicomm; PRINTING United
  Alliance

Patterson Printing Co
1550 Territorial Rd, Benton Harbor, MI 49022
Tel: 269-925-2177 *Toll Free Tel:* 800-848-8826
  Fax: 269-925-6057
E-mail: sales@patterson-printing.com
Web Site: www.patterson-printing.com
Key Personnel
Pres: Leroy Patterson
Plant Mgr: Pamela Thames *Tel:* 269-925-2177 ext
  542
Founded: 1956
Print Runs: 250 min

PBM Graphics Inc, an RR Donnelley Co
3700 S Miami Blvd, Durham, NC 27703
Tel: 919-544-6222 *Toll Free Tel:* 800-849-8100
  Fax: 919-544-6695
E-mail: info@pbmgraphics.com
Web Site: pbmgraphics.com

PCA Printing, see Printing Corporation of the
  Americas Inc

Perma Graphics
1356 S Jason St, Denver, CO 80223
Tel: 303-477-2070
E-mail: info@perma-graphics.com
Web Site: www.perma-graphics.com
Key Personnel
Owner: Erin Pfister
Founded: 1974

Pint Size Productions LLC
5745 Main St, Amherst, NY 14221
Tel: 716-204-3353
E-mail: sales@pintsizeproductions.com
Web Site: www.pintsizeproductions.com
Key Personnel
Pres & Creative Dir: Terry Ortolani
  E-mail: tortolani@pintsizeproductions.com
Founded: 2001
Print Runs: 2,500 min (no max)

POD Print
2012 E Northern St, Wichita, KS 67216
Tel: 316-522-5599 *Toll Free Tel:* 800-767-6066
E-mail: info@podprint.com
Web Site: www.podprint.com
Key Personnel
Owner: Grace Rishel; Jim Rishel
Prodn Opers Mgr: Traci Grote *E-mail:* tgrote@
  podprint.com
Founded: 1978
Print Runs: 1 min - 25,000 max (every service
  offered on-demand)
Membership(s): Print Services & Distribution As-
  sociation (PSDA); PRINTING United Alliance

PrairieView Press
625 Seventh St, Gretna, MB R0G 0V0, Canada
Mailing Address: PO Box 460, Gretna, MB R0G
  0V0, Canada
Tel: 204-327-6543 *Toll Free Tel:* 800-477-7377
  Toll Free Fax: 866-480-0253
Web Site: prairieviewpress.com
Key Personnel
Owner & Pres: Chester Goossen
Founded: 1968

Print It Plus
11420 Okeechobee Blvd, Royal Palm Beach, FL 33411
Tel: 561-790-0884 *Fax:* 561-790-9378
E-mail: info@printitplus.com
Web Site: printitplus.com
Key Personnel
Pres & CEO: David Leland *E-mail:* dave@printitplus.com
Mktg Mgr: Kimberly Leland *E-mail:* kim@printitplus.com
Founded: 1988
Membership(s): Florida Graphics Alliance (FGA); Print Image International

The Printer
2810 Cowell Blvd, Davis, CA 95618
Tel: 530-753-2519 *Fax:* 530-753-2528
E-mail: info@the-printer.net
Web Site: the-printer.net
Key Personnel
Owner & Estimator: Howard Galbreath
Founded: 1966
Print Runs: 1 min - 100,000 max
Membership(s): National Foundation of Independent Businesses (NFIB)

Printing Corporation of the Americas Inc
620 SW 12 Ave, Pompano Beach, FL 33069
Tel: 954-781-8100 *Toll Free Tel:* 866-721-1PCA (721-1722)
Web Site: pcaprintingplus.com
Key Personnel
Pres: Buddy Tuchman
Sales Mgr: Steven Konecky *E-mail:* steven@pcaprinting.com
Founded: 1980
Turnaround: 5-10 Workdays
Print Runs: 500 min - 100,000 max

Pro Laminators
1511 Avco Blvd, Sellersburg, IN 47172
Mailing Address: PO Box 274, Sellersburg, IN 47172-0274
Tel: 812-246-0900 *Toll Free Tel:* 800-357-6812
Fax: 812-246-1900
E-mail: customerservice@prolaminators.com
Web Site: prolaminators.com
Key Personnel
Pres: Karen Haywood
Mgr: Jack Haywood *E-mail:* jack@prolaminators.com
Sales: Doug Hamilton *E-mail:* dough@prolaminators.com
Founded: 1984
Membership(s): PRINTING United Alliance

ProductionPro
246 Park St, Bensenville, IL 60106
Tel: 847-696-1600
E-mail: sales@productionpro.com; graphics@productionpro.com
Web Site: www.productionpro.com
Key Personnel
Owner: Douglas Tello *Tel:* 847-696-1600 ext 101
 E-mail: douglas@productionpro.com
Founded: 1992

Progress Printing Plus
2677 Waterlick Rd, Lynchburg, VA 24502
Tel: 434-239-9213 *Toll Free Tel:* 800-572-7804
Fax: 434-832-7573
E-mail: info@progressprintplus.com
Web Site: www.progressprintplus.com
Key Personnel
Pres: Michael Thornton *E-mail:* mthornton@progressprintplus.com
Dir, Busn Devt: Gerald Bowles
 E-mail: gbowles@progressprintplus.com
Founded: 1962

Turnaround: 7-9 Workdays after final proof approval
Print Runs: 5,000 min - 500,000 max

Publishers Book Bindery (NY)
250 W 16 St, 4th fl, New York, NY 10011
Tel: 917-497-2950
Key Personnel
Pres: Ed Goldman
Founded: 1946
Print Runs: 100 min - 50,000 max

Publishers' Graphics LLC
131 Fremont St, Chicago, IL 60185
Tel: 630-221-1850
E-mail: contactpg@pubgraphics.com
Web Site: pubgraphics.com
Key Personnel
Pres: Nick A Lewis *E-mail:* nlewis@pubgraphics.com
VP: Kathleen Lewis *E-mail:* kmlewis@pubgraphics.com
Founded: 1996
Turnaround: 2-8 Workdays
Print Runs: 1 min - 20,000 max
Branch Office(s)
3777 Rider Trail S, St Louis, MO 63045
 Tel: 314-739-3777 *Fax:* 314-739-1436
Sales Office(s): Louisville, KY, VP, Sales: Cara Lahey *Tel:* 630-291-4867 *E-mail:* clahey@pubgraphics.com

Publishing Data Management Inc
39 Broadway, 28th fl, New York, NY 10006
Tel: 212-673-3210 *Fax:* 212-673-3390
E-mail: info@pubdata.com
Web Site: www.pubdata.com
Key Personnel
Pres: Addison Roverano *E-mail:* addison@pubdata.com
Founded: 1970
Turnaround: 1 Hour-3 Workdays

Puritan Press Inc
Division of Puritan Capital
95 Runnells Bridge Rd, Hollis, NH 03049 6565
Tel: 603-889-4500 *Toll Free Tel:* 800-635-6302
Fax: 603-889-6551
E-mail: print@puritancapital.com
Web Site: www.puritanpress.com
Key Personnel
Owner & Pres: Kurt A Peterson *E-mail:* kurt@puritancapital.com
Owner & VP: Michael Ames *E-mail:* michael@puritancapital.com; Jay Stewart *E-mail:* jay@puritancapital.com
Founded: 1976
Turnaround: 21 Workdays
Print Runs: 25 min - 25,000 max
Membership(s): Printing Industries of New England (PINE); PRINTING United Alliance

Quality Bindery Services Inc
501 Amherst St, Buffalo, NY 14207
Tel: 716-883-5185 *Toll Free Tel:* 888-883-1266
Fax: 716-883-1598
E-mail: info@qualitybindery.com
Web Site: www.qualitybindery.com
Key Personnel
Partner: David Borics; Charles Stachowiak, Jr
Pres: Kathleen Hartmans *E-mail:* kathie@qualitybindery.com
Founded: 1993
Turnaround: 1-3 Workdays
Print Runs: 1 min (no max)
Membership(s): Binding Industries Association (BIA); PRINTING United Alliance

Quantum Group
6511 Oakton St, Morton Grove, IL 60053
Tel: 847-967-3600 *Fax:* 847-967-3610

E-mail: info@quantumgroup.com
Web Site: www.quantumgroup.com
Key Personnel
CEO: Cheryl Kahanec
Founded: 1992
Membership(s): Great Lakes Graphics Association (GLGA); PRINTING United Alliance

V G Reed & Sons Inc
1002 S 12 St, Louisville, KY 40210-1302
Toll Free Tel: 800-635-9788 *Fax:* 502-560-0197
Web Site: www.vgreed.com
Key Personnel
Pres: Bobby Reed, Sr
VP, Natl Sales: Scott W Reed
Founded: 1938
Turnaround: 7-10 Workdays

Regal Press
79 Astor Ave, Norwood, MA 02062
Tel: 781-769-3900 *Toll Free Tel:* 800-447-3425
 Fax: 781-769-7361
E-mail: info@regalpress.com
Web Site: www.regalpress.com
Key Personnel
VP, Sales: Mike Simone *E-mail:* msimone@regalpress.com

Reindl Bindery Co Inc
W194 N11381 McCormick Dr, Germantown, WI 53022
Tel: 262-293-1444 *Toll Free Tel:* 800-878-1121
 Fax: 262-293-1445
E-mail: info@reindlbindery.com
Web Site: www.reindlbindery.com
Key Personnel
Pres: David C Reindl *E-mail:* david_reindl@reindlbindery.com
Founded: 1978
Print Runs: 1 min

The Renton Printery Inc
315 S Third St, Renton, WA 98057-2028
Tel: 425-235-1776
E-mail: info@rentonprintery.com
Web Site: www.rentonprintery.com
Key Personnel
Pres & CEO: Richard Sweeney
Founded: 1959
Turnaround: 2-7 Workdays
Print Runs: 1 min

RISO Inc
Subsidiary of RISO Kagaku Corp
10 State St, Suite 201, Woburn, MA 01801-2105
Tel: 978-777-7377 *Toll Free Tel:* 800-942-7476
 (cust support)
Web Site: us.riso.com
Key Personnel
Pres & CEO: Koji Sonobe
VP & CFO: Alex Olshan
VP, Corp Planning: Sho Fujiwara
Founded: 1986

Ross Gage Inc
8502 Brookville Rd, Indianapolis, IN 46239
Tel: 317-283-2323 *Toll Free Tel:* 800-799-2323
 Fax: 317-931-2108
E-mail: info@rossgage.com
Web Site: www.rossgage.com
Key Personnel
Pres: Thomas W Ross *E-mail:* tomross@rossgage.com
VP: Bill Main *E-mail:* bmain@rossgage.com
Opers Coord/Cust Serv: Carol Eads
 E-mail: ceads@rossgage.com
Founded: 1973

Roswell Bookbinding
2614 N 29 Ave, Phoenix, AZ 85009

Tel: 602-272-9338 *Toll Free Tel:* 888-803-8883
  Fax: 602-272-9786
Web Site: www.roswellbookbinding.com
Key Personnel
Pres: Michael Roswell
Trade Div Cust Serv Dir: Jim Menke
Specialty Div Mgr: Kortez Brown
Trade Prodn Mgr: Bryan Way
Specialty Div Estimating: Steve Jones
Trade Div Estimating: Nancy Scherba
Founded: 1960
Turnaround: 20 Workdays
Print Runs: 1 min - 1,000,000 max

St Joseph Communications-Print Group
50 Macintosh Blvd, Concord, ON L4K 4P3,
  Canada
Tel: 905-660-3111
E-mail: marketing@stjoseph.com
Web Site: stjoseph.com
Key Personnel
Pres: John Gagliano
EVP, Sales & Mktg: Ray D'Antonio
VP & Gen Mgr: Ryan Anderson
Branch Office(s)
119 Snow Blvd, Concord, ON L4K 4N9, Canada
  Tel: 905-695-8544
1165 Kenaston St, Ottawa, ON K1G 6S1, Canada
  Tel: 613-729-4303

Scientific Bindery Inc
8052 Monticello Ave, Suite 206, Skokie, IL
  60076
Mailing Address: PO Box 377, Highland Park, IL
  60035-6377
Tel: 847-329-0510 *Fax:* 847-329-0608
E-mail: info@scientificbindery.com
Web Site: www.scientificbindery.com
Key Personnel
Owner & Pres: Diane Czerwinski
Founded: 1912
Turnaround: 14-28 Workdays
Print Runs: 50 min - 15,000 max

Shepherd Inc
2223 Key Way Dr, Suite B, Dubuque, IA 52002
Tel: 563-584-0500
Web Site: www.shepherd-inc.com
Key Personnel
Prodn Mgr: Deb Leibfried
Founded: 1989

Sheridan GR
Division of CJK Group Inc
5100 33 St SE, Grand Rapids, MI 49512
Tel: 616-957-5100
Web Site: www.sheridan.com
Key Personnel
VP, Sales: Joe Thomson *E-mail:* joe.thomson@
  sheridan.com
Cust Serv Mgr: Tanya Eldred *E-mail:* tanya.
  eldred@sheridan.com
Estimating & Purch Mgr: Steve DeWeerd
  E-mail: steve.deweerd@sheridan.com
Plant Mgr: Jason Nelson *E-mail:* jason.nelson@
  sheridan.com
Founded: 1884
Turnaround: 2-5 Workdays
Print Runs: 1 min - 100,000 max

Sheridan MI
Division of CJK Group Inc
613 E Industrial Dr, Chelsea, MI 48118
Tel: 734-475-9145
Web Site: www.sheridan.com
Key Personnel
Pres: Paul Bozuwa *E-mail:* paul.bozuwa@
  sheridan.com
VP, Book Sales: Joe Thomson *E-mail:* joe.
  thomson@sheridan.com

VP, Fin: Nicole Mummert *E-mail:* nicole.
  mummert@sheridan.com
VP, HR: Ken Rapp *E-mail:* ken.rapp@sheridan.
  com
VP, Opers: Paul Loy *E-mail:* paul.loy@sheridan.
  com
Cust Serv Mgr: Ed Blissick *E-mail:* ed.blissick@
  sheridan.com
Direct Sales Rep: Jessica Ansorge *Tel:* 734-
  385-1544 *E-mail:* jessica.ansorge@sheridan.
  com; Kathy Brown *Tel:* 734-385-1540
  E-mail: kathy.brown@sheridan.com; Rebecca
  Humrich *Tel:* 734-385-1543 *E-mail:* rebecca.
  humrich@sheridan.com; Jennifer Riemen-
  schneider *Tel:* 734-385-1533 *E-mail:* jennifer.
  riemenschneider@sheridan.com
Founded: 1950

Sheridan NH
Division of CJK Group Inc
69 Lyme Rd, Hanover, NH 03755
Tel: 603-643-2220
Web Site: www.sheridan.com
Key Personnel
Pres: Paul Bozuwa *E-mail:* paul.bozuwa@
  sheridan.com
VP, Fin: Nicole Mummert *E-mail:* nicole.
  mummert@sheridan.com
VP, HR: Ken Rapp *E-mail:* ken.rapp@sheridan.
  com
VP, Opers: Paul Loy *E-mail:* paul.loy@sheridan.
  com
VP, Sales: Mike Klauer *E-mail:* mike.klauer@
  sheridan.com
Founded: 1843 (as The Dartmouth Press)
Print Runs: 5,000 min - 100,000 max (average
  press run: 20,000)
Membership(s): PRINTING United Alliance

Sheridan PA
Division of CJK Group Inc
450 Fame Ave, Hanover, PA 17331
Tel: 717-632-3535 *Toll Free Tel:* 800-352-2210
  Fax: 717-633-8900
Web Site: www.sheridan.com
Key Personnel
Pres: Paul Bozuwa *E-mail:* paul.bozuwa@
  sheridan.com
VP, Fin: Nicole Mummert *E-mail:* nicole.
  mummert@sheridan.com
VP, Opers: Paul Loy *E-mail:* paul.loy@sheridan.
  com
VP, Sales: Michael Klauer *E-mail:* mike.klauer@
  sheridan.com
Dir, Cust Serv: Ed Blissick *E-mail:* ed.blissick@
  sheridan.com
Technol Dir: Eric Biggins *E-mail:* eric.biggins@
  sheridan.com
Mgr, Sheridan Content Solutions: Amy Schriver
  E-mail: amy.schriver@sheridan.com
Founded: 1915
Turnaround: 7-10 Workdays
Print Runs: 1 min - 15,000 max (1 is for Digital
  Print on Demand Printing)
Membership(s): International Printers' Network
  (IPN)

Signature Book Printing Inc
8041 Cessna Ave, Gaithersburg, MD 20879
Tel: 301-258-8353 *Fax:* 301-670-4147
E-mail: book@sbpbooks.com
Web Site: sbpbooks.com
Key Personnel
Pres: Phil Nanzetta
Off Mgr: Linda Wood
Founded: 1986
We produce hard cover & soft cover, full color
& B&W books of (virtually) any type, in-
cluding children's, coffee table, travel &
cookbooks. Everything is produced by off-
set lithography. We print runs from 500 to
20,000 copies & can do as few as 500 copies

competitively for hard cover & full color
books. We are nationally recognized for
excellent quality, top value & smooth, easy
customer service.
Visit our web site at sbpbooks.com for extensive information on book printing & for a
large range of examples of our work. For
pricing, visit sbpbooks.com or call us at 301-
258-8353.
Print Runs: 500 min - 20,000 max

Signature Print Services
3565 Sierra Rd, San Jose, CA 95132
Mailing Address: PO Box 32464, San Jose, CA
  95152-2464
Tel: 408-213-3393 *Fax:* 408-213-3399
Web Site: www.signatureprint.com
Key Personnel
Pres & CEO: Meifang Xu
Secy & Dir: Peter B Martin
Print Runs: 10 min - 25,000 max

Smith & Sons Printers Inc
6403 Rutledge Pike, Knoxville, TN 37924
Tel: 865-523-1419
Web Site: www.ssprintinc.com
Key Personnel
Owner: Stephen Ownby *E-mail:* stephen@ssprint.
  com
Founded: 1979
Print Runs: 250 min - 100,000 max

Smith-Edwards-Dunlap Co
2867 E Allegheny Ave, Philadelphia, PA 19134
Tel: 215-425-8800 *Toll Free Tel:* 800-829-0020
  Fax: 215-425-9715
E-mail: sales@sed.com
Web Site: www.sed.com
Key Personnel
Pres: Jonathan Shapiro
Sales Mgr: Fred Binder
Founded: 1880

Southeastern Printing Co
3601 SE Dixie Hwy, Stuart, FL 34997
Tel: 772-287-2141 *Toll Free Tel:* 800-226-8221
  Fax: 772-288-3988
E-mail: sales@seprint.com
Web Site: www.seprint.com
Key Personnel
Pres: Don Mader
Founded: 1924
Turnaround: 20-40 Workdays
Print Runs: 5,000 min - 100,000 max
Branch Office(s)
950 SE Eighth St, Hialeah, FL 33010 *Tel:* 305-
  885-8707 *Fax:* 305-888-9903 *E-mail:* info@
  seprint.com
Sales Office(s): 6001 Park of Commerce Blvd,
  Suite 200, Boca Raton, FL 33487 *Tel:* 561-
  998-0870

Specialty Finishing Group
1401 Kirk St, Elk Grove Village, IL 60007
Tel: 847-290-0110 *Fax:* 847-290-9404
Web Site: www.sfgrp.com
Key Personnel
Pres: Jim Gallo
Gen Mgr: Jamie Morris *E-mail:* jmorris@sfgrp.
  com
Founded: 1981
Membership(s): Chicago Association of Direct
  Marketing (CADM); Print Image International;
  PRINTING United Alliance

Spectrum PrintGroup Inc
1535 Farmer's Lane, Suite 254, Santa Rosa, CA
  95405
Tel: 707-542-6044 *Toll Free Tel:* 888-340-6049
  Fax: 707-542-6045
E-mail: sales@spectrumprintgroup.com
Web Site: www.spectrumprintgroup.com

Key Personnel
Pres: Duncan McCallum *Tel:* 707-542-6044 ext 102 *E-mail:* duncan@spectrumprintgroup.com
Busn Devt Mgr: Elise Gochberg *Tel:* 415-461-1130 *E-mail:* elise@spectrumprintgroup.com
Founded: 1985
Print Runs: 500 min - 100,000 max

Spiral Binding LLC
One Maltese Dr, Totowa, NJ 07511
Mailing Address: PO Box 286, Totowa, NJ 07511
Tel: 973-256-0666 *Toll Free Tel:* 800-631-3572
Fax: 973-256-5981
E-mail: customerservice@spiralbinding.com; international@spiralbinding.com (outside US)
Web Site: spiralbinding.com
Key Personnel
CEO: Robert Roth
Pres: Douglas Nash
Founded: 1932
Turnaround: 2-10 Workdays
Print Runs: 100 min
Branch Office(s)
431 Calle San Pablo, Camarillo, CA 93012
Tel: 805-482-9100 *Toll Free Fax:* 800-215-2463
835 Bonnie Lane, Elk Grove Village, IL 60007
Tel: 847-437-3700 *Fax:* 847-437-4155
253 N Grand Ave, Poughkeepsie, NY 12603
Tel: 845-471-3408
9200 Waterford Centre Blvd, Suite 550, Austin, TX 78758 *Tel:* 512-832-7902 *Fax:* 512-832-7982
Membership(s): Binding Industries Association (BIA); Digital Solutions Cooperative (Dscoop); New Jersey Business & Industry Association (NJBIA); Printing Industries Alliance; PRINTING United Alliance

Springdale Bindery LLC
11411 Landan Lane, Cincinnati, OH 45246
Tel: 513-772-8500
E-mail: info@springdalebindery.com
Web Site: www.springdalebindery.com
Key Personnel
Pres: Steve DeHamer
Membership(s): National Foundation of Independent Businesses (NFIB); PRINTING United Alliance

Stephenson Printing
5731 General Washington Dr, Alexandria, VA 22312
Tel: 703-642-9000 *Toll Free Tel:* 800-336-4637
Fax: 703-354-0384
Web Site: www.stephensonprinting.com
Key Personnel
Pres: George W Stephenson
VP: Sandy Stephenson

Sterling Pierce Co Inc
395 Atlantic Ave, East Rockaway, NY 11518
Tel: 516-593-1170 *Fax:* 516-593-1401
Web Site: www.sterlingpierce.com
Key Personnel
Owner & Pres: William Burke
Mgr: Steven Cieslicki *E-mail:* scieslicki@sterlingpierce.com
Founded: 1980
Turnaround: 5-7 Workdays
Print Runs: 5 min - 5,000 max

The Studley Press Inc
151 E Housatonic St, Dalton, MA 01226
Mailing Address: PO Box 214, Dalton, MA 01227-0214
Tel: 413-684-0441 *Toll Free Tel:* 877-684-0441
Fax: 413-684-0220
Web Site: thestudleypress.com
Key Personnel
Owner: Suzanne K Salinetti *E-mail:* suzanne@thestudleypress.com

Founded: 1938
Print Runs: 100 min - 25,000 max

Styled Packaging LLC
PO Box 30299, Philadelphia, PA 19103-8299
Tel: 610-529-4122 *Fax:* 610-520-9662
Web Site: www.taylorbox.com
Key Personnel
Pres: William R Fenkel *E-mail:* jjibill@aol.com
Founded: 2003
Membership(s): Book Industry Guild of New York

Sun Graphics LLC
1818 Broadway, Parsons, KS 67357
Toll Free Tel: 800-835-0588 *Fax:* 620-421-2089
E-mail: info@sun-graphics.com
Web Site: www.sun-graphics.com
Key Personnel
VP, Mktg: John Hammett *Tel:* 918-695-2267
E-mail: jhammett@sun-graphics.com
VP, Sales: John Hohenshell *Tel:* 913-257-9420
E-mail: jhohenshell@sun-graphics.com
Commercial Sales & Book Div Sales: Melody Morris *Tel:* 620-660-0614 *E-mail:* mmorris@sun-graphics.com
Founded: 1998
Turnaround: 15-20 Workdays
Print Runs: 250 min - 100,000 max
Membership(s): Independent Book Publishers Association (IBPA); Publishers Association of the West (PubWest)

John S Swift Co Inc
999 Commerce Ct, Buffalo Grove, IL 60089
Tel: 847-465-3300 *Fax:* 847-465-3309
Web Site: www.johnswiftprint.com
Key Personnel
Pres: John S Swift *E-mail:* jss@johnswiftprint.com
Founded: 1912
Turnaround: 5 Workdays & up
Branch Office(s)
John S Swift Print of NJ Inc, 375 North St, Unit N, Teterboro, NJ 07608, Contact: Rick Frydrych *Tel:* 201-678-3232 *Fax:* 201-678-3001 *E-mail:* rickfry@johnswiftprint.com

Taylor Communications Inc
Subsidiary of Taylor Corp
1725 Roe Crest Dr, North Mankato, MN 56003
Toll Free Tel: 866-541-0937
Web Site: www.taylorcommunications.com
Key Personnel
CEO: Glen Taylor

Taylor Specialty Books
Division of Balfour/Taylor
1550 W Mockingbird Lane, Dallas, TX 75235
Tel: 214-819-8588 (cust serv) *Fax:* 214-819-5051 (cust serv) *Toll Free Fax:* 800-203-9778
E-mail: rfq@taylorpub.com (estimates)
Web Site: www.taylorspecialtybooks.com
Key Personnel
VP, Sales & Mktg, Specialty Books: Rick Parra *Tel:* 214-819-5027 *E-mail:* rick.parra@balfour.com
Sales Rep: Kim Hawley *E-mail:* khawley@taylorpub.com; George Levesque *E-mail:* glevesque@taylorpub.com; Mark McCombs *E-mail:* mmcombs@taylorpub.com
Founded: 1939
Turnaround: 25-30 Workdays
Print Runs: 250 min - 25,000 max

Thistle Printing Ltd
Division of DATA Communications Management Corp
35 Mobile Dr, Toronto, ON M4A 2P6, Canada
Tel: 416-288-1288 *Fax:* 416-288-0737
E-mail: sales@thistleprinting.com

Web Site: www.thistleprinting.com
Key Personnel
Gen Mgr: Mike Branov
Founded: 1931

Times Printing LLC
Division of Kappa Printing Management Associates LLC (KPMA)
100 Industrial Dr, Random Lake, WI 53075
Tel: 920-994-4396 *Toll Free Tel:* 800-236-4396 (sales)
E-mail: info@kappapma.com
Web Site: www.kappapma.com
Founded: 1918
Turnaround: 5-10 Workdays
Print Runs: 5,000 min - 250,000 max

Toof American Digital
4222 Pilot Dr, Memphis, TN 38118
Tel: 901-274-3632 *Toll Free Tel:* 800-722-4772
Web Site: www.toofamericandigital.com
Key Personnel
Pres: Stillman McFadden
Founded: 1864
Turnaround: 80 Workdays
Print Runs: 2,000 min - 500,000 max

TOP Engraving
106 Windsor Way, Berkeley Heights, NJ 07922
Tel: 212-239-9170; 201-223-4800
Key Personnel
Pres: Shane Levin *E-mail:* shane@hapengraving.com
Founded: 1934
Turnaround: 5-7 Workdays

Total Printing Systems
Division of TPS Enterprises Inc
201 S Gregory Dr, Newton, IL 62448
Mailing Address: PO Box 375, Newton, IL 62448-0365
Tel: 618-783-2978 *Toll Free Tel:* 800-465-5200
Fax: 618-783-8407
E-mail: sales@tps1.com
Web Site: www.tps1.com
Key Personnel
Pres: Rick Lindemann *Tel:* 800-465-5200 ext 346
E-mail: rick@tps1.com
Inside Sales: Darrin Sappenfield *Tel:* 800-465-5200 ext 325 *E-mail:* darrin@tps1.com
Dist Contact: Brenda Ochs *Tel:* 618-783-2219
E-mail: brenda@tps1.com
Founded: 1973
Turnaround: 3-10 Workdays
Print Runs: 1 min - 50,000 max (1-200 print-on-demand)
Branch Office(s)
204 E Morgan St, Newton, IL 62448
Membership(s): American Association of University Presses (AAUP); Evangelical Christian Publishers Association (ECPA); Independent Book Publishers Association (IBPA); Midwest Independent Publishing Association (MIPA); Print Services & Distribution Association (PSDA)

TotalWorks™ Inc
420 W Huron St, Chicago, IL 60654
Tel: 773-489-4313
E-mail: production@totalworks.net
Web Site: www.totalworks.net
Key Personnel
Principal, Pres & CEO: Gail Ludewig
Principal & EVP: Bruce Jensen
VP, Sales & Mktg: Louise Pauly
Founded: 1927
Membership(s): Women's Business Enterprise Network (WBENC)

Townsend Communications Inc
20 E Gregory Blvd, Kansas City, MO 64114
Tel: 816-361-0616

Web Site: www.townsendcommunications.com;
www.townsendprint.com
Key Personnel
Pres: Guy Townsend, III
VP: Joe Chambers
Founded: 1964

Trend Offset Printing Services
3791 Catalina St, Los Alamitos, CA 90720
Tel: 562-598-2446 *Fax:* 562-493-6840 (sales);
562-430-2373
E-mail: salesca@trendoffset.com
Web Site: www.trendoffset.com
Key Personnel
Owner: Anthony Lienau; Robert Lienau, Jr
CEO: Todd Nelson
Founded: 1986

Tribal Print Source
Division of Southern California Tribal Chairman's
Association
36146 Pala Temecula Rd, Bldg J, Pala, CA 92059
Mailing Address: 35008 Pala Temecula Rd, PMB
436, Pala, CA 92059
Tel: 760-597-2650
E-mail: sales@tribalprintsource.com
Web Site: www.tribalprintsource.com
Founded: 2003

TSO General Corp
79 Emjay Blvd, Brentwood, NY 11717
Tel: 631-952-5320 *Fax:* 631-952-5315
Web Site: www.tsogeneral.com
Key Personnel
Pres: Kirk Malandrakis *E-mail:* kmalan@
tsogeneral.com
Founded: 1969
Turnaround: 5 Workdays
Print Runs: 100,000 min

Tukaiz LLC
2917 N Latoria Lane, Franklin Park, IL 60131
Tel: 847-455-1588; 847-288-4968 (sales)
Toll Free Tel: 800-543-2674
E-mail: contacttukaiz@tukaiz.com
Web Site: www.tukaiz.com
Key Personnel
Founder & Mng Dir: Frank Defino, Sr
VP, Mng Dir & CFO: Christopher Calabra
VP & Mng Dir: Daniel Defino; Frank Defino, Jr
Founded: 1963

Turtleback Books
Division of Perfection Learning
1000 N Second Ave, Logan, IA 51546-0500
Toll Free Tel: 800-831-4190 *Toll Free Fax:* 800-
543-2745
E-mail: turtleback@perfectionlearning.com
Web Site: turtleback.perfectionlearning.com
Founded: 1961
Turnaround: 30 Workdays

Universal Bookbindery Inc
1200 N Colorado, San Antonio, TX 78207
Mailing Address: PO Box 7849, San Antonio, TX
78207
Tel: 210-734-9502 *Toll Free Tel:* 800-594-2015
Fax: 210-736-0867
E-mail: service@universalbookbindery.com
Web Site: www.universalbookbindery.com
Key Personnel
Cont: Cordell Reinhard *E-mail:* creinhard@
universalbookbindery.com
Pres: Trip Worden *E-mail:* tworden@
universalbookbindery.com
VP: Fred Daubert
Founded: 1923

Universal|Wilde
26 Dartmouth St, Westwood, MA 02090
Tel: 781-251-2700 *Fax:* 781-251-2613

Web Site: www.universalwilde.com
Key Personnel
Pres & CEO: Stephen Flood
COO: Christopher Armstrong
CFO: Joe Musanti
VP, HR: Jennifer MacAskill
VP, Sales: Jim Bailey
Mktg Mgr: Ryan Collins
Founded: 1958
Print Runs: 3,000 min - 100,000 max
Branch Office(s)
403 VFW Dr, Rockland, MA 02370 *Tel:* 781-
871-7744 *Fax:* 781-878-2967
48 Third Ave, Somerville, MA 02143 *Tel:* 617-
591-3000 *Fax:* 617-591-3091

VeronaLibri
124 Willowbrook Ave, Stamford, CT 06902
Tel: 203-614-8335
Web Site: www.veronalibri.com
Key Personnel
Sales Rep: Nancy Freeman *E-mail:* nancy.
freeman@veronalibri.com

Versa Press Inc
1465 Spring Bay Rd, East Peoria, IL 61611-9788
Tel: 309-822-8272 *Toll Free Tel:* 800-447-7829
Fax: 309-822-8141
Web Site: www.versapress.com
Key Personnel
Chmn: Joseph F Kennell
Pres: Steven J Kennell
Sales Mgr: Darold D Frerichs *E-mail:* dfrerichs@
versapress.com
Founded: 1937
Turnaround: 20 Workdays
Print Runs: 500 min - 50,000 max
Membership(s): Book Manufacturers' Institute
(BMI)

ViaTech Publishing Solutions Inc
11935 N Stemmons Fwy, Dallas, TX 75234
Tel: 214-827-8151
E-mail: marketing@viatechpub.com
Web Site: www.viatech.io
Key Personnel
CEO: Michael Bertuch
VP, Global Sales: Tom Bergenholtz
Founded: 1928
Turnaround: 5-20 Workdays
Print Runs: 50 min - 1,000,000 max
Branch Office(s)
8857 Alexander Rd, Batavia, NY 14020
5668 E 61 St, Commerce, CA 90040
5021 Old Dixie Rd, Forest Park, GA 30297
Kingston Business Park, Kingston Bagpuize,
Abingdon, Oxon OX13 5FE, United Kingdom
Tel: (01865) 822170
Membership(s): Book Manufacturers' Institute
(BMI)

Vicks Lithograph & Printing Corp
5166 Commercial Dr, Yorkville, NY 13495
Tel: 315-736-9344
E-mail: info@vicks.biz
Web Site: www.vicks.biz
Key Personnel
CEO: Dwight E Vicks, III
Founded: 1918
Turnaround: 10 Workdays
Print Runs: 1 min - 100,000 max
Membership(s): Book Manufacturers' Institute
(BMI); PRINTING United Alliance

VIP Digital Print Center
Affiliate of The Millenium Group
200 Circle Dr N, Piscataway, NJ 08854
Tel: 732-469-5400 *Fax:* 732-469-8414
E-mail: info@vipcopycenter.com
Web Site: www.vipcopycenter.com

Key Personnel
VP: Joe Errico
Founded: 1986
Turnaround: 2-3 Workdays

Viridiam LLC
3030 Lowell Dr, Green Bay, WI 54311
Tel: 920-465-3030 *Toll Free Tel:* 800-829-6555
Web Site: www.viridiam.com
Key Personnel
VP, Sales: Rob Butler
Founded: 1888
Turnaround: 15 Workdays
Print Runs: 250 min
Membership(s): Book Manufacturers' Institute
(BMI)

Walker360
2501 Fifth Ave E, Montgomery, AL 36107
Tel: 334-832-4975
E-mail: info@walker360.com
Web Site: walker360.com
Key Personnel
Pres: Taylor Blackwell *E-mail:* taylor@
walker360.com
Cont: Estella Riley *E-mail:* estella@walker360.
com
IT Dir: Connie Manoliu *E-mail:* connie@
walker360.com

Wallaceburg Bookbinding & Mfg Co Ltd
95 Arnold St, Wallaceburg, ON N8A 3P3,
Canada
Tel: 519-627-3552 *Toll Free Tel:* 800-214-BIND
(214-2463) *Fax:* 519-627-6922
E-mail: helpdesk@wbmbindery.com
Web Site: www.wbmbindery.com
Key Personnel
Pres: Clarence Dykhouse
VP: Gerrit Dykhouse
Founded: 1958
Turnaround: 15-20 Workdays
Membership(s): Atlantic Provinces Library Asso-
ciation (APLA); Canadian Library Association
(CLA); Michigan Library Association (MLA);
National Information Standards Organization
(NISO)

Walsworth
306 N Kansas Ave, Marceline, MO 64658
Toll Free Tel: 800-265-6795
Web Site: www.walsworth.com; www.
walsworthhistorybooks.com
Key Personnel
CEO: Don O Walsworth
COO: Jim Mead
Pres: Don Walsworth, Jr
VP, Mktg & Communs: Kristin Mateski
E-mail: kristin.mateski@walsworth.com
Founded: 1937
Print Runs: 100 min - 500,000 max
Branch Office(s)
803 S Missouri Ave, Marceline, MO 64658
(printing & bindery facility)
Donning Co Publishers, 731 S Brunswick St,
Brookfield, MO 64628 *Tel:* 660-675-5570 *Web
Site:* www.donning.com
The Ovid Bell Press, 1201 Bluff St, Fulton, MO
65251-0370 *Toll Free Tel:* 800-835-8919 *Web
Site:* www.ovidbell.com
903 E 104 St, Suite 700, Kansas City, MO 64131
(yearbook sales & mktg facility) *Toll Free
Tel:* 800-369-2965
7300 W 110 St, Suite 600, Overland Park, KS
66210 (sales & mktg)
2180 Maiden Lane, St Joseph, MI 49085 (printing
& bindery facility) *Toll Free Tel:* 888-563-3220
656 S Douglas St, Ripon, WI 54971 (printing &
bindery facility)

Webcom Inc
Division of Marquis Book Printing Inc

3480 Pharmacy Ave, Toronto, ON M1W 2S7,
Canada
Tel: 416-496-1000 *Toll Free Tel:* 800-665-9322
Fax: 416-496-1537
E-mail: webcom@webcomlink.com
Web Site: www.webcomlink.com
Key Personnel
Pres & CEO: Mike Collinge
Dir of HR & Cust Serv: Rhonda Suurd
Dir of Sales: Marc Doucet
Founded: 1975
Turnaround: 15 Workdays
Print Runs: 50 min - 100,000 max
Sales Office(s): 65 Spring Valley Ave, River
Edge, NJ 07661, Contact: Susan Ginch
Tel: 201-262-4301 *Fax:* 201-262-6375
E-mail: susan.ginch@webcomlink.com
Membership(s): Book Manufacturers' Institute
(BMI); Canadian Book & Periodical Council;
PRINTING United Alliance

Webcrafters Inc
2211 Fordem Ave, Madison, WI 53704
Tel: 608-244-3561 *Toll Free Tel:* 800-356-8200
Fax: 608-244-5120
E-mail: info@webcrafters-inc.com
Web Site: www.webcrafters-inc.com
Key Personnel
CEO: Chris Kurtzman
VP, Div Dir: Brad Koch
Membership(s): Book Manufacturers' Institute
(BMI)

Fred Weidner & Daughter Printers
99 Hudson St, 5th fl, New York, NY 10013
Tel: 646-706-5180
E-mail: info@fwdprinters.com
Web Site: www.fwdprinters.com
Key Personnel
Pres: Cynthia Weidner *E-mail:* cynthia@
fwdprinters.com
Creative Dir: Carol Mittelsdorf *E-mail:* carol@
fwdprinters.com
Founded: 1860
Turnaround: 5-10 Workdays
Print Runs: 1,000 min - 500,000 max

Wert Bookbinding Inc
9975 Allentown Blvd, Grantville, PA 17028
Tel: 717-469-0626 *Toll Free Tel:* 800-344-9378
Fax: 717-469-0629
E-mail: quotes@wertbookbinding.com
Web Site: www.wertbookbinding.com
Key Personnel
Owner: Kathryn E Wert
Pres: Gary L Wert *E-mail:* gary@
wertbookbinding.com
VP & Treas: Rodney D Wert *E-mail:* rod@
wertbookbinding.com
VP & Secy: Scott A Wert *E-mail:* scott@
wertbookbinding.com
Founded: 1966
Turnaround: 7-28 Workdays
Print Runs: 1 min - 3,000 max
Membership(s): Book Manufacturers' Institute
(BMI)

Whitehall Printing Co
4244 Corporate Sq, Naples, FL 34104
Tel: 239-643-6464 *Toll Free Tel:* 800-321-9290
Fax: 239-643-6439
E-mail: info@whitehallprinting.com
Web Site: www.whitehallprinting.com
Key Personnel
Chmn: Mike Hirsch
Pres: Jeff Hirsch
VP: Emil G Hirsch
Founded: 1959
Turnaround: 10-15 Business days
Print Runs: 250 min - 50,000 max

Wimmer Cookbooks
Division of Mercury Printing, an RR Donnelley
Co
4650 Shelby Air Dr, Memphis, TN 38118
Toll Free Tel: 800-548-2537 *Fax:* 901-363-1771
Web Site: www.wimmerco.com
Key Personnel
Acct Coord: Robyn Hite
Sales & Mktg: Terry Rayner
Founded: 1946
Turnaround: 49 Workdays
Print Runs: 1,000 min

Worzalla
3535 Jefferson St, Stevens Point, WI 54481
Tel: 715-344-9608 *Fax:* 715-344-2578
Web Site: www.worzalla.com
Key Personnel
Chmn of the Bd: Charles Nason
Pres: James Fetherston
VP, Fin: Samuel Crockett
VP, Opers: Brian McManus
VP, Sales: Richard Letchinger
Cust Serv Mgr: Kim Deuel
Field Sales: Rodger Beyer
Founded: 1892
Turnaround: 20 Workdays
Print Runs: 50 min - 1,000,000 max
Sales Office(s): 4819 W Berteau Ave, Chicago, IL
60641, Contact: Tim Taylor *Tel:* 773-383-7892
E-mail: ttaylor@worzalla.com
2231 Morris Ave, Suite 3, Union, NJ 07083, Con-
tact: Edmund Corvelli, III *Tel:* 201-749-7995
E-mail: ecorvelli@worzalla.com
222 W 37 St, 10th fl, New York, NY 10018,
Contact: Sam Gallucci *Tel:* 201-851-3292
E-mail: sgallucci@worzalla.com
Membership(s): Book Manufacturers' Institute
(BMI)

Yurchak Printing Inc
920 Links Ave, Landisville, PA 17538
Tel: 717-399-0209
E-mail: ypi.info@yurchak.com
Web Site: www.yurchak.com
Key Personnel
Founder & CEO: John Yurchak, Jr
Pres: John W Yurchak
VP, Opers: Jason Yurchak
Dir, Busn Devt: Randy Boyer
Founded: 1998
Turnaround: 5-20 Workdays
Print Runs: 1 min - 1,500 max
Membership(s): International Printers' Network
(IPN)

Manufacturing Materials Index

Manufacturing Materials

This section includes companies involved in the production of book manufacturing materials such as paper, book jacket & cover materials and binding supplies. The descriptions of the services provided are paid components.

The paper merchants listed maintain stocks of book, offset & advertising paper and handle orders from the book trade. The names of the principal mills they represent for book paper have been included when the information was available.

Most paper mills manufacture many grades and kinds of paperboard, some as stock items, others on special order only. The paper is usually distributed through merchants although larger paper users sometimes contract for their requirements directly with the mills. The mills listed are among the major mills in this country supplying large quantities of paper to book publishers.

Adams Magnetic Products Co
888 N Larch Ave, Elmhurst, IL 60126-1133
Tel: 630-617-8880 *Toll Free Tel:* 800-747-7543
   (sales) *Fax:* 630-617-8881 *Toll Free Fax:* 800-747-1323
E-mail: info@adamsmagnetic.com
Web Site: www.adamsmagnetic.com
Key Personnel
Pres: Scott Lewis
Dir, Mktg: Alice Martin *E-mail:* amartin@
   adamsmagnetic.com
Founded: 1950
Branch Office(s)
3198 Lionshead Ave, Carlsbad, CA 92010
2600 Ring Rd, Elizabethtown, KY 42701
   Tel: 270-763-9090 *Fax:* 270-763-0641
140A Metro Park, Suites 9 & 10, Rochester, NY
   14623

amb™, see Ambassador Press Inc

Ambassador Press Inc
1400 Washington Ave N, Minneapolis, MN 55411
Tel: 612-521-0123
E-mail: info@ambpress.com
Web Site: www.ambpress.com
Key Personnel
Co-Owner, Pres & CEO: Candice Engle-Fieldman
Co-Owner & EVP: Harold Engle
Founded: 1960

Arbor Books
244 Madison Ave, Box 254, New York, NY
   10016
Tel: 212-956-0950 *Toll Free Tel:* 877-822-2500
   Fax: 914-401-9385
E-mail: info@arborbooks.com; editorial@
   arborbooks.net
Web Site: www.arborbooks.com; www.
   arborservices.co
Key Personnel
Owner: Joel Hochman *Tel:* 877-822-
   2502 *E-mail:* arborbooksjoel@aol.com;
   Larry Leichman *Tel:* 877-822-2504
   E-mail: arborbookslarry@aol.com
Mktg Dir: Olga Vladi
Founded: 1992

Arbor Services, see Arbor Books

Bang Printing Co Inc
Division of CJK Group Inc
3323 Oak St, Brainerd, MN 56401
Tel: 218-829-2877 *Toll Free Tel:* 800-328-0450
Fax: 218-829-7145
E-mail: info@bangprinting.com
Web Site: www.bangprinting.com
Key Personnel
Pres: Todd Vanek *E-mail:* toddv@bangprinting.
   com
VP, Opers: Joe Saiko *E-mail:* joes@bangprinting.
   com

VP, Sales: Doug Walters *E-mail:* dougw@
   bangprinting.com
Founded: 1899

Richard Bauer & Co Inc
310 Cedar Lane, Teaneck, NJ 07666
Tel: 201-692-1005 *Toll Free Tel:* 800-995-7881
   Fax: 201-692-8626
E-mail: info@richardbauer.com
Web Site: www.richardbauer.com
Key Personnel
CEO: Robert Cipolaro
Founded: 1916
Book Paper Line(s) Sold: Abitibi; Badger; Finch
   Pruyn; Fraser; International; Miami Valley;
   Nashua; National Envelope; Riverside; Rolland;
   Wausau Paper
Cover Line(s) Sold: International; Wausau Paper

Bookmasters
Division of Baker & Taylor Publisher Services
30 Amberwood Pkwy, Ashland, OH 44805
Tel: 419-281-5100 *Toll Free Tel:* 800-537-6727
   Fax: 419-281-0200
E-mail: info@btpubservices.com
Web Site: www.btpubservices.com
Key Personnel
Dir of Mfg: Brad Sharp *E-mail:* bsharp@
   bookmasters.com
Founded: 1972

Bulkley Dunton
Division of Veritiv™ Corporation
One Penn Plaza, Suite 2814, 250 W 34 St, New
   York, NY 10119
Tel: 212-863-1800 *Toll Free Tel:* 800-347-9279
   Fax: 212-863-1872
Web Site: www.bulkleydunton.com
Key Personnel
SVP, Publg & Print Mgmt: John Biscanti
Dir of Sales: Terence Sheehy
Founded: 1833
Book Paper Line(s) Sold: Alberta Newsprint;
   American Eagle®; APC Paper Group; Apple-
   ton Coated; Asia Pulp and Paper; Boise Paper;
   Bollore Thin Papers; BPM Inc; Burgo; Canfor
   Premium One; Cascades; Catalyst; Chenming;
   Clearwater Paper; Coating Excellence Inc;
   Domtar; Dunn Paper; Evergreen Packaging;
   Expera Specialty Solutions; Finch Paper LLC;
   French Paper Co; Georgia Pacific; Glatfelter;
   International Paper; InterWrap Papers; Irving
   Paper; Kotkamills; Kruger Inc; Manchester In-
   dustries; Metsa Board; Mohawk Paper; Monad-
   nock Paper Mills Inc; Neenah Paper; New Leaf
   Paper; Nippon Paper; NORPAC; Novolex™;
   Parenco; Port Hawkesbury Paper; Reich Paper;
   Resolute Forest Products; Sappi; Scheufelen
   North America; Soporcel; Stora Enso; Suzano
   Pulp and Paper; Twin Rivers Paper Company;
   UPM Paper; Verso Corp; Wausau Paper; West
   Linn Paper Co; WestRock; Yupo Corporation
   America

Branch Office(s)
7500 Amigos Ave, Downey, CA 90242 *Tel:* 562-
   922-7814
850 N Arlington Heights Rd, Suite 100, Itasca, IL
   60143 *Tel:* 630-875-7037
7445 New Ridge Rd, Hanover, MD 21076
   Tel: 410-696-8500
4265 Trailer Dr, Charlotte, NC 28269 *Tel:* 704-
   599-6180
3120 N Marshall Rd, Appleton, WI 54915
   Tel: 920-749-2820 *Toll Free Tel:* 800-259-7974

Cenveo Inc
200 First Stamford Place, 2nd fl, Stamford, CT
   06902
Tel: 203-595-3000 *Fax:* 203-595-3070
E-mail: info@cenveo.com
Web Site: www.cenveo.com
Key Personnel
CEO: Robert G Burton, Jr
CFO: Mark Hiltwein
Pres: Michael Burton
Founded: 1830

Cenveo St Louis
101 Workman Ct, Eureka, MO 63025
Tel: 314-966-2000 *Toll Free Tel:* 800-800-8845
   Fax: 314-966-4725
Web Site: www.cenveo.com

CG Book Printers
Division of Corporate Graphics Commercial
   (CGC)
1750 Northway Dr, North Mankato, MN 56003
Tel: 507-388-3300 *Toll Free Tel:* 800-729-7575
   Fax: 507-386-6350
E-mail: cgbooks@corpgraph.com
Web Site: www.corpgraph.com
Key Personnel
Pres: Dan Kvasnicka *Tel:* 507-386-6340
   Fax: 507-344-5548 *E-mail:* dekvasnicka@
   corpgraph.com
Sales Exec, Book Mfg Sales: Mike Schmitt
   Tel: 507-386-6349 *E-mail:* mjschmitt@
   corpgraph.com
Founded: 1989

ColorPage
Division of Tri-State Associated Services Inc
81 Ten Broeck Ave, Kingston, NY 12401
Tel: 845-331-7581 *Toll Free Tel:* 800-836-7581
   Fax: 845-331-1571
E-mail: sales@colorpageonline.com
Web Site: www.colorpageonline.com
Key Personnel
Pres & Mktg Strategist/Consultant: Frank J Cam-
   pagna, II *E-mail:* fcampagna@colorpageonline.
   com
Acct Mgr & Cont: Kathy Riggins
   E-mail: kriggins@colorpageonline.com
Prodn Mgr: Randy Delanoy

Cust Serv Supv: Debbie Downes
  E-mail: ddownes@colorpageonline.com
Founded: 1976

Columbia Finishing Mills Inc
135 Boundary Rd, Cornwall, ON K6H 5T3,
  Canada
Mailing Address: Box 546, Cornwall, ON K6H
  5T3, Canada
Tel: 613-933-1462 *Toll Free Tel:* 800-267-9174
  Fax: 613-933-7717 *Toll Free Fax:* 800-242-
  9174
E-mail: info@columbiafinishingmills.com
Web Site: www.columbiafinishingmills.com
Key Personnel
Pres: Brian Lynch
Sales Mgr: Dan Plourde

Conservation Resources International LLC
7350 Lockport Place, Suite A, Lorton, VA 22079
Tel: 703-321-7730 *Toll Free Tel:* 800-634-6932
  Fax: 703-321-0629
E-mail: sales@conservationresources.com
Web Site: www.conservationresources.com
Key Personnel
COO: Catherine Hollinger
Pres: William K Hollinger, Jr
VP: Lavonia Hollinger
Membership(s): AIC

Coral Graphic Services Inc
Member of Bertelsmann Printing Group
840 S Broadway, Hicksville, NY 11801
Tel: 516-576-2100 *Fax:* 516-576-2168
E-mail: info@coralgraphics.com
Web Site: www.bpg-usa.com
Key Personnel
CEO: Christof Ludwig
COO: Jorge Velasco
CFO: Christoph Mittendorf
CTO: Yannic Schroeder
Founded: 1982
Branch Office(s)
4700 Commerce Crossing Dr, Louisville, KY
  40229 *Tel:* 502-962-5466 *Fax:* 502-962-9023
25 Jack Enders Blvd, Berryville, VA 22611
  Tel: 540-955-2750 *Fax:* 540-955-9164
Membership(s): Association of the Graphic Arts
  (AGA); Book Industry Guild of New York;
  PRINTING United Alliance

Corporate Graphics Book Printers, see CG
  Book Printers

Coverline Inc
13 Spruce Pond Rd, Franklin, MA 02038
Tel: 508-528-8511 *Fax:* 508-528-6838
Key Personnel
Pres: Paul Langley *E-mail:* pglcov@comcast.net

Cromwell Leather
147 Palmer Ave, Mamaroneck, NY 10543
Tel: 914-381-0100 *Fax:* 914-381-0046
E-mail: sales@cromwellgroup.com
Web Site: www.cromwellgroup.com
Key Personnel
Pres: Thomas Fleisch
VP, Sales: Margaret Zulkowsky *E-mail:* mz@
  cromwellgroup.com

D&K Group Inc
1795 Commerce Dr, Elk Grove Village, IL 60007
Tel: 847-956-0160; 847-956-4757 (tech support)
  Toll Free Tel: 800-632-2314 *Fax:* 847-956-8214
E-mail: info@dkgroup.net
Web Site: www.dkgroup.net
Key Personnel
Pres: Karl Singer
VP, Sales & Mktg: Tom Pidgeon *E-mail:* tom.
  pidgeon@dkgroup.net

Mktg Communs Specialist: Brian Biegel
  E-mail: brian.biegel@dkgroup.net
Founded: 1979

Dekker Bookbinding Inc
2941 Clydon Ave SW, Grand Rapids, MI 49519
Tel: 616-538-5160 *Toll Free Tel:* 800-299-BIND
  (299-2463)
E-mail: hello@dekkerbook.com
Web Site: www.dekkerbook.com
Key Personnel
Pres: Chris Dekker
VP: Corbin Dekker
Founded: 1928
Membership(s): Binding Industries Association
  (BIA); Forest Stewardship Council US (FSC-
  US); Printing Industries of Michigan Inc (PIM)

Desktop Miracles Inc
112 S Main St, Suite 294, Stowe, VT 05672
Tel: 802-253-7900 *Toll Free Fax:* 888-293-2676
E-mail: info@desktopmiracles.com
Web Site: www.desktopmiracles.com
Key Personnel
Pres & CEO: Barry T Kerrigan *E-mail:* barry@
  desktopmiracles.com
VP: Virginia Kerrigan *E-mail:* virginia@
  desktopmiracles.com
Founded: 1994

Dikeman Laminating Corp
181 Sargeant Ave, Clifton, NJ 07013
Tel: 973-473-5696 *Fax:* 973-473-2540
E-mail: office@dikemanlaminating.com
Web Site: dikemanlaminating.com
Key Personnel
Owner & Pres: Jeffrey W Snyder
Founded: 1949

DNP America LLC
Subsidiary of Dai Nippon Printing Co Ltd
335 Madison Ave, 3rd fl, New York, NY 10017
Tel: 212-503-1060
E-mail: gps@dnp-g.com
Web Site: www.dnpamerica.com
Key Personnel
VP & Gen Mgr: Norikatsu Nakamura
Founded: 1976
Branch Office(s)
2099 Gateway Place, Suite 490, San Jose, CA
  95110 *Tel:* 408-735-8880
3858 Carson St, Suite 300, Torrance, CA 90503
  Tel: 310-540-5123

Domtar Paper Co LLC
Division of Domtar
234 Kingsley Park Dr, Fort Mill, SC 29715
Tel: 803-802-7500 *Toll Free Tel:* 877-877-4685
E-mail: communications@domtar.com;
  commercialprinting@domtar.com
Web Site: www.domtar.com
Key Personnel
Pres, Pulp & Paper: Michael Garcia
Media & Community Rel: Jan Martin *Tel:* 803-
  802-8027 *E-mail:* jan.martin@domtar.com
Founded: 1965
Book Paper Line(s) Milled: Century® Premium
  Opaque; Cougar® Digital; Cougar® Digi-
  tal Color Copy; Cougar® Smooth; Cougar®
  Super Smooth; EarthChoice® Colors; Earth-
  Choice® HOTS®; EarthChoice® Tradebook;
  Guardian® Opaque; Husky® Digital; Husky®
  Opaque Offset; Husky® Recycled Digital;
  Husky® Recycled Opaque Offset; HuskyJET®;
  HuskyJET® 7 pt Card; Lynx® Digital; Lynx®
  Digital Super Smooth; Lynx® Opaque Ultra;
  LynxJET®; Printers Opaque; TitaniumJET™;
  Vista® Opaque; Vista® Ultra; Xerox® Bold
  Digital®; Xerox® Revolution®
Cover Line(s) Milled: Century® Premium
  Opaque; Century® Premium Opaque Pharma;

Century® Premium Pharma HiFold; Guardian®
  Opaque; Guardian® Opaque Pharma;
  Guardian® Pharma HiFold
Branch Office(s)
395 de Maisonneuve Blvd W, Montreal, QC H3A
  1L6, Canada *Tel:* 514-848-5555

RR Donnelley
35 W Wacker Dr, Chicago, IL 60601
Toll Free Tel: 800-742-4455
Web Site: www.rrd.com
Key Personnel
Pres & CEO: Daniel L Knotts
Pres, Busn Servs: John Pecaric
Pres, Mktg Solutions: Doug Ryan
EVP & CFO: Terry D Peterson
EVP & CIO: Ken O'Brien
EVP & Chief HR Offr: Sheila Rutt
EVP & Chief Strategy & Transformation Offr:
  Elif Sagsen-Ercel
EVP, Dom Opers & Chief Supply Chain Offr:
  Glynn Perry
EVP, Gen Coun, Chief Compliance Offr & Corp
  Secy: Deborah Steiner
SVP & Chief Acctg Offr: Michael J Sharp
Founded: 1864
Branch Office(s)
955 Gateway Center Way, San Diego, CA 92102
  Tel: 619-527-4600
40610 County Center Dr, Temecula, CA 92591
  Tel: 951-296-2890
151 Red Stone Rd, Manchester, CT 06042
  Tel: 860-649-5570
9125 Bachman Rd, Orlando, FL 32824 *Tel:* 407-
  859-2030
5800 Peachtree Rd, Atlanta, GA 30341 *Tel:* 770-
  458-6351
825 Riverside Pkwy, Suite 300, Austell, GA
  30168 *Tel:* 770-948-1330
1750 Wallace Ave, St Charles, IL 60174 *Tel:* 630-
  313-7000
609 S Kirk Rd, St Charles, IL 60174 *Tel:* 630-
  762-7600
One Poplar Ave, Thurmont, MD 21788 *Tel:* 301-
  271-7171
65 Sprague St, Hyde Park, MA 02136 *Tel:* 617-
  360-2000
18780 W 78 St, Chanhassen, MN 55317
  Tel: 952-937-9764
5500 12 Ave E, Shakopee, MN 55379 *Tel:* 952-
  941-7546
6305 Sunset Corporate Dr, Las Vegas, NV 89120
  Tel: 702-949-8500
5 Henderson Dr, West Caldwell, NJ 07006
  Tel: 973-882-7000
12301 Vance Davis Dr, Charlotte, NC 28269
  Tel: 704-949-3568
One Litho Way, Durham, NC 27703 *Tel:* 919-
  596-3660
3801 Gantz Rd, Grove City, OH 43123 *Tel:* 614-
  539-5527
700 Nestle Way, Suite 200, Breinigsville, PA
  18031 *Tel:* 610-391-3900
9985 Gantry Rd, Philadelphia, PA 19115
  Tel: 215-671-9500
218 N Braddock Ave, Pittsburgh, PA 15208
  Tel: 412-241-8200
1210 Key Rd, Columbia, SC 29201 *Tel:* 803-799-
  9550
1645 W Sam Houston Pkwy N, Houston, TX
  77043 *Tel:* 713-468-7175
1550 Lakeway Dr, Suite 600, Lewisville, TX
  75057 *Tel:* 972-353-7500
630 W 1000 N, Logan, UT 84321 *Tel:* 435-755-
  4000
201 E Progress Dr, West Bend, WI 53095
  Tel: 262-338-6101
Membership(s): Association of American Publishers (AAP); Book Industry Study Group
  (BISG); Book Manufacturers' Institute (BMI)

W R Draper Co
Division of The Arthur Press (1978) Ltd

162 Norfinch Dr, Toronto, ON M3N 1X6, Canada
Tel: 416-663-6001 *Fax:* 416-663-6043
E-mail: info@arthurpress.com
Web Site: www.arthurpress.com
Key Personnel
Pres: Jeremy Thorn
Founded: 1954

Dunn & Co Inc
Affiliate of Legacy Publishing Group
75 Green St, Clinton, MA 01510
Mailing Address: PO Box 1185, Clinton, MA
01510
Tel: 978-368-8505 *Fax:* 978-368-7867
E-mail: info@booktrauma.com
Web Site: www.booktrauma.com
Key Personnel
Chmn: David M Dunn
Pres: Peter R Heelan
VP: Rocco Windover
Founded: 1976

Ecological Fibers Inc
40 Pioneer Dr, Lunenburg, MA 01462
Tel: 978-537-0003 *Fax:* 978-537-2238
E-mail: info@ecofibers.com
Web Site: www.ecofibers.com
Key Personnel
Pres: John A Quill
VP, Sales: Dave Robbins *E-mail:* drobbins@
ecofibers.com
Dir, Book Group Sales: Jim McCafferty
E-mail: jmccafferty@ecofibers.com
Dir, Busn Opers: Joyce Hardell *E-mail:* joyce@
ecofibers.com
Founded: 1972
Book Paper Line(s) Milled: Rainbow® 80 &
100 lb cream & white endleaf; Rainbow® 80
NASTA spec colored endleaf, side & spine ma-
terial; Rainbow® 70 lb colored endleaf & side
material
Cover Line(s) Milled: Arizona; Corona; Lumina
Silver Pearlescent; Mirage; Mirage 325 gsm;
Prestige; Rainbow® 17; Rainbow® 3; Rain-
bow® 9 Type II coated cover; Rainbow® Eco-
Cover; Rainbow® Excel; Rainbow® LX; Ul-
tima
Book Paper Line(s) Sold: Rainbow® 80 & 100 lb
cream & white endleaf; Rainbow® 80 NASTA
spec colored endleaf, side & spine material;
Rainbow® 70 lb colored endleaf & side mate-
rial
Branch Office(s)
730 York Ave, Pawtucket, RI 02861 *Tel:* 401-725-
9700 *Fax:* 401-724-4970
Membership(s): Book Industry Guild of New
York; Book Manufacturers' Institute (BMI);
Bookbuilders of Boston; Publishing Professionals Network (PPN)

Edison Lithograph & Printing Corp
3725 Tonnelle Ave, North Bergen, NJ 07047-
2421
Tel: 201-902-9191 *Fax:* 201-902-0475
E-mail: info@edisonlitho.com
Web Site: www.edisonlitho.com
Key Personnel
COO: Joseph Ostreicher
Founded: 1958

Eska USA BV Inc
Subsidiary of Eska BV (Netherlands)
1910 Campostella Rd, Chesapeake, VA 23324
Tel: 757-494-7330
E-mail: usa@eska.com
Web Site: www.eska.com
Key Personnel
Gen Mgr: Vincent Tophoff

FIM
18 Central Blvd, South Hackensack, NJ 07606

Tel: 201-549-1037
Web Site: www.fimheadbands.com
Key Personnel
Pres: Jon Weingarten
Dir, Mfg & Dist: Milt Wolfson
Sales/Serv: Mariluz Yambao

Finch Paper LLC
One Glen St, Glens Falls, NY 12801
Tel: 518-793-2541 *Toll Free Tel:* 800-833-9983
Fax: 518-743-9656
E-mail: info@finchpaper.com
Web Site: www.finchpaper.com
Key Personnel
Chmn & CEO: Debabrata Mukherjee
E-mail: dmukherjee@finchpaper.com
Sales Dir, Eastern & Natl Accts: Ken Ritchie
Tel: 516-375-0256 *E-mail:* ken.ritchie@
finchpaper.com
Western Regl Sales Dir: Tom Dieckman *Tel:* 630-
450-2064 *E-mail:* tom.dieckman@finchpaper.
com
Founded: 1865
Book Paper Line(s) Milled: Alkaline base; Finch
Fine; Casa Opaque Book; Finch Casa Opaque
(recycled); Finch Digital Web XP; Finch Fine
Soft White; Finch Inkjet Pi; Finch Opaque
Book; Finch Vanilla Fine (natural white); Finch
Vanilla Opaque (natural white)
Cover Line(s) Milled: Finch Casa Opaque Cover;
Finch Fine Cover; Finch Fine Soft White
Cover; Finch Opaque Cover; Finch Vanilla Fine
Cover; Finch Vanilla Opaque Cover
Paper Type(s) Sold: Acid Free; Chlorine Free;
Recycled; Uncoated Free Sheet
Membership(s): Book Manufacturers' Institute
(BMI)

Flock Tex Inc
200 Founders Dr, Woonsocket, RI 02895
Tel: 401-765-2340 *Toll Free Tel:* 800-556-7286
Fax: 401-765-4915
Web Site: www.flocktex.com
Key Personnel
Owner & Pres: Edward T Abramek, Jr
VP: Brian Abramek; Gary Abramek
E-mail: garya@flocktex.com
VP, Sales: Walter Armstrong
Founded: 1967

French Paper
100 French St, Niles, MI 49120
Tel: 269-683-1100 *Toll Free Tel:* 800-253-5952
E-mail: frenchassetorders@frenchpaper.com;
frenchpaperco@gmail.com
Web Site: www.frenchpaper.com
Founded: 1871
Book Paper Line(s) Milled: Construction; acid-
free paper available; Dur-O-Tone; Finch Dig-
ital; Glo-Tone; Kraft-Tone; Parchtone; Pop-
Tone; Smart White; Speckletone; Vivitone

H B Fuller Co
1200 Willow Lake Blvd, St Paul, MN 55110-
5146
Tel: 651-236-5900 *Toll Free Tel:* 888-423-8553
E-mail: inquiry@hbfuller.com
Web Site: www.hbfuller.com
Key Personnel
Pres & CEO: Jim Owens
EVP & COO: Ted Clark
EVP & CFO: John Corkrean
VP & Cont: Robert Martsching
VP & Treas: Heidi Weiler
VP, Gen Coun & Corp Secy: Timothy Keenan

G & H Soho Inc
413 Market St, Elmwood Park, NJ 07407
Tel: 201-216-9400 *Fax:* 201-216-1778
E-mail: print@ghsoho.com
Web Site: www.ghsoho.com

Key Personnel
Pres: Gerry Burstein
Prodn Mgr: Jason Burstein
Founded: 1985
Membership(s): Association of Graphic Commu-
nications; Book Industry Guild of New York;
Digital Printing Council; PRINTING United
Alliance

Gane Brothers & Lane Inc
1400 Greenleaf Ave, Elk Grove Village, IL 60007
Tel: 847-593-3364 *Toll Free Tel:* 800-323-0596
Toll Free Fax: 800-784-2464
E-mail: sales@ganebrothers.com
Web Site: www.ganebrothers.com
Key Personnel
Owner & Pres: Glenn Brown
VP: Jack McLoraine
Founded: 1846

Glatfelter
Capitol Towers South, 4350 Congress St, Suite
600, Charlotte, NC 28209
Tel: 717-850-0170 *Toll Free Tel:* 866-744-7380
E-mail: info@glatfelter.com
Web Site: www.glatfelter.com
Key Personnel
Chmn & CEO: Dante C Parrini
SVP & Chief Commercial Offr: Chris W Astley
SVP & CFO: Samuel L Hillard
SVP, Integrated Global Supply Chain & IT: Wolf-
gang Laures
VP, Deputy Gen Coun & Corp Secy: Jill L Urey
VP, Fin & Chief Acctg Offr: David C Elder
VP, Global HR & Admin: Eileen L Beck
VP, Global Opers: Philippe Sevoz
Founded: 1864
Book Paper Line(s) Milled: Digibook; Ecolo-
text; Editors; EPA Reference; Glatfelter End-
Leaf; Glatfelter Hi-Brite; Glatfelter Hi-Opaque;
Glatfelter Offset; Natures; Restorecote; Spring
Forge; Supple Opaque; Thor; Writers
Branch Office(s)
8201 Chad Colley Blvd, Fort Smith, AR 72916
(mfg) *Tel:* 479-242-0754 *E-mail:* info.ambu@
glatfelter.com
351 Jesse Jewell Pkwy, Suite 301, Gainesville,
GA 30501 (sales & dist) *Tel:* 770-536-2400
1680 rue Atmec, Gatineau, QC J8P 7G7, Canada
(mfg) *Tel:* 819-669-8100
Membership(s): American Association of Univer-
sity Presses (AAUP); Association of American
Publishers (AAP); Book Industry Study Group
(BISG); Book Manufacturers' Institute (BMI);
OTT.X

Gould Paper Corp
99 Park Ave, 10th fl, New York, NY 10016
Tel: 212-301-0000 *Toll Free Tel:* 800-221-3043
Fax: 212-481-0067
E-mail: info@gouldpaper.com
Web Site: www.gouldpaper.com
Key Personnel
Pres & CEO: David H Berkowitz
Founded: 1924
Book Paper Line(s) Sold: A B Massa; Abitibi;
Appleton Papers; Beveridge; Cascade; Dom-
tar; Evergreen Packaging; Finch Paper LLC;
Fraser; Georgia-Pacific; Hazen; Kruger Inc;
Lincoln; Manistique; Mohawk Paper; Potlach;
St Mary's; Smart Papers; Stora Enso; Tem-
board; Wausau Paper; Whiting
Paper Type(s) Sold: Uncoated Groundwood
Branch Office(s)
Gould Paper South LLC, 10400 NW 21 St,
Suite 104, Doral, FL 33172 *Tel:* 305-470-0003
Fax: 305-470-0088 *Web Site:* www.gouldsouth.
com
Gould Publishing & Catalog, 25 East St, Winch-
ester, MD 01890 *Tel:* 781-729-2059 *Toll Free
Tel:* 800-882-2781 *Fax:* 781-721-1986

Gould Paper Corp (Metro), 319 Ridge Rd, Dayton, NJ 08810 *Tel:* 732-248-7800 *Toll Free Tel:* 800-672-7379 *Fax:* 732-248-5981
Membership(s): National Paper Trade Association (NPTA)

Henkel Corp
One Henkel Way, Rocky Hill, CT 06067
Tel: 860-571-5100 *Fax:* 860-571-5465
E-mail: corp.info@henkel.com
Web Site: www.henkel-northamerica.com; www.henkel-adhesives.com
Founded: 1876

HF Group LLC
8844 Mayfield Rd, Chesterland, OH 44026
Tel: 440-729-2445; 440-729-9411 (bindery)
E-mail: custservice-oh@hfgroup.com
Web Site: www.hfgroup.com
Key Personnel
CEO: Jay Fairfield *Tel:* 440-729-2445 ext 4
   E-mail: jayfairfield@hfgroup.com
VP & Gen Mgr: Jim Bratton *E-mail:* jbratton@hfgroup.com
Founded: 1821
Branch Office(s)
1010 N Sycamore St, North Manchester, IN 46962, Pres: Jim Heckman *Tel:* 260-982-2107 *E-mail:* jheckman@hfgroup.com
92 Cambridge St, Charlestown, MA 02129-0212, VP: John Parisi *Tel:* 617-242-1100 *E-mail:* jparisi@hfgroup.com
340 First St, Utica, NE 68456, Gen Mgr: Damon Osborne *Tel:* 402-534-2261 *E-mail:* dosborne@hfgroup.com
6204 Corporate Park Dr, Browns Summit, NC 27214-9745, Contact: Eric Fairfield *Tel:* 336-931-0800 *E-mail:* efairfield@hfgroup.com
45 N Main St, Unit 528, Hatfield, PA 19440 (transportation hub) *Tel:* 215-855-2293
105 W Thomas St, Atlanta, TX 75551-2736 (transportation hub) *Tel:* 260-982-2107 *Fax:* 260-982-1130

Hollinger Metal Edge Inc
9401 Northeast Dr, Fredricksburg, VA 22408
Tel: 540-898-7300 *Toll Free Tel:* 800-634-0491 *Toll Free Fax:* 800-947-8814
E-mail: info@hollingermetaledge.com
Web Site: www.hollingermetaledge.com
Key Personnel
Pres & CEO: Bob Henderson
Founded: 1945

Holliston Holdings LLC
Subsidiary of Holliston Mills
905 Holliston Mills Rd, Church Hill, TN 37642
Tel: 423-357-6141 *Toll Free Tel:* 800-251-0451; 800-251-0251 (cust serv) *Fax:* 423-357-8840 *Toll Free Fax:* 800-325-0351 (cust serv)
E-mail: custserv@holliston.com
Web Site: holliston.com
Key Personnel
Acct Exec: Jennifer Anderson
Founded: 1895
Cover Line(s) Milled: Arrestox®; Arrestox® Shimmer; Buckram® Lustre; Buckram® Roxite F; Kennett®; Linen-Set®; Luminaire®; Pearl Linen®; Pearl Linen® 2 Tone; Sturdite®
Membership(s): Book Manufacturers' Institute (BMI); Publishers Association of the West (PubWest)

Horizon Paper Co Inc
1010 Washington Blvd, Stamford, CT 06901
Tel: 203-358-0855 *Toll Free Tel:* 866-358-0855
E-mail: info@horizonpaper.com
Web Site: www.horizonpaper.com
Key Personnel
Chmn: Robert B Obernier
CEO: Jeffrey Hansen

Pres (Oak Park, IL off): Jeffrey A Hill
EVP, Sales: Matthew Asen
SVP, Sales: Michael P Hurley
VP, Sales: Mark Gerardi
Sales Mgr: Karl Pelikan
Sales: Thomas McGee
Founded: 1978
Book Paper Line(s) Sold: Alberta Newsprint; American Eagle®; APP; Burgo; Catalyst; Domtar; Evergreen Packaging; Finch Paper LLC; Inland Empire; Irving Paper; Kruger Inc; Lecta; Midwest Paper Group; Mitsubishi Paper Mills Ltd; ND Paper; New Indie/Catawaba; NORPAC; Pixelle Specialty Solutions™; Ponderay; Port Hawkesbury Paper; Rayonier Advanced Materials™; Resolute Forest Products; Rolland; Spruce Falls; Stora Enso; Suzano Pulp and Paper; Twin Rivers Paper Company; UPM Paper; Verso Corp; White Birch; Willamette Falls
Cover Line(s) Sold: Tembec; Verso Corp; WestRock

The P A Hutchison Co
400 Penn Ave, Mayfield, PA 18433
SAN: 991-5559
Tel: 570-876-4560 *Toll Free Tel:* 800-USA-PRNT (872-7768) *Fax:* 570-876-4561
E-mail: sales@pahutch.com
Web Site: www.pahutch.com
Key Personnel
Pres & CEO: Chris Hutchison
Dir, Sales & Admin: Erin Jones
Founded: 1911

Imago
110 W 40 St, New York, NY 10018
Tel: 212-921-4411 *Fax:* 212-921-8226
E-mail: sales@imagousa.com
Web Site: www.imagousa.com
Key Personnel
Pres & CEO: Howard Musk *E-mail:* howardm@imagogroup.com
Founded: 1985
Branch Office(s)
Imago West Coast, 23412 Moulton Pkwy, Suite 250, Laguna Hills, CA 92653 (sales), Contact: Tammy Simms *Tel:* 949-367-1635 *Fax:* 949-367-1639
Imago Australia, 10 Help St, Suite 27, Level 6, Chatswood, NSW 2067, Australia (sales) *Tel:* (04) 3753 3351 (cell); (04) 4806 8704 (cell) *E-mail:* sales@imagoaous.com
Imago Brazil, Domiciano Rossi, 340 unid 154, 09726-121 Sao Bernardo do Campo, Brazil (sales) *Tel:* (011) 2306 8546; (011) 2306 8547 *E-mail:* imagobra@gmail.com
Imago Shenzhen, Rm 2511-2512, Block A, United Plaza No 5022, Bin He Rd, Fu Tian Centre District, Shenzhen 518033, China (prodn), Contact: Kendrick Cheung *Tel:* (0755) 8304 8899 *Fax:* (0755) 8251 4073 *E-mail:* enquiries@imago.com.hk
Imago France, 23 rue Lavoisier, 75008 Paris, France (sales) *Tel:* 01 45 26 47 74 *Fax:* 01 78 94 14 44 *E-mail:* sales@imagogroup.com
Imago Services (HK) Ltd, Unit B309, 1/F, New East Sun Industrial Bldg, 18 Shing Yip St, Kwun Tong, Hong Kong (prodn), Contact: Kendrick Cheung *Tel:* 2811 3316 *E-mail:* enquiries@imago.com.hk
Imago Productions (Malaysia) Pte Ltd, No 43, Taman Emas, Jl Utama 31, Telok Panglima Garang, 42500 Kuala Langot, Selangor, Malaysia (prodn, incorporating South Africa sales) *Tel:* (017) 4288771 (cell) *E-mail:* enquiries@imago.com.sg
Imago Publishing, Albury Ct, Albury Thame, Oxon OX9 2LP, United Kingdom (sales), Dir: Simon Rosenheim *Tel:* (01844) 337000 *Fax:* (01844) 339935 *E-mail:* sales@imago.co.uk *Web Site:* imagogroup.com

International Paper Co
6400 Poplar Ave, Memphis, TN 38197
Tel: 901-419-9000 *Toll Free Tel:* 800-207-4003
Web Site: www.internationalpaper.com; facebook.com/internationalpaper; twitter.com/intlpaperco
Key Personnel
Chmn & CEO: Mark S Sutton
SVP & CFO: Tim S Nicholls
SVP, Gen Coun & Corp Secy: Sharon R Ryan
SVP, Corp Devt: C Cato Ealy
SVP, HR & Global Citizenship: Thomas J Plath
SVP, Mfg, Technol, EHS & Global Sourcing: Tommy S Joseph
SVP, Papers (Americas): W Michael Amick, Jr
Founded: 1898
Book Paper Line(s) Milled: Accent Opaque; by George!; CutLess®; DataSpeed®; DRM®; Hammermill®; HP; Postmark; Springhill; Williamsburg
Cover Line(s) Milled: Accent Opaque; Accent Opaque Digital; Hammermill®; Springhill Digital Opaque; Springhill Opaque; Springhill Vellum Bristol
Paper Type(s) Sold: Acid Free; Book Offset; Chlorine Free; Recycled
Branch Office(s)
International Paper Europe, Middle East & Africa, Chaussee de la Hulpe, 166, 1170 Brussels, Belgium *Tel:* (02) 774-1211
International Paper Latin America, Ave Eng Luis Carlos Berrini, 04571-010 Sao Paulo-SP, Brazil *Tel:* 0800 70 30070
International Paper Asia, 17-18F, West Bldg Greenland Ctr, 600 Middle Longhua Rd, Shanghai 200032, China *Tel:* (021) 6113 3200
International Paper India, 603 6th fl, Swapnalok Complex, 92/93 Sarojini Devi Rd, Seconderabad 500 003, India *Tel:* (040) 4002 0263
International Paper Japan Ltd, Kamiyacho Sq, 9th fl, Azabudai 1-chome, Bldg 7-3, Minato-ku, Tokyo 106-0041, Japan *Tel:* (03) 3560 7410
Ave 5 de Febrero No 1351, Edificio Sequoia PB Zona, Zona Industrial Benito Juarez, 76120 Santiago de Queretaro, QRO, Mexico *Tel:* (01442) 427 6150

Ironmark
9040 Junction Dr, Annapolis Junction, MD 20701
Toll Free Tel: 888-775-3737
E-mail: marketing@ironmarkusa.com
Web Site: ironmarkusa.com
Key Personnel
CEO: Scott Hargest *E-mail:* scott@ironmarkusa.com; Jeff Ostenso *E-mail:* jeff@ironmarkusa.com
Pres: Matt Marzullo *E-mail:* mmarzullo@ironmarkusa.com
SVP, Sales: Scott Kravitz *E-mail:* skravitz@ironmarkusa.com
VP, Opers: Chris Marzullo *E-mail:* cmarzullo@ironmarkusa.com
Sr Sales Exec: Larry Davis *E-mail:* ldavis@ironmarkusa.com
Founded: 1955

Kwikprint Manufacturing Co Inc
4868 Victor St, Jacksonville, FL 32207
Tel: 904-737-3755 *Toll Free Tel:* 800-940-5945 *Fax:* 904-730-0349
E-mail: info@kwikprint.net
Web Site: www.kwik-print.com
Key Personnel
Pres: Jay D Cann, Jr

Lake Book Manufacturing Inc
2085 N Cornell Ave, Melrose Park, IL 60160
Tel: 708-345-7000
E-mail: info@lakebook.com
Web Site: www.lakebook.com
Key Personnel
Pres & COO: Dan Genovese
VP, Fin & CFO: Bob Flatow
VP & Gen Mgr: Bill Richards

VP, Mfg: Steve Quagliato
VP, Opers: Bill Flavin
VP, Sales & Mktg: Nick Vergoth
VP, Technol: Paul Genovese

Larson Texts Inc
1762 Norcross Rd, Erie, PA 16510
Tel: 814-824-6365 *Toll Free Tel:* 800-530-2355
   Fax: 814-824-6377
Web Site: www.larsontexts.com
Key Personnel
CEO: Matt Totske
IT Mgr: Kathleen Williams
Sr Researcher: Tim Larson
Founded: 1983

LBS
Division of Library Binding Service
1801 Thompson Ave, Des Moines, IA 50316-
2751
Tel: 515-262-3191 *Toll Free Tel:* 800-247-5323
   Toll Free Fax: 800-262-4091
E-mail: info@lbsbind.com
Web Site: www.lbsbind.com
Key Personnel
Pres & CEO: Rob Mauritz *Tel:* 515-299-7402
   E-mail: robm@lbsbind.com
COO: Steve Deaton *Tel:* 515-299-1022
   E-mail: steved@lbsbind.com
CFO: Derek Stocking *Tel:* 515-299-1007
   E-mail: dereks@lbsbind.com
SVP & Gen Mgr: Joe Dunham *Tel:* 515-299-7416
   E-mail: joed@lbsbind.com
SVP, Corp Devt & Culture: Chris Paxson
   E-mail: chrisp@lbsbind.com
Acct Mgr: Shelly Davis *Tel:* 877-301-7421
   E-mail: shellyd@lbsbind.com
Sales Rep: Tony Nelson *Tel:* 866-331-7431
   E-mail: tonyn@lbsbind.com
Founded: 1936
Cover Line(s) Sold: Advantage 9; Advantage 7;
   Algora; Arrestox® B-Cloth; Arrestox® Shim-
   mer; Beaudiva; Buckram; C-1 Cloth; Canoso;
   Cezane; Chameleon; Chromo; Colibri; Colored
   Endleaf Paper; Cot-Linen; Diamond; Duo®;
   Dust; Eurobond®; euroBuckram; Excel-Tan®;
   Feincanvas; Fluctuations; Forest; Frankonia®;
   Hype; Imperial; Iris®; Ismara; Kashmir; Ken-
   nett®; Kensington® Leather; Leathers; Li-
   brary SUMMIT™; Linen Buckram; Linen
   Set®; Lino; Lipare; Liv; Lizard; Luminaire™;
   Lustre; Manhattan; Maple; Marano; Masanti;
   Medusa; Merino; Natural Papers; Nomad; Ot-
   tawa; Padusa; Pearl Linen®; Pellana; Printa
   Offset; Rebel; Record®; Reflections; Saffiano;
   Santina; Stingray; Sturdite®; Tango; Taratan
   II®; TexMex; Tsarina Crush; Velluto; Verona®;
   Walnut
Membership(s): Book Industry Guild of New
   York; Book Manufacturers' Institute (BMI)

Lindenmeyr Book Publishing Papers
Division of Central National Gottesman Inc
3 Manhattanville Rd, Purchase, NY 10577
Tel: 914-696-9300
Web Site: www.lindenmeyrbook.com
Key Personnel
Pres: Peter Harding
SVP: Tim Christie *Tel:* 914-696-9305
   E-mail: tchristie@lbppaper.com
Cust Serv Mgr: Michael A Yeager
   E-mail: myeager@lbppaper.com
Founded: 1859
Book Paper Line(s) Sold: Appleton; Domtar;
   Evergreen Packaging; Finch Pruyn; Georgia-
   Pacific; Glatfelter; International Paper; Kansaki;
   Kruger Inc; Madison International; Mohawk
   Paper; Monadnock Paper Mills Inc; Newton
   Falls; Plainwell; Rolland; Stora Enso; Ter-
   vakoski; Wausau Paper; Weyerhaeuser/NOR-
   PAC; Zanders

Cover Line(s) Sold: Eastex Inc; International Pa-
   per; Mead; Smart Papers; Temboard; UPM-
   Kymmene; Zanders
Paper Type(s) Sold: Book Offset; Coated Free
   Sheet; Coated Groundwood; Uncoated Free
   Sheet; Uncoated Groundwood
Membership(s): Association of American Pub-
   lishers (AAP); Book Industry Guild of New
   York; Book Industry Study Group (BISG);
   Book Manufacturers' Institute (BMI); Book-
   builders of Boston; Publishing Professionals
   Network (PPN)

Lindenmeyr Paper, see Lindenmeyr Book
Publishing Papers

McClain Printing Co
212 Main St, Parsons, WV 26287-1033
Mailing Address: PO Box 403, Parsons, WV
26287-0403
Tel: 304-478-2881 *Toll Free Tel:* 800-654-7179
   Fax: 304-478-4658
E-mail: mcclain@mcclainprinting.com
Web Site: www.mcclainprinting.com
Key Personnel
Pres: Kenneth E Smith
VP, Publg: Michelle McKinnie
Founded: 1958

McManus & Morgan
2506 W Seventh St, Los Angeles, CA 90057
Tel: 213-387-4433
Web Site: www.mcmanusandmorgan.com
Key Personnel
Owner: Gary Wolin *E-mail:* gary@
   mcmanusmorgan.com
Founded: 1923

Mekatronics Inc
85 Channel Dr, Port Washington, NY 11050
Tel: 516-883-6805 *Fax:* 516-883-6948
E-mail: office@mekatronicsinc.com
Web Site: mekatronicsinc.com
Key Personnel
Pres: Jack Bendror *E-mail:* jbendror@
   mekatronicsinc.com
Founded: 1960
Membership(s): The American Library Associa-
   tion (ALA)

Miami Wabash Paper LLC
Affiliate of Mafcote Inc
301 Wedcor Ave, Wabash, IN 46992
Tel: 260-563-4181 *Toll Free Tel:* 800-842-9112
   Fax: 219-563-2724
E-mail: miamivalley@mafcote.com
Web Site: www.mafcote.com
Key Personnel
Pres: Steven A Schulman
VP: Daryl Evans
Founded: 1965

Midland Paper, Packaging & Supplies
101 E Palatine Rd, Wheeling, IL 60090
Mailing Address: PO Box 9032, Wheeling, IL
60090-9032
Tel: 847-777-2700 *Toll Free Tel:* 800-323-8522;
   888-564-3526 (cust serv) *Fax:* 847-403-6320
   (cust serv)
E-mail: whl@midlandpaper.com; sales@
   midlandpaper.com; custservice@midlandpaper.
   com
Web Site: www.midlandpaper.com
Key Personnel
CEO: Mike Graves
EVP & CFO: Ralph DeLetto
EVP, Publg & Consulting: Jim O'Toole
Founded: 1907
Book Paper Line(s) Sold: BPM Inc; Cata-
   lyst; Cenveo; Clearwater Paper; CTI; Dec-
   orated; Domtar; FiberMark; French Paper

Co; Kallima® Coated Cover C1S; Kallima®
   Coated Cover C2S; Kruger Inc; Mactac;
   Magic; Mohawk Paper; Moorim; Neenah Pa-
   per; Nekoosa; Pixelle Specialty Solutions™;
   Reich Paper; Resolute Forest Products; SIHL
   Inc; Teslin®; Verso Corp; Yupo Corporation
   America
Branch Office(s)
363 N Third St, Des Plaines, IL 60016 *Toll
   Free Tel:* 800-323-8522 *Fax:* 847-403-6302
   E-mail: des@midlandpaper.com
150 S Unit Dr, Normal, IL 61761 *Toll Free
   Tel:* 866-289-2974 *Toll Free Fax:* 866-289-2975
   E-mail: nml@midlandpaper.com
1801 Hollister Whitney Pkwy, Quincy, IL 62305
   Toll Free Tel: 866-289-2974 *Fax:* 217-223-0905
   E-mail: qcy@midlandpaper.com
690 Southrock Dr, Rockford, IL 61102 *Toll
   Free Tel:* 800-929-3380 *Fax:* 847-403-6365
   E-mail: rok@midlandpaper.com
2050 W Iles Ave, Springfield, IL 62704 *Toll
   Free Tel:* 866-289-2974 *Fax:* 847-403-6385
   E-mail: spg@midlandpaper.com
2 Venture, Suite 455, Irvine, CA 92618 *Toll
   Free Tel:* 855-353-3922 *Fax:* 847-403-6303
   E-mail: nat@midlandpaper.com
CohereOne, 777 Grand Ave, Suite 204, San
   Rafael, CA 94901 *Tel:* 415-322-6986
   E-mail: info@cohereone.com
1375 Kings Hwy E, Suite 240, Fairfield, CT
   06824 *Toll Free Tel:* 888-615-5551 *Fax:* 203-
   256-1548 *E-mail:* nat@midlandpaper.com
1140A Maxwell Ave, Evansville, IN 47711 *Toll
   Free Tel:* 888-260-5270 *Fax:* 847-403-6260
   E-mail: evn@midlandpaper.com
2363 Perry Rd, Suite 150, Plainfield, IN 46168
   Toll Free Tel: 800-888-8291 *Fax:* 847-403-6308
   E-mail: ind@midlandpaper.com
801 S 19 St, West Des Moines, IA 50265 *Toll
   Free Tel:* 800-422-3174 *Fax:* 847-403-6305
   E-mail: dem@midlandpaper.com
14449 W 100 St, Lenexa, KS 66215 *Toll
   Free Tel:* 866-204-9700 *Fax:* 847-403-6278
   E-mail: len@midlandpaper.com
3805 Business Park Dr, Louisville, KY 40213
   Toll Free Tel: 888-260-6398 *Fax:* 502-969-8177
   E-mail: lou@midlandpaper.com
30 Constitution Dr, Southborough, MA 01801
   Tel: 847-777-2480 *E-mail:* nat@midlandpaper.
   com
1860 SE Elm St, Minneapolis, MN 55414 *Toll
   Free Tel:* 866-339-0414 *Fax:* 847-403-6886
   E-mail: mnp@midlandpaper.com
401 Hazelwood Logistics, Center Dr, Suite
   500, St Louis, MO 63042 *Toll Free Tel:* 888-
   260-4105 *Fax:* 847-403-6380 *E-mail:* stl@
   midlandpaper.com
4363 W Calhoun St, Suite A, Springfield, MO
   65802 *Toll Free Tel:* 888-832-8200 *Fax:* 847-
   403-6385 *E-mail:* spm@midlandpaper.com
40 Hillcrest Rd, Madison, NJ 07940 *Tel:* 847-
   777-2418 *E-mail:* nat@midlandpaper.com
440 Ivy Trails Dr, Cincinnati, OH 45244 *Toll
   Free Tel:* 855-549-2930 *Fax:* 847-403-6281
   E-mail: nat@midlandpaper.com
6749 E 12 St, Tulsa, OK 74112 *Toll Free
   Tel:* 888-260-5835 *Fax:* 847-403-6335
   E-mail: tul@midlandpaper.com
10200 Harwin Dr, Houston, TX 77036-1587
   Tel: 713-995-9510 *Fax:* 281-530-9619
   E-mail: hou@midlandpaper.com
195 NE Gilman Blvd, Suite 201, Issaquah, WA
   98027 *Toll Free Tel:* 855-900-2874 *Fax:* 847-
   403-6916 *E-mail:* nat@midlandpaper.com
4826 W Converters Dr, Appleton, WI 54913 *Toll
   Free Tel:* 800-242-3398 *Fax:* 847-403-6936
   E-mail: app@midlandpaper.com
1220 Femrite Dr, Suite 208, Madison, WI 53716
   Toll Free Tel: 866-339-0406 *Fax:* 847-403-6350
   E-mail: mad@midlandpaper.com

8601 N 91 St, Milwaukee, WI 53224 *Toll Free Tel:* 800-242-8917 *Fax:* 847-403-6910
E-mail: mke@midlandpaper.com
400 S 72 Ave, Wausau, WI 54401 *Toll Free Tel:* 800-688-1872 *Fax:* 847-403-6333
E-mail: wsa@midlandpaper.com

Midwest Paper Group
540 Prospect St, Combined Locks, WI 54113
Tel: 920-788-3550 *Toll Free Tel:* 800-828-1987
Fax: 920-968-3950
Web Site: mwpaper.com
Key Personnel
VP, Publg Papers: Mike Baker *Tel:* 920-968-3801
Founded: 1907
Book Paper Line(s) Milled: Ethos Offset Smooth; Ethos Offset Vellum; Utopia Coated Matte; Utopia Matte Inkjet

Mohawk Fine Papers Inc
465 Saratoga St, Cohoes, NY 12047
Tel: 518-237-1740 *Toll Free Tel:* 800-THE-MILL (843-6455) *Fax:* 518-237-7394
Web Site: www.mohawkconnects.com
Key Personnel
Chmn & CEO: Thomas D O'Connor, Jr
COO: Bruce M Hogan
EVP & CFO: John P Macy
Chief Revenue Offr: Melissa Stevens
Chief Strategy Offr: Paul J Biesiadecki
Founded: 1931
Book Paper Line(s) Milled: Mohawk Carnival; Mohawk Everyday Digital Uncoated; Mohawk Loop; Mohawk Opaque; Mohawk Options; Mohawk Skytone; Mohawk Superfine; Mohawk Via; Strathmore Premium; Strathmore Writing
Cover Line(s) Milled: Mohawk Carnival; Mohawk Everyday Digital Uncoated; Mohawk Loop; Mohawk Opaque; Mohawk Options; Mohawk Skytone; Mohawk Superfine; Mohawk Via; Strathmore Premium; Strathmore Writing
Book Paper Line(s) Sold: Chromolux; Curious Collection; Keaykolour; Mohawk Paper; Strathmore
Cover Line(s) Sold: Chromolux; Curious Collection; Keaykolour; Mohawk Paper; Strathmore
Paper Type(s) Sold: Acid Free; Recycled

Monadnock Paper Mills Inc
117 Antrim Rd, Bennington, NH 03442-4205
Tel: 603-588-3311 *Toll Free Tel:* 800-221-2159 (cust serv) *Fax:* 603-588-3158
E-mail: info@mpm.com
Web Site: www.mpm.com
Key Personnel
Dir, Mktg & Communs: Lisa Berghaum
Founded: 1819
Book Paper Line(s) Sold: Astrolite; Astrolite Digital+; Astrolite PC 100; Astrolite PC 100 Velvet C2S; Caress; Dulcet®
Cover Line(s) Sold: Astrolite; Astrolite Digital+; Astrolite PC 100; Astrolite PC 100 Velvet C2S; Caress; Dulcet®; Duraprint™
Membership(s): American Forest & Paper Association; University & College Designers Association

Neenah Inc
3460 Preston Ridge Rd, Suite 600, Alpharetta, GA 30005
Toll Free Tel: 800-344-5287
E-mail: publishing.team@neenah.com
Web Site: www.neenahperformance.com/products/neenah-performance/publishing-products
Key Personnel
Dir, Sales & Mktg: Melanie Calkins
Book Paper Line(s) Milled: Corvon®; HyFlex®; Kivar®; Kivarflex™; Lexide®; Lexotone®; Skivertex®
Branch Office(s)
5492 Bostwick St, Lowville, KY 13367
443B Shaker Rd, East Longmeadow, MA 01028

501 E Munising Ave, Munising, MI 49862
Bridge St, Brownville, NY 13615
45 N Fourth St, Quakertown, PA 18951
Membership(s): Book Manufacturers' Institute (BMI)

Iris Nevins Decorative Papers
PO Box 429, Johnsonburg, NJ 07846-0429
Tel: 908-813-8617
E-mail: irisnevins@verizon.net
Web Site: www.marblingpaper.com
Key Personnel
Owner: Iris Nevins
Founded: 1978

OGM USA
4333 46 St, Suite F2, Sunnyside, NY 11104
Tel: 212-964-2430
Web Site: www.ogm.it
Key Personnel
Chmn, CEO & Sales Rep: Rino Varrasso
E-mail: rvarrasso@ogm-usa.com
Founded: 1974

Omniafiltra LLC
9567 Main St, Beaver Falls, NY 13305
Mailing Address: PO Box 410, Beaver Falls, NY 13305
Tel: 315-346-7300
Web Site: www.omniafiltra.it/inglese/default_en.html
Key Personnel
Mill Mgr: Scott Sauer
Busn Devt & Sales Mgr: Peter Gendreau
Founded: 1955

O'Neil Digital Solutions LLC
12655 Beatrice St, Los Angeles, CA 90066
Tel: 310-448-6400
E-mail: sales@oneildata.com
Web Site: www.oneildata.com
Key Personnel
Pres & COO: Terry Chan
EVP, Sales & Mktg: Mark Rosson
Dir, HR: LaDonna Wise
Founded: 1973

Overseas Printing Corporation
Division of InnerWorkings Inc
4040 Civic Center Dr, Suite 200, San Rafael, CA 94903
Tel: 415-500-8331 *Fax:* 415-835-9899
Web Site: www.overseasprinting.com
Key Personnel
Sr Prodn Mgr: Shaun Garrett *E-mail:* sgarrett@inwk.com
Founded: 1972

The Ovid Bell Press Inc
Subsidiary of Walsworth Publishing Co
1201 Bluff St, Fulton, MO 65251
Mailing Address: PO Box 370, Fulton, MO 65251-0370
Tel: 573-642-2256 *Toll Free Tel:* 800-835-8919
E-mail: sales@ovidbell.com
Web Site: ovidbell.com
Key Personnel
CFO: Jill Custard *E-mail:* jillcustard@ovidbell.com
Pres: Troy Williams *Tel:* 573-310-2599
E-mail: troywilliams@ovidbell.com
VP, Sales & Mktg: David O'Donley *Tel:* 573-310-2630 *E-mail:* david@ovidbell.com
Plant Mgr: Kevin Werdehausen *Tel:* 573-310-2598
E-mail: kevin.werdehausen@ovidbell.com
Founded: 1927

Patterson Printing Co
1550 Territorial Rd, Benton Harbor, MI 49022
Tel: 269-925-2177 *Toll Free Tel:* 800-848-8826
Fax: 269-925-6057

E-mail: sales@patterson-printing.com
Web Site: www.patterson-printing.com
Key Personnel
Pres: Leroy Patterson
Plant Mgr: Pamela Thames *Tel:* 269-925-2177 ext 542
Founded: 1956

PCA Printing, see Printing Corporation of the Americas Inc

Peregrine Arts Bindery
7 Avenida Vista Grande, Suite B-7 119, Santa Fe, NM 87508
Tel: 505-466-0490
Web Site: www.peregrineartsbindery.etsy.com
Key Personnel
Pres: Katherine Loeffler

PrairieView Press
625 Seventh St, Gretna, MB R0G 0V0, Canada
Mailing Address: PO Box 460, Gretna, MB R0G 0V0, Canada
Tel: 204-327-6543 *Toll Free Tel:* 800-477-7377
Toll Free Fax: 866-480-0253
Web Site: prairieviewpress.com
Key Personnel
Owner & Pres: Chester Goossen
Founded: 1968

Pratt Paper Company LLC
20 Davis Rd, Marblehead, MA 01945
Tel: 781-639-9450 *Fax:* 781-639-9452
Key Personnel
Pres & CEO: A Diehl Jenkins *E-mail:* djenkins@prattpaper.com
CFO: Drew J Lemieux
Founded: 1907
Book Paper Line(s) Sold: Finch Pruyn; Glatfelter; International Paper; Monadnock Paper Mills Inc; Rolland; Stora Enso; Tervakoski; UPM-Kymmene
Cover Line(s) Sold: Glatfelter; Monadnock Paper Mills Inc; Rolland; Stora Enso

Printing Corporation of the Americas Inc
620 SW 12 Ave, Pompano Beach, FL 33069
Tel: 954-781-8100 *Toll Free Tel:* 866-721-1PCA (721-1722)
Web Site: pcaprintingplus.com
Key Personnel
Pres: Buddy Tuchman
Sales Mgr: Steven Konecky *E-mail:* steven@pcaprinting.com
Founded: 1980

PrintWest
1111 Eighth Ave, Regina, SK S4R 1C9, Canada
Tel: 306-525-2304 *Toll Free Tel:* 800-236-6438
Fax: 306-757-2439
E-mail: general@printwest.com
Web Site: www.printwest.com
Key Personnel
Pres & Dir, Opers: Corie Triffo
VP, Sales & Mktg: Ken Benson
Founded: 1992

Rayonier Advanced Materials
1301 Riverplace Blvd, Suite 2300, Jacksonville, FL 32207
Tel: 904-357-4600
Web Site: rayonieram.com
Key Personnel
Chmn, Pres & CEO: Paul G Boynton
SVP, Forest Prods, Paper & Board Busn: Chris Black
SVP, Mfg Opers: William R Manzer
Founded: 1937
Branch Office(s)
405 The West Mall, Suite 800, Toronto, ON M9C

5J1, Canada *Tel:* 416-775-2806 *Fax:* 416-621-3119

4 Place Ville-Marie, Suite 100, Montreal, QC H3B 2E7, Canada *Tel:* 514-871-0137 *Fax:* 514-397-0896

10 Gatineau Rd, PO Box 5000, Temiscaming, QC J0Z 3R0, Canada *Tel:* 819-627-4780 *Fax:* 819-627-1178

Sales Office(s): 4474 Savannah Hwy, Jesup, GA 31545, Contact: John Gegg *Tel:* 912-588-8007 *Fax:* 912-588-8300 *E-mail:* john.gegg@rayonieram.com

Hotel Equatorial, Unit 804, Off Bldg, 65, Yanan Rd W, Shanghai 200040, China, Contact: Wu Yaodong *Tel:* (021) 6248-2510; (021) 6249-6127; (0139) 01764581 (cell) *Fax:* (021) 6248-8929 *E-mail:* yaodong.wu@rayonieram.com

Cross Off Uchisaiwaicho, 1-18-6, Nishishimbashi, Minato-ku, Tokyo 105-0003, Japan, Contact: Tatsuro Miyachi *Tel:* (03) 6457-9530; (070) 2810-9913 (cell) *Fax:* (03) 6457-9532 *E-mail:* tatsuro.miyachi@rayonieram.com

Reichhold Inc
1035 Swabia Ct, Durham, NC 27703
Mailing Address: PO Box 13582, Research Triangle Park, NC 27709
Tel: 919-990-7500 *Toll Free Tel:* 800-448-3482 *Fax:* 919-990-7749
Web Site: www.reichhold.com
Key Personnel
Pres & CEO: John Gaither
SVP, Corp Servs: Mitzi Van Leeuwen
Founded: 1927
Branch Office(s)
237 S Motor Ave, Azusa, CA 91702 *Tel:* 626-334-4974 *Fax:* 626-969-6978
54 Wamsley Rd, Jacksonville, FL 32254 *Tel:* 904-695-7500 *Fax:* 904-695-7517
425 S Pace Blvd, Pensacola, FL 32502 *Tel:* 850-433-7621 *Fax:* 850-433-7699
6350 E Collins Rd, Morris, IL 60450 *Tel:* 815-942-4600 *Fax:* 815-942-4722
249 Saint Louis Ave, Valley Park, MO 63088 *Tel:* 636-225-5226 *Fax:* 636-225-2954
1503 Haden Rd, Houston, TX 77015 *Tel:* 713-453-5431 *Fax:* 713-453-1093

Resolute Forest Products
111 Robert-Bourassa Blvd, Suite 5000, Montreal, QC H3C 2M1, Canada
Tel: 514-875-2160 *Toll Free Tel:* 800-361-2888
E-mail: info@resolutefp.com
Web Site: www.resolutefp.com
Key Personnel
Pres & CEO: Yves Laflamme
SVP & CFO: Jo-Ann Longworth
SVP, Corp Aff & Chief Legal Offr: Jacques Vachon
SVP, HR: Daniel Ouellet
SVP, Pulp & Paper Opers: Richard Tremblay
SVP, Pulp & Paper Sales & Mktg: John Lafave
SVP, Tissue Group: Patrice Minguez
Founded: 2011
Book Paper Line(s) Milled: Alternative Book; Alternative Book Cream; Alternative Offset; Alternative Opaque; Ecopaque Offset; Equal Book; Equal Offset; Resolute Connect; ResoluteBook 70; ResoluteBook 70 Cream; ResoluteBook 75; ResoluteBook 60; ResoluteBook 65; ResoluteLite; ResoluteSCA; ResoluteSCA+; ResoluteSCA++; ResoluteSCB; ResoluteSelect 70; ResoluteSelect 75; ResoluteSelect 65; ResoluteSNC
Book Paper Line(s) Sold: Alternative Book; Alternative Book Cream; Alternative Offset; Alternative Opaque; Ecopaque Offset; Equal Book; Equal Offset; Resolute Connect; ResoluteBook 70; ResoluteBook 70 Cream; ResoluteBook 75; ResoluteBook 60; ResoluteBook 65; ResoluteLite; ResoluteSCA; ResoluteSCA+; ResoluteSCA++; ResoluteSCB;

ResoluteSelect 70; ResoluteSelect 75; ResoluteSelect 65; ResoluteSNC
Paper Type(s) Sold: Coated Mechanical No 4; Coated Mechanical No 5; Directory; Supercalendered; Uncoated Free Sheet; Uncoated Mechanical
Membership(s): American Forest & Paper Association; American Wood Council (AWC); Forest Products Association of Canada (FPAC); FPInnovations; Quebec Forest Industry Council (QFIC); Two Sides North America Inc

Rolland Enterprises
256 JB Rolland W, St-Jerome, QC J7Y 0L6, Canada
Toll Free Tel: 800-567-9872 (CN); 800-388-0882 (US)
E-mail: media@rollandinc.com; marketing@rollandinc.com
Web Site: www.rollandinc.com
Founded: 1882
Book Paper Line(s) Milled: Rolland Enviro® Book; Rolland Enviro® Opaque Offset; Rolland Enviro® Print; Rolland Enviro® Satin; Rolland HiBulk; Rolland Kraft®; Rolland Opaque®

Roosevelt Paper Co
One Roosevelt Dr, Mount Laurel, NJ 08054
Tel: 856-303-4100 *Toll Free Tel:* 800-523-3470 *Fax:* 856-642-1949
E-mail: marketing@rooseveltpaper.com
Web Site: www.rooseveltpaper.com
Key Personnel
Chmn & CEO: Ted Kosloff
CFO: Tony Janulewicz
CIO: John Gordon, Jr
Pres: David Kosloff
VP, Sales & Mktg: Dean T Egan
Sales Mgr: Dennis Carney
Founded: 1932
Branch Office(s)
5100 W 123 St, Alsip, IL 60803, Div Mgr: Donald Raugh *Tel:* 708-653-5121 *Toll Free Tel:* 800-323-1778 *Fax:* 708-653-3103
11001 Paper Blvd, Richwood, KY 41094-9341, Div Mgr: Donald Raugh *Tel:* 859-485-8100 *Toll Free Tel:* 800-354-9829 *Fax:* 859-485-9724

St Armand Paper Mill
3700 St Patrick, Montreal, QC H4E 1A2, Canada
Tel: 514-931-8338 *Fax:* 514-931-5953
Web Site: www.st-armand.com
Key Personnel
Prop: David Carruthers
VP: Denise Lapointe
Founded: 1979
Book Paper Line(s) Milled: Canal Paper; Old Masters
Cover Line(s) Milled: St Armand Colours
Membership(s): Alcuin Society; Canadian Bookbinders & Book Artists Guild (CBBAG); Pulp & Paper Technical Association of Canada (PAPTAC)

Sappi Fine Paper North America
Subsidiary of Sappi Ltd
255 State St, Boston, MA 02109
Tel: 617-423-7300 *Toll Free Tel:* 800-882-4332
E-mail: webqueriesna@sappi.com
Web Site: www.sappi.com/na
Key Personnel
Pres & CEO: Mike Haws
VP & CFO: Annette Luchene
VP, Graphics, Packaging & Specialties: Deece Hannigan
VP, HR & Gen Coun: Sarah Manchester
VP, Mfg: Mike Schultz
VP, Pulp Busn & Supply Chain: Anne Ayer
VP, Res, Devt & Sustainability: Beth Cormier
Founded: 1854 (as S D Warren Co which was acquired by Sappi in 1994)

Book Paper Line(s) Milled: EuroArt Plus (sheet); Flo (sheet, web & digital); Galerie Brite (web); Galerie Fine (web); Galerie Lite (web); McCoy (sheet, web & digital); Opus (sheet, web & digital); Opus PS (sheet & web); Somerset (web)
Cover Line(s) Milled: EuroArt Plus (sheet); Flo (sheet, web & digital); Galerie Brite (web); Galerie Fine (web); Galerie Lite (web); McCoy (sheet, web & digital); Opus (sheet, web & digital); Opus PS (sheet & web); Somerset (web)
Sales Office(s): Western Region Sales Office, 333 S Anita Dr, Suite 840, Orange, CA 92868 *Tel:* 714-456-0600
Southern Region Sales Office, 3700 Mansell Rd, Suite 140, Alpharetta, GA 30322 *Tel:* 404-751-2600
Chicago Sales Office, 10600 W Higgins Rd, Suite 701, Rosemont, IL 60018 *Toll Free Tel:* 800-333-9855
Great Lakes Region Sales Office, 1717 Dixie Hwy, Suite 150B, Fort Wright, KY 41011 *Toll Free Tel:* 888-739-6601
Pulp Sales Office-North America, 20 N 22 St, Cloquet, MN 55720 *Tel:* 218-879-2300
Northern Region Sales Office, 287 Bowman Ave, Suite 225, Purchase, NY 10577-2544 *Tel:* 914-696-5544

Sepp Leaf Products Inc
381 Park Ave S, No 13, New York, NY 10016
Tel: 212-683-2840 *Fax:* 212-725-0308
E-mail: sales@seppleaf.com
Web Site: www.seppleaf.com
Key Personnel
Pres: Peter Sepp

Sheridan MI
Division of CJK Group Inc
613 E Industrial Dr, Chelsea, MI 48118
Tel: 734-475-9145
Web Site: www.sheridan.com
Key Personnel
Pres: Paul Bozuwa *E-mail:* paul.bozuwa@sheridan.com
VP, Book Sales: Joe Thomson *E-mail:* joe.thomson@sheridan.com
VP, Fin: Nicole Mummert *E-mail:* nicole.mummert@sheridan.com
VP, HR: Ken Rapp *E-mail:* ken.rapp@sheridan.com
VP, Opers: Paul Loy *E-mail:* paul.loy@sheridan.com
Cust Serv Mgr: Ed Blissick *E-mail:* ed.blissick@sheridan.com
Direct Sales Rep: Jessica Ansorge *Tel:* 734-385-1544 *E-mail:* jessica.ansorge@sheridan.com; Kathy Brown *Tel:* 734-385-1540 *E-mail:* kathy.brown@sheridan.com; Rebecca Humrich *Tel:* 734-385-1543 *E-mail:* rebecca.humrich@sheridan.com; Jennifer Riemenschneider *Tel:* 734-385-1533 *E-mail:* jennifer.riemenschneider@sheridan.com
Founded: 1950

Simon Miller Paper & Packaging
3409 W Chester Pike, Suite 204, Newton Square, PA 19073
Tel: 215-923-3600 *Toll Free Tel:* 800-642-1899 *Fax:* 610-355-9330
E-mail: info@simonmiller.com
Web Site: www.simonmiller.com
Key Personnel
Chmn & CEO: Henri C Levit *E-mail:* henri.levit@simonmiller.com
Dir, Opers: Jeffrey Levit
Dir, Sales & Mktg: G Scott Earls
Founded: 1926
Cover Line(s) Milled: New Age
Book Paper Line(s) Sold: Domtar; Finch Pruyn; Glatfelter; Manistique; Seaman; Stora
Paper Type(s) Sold: Acid Free; Recycled

Membership(s): Forest Stewardship Council US (FSC-US); Graphic Arts Association; National Paper Trade Association (NPTA); Two Sides North America Inc

Smith-Edwards-Dunlap Co
2867 E Allegheny Ave, Philadelphia, PA 19134
Tel: 215-425-8800 *Toll Free Tel:* 800-829-0020
Fax: 215-425-9715
E-mail: sales@sed.com
Web Site: www.sed.com
Key Personnel
Pres: Jonathan Shapiro
Sales Mgr: Fred Binder
Founded: 1880

Solar-Screen Co Inc
53-11 105 St, Corona, NY 11368
Tel: 718-592-8222 *Toll Free Tel:* 800-347-6527
Toll Free Fax: 888-271-0891
E-mail: solarscreen@prodigy.net
Web Site: www.solar-screen.com
Key Personnel
Pres: Miles Joseph
Founded: 1960

Southeastern Printing Co
3601 SE Dixie Hwy, Stuart, FL 34997
Tel: 772-287-2141 *Toll Free Tel:* 800-226-8221
Fax: 772-288-3988
E-mail: sales@seprint.com
Web Site: www.seprint.com
Key Personnel
Pres: Don Mader
Founded: 1924
Branch Office(s)
950 SE Eighth St, Hialeah, FL 33010 *Tel:* 305-885-8707 *Fax:* 305-888-9903 *E-mail:* info@seprint.com
Sales Office(s): 6001 Park of Commerce Blvd, Suite 200, Boca Raton, FL 33487 *Tel:* 561-998-0870

Spectrum PrintGroup Inc
1535 Farmer's Lane, Suite 254, Santa Rosa, CA 95405
Tel: 707-542-6044 *Toll Free Tel:* 888-340-6049
Fax: 707-542-6045
E-mail: sales@spectrumprintgroup.com
Web Site: www.spectrumprintgroup.com
Key Personnel
Pres: Duncan McCallum *Tel:* 707-542-6044 ext 102 *E-mail:* duncan@spectrumprintgroup.com
Busn Devt Mgr: Elise Gochberg *Tel:* 415-461-1130 *E-mail:* elise@spectrumprintgroup.com
Founded: 1985

Spicers Paper
Division of Central National Gottesman Inc
12310 E Slauson Ave, Santa Fe Springs, CA 90670
Toll Free Tel: 800-774-2377 *Fax:* 562-693-8339
Web Site: www.spicers.com
Key Personnel
Pres: Jan Gottesman
SVP: Rick Anderson
Book Paper Line(s) Milled: Moorim; Sappi
Cover Line(s) Milled: Clearwater; Moorim; MWV; Tango
Book Paper Line(s) Sold: CTI; Domtar; French Paper Co; Mohawk Paper; Neenah Paper; Sappi; Verso Corp; West Linn Paper Co; Yupo Corporation America
Cover Line(s) Sold: Appleton; Clearwater Paper; Tango
Paper Type(s) Sold: Acid Free; Book Offset; Chlorine Free; Coated Free Sheet; Coated Groundwood; Contract Embossings; Fancy; Printed; Recycled; Uncoated Free Sheet; Uncoated Groundwood

Branch Office(s)
47422 Kato Rd, Fremont, CA 94538, Contact: Jeff Jarvis *Tel:* 510-476-7700 *Fax:* 510-476-7755
105 S 41 Ave, Suite 2, Phoenix, AZ 85009, Contact: Kathy Markley *Tel:* 602-484-7337 *Fax:* 602-484-7388
14209 E 35 Place, Suite 103, Aurora, CO 80011, Contact: George Seymour *Tel:* 303-373-9655 *Fax:* 303-373-9658
320C Waiakamilo, Honolulu, HI 96817, Contact: Mr Jody Kadokawa *Tel:* 808-832-0001 *Fax:* 808-832-0016
4161 NE 189 Ave, Gresham, OR 97230 *Tel:* 503-405-0100 *Fax:* 503-405-0130
2454 S 3600 W, Suite A, West Valley City, UT 84119, Contact: Heath Lawrence *Tel:* 801-364-0113 *Fax:* 801-364-0302
21527 64 Ave S, Kent, WA 98032 *Tel:* 253-518-0030 *Fax:* 253-395-4849
Membership(s): National Paper Trade Association (NPTA); Visual Media Alliance (VMA)

StoraEnso North American Sales Inc
Canterbury Green, 201 Broad St, Stamford, CT 06901
Tel: 203-541-5100 *Fax:* 203-353-1143
Web Site: www.storaenso.com
Key Personnel
Pres: Peter Mersmann
Sales Dir, Paper: Courtney Wemyss *Tel:* 203-541-5194 *E-mail:* courtney.wemyss@storaenso.com
Book Paper Line(s) Milled: Belle; Bulky; Classic; Creamy; Lux; Lux Cream; Novel 80; Novel 76
Cover Line(s) Milled: LumiArt; LumiSilk; Novapress

The Studley Press Inc
151 E Housatonic St, Dalton, MA 01226
Mailing Address: PO Box 214, Dalton, MA 01227-0214
Tel: 413-684-0441 *Toll Free Tel:* 877-684-0441
Fax: 413-684-0220
Web Site: thestudleypress.com
Key Personnel
Owner: Suzanne K Salinetti *E-mail:* suzanne@thestudleypress.com
Founded: 1938

Styled Packaging LLC
PO Box 30299, Philadelphia, PA 19103-8299
Tel: 610-529-4122 *Fax:* 610-520-9662
Web Site: www.taylorbox.com
Key Personnel
Pres: William R Fenkel *E-mail:* jjibill@aol.com
Founded: 2003
Membership(s): Book Industry Guild of New York

Sun Chemical Corp
Member of DIC Group
35 Waterview Blvd, Parsippany, NJ 07054-1285
Tel: 973-404-6000
E-mail: globalmarketing@sunchemical.com
Web Site: www.sunchemical.com
Key Personnel
Pres & CEO: Myron Petruch
Chief Admin Offr, Gen Coun & Secy: James R Van Horn
Founded: 1830
Branch Office(s)
135 W Lake St, Northlake, IL 60164 (North American inks)
5020 Spring Grove Ave, Cincinnati, OH 45232 (performance pigments)
Av Justino de Maio, 140 Guarulhos, 07222-000 Sao Paulo-SP, Brazil *Tel:* (011) 2462 2500 *Fax:* (011) 2462 2520

Leeuwenveldsweg 3-T, 1382 LV Weesp, Netherlands
Wexham Springs, Framewood Rd, Slough SL3 6PJ, United Kingdom *Tel:* (0203) 139 0000 *Fax:* (0203) 139 0001

Superior Printing Ink Co Inc
100 North St, Teterboro, NJ 07608
Tel: 201-478-5600 *Fax:* 201-478-5650
Web Site: www.superiorink.com
Key Personnel
CEO: Jeffrey I Simons
COO: Angel Torres
CFO: Peter Nunez
Founded: 1918
Branch Office(s)
666 E Linwood Ave, Maple Shade Township, NJ 08052 *Tel:* 856-482-9066
252 Wright St, Newark, NJ 07114 *Tel:* 973-824-0005
2125 Yates Ave, Commerce, CA 90040 *Tel:* 323-767-2173 *Fax:* 323-767-2192
750 Sherman Ave, Hamden, CT 06514 *Tel:* 203-281-1921
1220 NW 23 Ave, Fort Lauderdale, FL 33311 *Tel:* 954-587-0780
7498 Fullerton St, Jacksonville, FL 32256 *Tel:* 904-538-0601
300-A Shirley Way, Atlanta, GA 30336 *Tel:* 404-691-6759
1125 Republic Dr, Addison, IL 60101 *Tel:* 630-543-9770
120 Forbes Blvd, Mansfield, MA 02048 *Tel:* 508-337-8181
255 E Main St, Marlborough, MA 01752 *Tel:* 508-481-5015
2483 Walden Ave, Cheektowaga, NY 14225 *Tel:* 716-685-6763
4020 Rozzelles Ferry Rd, Charlotte, NC 28216-3343 *Tel:* 704-399-2523
309 Gallimore Dairy Rd, Suite 104, Greensboro, NC 27409 *Tel:* 336-931-3100
4440 Creek Rd, Cincinnati, OH 45242 *Tel:* 513-221-4707
7655 Hub Pkwy, Suite 205, Cleveland, OH 44125 *Tel:* 216-328-1720
1481 Goodale Blvd, Columbus, OH 43212 *Tel:* 614-486-2100
2708 S 163 St, New Berlin, WI 53151 *Tel:* 262-796-1499
Membership(s): National Association of Printing Ink Manufacturers (NAPIM)

Talas
330 Morgan Ave, Brooklyn, NY 11211
Tel: 212-219-0770
E-mail: info@talasonline.com; support@talasonline.com
Web Site: www.talasonline.com
Key Personnel
Pres: Aarol Salik
VP: Jillian Salik
Founded: 1962

Taylor Specialty Books
Division of Balfour/Taylor
1550 W Mockingbird Lane, Dallas, TX 75235
Tel: 214-819-8588 (cust serv) *Fax:* 214-819-5051 (cust serv) *Toll Free Fax:* 800-203-9778
E-mail: rfq@taylorpub.com (estimates)
Web Site: www.taylorspecialtybooks.com
Key Personnel
VP, Sales & Mktg, Specialty Books: Rick Parra *Tel:* 214-819-5027 *E-mail:* rick.parra@balfour.com
Sales Rep: Kim Hawley *E-mail:* khawley@taylorpub.com; George Levesque *E-mail:* glevesque@taylorpub.com; Mark McCombs *E-mail:* mmcombs@taylorpub.com
Founded: 1939

Technical Library Service Inc, see Talas

The Thomas Tape & Supply Co Inc
1713 Sheridan Ave, Springfield, OH 45505
Mailing Address: PO Box 207, Springfield, OH
45501-0207
Tel: 937-325-6414 *Fax:* 937-325-2850
Web Site: www.thomastape.com
Key Personnel
Pres: David Simonton *E-mail:* dave11@
thomastape.com
Founded: 1894

Times Printing LLC
Division of Kappa Printing Management Asso-
ciates LLC (KPMA)
100 Industrial Dr, Random Lake, WI 53075
Tel: 920-994-4396 *Toll Free Tel:* 800-236-4396
(sales)
E-mail: info@kappapma.com
Web Site: www.kappapma.com
Founded: 1918

Toof American Digital
4222 Pilot Dr, Memphis, TN 38118
Tel: 901-274-3632 *Toll Free Tel:* 800-722-4772
Web Site: www.toofamericandigital.com
Key Personnel
Pres: Stillman McFadden
Founded: 1864

TSO General Corp
79 Emjay Blvd, Brentwood, NY 11717
Tel: 631-952-5320 *Fax:* 631-952-5315
Web Site: www.tsogeneral.com
Key Personnel
Pres: Kirk Malandrakis *E-mail:* kmalan@
tsogeneral.com
Founded: 1969

Tukaiz LLC
2917 N Latoria Lane, Franklin Park, IL 60131
Tel: 847-455-1588; 847-288-4968 (sales)
Toll Free Tel: 800-543-2674
E-mail: contacttukaiz@tukaiz.com
Web Site: www.tukaiz.com
Key Personnel
Founder & Mng Dir: Frank Defino, Sr
VP, Mng Dir & CFO: Christopher Calabra
VP & Mng Dir: Daniel Defino; Frank Defino, Jr
Founded: 1963

Twin Rivers Paper Co
82 Bridge Ave, Madawaska, ME 04756
Tel: 207-728-3321 *Toll Free Tel:* 800-920-9988
Fax: 207-728-8701
E-mail: info@twinriverspaper.com
Web Site: www.twinriverspaper.com
Key Personnel
Pres: Ken Winterhalter

VP, Sales: Tony Rigelman *Tel:* 404-285-1864
E-mail: tony.rigelman@twinriverspaper.com
VP, Strategy & Mktg: Dave Deger *Tel:* 207-523-
2355 *E-mail:* dave.deger@twinriverspaper.com

Ulster Linen Co Inc
383 Moffit Blvd, Islip, NY 11751
Tel: 631-859-5244 *Fax:* 631-859-4990
E-mail: sales@ulsterlinen.com
Web Site: www.ulsterlinen.com
Key Personnel
Dir: Joseph H Larmor
Sales Mgr: Jackie Mihaley
Founded: 1933

University Products Inc
517 Main St, Holyoke, MA 01040
Mailing Address: PO Box 101, Holyoke, MA
01041-0101
Tel: 413-532-3372 *Toll Free Tel:* 800-628-1912
(orders) *Fax:* 413-533-4743 *Toll Free Fax:* 800-
532-9281
E-mail: info@universityproducts.com
Web Site: www.universityproducts.com
Key Personnel
VP & Gen Mgr: John A Dunphy
Mktg Mgr: Linda McInerney
Founded: 1968

Veritiv™ Corporation
400 Northpark Town Ctr, 1000 Abernathy Rd,
Suite 1700, Atlanta, GA 30328
Tel: 770-391-8200 *Toll Free Tel:* 844-VERITIV
(837-4848); 800-864-7687 (cust serv)
E-mail: contactus@veritivcorp.com
Web Site: www.veritivcorp.com
Key Personnel
Chmn & CEO: Mary A Laschinger
Group VP, Publg & Print Mgmt: John Biscanti
Dir, Fin Planning & Analysis: Mac Gayden
Cust Serv Mgr: Mary Beth Vitale
Founded: 2014 (as a result of the merger of
Unisource Worldwide Inc & xpedx)
Book Paper Line(s) Sold: Econosource®;
Endurance™; nordic+®; Park Avenue™;
PoliPrint™; Seville™; Showcase™; Starbrite®
Opaque Select; uBRAND®
Paper Type(s) Sold: Acid Free

Versa Press Inc
1465 Spring Bay Rd, East Peoria, IL 61611-9788
Tel: 309-822-8272 *Toll Free Tel:* 800-447-7829
Fax: 309-822-8141
Web Site: www.versapress.com
Key Personnel
Chmn: Joseph F Kennell
Pres: Steven J Kennell
Sales Mgr: Darold D Frerichs *E-mail:* dfrerichs@
versapress.com

Founded: 1937
Membership(s): Book Manufacturers' Institute
(BMI)

Fred Weidner & Daughter Printers
99 Hudson St, 5th fl, New York, NY 10013
Tel: 646-706-5180
E-mail: info@fwdprinters.com
Web Site: www.fwdprinters.com
Key Personnel
Pres: Cynthia Weidner *E-mail:* cynthia@
fwdprinters.com
Creative Dir: Carol Mittelsdorf *E-mail:* carol@
fwdprinters.com
Founded: 1860

Whitehall Printing Co
4244 Corporate Sq, Naples, FL 34104
Tel: 239-643-6464 *Toll Free Tel:* 800-321-9290
Fax: 239-643-6439
E-mail: info@whitehallprinting.com
Web Site: www.whitehallprinting.com
Key Personnel
Chmn: Mike Hirsch
Pres: Jeff Hirsch
VP: Emil G Hirsch
Founded: 1959

B W Wilson Paper Co Inc
2501 Brittons Hill Rd, Richmond, VA 23230
Tel: 804-358-6715 *Toll Free Tel:* 800-868-2868
Fax: 804-358-4742
E-mail: info@bwwilson.com; sales@bwwilson.
com
Web Site: www.bwwilson.com
Key Personnel
Pres: Lawrence H Rauppius, Jr
Dir, Sales & Mktg: Phil L Knab
Founded: 1904
Branch Office(s)
1015 Cavalier Blvd, Chesapeake, VA 27215
Tel: 757-487-7700 *Toll Free Tel:* 800-277-1136
Fax: 757-485-0710
2817 Carroll Ave, Lynchburg, VA 24501
Tel: 434-847-5220 *Toll Free Tel:* 888-511-3072
Fax: 434-847-5265
1006 Hauerhill Rd, Baltimore, MD 21229
308 S Anthony St, Burlington, NC 27215
Tel: 336-226-3226 *Toll Free Tel:* 800-277-9895
Fax: 336-226-3127
1219-B S Brightleaf Blvd, Smithfield, NC 27577
Toll Free Tel: 800-868-2868 *Fax:* 804-358-4742
2969 N Seventh St, Harris, PA 17110

Xerox Corp
26600 SW Parkway Ave, Wilsonville, OR 97070
Toll Free Tel: 800-835-6100 (cust serv)
Web Site: www.office.xerox.com

Manufacturing Services & Equipment Index

Manufacturing Services & Equipment

This section includes companies throughout the world offering manufacturing services. Services include distribution and mailing as well as companies that manufacture and distribute book manufacturing equipment, types and matrices. The descriptions of the services provided are paid components. For additional book distribution and mailing firms, see **Book Distributors & Sales Representatives** and **Shipping Services**.

A-R Editions Inc
1600 Aspen Commons, Suite 100, Middleton, WI 53562
Tel: 608-836-9000 *Fax:* 608-831-8200
E-mail: info@areditions.com
Web Site: www.areditions.com
Key Personnel
Pres & CEO: Patrick Wall *Tel:* 608-203-2575
  E-mail: patrick.wall@areditions.com
Dir, Spec Projs: James Zychowicz *Tel:* 608-203-2580 *E-mail:* james.zychowicz@areditions.com
Founded: 1962

AAVIM, see American Association for Vocational Instructional Materials

Adair Graphic Communications
Division of Printwell
26975 Northline Rd, Taylor, MI 48180
Tel: 734-941-6300 *Fax:* 734-942-0920
E-mail: adair@printwell.com
Web Site: www.adairgraphic.com
Key Personnel
Pres & CEO: Paul Borg
VP: Dennis Adair *E-mail:* dennis@adairgraphic.com
Founded: 1931

Agfa Graphics
611 River Dr, Center 3, Elmwood Park, NJ 07407
Tel: 201-440-2500 *Toll Free Tel:* 888-274-8626
  (cust serv)
E-mail: customercare.us@agfa.com
Web Site: agfagraphics.us
Key Personnel
Dir, Mktg: Deborah Hutcheson *E-mail:* deborah.hutcheson@agfa.com
Branch Office(s)
10798 Catawba Ave, Fontana, CA 92337 (dist ctr)
2240 Winton Ave, Hayward, CA 94545 (warehouse)
14303 Moncrieff Place, Suite C, Aurora, CO 80011 (dist ctr)
2544 E Landstreet Rd, Suite 100, Orlando, FL 32824 (dist ctr)
800 Bilter Rd, Aurora, IL 60502 (warehouse)
2650 Second St NE, Minneapolis, MN 55418 (dist ctr)
22 Stauffer Industrial Park, DC5, Taylor, PA 18517 (dist ctr)
3450 Roy Orr Blvd, Grand Prairie, TX 75050 (dist ctr)
Sales Office(s): 665 Raco Dr, Suite C, Lawrenceville, GA 30046 (sales/dist ctr)
Riverway West, 9399 W Higgens Rd, Suite 130W, Rosemont, IL 60018
200 Ballardvale St, Wilmington, MA 01887 (sales/R&D)

Amergraph Corp
Unit of HID Ultraviolet LLC
Rte 15, 520 Lafayette Rd, Sparta, NJ 07871
Tel: 973-383-8700 *Fax:* 973-383-9225
E-mail: sales@amergraph.com
Web Site: amergraph.com
Founded: 1975

American Association for Vocational Instructional Materials
220 Smithonia Rd, Winterville, GA 30683

Tel: 706-742-5355 *Fax:* 706-742-7005
Key Personnel
Dir: Gary Farmer
Founded: 1949

American Mathematical Society (AMS)
201 Charles St, Providence, RI 02904-2213
SAN: 201-1654
Tel: 401-455-4000 *Toll Free Tel:* 800-321-4267
  Fax: 401-331-3842; 401-455-4046 (cust serv)
E-mail: cust-serv@ams.org; ams@ams.org
Web Site: www.ams.org
Key Personnel
Exec Dir: Dr Catherine A Roberts
Publr: Dr Sergei Gelfand
Assoc Exec Dir: Dr Robert M Harrington
Assoc Exec Dir, Washington, DC: Dr Karen Saxe
Founded: 1888
Branch Office(s)
1527 18 St NW, Washington, DC 20036-1358
  (govt rel & sci policy) *Tel:* 202-588-1100
  Fax: 202-588-1853 *E-mail:* amsdc@ams.org
Mathematical Reviews®, 416 Fourth St, Ann Arbor, MI 48103-4820 (edit) *Tel:* 734-996-5250
  Fax: 734-996-2916 *E-mail:* mathrev@ams.org
Secretary of the AMS - Society Governance, Dept of Computer Science, North Carolina State University, Box 8206, Raleigh, NC 27695-8206 *Tel:* 919-515-7863 *Fax:* 919-515-7896
  E-mail: secretary@ams.org
Membership(s): Society for Scholarly Publishing (SSP)

Anderson & Vreeland Inc
15348 US Hwy 127 EW, Bryan, OH 43506
Tel: 419-636-5002 *Toll Free Tel:* 866-282-7697;
  888-832-1600 (CN) *Fax:* 419-636-4334
E-mail: info@andersonvreeland.com
Web Site: andersonvreeland.com
Key Personnel
Chmn & CEO: Howard Vreeland, Jr
Pres: Darin Lyon
VP: Joseph Anderson
Branch Office(s)
14106 Pontlavoy Ave, Santa Fe Springs, CA 90670 (warehouse), West Regl Warehouse Mgr: Ariel Hernandez *Toll Free Tel:* 800-446-7716
  E-mail: ahernandez@andvre.com
2196 Sweetwater Industrial Blvd, Suite A, Lithia Springs, GA 30122 (warehouse), East Regl Warehouse Mgr: Lonnie Grieser
  E-mail: lgrieser@andvre.com
1000 Estes Ave, Elk Grove Village, IL 60007 (warehouse)
8 Evans St, Fairfield, NJ 07004 (warehouse), East Regl Warehouse Mgr: Lonnie Grieser
  E-mail: lgrieser@andvre.com
8200 Tristar Dr, Suite 100, Irving, TX 75063-2836 (warehouse), South Warehouse Mgr: Ted Strenk *E-mail:* tstrenk@andvre.com
530 Andover Park W, Tukwila, WA 98188 (warehouse), West Regl Warehouse Mgr: Ariel Hernandez *Toll Free Tel:* 800-446-7716
  E-mail: ahernandez@andvre.com
719 Millennium Ct, De Pere, WI 54115 (warehouse), Midwest Regl Warehouse Mgr: Ted Strenk *Tel:* 920-347-6010 *E-mail:* tstrenk@andvre.com
1645 Cliveden Ave, Delta, BC V3M 6V5, Canada
1260 Lakeshore Rd E, Mississauga, ON L5E 3B8, Canada

5435 Rue Francois-Cusson, Lachine, QC H8T 3J4, Canada
Membership(s): Flexographic Technical Association (FTA)

Association for PRINT Technologies (APTech)
1896 Preston White Dr, Reston, VA 20191
Tel: 703-264-7200 *Fax:* 703-620-0994
E-mail: aptech@aptech.org
Web Site: www.printtechnologies.org
Key Personnel
Pres: Thayer Long *E-mail:* thayer_long@aptech.org
VP, Mktg & Communs: Sarah Markfield
  E-mail: smarkfield@aptech.org
Dir, Mktg & Communs: Jane Pratt
  E-mail: jpratt@aptech.org
Founded: 1933
Membership(s): American Society of Association Executives (ASAE); Council of Manufacturing Associations; International Association of Exhibitions and Events® (IAEE); National Association of Manufacturers (NAM)

AVT Inc
Subsidiary of Danaher Corp
8601 Dunwoody Place, Bldg 100, Suite 100, Sandy Springs, GA 30350
Tel: 770-541-9780
E-mail: support@avt-inc.com
Web Site: www.avt-inc.com
Branch Office(s)
AVT EMEA, Generaal Dewittelaan 9 Bus 3, 2800 Mechelen, Belgium *Tel:* (015) 56 03 80
  Fax: (015) 55 39 97
AVT Ltd, 6 Hanagar St, 4527703 Hod Hasharon, Israel (headquarters) *Tel:* (09) 7614444
  Fax: (09) 7614555

AWT World Trade Inc
Division of AWT World Trade Group
4321 N Knox Ave, Chicago, IL 60641-1906
Tel: 773-777-7100 *Fax:* 773-777-0909
E-mail: sales@awtworldtrade.com
Web Site: www.awt-gpi.com
Key Personnel
Owner: Michael Green
Branch Office(s)
8984 NW 105 Way, Medley, FL 33178 *Tel:* 305-887-7500 *Fax:* 305-887-2300
AWT World Trade Europe BV, Holland, Netherlands

Baumfolder Corp
Division of Heidelberg
1660 Campbell Rd, Sidney, OH 45365
Tel: 937-492-1281 *Toll Free Tel:* 800-543-6107
  Fax: 937-492-7280
E-mail: baumfolder@baumfolder.com
Web Site: www.baumfolder.com
Key Personnel
Pres & CEO: Janice Benanzer
Founded: 1917
Membership(s): Association for Supply Chain Management (ASCM); Dayton Region Manufacturers Association (DRMA); Print Industries Market Information and Research Organization (PRIMIR)

The Bear Wallow Publishing Co
809 S 12 St, La Grande, OR 97850
Tel: 541-962-7864
Web Site: www.bear-wallow.com
Key Personnel
Co-Owner: Cathy Gildemeister; Jerry Gildemeister *E-mail:* j-c@bear-wallow.com
Founded: 1976

Bindery & Distribution Service Inc
9 Overbrook Rd, South Barrington, IL 60010
Tel: 312-550-7000 *Fax:* 847-842-8800
Key Personnel
Pres: Dennis Uchimoto *E-mail:* uchimoto@aol.com
Founded: 1986

Blue Note Books, see Blue Note Publications Inc

Blue Note Publications Inc
721 North Dr, Suite D, Melbourne, FL 32934
Tel: 321-799-2583; 321-622-6289
   Toll Free Tel: 800-624-0401 (orders) *Fax:* 321-799-1942; 321-622-6830
E-mail: bluenotebooks@gmail.com
Web Site: bluenotepublications.com
Key Personnel
Pres: Paul Maluccio
Founded: 1988

Book Automation Inc
Division of Meccanotecnica Spa
458 Danbury Rd, Unit B10, New Milford, CT 06776
Tel: 860-354-7900 *Toll Free Tel:* 800-429-6305
E-mail: info@bookautomation.com
Web Site: www.bookautomation.com
Key Personnel
Pres: Manrico Caglioni
Founded: 1975

Book Machine Sales Inc
PO Box 297, Hamlin, PA 18427
Tel: 570-647-9111
Web Site: bookmachinesales.com
Key Personnel
Owner & Pres: Peter H Johnson *E-mail:* pete@bookmachinesales.com

Bookmasters
Division of Baker & Taylor Publisher Services
30 Amberwood Pkwy, Ashland, OH 44805
Tel: 419-281-5100 *Toll Free Tel:* 800-537-6727
   Fax: 419-281-0200
E-mail: info@btpubservices.com
Web Site: www.btpubservices.com
Key Personnel
Dir of Mfg: Brad Sharp *E-mail:* bsharp@bookmasters.com
Founded: 1972

Brackett Inc
7115 SE Forbes Ave, Topeka, KS 66619
Mailing Address: PO Box 19306, Topeka, KS 66619-0306
Tel: 785-862-2205 *Toll Free Tel:* 800-255-3506
   Fax: 785-862-1127
E-mail: brackett@brackett-inc.com; sales@brackett-inc.com
Web Site: brackett-inc.com
Key Personnel
Pres & CEO: J M "Mike" Murray
   E-mail: mmurray@brackett-inc.com
Founded: 1910

Brandtjen & Kluge LLC
539 Blanding Woods Rd, St Croix Falls, WI 54024
Tel: 715-483-3265 *Toll Free Tel:* 800-826-7320
   Fax: 715-483-1640

E-mail: sales@kluge.biz
Web Site: www.kluge.biz
Key Personnel
Pres: Michael C Aumann
Founded: 1919
Branch Office(s)
Kluge International, Springmill Industrial Estate, Unit 3, Avening Rd, Nailsworth, Glos GL6 0BS, United Kingdom *Tel:* (01453) 836 522 *Fax:* (01453) 836 009
Membership(s): Association for Print Technologies (APTech); Foil & Specialty Effects Association (FSEA); International Association of Diecutting & Diemaking (IADD)

Bunting Magnetics Co
500 S Spencer Rd, Newton, KS 67114
Mailing Address: PO Box 468, Newton, KS 67114-0468
Tel: 316-284-2020 *Toll Free Tel:* 800-835-2526; 877-576-0156 *Fax:* 316-283-4975
E-mail: bmc@buntingmagnetics.com
Web Site: www.buntingmagnetics.com
Key Personnel
Pres & CEO: Robert J Bunting, Sr
Gen Mgr: Robert Bunting, Jr
Prod Mgr: Barry Voorhees *E-mail:* bvoorhees@buntingmagnetics.com
Founded: 1959
Branch Office(s)
Flexible Die Division, 600 S Spencer Rd, Newton, KS 67114 *E-mail:* sales@flexdies.com *Web Site:* www.flexdies.com
Magnet Materials Division, 1150 Howard St, Elk Grove Village, IL 60007 *Tel:* 847-593-2060 *E-mail:* info@buymagnets.com *Web Site:* www.buymagnets.com
Bunting Magnetics Mexico S de RL de CV, Privada Liendo 708 Sur Despacho 4, Colonia Obispado, 64060 Monterey, NL, Mexico *Tel:* (0181) 8348 3943
Bunting Magnetics Europe Ltd, Northbridge Rd, Berkhamsted, Herts HP4 1EH, United Kingdom *Tel:* (01442) 87508 *E-mail:* sales@buntingeurope.com *Web Site:* www.buntingeurope.com

Busch LLC
516 Viking Dr, Virginia Beach, VA 23452
Tel: 757-463-7800 *Toll Free Tel:* 800-USA-PUMP (872-7867) *Fax:* 757-463-7407
E-mail: info@buschusa.com; marketing@buschusa.com
Web Site: www.buschvacuum.com/us
Key Personnel
Lead Prod Mktg Mgr: Antonio Mantilla
Founded: 1963
Sales Office(s): 373 Joseph Dr, South Elgin, IL 60177 *Tel:* 630-545-1310
39 Davis St, South Plainfield, NJ 07080 *Tel:* 908-561-3233
13123 NE David Circle, Portland, OR 97230 *Tel:* 408-782-0800
420 "E" St, Suite 4, Bayamon, PR 00959-1901 *Tel:* 787-798-5045
1100 E Howard Lane, Bldg 2, Suite 200, Austin, TX 78753 *Tel:* 512-835-0906
1901 S Starpoint Dr, Houston, TX 77032 *Tel:* 281-214-8400
Membership(s): Fab Owners Association (FOA); Facilities 450mm Consortium (F450C); Semiconductor Equipment & Materials International (SEMI)

CC1 Inc
170 West Rd, Suite 7, Portsmouth, NH 03801
Tel: 603-319-2000 *Fax:* 603-319-2200
E-mail: customerservice@cc1inc.com
Web Site: www.cc1inc.com
Founded: 1979

Century Direct LLC
15 Enter Lane, Islandia, NY 11749
Tel: 212-763-0600
E-mail: contact@centurydirect.net
Web Site: www.centurydirect.net
Key Personnel
VP, Sales & Busn Devt: Martin A Rego
   E-mail: regom@centurydirect.net
Founded: 1932
Membership(s): Direct Mail Fundraisers Association (DMFA); Greater Hudson Valley Postal Customers Council; Greater New York Postal Customers Council; Hudson Valley Direct Marketing Association; National Association of College & University Mail Services (NACUMS); National Catholic Development Conference Council

CG Book Printers
Division of Corporate Graphics Commercial (CGC)
1750 Northway Dr, North Mankato, MN 56003
Tel: 507-388-3300 *Toll Free Tel:* 800-729-7575
   Fax: 507-386-6350
E-mail: cgbooks@corpgraph.com
Web Site: www.corpgraph.com
Key Personnel
Pres: Dan Kvasnicka *Tel:* 507-386-6340
   Fax: 507-344-5548 *E-mail:* dekvasnicka@corpgraph.com
Sales Exec, Book Mfg Sales: Mike Schmitt
   Tel: 507-386-6349 *E-mail:* mjschmitt@corpgraph.com
Founded: 1989

Challenge Machinery Co
6125 Norton Center Dr, Norton Shores, MI 49441
Tel: 231-799-8484 *Fax:* 231-798-1275
E-mail: info@challengemachinery.com; sales@challengemachinery.com
Web Site: www.challengemachinery.com
Key Personnel
Pres & CEO: Tom Zant
Dir, Sales & Mktg: Britt Cary
Founded: 1870

Clamco Corp
Member of PAC Machinery Group
775 Berea Industrial Pkwy, Berea, OH 44017
Tel: 216-267-1911 *Toll Free Tel:* 800-985-9570 (headquarters) *Fax:* 216-267-8713
E-mail: info@clamcopackaging.com
Web Site: www.pacmachinery.com/clamcopackaging
Key Personnel
Mgr: Rob Patton
Founded: 1946

Clare Printing
206 S Keystone Ave, Sayre, PA 18840
Tel: 570-888-2244
E-mail: hr@clareprint.com
Web Site: www.clareprint.com
Key Personnel
Pres: Ian Clare
Prodn Mgr: Alicia Blokzyl
Founded: 1903

The Cleveland Vibrator Co
2828 Clinton Ave, Cleveland, OH 44113
Tel: 216-241-7157 *Toll Free Tel:* 800-221-3298
   Fax: 216-241-3480
E-mail: sales@clevelandvibrator.com
Web Site: www.clevelandvibrator.com
Key Personnel
Gen Sales Mgr: Jack Steinbuch
Founded: 1923

CONTECH (Converting Technologies)
1756 S 151 St W, Goddard, KS 67052
Tel: 316-722-6907 *Fax:* 316-722-2976

E-mail: info@contechusa.com
Web Site: www.contechusa.com
Key Personnel
VP: Max Ogden *E-mail:* mogden@contechusa.
   com
Founded: 1980

Corporate Graphics Book Printers, see CG
   Book Printers

Craftsmen Machinery Co Inc
1257 Worcester Rd, Unit 167, Framingham, MA
   01701
Mailing Address: PO Box 2006, Framingham,
   MA 01703-2006
Tel: 508-376-2001 *Fax:* 508-376-2003
E-mail: sales@craftsmenmachinery.com
Web Site: www.craftsmenmachinery.com
Key Personnel
Pres: Sherwin Marks

Crown Connect
250 W Rialto Ave, San Bernadino, CA 92408
Tel: 909-888-7531 *Fax:* 909-889-1639
E-mail: sales@crownconnect.com
Web Site: www.crownconnect.com
Key Personnel
CFO: Nicole Albright *Tel:* 909-888-7531 ext 204
Pres: Denny Shorett *Tel:* 909-888-7531 ext 225
VP, Opers: Ken Martin *Tel:* 909-888-7531 ext
   206
Mgr, Busn Devt: Erin Warren *Tel:* 909-888-7531
   ext 228
Prodn Mgr: Chris McPhate *Tel:* 909-888-7531 ext
   214
Founded: 1970

Cypress House
Imprint of Comp-Type Inc
155 Cypress St, Fort Bragg, CA 95437
Tel: 707-964-9520 *Toll Free Tel:* 800-773-7782
   Fax: 707-964-7531
Web Site: www.cypresshouse.com
Key Personnel
Pres: Cynthia Frank *E-mail:* cynthia@
   cypresshouse.com
Mng Ed: Joe Shaw *E-mail:* joeshaw@
   cypresshouse.com
Founded: 1986
Membership(s): American Booksellers Associa-
   tion (ABA); Bay Area Independent Publishers
   Association (BAIPA); California Independent
   Booksellers Alliance (CALIBA); Independent
   Book Publishers Association (IBPA); Pacific
   Northwest Booksellers Association (PNBA)

D&K Group Inc
1795 Commerce Dr, Elk Grove Village, IL 60007
Tel: 847-956-0160; 847-956-4757 (tech support)
   Toll Free Tel: 800-632-2314 *Fax:* 847-956-8214
E-mail: info@dkgroup.net
Web Site: www.dkgroup.com
Key Personnel
Pres: Karl Singer
VP, Sales & Mktg: Tom Pidgeon *E-mail:* tom.
   pidgeon@dkgroup.net
Mktg Communs Specialist: Brian Biegel
   E-mail: brian.biegel@dkgroup.net
Founded: 1979

Datalogic USA Inc
959 Terry St, Eugene, OR 97402-9150
Tel: 541-683-5700 *Toll Free Tel:* 800-227-2633
Web Site: www.datalogic.com
Founded: 1969
Branch Office(s)
55 W Del Mar Blvd, Pasadena, CA 91105
5775 W Old Shakopee Rd, Suite 160, Bloomington, MN 55437
511 School House Rd, Telford, PA 18969-1196
144 Milestone Way, Greenville, SC 29615

Desktop Miracles Inc
112 S Main St, Suite 294, Stowe, VT 05672
Tel: 802-253-7900 *Toll Free Fax:* 888-293-2676
E-mail: info@desktopmiracles.com
Web Site: www.desktopmiracles.com
Key Personnel
Pres & CEO: Barry T Kerrigan *E-mail:* barry@
   desktopmiracles.com
VP: Virginia Kerrigan *E-mail:* virginia@
   desktopmiracles.com
Founded: 1994

RR Donnelley
35 W Wacker Dr, Chicago, IL 60601
Toll Free Tel: 800-742-4455
Web Site: www.rrd.com
Key Personnel
Pres & CEO: Daniel L Knotts
Pres, Busn Servs: John Pecaric
Pres, Mktg Solutions: Doug Ryan
EVP & CFO: Terry D Peterson
EVP & CIO: Ken O'Brien
EVP & Chief HR Offr: Sheila Rutt
EVP & Chief Strategy & Transformation Offr:
   Elif Sagsen-Ercel
EVP, Gen Coun, Chief Compliance Offr & Corp
   Secy: Deborah Steiner
EVP, Dom Opers & Chief Supply Chain Offr:
   Glynn Perry
SVP & Chief Acctg Offr: Michael J Sharp
Founded: 1864
Branch Office(s)
955 Gateway Center Way, San Diego, CA 92102
   Tel: 619-527-4600
40610 County Center Dr, Temecula, CA 92591
   Tel: 951-296-2890
151 Red Stone Rd, Manchester, CT 06042
   Tel: 860-649-5570
9125 Bachman Rd, Orlando, FL 32824 *Tel:* 407-
   859-2030
5800 Peachtree Rd, Atlanta, GA 30341 *Tel:* 770-
   458-6351
825 Riverside Pkwy, Suite 300, Austell, GA
   30168 *Tel:* 770-948-1330
1750 Wallace Ave, St Charles, IL 60174 *Tel:* 630-
   313-7000
609 S Kirk Rd, St Charles, IL 60174 *Tel:* 630-
   762-7600
One Poplar Ave, Thurmont, MD 21788 *Tel:* 301-
   271-7171
65 Sprague St, Hyde Park, MA 02136 *Tel:* 617-
   360-2000
18780 W 78 St, Chanhassen, MN 55317
   Tel: 952-937-9764
5500 12 Ave E, Shakopee, MN 55379 *Tel:* 952-
   941-7546
6305 Sunset Corporate Dr, Las Vegas, NV 89120
   Tel: 702-949-8500
5 Henderson Dr, West Caldwell, NJ 07006
   Tel: 973-882-7000
12301 Vance Davis Dr, Charlotte, NC 28269
   Tel: 704-949-3568
One Litho Way, Durham, NC 27703 *Tel:* 919-
   596-3660
3801 Gantz Rd, Grove City, OH 43123 *Tel:* 614-
   539-5527
700 Nestle Way, Suite 200, Breinigsville, PA
   18031 *Tel:* 610-391-3900
9985 Gantry Rd, Philadelphia, PA 19115
   Tel: 215-671-9500
218 N Braddock Ave, Pittsburgh, PA 15208
   Tel: 412-241-8200
1210 Key Rd, Columbia, SC 29201 *Tel:* 803-799-
   9550
1645 W Sam Houston Pkwy N, Houston, TX
   77043 *Tel:* 713-468-7175
1550 Lakeway Dr, Suite 600, Lewisville, TX
   75057 *Tel:* 972-353-7500
630 W 1000 N, Logan, UT 84321 *Tel:* 435-755-
   4000

201 E Progress Dr, West Bend, WI 53095
   Tel: 262-338-6101
Membership(s): Association of American Pub-
   lishers (AAP); Book Industry Study Group
   (BISG); Book Manufacturers' Institute (BMI)

Douthitt Corp
245 Adair St, Detroit, MI 48207-4287
Tel: 313-259-1565 *Toll Free Tel:* 800-368-8448
   Fax: 313-259-6806
E-mail: em@douthittcorp.com
Web Site: www.douthittcorp.com
Key Personnel
Natl Sales Mgr: Jim Primo

Durr MEGTEC LLC
Division of Duerr AG
830 Prosper St, DePere, WI 54115
Mailing Address: PO Box 5030, DePere, WI
   54115-5030
Tel: 920-336-5715
E-mail: megtecinquiries@megtec.com
Web Site: www.durr-megtec.com
Key Personnel
SVP: Ken Zak
VP, Sales & Busn Devt: Rodney Schwartz
Founded: 1969
Branch Office(s)
Solvent Recovery Division, 1201 19 Place, No
   B301, Vero Beach, FL 32960 *Tel:* 772-567-
   1320
Solvent Recovery Division, 2120 Citygate Dr,
   Columbus, OH 43219 *Tel:* 614-324-2660
MEGTEC TurboSonic Inc, 550 Parkside Dr,
   No A-14, Waterloo, ON N2L 5V4, Canada
   Tel: 519-885-5513
MEGTEC Systems Australia Inc, 25, 21 Aristoc
   Rd, Glen Waverley, Victoria 3150, Australia
   Tel: (03) 9574 7450
MEGTEC Systems (Shanghai) Ltd, No 125, Lane
   1190, Jiujing Rd, Jiuting Town, Songjiang Dis-
   trict, Shanghai 201615, China *Tel:* (021) 6769
   7878
MEGTEC Systems SAS, Z I des Malines, 32 rue
   des Malines, 91090 Lisses, France *Tel:* 01 69
   89 47 93
Duerr Systems AG, Honeywellstr 18, 63477
   Maintal, Germany *Tel:* (06181) 94040
MEGTEC Systems India Pvt Ltd, Plot No 6/5,
   CTS No 8/5 Erandawana, Near Nal-Stop,
   Karve Rd, Behind Saraswat Bank, Pune 411
   004, India *Tel:* (020) 2546 6610
MEGTEC Systems AB, Olskroksgatan 30, Box
   6106, 40060 Gothenburg, Sweden *Tel:* (031) 65
   78 00
MEGTEC Environmental Ltd, Unit 133, Bradley
   Hall Trading Estate, Bradley Lane, Stan-
   dish Wigan WN6 0XQ, United Kingdom
   Tel: (01257) 42 7070
Membership(s): Flexible Packaging Association
   (FPA)

Dynaric Inc
5740 Bayside Rd, Virginia Beach, VA 23455
Tel: 757-363-5850 *Toll Free Tel:* 800-526-0827
   Fax: 757-363-8016
E-mail: gd@dynaric.com; order@dynaric.com
Web Site: www.dynaric.com
Key Personnel
Pres: Joseph Martinez
Founded: 1973

Eastman Kodak Co
343 State St, Rochester, NY 14650
Tel: 585-724-4000 *Toll Free Tel:* 866-563-2533
Web Site: www.kodak.com
Key Personnel
Exec Chmn: Jim Continenza
SVP & Pres, Print Systems Div: John O'Grady
Dir, Communs: Nicholas Rangel *E-mail:* nicholas.
   rangel@kodak.com
Founded: 1880

EMT International Inc
780 Centerline Dr, Hobart, WI 54155
Tel: 920-468-5475 *Fax:* 920-468-7991
E-mail: info@emtinternational.com
Web Site: www.emtinternational.com
Key Personnel
EVP, Sales & Mktg: Jim Driscoll
Regl Mgr: Jeff Messenger

Essex Products Group
30 Industrial Park Rd, Centerbrook, CT 06409-0307
Tel: 860-767-7130 *Toll Free Tel:* 800-394-7130
Fax: 860-767-9137
E-mail: sales@epg-inc.com
Web Site: www.epg-inc.com
Key Personnel
Pres: Peter Griffin
Admin: Kaylynn Washington

Evergreen Engravers
Division of Diecraft Dispatch Inc
1819 S Central Ave, Suite 24, Kent, WA 98032
Tel: 253-852-6766 *Toll Free Tel:* 800-852-6766
Fax: 253-850-3944
E-mail: emboss@evergreenengravers.com
Web Site: www.evergreenengravers.com
Key Personnel
Pres: Jeff Hilton
Founded: 1952

Fairfield Marketing Group Inc
Subsidiary of FMG Inc
The Direct Mail Ctr, 830 Sport Hill Rd, Easton, CT 06112-1241
Tel: 203-261-5585 *Fax:* 203-261-0884
E-mail: info@fairfieldmarketing.com
Web Site: www.fairfieldmarketing.com
Key Personnel
Pres & CEO: Edward P Washchilla, Jr
VP, Cust Serv: Mike Lozada *Tel:* 203-261-5585 ext 204
VP, Fulfillment: Jason Paul Miller *Tel:* 203-261-5585 ext 203 *E-mail:* jason@fairfieldmarketing.com
Founded: 1986
Membership(s): American Booksellers Association (ABA); Bridgeport Regional Business Council (BRBC); Education Market Association; United States Chamber of Commerce (USCC)

Ferry Associates Inc
49 Fostertown Rd, Medford, NJ 08055
Tel: 609-953-1233 *Toll Free Tel:* 800-257-5258
Fax: 609-953-8637
Web Site: www.ferryassociates.com
Key Personnel
Pres: Kevin Ferry *E-mail:* kferry@ferryassociates.com
Founded: 1982

Fife, see Maxcess International

Four Colour Print Group
2410 Frankfort Ave, Louisville, KY 40206
Tel: 502-896-9644 *Fax:* 502-896-9594
E-mail: sales@fourcolour.com
Web Site: www.fourcolour.com
Key Personnel
Pres & CEO: George C Dick *Tel:* 502-896-9644 ext 303 *E-mail:* gdick@fourcolour.com
Prodn Dir: Amy Martin *Tel:* 502-896-9644 ext 315 *E-mail:* amartin@fourcolour.com
Prodn Mgr: Cindy Jones *Tel:* 502-896-9644 ext 310 *E-mail:* cjones@fourcolour.com
Founded: 1985
Branch Office(s)
FCI Digital, 2032 S Alex Rd, Suite A, West

Carrollton, OH 45449 *Tel:* 931-859-9701
Fax: 931-859-9709 *E-mail:* sales@fcidigital.com *Web Site:* www.fcidigital.com

Fry Communications Inc
800 W Church Rd, Mechanicsburg, PA 17055
Tel: 717-766-0211 *Toll Free Tel:* 800-334-1429
Fax: 717-691-0341
E-mail: info@frycomm.com
Web Site: www.frycomm.com
Key Personnel
Chmn of the Bd: Henry Fry
CEO: Mike Lukas
CFO: Chris Wawrzyniak
CTO: David S Fry
VP, Sales: Kevin Quinn
Founded: 1934

Fujifilm North America Corporation, Graphic Systems Division
Division of Fujifilm Corporation
850 Central Ave, Hanover Park, IL 60133
Tel: 630-259-7200 *Toll Free Tel:* 800-877-0555
Fax: 630-259-7078
Web Site: www.fujifilmusa.com/products/graphic_arts_printing/index.html; www.fujifilmusa.com
Founded: 1965
Branch Office(s)
2507 W Erie Dr, Suite 103, Tempe, AZ 85282
Toll Free Tel: 800-279-1673 *Fax:* 602-437-8483
6200 Phyllis Dr, Cypress, CA 90630 *Tel:* 714-933-3300 *Toll Free Tel:* 800-879-2355
Fax: 714-899-4707
30962 San Benito St, Hayward, CA 94544 *Toll Free Tel:* 800-734-8745 *Fax:* 510-266-0707
4424 Seaboard Rd, Suite C, Orlando, FL 32808, Regl Sales Mgr: Jim Kornmeyer *Toll Free Tel:* 800-940-6366 *Fax:* 407-898-0818
6810 Deerpath Rd, Suite 405, Elkridge, MD 21075, Regl Sales Mgr: Tony Aquino *Tel:* 301-317-7480 *Toll Free Tel:* 800-729-3600
Fax: 301-317-7480
France Avenue Business Park IV, 4001 Lakebreeze Ave N, Suite 400, Brooklyn Center, MN 55429-3860 *Tel:* 651-855-6000 *Toll Free Tel:* 800-758-8421 *Fax:* 651-855-6025
2001 NE 46 St, Suite 250, Kansas City, MO 64116, Regl Sales Mgr: John Steege *Tel:* 913-233-0355 *Toll Free Tel:* 800-776-4019
Fax: 913-233-0125
1100 King Georges Post Rd, Edison, NJ 08837, Regl Sales Mgr: Fred Heinkel *Tel:* 732-857-3280 *Fax:* 732-857-3470
1650 Magnolia Dr, Cincinnati, OH 45215, Regl Sales Mgr: Kurt Paskert *Toll Free Tel:* 800-582-7406 *Fax:* 513-563-0377
3926 Willow Lake Blvd, Memphis, TN 38118, Regl Sales Mgr: Tony Aquino *Toll Free Tel:* 800-365-2457 *Fax:* 901-795-1251
330 West Way Place, No 446, Arlington, TX 76018, Regl Sales Mgr: Bob O'Shea *Toll Free Tel:* 800-404-3228 *Fax:* 817-467-7351
1795 Fremont Dr, Salt Lake City, UT 84104 *Tel:* 801-975-1234 *Fax:* 801-972-3981
5103 "D" St NW, Suite 102, Auburn, WA 98001
Toll Free Tel: 800-628-0317 *Fax:* 253-852-4701
Toll Free Fax: 800-555-0776

H B Fuller Co
1200 Willow Lake Blvd, St Paul, MN 55110-5146
Tel: 651-236-5900 *Toll Free Tel:* 888-423-8553
E-mail: inquiry@hbfuller.com
Web Site: www.hbfuller.com
Key Personnel
Pres & CEO: Jim Owens
EVP & COO: Ted Clark
EVP & CFO: John Corkrean
VP & Cont: Robert Martsching
VP & Treas: Heidi Weiler
VP, Gen Coun & Corp Secy: Timothy Keenan

Gallus Group
Subsidiary of Heidelberg
One Ivybrook Blvd, Suite 180, Ivyland, PA 18974
Tel: 215-677-9600 *Fax:* 215-677-9700
E-mail: info@gallus-group.com
Web Site: gallus.contento.ch
Founded: 1980
Membership(s): Flexographic Technical Association (FTA); Tag & Label Manufacturers Institute (TLMI)

Graphics Two
819 S Main St, Burbank, CA 91506
Tel: 818-841-4922
Key Personnel
Owner: Bert Johnson *E-mail:* cabert@aol.com; Jeanne Vlazny
Founded: 1973

GTI Graphic Technology Inc
211 Dupont Ave, Newburgh, NY 12550
Mailing Address: PO Box 3138, Newburgh, NY 12550-0651
Tel: 845-562-7066 *Fax:* 845-562-2543
E-mail: sales@gtilite.com
Web Site: www.gtilite.com
Key Personnel
Pres: Robert McCurdy
EVP: Louis Chappo
Sales & Mktg Coord: Linda Sutherland
Founded: 1975

HBP Inc
952 Frederick St, Hagerstown, MD 21740
Tel: 301-733-2000 *Toll Free Tel:* 800-638-3508
Fax: 301-733-6586
E-mail: contactus@hbp.com
Web Site: www.hbp.com
Key Personnel
Owner & Pres: John Snyder
VP, Busn Devt & Mktg: Ilene Lerner *Tel:* 703-289-9038 *E-mail:* ilerner@hbp.com
Founded: 1903
Sales Office(s): 2818 Fallfax Dr, Falls Church, VA 22042 *Tel:* 703-289-9000
Membership(s): CUA; Printing & Graphics Association MidAtlantic (PGAMA); Printing Industries of Virginia (PIVA); PRINTING United Alliance

Heidelberg Graphics
2 Stansbury Ct, Chico, CA 95928
SAN: 211-5654
Tel: 530-342-6582 *Fax:* 530-342-6582
E-mail: heidelberggraphics@gmail.com; service@heidelberggraphics.com
Web Site: www.heidelberggraphics.com
Key Personnel
Owner & Pres: Larry S Jackson
Founded: 1972

Heidelberg USA Inc
Division of Heidelberg Druckmaschinen AG
1000 Gutenberg Dr, Kennesaw, GA 30144
Tel: 770-419-6500 *Toll Free Tel:* 800-437-7388
E-mail: info@heidelberg.com
Web Site: www.heidelberg.com/us
Key Personnel
Pres: Felix Mueller

Heraeus Noblelight America LLC
910 Clopper Rd, Gaithersburg, MD 20878-1361
Tel: 301-527-2660 *Toll Free Tel:* 888-276-8600
Fax: 301-527-2661
E-mail: info.hna.uvp@heraeus.com
Web Site: www.heraeus-noblelight.com/uvamericas
Key Personnel
Pres: P K Swain
Dir, Sales: Kevin Joesel
Mktg Communs Mgr: Gina Gonzalez
Founded: 1971

HID Ultraviolet LLC
520 Lafayette Rd, Sparta, NJ 07871
Tel: 973-383-8535 *Fax:* 973-383-1606
E-mail: sales@hid.com
Web Site: www.hid.com
Founded: 1981

Holo Image Technology Inc
101 William Leigh Dr, Tullytown, PA 19007
Tel: 215-946-2190 *Fax:* 215-946-2129
E-mail: info@holoimagetechnology.com
Web Site: www.holoimagetechnology.com
Key Personnel
Pres: Tom Chiang
Founded: 1992
Membership(s): SPIE, The international society
   for optics and photonics

The P A Hutchison Co
400 Penn Ave, Mayfield, PA 18433
SAN: 991-5559
Tel: 570-876-4560 *Toll Free Tel:* 800-USA-PRNT
   (872-7768) *Fax:* 570-876-4561
E-mail: sales@pahutch.com
Web Site: www.pahutch.com
Key Personnel
Pres & CEO: Chris Hutchison
Dir, Sales & Admin: Erin Jones
Founded: 1911

I-Web
175 Bodwell St, Avon, MA 02322
Tel: 508-580-5809 *Fax:* 508-580-5632
E-mail: info@iwebus.com
Web Site: iwebus.com
Key Personnel
Owner: Robert Williams *E-mail:* bwilliams@
   iwebus.com

Imago
110 W 40 St, New York, NY 10018
Tel: 212-921-4411 *Fax:* 212-921-8226
E-mail: sales@imagousa.com
Web Site: www.imagousa.com
Key Personnel
Pres & CEO: Howard Musk *E-mail:* howardm@
   imagogroup.com
Founded: 1985
Branch Office(s)
Imago West Coast, 23412 Moulton Pkwy, Suite
   250, Laguna Hills, CA 92653 (sales), Contact:
   Tammy Simms *Tel:* 949-367-1635 *Fax:* 949-
   367-1639
Imago Australia, 10 Help St, Suite 27, Level
   6, Chatswood, NSW 2067, Australia (sales)
   Tel: (04) 3753 3351 (cell); (04) 4806 8704
   (cell) *E-mail:* sales@imagaoaus.com
Imago Brazil, Domiciano Rossi, 340 unid 154,
   09726-121 Sao Bernardo do Campo, Brazil
   (sales) *Tel:* (011) 2306 8546; (011) 2306 8547
   E-mail: imagobra@gmail.com
Imago Shenzhen, Rm 2511-2512, Block A,
   United Plaza No 5022, Bin He Rd, Fu
   Tian Centre District, Shenzhen 518033,
   China (prodn), Contact: Kendrick Cheung
   Tel: (0755) 8304 8899 *Fax:* (0755) 8251 4073
   E-mail: enquiries@imago.com.hk
Imago France, 23 rue Lavoisier, 75008 Paris,
   France (sales) *Tel:* 01 45 26 47 74 *Fax:* 01 78
   94 14 44 *E-mail:* sales@imagogroup.com
Imago Services (HK) Ltd, Unit B309, 1/F,
   New East Sun Industrial Bldg, 18 Shing
   Yip St, Kwun Tong, Hong Kong (prodn),
   Contact: Kendrick Cheung *Tel:* 2811 3316
   E-mail: enquiries@imago.com.hk
Imago Productions (Malaysia) Pte Ltd, No
   43, Taman Emas, Jl Utama 31, Telok Pan-
   glima Garang, 42500 Kuala Langot, Selan-
   gor, Malaysia (prodn, incorporating South
   Africa sales) *Tel:* (017) 4288771 (cell)
   E-mail: enquiries@imago.com.sg

Imago Publishing, Albury Ct, Albury Thame,
   Oxon OX9 2LP, United Kingdom (sales),
   Dir: Simon Rosenheim *Tel:* (01844) 337000
   Fax: (01844) 339935 *E-mail:* sales@imago.co.
   uk *Web Site:* imagogroup.com

International Press Publication Inc
Spadina Rd, Richmond Hill, ON L4B 3C5,
   Canada
Tel: 905-883-0343
E-mail: sales@ippbooks.com
Web Site: www.ippbooks.com; www.facebook.
   com/ippbooks; twitter.com/ippbooks2
Key Personnel
Pres: Bali Sethi
Founded: 1976
Membership(s): The American Library Associa-
   tion (ALA); Children's Literature Association
   (ChLA); Ontario Library Association

Ironmark
9040 Junction Dr, Annapolis Junction, MD 20701
Toll Free Tel: 888-775-3737
E-mail: marketing@ironmarkusa.com
Web Site: ironmarkusa.com
Key Personnel
CEO: Scott Hargest *E-mail:* scott@ironmarkusa.
   com; Jeff Ostenso *E-mail:* jeff@ironmarkusa.
   com
Pres: Matt Marzullo *E-mail:* mmarzullo@
   ironmarkusa.com
SVP, Sales: Scott Kravitz *E-mail:* skravitz@
   ironmarkusa.com
VP, Opers: Chris Marzullo *E-mail:* cmarzullo@
   ironmarkusa.com
Sr Sales Exec: Larry Davis *E-mail:* ldavis@
   ironmarkusa.com
Founded: 1955

Koenig & Bauer (US) Inc
Member of KBA (Koenig & Bauer AG) Group
2555 Regent Blvd, Dallas, TX 75229
Mailing Address: PO Box 619006, Dallas, TX
   75261
Tel: 469-532-8000 *Fax:* 469-532-8190
Web Site: us.koenig-bauer.com
Key Personnel
Pres & CEO: Mark Hischar *E-mail:* mark.
   hischar@koenig-bauer.com
SVP, Fin & CFO: Gerrit Zwergel *Tel:* 469-532-
   8050 *E-mail:* gerrit.zwergel@koenig-bauer.com
SVP, Mktg & Prod Mgmt: Eric Frank *Tel:* 469-
   532-8040 *E-mail:* eric.frank@koenig-bauer.com
SVP, Sheetfed Sales: Richard Dreshfield *Tel:* 469-
   532-8030 *E-mail:* richard.dreshfield@koenig-
   bauer.com
VP, Web & Specialty Press Div: Jeff Dietz
   Tel: 469-532-8029 *E-mail:* jeff.dietz@koenig-
   bauer.com
Branch Office(s)
Koenig & Bauer (CA) Inc, 181 Bay St, No 1800,
   Box 754, Toronto, ON M5J 2T9, Canada

Lake Book Manufacturing Inc
2085 N Cornell Ave, Melrose Park, IL 60160
Tel: 708-345-7000
E-mail: info@lakebook.com
Web Site: www.lakebook.com
Key Personnel
Pres & COO: Dan Genovese
VP, Fin & CFO: Bob Flatow
VP & Gen Mgr: Bill Richards
VP, Mfg: Steve Quagliato
VP, Opers: Bill Flavin
VP, Sales & Mktg: Nick Vergoth
VP, Technol: Paul Genovese

Lassco-Wizer Equipment & Supplies
Division of Woerner Industries
485 Hague St, Rochester, NY 14606-1296

Tel: 585-436-1934 *Toll Free Tel:* 800-854-6595
Fax: 585-464-8665
E-mail: info@lasscowizer.com; sales@
   lasscowizer.com
Web Site: www.lasscowizer.com
Key Personnel
Busn Mgr: Jennifer Weinschreider

MacDermid Graphics Solutions LLC
Division of Element Solutions
5210 Phillip Lee Dr, Atlanta, GA 30336
Tel: 404-696-4565 *Toll Free Tel:* 800-348-7201
E-mail: mpsproductinfo@macdermid.com
Web Site: graphics.macdermid.com
Key Personnel
Pres & COO: Scot Benson

Magna Visual Inc
28271 Cedar Park Blvd, Perrysburg, OH 43551
Tel: 314-843-9000 *Toll Free Tel:* 800-843-3399
   Fax: 314-843-0000
E-mail: magna@magnavisual.com; mvsales@
   magnavisual.com
Web Site: www.magnavisual.com
Key Personnel
Co-Pres: Joseph L Young
Branch Office(s)
9400 Watson Rd, St Louis, MO 63126-1596

MAGPOWR®, see Maxcess International

manroland Goss web systems Americas LLC
121 Technology Dr, Durham, NH 03824
Tel: 603-749-6600 *Toll Free Tel:* 800-323-1200
   (parts & serv) *Fax:* 603-750-6860
E-mail: info@manrolandgoss.com
Web Site: www.manrolandgoss.com
Key Personnel
Mng Dir: Dave Soden
Branch Office(s)
Alois-Senefelder-Allee 1, 86153 Augsburg, Ger-
   many (world headquarters) *Tel:* (0821) 424-0
   Fax: (0821) 424-33 03

Manroland Inc
Subsidiary of Manroland Sheetfed GmbH
800 E Oak Hill Dr, Westmont, IL 60559
Tel: 630-920-2000
E-mail: info.us@manrolandsheetfed.com
Web Site: manrolandsheetfed.com
Key Personnel
CEO: Sean Springett

Maple Press
480 Willow Springs Lane, York, PA 17406
Mailing Address: PO Box 2695, York, PA 17405-
   2695
Tel: 717-764-5911 *Toll Free Tel:* 800-999-5911
   Fax: 717-764-4702
E-mail: sales@maplepress.com
Web Site: www.maplepress.com
Key Personnel
Pres: James S Wisotzkey
VP, Opers: Chris Benyovszky
VP, Sales: Bob Bethune
VP, Sales & Mktg: Andrew J Van Sprang
   E-mail: vansprang@maplepress.com
Founded: 1901
Branch Office(s)
92 Rockvale Rd, Tewksbury, MA 01876, VP,
   Sales: Bob Bethune *Tel:* 978-585-0900
   Fax: 978-858-0920 *E-mail:* bethune@
   maplepress.com
Membership(s): Book Industry Study Group
   (BISG); Book Manufacturers' Institute (BMI)

Markwith Tool Co Inc
5261 State Rte 49 S, Greenville, OH 45331
Tel: 937-548-6808 *Fax:* 937-548-7051

Web Site: markwithtool.com
Key Personnel
Pres: Merlin Miller *E-mail:* merlin@
markwithtool.com

Marrakech Express Inc
720 Wesley Ave, No 10, Tarpon Springs, FL
34689
Tel: 727-942-2218 *Toll Free Tel:* 800-940-6566
Fax: 727-937-4758
E-mail: print@marrak.com
Web Site: www.marrak.com
Key Personnel
CEO: Peter Henzell
Prodn Mgr: Steen Sigmund
Sales/Estimator: Shirley Copperman
Founded: 1976

Master Flo Technology Inc
154 Seale Rd, Wentworth, QC J8H 0G9, Canada
Tel: 450-533-0088 *Fax:* 450-533-4597
E-mail: info@mflo.com; sales@mflo.com
Web Site: www.mflo.com
Key Personnel
VP, Opers: Tim Duffy
Founded: 1984

Maxcess International
222 W Memorial Rd, Oklahoma City, OK 73114
Mailing Address: PO Box 26508, Oklahoma City,
OK 73126
Tel: 405-755-1600 *Toll Free Tel:* 800-639-3433
Fax: 405-755-8425
E-mail: sales@maxcessintl.com
Web Site: www.maxcessintl.com
Key Personnel
VP, Global Mktg & Devt: Sean Craig
Mktg Communs Mgr: Ben Bowlware
E-mail: bbowlware@maxcessintl.com
Membership(s): Paper Industry Machine Associa-
tion (PIMA); Technical Association of the Pulp
& Paper Industry (TAPPI)

McClain Printing Co
212 Main St, Parsons, WV 26287-1033
Mailing Address: PO Box 403, Parsons, WV
26287-0403
Tel: 304-478-2881 *Toll Free Tel:* 800-654-7179
Fax: 304-478-4658
E-mail: mcclain@mcclainprinting.com
Web Site: www.mcclainprinting.com
Key Personnel
Pres: Kenneth E Smith
VP, Publg: Michelle McKinnie
Founded: 1958

Miles 33 International LLC
Subsidiary of Miles 33 Ltd
40 Richards Ave, Norwalk, CT 06854
Tel: 203-838-2333 *Fax:* 203-838-4473
E-mail: info@miles33.com
Web Site: www.miles33.com
Key Personnel
VP, US Opers: Jeff Malik

Muller Martini Corp
456 Wheeler Rd, Hauppauge, NY 11788
Tel: 631-582-4343 *Toll Free Tel:* 888-268-5537
Fax: 631-348-1961
E-mail: info@us.mullermartini.com
Web Site: www.mullermartiniusa.com
Key Personnel
Pres & CEO: Werner Naegeli *Tel:* 631-486-1351
Founded: 1946
Membership(s): Association for Print Technolo-
gies (APTech); Book Manufacturers' Institute
(BMI)

Neenah Inc
3460 Preston Ridge Rd, Suite 600, Alpharetta,
GA 30005

Toll Free Tel: 800-344-5287
E-mail: publishing.team@neenah.com
Web Site: www.neenahperformance.com/products/
neenah-performance/publishing-products
Key Personnel
Dir, Sales & Mktg: Melanie Calkins
Branch Office(s)
5492 Bostwick St, Lowville, KY 13367
443B Shaker Rd, East Longmeadow, MA 01028
501 E Munising Ave, Munising, MI 49862
Bridge St, Brownville, NY 13615
45 N Fourth St, Quakertown, PA 18951
Membership(s): Book Manufacturers' Institute
(BMI)

Nevada Publications
4135 Badger Circle, Reno, NV 89519
Tel: 775-747-0800
Web Site: nevadapublicationsonline.com
Key Personnel
Owner & Author: Stanley W Paher
E-mail: swpaher@gmail.com
Founded: 1970

The Ohio Blow Pipe Co
446 E 131 St, Cleveland, OH 44108-1684
Tel: 216-681-7379 *Fax:* 216-681-7713
E-mail: sales@obpairsystems.com
Web Site: www.obpairsystems.com
Key Personnel
Pres & CEO: Edward G Fakeris
VP, Engg: Bill Roberts
Founded: 1932

On Demand Machinery
150 Broadway, Elizabeth, NJ 07206
Tel: 908-351-6906 *Fax:* 908-351-7156
E-mail: info@odmachinery.com
Web Site: www.odmachinery.com

O'Neil Digital Solutions LLC
12655 Beatrice St, Los Angeles, CA 90066
Tel: 310-448-6400
E-mail: sales@oneildata.com
Web Site: www.oneildata.com
Key Personnel
Pres & COO: Terry Chan
EVP, Sales & Mktg: Mark Rosson
Dir, HR: LaDonna Wise
Founded: 1973

Overseas Printing Corporation
Division of InnerWorkings Inc
4040 Civic Center Dr, Suite 200, San Rafael, CA
94903
Tel: 415-500-8331 *Fax:* 415-835-9899
Web Site: www.overseasprinting.com
Key Personnel
Sr Prodn Mgr: Shaun Garrett *E-mail:* sgarrett@
inwk.com
Founded: 1972

The Ovid Bell Press Inc
Subsidiary of Walsworth Publishing Co
1201 Bluff St, Fulton, MO 65251
Mailing Address: PO Box 370, Fulton, MO
65251-0370
Tel: 573-642-2256 *Toll Free Tel:* 800-835-8919
E-mail: sales@ovidbell.com
Web Site: ovidbell.com
Key Personnel
CFO: Jill Custard *E-mail:* jillcustard@ovidbell.
com
Pres: Troy Williams *Tel:* 573-310-2599
E-mail: troywilliams@ovidbell.com
VP, Sales & Mktg: David O'Donley *Tel:* 573-
310-2630 *E-mail:* david@ovidbell.com
Plant Mgr: Kevin Werdehausen *Tel:* 573-310-2598
E-mail: kevin.werdehausen@ovidbell.com
Founded: 1927

Pantone Inc
Subsidiary of X-Rite Inc
590 Commerce Blvd, Carlstadt, NJ 07072-3098
Tel: 201-935-5500 *Toll Free Tel:* 866-PANTONE
(726-8663) *Fax:* 201-896-0242
E-mail: pantoneorders@pantone.com
Web Site: www.pantone.com
Key Personnel
SVP & Gen Mgr: Ron Potesky
VP, Opers: Brooks Tippett
Founded: 1963
Branch Office(s)
AXA Tower, Landmark East, 28th fl, 100 How
Ming St, Suite 2801, Kwun Tong, Kowloon,
Hong Kong *Tel:* 2724 8822 *Fax:* 2885 8610
Web Site: www.pantone.com.hk
Pantone LLC, The Acument Centre, First Ave,
Poynton, Cheshire SK12 1FJ, United King-
dom *Tel:* (01625) 871100 *Web Site:* www.store.
pantone.com

Patterson Printing Co
1550 Territorial Rd, Benton Harbor, MI 49022
Tel: 269-925-2177 *Toll Free Tel:* 800-848-8826
Fax: 269-925-6057
E-mail: sales@patterson-printing.com
Web Site: www.patterson-printing.com
Key Personnel
Pres: Leroy Patterson
Plant Mgr: Pamela Thames *Tel:* 269-925-2177 ext
542
Founded: 1956

PrairieView Press
625 Seventh St, Gretna, MB R0G 0V0, Canada
Mailing Address: PO Box 460, Gretna, MB R0G
0V0, Canada
Tel: 204-327-6543 *Toll Free Tel:* 800-477-7377
Toll Free Fax: 866-480-0253
Web Site: prairieviewpress.com
Key Personnel
Owner & Pres: Chester Goossen
Founded: 1968

Printer's Repair Parts
2706 Edgington St, Franklin Park, IL 60131-3438
Tel: 847-288-9000 *Toll Free Tel:* 800-444-4338
Fax: 847-288-9010
E-mail: prpsales@printersrepairparts.com
Web Site: www.printersrepairparts.com
Key Personnel
Sales Mgr: Ken Schelberger *Tel:* 847-228-9000
ext 1054 *E-mail:* ken@printersrepairparts.com

Printing Research Inc (PRI)
10760 Shady Trail, Suite 300, Dallas, TX 75220
Tel: 214-353-9000 *Toll Free Tel:* 800-627-5537
(US only) *Fax:* 214-357-5847
E-mail: info@superblue.net
Web Site: www.printingresearch.com; www.
superblue.net
Key Personnel
Global Sales Dir: Phillip Jones *E-mail:* pjones@
superblue.net
Founded: 1968

PrintWest
1111 Eighth Ave, Regina, SK S4R 1C9, Canada
Tel: 306-525-2304 *Toll Free Tel:* 800-236-6438
Fax: 306-757-2439
E-mail: general@printwest.com
Web Site: www.printwest.com
Key Personnel
Pres & Dir, Opers: Corie Triffo
VP, Sales & Mktg: Ken Benson
Founded: 1992

Publishers Book Bindery (NY)
250 W 16 St, 4th fl, New York, NY 10011
Tel: 917-497-2950

Key Personnel
Pres: Ed Goldman
Founded: 1946

Publishers' Graphics LLC
131 Fremont St, Chicago, IL 60185
Tel: 630-221-1850
E-mail: contactpg@pubgraphics.com
Web Site: pubgraphics.com
Key Personnel
Pres: Nick A Lewis *E-mail:* nlewis@pubgraphics.
  com
VP: Kathleen Lewis *E-mail:* kmlewis@
  pubgraphics.com
Founded: 1996
Branch Office(s)
3777 Rider Trail S, St Louis, MO 63045
  Tel: 314-739-3777 *Fax:* 314-739-1436
Sales Office(s): Louisville, KY, VP, Sales: Cara
  Lahey *Tel:* 630-291-4867 *E-mail:* clahey@
  pubgraphics.com

Sakurai USA Inc
Subsidiary of Sakurai Graphic Systems Corp
1700 N Basswood Rd, Schaumburg, IL 60173
Tel: 847-490-9400 *Toll Free Tel:* 800-458-4720
  Fax: 847-490-4200
E-mail: inquiry@sakurai.com
Web Site: www.sakurai.com
Key Personnel
Pres: Ryuta Sakurai
VP: David Rose

Samuel Packaging Systems
4020 Gault Ave S, Fort Payne, AL 35967
Tel: 256-845-1928
Web Site: www.samuel.com

Santec Corp
84 Old Gate Lane, Milford, CT 06460
Tel: 203-878-1379 *Fax:* 203-876-0949
E-mail: info@santeccorp.com
Web Site: www.santeccorp.com
Key Personnel
Pres: Laura M Lombardo
Opers Mgr: Vito Lombardo
Founded: 1983

Schaefer Machine Co Inc
200 Commercial Dr, Deep River, CT 06417
Tel: 860-526-4000 *Toll Free Tel:* 800-243-5143
  Fax: 860-526-4654
E-mail: schaefer@schaeferco.com
Web Site: www.schaeferco.com
Key Personnel
Pres: Robert Gammons

E C Schultz & Company Inc
333 Crossen Ave, Elk Grove Village, IL 60007-
  2001
Tel: 847-640-1190
E-mail: jobfiles@ecschultz.com
Web Site: www.ecschultz.com
Key Personnel
Pres: Michael Pautz
Founded: 1895
Membership(s): Foil & Specialty Effects Associa-
  tion (FSEA)

SCREEN Americas
Subsidiary of SCREEN Graphic & Precision So-
  lutions
5110 Tollview Dr, Rolling Meadows, IL 60008-
  3715
Tel: 847-870-7400 *Toll Free Tel:* 800-372-7737
E-mail: info@screenamericas.com
Web Site: www.screenamericas.com
Key Personnel
Pres: Ken Ingram
Founded: 1967

Simco-Ion
Subsidiary of ITW Co
2257 N Penn Rd, Hatfield, PA 19440
Tel: 215-822-6401 *Toll Free Tel:* 800-203-3419
E-mail: customerservice@simco-ion.com
Web Site: www.simco-ion.com
Founded: 1936

SITMA USA Inc
Subsidiary of Sitma Machinery SpA
45 Empire Dr, St Paul, MN 55103-1856
Tel: 651-222-2324 *Fax:* 651-222-4652
E-mail: sales@sitma.com
Web Site: www.sitma.it
Key Personnel
Mng Dir: Kevin Curran
Founded: 1965

Southeastern Printing Co
3601 SE Dixie Hwy, Stuart, FL 34997
Tel: 772-287-2141 *Toll Free Tel:* 800-226-8221
  Fax: 772-288-3988
E-mail: sales@seprint.com
Web Site: www.seprint.com
Key Personnel
Pres: Don Mader
Founded: 1924
Branch Office(s)
950 SE Eighth St, Hialeah, FL 33010 *Tel:* 305-
  885-8707 *Fax:* 305-888-9903 *E-mail:* info@
  seprint.com
Sales Office(s): 6001 Park of Commerce Blvd,
  Suite 200, Boca Raton, FL 33487 *Tel:* 561-
  998-0870

Specialty Product Technologies
Subsidiary of Dynapar Corp
2100 W Broad St, Elizabethtown, NC 28337
Tel: 910-862-2511 *Toll Free Tel:* 800-390-6405
  Fax: 910-879-5486
E-mail: customer.service@sptech.com
Web Site: www.specialtyproducttechnologies.com
Key Personnel
Gen Mgr: Sally Creasy
Founded: 1969

Spraymation Inc
Division of Spraymation Development Corp
4180 NW Tenth Ave, Fort Lauderdale, FL 33309
Tel: 954-484-9700 *Toll Free Tel:* 800-327-4985
  Fax: 954-301-0842
E-mail: orders@spraymation.com
Web Site: www.spraymation.com
Key Personnel
CEO: Grant Fitzwilliam
VP: Jim McMillen; Michael Moran
Founded: 1958

Spring Arbor Distributors Inc
Unit of Ingram Content Group LLC
One Ingram Blvd, La Vergne, TN 37086-1986
Toll Free Tel: 800-395-4340 *Toll Free Fax:* 800-
  876-0186
E-mail: customerservice@ingramcontent.com
Web Site: www.ingramcontent.com
Key Personnel
Sales Rep: Mary Lou Alexander *Tel:* 615-
  213-3319 *E-mail:* marylou.alexander@
  ingramcontent.com
Founded: 1978
Branch Office(s)
Indiana Distribution Center, 7315 Innovation
  Blvd, Fort Wayne, IN 46818-1371
Oregon Distribution Center, 201 Ingram Dr, Rose-
  burg, OR 97471
Chambersburg Distribution Center, 1240 Ingram
  Dr, Chambersburg, PA 17202

Standard Finishing Systems
Division of Standard Duplicating Machines Corp
10 Connector Rd, Andover, MA 01810

Tel: 978-470-1920 *Toll Free Tel:* 877-404-4460
  Fax: 978-470-0819
E-mail: marketing@sdmc.com
Web Site: www.sdmc.com
Key Personnel
Dir, Mktg: Don Dubuque *E-mail:* don_dubuque@
  sdmc.com

Staplex® Electric Stapler Division
Division of The Staplex® Co Inc
777 Fifth Ave, Brooklyn, NY 11232-1626
Tel: 718-768-3333 *Toll Free Tel:* 800-221-0822
  Fax: 718-965-0750
E-mail: info@staplex.com
Web Site: www.staplex.com
Key Personnel
Sales Mgr: Doug Butler
Founded: 1949

Stoesser Register Systems
610 Whitetail Blvd, River Falls, WI 54022
Tel: 715-425-1900 *Toll Free Tel:* 888-407-4808
  Fax: 715-425-1901
E-mail: info@nela-usa.com
Web Site: www.nela-usa.com
Key Personnel
Inside Sales: Dave Kurz

Styled Packaging LLC
PO Box 30299, Philadelphia, PA 19103-8299
Tel: 610-529-4122 *Fax:* 610-520-9662
Web Site: www.taylorbox.com
Key Personnel
Pres: William R Fenkel *E-mail:* jjibill@aol.com
Founded: 2003
Membership(s): Book Industry Guild of New
  York

Suspension Feeder
Division of Roessner Holdings Inc
631 E Washington St, St Henry, OH 45883
Tel: 419-763-1377 *Toll Free Fax:* 888-210-9654
Web Site: www.suspensionfeeder.com
Key Personnel
Owner & Pres: Jeff Roessner
Founded: 1969

Taconic Wire
250 Totoket Rd, North Branford, CT 06471
Tel: 203-484-2863 *Toll Free Tel:* 800-253-1450
  Fax: 203-484-2865
E-mail: sales@taconicwire.com;
  taconicwiresales@gmail.com
Web Site: www.taconicwire.com
Key Personnel
Pres: Angela Watrous *E-mail:* angela@
  taconicwire.com
VP, Sales & Mktg: Anthony Candelora
  E-mail: anthony@taconicwire.com
Sales & Cust Serv: Michele Pollock
  E-mail: michele@taconicwire.com

Tecnau Inc
4 Suburban Park Dr, Billerica, MA 01821
Tel: 978-608-0500 *Fax:* 978-608-0558
E-mail: info.us@tecnau.com
Web Site: www.tecnau.com
Key Personnel
District Sales Mgr: Chris Markley *Tel:* 610-469-
  2008 *E-mail:* cmarkley@tecnau.com
Founded: 2011 (from acquisition of Lasermax
  Roll Systems by Tecnau)
Branch Office(s)
Tecnau NV, Stoofstr 39/a, 1785 Merchtem, Bel-
  gium *Tel:* (0524) 82 444 *E-mail:* info@tecnau.
  com
Tecnau Ltd, North Bldg, Rm 200, 223 XiKang
  Rd, Jing An District, Shanghai 200040, China
  Tel: (0159) 00710147 *Fax:* (0216) 2898662
  E-mail: info.cn@tecnau.com

Tecnau SRL, Via Torino, 603, 10015 Ivrea TO, Italy *Tel:* (0125) 63 16 78 *Fax:* (0125) 23 90 35 *E-mail:* info.it@tecnau.com

Tecnau Pte Ltd, Block 829, Jurong West St 81, No 03-314, Singapore 640829, Singapore *Tel:* 6793 9478 *Fax:* 6793 9476 *E-mail:* info.sg@tecnau.com

Tecnau AB, Langgatan 21, 341 32 Ljungby, Sweden *Tel:* (0372) 256 00 *Fax:* (0372) 828 37 *E-mail:* info.se@tecnau.com

Tidland, see Maxcess International

Times Printing LLC
Division of Kappa Printing Management Associates LLC (KPMA)
100 Industrial Dr, Random Lake, WI 53075
Tel: 920-994-4396 *Toll Free Tel:* 800-236-4396 (sales)
E-mail: info@kappapma.com
Web Site: www.kappapma.com
Founded: 1918

Timsons Inc
385 Crossen Ave, Elk Grove Village, IL 60007
Tel: 847-884-8611 *Fax:* 847-884-8676
E-mail: sales@timsonsinc.com
Web Site: www.timsonsinc.com
Key Personnel
VP, Opers: Nancy Panzarella *E-mail:* nancyp@timsonsinc.com
Founded: 1896

Tobias Associates Inc
50 Industrial Dr, Ivyland, PA 18974
Mailing Address: PO Box 2699, Ivyland, PA 18974
Tel: 215-322-1500 *Toll Free Tel:* 800-877-3367 *Fax:* 215-322-1504
E-mail: sales@tobiasinc.com
Web Site: www.densitometer.com
Key Personnel
Pres: Eric Tobias
Founded: 1959

Tompkins Printing Equipment Co
5050 N Rose St, Schiller Park, IL 60176
Tel: 847-671-5050 *Fax:* 847-671-5538
E-mail: sales@tompkins.com
Web Site: www.tompkins.com
Key Personnel
Pres: Steve Tompkins
VP: Bill Tompkins
Founded: 1932

Townsend Communications Inc
20 E Gregory Blvd, Kansas City, MO 64114
Tel: 816-361-0616

Web Site: www.townsendcommunications.com; www.townsendprint.com
Key Personnel
Pres: Guy Townsend, III
VP: Joe Chambers
Founded: 1964

Tukaiz LLC
2917 N Latoria Lane, Franklin Park, IL 60131
Tel: 847-455-1588; 847-288-4968 (sales)
    Toll Free Tel: 800-543-2674
E-mail: contacttukaiz@tukaiz.com
Web Site: www.tukaiz.com
Key Personnel
Founder & Mng Dir: Frank Defino, Sr
VP, Mng Dir & CFO: Christopher Calabra
VP & Mng Dir: Daniel Defino; Frank Defino, Jr
Founded: 1963

Valley Roller, see Maxcess International

Videojet Technologies Inc
Subsidiary of Danaher Corp
1500 N Mittel Blvd, Wood Dale, IL 60191-1073
Tel: 630-860-7300 *Toll Free Tel:* 800-843-3610
    Toll Free Fax: 800-582-1343
E-mail: info@videojet.com
Web Site: www.videojet.com
Key Personnel
Sr Mktg Communs Specialist: Theresa DiCanio
    E-mail: theresa.dicanio@videojet.com
Founded: 1980

Webcom Inc
Division of Marquis Book Printing Inc
3480 Pharmacy Ave, Toronto, ON M1W 2S7, Canada
Tel: 416-496-1000 *Toll Free Tel:* 800-665-9322 *Fax:* 416-496-1537
E-mail: webcom@webcomlink.com
Web Site: www.webcomlink.com
Key Personnel
Pres & CEO: Mike Collinge
Dir of HR & Cust Serv: Rhonda Suurd
Dir of Sales: Marc Doucet
Founded: 1975
Sales Office(s): 65 Spring Valley Ave, River Edge, NJ 07661, Contact: Susan Ginch
    Tel: 201-262-4301 *Fax:* 201-262-6375
    E-mail: susan.ginch@webcomlink.com
Membership(s): Book Manufacturers' Institute (BMI); Canadian Book & Periodical Council; PRINTING United Alliance

Webcrafters Inc
2211 Fordem Ave, Madison, WI 53704
Tel: 608-244-3561 *Toll Free Tel:* 800-356-8200 *Fax:* 608-244-5120
E-mail: info@webcrafters-inc.com
Web Site: www.webcrafters-inc.com

Key Personnel
CEO: Chris Kurtzman
VP, Div Dir: Brad Koch
Membership(s): Book Manufacturers' Institute (BMI)

Webex, see Maxcess International

Fred Weidner & Daughter Printers
99 Hudson St, 5th fl, New York, NY 10013
Tel: 646-706-5180
E-mail: info@fwdprinters.com
Web Site: www.fwdprinters.com
Key Personnel
Pres: Cynthia Weidner *E-mail:* cynthia@fwdprinters.com
Creative Dir: Carol Mittelsdorf *E-mail:* carol@fwdprinters.com
Founded: 1860

Western Printing Machinery Co (WPM)
9228 Ivanhoe St, Schiller Park, IL 60176
Tel: 847-678-1740 *Fax:* 847-678-6176
E-mail: info@wpm.com
Web Site: www.wpm.com
Key Personnel
Pres & CEO: Paul Kapolnek
CFO: Kelvin O'Meara
Dir, Cust Servs: Renee Reckamp *Tel:* 847-994-8622
Founded: 1933
Membership(s): International Association of Diecutting & Diemaking (IADD)

X-Rite Inc
Subsidiary of Danaher Corp
4300 44 St SE, Grand Rapids, MI 49512
Tel: 616-803-2100 *Toll Free Tel:* 800-248-9748; 888-800-9580 (sales)
E-mail: info@xrite.com
Web Site: www.xrite.com
Key Personnel
CFO: Jeff McKee
CTO: Dr Francis Lamy
Pres: Ondrej Kruk
Founded: 1958

Yurchak Printing Inc
920 Links Ave, Landisville, PA 17538
Tel: 717-399-0209
E-mail: ypi.info@yurchak.com
Web Site: www.yurchak.com
Key Personnel
Founder & CEO: John Yurchak, Jr
Pres: John W Yurchak
VP, Opers: Jason Yurchak
Dir, Busn Devt: Randy Boyer
Founded: 1998
Membership(s): International Printers' Network (IPN)

Sales & Distribution

Book Distributors & Sales Representatives

Featuring freelance book salespersons who represent publishers in various parts of the country as well as publishers' distributors that, in addition to representing groups of smaller publishers throughout the United States and Canada, may also provide marketing and sales services.

Abraham Associates Inc
5120-A Cedar Lake Rd, Minneapolis, MN 55416
Tel: 952-927-7920 *Toll Free Tel:* 800-701-2489
Fax: 952-927-8089
E-mail: info@abrahamassociatesinc.com
Web Site: www.abrahamassociatesinc.com
Key Personnel
Founder: Stu Abraham *E-mail:* stu@
abrahamassociatesinc.com
Owner: John Mesjak *E-mail:* john@
abrahamassociatesinc.com
Sales Rep: Emily Johnson *E-mail:* emily@
abrahamassociatesinc.com; Sandra Law
E-mail: sandra@abrahamassociatesinc.com
Off Mgr: Ted Seykora *E-mail:* ted@
abrahamassociatesinc.com
Founded: 1992
Trade sales representatives.
Territory: Midwestern States

ACC Distribution Ltd
Division of ACC Art Books
6 W 18 St, Suite 4B, New York, NY 10011
Tel: 212-645-1111 *Toll Free Tel:* 800-252-5231
Fax: 716-242-4911
E-mail: ussales@accpublishinggroup.com
Web Site: www.accpublishinggroup.com/us
Key Personnel
VP & Gen Mgr: John Brancati
E-mail: jbrancati@accpublishinggroup.com
Press: Jennifer Burch *E-mail:* jburch@
accpublishinggroup.com
Represents over 150 publishing houses with distribution worldwide. Focus on antiques & decorative art books. Foreign office in the UK.
Distributor for ACC Art Books; ACC Editions; ACR Edition; John Adamson; Adler Planetarium & Astronomy; America's Greatest Brands; Anniversary Books; Archetype Books; Arkivia Books SRL; Arnoldsche Art Publishers; Art of Power Publishing; Artis; Artist Book Foundation; Artmedia; ArtPostAsia; Artpower International Publishers; Ashmolean Museum Publications; AV Edition; Barn Elms; Bauer & Dean; Belmont Press/Fiske & Freeman; Beta Plus Publishing; Bierke Publishing; Books & Projects; Brown & Brown; Callaway; Callwey Verlag; Cannibal/Hannibal; Carlton Books Ltd; Centro Di; Editions Cercle d'Art; Chameleon Books; Circa Press; Editions du Chene; William G Congdon Foundation; Congedo Editore; DAAB Media; De Menil Gallery; Diane de Selliers; Debrett's; Delius Klasing Verlag; Richard Dennis Publications; Duval & Hamilton; Editemos; Ediciones El Viso; Ediciones El Viso America; Emons; Fawn's Leap Publications; Fine Arts Society/Atelier Books; Floating World Editions; M Shafik Gabr; Gallimard; Gambero Rosso; Garden Art Press; Editions Gourcuff Gradenigo; Grayson Publishing; Guido Tomassi Editore; Hasson Editorial; Hathi Chiti/Shunya Inc; Heel Verlag; Hudson Hills Press LLC; The Images Publishing Group; Jaico Publishing House; Jensen Fine Arts; Johan & Levi SRL; Urban Juergensen; KMW Studio; LACMA; Edition Lammerhuber; Lange Uhren; Lannoo Publishers; London Editions Turkey Ltd; Luster; Macklowe Gallery; Mandragora SRL; Mapin Publishing; The Marg Foundation; Luca Maroni; Marquand Books; Merrick & Day; David Messum; Monaco Books; Andrea Monfried Editions; MT Train; Museum of Arts & Design; Museum of Brands; National Galleries of Scotland; National Museums of Scotland; New Cavendish; Nicolai; Niyogi Books; Editions Norma; North Carolina Museum of Art; Officina Libraria SRL; Orchid Press; Franco Cosimo Panini Editore SpA; Papadakis Publisher; Pelluceo; Grupo Penin; Plurabelle; Pointed Leaf Press; Quart Architektur; Red Dot; Ridgewood Publishing LLC; River Books; Roads Publishing; Roli Books; Rovakada; Royal Pavilion Libraries & Museums; San Diego Museum of Art; Scala Arts Publishers Inc; Shannongrove Press; Sieveking; Smallwood + Stewart; Spacemaker Press; Stichting Kunstboek; teNeues Verlag; Tf Editores; Third Millenium Publishing/Profile Books; Trilce Ediciones; Two Red Roses Foundation; 24 ORE Cultura; Vadehra Art Gallery; Vendage Press; Grafiche Vianello/Vianello Libri; Visionary World; Wartski; Watchprint; Watermark Press; WBooks Publishers; Winterthur Museum; Wonderland

Actar D
440 Park Ave S, 17th fl, New York, NY 10016
Tel: 212-966-2207
E-mail: salesnewyork@actar-d.com
Web Site: www.actar.com
Key Personnel
Pres: Brian Brash *E-mail:* brian@actar-d.com
Founded: 2006
Distributor of architecture & design books.
Distributor for Actar; Artifice Books on Architecture; DOM Publishers; Evolo; ORO Editions; Yale School of Architecture
Territory: worldwide exc Europe

Les Messageries ADP
Subsidiary of Quebecor Media Inc
2315, rue de la Province, Longueuil, QC J4G 1G4, Canada
Tel: 450-640-1234 (commercial); 450-640-1237 (sales) *Toll Free Tel:* 800-771-3022 (commercial); 866-874-1237 (sales) *Fax:* 450-640-1251 (commercial); 450-674-6237 (sales) *Toll Free Fax:* 800-603-0433 (commercial); 866-874-6237 (sales)
E-mail: adpcommandes@messageries-adp.com
Web Site: www.messageries-adp.com

Key Personnel
SVP: Lyne Robitaille
Commercial Dir: Ronald Blouin
Gen Mgr: Charles Cusson
Founded: 1967
Represents Adventure Press; Les Editions Alaska Inc; L'Alchimiste Editions; Alire; Alma Ma Terre; Alter Real; Des Ameriques; Archipel; Atma; Atramenta; Aupel; De la Bagnole; Berlicoco; Boomerang Editeur Jeunesse; Bravo!; Marcel Broquet Editeur; Calligram; Catalogue Lsuk; CEC Parasco; Centre quebecois de lutte aux dependances; Chouette; Editions Cinq-Cygne; Couer de Pomme; Coup de Pouce; Crackboom!; Editions de l'ecole de Guerre; L'Ecrivain de l'Est; Fonfon; Fontea; Les Editions Goelette; La Griffe; H Tag Editions; Les Editions de l'Hexagone; Les Editions de l'Homme; Houle; Les Editions Inst-Art; Maison Jacynthe; Les Editions JCL; Jeux Ludex; Jobboom; Le Jour; Les Editions du Journal; Klorofil; Kmag; Michel Lafon; Michel Lafon Poche; Editions LaLucia; Peter Lang Group; Linda Leith Editions; Libre Expression; Livresque Edit; Les Editions Logiques; Le Maitre-Routier; Mega Editions; Albin Michel Jeunesse; Albin Michel Litterature; Modus Vivendi; Un Monde Different; Option Sante Editions; Origo; Orinha Media; Otherlands Editions; Perro Editeur; Petit homme; Groupe Phaneuf; Pratico-Pratiques; Presses Aventure; Prive; Publistar; Les Editions Quebec-Livres; Editions Michel Quintin; Recrealire; Recto-Verso; Rouge; Editions Caroline Roy; Selection du Reader's Digest; Editions La Semaine; Solaris; Something Else; Soulieres Editeur; Stanke; Alexandre Stanke Editions; Editions Theatre des Varietes (TDV); Trapeze; Trecarre; Editions du Tresor cache; Typo; Utilis; Velo Quebec; VLB Editeur; Voyel; Wilson & Lafleur; Z'Ailees
Territory: Canada (French-speaking)

Aeon Books/Vishaal
Affiliate of Aeon Group
PO Box 396, Accord, NY 12404-0396
Tel: 845-658-3068 *Fax:* 845-658-3068
E-mail: aeongroup@msn.com
Web Site: www.aeongroup.com
Key Personnel
Dist Mgr: Jeanette Caurant *E-mail:* caurant@msn.com
Dist Asst: Jan Shapiro *Tel:* 845-895-9133
E-mail: jans963@gmail.com
Founded: 1975
Distributor of books by author Patrizia Norelli-Bachelet.
Territory: USA

AIMS International Books Inc
7709 Hamilton Ave, Cincinnati, OH 45231

Tel: 513-521-5590 *Fax:* 513-521-5592
E-mail: info@aimsbooks.com
Web Site: www.aimsbooks.com
Key Personnel
Pres: Georgia W Crowell
Secy & Treas: David Crowell
Distributes books in Spanish & other foreign languages.
Represents Another Language Press
Territory: Canada, USA

AKJ Education
4702 Benson Ave, Halethorpe, MD 21227
Tel: 410-242-1602 *Toll Free Tel:* 800-922-6066
  Fax: 410-242-6107 *Toll Free Fax:* 888-770-2338
E-mail: info@akjeducation.com
Web Site: www.akjeducation.com
Key Personnel
Owner & Pres: Tim Thompson
Founded: 1974
Children's book distributor specializing in infant–12th grade educational sales & literacy programs. Also services literacy programs like Reading is Fundamental, Reach Out & Read & others.
Territory: USA
Membership(s): Educational Book & Media Association (EBMA); Reading Recovery Council of North America

Amazon Advantage, see Fulfillment by Amazon (FBA)

Amazon Fulfillment Services, see Fulfillment by Amazon (FBA)

American International Distribution Corp (AIDC)
82 Winter Sport Lane, Williston, VT 05495
Mailing Address: PO Box 80, Williston, VT 05495-0080
Tel: 802-862-0095 *Toll Free Tel:* 800-678-2432
  Fax: 802-864-7749
Web Site: www.aidcvt.com
Key Personnel
Pres & CEO: Marilyn McConnell
Dir, Opers: Michael Pelland
Founded: 1986
Comprehensive order processing, payment processing, pick, pack, ship & processing, collection services; inventory receipt, management & preparation services; comprehensive data management & reporting via e-mail & web; membership & association services, subscription services; lettershop services, web site hosting & development.
Distributor for Air Age Media; American Agora Foundation; Belvoir Media Group; Berrett-Koehler Publishers; Business Expert Press; Chooseco; Crown House Publishers; The Geological Society of London; Hardspring Publishing; Height of Land Pubications; International Monetary Fund; Jolly Learning Ltd; Kugler Publications; MCC Magazines; Metropolis Magazine; Momentum Press; More Press; Morgan & Claypool Publishers; National Geographic; Outside Magazine; People's Medical Publishing House; Reef to Rainforest Media; Rethinking Schools; SAP Press; Society of Biblical Literature; Source Interlink Media; String Letter Publishing; Teachers College Press; Trusted Media Brands; Vermont Department of Health; Wine Enthusiast Magazine; Zeig, Tucker & Theisen
Membership(s): Book Industry Study Group (BISG); Independent Publisher's Guild (IPG)

American West Books Inc
1254 Commerce Way, Sanger, CA 93657
SAN: 630-8570

Tel: 559-876-2170 *Fax:* 559-876-2180
E-mail: info@americanwestbooks.com
Web Site: www.americanwestbooks.com
Key Personnel
Pres & CEO: Christopher Robbins
  E-mail: crobbins@americanwestbooks.com
Founded: 1993
Book wholesaler that focuses on niche titles & regional titles thoughout the nation.
Represents Abbeville Press; AJ Hauntings; Frank Amato Publications Inc; American River Natural History; Arbutus Press; Arcadia Publishing; Automobile Club of Southern California; Azalea Creek Publishing; Backdoor Publishing; Bear State Books; Bellerophon Books; Big Lost River Press; Big Valley Publishing; Bike Map Dude Productions; Bluebird Publishing; BMC Publications; Bored Feet Press; Burford Books; Cachuma Press; Calaveras Big Tree Associates; California Genealogical Society; Cameron & Co; Central Coast Press; Chapel Hill Press; Charlesbridge Publishing; Cherbo Publishing; Chilnoalna Books; Chrispaul Publishing Co; Ciao Bella Publishing; City of Palm Desert; Clear Light Publishers; Clock Tower Press; Clover Publications; Cody Ben Taylor Publishing; Coldstream Press; Collier Publishing; Color & Light Editions; Commonwealth Editions; Community Action Publications; Conejo Valley Historical Society; Constellation Press; Crabtree Publishing; Creative Arts; Creative Design Group; Crest Publishers; Cumberland House Publishing; Cypress House; Dawn Press; Desert Discovery Publication; Diamond Valley Co; Document Media LLC; Dona Ana County Historical Society; Electric Canvas; Encounter Books; Farcountry Press; Faultline Books; Fine Edge; Folson Historical Society; Fulcrum Publishing; Gallopade International; Give-it-A-Go Enterprises; Globe Pequot Press; Grand Canyon Association; Graphic Arts Center Publishing; Great West Books; Heyday Books; High Plains Press; Houghton Mifflin Harcourt Publishing Co; Joshua Tree National Park Association; Linden Publishing; Lonely Planet; Lone Pine Publishing; Los Angeles Times; Map Link; MBI Publishers; Mountaineers; Mountain Press; Natruregraph Publishing; Thomas Nelson Inc; Pioneer Press; Pomegranate Communications Inc; Poppyland Publishing Co; Positively for Kids; Princeton University Press; Quill Driver Books/Word Dancer; Random House Inc; Red Rabbit Press; Carl L Sams II Photography; Sequoia Natural History Association; Shafdog Publications Inc; Sierra Press; Sleeping Bear; Stackpole Books; Stagecoach Publishing; Stauffer Publishing; T & N Children's Publishing; Ten Speed Press; 3D Press; Timber Press Inc; Tomato Enterprises; Track & Trail Publishing; Trail Tracks; Twin Lights Publishers Inc; University of California Press; University of Nevada Press; Welcome Enterprises Inc; Wesanne Publishing; Western Reflections Publishing; West Press; Wilderness Press; John Wiley & Sons; Willow Creek Press; Windgate Press; Windy Hill Publications; Yosemite Association
Territory: USA
Membership(s): California Independent Booksellers Alliance (CALIBA)

APG Sales & Distribution
1501 County Hospital Rd, Nashville, TN 37218
Tel: 615-254-2488 *Toll Free Tel:* 800-327-5113
  Toll Free Fax: 800-510-3650
Web Site: www.apg-sales.com
Sales, consultation & distribution group that services the book, gift & decorative accessories market nationwide.
Distributor for Aslan Publishing; Concept Inc; Foundation House Publishing
Represents Aequus Institute; Aristata Publishing; Aslan Publishing; Borgata Books; BTS Pub-

lishing; Celebrity Books; Compendium Inc; Eager Minds Press; Everywhere Press; Forrason Press; Foulsham; David Icke Books; Inclusive Books; Knowledge Products; Legacy Publishing; Life Action Press; Ned's Head Productions; Peace Publishing; Pers Publishing; Prelude Press/Mary Books; Recovery Communications; Rock House Way; Simple Dream Publishing; SOS Publishing; Summerjoy Press; Zoetic Publishing; Zulu Publishing
Territory: USA

Arrow Publications Inc
5270 N Park Place NE, Suite 114, Cedar Rapids, IA 52402
Mailing Address: PO Box 10102, Cedar Rapids, IA 52410
Tel: 319-395-7833 *Toll Free Tel:* 877-363-6889
  Fax: 319-395-7353
Web Site: www.frangipane.org; www.arrowbookstore.com
Key Personnel
Admin Asst: Terri Rowray *Tel:* 319-395-7131
  E-mail: trowray@frangipane.org
Publish & distribute Christian books & teaching materials.

Ars Medica, see RAmEx Ars Medica Inc

Art Media Resources Inc
1965 W Pershing Rd, Chicago, IL 60605
Tel: 312-663-5351 *Fax:* 312-663-5177
E-mail: paragon@paragonbook.com
Web Site: www.artmediaresources.com
Key Personnel
Owner: Amy Lee
Publishers & distributors of Asian art books.

Athena Productions Inc
2204 S Ashford Ct, Nashville, TN 37214
Tel: 305-807-8607
E-mail: atheprod@aol.com
Key Personnel
Pres: Athena Millas Kaiman
EVP: Ken Kaiman
Founded: 1969
Sales representatives & consultants. Foreign rights agency.
Represents Book Publishing Co; New Leaf Distributing Co; Square One Publishers
Territory: USA, worldwide
Membership(s): Independent Book Publishers Association (IBPA)

Auromere Ayurvedic Inc
Division of Integral Yoga
2621 W Hwy 12, Lodi, CA 95242
Toll Free Tel: 800-735-4691
Web Site: www.auromere.com
Key Personnel
Pres & Mktg Dir: Dakshina Vanzetti
Book distribution.
Territory: Canada, USA

AzureGreen
16 Bell Rd, Middlefield, MA 01243
Mailing Address: PO Box 48, Middlefield, MA 01243-0048
Tel: 413-623-2155 *Fax:* 413-623-2156
E-mail: azuregreen@azuregreen.com
Web Site: www.azuregreen.net
Key Personnel
Owner: Adair Cafarella *E-mail:* adair@abyssdistribution.com
Founded: 1986
Distributors of specialty books & gifts for spiritual seekers. Leaders in providing titles on: magick, wicca, tarot, New Age, goddess studies, herbs, healing, shamanism, Celtic lore, western mystery traditions, occult, ancient

Egypt, magical children's stories & related subjects. Suppliers of merchandise to New Age retail stores & mail-order companies.

Baha'i Distribution Service
401 Greenleaf Ave, Wilmette, IL 60091
Tel: 847-425-7950 *Toll Free Tel:* 800-999-9019
Fax: 847-425-7951
E-mail: bds@usbnc.org
Web Site: www.bahaibookstore.com
Key Personnel
Gen Mgr: Nat Yogachandra
Founded: 1902
Distributor of literature on or related to the Baha'i Faith.
Distributor for Baha'i Books UK; Baha'i Distribution Services of Australia; Baha'i Publishing Trust of the United States
Represents Baha'i Distribution Services of Canada; Oneworld Publications; Palabra Publications; George Ronald Publishers
Territory: worldwide

Baker & Taylor LLC
Division of Follett Corporation
2550 W Tyvola Rd, Suite 300, Charlotte, NC 28217
Tel: 704-998-3100 *Toll Free Tel:* 800-775-1800
(info servs) *Fax:* 704-998-3319
E-mail: btinfo@baker-taylor.com
Web Site: www.baker-taylor.com
Key Personnel
EVP & Gen Mgr: Amandeep Kochar
EVP, Opers: Gary Dayton
Founded: 1828
Aggregator & distributor of books, digital content & entertainment products. The company leverages its unsurpassed worldwide distribution network to deliver rich content in multiple formats, anytime & anywhere. Offers cutting-edge digital media services & innovative technology platforms to thousands of publishers & libraries. Baker & Taylor also offers industry-leading customized library services. Baker & Taylor is proud to power Blio (blioreader.com), a flexible engaging & revolutionary e-reading application.
Branch Office(s)
Commerce Service Center, 251 Mount Olive Church Rd, Dept R, Commerce, GA 30599 *Tel:* 706-335-5000 *Toll Free Tel:* 800-775-1200
Momence Service Center, 501 S Gladiolus St, Momence, IL 60954, VP, Opers/Gen Mgr: Terrell Osborne *Tel:* 815-802-2444 *Toll Free Tel:* 800-775-2300
Pittsburgh Service Center, 875 Greentree Rd, Suite 678, Pittsburgh, PA 15220 *Tel:* 412-787-8890 *Toll Free Tel:* 800-775-2600
Territory: worldwide
Membership(s): The American Library Association (ALA); Book Industry Study Group (BISG)

Baker & Taylor Publisher Services
30 Amberwood Pkwy, Ashland, OH 44805
Tel: 567-215-0030 *Toll Free Tel:* 888-814-0208
E-mail: info@btpubservices.com; orders@btpubservices.com
Web Site: www.btpubservices.com
Key Personnel
SVP, Sales & Client Servs: Mark Suchomel
SVP, Opers: Bob Gospodarek
Founded: 2017
Baker & Taylor Publisher Services can efficiently get your books to market. For print books, in-house & contracted field sales professionals call on major industry buyers & we can help you reach independent bookstores, libraries, mass merchandisers & special markets. For eBooks, connect with Amazon, Barnes & No-

ble, Apple, Kobo & Overdrive. Also offers warehousing, commercial & direct-to-consumer fulfillment & online account management.

Balogh International Inc
1911 N Duncan Rd, Champaign, IL 61822
Tel: 217-355-9331 *Fax:* 217-355-9413
E-mail: balogh@balogh.com
Web Site: www.balogh.com
Key Personnel
Pres: Scott Michael Balogh *E-mail:* scott@balogh.com
Booksellers & distributors of international publishers.

BCH Fulfillment & Distribution
33 Oakland Ave, Harrison, NY 10528
Tel: 914-835-0015 *Toll Free Tel:* 800-431-1579
Fax: 914-835-0398
E-mail: bookch@aol.com
Web Site: www.bookch.com
Key Personnel
Pres: Diane Musto
Founded: 1934
Represent over 700 self-publishers. Approved vendor for Ingram, Baker & Taylor, Amazon & Barnes & Noble.
Membership(s): Independent Book Publishers Association (IBPA)

Beacon Audiobooks
Subsidiary of Spectra Music Group
7075 Cross County Rd, Box 41573, Charleston, SC 29423
Toll Free Tel: 800-817-8480
E-mail: info@beaconaudiobooks.com
Web Site: www.beaconaudiobooks.com
Specialize in narration & distribution of audiobooks worldwide.

Beacon of Grace Publications, see Publicaciones Faro de Gracia (PFG)

Bernan
Imprint of Rowman & Littlefield Publishing Group
4501 Forbes Blvd, Suite 200, Lanham, MD 20706
Mailing Address: PO Box 191, Blue Ridge Summit, PA 17214-0191
Tel: 717-794-3800 (cust serv & orders)
Toll Free Tel: 800-462-6420 (cust serv & orders) *Fax:* 717-794-3803 *Toll Free Fax:* 800-338-4550
E-mail: customercare@bernan.com
Web Site: rowman.com/page/bernan
Key Personnel
Mktg Mgr: Veronica M Dove *Tel:* 301-459-2255 ext 5716 *Fax:* 301-459-0056 *E-mail:* vdove@bernan.com
Founded: 1952
Standing order & one-time order service for US government publications.
Represents Government Printing Office; Library of Congress; National Technical Information Service (NTIS)

Bilingual Educational Services Inc
2514 S Grand Ave, Los Angeles, CA 90007
SAN: 169-0388
Tel: 213-749-6213 *Toll Free Tel:* 800-448-6032
Key Personnel
Pres: Jeff Penichet
Textbooks, books, posters, study prints & AV programs for bilingual & multicultural education.

Book Travelers West
3614A California Ave SW, No 228, Seattle, WA 98116
Tel: 206-932-7865 *Toll Free Fax:* 800-440-0818
Web Site: www.booktravelerswest.com

Key Personnel
Group Head: Kurtis Lowe *E-mail:* kurtis@booktravelerswest.com
Founded: 1951
Commissioned sales group calling on bookstores, book wholesalers, college & university bookstores, museum shops, art supply & related book retailers.
Branch Office(s)
110 Pine Ridge Rd, PO Box 3328, Crestline, CA 92325 (Southern CA & Las Vegas, NV), Contact: Kevin Peters *Tel:* 310-710-1306 *Toll Free Fax:* 800-400-0818 *E-mail:* john@booktravelerswest.com
1026 Florin Rd, No 164, Sacramento, CA 95831 (Northern CA & Reno, NV), Contact: Kevin Peters *Tel:* 916-837-3604 *Toll Free Fax:* 800-440-0818 *E-mail:* kevin@booktravelerswest.com
303 S Broadway, Suite 200-335, Denver, CO 80209 (AZ, CO, HI, NM, UT, WY), Contact: Phoebe Gaston *Tel:* 513-886-1130 *Toll Free Fax:* 800-440-0818 *E-mail:* phoebe@booktravelerswest.com
Represents Algonquin Books of Chapel Hill; Algonquin Young Readers; Artisan; Aurum Press; Colin Baxter Photography; Capstone; Capstone Digital; Capstone Press; Cartech; Caxton Press; Chooseco; Compass Point Books; Cool Springs Press; Creative Publishing International; Duopress; The Experiment; Fair Winds Press; Familius; Walter Foster; Harvard Common Press; Heinemann-Raintree; HMH Books & Media (western US); Hove Books; Kumon Publishing North America; Liberty Street; Frances Lincoln; Litographs; Meredith; Merrymakers Inc; Mitchell Geography; Motorbooks; MVP Books; Naval Institute Press; Oregon State University Press; Picture Window Books; Quarry Books; Quarto Publishing Group USA; Quiver; Rockport Publishers; Shelter Harbor Press; Specialty Press; Sterling Publishing Inc; Stone Arch Books; Storey Publishing; Tetra Press; Theo Chocolate; Tiger Tales; Timber Press; Time Books Inc; Union Books; University of Washington Press; Vintage Bookmarks; Voyageur Press; Washington State University Press; Workman Publishing Co; Zenith Press; Zigamedia
Territory: 13 Western States

Book Vine for Children
3980 Albany St, Suite 7, McHenry, IL 60050-8397
Tel: 815-363-8880 *Toll Free Tel:* 800-772-4220
Fax: 815-363-8883
E-mail: info@bookvine.com
Web Site: www.bookvine.com
Key Personnel
Owner & Pres: Isabel Baker
Founded: 1989
Distributor of children's books.

B Broughton Co Ltd
322 Consumers Rd, North York, ON M2J 1P8, Canada
Tel: 416-690-4777 *Toll Free Tel:* 800-268-4449
Fax: 416-690-5357
E-mail: sales@bbroughton.com
Web Site: www.bbroughton.com
Key Personnel
Owner & Pres: Brian Broughton *E-mail:* brian@bbroughton.com
Founded: 1970
Religious education books & AV.
Distributor for Hermitage Art; Ignatius Press; Liturgical Press; Malhame Publishing; Our Sunday Visitor; Regina Press; Saint Mary's Press
Represents Hermitage Art; Ignatius Press; Liturgical Press; Malhame Publishing; Our Sunday Visitor; Regina Press; Saint Mary's Press

Territory: Canada
Membership(s): National Church Goods Association (NCGA)

Brunswick Books
14 Afton Ave, Toronto, ON M6J 1R7, Canada
Tel: 416-703-3598 *Fax:* 416-703-6561
E-mail: info@brunswickbooks.ca; orders@brunswickbooks.ca
Web Site: brunswickbooks.ca
Key Personnel
Pres: Lindsay Sharpe *E-mail:* lindsay@brunswickbooks.ca
Off Mgr: Michael Jackel *E-mail:* michael@brunswickbooks.ca
Founded: 1978
Sales & distribution.
Distributor for Baylor University Press; Between the Lines; Catholic University of America Press; Daraja Press; Demeter Press; Duke University Press; Fernwood Publishing; Georgetown University Press; Inanna Publications; Johns Hopkins University Press; Maryland Historical Society; Monthly Review Press; New Star Books; New York University Press; Pluto Books; Roseway Publishing; University of Massachusetts Press; University Press of Kentucky
Territory: Canada

Calvary Distribution
3232 W MacArthur Blvd, Santa Ana, CA 92704
Tel: 714-545-6548 *Toll Free Tel:* 800-444-7664
Fax: 714-641-8201
E-mail: info@calvaryd.org
Web Site: www.calvaryd.org
Key Personnel
Purch: Megan Yorimitsu *E-mail:* megany@calvaryd.org
Religious book distributor.

Canadian Manda Group
664 Annette St, Toronto, ON M6S 2C8, Canada
Tel: 416-516-0911 *Fax:* 416-516-0917
Toll Free Fax: 888-563-8327 (CN only)
E-mail: general@mandagroup.com; info@mandagroup.com
Web Site: www.mandagroup.com
Key Personnel
Pres & Partner: Nick Smith *Tel:* 416-516-0911 ext 236 *E-mail:* nsmith@mandagroup.com
VP & Partner: Carey Low *Tel:* 416-516-0911 ext 237 *E-mail:* clow@mandagroup.com
Founded: 1977
Sales agency of books, stationery & gift products offering renowned international & local publishers to retailers, libraries & wholesalers.

CannonBertelli LLC, see Parson Weems' Publisher Services LLC

Cardinal Publishers Group
2402 N Shadeland Ave, Suite A, Indianapolis, IN 46219
Tel: 317-352-8200 *Toll Free Tel:* 800-296-0481 (cust serv) *Fax:* 317-352-8202
E-mail: customerservice@cardinalpub.com
Web Site: cardinalpub.com
Key Personnel
Opers: Adriane Doherty *E-mail:* adoherty@cardinalpub.com
Cust Serv: Barbara Carter
Sales & Mktg: Thomas McLean *E-mail:* tmclean@cardinalpub.com
Founded: 2000
Provides full service book distribution to publishers throughout North America & beyond.
Distributor for AFN; AGA Institute Press; AMI Publishers; Amity University Press; Axel & Ash Journals; Big Blue Marble Books; Blog Into Book; Blue River Press; Body & Breath Inc; C C Fine Tea Books; Crestwood Publishing; Crew Press; CS Publishing; DeBenedictis Books; Direct Hits; Emerald Career Publishing; EMS Publishing; Executive Suite Press; Gem Multimedia LLC; Gluten Free RN; Great Day Press; Halfcourt Press; Harrison & Hampton Publishing; Terry Hutchens Publications; ISR Books (Baylor University); Jamenair Publishing; Jazzy Vegetarian; L & L Pardey Publications; Lotus Publishing; La Luz Press Inc; MicMac Margins; Meyer & Meyer Sport; Momentum Media; Mountain Lion Inc; Mountainside MD Press; Naturally Healthy Desserts; Norris Associates; Northeast Books & Publishing; Paleo Media Group LLC; Panda Guides; PeopleSpeak; Price World Publishing; Propriometrics Press; Quixotic Travel Guides; Reedswain; Resume Place Inc; Rite Site Custom Career Services; Rubber Ducky Press; Salut Studio Lifestyle Publishing; SJJ Inc; SportsWorkout.com; Stone Road Press; Strategic Media Books

Casemate | academic
Affiliate of Oxbow Books (UK)
1950 Lawrence Rd, Havertown, PA 19083
Tel: 610-853-9131 *Fax:* 610-853-9146
E-mail: info@casemateacademic.com
Web Site: www.oxbowbooks.com/dbbc
Key Personnel
VP, Busn Devt: Simone Drinkwater
Cust Serv Rep: Jen Romano
Distribution of academic, scholarly & specialist literature.
Distributor for Akanthina; American Numismatic Society; American Research Center in Sofia; American School of Classical Studies at Athens (ASCSA); American School of Prehistoric Research; American Society of Papyrologists; Ancient Egypt Research Associates; Anglo-Saxon Books; Archaeolingua; Archaeopress; Armatura Press; ASTENE; Ekdotike Athenon; Australian Centre for Ancient Numismatic Studies; Australian Centre for Egyptology; Australian Theological Forum; Axioma; Azimuth Editions; Bannerstone Press; Barkhuis; Bellview; British Academy; British Institute at Ankara; British Institute for the Study of Iraq; British Institute in Eastern Africa; British Institute of Persian Studies; British Museum Press; British School at Athens; British School at Rome; Brown University, Department of Egyptology & Ancient Western Asian Studies; Bryn Mawr Archaeological Monographs; Butrint Foundation; Francis Cairns Publications; Cambridge Archaeological Unit; Cambridge Philological Society; Canterbury Archaeological Trust; CB Edizioni; Celtic Studies Publications; Christianity & Culture; Citeaux; Concordia University; Cotswold Archaeology; Council for British Archaeology; Council for British Research in the Levant; Countryside Books; Librairie Cybele; Cyclamen Press; Czech Institute of Egyptology; Discussions in Egyptology; East Anglian Archaeology; Edinburgh University, Department of Archaeology; Egyptological Seminar of New York; Etruscan Foundation; Ezekiel; Fine Arts Department of Thailand; Footwork; Friends of Canterbury Cathedral; Gibb Memorial Trust; Golden House Publications; Grant & Cutler (Foyles); Griffith Institute, University of Oxford; Halgo; Highfield Press; Hirmer Verlag; Illuminata; INSTAP Academic Press; Institute for Philosophical Research; Institute of Classical Archaeology; International Centre for Albanian Archaeology; International Monographs in Prehistory; Joukowsky Institute for Archaeology & the Ancient World, Brown University; Journal of Juristic Papyrology; Khalili Collections; Logogram Publishing; London Association of Classical Teachers Occasional Research Series (LACTOR); Lutterworth Press; Maney Publishing; McDonald Institute for Archaeological Research; Medina Publishing; Medstroms Bokforlag; Midsea Books; Mistra Estate; Museum of Fine Arts, Boston; Museum of London Archaeology (MoLA); Northcote House Publishers; Northgate Publishers; Ocarina Books; On-Site Archaeology; Onassis Foundation; Orcadian; Oriental Institute of the University of Chicago; Oxbow Books; Oxford Archaeology; Oxford Centre for Maritime Archaeology; Oxford University School of Archaeology; Pallas Athene; Peartree Publishing; Pierides Foundation; Pindar Press; Edizioni Polistampa; Portcullis Publishing; Pre-Construct Archaeology; Princeton University Library; Pro Calima Foundation; Ravenhall Books; Regatta Press; Riksantikvarieabetet (National Heritage Board of Sweden); Mary Rose Trust; Royal Commission on the Ancient & Historic Monuments of Scotland; Andrzej Rozwadowski; Rutherford Press; St George's Chapel; St John's College, Oxford; San Diego Museum of Man; Scientia; Sidestone Press; Siduri Books; Societas Archaeologica Upsaliensis; Society for Libyan Studies; Society for the Promotion of Roman Studies; Society of Antiquaries of London; Spire Books; SSEA-Benben Publications; Stacey International; Statens Maritima Museer; Franz Steiner Verlag; Stobart Davies; Stone Age Institute Press; Summanus; University College Cork, Ireland; University of Iceland Press; University of Leiden; Viking Ship Museum, Roskilde; Wessex Archaeology; Wiltshire Archaeological & Natural History Society; Windgather Press; York University Department of Archaeology
Territory: North America

Casemate | IPM
Division of Casemate Group
1950 Lawrence Rd, Havertown, PA 19083
Tel: 610-853-9131 *Fax:* 610-853-9146
E-mail: casemate@casematepublishers.com
Web Site: www.casemateipm.com
Key Personnel
VP, Busn Devt: Simone Drinkwater
Sales Dir: Jane R Graf *E-mail:* jane.graf@casematepublishers.com
Founded: 1995
Provides sales, marketing & distribution services for book publishers, in both the academic & trade fields.
Distributor for Allison & Busby; Amber Books; Anomie Publishing; Ayebia Clarke Publishing; Bartleby Press; Barzipan Publishing; Bauhan Publishing; Big Sky Publishing; Birlinn Ltd; Blackstaff Press; Boydell & Brewer Ltd; Brandon; British Museum Press; Capital Books; Capuchin Classics; Carnegie Publishing; Choc Lit; Classics Illustrated Comics; Claymore Press; Collins Press; Colourpoint; Columba Press; Countryside Books; Currach Press; Delicious Stationery; Dufour Editions; Educator's International Press; Eland Publishing; ElStreet Educational; Enodare Ltd; Eshel Books; Fernhurst Books; Fonthill Media; Frontline Books; Gill Books; Goblinshead; Gremese Editore (English language books in North America); Grub Street Cookery; Histoire & Collections; Histria Books; Paul Holberton Publishing; International Polar Institute; International Publishers Marketing; Jantar Publishing; JJ Books; Kashi House; Kolibri Languages; Liberties Press; Library of the Holocaust; Liffey Press; Liss Llewellyn Fine Art; Litera Publications; Y Lolfa; Medina Publishing; Mercier Press; Mereo Books; Messenger Publications; Neem Tree Press; 9crows Publishing; O'Brien Press; Oratia Books; Papillote Press; Pen & Sword; Penguin Random House South Africa; Piano Nobile; Publishing 451; Protea Boekhuis; Real Reads; Remember When; Salmon Poetry; Sandstone Press; Savas Beatie; Schreiber Publishing; Seaforth Publishing; Solomon Berl Media; Somerville

Press; Stacey International; Struik Inspirational Gifts; George F Thompson Publishing; Tilde Publishing & Distribution; University of Buckingham Press; Vagabond Voices; Veritas Books; Waverly Lee Media; Wharncliffe; Wordwell Books; WTM Publishing & Communications

Chesapeake & Hudson Inc
115 W Potomac St, Brunswick, MD 21716
Tel: 301-834-7170 *Toll Free Tel:* 800-231-4469
Toll Free Fax: 800-307-5163
E-mail: office@cheshud.com
Web Site: www.cheshud.com
Key Personnel
Pres: Bill Hoar
VP: Ted Wedel
Dir, Opers: Robin Bell
Sales Rep: Keith Arsenault; Michael Gourley; Janine Jensen; Steve Straw
Founded: 1992
Publishers representatives.
Territory: Mid-Atlantic States, New England

Chicago Distribution Center (CDC)
Division of University of Chicago Press
11030 S Langley Ave, Chicago, IL 60628
Tel: 773-702-7010 *Toll Free Fax:* 800-621-8476
Web Site: press.uchicago.edu/cdc
Key Personnel
Dir: Joe D'Onofrio
Dir, Client Servs & Busn Opers: Saleem Dhamee *Tel:* 773-702-7014 *E-mail:* sdhamee@press.uchicago.edu
Sr Opers Mgr: Mark Stewart *Tel:* 773-702-7024 *E-mail:* mstewart@press.uchicago.edu
Accts Receivable Mgr: Cynthia Bastion *Tel:* 773-702-7164 *E-mail:* cab9@press.uchicago.edu
BiblioVault Mgr: Kate Davey *Tel:* 773-834-4417 *E-mail:* kdavey@press.uchicago.edu
Cust Serv Mgr: Karen Hyzy *Tel:* 773-702-7109 *E-mail:* khyzy@press.uchicago.edu
Info Systems Mgr: Christopher Jones *Tel:* 773-702-7229 *E-mail:* cjones@press.uchicago.edu
Inventory Control Mgr: Dennis Kraus *Tel:* 773-834-3499 *E-mail:* kraus@uchicago.edu
Returns Mgr: Jenn Stone *Tel:* 773-834-3687 *E-mail:* jstone@press.uchicago.edu
Royalty & Rts Mgr: Cassie Wisniewski *Tel:* 773-702-7062 *E-mail:* cwisniewski@press.uchicago.edu
Warehouse Asst Supv: Tammy Paul *Tel:* 773-702-7081 *E-mail:* tpaul@press.uchicago.edu
Warehouse Off Mgr: Gail Szwet *Tel:* 773-702-7080 *E-mail:* gszwet@press.uchicago.edu
Founded: 1991
CDC began in 1966 as a distributor for University of Chicago Press & in 1991 began offering distribution services to other university presses. Today CDC handles distribution for more than 100 publishers.
Distributor for ACMRS Publications; Aksant-Royal Netherlands; American Institute of Musicology; American Library Association (ALA); American Meteorological Society; AmP Publishers; Amsterdam University Press; Arizona Center for Medieval & Renaissance Studies (ACMRS) Press; Association of College & Research Libraries (ACRL); Autumn House Press; Bard Graduate Center; Bayeux Arts; Bodleian Library; Brandeis University Press; Brigham Young University; Campus Verlag GmbH; Carnegie Mellon University Press; Casel; Catholic University Press; CavanKerry Press; Central Conference of American Rabbis/CCAR Press; Columbia College Chicago; CSLI Publications; DaltonWatson; Dana Press; Dartmouth College Press; diaphanes; Eburon Academic Publishers; EPFL Press; French National Museum of Natural History; Front Forty Press; Gallaudet University Press; J Paul Getty Trust; Gingko Library; GTA Verlag Publishers; Guerra Edizioni; HAU; Haus Publishing; Hirmer Verlag; Hong Kong University Press;

Intellect Ltd; Historic England Publishing; ISI Books; Island Press; Karolinum/Charles University Prague; Koc University Publishing (KUP); Leiden University Press; McGill-Queen's University Press; Michigan Publishing Services; Michigan State University Press; Missouri History Museum Press; MMA in Warsaw; Museum Tusculanum; National Journal Group; New Issues Poetry & Prose; Northern Illinois University Press; Northwestern University Press; NUS Press Singapore; Oberlin College Press; Ohio State University Press; Ohio University Press; Omnidawn Publishing; Oregon State University Press; Park Books; Parkhurst Brothers Inc; Parmenides Publishing; Passionaries Press; Penultimate Press Inc; Pluto Press; Policy Press at the University of Bristol; Prickly Paradigm; Reaktion Books Ltd; Research Publishers LLC; Royal Botanic Gardens, Kew; Royal Collection Trust; Russel Sage Foundation; St Augustine's Press; Scheiddegger & Spiess; School of the Art Institute of Chicago; Scion Publishing Ltd; Seagull Books; Sidewalks Books Co; Signature Books; Solar Books; Southern Illinois University Press; Swan Isle Press; Swedenborg Foundation Press; Temple University Press; Templeton Foundation Press; Tenov Books; 2Leaf Press; Unicorn Press Ltd; University College Dublin Press; University of Alabama Press; University of Alaska Press; University of Arizona Press; University of Arkansas Press; University of British Columbia Press; University of Chicago Department of Medicine; University of Chicago Press; University of Exeter Press; University of Illinois Press; University of Iowa Press; University of Michigan Press; University of Minnesota Press; University of Missouri Press; University of Nevada Press; University of North Texas Press; University of Pittsburgh Press; University of Scranton Press; University of Tennessee Press; University of Texas Press; University of Utah Press; University of Wales Press; University of Wisconsin Press; University Press of Colorado; Utah State University Press; Vu Boekhandel/Uitgeverij; West Virginia University Press; Westholme Publishing; WhiteWalls Inc; Wisconsin Historical Society; Zed Books

Consortium Book Sales & Distribution, an Ingram brand
The Keg House, Suite 101, 34 13 Ave NE, Minneapolis, MN 55413-1007
SAN: 200-6049
Tel: 612-746-2600 *Toll Free Tel:* 800-283-3572 (cust serv, Jackson, TN) *Fax:* 612-746-2606
E-mail: info@cbsd.com
Web Site: www.cbsd.com
Key Personnel
Pres: Julie Schaper
VP & Dir, Mktg: Jennifer Swihart *E-mail:* jswihart@cbsd.com
VP & Gen Mgr: Mark Ouimet
VP, Sales: Jim Nichols
Dir, Client Rel: Michael Cashin
Natl Accts: Michael Croy; Bill Mockler; Jaime Starling
Founded: 1985
Provides full service distribution for US, UK & European independent publishers in the US & Canada.
Distributor for Agnes & Aubrey; AK Press; Akashic Books; Albatros Media; Alternative Comics; And Other Stories; Animal Media Group; Arsenal Pulp Press; Auzou; Beehive Books; Behler Publications; Bellevue Literary Press; Berbay Publishing; Biblioasis; BIS Publishers; Biteback Publishing; Bitter Lemon Press; Black Inc; Black Ocean; Blair; Bloodaxe Books; BOA Edition Ltd; Marion Boyars Publishers; Braun Publishing; Breakaway Books; Bywater Books; CarTech Inc (digital only); Cassava Republic Press; Catalyst Press; Cen-

tipede Press; Central Recovery Press; Centrala; Charco Press; Chin Music Press; ChiZine Publications; Cicada Books; Cinco Puntos Press; Cinestate; City Lights Publishers; Coach House Books; Coffee House Press; Common Notions; Contrasto; Copper Canyon Press; The Critical Press; Curbside Splendor Publishing; Daylight Books; Deep Vellum Publishing; DoppelHouse Press; Dottir Press; Paul Dry Books; The Eighth Mountain Press; Enchanted Lion Books; Engine Books; Etruscan Press; Exterminating Angel Press; Eye of Newt; Fabled Films Press; The Feminist Press at CUNY; Fence Books; Feral House; Fitzcarraldo Editions; Floating World Comics; Floris Books; Frame Publishers; Gallic Books; Garnet Publishing; Gentle Path Press; GILES; Gilgamesh Publishing; Global Book Sales; Green Card Voices; Green Integer; The Gryphon Press; h.f.ullmann publishing; Haymarket Books; Hazy Dell Press; High Conflict Institute Press; Hispabooks; Holy Cow! Press; Hoxton Mini Press; Ig Publishing; Image Continuum Press; Immedium; Imperfect Publishing; Inhabit Media; Iron Circus Comics; Alice James Books; Karadi Tales; Kehrer Verlag; Koyama Press; Kube Publishing Ltd; Leapfrog Press; Lesser Gods; Dewi Lewis Publishing; Lookout Books; Mandel Vilar Press; Manic D Press; MCCM Creations; Milo Books; Monkfish Book Publishing; National Association for the Education of Young Children; New Europe Books; New Internationalist; New Society Publishers; New Vessel Press; New Village Press; Nicolo Whimsey Press; Nighboat Books; 1984 Publishing; Nobrow Press; Not a Cult; NubeOcho; Oberon Books; Ocean Press; Joshua Odell Editions; Open Letter; OR Books; Postcart Editions; Process; Profile Books; Promopress; Rabsel Editions; Redleaf Press; Salamander Street; Saqi Books; Sarabande Books Inc; The School of Life; Scribe Publications; Secret Acres; Serpent's Tail; Small Beer Press; Stark Raving Group (digital only); Stone Bridge Press; Street Noise Books; Sunrise River Press (digital only); Sweetmeats Press; Talonbooks; Telegram Books; Text Publishing Co; Theatre Communications Group/Nick Hern Books/Oberon Books; Third Man Books; 3D Total Publishing; Tiny Owl Publishing; TOON Books; Torrey House Press; Transit Books; Turtle Point Press; 2dcloud; Tyrant Books; Unbound; Uncivilized Books; Unfiltered Media; Vodka & Milk; Wave Books; White Pine Press; Windhorse Publications; World Editions; Yoffy Press; Zephyr Press; Zuccotti Park Press
Territory: Canada, USA
Membership(s): American Booksellers Association (ABA)

Continental Book Co Inc
7000 Broadway, Suite 102, Denver, CO 80221-2913
Tel: 303-289-1761 *Toll Free Fax:* 800-279-1764
E-mail: cbc@continentalbook.com
Web Site: www.continentalbook.com
Key Personnel
Dir: Linette Hayat *E-mail:* linette@continentalbook.com
Founded: 1961
Importers & distributors of language materials. Specialize in Spanish, French, German, Italian, Latin, Chinese, Arabic, Bilingual Spanish, Heritage Spanish, ELL, ESL, Common Core, English Novels, ASL, juvenile to advanced levels.
Territory: USA

Continental Sales Inc
213 W Main St, Barrington, IL 60010
Tel: 847-381-6530 *Fax:* 847-382-0385; 847-382-0419
Web Site: www.continentalsalesinc.com

Key Personnel
Pres: Ron Prazuch *E-mail:* prazur@wybel.com
Founded: 2001
Complete sales, marketing & distribution services for independent publishers. US coverage.
Represents Aveditions GmbH; Becker Joest Volk Verlag; Braun; Brunswick House; Callisto Publishing; Diamond Cutter; Editions Didier Millet; Hal Leonard; Links International; Momosa Publishing; New in Chess; Parker House; Marco Polo; RSD Publishing; Regina Orthodox Press; Scientific Publishing; Seltmann & Sohne; Swedenborg Foundation; Templeton Foundation Press; Visual Profile Books; XPat Media/Scriptum
Membership(s): American Booksellers Association (ABA)

Diffusion Inter-Livres

Division of Ligue pour la Lecture de la Bible Inc
1701 Belleville, Lemoyne, QC J4P 3M2, Canada
Tel: 450-465-0037 *Toll Free Tel:* 866-465-5579
E-mail: interlivres@llbquebec.ca
Web Site: www.inter-livres.ca
Key Personnel
Dir: Guillaume Duvieusart
Founded: 1982
Distribute religious books (French language).
Distributor for A Auderset; Editions du Cedre; De la Colline; Editions ELLB; Emmaus; Excelsis; Editions Exit; Famille Je t'aime; Farel; Editions Foi et Victoire; iCharacter; Editions Inspiration Publishings; Jeunesse en Mission; Ligue de Belgique; Ligue de Suisse; Editions Missionnaire Francophone; Editions Oladios; Parole de Vie; Editions Passiflores; Pretexte; Derek Prince Ministries France; Editions Raphael; Editions RDF; Editions sur Ses Traces
Territory: Canada, USA

Distribooks Inc

Subsidiary of MEP Inc
8154 N Ridgeway Ave, Skokie, IL 60076-2911
Tel: 847-676-1596 *Toll Free Fax:* 888-266-5713
E-mail: info@distribooks.com
Key Personnel
Pres: Nicolas Mengin
Dir, Mktg & Sales: Daniel Eastman
E-mail: deastman@mep-inc.net
Sale of foreign language books to high schools, universities, bookstores, trade bookstores & libraries at trade discount. Branch office located in Boston, MA.
Represents Assimil; Book King International; ELI
Territory: USA

Distributed Art Publishers (DAP)

75 Broad St, Suite 630, New York, NY 10004
Tel: 212-627-1999 *Toll Free Tel:* 800-338-2665 (cust serv) *Fax:* 212-627-9484
Toll Free Fax: 800-478-3128
E-mail: orders@dapinc.com
Web Site: www.artbook.com
Key Personnel
Pres & Publr: Sharon Gallagher
SVP & Dir, Mktg & Admin: Avery Lozada
Tel: 212-627-1999 ext 209 *E-mail:* alozada@dapinc.com
Sales Dir: Jane Brown *E-mail:* jbrown@dapinc.com
Founded: 1990
Contemporary art, photography, design & aesthetic culture titles. Major international distributor of books, special editions & rare publications from major publishers, museums & cultural institutions.
Distributor for Actes Sud; T Adler Books; Adult Magazine; Apology; Arbor Vitae; Archive of Modern Conflict; Arquine; Art / Books; Art Gallery of York University; Art Insights; Art Issues Press; Artspace Books; ASAP; Aspen Art Museum; Atlas Press; Badlands Unlimited; Bald Ego Publishing; Editions Xavier Barral; Berkeley Art Museum; Blue Kingfisher Ltd; Peter Blum; Boo-Hooray; Chris Boot; Kunsthaus Bregenz; Cabinet; Candela Books; Carnegie Museum of Art; Center for Art, Design & Visual Culture, UMBC; Contemporary Art Museum, Houston; Contemporary Art Museum, St Louis; Cooper-Hewitt, Smithsonian Design Museum; Corraini Editions; Damiani; Dancing Foxes Press; DAP Publishing; DC Moore; Deitch Projects Archive; DelMonico Books; Deste Foundation for Contemporary Art; Dia Center for the Arts; Editions Dis Voir; The Drawing Center; Dumont; Dung Beetle; Dust to Digital; George Eastman House; Errant Bodies; Errata Editions; Esopus; Exact Change; Exhibitions International; La Fabrica; Fondazione Prada; Forlaget Press; Forum Gallery, New York; Foundation 20 21; Four Corners Books; Fraenkel Gallery; Free News Projects; Frieze; FUEL; Fundacion Juan March; Garage Museum of Contemporary Art; Glenstone Museum; Levy Gorvy; Granary Books; Garth Greenan Gallery; Guggenheim Museum; Hatje Cantz; Hauser & Wirth Publishers; Hayward Gallery Publishing; Heni Publishing; Hips Road/Tzadik; Holzwarth Publications; ICA Philadelphia; Ice Plant; Ideal World Books; Independent Curators International; Inventory Press; Irish Museum of Modern Art; J&L Books; Jovis Verlag; JRP|Ringier; Kant; Karma, New York; Kasmin; Kaya Press; Kerber Verlag; Kiito-San; Walther Konig Verlag; Lisson Gallery; Locus+; Los Angeles County Museum of Art; Louisiana Museum of Modern Art; Lucia|Marquand; Ludion Publishers; Matthew Marks Gallery; MCA Chicago; MER Paper Kunsthalle; Metropolis Books; MFA Publications; Gregory R Miller & Co; MIT List Visual Arts Center; Mitchell-Innes & Nash; Verlag fuer Moderne Kunst; MoMA; MoMA PS1; Mousse Publishing; Lars Mueller; Museum of Contemporary Art, Los Angeles (MOCA); Museum of Contemporary Art, San Diego; MW Editions; nai010 Publishers; National Gallery of Victoria; National Portrait Gallery; New Museum; Nieves; Nova Scotia College of Art & Design; Osmos; Other Criteria Books; Parkett Publishers; PictureBox; Pioneer Works; Ediciones Poligrafa; Pomona College Museum of Art; Power Plant; Primary Information; R & Co; Radius Books; Reel Art Press; Richter Verlag; RM; Galerie Thaddaeus Ropac; Andrew Roth; Royal Academy of Arts, London; Rubell Family Collection Contemporary Arts Foundation; Saint Louis Art Museum; Scala Group SpA; Schaulager/Laurenz Foundation; Jordan Schnitzer Family Foundation; Secret Behavior; Galerie Patrick Seguin; Seraphin Gallery; Siglio; Silvana Editoriale; Sinecure Books; SITE Santa Fe; Skarstedt Gallery; Skira; Soul Jazz; SPBH Editions; Spector Books; Standards Manual; Steidl; Max Strom; Swiss Institute Contemporary Art New York; TamTam Books; Testify Books; Thyssen-Bornemisza Art Contemporary; Torst; Triple Canopy; Turner; Ullens Center for Contemporary Art; Um Yeah Arts; University Galleries of Illinois State University; Valiz; Violette Editions; Visionaire Publishing; Vitra Design; Wakefield Press; Walker Art Center; Warhol Musuem; Wexner Center for the Arts; White Cube; Whitechapel Gallery; Witte de With, Rotterdam; Yerba Buena Center for the Arts
Territory: worldwide

Empire Publishing Service

PO Box 1344, Studio City, CA 91614-0344
Tel: 818-784-8918 *Fax:* 818-990-2477
E-mail: empirepubsvc@att.net
Distributes worldwide entertainment books, plays, film scripts, tele-scripts, general books, choral music, orchestra, vocals & Sherlock Holmes books, plays, film & radio scripts. Represents US & non-US publishers all language rights.
Distributor for Amusement One; Arabesque; Arte Publico Press (drama); D-Books; Empire Music & Percussion; Empire Publishing; Gaslight Publications; Helios Music; Ian Henry Publishers Ltd; ISH Group (worldwide exc Australia); Paul Mould Publishing; Phantom Publications Inc; Jack Spratt Music; Strutter; USA Music Group
Represents Amusement One; Arabesque; Arte Publico; Empire Music & Percussion; Empire Publishing; Gaslight Publications; Ian Henry Publishers; ISH Group (worldwide exc Australia); Paul Mould Publishing; Showcase Publishers
Territory: worldwide

Faherty & Associates Inc

Division of Left Coast Book Sales Inc
6665 SW Hampton St, Suite 100, Portland, OR 97223
Tel: 503-639-3113 *Toll Free Tel:* 800-824-2888
Fax: 503-598-9850
Web Site: www.fahertybooks.com
Key Personnel
Owner, Club Sales & Key Accts: Ken Guerins
Tel: 503-597-2213 *E-mail:* ken@fahertybooks.com
Online & Key Accts Mgr: Lisa Stone *Tel:* 503-597-2212 *E-mail:* lisa@fahertybooks.com
Sales Coord: Shea Petty *Tel:* 503-639-3113
E-mail: shea@fahertybooks.com
Rep: Trevin Matlock *Tel:* 909-263-2346
E-mail: trevin@fahertybooks.com; Richard McNeace *Tel:* 323-478-9013 *E-mail:* richard@fahertybooks.com
Commission based sales group.
Represents ACC Distribution; Actar (IPS); Amber Lotus Publishing; APG Sales & Distribution; Applied Research + Design (IPS); Art Stock; Artifice (IPS); Ave Maria Press; Avedition (NBN); Becker Joest (NBN); Benteli; Birkhauser; Bloomsbury Academic (AZ, CA, NM, NV only); Braun Publishing; Brunswick House Press (NBN); Callisto Publishing (NBN); Career Press & New Page Books; Daudin Distribution; Diamond Cutter Press (NBN); DOM Publishers (IPS); Earlswood Press; Eksmo Publishing House; Flamant; Forefront Publishing; Fox Chapel Publishing; Independent Publishers Group (IPG); IRH Press; Island Press (AZ, CA, HI, NM, NV only); Leuchtturm1917 & Semikolon; Links International (NBN); Marco Polo Travel Publishing (NBN); McGraw-Hill Education; Editions Didier Millet (NBN); Momosa Publishing; New Harbinger Publications; New in Chess; Niggli; Offshoot Press (Kalabindu Enterprises); ORO Editions (IPS); Phaidon Press (select accts); Pictoplasma; RAM Publications; Red Dot (NBN); Red Wheel/Weiser/Conari (Hampton Roads Publishing); Regina Orthodox Press (NBN); Oscar Riera Ojeda Publishing; River North Editions; RSD Publishing (NBN); Scientific Publishing (NBN); Sellers Publishing; Seltmann & Sohne (NBN); SPU (Small Press United); Swedenborg Foundation; Templeton Foundation Press; TF Publishing; Toon Studio Press; Trafalgar Square; Visual Profile Books (NBN); XPat Media (NBN); Zebra Publishing
Territory: Alaska, Hawaii, 13 Western States
Membership(s): California Independent Booksellers Alliance (CALIBA); Mountains & Plains Booksellers Association (MPBA); Pacific Northwest Booksellers Association (PNBA); Southern California Children's Booksellers Association

Far Eastern Books

250 Cochrane Dr, Suite 14, Markham, ON L3R 8E5, Canada
SAN: 159-0227

Tel: 905-477-2900 *Toll Free Tel:* 800-291-8886
Fax: 905-479-2988
E-mail: books@febonline.com
Web Site: fareasternbooks.com
Key Personnel
Owner & Pres: Virender Malik
Founded: 1976
Distributor of books, periodicals & multimedia material in international languages including dual-language books, large print books, language learning material, dictionaries (adult & picture), DVDs, music CDs & talking books.
Represents Ferozsons; HarperCollins India; Ingram Yates; Magi; Mantra; Motilal Banarsidas Publishing House; Navbharat Sahitya Mandir; Penguin India; Scholastic India; R R Sheth & Co Pvt Ltd; Sterling; Tulika; Vani Publications
Territory: Australia, Europe, North America, South Africa

Publicaciones Faro de Gracia (PFG)
1317 Railroad St, Burlington, NC 27217
Mailing Address: PO Box 1043, Graham, NC 27253
Tel: 336-792-2690
E-mail: oficina@farodegracia.org
Web Site: www.farodegracia.org
Key Personnel
Pres: R Wayne Andersen
Founded: 1998
Reformed Spanish publisher & distributor.
Distributor for Publicaciones Aquila; Banner of Truth; B&H/Lifeway; Campamentos Cristianos Internacionales; CLC; Editorial CLIR; Editorial Concordia; DIME; HarperCollins; JUCUM; Moody Publishers; Editorial Patmos; Editorial Peregrino; Poiema Publicaciones; Editorial Portavoz; Tyndale Espanol; Editorial Unilit
Territory: Latin America, Mexico, USA
Membership(s): The Association of Publishers for Special Sales (APSS); Evangelical Christian Publishers Association (ECPA); Letra Viva; SEPA

Fire Engineering Books & Videos
Division of PennWell Books
1421 S Sheridan Rd, Tulsa, OK 74112
Tel: 918-831-9421 *Toll Free Tel:* 800-752-9764
Fax: 918-831-9555
E-mail: sales@pennwell.com
Web Site: www.pennwellbooks.com
Key Personnel
Mktg Coord: Holly Fournier *Tel:* 918-832-9380
E-mail: hollyf@pennwell.com
Publishes, produces & distributes training & instructional materials (books, videos, magazines, software) for firefighters.
Represents ASVP; Brady; Emergency Film Group; Idea Bank; IFSTA/Fire Protection Publications; ISFSI; Krieger; Macmillan; Mosby Yearbook
Territory: worldwide

Firefly Books Ltd
50 Staples Ave, Unit 1, Richmond Hill, ON L4B 0A7, Canada
Tel: 416-499-8412 *Toll Free Tel:* 800-387-6192 (CN); 800-387-5085 (US) *Fax:* 416-499-8313
Toll Free Fax: 800-450-0391 (CN); 800-565-6034 (US)
E-mail: service@fireflybooks.com
Web Site: www.fireflybooks.com
Key Personnel
Pres: Lionel Koffler
Dir, Foreign Rts, Licensing & Contracts: Parisa Michailidis *Tel:* 416-499-8412 ext 157
E-mail: parisa@fireflybooks.com
Founded: 1977
North American publisher & distributor of nonfiction adult & children's books.
Represents The Boston Mills Press; Cottage Life; Firefly Books; Fitzhenry & Whiteside; Kiddy

Chronicles Publishing; Mikaya Press; Robert Rose Inc
Territory: North America
Membership(s): American Booksellers Association (ABA); Association of Canadian Publishers (ACP)

Follett School Solutions Inc
Division of Follett Corporation
1340 Ridgeview Dr, McHenry, IL 60050
SAN: 169-1902
Tel: 815-759-1700 *Toll Free Tel:* 888-511-5114 (cust serv); 877-899-8550 (sales) *Fax:* 815-759-9831 *Toll Free Fax:* 800-852-5458
E-mail: info@follettlearning.com; customerservice@follett.com
Web Site: www.follettlearning.com; www.follett.com/prek12; www.titlewave.com
Key Personnel
EVP: Britten Follett
Sales Exec: Erica Moore
Suppliers of books (new & pre-owned), reference materials, digital resources, ebooks & AV materials to PreK-12 libraries, classrooms, learning centers & school districts.

Fotofolio
561 Broadway, New York, NY 10012
Tel: 212-226-0923 *Toll Free Tel:* 800-955-FOTO (955-3686)
E-mail: contact@fotofolio.com
Web Site: www.fotofolio.com
Key Personnel
Dir: Martin Bondell
Founded: 1975
Publishers & distributors of art & photographic postcards, note cards, boxed cards, holiday cards, posters, calendars, postcard books, books, art t-shirts & art coloring books, blank books & puzzles.
Represents Artkeeping (Spain); Artpost & Fotofolio; Bizarr (Germany); L M Kartenvertrieb (Germany); Point It (Germany); Polite (UK); Printed Matter (NY); Cheim Read Gallery; Reunion des Musees Nationoux (Nat'l Museums of France); Edition Toube (Germany)
Membership(s): American Booksellers Association (ABA); Museum Store Association (MSA)

Fujii Associates Inc
75 Sunny Hill Dr, Troy, MO 63379
Tel: 636-528-2546 *Fax:* 636-600-5153
Web Site: www.fujiiassociates.com
Key Personnel
Pres: Eric Heidemann
Mng Partner: Don Sturtz
Assoc: Jennifer Allen; Tom Bowen; Beth Chang; Mark Fleeman; Adrienne Franceschi; Andy Holcomb
Off Mgr: Kathy Bogs *E-mail:* kathybogs@fujiiassociates.com
Sales representatives.
Represents Abrams; Arte Publico Press; Baker & Taylor Publisher Services (select group of publrs); Brilliance Publishing; Capstone Press; Chico Bag; Chihuly Workshop; Childs Play; Chooseco; Familius; Flowerpot Press; Gardner; Gibbs Smith Publisher; Houghton Mifflin Harcourt; Interlink Publishing; Independent Publishers Group-Trade; Island Press; Jessica Kingsley Publishers; Kumon Publishing; Litographs; McGraw-Hill; Merrymakers Inc; Mountain Press; Mountaineers Books; Naval Institute Press; Octane; Peachtree Publishers; Scholastic/Grolier; Shelter Harbor Press; Sounds True; Sourcebooks; Sterling; TF Publishing; Tiger Tales; Time Home; UPG; US Games Systems; Workman; Zebra Publishing
Territory: Arkansas, Illinois, Indiana, Iowa, Kansas, Kentucky, Louisiana, Michigan, Minnesota, Missouri, Nebraska, North Dakota, Ohio, Oklahoma, South Dakota, Texas, Wisconsin

Fulfillment by Amazon (FBA)
Subsidiary of Amazon Services LLC
440 Terry Ave N, Seattle, WA 98109
Web Site: services.amazon.com; www.amazon.com/advantage
Founded: 2002
Amazon has the unique ability to match specialized, niche, or "hard-to-find" books with the customers most likely to purchase them & Amazon.com has a world-renowned reputation for service, reliability & security. Amazon.com Advantage is a consignment program that enables authors & publishers to list & sell their books on Amazon.com right alongside products that have massive marketing & distribution. The Advantage program provides a simple, efficient way to have a direct relationship with Amazon.com. The Advantage program includes listing your book in stock & ready to ship, the ability to control your detail page on Amazon.com, automatic reordering, sales & inventory reports, quick invoice-free payments, Search Inside the Book™ & hassle-free fulfillment to customers.
Territory: worldwide

Gaunt Inc
Gaunt Bldg, 3011 Gulf Dr, Holmes Beach, FL 34217
SAN: 202-9413
Tel: 941-778-5211 *Toll Free Tel:* 800-WGAUNT3 (942-8683) *Fax:* 941-778-5252
E-mail: info@gaunt.com
Web Site: www.gaunt.com
Founded: 1968
Law books: reprints, textbooks-college.

Genesis Marketing Group Inc
850 Wade Hampton Blvd, Bldg A, Suite 100, Greenville, SC 29609
Tel: 864-233-2651 *Toll Free Tel:* 800-627-2651
Toll Free Fax: 800-849-4363
E-mail: orders@genesislink.com
Web Site: www.genesislink.com
Key Personnel
CEO: Tim Morgan
Pres: David George *Tel:* 864-233-2651 ext 1605
Founded: 1970
Group of sales representatives to the Christian retail market.
Territory: worldwide

Girol Books Inc
PO Box 5473, LCD Merivale, Ottawa, ON K2C 3M1, Canada
Tel: 613-233-9044 *Fax:* 613-233-9044
E-mail: info@girol.com
Web Site: www.girol.com
Key Personnel
Owner: Miguel Angel Giella; Peter Roster
Mgr: Leslie Roster *E-mail:* lroster@girol.com
Founded: 1975
Sales & publishing of books in Spanish & Portuguese from Spain, Portugal, Central & South America, plus North American books in Spanish.
Territory: worldwide

GoodMinds.com
Six Nations of the Grand River Territory, 188 Mohawk St, Brantford, ON N3S 2X2, Canada
Tel: 519-753-1185 *Toll Free Tel:* 877-862-8483 (CN & US) *Fax:* 519-751-3136
E-mail: helpme@goodminds.com
Web Site: www.goodminds.com
Key Personnel
Founder & Pres: Jeff Burnham
E-mail: burnhamj@goodminds.com

Owner & Operator: Linda Burnham
Founded: 2000
Native American, Aboriginal, First Nations, Metis & Inuit books.
Territory: Canada, USA

Greenleaf Book Group LLC

3 Park Place, 4005 Banister Lane, Suite B, Austin, TX 78704
Mailing Address: PO Box 91869, Austin, TX 78709
Tel: 512-891-6100 *Fax:* 512-891-6150
E-mail: contact@greenleafbookgroup.com
Web Site: www.greenleafbookgroup.com
Key Personnel
Founder: Clint Greenleaf
CEO: Tanya Hall
CFO: Brian Viktorin
Gen Coun: Sujan Trivedi
Dir, Consulting: Justin Branch
Dir, Dist: Steve Elizalde
Dir, Mktg & Branding: Corrin Foster
Dir, Prodn: Carrie Jones
Mgr, Busn Devt: Kesley Smith *E-mail:* ksmith@ greenleafbookgroup.com
Founded: 1997
Publisher & distributor specializing in the development of independent authors & the growth of small presses. Our publishing model was designed to support independent authors & allow writers to retain the rights to their work & still compete with major publishing houses. We also distribute select titles from small & independent publishers to major trade outlets, including bookstores, libraries & airport retailers. We serve the small & independent publishing community by offering industry guidance, business development, production, distribution & marketing services.
Distributor for Thundersnow Publications; Western Classics
Membership(s): The Association of Publishers for Special Sales (APSS); Independent Book Publishers Association (IBPA)

Greenleaf Book Group Press, see Greenleaf Book Group LLC

Hanser Publications LLC

Subsidiary of Carl Hanser Verlag GmbH & Co KG
414 Walnut St, Suite 323, Cincinnati, OH 45202
Toll Free Tel: 800-950-8977; 888-558-2632 (orders)
E-mail: info@hanserpublications.com
Web Site: www.hanserpublications.com
Key Personnel
Mktg Mgr: Valerie Lauer *Tel:* 513-527-8896
   E-mail: valerie.lauer@hanserpublications.com
Premier source for plastics-related reference & educational materials in North America. Over 150 books written by industry experts are available.

HBG Productions/International Publishers Alliance

PO Box 5560, Chico, CA 95927-5560
Tel: 530-893-4699
Web Site: www.hbgproductions.com
Key Personnel
Exec Dir: Deanna Leah *E-mail:* deanna@ hbgproductions.com
Founded: 1987
HBG Productions represents independent publishers & authors in the international marketplace. We specialize in hands-on representation of select books which are life-affirming & empowering. We bring your work to the attention of like-minded international publishers. In 2007 HBG Productions joined forces with International Publishers Alliance, founded in 1987 & they have been working together to represent

creative works at book fairs & trade shows ever since. Our services include: author representation & coaching, foreign & translation rights negotiation, international trade show presentations, specializing in the Mind-Body-Spirit market.
Territory: worldwide
Membership(s): Book Publicists of Southern California (BPSC)

HFS

Division of Johns Hopkins University Press
2715 N Charles St, Baltimore, MD 21218
Mailing Address: PO Box 50370, Baltimore, MD 21211-4370
Tel: 410-516-6965 *Toll Free Tel:* 800-537-5487 (US & CN) *Fax:* 410-516-6998
E-mail: hfscustserv@press.jhu.edu
Web Site: hfs.jhu.edu; www.hfsbooks.com
Key Personnel
Dir: Davida Breier *E-mail:* dgb@press.jhu.edu
Mgr: Terrence Melvin *E-mail:* tjm@press.jhu.edu
Founded: 1977
Order processing, collection management, warehousing & fulfillment for university presses & nonprofit institutions.
Distributor for The Catholic University of America Press; Central European University Press (CEU Press); Family Development Press; Georgetown University Press; Johns Hopkins University Press; Maryland Historical Society; Modern Language Association of America (MLA); Northeastern University Press; University of Massachusetts Press; University of South Carolina Press; University of Washington Press; The University Press of Kentucky; UNO Press; Wesleyan University Press

Hopkins Fulfillment Services, see HFS

Imprint Group West

2070 Cherry St, Denver, CO 80207
Toll Free Tel: 800-738-3961 *Toll Free Fax:* 888-867-3869
Web Site: imprintgroupwest.com
Key Personnel
Owner/Principal: Derek Lawrence
   E-mail: derek@imprintgroupwest.com
Founded: 1987
Commission sales group & publisher services.
Represents Adventure Publications; Angel City Press; Bower House; Brown Books; Candlewick; Cottage Door Press; EDC/Usborne/ Kane Miller; John Fielder Publishing; Firefly Books; Kids Can Press; Midpoint Trade Books; Mountain Press; Norwood House Press; Peachtree Publishers; Peter Pauper Press; Scholastic Library Publishers; Sleeping Bear Press; Sourcebooks; Treasure Bay; Wiley
Territory: Alaska, Arizona, California, Colorado, Hawaii, Idaho, Montana, Nevada, New Mexico, Oregon, Utah, Washington, Wyoming
Membership(s): California Independent Booksellers Alliance (CALIBA); Mountains & Plains Independent Booksellers Association (MPIBA); National Association of Independent Publishers (NAIP); Pacific Northwest Booksellers Association (PNBA); Southern California Booksellers Association

Independent Publishers Group (IPG)

Division of Chicago Review Press
814 N Franklin St, Chicago, IL 60610
Tel: 312-337-0747 *Toll Free Tel:* 800-888-4741 (orders) *Fax:* 312-337-5985
E-mail: frontdesk@ipgbook.com; orders@ ipgbook.com
Web Site: www.ipgbook.com
Key Personnel
CEO: Joe Matthews
CFO: Frank Autunnale
CTO: Clark Matthews

VP & Dir, Natl Accts: Jeff Palicki *Tel:* 312-337-0747 ext 281
VP, Busn Devt: Alex Kampmann
VP, Mktg & Publicity: Annette Hobbs Magier
VP, Prof & Academic Mkts: Paul Murphy
   Tel: 312-337-0747 ext 229
VP, Publr Devt: Richard T Williams
VP, Sales: Michael Riley *Tel:* 312-337-0747 ext 258
VP, Supply Chain: Mark Noble
Mng Dir, Spanish Prog: Kelsey Wayne
Dir, Data Mgmt: Salma Yaqubi
Dir, Intl Sales: Scott Hatfill
Dir, Lib & Educ Sales: Sharon Shell
Dir, Mktg: Lauren Klouda
Dir, Opers: Amber McKown-Finken
Dir, Publicity: Caitlin Eck
Dir, Spec Sales: Ilene Schreider
Sr Sales Mgr, Trade & Spec Sales: Aaron Howe
Cust Serv Mgr: David Gebhart
Digital Servs Mgr: Mallori Bontrager
Lib Sales Mgr: Cynthia Murphy
Natl Accts Mgr: Lara Alexander
Trade Sales Mgr: Chris Conti
Founded: 1971
Sales & distribution services for independent publishers.
Six distribution programs: IPG; Trafalgar Square Publishing; River North Editions; IPG Spanish Books; Art Stock Books; Small Press United.
Distributor for AA Publishing; Aalborg University Press; A&C Publishing; Aboriginal Studies Press; Academic Foundation; Academy & Finance; Academy of Nutrition & Dietics; Acapella Publishing; ACER Press; Addicus Books; African American Images; AH Comics Inc; AJR Publishing; Akiara Books; Alamo Press; Alazar Press; Alephactory Press; Alexandria Press; Ediciones Aljibe SL; All Clear Publishing; Allen & Unwin; ALM Media LLC; Editorial Alma; Ediciones Alpha Decay; Alterna; Amalion Publishing; Amazing People Worldwide; Amberley Publishing; American Academy of Pediatrics; American Cancer Society Inc; American Legacy Media; American Museum of Radio & Electricity; Ammonite Press; Analogue Media; Analytics Press; Angry Penguin Ltd; Annelidical Books; Annie's; Anqa Publishing; Arissa Media Group LLC; Arkin Publishing; Art on Dekz/Goodman; ASP-VUB Press; Aspen Books; Libros del Asteroide; A Thousand Words Press LLC; At Bay Press; Atelier Saint-Luc Press; Atelier26 Books; ATH-LiTACOMiCS; Atlantic Books Ltd; Auckland University Press; AudKnits LLC; Aurora Publishers Inc; Austin Lamp Press; Autumn Hill Books; Awa Press; Ayurveda Holistic Center; Azure Moon Publishing; B Brothers Press; b small publishing; BackPage Press; Baha'i Publishing; Baker Street Press; Balance for Health Publishing; Balanced Living Press; Ball Publishing (BPU); Ball Publishing (CRP); Baraka Books; Ediciones Barataria; Barbican Press; Bay Otter Press; Bedazzled Ink Publishing; Bees Knees Books; Bella Figura Publications; Bella Musica Publishing; Belle Publishing LLC; Belly Song Press; Belt Publishing; Laurence Bennett; BennettKnepp Publishing; benton buckley books; Berbay Publishing; Berlinica; Bertz + Fischer Verlag; Bienville Ray LLC; Thom Bierdz Inc; Big Kid Science; BIICL; Birdsong Books; Birlinn Ltd; Black & White Publishing; Black Belt Communications; Black Heron Press; BlackBook Media Corp; Blackwell & Ruth Ltd; John Blake; Blink Publishing; Bloomin Books; Bloomsbury Professional; blue manatee press; Blume; BMG Books; Board & Bench Publishing; Bocconi University Press; Bonnier Publishing Australia; Bonnier Zaffre; Book Club Productions; Booklife; Bookmark Publishers; Bosco Publishing; Boutique of Quality Books; Bowhead Press; Bowman Sculpture; Boxing Clever Publishing; Boy's & Girl's Guide Books; The Brain-

storm Co; Brand Nu Words; Bravebird Publishing; Breckling Press; Bright Ideas Publishing; British Library Publishing; Broken Shell Press; Brookside Press; Bucket Fillers; Budding Biologist; Bull Publishing; Burnt Cheese Press; Butterfly Bliss Productions; By Architect Publications; Caboodle Books Ltd; Cadillac Press; Cadmos Verlag GmbH; Calithumpian Press; Campbell Hall Press; CAMRA Books; Cannonball Books; Canterbury University Press; La Caravane Publishing; Carcanet Press Ltd; Cardinal Rule Press; Cargo Publishing; Carlton Publishing Group; Carysfort Press Ltd; Editorial Casals; CAST Professional Publishing; Catbird Press; CBAY Books; CCC Publishing; Cedar Grove Publishing; Central Avenue Publishing; Chalk Hill Books; Change the Universe Press; Chase Sequence Co; Chawton House Press LC; Cherry Red Books; Cherrytree Books; Chicago Children's Museum; Chicago International Poster Biennial Association; Chicago Review Press; Childhood Cancer Guides; ChiLiving Inc; Chirp Publishing; Cinco Tintas; Claeys & Casteels Publishing; Clarus Press Ltd; Co & Bear Productions UK Ltd; Code Babies Media; Cognella Press; Cohesion Press; Colorful Cities; Comma Press; Commonwealth Secretariat; Companion Press; Compass Publishing; Connell Publishing; Construction Trade Press; Contra; Conversation Arts Media; Ruth Beaumont Cook; Copenhagen Business School Press; Copernicus Center Press; Copper Ridge Press; Coralstone; Ediciones Corona Borealis; Corporativo V y T; Council Oak Books; Arthur Coyle Press; CPA911 Publishing; Craigmore Creations; Creative Noggin; Creotz; Critical Publishing; The Crossroad Publishing Co; Crown King Books; Crowood Press; CTO Editorial; Cupola Press; Cute Ediciones; Gus D'Angelo; de Monza; de Sitter Publications; Debrett's; Del Nuevo Extremo; Demeter Press; Designer-Books; Deutscher Kunstverlag; Dhyanyoga Centers; Die Neue Sachlichkeit; Dike Publishers; Dine Out LLC; Diplomat Books; Discover Art; The Discovery Box; Disruption Books; Djoef Publishing; The Do-It-Yourself Florist Enterprises; do re mi Languages; Doodles Ave; Double Dove Press; Double-Barrelled Books; Draft2Digital; Drag City; Dragon Threads; Dragonfly Group; Dream Character Inc; Dreamspinner Press; DreamTitle Publishing; Duckbill Books; Dunedin Academic Press; Dunemere Books; e-artnow; Earnshaw Books; Edimat Libros; Educational Resources Ltd; Edward & Dee; Egmont UK; Elder Signs Press; Elephant Rock Productions Inc; Eleven International Publishing; Elliott & Thompson; Elva Resa Publishing; Elysian Editions; Enitharmon Press; Enterprise Publishing; Ess Ess Publications; Europa Law Publishing; evenSO Press LLC; Exile Editions; Experience Publishing; Eye Books; EZChinesey.com; Fagbokforlaget; Fairyfaye Publications Ltd; Fanfare; Fantasmus; Fields Publishing; Fifth Star Press; Filbert Press; Adam Filippi; Filles Vertes Publishing; Finch Publishing; Fine Feather Press; Editorial Fineo; Firehouse Publications; FireStarter Speaking & Consulting; Firewater Media Group; Fish Out of Water Books; Five Mile; 5m Publishing; Flashlight Press; Flora Publishing LLC; Fons Vitae; Footsteps Media; 45th Parallel Press; Four Courts Press; La Fragatina; Fragmenta Editorial; Free Association Books; Freight Books; Freizeit Publishers; Fremantle Press; Fresh Baby LLC; Fulcrum Publishing; Future House Publishing; Gainsborough House; Galt Publishing; Gao House Press; Garant Publishers; Garlic Press; Gateways Books & Tapes; Gathering Wave Press; The Gelofer Press; Gia Publications Inc; Gibson House Press; Gilgamesh Publishing; Gingerbread House; Glass Books Pty Ltd; Golden Pheasant Press; The Golden Sufi Center; Gomer Press

Ltd; Good Luck Black Cat Books; Graffeg; Graffito Books; Granite Peak Publications; Grimdark Magazine; Grip Press; G2 Entertainment; Gylendal Akademisk; Robert Hale; Hall & Stott Publishing Ltd; Handfinger Press; HarperCollins UK; Hart Publishing; Hawthorn Press; HCNY Press; Head of Zeus; Health Administration Press; Health Inspired Publishing; Heartstrings Press; Hesperus Press; Hide Stationery Ltd; High Rock Press; HighLine Editions; Lawrence Hill Books; Historical Society of Michigan; The History Press; Hodos Historia; Hogs Back Books; Holladay House; Holy Macro! Books; Holy Trinity Publications; Honeybee in the Garden; Honno Press; Hoover Institution Press; HopeRoad; House of Stratus; Huckleberry Sweet Pie Publishing Ltd; The Human Sciences Research Council; Hunter Press; Huron Street Press; IAD Press; IFWG Publishing International; IHS Press; Ikeda Center for Peace Learning & Dialogue; Illumination Press; Imagine That UK; Michael Imhof Verlag; Editorial Impedimenta; Impossible Foods; InData Group Inc; Independent Institute; India Research Press; Indigo Press; Information Today, Inc; Inhabit Media; Inner Coaching; Inscribe Digital Small Press United; INscribe UNassigned; Insight Press; Inspired Studios; Institute for Collaborative Communication; Institute of Art & Law; Institute of Economic Affairs; Interlude Press; International Courts Association; Intersentia; Into the Void; Intrigue Publishing LLC; Invisible Cities Press LLC; Irish Academic Press; Islamic Texts Society; Istros Books; IWP Book Publishers; Jacana Media; Jam Graphics & Publishing; JB Max Publishing; Jora Books; Jordan Publishing Ltd; Just World Books; K F Enterprises; Editorial Kairos; KAMA Publishing; Karolinger Verlag; Keep It Simple Books; Kent Press; KettleDrummer Books; KiCam Projects; Kidsbooks; Knitbot; Kombi-Nation Sweden AB; Korero Books; Korero Press; KPO Creative LLC; Krittergitters; Kunati; Kuperard; Libros del Kultrum; Kyoto University Press; Laburnum Press; Lafayette Publishers; Lakeview Research; Lao Tse Press; Larkfield Publishing; Ediciones Larousse; Last Syllable Books; Ediciones Lea; Lectio Ediciones; Lectura Colaborativa; Leete's Island Books; Legend Times Group; La Librairie Parisienne; Libri Publishing; Liesl + Co; Life of Reiley; Light Beams Publishing; Linkgua; Lion Hudson; LIT Verlag; Little Hare; Little House Press; Little Island Books; Little Island Press; Little Lamb Books; Live Model Books LLC; Long Haul Press; Long Stride Books; Looking Glass Books Inc; Lost the Plot; Love the World Books; Lucky Bamboo Crafts; Lucky Sky Press; Lund Humphries; Machillock Publishing; MacIntyre Purcell Publishing; Madder; madebyfae; The Magenta Foundation; Mainstream Publishing; Maklu Publishers; Malpaso Editorial; Malt Shop Publishing; Malyszko Photography; Manitenahk Books; Marion Street Press; Markelle Media; Marlor Press Inc; Massey University Press; Mattamayura Press; Maverick Arts Publishing; Maximilian Verlag; Maximo Potencial; MC Press; Graham McDonald Stringed Instruments; Medford Books/Plexus Publishing; Meg & Lucy Books; Melbourne University Press; Melbournestyle Books; Merlin Press; Robert G Merrick; Meteoor Books; Metro Publications; Micro Publishing Media; Middleway Press; Milet Publishing; Millfree Mursaps Media; Minted Prose LLC; Mira Vista Press; Missouri's Civil War Heritage Foundation; Ernest Mitchell Publishing; MMS Gold; modo Verlag; Monash University Publishing; Month9Books LLC; Moonlight Publishing; Moonstone Press LLC; Mortar & Press; Mo's Nose LLC; Mosaic Press; Motorcycle Misadventures; Mount Castle Co; Mountain Lake Press; Mountain Trail Press; Move Books; MR

Publishing LLC; Museyon; Myrmidon Books; Mystic Productions Press; NADD; National Association of Home Builders; National Museum of Australia Press; Natural History Museum, London; NBM Publishing; NBS Publications; Nebulous Arts LLC; Nehora Press; Stephen L Nelson Inc; Neofelis Verlag; Netribution; Never Lose Heart LLC; New Century Publications; New Chapter Press; New Island; New World Publishing; NewRoad Publishing; The Next Big Think; Next Step Test Preparation Publishing; Nite Owl Books; NNK Press; Noah Publications; Nordic Academic Press; Nordica Libros; Ediciones Norte; Nostra Ediciones; Nourish Publishing; NSTA Kids; NTI Upstream; NW1 Books; Oak Grove Press; Oak Lane Press; Ediciones Oblicuas Inc; Editorial Oceano de Mexico; Odyssey Books & Maps; Odyssey Publishing LLC; Old Bow Publishing; The Old Mill Press; Oldcastle Books Ltd; Edition Olms; Georg Olms Verlag AG; Michael O'Mara Books; Omnibus Press; OnWord Bound Books LLC; 121 Publications; Opal Publishing Co; Orbit Media Studios Inc; Orenda Books; Otago University Press; Out of Your Mind...and Into the Marketplace™; Outlook Words & Art; Oval Books; Peter Owen Publishers; Ozone Zone Books; Paginas Libros de Magia; Paladin Communications; Palazzo Editions; Pallas Athene; Palm Island Press; Palmer/Pletsch Publishing; Palmyra Publishing; Pan Macmillan; Pandasaur Press; Pangolin London; Paper Books LLC; Paper Chase Farms Publishing Group; Paragon Garage Co Ltd; Parent Guide Books; Parenting Press; Pariyatti Publishing; Park Publishing Inc; Partera Press; Parthian Books Ltd; Pathfinder Equine Publications; Paths International Ltd; PatrickGeorge; Pavilion Books Group; Pavilion Publishing & Media; Editorial Pax Mexico; Peepal Tree Press Ltd; Pelican Book Group; Pendo Press; Penguin Books China; Penguin Books New Zealand; Penguin Random House Australia; Penguin UK; Penlight Publications; Penny Publishing; Editorial Periferica; Perronet Press; Personhood Press; Phoenix Yard Books; Pikku Publishing; Pimpernel Press; Pitch Publishing; Pitchstone Publishing; Plaid People Press; Plaintales Inc; The Plan Editions; Plaza y Valdes; PM Press; Poorhouse Publishing; Popular Kinetics Press; Portal Books; Posthuman Studios; Practical Psychology Press; Editorial Primapersona; Princeton Book Co; The Print Project; Prion; Prison Radio; Privateer Publications; Probitas Press; Project Management Institute; Psychodynamic Diagnostic Manual; PublikumArt; Pucci Books; Pucci Publishing; PuddleDancer Press; Pukka Publishing; Pumpkin House Ltd; Verlag Anton Pustet; The PuzzleWorks; Qi Works; Quarto Iberoamericana; Quiller Publishing; Quince & Co; Racing Post Books; Marian Rae Publications; Ragged Bears; Rainbow Morning Music; Raincloud Press; Rakennusticto Publishing; Random House Australia Pty Ltd; Random House UK; Rawat Publications; RCR Creative Press; Reading Rainbow; ReadZone Books; Real African Publishers; Redbook Ediciones; RedDoor Publishing; Dietrich Reimer Verlag GmbH; Resonance House LLC; Reynolds Hearn (Cherry); RHINO Poetry; River Horse Press; Rivers Turn Press; ROCK International; Rockpool Publishing; Ediciones Rodeno; Rolling Homes Press; Rosarium Publishing; Rosenberg Publishing; J Ross Publishing; Roundup Press; Rowhouse Publishing; Royal British Columbia Museum; Royal Collins Publishing Group; Royal Irish Academy; Ruka Press; Russell House Publishing Ltd; Sad Hill LLC; SAFE for Children Publishing; Saint Andrew's Press; St James's House; Salor Press; Salvia Press; Samfundslitteratur; Sandalwood Passage; Sandorf Passage (North America & UK); Sandy Point Ink LLC; Santa Fe Writer's Project; Saraband; Scan-

dinavia House Publishing; Schaffner Press; Schlebruegge Editor; Schnell und Steiner; Science Literacy Books; Scribble & Sons; Scribe Publications Pty Ltd; Scruffie Munster Media; Search Institute Press; Second Base Publishing; The Secret Mountain; Secret Passage Press; Sedro Publishing; See Sharp Press; Seemann Henschel; Self-Counsel Press; Selwa Press; Seren; Seven Gates Media; Shepheard-Walwyn Publishers; Sheldrake Press; Shinola; Shogam Publications; Siddha Yoga Publications; Signature Publishing Group; Silent 7 Publishing; Silk Web Publishing; Simax; Skeezel Press; Edition Skylight; Sladmore Gallery; The Sleepy Animals LLC; Slovart Publishing Ltd; Small Mountain Press; Smart Guide Publications Inc; Smoking Gun Publishing LLC; Society for Human Resource Management; Solana Press; Soluble LLC; Solum Forlag; Somogy Art Publishers; Soul Support; SourceAid LLC; Southeast Missouri State University Press; Souvenir Press; Spark Avenue; Specialty Press/ADD Warehouse; Spinifex Press; Spinning Wheel Press; Spiramus Press; Spy Publishing Ltd; Square Monkey Publishing; Staghorn Press; Starfish Bay Publishing; Dr Steven D Stark Podiatric Corp; Stone Skin Press; Stonemark Publishing; Strauss House Productions; Streamline Press; Suitcase Media International; Summersdale Publishers Ltd; SummitView Publishing Inc; Susaeta Ediciones SA; Sussex Academic Press; Symphony Space Inc; Tabula Books; Tamarisk Books LLC; Tango Books Ltd; Tantan Publishing; Tell-A-Gram Publishing LLC; Temenos Press; Te Papa Press; Terrace Publishing; Thircuir; Thompson Mill Press; Thorntree Press; Three Pebble Press LLC; Thrums Books; Thule Ediciones; TI Inc Books; Tightrope Books; Tiller Publishing; Titiris; TJ Studios; TOKYOPOP GmbH; Top That Publishing US; Tortuga Press; Tot Toppers; Touche Publishing; Tracks Publishing; Tradart Institut; Trans Pacific Press; Transworld Publishers; Trellis Publishing; Triarchy Press Ltd; Tribeca View Press LLC; Trigger Publishing; Trine Day; Triplekite Publishing; Trism Books; Triumph Books; Troika Books; Tulip Books; Tumblehome Learning Inc; TuTu's Green World LLC; Tuva Publishing; Two Thousand Three Associates; UIT Cambridge Ltd; Umiya Publishing; Unisa Press; Presses de l'Universite du Quebec; University of Hertfordshire Press; University of KwaZulu-Natal Press; University of New South Wales Press; University of Queensland Press; University Press of Southern Denmark; Upstart Press; Urban Land Institute; Urbane Publications; Urim Publications; USNA Publishing Inc; USRSA; UWA Publishing; Vallentine Mitchell; Variant Press; Vegueta Ediciones; Vehicule Press; Velociteach; Vesuvian Media Group; Victoria University Press; Visual Steps Publishing; Wachholtz Verlag GmbH; Wacky Bee Books; Wake Forest University Press; Walnut Cracker Publishing LLC; Water Environment Federation; Weddle's LLC; Welsh Academic Press; Weslo Publishing; Whimsical Designs by CJ LLC; Wienand Verlag; Wild Iris Publishing; Wild River Press; Wilkins Farago Pty Ltd; Willow Tree Books; Wings Press; Wishland LLC; Wits University Press; Wolf Legal Publishers; Wolsak & Wynn Publishers Ltd; World Council of Churches; WorldRider Publishing & Press; Verlagshaus Wuerzburg; Wilkinson Publishing; XRX Books; Yan Lei Press; You Can Publishing; ZuZu Petals Books
Territory: worldwide

Indigo Books & Music Inc
468 King St W, Suite 500, Toronto, ON M5V 1L8, Canada
Tel: 416-364-4499
E-mail: cisales@indigo.ca
Web Site: www.chapters.indigo.ca

Key Personnel
CEO: Heather Reisman
Chief Creative Offr: Scott Formby
EVP & CFO: Hugues Simard
EVP & Chief Mdsg Offr: Tod Morehead
EVP & CTO: Bo Parizadeh
EVP, E-Commerce & Chief Mktg Offr: Kristen Chapman
EVP, Gen Coun & Corp Secy: Kathleen Flynn
EVP, Retail & HR: Gil Dennis
Founded: 2001
Distributor for Audio & Video; Children's Book Store
Territory: Canada, USA

Ingram Content Group LLC
One Ingram Blvd, La Vergne, TN 37086-1986
Tel: 615-793-5000 *Toll Free Tel:* 800-937-8000 (retailers); 800-937-5300 (ext 1, libs)
E-mail: customerservice@ingramcontent.com
Web Site: www.ingramcontent.com
Key Personnel
Chmn: John Ingram
Pres & CEO: Shawn Morin
Chief Commercial Offr: Shawn Everson
Chief Content Offr: Phil Ollila
CFO: Brian Dauphin
Chief HR Offr: Wayne Keegan
CIO: Steve Marshall
Chief Legal Offr: Kelly Arnold
Chief Logistics Offr: John Secrest
Chief Strategy & Devt Offr: Kent Freeman
Chief Venture Capital Offr: David Roland
VP & Cont: Tina Elmore
VP & Gen Mgr: Sabrina McCarthy
VP, Application Servs: Lori Dunbar
VP, Credit: Roger Lee
VP, Community Rel: Emily Weiss
VP, Content Acq: Kelly Gallagher
VP, HR: Jacqueline Letson
VP, Mktg: Brian McKinley
VP, Mdsg: George Tattersfield
VP, Retail Sales: Donald Roseman
Dir, Academic Servs: Kurt Hettler
Dir, Application Servs: Robert Barnard
Dir, Consumer Mktg: Kim Schutte
Dir, Digital Servs: Margaret Harrison
Dir, Mass Merchandisers Sales: Lisa Tomasello
Dir, Natl Accts: Michael Bell
Dir, Sales Opers: Tammy Spurlock
Sales Dir: Sharon Swados
Sr Mgr, Content Acqs: John Hussey
Sr Mgr, Mktg Servs: Ann Zangri
Sr Mgr, PR & Communs: Kris Wiese
Lib Sales & Servs Mgr: Tricia Racke Bengel
Mgr, Client Rel: Louisa Brody
Prod Mktg Mgr: Catherine Robinson
Proj Mgr, Integration & Outsource: Sterling Crawford
Specialty Retail Mgr: Megan Smith
Sales & Support Rep, Mass Mdse Group: Tori Cushman
Founded: 1964
Comprehensive publishing industry services company that offers numerous solutions, including physical book distribution, print-on-demand & digital services. Ingram works closely with publishers, retailers, libraries & schools around the world to provide them with the right products & services to help them succeed in the dynamic & increasingly complex world of content publishing. Ingram's operating units are Ingram Book Group LLC, Lightning Source LLC, VitalSource Technologies LLC, Ingram International Inc, Ingram Library Services LLC, Spring Arbor Distributors Inc, Ingram Publisher Services LLC & Tennessee Book Co LLC.
Branch Office(s)
6050 Dana Way, Antioch, TN 37013
7315 Innovation Blvd, Fort Wayne, IN 46818
4260 Port Union Rd, Fairfield, OH 45011
201 Ingram Dr, Roseberg, OR 97470

860 Nestle Way, Breinigsville, PA 18031
1200 Ingram Dr, Chambersburg, PA 17202
Territory: worldwide

Ingram Publisher Services, an Ingram brand
Subsidiary of Ingram Content Group LLC
One Ingram Blvd, La Vergne, TN 37086
SAN: 631-8630
Tel: 615-793-5000 *Toll Free Tel:* 866-400-5351 (cust serv)
E-mail: ips@ingramcontent.com
Web Site: www.ingramcontent.com
Key Personnel
VP & Gen Mgr: Sabrina McCarthy
Dir, Acqs: Gonzalo Ferreyra
Dir, Busn Opers: Alison Black
Dir, Mktg: Peter Antone
Sr Client Rel Mgr: Leah Rex McCracken
Client Rel Mgr: Sarah Armstrong
European Sales Mgr: Matthew Dickie
Mgr, Busn Opers Support: Kristal Smith
Mgr, Sales: Johanna Hynes
Mgr, Sales & Support: Leslie Jobson
Assist publishers in a variety of ways including sales, distribution & account management. Provides distribution to 220 countries & territories with 19 offices, distribution centers & manufacturing plants worldwide.
Distributor for Academic Studies Press; Actar D; Adaptive Studios; Advantage Media Group Inc; AMMO Books LLC; Anomaly Productions Inc; Anthology Editions; Apa Publications; Aperture; APL Publishing; Apollo Publishers; Applewood Books Inc; Arcas Publishing; Arundel Publishing; Australian Academic Press; Bella & Harry; BiggerPockets Publishing Inc; Blue Star Press; Books & Books; Bottom Dog Press; Burleigh Dodds Science Publishing; Calexia Press; Callaway Arts & Entertainment; Callisto Media Inc; Cambridge International Science; Carpet Bombing Culture; Chiltern Publishing (US & CN); Clovercroft Publishing; CN Times Books; Conari Press; Cooking Lab; Dabel Brothers Publishing; Dalkey Archive Press; Design Studio Press; Diversion Books; The Do Book Co; Dovetail Press; Drago Media; Dreamscape Media (audio); Dundurn Press; Elevate Publishing; The Enthusiast; Esri Press; Fodor's Travel; Fordham University Press; Le French Book; Future Horizons Inc; Gemma Open Door; GemmaMedia; Gestalten; Ghost Mountain Books; Gingko Press; Bruno Gmuender; Granta Books; Grim Oak Press; Hanser Publications LLC; Harriman House; Hodder Education; Hoffman Media; Ideapress Publishing; Imprint Academic; Indiana University Press; Inkshares; The Institution of Engineering & Technology; International Society for Technology in Education; Morgan James Publishing; Jumping Jack Press; Kogan Page; Danielle LaPorte Inc; Laughing Elephant; Wilfrid Laurier University Press; The Law School Admission Council; Lemniscaat USA; Liberty Fund Inc; Linden Publishing; Made for Success Publishing; Maiden Lane Press; Mandevilla Press; Mango Media; Mango Publishing; Warren Miller Co; Minnesota Historical Society Press; ML Books International; MONKEY; Montana Publishing; The Mother Co; Mouse Prints Press; Museum of Jewish Heritage; NewSouth Books; Nippan IPS; No Nonsense Fly Fishing; Nolo; NYU Press; Oceanview Publishing; Ooligan Press; Open Road Integrated Media; O'Reilly Media; Outpost19 Books; Oxford University Press; Pajama Press; ParentMap; Parkstone Press; Perilous Worlds (US & CN); PIE International Inc; The Planning Shop; Plough Publishing House; Poisoned Pen Press; Popular Book Co; Prospect Park Books; Ramsey Press; Recorded Books; Red Pen Press; Rocky Nook; Rosenfield Media: Two Waves Books & Digital Reality Checks; Rough Guides; RSC Publishing; St Lynn's

Press; Susan Schadt Press; Schilt Publishing; Sensory Focus; Severn House Publishers; She Writes Press; Simply Read Books; SparkPress; Spring House Press; Tantor Media; Taschen America; Tate's Bake Shop; Taunton Press; Terra Galleria Press; Third World Press; Three Hands Press; The TMG Firm; Trope Reader; Turner Publishing Co; University of Regina Press; US News & World Report; VanitaBooks; VeloPress; Waterhouse Press; West Margin Press®; What on Earth Publishing; Michael Wiese Productions; Windsor Peak Press; XAM-online.com

Institute for the Study of Human Knowledge (ISHK)
1702-L Meridian Ave, No 266, San Jose, CA 95125-5586
Tel: 617-497-4124 *Toll Free Tel:* 800-222-4745 (orders) *Fax:* 617-500-0268 *Toll Free Fax:* 800-223-4200 (orders)
E-mail: ishkadm@aol.com; ishkbooks@aol.com (orders)
Web Site: www.ishk.com
Key Personnel
Founder & Pres: Robert Ornstein, PhD
Founded: 1969
Represents Hoopoe Books; Malor Books
Territory: Canada, Central America, Mexico, South America, USA

International Press Publication Inc
Spadina Rd, Richmond Hill, ON L4B 3C5, Canada
Tel: 905-883-0343
E-mail: sales@ippbooks.com
Web Site: www.ippbooks.com; www.facebook.com/ippbooks; twitter.com/ippbooks2
Key Personnel
Pres: Bali Sethi
Founded: 1976
Library & wholesale suppliers of all types of publications, directories, dictionaries, foreign language books. Supply to the book trade & to individuals.
Distributor for ABC-CLIO; ABC-CLIO/Greenwood; Academic Press; Addison Wesley Longman; Blackwell Publishers; Bowker; Cambridge University Press; Career Press; Contact Canada; CQ Press; CRC Press; CSA; Elsevier; Europa Publications; Ferguson; Gale Research Inc; Grey House; Harcourt; HarperCollins; Information Today, Inc; International Code Council (ICC); ISO; Jist; Kluwer Academic Publishers; Libraries Unlimited; Library of Congress (USA); Macmillan; McGraw-Hill; Mediacorp; MIT Press; Monarch; Nelson Stationery Office; W W Norton & Company Inc; Omnigraphics; Orderline; Oxford University Press; Palgrave; Pearson; Penguin Group (USA) LLC; Prentice Hall; Project Management Institute; Raincoast; Random House; Lynn Reiner; Routledge; Sage; Self-Counsel Press; Simon & Schuster; Springer Verlag; Taylor & Francis Group, an Informa Business (USA); Techstreet; Thames & Hudson; Thomson Publishing; Time Warner; United Nations Publishing; John Wiley & Sons; H W Wilson
Territory: worldwide
Membership(s): The American Library Association (ALA); Children's Literature Association (ChLA); Ontario Library Association

Jonathan David Publishers Inc
52 Tuscan Way, Suite 202-371, St Augustine, FL 32092
SAN: 169-5274
Tel: 718-456-8611
E-mail: customerservice@jdbooks.com
Web Site: www.jdbooks.com
Key Personnel
Pres & Edit Dir: David Kolatch

VP, Sales & Mktg: Marvin Sekler
Cont: Carol A Zelezny
Acct Exec: Barbara Burke
Founded: 1948
Nonfiction trade book publishing.
Territory: Australia, Canada, Israel, South Africa, UK, USA

The Karel/Dutton Group
3145 Geary Blvd, PMB 619, San Francisco, CA 94118
Tel: 415-668-0829 *Fax:* 415-668-2463
Key Personnel
Owner & Partner: Howard Karel *E-mail:* hkarel@comcast.net
Partner: Doris Dutton
Assoc: Lisa Solomon; Ellen Towell
Represents Abrams Publishing; Consortium; Gibbs Smith Publishing; Inner Traditions; Lonely Planet; Mountaineers; Pomegranate Art; Tuttle Publishing

Kitzmiller Sales & Marketing Co
35 Flint St, Suite 304, Salem, MA 01970-3264
Tel: 978-985-1144 (cell) *Fax:* 978-744-0232
E-mail: dnd.kitzmiller@gmail.com
Key Personnel
Pres: David E Kitzmiller
Founded: 1992
Remainder & bargain book specialist.
Represents Book Country Clearing House LLC; Nationwide Book Industries LLC
Territory: Connecticut, Maine, Massachusetts, New Hampshire, Rhode Island, Vermont

Lerner Publisher Services
Division of Lerner Publishing Group Inc
241 First Ave N, Minneapolis, MN 55401
Tel: 612-332-3344 *Toll Free Tel:* 800-328-4929 (orders) *Fax:* 612-215-6230
E-mail: info@lernerpublisherservices.com; custserve@lernerpublisherservices.com
Web Site: www.lernerpublisherservices.com
Key Personnel
EVP, Sales: David Wexler *E-mail:* dwexler@lernerpublisherservices.com
Distributes titles from high quality children's publishers to the school, library & retail markets.
Distributor for Andersen Press; Big & Small; Creston Books; Full Tilt Press; Gecko Press; Hungry Tomato®; JR Comics®; Kane Press; Lantana Publishing; Live Oak Media; Lorimer Children & Teens; Maverick Arts Publishing; New Frontier Publishing; The Page Education Foundation; Quarto Library; Red Chair Press; Ruby Tuesday Books; StarBerry Books; We Do Listen Foundation
Territory: worldwide

Maple Logistics Solutions
60 Grumbacher Rd, York, PA 17406
Mailing Address: PO Box 15100, York, PA 17405-7100
Tel: 717-764-4596 *Fax:* 717-764-4494
E-mail: info@maplesoln.com
Web Site: www.maplelogisticssolutions.com
Key Personnel
Pres: James S Wisotzkey
VP, Dist Opers: Chris Benyovszky
VP, Dist, Sales & Mktg: Andrew J Van Sprang
VP, Sales & Mktg: William S Long
  E-mail: long@maplepress.com
Warehousing, distribution, fulfillment, print-on-demand, drop shipping, invoicing & value added services.
Territory: North America, worldwide
Membership(s): Associated Warehouses Inc (AWI); Book Manufacturers' Institute (BMI); Council of Supply Chain Management Professionals (CSCMP); Distributors & Consolidators of America (DACA); Express Carriers Associ-

ation (ECA); Warehousing Education and Research Council (WERC); World Trade Center Harrisburg

Matthews Book Co
11559 Rock Island Ct, Maryland Heights, MO 63043
SAN: 169-4316
Tel: 314-432-1400 *Toll Free Tel:* 800-633-2665 *Fax:* 314-432-7044 *Toll Free Fax:* 800-421-8816
E-mail: orders@mattmccoy.com
Web Site: www.matthewsbooks.com
Key Personnel
CEO: Linda Nash
Founded: 1889
Wholesale distributor of medical, nursing, allied health, dental, veterinary, scientific & technical books.
Represents Academic Press; Acindes; Addison-Wesley (Prentiss Hall Health); Advanced Medical Publishing; Airway Cam Technologies; Alert & Oriented Publishing; American Academy of Orthopaedic Surgeons; American Academy of Pediatrics; American College of Obstetricians & Gynecologists (ACOG); American College of Physicians (ACP); American Dietetic Association; American Hospital Association; American Institute of Cancer Research; American Medical Association; American Pharmaceutical Association (APhA); American Psychiatric Publishing Inc; American Psychological Association; American Public Health Association (Benenson); American Society for Microbiology; American Society of Health System Pharmacists (ASHP); American Wolf; Anadem Publishing Inc; Anatomical Chart Co (LWW); Annie Enterprises; Anshan Publishing; Anson Publishing LLC; Antimicrobial Therapy Inc; Anup Research; Apollos Voice; Appleton (Prentiss Hall Health); Applied Therapeutics Inc (LWW); Jason Aronson (Rowman Littlefield); Artech House; Arts End Books; Ashbury Press; Ashgate Publishing Co (Wiley); Aspen Publishers (Jones & Bartlett); Atheneum Press; Ausmed Publications; Baja Books; Bandido Books (HCPro); BarCharts Publishing Inc; Basic Books Inc; Birkhauser Boston Inc; BL Publishing Co; Blackwell Publishing (Wiley); Bontrager Publishing; Book Smythe; Books of Discover; Ken Bookstein; Borm Bruckmeier Publishing LLC; Brady (Prentice Hall Health); BrainX; Brookes Publishing (Paul H Brooks); Brunner Mazel Inc (Taylor & Francis); Bryan Edwards/Flash Anatomy; Butterworth (Elsevier); Butterworth-Heinemann; Cache River Press; Cambridge University Press; Canadian Nurses Association; Cardiotext; CCNM Press; Cengage; Chapman & Hall; Charles Press Publishers; Chicago Review Press; Clinical EKG Guide; Clinical Publishing; The Coding Institute; Cold Spring Harbor; Colon Publishing; Columbia University Press; Cover Publishing Co; CRC Press; Creative Healthcare; Cricket Science; Critical Care Research & Associates; Critical Concepts; Current Clinical Strategies; Current Medicine (Springer); Curties-Overzet; Dalhousie University (Midnight Medicine); Data Trace Publishing Co; Davies Publishing; Davis Associates; F A Davis; B C Decker; Marcel Dekker Inc; Dudley Delaney; Delmar Publishers (Cengage); Demos Publications Inc; Martin Dunitz (Taylor & Francis); E D Insight; Educational Communications; Edu Rad; Elsevier Science Publishing Co; Lawrence Erlbaum & Associates (LEA) (Taylor & Francis); Exam Master Corporation; Facts & Comparisons Inc; Family Health Publications; W H Freeman & Co; Futura Publishing Co Inc; Galen Press Ltd; Garland Publishing (Taylor & Francis); Gordon & Breach Science Publishers (Taylor & Francis); Greenbranch Publishing LLC; Greenwich Medical Media (Cambridge); Guilford Pub-

lications Inc; GW Medical Publishing (STM Learning); H & H Publications; H & H Publishing Co Inc; Hampton Medical; Hancock Surgical Consultants; Handbooks in Health Care Co (HHC); HarperCollins Publishers; Haworth Press; HC Pro (Opus Communications); Health Emergency Publishing; Health Leadership (J&B); Health Press International; Health Professions Institute; Health Professions Press; HIMSS; Hogrefe & Huber Publishers; Human Kinetics; Human Sciences Press Inc; Humana Press; I-Can; I D G Books (Wiley); Ideas2Pen; IGI Global; IMP Publishing; In the Spotlight; Informed/Creative Ventures; Ingenix; Inner Traditions International; Insight Therapeutics LLC; InterLingua Publishing; International Medical Publishers; International University Press; Interpretive Laboratory Data; IOS Press Inc; Iowa State University Press; IRL Press (Oxford); Isis Medical (Taylor & Francis); IWA Publishing; J & S Publishing Co; Jeff Computers; JLW Publications; Joint Commission Resources (JCR); Jones & Bartlett Publishing; Jossey-Bass Inc Publishers (Wiley); JP Medical; Karger; KG/EKG Press; Jessica Kingsley (Taylor & Francis); Kluwer Academic Publishers; Lander-Drysdale; LearningExpress; Lewis Publishers Inc (Taylor & Francis); Lexi-Comp Inc; Lippincott, Williams & Wilkins; Mainely Physical Therapy; Margol Publishing LLC; Maxwell Publishing Co; McGraw-Hill Inc; MD Pocket; MD2B; Medconsult Publishing; Medhumor Publications; Medical Group Management Association (MGMA); Medical Management Institute (MMI); Medical Surveillance; Medlearn; Medmaster Inc; Megabooks; Megusta Publishing; Merck & Co; Merriam-Webster; Milady; Minireview LLC; Miracle Press; MIT Press (selected titles); Modern Language Association; Morgan & Claypool Publishers; Morrow, William & Co Inc; Mountainside MD Press; Mudpiles.com; National Academy Press; National League for Nursing (Jones & Bartlett); National Nursing Review; National Safety Council (Jones & Bartlett); New Harbinger Publications; NNCC Inc; North Atlantic Books; W W Norton & Company Inc; Nursecom Inc; Nurse's Station; Nursing Education Consultants; Oakwood Publishing; OEM/Managed Medical Services; Ohio State University; Oncology Nursing Society (ONS); Open Heart Publishing; OPP Crunch; Optum; Osote Publishing; Oxford University Press Inc; Pan American Health Organization (PAHO); Parthenon Publications Group (Taylor & Francis); People's Medical Publishing House (PMPH); Pergamon Press Inc (Elsevier); Peterson's Guides Inc; Pharmaceutical Press; Physician Support Resources (PSR); Physician's Desk Reference (PDR); Physician's Press; Plenum Publishing Corp (Kluwer); Plural Publishing Inc; Pluribus Press (Precept); PMIC; Porter & Associates; Precept Press; Prentice Hall Health; Pro-Ed; Psych Products Press; Quintessence Publishing Co Inc; Quiz Me A&P; Radcliff Medical; Random House; Rapid Psychler Press; Raspberry Publishing Co; Remedica Publishing Ltd; RennieMatrix Inc; Reveneco; Review for Nurses Inc; Rheum Info; Rodram Corp Sa De CV; Routledge (Taylor & Francis); Rowman & Littlefield Publishers; Royal College of Physicians (American Psychiatric Publishing Inc); RSM Press; RuveneCo Publishing; St Lucie Press (CRC); St Martin's Press Inc; Scientific Publishing Ltd; Scrub Hill Press; Scymed Sa De Cv; Seak Inc; SFI Medical; Sigma Theta Tau International; Simon & Schuster; Simply Books; Sinauer & Associates; Slack Inc; SmartDraw.com; Sportsmed Press; Springer New York Inc; Springer Publishing Co Inc; Springhouse Publishing (LWW); Tarascon Publishing (J&B); Taylor & Francis Inc; Tell Me Press; Teton New Media; TFM Publishing; Therapeutic Ar-

ticulations; Thieme Medical Publishers Inc; Transmedical Corp; VCH Publishers (Wiley); Visual-Edge; Waveland Press; Whurr Publishing (Wiley); John Wiley & Sons Inc; World Bank Publications; World Scientific Publishing; Wysteria Ltd

Territory: Puerto Rico, USA

McGarr & Associates
5692 Heathwood Ct, Covington, KY 41015
Tel: 859-356-9295 *Fax:* 859-356-7804
Key Personnel
Pres: William D McGarr *E-mail:* wdmcgarr@aol.com
Representing book publishers, calendars & audio, bookmarks, journals & other sidelines to bookstores, wholesaler & specialty accounts.
Territory: Illinois, Indiana, Iowa, Kansas, Kentucky, Michigan, Minnesota, Missouri, Nebraska, North Dakota, Ohio, South Dakota, West Virginia, Wisconsin

Melman-Moster Associates Inc
48 Post Ave, Hawthorne, NJ 07506
Tel: 862-452-6196 *Fax:* 973-304-4923
E-mail: books@melman-moster.com
Key Personnel
Owner: Meg Moster; Nancy Moster
Publishers' representatives.
Represents Braun; Brown Books; Brunswick Books; Callisto Publishing; Crabtree; Diamond Cutter Press; Didier Millet Publishing; Earlswood Press; Eksmo Publishing House; Forefront Publishing Co; Fresh Frances; Greenleaf Book Group; IRH Press; Lerner Publications; Links International; Marco Polo; Millichap Books; Momosa Publishing; New Harbinger; New In Chess; Offshoot; Peter Pauper Press; Pictoplasma; Pomegranate Calendars; Pomegranate Press; Regina Orthodox Press; Oscar Riera Ojeda Publishers Ltd; Scientific Publishing; Seltmann & Sohne; Swendenborg Foundation Press; Templeton Press; teNeues; teNeues Stationary; Toon Studio Press; xPat Media/Scriptum
Territory: Mid-Atlantic States

MEP Education
8154 N Ridgeway Ave, Skokie, IL 60076
Tel: 847-676-1596 *Fax:* 847-676-1195
E-mail: info@mep-inc.net
Web Site: www.mepeducation.net
Founded: 1856
Distribute imported foreign language (French, German, Italian, Spanish) materials; books, software, audio, video, periodicals, to schools, libraries, teachers & general public. Office of Publication of European Language Institute for ELI magazines. Also distribute for US & foreign publishers in ESL/bilingual & foreign language materials.
Territory: USA

Midpoint National Inc
1263 Southwest Blvd, Kansas City, KS 66103
Tel: 913-362-7400 *Toll Free Tel:* 800-228-4321
E-mail: info@midpt.com
Web Site: www.midpt.com
Key Personnel
Pres: Ron Freund
EVP: Kent Gedman
Founded: 1988
Full service order fulfillment operations for book publishers, direct marketers, continuity book clubs, video & audio tape suppliers. Fully conveyorized 60,000 square foot distribution center, shipping nationwide from a "Midpoint USA" location. Services tailored to each client's needs include 800 number call center; complete or partial invoicing, accounting, credit management & collection; mailing list management; inventory reporting, computerized credit

card authorization & processing; complete handling of returned merchandise; full pick, pack & ship capability ranging from individual consumer orders & small store retail shipments to truckload quantities.

Midpoint Trade Books
Division of Independent Publishers Group (IPG)
814 N Franklin St, Suite 100, Chicago, IL 60610
Tel: 312-337-0747 *Fax:* 312-337-5985
E-mail: orders@ipgbook.com
Web Site: www.midpointtrade.com
Key Personnel
Pres: Eric Kampmann *E-mail:* eric@midpointtrade.com
VP & Gen Mgr: Alex Kampmann *E-mail:* alex@midpointtrade.com
Mktg Mgr: Alison Kampmann
Natl Accts Mgr: William Huhn *E-mail:* bill@midpointtrade.com
Natl Sales Acct Mgr: Annette Hughes
Ebook Coord: Casey Park
Founded: 1996
Full service book distribution company. Provides an important new model of marketing & distribution for independent publishers, with hands-on sales management. Represents US, Canadian & UK publishers in the US market.
Distributor for AAPC Inc; AAPC Publishing; Active Planet Kids Inc; ACW Press; Adams Printing Press; Affinitas Publishing; Albion Press; Alexander & Smith Publishing; Alicon Holdings Ltd; Allen Lane; Alliance Quebecoise editeurs independants; American Series; Amphorae Publishing Group LLC; Anglican House Media Ministries Inc; Anglican House Publishers Inc; APC Books; Apostle Press; Appalachian Trail Conservancy; Archetype; Artemisia Publishing LLC; Artichoke Publishers; Ash Tree Publishing; Asphodel Press; Atomic Fez Publishing; Austin Macauley Publishers Ltd; Authority Press; AWSNA Publications; B-Strong LLC; Backcountry Publishing; Backpack Editions; Balfour Books; Barlow Publishing; Barrytown/Station Hill Press Inc; Beaufort Books; John Beaufoy Publishing; Becoming Journey LLC; Beijing Mediatime United Publishing Co Ltd; Believe Books LLC; Bellekeep Books; Benjamin Press; Ensign Benson Books LLC; Beyond Dreams Publishing Group; Big Mind Publishing; Big Tent Entertainment; Bitingduck Press; Black Heron Press; Black Moss Press; Blank Slate Communications LLC; Blank Slate Press; blewointment; Bluebonnet Kids; Bluefield Books; Book Publishers Network; Book Ripple; Bookhaven Press; Bookstorm; Boulder Publications; BP Books; Brand Artist Press; Robin Brass Studio Inc; Bridgeway Publishing; Broken Hill; Brolga Publishing; Buckingham Book Publishing Ltd; Buffalo Heritage Press; Burke Publishing; Byword Books; Caffeine Nights Publishing; Caitlin Press Inc; Callinectes Press; Cameo Press; Canine Wellness LLC; Canon Publishers; Cappuccino Books Publishing; CareNet Pregnancy Centers; Casino Vacations Press Inc; CELA Publishing; Central Park Tutors; Changing Lives Press; Nina Charles LLC; Chef Media; China Resource Center Press; Chowder Inc; Chronology Books; Church Media; Cicerone Press Ltd; Circle Publishing; CJ Books; Clarens Publishing; Clarity Marketing USA LLC; Clean Teen Publishing; CLM Publishing; Clockwise Press; Clotho Press; CN Times Books Inc; Cogin Inc; Comfort Publishing LLC; Conquill Press; Convergence Press; Cool Titles; Corgi Bits; Cormorant Books; Cosmos Internet Sdn Bhd; Cosmos Press Inc; Courtright; David & Nicole Crank Ministries; Creality Publishing; Creative Production Services Inc; Crimson Tree Publishing; Cross House Books; Crow Flies Press; Cuidono Press; CulturAle Press; Jean Cunningham Consulting; Curtis Christine Press; Jen Dafoe Publishing;

Dagger Editions; Dalsimer Press Inc; Darton Longman & Todd Ltd; DC Books; DCDESIGN Books; Defiance Press; Difference Press; Don't Rent Inc; Dragon Door Publications; Dragon Moon Press; Dram Good Books; Dreams Shared Publications; Dreamtitle Publishing; Dunham Books; Early Learning Foundation; East End Press; eBury Press; Ecademy Press Ltd; EDGE Science Fiction & Fantasy Publishing; Editions Mundo; Editions Veritas Quebec; Elijah Books; Entangled Books; Executive Books; Expert Subjects LLC; Facing History & Ourselves; FAL Enterprises LLC; Family Health Publications; Famous Publishing; Fayetteville Mafia Press; The Fedd Agency; Fidelis Publishing; Fieldhouse; Fifth House Publishers; The Fine Print Press Ltd; First Base Sports; Fitch & Madison Publishers LLC; Fitzhenry & Whiteside; Five Elements Press; 5Points Publishing; Five Wisdoms Press; Flowers in Bloom Publishing; Foragers Harvest Press; Forever Young Publishers; 498 Productions LLC; 4GenPress; Fortem Press; Foxglove Press; Fracas Press; Franklin Green Publishing LLC; Franklin Square Press; Frederick Fell Publishers Inc; FRI Research; Frigate Books; Front Porch Press; Frontrunner; Gateway Entertainment Inc; Gavia Books; Gazelles Inc; Gelos Publications; Genesis Publishing; Glass House Nocturnal; Glass House Press; GMF Publishing; Gold Star Publishing; Goldminds Publishing; Goodman Beck Publishing; Good2Go Kids; Jeff Gordon Inc; Great River Books; Green Jellybean Press; Green Kids Press LLC; Green Place Books; Green Sprouts; Green Writers Press; Grid Press; Guernica Editions; Habits of Health Press; Hamish Hamilton; Hank Enterprises LLC; Harbour; Harbour Publishing; Haute Life Press; HeartWork Publishing; Heaven's Library; Hellgate Press; HigherLife Publishing; Hiraeth Press; HL Special Ebook Imprint; HnL; Homebound Publications; Hometown Fanfare Publishing LLC; House of David Publishers; HPN Books; h2 press; Hummingbird Books; Hummingbird World Media; Ignatius Press; Illumify Media Global; Illumify Press; In-Depth Editions LLC; Incorgnito Publishing Press; Influence Publishing Inc; Influencers; Inked; Integrative Nutrition Inc; Interactive Publishing Corp; Isaac Publishing LLC; ISB Publishing; Island Heritage Publishing; JAFS Inc; JahBread LLC; JCC Press; JEC Press; Jinda Corp; John August Media LLC; Junction; Kalpa Tree Press; Kingdom Driven Publishing; Kinkajou Press; KMG Publishing; Knox Robinson Publishing; Kokoro; Koebele Weaver Enterprises; Krazy Coupon Lady LLC; Ladyslipper Press; Lagniappe Publishing; Lambert Hill; Lamplight Ministries Inc; Layla Dog Press; Leadership First; The Leading Edge Publishing Co; Level 4 Press Inc; Lexington Marshall Publishing LLC; Life Journey Publishing; Life's Plan Publishing; LifeBridge Books; Lifestyle Entrepreneurs Press; Lighthouse Press; Little Adventures; Little Bound Books; Living Clay; Living Waters Publications; London Wall Publishing; Lorimer Press; Lost Moose; Lotus Publications; Loving On Purpose; Luath Press Ltd; Luminescent Herbivore; Mad Norwegian Press; Magic Light Publishing; Magnificat; Managing Times Press; Marching Band; Barbara McLennan; Meerkat Press LLC; Mehta Publishers; Mentobe Press; Merril Press; Messenger International; Mile Oak Publishing Inc; Mr Mark's Classroom; Mitchell Street Press; Mithras Books; MKids; Mokum Media; Monkeyfeather; Moonshots Press; Brett Morgan Publishing; Motivating The Masses Press; Motivational Press; Moyer Bell; MP Publishing Ltd; Mutasian Entertainment LLC; Mwella Publishing; Myndset Press; New Atlantean Press; New Awareness Network; New Chapter Publisher; New Holland Publishers; NEWTYPE; Next; Next Century

Publishing; NEXT SAS; NEXTBOOK Ltd; NEXTBOOK SAS; Nightwood; Nightwood Editions; 9 Heads Media Inc; NK Publications Inc; North Star Press of St Cloud; Notable Kids Publishing; Nunavut Arctic College; Obstacles Press; Oceanview Publishing; Old Dog Books; Olmstead Press; Olympic Press; 1-Take MultiMedia; Onward; Owl House Books; Paloma Books; PaperUp Publishing; Papier-Mache Press; Annika Parance Publishing; Park Avenue Press; PCG Business; PCG Kids; PCG Legacy; Pemmican Publications; Penguin; Penguin Ananda; Penguin Classics; Penguin Enterprise; Penguin Metro Reads; Penguin Modern Classics; Penguin Random House India Pvt Ltd; Penguin Studio; Penguin Young Adult; Penguin Zubaan; Penrhyn Press; Pentatonic Press; Perichoresis Press; Personal Power Press; Pilot Communications Group; Pinata Publishing; PMP; Pokeweed Press; Polar Horizons; Polaris Publications; Ponent Mon SL; Portfolio; Press Syndication Group; Primal Nutrition Inc; Primus Books; Printopya; Project Restored Press; Prolance; Promontory Press Inc; Puffin; Puffin Young Zubaan; Quinn & Associates Publishing & Consulting; Khalil Rafati; Ransom Note Press LLC; Ratna Sagar; Ratna Sagar P Ltd; Readers Legacy Inc; Reading With Peaches LLC; Real Magic Design LLC; Real Western; Rebel Press; Red Deer Press; Red Press Ltd; Redwood Publishing LLC; Robert Reed Publishers; Reservoir Square Books; Retire Secure Press; Walter Reutiman Publishing; RFI Publishing; Risen Son Publishing LLC; River Publishing; Riverrun LLC; RLM Publishing; Rock Foundations Press; Rogue Bear Press; Rollerbird; Warren K Ross Jr; Roundup Press; Sandbox Publishing LLC; S&J Multimedia LLC; Sands Press; Satya House Publications; Jeff Schmidgall Ministries; Schoolside Press; Scribe Publishing Co; Search for the Truth Ministry; SelectBooks; Shadow Dragon Press; Sharitt Publications; Shobha De Books; Singing Turtle Press; Six Points Press; SK Halliburton Enterprises; Smart Travel Press; Snow & Associates Inc; Soar in Trust; Solo Roma Inc; Sonflower Publishing Co; SOS Publishing; Space Goat Productions Inc; Sparrow Publishing; Special Yoga Publications; Spence City; Spencer Hill Contemporary; Spencer Hill Middle Grade; Spencer Hill Press; SSE Publishing; Star of Light Publications; The Star Trilogy; Steamboat Springs Publishing; Summer Fit Learning; Super Senses Productions; taotime verlag; Tatra Press; 10 Finger Press; 3 Dreams Creative Enterprises LLC; Thunder Bay Press Michigan; Tiara Publishing; Tiger Blood International; Times Media Group Inc; Timothy & Titus; Titletown Publishing LLC; TM Publishing; Today is the Day Publishing; Today's Books; Tomahawk Press; Top Executive Media; Topos Books; Totus Tuus Press; Tourist Town Guides; TreeGirl Studios LLC; Treehouse Publishing Group; Trifolium Books; Trinacria Editions LLC; True North Publishing; Trueface; Truth in Science; Tulip; 12 Pines Press; Under the Maple Tree Books; Upper Access Inc; Van der Plas/Cycle Publishing; Vesst Investment Partnership LP; VESST Publishing; Veterans Publishing Inc; Viking; Vision Life Ministries International Inc; Vista Communications; Walrus Books; Wapner & Brent Books; Westminster Institute; Whitecap America; Whitecap Books Ltd; Why Not Books; Wild Thorn Publishing LLC; Buck Wilder Inc; Windhill Books LLC; Windsor-Brooke Books LLC; Dortha Withrow Books; WND Books; WND Films; World Ahead Publishing; X-Communication LLC
Territory: Canada, UK, USA, worldwide
Membership(s): American Booksellers Association (ABA); California Independent Booksellers Alliance (CALIBA); Great Lakes Independent Booksellers Association (GLIBA); Independent Book Publishers Association (IBPA); Mountains & Plains Booksellers Association (MPBA); New Atlantic Independent Booksellers Association (NAIBA); Pacific Northwest Booksellers Association (PNBA)

Miller Trade Book Marketing Inc
1426 W Carmen Ave, Chicago, IL 60640
Tel: 773-307-3446
Key Personnel
Pres: Bruce Miller *E-mail:* bruce@millertrade.com
Founded: 1985
Sales representative for midwest territory for book marketing.
Represents Duke University Press; Johns Hopkins University Press; Kent State University Press; Michigan State University Press; Minnesota Historical Society Press; Rutgers University Press; Springer Nature; Syracuse University Press; Temple University Press; University of Georgia Press; University of Iowa Press; University of Minnesota Press; University of Texas Press; University Press of Kansas; University Press of Kentucky; University Press of Mississippi; Wayne State University Press; Wisconsin Historical Society Press
Territory: Midwestern States
Membership(s): Great Lakes Independent Booksellers Association (GLIBA); Midwest Independent Booksellers Association (MIBA)

National Association of Book Entrepreneurs (NABE)
PO Box 606, Cottage Grove, OR 97424
Tel: 541-942-7455 *Fax:* 541-942-7455
E-mail: nabe@bookmarketingprofits.com
Web Site: www.bookmarketingprofits.com
Key Personnel
Exec Dir: Al Galasso
Founded: 1980
Book marketing consultations, publishing seminars, NABE Book Showcase combined book exhibits, mail order marketing through "Publishers Preview." Over 1,000 independent & small press publishers, electronic marketing service.
Distributor for Moore Publishing; Publishers Media
Territory: USA

National Book Network (NBN)
Subsidiary of Rowman & Littlefield Publishing Group
4501 Forbes Blvd, Suite 200, Lanham, MD 20706
Tel: 301-459-3366 *Toll Free Tel:* 800-462-6420 (orders only) *Fax:* 301-429-5746
Toll Free Fax: 800-338-4550 (orders only)
E-mail: customercare@nbnbooks.com
Web Site: www.nbnbooks.com
Key Personnel
CEO: Jed Lyons
COO: Robert S Marsh *E-mail:* rmarsh@rowman.com
SVP & CFO: Michael Lippenholz *E-mail:* mlippenholz@rowman.com
Pres: Jason Brockwell *E-mail:* jbrockwell@nbnbooks.com
VP, Opers: Mike Cornell *E-mail:* mcornell@nbnbooks.com
VP, Publr & Cust Servs: Carla Quental *E-mail:* cquental@nbnbooks.com
Dir, Sales Admin: Sylvia Williams *E-mail:* swilliams@nbnbooks.com
Intl Sales Dir: Les Petriw *E-mail:* lpetriw@nbnbooks.com
Mgr, Dist: Sue Bumbaugh *E-mail:* sbumbaugh@nbnbooks.com
Publr Servs Mgr: Karen Mattscheck *E-mail:* kmattscheck@nbnbooks.com
Founded: 1986

Sales, marketing & distribution for publishers to the trade.

Distribution center located in Blue Ridge Summit, PA.

Represents Active Parenting; Advantage Books; AEI Press; American Bar Association; Anness Publishing; Appalachian Mountain Club Books; Applause Theatre & Cinema Books; Aquila Polonica Publishing; Army War College; Association for Talent Development; Astragal Press; Astronaut Projects (BizBookLab LLC); August House; Axios Press; Backbeat Books; Bard Press; Baron Barclay Bridge; Barricade Books; Bay Tree Publishing; Black Widow Press/Commonwealth Books Inc; Blacksmith Club; Blood Moon Productions; Blue Dome Press; Bnei Baruch/Laitman Kabbalah Publishers; Boone & Crockett Club; Bradt Travel Guides; Bragg/Health Science; Brewers Publications; Bristol Park Books; British American Publishing; Burford Books; C&T Publishing; Capizon Publishing; Cato Institute; Cinebook; Common Deer Press; Continental Sales Inc (CSI); Crimson Publishing; Crystal Clarity Publishers; D&B Publishing; Day Hike Books; Dharma Publishing; Dillman Karate International; Don't Eat Any Bugs Productions; Earthbound Sports; Everyman Chess; ExPress; Facts on Demand Press; Felony & Mayhem; Fitness Information Technology; Flower Press; Footprint Travel Guides; Garrett County Press; Globe Pequot; Good Sam Club; Goofy Foot Press; Green Editorial; Green Lion Press; Harbor Press; Headwater Books; Himalayan Institute Press; Hobar Publications; Alan C Hood; A C Hubbard; Impact Publications; Jeffers Press; Jonglez Publishing; Jupitalia; Kidwick Books; Lake Isle Press; Larson Publications; Learning Express; Limelight Editions; Lost Classics Book Co; Lotus Press; Marshall Cavendish; McBooks Press; Axel Menges; Michelin Travel & Lifestyle; Milepost; Moffly Media; Mongoose Press; Monsoon Books; Mount Alpha Media; Mustang Publishing; New Academy Publishers; NewTrends Publishing Inc; NIMBUS; No Voice Unheard; Nomad Press; Oak Hill Publishing; Octobre LLC; Peak Performance Press; Phobos Books; Photo Tour Books Inc; Pineapple Press; Pinter & Martin; Platypus Media/Science, Naturally; PopOut; Practising Law Institute; Prometheus Books; Quality Chess; Quiller Publishing Ltd; Radical Honesty Enterprises Inc; Rainforest Books; RAND Corp; Riverbend Publishing; Edward Everett Root; Rowman & Littlefield; Royal College of General Practitioners; Ryton Publications; Safari Press; Sausage Maker; Scientific Publishing; Seapoint Books & Media; Sentient Publications; Shalem Press; Smart Publications; Speechmark Publishing; Stoecklein Photography; The Story Plant; Survival Books Ltd; Trailblazer Publications; Tughra Books; Velocity Press; Vij Books India; Visions International Publishing; Waterford Press; Welcome Rain Publishers; Western Horseman; Whittles Publishing; Windsor Books; Windward Publishing; Wisdom Waters Press; Woodland Press; World Wisdom/Wisdom Tales; Yale University Art Gallery; YMAA Publication Center; Zeshan Qureshi

Territory: Australia, Caribbean, Central America, Mexico, New Zealand, South America, UK, USA

Membership(s): Independent Book Publishers Association (IBPA)

New Leaf Distributing Co
Subsidiary of Shakti LLC
401 Thornton Rd, Lithia Springs, GA 30122-1557
SAN: 169-1449
Tel: 770-948-7845 *Toll Free Tel:* 800-326-2665 (orders) *Fax:* 770-944-2313 *Toll Free Fax:* 800-326-1066 (orders)

E-mail: customerservice@newleaf-dist.com
Web Site: newleafdist.com
Key Personnel
Pres: Santosh Krinsky
VP, Opers: Karen Price
Founded: 1975
Serves publishers both inside & outside of New Leaf's usual Body, Mind & Spirit niche. Founded on the premise that in the present publishing environment, the traditional one size fits all distribution scheme may no longer meet the needs of many small presses. We offer a service that is uniquely flexible & designed to ensure that worthy books are presented effectively to important buyers. Additional services include ebook distribution, digital short run printing, plus freight consolidation & logistics for small publishers.

Distributor for Beech Hill Publishing; Blue Juice Comics; Brotherhood of Life; BurmanBooks Media Corp; George Cappannelli; Center for Touch Drawing; DBM Press; Enrealment Press; Expansion Publishing; Foundation for Inner Peace; Grail Press; Kitchen Sink Publishing (one title only); Pari Publishing; Promontory Press; Sky Grove; Sounding Light Publishing; Spiritual Journeys; Carl Studna; Sufi Ruhaniat International; Thoth Publications; TV Guestpert; Whitedove Press; World Tree Press; Zen Publications (one title only)

Northeast Publishers Reps
Montville Chase, 20 Davenport Rd, Montville, NJ 07045
Tel: 973-299-0085 *Fax:* 973-263-2363
E-mail: siraksirak@aol.com
Web Site: www.nepubreps.com
Key Personnel
Owner: James F Sirak
Sales Off Mgr: Mariel Dryl *Tel:* 973-625-3694
Contact: Beth Martin; Bill Palizzolo; Lisa Sirak
Founded: 1981
Sales organization that represents publishers & manufacturers to the book trade in the northeastern US.

Represents Amber Lotus; Artgame; Bar Charts Publishing; Bookmasters; Earthbound Journals; EDC Publishing/Usborne Books; Enchanted World of Boxes; Endless Possibilities/Boink Fidgets; FoxMind; Fridolin; From There to Here Imports (FTTH); Gift Trenz; Gold Crest/Mighty Bright; Good Cause Greetings; Holiday House; InterLink; Lang Companies/Turner; Mark-My-Time; Masterpiece Puzzles; Northwoods Guides; Parody Productions; Quarto Publishing Group; Round World Products; Sellers Publishing; Sock It to Me; Soundstrue; Sourcebooks; 3 Oak Publishing; Tide-Mark Calendars; University of Hawaii Press; White Mountain Puzzles; Willow Creek; Zebra Publishing; Ziga Media Calendars
Territory: Mid-Atlantic States, New England
Membership(s): New Atlantic Independent Booksellers Association (NAIBA); New England Independent Booksellers Association (NEIBA)

OverDrive Inc
One OverDrive Way, Cleveland, OH 44125
Tel: 216-573-6886 *Fax:* 216-573-6888
E-mail: info@overdrive.com
Web Site: www.overdrive.com
Key Personnel
Pres & CEO: Steve Potash
COO: Lori Franklin
CFO: Greg Farmer
Chief Sales & Mktg Offr: Adam Eberle
Gen Coun: Erica Lazzaro
Intl Busn Devt Exec: Steve Rosato
Founded: 1986
Leading full service digital distributor of ebooks, audiobooks & other digital content.

Parasource Marketing & Distribution Ltd
55 Woodslee Ave, Paris, ON N3L 3E5, Canada
Mailing Address: PO Box 98, Paris, ON N3L 3E5, Canada
Tel: 519-442-7853 *Toll Free Tel:* 800-263-2664 *Fax:* 519-442-1303 *Toll Free Fax:* 800-461-8575
E-mail: custserv@parasource.com
Web Site: parasource.com
Key Personnel
Pres: Greg Tombs *Tel:* 519-442-7853 ext 231 *E-mail:* greg.tombs@parasource.com
Dir, Sales & Mktg: Debbie Tempelmeyer *Tel:* 519-442-7853 ext 252 *E-mail:* deb.tempelmeyer@parasource.com
Sales & marketing distribution.
Distributor for Abingdon; Alpha; B & H Publishing Group; Baker Group Publishing; Beacon Hill Press; Blossom Bucket; CA Gifts; David C Cook; Concordia; Crusade World Revival; Dayspring; Eerdmans; 1517 Media (formerly Augsburg Fortress); Growing Families; Hendrickson Publishing; Inter Varsity Publishing; Kregel Publishing; Lifeway Publishing; Moody Publishers; Rainbow; Random House; Rose Publishing; Simon & Schuster; Warner Press; Westminster John Knox Press
Territory: Canada

Parson Weems' Publisher Services LLC
3811 Canterbury Rd, No 707, Baltimore, MD 21218
Tel: 914-948-4259 *Toll Free Fax:* 866-861-0337
E-mail: office@parsonweems.com
Web Site: www.parsonweems.com
Key Personnel
Partner/Owner & Sales Rep, Mid Atlantic Region: Eileen Bertelli *Tel:* 845-987-7233 *Fax:* 866-761-7112 *E-mail:* eileenbertelli@parsonweems.com
Partner: Chris Kerr *Tel:* 914-329-4961 *E-mail:* chriskerr@parsonweems.com
Mgr: Causten Stehle *Tel:* 914-948-4259 *Fax:* 866-861-0337
Sales Rep, Mid Atlantic Region: Jason Kincade *Tel:* 347-244-2165 *E-mail:* jasonkincade@parsonweems.com; Kevin Moran *Tel:* 848-303-4164 *E-mail:* kevinmoran@parsonweems.com
Founded: 1997
Independent trade sales representatives & marketing consultants specializing in art & lifestyle illustrated books, business, travel, regional, reference, children's books, scholarly & professional, calendars, museum products, promotional books & note cards.
Represents Actar/ORO (New England only); Berghahn; Birkhauser (New England only); Bloomsbury Academic; Capstone; Casemate | IPM; Children's Press; Child's Play (New England only); ChooseCo; Consortium; Dawn Publications; Diamond Books; Familius; Fine Print Publishing; Gardner (New England only); Geotoys; Inner Traditions; Island Press; Jessica Kingsley Publishers; LSU Press; MACK Publications; McGraw-Hill Professional; Midpoint/Green Writers Press; Mountaineers Books; Naval Institute Press; Penn State University Press; Rutgers University Press; Shelter Harbor Press; Stillman & Birn; Stylus Publishing; University of Kansas Press; University of Pennsylvania Press; University of Tennessee Press; University of Toronto Press; University Press of Kentucky; Wayne State University Press
Territory: Connecticut, Delaware, District of Columbia, Maine, Maryland, Massachusetts, New Hampshire, New Jersey, New York, Pennsylvania, Rhode Island, Vermont, West Virginia
Membership(s): Association of Book Travelers; New Atlantic Independent Booksellers Association (NAIBA); New England Independent Booksellers Association (NEIBA)

Penguin Random House Canada
Division of Penguin Random House LLC
320 Front St W, Suite 1400, Toronto, ON M5V
  3B6, Canada
SAN: 201-3975
Tel: 416-364-4449 *Toll Free Tel:* 888-523-9292
  (cust serv) *Fax:* 416-598-7764
Web Site: www.penguinrandomhouse.ca
Key Personnel
CEO: Kristin Cochrane
CFO: Barry Gallant
COO: Robert Wheaton
Exec Publr & EVP: Louise Dennys
SVP & Dir, Prodn: Janine Laporte
VP & Deputy Publr: Marion Garner
VP, Mktg & Communs: Beth Lockley
VP, PRHC & Publr, Penguin Canada: Nicole
  Winstanley
VP, Sales: Charidy Johnston
VP, Subs Rts: Adrienne Tang
Sr Dir, Independent, Lib & Academic Sales:
  Mary Giuliano
Group Sales Dir: Val Gow
Dir, Consumer Engagement: Shannon Poos
Dir, Sales Mgmt: Brent Richard
Dir, Spec Mkts & New Busn: Lavanya
  Narasimhan
Prodn Dir: Carla Kean
Publicity Dir: Josh Glover
Sales Mgr, Natl Accts: Karen Ma
Group Sales Coord: Leah Persaud
Ad Coord: Anais Loewen-Young
Online & Digital Sales Rep: Jessica Reid
Sales, marketing, warehouse & accounting ser-
  vices for Bantam, Seal, Doubleday Canada,
  Knopf Canada, McClelland & Stewart, Vintage
  Canada, etc.
Distributor for Appetite; Bantam; Charlesbridge
  Publishing; Crown; Delacorte; Dell; Double-
  day; McClelland & Stewart; Seal Books; Tun-
  dra
Represents Doubleday Canada; Knopf Canada;
  Vintage Canada
Territory: Canada

Power Engineering Books Ltd
Division of Book Order Service of Canada
7 Perron St, St Albert, AB T8N 1E3, Canada
SAN: 115-4850
Tel: 780-458-3155; 780-459-2525
  Toll Free Tel: 800-667-3155 *Fax:* 780-460-2530
E-mail: power@nucleus.com
Web Site: www.powerengbooks.com
Key Personnel
Dir: Kim Borle
Founded: 1973
Distributors of technical books, codes & stan-
  dards to private individuals, trade shows &
  businesses in Canada.
Distributor for Reeds
Represents ACGIH®; American Petroleum In-
  stitute (API); American Society for Testing &
  Materials (ASTM); American Society of Me-
  chanical Engineers (ASME); American Weld-
  ing Society (AWS); Canadian Standards Asso-
  ciation (CSA); DEWALT®; Institute of Elec-
  trical & Electronics Engineers (IEEE); Manu-
  facturers Standardization Society of the Valve
  & Fittings Industry Inc; National Association
  of Corrosion Engineers (NACE); National Fire
  Protection Association (NFPA); National Research Council Canada (NRCC); RSMeans;
  Reeds
Territory: Canada

Printed Matter Inc
231 11 Ave, Ground fl, New York, NY 10001
Tel: 212-925-0325 *Fax:* 212-925-0464
E-mail: info@printedmatter.org
Web Site: www.printedmatter.org
Key Personnel
Exec Dir: Max Schumann *E-mail:* mschumann@
  printedmatter.org

Gen Mgr & Asst to Dir: Cory Siegler
  E-mail: cory@printedmatter.org
Founded: 1976
Nonprofit distributor of artists' books; more than
  15,000 titles.
Represents Bookworks; Lapp Princess; Nexus;
  Visual Studies Workshop; WeProductions
Territory: worldwide
Membership(s): Art Libraries Society (ARLIS)

Prologue Inc
1650 Blvd Lionel-Bertrand, Boisbriand, QC J7H
  1N7, Canada
Tel: 450-434-0306 (ext 231) *Toll Free Tel:* 800-
  363-2864 *Fax:* 450-434-2627
  Toll Free Fax: 800-361-8088 (cust serv)
E-mail: prologue@prologue.ca
Web Site: www.prologue.ca; www.
  prologuenumerique.ca
Key Personnel
Exec Asst: Genevieve Gamache
  E-mail: ggamache@prologue.ca
Founded: 1976
Distributes books in Canada in French for chil-
  dren & adults.
Distributor for Academie Culinaire du Quebec;
  Accarias/L'Originel; Accent Grave; Agni Yoga;
  Agora; Almora; Alpen; Andara; ARA; Assimil;
  Athena; Au Carre; Auralog; Beerlandt Publi-
  cations; Beliveau Editeur; Berger; Bertrand-
  Lacoste; BFLY; Blake et Mortimer; Bonhomme
  de Chemin; La Bonne Chanson; Bouton d'or
  Acadie; Breal; Broquet; Michel Brule; Budo;
  Calligram; Caractere; CARD; Cardoza; Carto-
  vision; Chalet; Editions Charlevoix; Chiffon
  Bleu; Chronique; Editions du CHU Sainte-
  Justine; Clairance; Clavis; Colloidales; Compe-
  tence Micro; Cornac; Louise Courteau; Editions
  Cristal; Dargaud; Le Dauphin Blanc; Rose de
  la Fontaine; Del Pierre; Demi Lune; Le Dernier
  Havre; Desclee; Detrad/AVS; Dixit; DLL
  Presse; Droguet et Ardant; Druide Editions;
  Druide Informatique; Dupuis Editeur de Carac-
  tre; Ecrits des Forges; EDIFA; Editions Edit'as;
  Educ'argent; Education 4 Peace; Elfes de la
  Vapeur; ENI Editions; Editions de l'Envolee;
  Essenia; ESSOR Editeur; Les Editions ETC;
  Evergreen; Editions Exclusif; Editions Fab-
  ulle; Les Editions Fei; Editions Fleurus; Fleu-
  rus Religion; Flic Flac; Fondation Urantia;
  Editions FouLire; Front Froid; Le Genevrier;
  J C Godefroy; Gouttiere; La Grande Maree;
  L'Harmattan; Andre Harvey; Horay; Huginn
  et Muninn; Imagine Publications; Les Impa-
  tients; Les Editions Interligne; Les Intouch-
  ables; IQRC; IRMA; IUGM (Institut Universi-
  taire de Geriatrie de Montreal)/CIUSS; Jaune;
  Kana; Kunchab; Lanctot; Fernand Lanore; Lito;
  Livres Brian; Lombard; Lounak; Lucis Trust;
  Lucky Comics; Lumiere d'El Morya; M Edi-
  teur; MA Bulle; MA Editeur; MA Editions;
  Macro; Magnard Jeunesse; Magnificat; Mai-
  son de Vie; Groupe Mame Liturgie; Groupe
  Mame Religieux; Mango; Editions Marie-
  Claire; Marsu Productions; Massin; McGray;
  Media-Participation; Medispaul; Yves Michel;
  Michelin; Micro Application; Midi Trente
  Editions; Mijade; Lyette Morin; Editions de
  Mortagne; Nectar; NKS; Nord-Sud; Nouveaux
  Contes de Perrault; Nouvelles Editions de l'arc;
  Nuinui; Octave Editions; Oracom; Oser la Vie;
  Parramon; Les Editions du Passage; Le Passe-
  Monde; Passe-Temps; Performance Edition;
  Editions Phidal; Editions du Phoenix; Picco-
  lia; Pix'n Love Editions; Plume de Pluie; Edi-
  tions Pochette; Les Editions Porte-Bonheur;
  Editions Pratiko; Les Presses de l'Universite
  d'Ottawa; Presses de l'Universite du Quebec;
  Presses de l'Universite Laval; Publications
  Quebec Francais; Les Editions du Quebecois;
  Isabelle Quentin; Paskal Rainville; Rameau;
  RDL; Recre Jeux; Du Renouveau Quebecois;
  Les Editeurs Reunis; Romart Editions; Rustica

  Editions; Daniel St Amour; Guy Saint-Jean;
  Les Editions Saint-Yves; SAM; Les Editions
  du Saxe; Scholastic; Sedirep; Sgraff; Shoebox
  Media; Les Six Brumes; Editions de la Smala;
  Soleil de Minuit; Soleil Noir; Editions du Som-
  met; Le Souffle d'Or; SRAM; Studio Boule
  et Bill; Studyrama; Sully; Sur l'Air des Mots;
  Tardy; Taschen International; TC Media Livres;
  Texte Vivant; Editions Pierre Tisseyre; Editions
  du Tonnerre; Toundra; Editions Touristiques du
  Quebec; Editions Trampoline; Editions Trois-
  Pistoles; Ubisoft; Univers/Cite Mikael; Editions
  Universitaires; Urban China; Urban Comics;
  Vagnon; Editions Vaudreuil; Editions Vents
  d'Ouest; Editions Vial; Editions Vigot; Viseo;
  Librairie Vuibert; Web Tech; Wellan Inc; Win
  Novation Informatique; Yoyo; Zephyr Editions
Territory: Canada

**Publishers Group West (PGW), an Ingram
brand**
Division of Ingram Content Group LLC
1700 Fourth St, Berkeley, CA 94710
SAN: 202-8522
Tel: 510-809-3700 *Toll Free Tel:* 866-400-5351
  (cust serv) *Fax:* 510-809-3777
E-mail: info@pgw.com
Web Site: www.pgw.com
Key Personnel
VP & Gen Mgr: Mark Ouimet
VP, Busn Devt: Kevin Votel *E-mail:* kevin.votel@
  ingramcontent.com
Founded: 1976
Marketing & distribution services for more than
  100 independent publishers.
Branch Office(s)
154 W 14 St, 12th fl, New York, NY 10011 (natl
  accts off)
Distributor for A Public Space; Adventure Pub-
  lications; AdventureKEEN; Agate Digital;
  Agate Publishing; American Diabetes Asso-
  ciation; Amherst Media; Annick Press; Au-
  gustus Publishing; Automatic Publishing;
  Aviation Supplies & Academics; Bailiwick
  Press; Baobab Press; Beginning Press; Be-
  liever Magazine; Belt Publishing; Bilingual
  Books Inc; Black Classic Press; Black Sands
  Entertainment; Black Ship Publishing; Blast
  Books; Blizzard Entertainment LLC; Blue Dot
  Press; Bluebridge; The Book Peddlers; Bread-
  pig; Breathing Books; Button Books; Cadmus
  Editions; Canongate Books; Cartoon Books;
  Carus Books; Chouette Publishing Inc; City-
  files Press; Classical Comics; Clavis; Clerisy
  Press; Coconut Press; Columbia Global Re-
  ports; Come & Get It Publishing; Cool Tools
  Lab; Cornell Lab Publishing Group; Counter-
  point; Creston Books; Crooked Lane Books;
  Cuento de Luz; Cune Press; Curiosity Books;
  Cursor; Deletrea; Destination Press; Douglas &
  McIntyre; Dry Climate Studios; Dzanc Books;
  826 Valencia; Encantos Media; Entrepreneur
  Press; Europa Editions; Faber & Faber; Fang
  Duff Kahn Publishers; Featherproof Books;
  Felony & Mayhem; Fig Tree Books; Figure
  1 Publishing; Flesk Publications; Forest Ave-
  nue Press; Four Elephants Press; Four Winds
  Press; Fourth Chapter Books; Franklin Pub-
  lishers; Frommer Media; Genesis Publica-
  tions; Gibson House Press; Gingko Press; Pe-
  ter Glickman Inc; Global Travel Publishers;
  Goosebottom Books; John Gray's Mars Venus
  LLC; Green Candy Press; Greystone Books;
  Groundwood Books; Grove/Atlantic Inc; Har-
  bour Publishing; Hartley & Marks Publishers; Hawthorne Books; Healthy Travel Media;
  Heritage Builders; Heyday; Hopscotch Press;
  House of Anansi Press; Hub City Press; Hun-
  dreds of Heads Books; Huntington Press; Icon
  Books; Imbrifex Books; In Easy Steps Ltd;
  Insight Press; Into Action Publications; Inter-
  link Publishing; Invisible Publishing; Kalm-
  bach Publishing; Kelcy Press; KO Kids Books;
  HJ Kramer; Laboratory Books; LARB Books;

Leaf Storm Press; Let's Go Inc; London Town Press; Machines of Death; Maven House; Mayo Clinic; McWitty Press; Medallion Media Group; Menasha Ridge Press; Microcosm Publishing; Mighty Media Inc; Milkweed Editions; Minoan Moon Publishing; Missionday LLC; Morpheus International; Mount Vernon Press; M27 Editions LLC; Namaste Publishing; Namchak Publishing LLC; Nature Study Guides; Naval Institute Press; Need To Know; New World Library; NewSage Press; Nilgiri Press; Nolo Press Occidental; Nothing But The Truth Publishing; Open Court; OR Books; Osho Media International; Otter-Barry Books; Owlkids Books; Owners Manual Press; Page Two; Papaloa Press; Passporter Travel Press; Patagonia Books; PDR Consumer; PDR Network; Penngrove Publications; Penny Candy Books; Pharos Editions; Phoneme Media; Plexus Publishing; PM Press; Polis Books; Pomegranate Press; Pritzker Military; Public Lands Alliance; Quick American Archives; Raincoast Books; Rare Bird Books; RE/Search Publications; Readers to Eaters; Red Comet Press; Restless Books; Resurrection House; Roaring Forties Press; Ronin Publishing; Roundtree Press; Sandow Media; Santa Monica Press; Seven Footer Press; Shelter Publications; Sierra Club/Counterpoint; Soft Skull Press; Source Book Publications; Sudden Oak Books; Supercollege; Surrey Books; Synergetic Press; Tachyon Publications; Tahrike Tarsile Qur'an; TalentSmart; Tara Books; Three Rooms Press; Time Out; Tinderbox Press; Tinwood Books; Trafalgar Square Books; Travelers' Tales; Trinity University Press; Tuttle Publishing; Two Dollar Radio; Two Lines Press; 2.13.61; Udon Entertainment; Unbridled Books; Underwood Books; The Unnamed Press; Unofficial Guides; Urantia Foundation; Val De Grace Books; Verse Chorus Press; Visible Ink Press; Waterford Press Inc; Watershed Media; Web of Life Children's Books; Wellstone Books; West Hills Press; Whereabouts Press; White Cloud Press; Wide World Publishing; Wild Strawberry Productions; Wilderness Press; Wildlands Press; Wine House Press; Yellow Pear Press; Rangjung Yeshe Publications; Yosemite Conservancy; You Live Right Publishing; Zakka Workshop
Territory: worldwide

QDS, see Quarto Distribution Services (QDS)

Quarto Distribution Services (QDS)
Division of Quarto Publishing Group USA
100 Cummings Ctr, Suite 265D, Beverly, MA 01915
Tel: 978-282-9590
E-mail: qds@quarto.com
Web Site: www.quartoknows.com/qds
Key Personnel
Dir, Dist Servs: John Groton *Tel:* 978-282-3562
  E-mail: john.groton@quarto.com
Distributor for Brooklands Books Ltd; Clever Publishing; The Crowood Press Ltd; Enthusiast Books; Evro; Exisle Publishing Ltd; Haynes Publishing; Herridge & Sons Ltd; Icon Publishing Ltd; Jawbone Press; James Mann; Murdoch Books; Giorgio Nada Editore SRL; Orca Publishing; Porter Press; TPR; Veloce Publishing Ltd

R & R Book Co LLC
666 Godwin Ave, Suite 120-C, Midland Park, NJ 07432
Tel: 201-337-3400
Web Site: www.rrbookcompany.com
Key Personnel
Partner: Ruth Alden Hook *E-mail:* ruth@rrbookcompany.com
Founded: 2005

Publisher sales & marketing representatives.
Represents Actar Publishing; Child's Play; Firefly; Free Spirit; Gardner Publishing; Gryphon House; Holiday House; Peachtree; Pepin; Prestel; Ronnie Sellers Productions
Territory: USA

Raincoast Books Distribution Ltd
2440 Viking Way, Richmond, BC V6V 1N2, Canada
SAN: 115-0871
Tel: 604-448-7100 *Toll Free Tel:* 800-663-5714 (CN only) *Fax:* 604-270-7161
  Toll Free Fax: 800-565-3770
E-mail: info@raincoast.com; customerservice@raincoast.com
Web Site: www.raincoast.com
Key Personnel
CEO: John Sawyer *E-mail:* johns@raincoast.com
Head, Raincoast Books: Peter MacDougall
  E-mail: pete@raincoast.com
VP, Mktg: Jamie Broadhurst *E-mail:* jamie@raincoast.com
Founded: 1979
Distributor for Alma Books; Beginning Press; Bilingual Books; Bloomsbury; Chronicle Books; CollegeBoard; The Do Book Co; Drawn & Quarterly; Entangled Publishing; Familius; Farrar, Straus and Giroux; Feiwel & Friends; Figure 1; First Second; Flatiron Books; Graywolf Press; Hardie Grant; Henry Holt & Co; Houghton Mifflin Harcourt; Imprint; Laurence King; Kingfisher; Lonely Planet; Macmillan Audio; Macmillan Children's Publishing Group; Magnetic Poetry; Media Lab Books; Minotaur; Mountaineers Books; New Harbinger Publications; Osprey; Page Two; Papercutz; Picador; Priddy Books; Princeton Architectural Press; Prufrock Press; Quadrille; St Martin's Press; Gibbs Smith; Sourcebooks; The Tite Group; Tor/Forge; Twirl; Wattpad Books
Represents Alma Books; Beginning Press; Bilingual Books; Bloomsbury; Chronicle Books; CollegeBoard; The Creative Co; The Do Book Co; Drawn & Quarterly; Entangled Publishing; Familius; Farrar, Straus and Giroux; Feiwel & Friends; Figure 1; First Second; Flatiron Books; Graywolf Press; Hardie Grant; Henry Holt & Co; Houghton Mifflin Harcourt; Imprint; Laurence King; Kingfisher; Lonely Planet; Macmillan Audio; Macmillan Children's Publishing Group; Magnetic Poetry; Media Lab Books; Minotaur; Mountaineers Books; New Harbinger Publications; Osprey; Page Two; Papercutz; Picador; Priddy Books; Princeton Architectural Press; Prufrock Press; Quadrille; St Martin's Press; Gibbs Smith; Sourcebooks; The Tite Group; Tor/Forge; Twirl; Wattpad Books
Territory: Canada

RAM Publications & Distribution Inc
2525 Michigan Ave, Bldg A2, Santa Monica, CA 90404
Tel: 310-453-0043 *Fax:* 310-264-4888
E-mail: info@rampub.com; orders@rampub.com
Web Site: www.rampub.com
Key Personnel
Founder: Theresa Luisotti *E-mail:* theresa@rampub.com
Dir: Paul Schumacher *E-mail:* paul@rampub.com
Warehouse Mgr: John Melendez
Founded: 1984
Distributor for Alvar Aalto Foundation; AC Books; Arquine; Art 21 Inc; Armory Center for the Arts; Arvinius + Orfeus Publishing; Morris & Helen Belkin Art Gallery (University of British Columbia); BNN Inc; Book Works; Clouds; Eakins Press Foundation; Falkenstein Foundation; Fotohof Editions; Editions Patrick Frey; Inventory Press; Jap Sam Books; David Kordansky Gallery; LA Forum for Architecture

& Urban Design; Los Angeles Contemporary Exhibitions (LACE); M/M (Paris); Museum of Contemporary Art; Nohara Co Ltd; Office for Discourse Engineering; Onomatopee; Oslo Editions; Passenger Books; Post Editions; Raking Leaves; Rice University Architectural Dept; Ridinghouse; Santa Barbara Museum of Art; Smart Art Press; Snoeck Verlag; Spector Books; Sternberg Press; Wright

RAmEx Ars Medica Inc
Subsidiary of Rampertab American Exports Inc
1714 S Westgate Ave, No 2, Los Angeles, CA 90025-3852
SAN: 631-6573
Tel: 310-826-4964 *Toll Free Tel:* 800-633-9281
  Fax: 310-826-9674
E-mail: ars.medica@ramex.com
Web Site: www.ramex.com
Key Personnel
CEO: Ramesh Rampertab *Tel:* 310-826-3489
  E-mail: zerohourzulu@yahoo.com
Founded: 1994
International distributor of medical multimedia products including CD-ROMs, videos, slides, books & other software. Products are for reference, teaching, training, administration & research. Represent over 500 medical publishers.
Represents Academic Press; ADAM; Addison Wesley; AHC; American Academy of Orthopaedic Surgeons; American Diabetes Association; American Hospital Association; American Psychiatric Publishing Inc; American Society of Health-System Pharmacists; Andromeda Software Inc; Aspen Publishers; ASTM International; Auerbach Publishers; Belson/Hanwright Video; Blackwell Science; Blanchard & Loeb Publishers; Butterworth-Heinemann; Canon Communications LLC; Cardionics; CG; Chapman & Hall/CRC; Churchill-Livingstone; Ciba Geigy; Clinics in Motion; Concept Media; CP Inc; CRC Press; Creative Educational Options LLC; Critical Concepts; CTT; Benjamin Cummings; Current Medicine Inc; Current Science Group; Database Publishing Group; FA Davis Co; Marcel Dekker; Delmar; DP; DxR Development Group Inc; Elsevier Science; Facts & Comparisons; FITNE Electronic Vision Inc; Fleetwood; Food Chemical News; Franklin Electronic Publishers; G W Medical Publishing; Garland Science Publishing; Graphic Education Corp; Grey House Publishing; Harcourt Health Sciences; Health Professions Press; Health Stream Inc; Mike Holt Publications; Humana Press; Icon Learning Systems; IM; Informa Healthcare; Ingenix; Intercollegiate Center for Nursing Education; International Thompson Publishing; Johns Hopkins University Press; Lange Video Production; Lewis Publishers; Lexi-Comp; LifeART; Lippincott Williams & Wilkins; Mayo Clinic Scientific Press; McGraw-Hill; Medcom-Trainex Inc; Medical Economics Co; Medical Multimedia Systems; Medicode; Medifor Inc; Meds Publishing; Merck; Miscellaneous Publishers; Mosby; National Technical Information Services; NEVCO; Novartis; Nursing Videos; Oxford University Press; Parthenon Publishing; Pearson Education; Pharmaceutical Press; Prentice Hall; Primal Pictures; Professional Pharmaceutical Index; Quality Medical Publishing; Reality Surgery; Relax Herbals & Exports Pvt Ltd; St Anthony Publishing; St Lucie Press; WB Saunders; Scientific American Medicine; Seak Inc; Silver Platter Information; Software & Medical Image SL; Spellex Corp; Springer-Verlag; Springhouse Publishing; Stedman's; Stethographics Inc; Stokes Publishing Co; Taylor & Francis; Thieme Medical Publishing; Thomson Healthcare; TVMED Corp; US Government Publications; US Pharmacopoeia; Vi Me S Publishing; Victory Technology; Virtual Learning Center; WebMD; John Wiley & Sons

Publishing Inc; John Wiley Current Protocols;
Yale/CAIM
Territory: worldwide

Readerlink Distribution Services LLC
1420 Kensington Rd, Suite 300, Oakbrook, IL
60523-2164
SAN: 169-197X
Tel: 708-547-4400 *Toll Free Tel:* 800-549-5389
E-mail: info@readerlink.com;
marketingservices@readerlink.com
Web Site: www.readerlink.com
Key Personnel
Pres, Chmn & CEO: Dennis Abboud
EVP & COO: John Bode
EVP & Chief Mktg Offr: David Barker
SVP, Fin & Busn Analytics: Jeremy Armer
SVP, Mktg & Procurement: Corey Berger
SVP, Sales: David Travettoo
VP, Enterprise Analytics: Kyle Marx
VP, Prod Mgmt & Mktg: John Norris
VP, Publr Rel & Mktg: Kristin Bartelme
Founded: 2011
Full service distributor of hardcover, trade & pa-
perback books to non-trade channel booksellers
in North America.
Branch Office(s)
812 SW Raintree Lane, Suite 6, Bentonville, AR
72712 *Tel:* 479-464-4932
50 S Tenth St, Suite 600, Minneapolis, MN
55403 *Tel:* 612-339-3249

Renouf Publishing Co Ltd
22-1010 Polytek St, Ottawa, ON K1J 9J1, Canada
Tel: 613-745-2665 *Toll Free Tel:* 866-767-6766;
888-551-7470 (North America) *Fax:* 613-745-
7660
E-mail: order.dept@renoufbooks.com
Web Site: www.renoufbooks.com
Key Personnel
Pres: Gordon Grahame *E-mail:* g.grahame@
renoufbooks.com
Compt: Sheena Challenger
Gen Mgr: Brigid Grahame
Serials Mgr: Lise St-Jean
Mktg Coord: Lucy Dodds
Founded: 1888
Distributor of governmental, international, busi-
ness, environment, health, social & legal publi-
cations. With offices in Canada & the US, the
company distributes throughout North America
& worldwide.
Branch Office(s)
808 Commerce Park Dr, Ogdensburg, NY 13669-
2208 *Toll Free Fax:* 888-551-7471
Distributor for Asian Development Bank; Cana-
dian Government Publishing; The Common-
wealth Secretariat; Council of Europe; Food
& Agriculture Organization; The C D Howe
Institute; IDRC Books; International Atomic
Energy Agency; International Labour Organization (ILO); International Monetary Fund
(IMF); Office for Official Publications of the
European Communities; Organization for Eco-
nomic Cooperation & Development (OECD);
TSO; UNESCO; United Nations Association
in Canada; United Nations Environment Pro-
gramme (UNEP); United Nations Publications;
United States Government Printing Office;
The World Bank; World Health Organization
(WHO); World Intellectual Property Organi-
zation; World Meteorological Organization;
World Organization for Animal Health; World
Tourism Organization; World Trade Organiza-
tion
Territory: worldwide
Membership(s): The American Library Associa-
tion (ALA)

Rights & Distribution Inc
7519 LaPaz Blvd, Suite C303, Boca Raton, FL
33433

Tel: 954-925-5242
E-mail: rightsinc@aol.com
Key Personnel
Pres & Publr: Donald L Lessne
Founded: 1943
The only company in the US that sells both for-
eign rights & handles all foreign distribution
for our small & medium-sized publishers.
Distributor for Bancroft Press; Bartleby Press;
Frederick Fell Publishers; Gulliver Publishing;
YMAA Publication Center
Territory: USA, worldwide

St Catharines Museum
1932 Welland Canals Pkwy, RR 6, St Catharines,
ON L2R 7K6, Canada
Mailing Address: PO Box 3012, St Catharines,
ON L2R 7C2, Canada
Tel: 905-984-8880 *Toll Free Tel:* 800-305-5134
Fax: 905-984-6910
E-mail: museum@stcatharines.ca
Web Site: www.stcatharines.ca
Key Personnel
Supv, Museum Opers & Curator: Kathleen Powell
Publishing & retail sales.

Saunders Book Co
Division of Saunders Office & School Supplies
Ltd
PO Box 308, Collingwood, ON L9Y 3Z7, Canada
Tel: 705-445-4777 *Toll Free Tel:* 800-461-9120
Fax: 705-445-9569 *Toll Free Fax:* 800-561-
1763
E-mail: info@saundersbook.ca
Web Site: librarybooks.com
Key Personnel
Pres: John Saunders *Fax:* 705-445-5804
E-mail: johns@saundersbook.ca
VP, Direct Sales: James Saunders
E-mail: jamess@saundersbook.ca
Dir, Mktg: Carol Saunders *Tel:* 800-461-9120
ext 2000 *Fax:* 705-445-5804 *E-mail:* carols@
saundersbook.ca
Gen Mgr: Judy Purdy
Sales to schools, public libraries & school/library
wholesalers.
Distributor for Mason Crest
Represents Amicus; Arcturus Publishing Ltd;
Beech Street Books; Bellwether Media; Black
Rabbit Books; Brown Bear Books; Cherry
Lake Publishing; Creative Editions; Creative
Education; Lerner Publishing Group Inc; Mill-
brook; Reference Point Press; Saddleback Ed-
ucational Publishing; Smart Apple Media; 12-
Story Press; 21st Century
Territory: Canada

SCB Distributors
Subsidiary of ABP Inc
15608 S New Century Dr, Gardena, CA 90248
Tel: 310-532-9400 *Toll Free Tel:* 800-729-6423
Fax: 310-532-7001
E-mail: scb@scbdistributors.com
Web Site: www.scbdistributors.com
Key Personnel
Pres: Aaron Silverman *E-mail:* aaron@
scbdistributors.com
Gen Mgr: Victor Duran *E-mail:* victor@
scbdistributors.com
Sales & Mktg Mgr: Gabriel Wilmoth
E-mail: gabriel@scbdistributors.com
Full service distributor, fulfillment, order entry,
national sales representation.
Distributor for Acrobat Books; Adventures Un-
limited Press; Editions Akileos; Alchimia;
Amok Books; Anacapa Press; Arcata Arts;
Sherman Asher Publishing; Atides Publish-
ing; Auad Publishing; Ayerware Publishing;
Baby Tattoo Books; Bascom-Hall Publishing;
BDSM Press; Belly Kids; BEST Life Media;
Beyond Binary Books; Aaron Blake Publish-
ers; Blenheim Press; Blind Eye Books; Blue

Bird Press; Bluewater Productions; Bluewood
Books; Braided Worlds Publishing; Bristol
Books; Bullet Point Publishing; CCNM Press;
Centrala; Chopra Center Press; Circlet Press
Inc; Clarity Press Inc; CLU Press; Coffee Table
Comics; CRCS Publications; Creation Books;
Creation Oneiros; Cricket Feet Publishing;
Daedalus Publishing; Daje Publishing; Dam-
ron Guides; Dancing Hands Music; Daniel
& Daniel Publishers; Dark Dragon Books;
Dedalus Ltd; Deicide Press; Devastator Press;
Dokument Press; Down There Press; Dunhill
Publishing; Ermor Enterprises; FAB Press; Fair
Oaks Press; Food for Talk; Fox Music Books;
Fox Women's Books; Freedom Press; From
Here to Fame; Gatehouse Publishing; Ghost &
Co; Glorian Publishing; Goliath Books; Gorsky
Press; Gothic Image Publications; Grand Cen-
tral Press; Greenery Press; Happy Hen Books;
Headpress; Hohm Press; Hybrid Cinema; I
Love Mel; Iam8bit Productions; IamCoach
Publishing; Illustre Books; Infilpress; Ingenuity
Press; Inner Health Books; Inner Travel Books;
International Neighborhood; K Publications;
Kahboom; Kalindi Press; Kingyo Press; Kontur
Publishing; Kopetkai Press; Lange Media; Lasp
Gasp; Lebowski Publishers; Herb Lester As-
sociates; Lightpoint Press; Limehouse Books;
Luxe City Guides; MapMania Publishing; Mas-
teryear Publishing; McCarty PhotoWorks; Milk
Mug Publishing; Mindpower Press; New Cen-
tury Publishers; Nicotext; One Love Books;
One Peace Books; Over & Above Creative;
Overcup Press; Pacific Highlands Press; Penny-
Ante Editions; Perseverance Press; Pet Friendly
Publications; Pier 99 Publishing; Polair Pub-
lishing; Power Press; Quarry Press; Quintessen-
tial Healing Inc; Quotable Zodiac Publishing;
Ram Publishing; Rankin Photography; Raw
Vision; Resources for Infant Educators (RIE);
Rock Out Books; Rock Point Press; Russell
Enterprises Inc; RVP Publishers; Scratter &
Pomace; Sedona Press; September Publishing;
Shake It!; Shinbaku Books; Silver Lake Pub-
lishing; Soaring Penguin Press; Soundcheck
Books; Steller Press; Street Smart Press; Sugoi
Books; Sun Vision Press; Synergetic Press;
Tallfellow Press; Tangent Books; Tavin Press;
The Temple Publications; Terra Nova Books;
Three Wings Press; Toddler Press; Twisted
Spoon Press; Merlin Unwin Books; Vidov Pub-
lishing; Vision Sports Publishing; We Heard
You Like Books; Wet Angel Books; Winged
Horse Publishing; Wisdom Tree Publishers;
Wizarding World Press; Wolf Creek Books;
Wordslinger Press; Write Bloody Publishing
Territory: Canada, USA

Scholarly Book Services Inc
289 Bridgeland Ave, Unit 105, Toronto, ON M6A
1Z6, Canada
Toll Free Tel: 800-847-9736 *Toll Free Fax:* 800-
220-9895
E-mail: customerservice@sbookscan.com
Web Site: www.sbookscan.com
Key Personnel
Pres & CEO: Laura Rust *E-mail:* laura@
sbookscan.com
Distributors & sales representatives for university,
literary & specialist presses in Canada.
Distributor for Boydell & Brewer Inc; Cork Uni-
versity Press; International Society for Technol-
ogy in Education; Kent State University Press;
Liberty Fund Books; Louisiana State University
Press (CN only); Marquette University Press
(CN only); Minnesota Historical Society Press;
Naval Institute Press; Northwestern Univer-
sity Press; Notre Dame University Press; Ohio
University Press; Oklahoma University Press;
Polebridge Publishing; Purdue University Press
(CN only); Rutgers University Press (CN only);
Southern Illinois University Press (CN only);
Syracuse University Press; Texas A&M Univer-

sity Press; University of Arkansas Press; University of Hawaii Press (CN only); University of Illinois Press (CN only); University of Missouri Press (CN only); University of Nevada Press (CN only); University of North Carolina Press (CN only); University of Pennsylvania Press (CN only); University of Pittsburgh Press (CN only); University of South Carolina Press (CN only); University of the West Indies; University of Virginia Press (CN only); University Press of Florida (CN only); University Press of Kansas; University Press of Mississippi (CN only); Vanderbilt University Press; Wayne State University Press (CN only); World Scientific Publishing (CN only)
Territory: Canada

Scholar's Choice Ltd
2323 Trafalgar St, London, ON N5Y 5S7, Canada
Mailing Address: PO Box 7214, London, ON N5Y 5S7, Canada
Tel: 519-453-7470 *Toll Free Tel:* 800-265-1095
Fax: 519-455-2853 *Toll Free Fax:* 800-363-3398 (CN only)
E-mail: sales@scholarschoice.ca
Web Site: www.scholarschoice.ca
Key Personnel
Pres: Scott Webster
Founded: 1952
Distributor & retailer of educational toys & teaching materials to parents, teachers & early childhood educators in Canada & around the world. 25 retail locations in Canada.
Distributor for Check & Double Check Workbooks; Scholar's Choice
Territory: North America

Scholastic Book Fairs®
Division of Scholastic Inc
1080 Greenwood Blvd, Lake Mary, FL 32746
Tel: 407-829-8000 *Fax:* 407-829-2600
E-mail: custservbf@scholasticbookfairs.com
Web Site: www.scholastic.com/bookfairs
Key Personnel
Pres & EVP, Scholastic Inc: Sasha Quinton
VP, Busn Devt & Strategy: Ben Stone
VP, Fin: Phil Bernhardt
VP, Sales & Serv (North): Jeff Marty
VP, Sales & Serv (South): Shane Kyle
VP, Mktg: Laura Lundgren
VP, Prod Category Mgmt: Eric Compton
VP, Field Deployment & Optimization: Brian Carter
VP, HR: Tim Vuolo
Founded: 1981
Scholastic Book Fairs®, in partnership with schools across the country, hosts more than 120,000 book-sale events each year, reaching more than 35 million children & their families in preschool-9th grade. Book Fairs provide students, teachers & parents access to thousands of affordable books & educational products & is responsible for putting more than 100 million books in the hands of children, helping to foster enthusiasm for reading & generating more than $200 million annually in fundraising for school projects & classroom materials.

Small Press Distribution Inc
1341 Seventh St, Berkeley, CA 94710-1409
SAN: 204-5826
Tel: 510-524-1668 *Toll Free Tel:* 800-869-7553 (within the US) *Fax:* 510-524-0852
E-mail: spd@spdbooks.org
Web Site: www.spdbooks.org
Key Personnel
Interim Exec Dir: Cindy Myers
Mng Dir: Brent Cunningham *Tel:* 510-524-1668 ext 308 *E-mail:* brent@spdbooks.org
Fin Dir: Andrew Pai *E-mail:* andrew@spdbooks.org

Data Mgr: Janice Worthen *E-mail:* janice@spdbooks.org
Publicity Mgr: Trisha Low *E-mail:* trisha@spdbooks.org
Warehouse Mgr: John Sakkis *E-mail:* john@spdbooks.org
Cust Serv Coord: Johnny Hernandez *E-mail:* johnny@spdbooks.org
Cust Serv & Publicity Assoc: Ari Banias *E-mail:* ari@spdbooks.org
Founded: 1969
Book distribution, information services & public advocacy programs to hundreds of small publishers. Dedicated exclusively to independently published literature.
Represents A Barnacle Book; Able Muse Press; Acre Books; Action Books; Ad Lumen Press; Adastra Press; Adventures in Poetry; Aequitas Books; Aforementioned Productions; Agincourt Press; Ahadada Books; Ahsahta Press; Airlie Press; AJAR; Allardyce, Barnett, Publishers; Almost Island; American Books; Androgyne Books; Anhinga Press; Annex Press; Anomalous Press; Antilever Press; AntiSentimental Society; Anvil Press; Apogee Press; Apostrophe Books; Aquarius Press; Arctos Press; Argos Books; Ashland Poetry Press; Astrophil Press; Atelos; Audubon Terrace Press; Augury Books; Aunt Lute Books; Ausubo Press; Autonomedia; Avenue B; Avian Press; Awst Press; Ayin Press; Aztlan Libre Press; Bamberger Books; Bamboo Ridge Press; Barrelhouse Books; Barrow Street Press; Bateau Press; Bear Star Press; Belladonna; Benu Press; Beyond Baroque Press; Big Lucks Books; Big Sky Books; Bilingual Review Press; Bird Dog Publishing; Birds LLC; Bitingduck Press; Bitter Cherry Books; The Bitter Oleander Press; BkMk Press; Black Lawrence Press; Black Ocean; Black Radish Books; Black Square Editions; Black Sun Lit; Blackberry Books; Blaft Publications; BlazeVOX Books; BOAAT Press; Bona Fide Books; BookThug; Bootstrap Press; Bordighera Press; BOTH BOTH Books; Box Turtle Press; Braddock Avenue Books; Brick Books; BrightCity Books; Bright Hill Press; Broadstone Books; Bronx Museum/Phoenix Art Museum; Bronx River Press; Brooklyn Arts Press; Browser Books Publishing; Bull City Press; Bureau of Public Secrets; Burning Books; Burning Deck; Burnside Review; C&R Press; Cadmus Editions; Cahuenga Press; Calamari Press; Canarium Books; Cape Ann Museum; Caravel Mystery Books; Cardboard House Press; Carville Annex Press; CDA Press; Center for the Humanities, The Graduate Center, CUNY; Ceratonia Siliqua Press; Cervena Barva Press; ChainLinks; Chax Press; Chelsea Editions; Chicago Network for Justice & Peace; China Books; Dr Cicero Books; Cider Press Review; City Lights Publishers; Cleveland State University Poetry Center; co-impress; Coconut Books; Combo Books; Compline; Content; Convolution; Cool Grove Press; Copper Beech Press; Copper Canyon Press; Cordite Books; Counterpath Press; Cracked Slab Books; Creative Arts Book Co; Cross-Cultural Communications; Crown Point Press; Cubanabooks; The Cultural Society; Cuneiform Press; Cypher Books; Deerbrook Editions; Delete Press; Dialogos; Displaced Press; Dock Street Press; Dorothy, A Publishing Project; Dos Gatos Press; Dos Madres Press; Downstate Legacies; Dracopis Press; Drunken Boat Media; Drunken Boat Media/Ethos Books; Durga Press; Dryad Press; East Bay Municipal Utility District; Edge Books; Edition Muta; Edition Solitude; Editions Michel Eyquem; ElephantEars Press; The Elephants; Eleven Eleven; Elis Press; Elixir Press; ELJ Editions; Ellipsis Press; Empty Bowl; Entasis Press; Entre Rios Books; EOAGH Books; Equus Press; Essay Press; etruscan books; EXIT Press; Eyewear Publishing; Factory Hollow Press; Fac-

tory School; Fairy Tale Review Press; Fast Forward Press; Faux Press; Fence; Fiction Advocate; Fifth Planet Press; 53rd State Press; Les Figues Press; The Figures; firthFORTH; Five Seasons Press; Flood Editions; Flow Press; Fonograf Editions; Forthcoming Books; 42 Miles Press; 421 Atlanta; Fourteen Hills Press; Frank/Wynkin de Worde; French Connection Press; Furniture Press Books; Further Other Book Works; Future Tense Books; Futurepoem Books; Garland Press; GenPop Books; Georgetown Review Press; Get Fresh Books LLC; The Gig; Gnomon Press; Gold Line Press; Gorgeous Notions Press; John Gosslee Books; Gramma Poetry; The (Great) Indian Poetry Collective; Green Lantern Press; Green Mountains Review Books; The Greenfield Review Press; Greenhouse Review Press; Grey Fox; Grid Books; Grolier Poetry Press; Groundhog Poetry Press LLC; The Groundwater Press; Hambone; Hanging Loose Press; Harbor Mountain Press; The Head & The Hand Press; Hobart & William Smith College Press/Seneca Review Books; Hobblebush Books; W D Hoffstadt & Sons; Holland Park Press; Holon Press; Horse Less Press; Host Publications; House of Nehesi Publishers; Howling Bird Press; Ibis Editions; ID8; IF SF Publishing; Imprint Press Inc; Inanna Publications; Information as Material; Ink; Inkworks Press; Insert Press; Instance Press; Instar Books; Intermezzo Press; Invisible Publishing; Ithuriel's Spear; Itna Press; ixnay press; Jambu Press; JEF Books; Jensen/Daniels Publishers; Juan de la Cosa; Junction Press; Kalina; Kasva Press LLC; Kat Ran Press; Kaya Press; Kelsey Street Press; Kelson Books; Kenning Editions; KERNPUNKT Press; Kiwai Media; Koja Press; kookbooks; Kore Press; Krupskaya; Lavender Ink; Linda Leith Publishing; El Leon Literary Arts; Leon Works; Leroy Chapbook Series; Letter Machine Editions; Libellum Books; LINEbooks; The Literary House Press; Lithic Press; Litmus Press; Litteraria Pragensia Books; Livingston Press; Logosophia LLC; Long River Press; Lost Roads Publishers; Loyola Marymount University & the Department of English; Luna Bisonte Prods; Lunar Chandelier Press; Luquer Street Press; Lyric & Press; Magic Helicopter Press; Make Now Press; Make Now Press/lx Press; MAMMOTH books; Mango Publishing; The Mantle; Many Mountains Moving Press; Many Voices Press; Manzanita Writers Press; Marfa Book Co; Marin Poetry Center Press; Marsh Hawk Press; Mawenzi House/TSAR Publishers; Mayapple Press; Mediumless; Meeting Eyes Bindery; Membrane Press; The Menard Press; Mercury House; Metatron; Metonymy Press; Miami University Press; A Midsummer Night's Press; Mimeo Mimeo; Missouri Review Books; Monk Books; Monster House Press; Mount Vision Press; Mouthfeel Press; MPMP; Muumuu House; Narrow House; National Poetry Foundation; Natural History Press; Negative Capability Press; New Herring Press; New Native Press; New Rivers Press; New Star Books; Night Heron Media; Nine Mile Press; 1913 Press; 99: The Press; Noctuary Press; Nocturnes Editions; Noemi Press; Nomadic Press; Nouvella; NYQ Books; O Books; Oblio Press; obnaZHENle priema; Octopus Books; Off the Park Press; Ohio Edit; Old Cove Press; ON Contemporary Practice; Open Field Press; The Operating System; Oread Press; Otis Books/Seismicity Editions; Otoliths; Outriders Poetry Project; Oyster Moon Press; PANK Books; Passager Books; Passing 4 Normal; Past Tents Press; Patmos Press; Pelekinesis; Peninsula Road Press; Penmanship Books; plain wrap press; Plays Inverse Press; Pleasure Boat Studio; Pleiades Press; Plein Air Editions; Poetic Matrix Press; Poetry Hotel Press; Poor Claudia; Portable Press at Yo-Yo Labs; The Post-Apollo Press; Prelude; Press Other-

wise; La Presse; Pressed Wafer; Presses Universitaires de Rouen; Publishing Genius Press; Quale Press; Quantum Prose; Quercus Review Press; Racing Form Press; Rail Editions; Rain Mountain Press; RAW ArT PRESS; Red Dragonfly Press; Red Dust; The Red Hill Press; Red Letter Press; Red Mountain Press; RedBone Press; Redwood Coast Press; Rescue Press; Resonant Books; Ricochet Editions; The Ridgeway Press; Rixdorf Editions; Rocky Ledge; Rogue Art; Ronsdale Press; Roof Books; Rose Metal Press; Roundabout Press; Rumor Books/Listening Chamber; Sagging Meniscus Press; San Francisco Bay Press; Sand Paper Press; Sator Press; Saturnalia Books; Scablands Books; Scarlet Tanager Books; Scrambler Books; Secretary Press; SeedStar Books; selva oscura press; Senal; Sententia Books; Seoul Selection; Shade Mountain Press; Shark Books; Shearsman Books; Short Flight/Long Drive Press; Side Street Press; Sidebrow Books; sight / for / sight books; Silverfish Review Press; Singing Horse Press; Six Gallery Press; Sixteen Rivers Press; Skeleton Man; Slapering Hol Press; Slope Editions; Small Doggies Press; Soberscove Press; Solid Objects; The Song Cave; Soultheft Records Inc; Southern Indiana Review Press; Split Shift; SplitLevel Texts; Spork Press; Spout Press; SpringGun Press; Spurl Editions; Standing Stone Books; Station Hill Press of Barrytown; Steerage Press; A Strange Object; Straw Gate Books; Subito Press; Subpress; sunnyoutside; Supermachine; Swan Scythe Press; Switchback Books; Synecdoche; Talisman House, Publishers; The Tangent Press; Tarpaulin Sky Press; Taurean Horn Press; Tavern Books; Tebot Bach; Tender Buttons Press; Test Centre; theenk Books; There Press; This Press; Thoughtcrime Press; Three Count Pour; 3 Hole Press; Three Mile Harbor Press; Tiger Bark Press; Timeless, Infinite Light; Tinderbox Editions; Tinfish Press; Tombouctou Books; Trembling Pillow Press; Tres Chicas Books; Trip Street Press; Triton Books; Truck Books; Tupelo Press; Tuumba Press; Twisted Road Publications; UCLA American Indian Studies Center; UCLA Asian American Studies Center; Ugly Duckling Presse; Un-Gyve Press; Unicorn Press; United Artists Books; Upper West Side Philosophers Inc; Vagabond Press; Vala Book Press; Vanitas; Vehicle Editions; Veliz Books; Verge Books; Viz. Inter-Arts; Volt; Wave Books; The Waywiser Press; Weavers Press; West of West Books; What Books Press; Whit Press; White Deer Books; Wild Ocean Press; Willow Springs Books; Wolf Ridge Press; Wolfman Books; Wonder; Word Riot Inc; The Word Works; WordFarm; World Poetry Books; WriteGirl Publications; Writers' Collective of Kristiania Inc; Writing Our World Press; WTAW Press; Xenos Books; YesYes Books; ZKM; Zone 3 Press
Territory: worldwide

Socadis Inc
Subsidiary of Groupe Madrigall
420 rue Stinson, Ville St-Laurent, QC H4N 3L7, Canada
Tel: 514-331-3300 *Toll Free Tel:* 800-361-2847 (CN only) *Fax:* 514-745-3282
Toll Free Fax: 866-803-5422
E-mail: socinfo@socadis.com; direction@socadis.com
Web Site: www.socadis.com
Key Personnel
Dir, Fin: Genevieve Castomguay
Founded: 1970
French language book distributor for 1,000 publishers.

Social Studies School Service
10200 Jefferson Blvd, PO Box 802, Culver City, CA 90232
Tel: 310-839-2436 *Toll Free Tel:* 800-421-4246 *Fax:* 310-839-2249 *Toll Free Fax:* 800-944-5432 (US & CN)
E-mail: access@socialstudies.com
Web Site: www.socialstudies.com
Key Personnel
CEO: David Weiner
Chief Learning Offr: Aaron Willis
Founded: 1965

Southern Territory Associates
4508 64 St, Lubbock, TX 79414
E-mail: sta77@suddenlink.net
Web Site: www.southernterritory.com
Key Personnel
Pres: Geoff Rizzo *Tel:* 772-223-7776 *Fax:* 877-679-6913
Secy & Treas: Judy Stevenson
Assoc: Tom Caldwell *Tel:* 773-450-2695; Rayner Krause *Tel:* 972-618-1149 *Fax:* 972-618-1149; Teresa Rolfe Kravtin *Tel:* 706-882-9014 *Fax:* 706-882-4105; Angie Smits *Tel:* 336-574-1879 *Fax:* 336-275-3290
Founded: 1976
Represents Baker & Taylor Publisher Services (southeastern US & select southern states)
Territory: Alabama, Arkansas, Florida, Georgia, Louisiana, Mississippi, North Carolina, Oklahoma, South Carolina, Tennessee, Texas, Virginia

Southwest Book Co
Division of Scholastic Book Fairs®
13003 Murphy Rd, Suite H1, Stafford, TX 77477-3934
Tel: 281-498-2603 *Fax:* 281-498-7566
Key Personnel
Gen Mgr: Peter M Randles
Founded: 1980
Distribute paperbacks to book fairs & classrooms. Reading Is Fundamental programs.
Branch Office(s)
2956 Reward Lane, Dallas, TX 75220 *Tel:* 214-357-9656 *Fax:* 214-357-0222

SPD, see Small Press Distribution Inc

Spring Arbor Distributors Inc
Unit of Ingram Content Group LLC
One Ingram Blvd, La Vergne, TN 37086-1986
Toll Free Tel: 800-395-4340 *Toll Free Fax:* 800-876-0186
E-mail: customerservice@ingramcontent.com
Web Site: www.ingramcontent.com
Key Personnel
Sales Rep: Mary Lou Alexander *Tel:* 615-213-3319 *E-mail:* marylou.alexander@ingramcontent.com
Founded: 1978
Distributor of Christian books, Bibles, music & video, to Christian retail stores.
Branch Office(s)
Indiana Distribution Center, 7315 Innovation Blvd, Fort Wayne, IN 46818-1371
Oregon Distribution Center, 201 Ingram Dr, Roseburg, OR 97471
Chambersburg Distribution Center, 1240 Ingram Dr, Chambersburg, PA 17202

Stylus Publishing LLC
22883 Quicksilver Dr, Sterling, VA 20166-2019
SAN: 299-1853
Tel: 703-661-1504 (edit & sales); 703-661-1581 (orders & cust serv); 703-996-1036 *Toll Free Tel:* 800-232-0223 (orders & cust serv) *Fax:* 703-661-1547; 703-661-1501 (orders & cust serv)

E-mail: stylusinfo@styluspub.com; stylusmail@styluspub.com (orders & cust serv)
Web Site: styluspub.presswarehouse.com
Key Personnel
Pres & Publr: John von Knorring *E-mail:* jvk@styluspub.com
VP, Mktg & Publicity Mgr: Andrea Ciecierski *Tel:* 703-996-1036 *E-mail:* andrea@styluspub.com
Mktg Mgr, Educ & Higher Educ: Patricia Webb *E-mail:* patricia@styluspub.com
Sales & Mktg Admin: Jane Leathem *E-mail:* jane.leathem@styluspub.com
Founded: 1996
Publishes in higher education. Distributes books for trade, education, engineering, higher education, scholarly, professional & NGO markets in the following subjects: agriculture, business, education, environment & conservation, international studies, Third World development, politics & policy, public health, psychology & psychotherapy.
Distributor for Baseball Prospectus; Cabi Books; Campus Compact; Commonwealth Scientific & Industrial Research Organization (CSIRO); CSREA; Mercury Learning & Information; Myers Education Press; National Resource Center for The First-Year Experience & Students in Transition; River Publishers; Thorogood Publishing; Trentham Books Ltd; UCL IOE Press; World Health Organization (WHO)
Represents Baseball Prospectus; Cabi Books; Campus Compact; Commonwealth Scientific & Industrial Research Organization (CSIRO); CSREA; Mercury Learning & Information; Myers Education Press; National Resource Center for The First-Year Experience & Students in Transition; River Publishers; Thorogood Publishing; Trentham Books Ltd; UCL IOE Press; World Health Organization (WHO)
Territory: North America, South America

Chip Taylor Communications LLC
2 East View Dr, Derry, NH 03038
Tel: 603-434-9262 *Toll Free Tel:* 800-876-2447 *Fax:* 603-432-2723
Web Site: www.chiptaylor.com
Key Personnel
Pres: Chip Taylor
Founded: 1985
Producer, distributor of 4,000+ exclusive DVDs, streaming digital files, videos, associated books, posters & CDs for educators, librarians, TV programmers & the home use markets.
Distributor for SquareOne Publishers Inc
Represents SquareOne Publishers Inc
Territory: worldwide
Membership(s): AASL; AIME; The American Library Association (ALA); Consortium of College & University Media Centers (CCUMC); Music Business Association (Music Biz); National Association of Media & Technology Centers (NAMTC); National Association of Television Program Executives (NATPE); National Science Teachers Association (NSTA); NSBA; Public Library Association (PLA)

Teacher's Discovery®
Division of American Eagle Co Inc
2741 Paldan Dr, Auburn Hills, MI 48326
Toll Free Tel: 800-TEACHER (832-2437) *Toll Free Fax:* 800-287-4509
E-mail: help@teachersdiscovery.com; orders@teachersdiscovery.com
Web Site: www.teachersdiscovery.com
Key Personnel
Owner: Skip McWilliams
Dir, Mktg: Steve Giroux
Founded: 1968
Sell supplemental classroom teaching materials for Spanish, French, German, English & Social Studies. See www.vocesdigital.com for prize-winning digital courseware (e-textbooks).

Terry & Read LLC
4471 Dean Martin Dr, The Martin 3302, Las Vegas, NV 89103
Tel: 510-813-9854 *Toll Free Fax:* 866-214-4762
Key Personnel
Dir: David M Terry *E-mail:* dmterry@aol.com
Assoc: Alan Read
Founded: 1943
Represents Atlas Books; Babalu Inc; Brookings; Casemate; Catholic University Press; Holiday House; Johns Hopkins University Press; Illinois University Press; International Publishers Marketing (IPM); Jessica Kingsley; Louisiana State University Press; North Carolina University Press; Springer; Stylus Publications; Transaction Publishers; University of Georgia; University of Mississippi; University of Texas Press; University of Toronto; University of Wisconsin Press
Territory: Alaska, Arizona, California, Colorado, Hawaii, Idaho, Montana, Nevada, New Mexico, Oregon, Utah, Washington, Wyoming
Membership(s): American Booksellers Association (ABA)

David M Terry, see Terry & Read LLC

Thomas Allen & Son Ltd
195 Allstate Pkwy, Markham, ON L3R 4T8, Canada
SAN: 115-1762
Tel: 905-475-9126 *Toll Free Tel:* 800-387-4333
Fax: 905-475-6747 *Toll Free Fax:* 800-458-5504
E-mail: info@t-allen.com
Web Site: www.thomasallen.ca
Key Personnel
Pres & CEO: T James Allen
Dir, Mktg & Publicity: David Glover
Natl Sales Mgr: Darryl Scott
Founded: 1916
Distribution, marketing & publishing to the Canadian book trade.
Represents Algonquin Books; Algonquin Young Readers; Amazon Publishing; Artisan; Brilliance Audio; Carlton Publishing Group; Cottage Door Press; duopress LLC; Flowerpot Press; Fox Chapel Publishing; Robert Frederick; Interlink Publishing; Lerner Publishing Group Inc; Llewellyn Publications; Merriam-Webster Inc; Midnight Ink; North Parade Publishing Ltd; Ryland, Peters & Small; Schiffer Publishing Ltd; Square One Publishers; Storey Publishing; Timber Press; Willow Creek Press; Workman Publishing Co; Yankee/The Old Farmer's Almanac
Territory: Canada
Membership(s): BookNetCanada

Tri-Fold Books
PO Box 534, King City, ON L7B 1A7, Canada
Tel: 905-726-0142 *Fax:* 905-727-1068
E-mail: info@trifoldbooks.com
Key Personnel
Owner & Prop: Gabriele Freydank
Founded: 1982
Distribution to book trade, institutions, schools & libraries. Mail order to general public.
Distributor for Bell Pond Books (USA); Bio-Dynamic Literature (USA); Claiview Book (UK); Floris Books (UK); Hawthorne Press (UK); Lindisfarne Books (USA); New Trends Publishing (USA); Rudolf Steiner Press (UK); SteinerBooks (USA); Temple Lodge Publishing (UK)
Represents Bell Pond Books (USA); Bio-Dynamic Literature (USA); Hawthorne Press (UK); Lindisfarne Books (USA); Rudolf Steiner Press (UK); SteinerBooks (USA); Temple Lodge Publishing (UK)
Territory: Canada

Two Rivers Distribution, an Ingram brand
Member of Ingram Publisher Services
1400 Broadway, Suite 520, New York, NY 10018
Toll Free Tel: 866-400-5351
E-mail: ips@ingramcontent.com (orders, independent bookstores & gift accts)
Web Site: www.tworiversdistribution.com
Key Personnel
VP & Gen Mgr: Sabrina McCarthy
Dir: Nick Parker
Mgr, Client Rel: Louisa Brody; Jessica Morales
Founded: 1999
Sales, print, ebook & distribution services for independent publishers.
Branch Office(s)
IPS Jackson, 193 Edwards Dr, Jackson, TN 38301 (shipping) *Toll Free Tel:* 800-343-4499 *Toll Free Fax:* 800-351-5073
E-mail: ipsjacksonorders@ingramcontent.com
Distributor for Abbeville Press; American Academy of Pediatrics; Architecture/Interiors Press; Assouline; Bard Press; Bella Books; Black Dog Publishing Ltd London; Brisance Books Group; CompanionHouse; David & Charles Ltd; Distributed Art Publishers; Easton Studio Press; Encounter Books; G Editions; Girl Friday Books; David R Godine Inc; Hamilcar Publications; Handheld Press; Harvard Business Review Press; Hippocrene Books; Humanix Books; The Infatuation Inc; Justice Studios; LifeLines; Melcher Media Inc; Merrell Publishers; The New Press; Park Avenue Publishers; Pear Press; Penguin Random House Grupo Editorial; Peterson's; Planeta Publishing Corp; Plata Publishing; Platform Books; RDA Press LLC; Regnery Publishing; Editorial Reverte SA; SelectBooks; Seven Press; Spiegel & Grau; Spry Publishing LLC; Starry Forest Books; Ta-Da! Language Productions; Waterside Publishing; Welbeck Publishing Group; WS Publishing Group; ZAGAT Survey
Territory: USA

P Tyrrell Associates
321 Monica Crescent, Burlington, ON L7N 1Z5, Canada
Tel: 289-937-6436 *Fax:* 905-639-2640
E-mail: pgtyrrell@cogeco.ca
Key Personnel
Prop: Paul Tyrrell
Founded: 1991
Agent representing educational publishers.
Represents Curriculum Associates; McGraw-Hill/Macmillan; SRA
Territory: Southwestern Ontario

Ulverscroft Large Print (USA) Inc
Member of The Ulverscroft Group
950A Union Rd, Suite 427, West Seneca, NY 14224
Mailing Address: PO Box 1230, West Seneca, NY 14224-1230
Tel: 716-674-4270; 905-637-8734 (CN)
Toll Free Tel: 800-955-9659; 888-860-3365 (CN) *Fax:* 716-674-4195; 905-333-6788 (CN)
E-mail: sales@ulverscroftusa.com; sales@ulverscroftcanada.com (CN)
Web Site: www.ulverscroft.com
Key Personnel
Dir: Charlene Kessel
Sales of large print books, unabridged & abridged audiobooks & CDs.

University of Toronto Press Guidance Centre
Division of University of Toronto Press
5201 Dufferin St, Toronto, ON M3H 5T8, Canada
Tel: 416-667-7791 *Toll Free Tel:* 800-565-9523
Fax: 416-667-7832 *Toll Free Fax:* 800-221-9985
E-mail: utpbooks@utpress.utoronto.ca
Web Site: www.utpguidancecentre.com
Key Personnel
Mgr: Cindy Hall *Tel:* 416-667-8731
E-mail: chall@utpress.utoronto.ca
Distributes a variety of resources in all areas of education for teachers, teacher educators, administrators, school board members, students & parents.
Distributor for Alta Book Centre; ALTA English Publishers; Boys Town Press; Brookes Publishing Co; Corwin; Gryphon House Inc; Guidance Centre; Kaplan Press; The Laboratory School at the Dr Eric Jackman Institute of Child Study, Ontario Institute for Studies in Education; NSTA Press; Pippin Publishing; Prometheus Nemesis Book Co; Rec Room Publishing; Teachers College Press; University of Toronto Press; University of Toronto Press, Higher Education Division; University of Toronto Press, Scholarly Publishing Division; Woodbine House
Territory: Canada

USCIB International Bookstore
Division of United States Council for International Business
1212 Avenue of the Americas, 21st fl, New York, NY 10036
Tel: 212-703-5066 *Fax:* 212-944-0012
E-mail: bookstore@uscib.org
Web Site: store.internationaltradebooks.org
Founded: 1980
International trade including banking, commercial trade terms, law & arbitration, counterfeiting & fraud, model commercial contracts to advertising & environmental matters.

Christopher Ward & Co
11515 Kruhm Rd, Burtonsville, MD 20866
Tel: 860-355-8273
E-mail: cwardandco@gmail.com
Key Personnel
Owner: Chris Ward
Founded: 1978
Represents Leafwood Publishers
Territory: Mid-Atlantic States

West Virginia Book Co
1125 Central Ave, Charleston, WV 25302
Tel: 304-342-1848 *Fax:* 304-343-0594
E-mail: wvbooks@wvbookco.com
Web Site: www.wvbookco.com
Key Personnel
Owner: Bill Clements
Founded: 1995
Distributor of WV books.
Distributor for Elk River Press; Mountain Memories Books; Pictorial Histories Publishing Co; Quarrier Press

Wimmer Cookbooks
Division of Mercury Printing, an RR Donnelley Co
4650 Shelby Air Dr, Memphis, TN 38118
Toll Free Tel: 800-548-2537 *Fax:* 901-363-1771
Web Site: www.wimmerco.com
Key Personnel
Acct Coord: Robyn Hite
Sales & Mktg: Terry Rayner
Founded: 1946
Development, publishing, manufacturing, marketing & distribution of cookbooks by nonprofit organizations or self-publishers.
Territory: USA

Worldwide Books
1001 W Seneca St, Ithaca, NY 14850-3342
Tel: 607-272-9200 *Toll Free Tel:* 800-473-8146 (US/CN orders only) *Fax:* 607-272-0239
E-mail: info@worldwide-artbooks.com
Web Site: www.worldwide-artbooks.com
Key Personnel
Pres: Mr Kelly M Fiske *E-mail:* fiske@worldwide-artbooks.com

Mgr, Exhibit Catalog Prog: Eileen Baker
  E-mail: ebaker@worldwide-artbooks.com
Mgr, Approval Plan Prog: David Fogel
  E-mail: dfogel@worldwide-artbooks.com
Founded: 1962
Library vendor specializing in the selection, review & distribution of museum & gallery exhibition catalogues from around the globe. Also supplying trade & university press books on art, architecture, design & photography. Approval plans available.
Membership(s): Art Libraries Society of North America (ARLIS/NA)

Wybel Marketing Group Inc
213 W Main St, Barrington, IL 60010
Tel: 847-382-0384; 847-382-0382
  Toll Free Tel: 800-323-5297 *Fax:* 847-382-0385
  Toll Free Fax: 800-595-5252
E-mail: bookreps@wybel.com

Key Personnel
Pres: Ronald J Prazuch *E-mail:* prazur@wybel.com
VP: Sheryl L Wybel *E-mail:* wybels@wybel.com
Assoc: Laurie Kendziora *E-mail:* lauriek@wybel.com; Bill McGarr *E-mail:* wdmgarr@aol.com
Founded: 1976
Sales representatives.
Territory: Midwestern States
Membership(s): American Booksellers Association (ABA); Midwest Independent Booksellers Association (MIBA)

Wholesalers — Activity Index

TEXTBOOKS - ELEMENTARY

TEXTBOOKS - SECONDARY

TEXTBOOKS - COLLEGE

UNIVERSITY PRESS BOOKS

Wholesalers

Included is a partial list of active book wholesalers, including wholesale remainder dealers (buyers of bulk remainder stock from publishers and other sources). *The American Book Trade Directory* (Information Today, Inc., 121 Chanlon Road, Suite G-20, New Providence, NJ 07974-2195) lists wholesalers (including paperback wholesalers), jobbers and remainder houses in all fields. See also **Book Exporters & Importers**.

A-M Church Supply
3220 Bay Rd, Suite E, Saginaw, MI 48603
Tel: 989-249-9174 *Toll Free Tel:* 800-345-4694
Web Site: www.am-church.com
Key Personnel
Pres: Karrie Rapin-Klopp *E-mail:* rapin1974@
 yahoo.com
Founded: 1902
Religious goods, church supplies.
Number of Titles Warehoused: 300
Publication(s): *Annual catalog* (circ 1,200)

Adams Book Co Inc
80 Broad St, 5th fl, New York, NY 10004
Tel: 718-875-5464 *Toll Free Tel:* 800-221-0909
 Fax: 718-852-3212 *Toll Free Fax:* 888-229-
 2650
E-mail: customerservice@adamsbook.com;
 orders@adamsbook.com; sales@adamsbook.
 com; returns@adamsbook.com
Web Site: www.adamsbook.com
Key Personnel
VP: Glen Schattner
Founded: 1945
Textbooks, paperbacks, digital books & ebooks;
 all subjects for elementary through high school
 & college.

Mark A Adams Inc
425 Riverside Dr, New York, NY 10025
Tel: 212-864-0416 *Fax:* 212-316-6496
E-mail: mark@markadamsinc.com
Technical & medical text remainders.

AKJ Education
4702 Benson Ave, Halethorpe, MD 21227
Tel: 410-242-1602 *Toll Free Tel:* 800-922-6066
 Fax: 410-242-6107 *Toll Free Fax:* 888-770-
 2338
E-mail: info@akjeducation.com
Web Site: www.akjeducation.com
Key Personnel
Owner & Pres: Tim Thompson
Founded: 1974
Wholesaler of paperback books for schools &
 literacy programs.
Catalog available.
Number of Titles Warehoused: 25,000
Membership(s): Educational Book & Media Asso-
 ciation (EBMA)

American Camp Association Inc
5000 State Rd 67 N, Martinsville, IN 46151-7902
Tel: 765-342-8456 *Toll Free Tel:* 800-428-2267
 Fax: 765-342-2065
E-mail: contactus@acacamps.org
Web Site: www.acacamps.org
Key Personnel
Chief Prog Offr: Amy Katzenberger *Tel:* 765-349-
 3515 *E-mail:* akatzenberger@acacamps.org
Founded: 1910
Accreditation of children's camps; educational
 conferences & print resources (magazine &
 books), membership.
Catalog available.
Number of Titles Warehoused: 400

**American International Distribution Corp
 (AIDC)**
82 Winter Sport Lane, Williston, VT 05495

Mailing Address: PO Box 80, Williston, VT
 05495-0080
Tel: 802-862-0095 *Toll Free Tel:* 800-678-2432
 Fax: 802-864-7749
Web Site: www.aidcvt.com
Key Personnel
Pres & CEO: Marilyn McConnell
Dir, Opers: Michael Pelland
Founded: 1986
Fulfillment, credit, collections, reporting, cus-
 tomer service, data processing & subscriptions,
 continuity, call center, comprehensive suite of
 web services. Catalog available upon request.
Number of Titles Warehoused: 75,000
Membership(s): Book Industry Study Group
 (BISG); Independent Publisher's Guild (IPG)

American West Books Inc
1254 Commerce Way, Sanger, CA 93657
SAN: 630-8570
Tel: 559-876-2170 *Fax:* 559-876-2180
E-mail: info@americanwestbooks.com
Web Site: www.americanwestbooks.com
Key Personnel
Pres & CEO: Christopher Robbins
 E-mail: crobbins@americanwestbooks.com
Founded: 1993
Book wholesaler currently focusing on nonfiction
 books that deal with the natural history, history
 & recreation of regional areas in the US. Buys
 books from individuals & publishers & sells
 to booksellers & special markets. Regional &
 national distribution.
Catalog available.
Number of Titles Warehoused: 10,000
Membership(s): California Independent Book-
 sellers Alliance (CALIBA)

Ancient Healing Ways
PO Box 459, Espanola, NM 87532
Tel: 505-747-2860 *Toll Free Tel:* 877-753-5351
Web Site: www.a-healing.com
Key Personnel
Owner & Pres: Siri Ram Singh
 E-mail: sirirams@windstream.net
Founded: 1976
Health, yoga, herbs, teas, oils, organic foods bulk
 & packaged.
Catalog available.
Number of Titles Warehoused: 100

The Antiquarian Bookstore
1070 Lafayette Rd, US Rte 1, Portsmouth, NH
 03801-5408
Tel: 603-436-7250
Web Site: www.antiquarianbookstore.com
Key Personnel
Mgr & Buyer: John W Foster
Founded: 1973
Rare books & periodicals.
Catalog available.
Number of Titles Warehoused: 250,000

Ariane Editions
1217 Bernard W, Suite 101, Montreal, QC H2V
 1V7, Canada
Tel: 514-276-2949 *Fax:* 514-276-4121
E-mail: info@editions-ariane.com
Web Site: www.editions-ariane.com

Key Personnel
Pres: Marc Vallee
Founded: 1983
Catalog available.
Number of Titles Warehoused: 250

**Art Consulting Scandinavia: Books on Art &
 Architecture**
25777 Punto de Vista Dr, Monte Nido, CA
 91302-2155
Tel: 310-456-8762 *Fax:* 310-456-5714
E-mail: info@nordicartbooks.com
Web Site: www.nordicartbooks.com
Key Personnel
Owner: Lena Torslow Hansen
Founded: 1985
Importing & distributing of books on art & ar-
 chitecture & related subjects from Scandinavia.
 Catalogue available online.
Catalog available.
Number of Titles Warehoused: 4,000

Art Image Publications
Division of GB Publishing Inc
PO Box 160, Derby Line, VT 05830
Toll Free Tel: 800-361-2598 *Toll Free Fax:* 800-
 559-2598
E-mail: customer.service@artimagepublications.
 com
Web Site: www.artimagepublications.com
Key Personnel
Pres: Yvan Boulerice
Secy: Francoise Desjardins
Founded: 1998
Publisher & distributor. Art education, school
 books.
Catalog available.
Number of Titles Warehoused: 45

**Augsburg Fortress Publishers, Publishing
 House of the Evangelical Lutheran Church
 in America**
510 Marquette Ave S, Minneapolis, MN 55402
SAN: 169-4081
Mailing Address: PO Box 1209, Minneapolis,
 MN 55440-1209
Tel: 612-330-3300 *Toll Free Tel:* 800-426-0115
 (ext 639, subns); 800-328-4648 (orders)
 Fax: 612-330-3455 *Toll Free Fax:* 800-722-
 7766 (orders)
E-mail: customercare@augsburgfortress.org;
 copyright@augsburgfortress.org (reprint
 permission requests); info@augsburgfortress.
 org
Web Site: www.augsburgfortress.org; www.1517.
 media
Key Personnel
Pres & CEO: Tim Blevins *Tel:* 612-330-3300 ext
 400 *E-mail:* blevinst@1517.media
CFO: John Rahja *E-mail:* rahjaj@1517.media
VP & Publr, Fortress Press: Will Bergkamp
 E-mail: bergkampw@1517.media
VP & Publr, Sparkhouse: Tim Paulson
 E-mail: paulsont@1517.media
VP, HR: Sandy Amundson *E-mail:* amundsons@
 1517.media
Publr, Worship & Music: Martin Seltz
 E-mail: seltzm@1517.media
Perms, Pubns: Michael Moore *E-mail:* moorem@
 1517.media

Founded: 1855
Catalog available.
Number of Titles Warehoused: 1,200

AzureGreen
16 Bell Rd, Middlefield, MA 01243
Mailing Address: PO Box 48, Middlefield, MA
01243-0048
Tel: 413-623-2155 *Fax:* 413-623-2156
E-mail: azuregreen@azuregreen.com
Web Site: www.azuregreen.net
Key Personnel
Owner: Adair Cafarella *E-mail:* adair@
abyssdistribution.com
Founded: 1986
Distributors of specialty books & gifts for spiritual seekers. Leaders in providing titles on:
magic, wicca, tarot, New Age, goddess studies,
herbs, healing, shamanism, Celtic lore, western
mystery traditions, occult, ancient Egypt, magical children's stories & related subjects. Distribute mail-order catalog. Supply merchandise
to New Age retail stores & mail-order companies.
Catalog available.
Number of Titles Warehoused: 2,500

Baker & Taylor LLC
Division of Follett Corporation
2550 W Tyvola Rd, Suite 300, Charlotte, NC
28217
Tel: 704-998-3100 *Toll Free Tel:* 800-775-1800
(info servs) *Fax:* 704-998-3319
E-mail: btinfo@baker-taylor.com
Web Site: www.baker-taylor.com
Key Personnel
EVP & Gen Mgr: Amandeep Kochar
EVP, Opers: Gary Dayton
Founded: 1828
Global information & entertainment services company that offers print & digital books & en-
tertainment products along with value-added
services to libraries & educational institutions.
Based in Charlotte, NC, the company has been
in existence for more than 180 years, develop-
ing long-term relationships with major suppli-
ers, including book publishers, movie studios
& music labels. Baker & Taylor maintains one
of the largest combined in-stock book, video &
music inventories in the US.
Branch Office(s)
Commerce Service Center, 251 Mount Olive
Church Rd, Dept R, Commerce, GA 30599
Tel: 706-335-5000 *Toll Free Tel:* 800-775-1200
Momence Service Center, 501 S Gladiolus St,
Momence, IL 60954, VP, Opers/Gen Mgr:
Terrell Osborne *Tel:* 815-802-2444 *Toll Free
Tel:* 800-775-2300
Pittsburgh Service Center, 875 Greentree Rd,
Suite 678, Pittsburgh, PA 15220 *Tel:* 412-787-
8890 *Toll Free Tel:* 800-775-2600
Membership(s): The American Library Asso-
ciation (ALA); Book Industry Study Group
(BISG)

BCH Fulfillment & Distribution
33 Oakland Ave, Harrison, NY 10528
Tel: 914-835-0015 *Toll Free Tel:* 800-431-1579
Fax: 914-835-0398
E-mail: bookch@aol.com
Web Site: www.bookch.com
Key Personnel
Pres: Diane Musto
Founded: 1934
Distributor & small press fulfillment. Approved
vendor for Ingram, Baker & Taylor, Amazon &
Barnes & Noble.
Catalog available.
Number of Titles Warehoused: 5,000
Membership(s): Independent Book Publishers As-
sociation (IBPA)

Beaming Books, see Augsburg Fortress
Publishers, Publishing House of the
Evangelical Lutheran Church in America

Beijing Book Co Inc
Subsidiary of China National Publications Import
& Export (Group) Corp (People's Republic of
China)
701 E Linden Ave, Linden, NJ 07036
Tel: 908-862-0909 *Fax:* 908-862-4201
E-mail: journals@cnpbbci.com
Key Personnel
Mgr: Donna Jacik
Founded: 1981
Export American publications (books, periodi-
cals, other serials & government publications)
to China for Chinese libraries. Purchase news-
papers, music products, micro products, CD-
ROM.

Benjamin News Group
1701 Rankin St, Missoula, MT 59808
Mailing Address: PO Box 16147, Missoula, MT
59808
Tel: 406-721-7801 *Toll Free Tel:* 800-823-6397
(MT only); 800-735-8557 (outside MT)
E-mail: customerservice@bngmsla.com
Web Site: www.bngmsla.com; www.facebook.
com/Benjamin-News-Group-168874803126737/
Wholesale distributor of books, magazines & at-
lases.
Branch Office(s)
2701 N Van Marter, Spokane Valley, WA 99206
Tel: 509-928-0122 *Toll Free Tel:* 800-863-6278

Bernan
Imprint of Rowman & Littlefield Publishing
Group
4501 Forbes Blvd, Suite 200, Lanham, MD
20706
Mailing Address: PO Box 191, Blue Ridge Sum-
mit, PA 17214-0191
Tel: 717-794-3800 (cust serv & orders)
Toll Free Tel: 800-462-6420 (cust serv & or-
ders) *Fax:* 717-794-3803 *Toll Free Fax:* 800-
338-4550
E-mail: customercare@bernan.com
Web Site: rowman.com/page/bernan
Key Personnel
Mktg Mgr: Veronica M Dove *Tel:* 301-459-2255
ext 5716 *Fax:* 301-459-0056 *E-mail:* vdove@
bernan.com
Founded: 1952
Distributor of publications from the US govern-
ment & intergovernmental agencies. Publisher
of government-related reference works.
Catalog available.

Bilingual Educational Services Inc
2514 S Grand Ave, Los Angeles, CA 90007
SAN: 169-0388
Tel: 213-749-6213 *Toll Free Tel:* 800-448-6032
Key Personnel
Pres: Jeff Penichet
Founded: 1971
Textbooks, books, posters, study prints & AV pro-
grams for bilingual & multicultural education.
Number of Titles Warehoused: 5,000

BMI Educational Services Inc
26 Haypress Rd, Cranbury, NJ 08512
SAN: 169-4669
Mailing Address: PO Box 800, Dayton, NJ
08810-0800
Tel: 732-329-6991 *Toll Free Tel:* 800-222-
8100 (orders only) *Fax:* 732-329-6994
Toll Free Fax: 800-986-9393 (orders only)
E-mail: info@bmionline.com
Web Site: bmionline.com
Key Personnel
Owner & Secy-Treas: Lynda Bradley

Pres: Jerry Wagner *E-mail:* jwagner@bmionline.
com
Founded: 1964
Distributors of popular & classic fiction & non-
fiction paperback titles for K-12, leveled book
collections for schools, teacher's guides. Also
offers book binding services.
Catalog available.
Number of Titles Warehoused: 10,000
Publication(s): *Catalogs for grades K-12*
Membership(s): International Literacy Association
(ILA); National Council of Teachers of English
(NCTE)

Book Express
Division of Raincoast Book Distribution Ltd
2440 Viking Way, Richmond, BC V6V 1N2,
Canada
SAN: 115-0871
Tel: 604-448-7100 *Toll Free Tel:* 800-663-5714
Fax: 604-270-7161 *Toll Free Fax:* 800-565-
3770
E-mail: info@raincoast.com
Web Site: www.raincoast.com
Key Personnel
CEO, Raincoast Books: John Sawyer
E-mail: johns@raincoast.com
Buyer: Debra Berglind
Founded: 1975
Book wholesaler. Trade wholesale in Canada.
Catalog available.
Number of Titles Warehoused: 5,000

Book Sales
Division of Quarto Publishing Group USA Inc
142 W 36 St, 4th fl, New York, NY 10018
SAN: 299-4062
Tel: 212-779-4971; 212-779-4972 *Fax:* 212-779-
6058
Web Site: www.quartoknows.com
Key Personnel
Sales Dir: Steven Wilson *Tel:* 212-779-4973
E-mail: steve.wilson@quarto.com
Founded: 1952
Publisher & supplier of books to wholesalers,
mail order companies & retail stores for over
60 years. In addition to books published, we
are one of the largest purchasers of other pub-
lishers' remainder +/or overstock titles for re-
sale at significantly reduced prices. Categories
include novels, cookbooks, history, juvenile,
Civil War, militaria, fine art, art instruction,
how-to craft books, natural history, gardening
& more.
Catalog available.
Membership(s): American Booksellers Association (ABA)

Bookazine Co Inc
75 Hook Rd, Bayonne, NJ 07002
SAN: 169-5665
Tel: 201-339-7777 *Toll Free Tel:* 800-221-8112
Fax: 201-339-7778
E-mail: info@bookazine.com
Web Site: www.bookazine.com
Key Personnel
Pres & CEO: Robert Kallman
COO: Richard Kallman
Pres, Sales: Cindy Raiton
VP, Mdse: Andrew Collings
VP, Dist: Allan Davis
Dir, Natl Accts: Steven Goldberg
Northeast Sales Dir: Josh Harwood
Mktg Mgr: Lani Buess
Founded: 1929
General book wholesaler to bookstores & li-
braries. Specialize in books of Jewish inter-
est, Black interest books, juvenile books, gay-
lesbian books, computer books, international
services.
Number of Titles Warehoused: 80,000
Publication(s): *Gift Books for the Holidays*

The Booksource Inc
Division of GL group Inc
1230 Macklind Ave, St Louis, MO 63110
Tel: 314-647-0600 *Toll Free Tel:* 800-444-0435
Fax: 314-647-6850 *Toll Free Fax:* 800-647-
1923
E-mail: service@booksource.com
Web Site: www.booksource.com
Key Personnel
Owner: Neil Jaffe *Tel:* 314-647-0600 ext 245
E-mail: njaffe@booksource.com
CEO: Gary Jaffe
Founded: 1974
K-12 school wholesaler, hardcover & paperbacks.
Vinaclad, prebound paperback books.
Catalog available.
Number of Titles Warehoused: 30,000
Publication(s): *K-12 Education Catalog* (annual,
circ 50,000); *Leveled Reading K-6 Catalog* (an-
nual, circ 20,000)
Membership(s): Educational Book & Media Asso-
ciation (EBMA)

Bound to Stay Bound Books Inc
1880 W Morton Rd, Jacksonville, IL 62650
SAN: 169-1996
Tel: 217-245-5191 *Toll Free Tel:* 800-637-6586
Fax: 217-245-0424 *Toll Free Fax:* 800-747-
7872
E-mail: btsb@btsb.com
Web Site: www.btsb.com
Key Personnel
Pres: Robert L Sibert
Founded: 1920
Prebinder of children's books which are sold to
schools & libraries all over the country. Sea-
sonal catalogs available.
Number of Titles Warehoused: 19,000

Broadleaf Books, see Augsburg Fortress
Publishers, Publishing House of the
Evangelical Lutheran Church in America

Brodart Books & Library Services
500 Arch St, Williamsport, PA 17701
Tel: 570-326-2461 *Toll Free Tel:* 800-233-8467
Fax: 570-651-1639 *Toll Free Fax:* 800-999-
6799
E-mail: support@brodart.com
Web Site: www.brodartbooks.com
Key Personnel
Pres & CEO: George Coe
CFO: Richard Dill
VP, Books Div: Gretchen Herman
Founded: 1939
Delivers shelf-ready books, exclusively serving
libraries. Professional selection & customized
cataloging & processing are avilable for En-
glish & Spanish language titles.
Catalog available.
Number of Titles Warehoused: 1,000,000

B Broughton Co Ltd
322 Consumers Rd, North York, ON M2J 1P8,
Canada
Tel: 416-690-4777 *Toll Free Tel:* 800-268-4449
Fax: 416-690-5357
E-mail: sales@bbroughton.com
Web Site: www.bbroughton.com
Key Personnel
Owner & Pres: Brian Broughton *E-mail:* brian@
bbroughton.com
Founded: 1970
Religious education books, AV & trade.
Catalog available.
Number of Titles Warehoused: 6,000
Membership(s): National Church Goods Associa-
tion (NCGA)

Burlington News Agency Inc
382 Hercules Dr, Suite 2, Colchester, VT 05446

Tel: 802-655-7000 *Fax:* 802-655-7002
E-mail: burlnews@aol.com
Key Personnel
Pres: Glenn E Murphy
VP: Brian T Murphy
Founded: 1942
Wholesaler & distributor of newspapers, maga-
zines, paperback books & periodicals.

C J Traders Inc
555 Second Ave, Suite C700, Collegeville, PA
19426
Tel: 484-902-8057 *Fax:* 484-902-8093
E-mail: cjtraders714@gmail.com
Key Personnel
Pres: John Jacobs
Founded: 1995
Specialize in cookbooks, children's books, craft,
gardening; hardcover, trade, fiction, nonfiction
& textbooks.
Number of Titles Warehoused: 1,000

Carolina Biological Supply Co
2700 York Rd, Burlington, NC 27215-3398
Mailing Address: PO Box 6010, Burlington, NC
27216-6010
Tel: 336-586-4399 (intl sales); 336-538-6211
Toll Free Tel: 800-334-5551 *Fax:* 336-584-7686
(intl sales) *Toll Free Fax:* 800-222-7112
E-mail: quotations@carolina.com; product@
carolina.com
Web Site: www.carolina.com
Key Personnel
Pres & CEO: Jim Parrish
VP: Bruce Wilcox *E-mail:* bruce.wilcox@
carolina.com
HR Mgr: Jim Scruggs
Founded: 1927
Publish & distribute books, charts, audiovisuals,
CD-ROMs.
Catalog available.
Number of Titles Warehoused: 1,700
Publication(s): *Carolina Tips* (quarterly, circ
100,000)

Wm Caxton Ltd - Bookseller & Publisher
12037 Hwy 42, Ellison Bay, WI 54210
SAN: 664-7901
Mailing Address: Box 220, Ellison Bay, WI
54210
Tel: 920-854-2955
Key Personnel
Owner: Kubet Luchterhand
Founded: 1986
Number of Titles Warehoused: 24

Cheneliere Education Inc
Division of TC Media
5800, rue St Denis, bureau 900, Montreal, QC
H2S 3L5, Canada
Tel: 514-273-1066 *Toll Free Tel:* 800-565-5531
Fax: 514-276-0324 *Toll Free Fax:* 800-814-
0324
E-mail: info@cheneliere.ca
Web Site: www.cheneliere.ca
Key Personnel
VP, Prodn: Michel Carl Perron
E-mail: mcperron@cheneliere.ca
Gen Mgr: Patrick Lutzy *E-mail:* patrick.lutzy@tc.
tc
Founded: 1985
Publish & distribute.
Catalog available.
Number of Titles Warehoused: 2,500

Cheng & Tsui Co Inc
25 West St, 2nd fl, Boston, MA 02111-1213
Tel: 617-988-2400 *Toll Free Tel:* 800-554-1963
Fax: 617-426-3669
E-mail: service@cheng-tsui.com; orders@cheng-
tsui.com

Web Site: www.cheng-tsui.com
Key Personnel
Pres: Jill Cheng
Founded: 1979
Distribute & publish Asian studies related text-
books, literature, software, DVDs & more.
Catalog available.

**The Children's Book Store Distribution
(CBSD)**
Division of IDLA Associated Label Distribution
23 Griffin St, Waterdown, ON L0R 2H0, Canada
Mailing Address: PO Box 170, Waterdown, ON
L0R 2H0, Canada
Tel: 905-690-9397 (ext 237) *Toll Free Tel:* 800-
757-8372 (cust serv, CN & US) *Fax:* 905-690-
3419
E-mail: info@childrensgroup.com; sales@idla.ca
Web Site: www.childrensgroup.com
Key Personnel
Sales: Judy Smyth
Founded: 1991
Children's audio recordings, teacher resource ma-
terials & DVDs.
Catalog available.
Number of Titles Warehoused: 2,000

China Books
Division of Sinomedia International Group
360 Swift Ave, Suite 48, South San Francisco,
CA 94080
SAN: 169-0167
Fax: 650-872-7808
E-mail: editor.sinomedia@gmail.com
Key Personnel
Edit Dir: Chris Robyn *Tel:* 650-872-7718 ext 312
E-mail: chris@sinomediausa.com
Sales Mgr: Kelly Feng *Tel:* 650-872-7076 ext 310
E-mail: kelly@chinabooks.com
Founded: 1960
Publisher, distributor & importer of books from &
about China.
Catalog available.
Number of Titles Warehoused: 3,000

China Books & Periodicals Inc, see China
Books

China Institute in America
100 Washington St, New York, NY 10006
Tel: 212-744-8181 *Fax:* 212-628-4159
E-mail: gallery@chinainstitute.org
Web Site: www.chinainstitute.org
Key Personnel
Gallery Dir: Willow Weilan Hai
Asst Dir: Insher Pan
Founded: 1926
Exhibitions of masterpieces of Chinese art & folk
art. Exhibitions are accompanied by scholarly
catalogs.
Catalog available.
Number of Titles Warehoused: 20

Chinese Christian Mission Bookroom
1269 N McDowell Blvd, Petaluma, CA 94954-
1133
Mailing Address: PO Box 750759, Petaluma, CA
94975-0759
Tel: 707-762-2688; 707-762-1314 *Fax:* 707-762-
1713
E-mail: bookroom@ccmusa.org; ccm@ccmusa.
org
Web Site: www.ccmusa.org; www.ccmbookroom.
org
Key Personnel
Mgr: Jenny Sit
Founded: 1972
Chinese Bibles, Christian books & tracts, mail
order service, Christian gift items.
Catalog available.

Choice Books
2387 Grace Chapel Rd, Harrisonburg, VA 22801
Tel: 540-434-1827 *Fax:* 540-434-9894
E-mail: info@choicebooks.org
Web Site: www.choicebooks.org
Key Personnel
CEO: Kenneth E Gonyer
Prog Asst: E Dale Mast *E-mail:* mastd@
    choicebooks.org
Founded: 1962
Rack jobber/wholesale vendor of trade & mass
    market paperbacks.
Number of Titles Warehoused: 2,000
Branch Office(s)
Choice Books of Northern Virginia, 10100 Piper
    Lane, Bristow, VA 20136-1419, Contact: Joe
    Bacher *Tel:* 703-530-9993
Choice Books of Gulf States, 6115 Old
    Pascagoula Rd, Theodore, AL 36582-9166,
    Contact: Jason Miller *Tel:* 251-653-0560
Choice Books of West Coast, 856 S Reed Ave,
    Suite 10, Reedley, CA 93654-3348, Contact:
    Steve Isaak *Tel:* 559-638-1745
Choice Books of Midwest, 1705 W Mount Ver-
    non, Metamora, IL 61548, Contact: Jerry
    Eicher *Tel:* 309-367-2152
Choice Books of Kansas, 4405 S Whiteside Rd,
    Hutchinson, KS 67501-9062, Contact: Arno
    Miller *Tel:* 620-662-3900
Choice Books of Great Lakes, 10154 Rosedale
    Milford Center Rd, Irwin, OH 43029, Contact:
    Nathan Miller *Tel:* 740-857-1368
Choice Books of Pennsylvania, 121 S Main
    St, Manheim, PA 17545-1601, Contact: Ray
    Brubaker *Tel:* 717-665-3933

Christianbook Inc
140 Summit St, Peabody, MA 01960-5156
Mailing Address: PO Box 7000, Peabody, MA
    01961-7000
Tel: 978-977-5060; 978-977-5000 (intl calls)
    Toll Free Tel: 800-CHRISTIAN (247-4784)
    Fax: 978-977-5010
E-mail: customer.service@christianbook.com
Web Site: www.christianbook.com
Key Personnel
Pres & CEO: Ray Hendrickson
COO: Kevin Hendrickson
EVP: Ken Davis
Dist Ctr Systems Mgr: Gary Lussier
Founded: 1978
Direct mail to individuals throughout the world.
    Religious reference, language, popular, youth
    counseling, sermon resources, Bibles, theolog-
    ical reference, juvenile, young adult books &
    videos.
Number of Titles Warehoused: 12,000

CLC Ministries
701 Pennsylvania Ave, Fort Washington, PA
    19034
SAN: 169-7358
Mailing Address: PO Box 1449, Fort Washington,
    PA 19034-8499
Tel: 215-542-1240 *Toll Free Tel:* 800-659-1240
    Fax: 215-542-7580
E-mail: orders@clcpublications.com
Web Site: www.clcpublications.com
Key Personnel
Dir: Jim Pitman *E-mail:* jpitman@clcusa.org
Dist/Sales Dir: Charlie Hurd
Founded: 1941
Also sells to ministries.
Catalog available.
Number of Titles Warehoused: 440
Membership(s): EFMA

Clear Concepts
1329 Federal Ave, Suite 6, Los Angeles, CA
    90025
Tel: 323-285-0325

Key Personnel
Owner: Karen Kleiner
Brokers remainders & overstock, books & au-
    dio, fiction & nonfiction. Subjects include chil-
    dren's, cookbooks, artbooks, how-to, health,
    reference books & best sellers. Prefers exclu-
    sive representation.

Comag Marketing Group LLC (CMG)
Division of The Jim Pattison Group
155 Village Blvd, Suite 300, Princeton, NJ 08540
Tel: 609-524-1800 *Fax:* 609-524-1629
Web Site: www.i-cmg.com
Key Personnel
Pres: James W Felts
EVP: Michael P Herrington
SVP: Robert F Brassell; Michael Gillen
Founded: 1919
Our client services team works with publishers on
    developing & implementing a targeted single-
    copy sales business plan. We act as the liaison
    between our publishers & all our channel part-
    ners (internal & external) to make sure that
    our clients' objectives are communicated & put
    into practice. Our goal is to exceed our clients'
    expectations every day.

Continental Book Co Inc
7000 Broadway, Suite 102, Denver, CO 80221-
    2913
Tel: 303-289-1761 *Toll Free Fax:* 800-279-1764
E-mail: cbc@continentalbook.com
Web Site: www.continentalbook.com
Key Personnel
Dir: Linette Hayat *E-mail:* linette@
    continentalbook.com
Founded: 1961
Distributors of French, Spanish, ELL, Italian,
    German, Arabic, Chinese, Heritage Spanish &
    American publications, imported & domestic,
    juvenile to advanced levels.
Catalog available.
Number of Titles Warehoused: 15,000

Cooperative Etudiante de Polytechnique
Pavillon Principal Local C-220, 2900 Edouard
    Mont Petit, Montreal, QC H3T 1J4, Canada
Mailing Address: Box 6079, Succursale Centre-
    Ville, Montreal, QC H3C 3A7, Canada
Tel: 514-340-4851 *Fax:* 514-340-4543
E-mail: andre.daneau@polymtl.ca
Web Site: www.coopoly.ca
Key Personnel
Bookstore Dir: Jacques Desharnais *Tel:* 514-340-
    4362 *E-mail:* jacques.desharnais@polymtl.ca
Gen Mgr: Yves Daigneault *Tel:* 514-340-5229
    E-mail: yves.daigneault@polymtl.ca
Founded: 1944
Engineering publications.
Number of Titles Warehoused: 10,000

Coronet Books Inc
33 Ashley Dr, Schwenksville, PA 19473
SAN: 210-6043
Tel: 215-925-2762 *Fax:* 215-925-1912
Web Site: www.coronetbooks.com
Key Personnel
Pres: Ronald P Smolin
VP: Jeff Goldstein *E-mail:* jeffgolds@comcast.net
Founded: 1985

Crescent Imports
PO Box 721, Union City, CA 94587
Tel: 734-665-3492 *Toll Free Tel:* 800-521-9744
    Fax: 734-677-1717
E-mail: message@crescentimports.com
Web Site: www.crescentimports.com; www.
    crescentcatalog.com
Key Personnel
Co-Owner & CEO: Ashfaq Ibrahim
Co-Owner: Gulshan Ibrahim

Founded: 1978
Distribute books on Islamic religion & African-
    American literature, free catalog & Islamic
    supplies.
Catalog available.
Number of Titles Warehoused: 10,000
Publication(s): *Catalog* (semiannual, circ 50,000)

Ralph Curtis Books
16956 McGregor Blvd, Suite 9, Fort Myers, FL
    33908
Mailing Address: PO Box 349, Sanibel, FL
    33957-0349 SAN: 281-5842
Tel: 239-454-0010 *Fax:* 239-395-2727
E-mail: rcurtisbks@yahoo.com
Web Site: www.ralphcurtisbooks.com
Key Personnel
Owner & CEO: Ralph C Curtis
Founded: 1965
Book publisher, import remainder titles, whole-
    sale selected titles from domestic & foreign
    publishers.
Number of Titles Warehoused: 40

De Ru's Fine Art
Subsidiary of De Ru's Fine Arts Gallery
9100 E Artesia Blvd, Bellflower, CA 90706-6205
SAN: 216-3667
Tel: 562-920-1312 *Fax:* 562-920-3077
E-mail: derusgal@aol.com
Web Site: www.derusfinearts.com
Key Personnel
Owner: Dewitt C McCall
Founded: 1969
Art gallery, art restoration, art reference books,
    library bound catalogs from museums & gal-
    leries dealing with early California art.
Catalog available.
Number of Titles Warehoused: 80
Branch Office(s)
1590 S Coast Hwy, Suite 5, Laguna Beach, CA
    92651 *Tel:* 949-376-3785 *Fax:* 949-376-9915

DeHoff Christian Bookstore
749 NW Broad St, Murfreesboro, TN 37129
Tel: 615-893-8322 *Toll Free Tel:* 800-695-5385
    Fax: 615-896-7447
E-mail: dehoffbooks@gmail.com
Web Site: www.dehoffpublications.com
Key Personnel
Owner & Mgr: Bonnie Fakes
Founded: 1939
Religious books, literature, workbooks & publica-
    tions.
Catalog available.
Number of Titles Warehoused: 100

Devin-Adair Publishers
Subsidiary of Seagrace Partners LLC
9 Lafayette Ct, Suite 3, Greenwich, CT 06830
Tel: 203-622-1010 *Fax:* 718-359-8568
Key Personnel
VP: Roger H Lourie
Cust Serv Mgr: Chris Dowdell
Founded: 1911
Mail order & trade sales to libraries, retail stores,
    institutions, individuals & private organizations.
Catalog available.
Number of Titles Warehoused: 820
Membership(s): American Booksellers Associa-
    tion (ABA); Association of Research Libraries
    (ARL); Connecticut Business & Industry Asso-
    ciation (CBIA)

DeVorss & Co
553 Constitution Ave, Camarillo, CA 93012-8510
SAN: 168-9886
Tel: 805-322-9010 *Toll Free Tel:* 800-843-5743
    Fax: 805-322-9011
E-mail: service@devorss.com
Web Site: www.devorss.com

Key Personnel
Pres: Gary R Peattie *Tel:* 805-322-9010 ext 14
 E-mail: gpeattie@devorss.com
Founded: 1929
Metaphysical, spiritual, inspirational, self-help,
 body/mind/spirit, New Thought. CDs & DVDs.
 Announcements of new books as available.
Catalog available.
Number of Titles Warehoused: 10,000
Publication(s): *DeVorss Publications Catalog* (an-
 nual); *DeVorss Wholesale Distributors Catalog*
 (annual)

Distribooks Inc
Subsidiary of MEP Inc
8154 N Ridgeway Ave, Skokie, IL 60076-2911
Tel: 847-676-1596 *Fax:* 847-676-1195
 Toll Free Fax: 888-266-5713
E-mail: info@distribooks.com; info@schoenhofs.
 com
Web Site: www.schoenhofs.com
Key Personnel
Pres: Nicolas Mengin
Dir, Mktg & Sales: Daniel Eastman
 E-mail: deastman@mep-inc.net
Founded: 1989
Foreign language book distributor. Branch office
 located in Boston, MA.
Catalog available.
Number of Titles Warehoused: 8,000

Eaglecrafts Inc
168 W 12 St, Ogden, UT 84404
SAN: 630-6381
Tel: 801-393-3991 *Fax:* 801-393-4647
E-mail: sales@eaglefeathertrading.com
Web Site: www.eaglefeathertrading.com
Key Personnel
Publr: Monte Smith
Sales Mgr: Sue Smith
Founded: 1972
Native American & early American frontier titles
 & related subjects: crafts, history & mountain
 men titles.
Catalog available.
Number of Titles Warehoused: 2,500

East-West Health Arts
45 Academy Circle, Oakland, NJ 07436-0945
Tel: 201-337-8787
Key Personnel
Owner: Martin S Ruback
Founded: 2006
Wholesale to New Age stores, massage schools &
 Judaica stores.

Eastern Book Co
7 Lincoln Ave, Scarborough, ME 04074
SAN: 169-3050
Tel: 207-856-1370 *Toll Free Tel:* 800-937-0331
 Toll Free Fax: 800-214-3895
E-mail: info@ebc.com; sales@ebc.com
Web Site: www.ebc.com
Key Personnel
Owner: Stephen P Coyne
Founded: 1957
Wholesaler for all publishers to schools & li-
 braries.
Number of Titles Warehoused: 15,000

Eastwind Books & Arts Inc
1435 Stockton St, San Francisco, CA 94133
SAN: 127-3159
Tel: 415-772-5888 *Fax:* 415-772-5885
E-mail: contact@eastwindbooks.com
Web Site: www.eastwindbooks.com
Key Personnel
Mgr: Cat Deng
Founded: 1978
Books on Asia, Asian-American, China in En-
 glish +/or Chinese language.

Number of Titles Warehoused: 30,000
Membership(s): American Booksellers Association (ABA)

Edipresse Inc
945, ave Beaumont, Montreal, QC H3N 1W3,
 Canada
Tel: 514-273-6141 *Toll Free Tel:* 800-361-1043
 Fax: 514-273-7021
E-mail: information@edipresse.ca
Web Site: www.edipresse.ca
Key Personnel
Pres: Ms Leone Giannone Rameau
Gen Mgr: Pascal Chamaillard *Tel:* 514-273-6141
 ext 203 *E-mail:* chamaillard@edipresse.ca
Founded: 1979
Distribute French books.
Number of Titles Warehoused: 24,000
Membership(s): Association des Distributeurs
 Exclusifs de Livres en Langue Francaise
 (ADELF)

Les Editions Themis
Faculte de droit, Universite de Montreal, CP
 6128, Succursale Centreville, Montreal, QC
 H3C 3J7, Canada
Tel: 514-343-6627 *Fax:* 514-343-6779
E-mail: info@editionsthemis.com
Web Site: ssl.editionsthemis.com
Key Personnel
Pres: Stephane Rousseau *E-mail:* stephane.
 rousseau@umontreal.ca
Deputy Dir: Michel Morin *E-mail:* direction.
 rjtum@editionsthemis.com
Founded: 1969
Law books, reference books, journals & profes-
 sional books.
Catalog available.
Number of Titles Warehoused: 100
Publication(s): *La Revue Juridique Themis* (3 is-
 sues/yr)

Elder's Bookstore
101 White Bridge Rd, Nashville, TN 37209
Tel: 615-352-1562
E-mail: info@eldersbookstore.com
Web Site: eldersbookstore.com
Key Personnel
Owner: Randy Elder
Founded: 1950
Book search; wholesale, retail, rare.
Number of Titles Warehoused: 60,000

Emery-Pratt Co
1966 W M 21, Owosso, MI 48867-1397
SAN: 170-1401
Tel: 989-723-5291 *Toll Free Tel:* 800-762-5683
 (orders); 800-248-3887 (cust serv) *Fax:* 989-
 723-4677 *Toll Free Fax:* 800-523-6379 (cust
 serv)
E-mail: customer.service@emery-pratt.com
Web Site: www.emery-pratt.com
Key Personnel
Pres: Maurie Shattuck
Dir, Busn Devt: Byron Shattuck
Mktg Mgr: Mo Shattuck *E-mail:* mo.shattuck@
 emery-pratt.com
Book Buyer: Kathi Strong
Founded: 1873
Book distributors dedicated to meeting the needs
 of academic, public & hospital libraries & in
 turn, the communities they serve. Everything
 we do is designed around your needs. Have
 over 70,000 publishing sources to find any of
 the 3.4 million titles currently in print. Along
 with that, we have a wide range of services
 available to streamline operations saving you
 time & money.
Number of Titles Warehoused: 100,000
Publication(s): *New Titles Trade* (weekly); *Technical & Reference* (weekly)

Encyclopaedia Britannica Inc
325 N La Salle St, Suite 200, Chicago, IL 60654
Tel: 312-347-7000 (all other countries)
 Toll Free Tel: 800-323-1229 (US & CN)
 Fax: 312-294-2104
E-mail: contact@eb.com
Web Site: www.britannica.com
Key Personnel
Global CEO: Karthik Krishnan
EVP, Corp Secy & Gen Coun: Douglas Eveleigh
SVP & CFO: Jim Conners
SVP, Britannica Digital Learning Intl: Leah Man-
 soor
VP, Consumer Mkts: Chris Mayland
VP, Mktg & Channel Devt: Sal De Spirito
VP, Sales: Matthew Krise
Exec Dir, Cust Success: Rick Lumsden
Founded: 1768

European Books & Media
6600 Shattuck Ave, Oakland, CA 94609
Tel: 510-922-9157
E-mail: info@europeanbook.com
Web Site: www.europeanbook.com
Key Personnel
Owner & Mng Memb: Nicolas Pellerin
 E-mail: nicolas.pellerin@europeanbook.com
Founded: 1963
Foreign language & bilingual materials. Special-
 izes in French books. Online catalog.
Catalog available.
Number of Titles Warehoused: 100,000

Fall River News Co Inc
144 Robeson St, Fall River, MA 02720
Tel: 508-679-5266
E-mail: frnewco@gmail.com
Key Personnel
Owner & Pres: David W Boland, III
Founded: 1935
Distribute mass market paperbacks, hardcovers,
 periodicals, maps, newspapers & atlases to con-
 venience & drug stores, bookstores, schools,
 libraries, etc.
Membership(s): American Booksellers Associa-
 tion (ABA)

Philipp Feldheim Inc, see Feldheim Publishers

Feldheim Publishers
208 Airport Executive Park, Nanuet, NY 10954
SAN: 207-0545
Tel: 845-356-2282 *Toll Free Tel:* 800-237-7149
 (orders) *Fax:* 845-425-1908
E-mail: sales@feldheim.com
Web Site: www.feldheim.com
Key Personnel
Pres: Yitzchak Feldheim
Mng Dir: Eli M Hollander *E-mail:* eli@feldheim.
 com
Sales Mgr: Suzanne Brandt *E-mail:* suzanne@
 feldheim.com
Founded: 1939
Publishers & distributors of English language Ju-
 daica.
Catalog available.
Number of Titles Warehoused: 800

Reginald F Fennell Subscription Service Inc
1002 W Michigan Ave, Jackson, MI 49202
Tel: 517-782-3132 *Toll Free Tel:* 800-603-5557
 Fax: 517-782-1109
E-mail: fennellss@acd.net
Key Personnel
Pres: Reg Fennell
Founded: 1910
Ordering service & maintenance, magazines,
 newspapers.

1517 Media, see Augsburg Fortress Publishers,
 Publishing House of the Evangelical Lutheran
 Church in America

Follett Higher Education Group
Division of Follett Corporation
3 Westbrook Corporate Ctr, Suite 200, Westchester, IL 60154
Tel: 708-884-0000 Toll Free Tel: 800-FOLLETT
(365-5388)
Web Site: www.follett.com/higher-ed
Key Personnel
Pres & CEO: Patrick E Connolly
Founded: 1873
Wholesaler of new & used college textbooks.
Number of Titles Warehoused: 125,000

Forest Sales & Distributing Co
139 Jean Marie St, Reserve, LA 70084
SAN: 157-5511
E-mail: forestsales@juno.com
Key Personnel
Contact: Rob Schauffler
Founded: 1967
Wholesaler & distributor of primarily regional titles; cookbooks.
Catalog available.
Number of Titles Warehoused: 2,400
Membership(s): American Booksellers Association (ABA); New Orleans Gulf South Booksellers Association (NOGSBA)

Fortress Press, see Augsburg Fortress Publishers, Publishing House of the Evangelical Lutheran Church in America

Samuel French Inc
235 Park Ave S, 5th fl, New York, NY 10003
Tel: 212-206-8990 Toll Free Tel: 866-598-8449
Fax: 212-206-1429
E-mail: info@samuelfrench.com
Web Site: www.samuelfrench.com
Key Personnel
Pres: Nate Collins E-mail: ncollins@samuelfrench.com
Founded: 1830
Branch Office(s)
•Samuel French Ltd, 24-32 Stephenson Way, London NW1 2HD, United Kingdom, Webster Tel: (020) 7387 9373
E-mail: customerservices@samuelfrench.co.uk
Web Site: www.samuelfrench.co.uk

GBS Books
11226 N 23 Ave, Suite 103, Phoenix, AZ 85029
Tel: 602-863-6000 Toll Free Tel: 800-851-6001
E-mail: gbsbooks@gbsbooks.com
Web Site: www.gbsbooks.com
Key Personnel
Book Buyer: Eileen Baughman
Gen Mgr: Troy Williams E-mail: twilliams@gbsbooks.com
Mktg: Abigail Williams
Founded: 2013
Juvenile & young adult books, trade & mass market paperback books, library accounts.
Number of Titles Warehoused: 28,000
Membership(s): American Booksellers Association (ABA)

Gem Guides Book Co
1155 W Ninth St, Upland, CA 91786
Tel: 626-855-1611 Toll Free Tel: 800-824-5118
(orders) Fax: 626-855-1610
E-mail: info@gemguidesbooks.com; sales@gemguidesbooks.com (orders)
Web Site: www.gemguidesbooks.com
Key Personnel
Opers Mgr: Matt Warner
Ed: Nancy Fox
Off Mgr: Nannette Becerra
Sales: Michael Moran
Founded: 1965
Western publisher & distributor of regional titles on Western Americana, Native American,

travel, outdoor, recreational prospecting, historical/ghost towns, railroads, rocks & minerals, jewelry making, bead crafts & New Age crystal.
Catalog available.
Number of Titles Warehoused: 1,000

Dot Gibson Publications
PO Box 117, Waycross, GA 31502
SAN: 200-4143
Tel: 912-285-2848 Toll Free Tel: 800-336-8095
(for orders) Fax: 912-285-2848
E-mail: info@dotgibson.com
Web Site: www.dotgibson.com
Key Personnel
CEO: Dot Gibson
Pres: N Gilbert Gibson, Jr
Founded: 1975
Distribution & publishing of cookbooks, giftbooks & children's books.
Catalog available.
Number of Titles Warehoused: 400
Publication(s): Dot Gibson Bestsellers catalog (annual); Dot Gibson Bestsellers newsletter (quarterly)

Gift of Words, see GBS Books

Gilman's LRC (Lost River Caverns)
726 Durham St, Hellertown, PA 18055
SAN: 130-7452
Mailing Address: PO Box M, Hellertown, PA 18055
Tel: 610-838-8767 Toll Free Tel: 888-529-1907
Fax: 610-838-2961
E-mail: info.lostcave@gmail.com
Web Site: www.lostcave.com
Key Personnel
Partner: Beverly Rozewicz
Founded: 1930
Wholesaler to rock, gem & geology stores.

Girol Books Inc
PO Box 5473, LCD Merivale, Ottawa, QN K2C 3M1, Canada
Tel: 613-233-9044 Fax: 613-233-9044
E-mail: info@girol.com
Web Site: www.girol.com
Key Personnel
Owner: Miguel Angel Giella; Peter Roster
Founded: 1975
Importers & distributors of books in Spanish & Portuguese. Publishers of Latin American theater titles & theater criticism.

Glenbow Museum Shop
Division of Glenbow Museum
130 Ninth Ave SE, Calgary, AB T2G 0P3, Canada
SAN: 157-0048
Tel: 403-268-4119 Fax: 403-262-4045
E-mail: shop@glenbow.org
Web Site: www.glenbow.org
Key Personnel
Mgr: Cherry Deacon
Founded: 1957
Catalog production, nonfiction (native & Canadian titles) publications, maps, note cards & videos.
Number of Titles Warehoused: 100

GoalsGuy Learning Systems
36181 E Lake Rd, Suite 139, Palm Harbor, FL 34685
Toll Free Tel: 877-462-5748 Fax: 813-435-2022
Toll Free Fax: 877-903-2284
E-mail: info@goalsguy.com
Web Site: www.100daychallenge.com
Key Personnel
Owner: Gary Ryan Blair

Buy & sell books for corporate libraries nationwide.
Branch Office(s)
201 E Jefferson St, Suite 269, Fayetteville, NY 13066 Tel: 315-446-4960

GOBI® Library Solutions from EBSCO
Division of EBSCO Information Services
999 Maple St, Contoocook, NH 03229
SAN: 169-4510
Tel: 603-746-3102 Toll Free Tel: 800-258-3774
(US & CN) Fax: 603-746-5628
E-mail: information@ebsco.com
Web Site: gobi.ebsco.com
Key Personnel
COO: Darby Kopp
VP, Content Devt & Partner Rel: Michael Zeoli
VP, Content Mgmt: Nat Bruning
VP, Fin & Acctg: Kate Hartnett
VP, Opers & Lean Mgmt: Jeffrey Pickert
VP, Strategic Projs, Consortia & Admin: Kristine Baker
Founded: 2015 (1971 as Yankee Book Peddler Inc)
Full service bookseller to libraries; monographic order fulfillment, series standing orders & approval plans. National library book jobber: university presses; university affiliated departments; scientific, technical & business publishers; medical publishers; societies; museums; trade; juvenile & young adult.
Publication(s): Dialogue: The Business of Publishing (Feb, June, Oct, circ 1,000)
Membership(s): Book Industry Study Group (BISG)

Louis Goldberg Library Book Supplier
45 Belvidere St, Nazareth, PA 18064
SAN: 169-7536
Tel: 610-759-9458
E-mail: orders@goldberg-books.com
Web Site: www.goldberg-books.com
Key Personnel
Owner: Dianne Duignam; Katherine Hoadley
Founded: 1951

Guardian Book Co
7019 Edinburgh Dr, Lambertville, MI 48144
Mailing Address: PO Box 6566, Toledo, OH 43612
Tel: 734-856-1765 Toll Free Tel: 800-560-6697
Fax: 734-854-7638
Web Site: guardianbookcompany.com; gbcbooks.com
Key Personnel
Owner & Dir: Norm Black E-mail: nblack726@aol.com
Founded: 1972
Educational materials & exhibits; children's books.
Catalog available.
Number of Titles Warehoused: 8,500

Harvard Art Museums
32 Quincy St, Cambridge, MA 02138
Tel: 617-495-9400 Fax: 617-495-9985
Web Site: www.harvardartmuseums.org
Founded: 1901
Reproductions & bookshop.
Number of Titles Warehoused: 50

William S Hein & Co Inc
2350 N Forest Rd, Getzville, NY 14068
Tel: 716-882-2600 Toll Free Tel: 800-828-7571
Fax: 716-883-8100
E-mail: mail@wshein.com; marketing@wshein.com
Web Site: www.wshein.com
Key Personnel
Chmn of the Bd: William S Hein, Jr
E-mail: whein@wshein.com
Pres & CEO: Shane P Marmion Tel: 716-882-2600 ext 129 E-mail: smarmion@wshein.com

Chief Resource Offr: Daniel P Rosati
  E-mail: drosati@wshein.com
VP, Sales: W Shannon Hein *E-mail:* shein@
  wshein.com
VP, Technol: Kyle Daving
Dir, Mktg: Shannon Furtak *E-mail:* sfurtak@
  wshein.com
Founded: 1961
Online publisher, law book publishers, legal peri-
  odicals, subscription, continuation, law libraries
  & micropublishers.
Catalog available.
Number of Titles Warehoused: 4,000
Membership(s): American Association of Law
  Libraries; The American Library Association
  (ALA)

Historic Aviation Books
Division of Sky Media LLC
640 Taft St NE, Minneapolis, MN 55413-2815
Tel: 612-206-3200 *Toll Free Tel:* 800-225-5575
  Fax: 612-877-3160
E-mail: info@historicaviation.com;
  customerservice@historicaviation.com
Web Site: www.historicaviation.com
Key Personnel
Owner: Greg E Herrick
Founded: 1969
Aviation books, videos, art prints, models & kits,
  puzzles & games, calendars, apparel, software,
  home decor & accessories.
Number of Titles Warehoused: 1,000

Historic Cherry Hill
523 1/2 S Pearl St, Albany, NY 12202
SAN: 111-3178
Tel: 518-434-4791 *Fax:* 518-434-4806
E-mail: info@historiccherryhill.org
Web Site: www.historiccherryhill.org
Key Personnel
Pres: Maryrita Dobiel
Dir: Liselle La France *E-mail:* liscllc@
  historiccherryhill.org
Founded: 1964
Historic house museum, tours, museum shop;
  publisher.
Number of Titles Warehoused: 5

The Hubbard Co
612 Clinton St, Defiance, OH 43512
Mailing Address: PO Drawer 100, Defiance, OH
  43512
Tel: 419-784-4455 *Toll Free Tel:* 888-448-2227
Web Site: www.hubbardcompany.com
Key Personnel
Pres: Thomas K Hubbard *E-mail:* tom@
  hubbardcompany.com
Founded: 1906
Class record & plan books. Commercial printer.
Catalog available.
Membership(s): Epicomm

Ideal Foreign Books LLC
132-10 Hillside Ave, Richmond Hill, NY 11418
Tel: 718-297-7477 *Toll Free Tel:* 800-284-2490
  Fax: 718-297-7645
E-mail: idealforeignbooks@att.net
Key Personnel
Owner & Pres: Alain Fetaya
Founded: 1977
Distribute foreign language books & materials,
  from elementary to college level, to bookstores,
  libraries & schools; specialize in French, Span-
  ish, German & Italian.
Catalog available.
Number of Titles Warehoused: 1,500
Membership(s): National Association of College
  Stores (NACS)

Independent Campus Stores Collaborative, see
  indiCo

indiCo
Subsidiary of National Association of College
  Stores (NACS)
528 E Lorain St, Oberlin, OH 44074-1298
SAN: 169-6823
Toll Free Tel: 800-622-7498; 800-321-3883 (or-
  ders)
E-mail: cs@goindico.com; info@goindico.com;
  orders@goindico.com; service@goindico.com
Web Site: www.goindico.com
Founded: 1963
Wholesaler of trade paperbacks, mass market
  paperbacks, hardcovers, calendars, computer
  products & peripherals, remainders & assort-
  ments, textbooks.
Number of Titles Warehoused: 2,000,000

Ingram Content Group LLC
One Ingram Blvd, La Vergne, TN 37086-1986
Tel: 615-793-5000 *Toll Free Tel:* 800-937-8000
  (retailers); 800-937-5300 (ext 1, libs)
E-mail: customerservice@ingramcontent.com
Web Site: www.ingramcontent.com
Key Personnel
Chmn: John Ingram
Pres & CEO: Shawn Morin
Chief Commercial Offr: Shawn Everson
Chief Content Offr: Phil Ollila
CFO: Brian Dauphin
Chief HR Offr: Wayne Keegan
CIO: Steve Marshall
Chief Legal Offr: Kelly Arnold
Chief Strategy & Devt Offr: Kent Freeman
Chief Venture Capital Offr: David Roland
VP & Cont: Tina Elmore
VP & Gen Mgr: Sabrina McCarthy
VP, Application Servs: Lori Dunbar
VP, Community Rel: Emily Weiss
VP, Content Acq: Kelly Gallagher
VP, Credit: Roger Lee
VP, HR: Jacqueline Letson
VP, Mktg: Brian McKinley
VP, Mdsg: George Tattersfield
VP, Retail Sales: Donald Roseman
Dir, Academic Servs: Kurt Hettler
Dir, Application Servs: Robert Barnard
Dir, Consumer Mktg: Kim Schutte
Dir, Digital Servs: Margaret Harrison
Dir, Mass Merchandisers Sales: Lisa Tomasello
Dir, Natl Accts: Michael Bell
Dir, Sales Opers: Tammy Spurlock
Sales Dir: Sharon Swados
Sr Mgr, Content Acqs: John Hussey
Sr Mgr, Mktg Servs: Ann Zangri
Sr Mgr, PR & Communs: Kris Wiese
Sr Mgr, Specialty Retail: Lori Bowen
Lib Sales & Servs Mgr: Tricia Racke Bengel
Mgr, Client Rel: Louisa Brody
Prod Mktg Mgr: Catherine Robinson
Proj Mgr, Integration & Outsource: Sterling
  Crawford
Specialty Retail Mgr: Megan Smith
Sales & Support Rep, Mass Mdse Group: Tori
  Cushman
Founded: 1964
Wholesaler of trade books, audiobooks, calendars,
  interactive information & inventory systems &
  periodicals to retailers, libraries, specialty mar-
  kets, higher education stores.
Number of Titles Warehoused: 500,000
Publication(s): *Advance* (monthly); *African American Connection* (3 issues/yr); *Business Connections* (semiannual); *Calendar Catalog* (annual); *Children's Advance* (6 issues/yr); *Children's Backlist* (annual); *Christian Advance*
  (6 issues/yr); *Computer Books Catalog* (6 is-
  sues/yr); *Cooking Catalog* (annual); *Holiday*
  (annual); *Libros en Espanol* (annual); *Paperback Advance* (monthly); *Professional/Techni-
  cal/Reference Cat* (semiannual); *Spring/Summer*
  (annual); *Trade Books for the Class Room* (annual); *Travel* (semiannual)

Branch Office(s)
6050 Dana Way, Antioch, TN 37013
7315 Innovation Blvd, Fort Wayne, IN 46818
4260 Port Union Rd, Fairfield, OH 45011
201 Ingram Dr, Roseberg, OR 97470
860 Nestle Way, Breinigsville, PA 18031
1200 Ingram Dr, Chambersburg, PA 17202

Ingram Micro Inc
3351 Michelson Dr, Suite 100, Irvin, CA 92612
Tel: 714-566-1000
E-mail: customerexperience@ingrammicro.com
Web Site: www.ingrammicro.com
Key Personnel
CEO: Alain Monie
CFO: Gina Mastantuono
EVP & Chief Info & Digital Offr: Tom Peck
EVP, Secy & Gen Coun: Augusto P Aragone
EVP, HR: Scott D Sherman
Founded: 1979
Full service distributor of microcomputer soft-
  ware, hardware, peripherals & accessories to
  resalers.
Number of Titles Warehoused: 4,500
Publication(s): *The Dealer Price Book* (quarterly);
  The Ingram Journal (weekly)
Branch Office(s)
1759 Wehrle Dr, Williamsville, NY 14221
  Tel: 716-633-3600

Institute of Intergovernmental Relations
Queen's University, Robert Sutherland Hall, Rm
  301, Kingston, ON K7L 3N6, Canada
Tel: 613-533-2080
E-mail: iigr@queensu.ca
Web Site: www.queensu.ca/iigr
Key Personnel
Dir: Dr Christian Leurpecht
Pubns Coord & Admin Secy: Mary Kennedy
Founded: 1965
Publish & distribute research & other scholarly
  work on Canadian federalism & intergovern-
  mental relations as it affects public policy.
Number of Titles Warehoused: 115

International Book Centre Inc
2391 Auburn Rd, Shelby Township, MI 48317
SAN: 208-7022
Tel: 586-254-7230 *Fax:* 586-254-7230
E-mail: ibc@ibcbooks.com
Web Site: www.ibcbooks.com
Key Personnel
Owner & Sales Mgr: Doris Mukalla
Founded: 1974
Importer, distributor of foreign language books.
  Distribute Arabic language textbooks, dictionar-
  ies, imports to bookstores, libraries & schools;
  distributor of University of Michigan textbooks
  on Arabic languages & all Librairie du Liban
  publications (Beirut, Lebanon). Distributor of
  English language learning books.
Number of Titles Warehoused: 200

International Institute of Reflexology Inc
PO Box 12642, St Petersburg, FL 33733-2642
Tel: 727-343-4811
E-mail: info@reflexology-usa.net; orderdept@
  reflexology-usa.net
Web Site: reflexology-usa.net
Key Personnel
Pres: Gail Byers *E-mail:* gailbyers@reflexology-
  usa.net
Founded: 1975
Paperbacks, hardbound & charts.
Number of Titles Warehoused: 7

International Press Publication Inc
Spadina Rd, Richmond Hill, ON L4B 3C5,
  Canada
Tel: 905-883-0343
E-mail: sales@ippbooks.com
Web Site: www.ippbooks.com; www.facebook.
  com/ippbooks; twitter.com/ippbooks2

Key Personnel
Pres: Bali Sethi
Founded: 1976
Reference books, yearbooks, directories, language dictionaries, library sales, trade, government research, business libraries, mail order & subscriptions: international, US, UK, India, China, Hong Kong & Canada.
Number of Titles Warehoused: 100,000
Membership(s): The American Library Association (ALA); Children's Literature Association (ChLA); Ontario Library Association

International Service Co
International Service Bldg, 333 Fourth Ave, Indialantic, FL 32903-4295
SAN: 169-5134
Tel: 321-724-1443 *Fax:* 321-724-1443
Key Personnel
Pres: Dennis Samuels
Compt: F Schneider
Mng Dir: Katherine Swanberg
Coord Dir: Ann C Samuels
Shipping & Receiving Mgr: Larry A Whobrey
Systems Supv: Suzanne Jones
Admin Asst: Irene August
Asst to Pres: Robert Cohen
Founded: 1958
Exporters & importers of books, quantity & single copy, periodicals & school supplies, commissionaires.

Interstate Books4School
Division of Interstate Promotional Distributors Inc
201 E Badger Rd, Madison, WI 53713
Tel: 608-277-2407 *Toll Free Tel:* 800-752-3131
  Fax: 608-277-2410
E-mail: sales@books4school.com
Web Site: www.books4school.com
Key Personnel
Pres: Marty Fields *Tel:* 608-277-2407 ext 14
  E-mail: mfields@books4school.com
Founded: 1924
Hardback & paperback books. Distribution of paperback books to educational institutions, K-12. Catalog also available online.
Catalog available.
Number of Titles Warehoused: 12,000

Iranbooks
PO Box 30087, Bethesda, MD 20824
Tel: 301-718-8188 *Toll Free Tel:* 888-718-8188
  Fax: 301-907-8707
E-mail: info@iranbooks.com
Web Site: www.iranbooks.com
Key Personnel
Mgr: Farhad Shirzad
Founded: 1979
Distribute for most Iranian publishers & Persian language publishers outside of Iran.

The Islander Group
269 Palii St, Mililani, HI 96789
Tel: 808-676-0116 *Toll Free Tel:* 877-828-4852
  Fax: 808-676-5156
E-mail: customerservice@islandergroup.com
Web Site: www.islandergroup.com
Key Personnel
CEO: Jeff Swartz
Pres & COO: Steve Holmberg
Founded: 1976
Hardcover & quality paperback supplier of Hawaiian & Pacific titles to stores & libraries, children's books.
Catalog available.
Number of Titles Warehoused: 6,500

Israel's Judaica Center
441 Clark Ave W, Thornhill, ON L4J 6W7, Canada

Tel: 905-881-1010 *Toll Free Tel:* 877-511-1010
  Fax: 905-881-1016
E-mail: contact@israelsjudaica.com; thornhill@israelsjudaica.com (retail store)
Web Site: www.israelsjudaica.com
Key Personnel
Pres: Joseph Segal *Tel:* 905-881-1010 ext 23
  E-mail: jsegal@israelsjudaica.com
Founded: 1982
Books & gift retail & wholesale, Judaica.
Number of Titles Warehoused: 2,500
Branch Office(s)
1172 Eglinton Ave W, Toronto, ON M6C 2E3, Canada *E-mail:* eglinton@israelsjudaica.com

The James & Law Co
217 W Main St, Clarksburg, WV 26301
SAN: 169-894X
Tel: 304-624-7401 *Toll Free Tel:* 800-253-5428
  Fax: 304-624-9331
E-mail: sales@jamesandlaw.com
Web Site: jamesandlaw.com
Key Personnel
Pres: George I Brown
VP & Retail Sales: Alice Godfrey
  E-mail: agodfrey@jamesandlaw.com
Founded: 1905
Suppliers of hardcover & paperback trade books, school supplies, reference books & microcomputer software to libraries & schools.

Kazi Publications Inc
3023 W Belmont Ave, Chicago, IL 60618
Tel: 773-267-7001 *Fax:* 773-267-7002
E-mail: info@kazi.org
Web Site: www.kazi.org
Key Personnel
Pres: Liaquat Ali
Mktg Dir: Mary Bakhtiar
Founded: 1972
Islamic books & supplies; books on Islam & Muslim world; Sufism.
Catalog available.
Number of Titles Warehoused: 1,963
Publication(s): *Catalog of Books on Islam & the Muslim World* (2 issues/yr)

Ketab Corp
12701 Van Nuys Blvd, Unit H, Pacoima, CA 91331
Tel: 310-477-7477 *Toll Free Tel:* 800-FOR-IRAN (367-4726) *Fax:* 818-908-1457
E-mail: ketab1@ketab.com
Web Site: www.ketab.com
Key Personnel
Pres: Bijan Khalili
Founded: 1981
Distribute Persian books & books in English about Iran.
Catalog available.
Number of Titles Warehoused: 5,000

Kinokuniya Bookstores of America Co Ltd
Subsidiary of Kinokuniya Co Ltd (Japan)
1581 Webster St, San Francisco, CA 94115
SAN: 121-8441
Tel: 415-567-6787 *Fax:* 415-567-4109
E-mail: sales@kinokuniya.com; san_francisco@kinokuniya.com; bookwebusa@kinokuniya.com (cust serv)
Web Site: usa.kinokuniya.com
Founded: 1969
Retail & wholesale Japanese books & magazines.
Number of Titles Warehoused: 80,000
Branch Office(s)
Little Tokyo, 123 Astronaut E S Onizuka St, Los Angeles, CA 90012 *Tel:* 213-687-4480
  E-mail: los_angeles@kinokuniya.com
Mitsuwa Marketplace, 3760 S Centinela Ave, Los Angeles, CA 90066 *Tel:* 310-482-3382
  E-mail: santamonica@kinokuniya.com

Mitsuwa Marketplace, 675 Saratoga Ave, San Jose, CA 95129 *Tel:* 408-252-1300
  E-mail: san_jose@kinokuniya.com
Mitsuwa Marketplace, 100 E Algonquin Rd, Arlington Heights, IL 60005 *Tel:* 847-427-2665
  E-mail: chicago@kinokuniya.com
Mitsuwa Marketplace, 595 River Rd, Edgewater, NJ 07020 *Tel:* 201-496-6910 *E-mail:* nj@kinokuniya.com
1073 Avenue of the Americas, New York, NY 10018 *Tel:* 212-869-1700 *E-mail:* nyinfo@kinokuniya.com
Uwajimaya Plaza, 10500 SW Beaverton-Hillsdale Hwy, Beaverton, OR 97005 *Tel:* 503-641-6240
  E-mail: beaverton@kinokuniya.com
6929 Airport Blvd, No 121, Austin, TX 78752
  Tel: 512-291-2026 *E-mail:* austin@kinokuniya.com
Carrollton Town Ctr, 2540 Old Denton Rd, Suite 114, Carrollton, TX 75006 *Tel:* 214-731-6800
  E-mail: carrollton@kinokuniya.com
Mitsuwa Marketplace, 100 Legacy Dr, Plano, TX 75023 *Tel:* 972-517-0226 *E-mail:* plano@kinokuniya.com
Uwajimaya Village, 525 S Weller St, Seattle, WA 98104 *Tel:* 206-587-2477 *E-mail:* seattle@kinokuniya.com

Learning World Inc
Subsidiary of Okhai Educational Inc
287 Wycliffe Ave, Vaughan, ON L4L 3N7, Canada
Key Personnel
Pres: Adam Okhai *E-mail:* ceo@tlcq.com
VP: Dr A Osman
Founded: 1884
Distributor of educational supplies, including law books & K-12 educational software.
Catalog available.
Number of Titles Warehoused: 730

Lectorum Publications Inc
205 Chubb Ave, Lyndhurst, NJ 07071
Tel: 201-559-2200 *Toll Free Tel:* 800-345-5946
  Fax: 201-559-2201 *Toll Free Fax:* 877-532-8676
E-mail: lectorum@lectorum.com
Web Site: www.lectorum.com
Key Personnel
Pres & CEO: Alex Correa *E-mail:* acorrea@lectorum.com
Lib & Trade Sales Mgr: Ingeborg Portales
  E-mail: iportales@lectorum.com
Opers Mgr: Fernando Febus *E-mail:* ffebus@lectorum.com
Collection Devt: Marjorie Samper
  E-mail: msamper@lectorum.com
Founded: 1960
America's oldest & largest distributor of children & adult books in Spanish, with titles from more than 500 domestic & foreign publishers. Lectorum serves schools & libraries, as well as the trade & various specialized markets, with the best selection of children's books in Spanish, including works originally written in Spanish, translations from other languages & the Spanish language editions of many popular children's books.
Catalog available.
Number of Titles Warehoused: 25,000

Library Bound Inc
100 Bathurst Dr, Unit 2, Waterloo, ON N2V 1V6, Canada
SAN: 116-9203
Tel: 519-885-3233 *Toll Free Tel:* 800-363-4728
  Fax: 519-885-2662
Web Site: www.librarybound.com
Key Personnel
Pres: Heather Bindseil *E-mail:* heatherb@librarybound.com

COO: Duncan Hamilton *E-mail:* duncan@
librarybound.com
Dir, Sales & Mktg: Terry Palmer *E-mail:* terry.
palmer@librarybound.com
Music & Video Games Mgr: Tracy Reid
E-mail: tracy@librarybound.com
Print Mgr: Ron Stadnik *E-mail:* ron@
librarybound.com
Founded: 1993
National Canadian wholesaler for print materi-
als & AV products to public libraries. Full
cataloging including MARC records & cus-
tomized processing available for all material
types, print, bestsellers, audiobooks, CD music,
DVD/Blu-ray & video games.
Catalog available.
Branch Office(s)
LBI West, 8370 Prince Edward St, Vancouver,
BC V5X 3R9, Canada *Tel:* 604-434-5242
Fax: 604-434-5262
Membership(s): BCLA; Ontario Library Associa-
tion

The Library Services Centre
131 Shoemaker St, Kitchener, ON N2E 3B5,
Canada
SAN: 319-2024
Tel: 519-746-4420 *Toll Free Tel:* 800-265-3360
(CN only) *Fax:* 519-746-4425
Web Site: www.lsc.on.ca
Key Personnel
CEO: Michael Monahan
CFO: Kirk Oliver
CIO: Marta Gonzalez
VP, Sales & Mktg: Cecile Dillon
VP, Servs: Trish Hayes
Founded: 1985
Wholesalers.
Publication(s): *Spotlight* (irregular)

Login Canada
300 Saulteaux Crescent, Winnipeg, MB R3J 3T2,
Canada
Tel: 204-837-2987 *Toll Free Tel:* 800-665-
1148 (CN only) *Fax:* 204-837-3116
Toll Free Fax: 800-665-0103
E-mail: sales@lb.ca
Web Site: www.lb.ca
Key Personnel
Pres & CEO: Mark Champagne *E-mail:* markc@
lb.ca
CFO: Sharon Murray *E-mail:* sho@lb.ca
Chief Mktg Offr: Russell Friesen
E-mail: russellf@lb.ca
Founded: 1991
Health science books.
Number of Titles Warehoused: 30,000

Lushena Books Inc
607 Country Club Dr, Unit E, Bensenville, IL
60106
Tel: 630-238-8708 *Toll Free Tel:* 800-785-1545
Fax: 630-238-8824
E-mail: lushenabks@yahoo.com
Web Site: lushenabks.com
Key Personnel
Pres & Gen Mgr: Luther A Warner
Founded: 1988
African-American books to retailers.
Catalog available.
Number of Titles Warehoused: 1,000

Mackin Educational Resources
3505 County Rd 42 W, Burnsville, MN 55306
Tel: 952-895-9540 *Toll Free Tel:* 800-245-9540
Fax: 952-894-8806 *Toll Free Fax:* 800-369-
5490
E-mail: mackin@mackin.com
Web Site: www.mackin.com
PreK-12 book resellers.

Maison de l'Education Inc
10840 Ave Millen, Montreal, QC H2C 0A5,
Canada
Tel: 514-384-4401 *Fax:* 514-384-4844
E-mail: librairie@maisondeleducation.com
Web Site: maisondeleducation.com
Key Personnel
Dir Gen: Danielle Dion
Founded: 1967
Bookstore & distributor.

Manning's Book & Prints
Subsidiary of Prints Old & Rare
580-M Crespi Dr, Pacifica, CA 94044
Tel: 415-621-3565 *Toll Free Tel:* 800-TRY-MAPS
(879-6277) *Fax:* 650-355-1851
E-mail: staff@printsoldandrare.com;
manningsbk@aol.com
Web Site: www.printsoldandrare.com
Key Personnel
Owner: Kathleen Manning
Founded: 1972
Buy, sell, rent old prints, maps, books; wholesale
antique prints.
Catalog available.
Membership(s): Antiquarian Booksellers Associa-
tion of America (ABAA)

The Mazel Co
31000 Aurora Rd, Solon, OH 44139-2769
Tel: 440-248-5200 *Toll Free Tel:* 800-443-4789
Fax: 440-349-1931
Web Site: www.themazelcompany.com
Closeout & remainder liquidator.
Branch Office(s)
1020 Taylor Station Rd, Suite A, Gahanna, OH
43230-6674 *Tel:* 614-239-2331 *Fax:* 614-239-
2357
9555 Foster Ave, Suite 595, Schiller Park, IL
60176 *Tel:* 847-261-9680 *Fax:* 847-261-9679
230 Fifth Ave, Suite 918, New York, NY 10001-
7704 *Tel:* 212-696-0200 *Fax:* 212-696-0073

MBS Textbook Exchange Inc
2711 W Ash, Columbia, MO 65203
Mailing Address: PO Box 637, Columbia, MO
65205-0637
Tel: 573-445-2243 *Toll Free Tel:* 800-325-0530
(textbook solutions); 800-325-4138 (bookstore
systems) *Fax:* 573-446-5256
E-mail: cserv@mbsbooks.com
Web Site: www.mbsbooks.com
Key Personnel
Pres: Mark Henderson
VP, Sales & Mktg: Jeff Miller
Founded: 1973
College textbook wholesaler.

**Le Messager Chretien (The Christian
Messenger)**
185 Gatineau Ave, Gatineau, QC J8T 4J7, Canada
Tel: 819-243-8880 *Toll Free Tel:* 800-263-8086
Fax: 819-243-1220
E-mail: info@messagerchretien.com
Web Site: www.messagerchretien.com
Key Personnel
Contact: Luc Deschenes
Founded: 1981
Christian books & Bibles.
Number of Titles Warehoused: 3,000
Branch Office(s)
1148 rue des Cascades, St-Hyacinthe, QC J2S
3G8, Canada, Contact: Marielle Charland
Tel: 450-774-8086 *Toll Free Tel:* 866-774-8086

Metro 360
120 Sinnott Rd, Scarborough, ON M1L 4N1,
Canada
Tel: 416-752-8720 *Toll Free Tel:* 888-260-2208
Web Site: www.metro360.ca

Key Personnel
Pres & CEO: Daniel Shapiro
Founded: 1915
Wholesaler of magazines & books. Branch of-
fices in Calgary, Edmonton, Montreal, Regina,
Saskatoon & Winnipeg.
Number of Titles Warehoused: 20,000

Midwest Library Service
11443 Saint Charles Rock Rd, Bridgeton, MO
63044
SAN: 169-4243
Tel: 314-739-3100 *Fax:* 314-739-1326
E-mail: mail@midwestls.com
Web Site: www.midwestls.com
Key Personnel
Pres: Howard N Lesser
VP: Herbert M Lesser
Gen Mgr: Georgia Willen *E-mail:* willen@
midwestls.com
Book Buyer: Melissa Williams
Founded: 1959
Service to academic & public libraries for more
than half a century. Complete order fulfillment
is a paramount objective, coupled with prompt,
personalized assistance from an expert staff of
professionals. Midwest's comprehensive ser-
vices, products & resources are all designed to
improve your library's efficiency.
Number of Titles Warehoused: 75,000
Publication(s): *Choice's Outstanding Academic
Titles Catalog*; *Sci-Tech-Health Sciences Catalog*; *University Press Catalog*; *University Press
Law Catalog*
Membership(s): The American Library Association (ALA)

MMoCA Museum Store
227 State St, Madison, WI 53703
Tel: 608-257-3222 *Fax:* 608-257-1219
E-mail: store@mmoca.org
Web Site: www.mmoca.org
Key Personnel
Dir, Retail Opers: Leslie Genszler
Mgr & Buyer: Laurie Stacy
Founded: 1951
Art catalogues & museum store.
Number of Titles Warehoused: 20
Membership(s): Museum Store Association
(MSA)

Montfort Publications
Division of Montfort Missionaries
26 S Saxon Ave, Bay Shore, NY 11706-8993
SAN: 169-5053
Tel: 631-665-0726; 631-666-7500 *Fax:* 631-665-
0726
E-mail: info@montfortpublications.com
Web Site: www.montfortpublications.com
Key Personnel
Dir: Hugh Guillespie
Founded: 1947
Religious & Catholic books, devotional & theo-
logical, about Mariology & Marian spirituality
only.
Catalog available.
Number of Titles Warehoused: 20

Motorbooks
Division of Quarto Publishing Group USA Inc
100 Cummings Ctr, Suite 265D, Beverly, MA
01915
Tel: 978-282-9590 *Toll Free Tel:* 800-759-0190
(orders)
Web Site: www.quartoknows.com/motorbooks
Key Personnel
SVP & Group Publg Dir, US: Winnie Prentiss
E-mail: winnie.prentiss@quarto.com
Publr: Zack Miller *E-mail:* zack.miller@quarto.
com
Sr Acqs Ed: Dennis Pernu *E-mail:* dennis.pernu@
quarto.com

Mgr, Spec Mkt Sales: Nichole Schiele
    E-mail: nichole.schiele@quarto.com
Mktg Mgr: Steve Roth E-mail: steve.roth@quarto.
    com
Founded: 1965
Number of Titles Warehoused: 14,000

National Book Co Inc
Division of W W Norton & Company Inc
Keystone Industrial Park, Dunmore, PA 18512
SAN: 157-1869
Tel: 570-346-2029 *Toll Free Tel:* 800-233-4830
Founded: 1960
Fulfillment center; invoicing & shipping; special-
    ize in college text & trade paperbacks.
Number of Titles Warehoused: 13,000

National Book Network (NBN)
Subsidiary of Rowman & Littlefield Publishing
    Group
4501 Forbes Blvd, Suite 200, Lanham, MD
    20706
Tel: 301-459-3366 *Toll Free Tel:* 800-462-
    6420 (orders only) *Fax:* 301-429-5746
    Toll Free Fax: 800-338-4550 (orders only)
E-mail: customercare@nbnbooks.com
Web Site: www.nbnbooks.com
Key Personnel
CEO: Jed Lyons
COO: Robert S Marsh E-mail: rmarsh@rowman.
    com
SVP & CFO: Michael Lippenholz
    E-mail: mlippenholz@rowman.com
Pres: Jason Brockwell E-mail: jbrockwell@
    nbnbooks.com
VP, Opers: Mike Cornell E-mail: mcornell@
    nbnbooks.com
VP, Publr & Cust Servs: Carla Quental
    E-mail: cquental@nbnbooks.com
Dir, Sales Admin: Sylvia Williams
    E-mail: swilliams@nbnbooks.com
Intl Sales Dir: Les Petriw E-mail: lpetriw@
    nbnbooks.com
Mgr, Dist: Sue Bumbaugh E-mail: sbumbaugh@
    nbnbooks.com
Publr Servs Mgr: Karen Mattscheck
    E-mail: kmattscheck@nbnbooks.com
Founded: 1986
National sales, marketing, order fulfillment, dis-
    tribution & collections services for independent
    trade book publishers.
Distribution center located in Blue Ridge Summit,
    PA.
Number of Titles Warehoused: 25,000

National Learning Corp
212 Michael Dr, Syosset, NY 11791
Tel: 516-921-8888 *Toll Free Tel:* 800-632-8888
    Fax: 516-921-8743
E-mail: info@passbooks.com
Web Site: www.passbooks.com
Key Personnel
Pres & CEO: Michael P Rudman
Founded: 1967
Educational, commercial, industrial & government
    sales.
Catalog available.
Number of Titles Warehoused: 6,000
Publication(s): *Passbooks*
Membership(s): Association of American Publish-
    ers (AAP)

Mrs Nelson's Library Services
Division of Mrs Nelson's Toy & Book Shop
1650 W Orange Grove Ave, Pomona, CA 91768
SAN: 168-9703
Tel: 909-397-7820 *Toll Free Tel:* 800-875-9911
    Fax: 909-397-7833
E-mail: bookcompany@mrsnelsons.com
Web Site: www.mrsnelsons.com
Key Personnel
Pres: Judy Nelson

Mgr: Patrick Nelson *E-mail:* pnelson@
    mrsnelsons.com
Founded: 1985
Prebound novels, wholesale book orders & text-
    book rebinding.
Catalog available.
Membership(s): California School Library Associ-
    ation (CSLA)

New England Book Service Inc
7000 Vt Rte 17 W, Addison, VT 05491
Tel: 802-759-3000 *Toll Free Tel:* 800-356-5772
    Fax: 802-759-3220
E-mail: nebs@together.net
Web Site: www.nebooks.com
Key Personnel
Pres: Fred Morrow
VP: Dee Morrow
Founded: 1959
Book service/book store. All books available.

The New England Mobile Book Fair®
241 Needham St, Newton, MA 02464
SAN: 169-3530
Tel: 617-527-5817; 617-964-7440
E-mail: customerservice@nebookfair.com
Web Site: nebookfair.com
Key Personnel
Owner: Tom Lyons
Founded: 1958
Juveniles, adult hardcovers, paperbacks, trade pa-
    perbacks & remaindered books.

New Leaf Distributing Co
Subsidiary of Shakti LLC
401 Thornton Rd, Lithia Springs, GA 30122-1557
SAN: 169-1449
Tel: 770-948-7845 *Toll Free Tel:* 800-326-2665
    (orders) *Fax:* 770-944-2313 *Toll Free Fax:* 800-
    326-1066 (orders)
E-mail: customerservice@newleaf-dist.com
Web Site: newleafdist.com
Key Personnel
Pres: Santosh Krinsky
VP, Opers: Karen Price
Founded: 1975
Health & metaphysics.
Catalog available.
Number of Titles Warehoused: 30,000
Membership(s): American Booksellers Associa-
    tion (ABA)

**Newborn Enterprises Inc (Altoona News
    Agency)**
808 Green Ave, Altoona, PA 16601
Tel: 814-944-3593
Key Personnel
Pres: Barry Newborn
Wholesale distributor of magazines, books, news-
    papers & videos.

North 49 Books
Division of Waldock Publishing Ltd
35 Prince Andrew Place, Toronto, ON M3C 2H2,
    Canada
SAN: 117-2689
Tel: 416-449-4000 *Toll Free Tel:* 800-490-4049
    Fax: 416-449-9924 *Toll Free Fax:* 888-349-
    2221
E-mail: sales@north49books.com
Web Site: www.north49books.com
Key Personnel
Pres: Peter Mikos
Founded: 1992
Catalog available in Winter, Spring & Fall.
Catalog available.
Number of Titles Warehoused: 2,500

Ollis Book Co
28 E 35 St, Steger, IL 60475
SAN: 169-2224

Mailing Address: PO Box 258, Steger, IL 60475
Tel: 708-755-5151 *Toll Free Tel:* 800-323-0343
    (natl) *Fax:* 708-755-5153
Key Personnel
Pres: Kenneth R Ollis
Founded: 1965
Juvenile books only.
Number of Titles Warehoused: 2,500

Osa's Ark Museum Shop
Division of The Martin and Osa Johnson Safari
    Museum Inc
111 N Lincoln Ave, Chanute, KS 66720
Tel: 620-431-2730 *Fax:* 620-431-2730
E-mail: osajohns@safarimuseum.com; osasark@
    yahoo.com
Web Site: www.safarimuseum.com
Key Personnel
Dir: Conrad G Froehlich
Mgr: Shirley Rogers-Naff
Founded: 1961
Wholesaler.
Number of Titles Warehoused: 20

Oyster River Press
36 Oyster River Rd, Durham, NH 03824-3029
Tel: 603-868-5006
E-mail: oysterriverpress@comcast.net
Web Site: www.oysterriverbooks.com; www.
    facebook.com/OysterRiverPress
Key Personnel
Publr & Ed: Cicely Buckley
Founded: 1987
Edit, format, illustrate, publish & distribute. Also
    wholesaler of bilingual poetry publications.
Number of Titles Warehoused: 39
Publication(s): *Vatis Warme Hande*

Pannonia Bookstore
300 Sainte Clair Ave W, Suite 103, Toronto, ON
    M4V 1S4, Canada
Tel: 416-966-5156
E-mail: info@pannonia.ca
Web Site: www.pannonia.ca
Key Personnel
Owner: Zsolt Bede Fazekas; Hortenzia Papp
Founded: 1957
Subscriptions, mail order, retail.
Number of Titles Warehoused: 15,000

Paperbacks For Educators
426 W Front St, Washington, MO 63090
SAN: 103-3379
Tel: 314-960-3015
E-mail: paperbacks@usmo.com
Web Site: www.any-book-in-print.com
Key Personnel
Pres: David L Craig *E-mail:* davecraig@usmo.
    com
Founded: 1978
Wholesaler to schools. Specialize in counseling,
    bibliotherapy for children & teens, career, staff
    development, teacher resources & parenting.
Number of Titles Warehoused: 8,000

Parasource Marketing & Distribution Ltd
55 Woodslee Ave, Paris, ON N3L 3E5, Canada
Mailing Address: PO Box 98, Paris, ON N3L
    3E5, Canada
Tel: 519-442-7853 *Toll Free Tel:* 800-263-2664
    Fax: 519-442-1303 *Toll Free Fax:* 800-461-
    8575
E-mail: custserv@parasource.com
Web Site: parasource.com
Key Personnel
Pres: Greg Tombs *Tel:* 519-442-7853 ext 231
    E-mail: greg.tombs@parasource.com
Dir, Sales & Mktg: Debbie Tempelmeyer
    Tel: 519-442-7853 ext 252 *E-mail:* deb.
    tempelmeyer@parasource.com
Founded: 1912

Distribute to bookstores, libraries & schools. Drop shipping available. General trade books, juvenile & young adult, large print, mass market, trade & paperback.

Pathway Book Service
Division of The No Tomorrow Book Co
34 Production Ave, Keene, NH 03431
SAN: 170-0545
Tel: 603-357-0236 *Toll Free Tel:* 800-345-6665
Fax: 603-965-2181
E-mail: pbs@pathwaybook.com
Web Site: www.pathwaybook.com
Key Personnel
Partner: George Corrette; Robert Zipoli
Founded: 1978
Complete distribution & fulfillment company distributing titles to all of the major wholesalers, including Ingram, Baker & Taylor, Barnes & Noble & Books-A-Million as well as Amazon & the popular online digital catalog used by bookstore buyers, Edelweiss+.
Number of Titles Warehoused: 8,200

Paulist Press
997 Macarthur Blvd, Mahwah, NJ 07430-9990
SAN: 202-5159
Tel: 201-825-7300 *Toll Free Tel:* 800-218-1903
Fax: 201-825-6921 *Toll Free Fax:* 800-836-3161
E-mail: info@paulistpress.com
Web Site: www.paulistpress.com
Key Personnel
Pres & Publr: Mark-David Janus, CSP
Edit Dir: Trace Murphy
Dir, Mktg: Gloria Capik
Dir, Mktg & Sales: Bob Byrns *E-mail:* bbyrns@paulistpress.com
Sr Academic Ed: Donna Crilly
Founded: 1865
Religious & Catholic books.
Catalog available.
Number of Titles Warehoused: 1,650
Membership(s): Association of Catholic Publishers Inc

Penfield Books
215 Brown St, Iowa City, IA 52245
SAN: 221-6671
Tel: 319-337-9998 *Toll Free Tel:* 800-728-9998
Fax: 319-351-6846
E-mail: penfield@penfieldbooks.com; orders@penfieldbooks.com
Web Site: www.penfieldbooks.com
Key Personnel
Publr: Joan Liffring-Zug Bourret
Founded: 1979
Publisher & distributor of cookbooks, ethnic cultural cookbooks, crafts & folk art & ethnic subjects.
Catalog available.
Number of Titles Warehoused: 200

The Penworthy Company LLC
219 N Milwaukee St, 4th fl, Milwaukee, WI 53202
Tel: 414-287-4600 *Toll Free Tel:* 800-262-2665
Fax: 414-287-4602
E-mail: info@penworthy.com
Web Site: www.penworthy.com
Key Personnel
Pres: Holly Ritz
EVP: Julie Plantz *Tel:* 414-287-4600 ext 211
E-mail: julie.plantz@penworthy.com
Founded: 1982
Prebinding; specialize in juvenile books.
Number of Titles Warehoused: 2,000

Perma-Bound Books
Division of Hertzberg-New Method Inc
617 E Vandalia Rd, Jacksonville, IL 62650

Tel: 217-243-5451 *Toll Free Tel:* 800-637-6581
Fax: 217-243-7505 *Toll Free Fax:* 800-551-1169
E-mail: books@perma-bound.com
Web Site: www.perma-bound.com
Key Personnel
Owner & Pres: James Orr
Founded: 1954
Bookbinding; education market; wholesale books K-12.
Catalog available.
Number of Titles Warehoused: 5,000,000
Branch Office(s)
PO Box 868, Sta Main, Peterborough, ON K9J 7A2, Canada *Tel:* 705-742-1513 *Toll Free Tel:* 800-461-1999 *Toll Free Fax:* 888-250-3811
E-mail: perma-bound.ca@sympatico.ca *Web Site:* www.perma-bound.com/canada

Polybook Distributors
Subsidiary of Main Street Book Shop Inc
501 Mamaroneck Ave, White Plains, NY 10605
SAN: 169-5568
Mailing Address: PO Box 248, White Plains, NY 10605
Tel: 914-328-6346 *Fax:* 914-328-6348
Key Personnel
Owner & Pres: Joshua H Makanoff
Founded: 1965
School book fairs, RIF distributor, rack jobbing.
Number of Titles Warehoused: 50,000

Promotional Book Co
Division of Strathearn Books Inc
12 Cranfield Rd, No 100, Toronto, ON M4B 3G8, Canada
Tel: 416-759-2226 *Fax:* 416-759-2150
Key Personnel
Pres: Ron Goelman *Tel:* 416-759-2226 ext 236
VP, Sales & Purch: Joan Rickerby *Tel:* 416-759-2226 ext 232 *E-mail:* joanr@promobookco.com
Founded: 1981
Remainders & overstock.

Redwing Book Co
202 Bendix St, Taos, NM 87571
Tel: 575-758-7758 *Toll Free Tel:* 800-873-3946 (US); 888-873-3947 (CN) *Fax:* 575-758-7768
E-mail: info@redwingbooks.com; custsrv@redwingbooks.com
Web Site: www.redwingbooks.com
Key Personnel
Pres & Publr: Robert Felt
Founded: 1973
Wholesale & direct mail, trade paperbacks & scholarly books; specialize in acupuncture & oriental medicine. Publish scholarly works in oriental medicine under the imprint Paradigm Publications. Distribute selected titles for a variety of publishers, US & foreign.
Number of Titles Warehoused: 1,500
Publication(s): *Redwing Reviews* (biennial, circ 50,000)

Regent Book Co
PO Box 37, Liberty Corner, NJ 07938
SAN: 169-4715
Tel: 973-574-7600 *Toll Free Tel:* 800-999-9554
Fax: 973-944-5073 *Toll Free Fax:* 888-597-3661
E-mail: info@regentbook.com
Web Site: www.regentbook.com
Key Personnel
Owner: Janice Zucker
VP: Josh Zucker
Founded: 1958
Juveniles (kits available), K-12, library bound juvenile books & cataloging services available.
Number of Titles Warehoused: 3,000

Rising Sun Book Co
1424 Stony Brook Rd, Stony Brook, NY 11790

Tel: 631-473-7000 *Fax:* 631-473-7447
Web Site: risingsunbook.com
Key Personnel
Pres: Arun Shanbhag *E-mail:* shanbhagarun@aol.com
Founded: 1983
Book wholesaler & exporter.
Number of Titles Warehoused: 10,000

Riverside Book Co Inc
PO Box 237043, New York, NY 10023-0028
Tel: 212-595-0700 *Fax:* 212-595-0700
Web Site: www.riversidebook.com
Key Personnel
Pres: Victor Eskenazi
Publr: Brian Eskenazi *E-mail:* eskenazi@riversidebook.com
Founded: 1987
Art, architecture/design, photography, gardening, cookbooks & reprints.
Number of Titles Warehoused: 30

Rizzoli Bookstores
1133 Broadway, New York, NY 10010
Tel: 212-759-2424 *Toll Free Tel:* 800-52-BOOKS (522-6657) *Fax:* 212-826-9754
Web Site: rizzolibookstore.com; www.rizzoliusa.com
Art books.

Richard Owen Roberts, Booksellers & Publishers
139 N Washington St, Wheaton, IL 60189
SAN: 239-4847
Mailing Address: PO Box 21, Wheaton, IL 60187-0021
Tel: 630-752-4122
E-mail: sales@rorbooks.com
Web Site: www.rorbooks.com
Key Personnel
Pres: Richard Owen Roberts
VP: Margaret J Roberts
Founded: 1961
Book distribution to stores, schools & libraries.
Number of Titles Warehoused: 51

Rushmore News Inc
924 E Saint Andrew, Rapid City, SD 57701
SAN: 169-7846
Tel: 605-342-2617 *Toll Free Tel:* 800-423-0501
Key Personnel
Gen Mgr: Michael Freese *E-mail:* mfrushmore@rushmore.com
Founded: 1956
Number of Titles Warehoused: 24,000

Ryukyu Books & Periodicals Inc
PO Box 535, Olathe, KS 66051
Tel: 913-782-3920 *Toll Free Tel:* 800-383-4017
Fax: 913-780-1750
E-mail: info@ryukyubooks.com
Web Site: www.ryukyu.com
Key Personnel
Pres & CEO: Bill Wiswell
Founded: 1984
Wholesale books on martial arts.
Number of Titles Warehoused: 1,683

S & L Sales Co Inc
2165 Industrial Blvd, Waycross, GA 31503
Tel: 912-283-0210 *Toll Free Tel:* 800-243-3699
Fax: 912-283-0261 *Toll Free Fax:* 800-736-7329
E-mail: sales@slsales.com
Web Site: slsales.com
Key Personnel
Pres: Rickey L Perritt
Founded: 1965
Remainders.
Number of Titles Warehoused: 25,000

San Diego Museum of Art
Balboa Park, 1450 El Prado, San Diego, CA 92112
SAN: 121-3679
Mailing Address: PO Box 122107, San Diego, CA 92112-2107
Tel: 619-232-7931 *Fax:* 619-232-9367
Web Site: www.sdmart.org
Key Personnel
Assoc Dir, Earned Income: Chacho Herman *E-mail:* cherman@sdmart.org
Publish, wholesale & retail.
Publication(s): *Exhibition Art Catalogs*

Sandhill Book Marketing Ltd
Millcreek Industrial Park, Unit 4, 3308 Appaloosa Rd, Kelowna, BC V1V 2W5, Canada
SAN: 115-2181
Tel: 250-491-1446 *Toll Free Tel:* 800-667-3848 (CN only) *Fax:* 250-491-4066
E-mail: info@sandhillbooks.com
Web Site: www.sandhillbooks.com
Key Personnel
Pres: Nancy Wise
Founded: 1984
Trade book distribution (no imprints from the US); specialty store, only carry Canadian titles/publishers.
Number of Titles Warehoused: 1,000

Schoenhof's Foreign Books Inc
Subsidiary of MEP Inc
76 A Mount Auburn St, Cambridge, MA 02138
SAN: 122-7963
Tel: 617-547-8855
E-mail: info@schoenhofs.com
Web Site: www.schoenhofs.com
Key Personnel
Pres: Nicolas Mengin
Mgr: Daniel Eastman
Founded: 1856
French, Spanish, German, Italian, Russian, Portuguese, Arabic, Slavic, Scandinavian, Greek & Latin literature, children's books & nonfiction. Dictionaries, audio courses & grammars in over 700 languages & dialects.
Number of Titles Warehoused: 75,000

Scholastic Book Fairs®
Division of Scholastic Inc
1080 Greenwood Blvd, Lake Mary, FL 32746
Tel: 407-829-8000 *Fax:* 407-829-2600
E-mail: custservbf@scholasticbookfairs.com
Web Site: www.scholastic.com/bookfairs
Key Personnel
Pres & EVP, Scholastic Inc: Sasha Quinton
VP, Busn Devt & Strategy: Ben Stone
VP, Fin: Phil Bernhardt
VP, Sales & Serv (North): Jeff Marty
VP, Sales & Serv (South): Shane Kyle
VP, Mktg: Laura Lundgren
VP, Prod Category Mgmt: Eric Compton
VP, Field Deployment & Optimization: Brian Carter
VP, HR: Tim Vuolo
Founded: 1981
Scholastic Book Fairs®, in partnership with schools across the country, hosts more than 120,000 book-sale events each year, reaching more than 35 million children & their families in preschool-9th grade. Book Fairs provide students, teachers & parents access to thousands of affordable books & educational products & is responsible for putting more than 100 million books in the hands of children, helping to foster enthusiasm for reading & generating more than $200 million annually in fundraising for school projects & classroom materials.
Number of Titles Warehoused: 2,000

Schroeder's Book Haven
104 Michigan Ave, League City, TX 77573

SAN: 122-7998
Tel: 281-332-5226
E-mail: info@bookhaventexas.com
Web Site: www.bookhaventexas.com
Key Personnel
Mgr & Buyer: Bert Schroeder
Founded: 1968
Wholesale to schools & libraries.
Number of Titles Warehoused: 15,000

SEBCO Books, see Southeastern Book Co

Sheriar Foundation Bookstore
603 Briarwood Dr, Myrtle Beach, SC 29572
SAN: 203-2457
Tel: 843-272-1339 *Fax:* 843-361-1747
Web Site: www.sheriarbooks.org
Key Personnel
Mgr: Laura Smith *E-mail:* laura@sheriarbooks.org
Founded: 1971
Publishes & distributes books by & about Meher Baba, videos, music & photos.
Catalog available.
Number of Titles Warehoused: 60

Small Changes
1418 NW 53 St, Seattle, WA 98107
Mailing Address: PO Box 70740, Seattle, WA 98127
Tel: 206-382-1980 *Fax:* 206-382-1514
E-mail: info@smallchanges.com
Web Site: www.smallchanges.com
Key Personnel
Owner: Shari Basom
Founded: 1977
Wholesale distribution magazines, calendars, natural foods stores.
Number of Titles Warehoused: 550
Membership(s): California Independent Booksellers Alliance (CALIBA); Pacific Northwest Booksellers Association (PNBA)

Social Studies School Service
10200 Jefferson Blvd, PO Box 802, Culver City, CA 90232
Mailing Address: PO Box 802, Culver City, CA 90232-0802
Tel: 310-839-2436 *Toll Free Tel:* 800-421-4246 *Fax:* 310-839-2249 *Toll Free Fax:* 800-944-5432 (US & CN)
E-mail: access@socialstudies.com
Web Site: www.socialstudies.com
Key Personnel
CEO: David Weiner
Chief Learning Offr: Aaron Willis
Founded: 1965
Provide a wide variety of supplementary curriculum materials to schools, including books, videos, computer software, maps & globes.
Catalog available.
Number of Titles Warehoused: 15,000

SOM Publishing
Division of School of Metaphysics
163 Moon Valley Rd, Windyville, MO 65783
SAN: 159-5423
Tel: 417-345-8411 *Fax:* 417-345-6668
E-mail: som@som.org; dreams@dreamschool.org
Web Site: www.som.org; www.dreamschool.org
Key Personnel
Pres: Dr Christine Spretnjak
Founded: 1973
Publishing & wholesale distribution.
Number of Titles Warehoused: 15,000

Southeastern Book Co
Division of Library Sales Inc
2001 SW 31 Ave, Pembroke Park, FL 33009
Tel: 954-985-9400 *Toll Free Tel:* 800-223-3251 *Fax:* 954-987-2200

E-mail: staff@sebcobooks.com
Web Site: www.sebcobooks.com
Key Personnel
Pres: Dan Comer *E-mail:* dan@sebcobooks.com
Founded: 1984
Distributor of paperback classroom sets, library bound books & ebooks to schools & libraries.

Southern Book Service
Affiliate of Book Warehouse Inc
4360 NW 135 St, Opa-locka, FL 33054
Tel: 305-681-3424 *Fax:* 305-681-8427
Founded: 1996
Wholesaler of hardcover & paperback books; distributor of Florida regional books, audios, hardcover, quality paper, mass market paper, regional & audio, Spanish books.
Catalog available.
Number of Titles Warehoused: 100,000
Publication(s): *Advance Daily* (circ 2,000); *Book Catalog* (circ 2,000)

Southern Tier News Company, Inc
353 Upper Oakwood Ave, Elmira Heights, NY 14903
Mailing Address: PO Box 2128, Elmira Heights, NY 14903-0128
Tel: 607-734-7108 *Toll Free Tel:* 888-287-4786 *Fax:* 607-734-6825
Web Site: www.southerntiernews.com
Key Personnel
Pres: Jeff Rubin
Founded: 1909
Hardcover, trade paperback, mass market & educational paperbacks & newspapers, children's books & magazines. Periodical distribution.

Southern Wisconsin News Co
Subsidiary of Purnell Brothers Inc
58 Artisan Dr, Edgerton, WI 53534
Tel: 608-884-2600 *Fax:* 608-884-2636
Web Site: www.southernwisconsinnews.com
Key Personnel
Owner & Pres: Thomas Purnell *E-mail:* tpurnell@southernwisconsinnews.com
Founded: 1933
Wholesaler of magazines & books.
Number of Titles Warehoused: 4,000

Sparkhouse, see Augsburg Fortress Publishers, Publishing House of the Evangelical Lutheran Church in America

Sparkhouse Family, see Augsburg Fortress Publishers, Publishing House of the Evangelical Lutheran Church in America

Spring Arbor Distributors Inc
Unit of Ingram Content Group LLC
One Ingram Blvd, La Vergne, TN 37086-1986
Toll Free Tel: 800-395-4340 *Toll Free Fax:* 800-876-0186
E-mail: customerservice@ingramcontent.com
Web Site: www.ingramcontent.com
Key Personnel
Sales Rep: Mary Lou Alexander *Tel:* 615-213-3319 *E-mail:* marylou.alexander@ingramcontent.com
Founded: 1978
Distribute Christian books, Bibles, music & videos to Christian retail stores.
Number of Titles Warehoused: 260,000
Branch Office(s)
Indiana Distribution Center, 7315 Innovation Blvd, Fort Wayne, IN 46818-1371
Oregon Distribution Center, 201 Ingram Dr, Roseburg, OR 97471
Chambersburg Distribution Center, 1240 Ingram Dr, Chambersburg, PA 17202

Sunbelt Publications Inc
1250 Fayette St, El Cajon, CA 92020-1511
SAN: 630-0790
Tel: 619-258-4911 *Toll Free Tel:* 800-626-6579
(cust serv) *Fax:* 619-258-4916
E-mail: info@sunbeltpublications.com;
sunbeltbook@sunbeltpub.com
Web Site: sunbeltpublications.com
Key Personnel
CEO: Lowell Lindsay *E-mail:* llindsay@
sunbeltpub.com
Pres: Diana Lindsay *Tel:* 619-258-4911 ext 104
E mail: dlindsay@sunbeltpub.com
Pubns Mgr: Debi Young *Tel:* 619-258-4905 ext
103 *E-mail:* dyoung@sunbeltpub.com
Sales Mgr: Lisa Gulick *Tel:* 619-258-4911 ext
112
Acctg Coord: Maria Groschup-Black *Tel:* 619-
258-4905 ext 108 *E-mail:* maria@sunbeltpub.
com
Mktg Coord: Rebecca Kriz *Tel:* 619-258-4911 ext
114
Founded: 1984
Specialty wholesaler, distributor & publisher;
regional reference & travel books on Southwest US & Baja, California; outdoor adventure,
sports; natural history & science.
Catalog available.
Number of Titles Warehoused: 800
Membership(s): Association of Earth Science Editors (AESE); Independent Book Publishers Association (IBPA); Outdoor Writers Association
of America (OWAA); Publishers Association of
the West (PubWest)

The Supreme Co
Division of Supreme Company Wholesaler of
Books Inc
1909 Lagneaux Rd, Lafayette, LA 70506
SAN: 631-3388
Tel: 337-453-1028 *Toll Free Fax:* 888-600-4180
E-mail: information@supremebooks.com
Web Site: www.supremebooks.com
Key Personnel
Pres: Sandra Curley
Founded: 1992
Wholesaler for all publishers to schools & li-
braries throughout the US & Canada. Distribute
all hardbound & paperback titles, reference,
audios & videos, music & software suitable to
the library or school market. Library cataloging
kits & cards, full book processing available.
Able to supply almost any book in print.
Catalog available.
Number of Titles Warehoused: 150,000
Publication(s): *Books For Schools & Libraries*
(annual catalog)

Swedenborg Foundation
320 N Church St, West Chester, PA 19380
SAN: 202-5280
Tel: 610-430-3222 *Toll Free Tel:* 800-355-3222
(cust serv) *Fax:* 610-430-7982
E-mail: info@swedenborg.com
Web Site: swedenborg.com
Key Personnel
Exec Dir: Morgan Beard *Tel:* 610-430-3222 ext
102 *E-mail:* mbeard@swedenborg.com
Mktg Coord: Amy Acquarola *Tel:* 610-430-3222
ext 103 *E-mail:* aacquarola@swedenborg.com
Founded: 1849
Publishers of theological works of Emanuel Swe-
denborg & related literature; books on spiritual
transformation.
Catalog available.
Number of Titles Warehoused: 190

Talas
330 Morgan Ave, Brooklyn, NY 11211
Tel: 212-219-0770
E-mail: info@talasonline.com; support@
talasonline.com

Web Site: www.talasonline.com
Key Personnel
Pres: Aarol Salik
VP: Jillian Salik
Founded: 1962
Art & book conservation materials.
Number of Titles Warehoused: 50

TEACH Services Inc
11 Quartermaster Circle, Fort Oglethorpe, GA
30742-3886
SAN: 246-9863
Tel: 706-504-9192 *Toll Free Tel:* 800-367-1844
(sales) *Toll Free Fax:* 866-757-6023
E-mail: sales@teachservices.com; info@
teachservices.com
Web Site: www.teachservices.com
Key Personnel
Owner & Pres: Timothy Hullquist *E-mail:* t.
hullquist@teachservices.com
Publr & Opers Mgr: Bill Newman *E-mail:* b.
newman@teachservices.com
Founded: 1984
Publisher & distributor of Seventh-Day Adven-
tist books. Offer editing, design, typesetting &
printing services.
Catalog available.
Number of Titles Warehoused: 2,500
Membership(s): Independent Book Publishers As-
sociation (IBPA)

Teacher's Discovery®
Division of American Eagle Co Inc
2741 Paldan Dr, Auburn Hills, MI 48326
Toll Free Tel: 800-TEACHER (832-2437)
Toll Free Fax: 800-287-4509
E-mail: help@teachersdiscovery.com; orders@
teachersdiscovery.com
Web Site: www.teachersdiscovery.com
Key Personnel
Owner: Skip McWilliams
Dir, Mktg: Steve Giroux
Founded: 1968
Proprietary products; English, social studies, for-
eign language, science; full color maps.
Catalog available.

Technical Library Service Inc, see Talas

Tennessee Book Co
Subsidiary of Ingram Industries Inc
1550 Heil Quaker Blvd, La Vergne, TN 37086
SAN: 150-6897
Mailing Address: PO Box 3009, La Vergne, TN
37086-1986
Tel: 615-793-5040 *Toll Free Tel:* 800-456-0418
Fax: 615-213-9545
Web Site: www.tennesseebook.com
Key Personnel
VP & Gen Mgr: Todd Svec
Dir, Admin & Fin Servs: Mandy Bolin
Dir, Digital Solutions: Andrew McGarrity
Sr Mgr, Cust Success: Derrick Greer
Mgr, Cust Rel: Kellie Dumas
Mgr, Prod & Publr Rel: Carol Anne Brown
Founded: 1935
School book depository/wholesaler.

Texas Art Supply
2001 Montrose Blvd, Houston, TX 77006
Tel: 713-526-5221
E-mail: customerservice@texasart.com
Web Site: www.texasart.com
Founded: 1948
Wholesale books sold through retail bookstores &
online.
Number of Titles Warehoused: 5,000
Branch Office(s)
1507 Baybrook Mall Dr, Friendswood, TX 77546
Tel: 281-486-9320

2237 S Voss, Houston, TX 77057 *Tel:* 713-780-
0440
Membership(s): American Booksellers Associa-
tion (ABA); Craft Hobby Association (CHA);
NAMTA; National Association of College
Stores (NACS)

Texas Book Co
8501 Technology Circle, Greenville, TX 75402
Tel: 903-455-6969 *Toll Free Tel:* 800-527-1016
E-mail: customerservice@texasbook.com
Web Site: www.texasbook.com
Key Personnel
CEO: C Brent Dyer
Pres: Darren Croom
Dir, Campus Rel & Busn Devt: Stacy Dyer
E-mail: sdyer@texasbook.com
Founded: 1975
Wholesale books.
Number of Titles Warehoused: 20,000

Texas Bookman
Division of Half Price Books, Records, Magazine
Inc
2700 Lone Star Dr, Dallas, TX 75212
Tel: 214-678-6680 *Toll Free Tel:* 800-566-2665
Fax: 214-678-6699
E-mail: orders@texasbookman.com
Web Site: www.texasbookman.com
Key Personnel
Dir, Sales & Opers: Crystal Reyes
E-mail: creyes@texasbookman.com
Sales: Mark Wren *E-mail:* mwren@
texasbookman.com
Founded: 1983
Scholarly & general remainders.
Catalog available.
Number of Titles Warehoused: 2,000
Publication(s): *Catalog* (monthly); *E-mail*
(monthly)
Membership(s): Museum Store Association
(MSA)

TNG
Member of The Jim Pattison Group
3320 S Service Rd, Burlington, ON L7N 3M6,
Canada
Toll Free Tel: 800-201-8127 *Toll Free Fax:* 877-
664-9732
E-mail: cs@tng.com
Web Site: www.tng.com
Key Personnel
Pres, CN: Peter Olson
SVP: Scott Shepherd
VP, Purch: Carm Alfano
VP, Sales & Mktg: Rob Smith
Founded: 1914
Wholesaler of magazines & books.

United Library Services Inc
7140 Fairmount Dr SE, Calgary, AB T2H 0X4,
Canada
SAN: 169-9342
Tel: 403-252-4426 *Toll Free Tel:* 888-342-
5857 (CN only) *Fax:* 403-258-3426
Toll Free Fax: 800-661-2806 (CN only)
E-mail: info@uls.com
Web Site: www.uls.com
Key Personnel
Gen Mgr: Robin Hoogwerf *E-mail:* robin@uls.
com
Mgr, Children's Books & Schools/French Book
Buyer: Keitha Langston *E-mail:* klangston@
uls.com
Mgr, Prod Devt: Jana Seshadri *E-mail:* jana@uls.
com
Natl Sales Mgr: Ren Speer *E-mail:* rspeer@uls.
com
Adult Book Buyer/ARP Mgmt: Nadia Fortuna
E-mail: nadia@uls.com
Fin & Admin: Yolanda Arambarri
E-mail: accounting@uls.com

Founded: 1939
Book wholesaler; automatic release plans & profile purchasing.
Catalog available.
Number of Titles Warehoused: 15,000
Publication(s): *Accelerated Reader*; *Adult Large Print* (monthly); *Alberta Education Authorized Novels & Nonfiction*; *Alberta Social Studies*; *Best New Books for Children & Young Adults* (daily); *Book Club Picks*; *First Nations Metis Inuit*; *French Collection-Children's*; *French Titles for Adults* (2 times/yr, Spring & Autumn); *Hotlist Catalogue*; *Levelled Books for Guided Reading*; *Nonfiction Reading Power: Teaching Students How to Think While They Read All Kinds of Information*; *Novel Sets*; *Reading Power: Teaching Students to Think While They Read*; *Super Forthcoming Catalogue*; *Top New Titles-Children's* (3 times/yr); *Top New Titles-Young Adult* (3 times/yr); *Top 10 Adult Paperback Bestsellers* (3 times/yr); *Young Reader's Choice Awards*
Branch Office(s)
101-B 3430 Brighton Ave, Burnaby, BC V5A 3H4, Canada, Showroom Mgr: Ria Bleumer
Tel: 604-421-1154 *Toll Free Tel:* 877-853-1200 (CN only) *Fax:* 604-421-2216
Toll Free Fax: 866-421-2216 (CN only)
E-mail: burnaby@uls.com
Membership(s): Association of Canadian Book Wholesalers; BCLA

Upstart Books™
Division of Demco Inc
PO Box 7488, Madison, WI 53707
Tel: 608-241-1201 *Toll Free Tel:* 800-356-1200 (orders); 800-962-4463 (cust serv)
Toll Free Fax: 800-245-1329 (orders)
E-mail: custserv@demco.com; order@demco.com
Web Site: www.demco.com/upstart
Key Personnel
Prod Devt Mgr, Lib Mkts: Heidi Green
Founded: 1956
Distributor of penworthy prebound books & library bound books.
Number of Titles Warehoused: 50
Membership(s): The American Library Association (ALA)

Valley News Co
1305 Stadium Rd, Mankato, MN 56001
Tel: 507-345-4819 *Fax:* 507-345-6793
Web Site: www.valleynewscompany.com
Key Personnel
Pres: Troy Leiferman *E-mail:* tleiferman@valleynewscompany.com
Gen Mgr: Paul Dirks *E-mail:* pauldirks@valleynewscompany.com
Off Mgr: Nancy Nickels *E-mail:* nnickels@valleynewscompany.com
Founded: 1940
Wholesale book & magazine distributor.

Vedanta Book Center
Subsidiary of Vivekananda Vedanta Society
14630 S Lemont Rd, Homer Glen, IL 60491
Tel: 708-301-9062 *Fax:* 708-301-9063
Web Site: www.vedantabooks.com
Key Personnel
Mgr: Swami Varadananda
E-mail: swamivaradananda@yahoo.com
Founded: 1930
Retail & wholesale.
Number of Titles Warehoused: 1,100

Virginia Publications
Unit of Washington Book Distributors
4930A Eisenhower Ave, Alexandria, VA 22304

Tel: 703-212-9113 *Toll Free Tel:* 800-699-9113
Fax: 703-212-9114
E-mail: vapub@msn.com
Web Site: www.washingtonbk.com
Key Personnel
Opers Mgr: Jill Zacharie
Founded: 1992
Number of Titles Warehoused: 3,000

VisionWorks
PO Box 92, Greenfield, MA 01302
Tel: 413-772-6569 *Toll Free Tel:* 800-933-7326 (orders) *Fax:* 413-772-6559
E-mail: dreaming@changingworld.com
Web Site: www.changingworld.com
Key Personnel
Owner: Dick McLeester
Founded: 1986
Postcard & note card publisher; promotion & wholesale distribution for cards, books & calendars & bumper stickers.
Catalog available.
Number of Titles Warehoused: 400
Publication(s): *Annual catalog*

VistaBooks LLC
637 Blue Ridge Rd, Silverthorne, CO 80498-8931
Tel: 970-468-7673 *Fax:* 970-468-7673
E-mail: email@vistabooks.com
Web Site: www.vistabooks.com
Key Personnel
Partner & Ed: William R Jones
Founded: 1972
Catalog available.
Number of Titles Warehoused: 500

Warehouse Books Inc
1006 Ballantine Blvd, Norfolk, VA 23504
Tel: 757-627-4160
E-mail: sales@warehousebooksinc.com
Web Site: www.warehousebooksinc.com
Key Personnel
Owner: Marie Roukas
Founded: 1990
Buying & selling remainders.
Number of Titles Warehoused: 2,850

Washington Book Distributors
4930-A Eisenhower Ave, Alexandria, VA 22304-4809
SAN: 631-0095
Tel: 703-212-9113 *Toll Free Tel:* 800-699-9113
Fax: 703-212-9114
Web Site: www.washingtonbk.com
Key Personnel
Pres: Victor Zacharie *E-mail:* wbdvapub@hotmail.com
Founded: 1992
Book & map wholesaler.
Catalog available.
Number of Titles Warehoused: 3,000

WeWrite LLC
11040 Alba Rd, Ben Lomond, CA 95005
Tel: 831-336-3382
E-mail: info@wewrite.net
Web Site: www.wewrite.net
Key Personnel
Pres & CEO: Delores L Palmer
E-mail: dpalmer@wewrite.net
Dir, Mktg: Rickey Bowen *E-mail:* rbowen@wewrite.net
Ed: Jan Hansen *E-mail:* jhansen@wewrite.net
Founded: 1993
Regional & national publisher, book & interactive comic books created from workshop setting, by children for children. *We Write Kids!™*.

Catalog available.
Number of Titles Warehoused: 10

Whitehots Inc
205 Industrial Pkwy N, Unit 3, Aurora, ON L4G 4C4, Canada
Tel: 905-727-9188 *Toll Free Tel:* 888-567-9188
Fax: 905-727-8756 *Toll Free Fax:* 888-563-0020
E-mail: admin@whitehots.com
Web Site: www.whitehots.com
Key Personnel
CEO: Russ Culver *Tel:* 905-727-9188 ext 142
E-mail: rculver@whitehots.com
CFO: Sharon Culver *E-mail:* sculver@whitehots.com
Pres: Edmund Salt *E-mail:* esalt@whitehots.com
Natl Accts Mgr: Eleanor Heidt *E-mail:* eheidt@whitehots.com
Founded: 1987
Membership(s): Association of Canadian Book Wholesalers; Aurora Chamber of Commerce; Ontario Library Association; Vistage

Wilshire Book Co
22647 Ventura Blvd, Suite 314, Woodland Hills, CA 91364
SAN: 205-5368
Tel: 818-700-1522
E-mail: sales@mpowers.com
Web Site: www.mpowers.com
Key Personnel
Pres & Rts & Perms: Marcia Powers
Founded: 1967 (by Melvin Powers)
Psychological, self-help, motivational & inspirational books, adult fables; mail order, business, advertising & marketing; bridge, originals & reprints.
Number of Titles Warehoused: 23

Wimmer Cookbooks
Division of Mercury Printing, an RR Donnelley Co
4650 Shelby Air Dr, Memphis, TN 38118
Toll Free Tel: 800-548-2537 *Fax:* 901-363-1771
Web Site: www.wimmerco.com
Key Personnel
Acct Coord: Robyn Hite
Sales & Mktg: Terry Rayner
Founded: 1946
Development, publishing, manufacturing, marketing & distribution of cookbooks by nonprofit organizations or individuals.
Number of Titles Warehoused: 250

Woodcrafters Lumber Sales Inc
212 NE Sixth Ave, Portland, OR 97232-2976
Tel: 503-231-0226 *Toll Free Tel:* 800-777-3709
Fax: 503-232-0511
Web Site: www.woodcrafters.us
Key Personnel
Pres: Stephen Penberthy
Sales Mgr: Carl Paasche
Founded: 1973
Woodworking & wood titles.
Catalog available.
Number of Titles Warehoused: 1,465

World Exonumia Press
PO Box 4143, Rockford, IL 61110-0643
Tel: 815-226-0771
Web Site: www.exonumia.com
Key Personnel
Pres: Rich Hartzog *E-mail:* hartzog@exonumia.com
Founded: 1972
Tokens/medals/World's Fair, other collectibles.
Number of Titles Warehoused: 300

Prebinders to Schools & Libraries

These firms handle prebound books, usually juvenile titles, for which publishers' bindings have been replaced by stronger bindings prior to sale to schools or libraries. Some of the firms handle only the titles listed in their own catalogs, which they usually purchase in sheets from the publishers and bind in quantity. Others will prebind any book on request, removing the publisher's case and replacing it with a stronger one.

Arizona Library Binding Service
1337 W McKinley, Phoenix, AZ 85007
Tel: 602-253-1861
E-mail: info@azlbinding.com
Key Personnel
Pres: Tom Couturier
VP: Greg Couturier
Founded: 1938
Binding of books & related work, some trade-
  work oversewing & saddle (smyth) sewing. No
  perfect binding.

BMI Educational Services Inc
26 Haypress Rd, Cranbury, NJ 08512
SAN: 169-4669
Mailing Address: PO Box 800, Dayton, NJ
  08810-0800
Tel: 732-329-6991 *Toll Free Tel:* 800-222-
  8100 (orders only) *Fax:* 732-329-6994
  Toll Free Fax: 800-986-9393 (orders only)
E-mail: info@bmionline.com
Web Site: bmionline.com
Key Personnel
Owner & Secy-Treas: Lynda Bradley
Pres: Jerry Wagner *E-mail:* jwagner@bmionline.
  com
Founded: 1964
Complete prebinding service for all books; in-
  cluding mass market & trade paperback, dictio-
  naries & reference books.
Catalog available.
Number of Titles Warehoused: 10,000
Membership(s): International Literacy Association
  (ILA); National Council of Teachers of English
  (NCTE)

Bound to Stay Bound Books Inc
1880 W Morton Rd, Jacksonville, IL 62650
SAN: 169-1996
Tel: 217-245-5191 *Toll Free Tel:* 800-637-6586
  Fax: 217-245-0424 *Toll Free Fax:* 800-747-
  7872
E-mail: btsb@btsb.com
Web Site: www.btsb.com
Key Personnel
Pres: Robert L Sibert
Founded: 1920
Prebound books, grades K-12.
Catalog available.
Number of Titles Warehoused: 19,000

Bridgeport National Bindery Inc
662 Silver St, Agawam, MA 01001
Mailing Address: PO Box 289, Agawam, MA
  01001-0289
Tel: 413-789-1981 *Toll Free Tel:* 800-223-5083
E-mail: info@bnbindery.com
Web Site: www.bnbindery.com
Key Personnel
Pres: James M Larsen
EVP: Bruce F Jacobsen
VP, Print on Demand Div: Kent Larson
Founded: 1947
Prebinding services (library bound), short run edi-
  tion binding, print on demand (POD), textbook
  rebinding, conservation services.
Membership(s): Book Manufacturers' Institute
  (BMI)

Brodart Books & Library Services
500 Arch St, Williamsport, PA 17701
Tel: 570-326-2461 *Toll Free Tel:* 800-474-9816
  Fax: 570-651-1639 *Toll Free Fax:* 800-999-
  6799
E-mail: support@brodart.com
Web Site: www.brodartbooks.com
Key Personnel
Pres & CEO: George Coe
CFO: Richard Dill
VP, Books Div: Gretchen Herman
Founded: 1939
Premier supplier of shelf-ready materials to li-
  braries delivering carefully selected, cataloged
  & processed books. Today, Brodart offers state-
  of-the-art online tools, bibliographic services &
  consulting exclusively to libraries. Customers
  select from English language titles, Spanish
  language materials, plus audio & video prod-
  ucts.
Catalog available.
Number of Titles Warehoused: 1,000,000

The Campbell-Logan Bindery Inc
7615 Baker St NE, Fridley, MN 55432
Tel: 612-332-1313 *Toll Free Tel:* 800-942-6224
E-mail: info@campbell-logan.com
Web Site: www.campbell-logan.com
Key Personnel
Pres: Greg Campbell *E-mail:* greg@campbell-
  logan.com
VP: Duncan Campbell *E-mail:* duncan@
  campbell-logan.com
Founded: 1949
Bookbinding, book design, art & design, edition
  hardcover binding, covers, paper & paper prod-
  ucts, printing & publishing. Consulting to li-
  braries.

Denver Bookbinding Co Inc
Affiliate of Creatively Ever After
1401 W 47 Ave, Denver, CO 80211
Mailing Address: PO Box 11187, Denver, CO
  80211-3995
Tel: 303-455-5521
E-mail: dbbc@denverbook.com; info@
  denverbook.com
Web Site: www.denverbook.com
Founded: 1929
Bookbinder, leather binding, restorations & short
  run editions, book making kits, story making
  kits.
Catalog available.
Number of Titles Warehoused: 1
Publication(s): *My Own Storybook*

HF Group LLC
8844 Mayfield Rd, Chesterland, OH 44026
Tel: 440-729-2445; 440-729-9411 (bindery)
E-mail: custservice-oh@hfgroup.com
Web Site: www.hfgroup.com
Key Personnel
CEO: Jay Fairfield *Tel:* 440-729-2445 ext 4
  E-mail: jayfairfield@hfgroup.com
VP & Gen Mgr: Jim Bratton *E-mail:* jbratton@
  hfgroup.com
Founded: 1821
Prebinding, rebinding, binding of short runs.
Branch Office(s)
1010 N Sycamore St, North Manchester, IN

46962, Pres: Jim Heckman *Tel:* 260-982-2107
  E-mail: jheckman@hfgroup.com
92 Cambridge St, Charlestown, MA 02129-
  0212, VP: John Parisi *Tel:* 617-242-1100
  E-mail: jparisi@hfgroup.com
340 First St, Utica, NE 68456, Gen Mgr: Damon
  Osborne *Tel:* 402-534-2261 *E-mail:* dosborne@
  hfgroup.com
6204 Corporate Park Dr, Browns Summit, NC
  27214-9745, Contact: Eric Fairfield *Tel:* 336-
  931-0800 *E-mail:* efairfield@hfgroup.com
45 N Main St, Unit 528, Hatfield, PA 19440
  (transportation hub) *Tel:* 215-855-2293
105 W Thomas St, Atlanta, TX 75551-2736
  (transportation hub) *Tel:* 260-982-2107
  Fax: 260-982-1130

Houchen Bindery Ltd
340 First St, Utica, NE 68456
Tel: 402-534-2261 *Toll Free Tel:* 800-869-0420
  Fax: 402-534-2761
E-mail: email@houchenbindery.com
Web Site: www.houchenbindery.com
Key Personnel
Pres: H Damon Osborne
VP, Opers: John C Salistean
Founded: 1935
Library, edition & comic book binding; repair &
  restoration services.
Branch Office(s)
University Bindery Div, 7917 Watson Rd, St
  Louis, MO 63119 *Tel:* 314-918-7017 *Fax:* 314-
  918-7133

International Service Co
International Service Bldg, 333 Fourth Ave, Indi-
  alantic, FL 32903-4295
SAN: 169-5134
Tel: 321-724-1443 *Fax:* 321-724-1443
Key Personnel
Pres: Dennis Samuels
Compt: F Schneider
Mng Dir: Katherine Swanberg
Coord Dir: Ann C Samuels
Shipping & Receiving Mgr: Larry A Whobrey
Systems Supv: Suzanne Jones
Asst to Pres: Robert Cohen
Admin Asst: Irene August
Founded: 1958
Exporter & importer of books, quantity & single
  copies; periodicals & school supplies; commis-
  sionaires.

Long's Roullet Bookbinders Inc
2800 Monticello Ave, Norfolk, VA 23504
Tel: 757-623-4244 *Fax:* 757-627-1404
E-mail: bindlrbi@gmail.com
Web Site: longs-roullet.com
Key Personnel
Pres: Alain Roullet
VP: Eileen Roullet
Founded: 1975
Library & edition binding.

**National Library Bindery Co of Indiana Inc
(NLBCo)**
55 S State Ave, Suite 100, Indianapolis, IN 46201
Tel: 317-636-5606
E-mail: nlbco@nlbco.com
Web Site: www.nlbco.com

Key Personnel
Pres: Joseph A Cox
Founded: 1873
Library & small edition binding, textbooks.

The Penworthy Company LLC
219 N Milwaukee St, 4th fl, Milwaukee, WI 53202
Tel: 414-287-4600 *Toll Free Tel:* 800-262-2665
  Fax: 414-287-4602
E-mail: info@penworthy.com
Web Site: www.penworthy.com
Key Personnel
Pres: Holly Ritz
EVP: Julie Plantz *Tel:* 414-287-4600 ext 211
  E-mail: julie.plantz@penworthy.com
Founded: 1982
Prebound juvenile books, cataloging, bar coding, complete processing.
Number of Titles Warehoused: 2,000

Perma-Bound Books
Division of Hertzberg-New Method Inc
617 E Vandalia Rd, Jacksonville, IL 62650
Tel: 217-243-5451 *Toll Free Tel:* 800-637-6581
  Fax: 217-243-7505 *Toll Free Fax:* 800-551-1169
E-mail: books@perma-bound.com
Web Site: www.perma-bound.com
Key Personnel
Owner & Pres: James Orr
Founded: 1954
Prebinder of paperbacks & educational vendor of Perma-Bound books & related media.

Catalog available.
Number of Titles Warehoused: 5,000,000
Branch Office(s)
PO Box 868, Sta Main, Peterborough, ON K9J 7A2, Canada *Tel:* 705-742-1513 *Toll Free Tel:* 800-461-1999 *Toll Free Fax:* 888-250-3811
E-mail: perma-bound.ca@sympatico.ca *Web Site:* www.perma-bound.com/canada

Roswell Bookbinding
2614 N 29 Ave, Phoenix, AZ 85009
Tel: 602-272-9338 *Toll Free Tel:* 888-803-8883
  Fax: 602-272-9786
Web Site: www.roswellbookbinding.com
Key Personnel
Pres: Michael Roswell
Trade Div Cust Serv Dir: Jim Menke
Specialty Div Mgr: Kortez Brown
Trade Prodn Mgr: Bryan Way
Specialty Div Estimating: Steve Jones
Trade Div Estimating: Nancy Scherba
Founded: 1960
Prebinders to schools & libraries, library binding, edition binding, specialty binding & book restoration.

Shaffner's Bindery
3305 Pattee Canyon Rd, Missoula, MT 59803
Tel: 406-251-2699
E-mail: shaffnersbindery@centric.net
Web Site: shaffnersbindery.com
Key Personnel
Owner: Carol Shaffner; Jeff Shaffner

Founded: 1965
Bookbinding, library rebinding & restoration.

Turtleback Books
Division of Perfection Learning
1000 N Second Ave, Logan, IA 51546-0500
Toll Free Tel: 800-831-4190 *Toll Free Fax:* 800-543-2745
E-mail: turtleback@perfectionlearning.com
Web Site: turtleback.perfectionlearning.com
Founded: 1961
Dedicated to providing children & adults with the most popular literature in a sturdy hardcover library binding created for the highly demanding school & library environment.

Wallaceburg Bookbinding & Mfg Co Ltd
95 Arnold St, Wallaceburg, ON N8A 3P3, Canada
Tel: 519-627-3552 *Toll Free Tel:* 800-214-BIND (214-2463) *Fax:* 519-627-6922
E-mail: helpdesk@wbmbindery.com
Web Site: www.wbmbindery.com
Key Personnel
Pres: Clarence Dykhouse
VP: Gerrit Dykhouse
Founded: 1967
Bookbinding, library binding, rare book restoration. Specialize in archival boxes.
Membership(s): Atlantic Provinces Library Association (APLA); Canadian Library Association (CLA); Michigan Library Association (MLA); National Information Standards Organization (NISO)

Book Exporters & Importers

For more complete lists of book exporters and importers, see the latest edition of *The American Book Trade Directory* (Information Today, Inc., 121 Chanlon Road, Suite G-20, New Providence, NJ 07974-2195).

AK Press Distribution
Subsidiary of AK Press Inc
370 Ryan Ave, Unit 100, Chico, CA 95973
Tel: 510-208-1700 *Fax:* 510-208-1701
E-mail: info@akpress.org; orders@akpress.org; sales@akpress.org
Web Site: www.akpress.org
Key Personnel
Ed: Charles Weigl
Founded: 1994
Radical publishing & distribution.
Number of Titles Warehoused: 4,000

Amcorp Ltd
10 Norden Lane, Huntington Station, NY 11746
Tel: 631-271-0548 *Fax:* 631-549-8849
E-mail: amcorpltd@aol.com
Key Personnel
Pres: Durga Edson
VP: Chandru Mahtani; Lal Uttam
Founded: 1946
Exporters of all published materials to Hong Kong, Singapore, Philippines, Malaysia, Australia & India. Branch offices at Singapore Magazine Distributors, Singapore & Far East Media (HKG) Ltd, Hong Kong.

Auromere Ayurvedic Inc
Division of Integral Yoga
2621 W Hwy 12, Lodi, CA 95242
SAN: 211-7207
Toll Free Tel: 800-735-4691
Web Site: www.auromere.com
Key Personnel
Pres & CEO: Dakshina Vanzetti
Founded: 1974
Importers of spiritual & classical Indian texts. Specialize in Sri Aurobindo & the Mother, yoga, health literature & children's books from India.
Number of Titles Warehoused: 500

Avanti Enterprises Inc
18901 Springfield Ave, Flossmoor, IL 60422-1071
SAN: 158-3727
Tel: 630-850-3245 *Toll Free Tel:* 800-799-6464 *Fax:* 708-799-6474 *Toll Free Fax:* 877-799-6474
E-mail: sales@avantiusa.com
Web Site: www.avantiusa.com
Key Personnel
Pres: Nilima Kumar *E-mail:* kumar@avantiusa.com
Founded: 1971
Export wholesale book distribution, medical, fiction, nonfiction, children's, textbooks, maps, dictionaries, trade library; subscription agency; import from UK, Europe, Asia & India.
Number of Titles Warehoused: 175,000

Beijing Book Co Inc
Subsidiary of China National Publications Import & Export (Group) Corp (People's Republic of China)
701 E Linden Ave, Linden, NJ 07036
Tel: 908-862-0909 *Fax:* 908-862-4201
E-mail: journals@cnpbbci.com
Key Personnel
Mgr: Donna Jacik
Founded: 1981

Export American publications (books, periodicals, other serials & government publications) to China for Chinese libraries. Purchase newspapers, music products, micro products, CD-ROM.

Bentley Publishers
Division of Robert Bentley Inc
1734 Massachusetts Ave, Cambridge, MA 02138-1804
SAN: 213-9839
Tel: 617-547-4170 *Toll Free Tel:* 800-423-4595 *Fax:* 617-876-9235
E-mail: sales@bentleypublishers.com
Web Site: www.bentleypublishers.com
Key Personnel
Chmn & Pres: Michael Bentley
Dir, Publg: Janet Barnes
Founded: 1949
Official factory automobile service manuals & other automobile manuals, sports car & automobile books; hardcover fiction reprints.
Number of Titles Warehoused: 8,100

Bible Truth Publishers
59 Industrial Rd, Addison, IL 60101
Mailing Address: PO Box 649, Addison, IL 60101-0649
Tel: 630-543-1441 *Fax:* 630-543-1476
E-mail: btporders@bibletruthpublishers.com
Web Site: www.bibletruthpublishers.com
Key Personnel
Mgr: Donald Rule
Founded: 1947
Exporter of books.
Number of Titles Warehoused: 3,000

Bookazine Co Inc
75 Hook Rd, Bayonne, NJ 07002
SAN: 169-5665
Tel: 201-339-7777 *Toll Free Tel:* 800-221-8112 *Fax:* 201-339-7778
E-mail: info@bookazine.com
Web Site: www.bookazine.com
Key Personnel
Pres & CEO: Robert Kallman
COO: Richard Kallman
Pres, Sales: Cindy Raiton
VP, Dist: Allan Davis
VP, Mdse: Andrew Collings
Dir, Natl Accts: Steven Goldberg
Northeast Sales Dir: Josh Harwood
Mktg Mgr: Lani Buess
Founded: 1929
Exporters of hardcover, paperback, computer books & audios to bookstores, schools & libraries.
Number of Titles Warehoused: 80,000

Catholic Books & Tapes
Subsidiary of Fidelis Et Verus
PO Box 350333, Fort Lauderdale, FL 33335-0333
Tel: 954-583-5108 *Fax:* 954-583-5108
E-mail: mascmen7@yahoo.com
Web Site: www.catholicbook.com
Key Personnel
Owner, CEO & Dir: John R Walsh
Founded: 1983
Exporters & importers; apparitions of holy persons, traditional Catholic books printed before 1965, patriotic books, money question, world

rulers & conspiracy theory books. English & Spanish.
Number of Titles Warehoused: 500

Cedar Fort Inc
2373 W 700 S, Springville, UT 84663
Tel: 801-489-4084 *Toll Free Tel:* 800-SKY-BOOK (759-2665)
Web Site: cedarfort.com
Key Personnel
Owner & Chmn: Bryce Mortimer *E-mail:* bmortimer@cedarfort.com
Sr Commodities Mgr: Kim Clemons *Tel:* 801-477-9029 *E-mail:* kclemons@cedarfort.com
Founded: 1986
Number of Titles Warehoused: 1,800

China Books
Division of Sinomedia International Group
360 Swift Ave, Suite 48, South San Francisco, CA 94080
SAN: 169-0167
Fax: 650-872-7808
E-mail: editor.sinomedia@gmail.com
Key Personnel
Edit Dir: Chris Robyn *Tel:* 650-872-7718 ext 312 *E-mail:* chris@sinomediausa.com
Sales Mgr: Kelly Feng *Tel:* 650-872-7076 ext 310 *E-mail:* kelly@chinabooks.com
Founded: 1960
Publisher & importer of books & periodicals in English from China (Foreign Language Press, etc). Subscription agents for Chinese periodicals in English & Chinese.
Number of Titles Warehoused: 5,000

China Books & Periodicals Inc, see China Books

Continental Book Co Inc
7000 Broadway, Suite 102, Denver, CO 80221-2913
Tel: 303-289-1761 *Toll Free Fax:* 800-279-1764
E-mail: cbc@continentalbook.com
Web Site: www.continentalbook.com
Key Personnel
Dir: Linette Hayat *E-mail:* linette@continentalbook.com
Founded: 1961
Importers & distributors of language materials. Specialize in Spanish, French, German, Italian, Latin, Chinese, Arabic, Bilingual Spanish, Heritage Spanish, ELL, ESL, Common Core, English Novels, ASL, juvenile to advanced levels.
Number of Titles Warehoused: 15,000

Cranbury International LLC
7 Clarendon Ave, Suite 2, Montpelier, VT 05602
Tel: 802-223-6565 *Fax:* 802-223-6824
E-mail: inquiries@cranburyinternational.com
Web Site: www.cranburyinternational.com
Key Personnel
Pres: Ethan Atkin *E-mail:* eatkin@cranburyinternational.com
Book export agency. Publishers representatives agents in South America, Central America, Mexico & Caribbean.

Crescent Imports
PO Box 721, Union City, CA 94587
Tel: 734-665-3492 *Toll Free Tel:* 800-521-9744
Fax: 734-677-1717
E-mail: message@crescentimports.com
Web Site: www.crescentimports.com; www.
crescentcatalog.com
Key Personnel
Co-Owner & CEO: Ashfaq Ibrahim
Co-Owner: Gulshan Ibrahim
Founded: 1978
Islamic books; free catalog upon request.
Number of Titles Warehoused: 10,000

Ralph Curtis Books
16956 McGregor Blvd, Suite 9, Fort Myers, FL
33908
Mailing Address: PO Box 349, Sanibel, FL
33957-0349 SAN: 281-5842
Tel: 239-454-0010 *Fax:* 239-395-2727
E-mail: rcurtisbks@yahoo.com
Web Site: www.ralphcurtisbooks.com
Key Personnel
Owner & CEO: Ralph C Curtis
Founded: 1965
Book publisher, imports & import remainder ti-
tles.
Number of Titles Warehoused: 40

Eastwind Books & Arts Inc
1435 Stockton St, San Francisco, CA 94133
SAN: 127-3159
Tel: 415-772-5888 *Fax:* 415-772-5885
E-mail: contact@eastwindbooks.com
Web Site: www.eastwindbooks.com
Key Personnel
Mgr: Cat Deng
Founded: 1978
Export & import, specialize in China or Asia-
related titles.

European Books & Media
6600 Shattuck Ave, Oakland, CA 94609
Tel: 510-922-9157
E-mail: info@europeanbook.com
Web Site: www.europeanbook.com
Key Personnel
Owner & Mng Memb: Nicolas Pellerin
E-mail: nicolas.pellerin@europeanbook.com
Founded: 1963
Importer/distributor of French books.
Number of Titles Warehoused: 100,000

French & European Publications Inc
425 E 58 St, Suite 27-D, New York, NY 10022
Tel: 212-581-8810 *Fax:* 212-202-4356
E-mail: livresny@gmail.com; frenchbookstore@
aol.com
Web Site: www.frencheuropean.com
Key Personnel
Pres: Emanuel Molho
Founded: 1928
Importers & exporters of language-learning books
in all languages. Specialize in French & Span-
ish books & dictionaries in all languages.
Number of Titles Warehoused: 80,000
Membership(s): American Booksellers Associa-
tion (ABA); National Association of College
Stores (NACS)

Girol Books Inc
PO Box 5473, LCD Merivale, Ottawa, ON K2C
3M1, Canada
Tel: 613-233-9044 *Fax:* 613-233-9044
E-mail: info@girol.com
Web Site: www.girol.com
Key Personnel
Owner: Miguel Angel Giella; Peter Roster
Mgr: Leslie Roster *E-mail:* lroster@girol.com

Founded: 1975
Importers & distributors of books in Spanish &
Portuguese. Publishers of Latin American the-
ater titles & theater criticism.

Gurarys Books & Trade Inc, see Gurarys Israeli
Trading Co Inc

Gurarys Israeli Trading Co Inc
724 Eastern Pkwy, Brooklyn, NY 11213
Tel: 718-493-5225
E-mail: hebbook@gmail.com
Key Personnel
Mgr: Hyam Lieberman

Haynes North America Inc
Division of The Haynes Publishing Group
859 Lawrence Dr, Newbury Park, CA 91320-1514
Tel: 805-498-6703 *Toll Free Tel:* 800-4-HAYNES
(442-9637) *Fax:* 805-498-2867
E-mail: cstn@haynes.com
Web Site: www.haynes.com
Key Personnel
Chmn: E Bell
SVP: Harvey Wolff
Mktg Dir: Reed Trueblood
Founded: 1960
Publisher & importer of books on domestic &
foreign autos & motorcycles, historical & tech-
nical motoring. Export to all countries except
England.
Number of Titles Warehoused: 800

Independent Publishers Group (IPG)
Division of Chicago Review Press
814 N Franklin St, Chicago, IL 60610
Tel: 312-337-0747 *Toll Free Tel:* 800-888-4741
(orders) *Fax:* 312-337-5985
E-mail: frontdesk@ipgbook.com; orders@
ipgbook.com
Web Site: www.ipgbook.com
Key Personnel
CEO: Joe Matthews
CFO: Frank Autunnale
CTO: Clark Matthews
VP & Dir, Natl Accts: Jeff Palicki *Tel:* 312-337-
0747 ext 281
VP, Busn Devt: Alex Kampmann
VP, Mktg & Publicity: Annette Hobbs Magier
VP, Prof & Academic Mkts: Paul Murphy
Tel: 312-337-0747 ext 229
VP, Publr Devt: Richard T Williams
VP, Sales: Michael Riley *Tel:* 312-337-0747 ext
258
VP, Supply Chain: Mark Noble
Mng Dir, Spanish Prog: Kelsey Wayne
Dir, Data Mgmt: Salma Yaqubi
Dir, Intl Sales: Scott Hatfill
Dir, Lib & Educ Sales: Sharon Shell
Dir, Publicity: Caitlin Eck
Dir, Spec Sales: Ilene Schreider
Sr Sales Mgr, Trade & Spec Sales: Aaron Howe
Lib Sales Mgr: Cynthia Murphy
Natl Accts Mgr: Lara Alexander
Trade Sales Mgr: Chris Conti
Founded: 1971
Exporter & importer.
Number of Titles Warehoused: 50,000

International Book Import Service Inc
161 Main St, Lynchburg, TN 37352-8300
SAN: 175-8179
Mailing Address: PO Box 8188, Lynchburg, TN
37352-8188
Tel: 931-759-7400 *Toll Free Tel:* 800-277-4247
Fax: 931-759-7555 *Toll Free Fax:* 866-277-
2722
E-mail: ibis@ibiservice.com
Web Site: www.ibiservice.com
Key Personnel
Pres: Barbara L Patten

Founded: 1989
Import German, French & Italian books; can supply any title published in Germany, Switzerland, Austria, France & Italy.
Number of Titles Warehoused: 10,000
Membership(s): American Association of Teachers of German (AATG); National Association
of College Stores (NACS)

International Institute of Reflexology Inc
PO Box 12642, St Petersburg, FL 33733-2642
Tel: 727-343-4811
E-mail: info@reflexology-usa.net; orderdept@
reflexology-usa.net
Web Site: reflexology-usa.net
Key Personnel
Pres: Gail Byers *E-mail:* gailbyers@reflexology-
usa.net
Export/import hardbound, paperbacks & charts.
Number of Titles Warehoused: 7

International Service Co
International Service Bldg, 333 Fourth Ave, Indi-
alantic, FL 32903-4295
SAN: 169-5134
Tel: 321-724-1443 *Fax:* 321-724-1443
Key Personnel
Pres: Dennis Samuels
Compt: F Schneider
Mng Dir: Katherine Swanberg
Coord Dir: Ann C Samuels
Shipping & Receiving Mgr: Larry A Whobrey
Systems Supv: Suzanne Jones
Asst to Pres: Robert Cohen
Admin Asst: Irene August
Founded: 1958
Exporters & importers of books; quantity & sin-
gle copy.

Iranbooks
PO Box 30087, Bethesda, MD 20824
Tel: 301-718-8188 *Toll Free Tel:* 888-718-8188
Fax: 301-907-8707
E-mail: info@iranbooks.com
Web Site: www.iranbooks.com
Key Personnel
Mgr: Farhad Shirzad
Founded: 1979
Import & distribute for most publishers from Iran.

The Islander Group
269 Palii St, Mililani, HI 96789
Tel: 808-676-0116 *Toll Free Tel:* 877-828-4852
Fax: 808-676-5156
E-mail: customerservice@islandergroup.com
Web Site: www.islandergroup.com
Key Personnel
CEO: Jeff Swartz
Pres & COO: Steve Holmberg
Founded: 1992
Wholesale distributor, specialize in Hawaiian &
Pacific Rim material.
Number of Titles Warehoused: 6,000

Kazi Publications Inc
3023 W Belmont Ave, Chicago, IL 60618
Tel: 773-267-7001 *Fax:* 773-267-7002
E-mail: info@kazi.org
Web Site: www.kazi.org
Key Personnel
Pres: Liaquat Ali
Mktg Dir: Mary Bakhtiar
Founded: 1972
Number of Titles Warehoused: 1,963

kfa.org, see Krishnamurti Publications of
America

Kinokuniya Bookstores of America Co Ltd
Subsidiary of Kinokuniya Co Ltd (Japan)
1581 Webster St, San Francisco, CA 94115

SAN: 121-8441
Tel: 415-567-6787 *Fax:* 415-567-4109
E-mail: sales@kinokuniya.com; san_francisco@
kinokuniya.com; bookwebusa@kinokuniya.com
(cust serv)
Web Site: usa.kinokuniya.com
Founded: 1969
Import & retail sales.
Number of Titles Warehoused: 80,000
Branch Office(s)
Little Tokyo, 123 Astronaut E S Onizuka St,
Los Angeles, CA 90012 *Tel:* 213-687-4480
E-mail: los_angeles@kinokuniya.com
Mitsuwa Marketplace, 3760 S Centinela Ave,
Los Angeles, CA 90066 *Tel:* 310-482-3382
E-mail: santamonica@kinokuniya.com
Mitsuwa Marketplace, 675 Saratoga Ave,
San Jose, CA 95129 *Tel:* 408-252-1300
E-mail: san_jose@kinokuniya.com
Mitsuwa Marketplace, 100 E Algonquin Rd, Ar-
lington Heights, IL 60005 *Tel:* 847-427-2665
E-mail: chicago@kinokuniya.com
Mitsuwa Marketplace, 595 River Rd, Edgewa-
ter, NJ 07020 *Tel:* 201-496-6910 *E-mail:* nj@
kinokuniya.com
1073 Avenue of the Americas, New York, NY
10018 *Tel:* 212-869-1700 *E-mail:* nyinfo@
kinokuniya.com
Uwajimaya Plaza, 10500 SW Beaverton-Hillsdale
Hwy, Beaverton, OR 97005 *Tel:* 503-641-6240
E-mail: beaverton@kinokuniya.com
6929 Airport Blvd, No 121, Austin, TX 78752
Tel: 512-291-2026 *E-mail:* austin@kinokuniya.
com
Carrollton Town Ctr, 2540 Old Denton Rd, Suite
114, Carrollton, TX 75006 *Tel:* 214-731-6800
E-mail: carrollton@kinokuniya.com
Mitsuwa Marketplace, 100 Legacy Dr, Plano,
TX 75023 *Tel:* 972-517-0226 *E-mail:* plano@
kinokuniya.com
Uwajimaya Village, 525 S Weller St, Seattle, WA
98104 *Tel:* 206-587-2477 *E-mail:* seattle@
kinokuniya.com

Krishnamurti Publications of America
Division of Krishnamurti Foundation of America
1070 McAndrew Rd, Ojai, CA 93023
Mailing Address: PO Box 1560, Ojai, CA 93024
Tel: 805-646-2726
E-mail: kfa@kfa.org
Web Site: www.kfa.org
Key Personnel
Exec Dir: Jaap Sluijter
Pubns: Cory Fisher
Founded: 1999
Publisher & distributor of the books, CDs of the
writings, talks & dialogues of author, educator
& philosopher J Krishnamurti.
Number of Titles Warehoused: 200
Membership(s): American Booksellers Associa-
tion (ABA); Independent Book Publishers As-
sociation (IBPA); Small Publishers Marketing
Association

The Latin American Book Store Ltd
PO Box 7328, Redlands, CA 92375
Toll Free Tel: 800-645-4276 *Fax:* 909-335-9945
E-mail: libros@latinamericanbooks.com
Web Site: www.latinamericanbooks.com
Key Personnel
Contact: Alfonso Vijil
Founded: 1982
Importer of Latin American & Spanish academic
publications.
Number of Titles Warehoused: 4,000

LEA Book Distributors, see LEA Libros de
Espana y America

LEA Libros de Espana y America
170-23 83 Ave, Jamaica, NY 11432
SAN: 170-5407

Tel: 718-291-9891 *Fax:* 718-291-9830
E-mail: lea@leabooks.com; orders@leabooks.com
Web Site: www.leabooks.com
Key Personnel
Owner: Dr Angel Capellan
Founded: 1977
Service basis only. Specialize in sale of any type
of book published in US for export to foreign
academic institutions & bookstores; distribute
to certain American publishers for American
university libraries. Also import Spanish books
from Spain, Latin America & Mexico for sale
to American academic institutions & bookstores. Sale of CD-ROM multimedia products
in Spanish to US markets. Audiobooks. Spanish literary videos.
Number of Titles Warehoused: 10,000
Membership(s): ABE

Motorbooks
Division of Quarto Publishing Group USA Inc
100 Cummings Ctr, Suite 265D, Beverly, MA
01915
Tel: 978-282-9590 *Toll Free Tel:* 800-759-0190
(orders)
Web Site: www.quartoknows.com/motorbooks
Key Personnel
SVP & Group Publg Dir, US: Winnie Prentiss
E-mail: winnie.prentiss@quarto.com
Publr: Zack Miller *E-mail:* zack.miller@quarto.
com
Sr Acqs Ed: Dennis Pernu *E-mail:* dennis.pernu@
quarto.com
Mgr, Spec Mkt Sales: Nichole Schiele
E-mail: nichole.schiele@quarto.com
Mktg Mgr: Steve Roth *E-mail:* steve.roth@quarto.
com
Founded: 1965
Exporters & importers of European & British
books; publish & distribute own books, trans-
portation, military history & aviation books.
Number of Titles Warehoused: 9,000

OCS America Inc
Subsidiary of Overseas Courier Service Co Ltd
(Japan)
195 Anderson Ave, Moonachie, NJ 07074
Tel: 201-460-2888 *Toll Free Tel:* 800-367-3405
E-mail: info@ocsworld.com
Web Site: www.ocsworld.com
Key Personnel
Pres & CEO: Tsukasa Shibata
Sales Rep: Edward Ho
Founded: 1957
Courier service worldwide; mailing service
to Asian countries; subscription agency for
Japanese publications.
Number of Titles Warehoused: 1,000

Pannonia Bookstore
300 Sainte Clair Ave W, Suite 103, Toronto, ON
M4V 1S4, Canada
Tel: 416-966-5156
E-mail: info@pannonia.ca
Web Site: www.pannonia.ca
Key Personnel
Owner: Zsolt Bede Fazekas; Hortenzia Papp
Founded: 1957
Importers of books & periodicals on Hungary or
published in Hungarian, including history, cul-
ture, music, geography, science, CDs & tapes,
maps & playing cards.
Number of Titles Warehoused: 15,000

Redwing Book Co
202 Bendix St, Taos, NM 87571
Tel: 575-758-7758 *Toll Free Tel:* 800-873-3946
(US); 888-873-3947 (CN) *Fax:* 575-758-7768
E-mail: info@redwingbooks.com; custsrv@
redwingbooks.com
Web Site: www.redwingbooks.com

Key Personnel
Pres & Publr: Robert Felt
Founded: 1973
Oriental traditional medicine, acupuncture, herbol-
ogy, homeopathy, massage, dietary therapy, tai
chi chuan.
Number of Titles Warehoused: 1,500

Rising Sun Book Co
1424 Stony Brook Rd, Stony Brook, NY 11790
Tel: 631-473-7000 *Fax:* 631-473-7447
Web Site: risingsunbook.com
Key Personnel
Pres: Arun Shanbhag *E-mail:* shanbhagarun@aol.
com
Founded: 1983
Book wholesaler & exporter, domestic US.
Number of Titles Warehoused: 10,000

Ryukyu Books & Periodicals Inc
5005 Merriam Dr, Merriam, KS 66203
Tel: 913-782-3920 *Toll Free Tel:* 800-383-4017
Fax: 913-780-1750
Web Site: www.ryukyu.com
Key Personnel
CEO & Buyer: Bill Wiswell *Tel:* 913-782-3920
Founded: 1970
Wholesale & retail import of martial arts only.
Number of Titles Warehoused: 1,521
Branch Office(s)
PO Box 535, Olathe, KS 66051

Schoenhof's Foreign Books Inc
Subsidiary of MEP Inc
76 A Mount Auburn St, Cambridge, MA 02138
SAN: 122-7963
Tel: 617-547-8855
E-mail: info@schoenhofs.com
Web Site: www.schoenhofs.com
Key Personnel
Pres: Nicolas Mengin
Mgr: Daniel Eastman
Founded: 1856
Importers & distributors of foreign language
books in over 700 languages & dialects from
50 countries. Book listings available.
Number of Titles Warehoused: 75,000

Silvermine International Books LLC
25 Perry Ave, Suite 11, Norwalk, CT 06850
SAN: 760-6338
Tel: 203-451-2396
E-mail: info@jawilsons.com
Web Site: jawilsons.com/pages/who-we-are
Key Personnel
Pres: John Atkin *E-mail:* jatkin@
silvermineinternational.com
Founded: 2006
Represents clients in the US market from all parts
of the world. Specialize in academic, Spanish
language, photography, engineering, reference,
architectural & trade publications. Provide distribution, warehousing, fulfillment, ebook, sales
& marketing services, online listings & sales,
trade show displays & other support services.

Skylark Co Inc
PO Box 237043, New York, NY 10023-0028
Tel: 212-595-0700 *Fax:* 212-595-0700
Key Personnel
Pres: Brian Eskenazi *E-mail:* eskenazi@rcn.com
Founded: 1982
Exporters of books from all publishers. Buying
service, shipping, banking, documentation &
insurance.

Square Deal Records Book Department
303 Higuera St, San Luis Obispo, CA 93401-
1002
Tel: 805-543-3636 *Toll Free Tel:* 800-235-4114
Fax: 805-543-3938

E-mail: web@squaredealonline.com
Web Site: www.squaredealonline.com
Key Personnel
Pres & CEO: R W Ferris *E-mail:* rferris@sdrs.biz
Sales Mgmt: Kjerstin Ferris *E-mail:* kj@sdrs.biz
Founded: 1971
Export & import books on music & related subject matter; sound recordings & comics.
Number of Titles Warehoused: 150,000

Thinkers' Press Inc
1524 Le Claire St, Davenport, IA 52803
SAN: 176-4632
Tel: 563-271-6657
E-mail: info@chessbutler.com
Web Site: www.thinkerspressinc.com

Key Personnel
Pres & Busn Mgr: Bob Long
Founded: 1971
Specialize in books on chess.

Trophy Room Books
PO Box 3041, Agoura, CA 91301
Tel: 818-889-2469 *Fax:* 818-889-4849
E-mail: info@trophyroombooks.com
Web Site: www.trophyroombooks.com
Key Personnel
Co-Owner: Jim Herring; Ellen Herring
Founded: 1971
Antiquarian big game hunting; all 30 titles we publish are signed limited editions.
Number of Titles Warehoused: 30

Membership(s): Antiquarian Booksellers Association of America (ABAA); Independent Book Publishers Association (IBPA); International League of Antiquarian Booksellers (ILAB)

Vedanta Book Center
Subsidiary of Vivekananda Vedanta Society
14630 S Lemont Rd, Homer Glen, IL 60491
Tel: 708-301-9062 *Fax:* 708-301-9063
Web Site: www.vedantabooks.com
Key Personnel
Mgr: Swami Varadananda
   E-mail: swamivaradananda@yahoo.com
Founded: 1930
Imported & US titles.
Number of Titles Warehoused: 1,100

Export Representatives

International Service Co
International Service Bldg, 333 Fourth Ave, Indi-
   alantic, FL 32903-4295
SAN: 169-5134
Tel: 321-724-1443 *Fax:* 321-724-1443
Key Personnel
Pres: Dennis Samuels

Compt: F Schneider
Mng Dir: Katherine Swanberg
Coord Dir: Ann C Samuels
Shipping & Receiving Mgr: Larry A Whobrey
Systems Supv: Suzanne Jones
Asst to Pres: Robert Cohen
Admin Asst: Irene August

Founded: 1958
Exporter & importer of books, quantity & single
   copy; periodicals & school supplies; commissionaires. Specialize in science, technology &
   medicine.

Shipping Services

ABDI Inc
16 Avenue "A", Leetsdale, PA 15056
Toll Free Tel: 800-796-6471 *Fax:* 412-741-4161
E-mail: e-fulfillment@abdintl.com
Web Site: www.abdi-ecommerce10.com/abdintl;
www.abdintl.com/abdintl
Key Personnel
CEO: Michael D Cheteyan, II
Pres: Judy G Cheteyan *E-mail:* j.cheteyan@
abdintl.com
VP, Fin & IT: Bryan A Cox
Gen Opers Mgr: Ericka D Giles
Founded: 1985
Provide associations with highly responsive,
member-focused order fulfillment, customer-
client care call center, membership processing,
e-commerce solutions, specialized web-enabled
applications & variable data/digital printing.
Based on your requirements, we use your association's or our specialized systems. Our primary goals are to help improve your member
satisfaction & retention while reducing your
overall costs.
BISAC compatible software
Membership(s): American Booksellers Association (ABA); ASAE

**American International Distribution Corp
(AIDC)**
82 Winter Sport Lane, Williston, VT 05495
Mailing Address: PO Box 80, Williston, VT
05495-0080
Tel: 802-862-0095 *Toll Free Tel:* 800-678-2432
Fax: 802-864-7749
Web Site: www.aidcvt.com
Key Personnel
Pres & CEO: Marilyn McConnell
Dir, Opers: Michael Pelland
Founded: 1986
Order fulfillment, distribution, warehouse ser-
vices, call center, computerized reporting,
credit & collections, list maintenance, data
management, lettershop, subscription, Pubnet,
Advantis, web site hosting & development.
BISAC compatible software
Membership(s): Book Industry Study Group
(BISG); Independent Publisher's Guild (IPG)

Baker & Taylor Publisher Services
30 Amberwood Pkwy, Ashland, OH 44805
Tel: 567-215-0030 *Toll Free Tel:* 888-814-0208
E-mail: info@btpubservices.com; orders@
btpubservices.com
Web Site: www.btpubservices.com
Key Personnel
SVP, Sales & Client Servs: Mark Suchomel
SVP, Opers: Bob Gospodarek
Founded: 2017
Complete warehousing, shipping & order fulfillment. Our dedicated call center takes orders &
ships products directly from our distribution
centers. Baker & Taylor Publisher Services'
online Publisher Dashboard allows you to ac-
cess sales information, track inventory & place
orders. Customized reports also available.

Books International Inc
22883 Quicksilver Dr, Dulles, VA 20166
Mailing Address: PO Box 605, Herndon, VA
20172-0605
Tel: 703-661-1500 *Fax:* 703-661-1501
E-mail: hdqtrs@booksintl.com
Web Site: booksintl.presswarehouse.com
Key Personnel
CFO: Vartan Ajamian

Dir, Busn Devt: Ellen Loerke *E-mail:* ellen.
loerke@booksintl.com
Founded: 1984
Complete fulfillment services for medium &
large-sized book publishers since 1984. Order
processing, EDI, customer service, collections,
royalties, commissions, reports, Internet access
to live data, 24-hour turn-around, on-site digital printing (color & B&W) & digital content
support. Ebook distribution direct from your
web site. We ship worldwide. Call for a free
estimate.
BISAC compatible software
Membership(s): American Association of University Presses (AAUP); Association of American
Publishers (AAP)

Canon Business Process Services
Division of Canon Group
460 W 34 St, 6th fl, New York, NY 10001
Tel: 212-502-2100 *Toll Free Tel:* 800-937-2724;
888-623-2668 (ext 108)
E-mail: info@cbps.canon.com
Web Site: cbps.canon.com
Key Personnel
Pres & CEO: Joseph R Marciano
Provides on-site total management of mailroom,
messenger & copy center, including equipment,
professional personnel, supplies, systems &
controls; copy, fax, records management, mes-
senger service & word processing.
BISAC compatible software

Clark Distribution Systems (CDS)
Unit of The Clark Group Inc
3705 Quakerbridge Rd, Suite 116, Hamilton, NJ
08169
Tel: 609-528-7660 *Fax:* 609-528-4526
Web Site: www.clarkdistribution.net
Founded: 1984
Full service logistic company providing solu-
tions & transportation for publishers & print-
ers of magazines & books, regional & national.
Weekly consolidation & delivery to magazine
& book wholesaler & postal facilities located
throughout the US & Canada; specialized trans-
portation; warehousing; Pic N Pac. Distribution
centers located in Bethany, CT; Woodridge, IL;
Kansas City, MO; Harrisburg, PA; La Vergne,
TN & Carrollton, TX.
BISAC compatible software

The Clark Group Inc
Subsidiary of The Gores Group
3705 Quakerbridge Rd, Suite 116, Hamilton, NJ
08619
Tel: 609-528-7660 *Fax:* 609-528-7710
E-mail: service@clarkworldwide.com
Web Site: www.clarkgroupinc.com
Key Personnel
Pres & CEO: Charles H "Skip" Fischer, III
E-mail: sfischer@clarkworldwide.com
EVP, Sales & Mktg: Dave Alleger
E-mail: dalleger@clarkgroupinc.com
VP, Transportation, Clark Distribution Systems:
Marc Wallman
Leading independent third party logistics provider
of value-added distribution, transportation man-
agement & international air & ocean freight
forwarding services to the print media & other
highly service sensitive industries. Clark's 4
unique business units, Clark Distribution Ser-
vices (CDS), Highway Distribution Systems
(HDS), Clark Worldwide Transportation (CWT)

& Preprint Logistics (PP) provide customers
with a single source supply chain solution.
Branch Office(s)
Clark Worldwide Transportation Inc, 10 New
Maple Ave, Suite 304, Pine Brook, NJ 07058,
VP & Gen Mgr: Neil Dale *Tel:* 973-628-
8880 *Fax:* 973-628-8330 *E-mail:* ndale@
clarkworldwide.com
Clark Worldwide Transportation Inc, 8200 E
Stausen Ave, Decks 25 & 26, Pico Rivera, CA
90660 *Tel:* 310-952-9595 *Fax:* 310-763-0016
Clark Distribution Systems, 6 Old Amity
Rd, Bethany, CT 06524 *Tel:* 203-393-0660
Fax: 203-393-1813
Preprint Logistics Management, 105 Filley St,
Unit A, Bloomfield, CT 06002 *Tel:* 860-286-
9240 *Fax:* 860-286-9290 *Web Site:* www.
preprintlogistics.com
Clark Distribution Systems Inc, 2145 Interna-
tionale Pkwy, Suite 400, Woodridge, IL 60517
Tel: 630-783-8713 *Fax:* 630-783-8792
Highway Distribution Systems Inc, 8250 NE Un-
derground Dr, Pillar 158, Kansas City, MO
64161 *Tel:* 816-453-5204 *Fax:* 816-453-9137
Clark Distribution Systems Inc, 400 Capital Lane,
Middletown, PA 17057 (Opers Ctr) *Tel:* 717-
616-5726 *Fax:* 717-761-3320
Clark Distribution Systems Inc, 1630 Corporate
Place, La Vergne, TN 37086 *Tel:* 615-501-0120
Fax: 615-501-0115
Highway Distribution Systems Inc, 2848 Anode
Lane, Dallas, TX 75220 *Tel:* 615-535-4058
Clark Worldwide Transportation Inc, 8920
San Mateo Dr, Suite A, Laredo, TX 78045
Tel: 956-717-3266 *Fax:* 956-717-3267
Membership(s): Distripress

Courier Systems Inc
180 Pulaski St, Bayonne, NJ 07002
Tel: 201-432-0550 *Toll Free Tel:* 800-252-0353
Fax: 201-432-9686
E-mail: sales@csweb.biz
Web Site: www.csweb.biz
Key Personnel
Owner & Pres: Richard Murad *Tel:* 201-432-0550
ext 211 *E-mail:* rick.murad@csweb.biz
Warehousing, pick-pack shipping, trucking,
import-export, hand assembly.
BISAC compatible software
Branch Office(s)
415 Bank St, Bridgeton, NJ 08302
45 Rosenhayn Ave, Bridgeton, NJ 08302, Con-
tact: Tori Morris *Tel:* 856-455-3600 *Toll Free
Tel:* 800-252-0353 *E-mail:* tori.morris@csweb.
biz

Direct Link™ Worldwide Inc
Subsidiary of PostNord
700 Dowd Ave, Elizabeth, NJ 07201
Tel: 908-289-0703 *Toll Free Tel:* 800-223-7967
Fax: 908-289-0705
E-mail: infousa@directlink.com
Web Site: www.directlink.com
Key Personnel
Pres: John Cucciniello *E-mail:* jjc@directlink.com
VP: Soren Muller
Founded: 1986
Provider of international remail services.
BISAC compatible software
Branch Office(s)
1872 Brummel Dr, Elk Grove Village, IL 60007
Tel: 847-290-6420 *Fax:* 847-290-6421

Disticor Magazine Distribution Services
Division of MicroVite Investments Ltd

1000 Thornton Rd S, Oshawa, ON L1J 7E2, Canada
Tel: 905-619-6565 *Toll Free Tel:* 800-668-7724 (CN only) *Fax:* 905-619-2903
Web Site: www.disticor.com; www.magamall.com
Key Personnel
CEO: John Lafranier *E-mail:* johnl@disticor.com
National distributor of newsstand publications.
BISAC compatible software

RR Donnelley & Sons Company
35 W Wacker Dr, Chicago, IL 60601
Tel: 312-326-8000 *Toll Free Tel:* 800-742-4455
Web Site: www.rrd.com
Key Personnel
Pres & CEO: Daniel L Knotts
Pres, Busn Servs: John Pecaric
Pres, Mktg Solutions: Doug Ryan
EVP & CIO: Ken O'Brien
EVP & CFO: Terry D Peterson
EVP & Chief Human Resources Offr: Sheila Rutt
EVP, Dom Opers & Chief Supply Chain Offr: Glynn Perry
EVP, Gen Coun, Chief Compliance Offr & Corp Secy: Deborah Steiner
EVP, Chief Strategy & Transformation Offr: Elif Sagsen-Ercel
SVP & Chief Acctg Offr: Michael J Sharp
Founded: 1864
Order processing; shrink wrapping, product assembly, pick-pack, mass mailing, drop & bulk shipping, warehousing & inventory control, customer service, royalties, credit & collections, trucking services.
BISAC compatible software

eFulfillment Service Inc
807 Airport Access Rd, Traverse City, MI 49686
Tel: 231-276-5057 *Toll Free Tel:* 866-922-6783
Web Site: www.efulfillmentservice.com
Key Personnel
Pres: John Lindberg *E-mail:* jal@efulfillmentservice.com
VP, Sales & Mktg: Steve Bulger *E-mail:* bulger.s@efulfillmentservice.com
Founded: 2000
Internet based order fulfillment services for book, tape, CD & DVD publishers.
BISAC compatible software
Membership(s): Better Business Bureau (BBB); Mailing & Fulfillment Service Association (MFSA)

FedEx Ground
Subsidiary of FedEx Corp
1000 FedEx Dr, Coraopolis, PA 15108
Mailing Address: PO Box 108, Coraopolis, PA 15230
Tel: 412-269-1000 *Toll Free Tel:* 800-762-3725
Web Site: www.fedex.com
Key Personnel
Pres & CEO: Henry J Maier
EVP & COO: Ward B Strang
EVP & CFO: Robert D Henning
Transport small packages, ground, US, Canada, Mexico.
BISAC compatible software

FedEx Supply Chain
Division of FedEx Corp
6700 Cranberry Woods Dr, Cranberry Township, PA 16066
Toll Free Tel: 800-677-3110
E-mail: solution@fedex.com
Web Site: supplychain.fedex.com
Key Personnel
Pres & CEO: Art Smuck
SVP & COO: Andy Smith
SVP & Gen Coun: Bradley R Peacock
SVP, Sales, Strategy & Communs: Ryan Kelly
VP & CFO: Michael Fox
VP, HR: Stacey Heitzenrater

Founded: 1898
Third-party logistics provider. Value-added warehousing & transportation services.
BISAC compatible software

Global Order Fulfillment, see ABDI Inc

Gordon Management Inc (GMI)
305 Churchill Ave, Somerset, NJ 08873
Tel: 732-846-4800 *Fax:* 732-846-4709
E-mail: info@gmidistribution.com
Web Site: www.gmidistribution.com
Key Personnel
Pres: Keith Gordon
VP: Kenneth Gordon
Founded: 1978
Physical distribution for gift, trade & textbook publishers, book clubs, catalog & continuity programs; freight savings programs (in-bound & out-bound). Pick-pack, shrink wrapping, hot stamping, hand assembly of displays, kits & prepacks; mail services.

Hassett Express
18W100 22 St, Suite 109, Oakbrook Terrace, IL 60181
Tel: 630-530-6515 *Toll Free Tel:* 800-323-9422 *Fax:* 630-530-6538
Web Site: www.hassettexpress.com
Founded: 1980
The nation's leading forwarder of daily, weekly, biweekly & monthly periodicals, magazines & newspapers specializing in newsstand & subscriber copies. We currently service over 200 post offices & 250 wholesalers, as well as office & show copies. A full service logistical transportation company providing business with time-definite transportation & personalized logistic solutions including: same, next, second, third, fourth & fifth day; international; charter; & exclusive truck. Offices also in Los Angeles, CA, San Francisco, CA; Atlanta, GA; Chicago O'Hare Annex, Chicago, IL; Newark, NJ; Philadelphia, PA; Dallas, TX; Dulles, VA.
BISAC compatible software

Integrated Distribution Services (IDS)
9431 AllPoints Pkwy, Plainfield, IN 46168
Toll Free Tel: 866-232-6533
E-mail: adale@idsfulfillment.com
Web Site: www.idsfulfillment.com
Key Personnel
CEO: Mark DeFabis *E-mail:* mdefabis@idsfulfillment.com
CFO: Rick LaGore *E-mail:* rlagore@idsfulfillment.com
Pres, Warehousing & Fulfillment: Mike Jones *E-mail:* mjones@idsfulfillment.com
VP, Busn Devt: Mike DeFabis *E-mail:* mcdefabis@idsfulfillment.com; Robert Hartley *E-mail:* rhartley@idsfulfillment.com
Ecommerce, retail & direct selling order fulfillment (direct to consumer).
BISAC compatible software
Membership(s): DSA; International Warehouse Logistics Association (IWLA); Internet Assigned Numbers Authority (IANA); Toy International Association (TIA)

Kable Packaging Services
4275 Thunderbird Lane, Fairfield, OH 45014
Tel: 513-671-2800
E-mail: info@kable.com
Web Site: www.kablefulfillment.com
Key Personnel
VP, Sales: Charles J Walker
Multichannel fulfillment & custom repackaging.

Magnum Book Services
Member of The Magnum Group

180 Raritan Center Pkwy, Suite 105, Edison, NJ 07737
Tel: 908-349-2300 *Fax:* 732-225-2037
E-mail: sales@magnumbookservices.com
Web Site: www.magnumbookservices.com; www.linkedin.com/company/magnum-book-services; www.facebook.com/magnumbookservices
Key Personnel
Pres: Scott B Bramson
Supplier of shipping & consolidation services to the global publishing industry. With office-depots in Edison, NJ & Essex, UK, plus our overseas partners we offer specific door-to-door services covering the US, Far East, Australasia & the UK, plus a fully integrated European network. Our emphasis is on total customer care, flexibility & resourcefulness to solve your shipping issues.
Branch Office(s)
Unit 8, Repton Close, Burnt Mills Industrial Area, Basildon, Essex SS13 1LJ, United Kingdom (headquarters) *Tel:* (01268) 244 211 *Fax:* (01268) 244 212

Maple Logistics Solutions
60 Grumbacher Rd, York, PA 17406
Mailing Address: PO Box 15100, York, PA 17405-7100
Tel: 717-764-4596 *Fax:* 717-764-4494
E-mail: info@maplesoln.com
Web Site: www.maplelogisticssolutions.com
Key Personnel
Pres: James S Wisotzkey
VP, Dist Opers: Chris Benyovszky
VP, Dist, Sales & Mktg: Andrew J Van Sprang
VP, Sales & Mktg: William S Long *E-mail:* long@maplepress.com
Warehousing, distribution, fulfillment, print-on-demand, drop-shipping, invoicing & value added services.
BISAC compatible software
Membership(s): Associated Warehouses Inc (AWI); Book Manufacturers' Institute (BMI); Council of Supply Chain Management Professionals (CSCMP); Distributors & Consolidators of America (DACA); Express Carriers Association (ECA); Warehousing Education and Research Council (WERC); World Trade Center Harrisburg

NCS Inc
149 N Railroad St, Selmer, TN 38375
Tel: 731-645-4496
E-mail: service@ncsmags.com
Key Personnel
CEO: Ross Capwell
Single-copy sales, subscription fulfillment, product/premium fulfillment & reader service.
BISAC compatible software

Omeda
555 Huehl Rd, Northbrook, IL 60062
Tel: 847-564-8900 *Fax:* 847-559-7555
E-mail: sales@omeda.com
Web Site: ww3.omeda.com
Key Personnel
VP, Sales & Mktg: Randy Renner *E-mail:* rrenner@omeda.com
Founded: 1980
Fulfillment & database management for business-to-business trade publications & business marketers.
BISAC compatible software

The Order Fulfillment Group
7313 Mayflower Park Dr, Zionsville, IN 46077
Tel: 317-733-7755 *Fax:* 317-733-8799
Web Site: www.tofg.com
Key Personnel
Owner & Pres: Tony Hughes *E-mail:* thughes@tofg.com
Founded: 1989

Complete fulfillment services for publishers including call center, cashiering, pick/pack, storage, kitting & online reports portal.
BISAC compatible software

PBD Worldwide Inc
Affiliate of Georgia School Book
1650 Bluegrass Lakes Pkwy, Alpharetta, GA 30004
Tel: 470-769-1000 *Toll Free Tel:* 866-998-4PBD (998-4723)
E-mail: sales.marketing@pbd.com; customerservice@pbd.com
Web Site: www.pbd.com
Key Personnel
Pres & CEO: Scott A Dockter
SVP & CFO: David S Ferguson
SVP: Gregory R Dockter
SVP, Client Rel: Brion Zaeh
SVP, Opers: Lisa Williams
VP/Cont: Jeff Wells
VP, Sales: Jan Jones
Mktg Mgr: Jeanna Akins
Founded: 1976
Fulfillment & distribution services for e-commerce companies, retailers, corporations, publishers, associations, nonprofits & faith-based organizations. Provides order fulfillment solutions for over 120 B2C & B2B clients that enable growth & streamline operations.
BISAC compatible software
Branch Office(s)
8215 Roswell Rd, Suite 925, Atlanta, GA 30350
3280 Summit Ridge Pkwy, Duluth, GA 30096, Dir, Opers: Tim Krupel *Tel:* 470-769-1300
905 Carlow Dr, Unit B, Bolingbrook, IL 60490 *Tel:* 470-769-1400
8779 Greenwood Place, Suite A, Savage, MD 20763 *Tel:* 470-769-1500
7055 S Decatur Blvd, No 180, Las Vegas, NV 89118

Publishers Storage & Shipping Corp
46 Development Rd, Fitchburg, MA 01420
Tel: 978-345-2121 *Fax:* 978-348-1233
Web Site: www.pssc.com
Key Personnel
Pres: Mike Seagram
VP, Massachusetts Opers: Carol Braman
Dir, Sales & Mktg: Pam Nuffer
Founded: 1974
Full order processing, warehousing & shipping services for small- & medium-sized publishers. Customer service: invoicing, web shopping cart integration, real time credit card processing, back orders, credit memos. Handle all types of published materials: books, calendars, CDs, back issues. Ship any quantity singles to thousands, domestic & foreign. Set assembly & shrink wrapping.
BISAC compatible software
Branch Office(s)
660 S Mansfield, Ypsilanti, MI 48197 *Tel:* 734-487-9720 *Fax:* 734-487-1890 SAN: 991-2665

Styled Packaging LLC
PO Box 30299, Philadelphia, PA 19103-8299
Tel: 610-529-4122 *Fax:* 610-520-9662
Web Site: www.taylorbox.com

Key Personnel
Pres: William R Fenkel *E-mail:* jjibill@aol.com
Founded: 2003
Design & manufacture slipcases, box sets, set-up-boxes, folding cartons, inserting; POP displays & corrugated packaging, plastic rigid & folding boxes, vacuum-formed components & custom packaging.
BISAC compatible software
Membership(s): Book Industry Guild of New York

Swan Packaging Fulfillment Inc
415 Hamburg Tpke, Wayne, NJ 07470
Tel: 973-790-8417 *Fax:* 973-790-0216
Web Site: www.swanpackaging.com
Key Personnel
Pres: Timothy S Werkley *E-mail:* tim@swanpackaging.com
Founded: 1986
SPF provides third party fulfillment (pick-pack) & project packaging services (kit assembly, automated cartoning & shrink wrapping). Operate from a 125,000 sq ft facility located approximately 20 miles west of New York City.
BISAC compatible software
Membership(s): Direct Marketing Club of New York (DMCNY); FMA

UPS Supply Chain Solutions
12380 Morris Rd, Alpharetta, GA 30005
Tel: 913-693-6151 (outside US & CN)
Toll Free Tel: 800-742-5727 (US & CN)
Web Site: upsscs.com
Key Personnel
Mng Dir: Ken Warech
Specialize in arranging consolidated ocean & air shipments for books, magazines & printed matter. Provide the export-import link between publishers, booksellers & distributors. Custom house brokers. Freight forwarders. Warehousemen.
BISAC compatible software

US Postal Service Global Business
Division of US Postal Service
475 L'Enfant Plaza SW, Rm 5100, Washington, DC 20260-4016
Tel: 202-268-2178
Web Site: www.usps.com
Key Personnel
Mng Dir: Franca S Davis
Founded: 2006
International mail & distribution.
BISAC compatible software

Value Added Resources
Subsidiary of Wilson Logistics Inc
7900 Rockville Rd, Indianapolis, IN 46214
Tel: 317-899-1000 *Fax:* 317-899-2259
E-mail: info@valueaddedres.com
Web Site: www.valueaddedres.com
Key Personnel
Owner: Scott Wilson *E-mail:* swilson@valueaddedres.com
Founded: 2005
Quality provider of fulfillment services to publishers, distributors & manufacturers. Over 13 years of experience in publishing distribution. Provide services such as order entry/customer

service, pick/pack/shipping, kitting, display building, product labeling & shrink wrapping. Specialize in the small- to medium-size publisher who wants to be treated like they are our only client.
BISAC compatible software
Membership(s): Book Industry Study Group (BISG); Council of Supply Chain Management Professionals (CSCMP); Distribution Executive Interest Group (DEIG); Warehousing Education and Research Council (WERC)

Ware-Pak LLC
2427 Bond St, University Park, IL 60484
Tel: 708-534-2600 *Fax:* 708-534-7803
Web Site: www.ware-pak.com
Key Personnel
Pres & CEO: Keith F Shay *E-mail:* kshay@ware-pak.com
Busn Devt Mgr: Matthew Kurtis *E-mail:* mkurtis@ware-pak.com
Founded: 1963
Complete fulfillment services for publishers including call center services, pick-pack fulfillment, storage, kit assembly & complete account information online, anytime, 24/7.
BISAC compatible software

Whitehurst & Clark Book Fulfillment
1200 County Rd, Rte 523, Flemington, NJ 08822
Tel: 908-782-2323 *Toll Free Tel:* 800-488-8040 *Fax:* 908-237-2407
E-mail: wcbooks@aol.com
Web Site: www.wcbks.com
Key Personnel
Pres: Bradley J Searles
IT Mgr: Jay Makuch
Logistics Mgr: Maria Silva
Plant Mgr: Elayne Suckno
Warehouse Mgr: Sean Colril
Computerized order processing, customer service, sales analysis & inventory control. Complete warehousing for book publishers of all types including nonprofit associations & scientific. Full shrink wrapping operation. Pick, pack, shipping & pallet storage.
BISAC compatible software

Wood & Associates Direct Marketing Services Ltd
9-1410 Bayly St, Pickering, ON L1W 3R3, Canada
Tel: 416-293-2511 *Fax:* 416-293-2594
E-mail: clientservices@wood-and-associates.com
Web Site: www.wood-and-associates.com
Key Personnel
VP, Sales & Mktg: Brian Davidson *Tel:* 416-293-2511 ext 105
Founded: 1979
Mailing services, fulfillment & distribution, lasering, inkjetting, data capture & processing, communication fulfillment process design & management.
BISAC compatible software
Membership(s): Canadian Federation for Independent Business (CFIB); Canadian Marketing Association (CMA); Canadian Society of Association Executives (CSAE); National Association of Major Mail Users (NAMMU); Scarborough Chamber of Commerce; Toronto Board of Trade

Shipping Suppliers

Citation Box & Paper Co
4700 W Augusta Blvd, Chicago, IL 60651-3397
Tel: 773-378-1400
E-mail: info@citationbox.com
Web Site: www.citationbox.com
Key Personnel
Pres: Tony Kostiuk
Founded: 1951
Corrugated boxes.
BISAC compatible software

The Gluefast Co Inc
3535 State Rte 66, Bldg No 1, Neptune, NJ
  07753
Tel: 732-918-4600 *Toll Free Tel:* 800-242-7318
  Fax: 732-918-4646
E-mail: info@gluefast.com
Web Site: www.gluefast.com
Key Personnel
Pres: Lester Mallet *E-mail:* lmallet@gluefast.com
VP: Amy Altman *E-mail:* aaltman@gluefast.com
Gen Mgr: Joe Benenati *E-mail:* jbenenati@
  gluefast.com
Manufacturer of adhesives, liquid glues, manual
  & electric label gluers & moisteners as well as
  case making equipment & products for the wall
  art industry.
BISAC compatible software
Membership(s): PMMI: The Association for
  Packaging and Processing Technologies

Stephen Gould Corp
35 S Jefferson Rd, Whippany, NJ 07981
Tel: 973-428-1500; 973-428-1510
E-mail: info@stephengould.com
Web Site: www.stephengould.com
Key Personnel
CEO: Michael Golden
CFO: Anthony Lupo
Pres: Justin Golden
EVP: John Golden
Cont: Kim Ings
Dir, Info Systems: Nanette Rosenbaum
Dir, Opers: Jason Rosario
Founded: 1939
Design & manufacture corrugated & chipboard
  containers for book publishers & suppliers; die-
  cut specialties.
BISAC compatible software

Styled Packaging LLC
PO Box 30299, Philadelphia, PA 19103-8299
Tel: 610-529-4122 *Fax:* 610-520-9662
Web Site: www.taylorbox.com
Key Personnel
Pres: William R Fenkel *E-mail:* jjibill@aol.com
Founded: 2003
Design & manufacture slipcases, box sets, set-up-
  boxes, folding cartons, inserting; POP displays
  & corrugated packaging, plastic rigid & folding
boxes, vacuum-formed components & custom
packaging.
BISAC compatible software
Membership(s): Book Industry Guild of New
  York

Swan Packaging Fulfillment Inc
415 Hamburg Tpke, Wayne, NJ 07470
Tel: 973-790-8417 *Fax:* 973-790-0216
Web Site: www.swanpackaging.com
Key Personnel
Pres: Timothy S Werkley *E-mail:* tim@
  swanpackaging.com
SPF provides third party pick-pack fulfillment
  services for B2C & B2B product marketers in
  the e-commerce & catalog markets, specializing in books, CDs, clothing, gifts & other
  products. Offers electronic order import &
  shipment confirmation export, returns processing, electronic reports & shipping via USPS,
  UPS & FedEx. 125,000 sq ft facility is located approximately 20 miles west of New
  York City & maintains secured client storage in
  flow racks, shelving & pallet storage environ-
  ments. SPF also provides value-added packaging services such as kit assembly & automated
  packaging.
BISAC compatible software
Membership(s): Direct Marketing Club of New
  York (DMCNY); FMA

Services & Suppliers

Consultants — Activity Index

CONSULTANTS — ACTIVITY INDEX

Consultants

This section includes firms and individuals who offer consultation on matters such as advertising and promotion, book production, finance, management, marketing and printing.

A-R Editions Inc
1600 Aspen Commons, Suite 100, Middleton, WI 53562
Tel: 608-836-9000 *Fax:* 608-831-8200
E-mail: info@areditions.com
Web Site: www.areditions.com
Key Personnel
Pres & CEO: Patrick Wall *Tel:* 608-203-2575
   E-mail: patrick.wall@areditions.com
Dir, Spec Projs: James Zychowicz *Tel:* 608-203-2580 *E-mail:* james.zychowicz@areditions.com
Founded: 1962
Complete production services & project management from editorial & design through typesetting, printing, art creation, indexing, printing & mailing for journal, book & magazine publishers; specialize in computerized music engraving, integration of music & text, foreign language, scientific & non-Roman alphabet. Typesetting on Mac/Quark systems. Disk conversion; automatic pagination; Postscript & PDF output; customized music engraving.

Accurate Writing & More
16 Barstow Lane, Hadley, MA 01035
Tel: 413-586-2388
Web Site: frugalmarketing.com
Key Personnel
Owner & Dir: Shel Horowitz *E-mail:* shel@principledprofit.com
Dir: Dina Friedman
Founded: 1981
Marketing, promotion & advertising consulting emphasizing green & ethical practices & highest return for lowest cost. Also consulting to authors on traditional & independent publishing options, preparation of book proposals, vendor selection & project management for self-publishers.
Membership(s): Connecticut Authors & Publishers Association; Independent Book Publishers Association (IBPA); Independent Publishers of New England (IPNE); National Writers Union (NWU); Western New England Editorial Freelancers Network

Alice B Acheson
Unit of Acheson-Greub Inc
PO Box 735, Friday Harbor, WA 98250
Tel: 360-378-2815 *Fax:* 360-378-2815
E-mail: aliceba7@gmail.com
Founded: 1988
Consultation in all aspects of publicity (launching, reviews, interviews, press materials) & marketing for publishers, booksellers & authors. Specialize in assisting authors & independent presses enter the mainstream +/or improve expertise through enhanced contacts, timing, positioning, rights sales & distribution.
Membership(s): Book Promotion Forum; Independent Book Publishers Association (IBPA); Pacific Northwest Booksellers Association (PNBA); Pacific Northwest Writers Association; Publishers' Publicity Association

Advanced Telecom Services, see ATS Mobile

AEI (Atchity Entertainment International Inc)
9601 Wilshire Blvd, Unit 1202, Beverly Hills, CA 90210
Tel: 323-932-1685

Web Site: www.aeionline.com
Key Personnel
CEO: Dr Kenneth Atchity *E-mail:* kja@aeionline.com
Pres & COO: Ms Chi-Li Wong
VP, Devt: Brenna Lui *E-mail:* bl@aeionline.com
Submissions Coord: Jennifer Pope
Founded: 1996
Full service literary company that deals with editing & developing, book publishing, TV production, motion picture production, licensing & merchandising.
Sister companies: Atchity Productions; Story Merchant; Story Merchant Books; The Writer's Lifeline Inc.

Agent Research & Evaluation Inc (AR&E)
44 Park Rd, Woodbury, CT 06798
Tel: 203-586-1397
Web Site: www.agentresearch.org
Key Personnel
Pres: Beverly Swerling Martin *E-mail:* beverly@agentresearch.org
Founded: 1996
Directs you to the literary agents right for you, twentieth book or your first. We keep in contact by exchange of e-mail +/or telephone & use our wide experience to produce a highly individualized, nuanced & in-depth report with full data on the sales records of the recommended agents & how to design your approach to them. Author web sites: In this mass-media age, you now need three things to make it as an author, your own talent, the right literary agent & a successful web site. The Internet has become the most powerful tool for selling the maximum number of books to the widest possible readership & we're talking mainstream royalty-paying publishers, not self-publishing. We recommend developers & promoters of author web sites, without any kick-backs or finders fees.

Altman Dedicated Direct
853 Academy St, Rural Hall, NC 27045-9329
Tel: 336-969-9538 *Fax:* 336-969-0187
Web Site: www.altmandedicateddirect.com
Key Personnel
Pres: Shari Altman *E-mail:* saltman@altmandedicateddirect.com
Founded: 1999
Direct response marketing consultancy.

Ampersand Inc/Professional Publishing Services
515 Madison St, New Orleans, LA 70116
Tel: 312-280-8905 *Fax:* 312-944-1582
E-mail: info@ampersandworks.com
Web Site: www.ampersandworks.com
Key Personnel
Pres & Publr: Suzanne T Isaacs
Founded: 1995 (began consulting in 2005)
Provides a wide range of publishing services including private publishing. Branch office in Chicago, IL.
Membership(s): Association of Independent Authors (AIA); The Association of Publishers for Special Sales (APSS); Independent Book Publishers Association (IBPA); Society of Children's Book Writers & Illustrators (SCBWI)

Applied Information Sciences Corp
PO Box 9182, Calabasas, CA 91372-9182
Tel: 818-222-0926 *Fax:* 818-222-4329
E-mail: sales@aisciences.com
Web Site: www.aisciences.com
Key Personnel
Pres: Norm Mazer *E-mail:* nmazer@aisciences.com
Founded: 1984
Software products for companies selling books to libraries. Products include SmartSearch® Offline Sales Tool, SmartSearch® Web Module & VendorCat™ Book Processing Software. The SmartSearch® Web Module integrates into a vendor's web site & enables libraries to upload their collections, perform a complete collection analysis & create complete book lists that fill the libraries collection deficiencies within an overall budget. Consulting services include: central database creation & maintenance, upgrading & enhancing incomplete book data & custom software development.

Aptara Inc
Subsidiary of iEnergizer
2901 Telestar Ct, Suite 522, Falls Church, VA 22042
Tel: 703-352-0001
E-mail: moreinfo@aptaracorp.com
Web Site: www.aptaracorp.com
Key Personnel
Pres: Samir Kakar
EVP, Fin & Cont: Prashant Kapoor
SVP, Busn & Contact Ctr Opers: Ashish Madan
Busn Devt: Michael Scott *E-mail:* michael.scott@aptaracorp.com
Founded: 1988
Liaison for complete or any combination of production services, ranging from simple 1-color to complex 4-color projects. Copy-editing.
Branch Office(s)
150 California St, Suite 301, Newton, MA 02458
   Tel: 617-423-7755
11009 Metric Blvd, Bldg J, Suite 150, Austin, TX 78758 *Tel:* 512-876-5997
299 Elizabeth St, Level 1, Sydney 2000, Australia
   Tel: (02) 8251 0070
Tower 1 & 2, 8/100, Acharya Thulasi Rd (Shandy Rd), Pallavaram, Chennai 600 043, India
   Tel: (044) 22640676
No 2310, Doon Express Business Park, Saharanpur Rd, Bldg 2000, Dehradun 248 002, India
   Tel: (0135) 2644055
7B, Leela Infopark, Technopark, Trivandrum, Kerala 695 581, India *Tel:* (047) 14063370
A-37, Sector-60, Noida 201 301, India
   Tel: (0120) 7182424
D-10, Sector-2, Noida 201 301, India *Tel:* (0120) 24423678
SEZ Bldg 4A, 1st fl, S P Infocity, Pune Saswad Rd, Phursungi, Pune 412 308, India *Tel:* (020) 66728000

Arbor Books
244 Madison Ave, Box 254, New York, NY 10016
Tel: 212-956-0950 *Toll Free Tel:* 877-822-2500
   Fax: 914-401-9385
E-mail: info@arborbooks.com; editorial@arborbooks.net
Web Site: www.arborbooks.com; www.arborservices.co

Key Personnel
Owner: Joel Hochman *Tel:* 877-822-2502 *E-mail:* arborbooksjoel@aol.com; Larry Leichman *Tel:* 877-822-2504 *E-mail:* arborbookslarry@aol.com
Mktg Dir: Olga Vladi
Founded: 1992
Full service book production from ghostwriting & editing to cover design, printing, publishing & marketing. Arbor Books works for both 1) corporations (business books, corporate histories, CEO bios) & 2) individuals: novels (all genres), memoirs, children's books, biz books, etc. Services include supervised (& insured) ghostwriting, copy-editing, translation, proofreading, design (even the most complex, including model shoots, illustrations, photo reconstruction & manipulation, book jacket design, album cover & magazine design), word processing (including transcription), scanning, layout, typesetting, obtaining registrations & endorsements, B&W & 4-color printing, marketing, promotion & advertising. We also create logos, letterheads, annual reports, posters & promotional flyers. We can be hired for part of the job or all of the job. Personal attention & quality are guaranteed. Fully insured, including Media Insurance. Writers include Pulitzer Prize winners & "NY Times" best-selling authors; listed with Dun & Bradstreet; firm is featured regularly "The New York Times Book Review." Our self-publishing services include: press kits, press releases, booking TV & radio programs, speaking tours & book signings & negotiating with producers & agents.

Arbor Services, see Arbor Books

Asia Marketing & Management (AMM)
2014 Naudain St, Philadelphia, PA 19146-1317
Tel: 215-735-7670; 267-324-6227 (cell phone)
Web Site: www.asiamarketingmanagement.com
Key Personnel
Pres: James W Chan, PhD *E-mail:* jameschan@asiamarketingmanagement.com
Founded: 1983
James Chan consults on doing business in China & exporting American-made products & services to China & Asia.

Atchity Entertainment International Inc, see AEI (Atchity Entertainment International Inc)

ATS Mobile
1150 First Ave, Suite 105, King of Prussia, PA 19406
Tel: 610-688-6000 *Toll Free Tel:* 800-247-1287 *Fax:* 610-964-9117
Web Site: www.atsmobile.com
Key Personnel
CFO: Margie Varallo
Pres & Dir, Mktg & Sales: Bob Bentz *Tel:* 610-254-7191 *E-mail:* bobb@advancedtele.com
Sr Acct Exec: Scott Bronenberg
Founded: 1989
Mobile marketing services.
Branch Office(s)
Advanced Telecom Services, 34 Eglinton Ave W, Suite 180, Toronto, ON M4R 2J6, Canada *Tel:* 416-800-2490 *E-mail:* sales@atsmobile.ca
Advanced Telecom Services sro, Rosemarin Business Ctr, Delnicka 12, 170 00 Prague 7, Czechia *Tel:* 296 363 205 *Fax:* 296 363 204 *E-mail:* info@atspraha.cz *Web Site:* www.atspraha.cz
Advanced Telecom Services (UK) Ltd, 5 St John's Lane, London EC1M 4BH, United Kingdom *Tel:* (0800) 592 360 *E-mail:* uksales@advancedtele.co.uk *Web Site:* www.advancedtele.co.uk

Atwood Capital Partners LLC
The DuMont Bldg, 515 Madison Ave, 35th fl, New York, NY 10022
Tel: 212-355-1390 *Fax:* 212-355-1391
E-mail: info@atwoodcp.com
Web Site: www.atwoodadvisors.com
Key Personnel
Partner: John Wickersham
Founded: 1996
Consultants & intermediaries in the US & Europe in mergers & acquisitions. Assists clients exclusively in the business information industry.

Audiobook Department
6429 N Talman Ave, Chicago, IL 60645
Tel: 773-338-8813 *Fax:* 773-338-8813
Web Site: www.judithwest.com
Key Personnel
Owner & Prodr: Judith West *E-mail:* judith@judithwest.com
Founded: 2000
Full service audiobook development & production, with a diverse talent pool & on-site production facilities. Special consulting for publishers new to audiobooks: from concept to design, through digital or hard copy formats, reviewers & special markets. Free estimates available.
Membership(s): The Association of Publishers for Special Sales (APSS); Audio Publishers Association; The Authors Guild; Chicago Women in Publishing

Author Planet Consulting Services
Subsidiary of Jody Rein Books Inc
7741 S Ash Ct, Centennial, CO 80122
Tel: 303-253-1702
Web Site: authorplanet.org; jodyreinbooks.com
Key Personnel
Owner & Pres: Jody Rein *E-mail:* jodyrein@jodyreinbooks.com
Literary Assoc & Off Mgr: Caitlin Marshall *E-mail:* assistant@jodyreinbooks.com
Founded: 2011
Executive-level consulting, strategic branding & editorial services for writers & publishers. Platform development, author web sites, social media creation & management, writing & editorial services, branding strategies & concept development.

AuthorBytes
PO Box 382103, Cambridge, MA 02238-2103
Tel: 617-492-0442
E-mail: info@authorbytes.com
Web Site: www.authorbytes.com
Key Personnel
Founder: Steve Bennett
Founded: 2000
Web design, blogs, multimedia previews, social media consulting for authors.

Author's, Writer's & Book Publisher's Advice Line™
Division of The Linick Group Inc
Communications Tower, 7 Putter Lane, Middle Island, NY 11953-1920
Mailing Address: PO Box 102, Middle Island, NY 11953-0102
Tel: 631-924-3888; 631-924-8555; 631-604-8599
E-mail: topmarketingadvisor@gmail.com; awbpal@gmail.com
Web Site: TopMarketingAdvisor.com
Key Personnel
EVP: Roger Dextor
Sr Consultant: Andrew S Linick, PhD *E-mail:* topmarketingadvisor@gmail.com
Dir, Spec Projs: Barbara Deal
Founded: 1978
Advice for first-timers, entrepreneurs, small to medium-size publishers by phone, fax & e-mail. Specialize in getting your book published,

ebook & book promotion, direct response advertising, cross selling, self-publishing, social media marketing, sales promotion, Internet promotion & digital marketing. Consultation & critique service by phone on 100% money back guarantee. Provides comprehensive graphic redesign/new web site content development, interactive services with web site marketing makeover advice for first-time authors, self-publishers, professionals & entrepreneurs. Specialize in building a profitable author web site, 24/7 Editor's Choice newsroom, SEO/SEM, online advertising/PR, lead magnets, links to top bookselling search engines. Free marketing checklist for LMP readers: 49 Action Steps to Drive & Convert Traffic to Your Web Site.

Bashian & Associates Inc
28915 S Village Lane, Glenwillow, OH 44139
E-mail: adsales@bashian.com
Web Site: www.bashian.com
Key Personnel
Owner & Pres: Alison Bashian *E-mail:* alisonb@bashian.com
Sales & Busn Dvt: Laure Curva
Off Mgr: Anna Mazzolini
Founded: 1972
Advertising space sales for association, business-to-business & technical publications & directories; trade show exhibit sales management.
Membership(s): Association Media & Publishing; NAPR

Beidel Printing House Inc
Division of White Mane Publishing Co Inc
225 S Fayette St, Shippensburg, PA 17257
Mailing Address: PO Box 708, Shippensburg, PA 17257-0708
Tel: 717-532-5063 *Fax:* 717-532-2502
E-mail: customerservice@dreamprint.com
Web Site: dreamprint.com
Key Personnel
VP & Ed: Harold Collier
VP, Opers: Thomas M Fritz
Founded: 1917
Full service company.

Hal Zina Bennett
Affiliate of Tenacity Press Productions
9827 Irvine Ave, Upper Lake, CA 95485
Tel: 707-275-9011 *Toll Free Tel:* 800-738-6721
E-mail: halbooks@halzinabennett.com
Web Site: www.halzinabennett.com
Founded: 1971
Publishing consultant.
Membership(s): The Authors Guild; Poets & Writers

J R Blitman Marketing Inc
93 Einstein Way, East Windsor, NJ 08512
Tel: 609-448-2490; 301-758-2334
E-mail: jrblitman@gmail.com
Key Personnel
Pres: Joan R Blitman
Specializing in professional & STM publishing, executive search, strategic planning, business development, product development, competitive intelligence, market planning, direct response, market research, international sales & marketing, project management, conference planning & interactive marketing. Whether it is planning, implementation, or evaluation, expert, personalized services are available to you on a project or ongoing basis.
Branch Office(s)
7805 Stanza St, Boynton Beach, FL 33437
Tel: 561-200-4730 *Fax:* 302-348-2490
E-mail: joanroy@brandeis.edu

Joan R Blitman, see J R Blitman Marketing Inc

Blue Fox Associates
9 Barnacle Rd, Hilton Head Island, SC 29928-5518
Tel: 843-681-6939
E-mail: Island120@aol.com
Key Personnel
Pres: Janice M Blaufox
Founded: 1980
Directory, database, mailing list, computer consultant. Freelance book reviews.

BMR Associates
60 Corte Amado, Greenbrae, CA 94904
Tel: 415-927-1564
E-mail: info@bmrassoc.com
Web Site: www.bmrassoc.com
Key Personnel
Chairman: J Peter Kiers
Pres: Walter Parsons
Sr VP, Opers: Robert Parzival *E-mail:* rparzival@bmrassoc.com
Sr Assoc: John Hershberger; Peter Massik
Consultant: Pete Alcorn; Mark Brokering; David Brugger; Craig Havemeyer; Carla Ruff; Eugene Schwartz
Founded: 1983
Publishing & media management consultants emphasizing strategic & operational planning, new business & market development, marketing, sales & financial management for trade, educational & reference publishers. Advise, develop & assist in the implementation of new publishing programs; assess & reposition existing publishing programs. Develop business plans for new ventures. Merger & acquisition representation & valuations, founder transitions, liquidity strategies.

J B Bryans Literary
7 Meetinghouse Ct, Indian Mills, NJ 08088
Tel: 609-922-0369
E-mail: info@brylit.com
Web Site: brylit.com
Key Personnel
Pres: John B Bryans *E-mail:* john@brylit.com
Founded: 2017
Provides strategic, customized consulting services that help independent, association, non-profit, corporate, niche & regional publishers & content developers succeed critically & commercially & avoid costly missteps. Innovative consulting modules cover: publishing business models, sales strategy development, finding & serving profitable niche markets, customized social media marketing, affordable market & competitor research, shoe-stringing the startup, content & author acquisition strategies, building the evergreen backlist, content & subsidiary rights licensing, editorial services management, publication design & production, & strategic outsourcing.

R E Carsch, MS-Consultant
1453 Rhode Island St, San Francisco, CA 94107-3248
Tel: 415-533-8356
E-mail: recarsch@mzinfo.com
Founded: 1973
Full range custom information services including library marketing, research organization; analytical reporting; publications development; space planning. Unique & rare collections development & management. Specialize in art, business, architecture & engineering, information literacy, philanthropy & funding development.
Membership(s): Art Libraries Society of North America (ARLIS/NA)

Casemate | IPM
Division of Casemate Group
1950 Lawrence Rd, Havertown, PA 19083
Tel: 610-853-9131 *Fax:* 610-853-9146
E-mail: casemate@casematepublishers.com
Web Site: www.casemateipm.com
Key Personnel
VP, Busn Devt: Simone Drinkwater
Sales Dir: Jane R Graf *E-mail:* jane.graf@casematepublishers.com
Founded: 1995
Full service sales, marketing & distribution firm, offering strategic planning, direct mail, advertising & publicity campaigns, sales representation & POD on web site to book publishers.

Cat's Eye Consultancy
4120 Durham Ct, Eagan, MN 55122
Tel: 651-270-3190
Key Personnel
Independent Literary Consultant: Cassandra Faulkner *E-mail:* cjfaulkner243@gmail.com
Founded: 2014
Experienced consultant providing the following services: editing, copywriting, proofreading, research, indexing, database & library archiving, photography, copyright/Library of Congress, book fair/trade show coordination, author/artist relations.

CeciBooks Editorial & Publishing Consultation
7057 26 Ave NW, Seattle, WA 98117
Mailing Address: PO Box 17229, Seattle, WA 98127
E-mail: ceci@cecibooks.com
Web Site: www.cecibooks.com
Key Personnel
Owner: Ceci Miller *E-mail:* ceci@cecibooks.com
Founded: 1988
We provide expert publishing, writing, editing & editorial coaching services to authors & other professionals in the US & Canada. We offer a professional orientation to publishing, as well as effective, respectful coaching to develop a book & marketing strategy that expresses our client's highest intention. E-mail to set up a phone consultation.
Membership(s): Independent Book Publishers Association (IBPA); Northwest Editors Guild; Society of Children's Book Writers & Illustrators (SCBWI)

City Diecutting
Affiliate of Bookdisplays LLC
One Cory Rd, Morristown, NJ 07960
Tel: 973-270-0370 *Fax:* 973-270-0369
E-mail: sales@bookdisplays.com
Web Site: www.bookdisplays.com
Key Personnel
CEO: Eric De Vos *Tel:* 973-270-0370 ext 11
 E-mail: edevos@bookdisplays.com
Pres: Robert Dembowski *Tel:* 973-270-0370 ext 17 *E-mail:* rdembowski@bookdisplays.com
Founded: 1989
Retail point of purchase cardboard & corrugated displays for merchandising books. In-stock displays for most standard trim sizes. 4/C Branding on Headers/Risers. Custom displays for national rollouts. Sturdy displays designed for books. Proudly made in the USA using American materials & labor.
Membership(s): American Booksellers Association (ABA); The Association of Publishers for Special Sales (APSS); Independent Book Publishers Association (IBPA)

Clear Concepts
1329 Federal Ave, Suite 6, Los Angeles, CA 90025
Tel: 323-285-0325
Key Personnel
Owner: Karen Kleiner
Communications consultant. Marketing plans, research, writing & editing.

Dwight Clough
W7502 County Rd "G", Pardeeville, WI 53954
Tel: 608-429-1440
E-mail: lmp@dwightclough.com
Web Site: dwightclough.com
Founded: 1983
Serving authors, especially first-time authors & publishers, to help write & self-publish their books on Amazon.

Herbert J Cohen
281 Hicks St, Brooklyn Heights, NY 11201
Tel: 718-875-4092 *Fax:* 718-875-5065
E-mail: herbertjcohen@aol.com
Founded: 1992
Consult in all phases of book marketing with special expertise in book clubs. Also have wide experience in negotiation & purchasing of all phases of book manufacturing, including various kinds of binding, paper, cover material & special ingredients.

Cohesion®
511 W Bay St, Suite 480, Tampa, FL 33606
Tel: 813-999-3111 *Toll Free Tel:* 866-727-6800
Web Site: www.cohesion.com
Key Personnel
CEO: John Owens
Chief Strategy Offr: John Larson
Founded: 1982
Complete book, journal, electronic & CD-ROM development & production services. Web design, content, development & production, project management, writing, editing (including online), indexing, proofreading, design & art management. XML-based production processes for both print & electronic products & content management support. Specialize in educational, reference, medical & allied health, computer science, law, physical & life sciences, engineering & technical.
Branch Office(s)
6760 Alexander Bell Dr, Suite 120, Columbia, MD 21046 *Toll Free Tel:* 800-560-0630
5151 Pfeiffer Rd, Suite 105, Cincinnati, OH 45242 *Tel:* 513-587-7700

Color House Graphics Inc
3505 Eastern Ave SE, Grand Rapids, MI 49508
Toll Free Tel: 800-454-1916 *Fax:* 616-245-5494
Web Site: www.colorhousegraphics.com
Key Personnel
Gen Mgr: Phil Knight *E-mail:* pknight@colorhousegraphics.com
Founded: 1987
CHG is a full service book manufacturing company.
Membership(s): The Association of Publishers for Special Sales (APSS); Colorado Independent Publishers Association (CIPA); Evangelical Christian Publishers Association (ECPA); Florida Authors & Publishers Association Inc (FAPA); Independent Book Publishers Association (IBPA); Printing Industries of Michigan Inc (PIM); Publishers Association of the West (PubWest)

Concierge Marketing Inc
4822 S 133 St, Omaha, NE 68137
Tel: 402-884-5995 *Fax:* 413-669-8870
Web Site: www.conciergemarketing.com
Key Personnel
Pres: Lisa K Pelto *E-mail:* lisa@conciergemarketing.com
Founded: 2004
Audio production, design & ebook programming. Consultant for small publishers, illustrators, editorial, marketing & product development. Help independent authors become high quality publishers.
Membership(s): American Advertising Federation (AAF); American Marketing Association; The Association of Publishers for Special Sales

(APSS); Greater Omaha Chamber of Commerce; Independent Book Publishers Association (IBPA)

Conspire Creative
Division of Everything Goes Media LLC
PO Box 1524, Milwaukee, WI 53201
Tel: 312-226-8400 *Fax:* 312-226-8420
Web Site: www.conspirecreative.com
Key Personnel
Owner: Sharon Woodhouse *E-mail:* sharon@ everythinggoesmedia.com
Founded: 2005
Publishing consulting, author services & publishing business solutions, especially content enterprises, entrepreneurial publishing, project management for self-publishers, author coaching & editorial services, $1.50/minute e-mail advice.

Copyright Clearance Center Inc (CCC)
222 Rosewood Dr, Danvers, MA 01923
Tel: 978-750-8400 (sales); 978-646-2600 (cust serv)
E-mail: info@copyright.com
Web Site: www.copyright.com
Key Personnel
Pres & CEO: Tracey L Armstrong
VP, CFO & Treas: Richard A Ruf
CTO & VP, Engg: Haralambos "Babis" Marmanis
SVP, Prod & Opers: Gretchen L Gasser-Ellis
VP, HR: Michele R Nivens
VP, Licensing & Busn Devt: A Miles McNamee
VP, Opers: Debra Mariniello
Exec Dir, Intl Rel: Michael Healy
Mng Dir, New Ventures: Roy S Kaufman
Dir, Rightsholder Rel & Global Alliances: Emilie Delquie
HR: Christine Cozzi-James
Founded: 1978
Leading global rights-licensing technology organization which provides solutions that simplify compliance for content users, promotes the work of creators & supports the principles of copyright. A rights broker for the world's most sought-after journals, books, blogs, movies & more, CCC makes it easy for businesses & academic institutions to use, share & store copyrighted material while compensating content creators for their works. With its international subsidiary, RightsDirect, CCC serves more than 35,000 customers & 12,000 publishers around the world. Locations in US, UK, Netherlands, Spain, Romania & Japan.
Branch Office(s)
PO Box 7102, 20 Westport Rd, Wilton, CT 06879 *Tel:* 203-423-2130 *Fax:* 203-423-2155 *E-mail:* marketing@copyright.com

Copywriters' Council of America™ (CCA)
Division of The Linick Group Inc
CCA Bldg, 7 Putter Lane, Middle Island, NY 11953-1920
Mailing Address: PO Box 102, Middle Island, NY 11953-0102
Tel: 631-924-3888; 631-924-8555; 631-604-8599
Key Personnel
Founder & CEO: Andrew S Linick, PhD *E-mail:* cca4dmcopy@gmail.com
Sr Consultant: Gaylen Andrews
Dir, Spec Projs: Barbara Deal
EVP & Creative Dir: Roger Dextor
Treas: Milt Sosinsky
Edit Dir: Kelly Boyles
Art Dir: Keith Yates
Photos: Johnathan Gerson; Laura Covas; Tim Deos
Founded: 1970
Free referral service to 35,000 independent full service consultative talent. Member consultants cover over 1,550 areas of expertise. Specialize in working with authors, Internet publishers

& Infomarketers, advertising, direct marketing, public relations in-house & outside agencies; government agencies, profit & nonprofit associations, corporations, independent publishers, self-publishers, speakers, talent agencies, celebrities & entertainers, other consulting firms & professionals; developers of trade shows, webinars, seminars & workshops, meetings & conventions; book, video & continuity clubs. Call for CCA's Free InfoActive™ Marketing Communications Audit. Provides comprehensive graphic redesign/new web site content development, interactive services with web site marketing makeover advice for first-time authors, self-publishers, professionals & entrepreneurs. Specializes in online advertising/PR, links to top search engines, consulting on a 100% satisfaction guarantee. Free site evaluation marketing checklist (a $250 value) for LMP readers.
Branch Office(s)
7 Lincoln Ave, Smithtown, NY 11787
Membership(s): The Imaging Alliance

Creative Direct Marketing Group Inc (CDMG)
21171 S Western, Suite 260, Torrance, CA 90501
Tel: 310-212-5727 *Fax:* 310-212-5773
Web Site: www.cdmginc.com
Key Personnel
Pres: Craig Huey *E-mail:* craig@cdmginc.com

Creative Trust Inc
Division of Creative Trust Ventures
210 Jamestown Park Dr, Suite 200, Brentwood, TN 37027
Tel: 615-297-5010 *Fax:* 615-297-5020
E-mail: info@creativetrust.com
Web Site: creativetrust.com
Key Personnel
Founder & Pres: Daniel Raines
Mng Partner, Creative Trust Literary Group: Kathryn A Helmers
Founded: 1989
Literary representation.

CS International Literary Agency
43 W 39 St, New York, NY 10018
Tel: 212-921-1610; 212-391-9208
E-mail: query@csliterary.com; csliterary08@ gmail.com
Web Site: www.csliterary.com
Key Personnel
Literary Agent: Cynthia Neesemann
Founded: 1996
Assist writers in developing strategies to achieve ms publication or film production & to find the writing niche that suits their talents & personality in general or specialized markets. We analyze ideas & help develop proposals for writing projects or evaluate existing projects by critiquing mss +/or proposals & suggesting further research or other ways of developing or improving content if necessary. Sometimes a writer wonders whether he should seek a publisher or self-publish. We can help him decide how to proceed & provide personal attention because we are interested in supporting writers & promoting their creative efforts.

CVI Capital
Division of CVI Capital Holdings LLC
165 Annursnac Hill Rd, Concord, MA 01742
Mailing Address: PO Box 10, Concord, MA 01742-0010
Tel: 978-371-0995 *Fax:* 978-287-5869
E-mail: admin@cvicapital.com
Web Site: www.cvicapital.com
Key Personnel
Mng Dir & CEO: H Mason Fackert, III *Tel:* 617-759-2704 (cell) *E-mail:* hmfackert@cvicapital.com
EVP & CFO: Patricia A Stickney

Mng Dir: Paul V McLaughlin
Res Dir: Tatyana Zachary *E-mail:* tatyana2@ cvicapital.com
Registered Assoc: Lisa Gelin
Founded: 1987
Investment banking services for book & magazine publishers; medical information companies.
Membership(s): Association for Corporate Growth (ACG); Association of American Publishers (AAP); Book Industry Study Group (BISG); National Association of Corporate Directors (NACD); Specialized Information Publishers Association (SIPA)

Cypress House
Imprint of Comp-Type Inc
155 Cypress St, Fort Bragg, CA 95437
Tel: 707-964-9520 *Toll Free Tel:* 800-773-7782 *Fax:* 707-964-7531
Web Site: www.cypresshouse.com
Key Personnel
Pres: Cynthia Frank *E-mail:* cynthia@ cypresshouse.com
Project coordination, prepress, typesetting, page design, complete page make-up to camera ready, book cover preparation, color separations, cover design & layout, printer selection & supervision, press release development, solicitation & coordination of media interviews, press kit development, packaging & mailing review & advance copies.
Membership(s): American Booksellers Association (ABA); Bay Area Independent Publishers Association (BAIPA); California Independent Booksellers Alliance (CALIBA); Independent Book Publishers Association (IBPA); Pacific Northwest Booksellers Association (PNBA)

Jeff Davidson MBA, CMC, Breathing Space Institute
3202 Ruffin St, Raleigh, NC 27607
Tel: 919-932-1996
Web Site: www.breathingspace.com; www. ghostwiththemost.com
Key Personnel
Founder & Exec Dir: Jeff Davidson *E-mail:* jeff@ breathingspace.com
Founded: 1995
Advertising, promotion, marketing, publicity, foreign sales, bookclubs, subsidiary sales, negotiations, second editions, ghostwriting & script writing. Foreign reps.
Membership(s): Authors Registry; IMC; National Speakers Association (NSA); Triangle Area Freelancers

Peter L DeGiglio
6 Overlook Dr, Washingtonville, NY 10992
Tel: 914-850-3803
E-mail: pdegiglio@gmail.com
Founded: 2011
Consulting services to publishers, authors & agents with a full range of expertise in the areas of finance, strategic planning, mergers & acquisitions, building infrastructure & business development.

Del Commune Enterprises Inc
307 Seventh Ave, Suite 807, New York, NY 10001
Tel: 212-226-6664
E-mail: mail@dcescouts.com
Web Site: www.dcescouts.com
Key Personnel
Founder & Pres: Lauri del Commune
Sr Scout: Olivia Geraci
Founded: 1996
International book scouting agency.

Steven Diamond Inc
104 W 17 St, Suite 3-E, New York, NY 10011
Tel: 212-675-0723 *Fax:* 212-675-0762
E-mail: steven.diamond@verizon.net

Key Personnel
Pres: Steven Diamond
VP: Carol Poticny
Visual research of all kinds, with an emphasis on fine art, both painting & photography. In addition to the standard services we provide, we have our own fine art reference library on the premises.
Membership(s): American Society of Picture Professionals (ASPP)

Direct Marketing Solutions Inc
1275 Fairfax Ave, San Francisco, CA 94124
Tel: 415-642-8600 *Fax:* 415-642-8640
E-mail: dmsi@directmailing.com
Web Site: www.directmailing.com
Key Personnel
Principal: Glenn Chase *Tel:* 415-642-8600 ext 128
Mail order marketing, catalog venture startups, marketing plans, direct response & database management.

Double Play
303 Hillcrest Rd, Belton, MO 64012-1852
Tel: 816-651-7118
Key Personnel
Pres: Lloyd Johnson *E-mail:* wlloydj@yahoo.com
VP: Connie Johnson
Writing & research on baseball; baseball museum consultant.
Membership(s): Society for American Baseball Research

Energy Psychology Press
3340 Fulton Rd, No 442, Fulton, CA 95439
Tel: 707-525-9292 *Toll Free Fax:* 800-330-9798
E-mail: energypsychologypress@gmail.com
Web Site: www.energypsychologypress.com
Founded: 1994
Consulting & production services for publishers & authors, including national sales & distribution, book manufacturers & fulfillment & strategic planning.
Membership(s): Independent Book Publishers Association (IBPA)

Bob Erdmann
1116 Oakmont Dr, No 6, Walnut Creek, CA 94595
Tel: 925-451-8201
E-mail: info@bob-erdmann.com
Web Site: www.columbinecommunications.com
Founded: 1978
Full service foreign rights consultancy to publishers & self-published authors. Foreign rights agent.
Membership(s): The Association of Publishers for Special Sales (APSS); Independent Book Publishers Association (IBPA)

Exhibit Promotions Plus Inc
11620 Vixens Path, Ellicott City, MD 21042-1539
Tel: 410-997-0763 *Fax:* 410-997-0764
E-mail: exhibit@epponline.com
Web Site: www.epponline.com
Key Personnel
Founder & Pres: Harve C Horowitz, Esq
CFO: Eileen S Horowitz
Sr Mgr, Cust Rel: Kelly K Marshall
Founded: 1969
Advise publishers where to advertise & exhibit their books; advertising & exhibit representative for scholarly & other professional trade associations. Generate program & journal advertising in conjunction with international, national, regional & state exhibits in subject-arranged collections. Comprehensive convention management.

Taryn Fagerness Agency
4810 Point Fosdick Dr NW, PMB 34, Gig Harbor, WA 98335
Tel: 858-254-7711
E-mail: taryn.fagerness@gmail.com
Web Site: www.tarynfagernessagency.com
Founded: 2009
Represents foreign subsidiary rights on behalf of North American literary agents.

Fairfield Marketing Group Inc
Subsidiary of FMG Inc
The Direct Mail Ctr, 830 Sport Hill Rd, Easton, CT 06112-1241
Tel: 203-261-5585 *Fax:* 203-261-0884
E-mail: info@fairfieldmarketing.com
Web Site: www.fairfieldmarketing.com
Key Personnel
Pres & CEO: Edward P Washchilla, Jr
VP, Cust Serv: Mike Lozada *Tel:* 203-261-5585 ext 204
VP, Fulfillment: Jason Paul Miller *Tel:* 203-261-5585 ext 203 *E-mail:* jason@fairfieldmarketing.com
Founded: 1986
Mailing list brokerage & list management services. FMG clients rely on us for annual direct marketing programs. We are customer driven & accomodate. Specialty services: custom designed account management; expedient list rental approval; monthly usage reports; market & account analyses; fulfillment, mailing & mail response services; freelance art work; graphic design; advertising & promotional copywriting; binding services; lettershop services; computer services. FMG is a full service direct mail marketing firm.
Membership(s): American Booksellers Association (ABA); Bridgeport Regional Business Council (BRBC); Education Market Association; United States Chamber of Commerce (USCC)

Feigenbaum Publishing Consultants Inc
61 Bounty Lane, Jericho, NY 11753
Tel: 516-647-8314 (cell)
Key Personnel
Pres: Laurie Feigenbaum
E-mail: lauriefeigenbaum@gmail.com
Founded: 1990
Contract review & negotiation; permissions clearance; general publishing advice. Trademark & copyright registrations. Reasonable hourly rate.

Figaro
PO Box 848, Sharon, CT 06069
Tel: 860-248-8989; 860-364-0834
E-mail: design@figro.com
Web Site: www.figro.com
Key Personnel
Co-Pres & Creative Dir: Walter Schwarz
Co-Pres: Linda Swenson *E-mail:* ls@figro.com
Creative, editorial, production & photographic services for books, catalogs, promotional materials & packaging. Digital creation of text, art, maps, illustration & photos for current & out of print books. Consultation, graphic arts management & printing supervision. Web site development & maintenance. Photography of Suzanne Szasz & Ray Shorr.

Firebrand Technologies
44 Merrimac St, Newburyport, MA 01950
Tel: 978-465-7755 *Toll Free Tel:* 800-779-7345
Fax: 978-465-7759
E-mail: askburnie@firebrandtech.com
Web Site: www.firebrandtech.com
Key Personnel
Founder & CEO: Fran Toolan
CTO: Shane Archer
Pres: Doug Lessing
Community & Mktg Dir: Lindsey Lochner

Founded: 1987 (as Quality Solutions Inc)
Technology company offering solutions for publishers to help books succeed. Works with publishers to manage their internal workflows, digital distribution & marketing efforts. Community-focused approach helps create an optimal atmosphere for innovation & product success.
Membership(s): American Association of University Presses (AAUP); American Booksellers Association (ABA); The American Library Association (ALA); Audio Publishers Association; Bookbuilders of Boston; BookNetCanada; Evangelical Christian Publishers Association (ECPA); Independent Book Publishers Association (IBPA); Independent Publisher's Guild (IPG); Publishers Association of the West (PubWest); Society for Scholarly Publishing (SSP)

The Fisher Company
PO Box 89578, Tucson, AZ 85752-9578
Tel: 520-547-2460
Web Site: www.thefishercompany.com
Key Personnel
Mng Dir: Howard W Fisher *E-mail:* howard.fisher@thefishercompany.com
Founded: 2002
Offers international mergers & acquisitions brokerage & business development consulting. We work with you to improve your financial capabilities & develop your company. We provide advice on how to increase your profitability & add value to your publishing companies.
Membership(s): Independent Book Publishers Association (IBPA); Publishers Association of the West (PubWest)

Flannery Book Service
20258 Hwy 18, No 430-436, Apple Valley, CA 92307
Toll Free Tel: 800-456-3400 *Toll Free Fax:* 800-284-5600
E-mail: contact@fbs-now.com
Web Site: www.fbs-now.com
Key Personnel
COO: Heath Spurgeon
CFO: Eve Toles
Management consultants for K-12 school curriculum print & digital material logistics (K-12 textbooks).

Fournies Associates
1226 NW 19 Terr, Delray Beach, FL 33445
Tel: 561-445-5102
Key Personnel
Partner: Sandra Fournies
Founded: 1972
Book publisher of professional books, behavioral science & business; management consultant.

Franklin & Siegal Associates Inc
1350 Broadway, Suite 2015, New York, NY 10018
Tel: 212-868-6311 *Fax:* 212-868-6312
Web Site: www.franklinandsiegal.com
Key Personnel
Pres: Todd R Siegal *E-mail:* todd@franklinandsiegal.com
Dir, Adult Scouting: Danny Yanez
Dir, Film & TV: Erin Hennicke
Dir, Young Adult & Middle-Grade: Kalah McCaffrey
Scout: Nicole Thomas
Founded: 1992
Scouts for: Editora Rocco (Brazil); China Citic Press (China); Lindhardt & Ringhof & Carlsen (Denmark); WSOY (Finland); Flammarion/J'ai Lu & Nathan Jeunesse (France); Karl Blessing/Heyne Verlag & cbj (Germany); Europa/Alexandra/Cartaphilus (Hungary); Sperling & Kupfer/Frassinelli (Italy);

Hayakawa Publishing (Japan); Prometheus, Unieboek/Spectrum & Van Holkema-Van Goor (Netherlands); Aschehoug YA (Norway); Proszynski Media (Poland); Alianza & Molino (Spain); China Times Publishing Co (Taiwan); Hodder & Stoughton/Sceptre, John Murray Press/Two Roads (UK).

French Publishers' Agency
Subsidiary of BIEF (Bureau International de L'Edition Francaise)
30 Vandam St, Suite 5A, New York, NY 10013
Tel: 212-254-4540
Web Site: www.frenchpubagency.com
Key Personnel
Dir: Alice Tassel
Founded: 1983
Represent French publisher members of BIEF.

G & H Soho Inc
413 Market St, Elmwood Park, NJ 07407
Tel: 201-216-9400 *Fax:* 201-216-1778
E-mail: print@ghsoho.com
Web Site: www.ghsoho.com
Key Personnel
Pres: Gerry Burstein
Prodn Mgr: Jason Burstein
Membership(s): Association of Graphic Communications; Book Industry Guild of New York; Digital Printing Council; PRINTING United Alliance

Garvan Media, Management & Marketing Inc
PO Box 737, Sandpoint, ID 83864
Tel: 208-265-1718
Web Site: facebook.com/stephen.b.garvan
Key Personnel
CEO & Expediter: Stephen Bond Garvan
Tel: 303-809-1676 (cell) *E-mail:* steve@garvanmarketing.com
Founded: 1997
Strategic marketing & business guidance & development, 20+ years independent. Formerly in marketing/sales management, national accounts at: Workman, Morrow, Fulcrum, Roberts Rinehart & IABC. Overall marketing, business development, forecasting, analysis, budgeting & list building. Soliciting & managing sales/distribution in the US, Canada, Europe, Australia & New Zealand. Former AAP Telemarketing Committee, NEIBA & Pub West Boards. Numerous music industry, civic, cultural & community boards. Works also to place & strategize marketing & sales for music-oriented books. Has extensive music industry experience & contacts.
Membership(s): Mountains & Plains Independent Booksellers Association (MPIBA); Pacific Northwest Booksellers Association (PNBA); Publishers Association of the West (PubWest); Southern Independent Booksellers Alliance (SIBA)

GGP Publishing Inc
105 Calvert St, Suite 201, Harrison, NY 10528-3138
Tel: 914-834-8896 *Fax:* 914-834-7566
Web Site: www.GGPPublishing.com
Key Personnel
Pres & Publg Dir: Generosa Gina Protano
E-mail: GGProtano@GGPPublishing.com
Founded: 1991
Packager for trade & educational publishers. All editorial, art & design, production & printing services—from concept to bound books or any segment(s) of this publishing process. Trade (fiction & nonfiction) & children's books, textbooks (el-hi, college & adult education), professional, reference & how-to books, cookbooks, audiotapes, videotapes & CDs. Specialize in the development of materials for the study of foreign languages (such as French,

German, Italian, Japanese, Latin, Portuguese, Russian & Spanish) & ESL, as well as in the development of materials for bilingual education & language arts. In addition, we translate complete or partial programs from & into the various languages & act as literary agents & foreign publisher representatives.

Goldberg McDuffie Communications
250 Park Ave, 7th fl, New York, NY 10177
Tel: 212-705-4211
E-mail: bookpr@goldbergmcduffie.com
Web Site: www.goldbergmcduffie.com
Key Personnel
CEO: Lynn C Goldberg *E-mail:* lgoldberg@goldbergmcduffie.com
Founded: 1981
Consultation with authors, publishers & agents about how to build an author's platform, conceive & implement marketing programs, handle press outreach & placements & create an author's online & social networking identities, all with the goal of enhancing a books commercial success. Twice winner of the LMP Award.

Gordon Management Inc (GMI)
305 Churchill Ave, Somerset, NJ 08873
Tel: 732-846-4800 *Fax:* 732-846-4709
E-mail: info@gmidistribution.com
Web Site: www.gmidistribution.com
Key Personnel
Pres: Keith Gordon
VP: Kenneth Gordon
Founded: 1978
Physical distribution consultants to the book industry. Specialize in freight-savings programs (in-bound & out-bound), warehouse site selection, layout, staffing & equipment, freight forwarding, export shipping, customs brokerage, training programs for warehouse personnel, inventory management & control systems & quality controls for picking & packing.

Michael Grant
115 Carthage Rd, Scarsdale, NY 10583
Tel: 914-821-8315
E-mail: michael@michaelgrantdirect.com; michaelgrant12@optonline.net
Web Site: www.michaelgrantdirect.com
Founded: 1995
Marketing strategist with extensive consumer & business-to-business direct marketing background. Experienced manager with outstanding analytical skills, adept at defining client needs utilizing data assets & technology. Applies industry best practices to allocate media spend to acquire new customers & deepen relationships with existing ones. Experienced in consultant & account management positions. Expertise in: customer relationship management, direct & e-mail marketing, multi-channel marketing, catalog marketing & analysis, account management, service provider liaison, consumer marketing strategy, customer segmentation & database management.
Membership(s): New England Mail Order Association

Gropen Associates
9 Clubview Dr, Birmingham, AL 35223
Toll Free Tel: 888-3GROPEN (347-6736)
Toll Free Fax: 888-347-6736
Web Site: www.gropenassoc.com
Key Personnel
Principal: Marion Gropen *E-mail:* marion.gropen@gropenassoc.com
Founded: 2002
Provides financial & operational solutions on a By-the-Question basis. Also provides classes & free resources from www.gropenassoc.com.
Membership(s): Independent Book Publishers Association (IBPA)

Hartnett Inc
2308 Mount Vernon Ave, Suite 817, Alexandria, VA 22301
Tel: 703-660-6799
Web Site: www.hartnettinc.com
Key Personnel
Pres: Teresa Hartnett *E-mail:* teresa@hartnettinc.com
Founded: 1997
Publishing consultant for media savvy authors.

Heidelberg Graphics
2 Stansbury Ct, Chico, CA 95928
SAN: 211-5654
Tel: 530-342-6582 *Fax:* 530-342-6582
E-mail: heidelberggraphics@gmail.com; service@heidelberggraphics.com
Web Site: www.heidelberggraphics.com
Key Personnel
Owner & Pres: Larry S Jackson
Founded: 1972
Promotion, printing & publishing consultants; complete book preparation; advisors to self-publishers; copyrights; desktop publishing, imagesetting & disk conversion to type.

Albert Henderson
655 West Ave, Milford, CT 06461-3003
Tel: 203-301-0791
E-mail: 70244.1532@compuserve.com
Writer, editor, reviewer & management consultant to publishers. Scholarly, professional, scientific, technical books & journals; operations, production, marketing, fulfillment, importing & exporting, mergers, acquisitions & sale of business. Bibliography on request.

Henry Holmes Literary Agent/Book Publicist/Marketing Consultant
Mitchell Heights, Apt 205, 2100 S Main St, Fall River, MA 02724
Tel: 508-672-2258; 508-415-4062 (cell)
Key Personnel
Pres & Literary Agent: Henry Holmes
Founded: 1997
Nonfiction; no unsol mss, query first. Send query letter with chapters 1 & 2. If published, include past publicity, endorsement(s), etc with SASE. Ten mailings sent to preferred publishers via mss/CDs (this includes publisher research, query letter, packing, mailing, etc at $100/hour). Independent of my representation, professional consultation via freelance assignments/project work would be based on involvement & duration of project based on competitive fees. Specialize in consulting, marketing, media publicity, talk show placement, editorial, etc. 15% standard commission.

Nancy Humphreys Wordmaps
600 Humboldt St, Richmond, CA 94805
Tel: 510-215-9960
Web Site: authormaps.com
Key Personnel
Principal & CEO: Nancy K Humphreys
E-mail: nancy@authormaps.com
Founded: 1996
Advice on book production & marketing. Author of *Marketing Your Book to Libraries*.

HurleyMedia LLC
1477 Canyon Rd, Santa Fe, NM 87501
Tel: 505-603-6392
Web Site: www.hurleymedia.com
Key Personnel
Owner: Joanna Thorne Hurley *E-mail:* jth@hurleymedia.com
Founded: 1994
We offer full service packaging for photography & art books from concept through publication, including editorial, design, produc-

tion, as well as placement with a suitable publisher/distributor, marketing & publicity as needed to supplement publisher's efforts.

Idea Architects
523 Swift St, Santa Cruz, CA 95060
Tel: 831-465-9565
Web Site: www.ideaarchitects.com
Key Personnel
Founder & Pres: Douglas Carlton Abrams
Edit Dir & COO: Lara Love Hardin
Chief Strategy Offr & Sr Literary Agent, Children's: Rachel Neumann
Dir, Author Success & Contracts Mgr: Ty Gideon Love
Dir, Community Engagement: Cody Love
Dir, Global Prospecting & Res: Boo Prince
Founded: 2001
Literary agency, book & media development agency for visionary authors.
IA True Division focuses on inspirational & compelling memories & true stories that have the power to change hearts & minds.

The Idea Logical Co Inc
300 E 51 St, Apt 17C, New York, NY 10022
Tel: 212-758-5670
E-mail: info@idealog.com
Web Site: www.idealog.com
Key Personnel
Founder & CEO: Mike Shatzkin *E-mail:* mike@idealog.com
Founded: 1979
Innovative consulting for all aspects of the global book business; specialties are digital strategy & digital change, creating new models, new technology integration & supply chain management.

Imago
110 W 40 St, New York, NY 10018
Tel: 212-921-4411 *Fax:* 212-921-8226
E-mail: sales@imagousa.com
Web Site: www.imagousa.com
Key Personnel
Pres & CEO: Howard Musk *E-mail:* howardm@imagogroup.com
Founded: 1985
Global print & production services with a network of production & sales offices across Southeast Asia, Europe & America. Areas of expertise include the production of conventional & novelty books, packaging, stationery, plush toys & board games.
Branch Office(s)
Imago West Coast, 23412 Moulton Pkwy, Suite 250, Laguna Hills, CA 92653 (sales), Contact: Tammy Simms *Tel:* 949-367-1635 *Fax:* 949-367-1639
Imago Australia, 10 Help St, Suite 27, Level 6, Chatswood, NSW 2067, Australia (sales) *Tel:* (04) 3753 3351 (cell); (04) 4806 8704 (cell) *E-mail:* sales@imagaoaus.com
Imago Brazil, Domiciano Rossi, 340 unid 154, 09726-121 Sao Bernardo do Campo, Brazil (sales) *Tel:* (011) 2306 8546; (011) 2306 8547 *E-mail:* imagobra@gmail.com
Imago Shenzhen, Rm 2511-2512, Block A, United Plaza No 5022, Bin He Rd, Fu Tian Centre District, Shenzhen 518033, China (prodn), Contact: Kendrick Cheung *Tel:* (0755) 8304 8899 *Fax:* (0755) 8251 4073 *E-mail:* enquiries@imago.com.hk
Imago France, 23 rue Lavoisier, 75008 Paris, France (sales) *Tel:* 01 45 26 47 74 *Fax:* 01 78 94 14 44 *E-mail:* sales@imagogroup.com
Imago Services (HK) Ltd, Unit B309, 1/F, New East Sun Industrial Bldg, 18 Shing Yip St, Kwun Tong, Hong Kong (prodn), Contact: Kendrick Cheung *Tel:* 2811 3316 *E-mail:* enquiries@imago.com.hk

Imago Productions (Malaysia) Pte Ltd, No 43, Taman Emas, Jl Utama 31, Telok Panglima Garang, 42500 Kuala Langot, Selangor, Malaysia (prodn, incorporating South Africa sales) *Tel:* (017) 4288771 (cell) *E-mail:* enquiries@imago.com.sg
Imago Publishing, Albury Ct, Albury Thame, Oxon OX9 2LP, United Kingdom (sales), Dir: Simon Rosenheim *Tel:* (01844) 337000 *Fax:* (01844) 339935 *E-mail:* sales@imago.co.uk *Web Site:* imagogroup.com

Innodata Inc
55 Challenger Rd, Suite 202, Ridgefield Park, NJ 07660
Tel: 201-371-8000 *Toll Free Tel:* 877-454-8400
E-mail: info@innodata.com; marketing@innodata.com
Web Site: innodata.com
Key Personnel
Pres & CEO: Jack S Abuhoff
EVP & COO: Ashok Kumar Mishra
SVP & Gen Coun: Amy Agress
SVP, Prod Innovation: R Douglas Kemp
Founded: 1988
Innodata is a global services & technology solutions company. Our technology & services power leading information products & online retail destinations around the world. Our solutions help enterprises harness the power of digital data to reimagine how they operate & drive performance. We serve publishers, media & information companies, digital retailers, banks, insurance companies, government agencies & many other industries. We comprise a team of 5,000 diverse people in 8 countries who are dedicated to delivering services & solutions that help the world embrace digital data as a means of enhancing our lives & transforming our businesses. The company operates in 3 reporting segments: Digital Data Solutions (DDS), Innodata Data Solutions (IADS) & Media Intelligence Solutions (MIS).
Headquartered in Northern New Jersey, Innodata has offices & operations in the US, Canada, Germany, India, Israel, Philippines, Sri Lanka & UK.
Membership(s): The Association for Work Process Improvement; Association of American Publishers Professional & Scholarly Publishing Division; Center for Information Development & Content Management Strategies (CIDM); International Association of Outsourcing Professionals (IAOP); National Federation of Abstracting and Information Services (NFAIS); Society for Technical Communication (STC); Society of Knowledge Based Publishers (SKBP); Software & Information Industry Association (SIIA)

Integra Software Services Inc
Division of Integra Software Services Pvt Ltd
1110 Jorie Blvd, Suite 200, Oak Brook, IL 60523
Tel: 630-586-2579 *Fax:* 630-586-2599
E-mail: marketing@integra.co.in
Web Site: www.integra.co.in
Key Personnel
Dir, Edit Devt: Ingrid Benson *E-mail:* ingrid.benson@integra.co.in
Design Mgr: Emily Friel *E-mail:* emily.friel@integra.co.in
Founded: 1991
Project management, development & production support for book publishers.

The Intermarketing Group-Art Licensing Agency
29 Holt Rd, Amherst, NH 03031
Tel: 603-672-0499
Key Personnel
Founder & Principal: Linda Gerson

Founded: 1985
Art licensing agency, marketing/sales & international trade.

International Transactions Inc
28 Alope Way, Gila, NM 88038
Mailing Address: PO Box 97, Gila, NM 88038
Tel: 845-373-9696 *Fax:* 480-393-5162
E-mail: info@internationaltransactions.us
Web Site: www.intltrans.com
Key Personnel
Pres: Peter Riva *E-mail:* priva@intltrans.com
Founded: 1975

IP Royalty Auditors LLC
316 Perkins Ave, Oceanside, NY 11572
Tel: 516-503-5985
E-mail: royalty@aol.com
Web Site: www.iproyaltyauditors.com
Key Personnel
Pres: Gail R Gross
Founded: 2008
Conduct on our clients behalf, systematic reviews of books & records to verify proper payment of royalties due to intellectual property owners, i.e., authors, agents, attorneys & publishers, on sales of intellectual properties including books, merchandise licenses, electronic audio & video sales & subsidiary rights. In addition, our services include valuation of intellectual property as well as book office royalty consulting.
Membership(s): American Book Producers Association (ABPA); The Authors Guild; National Women's Book Association; Textbook & Academic Authors Association (TAA)

Law Offices of Lloyd J Jassin
The Paramount Bldg, 1501 Broadway, 12th fl, New York, NY 10036
Tel: 212-354-4442 *Fax:* 212-840-1124
E-mail: jassin@copylaw.com
Web Site: www.copylaw.org
Founded: 1991
Draft & negotiate publishing agreements; work for hire; distribution; subsidiary rights; trademark registration; copyright termination; prepublication review re: fair use, libel, invasion of privacy, right of publicity claims; film options; merchandise licensing claims; publishing consultant; literary agent.
Membership(s): The Authors Guild; Independent Book Publishers Association (IBPA)

Javelin Group
203 S Union St, Suite 200, Alexandria, VA 22314
Tel: 703-490-8845
E-mail: hello@javelindc.com
Web Site: javelindc.com
Key Personnel
Pres: Keith Urbahn *E-mail:* keith@javelindc.com
Founding Partner: Matt Latimer *E-mail:* matt@javelindc.com
Literary Agent/Foreign Rts Dir: Matt Carlini
Full service literary & communications firm. Representation, writing, editing & publicity.

Jenkins Group Inc
1129 Woodmere Ave, Suite B, Traverse City, MI 49686
Tel: 231-933-0445 *Toll Free Tel:* 800-706-4636 *Fax:* 231-933-0448
E-mail: info@bookpublishing.com
Web Site: www.bookpublishing.com
Key Personnel
CEO: Jerrold R Jenkins *Tel:* 231-933-0445 ext 1008 *E-mail:* jrj@bookpublishing.com
Pres & COO: James Kalajian *Tel:* 231-933-0445 ext 1006 *E-mail:* jjk@bookpublishing.com
Dir, Consulting & Mktg Servs: Kim Hornyak *Tel:* 231-933-0445 ext 1013 *E-mail:* khornyak@bookpublishing.com

Book Prodn Mgr: Leah Nicholson *Tel:* 231-933-0445 ext 1015 *E-mail:* lnicholson@bookpublishing.com
Founded: 1988
Provide consulting services to Fortune 500 companies, associations, booksellers, publishers, corporations & organizations attempting to reach the publishing community. Unparalleled access & experience with all aspects of the publishing industry, providing knowledge for trade distributors & library wholesalers; assistance with galley presentation for pre-publication reviews; media publicity & promotion, literary agent acquisition; recommendations for public relations firms; contacts for book clubs, catalogs & corporate level bookstores; necessary information & guidance to assist independent publishers in building a presence within the industry.

JMB Associates
PO Box 425, Woodstock, NY 12498
Tel: 845-679-5719
E-mail: contact@joannemichaels.com
Web Site: www.joannemichaels.com
Key Personnel
Pres: Joanne Michaels
Founded: 1990
Assist clients through the publishing process. How to write a selling book proposal, query letter, market to literary agents as well as ms critiques, line-editing, revisions, ghostwriting, self-publishing & print on demand; reasonable rates. Also a literary scout.
Membership(s): The Authors Guild

JMW Group Inc
347 Rte 6, No 867, Mahopac, NY 10541
Tel: 914-841-7105 *Fax:* 914-248-8861
E-mail: jmwgroup@jmwgroup.net
Web Site: jmwforlife.com
Key Personnel
Pres: Patti DeMatteo
VP, Rts: Pete Allen
Dir, Licensing: Sara Castle
Founded: 1949
Licenses rights to nonfiction books & other copyrighted material in a range of subjects on a worldwide basis, including self-help, self-improvement & business.

JPMC Associates
7037 Snapdragon Dr, Carlsbad, CA 92011
Tel: 916-203-3693 *Fax:* 760-931-6878
E-mail: jpmcaso@aol.com
Key Personnel
Pres: Jim McGough
Founded: 1979

JVW Direct
309 W Hutchinson Ave, Pittsburgh, PA 15218
Key Personnel
Pres: Jay Van Wagenen
Founded: 1981
Direct response for publishers.
Membership(s): ECHO Academy of Direct Marketing Arts & Sciences

Kaplan/DeFiore Rights
47 E 19 St, 3rd fl, New York, NY 10003
Tel: 212-925-7244
Web Site: kaplanrights.com
Key Personnel
Dir: Linda Kaplan *Tel:* 212-925-7744 ext 106 *E-mail:* linda@defliterary.com
Offers publishers & literary agents full service international licensing solutions, including early proposal/ms reports, solicitation & negotiation of contracts, tax forms & financial analysis of royalty statements.

Kensai International Ltd
75 Nottingham Rd, Malverne, NY 11565
Tel: 516-593-0480
E-mail: info@kensai.net
Web Site: www.kensai.net
Key Personnel
Pres: Edwin Fager *E-mail:* edwin@kensai.net
Founded: 1997
Provides ERP software consultancy & implementation project management services to book publishers worldwide.

Kinokuniya Publications Service of New York (KPS-NY)
Subsidiary of Kinokuniya Co Ltd (Tokyo, Japan)
1073 Avenue of the Americas, New York, NY 10018-3701
Tel: 212-765-1465 *Fax:* 212-307-5593
E-mail: nyinfo@kinokuniya.com
Web Site: www.kinokuniya.co.jp; www.kinokuniya.com
Key Personnel
VP: Shigeharu Ono
Bookstore, book & subscription agency, wholesaler.
Membership(s): Association of American Publishers (AAP)

Klopotek North America Inc
2001 Rte 46, Suite 203, Parsippany, NJ 07054
Tel: 973-331-1010 *Toll Free Tel:* 800-239-9254 *Fax:* 973-331-0042
E-mail: info@klopotek.com
Web Site: www.klopotek.com; www.gtsystems.com
Key Personnel
VP, Sales & Mktg: George Logan *Tel:* 862-261-9404 *E-mail:* g.logan@klopotek.com
Founded: 1992
Leading supplier of software & consulting services for publishers of books & journals, print & online. Publishers rely on our programs to help them manage their business & achieve their goals. Over 15 years experience in delivering innovative solutions to publishers around the world. Our software supports the entire publishing value chain for print & digital products, including contracts, rights & royalties management, editorial planning, production management, product promotion, marketing, sales & distribution all the way through to order processing & customer service support.
Membership(s): Book Industry Study Group (BISG)

knk Software LP
Member of knk Group
89 Headquarters Plaza N, No 1478, Morristown, NJ 07960
Tel: 908-206-4599
E-mail: info@knk.com
Web Site: www.knkpublishingsoftware.com
Key Personnel
Busn Devt Mgr: Steve Rutberg
Mktg Mgr: Oliver Holden *Tel:* 781-772-2213 *E-mail:* oliver.holden@knk.com
Sales Mgr: Jason Spanos *Tel:* 206-769-9245 *E-mail:* jason.spanos@knk.com
Founded: 1988
As an expert in the publishing industry, knk combines the strengths of a business consultancy & the solution expertise of a software company. knk develops & markets knkPublishing - the only Microsoft certified publishing software in the world. knkPublishing combines the classical ERP functions (financial accounting, supply chain management & sales & marketing), with industry specific functions for modern publishers & media companies.

David W Koehser Attorney at Law
322 First Ave N, Suite 402, Minneapolis, MN 55401
Tel: 612-910-6468
E-mail: dk@dklex.com
Web Site: www.dklex.com
Founded: 1996
Law firm providing representation for copyrights, publishing agreements & agent agreements.

Maggie Lichtenberg, Book Publishing Coach & Marketing Strategist, see Margaret Klee Lichtenberg Coaching

Margaret Klee Lichtenberg Coaching
4 Cosmos Ct, Santa Fe, NM 87508
Tel: 505-986-8807 *Toll Free Tel:* 866-986-8807 *Fax:* 505-986-8794
E-mail: maggie@maggielichtenberg.com; maggie@publishing-options.com
Web Site: www.maggielichtenberg.com; www.openheartcoach.com; www.publishing-options.com
Key Personnel
Book Publg Coach & Mktg Strategist: Maggie Lichtenberg
Founded: 1995
Book publishing & marketing coaching service for authors & independent publishers via telephone appointment & e-mail; advice & mentoring on every aspect of traditional publishing, independent publishing, ebook publishing, ebook conversion guidance, POD; querying, ms evaluation, selecting the right publishing route, finding an agent, writing a proposal that sells, relationship building, contract negotiation, planning & budgeting, sales, distribution, domestic & foreign subsidiary rights, publicity online & offline, promotion & generally "partnering" with your publisher to achieve publishing goals.
Membership(s): Independent Book Publishers Association (IBPA); International Coach Federation (ICF); New Mexico Book Association

Andrew S Linick PhD, The Copyologist®
Division of The Linick Group Inc
Linick Bldg, 7 Putter Lane, Middle Island, NY 11953
Mailing Address: PO Box 102, Middle Island, NY 11953-0102
Tel: 631-924-3888; 631-924-8555; 631-604-8599
E-mail: linickgroup@gmail.com
Web Site: topmarketingadvisor.com
Key Personnel
CEO & Creative Dir: Andrew S Linick, PhD *E-mail:* topmarketingadvisor@gmail.com
EVP: Roger Dextor
Edit Dir: Kelly Boyles
International & North American Internet marketing direct response advertising/PR specialist for the publishing industry. New product selection & development, business planning; select mailing lists/media, print, DM Publications; co-ops, inbound/outbound telemarketing scripts; generate inquiries/conversion to sales/orders programs; pretesting, direct response copy, offers, premiums; market research; copy analysis, critique/redesign service on ads & mailing packages; price & offer testing; mail order fulfillment, budgeting & accounting systems. Customer profile surveys & tele-research; personnel & supplier relations; counsels book & newsletter publishers; first time authors; book clubs; convention & trade show exhibitors & management; book producers; ad agencies, entrepreneurs, mail order dealers. Free initial 15 minute consultation; 100% satisfaction guarantee on all consultations & assignments. Provides comprehensive graphic redesign/new web site content development, interactive services with web site marketing makeover advice for

first-time authors, self-publishers, professionals & entrepreneurs. Specializes in online advertising/PR, links to top search engines, consulting on a 100% satisfaction guarantee. Free site evaluation marketing checklist (a $250 value) for LMP readers.

Membership(s): ADA; American Association of Advertising Agencies (4A's); The Association of Publishers for Special Sales (APSS); Independent Book Publishers Association (IBPA)

Linick International Inc
Division of The Linick Group Inc
Linick Bldg, 7 Putter Lane, Middle Island, NY 11953
Mailing Address: PO Box 102, Middle Island, NY 11953-0102
Tel: 631-924-3888; 631-924-8555; 631-604-8599
E-mail: topmarketingadvisor@gmail.com
Web Site: topmarketingadvisor.com
Key Personnel
Chmn & CEO: Andrew S Linick, PhD
  E-mail: linickgroup@gmail.com
EVP: Roger Dextor
Natl Sales Mgr: Jim Figurniak
VP, Direct Mktg: Shane Clarke
Mng Dir, Global Mail Order Sales: Robert Kaplan
Dir, Spec Projs: Barbara Deal
Subs Rts & Perms Consultant: Laurie Felgenbaum
Creative Copy & Mgmt Consultant: Charlene Hoey
PR Consultant: Bernadette Fasching
Graphic Arts & Design Consultant: Hal Klein
Edit Commun Consultant: James Rada, Jr; Kelly Boyles
Founded: 1968
Provides maximum exposure free publicity for books, videos, products, services, organizations, inventions & ideas through integrated, targeted public relations & other marketing communications; publishing, sales promotion & direct response advertising; measurable response database promotions; printing; mail-order & direct mail selling; planning & counseling: 12 month communications action plans; public relations seminars; media, special events planning; media press kits; creation, design & implementation, new product introductions, corporate backgrounders, fact sheets, executive biographies, question & answer sheets; persuasive copywriting; news releases to Internet-all electronic & print media, technical articles, by-line articles, speeches, speaker proposals, brochures, newsletters, annual reports, lead generation & conversion sales letters; advertising copy; editorial contact & interviews; Internet direct mail, e-commerce campaigns. Provides comprehensive graphic redesign/new web site content development, interactive services with web site marketing makeover advice for first-time authors, self-publishers, professionals & entrepreneurs. Specializes in online advertising/PR, links to top search engines, consulting on a 100% satisfaction guarantee. Free site evaluation marketing checklist (a$ 250 value) for LMP readers.
Branch Office(s)
7 Lincoln Ave, Smithtown, NY 11787

The Live Oak Press LLC
PO Box 60036, Palo Alto, CA 94306-0036
E-mail: info@liveoakpress.com
Web Site: www.liveoakpress.com
Key Personnel
Founder & Pres: David M Hamilton
Founded: 1982
Offers consulting & publishing services (editorial & production).
Membership(s): The American Library Association (ALA); Association of College & Research Libraries (ACRL); The Authors Guild; Book

Club of California (BCC); Independent Book Publishers Association (IBPA); Publishing Professionals Network (PPN); Society for Scholarly Publishing (SSP)

Lorimer Literary Consulting
1033 SW Yamhill St, Suite 205, Portland, OR 97205
Tel: 503-481-5847
E-mail: lorimerliterary@yahoo.com
Key Personnel
Owner & Pres: Kevin L Faherty
Founded: 2003
Consultancy to independent authors, self-publishers, ms development, sales representative hiring & trade show participation. Over 25 years of publishing & sales experience, specialty sales & club penetration. Branch office in Portland, OR.

Lumina Datamatics Inc
Affiliate of Datamatics Global Services (Mumbai)
4 Collins Ave, Plymouth, MA 02360
Tel: 508-746-0300 *Fax:* 508-746-3233
Web Site: luminadatamatics.com
Key Personnel
SVP: Jack Mitchell *Tel:* 508-746-0300 ext 203
  E-mail: jack.mitchell@luminad.com
SVP, Content Technol: John Wheeler
  E-mail: john.wheeler@luminad.com
SVP, Prod Devt: Gordon Laws *E-mail:* gordon.laws@luminad.com
SVP, Sales: Prashant Prabhu *E-mail:* prashant.prabhu@luminad.com
VP, Fin & Acctg: John Chappell *E-mail:* john.chappell@luminad.com
Founded: 1974
Providing full service content creation, design/packaging & media delivery systems to publishers. Services include authoring/writing, editorial research & development, media development & production, editing, photo & text research/permissions, photography/photo shoot direction, indexing, proofreading, fact checking, design/design direction, art direction/editing, technical/illustrative art packages, photo manipulation & page make-up/composition services. Employs over 1,200 US & offshore resources specializing in content/media creation & make-up including file conversions/re-purposing & content management & delivery services. All services are offered both in the US & at offshore facilities. Areas of specialization include school, higher education & professional publishing: mathematics (grade school/algebra/calculus/physics), foreign language (French/Spanish/German/Italian), English & English composition, history, political science, science (chemistry/biology/astronomy), social studies, computer science, business (economics/finance/marketing), engineering & technical trades as well as professional/reference material. Products range from simple one-color ancillaries components to highly complex design & art intensive core content.
Branch Office(s)
31572 Industrial Rd, Suite 400, Livonia, MI 48150 *Toll Free Tel:* 800-717-9153 *Fax:* 734-525-4455
510 Thornall St Metropark, Suite 100, Edison, NJ 08837 (sales) *Toll Free Tel:* 888-772-5532 *Fax:* 732-635-0600
345 Seventh Ave, 4th fl, New York, NY 10001 *Tel:* 646-453-1000 *Fax:* 212-564-8285
1797 Seddon Ct, Ashland, OH 44805 *Tel:* 419-289-0558 *Fax:* 419-289-8923
3265 Farmtrail Rd, York, PA 17406 *Tel:* 717-764-4000
Datamatics Global Services GmbH doo, Gunduliceva br 33, 78000 Banja Luka, Bosnia and Herzegovina *Tel:* 51304120

Im Leuschner, Park 3, 64347 Griesheim, Germany *Tel:* (06155) 862 99-0 *Fax:* (06155) 862 99-19
Ascendas International Tech Park, Taramani Rd, 12th fl, Phase II, Chennai 600 113, India *Tel:* (044) 6604 6000; (044) 6604 6001; (044) 6604 6002 *Fax:* (044) 6604 6098
Knowledge Ctr, St No 17, MIDC, Andheri (E), Mumbai 400 093, India *Tel:* (022) 6102 0000 *Fax:* (022) 2834 3669
Suyojit Datamatics Knowledge Center, Suyojit IT Park, Survey No 804, Unit No S1-S3, Nashik-Mumbai Hwy, Nashik 422 002, India *Tel:* (0253) 610 2222 *Fax:* (0253) 610 2271
Off No 5, 2nd fl, Tower 1, Stellar IT Park, C-25, Sector 62, Noida 201 301, India *Tel:* (0120) 494 0999
Plot No 29-34, East Coast Rd, Saram Revenue Village, Oulgaret Municipality, Lawspet Post, Puducherry 605 008, India *Tel:* (0413) 660 4500; (0413) 660 4501

Market Partners International Inc
232 Madison Ave, Suite 1400, New York, NY 10016
Tel: 212-447-0855 *Fax:* 212-447-0785
E-mail: info@marketpartnersinternational.com
Web Site: www.marketpartnersinternational.com
Key Personnel
Dir: Amy Rhodes; Lorraine W Shanley
Consulting services to adult & children's publishers, book clubs, retailers, packagers & institutions including a full range of online & retail marketing expertise, digital strategy, business & strategic planning, special sales, mergers & acquisitions & executive search. Publishers of www.PublishingTrends.com, a web site dedicated to the book publishing industry. Member of the Publishers Lunch Club.
Membership(s): Book Industry Study Group (BISG); Women's Media Group

McCarthy Digital
15 Mountain Trail, Croton-on-Hudson, NY 10520
Tel: 914-334-0408 *Toll Free Fax:* 866-618-8605
Web Site: www.mccarthy-digital.com
Key Personnel
Founder & Principal Consultant: Peter McCarthy
  E-mail: pete@mccarthy-digital.com
Founded: 2012
A consultancy at the intersection of publishing, technology & marketing.

Anita D McClellan Associates
464 Common St, Suite 142, Belmont, MA 02478-2704
Tel: 617-575-9203
E-mail: adm@anitamcclellan.com
Web Site: www.anitamcclellan.com
Founded: 1988
From concept into print: consulting by top corporate trade & scholarly publishing professional; trade & scholarly books, nonfiction & fiction written for adults & juveniles/YA. Clientele: publishers, literary agents, authors, content providers & book packagers across the English-language world. Scope: Contracts: negotiations, agreement vetting. Editorial services: developmental editing; mss & project analysis; revision, restructuring; nonfiction book & series proposals; fiction synopses; queries; cover letters. Marketing: cover design evaluation, market positioning, jacket & catalog copywriting, marketing plans; writers' coach.
Membership(s): The Authors Guild; Bay Area Editors' Forum; Editorial Freelancers Association (EFA); Independent Book Publishers Association (IBPA); International Women's Writing Guild (IWWG); National Book Critics Circle (NBCC); Sisters in Crime; Society of Children's Book Writers & Illustrators (SCBWI); Women's National Book Association (WNBA)

Virginia McCullough
2527 Telluride Trail, Suite D, Green Bay, WI
54313
Tel: 920-662-9633
E-mail: vemccullough@earthlink.net
Web Site: www.virginiamccullough.com
Novelist & fiction consultant: coach, edit & ad-
vise at all stages of publishing.
Membership(s): The Authors Guild; Romance
Writers of America (RWA)

John B McHugh Publishing Consultant
PO Box 170665, Milwaukee, WI 53217-8056
Tel: 414-351-3056
E-mail: jack@johnbmchugh.com
Web Site: www.johnbmchugh.com
Key Personnel
Principal & Consultant: John B McHugh
Contact: Jan Aline Franzelle
Founded: 1979
Management consulting for publishers. Special-
ize in business finance, management, publish-
ing & rights & permissions, college market &
association/not-for-profit, self-employment &
social media.
Membership(s): ASAE; Council of Science Ed-
itors (CSE); Society for Scholarly Publishing
(SSP)

Media Masters Publicity
61 Depot St, Tryon, NC 28782
Tel: 828-859-9456
E-mail: info@mmpublicity.com
Web Site: www.mmpublicity.com
Key Personnel
Sr Partner: Tracey Daniels *E-mail:* tracey@
mmpublicity.com
Founded: 1998
Full service literary publicity agency. Specialize
in publicity for children's & teen books, cookbooks & lifestyle titles. Personalized service
for every client with emphasis on procuring
quality media results. Services: implementing
& executing national & local media campaigns,
author tours & appearances, TV & radio satellite tours, press kit design & consulting. Per-
project or retainer services. Client list includes
large & small publishing houses.
Branch Office(s)
6106 Majestic Pines Dr, Kingwood, TX 77345,
Partner: Karen Wadsworth *Tel:* 617-869-5854
E-mail: karen@mmpublicity.com
Membership(s): The American Library Association (ALA); Society of Children's Book Writers & Illustrators (SCBWI); Young Adult Library Services Association (YALSA)

Tom Mellers Publishing Services (TMPS)
60 Second Ave, Suite 8, New York, NY 10003
Tel: 212-254-4958
E-mail: tmps71@yahoo.com
Key Personnel
Pres: Tom Mellers
Founded: 1971
Permissions: general & project-specific advice to
publishers & authors seeking permissions; pro-
cedures setup; trouble shooting. Specialize in
image research & international work with museums. Administrative guidance for authors &
literary estates with rights to administer, also
write contracts. Mss: analysis & advice for authors & publishers.
Branch Office(s)
4629 Vestal Pkwy E, Vestal, NY 13850 *Tel:* 607-
798-7994

Mendon Associates Inc
4195 Dundas St W, Suite 346, Toronto, ON M8X
1Y4, Canada
Tel: 416-239-9661 *Toll Free Tel:* 800-361-1325
Fax: 416-239-1076
E-mail: info@mendon.com

Web Site: www.mendon.com
Key Personnel
Owner & Partner: A Jorge de Mendonca
E-mail: jd@mendon.com
Founded: 1983
Media research & computer consulting for pub-
lishers.

MetaComet Systems
29 College St, South Hadley, MA 01075
Tel: 413-536-5989
Web Site: www.metacomet.com
Key Personnel
COO: Khalid Elkalai *E-mail:* kelkalai@
metacomet.com
Pres: David Marlin *E-mail:* dmarlin@metacomet.
com
Founded: 2000
Leading provider of royalty automation solutions
designed to reduce effort by 90% while reduc-
ing risk & improving author relations.
Membership(s): Audio Publishers Association;
Book Industry Study Group (BISG); Evangeli-
cal Christian Publishers Association (ECPA);
Independent Book Publishers Association
(IBPA); Independent Publisher's Guild (IPG);
Publishers Association of the West (PubWest)

MGP Direct Inc
17814 Shotley Bridge Place, Olney, MD 20832
Tel: 240-755-6976
Web Site: www.mgpdirect.com
Key Personnel
Pres & CEO: Roberta Rosenberg
E-mail: roberta@mgpdirect.com
Founded: 1987
Marketing consulting & direct marketing &
search engine optimization (SEO) copywriting
services for print, electronic & web information
publishers.

Mobium Creative Group
200 S Michigan Ave, 17th fl, Chicago, IL 60604
Tel: 312-422-8950; 312-422-5995 *Fax:* 312-422-
5901
Web Site: www.mobium.com
Key Personnel
SVP, Acct Mgr: Patti Bridge
E-mail: pattibridge@mobium.com
SVP, Acct Servs: Pat McAuley
E-mail: pmcauley@mobium.com
Full service integrated marketing communica-
tions & business to business brand development
company. Specialize in advertising, direct mail,
collateral & interactive web.

OBS, see Open Book Systems Inc®

Odyssey Books
Division of The Ciletti Publishing Group Inc
2421 Redwood Ct, Longmont, CO 80503
Tel: 720-494-1473 *Fax:* 720-494-1471
E-mail: books@odysseybooks.net
Key Personnel
Pres & Publr: Barbara Ciletti
Founded: 1995
Book publishers specializing in fiction & non-
fiction. Subject areas include social science,
adult nonfiction, children's books, gardening &
crafts.
Membership(s): The American Library Associ-
ation (ALA); APPL; International Associa-
tion of Culinary Professionals (IACP); Inter-
national Literacy Association (ILA); National
Science Teachers Association (NSTA); Society
of American Poets

Open Book Systems Inc®
21 Broadway, Suite 5, Rockport, MA 01966
Tel: 978-546-7346 *Fax:* 978-231-0222
E-mail: info@obs.com

Web Site: www.obs.com
Key Personnel
Pres: Laura Fillmore
Founded: 1982
Consult with publishers & educators on digital
strategy. Specialize in: Standards & workflows
for traditional & digital publishing; ebook conversion & distribution; sci-tech-medical (STM)
& educational publishing; institutional sales
& access; re-purposing of print & electronic
content; backend content & digital asset management; proprietary code development; cus-
tomization of open source software.
Membership(s): Book Industry Study Group
(BISG); Independent Book Publishers Association (IBPA); Internet Society

Open Horizons Publishing Co
PO Box 2887, Taos, NM 87571
Tel: 575-751-3398
E-mail: books@bookmarketingbestsellers.com
Web Site: bookmarketingbestsellers.com
Key Personnel
Owner & Publr: John Kremer
E-mail: johnkremer@bookmarket.com
Founded: 1982
Book marketing, publicity, direct marketing, pric-
ing & general planning for book publishers of
all sizes as well as for individual authors. Most
consulting is done over the phone, but also pro-
vides on-site consulting services; book covers;
news releases, Internet marketing.
Membership(s): The Association of Publishers
for Special Sales (APSS); Independent Book
Publishers Association (IBPA)

Orobora Inc
Affiliate of Staunton Media Lab
644 Greenville Ave, Suite 234, Staunton, VA
24401
Tel: 540-324-7023
E-mail: info@orobora.com
Web Site: orobora.com
Key Personnel
Pres: Steve O'Keefe *E-mail:* steve.okeefe@
orobora.com
Founded: 1994
Provides online public relations for the publishing
trade.
Membership(s): Independent Book Publishers As-
sociation (IBPA); International Association of
Online Communicators (IAOC); Public Rela-
tions Society of America Inc (PRSA)

**Paz & Associates: The Bookstore Training &
Consulting Group**
1417 Sadler Rd, No 274, Fernandina Beach, FL
32034
Tel: 904-277-2664 *Fax:* 904-261-6742
Web Site: www.pazbookbiz.com
Key Personnel
Owner & Partner: Donna Paz Kaufman
E-mail: dpaz@pazbookbiz.com
Partner: Mark Kaufman *E-mail:* mkaufman@
pazbookbiz.com
Founded: 1992
Bookstore consultants with specialties in store
design, inventory selection, marketing, staff
training & business management. Also used by
public libraries for design & marketing.
Membership(s): American Booksellers Asso-
ciation (ABA); American Institute of Archi-
tects; Association of Booksellers for Children;
Women's National Book Association (WNBA)

The Permissions Group Inc
401 S Milwaukee Ave, Suite 180, Wheeling, IL
60090
Tel: 847-635-6550 *Toll Free Tel:* 800-374-7985
Fax: 847-635-6968
E-mail: info@permissionsgroup.com
Web Site: www.permissionsgroup.com

Key Personnel
Dir: Sherry Hoesly *E-mail:* sherry_hoesly@
permissionsgroup.com
Founded: 1990
Full service copyright & permissions consulting
company. Specialize in ms review & analysis,
rights negotiation, individualized consulting.

**Law Office of Robert G Pimm Attorney at
Law**
2977 Ygnacio Valley Rd, Suite 265, Walnut
Creek, CA 94598-3535
Tel: 925-374-1442 *Fax:* 925-281-2888
Web Site: www.rgpimm.com
Key Personnel
Literary Attorney: Robert G Pimm *E-mail:* bob@
rgpimm.com
Founded: 2001
Represents authors & publishers, artists & illus-
trators, agents, printers & other participants in
the book industry. Areas of practice include
copyright, trademark, trade secrets & contract
negotiations in the book industry. Also, forma-
tion of book industry corporations & advising
corporate directors & officers.
Membership(s): American Bar Association
(ABA); Authors Alliance; The Authors Guild;
California Lawyers for the Arts; National Writers Union (NWU)

Promote A Book
591 Mantua Blvd, Sewell, NJ 08080
Tel: 512-586-6073
Web Site: promoteabook.media
Key Personnel
Founder & Publicist: Michael R Drew
E-mail: michael@promoteabook.com
Book marketing, author video bio's, book video
trailers, broadcast & syndication service.

Generosa Gina Protano Publishing, see GGP
Publishing Inc

ps ink LLC
857 Post Rd, Suite 367, Fairfield, CT 06824
Tel: 203-255-9789
Web Site: www.ps-ink.com
Key Personnel
Mng Partner: Patty Sullivan *E-mail:* patty@ps-
ink.com
Founded: 1999
Publishing solutions company offering consulting services, licensing, property development
& book/series packaging. Client base includes
educational & trade publishers, toy manufacturers, authors, illustrators & photographers as
well as companies representing children's products & programs. Our expertise has its roots
in the development of underlying intellectual
properties with a focus on identifying ways to
leverage those properties across multiple formats in print publishing, digital expression,
licensed categories & other media.
Membership(s): Women's Media Group

Publishing Management Associates Inc
129 S Phelps Ave, Suite 312, Rockford, IL 61108
Tel: 815-398-8569 *Fax:* 815-398-8579
E-mail: pma@pma-inc.net
Web Site: www.pma-inc.net
Key Personnel
Pres: Richard A Vaughan
Founded: 1989
Publishing consulting firm providing marketing,
advertising & business management services
for a wide range of publications.

R J Promotions & Advertising
120 Holton Ave S, Hamilton, ON L8M 2L5,
Canada
Tel: 905-548-0389

E-mail: rjpromo@cogeco.ca
Key Personnel
Mktg Consultant: Jacqueline Rotterman
Founded: 1984
Marketing & media plans, budgets; creative writ-
ing, art & logo designs; computer graphic de-
sign & production (Mac).

Raab Associates Inc
730 Yale Ave, Swarthmore, PA 19081
Tel: 914-241-2117
E-mail: info@raabassociates.com
Web Site: www.raabassociates.com
Key Personnel
Pres: Susan Salzman Raab
Founded: 1986
Consulting in direct marketing of books, conti-
nuities & magazines. Database development,
list segmentation models, vendor evaluation,
system development, project management, new
business planning & analytical techniques; chil-
dren's book publicity.

Nina J Reznick Esq
28 E Tenth St, New York, NY 10003
Tel: 212-473-6279
E-mail: ninarezesq@icloud.com
Founded: 1980
All legal work for writers & producers in all ar-
eas of the entertainment business with special
emphasis on publishing, theatre, film & TV.
Membership(s): American Bar Association
(ABA); National Lawyers Guild (NLG); New
York State Bar Association

Law Offices of Lloyd L Rich
1163 Vine St, Denver, CO 80206
Tel: 303-388-5215
E-mail: rich@publishingattorney.com
Web Site: www.publaw.com
Key Personnel
Attorney: Lloyd L Rich

Judith Riven Literary Agent LLC
250 W 16 St, Suite 4F, New York, NY 10011
Tel: 212-255-1009 *Fax:* 212-255-8547
E-mail: rivenlitqueries@gmail.com
Web Site: rivenlit.com
Key Personnel
Owner & Pres: Judith Riven
Founded: 1993
Advising & consulting writers on how to develop
& strategize their careers.

Stephanie Rogers & Associates
Affiliate of Philipico Pictures Co
8737 Carlitas Joy Ct, Las Vegas, NV 89117
Tel: 702-255-9999
E-mail: sjrlion@aol.com; write2wow@aol.com
Web Site: www.write2wow.com
Key Personnel
Owner: Stephanie Rogers
Founded: 1980
Represent writers, producers & directors in film
& TV. No unsol mss, screenplays or teleplays
(must have industry referral/recommendation).
We do not represent mss to publishers, only
published books, screenplays & teleplays to
the film & television trade along with writ-
ers, directors & producers for hire. No reading
fee. Will accept query letters with a SASE &
e-mail queries (without attachments).

Sherri Rosen Publicity Intl NYC
454 Manhattan Ave, Suite 3-J, New York, NY
10026
Tel: 212-222-1183
E-mail: sherri@sherrirosen.com
Web Site: www.sherrirosen.com
Key Personnel
Pres: Sherri Rosen

Founded: 1999
Publicity firm which gives a powerful voice to
people doing great things in the world. Specialize in literary with emphasis on sex, spirituality
& relationships, multicultural publicity, science
fiction, publicizing published or self-published
books. Creates specific media lists for genre of
client, ghostwright, ms development, web sites,
Internet, ebooks, videos, virtual tours, blogging,
live storytelling. Writes for Redhead's Rap,
Elephant Journal & The Good Men Project.
Created her own award-winning ebook *Give
Me Your Truth* & author of award-winning
*Publicity from the Trenches: For Published &
Self-Published Authors.*
Membership(s): International Women's Writ-
ing Guild (IWWG); National Writers Union
(NWU)

Dick Rowson
4701 Connecticut Ave NW, Suite 503, Washington, DC 20008
Tel: 202-244-8104
E-mail: rcrowson2@aol.com
Founded: 1990
Management & placement of mss with publishers
for authors.
Membership(s): Association for Slavic, East European & Eurasian Studies (ASEEES); Overseas Press Club

Royalty Review LLC
Member of The JR Group LLC
485 Madison Ave, 9th fl, New York, NY 10022
Tel: 212-792-6300 *Fax:* 212-792-6350
E-mail: info@janoverllc.com
Web Site: www.jrllc.com
Key Personnel
Partner: Steven White *Tel:* 212-792-6300 ext
6413 *E-mail:* steven.white@janoverllc.com
Founded: 1991
Examinations of publishers books & records, per
royalty contracts. Consulting on royalty matters
for agents, authors & copyright owners. Exami-
nation of subs-rights transactions & reports for
publishers. Valuations & appraisals for estates
& litigation support.

Bernard Schleifer Co
200 W 20 St, Suite 212, New York, NY 10011
Tel: 212-675-2615
Key Personnel
Owner: Bernard Schleifer
Complete book design & production; dummying
& mechanicals; publishing consultants; Quark
Express desktop.

Schnoll Media Consulting
1253 Springfield Ave, PMB 338, New Provi-
dence, NJ 07974
Tel: 908-522-3190 *Fax:* 908-273-2667
Web Site: www.schnollconsult.com
Key Personnel
Mng Dir: Steven Schnoll *E-mail:* steven@
schnollconsult.com
Founded: 1998
Marketing technology issues, workflow, process
control, printing, manufacturing & production.
Membership(s): Electronic Document Systems
Foundation (EDSF); Epicomm; PRINTING
United Alliance

Bettina Schrewe Literary Scouting
220 E 23 St, Suite 409, New York, NY 10010
Tel: 212-414-2515 *Fax:* 212-414-2516
E-mail: bschrewe@bschrewe.com
Web Site: www.bschrewe.com
Key Personnel
Scout: Amy Gordon *E-mail:* agordon@
bschrewe.com; Bettina Schrewe; Flora Esterly
E-mail: festerly@bschrewe.com

Scribe Inc
842 S Second St, Philadelphia, PA 19147
Tel: 215-336-5094 *Fax:* 215-336-5092
E-mail: contact@scribenet.com
Web Site: www.scribenet.com
Key Personnel
Pres: David Alan Rech *E-mail:* drech@scribenet.com
Founded: 1993
Provides a full range of publishing services, including OCR/data conversion, editing, typesetting & ebook creation, with expertise in XML, Well-Formed Document Workflow & staff training. Assists with multipurpose publishing through services & training. Branch offices located in Dania Beach, FL & Allentown, PA.
Branch Office(s)
7540 Windsor Dr, Suite 200B, Allentown, PA 18195
3758 SW 30 Ave, Fort Lauderdale, FL 33312

SDP Publishing Solutions LLC
36 Captain's Way, East Bridgewater, MA 02333
Tel: 617-775-0656
E-mail: info@sdppublishing.com
Web Site: sdppublishing.com
Key Personnel
Publr & Publg Consultant: Lisa Akoury-Ross
E-mail: lross@sdppublishing.com
Founded: 2009
Offer consulting services in all related publishing aspects such as ms review of all genres. Offer editorial & ghostwriting services, international rights, custom book covers, interior design, marketing & distribution services. Offer publishing solutions for authors worldwide.
Membership(s): Independent Book Publishers Association (IBPA)

Selden Associates
150 S Mountain Ave, Montclair, NJ 07042
Tel: 973-746-0421
Key Personnel
CEO: Charles J Selden *E-mail:* charles.selden@mac.com
Founded: 1986
Writer.
Branch Office(s)
639 Forest Ave, Palo Alto, CA 94301
Membership(s): The Authors Guild

Sensible Solutions Inc
500 Croton Lake Rd, Mount Kisco, NY 10549
Tel: 914-241-4749 *Fax:* 914-241-1942
Web Site: www.happilypublished.com
Key Personnel
Mng Dir: Judith Appelbaum *E-mail:* judith@happilypublished.com
Founded: 1981
Marketing consultants to authors & publishers. Guidance & assistance on target marketing books from their earliest stages through & after publication regarding editing, design, publicity, subsidiary rights; bookstore, online, mail order, library & special sales.
Membership(s): The Authors Guild; Book Industry Study Group (BISG); Independent Book Publishers Association (IBPA); PEN America; Women's Media Group

Specialty Book Marketing Inc
87-80 115 St, Richmond Hill, NY 11418
Tel: 212-696-0415 *Fax:* 718-849-5131
Web Site: www.specialtybooks.com
Key Personnel
Pres: William L Corsa *E-mail:* billbooky@aol.com
Founded: 1986
An independent services company to the publishing community. We consult on strategic planning, partnerships, project management, marketing & sales, rights management & disposition.

Jane Starr Literary Scouts
1350 Avenue of the Americas, Suite 1205, New York, NY 10019
Tel: 212-421-0777
E-mail: jane@janestarr.com
Key Personnel
Owner: Jane Starr
Founded: 1995
An international scouting agency for: Allen & Unwin (Australia), Bastei Luebbe, Eichborn, Baumhaus Verlag & Boje Verlag (Germany), Japan Uni Agency (Japan), Editions Michel Lafon (France), Editora Autentica (Brazil), Newton Compton Editori (Italy), Vulkan Publishing (Serbia), RBA Libros (Spain), Uitgeverij De Fontein (The Netherlands), Vigmostad & Bjoerke (Norway).

Story Monsters LLC
4696 W Tyson St, Chandler, AZ 85226-2903
Tel: 480-940-8182 *Fax:* 480-940-8787
Web Site: www.StoryMonsters.com
Key Personnel
Pres: Linda F Radke *E-mail:* Linda@StoryMonsters.com
Founded: 1985
Offers consulting in book production, marketing, publicity, distribution, book trailers, social media, web sites & book ms evaluations. Story Monsters has been producing & marketing books since 1985 & has helped numerous authors achieve success. Story Monsters can help you avoid the inevitable pitfalls that frustrate even experienced writers.
Membership(s): Better Business Bureau (BBB); The Children's Book Council (CBC); Independent Book Publishers Association (IBPA); National Federation of Press Women

Tanenbaum International Literary Agency Ltd (TILA)
1035 Fifth Ave, Suite 15D, New York, NY 10028
Tel: 212-371-4120 *Fax:* 212-988-0457
E-mail: tips001@aol.com
Web Site: www.tanenbauminternational.com
Key Personnel
Owner & Pres: Ann Tanenbaum
Ed: Ella Snow
Founded: 1980
Editorial, marketing & management services for books on the fine & performing arts, museum books, nonfiction & children's picture & chapter books. Also a literary agency.

To Press & Beyond
825 E Pedregosa St, Suite 2, Santa Barbara, CA 93103
Tel: 805-898-2263
E-mail: info@topressandbeyond.com
Web Site: www.topressandbeyond.com
Key Personnel
Owner & Pres: Gail M Kearns *E-mail:* gail@topressandbeyond.com
Partner: Penelope C Paine *E-mail:* pennypaine@aol.com
Founded: 2001
Book publishing consulting & support services. We shepherd your print +/or ebook through writing, editing, design & layout, printing, distribution, sales & marketing & promotion, both in trade & niche markets & on the Web. We have worked with over 400 authors & independent publishers worldwide. You can contact Gail Kearns for a half-hour gratis phone consult about your project.
Membership(s): The Association of Publishers for Special Sales (APSS); Independent Book Publishers Association (IBPA)

Upper Access Inc
87 Upper Access Rd, Hinesburg, VT 05461
SAN: 667-1195
Tel: 802-482-2988
E-mail: upperaccessbooks@gmail.com
Web Site: www.upperaccess.com
Key Personnel
Pres: Lisa Carlson
VP & Publr: Stephen T Carlson *E-mail:* steve@upperaccess.com
Publicist: Kristen Lewis
Computer Progammer: Ron Lawrence
Founded: 1986
Publisher of books & software, consultants to other publishers on book production, publicity & business operation, Specialties include promotion, business/finance, computer technology & marketing.
Membership(s): The Association of Publishers for Special Sales (APSS); Independent Book Publishers Association (IBPA); Independent Publishers of New England (IPNE); Publishers North (PubNorth)

UTA News & Broadcast
Division of United Talent Agency (UTA)
888 Seventh Ave, 7th fl, New York, NY 10106
Tel: 212-765-3040 *Fax:* 212-757-6411
E-mail: nsb@nsbtalent.com
Web Site: bienstock.unitedtalent.com
Key Personnel
Co-Founder & Co-Pres: Carole Cooper; Richard Leibner
COO & Gen Coun: Jonathan Leibner
Literary Agent: Paul Fedorko
Broker publishing deals in fiction & nonfiction. Assist clients in developing book concepts & proposals.

VillageSoup®
Unit of Courier Publications LLC
91 Camden St, Suite 403, Rockland, ME 04841
Tel: 207-594-4401 *Fax:* 207-594-1679
E-mail: info@villagesoup.com
Web Site: www.villagesoup.com
Key Personnel
Pres & CEO: Bryan Gess *Tel:* 207-594-4401
E-mail: bryan@villagesoup.com
Community Internet station & community newspaper; marketing, promotion & publishing consultants; combined editorial & visual services.

Visual Artists & Galleries Association Inc (VAGA)
111 Broadway, Suite 1006, New York, NY 10006
Tel: 212-736-6666 *Fax:* 212-736-6767
E-mail: info@vagarights.com
Web Site: vagarights.com
Key Personnel
Exec Dir: Robert Panzer *E-mail:* rpanzer@vagarights.com
Represent reproduction rights (copyright) for approximately 18,000 artists worldwide including painters, sculptors, photographers etc. Publishers & others should contact VAGA to obtain repro rights clearance to use art in books, magazines, posters, postcards, calendars, merchandise, film, television etc. Provides research services to locate B&W photographs & color transparencies along with ancillary rights. Expert in all areas of copyright.

Wagner & Schell LLP
780 Lee St, Suite 102, Des Plaines, IL 60016
Tel: 847-759-9833 *Fax:* 847-759-9834
Web Site: www.wagneruslaw.com
Key Personnel
Attorney: Debbie M Schell *E-mail:* schell@wagneruslaw.co; Richard E Schell; Kurt A Wagner *E-mail:* wagner@wagneruslaw.com
Founded: 1994

Law firm offering intellectual property, international business & immigration services, publishing law, author & publisher representation, including rights & permissions. Branch office in Villach, Austria.
Membership(s): Independent Book Publishers Association (IBPA); Midwest Writers Association

Jayne Walker Editorial
1406 Euclid Ave, Suite 1, Berkeley, CA 94708
Tel: 510-843-8265
Key Personnel
Pres & Owner: Jayne Walker
  E-mail: jaynelwalker@earthlink.net
Services to writers: editorial & marketing consultations. Trade books (fiction & nonfiction), university press & textbooks.

Warwick Associates
18340 Sonoma Hwy, Sonoma, CA 95476
Tel: 707-939-9212 *Fax:* 707-938-3515
E-mail: warwick@vom.com
Web Site: www.warwickassociates.com
Key Personnel
Pres: Simon Warwick-Smith
Founded: 1985
Consulting on all aspects of publishing, from sales & distribution, to marketing & publicity. Steps include creating a winning ms, cover & design, getting printed successfully, getting excellent distribution, the launch & managing sales (trade, special sales, foreign rights). Also offers guidance on reviews, interviews, press materials, getting national radio & TV for publishers & authors. One-stop shop for creating & implementing successful publishing strategies. Specializations include spirituality, business, how-to, nonfiction, celebrity autobiographies, sports & general trade. Expert witness on all aspects of publishing.

Weidner Communications International Inc
1468 Alton Way, Downingtown, PA 19335
Tel: 610-486-6525 *Fax:* 610-486-6527
Web Site: www.weidcom.com
Key Personnel
Pres: Matthew T Weidner *E-mail:* mtw@
  weidcom.com
Founded: 1982
Publisher's representatives for trade & professional journals.
Membership(s): NAPR

Fred Weidner & Daughter Printers
99 Hudson St, 5th fl, New York, NY 10013
Tel: 646-706-5180
E-mail: info@fwdprinters.com
Web Site: www.fwdprinters.com
Key Personnel
Pres: Cynthia Weidner *E-mail:* cynthia@
  fwdprinters.com
Creative Dir: Carol Mittelsdorf *E-mail:* carol@
  fwdprinters.com
Founded: 1860
Incorporated in 1860 in the city of Brooklyn, the Weidner family has, for five generations, provided complete printing & production services for small to medium volume buyers of print-

ing who wish to have all their graphic needs conveniently met by one supplier.
Design, copy-editing & all types of printing, binding & die-cutting techniques can be readily utilized for everything from business cards to large runs of 4-color brochures & catalogues. Economy of scale is applied on continuous or repeated work.
Our unique & long-time trade arrangement with specialized firms in all parts of the country allow us to be competitive with the finest printing firms in the production of museum quality brochures & posters.
Call us & discover how the cumulative experience of a century & a half can benefit you.

Westwind Communications
1310 Maple St, Plymouth, MI 48170
Tel: 734-667-2090
Web Site: www.book-marketing-expert.com
Key Personnel
Pres: Scott Lorenz *E-mail:* scottlorenz@
  westwindcos.com
Founded: 1981
Book marketing, publicity & promotion.

Wheatmark Inc
2030 E Speedway Blvd, Suite 106, Tucson, AZ 85719
Tel: 520-798-0888 *Toll Free Tel:* 888-934-0888
  Fax: 520-798-3394
E-mail: info@wheatmark.com
Web Site: www.wheatmark.com
Key Personnel
Pres & Founder: Sam Henrie *E-mail:* sam@
  wheatmark.com
VP: Atilla Vekony *E-mail:* atilla@wheatmark.com
Dir, Mktg: Grael Norton *E-mail:* grael@
  wheatmark.com
Founded: 1999
Provider of editing, publishing & online marketing services to authors.
Membership(s): Independent Book Publishers Association (IBPA)

Wimmer Cookbooks
Division of Mercury Printing, an RR Donnelley Co
4650 Shelby Air Dr, Memphis, TN 38118
Toll Free Tel: 800-548-2537 *Fax:* 901-363-1771
Web Site: www.wimmerco.com
Key Personnel
Acct Coord: Robyn Hite
Sales & Mktg: Terry Rayner
Founded: 1946
Conduct seminars on publication development & national marketing/promotion & leadership training. Specialize in regional books, community cookbooks & publishing projects produced by nonprofit organizations & individual self-publishers.

Wittman Associates
43 Valley Lane N, Valley Stream, NY 11581
Tel: 516-791-3779
Key Personnel
Partner: Allan Wittman *E-mail:* allanwittman@
  juno.com; Ruth Wittman

Founded: 1988
Consultants to commercial & nonprofit publishers & professional societies; specialize in professional & scholarly publishing for books, magazines & journals in science, technology, medicine, reference & business; acquisitions, divestitures & mergers; represent principals in negotiating & drafting publishing agreements. Expert witness in publishing litigation.

Word-Wise Advertising
3500 Virginia Bcach Blvd, Suite 611, Virginia Beach, VA 23452
Tel: 757-455-5020
Key Personnel
Owner & Dir: Bruce Price
Founded: 1980
Advertising, promotion, direct mail; copy & design for ads, brochures, mailing pieces. Specialize in logos & corporate design for smaller firms.

write 2 wow, see Stephanie Rogers & Associates

The Writer's Lifeline Inc
400 S Burnside Ave, Suite 11B, Los Angeles, CA 90036
Tel: 323-932-1685
Web Site: www.thewriterslifeline.com
Key Personnel
CEO: Kenneth Atchity, PhD *E-mail:* kja@
  thewriterslifeline.com
Mgr: Yasemin Isil *E-mail:* yasemin@
  storymerchant.com; Samantha Skelton
  E-mail: sam@storymerchant.com
Assoc Mgr: Chris Kuhne *E-mail:* chris@
  storymerchant.com
Founded: 1996
A full service editorial company, providing nonfiction book writers, novelists, business, professional, technical & screenwriters with assistance in storytelling, mentoring, perfecting their style & craft, style-structure-concept-line editing, ghostwriting, publishing consulting, development, translation, advertising & promotion, printing & self-publishing, distribution & research. Branch office in New York.
Sister companies: Atchity Productions; Story Merchant; Story Merchant Books.
Membership(s): American Comparative Literature Association; The Authors Guild; National Academy of Television Arts & Sciences (NATAS); PEN America; Women in Film (WIF); Writers Guild of America (WGA)

Writer's Relief, Inc
18766 John J Williams Hwy, Unit 4, Box 335, Rehoboth Beach, DE 19971
Toll Free Tel: 866-405-3003 *Fax:* 201-641-1253
E-mail: info@writersrelief.com
Web Site: www.WritersRelief.com
Key Personnel
Pres: Ronnie L Smith *E-mail:* ronnie@wrelief.com
Founded: 1994
Free submission leads/guidelines. Cover/query letters. Join 60,000+ writers subscribing to *Submit Write Now!* Best for poetry, short prose, book projects.

Book Producers

Book producers (also called book packagers) provide publishers with complete book preparation services from outline to final book, sometimes including marketing and distribution services as well. Some of the book producers listed here are also book publishers and as such are listed in **U.S. Publishers** or **Canadian Publishers** (both in volume 1). For related listings, see **Editorial Services** (volume 1), **Consultants, Artists & Art Services, Complete Book Manufacturers** and **Prepress Services**.

Adler & Robin Books Inc
3000 Connecticut Ave NW, Washington, DC 20008
Tel: 202-986-9275
E-mail: adlerrobininfo@my.netmails.net
Web Site: www.AdlerRobin.com
Key Personnel
Pres: Bill Adler, Jr
VP: Peggy Robin
Packages & publishes books. Now accepting unsol proposals (biography/memoir, careers, gift books, how-to, humor, lifestyle, local history, pop culture, reference books, self-help).
Membership(s): American Booksellers Association (ABA); Washington Publishers (WP)

Agincourt Press
25 Main St, Chatham, NY 12037
Tel: 518-392-2898
E-mail: aginpress@aol.com
Key Personnel
Pres: David Rubel
Founded: 1990
Book packager, adult & children's.
Number of titles produced annually: 1 Print

AGS Bookworks
Division of American Graphic Systems
PO Box 460313, San Francisco, CA 94146-0313
Tel: 415-285-8799
Web Site: www.agsbookworks.com
Key Personnel
Pres: Bill Yenne *E-mail:* bill_yenne@msn.com
Founded: 1981
High quality illustrated books for international trade publishers on subjects such as history, biography, natural history, transportation & pop culture. Company provides full service book production services & licenses its vast library of verbal & pictorial content to print & electronic publishers.
Number of titles produced annually: 1 Print

American BookWorks Corp
309 Florida Hill Rd, Ridgefield, CT 06877
Mailing Address: PO Box 294, Georgetown, CT 06829
Fax: 203-244-9522 (orders)
E-mail: info@abwcorporation.com
Key Personnel
Pres: Fred N Grayson
EVP & Gen Coun: Valerie Levy-Grayson
Founded: 1976
Package general, self-help & educational paperbacks, trade & mass market reference books, premiums, textbook supplements & ancillaries, review books (K-Graduate) & test preparation.
Number of titles produced annually: 10 Print

American Graphic Systems, see AGS Bookworks

Aptara Inc
Subsidiary of iEnergizer
2901 Telestar Ct, Suite 522, Falls Church, VA 22042
Tel: 703-352-0001
E-mail: moreinfo@aptaracorp.com

Web Site: www.aptaracorp.com
Key Personnel
Pres: Samir Kakar
EVP, Fin & Cont: Prashant Kapoor
SVP, Busn & Contact Ctr Opers: Ashish Madan
Busn Devt: Michael Scott *E-mail:* michael.scott@aptaracorp.com
Founded: 1988
Liaison for complete or any combination of production services, ranging from simple 1-color to complex 4-color projects. Copy-editing.
Number of titles produced annually: 6 Print
Branch Office(s)
150 California St, Suite 301, Newton, MA 02458
Tel: 617-423-7755
11009 Metric Blvd, Bldg J, Suite 150, Austin, TX 78758 *Tel:* 512-876-5997
299 Elizabeth St, Level 1, Sydney 2000, Australia *Tel:* (02) 8251 0070
Tower 1 & 2, 8/100, Acharya Thulasi Rd (Shandy Rd), Pallavaram, Chennai 600 043, India *Tel:* (044) 22640676
No 2310, Doon Express Business Park, Saharanpur Rd, Bldg 2000, Dehradun 248 002, India *Tel:* (0135) 2644055
7B, Leela Infopark, Technopark, Trivandrum, Kerala 695 581, India *Tel:* (047) 14063370
A-37, Sector-60, Noida 201 301, India *Tel:* (0120) 7182424
D-10, Sector-2, Noida 201 301, India *Tel:* (0120) 24423678
SEZ Bldg 4A, 1st fl, S P Infocity, Pune Saswad Rd, Phursungi, Pune 412 308, India *Tel:* (020) 66728000

Arbor Books
244 Madison Ave, Box 254, New York, NY 10016
Tel: 212-956-0950 *Toll Free Tel:* 877-822-2500
Fax: 914-401-9385
E-mail: info@arborbooks.com; editorial@arborbooks.net
Web Site: www.arborbooks.com; www.arborservices.co
Key Personnel
Owner: Joel Hochman *Tel:* 877-822-2502 *E-mail:* arborbooksjoel@aol.com; Larry Leichman *Tel:* 877-822-2504 *E-mail:* arborbookslarry@aol.com
Mktg Dir: Olga Vladi
Founded: 1992
Full service book production from ghostwriting & editing to cover design, printing, publishing & marketing. Works for both corporations: business books, corporate histories, CEO bios & individuals: novels (all genres), memoirs, children's books, biz books, etc. Services include supervised (& insured) ghostwriting, copy-editing, translation, proofreading, design (even the most complex, including model shoots, illustrations, photo reconstruction & manipulation, book jacket design, album cover & magazine design), word processing (including transcription), scanning, layout, typesetting, obtaining registrations & endorsements, B&W & 4-color printing, marketing, promotion & advertising. Create logos, letterheads, annual reports, posters & promotional flyers. We can be hired for part of the job or all of the job. Personal attention & quality are guaranteed.

Fully insured, including media insurance. Self-publishing services include press kits, press releases, booking TV & radio programs, speaking tours & book signings & negotiating with producers & agents.
Number of titles produced annually: 100 Print

Arbor Services, see Arbor Books

Archetype Press Inc
11272 N Meadow Sage Dr, Oro Valley, AZ 85737-7250
Tel: 302-249-5879
E-mail: archepress@aol.com
Key Personnel
Pres: Diane Maddex *E-mail:* dimaddex@gmail.com
Founded: 1990
Complete editorial services to bound books. Produces illustrated books, calendars & sidelines on lifestyles, architecture, design, the arts & American culture for trade publishers, museums, hotels & associations.
Number of titles produced annually: 5 Print

Arrow Graphics Inc
PO Box 380291, Cambridge, MA 02238
E-mail: info@arrow1.com
Web Site: www.arrow1.com
Key Personnel
Pres: Alvart Badalian
Sr Graphic/Pubn Designer: Aramais Andonian
Founded: 1988
Complete book production services with state-of-the-art electronic design & publishing capabilities: copy-editing; indexing; typesetting & page composition; typography; design & art direction from concept to finished product; printing; consultation; project management. Novels, poetry, monographs, self-help, how-to, guides, ebooks & children's picture books. From ms to camera-ready to bound book, serving the publishing industry & self-publishing community. Call or write for free information, or visit our web site.
Number of titles produced annually: 25 Print

Bascom Communications LLC
200 E 72 St, Suite 6-L, New York, NY 10021-4500
Tel: 212-988-4212
E-mail: bascomllc@aol.com
Key Personnel
Pres: Betsy Ryan
VP: William Devereaux
Edit Dir: M L Bascom
Ed: Dorothy Devereaux
Founded: 1983
Complete preparation from concept through bound books. We specialize in adult & young adult trade nonfiction & reference. The company also publishes a selected number of young adult fiction titles. African-American biography; general & women's health issues & young adult self-help. All genres have received critical praise, literary prizes & a wide international audience.
Recent Title(s): *A Year in Poetry* (Crown Publishing); *Heart Full of Grace, A Thousand Years*

of Black Wisdom (Simon & Schuster); *The Scholastic Encyclopedia of the Unites States* (Scholastic Inc); *Voices of the Dream: African-American Women Speak* (Chronicle Books)
Membership(s): The Authors Guild; PEN America; The Science Advisory Board of the United States

becker&mayer!, LLC
11120 NE 33 Place, Suite 101, Bellevue, WA 98004
Tel: 425-827-7120 *Fax:* 425-828-9659
E-mail: infobm@beckermayer.com
Founded: 1978
Write, design & produce adult, nonfiction & children's nonfiction/book-plus.
Number of titles produced annually: 50 Print
Recent Title(s): *Extreme 3D: World's Most Dangerous Animals* (Scholastic); *Hello Kitty Super Sweet Stencils* (Abrams); *Kittenhood: Lifesize Portraits of Kittens in Their First 12 Weeks* (Abrams); *Star Trek Federation: The First 150 Years* (47 North); *Star Wars: Book of Sith* (47 North); *Star Wars Mega Models* (DK)
Membership(s): American Book Producers Association (ABPA)

Beckon Books, see Southwestern Publishing House Inc

Book Creations Inc
5075 56 Place, Vero Beach, FL 32967
Tel: 518-366-4636 (cell)
Key Personnel
Pres: George S Engel *E-mail:* george.engel@att.net
Edit Dir: Elizabeth Tinsley
Founded: 1973
Producing mass market fiction, both historical & contemporary & nonfiction; provides full editing services, as well as book design, typesetting & camera-ready pages & electronic publishing services.
Recent Title(s): *Wagons West: Colorado!*; *Wagons West: Texas!*; *Wagons West: Wyoming!*

BookComp Inc
6124 Belmont Ave NE, Belmont, MI 49306
Tel: 616-774-9700
E-mail: production@bookcomp.com
Web Site: www.bookcomp.com
Key Personnel
Pres: Jon F Dertien *E-mail:* jd@bookcomp.com
Prodn Mgr: JoAnn Sikkes
Founded: 1989
A privately owned company located in the greater Grand Rapids, MI area providing publishing service solutions for publishers of trade, professional & scholarly, scientific & university presses on a global scale.
Number of titles produced annually: 325 Print
Recent Title(s): *The Best Writing on Mathematics* (Princeton University Press); *Conflict in the Middle East* (ABC-CLIO); *The Pearl Harbor Secret* (ABC-CLIO); *Unmanning: How Humans, Machines and Media Perform Drone Warfare* (Rutgers University Press)
Membership(s): American Association of University Presses (AAUP); Book Industry Guild of New York

Bookwrights Design
1060 Old Ridge Rd, Lovingston, VA 22949
Tel: 434-263-4818
E-mail: design@bookwrights.com
Web Site: www.bookwrights.com
Key Personnel
Owner & Designer: Mayapriya Long *E-mail:* mayapriya@bookwrights.com
Prodn Designer: Jennylene Scheuch
Founded: 1990

Trade hardback, paperback & scholarly book & jacket design & production. Interior design & production. Print brokering & editorial services available. Samples & references available including social media. Ebook conversion & author/book web sites.
Number of titles produced annually: 30 Print
Recent Title(s): *Consumed in Freedom's Flame* (St Padraic); *The Natural Medicine Guide to Autism* (Hampton Roads Publishing); *The People's Business* (Berrett-Koehler); *Riddle in the Mountain* (Nomad Press); *Rolling Stones 1000 Best Movies of DVD* (Wenner Media); *Schools That Rock* (Wenner Media); *Wild Open Spaces* (Maverick Spirit Press)
Membership(s): Independent Book Publishers Association (IBPA)

Bowen Books LLC
971 First Ave, New York, NY 10022
Tel: 212-421-5797
E-mail: bowenbooks@aol.com
Key Personnel
Pres: Barbara Bowen
Founded: 1989
Books that provide insight into human potential, awareness & all areas of life improvement. While developing projects through fully edited mss or finished books, the company also serves as literary agent & offers consulting services.
Recent Title(s): *The Secrets of Power (2 vols)* (Ingo Swann Books)

Cenveo Publisher Services
555 Virginia Dr, Fort Washington, PA 19034
Tel: 267-470-1590 *Fax:* 215-591-9093
E-mail: info.psg@cenveo.com
Web Site: www.cenveopublisherservices.com
Key Personnel
CFO: John Pennie
Pres: Atul Goel
VP, Journal Publg Servs: Debbie McClanahan
VP, Learning Solutions: Waseem Andrabi
VP, Media & Intl Delivery Ctr: Dwayne Reed
Dir, Mktg: Mike Groth *E-mail:* mike.groth@cenveo.com
Founded: 1998
We offer complete book production services for educational markets including PreK-12 & higher education. Our editorial services include conceptual development, prototype development, research, writing, content editing, copyediting, fact checking & production editing. Our production services include instructional design, page layouts, art creation & art services, photo research/shoots, electronic composition & prepress services. We specialize in full service project management.
Branch Office(s)
3575 Hempland Rd, Lancaster, PA 17601
Tel: 717-285-9095
5457 Twin Knolls Rd, Suite 200, Columbia, MD 21045 *Tel:* 410-850-0500 *Toll Free Tel:* 800-257-5529
2905 Byrdhill Rd, Richmond, VA 23228
No 31 Kempapura, Hebbal, Bangalore 560 024, India *Tel:* (080) 4000 4888
36 Barnaby Rd, Kilpauk, Chennai, Tamil Nadu 600 010, India *Tel:* (044) 4205 8888
Marwah Ctr, 5th fl, Krishanlal Marwah Marg, Andheri East, Mumbai 400 072, India *Tel:* (022) 4098 5200
Steller IT Park, Tower I, 3rd fl, C 25, Sector 62, Noida 201 301, India *Tel:* (0120) 461 3700
One Mulgrave Chambers, 26-28 Mulgrave Rd, Sutton, Surrey SM2 6LE, United Kingdom

CG Book Printers
Division of Corporate Graphics Commercial (CGC)
1750 Northway Dr, North Mankato, MN 56003

Tel: 507-388-3300 *Toll Free Tel:* 800-729-7575
Fax: 507-386-6350
E-mail: cgbooks@corpgraph.com
Web Site: www.corpgraph.com
Key Personnel
Pres: Dan Kvasnicka *Tel:* 507-386-6340
Fax: 507-344-5548 *E-mail:* dekvasnicka@corpgraph.com
Sales Exec, Book Mfg Sales: Mike Schmitt
Tel: 507-386-6349 *E-mail:* mjschmitt@corpgraph.com
Founded: 1989
CG Book Printers currently provides book manufacturing services for publishers who sell product to school library & trade markets. In addition, we offer fulfillment services for those publishers wishing to maintain their inventories in the same location where their books are manufactured.
We bind books in hard case & paperback formats. We use Smyth sewn, side sew & adhesive bound for hard case trade or library bound books & section sew, or adhesive bind for paperback books.

Chernow Editorial Services Inc
16 W 16 St, Suite 2DS, New York, NY 10011
Tel: 212-675-0605
Key Personnel
Pres: Barbara A Chernow *E-mail:* bchernow@chernow.com
Founded: 1982
Project development & management of reference, professional & text information products. Full range of services, including ms development, technical editing, indexing, creation of art, print & electronic media design & production.
Number of titles produced annually: 20 Print
Recent Title(s): *Anatomy: The Essential Text* (Thieme); *Color Atlas of Brainstem Surgery* (Thieme); *75 Ways for Managers to Hire, Develop, and Keep Great Employees* (Amacon)

Concord Editorial & Design LLC
9450 SW Gemini Dr, Suite 68669, Beaverton, OR 97008
Tel: 616-827-7537 *Fax:* 616-825-6048
E-mail: info@concordeditorial.com
Web Site: www.concordeditorial.com
Key Personnel
Pres & Proj Dir: David Fideler, PhD
Founded: 2005
Offers complete design, book production, prepress & editorial services for publishers at extremely competitive rates with over 25 years of experience. Produce both general trade, academic & highly illustrated titles through high-resolution, press-ready Adobe Acrobat files. We offer fast turnaround, free FTP sites for clients & guarantee total customer satisfaction.
Number of titles produced annually: 30 Print

Cookbook Marketplace, see Southwestern Publishing House Inc

Copywriters' Council of America™ (CCA)
Division of The Linick Group Inc
CCA Bldg, 7 Putter Lane, Middle Island, NY 11953-1920
Mailing Address: PO Box 102, Middle Island, NY 11953-0102
Tel: 631-924-3888; 631-924-8555; 631-604-8599
Key Personnel
Chmn, Consulting Group: Andrew S Linick, PhD *E-mail:* cca4dmcopy@gmail.com
EVP: Roger Dextor
Ms Ed: Kelly Boyles
Founded: 1964
Complete book preparation & production; trade books, premiums, self liquidators, mass market paperbacks, manuals, reports, guides & directories, all information products. Target audiences:

book clubs, small to large development presses, entrepreneurs, information marketers of products including: books, ebooks, digital copy, audio & all other information products requiring packaging, sales & distribution via unique direct response advertising methods. Provides comprehensive graphic redesign/new web site content development, interactive services with web site marketing makeover advice for first-time authors, self-publishers, professionals & entrepreneurs. Specializes in online advertising/PR, links to top search engines, consulting on a 100% satisfaction guarantee. Free site evaluation marketing checklist (a $250 value) for LMP readers.

Number of titles produced annually: 75 Print

Recent Title(s): *Mail Order Fortunaire*™ (Linick International); *Picture Profits® How to Make Over $75,000 with Your Camera* (NAPS); *Secrets of a Successful Freelance Photographer* (NAPS); *Timeless Copywriting Wisdom*™ (Newsworldpressbooks.com)

Branch Office(s)

7 Lincoln Ave, Smithtown, NY 11787

Membership(s): The Association of Publishers for Special Sales (APSS); The Imaging Alliance

Corporate Graphics Book Printers, see CG Book Printers

Course Crafters Inc
243 Greenleaf Rd, Anson, ME 04911
Mailing Address: PO Box 100, Amesbury, MA 01913
Tel: 207-696-4050
E-mail: info@coursecrafters.com
Web Site: www.coursecrafters.com
Key Personnel
Publr & CEO: Lise B Ragan
Founded: 1993
Consultants & publishers specializing in the English Language Learner (ELL) market. Provides consulting services, professional development & authoring & publishing own materials for English Language Learners to ensure these students' academic success.

Recent Title(s): *Academic Language Notebooks: The Language of Math* (Perfection Learning); *HMH Family Engagement* (Houghton Mifflin Harcourt)

Membership(s): International Literacy Association (ILA); National Association for Bilingual Education; National Council of Teachers of Mathematics (NCTM); TESOL International Association

The Creative Spark
7010 85 Street Ct E, Bradenton, FL 34202
Tel: 941-356-2514
E-mail: info@creativespark.com
Web Site: www.creativespark.com
Key Personnel
Owner & Proj Dir: Mary Francis McGavic *E-mail:* mary@creativespark.com
Traditional hard bound books. Provide design & production through final disc, composed film or finished product. Generation & coordination of mss, editing, photo acquisition, indexing & illustration. School library & children's retail.

Recent Title(s): *Ace It! Information Literacy Series* (Enslow Publishers); *Mighty Math* (The Childs World Inc); *Presidents of the USA* (The Childs World Inc); *A Proud Heritage: Hispanic Library* (The Childs World Inc); *Top Pets for Kids with American Humane* (Enslow Publishers); *Welcome to the World* (The Childs World Inc); *Wild Wheels* (Enslow Publishers)

Delgado & Co Inc
3900 Greystone Ave, Suite 21A, Riverdale, NY 10463
Tel: 718-708-4419

E-mail: mail@delgadoandcompany.com
Web Site: www.delgadoandcompany.com
Key Personnel
Founder & Pres: Lisa Delgado *E-mail:* lisa@delgadoandcompany.com
Founded: 1981
Complete publishing services, including design, copy-editing & paging/prepress.
Number of titles produced annually: 50 Print
Recent Title(s): *Childhood* (Cengage Learning); *Evidence-Based Cardiology* (Wolters-Kluwer); *K-2 Reading Series* (Benchmark Education)

Dell Magazines
Division of Penny Publications LLC
44 Wall St, Suite 904, New York, NY 10005-2401
Tel: 212-686-7188 *Toll Free Tel:* 800-220-7443 (corp sales) *Fax:* 212-480-5751
E-mail: customerservice@pennydellpuzzles.com
Web Site: www.pennydellpuzzles.com
Key Personnel
Pres: Peter Kanter
VP, Edit & Prod Devt: Christine Begley
SVP: Bruce W Sherbow
Sr Art Dir: Victoria Green
Dir, Mktg, E-Commerce & Brand Licensing: Abigail Browning
Founded: 1931
Packaging puzzle books compiled from 26 puzzle magazines & science fiction & mystery anthologies based on stories from 4 fiction magazines: *Alfred Hitchcock Mystery Magazine, Ellery Queen's Mystery Magazine, Asimov's Science Fiction, Analog Science Fiction & Fact.* Provide book packaging services for mass market paperbacks, promotional & trade books.
Number of titles produced annually: 6 Print

Desktop Miracles Inc
112 S Main St, Suite 294, Stowe, VT 05672
Tel: 802-253-7900 *Toll Free Fax:* 888-293-2676
E-mail: info@desktopmiracles.com
Web Site: www.desktopmiracles.com
Key Personnel
Pres & CEO: Barry T Kerrigan *E-mail:* barry@desktopmiracles.com
VP: Virginia Kerrigan *E-mail:* virginia@desktopmiracles.com
Founded: 1994
Full service book design & production studio for publishers large & small. Turnkey services from concept to editorial to design to production.

diacriTech Inc
4 S Market St, 4th fl, Boston, MA 02109
Tel: 617-600-3366 *Fax:* 617-848-2938
Web Site: www.diacritech.com
Key Personnel
EVP: Madhu Rajamani *E-mail:* madhu@diacritech.com
Dir, Prodn & Edit Servs: Maureen Ross *E-mail:* m.ross@diacritech.com
Founded: 1997
Specialize in meeting educational publishing needs. Full service development includes project management, editorial & content development services, print & digital production, art & prepress services. In-house staff of over 800 are experienced with all phases & disciplines of K-12, college & STM. Facilities in Boston, MA, Manchester, NH & in Chennai, Madurai & Kottayam in India.

DWJ BOOKS LLC
14 Hill Side Lane, East Hampton, NY 11937
Tel: 631-267-8270
E-mail: info@dwjbooks.com
Web Site: www.dwjbooks.com

Key Personnel
EVP: Lauren Fedorko *E-mail:* lfedorko@dwjbooks.com
Edit Dir: Darrell Kozlowski
Founded: 1988
Full service content provider of library & general reference, nonfiction textbook.
Membership(s): American Book Producers Association (ABPA); The American Library Association (ALA)

Eriako Associates
1380 Morningside Way, Venice, CA 90291
Tel: 310-392-6537 *Fax:* 310-392-6537
E-mail: eriakoassociates@gmail.com
Key Personnel
CEO: Erika Fabian
Founded: 1972
Create & package illustrated books to invite investment to a country or profile a company, worldwide; travel, photography oriented guides & multicultural children's books based on the culture & customs of a variety of exotic countries. Package books of general interest & self-help.
Recent Title(s): *Driver to Sky; Liars' Paradise; Pro Ways to Great Photos; Stolen Minds* (Eriako Associates); *The Travel Photographer's Handbook* (Eriako Associates)
Membership(s): American Society of Media Photographers (ASMP); Independent Writers of Southern California; Publishers Association of Los Angeles

f-stop Fitzgerald Inc
88 James St, Rosendale, NY 12472
E-mail: fstopf@gmail.com
Key Personnel
CEO: Richard Minissali
Adult trade, travel, reference, sports, biography & photography.
Membership(s): American Book Producers Association (ABPA); Professional Photographers of America (PPA)

Favorite Recipes Press, see Southwestern Publishing House Inc

Figaro
PO Box 848, Sharon, CT 06069
Tel: 860-248-8989; 860-364-0834
E-mail: design@figro.com
Web Site: www.figro.com
Key Personnel
Co-Pres & Creative Dir: Walter Schwarz
Co-Pres: Linda Swenson *E-mail:* ls@figro.com
Copy-editing, design, page make-up, illustration & prepress.
Number of titles produced annually: 20 Print

Focus Strategic Communications Inc
15 Hunter Way, Brantford, ON N3T 6S3, Canada
Tel: 519-756-3265
E-mail: info@focussc.com
Web Site: www.focussc.com
Key Personnel
Dir: Adrianna Edwards *E-mail:* aedwards@focussc.com; Ron Edwards *E-mail:* redwards@focussc.com
Founded: 1988
North American full service book packaging firm providing complete book development & production, from original concept to finished product, both print & digital. Specialize in children's nonfiction books for the trade, library & classroom markets as well as educational materials such as K-12 classroom books & teacher resources. Curriculum experts guide clients in the best approaches to the CCSS & NGSS. Innovative in assembling tailored & creative teams of experts to develop & produce superior products. Excellent track record & reputation.
Number of titles produced annually: 50 Print

Fortunato Book Packaging

Subsidiary of The Chris Fortunato Literary
Agency
500 Angell St, No 203, Providence, RI 02906
Tel: 845-826-3675
Web Site: twitter.com/chrisfortunato
Key Personnel
Owner & Edit Dir: Chris Fortunato
E-mail: cefort20@gmail.com
Founded: 1999
Agent for quality nonfiction, thrillers & literary
novels. Also provides full editorial & produc-
tion packaging services to publishers.
Number of titles produced annually: 3 Print
Recent Title(s): *Blood in the Soil* (Skyhorse);
Gasping for Air (Rowman & Littlefield)

G & H Soho Inc

413 Market St, Elmwood Park, NJ 07407
Tel: 201-216-9400 *Fax:* 201-216-1778
E-mail: print@ghsoho.com
Web Site: www.ghsoho.com
Key Personnel
Pres: Gerry Burstein
Prodn Mgr: Jason Burstein
Founded: 1985
Complete service, beginning with development
through copy-editing & production edit-
ing. Text & cover design. Production service
through bound books. Specialize in short run,
on-demand book manufacturing with variable
data.
Number of titles produced annually: 10 Print
Membership(s): Association of Graphic Commu-
nications; Book Industry Guild of New York;
Digital Printing Council; PRINTING United
Alliance

Garcia Publishing Services

919 Tappan St, Woodstock, IL 60098
Tel: 815-338-5512 *Fax:* 815-338-5512
Web Site: www.gpsdesign.net
Key Personnel
Owner: Robert T Garcia *E-mail:* rgarcia@
gpsdesign.net
CFO: Nancy Garcia
Founded: 1991
Provide editorial, consulting & design services
to presses throughout the US. Design books,
magazines, advertising, catalogs, sell-sheets,
direct-mail pieces, flyers, corporate identity,
etc. As a Mac consultant, analyze businesses'
needs & make recommendations for purchases
& upgrades of hardware & software & provide
on-site support. Manage the work of several
freelance artists & designers during the course
of any given year; create & produce consumer
newsletters for bookstores.
Number of titles produced annually: 12 Print
Recent Title(s): *Tarzan Trilogy* (Edgar Rice Bur-
roughs Inc); *Weinberg Tales* (American Fantasy)

GEX Inc

2 Industrial Way, Atkinson, NH 03811
Tel: 603-870-9292
Web Site: www.gexinc.com
Key Personnel
Pres: Gary Russell
VP: Jim LaPierre; Karla Russell
Founded: 1986
Full service educational publishing services com-
pany, providing content development, digital
& production services to the world's foremost
publishers. With over 30 years of experience,
GEX designs courses, creates engaging content
& provides services that deliver content to a
variety of media with digital & print solutions.

GGP Publishing Inc

105 Calvert St, Suite 201, Harrison, NY 10528-
3138
Tel: 914-834-8896 *Fax:* 914-834-7566
Web Site: www.GGPPublishing.com
Key Personnel
Pres & Publg Dir: Generosa Gina Protano
E-mail: GGProtano@GGPPublishing.com
Founded: 1991
Packager for trade & educational publishers. All
editorial, art & design, production & printing
services—from concept to bound books or any
segment(s) of this publishing process. Trade
(fiction & nonfiction) & children's books, textbooks (el-hi, college & adult education), professional, reference & how-to books, cookbooks, audiotapes, videotapes & CDs. Specialize in the development of materials for the
study of foreign languages (such as French,
German, Italian, Japanese, Latin, Portuguese,
Russian & Spanish) & ESL, as well as in the
development of materials for bilingual education & language arts. In addition, we translate
complete or partial programs from & into the
various languages & act as literary agents &
foreign publisher representatives.

P M Gordon Associates Inc

Affiliate of New Door Books
2115 Wallace St, Philadelphia, PA 19130
Tel: 215-769-2525
Web Site: www.pmgordonassociates.com
Key Personnel
Pres: Peggy M Gordon
VP: Douglas C Gordon *E-mail:* doug@
newdoorbooks.com
Founded: 1982
Complete book production from copy-editing &
design through bound books. Ms development
& writing services also available.
Number of titles produced annually: 15 Print
Recent Title(s): *Foundations of International
Macroeconomics* (MIT Press); *Practical Pul-
monary Pathology* (Elsevier); *Right Off the Bat:
Baseball, Cricket, Literature & Life* (Paul Dry
Books)

Greenleaf Book Group LLC

3 Park Place, 4005 Banister Lane, Suite B,
Austin, TX 78704
Mailing Address: PO Box 91869, Austin, TX
78709
Tel: 512-891-6100 *Fax:* 512-891-6150
E-mail: contact@greenleafbookgroup.com
Web Site: www.greenleafbookgroup.com
Key Personnel
Founder: Clint Greenleaf
CEO: Tanya Hall
CFO: Brian Viktorin
Gen Coun: Sujan Trivedi
Art Dir: Neil Gonzalez
Dir, Consulting: Justin Branch
Dir, Dist: Steve Elizalde
Dir, Mktg & Branding: Corrin Foster
Dir, Prodn: Carrie Jones
Mgr, Busn Devt: Kesley Smith *E-mail:* ksmith@
greenleafbookgroup.com
Founded: 1997
Publisher & distributor specializing in the devel-
opment of independent authors & the growth
of small presses. Our publishing model was de-
signed to support independent authors & allow
writers to retain the rights to their work & still
compete with major publishing houses. We also
distribute select titles from small & independent publishers to major trade outlets, including
bookstores, libraries & airport retailers. We
serve the small & independent publishing community by offering industry guidance, business
development, production, distribution & marketing services.
Number of titles produced annually: 100 Print
Recent Title(s): *The Exceptional Presenter Goes
Virtual*; *The Sandler Rules*; *Venus on Fire,*

Mars on Ice; *Kanye West Presents Thank You
& You're Welcome*
Membership(s): The Association of Publishers
for Special Sales (APSS); Independent Book
Publishers Association (IBPA)

Greenleaf Book Group Press, see Greenleaf
Book Group LLC

Homestead Publishing

Box 193, Moose, WY 83012-0193
Tel: 307-733-6248 *Fax:* 415-621-5039
Key Personnel
Owner & Publr: Carl Schreier
Founded: 1980
Complete book production service; design, layout,
editing, typesetting, marketing & promotion of
high-quality soft & hardcover editions. General
trade books, especially nature, travel, history,
biography, gift, art, children's & photography.
Number of titles produced annually: 12 Print
Recent Title(s): *Banff-Explorers Guide*; *Beaure-
gart the Bear*; *Flames, Friends and the Miracle
in Yellowstone*; *Glacier-Waterton*; *Greetings
from San Francisco*; *Grizzlies in the Mist*; *Hik-
ing Yellowstone Trails*; *Indian Lodge-Fire Stories*; *The Iron Shirt*; *Short Hikes*; *The Virginian*
Branch Office(s)
4388 17 St, San Francisco, CA 94114
Sales Office(s): 4388 17 St, San Francisco, CA
94114

Hourglass Press LLC

39 W 32 St, Suite 1404, New York, NY 10001
Tel: 917-449-3707
Web Site: www.hourglasspress.com
Key Personnel
Pres & Publr: Karen Matsu Greenberg
E-mail: karen@hourglasspress.com
Founded: 2010
Create book-based activity books, packages for
direct sales, publishers & specialty markets including crafts, paper products, kitchen tools,
children's books & illustrated books.
Number of titles produced annually: 10 Print
Recent Title(s): *Gourmet Pizza Made Easy* (Hourglass Press, Sterling Publishing); *Intensely In-
tricate Fractal Art Coloring Book* (Dover Publishing); *The Soldier's Story* (Quarto Publishing); *Thank You Notes for Kids* (Quarto Publishing); *To the Moon* (Laurence King Publishing); *To the Ocean Deep* (Laurence King Publishing); *Traditional Japanese Origami* (Rock
Point Publishing)
Membership(s): American Book Producers Association (ABPA); Book Industry Guild of New
York; Book Industry Study Group (BISG); National Association of Women Business Owners
(NAWBO)

Integra Software Services Inc

Division of Integra Software Services Pvt Ltd
1110 Jorie Blvd, Suite 200, Oak Brook, IL 60523
Tel: 630-586-2579 *Fax:* 630-586-2599
E-mail: marketing@integra.co.in
Web Site: www.integra.co.in
Key Personnel
Dir, Edit Devt: Ingrid Benson *E-mail:* ingrid.
benson@integra.co.in
Design Mgr: Emily Friel *E-mail:* emily.friel@
integra.co.in
Founded: 1991
Project management, development & production support for book publishers. Full range
of publishing services, including developmental editing, design, rights & permissions, photo
research, copy-editing & indexing, proofreading, language polishing, typesetting, XML &
conversion, illustrations & artwork, ebooks &
digital services. Specialty areas are business
& economics, computer science, mathematics,

science, medical, English, education & history texts.

Number of titles produced annually: 150 Print

Recent Title(s): *DK Guide to Public Speaking, 2nd ed* (Ford/Brown); *Horngren's Financial & Managerial Accounting, 4th ed* (Nobles/Horngren); *Intermediate Algebra: A Graphic Approach, 5th ed* (Martin-Gay); *Macroeconomics, 8th ed* (Abel/Bernanke/Croushore); *Math Lit, 1st ed* (Almy/Foes); *Political Science, 13th ed* (Roskin)

Membership(s): Chicago Women in Publishing

Jenkins Group Inc

1129 Woodmere Ave, Suite B, Traverse City, MI 49686

Tel: 231-933-0445 *Toll Free Tel:* 800-706-4636 *Fax:* 231-933-0448

E-mail: info@bookpublishing.com

Web Site: www.bookpublishing.com

Key Personnel

CEO: Jerrold R Jenkins *Tel:* 231-933-0445 ext 1008 *E-mail:* jrj@bookpublishing.com

Pres & COO: James Kalajian *Tel:* 231-933-0445 ext 1006 *E-mail:* jjk@bookpublishing.com

Book Prodn Mgr: Leah Nicholson *Tel:* 231-933-0445 ext 1015 *E-mail:* lnicholson@bookpublishing.com

Mng Ed, Independent Publisher Online: Jim Barnes *E-mail:* jimb@bookpublishing.com

Founded: 1988

Provides complete project management, development & production services for authors, corporations, associations & foundations. We offer a comprehensive range of production & editorial services that include art & text design, ghost-writing, copy-editing, proofreading, research, layout, composition, printing & packaging. Post-production services include fulfillment, distributing, marketing, publicity, consultation & an extensive special market sales program.

Number of titles produced annually: 40 Print

Lachina Precision Graphics Services

3791 S Green Rd, Cleveland, OH 44122

Tel: 216-292-7959

E-mail: info@lachina.com

Web Site: www.lachina.com

Key Personnel

Pres: Jeff Lachina *E-mail:* jeff@lachina.com

Dir, Prodn Servs: Whitney Philipp *E-mail:* wphilipp@lachina.com

Dir, Proj Mgmt Off: Shawn Vazinski *E-mail:* svazinski@lachina.com

Founded: 1978

Full service creative & business consulting agency that helps companies tackle creative, brand & business dilemmas with the right tools, methods & technology.

Number of titles produced annually: 50 Print

Larson Texts Inc

1762 Norcross Rd, Erie, PA 16510

Tel: 814-824-6365 *Toll Free Tel:* 800-530-2355 *Fax:* 814-824-6377

Web Site: www.larsontexts.com

Key Personnel

CEO: Matt Totske

IT Mgr: Kathleen Williams

Sr Researcher: Tim Larson

Founded: 1983

Author & develop educational materials in print, interactive multimedia & web formats for the elementary through college markets with a primary focus on mathematical instruction.

Number of titles produced annually: 5 Print

Layla Productions

370 E 76 St, Apt C-704, New York, NY 10021-2556

Tel: 212-879-6984

E-mail: laylaprod820@gmail.com

Key Personnel

Pres: Lori Stein

Founded: 1981

Complete book production & packaging from idea to bound book; trade books; production & editorial consulting.

Number of titles produced annually: 2 Print

Recent Title(s): *Butterfly Treats & Humming-bird Sweets* (Downtown Bookworks); *Let's Eat* (Rowman & Littlefield); *Master Pieces* (W W Norton & Company Inc); *Materializing The Immaterial* (Yale); *Recipes from America's Small Farms* (Villard)

The Learning Source Ltd

644 Tenth St, Brooklyn, NY 11215

E-mail: info@learningsourceltd.com

Web Site: www.learningsourceltd.com

Key Personnel

Dir: Gary Davis; Wendy Davis

Mng Ed: Brian Ableman

Founded: 1986

Provides a full range of book-producing activities from concept through ms, art & design to film & bound book. Specialty areas include classroom materials & trade reference.

Number of titles produced annually: 150 Print

Membership(s): ASCD; International Literacy Association (ILA); National Council for the Social Studies (NCSS); National Council of Teachers of English (NCTE); National Council of Teachers of Mathematics (NCTM)

The Philip Lief Group (PLG) Inc

2976 Pleasant Ridge Rd, Wingdale, NY 12594

Tel: 609-430-1000 *Fax:* 845-724-7139

E-mail: info@plg.us.com

Web Site: plg.us.com

Key Personnel

Pres: Philip Lief *Tel:* 609-430-1000 ext 108 *E-mail:* pl@plg.us.com

VP & Creative Dir: Sandy Davis *Tel:* 609-430-1000 ext 142

Admin: Megan Misiewicz *Tel:* 609-430-1000 ext 109 *E-mail:* megan@plg.us.com

Founded: 1978

Innovative content developer partnering with many Fortune 500 companies. Provides high impact content that expands & supports brand & publisher goals. Strategically planned books & multimedia from original ideas & client concepts in all areas of nonfiction are developed to generate visibility & drive revenue. Brings together the best minds & creative talent to provide the perfect team for each project. Provides publishing solutions that enhance brand image, educate consumers & drive sales.

Number of titles produced annually: 10 Print

Recent Title(s): *Diet Smoothies: 168 Delicious Recipes* (Science-Smart)

Membership(s): Custom Publishing Council (CPC)

Lifland et al., Bookmakers

442 William St, 2nd fl, Williamsport, PA 17701

Tel: 570-326-4100

E-mail: liflandh@comcast.net

Key Personnel

Partner: Jane Hoover; Sally Lifland

Founded: 1979

Production coordination, developmental editing, copy-editing, author relations, interior design, castoffs, illustration, photo research, proofreading, indexing. College textbooks & professional books.

Number of titles produced annually: 10 Print

Recent Title(s): *The Cosmic Perspective, 8th ed* (Pearson Education/Addison-Wesley); *Remix: Reading & Composing Culture, 3rd ed* (Bedford/St Martin's); *Statistical Reasoning for Everyday Life, 5th ed* (Pearson Education)

Lucia|Marquand

1400 Second Ave, Seattle, WA 98101

Tel: 206-624-2030 *Fax:* 206-624-1821

Web Site: luciamarquand.com

Key Personnel

Partner: Ed Marquand *E-mail:* ed@luciamarquand.com; Adrian Lucia *E-mail:* adrian@luciamarquand.com

Creative Dir: Donna Wingate

Design Dir: Tom Eykemans; Ryan Polich

Edit Dir: Melissa Duffes

Prodn Mgr: Lea Finger

Prodn Coord: Jeremy Linden

Founded: 1983

Art book packaging, editing, design, production; trade books, exhibition catalogs, museum collection handbooks. Develop fine art & illustrated books, delivering bound books or digital files.

Number of titles produced annually: 3 Print

Recent Title(s): *After Whistler: The Artist's Influence on American Painting*; *The Art of Adolfi Wolfli*; *Cherished Possessions: A New England Legacy*; *Manet & The Sea*; *Kara Walker: Pictures From Another Time*

Lumina Datamatics Inc

Affiliate of Datamatics Global Services (Mumbai)

4 Collins Ave, Plymouth, MA 02360

Tel: 508-746-0300 *Fax:* 508-746-3233

Web Site: luminadatamatics.com

Key Personnel

SVP: Jack Mitchell *Tel:* 508-746-0300 ext 203 *E-mail:* jack.mitchell@luminad.com

SVP, Content Technol: John Wheeler *E-mail:* john.wheeler@luminad.com

SVP, Prod Devt: Gordon Laws *E-mail:* gordon.laws@luminad.com

SVP, Sales: Prashant Prabhu *E-mail:* prashant.prabhu@luminad.com

VP, Fin & Acctg: John Chappell *E-mail:* john.chappell@luminad.com

Founded: 1974

Providing full service content creation, design/packaging & media delivery systems to publishers. Services include authoring/writing, editorial research & development, media development & production, editing, photo & text research/permissions, photography/photo shoot direction, indexing, proofreading, fact checking, design/design direction, art direction/editing, technical/illustrative art packages, photo manipulation & page make-up/composition services. Employs over 1,200 US & offshore resources specializing in content/media creation & make-up including file conversions/re-purposing & content management & delivery services. All services are offered both in the US & at offshore facilities. Areas of specialization include school, higher education & professional publishing: mathematics (grade school/algebra/calculus/physics), foreign language (French/Spanish/German/Italian), English & English composition, history, political science, science (chemistry/biology/astronomy), social studies, computer science, business (economics/finance/marketing), engineering & technical trades as well as professional/reference material. Products range from simple 1-color ancillaries components to highly complex design & art intensive core content.

Branch Office(s)

31572 Industrial Rd, Suite 400, Livonia, MI 48150 *Toll Free Tel:* 800-717-9153 *Fax:* 734-525-4455

510 Thornall St Metropark, Suite 100, Edison, NJ 08837 (sales) *Toll Free Tel:* 888-772-5532 *Fax:* 732-635-0600

345 Seventh Ave, 4th fl, New York, NY 10001 *Tel:* 646-453-1000 *Fax:* 212-564-8285

1797 Seddon Ct, Ashland, OH 44805 *Tel:* 419-289-0558 *Fax:* 419-289-8923

3265 Farmtrail Rd, York, PA 17406 *Tel:* 717-764-4000

Datamatics Global Services GmbH doo, Gunduliceva br 33, 78000 Banja Luka, Bosnia and Herzegovina *Tel:* 51304120

Im Leuschner, Park 3, 64347 Griesheim, Germany *Tel:* (06155) 862 99-0 *Fax:* (06155) 862 99-19

Ascendas International Tech Park, Taramani Rd, 12th fl, Phase II, Chennai 600 113, India *Tel:* (044) 6604 6000; (044) 6604 6001; (044) 6604 6002 *Fax:* (044) 6604 6098

Knowledge Ctr, St No 17, MIDC, Andheri (E), Mumbai 400 093, India *Tel:* (022) 6102 0000 *Fax:* (022) 2834 3669

Suyojit Datamatics Knowledge Center, Suyojit IT Park, Survey No 804, Unit No S1-S3, Nashik-Mumbai Hwy, Nashik 422 002, India *Tel:* (0253) 610 2222 *Fax:* (0253) 610 2271

Off No 5, 2nd fl, Tower 1, Stellar IT Park, C-25, Sector 62, Noida 201 301, India *Tel:* (0120) 494 0999

Plot No 29-34, East Coast Rd, Saram Revenue Village, Oulgaret Municipality, Lawspet Post, Puducherry 605 008, India *Tel:* (0413) 660 4500; (0413) 660 4501

March Tenth Inc
24 Hillside Terr, Montvale, NJ 07645
Tel: 201-387-6551 *Fax:* 201-387-6552
Web Site: www.march10th.com
Key Personnel
Pres: Sandra Choron *E-mail:* schoron@aol.com
VP: Harry Choron *E-mail:* hchoron@aol.com
Founded: 1981
Ms to camera-ready art or bound books in all areas of trade publishing (hardcover, trade paper, mass market, including heavily illustrated projects); graphic designs; consulting & editorial. Agenting services available.
Number of titles produced annually: 10 Print
Recent Title(s): *Deep Nutrition* (Flatiron); *Soundbreaking* (Higher Ground); *This is All a Dream We Dreamed* (Flatiron)

Maverick Publications Inc
63324 Nels Anderson Rd, Bend, OR 97701
Mailing Address: PO Box 5007, Bend, OR 97708
Tel: 541-382-6978
E-mail: moreinfo@maverickbooks.com
Web Site: www.maverickbooks.com; www.mavbooks.com
Key Personnel
Owner: Gary Asher
Founded: 1967
Complete book production, ms to fulfillment, including design, computerized phototypesetting, mechanical editing, graphics, photography, laser color separations, layout, proofing, page proofs, printing & binding. Book & author promotional materials. Free consultation on marketing & distribution. Specialize in deluxe trade paperbacks, handcrafted hardbound editions, short, fast production runs.
Number of titles produced annually: 5 Print

Meadows Design Office
3800 Yuma St NW, Washington, DC 20016
Tel: 202-966-6007
E-mail: mdo@mdomedia.com
Key Personnel
Pres & Creative Dir: Marc Meadows *E-mail:* marc@mdomedia.com
Curator & Image Res: Amy Meadows
Founded: 1981
A full service graphic design firm. Design & production of books, book jackets, illustrated books, cookbooks & publications; consultation, art direction, design, layout, type specification & mechanical art. Specialize in trade & textbooks. Conceptualize & prepare mockup covers & compositions & presentations & blads for publishers. State-of-the-art electronic publishing equipment & software. Typeset &

produce multilingual editions of our book designs.
Recent Title(s): *Palace of State: A History of the Eisenhower Executive Office Building* (US Government Printing Office)
Membership(s): AIGA, the professional association for design; Type Directors Club

Melcher Media Inc
124 W 13 St, New York, NY 10011
Tel: 212-727-2322 *Fax:* 212-627-1973
E-mail: info@melcher.com
Web Site: www.melcher.com
Key Personnel
CEO: Charles Melcher
VP, COO: Bonnie Eldon *E-mail:* beldon@melcher.com
Prodn Mgr: Susan Lynch *E-mail:* slynch@melcher.com
Exec Ed: Lauren Nathan *E-mail:* lnathan@melcher.com
Ed: Megan Worman *E-mail:* mworman@melcher.com
Founded: 1994
Innovative content production company, producing innovative, award-winning books, apps, ebooks & other multimedia content on a wide range of subjects including photography, popular culture, art, music, cooking & the environment.
Number of titles produced annually: 20 Print
Recent Title(s): *An Inconvenient Sequel: Truth to Power* (Rodale Books); *Dear Evan Hansen: Through the Window* (Grand Central Publishing); *The Wisdom of Sundays* (Flatiron Books)

Mount Ida Press
111 Washington Ave, Albany, NY 12210-2203
Tel: 518-426-5935 *Fax:* 518-426-4116
E-mail: info@mountidapress.com
Web Site: www.mountidapress.com
Key Personnel
Pres: Diana S Waite
Founded: 1985
Complete book production & marketing plans for associations, corporations, universities, government agencies, public relations firms & small presses. Trade & scholarly books, guides, directories, conference proceedings, journals, premiums, corporate histories, local histories, calendars & commemorative publications.
Number of titles produced annually: 3 Print
Recent Title(s): *Albany Architecture: A Guide to the City*; *Ornamental Ironwork: Two Centuries of Craftmanship in Albany & Troy, NY*; *The President as Architect*

Mountain Lion Inc
9 Voorhees Ct, Pennington, NJ 08534
Mailing Address: PO Box 799, Pennington, NJ 08534
Tel: 609-730-1665
E-mail: mtlion@me.com
Web Site: www.mtlioninc.net
Key Personnel
Pres: John J Monteleone *Tel:* 609-468-2661 (cell)
Founded: 1983
Book producer & packager. Deliver mss, photos, mechanical, disk or finished books. Consulting to publishing industry, associations & businesses; create books for adult trade, juvenile, educational & professional book market. Specialize in general reference, sports, health, fitness, how-to, children, trade & education, business & professional subjects. Also provide editing, marketing, production & direct sales; literary agency specializing in authors who write primarily about sports.
Number of titles produced annually: 6 Print

Norfleet Press Inc
PO Box 91, Bovina, NY 13740

Tel: 607-832-4749
Key Personnel
Pres: John Graham Tucker *E-mail:* jgtnor@aol.com
Founded: 1987
Fine large-format illustrated books on architecture, design, photography, travel, wine; will deliver finished books to publishers with whom we work.
Recent Title(s): *A Simpler Way of Life: Old Farmhouses of New York & New England* (Norfleet Press); *The Berkshires* (Norfleet Press); *The Finger Lakes of New York* (Norfleet Press); *Toward a Simpler Way of Life: The Arts & Crafts Architects of California* (University of California Press)

Online Training Solutions Inc (OTSI)
16794 Santanella St, San Diego, CA 92127
Toll Free Tel: 888-308-6874
E-mail: biz@otsi.com
Web Site: www.otsi.com
Key Personnel
Pres: Joan Lambert
Educational & professional book publishing services.
Membership(s): Women's Business Enterprise National Council

OTTN Publishing
16 Risler St, Stockton, NJ 08559
Tel: 609-397-4005 *Toll Free Tel:* 866-356-6886 *Fax:* 609-397-4007
E-mail: inquiries@ottnpublishing.com; sales@ottnpublishing.com
Web Site: www.ottnpublishing.com
Key Personnel
Publr: Jim Gallagher *E-mail:* jgallagher@ottnpublishing.com
Founded: 1998
Provides a full range of editorial services, from developing book or series ideas to providing a finished product all at a reasonable price. This allows the publisher to avoid the cost of maintaining a large editorial staff, thereby freeing up resources for promotion, sales & distribution. Our in-house staff includes writers, editors, photo researchers, graphic artists, proofreaders & indexers.
Number of titles produced annually: 40 Print
Recent Title(s): *Girls Guides* (Eldorado Ink); *Scientists and Their Discoveries* (Mason Crest Publishers)

Parachute Publishing LLC
Division of Parachute Properties LLC
157 Columbus Ave, Suite 518, New York, NY 10023
Tel: 212-691-1422
Key Personnel
Chmn & CEO: Joan Waricha *E-mail:* jwaricha@parachuteproperties.com
Chair: Jane Stine *E-mail:* jstine@parachuteproperties.com
Founded: 1983
Children's & adult fiction & nonfiction: original books & series, books from licensed properties, coloring books & other licensed merchandise.
Number of titles produced annually: 100 Print
Membership(s): American Book Producers Association (ABPA); The Children's Book Council (CBC)

Mel Parker Books LLC
75 Prospect Park West, 6B, Brooklyn, NY 11215
Tel: 212-982-8215
E-mail: info@melparkerbooks.com
Web Site: melparkerbooks.com
Key Personnel
Pres: Mel Parker *E-mail:* mel@melparkerbooks.com
Founded: 2004

Book producer & literary agent for a full range of trade books: business, health, psychology, spirituality, reference, memoir/biography, narrative, nonfiction, pop culture & fiction.
Number of titles produced annually: 8 Print
Recent Title(s): *The American Medical Association Complete Guide to Prevention & Wellness* (Wiley); *Date-onomics* (Workman Publishing); *Helping the Addict You Love* (Fireside/Simon & Schuster); *Leading from the Middle* (Putnam); *Locavesting* (John Wiley & Sons Inc); *The Loyalist Team* (Public Affairs/Hachette); *The New Digital Age* (Alfred A Knopf); *Not Built in a Day* (Da Capo Press); *Now I Know Who My Comrades Are* (Sarah Crichton Books/Farrar, Straus & Giroux); *One Minute Manners* (Broadway/Doubleday); *Structure House Weight Loss Plan* (Fireside/Simon & Schuster); *Unlatched* (Harper Perennial); *The Vertical Farm* (Thomas Dunne Books/St Martin's Press)

Generosa Gina Protano Publishing, see GGP Publishing Inc

Publishing Resources Inc
425 Carr 693, PMB 160, Dorado, PR 00646
Tel: 787-647-9342
E-mail: pri@chevako.net
Key Personnel
Pres: Ronald J Chevako
EVP & Ed: Anne W Chevako
Prodn: Jay A Chevako
Founded: 1982
Complete book preparation, from ms development through electronic publishing. Trade books; full editorial services, including translation & indexing. Design & art services; US trained professionals.
Number of titles produced annually: 3 Print

The Pushpin Group Inc
38 W 26 St, New York, NY 10010
Tel: 212-529-7590
Web Site: www.pushpininc.com
Key Personnel
Co-Founder, Pres & Dir: Seymour Chwast
E-mail: seymour@pushpininc.com
Founded: 1954
Full service book design & production, from concept to mechanicals. Handle a variety of genres, from graphic design texts & reference to children's books. Specialize in heavily illustrated books.
Recent Title(s): *At War With War* (7 Stories Press); *Bobo's Smile* (Creative Education); *Dante's Divine Comedy* (Boonesberry); *Get Dressed!* (Abrams); *Mr Merlin & the Turtle* (Greenwillow); *Moonride* (Houghton Mifflin Company); *My Daddy & Me* (Knopf Children's Books)

QBS Learning
242 W 30 St, Suite 900, New York, NY 10001
Tel: 929-841-5969
E-mail: sales@qbslearning.com
Web Site: www.qbslearning.com
Key Personnel
CEO: Hanut Singh *E-mail:* hanut.singh@qbslearning.com
COO, ADP: Brian Kobberger *E-mail:* brian.kobberger@qbslearning.com
EVP, Content Devt: Jane Petlinski *E-mail:* jane.petlinski@qbslearning.com
VP, Busn Devt: Michael Porter *E-mail:* michael.porter@qbslearning.com
Group HR Dir: Reggie Chua Singh
E-mail: reggie.singh@qbslearning.com
Founded: 1983 (as Bill Smith Group)
Full service partner for educational publishers & instructional technology firms. More than 60 professionals in New York & Austin creating

programs in American education. Provide end-to-end publishing solutions for early childhood through higher education publishing: both print & eMedia. Editorial, design, photo services & illustration, production & prepress, digital media.
Number of titles produced annually: 1,000 Print
Recent Title(s): *Big Day* (Scholastic); *Environmental Science* (Houghton Mifflin Harcourt); *Everything Weather* (National Geographic); *Lead21* (McGraw-Hill); *Science Fusion* (Houghton Mifflin Harcourt)

Quadrata Inc
15 Byron St, Wakefield, MA 01880
Tel: 781-245-1183 *Fax:* 781-246-9040
Key Personnel
Pres: Martha Morong *E-mail:* morong@rcn.com
Founded: 1985
Editorial, production services; college & general books.
Number of titles produced annually: 5 Print
Membership(s): Bookbuilders of Boston

Renaissance House
Imprint of Laredo Publishing Co
465 Westview Ave, Englewood, NJ 07631
Tel: 201-408-4048
Web Site: www.renaissancehouse.net
Key Personnel
Pres: Sam Laredo *E-mail:* laredo@renaissancehouse.net
VP & Exec Ed: Raquel Benatar *E-mail:* raquel@renaissancehouse.net
Founded: 1991
A full service book producer that takes projects through the conceptual, editorial & production stages that include the finished book. Short & long runs. Fine stock illustrations available. Specialize in highly illustrated children's books, multicultural projects (ESL, SSL, bilingual) & educational materials. Specializes in Spanish & French. Represents more than 80 illustrators specializing in children's books & multicultural projects. Editorial, translation, art, design & production services. Contact us for rights & availability.
Number of titles produced annually: 50 Print
Recent Title(s): *A Lime Says It's Time for a Pickle; An Honest Boy; The Ant and the Grasshopper; Chef Aiden & the Corn Maze; Daisy's New Day; Extraordinary People; The Flightless Adventures of Princess and Pearl; Go, Milka, Go! The Life of Milka Duno; Grandma's Garden; HippoDuck, Trouble at the Airport; I Do Not Want This on My Plate; The Icky, Sticky Tea Party; It's Snowing Gold; Magical Animals; Mother Oak; My Abuela is Sick; Peacock Blues; Postcard from Copenhagen; Postcard from London; Rabbit in the City or Turtle in the Park; Stories of the Americas; Super Jack; Super Smart Dog; There's Really No Way to Defunk a Skunk; Yes, You Can Too! The Life of Barack Obama*

Roundtable Press Inc
20 E Ninth St, New York, NY 10003
Tel: 917-597-2183
Web Site: www.roundtablepressinc.com
Key Personnel
Pres & Dir: Marsha Melnick *E-mail:* marsha@roundtablepressinc.com
Founded: 1981
Complete development of illustrated & non-illustrated nonfiction books; series & continuity programs; custom books for direct mail publishers, corporations & associations. Ideas developed with authors or clients. Specialize in trade books & popular reference on art & design, decorating & architecture, cooking, crafts, gardening, home improvement, health & fitness, nature & wildlife, American history, me-

dia tie-ins, popular culture, women's interests & parenting. Provide electronic files or bound books. Editorial & publishing consultants.
Number of titles produced annually: 10 Print
Membership(s): American Book Producers Association (ABPA)

Scarf Press
1385 Baptist Church Rd, Yorktown Heights, NY 10598
Tel: 914-245-7811
Key Personnel
Owner: Mark L Levine *E-mail:* mlev@pipeline.com
Founded: 1979
Originate projects & deliver copy-edited ms on computer disks. Specialize in religious & reference books, trade books, premiums.
Recent Title(s): *The Complete Book of Bible Quotations; Negotiating a Book Contract: A Guide for Authors, Agents & Lawyers*

Schenkman Books Inc
145 Bethel Mountain Rd, Rochester, VT 05767
Mailing Address: PO Box 119, Rochester, VT 05767
Tel: 802-767-3104
E-mail: schenkmanbooks@gmail.com
Web Site: www.schenkmanbooks.com
Key Personnel
Pres: Joe Schenkman
VP & Penstroke Press Publr: Kathryn Schenkman
E-mail: kms@penstrokepress.com
Founded: 1961
Academic nonfiction books.

Scribe Inc
842 S Second St, Philadelphia, PA 19147
Tel: 215-336-5094 *Fax:* 215-336-5092
E-mail: contact@scribenet.com
Web Site: www.scribenet.com
Key Personnel
Pres: David Alan Rech *E-mail:* drech@scribenet.com
Founded: 1993
A full range of publishing services, including OCR/data conversion, editing, proofreading, design, typesetting, & ebook creation, with expertise in XML, Well-Formed Document Workflow, & staff training. Also helps publishers do multipurpose publishing.
Number of titles produced annually: 1,200 Print
Branch Office(s)
7540 Windsor Dr, Suite 200B, Allentown, PA 18195
3758 SW 30 Ave, Fort Lauderdale, FL 33312

Shoreline Publishing Group LLC
125 Santa Rosa Place, Santa Barbara, CA 93109
Tel: 805-564-1004 *Toll Free Fax:* 800-840-6713
Web Site: shorelinepublishing.com
Key Personnel
Edit Dir: James Buckley, Jr *E-mail:* jbuckley@shorelinepublishing.com
Design Consultant: Thomas J Carling
Founded: 1999
Number of titles produced annually: 60 Print
Recent Title(s): *Animal Planet Animal Atlas* (Time Inc/Liberty Street); *Football Superstars 2017* (Beach Ball Books); *Scholastic Book of Sports 2017* (Scholastic); *Who Was Jules Verne?* (Penguin/Grosset & Dunlap)
Membership(s): American Book Producers Association (ABPA)

Sideshow Media LLC
315 St Johns Place, 1G, Brooklyn, NY 11238
Tel: 917-519-5335
E-mail: inquiries@sideshowbooks.com
Web Site: main.sideshowbooks.com
Key Personnel
Founding Partner: Daniel Tucker
E-mail: dtucker@sideshowbooks.com

Founded: 2000
Full service print & digital book developer, producer & agent. Specialize in the visual & performing arts, history, pop culture & travel.
Recent Title(s): *Citizen Woman* (Prestel); *The Hamilton Collection* (Black Dog & Leventhal/Hachette); *The Lincoln Notebooks* (Black Dog & Leventhal/Hachette); *The Only Way Out is Through* (Blue Sky/Bonnier); *Subversive Cross Stitch Coloring & Activity Book* (Blue Sky/Bonnier)

Smallwood & Stewart Inc
5 E 20 St, New York, NY 10003
Tel: 212-505-3268 *Fax:* 212-505-3624
Web Site: www.smallwoodandstewart.com
Key Personnel
Pres: John Smallwood *E-mail:* johnsmallwood@smastew.com
Founded: 1980
Complete packaging of popular reference books, illustrated trade books & sidelines; producer of international co-editions. Specialize in decorating & design, home how-to, food & wine, weddings. Ideas developed with authors, editors & private clients. Custom publishing.
Number of titles produced annually: 10 Print
Recent Title(s): *American Wine* (University of California Press)
Membership(s): American Book Producers Association (ABPA)

Southwestern Publishing House Inc
2451 Atrium Way, Nashville, TN 37214
Toll Free Tel: 800-358-0560 *Fax:* 615-391-2815
E-mail: info@swpublishinggroup.com
Web Site: www.swpublishinggroup.com
Key Personnel
Pres: Christopher Capen *E-mail:* ccapen@swpublishinggroup.com
Founded: 1855
Custom book packager.
Number of titles produced annually: 40 Print
Membership(s): International Association of Culinary Professionals (IACP)

Stonesong
270 W 39 St, Suite 201, New York, NY 10018
Tel: 212-929-4600
E-mail: editors@stonesong.com
Web Site: www.stonesong.com
Key Personnel
Partner & Literary Agent: Alison Fargis
Partner & Prodn Servs: Ellen Scordato
EVP & Literary Agent: Judy Linden
Contracts Mgr & Literary Agent: Madelyn Burt
Literary Agent: Leila Campoli; Melissa Edwards; Alyssa Jennette; Emmanuelle Morgan; Maria Ribas; Adrienne Rosado
Assoc Literary Agent: Kim Lindman
Founded: 1979
Representing nonfiction & fiction, including middle grade, young adult & adult titles. Create & develop commercial nonfiction & popular reference books on many subjects: cooking, business, how-to, self-help, memoir, beauty & fashion. Complete trade hardcover, paperback & ebook development, from concept to delivery. Consultants on backlist exploitation, acquisitions, publicity planning & editorial systems. Custom publishing for professional associations & magazines.
Recent Title(s): *A Lady's Guide to Etiquette and Murder* (Kensington); *ALFA Series* (InterMix); *Become an American Ninja Warrior* (St Martin's Press); *Color Me Floral: Stunning Monochromatic Arrangements for Every Season* (Chronicle Books); *Coloring in the Lions: Vintage Art from the Archives of The New York Public Library* (Holt); *The Cooks Atelier: Recipes, Techniques, and Stories from our French Cooking School* (Abrams); *Dosa*

Kitchen: Recipes for India's Favorite Street Food (Clarkson Potter); *Favorite Recipes from Melissa Clark's Kitchen: Family Meals, Festive Gatherings, and Everything In-between* (Black Dog & Leventhal/Hachette); *Get Off Your Acid: 7 Steps in 7 Days to Lose Weight, Fight Inflammation, and Reclaim Your Health and Energy* (Da Capo Lifelong Books); *Hardcore Carnivore: Cook Meat Like You Mean It* (Agate Surrey); *Hottest Heads of State* (Holt); *How to Get Sh*t Done: Why Women Need to Stop Doing Everything so They Can Achieve Anything* (North Star Way); *Italian Moms: Something Old, Something New* (Sterling Epicure); *Leaving Everest* (CreateSpace Independent Publishing Platform); *Love and Estrogen* (Amazon Original Stories); *Love and Lemons Meal Record and Market List* (Clarkson Potter); *The Memory of Forgotten Things* (Aladdin); *The Million-Dollar, One-Person Business: Make Great Money. Work the Way You Like. Have the Life You Want.* (Lorena Jones Books); *The Music of the Deep* (Lake Union Publishing); *Next is Now* (North Star Way); *On Pills and Needles: The Relentless Fight to Save My Son from Opiod Addiction* (Baker Books); *Once Upon a Chef, the Cookbook: 100 Tested, Perfected, and Family-Approved Recipes* (Chronicle Books); *The One-Bottle Cocktail* (Ten Speed Press); *Paris in Stride: An Insider's Walking Guide* (Rizzoli); *Pokemon GO! The Ultimate Unauthorized Guide*; *Pug Pals: Two's a Crowd* (Scholastic Press); *The Restaurant Diet: How to Eat Out Every Night and Still Lose Weight* (Mango); *Ruined Series* (Harper Teen); *Simply Vibrant: All-Day Vegetarian Recipes for Colorful Plant-Based Cooking* (Roost Books); *The Sister's Grimm Series: 10th Anniversary Edition* (Amulet Paperbacks); *Sweet Laurel: Recipes for Whole Food, Grain-Free Desserts* (Clarkson Potter); *The Vintage Baker* (Chronicle Books); *To Kill a Kingdom* (Feiwel & Friends); *When Likes Aren't Enough: A Crash Course in the Science of Happiness* (Grand Central Life & Style); *Where I Live* (Harper Teen); *Words That Built a Nation: Voices of Democracy That Have Shaped America's History* (Rodale Kids/Penguin Random House); *The World According to Rick* (Hachette)
Membership(s): American Book Producers Association (ABPA)

Story Monsters LLC
4696 W Tyson St, Chandler, AZ 85226-2903
Tel: 480-940-8182 *Fax:* 480-940-8787
Web Site: www.StoryMonsters.com
Key Personnel
Pres: Linda F Radke *E-mail:* Linda@StoryMonsters.com
Founded: 1985
Produce & market books.
Number of titles produced annually: 10 Print
Recent Title(s): *Jamie's Journey: Cancer from the Voice of a Sibling*; *Story Monster and Friends*; *Three Clever Coyote Pups*
Membership(s): Better Business Bureau (BBB); The Children's Book Council (CBC); Independent Book Publishers Association (IBPA); National Federation of Press Women

Studio 31 Inc
2740 SW Martin Downs Blvd, Suite 358, Palm City, FL 34990
Tel: 772-781-7195 *Fax:* 772-781-6044
Web Site: www.studio31.com
Key Personnel
Founder & Pres: James Wasserman *E-mail:* jim@studio31.com
Partner: Bill Corsa
Founded: 1977
Book production & design, including text, cover, project development, printing & editorial services.

Number of titles produced annually: 16 Print
Recent Title(s): *AHA!* (Aleister Crowley); *An Illustrated History of the Knights Templar* (James Wasserman); *The Egyptian Book of the Dead: The Book of Going Forth by Day* (Chronicle Books); *The Egyptian Book of the Dead: The Papyrus of Ani* (Chronicle Books); *Home Groan - A Pun for Everyone* (Carroll & Graf Publishers); *Moser Glass: The Klabin Collection* (Healing Wisdom Publications); *The Mystery Traditions* (James Wasserman); *Pyphagoras: His Life & Teaching* (Ibis Press); *Sacred Journey: A Pilgrimage to the Stations of the Cross in Jerusalem* (Nicolas Hays); *Secret Societies* (Una Birch); *Secrets of Masonic Washington* (James Wasserman); *The Temple of Solomon: Ancient Israel to Secret Societies* (James Wasserman)

Sweetgrass Books
Division of Farcountry Press
2750 Broadway Ave, Helena, MT 59602
Mailing Address: PO Box 5630, Helena, MT 59604
Tel: 406-422-1255 *Toll Free Tel:* 800-821-3874
Web Site: sweetgrassbooks.com
Key Personnel
Dir, Pubns: Kathy Springmeyer *E-mail:* kathy@farcountrypress.com
Custom publishing division of Farcountry Press. Professional editorial, design, production, print management & distribution services.
Number of titles produced annually: 34 Print

Tabby House
PO Box 544, Mineral, VA 23117
Tel: 540-895-5355
E-mail: tabbyhouse@gmail.com
Web Site: www.tabbyhouse.com
Key Personnel
Publr: Jim Salisbury
Founded: 1990
Full service, long & short runs, trade, hardcover, softcover; emphasis on developing quality products to fit its market (coffee table & children's books). Development & copy-editing, proofreading, cover design, typesetting, printing & binding, publishing.
Recent Title(s): *The Best Fried Chicken: Poems by Denny Burdette* (Tabby House); *I Call My "Child" Mom: Laughter, Joys and Tears of an Alzheimer's Companion* (Maxie Books); *Roadkill Round-up* (Tabby House); *The Sword and the Broom: The Exceptional Career and Accomplishments of John Mercer Langston* (Tabby House); *The War Years 1943-1945: George H Marshall* (Tabby House); *What Could Go Wrong? (A Bailey Fish Adventure, Book II)* (Tabby House); *What Happened to Joan?: A Haydn and Speaker Mystery* (Deernasus Publishing)
Membership(s): Florida Authors & Publishers Association Inc (FAPA)

Taylor Specialty Books
Division of Balfour/Taylor
1550 W Mockingbird Lane, Dallas, TX 75235
Tel: 214-819-8588 (cust serv) *Fax:* 214-819-5051 (cust serv) *Toll Free Fax:* 800-203-9778
E-mail: rfq@taylorpub.com (estimates)
Web Site: www.taylorspecialtybooks.com
Key Personnel
VP, Sales & Mktg, Specialty Books: Rick Parra *Tel:* 214-819-5027 *E-mail:* rick.parra@balfour.com
Sales Rep: Kim Hawley *E-mail:* khawley@taylorpub.com; George Levesque *E-mail:* glevesque@taylorpub.com; Mark McCombs *E-mail:* mmcombs@taylorpub.com
Founded: 1939
TSB is a full service book & catalog manufacturer specializing in 4-color case bound books:

juvenile, medical, trade, coffee table, oblong
trims & 4-color catalogs. Full in-house bindery
& case stamping/embossing capabilities with a
"Can Do!" attitude.
Number of titles produced annually: 4,600 Print

To Press & Beyond
825 E Pedregosa St, Suite 2, Santa Barbara, CA
93103
Tel: 805-898-2263
E-mail: info@topressandbeyond.com
Web Site: www.topressandbeyond.com
Key Personnel
Owner & Pres: Gail M Kearns *E-mail:* gail@
topressandbeyond.com
Partner: Penelope C Paine *E-mail:* pennypaine@
aol.com
Founded: 2001
Book publishing consulting & support services.
We shepherd your print +/or ebook through
writing, editing, design & layout, printing, dis-
tribution, sales & marketing & promotion, both
in trade & niche markets & on the Web. We
have worked with over 400 authors & inde-
pendent publishers worldwide. You can contact
Gail Kearns for a half-hour gratis phone con-
sult about your project.
Number of titles produced annually: 15 Print
Recent Title(s): *Best Foot Forward* (Booker
Press); *Courageous Gilbert the Groundhog*
(Blue Stone Healing Books); *Dad's War Photos*
(Cypress Cove Publishing); *Flossie Flies Home*
(Paper Posie); *Genocide: A Darcy McClain
and Bullet Thriller* (Thunder Glass Press); *Go-
ing to the Park* (Bowie Books); *The Gourmet
Girls Go Camping Cookbook* (Mise en Press);
Green Is Good (Bowie Books); *Happier You*
(Pralle Publishing); *Hidden Valley Homestead*
(7 Cross Productions); *I Love Books* (Zee Zee
Books); *The Journey of Not Knowing: How
21st Century Leaders Can Chart a Course
Where There Is None* (Morton Hill Press);
Journeys: Healing Through Nature's Wisdom
(Tim Hauf Photography); *Lust, Men, and Meth*
(Healing Path Press); *Night Buddies Go Sky
High* (Dune Buggy Press); *Only the Dead*
(Tremonto Press); *Splinters of Glass* (Soul At-
titude Press); *TubeLight* (Janet Rendall); *When
Miracles Aren't Enough* (Burro Publishing);
Write! Find the Truth in Your Fiction (CreateS-
pace)
Membership(s): The Association of Publishers
for Special Sales (APSS); Independent Book
Publishers Association (IBPA)

VanDam Inc
The VanDam Bldg, 121 W 27 St, New York, NY
10001
Tel: 212-929-0416 *Toll Free Tel:* 800-UNFOLDS
(863-6537) *Fax:* 212-929-0426
E-mail: info@vandam.com

Web Site: www.vandam.com
Key Personnel
Pres/Creative Dir: Stephan Van Dam *Tel:* 212-
929-0416 ext 10 *E-mail:* stephan@vandam.com
Dir, Opers: Jessy Cerda *Tel:* 212-929-0416 ext 16
E-mail: jessy@vandam.com
Design & Prodn: Eamonn Fitzmaurice *Tel:* 212-
929-0416 ext 17 *E-mail:* eamonn@vandam.com
R&D: Jon Tyillian *Tel:* 212-929-0416 ext 13
E-mail: jontyillian@vandam.com
VP, Soc Media: Patricia Grant *Tel:* 212-929-0416
ext 11 *E-mail:* patricia.grant@vandam.com
Founded: 1985
Publisher, licensor & developer of UNFOLDS®,
@tlas® & StreetSmart® brand maps, UN-
FOLDS® maps & book formats, extra-
dimensional reference, travel & educational
media; designer of multimedia reference in na-
ture & science; designs & produces new multimedia book formats, direct mail premiums &
custom specialties for publishers, government
agencies & financial services companies.
Recent Title(s): *Brooklyn@tlas*; *Manhattan@tlas*;
NY@tlas; *StreetSmart Boston*; *StreetSmart NY*;
StreetSmart Washington, DC
Membership(s): American Book Producers Association (ABPA)

Victory Productions Inc
55 Linden St, Worcester, MA 01609
Tel: 508-755-0051
E-mail: victory@victoryprd.com
Web Site: www.victoryprd.com
Key Personnel
Founder & CEO: Victoria Porras *E-mail:* victoria.
porras@victoryprd.com
Exec Dir: Neil Saunders
Deputy Exec Dir & CFO: Raul Porras
Dir, Busn Devt: Charles Hartford *E-mail:* charles.
hartford@victoryprd.com; Dan Souers
E-mail: danner.souers@victoryprd.com
Dir, Educ Technol: Haris Papamichael
Dir, Prod Devt: Joel Gendler *E-mail:* joel.
gendler@victoryprd.com
Dir, Strategic Technol: Owen Lawlor
Develops K-16 products for 21st century students. Content specialists develop STEM,
ELA, ELL, social studies & modern language
programs, high-stakes assessment items, performance tasks, knowledge graphs, Spanish
content in all curriculum areas & translations
in multiple languages. Instructional designers & digital learning experts develop online
courses & interactive activities, including sim-
ulations, technology enhanced items (TEIs),
complex digital learning objects (CDLOs) &
games. metacog™, a Victory spinoff, instruments digital-learning objects to collect, analyze, record & report student data in easily un-
derstood visualizations. For more information,
visit victoryprd.com & metacog.com.

VKH Media Resources
122 S Oneida Ave, Rhinelander, WI 54501
Tel: 715-369-4535
Web Site: www.victoriahouston.com
Key Personnel
Author: Victoria Houston *Tel:* 715-499-6800
(cell) *E-mail:* vhouston@charter.net
Founded: 1996
Package trade books; nonfiction; fly-fishing, hunt-
ing, gardening & nature; mysteries.
Number of titles produced annually: 1 Print
Recent Title(s): *Dead Loudmouth* (Gallery Books/
Simon & Schuster); *Dead Spider* (Gallery
Books/Simon & Schuster)
Membership(s): The Authors Guild; Mystery
Writers of America (MWA)

Welcome Enterprises Inc
Imprint of Welcome Enterprises
6 W 18 St, Unit 4B, New York, NY 10011
Tel: 212-989-3200 *Fax:* 212-989-3205
E-mail: info@welcomeenterprisesinc.com
Web Site: www.welcomeenterprisesinc.com
Key Personnel
Pres: Clark Wakabayashi *E-mail:* clark@
welcomeenterprisesinc.com
Publr: Lena Tabori *E-mail:* lena@
welcomeenterprisesinc.com
Founded: 1980
Complete book production from concept to deliv-
ery of bound books. Specialize in visual books
of all kinds for trade, hardcover & softcover;
art, gift, photography/illustration, how-to. Ser-
vices include packaging, agenting & distribu-
tion.
Number of titles produced annually: 20 Print
Recent Title(s): *Avedon at Work: In the Ameri-
can West* (University of Texas Press); *Grand-
mother Remembers: A Written Heirloom for
My Grandchild* (Stewart, Tabori & Chang);
New York, New York (Rizzoli); *The Toy Story
Films* (Disney Press)
Membership(s): American Book Producers Association (ABPA)

Wiley-Blackwell
111 River St, Hoboken, NJ 07030-5774
Tel: 201-748-6000 *Fax:* 201-748-6088
E-mail: info@wiley.com
Web Site: www.wiley.com
Medical meeting management & complete medical publishing facilities, from editing to marketing & worldwide distribution. Consultants
available for all types of medical publications
& symposia.

**John Wiley & Sons Inc Scientific, Technical,
Medical & Scholarly (STMS)**, see
Wiley-Blackwell

Publishing Systems, Services & Technology Index

HARDWARE

CD-ROM MASTERING

CD ROM Inc, pg 1374
CD Solutions Inc, pg 1374
Disc Makers, pg 1376
DSM Producers Inc, pg 1376
Hedquist Productions Inc, pg 1378
Imago, pg 1379
LG Electronics USA, pg 1380
Lumina Datamatics Inc, pg 1380
Microboards Technology Inc,
  pg 1381
OneTouchPoint, pg 1383
Scribe Inc, pg 1385
Sony DADC US Inc, pg 1385

DISPLAY DEVICES

alfa CTP Systems Inc, pg 1372
Alps Alpine North America Inc,
  pg 1372
ASC Systems, pg 1373
AZTEK Inc, pg 1373
Canvys® Visual Technology
  Solutions, pg 1374
Cenveo Publisher Services, pg 1374
Copywriters' Council of America™
  (CCA), pg 1375
Dell Wyse, pg 1376
Dotronix Technology Inc, pg 1376
Eizo Inc, pg 1376
Envision Peripherals Inc (EPI),
  pg 1377
HP Inc, pg 1378
Infocus® Corp, pg 1379
Kontron America Inc, pg 1380
LG Electronics USA, pg 1380
Matrox Graphics Inc, pg 1381
Planar, pg 1383
Rex Three Inc, pg 1384
Samsung Research America (SRA),
  pg 1385
Sceptre Inc, pg 1385
Scribe Inc, pg 1385
Sony Electronics Inc, pg 1385
Tamron USA Inc, pg 1386
Tatung Co of America Inc, pg 1386
Taylor Communications Inc,
  pg 1386
Unisys Corp, pg 1387
Victoria Productions Inc, pg 1387
VITEC Multimedia, pg 1387
Z-Axis, pg 1388

INPUT DEVICES

Agfa Graphics, pg 1372
alfa CTP Systems Inc, pg 1372
Alps Alpine North America Inc,
  pg 1372
ASC Systems, pg 1373
AZTEK Inc, pg 1373
BDT Products Inc, pg 1373
CD ROM Inc, pg 1374
Cenveo Publisher Services, pg 1374
Copywriters' Council of America™
  (CCA), pg 1375
Dynabook Americas Inc, pg 1376
Fujitsu Computer Products of
  America Inc, pg 1377
GTCO Calcomp, pg 1378
HP Inc, pg 1378
IMSI/Design LLC, pg 1379

Kensington Technology Group,
  pg 1380
Kontron America Inc, pg 1380
Lumina Datamatics Inc, pg 1380
Nissho Electronics USA Corp,
  pg 1382
Rex Three Inc, pg 1384
Scribe Inc, pg 1385
Tamron USA Inc, pg 1386
TEACH Services Inc, pg 1386
3M Touch Systems Inc, pg 1386
Videx Inc, pg 1387
VITEC Multimedia, pg 1387

INTERFACES

Aaron Marcus and Associates Inc,
  pg 1371
Agfa Graphics, pg 1372
alfa CTP Systems Inc, pg 1372
Apple Inc, pg 1372
Aptara Inc, pg 1373
ASC Systems, pg 1373
AZTEK Inc, pg 1373
Cenveo Publisher Services, pg 1374
Copywriters' Council of America™
  (CCA), pg 1375
Data Connect/RelComm Inc,
  pg 1375
Envision Peripherals Inc (EPI),
  pg 1377
HP Inc, pg 1378
Kontron America Inc, pg 1380
OneTouchPoint, pg 1383
Rex Three Inc, pg 1384
RISO Inc, pg 1385
Scribe Inc, pg 1385
TEACH Services Inc, pg 1386

MODEMS

Apple Inc, pg 1372
Cenveo Publisher Services, pg 1374
Clerical Plus, pg 1374
Copywriters' Council of America™
  (CCA), pg 1375
Data Connect/RelComm Inc,
  pg 1375
HP Inc, pg 1378
Kontron America Inc, pg 1380
Lumina Datamatics Inc, pg 1380
Multi-Tech Systems Inc, pg 1382
Rex Three Inc, pg 1384
Scribe Inc, pg 1385
Western Telematic Inc (WTI),
  pg 1388

OCR

Alps Alpine North America Inc,
  pg 1372
Cenveo Publisher Services, pg 1374
Copywriters' Council of America™
  (CCA), pg 1375
DocuWare Corp, pg 1376
HP Inc, pg 1378
Nuance Communications Inc,
  pg 1382
Pivar Computing Services Inc,
  pg 1383
Scribe Inc, pg 1385
SENCOR International, pg 1385
TEACH Services Inc, pg 1386

PHOTOTYPESETTERS

Agfa Canada Inc, pg 1371
alfa CTP Systems Inc, pg 1372
Cenveo Publisher Services, pg 1374
Copywriters' Council of America™
  (CCA), pg 1375
Rex Three Inc, pg 1384
Scribe Inc, pg 1385

PLATFORMS

Agfa Graphics, pg 1372
Apple Inc, pg 1372
ASC Systems, pg 1373
Cenveo Publisher Services, pg 1374
Copywriters' Council of America™
  (CCA), pg 1375
HP Inc, pg 1378
IBM Corp, pg 1378
NETS, pg 1382
Oracle America Inc, pg 1383
Sceptre Inc, pg 1385
Scribe Inc, pg 1385
Victoria Productions Inc, pg 1387

PRINTERS (LASER & NON-IMPACT)

Advantage Laser Products Inc,
  pg 1371
Agfa Canada Inc, pg 1371
alfa CTP Systems Inc, pg 1372
AlphaGraphics Inc, pg 1372
Alps Alpine North America Inc,
  pg 1372
Mark Andy Inc, pg 1372
Apple Inc, pg 1372
AZTEK Inc, pg 1373
BDT Products Inc, pg 1373
Cenveo Publisher Services, pg 1374
Citizen Systems America Corp,
  pg 1374
Clerical Plus, pg 1374
Copywriters' Council of America™
  (CCA), pg 1375
Delphax Solutions Inc, pg 1376
Fairfield Marketing Group Inc,
  pg 1377
Figaro, pg 1377
GEI WideFormat, A Visual Edge
  Technology Company, pg 1378
HID Global, pg 1378
HP Inc, pg 1378
Kroy LLC, pg 1380
OKI Data Americas Inc, pg 1382
Printronix Inc, pg 1383
Printware LLC, pg 1384
Rex Three Inc, pg 1384
Ricoh Americas Corp, pg 1384
Rimage Corp, pg 1385
RISO Inc, pg 1385
Scribe Inc, pg 1385
Sharp Electronics Corp, pg 1385
Star Micronics America Inc,
  pg 1386
Taylor Communications Inc,
  pg 1386
TEACH Services Inc, pg 1386
UniNet Imaging Inc, pg 1387
Xante Corp, pg 1388

SCANNERS & DIGITIZERS

Agfa Canada Inc, pg 1371
Agfa Graphics, pg 1372
alfa CTP Systems Inc, pg 1372
Alps Alpine North America Inc,
  pg 1372
Mark Andy Inc, pg 1372
AZTEK Inc, pg 1373
Cenveo Publisher Services, pg 1374
Copywriters' Council of America™
  (CCA), pg 1375
The Crowley Co, pg 1375
ECRM Imaging Systems, pg 1376
Figaro, pg 1377
Fujitsu Computer Products of
  America Inc, pg 1377
GEI WideFormat, A Visual Edge
  Technology Company, pg 1378
GTCO Calcomp, pg 1378
HP Inc, pg 1378
iCAD Inc, pg 1379
Kroy LLC, pg 1380
Megavision Inc, pg 1381
Nissho Electronics USA Corp,
  pg 1382
OneTouchPoint, pg 1383
Rex Three Inc, pg 1384
Ricoh Americas Corp, pg 1384
RISO Inc, pg 1385
SCREEN Americas, pg 1385
Scribe Inc, pg 1385
Sharp Electronics Corp, pg 1385
TEACH Services Inc, pg 1386
Videotex Systems Inc, pg 1387
Videx Inc, pg 1387

OTHER

Alliance Storage Technologies Inc
  (ASTI), pg 1372
CD ROM Inc, pg 1374
Copywriters' Council of America™
  (CCA), pg 1375
The Crowley Co, pg 1375
Data Connect/RelComm Inc,
  pg 1375
DisplayMate Technologies Corp,
  pg 1376
Dukane Corp, Audio Visual
  Products Division, pg 1376
Follett School Solutions Inc,
  pg 1377
GEI WideFormat, A Visual Edge
  Technology Company, pg 1378
GTCO Calcomp, pg 1378
OMRON Microscan Systems Inc,
  pg 1383
PrimeArray Systems Inc, pg 1383
Scribe Inc, pg 1385
Star Micronics America Inc,
  pg 1386
Tatung Co of America Inc, pg 1386
WeWrite LLC, pg 1388

SOFTWARE

AD PLACEMENT

Conway Greene Co, pg 1374
Copywriters' Council of America™
  (CCA), pg 1375
DSM Producers Inc, pg 1376

Publishing Systems, Services & Technology

Companies that offer publishing systems, services or technology are listed alphabetically. Entries include company name and address, phone numbers, and personnel to contact to receive further information on products & services. The descriptions of company products and services are paid components.

Preceding this section is a classified index that identifies entrants by specialization. This index is divided into four major categories; Hardware, Software, Systems and Services. The categories are further subdivided by the type of hardware, software or systems produced (for example Input Devices and Page Composition) or the service provided. Company names may appear under more than one category.

A&L Express Corp
PO Box 790733, San Antonio, TX 78279-0733
Tel: 210-262-6633
E-mail: sales@arts-letters.com; support@arts-letters.com
Web Site: www.arts-letters.com

Aaron Marcus and Associates Inc
1196 Euclid Ave, Berkeley, CA 94708-1640
Tel: 510-599-3195 (cell) *Fax:* 510-527-1994
Web Site: www.bamanda.com
Key Personnel
Principal: Aaron Marcus *E-mail:* aaron.marcus@bamanda.com
Founded: 1982
Membership(s): AIGA, the professional association for design; Association for Computing Machinery (ACM); Special Interest Group for Computer Human Interaction (SIGCHI); User Experience Professionals Association (UXPA)

Aatrix Software Inc
2100 Library Circle, Grand Forks, ND 58201
Tel: 701-746-6801; 701-746-6814 (Windows); 701-746-6017 (MacIntosh) *Toll Free Tel:* 800-426-0854 (sales) *Fax:* 701-746-4393
E-mail: sales@aatrix.com; support@aatrix.com
Web Site: www.aatrix.com
Key Personnel
Pres & CEO: Steve Lunseth
Founded: 1986

ACCUMEN Book®, see CyberWolf® Inc

AccuWeather Inc
385 Science Park Rd, State College, PA 16803
Tel: 814-235-8600; 814-237-0309
E-mail: salesmail@accuweather.com; support@accuweather.com
Web Site: www.accuweather.com; corporate.accuweather.com
Key Personnel
Founder & CEO: Dr Joel N Myers *Tel:* 814-235-8537 *E-mail:* joel.myers@accuweather.com
COO: Evan Myers *Tel:* 814-235-8505
E-mail: evan.myers@accuweather.com
CFO: Edward Arditte *Tel:* 814-235-8650
E-mail: ed.arditte@accuweather.com
CTO: Chris Patti *Tel:* 814-235-8694
E-mail: chris.patti@accuweather.com
Pres: Steven Smith *Tel:* 814-235-8695
E-mail: steven.smith@accuweather.com
VP, Busn Servs & Gen Mgr, Enterprise Solutions: Jonathan Porter *Tel:* 814-235-8681
E-mail: jonathan.porter@accuweather.com
Founded: 1962
Branch Office(s)
100 N Broadway, Suite 750, Wichita, KS 67202
Tel: 316-266-8000
250 Greenwich St, Manhattan, NY 10006
Tel: 212-554-4750

ACD Systems International Inc
129-1335 Bear Mountain Pkwy, Victoria, BC V9B 6T9, Canada
Toll Free Tel: 800-949-1457

E-mail: sales@acdsee.com
Web Site: www.acdsee.com
Founded: 1994

Ace Pro Inc, see Progressive Publishing Services (PPS)

Acxiom
301 E Dave Ward Dr, Conway, AR 72032
Toll Free Tel: 888-322-9466
Web Site: www.acxiom.com
Key Personnel
CEO: Chad Engelgau
Founded: 1997
Branch Office(s)
1901 Butterfield Rd, Suite 900, Downers Grove, IL 60515
100 W 33 St, 10th fl, New York, NY 10001
River Place Corporate Park 3, 6500 River Place Blvd, Bldg 3, Suite 300, Austin, TX 78730

Adobe Systems Inc
345 Park Ave, San Jose, CA 95110-2704
Tel: 408-536-6000 *Fax:* 408-537-6000
Web Site: www.adobe.com
Key Personnel
Chmn, Pres & CEO: Shantanu Narayen
EVP & CFO: John Murphy
EVP & Chief Mktg Offr: Ann Lewnes
EVP & Gen Mgr, Digital Experience: Anil Chakravarthy
EVP & Gen Mgr, Digital Media: Bryan Lamkin
EVP, Creative Cloud & Chief Prod Offr: Scott Belsky
EVP, Employee Experience & Chief HR Offr: Gloria Chen
EVP, Gen Coun & Corp Secy: Dana Rao
EVP, Strategy & Growth & CTO: Abhay Parasnis
EVP, Worldwide Field Opers: Matt Thompson
Branch Office(s)
1250 53 St, Emeryville, CA 94608 *Tel:* 510-817-6300
3640 Holdrege Ave, Los Angeles, CA 90016
601 Townsend St, San Francisco, CA 94103
Tel: 415-832-2000 *Fax:* 415-832-2020
100 Hooper St, San Francisco, CA 94107
Tel: 415-832-4700
901 Mariners Island Blvd, San Mateo, CA 94404
429 Santa Monica Blvd, Suite 222, Santa Monica, CA 90401 *Tel:* 310-633-2631
707 17 St, Denver, CO 80202
300 New Jersey Ave NW, Washington, DC 20001
420 N Wabash Ave, Suite 700, Chicago, IL 60611 *Tel:* 312-764-5598
7878 Diamondback Dr, College Park, MD 20742
One Broadway, Cambridge, MA 02142
One Newton Place, 3rd fl, Newton, MA 02458
Tel: 617-766-2360
3900 Northwoods, 3rd fl, Arden Hills, MN 55112
Tel: 651-766-4700 *Fax:* 651-766-4750
275 Fair St, Kingston, NY 12401
1540 Broadway, 17th fl, New York, NY 10036
Tel: 212-471-0904 *Fax:* 212-471-0990
100 Fifth Ave, New York, NY 10011 *Tel:* 212-597-0504
114 Fifth Ave, 9th fl, New York, NY 10011
Tel: 646-264-9101

1500 SW First Ave, Portland, OR 97201
Tel: 503-889-2800
11501 Domain Dr, Suite 110, Austin, TX 78758
316 W 12 St, Austin, TX 78701
3900 Adobe Way, Lehi, UT 84043 *Tel:* 385-345-0000
1300 W Traverse Pkwy, Lehi, UT 84043
7930 Jones Branch Dr, 5th fl, McLean, VA 22102
Tel: 571-765-5400 *Fax:* 571-765-5450
801 N 34 St, Seattle, WA 98103 *Tel:* 206-675-7000
830 Fourth Ave S, Suite 400, Seattle, WA 98134
Tel: 206-675-7600
343 Preston St, Ottawa, ON K1S 1N4, Canada
Tel: 613-940-3676 *Fax:* 613-594-8886
225 King St W, 14th fl, Toronto, ON M5V 3M2, Canada *Tel:* 613-940-4134
281 Ruben Dario, 11580 Mexico, CDMX, Mexico *Tel:* (0155) 5283-2401 *Fax:* (0155) 5281-3384
Membership(s): Association of American Publishers (AAP)

Advantage Laser Products Inc
1840 Marietta Blvd NW, Atlanta, GA 30318
Tel: 404-351-2700 *Toll Free Tel:* 800-722-2804 (cust serv) *Fax:* 404-351-0911
Toll Free Fax: 800-871-3305
E-mail: sales@advlaser.com
Web Site: www.advlaser.com
Key Personnel
Pres: Brian Chaney *E-mail:* brian@advlaser.com
VP, Sales & Cust Serv: John Miller
E-mail: john@advlaser.com
Founded: 1987

AdvantageCS
3850 Ranchero Dr, Ann Arbor, MI 48108
Tel: 734-327-3600 *Fax:* 734-327-3620
E-mail: sales-na@advantagecs.com
Web Site: www.advantagecs.com
Key Personnel
VP: Daniel D Heffernan
Mktg Dir: Cynthia M Twiss *Tel:* 734-327-3651
E-mail: cindy.twiss@advantagecs.com
Founded: 1979
BISAC compatible software
Membership(s): Association for Audience Marketing Professionals (AAMP); Media & Content Marketing Association (MCMA); Society for Scholarly Publishing (SSP); World Association of News Publishers (WAN-IFRA)

Agfa Canada Inc
5975 Falbourne St, Unit 2, Mississauga, ON L5R 3V8, Canada
Tel: 905-361-6982 *Toll Free Tel:* 800-540-2432
Fax: 905-502-9360
E-mail: can.customercare@agfa.com (orders)
Web Site: www.agfa.com/printing/worldwide/north-south-america/canada
Founded: 1867
Branch Office(s)
250 First Gulf Blvd, Brampton, ON L6W 4T5, Canada (dist ctr)

Agfa Graphics
611 River Dr, Center 3, Elmwood Park, NJ 07407
Tel: 201-440-2500 *Toll Free Tel:* 888-274-8626
(cust serv)
E-mail: customercare.us@agfa.com
Web Site: agfagraphics.us
Key Personnel
Dir, Mktg: Deborah Hutcheson *E-mail:* deborah.
hutcheson@agfa.com
Branch Office(s)
10798 Catawba Ave, Fontana, CA 92337 (dist ctr)
2240 Winton Ave, Hayward, CA 94545 (warehouse)
14303 Moncrieff Place, Suite C, Aurora, CO
80011 (dist ctr)
2544 E Landstreet Rd, Suite 100, Orlando, FL
32824 (dist ctr)
665 Raco Dr, Suite C, Lawrenceville, GA 30046
(sales/dist ctr)
800 Bilter Rd, Aurora, IL 60502 (warehouse)
Riverway West, 9399 W Higgens Rd, Suite
130W, Rosemont, IL 60018 (sales)
200 Ballardvale St, Wilmington, MA 01887
(sales/R&D)
2650 Second St NE, Minneapolis, MN 55418
(dist ctr)
22 Stauffer Industrial Park, DC5, Taylor, PA
18517 (dist ctr)
3450 Roy Orr Blvd, Grand Prairie, TX 75050
(dist ctr)

AGS
Subsidiary of RR Donnelley
4590 Graphics Dr, White Plains, MD 20695
Tel: 301-843-1800 *Fax:* 301-843-6339
E-mail: info@ags.com
Web Site: www.ags.com
Key Personnel
Pres: Mike Donohue *E-mail:* mike.donohue@rrd.
com
VP, Sales & Mktg: Alan Flint *E-mail:* aflint@ags.
com
Founded: 1975
Membership(s): American Society of Association
Executives (ASAE)

alfa CTP Systems Inc
Member of IPA Group
2503 Spring Ridge Dr, Unit D, Spring Grove, IL
60081
Tel: 815-474-7634
E-mail: info@alfactp.com
Web Site: www.alfactp.com
Key Personnel
CFO: Karen McAndrew
Pres: Tony Ford
VP, Opers: Keith Roeske *E-mail:* keith.roeske@
alfactp.com
Founded: 2007
Branch Office(s)
229 Billerica Rd, Suite 4, Chelmsford, MA
01824-3632 (headquarters) *Tel:* 603-689-1101
Fax: 978-689-0870

Alliance Storage Technologies Inc (ASTI)
10045 Federal Dr, Colorado Springs, CO 80908
Tel: 719-593-7900 *Toll Free Tel:* 888-567-6332
Fax: 719-598-3472
E-mail: sales@astiusa.com; info@astiusa.com
Web Site: www.alliancestoragetechnologies.com
Key Personnel
CEO: Chris Carr
VP, Prod Devt: Tim Summers
Admin Dir: Fran Rogers
Worldwide Dir, Sales & Mktg: Bill Gallagher
Founded: 2003

Allied Vaughn
7600 Parklawn Ave, Suite 300, Minneapolis, MN
55435
SAN: 920-8089
Tel: 952-832-3100 *Toll Free Tel:* 800-323-0281
Fax: 952-832-3203
Web Site: www.alliedvaughn.com
Key Personnel
CEO: E David Willette
CTO: James Laib *E-mail:* jim.laib@alliedvaughn.
com
Pres: Doug Olzenak
VP, Busn Devt: Mike Haney *E-mail:* mike.
haney@alliedvaughn.com
VP, Retail Mgmt: Cindy Verant *E-mail:* cindy.
verant@alliedvaughn.com
VP, Sales & Mktg: Richard Skillman
E-mail: richard.skillman@alliedvaughn.com
Branch Office(s)
901 Bilter Rd, Suite 150, Aurora, IL 60502, Gen
Mgr: Rick Polizzi *Tel:* 630-626-0215 *Toll
Free Tel:* 800-759-4087 *Fax:* 630-892-2672
E-mail: rick.polizzi@alliedvaughn.com
11923 Brookfield, Livonia, MI 48150, Gen
Mgr: Chris Barkoozis *Tel:* 734-462-5543 *Toll
Free Tel:* 800-462-5543 *Fax:* 734-462-4004
E-mail: chris.barkoozis@alliedvaughn.com

Allusion Studios & Pure Wave Audio
Division of Allusion Enterprises
248 W Elm St, Tucson, AZ 85705
Tel: 520-622-3895
E-mail: contact@allusionstudios.com
Web Site: www.allusionstudios.com; www.
purewaveaudio.com
Key Personnel
Owner & Operator: Jim Pavett

AlphaGraphics Inc
Division of MBE Worldwide
143 Union Blvd, Suite 650, Lakewood, CO 80228
Toll Free Tel: 800-955-6246 *Fax:* 801-595-7270
E-mail: contactus@alphagraphics.com
Web Site: www.alphagraphics.com
Key Personnel
CEO: Paolo Fiorelli
CFO: Camden Hodge
Pres, COO & CTO: Ryan Farris
Gen Coun: Kathleen Panek
VP, Franchise Devt: Bill McPherson
VP, HR: McKenzie Perez
VP, Mktg: Stephanie Johnson
VP, Network Sales & Opers: Tom Kennedy
VP, Purch: Cory Sawatzki
VP, Technol: Ira Shapiro
Founded: 1970

Alps Alpine North America Inc
Subsidiary of Alps Alpine Co Ltd
3151 Jay St, Suite 101, Santa Clara, CA 95054
Tel: 408-361-6400; 408-226-7301 *Fax:* 408-980-
9945; 408-226-7301
E-mail: alps-pr@jp.alps.com
Web Site: www.alpsalpine.com/na
Key Personnel
Pres: Toshihiro Kuriyqua
Founded: 1948
Branch Office(s)
1500 Altantic Blvd, Auburn Hills, MI 48326
Tel: 248-391-9950 *Fax:* 248-391-2500
4312 Tuller Rd, Dublin, OH 43017 *Tel:* 614-336-
1400 *Fax:* 614-336-1426
7100 International Pkwy, Suite 100, McAllen, TX
78503 *Tel:* 956-217-6500 *Fax:* 956-994-1400
2509 152 Ave NE, Suite MEZZ-D, Redmond,
WA 98052 *Tel:* 425-242-0343 *Fax:* 425-896-
8616

AM+A, see Aaron Marcus and Associates Inc

American Artist Studio
1114 W 26 St, Erie, PA 16508-1518
Mailing Address: PO Box 131, Erie, PA 16512-
0131
Tel: 814-455-4796 *Toll Free Tel:* 888-462-7813
Web Site: americanartiststudio.com
Key Personnel
Owner: Skip Niebauer *E-mail:* skipniebauer@
gmail.com
Founded: 1972

The American Audio Prose Library Inc
PO Box 842, Columbia, MO 65205
Tel: 573-449-7075
E-mail: aaplinc@centurytel.net
Key Personnel
Dir: Kay Callison
Founded: 1980

American Blackguard Inc
PO Box 680686, Franklin, TN 37068-0686
Tel: 615-599-4032
E-mail: contact@americanblackguard.com
Web Site: www.americanblackguard.com
Key Personnel
Pres & CEO: Clay Stafford
CFO: Jacqueline Stafford

Amgraf Inc
1501 Oak St, Kansas City, MO 64108-1424
Tel: 816-474-4797 *Toll Free Tel:* 800-304-4797
(sales & mktg) *Fax:* 816-842-4477
E-mail: support@amgraf.com
Web Site: www.amgraf.com
Key Personnel
Pres & CEO: Frank Garner, III
VP, Software Devt: Robert Kisel
Chief Design Engr: Huver Hu
Major Accts Sales Mgr: Raymond L Garner
Mfg Mgr: Jonathan Garner
Training & Documentation Mgr: Debra Poll
Founded: 1976
Membership(s): Business Forms Management As-
sociation (BFMA); DSA; NASPO INTERNA-
TIONAL; Print Services & Distribution Asso-
ciation (PSDA); Public Retirement Information
Systems Management (PRISM)

Mark Andy Inc
18081 Chesterfield Airport Rd, Chesterfield, MO
63005
Tel: 636-532-4433 *Toll Free Tel:* 800-447-1231
Toll Free Fax: 800-447-1231
Web Site: www.presstek.com; markandy.com;
shop.markandy.com
Key Personnel
VP, Offset Busn: Stuart Gallup
Dir, MAPP Offset Sales, North America: Ralph
Jenkins
Dir, Presstek EAMER: Ian Pollock

AOC, see Envision Peripherals Inc (EPI)

Apple Inc
One Apple Park Way, Cupertino, CA 95014
Tel: 408-996-1010
Web Site: www.apple.com
Key Personnel
CEO: Tim Cook
COO: Jeff Williams
SVP & CFO: Luca Maestri
SVP & Gen Coun: Katherine Adams
SVP, Hardware Engg: Dan Riccio
SVP, Hardware Technol: Johnny Srouji
SVP, Internet Software & Servs: Eddy Cue
SVP, Machine Learning & AI Strategy: John Gi-
annandrea
SVP, Opers: Sabih Khan
SVP, Retail & People: Deidre O'Brien
SVP, Software Engg: Craig Federighi
SVP, Worldwide Mktg: Philip W Schiller
VP, Corp Devt: Adrian Perica
VP, Environment, Policy & Social Initiatives: Lisa
Jackson
VP, Mktg Communs: Tor Myhren

Aptara Inc
Subsidiary of iEnergizer
2901 Telestar Ct, Suite 522, Falls Church, VA
  22042
Tel: 703-352-0001
E-mail: moreinfo@aptaracorp.com
Web Site: www.aptaracorp.com
Key Personnel
Pres: Samir Kakar
EVP, Fin & Cont: Prashant Kapoor
SVP, Busn & Contact Ctr Opers: Ashish Madan
Sr Dir, Edit: David George
Busn Devt: Michael Scott *E-mail:* michael.scott@
  aptaracorp.com
Founded: 1988
Branch Office(s)
150 California St, Suite 301, Newton, MA 02458
  Tel: 617-423-7755
11009 Metric Blvd, Bldg J, Suite 150, Austin,
  TX 78758 *Tel:* 512-876-5997
299 Elizabeth St, Level 1, Sydney 2000, Australia
  Tel: (02) 8251 0070
Tower 1 & 2, 8/100, Acharya Thulasi Rd (Shandy
  Rd), Pallavaram, Chennai 600 043, India
  Tel: (044) 22640676
No 2310, Doon Express Business Park, Saharan-
  pur Rd, Bldg 2000, Dehradun 248 002, India
  Tel: (0135) 2644055
7B, Leela Infopark, Technopark, Trivandrum,
  Kerala 695 581, India *Tel:* (047) 14063370
A-37, Sector-60, Noida 201 301, India
  Tel: (0120) 7182424
D-10, Sector-2, Noida 201 301, India *Tel:* (0120)
  24423678
SEZ Bldg 4A, 1st fl, S P Infocity, Pune Saswad
  Rd, Phursungi, Pune 412 308, India *Tel:* (020)
  66728000

Aquent LLC
101 W Elm St, Suite 300, Conshohocken, PA
  19428-2075
Tel: 610-828-0900 *Toll Free Fax:* 877-303-5224
E-mail: questions@aquent.com
Web Site: aquentstudios.com; aquent.com
Key Personnel
Mgr: Kelly Griffin
Founded: 1986

Arrow Graphics Inc
PO Box 380291, Cambridge, MA 02238
E-mail: info@arrow1.com
Web Site: www.arrow1.com
Key Personnel
Pres: Alvart Badalian
Sr Graphic/Pubn Designer: Aramais Andonian
Founded: 1988

Art Related Technology Inc
4 Brattle St, Rm 305, Cambridge, MA 02138
Tel: 617-661-1225 *Fax:* 617-491-0618
E-mail: artinc@artrelated.com
Web Site: www.artrelated.com
Key Personnel
Art Dir: Marvin Mortee

ASC Systems
Mack Place, B-566, St Clair Shores, MI 48080
Tel: 313-882-1133
E-mail: ascsystemss@live.com
Web Site: www.sites.google.com/site/
  ascsystemsusi
Key Personnel
Systems Mgr: R Martin
Founded: 1977
BISAC compatible software

Association for PRINT Technologies (APTech)
1896 Preston White Dr, Reston, VA 20191
Tel: 703-264-7200 *Fax:* 703-620-0994
E-mail: aptech@aptech.org
Web Site: www.printtechnologies.org

Key Personnel
Pres: Thayer Long *E-mail:* thayer_long@aptech.
  org
VP, Mktg & Communs: Sarah Markfield
  E-mail: smarkfield@aptech.org
Dir, Mktg & Communs: Jane Pratt
  E-mail: jpratt@aptech.org
Founded: 1933
Membership(s): American Society of Association
  Executives (ASAE); Council of Manufactur-
  ing Associations; International Association of
  Exhibitions and Events® (IAEE); National As-
  sociation of Manufacturers (NAM)

Autodesk Inc
111 McInnis Pkwy, San Rafael, CA 94903
Tel: 415-507-5000 *Fax:* 415-507-5100
Web Site: www.autodesk.com
Key Personnel
Pres & CEO: Andrew Anagnost
Founded: 1982

AutoGraph International Inc (AGI)
2500 Wilcrest Dr, Suite 324, Houston, TX 77042
Mailing Address: 650 W Bough Lane, Suite 150-
  117, Houston, TX 77024
Tel: 713-954-4848
E-mail: sales@myeasycopy.com
Web Site: myeasycopy.com
Founded: 1989

Automated Graphic Systems, see AGS

Avanti Computer Systems Ltd
Division of Ricoh Co Ltd
251 Consumers Rd, Suite 600, Toronto, ON M2J
  4R3, Canada
Tel: 416-445-1722 *Toll Free Tel:* 800-482-2908
  Fax: 416-445-6319
E-mail: askavanti@avantisystems.com
Web Site: www.avantisystems.com
Key Personnel
VP, Sales: John Alden
Gen Mgr: Duncan Ellis
Founded: 1984
Membership(s): Association for Print Technolo-
  gies (APTech); Epicomm; International Co-
  operation for Integration of Processes in Pre-
  press, Press & Postpress Organization (CIP4);
  National State Printing Association (NSPA);
  PRINTING United Alliance

Avery Dennison Corp
207 N Goode Ave, 6th fl, Glendale, CA 91203-
  1222
Tel: 626-304-2000
Web Site: www.averydennison.com
Key Personnel
Chmn of the Bd, Pres & CEO: Mitch Butier
SVP & CFO: Greg Lovins
SVP & Chief HR Offr: Anne Hill
SVP, Gen Coun & Secy: Sue Miller
VP & CIO: Nick Colisto
VP, Strategy & Corp Devt: Danny Allouche
Founded: 1935
Branch Office(s)
224 Industrial Rd, Fitchburg, MA 01420 *Tel:* 508-
  383-0511 *Fax:* 508-879-4259

Azalea Software Inc
PO Box 16660, Seattle, WA 98116-0660
Tel: 206-341-9500; 206-336-9559 (software sup-
  port); 206-336-9575 (sales & info) *Fax:* 206-
  299-5600
E-mail: salesinfo@azaleabarcodes.com
Web Site: www.azaleabarcodes.com
Key Personnel
Founder: Jerry Whiting
Pres: Miranda Pinero
Sales & Support: Scotty Carreiro
Founded: 1992

AZTEK Inc
13765-F Alton Pkwy, Irvine, CA 92618
Tel: 949-770-8787
E-mail: mail@aztek.com
Web Site: www.aztek.net
Founded: 1980

BCC Software Inc
75 Josons Dr, Rochester, NY 14623-3494
Toll Free Tel: 800-453-3130; 800-337-0442
  (sales)
E-mail: marketing@bccsoftware.com
Web Site: www.bccsoftware.com
Key Personnel
CFO: Eric Narowski
Pres: Chris Lien
VP, Opers: Jim Mann
VP, Prod Strategy: Shawn Ryan
VP, Sales: Marcus Banks
Founded: 1978

BDT Products Inc
Division of BDT Media Automation GmbH
250 E Rincon St, Suite 101, Corona, CA 92879
Tel: 949-263-6363
Key Personnel
CEO: David St Clair *Tel:* 949-263-6363 ext 101
Founded: 1979

BH Communications
115 E Ninth St, Unit 17-F, New York, NY 10003
Tel: 212-982-6502
Web Site: www.bhcommunications.com
Key Personnel
Principal: Brice Hammack *E-mail:* brice@
  bhcommunications.com
Membership(s): AIGA, the professional associa-
  tion for design; American Association of Uni-
  versity Presses (AAUP)

Biblical Archaeology Society
4710 41 St NW, Washington, DC 20016-1705
Tel: 202-364-3300 *Toll Free Tel:* 800-221-4644
  Fax: 202-364-2636
E-mail: info@biblicalarchaeology.org
Web Site: www.biblicalarchaeology.org
Key Personnel
Publr: Susan Laden
Mng Ed: Megan Sauter
Ed: Robert R Cargill
Prodn Mgr: Heather Metzger *Tel:* 202-364-3300
  ext 236
Founded: 1974

BJU Press
Unit of BJU Education Group
1430 Wade Hampton Blvd, Greenville, SC 29609-
  5046
SAN: 223-7512
Tel: 864-546-4600 *Toll Free Tel:* 800-845-5731
E-mail: bjupinfo@bjupress.com
Web Site: www.bjupress.com
Key Personnel
Pres: Bill Apelian

Brainworks Software
100 S Main St, Sayville, NY 11782
Tel: 631-563-5000 *Toll Free Tel:* 800-755-1111
  Fax: 631-563-6320
E-mail: info@brainworks.com; sales@brainworks.
  com; support@brainworks.com
Web Site: www.brainworks.com
Key Personnel
CEO: John Barry

BroadVision
Division of Aurea Inc
460 Seaport Ct, Suite 102, Redwood City, CA
  94063
Tel: 650-331-1000
Web Site: www.broadvision.com

Key Personnel
Pres, CEO & Chmn of the Bd: Dr Pehong Chen
VP & Gen Mgr, Global Servs: Stefano Gargioli
VP, Engg: Yuk Chan
VP, Sales: Fadi Micaelian
Founded: 1993
Branch Office(s)
255 Bear Hill Rd, Waltham, MA 02451 *Tel:* 781-290-0710

Burmar Technical Corp
106 Ransom Ave, Sea Cliff, NY 11579
Tel: 516-484-6000 *Fax:* 516-484-6356
Web Site: burmar.net
Key Personnel
Pres: Norma Novotny *E-mail:* norma.novotny@burmar.net
VP: Christine Jensen *E-mail:* christine.jensen@burmar.net

Canon USA Inc
One Canon Park, Milville, NY 11747
Tel: 516-328-5000; 631-330-5000
Web Site: www.usa.canon.com
Key Personnel
Pres & CEO: Kazuto Ogawa

Canvys® Visual Technology Solutions
Division of Richardson Electronics
40W267 Keslinger Rd, LaFox, IL 60147
Mailing Address: PO Box 393, LaFox, IL 60147-0393
Toll Free Tel: 888-735-7373 *Fax:* 630-208-2350
Web Site: www.canvys.com
Key Personnel
EVP & Gen Mgr: Jens Ruppert
VP, Global Engg: Brian Blanchett
Founded: 1992
Branch Office(s)
753 Forest St, Suite 100, Marlborough, MA 01752 *Tel:* 508-460-5400 *Toll Free Tel:* 800-291-1344 *Fax:* 508-460-5470

CD ROM Inc
3131 E Riverside Dr, Fort Myers, FL 33916
Tel: 239-332-2800 *Toll Free Tel:* 866-66-CDROM (662-3766) *Fax:* 239-332-2808
E-mail: sales@cdrominc.com
Web Site: www.cdrominc.com
Key Personnel
Owner & Pres: Roger Hutchison
Founded: 1988

CD Solutions Inc
100 W Monument St, Pleasant Hill, OH 45359
Mailing Address: PO Box 536, Pleasant Hill, OH 45359-0536
Tel: 937-676-2376 *Toll Free Tel:* 800-860-2376 *Fax:* 937-676-2478
E-mail: contact@cds.com
Web Site: www.cds.com
Key Personnel
Pres: Jerry Warner *E-mail:* jerryw@cds.com
Founded: 1993
Membership(s): International Disc Duplicating Association (IDDA)

CD/Works
Division of Zerious Electronic Publishing Corp
30 Doaks Lane, Marblehead, MA 01945
Tel: 978-922-4990 *Toll Free Tel:* 800-CDWORKS (239-6757) *Fax:* 978-922-5110
Web Site: www.cdworks.com
Key Personnel
Pres: Jeffrey Starfield *E-mail:* jbs@cdworks.com
Founded: 1993
Membership(s): International Disc Duplicating Association (IDDA)

Cenveo Publisher Services
555 Virginia Dr, Fort Washington, PA 19034

Tel: 267-470-1590 *Fax:* 215-591-9093
E-mail: info.psg@cenveo.com
Web Site: www.cenveopublisherservices.com
Key Personnel
CFO: John Pennie
Pres: Atul Goel
VP, Journal Publg Servs: Debbie McClanahan
VP, Learning Solutions: Waseem Andrabi
VP, Media & Intl Delivery Ctr: Dwayne Reed
Dir, Mktg: Mike Groth *E-mail:* mike.groth@cenveo.com
Founded: 1998
Branch Office(s)
3575 Hempland Rd, Lancaster, PA 17601 *Tel:* 717-285-9095
5457 Twin Knolls Rd, Suite 200, Columbia, MD 21045 *Tel:* 410-850-0500 *Toll Free Tel:* 800-257-5529
2905 Byrdhill Rd, Richmond, VA 23228
No 31 Kempapura, Hebbal, Bangalore 560 024, India *Tel:* (080) 4000 4888
36 Barnaby Rd, Kilpauk, Chennai, Tamil Nadu 600 010, India *Tel:* (044) 4205 8888
Marwah Ctr, 5th fl, Krishanlal Marwah Marg, Andheri East, Mumbai 400 072, India *Tel:* (022) 4098 5200
Steller IT Park, Tower 1, 3rd fl, C 25, Sector 62, Noida 201 301, India *Tel:* (0120) 461 3700
One Mulgrave Chambers, 26-28 Mulgrave Rd, Sutton, Surrey SM2 6LE, United Kingdom

CG Book Printers
Division of Corporate Graphics Commercial (CGC)
1750 Northway Dr, North Mankato, MN 56003
Tel: 507-388-3300 *Toll Free Tel:* 800-729-7575 *Fax:* 507-386-6350
E-mail: cgbooks@corpgraph.com
Web Site: www.corpgraph.com
Key Personnel
Pres: Dan Kvasnicka *Tel:* 507-386-6340 *Fax:* 507-344-5548 *E-mail:* dekvasnicka@corpgraph.com
Sales Exec, Book Mfg Sales: Mike Schmitt *Tel:* 507-386-6349 *E-mail:* mjschmitt@corpgraph.com
Founded: 1989

Charlesworth Author Services (USA) Inc
Unit of The Charlesworth Group (USA) Inc
c/o Suite 510 Constitution Place, 325 Chestnut St, Philadelphia, PA 19106
E-mail: usa@cwauthors.com
Web Site: www.cwauthors.com
Branch Office(s)
Charlesworth Author Services China, Room 1105, No 9 Bldg, Jianwai SOHO, No 39 Dongsanhuan Zhonglu, Chaoyang District, Beijing 100022, China *Tel:* (010) 5869 6201 *E-mail:* info@cwauthors.com.cn
Charlesworth Author Services UK, 250 Deighton Rd, Deighton, Huddersfield HD2 1JJ, United Kingdom *Tel:* (01484) 506250 *E-mail:* helpdesk@cwauthors.com

Citizen Systems America Corp
363 Van Ness Way, Suite 404, Torrance, CA 90501
Tel: 310-781-1460 *Toll Free Tel:* 800-421-6516
Web Site: www.citizen-systems.com
Key Personnel
Pres & CEO: Shuichi Ishiwata
Founded: 1930

Claris International Inc
Subsidiary of Apple Inc
5201 Patrick Henry Dr, Santa Clara, CA 95054
Tel: 408-727-8227 (sales & cust support) *Toll Free Tel:* 800-725-2747 (sales); 800-325-2747 (cust support) *Fax:* 408-987-7447
E-mail: claris_sales@claris.com
Web Site: www.claris.com

Key Personnel
CEO: Brad Freitag
Corp Coun & Secy: Sophia Yungen
VP, Engg: Peter Nelson
VP, Mktg: Britta Meyer Rock
VP, Prod Mgmt & Design: Srini Gurrapu
VP, Sales: Ryan McCann
VP, Worldwide Prod Release Engg: Lucy Chen
Founded: 1998
Branch Office(s)
20 Martin Place, Level 3, Sydney, NSW 2000, Australia *Tel:* (02) 8987 8300
B505 COFO Plaza, No 8 Jian Guo Men Nei Ave, Beijing 100005, China *Tel:* 400 601 5902
7 Place d'Iena, CS 81626, 75773 Paris Cedex 16, France *Tel:* 08 10 25 27 47
Katharina von Bora Str 3, 80333 Munich, Germany *Tel:* (089) 1 2089 5651
Roppongi Hills Mori Tower, 6-10-1 Roppongi, Minato-ku, Tokyo 106-6140, Japan *Tel:* (03) 4345 3333
2 Furzeground Way, Stockley Park, Uxbridge, Middx UB11 1BB, United Kingdom *Tel:* (020) 8268 6030

Claritas LLC
8044 Montgomery Rd, Suite 455, Cincinnati, OH 45236
Toll Free Tel: 888-981-0040
E-mail: findcustomers@claritas.com; marketing@claritas.com
Web Site: www.claritas.com
Key Personnel
CEO: Mike Nazzaro
COO: Karthik Iyer
Founded: 1971

Clerical Plus
97 Blueberry Lane, Shelton, CT 06484
Tel: 203-225-0879 *Fax:* 203-225-0879
E-mail: clericalplus@aol.com
Web Site: www.clericalplus.net
Key Personnel
Pres: Rose Brown
Founded: 1990

Dwight Clough
W7502 County Rd "G", Pardeeville, WI 53954
Tel: 608-429-1440
E-mail: lmp@dwightclough.com
Web Site: dwightclough.com
Founded: 1983

Cohesion®
511 W Bay St, Suite 480, Tampa, FL 33606
Tel: 813-999-3111 *Toll Free Tel:* 866-727-6800
Web Site: www.cohesion.com
Key Personnel
CEO: John Owens
Chief Strategy Offr: John Larson
Founded: 1982
Branch Office(s)
6760 Alexander Bell Dr, Suite 120, Columbia, MD 21046 *Toll Free Tel:* 800-560-0630
5151 Pfeiffer Rd, Suite 105, Cincinnati, OH 45242 *Tel:* 513-587-7700

Computer Analytics Corp
999 E Touhy Ave, Suite 130, Des Plaines, IL 60018-2736
Tel: 847-297-5290 *Fax:* 847-297-8680
Web Site: www.cacorp.com
Key Personnel
Principal: Dale C Jessen *E-mail:* dale.jessen@cacorp.com; Jay Cosentino *E-mail:* jay.cosentino@cacorp.com; Kenneth R Kosnik *E-mail:* ken.kosnik@cacorp.com
Founded: 1976

Conway Greene Co
1400 E 30 St, Suite 402, Cleveland, OH 44114

Tel: 216-965-3195
Web Site: www.conwaygreene.com
Key Personnel
Principal: Barry Conway *E-mail:* bconway@
conwaygreene.com

Copywriters' Council of America™ (CCA)
Division of The Linick Group Inc
CCA Bldg, 7 Putter Lane, Middle Island, NY
11953-1920
Mailing Address: PO Box 102, Middle Island,
NY 11953-0102
Tel: 631-924-3888; 631-924-8555; 631-604-8599
Key Personnel
Chmn, Consulting Group: Andrew S Linick, PhD
E-mail: cca4dmcopy@gmail.com
Pres: Gaylen Andrews
EVP: Roger Dextor
Dir, Spec Projs: Barbara Deal
Edit Dir: Kelly Boyles
BISAC compatible software
Branch Office(s)
7 Lincoln Ave, Smithtown, NY 11787
Membership(s): The Association of Publishers for
Special Sales (APSS); The Imaging Alliance

Corder Associates Inc
2602 W Baseline Rd, Suite 22, Mesa, AZ 85202
Mailing Address: PO Box 40518, Mesa, AZ
85274-0518
Tel: 480-752-8533 *Toll Free Tel:* 877-303-7575
Fax: 480-752-8534
E-mail: info@cordernet.com
Web Site: cordernet.com
Key Personnel
Pres: Kelly Corder
VP: Jennifer D Corder
Founded: 1991

Corel Corp
1600 Carling Ave, Ottawa, ON K1Z 8R7, Canada
Tel: 613-728-8200 (PR) *Toll Free Tel:* 877-582-
6735
Web Site: www.corel.com
Key Personnel
COO: Prasannaa Ganesan
CFO: Brad Jewett
Chief People Offr & Chief Legal Offr: Rene
Barreda
EVP, Global E-Commerce & Digital Mktg: Rob
Charlebois
EVP, Global Prods: Gerard Metrailler
EVP, Sales & Mktg: Jason Wesbecher
Founded: 1989

Corporate Disk Co
4610 Prime Pkwy, McHenry, IL 60050-7005
Tel: 815-331-6000 *Toll Free Tel:* 800-634-3475
Fax: 815-331-6030
E-mail: info@disk.com
Web Site: www.disk.com
Key Personnel
Owner & VP, Sales: Joe D Foley *Tel:* 815-331-
6000 ext 233 *E-mail:* jfoley@disk.com
Founded: 1984

Corporate Graphics Book Printers, see CG
Book Printers

Cosmos Communications Inc
11-05 44 Dr, Long Island City, NY 11101
Tel: 718-482-1800 *Toll Free Tel:* 800-223-5751
Fax: 718-482-1968
Web Site: www.cosmoscommunications.com
Key Personnel
CEO: Jack Weiss *E-mail:* jweiss@
cosmoscommunications.com
Founded: 1933

Courter Films LLC
1145 N Stoney Point, Crystal River, FL 34429

Tel: 352-563-7888 (cell) *Fax:* 352-795-3889
E-mail: info@courterfilms.com
Web Site: www.courterfilms.com
Key Personnel
Dir & Ed: Philip R Courter *E-mail:* phil@
courterfilms.com
Exec Prodr: Gay Courter *E-mail:* gay@
courterfilms.com

The Criterion Collection
215 Park Ave S, 5th fl, New York, NY 10003
Tel: 212-756-8822
E-mail: suggestions@criterion.com
Web Site: www.criterion.com
Key Personnel
Contact: Jon Mulvaney *E-mail:* mulvaney@
criterion.com
Founded: 1984

Cross-Cultural Communications
Division of Cross-Cultural Literary Editions Inc
239 Wynsum Ave, Merrick, NY 11566-4725
SAN: 208-6122
Tel: 516-868-5635 *Fax:* 516-379-1901
E-mail: cccpoetry@aol.com; cccbarkan@
optonline.net
Web Site: www.facebook.com/
CrossCulturalCommunications.NY/
Key Personnel
Publr & Ed-in-Chief: Stanley H Barkan
Art Ed: Bebe Barkan
Asst Ed: Mia Barkan Clarke
Founded: 1971
Branch Office(s)
3131 Mott Ave, Far Rockaway, NY 11691
HC 67, Box 1206, Big Sur, CA 93920-9629,
Contact: Patricia Holt *Tel:* 831-667-2433
E-mail: surph8@yahoo.com

The Crowley Co
5111 Pegasus Ct, Suite M, Frederick, MD 21704
Tel: 240-215-0224 *Fax:* 240-215-0234
E-mail: webrequest@thecrowleycompany.com
Web Site: www.thecrowleycompany.com
Key Personnel
Pres & CEO: Pat Crowley *E-mail:* pat@
thecrowleycompany.com
COO: Kevin Crowley
CFO: Jeffrey Manwiller
VP, Sales & Mktg: Matthew McCabe
E-mail: mattm@thecrowleycompany.com
Dir, Admin: Debbie Harris *E-mail:* debbie@
thecrowleycompany.com
Dir, Communs: Cheri Baker *E-mail:* cherib@
thecrowleycompany.com
Founded: 1980

CRW Graphics Communications
9100 Pennsauken Hwy, Pennsauken, NJ 08110
Tel: 856-662-9111 *Toll Free Tel:* 800-820-3000
Fax: 856-665-1789
E-mail: info@crwgraphics.com
Web Site: www.crwgraphics.com
Key Personnel
Pres: David Carpenter
EVP: George Slater
VP, Sales & Mktg: Will Glassman
E-mail: wglassman@crwgraphics.com
Cust Serv Mgr: Rich Quigley *E-mail:* rquigley@
crwgraphics.com

CyberWolf® Inc
1596 Pacheco, Suite 203, Santa Fe, NM 87505
Tel: 505-983-6463
E-mail: sales@cyberwolf.com
Web Site: www.cyberwolf.com;
www.accumenbook.com; www.
ebookdownloadservice.com
Key Personnel
Pres & CEO: Larry Wolf

VP, Sales & Mktg: Linda Masco *Tel:* 505-983-
6463 ext 618
Founded: 1988

Data Connect/RelComm Inc
Division of Data Connect Enterprise Inc
4868 Hwy 4, Suite G, Angels Camp, CA 95222
Tel: 301-924-7400 (ext 17) *Fax:* 301-924-7403
E-mail: sales@relcomm.com
Web Site: www.relcomm.com
Founded: 1989

Data Conversion Laboratory Inc (DCL)
61-18 190 St, Suite 205, Fresh Meadows, NY
11365
Tel: 718-357-8700 *Toll Free Tel:* 800-321-2816
(provider problems)
E-mail: info@dclab.com
Web Site: www.dataconversionlaboratory.com
Key Personnel
Pres: Mark Gross
COO: Amy Williams
CFO: Judy Gross
CIO: Tammy Bilitzky
Chief Revenue Offr: Jeff Wood
CTO & Dir, Res: Mike Gross
Natl Sales Dir: Brian Trombley
Sales Dir, Publg: Amber Watson
Founded: 1981
Membership(s): American Institute of Archi-
tects; Association for Enterprise Integration
(AFEI/CALS); Association of American Pub-
lishers (AAP); Graphic Communications Asso-
ciation (GCA); Society for Scholarly Publish-
ing (SSP)

Datalogics Inc
101 N Wacker, Suite 1800, Chicago, IL 60606
Tel: 312-853-8200 *Fax:* 312-853-8282
E-mail: sales@datalogics.com; marketing@
datalogics.com
Web Site: www.datalogics.com
Key Personnel
CEO: Kevin McNeill
CFO: Ruth Walker
CTO: Matt Zuznicki
VP, Sales: Maryanne Pavlin
Founded: 1967

DataStream Content Solutions LLC, see DSCS
LLC

DCA Inc
1515 E Pine St, Cushing, OK 74023
Tel: 918-225-0346 *Fax:* 918-225-1113
E-mail: sales@dcainc.com
Web Site: www.dcainc.com
Key Personnel
Chmn of the Bd & CEO: Doug Carson
Pres & COO: Mike Griffith
CTO: Henry Boon Kelly
Founded: 1988

Decker Intellectual Properties Inc
372 Richmond St W, Toronto, ON M5V 2L7,
Canada
Tel: 905-522-8526 *Toll Free Tel:* 855-647-6511
E-mail: customercare@deckermed.com
Web Site: www.deckerip.com
Key Personnel
Chief Content Offr: Ryan T Decker
CTO: Jeffrey B Decker
BISAC compatible software
Branch Office(s)
516 Tennessee St, Memphis, TN 38103

DeckerMed, see Decker Intellectual Properties
Inc

Dell EMC
Division of Dell Technologies
176 South St, Hopkinton, MA 01748

Tel: 508-435-1000 *Toll Free Tel:* 866-438-3622
Web Site: www.delltechnologies.com

Dell Wyse
Division of Dell Technologies
One Dell Way, Round Rock, TX 78682
Toll Free Tel: 866-438-3622 (sales)
Web Site: www.delltechnologies.com
Key Personnel
Chmn & CEO: Michael S Dell
VChmn & COO: Jeff Clarke
Chief Mktg Offr: Allison Dew

Delphax Solutions Inc
Unit of Air T Inc
2810 Argentia Rd, Unit 6, Mississauga, ON L5N
8L2, Canada
Toll Free Tel: 833-DELPHAX (335-7429)
Web Site: www.delphaxsolutions.com
Key Personnel
CEO: Richard Lee
Founded: 1981
Branch Office(s)
5000 W 36 St, Suite 130, Minneapolis, MN
55416 *Toll Free Tel:* 855-404-0026

Design Plus
1086 Main Rd, Aquebogue, NY 11931
Mailing Address: PO Box 1140, Aquebogue, NY
11931
Tel: 631-722-4384
E-mail: designplusonline@yahoo.com
Key Personnel
Creative Dir: Denise Lebrun
BISAC compatible software

Design Science Inc (DSI)
Division of Wiris
444 W Ocean Blvd, Suite 800, Long Beach, CA
90802
Tel: 562-432-2920 *Toll Free Tel:* 800-827-0685
(US sales only) *Fax:* 562-624-2859
E-mail: info@wiris.com; sales@wiris.com;
support@wiris.com
Web Site: www.dessci.com
Key Personnel
CEO: Robert Karmelich
Founded: 1986

DFI Technologies LLC
5501 Monte Claire Lane, Loomis, CA 95650
Tel: 916-568-1234
Web Site: dfitech.com
Key Personnel
Chmn & Pres: David Lu *E-mail:* david@dfitech.
com
Founded: 1985

Digimage Arts
100 S Eighth Ave, Winterset, IA 50273
Tel: 515-462-1874
E-mail: geninfo@digimagearts.com
Web Site: www.digimagearts.com
Key Personnel
Pres: Wayne Davis
Founded: 1987

Digital Wisdom Inc
PO Box 11, Tappahannock, VA 22560-0011
Tel: 804-443-9000 *Toll Free Tel:* 800-800-8560
E-mail: info@digitalwisdom.net
Web Site: www.digiwis.com; www.
mountainhighmaps.com
Key Personnel
Pres: David M Broad
Founded: 1992

Disc Makers
Division of DiY Media Group Inc

7905 N Crescent Blvd, Pennsauken, NJ 08110-
1402
Tel: 856-663-9030 *Toll Free Tel:* 800-468-9353
Fax: 856-661-3450
E-mail: info@discmakers.com
Web Site: www.discmakers.com
Key Personnel
EVP: David Olinsky
Founded: 1946
Membership(s): Content Delivery & Storage As-
sociation (CDSA); The Recording Academy
(NARAS); Society of Professional Audio
Recording Services (SPARS)

DisplayMate Technologies Corp
PO Box 550, Amherst, NH 03031
Tel: 603-672-8500 *Toll Free Tel:* 800-932-6323
(orders)
E-mail: info.dm@displaymate.com
Web Site: www.displaymate.com
Key Personnel
Founder, Pres & CEO: Dr Raymond Soneira
Founded: 1984

DocuWare Corp
4 Crotty Lane, Suite 200, New Windsor, NY
12553
Tel: 845-563-9045 *Toll Free Tel:* 888-565-5907
Fax: 845-563-9046
E-mail: dwsales@docuware.com; support.
americas@docuware.com
Web Site: www.docuware.com
Key Personnel
CFO: Paul Remington
VP, Prof Servs Americas: Brian Love
Mktg Communs Mgr: Mary K Williams *Tel:* 845-
563-9045 ext 221 *E-mail:* mary.williams@
docuware.com
Founded: 1988
Branch Office(s)
35 Thorpe Ave, Suite 201, Wallingford, CT
06492 *Tel:* 203-871-4984 *Fax:* 203-269-0322
E-mail: fortissupport@docuware.com
DocuWare SARL, 17 rue du Colisee, 75008 Paris,
France *Tel:* 01 57 19 03 23 *E-mail:* infoline@
docuware.com
DocuWare GmbH, Therese-Giehse-Platz 2, 82110
Germering, Germany (headquarters), Mng Dir:
Juergen Biffar *Tel:* (089) 894433-0 *Fax:* (089)
8419966 *E-mail:* docuware@docuware.com
DocuWare SL, Casp, 90 3º 1a, 08010 Barcelona,
Spain *Tel:* 933171771 *E-mail:* infoline@
docuware.com
DocuWare Ltd, Chiltern Chambers, 37 St Peters
Ave, Caversham, United Kingdom *Tel:* (0115)
7180353 *E-mail:* infoline@docuware.com

Dotronix Technology Inc
2420 Oakgreen Ave N, West Lakeland, MN
55082
Tel: 651-633-1742 *Fax:* 651-633-2152
E-mail: sales@dotronix.com
Web Site: dotronix.com
Key Personnel
Pres: Kurt Sadler *E-mail:* ksadler@dotronix.com

DSCS LLC
5000 College Ave, Suite 4100, College Park, MD
20742
Tel: 301-405-2883 *Fax:* 301-314-2799
E-mail: info@dscs.com
Web Site: www.dscs.com
Key Personnel
Pres: Jason Myers
Founded: 1995
BISAC compatible software

DSM Producers Inc
PO Box 1160, Marco Island, FL 34146-1160
Tel: 212-245-0006

Key Personnel
Owner & Pres: Suzan J Bader
Natl Sales Dir: Doris Kaufman
Founded: 1970
Membership(s): The American Society of Com-
posers, Authors and Publishers (ASCAP);
Broadcast Music Inc (BMI); SESAC

Dukane Corp, Audio Visual Products Division
Division of Dukane Corp
2900 Dukane Dr, St Charles, IL 60174
Tel: 630-584-2300 *Toll Free Tel:* 888-245-1966;
800-676-2487 (tech support) *Fax:* 630-584-
5156
E-mail: avsales@dukane.com
Web Site: dukaneav.com
Key Personnel
Pres: James Locascio *E-mail:* jlocascio@dukane.
com
Natl Sales Mgr: Scott Doornbos *Tel:* 800-269-
9715 *E-mail:* sdoornbos@dukane.com
Founded: 1922

Dynabook Americas Inc
5241 California Ave, Suite 100, Irvine, CA 92617
Tel: 949-583-3000
Web Site: us.dynabook.com
Key Personnel
Media Rel: Eric Paulsen *E-mail:* eric.paulsen@
dynabook.com

Eastgate Systems Inc
134 Main St, Watertown, MA 02472
Tel: 617-924-9044 *Toll Free Tel:* 800-562-1638
E-mail: info@eastgate.com
Web Site: www.eastgate.com
Key Personnel
Chief Scientist: Mark Bernstein
Founded: 1982

ECRM Imaging Systems
25 Commerce Way, North Andover, MA 01845-
1002
Tel: 978-851-0207 *Toll Free Tel:* 800-537-ECRM
(537-3276)
E-mail: sales@ecrm.com
Web Site: www.ecrm.com
Founded: 1969

Eizo Inc
5710 Warland Dr, Cypress, CA 90630
Tel: 562-431-5011 *Toll Free Tel:* 800-800-5202
Fax: 562-431-4811
E-mail: orders@eizo.com
Web Site: www.eizo.com
Key Personnel
VP, Sales: Dave Waletzki *Tel:* 888-925-6481
E-mail: david.waletzki@eizo.com
Mktg Coord: Julie De Anda *Tel:* 800-800-5202
ext 140 *E-mail:* julie.deanda@eizo.com
Founded: 1985

Electronics for Imaging Inc (EFI)
6750 Dumbarton Circle, Fremont, CA 94555
Tel: 650-357-3500 *Toll Free Tel:* 800-568-1917;
800-875-7117 (sales) *Fax:* 650-357-3907
E-mail: info@efi.com
Web Site: www.efi.com
Key Personnel
CEO: Guy Gecht
Chief Acctg Offr: Gene Zamiska
Chief Busn Devt Offr: Roy Douglass
CFO: Marc Olin
Chief HR Offr: Paul Sexton
CIO: Jill Norris
Chief Legal Offr: Alex K Grab
Chief Process Offr: Brandy Green
Chief Revenue Offr: Frank Mallozzi
CTO: Ghilad Dziesietnik
Chief of Staff: Vicki Sam
SVP & Gen Mgr, Fiery: Toby Weiss

SVP & Gen Mgr, Productivity Software: Gaby Matsliach
VP, Partner Alliance: Bernie Lepore
VP, Sales, Americas: Patrick Morrissey
VP, Sales, EMEA Opers: Paul Cripps
Founded: 1989
Branch Office(s)
15150 Avenue of Science, Suite 100, San Diego, CA 92128 *Tel:* 858-578-3550 *Fax:* 858-546-1401
9035 S Kyrene, Suite 106, Tempe, AZ 85284 *Tel:* 480-538-5800 *Fax:* 480-538-5882
5011 Gate Pkwy, Bldg 100, Suite 225, Jacksonville, FL 32256 *Tel:* 904-564-9690 *Fax:* 904-564-9691
4237 SW High Meadows Ave, Palm City, FL 34990 *Tel:* 772-220-7966
4955 Avalon Ridge Pkwy, Suite 300, Norcross, GA 30071 *Tel:* 770-448-9008 *Fax:* 770-448-3202
9 Aldrin Rd, Plymouth, MA 02360 *Tel:* 603-298-2490 *Fax:* 508-746-1569
1260 James L Hart Pkwy, Ypsilanti, MI 48197 *Tel:* 734-641-3062 *Fax:* 734-641-3065
1340 Corporate Center Curve, Eagan, MN 55121 *Tel:* 651-365-5300
8606 NW 107 Terr, Kansas City, MO 64153
79 E Wilder Rd, Lebanon, NH 03784 *Tel:* 603-298-2400 *Fax:* 603-298-2489
12 Innovation Way, Londondery, NH 03053 *Tel:* 603-279-4635 *Fax:* 603-279-6411
7 Campus Dr, 1st fl, Parsippany, NJ 07054 *Tel:* 973-451-7100 *Fax:* 973-451-7188
589 W Eighth Ave, 8th fl, New York, NY 10018 *Tel:* 212-629-9053 *Fax:* 212-629-9055
90 Earhart Dr, Suite 8, Williamsville, NY 14221 *Tel:* 716-631-3770 *Fax:* 716-631-3576
40 24 St, 1st fl, Pittsburgh, PA 15222 *Tel:* 412-456-1141 *Fax:* 412-456-1151
16825 48 Ave W, Suite 414, Lynnwood, WA 98037 *Tel:* 972-638-7490
121 Granton Dr, Unit 14, Richmond Hill, ON L4B 3N4, Canada *Tel:* 905-882-2500 *Fax:* 905-882-2535

Elixir Technologies Corp
1314 E Ojai Ave, Ojai, CA 93023
Tel: 805-641-5900 *Fax:* 805-648-9151
E-mail: info_us@elixir.com
Web Site: www.elixir.com
Key Personnel
CEO: Tarek Harry
Founded: 1985

Engineered Software™
PO Box 408, Grafton, MA 01519-0408
Tel: 336-299-4843
E-mail: info@engsw.com; sales@engsw.com
Web Site: www.engsw.com
Key Personnel
Pres & Dir, Software Devt: Todd Stanley

Envision Peripherals Inc (EPI)
490 N McCarthy Blvd, Suite 120, Milpitas, CA 95035
Web Site: us.aoc.com
Key Personnel
CEO: David Mo

Esko USA
Division of Danaher
8535 Gander Creek Dr, Miamisburg, OH 45342
Tel: 937-454-1721 *Toll Free Tel:* 800-743-7131 *Fax:* 937-454-1522
E-mail: info.usa@esko.com
Web Site: www.esko.com
Key Personnel
VP & Gen Mgr, North America: Stephen Bennett

Evolution Computing Inc
4228 E Andrea Dr, Cave Creek, AZ 85331

Tel: 602-299-1949
E-mail: support@fastcad.com; order_request@fastcad.com
Web Site: www.fastcad.com
Key Personnel
Owner: Michael Riddle
Tech Support: John Steen
Founded: 1985

Fairfield Marketing Group Inc
Subsidiary of FMG Inc
The Direct Mail Ctr, 830 Sport Hill Rd, Easton, CT 06112-1241
Tel: 203-261-5585 *Fax:* 203-261-0884
E-mail: info@fairfieldmarketing.com
Web Site: www.fairfieldmarketing.com
Key Personnel
Pres & CEO: Edward P Washchilla, Jr
VP, Cust Serv: Mike Lozada *Tel:* 203-261-5585 ext 204
VP, Fulfillment: Jason Paul Miller *Tel:* 203-261-5585 ext 203 *E-mail:* jason@fairfieldmarketing.com
Founded: 1986
BISAC compatible software
Membership(s): American Booksellers Association (ABA); Bridgeport Regional Business Council (BRBC); Education Market Association; United States Chamber of Commerce (USCC)

Falcon Safety Products Inc
25 Imclone Dr, Branchburg, NJ 08876
Tel: 908-707-4900 *Toll Free Tel:* 800-332-5266
E-mail: marketing@falconsafety.com
Web Site: www.falconsafety.com
Key Personnel
Dir, Cust Serv: Trish Dupuis-Jones
Dir, Mktg: Jennifer Rappaport
Founded: 1953

Figaro
PO Box 848, Sharon, CT 06069
Tel: 860-248-8989; 860-364-0834
E-mail: design@figro.com
Web Site: www.figro.com
Key Personnel
Co-Pres & Creative Dir: Walter Schwarz
Co-Pres: Linda Swenson *E-mail:* ls@figro.com

FileMaker Inc, see Claris International Inc

Firebrand Technologies
44 Merrimac St, Newburyport, MA 01950
Tel: 978-465-7755 *Toll Free Tel:* 800-779-7345 *Fax:* 978-465-7759
E-mail: askburnie@firebrandtech.com
Web Site: www.firebrandtech.com
Key Personnel
Founder & CEO: Fran Toolan
CTO: Shane Archer
Pres: Doug Lessing
Community & Mktg Dir: Lindsey Lochner
Founded: 1987 (as Quality Solutions Inc)
Membership(s): American Association of University Presses (AAUP); American Booksellers Association (ABA); The American Library Association (ALA); Audio Publishers Association; Bookbuilders of Boston; BookNetCanada; Evangelical Christian Publishers Association (ECPA); Independent Book Publishers Association (IBPA); Independent Publisher's Guild (IPG); Publishers Association of the West (PubWest); Society for Scholarly Publishing (SSP)

First Choice Copy
5208 Grand Ave, Maspeth, NY 11378
Tel: 718-381-1480 (ext 200) *Toll Free Tel:* 800-222-COPY (222-2679)

Web Site: www.firstchoice-copy.com
Key Personnel
Owner & Pres: Joe Meisner *Tel:* 718-381-1480 ext 212 *E-mail:* jmeisner@nyc.rr.com

Fluke Networks
Division of Fluke Electronics Corp
6920 Seaway Blvd, Everett, WA 98203
Mailing Address: PO Box 777, Everett, WA 98206-0777
Tel: 425-446-5500; 425-446-4519 (sales & support) *Toll Free Tel:* 800-283-5853
E-mail: info@flukenetworks.com
Web Site: www.flukenetworks.com
Key Personnel
Pres, Fluke Corp: Marc Tremblay
VP, Mktg: Tom Roth
Founded: 1984

Follett School Solutions Inc
Division of Follett Corporation
1340 Ridgeview Dr, McHenry, IL 60050
SAN: 169-1902
Tel: 815-759-1700 *Toll Free Tel:* 888-511-5114 (cust serv); 877-899-8550 (sales) *Fax:* 815-759-9831 *Toll Free Fax:* 800-852-5458
E-mail: info@follettlearning.com; customerservice@follett.com
Web Site: www.follettlearning.com; www.follett.com/prek12; www.titlewave.com
Key Personnel
EVP: Britten Follett
Sales Exec: Erica Moore

Fontlab Ltd
403 S Lincoln St, Suite 4-51, Port Angeles, WA 98362
Tel: 301-560-3208 *Toll Free Tel:* 866-571-5039
E-mail: orders@fontlab.com; contact@fontlab.com
Web Site: www.fontlab.com
Key Personnel
Pres: Ted Harrison
VP & Lead Developer: Yuri Yarmola
Dir, Prods: Adam Twardoch
Founded: 1992

Foster Travel Publishing
1623 Martin Luther King Jr Way, Berkeley, CA 94709
Tel: 510-549-2202
Web Site: www.fostertravel.com
Key Personnel
Owner & Pres: Lee Foster *E-mail:* lee@fostertravel.com
Founded: 1972
Membership(s): American Society of Media Photographers (ASMP); Bay Area Independent Publishers Association (BAIPA); Bay Area Travel Writers; Society of American Travel Writers (SATW)

Freestyle Software
Unit of FOG Software
9 Campus Dr, Parsippany, NJ 07054
Toll Free Tel: 800-474-5760 *Fax:* 973-237-9043
E-mail: info@freestylesolutions.com
Web Site: www.freestylesolutions.com
Key Personnel
CEO: Fred Lizza
CFO: Paul Kincaid
VP, Cust Satisfaction: Tony Kyberd *E-mail:* tony.k@freestylesolutions.com
Founded: 1986

Fujitsu Computer Products of America Inc
Subsidiary of Fujitsu Ltd
1250 E Arques Ave, Sunnyvale, CA 94085-4701
Tel: 408-746-6000 *Toll Free Tel:* 800-626-4686
E-mail: scanner-sales@us.fujitsu.com
Web Site: www.fujitsu.com/us

Key Personnel
Pres & CEO: Yasunari Shimizu
SVP, Partner Alliance: Yasuhiko Nagaoka
SVP, Planning, Serv Opers & Logistics: Masanori Shibusawa
VP, Serv Opers & Logistics: Glenn Wood

GEI WideFormat, A Visual Edge Technology Company
3874 Highland Park NW, North Canton, OH 44720
Toll Free Tel: 800-842-8448 (serv); 888-722-6434 (sales)
E-mail: sales@geiwideformat.com
Web Site: www.geiwideformat.com; www.visualedgetechnology.com
Key Personnel
Dir, Mktg: Denise Dennewitz-Hobson
Founded: 1970
BISAC compatible software

Getty Images Inc
605 Fifth Ave S, Suite 400, Seattle, WA 98104
Tel: 206-925-5000 *Toll Free Tel:* 800-IMAGERY (462-4379 sales); 888-888-5889
E-mail: enterprisesolutionssales@gettyimages.com
Web Site: www.gettyimages.com
Key Personnel
CEO: Craig Peters
Chief People Offr: Lizanne Vaughn
Chief Technol & Prod Offr: Nate Gandert
SVP & Chief Mktg Offr: Gene Foca
SVP, Content: Ken Mainardis
SVP, Creative Content: Andrew Saunders
SVP & Gen Coun: Kjelti Kellough
SVP, Strategic Devt: Peter Orlowsky
VP, Sales (Americas): Katie Calhoun
Founded: 1995
Branch Office(s)
6300 Wilshire Blvd, 16th fl, Los Angeles, CA 90048 *Tel:* 323-202-4200
55 E Monroe St, 17th fl, Suite 1700, Chicago, IL 60603 *Tel:* 312-344-4500
195 Broadway, New York, NY 10007 *Tel:* 646-613-4000
182 Blues Point Rd, Level 6, McMahons Point, NSW 2060, Australia *Tel:* 1800 500-141 *Fax:* (02) 9439 0476
Avenida Roque Petroni Junior, 1089 10° andar cj 1016, Jardim das Acacias, Sao Paulo-SP 04707-000, Brazil *Tel:* 0800 772 2074
UBP (Universal Business Park), Bldg B5, No 10 Jiuxianqiao St, Chaoyang District, Beijing 100015, China *Tel:* (010) 5795 0333; (010) 5795 0388 *Fax:* (010) 5692 0112; (010) 5692 0115
HuanZhi International Sq, Rm 901, No 436 Hengfeng Rd, ZhaBei District, Shanghai, China *Tel:* (021) 5385 0333 *Fax:* (021) 5385 0628
Haihang Bldg, Rm 2307-2308, No 8 Lin He Zhong Rd, Tianhe District, Guangzhou 510610, China *Tel:* (020) 8550 1070; (020) 8550 1955 *Fax:* (020) 8550 1073
4, Bd Poissonniere, 75009 Paris, France *Tel:* 01 55 33 66 00
Auenstr 5, 80469 Munich, Germany *Tel:* 0800 101 31 35
Rm 611, 6/F, Lee Garden 3, One Sunning Rd, Causeway Bay, Hong Kong *Tel:* 2832 0900 *Fax:* 3017 6747
Weesperstr 61, 1018 VN Amsterdam, Netherlands *Tel:* 0800 020 1532
PO Box 106671, Auckland City, Auckland 1143, New Zealand *Tel:* 0800 462 431
3 Church St, Level 8, Samsung Hub, Singapore 049483, Singapore *Tel:* 6410 3300 *Fax:* 6410 3301
c/o Wework, Paseo de la Castellana N° 77, 28046 Madrid, Spain *Tel:* 917 870 900 *Toll Free Tel:* 800 099 250

G Tower, 9 Rama 9 Rd, Level 33, No 3334, Huay Kwang District, Huay Kwang, Bangkok 10310, Thailand *Fax:* (02) 0260733
101 Bayham St, London NW1 0AG, United Kingdom

GEX Inc
2 Industrial Way, Atkinson, NH 03811
Tel: 603-870-9292
Web Site: www.gexinc.com
Key Personnel
Pres: Gary Russell
VP: Jim LaPierre; Karla Russell
Founded: 1986

Global Graphics Software Inc
Subsidiary of Global Graphics PLC
5996 Clark Center Ave, Sarasota, FL 34238
Tel: 941-925-1303
E-mail: info@globalgraphics.com; sales@globalgraphics.com
Web Site: www.globalgraphics.com/globalgraphics-software
Founded: 1986
Branch Office(s)
Global Graphics KK, 610 AIOS Nagatacho Bldg, 2-17-17 Nagatacho Chiyoda-ku, Tokyo 100-0014, Japan *Tel:* (03) 6273-3198 *Fax:* (03) 6273-3197
Global Graphics Software Ltd, Cambourne Busn Park, Bldg 2030, Cambourne, Cambridge CB23 6DW, United Kingdom *Tel:* (01954) 283100
Membership(s): Association for Print Technologies (APTech); DDAP; ICC; PRINTING United Alliance

Graphic World Inc, see GW Inc

GSB Digital
33-01 Hunters Point Ave, Long Island City, NY 11101
Tel: 212-684-3600 *Fax:* 212-684-3613
E-mail: questions@gsbdigital.com
Web Site: www.gsbdigital.com
Key Personnel
Pres: Stephan S Steiner
Founded: 1991
Branch Office(s)
51 Madison Ave, No 3B, New York, NY 10010 *Tel:* 212-500-6503 *E-mail:* litigation@gsbdigital.com

GTCO Calcomp
Division of Turning Technologies LLC
14557 N 82 St, Scottsdale, AZ 85260
Tel: 480-443-2264 *Toll Free Tel:* 800-220-1137 *Fax:* 480-948-1751
E-mail: sales@gtcocalcomp.com
Web Site: www.gtcocalcomp.com
Key Personnel
Natl Acct Mgr: Markie Nielsen
Founded: 1975

GTI Graphic Technology Inc
211 Dupont Ave, Newburgh, NY 12550
Mailing Address: PO Box 3138, Newburgh, NY 12550-0651
Tel: 845-562-7066 *Fax:* 845-562-2543
E-mail: sales@gtilite.com
Web Site: www.gtilite.com
Key Personnel
Pres: Robert McCurdy
EVP: Louis Chappo
Sales & Mktg Coord: Linda Sutherland

GTxcel Inc
144 Turnpike Rd, Suite 130, Southborough, MA 01772-2104
Toll Free Tel: 800-609-8994
Web Site: www.gtxcel.com

Key Personnel
Pres & CEO: Peter Stilson
CFO: Robert Epping
Sr Dir, Digital Servs: JoAnn Mauro
Dir, Engg: Mohammad Salih
Dir, Sales: Jim Clarke
Gen Mgr, Channel Partner Opers: Ted Stile
Founded: 1991
Membership(s): ASAE; Association of American Publishers (AAP)

GW Inc
2290 Ball Dr, St Louis, MO 63146
Tel: 314-567-9854
Web Site: www.gwinc.com
Key Personnel
CEO: Kevin Arrow
EVP: Andy Vosburgh; Mike Loomis
VP, Content Opers: Suzanne Kastner
Branch Office(s)
GW Tech Pvt Ltd, Atrium Bldg, Plot No A-45, Zone C, 2nd fl, Industrial Area Phase-VIII B, Mohali, Punjab 160 059, India *Tel:* (0172) 3006100 *Fax:* (0172) 3006128

Hedquist Productions Inc
PO Box 1475, Fairfield, IA 52556-1475
Tel: 641-472-6708 *Toll Free Fax:* 855-510-5726
Web Site: www.hedquist.com
Key Personnel
Pres & Creative Dir: Jeffrey P Hedquist *E-mail:* jeffrey@hedquist.com
Casting Dir: Jay Mattsson *E-mail:* jay@hedquist.com
Founded: 1985

Heidelberg Graphics
2 Stansbury Ct, Chico, CA 95928
SAN: 211-5654
Tel: 530-342-6582 *Fax:* 530-342-6582
E-mail: heidelberggraphics@gmail.com; service@heidelberggraphics.com
Web Site: www.heidelberggraphics.com
Key Personnel
Owner & Pres: Larry S Jackson
Founded: 1972

HID Global
611 Center Ridge Dr, Austin, TX 78753
Tel: 512-776-9000 *Toll Free Tel:* 800-872-5359 (cust serv) *Fax:* 512-776-9930
E-mail: customerservice@hidglobal.com
Web Site: www.hidglobal.com
Key Personnel
Sr Dir, Corp Communs & Pub Aff: Anthony Petrucci *E-mail:* apetrucci@hidglobal.com
Founded: 1991 (as Hughes Identification Devices)

HP Inc
1501 Paige Mill Rd, Palo Alto, CA 94304-1112
Tel: 650-857-1501 *Toll Free Tel:* 800-282-6672
Web Site: www.hp.com
Key Personnel
Pres & CEO: Enrique Lores
CFO: Steve Fieler
Chief Commercial Offr: Christopher Schell
Chief Communs Offr: Karen Kahn
Chief HR Offr: Tracy Keogh
Chief Legal Offr & Pres, Strategy & Busn Mgmt: Kim M Rivera
Chief Mktg Offr: Vikrant Batra
Chief Supply Chain Offr: Antoine Simonnet
Chief Transformation Offr: Richard Bailey
Pres, Imaging, Printing Solutions: Tuan Tran
Pres, Personal Systems: Alex Cho
Founded: 1939
Branch Office(s)
10300 Energy Dr, Spring, TX 77389

IBM Corp
One New Orchard Rd, Armonk, NY 10504

Tel: 914-499-1900 *Toll Free Tel:* 800-426-4968
E-mail: askibm@vnet.ibm.com
Web Site: www.ibm.com
Key Personnel
CEO: Arvind Krishna
CIO: Fletcher Previn
Pres: Jim Whitehurst
SVP & CFO: James J Kavanaugh
SVP & Chief HR Offr: Diane Gherson
SVP & Gen Coun: Michelle H Browdy
SVP, Digital Sales & Chief Mktg Offr: Michelle Peluso
SVP, Global Mkts: Bridget van Kralingen

iCAD Inc
98 Spit Brook Rd, Suite 100, Nashua, NH 03062
Tel: 603-882-5200 *Toll Free Tel:* 866-280-2239
E-mail: sales@icadmed.com; support@icamed.com
Web Site: www.icadmed.com
Key Personnel
Exec Chmn & CEO: Michael Klein
CFO: R Scott Areglado
CTO: Jonathan Go
Pres: Stacey Stevens

Imago
110 W 40 St, New York, NY 10018
Tel: 212-921-4411 *Fax:* 212-921-8226
E-mail: sales@imagousa.com
Web Site: www.imagousa.com
Key Personnel
Pres & CEO: Howard Musk *E-mail:* howardm@imagogroup.com
Founded: 1985
Branch Office(s)
Imago West Coast, 23412 Moulton Pkwy, Suite 250, Laguna Hills, CA 92653 (sales), Contact: Tammy Simms *Tel:* 949-367-1635 *Fax:* 949-367-1639
Imago Australia, 10 Help St, Suite 27, Level 6, Chatswood, NSW 2067, Australia (sales) *Tel:* (04) 3753 3351 (cell); (04) 4806 8704 (cell) *E-mail:* sales@imagoaus.com
Imago Brazil, Domiciano Rossi, 340 unid 154, 09726-121 Sao Bernardo do Campo, Brazil (sales) *Tel:* (011) 2306 8546; (011) 2306 8547 *E-mail:* imagobra@gmail.com
Imago Shenzhen, Rm 2511-2512, Block A, United Plaza No 5022, Bin He Rd, Fu Tian Centre District, Shenzhen 518033, China (prodn), Contact: Kendrick Cheung *Tel:* (0755) 8304 8899 *Fax:* (0755) 8251 4073 *E-mail:* enquiries@imago.com.hk
Imago France, 23 rue Lavoisier, 75008 Paris, France (sales) *Tel:* 01 45 26 47 74 *Fax:* 01 78 94 14 44 *E-mail:* sales@imagogroup.com
Imago Services (HK) Ltd, Unit B309, 1/F, New East Sun Industrial Bldg, 18 Shing Yip St, Kwun Tong, Hong Kong (prodn), Contact: Kendrick Cheung *Tel:* 2811 3316 *E-mail:* enquiries@imago.com.hk
Imago Productions (Malaysia) Pte Ltd, No 43, Taman Emas, Jl Utama 31, Telok Panglima Garang, 42500 Kuala Langot, Selangor, Malaysia (prodn, incorporating South Africa sales) *Tel:* (017) 4288771 (cell) *E-mail:* enquiries@imago.com.sg
Imago Publishing, Albury Ct, Albury Thame, Oxon OX9 2LP, United Kingdom (sales), Dir: Simon Rosenheim *Tel:* (01844) 337000 *Fax:* (01844) 339935 *E-mail:* sales@imago.co.uk *Web Site:* imagogroup.com

IMSI/Design LLC
384 Bel Marin Keys Blvd, No 150, Novato, CA 94949
Tel: 415-483-8000 *Toll Free Tel:* 800-833-8082 (sales)
E-mail: sales@imsidesign.com; support@imsidesign.com
Web Site: www.imsidesign.com

Key Personnel
Pres & CEO: Robert Mayer
Founded: 1983

Indexing Research
620 Park Ave, Suite 183, Rochester, NY 14607
Tel: 585-413-1819
E-mail: info@indexres.com
Web Site: www.indexres.com
Key Personnel
Owner: Frances S Lennie *E-mail:* flennie@indexres.com
Founded: 1986
Membership(s): American Society for Indexing (ASI); Australian and New Zealand Society of Indexers (ANZSI); Society of Indexers (UK)

Infinity Graphics
2277 Science Pkwy, Suite 5, Okemos, MI 48864
Tel: 517-349-4635 *Toll Free Tel:* 800-292-2633
Fax: 517-349-7608
E-mail: barcode@infinitygraphics.com
Web Site: www.infinitygraphics.com
Key Personnel
Owner & Partner: Brian Perry
Owner, Partner & Bar Code Specialist: Suzette Perry
Founded: 1972
BISAC compatible software
Membership(s): Independent Book Publishers Association (IBPA)

Infocus® Corp
13190 SW 68 Pkwy, Suite 120, Portland, OR 97223-8368
Tel: 503-207-4700 *Toll Free Tel:* 877-388-8360 (cust serv)
E-mail: salessupport@infocus.com
Web Site: www.infocus.com
Key Personnel
Pres: Liting Cai
Founded: 1986

Ingenta
317 George St, New Brunswick, NJ 08901
Tel: 732-563-9292 *Fax:* 732-563-9044
Web Site: www.ingenta.com
Key Personnel
CEO: Scott Winner
CFO & Secy: Jon Sheffield
Dir, Busn Growth: Heather Lantz
Dir, Strategic Partnerships: Nick Weir-Williams *Tel:* 732-564-6891 *E-mail:* nick.weir-williams@ingenta.com
Head, Prof Servs: Matt Williams
Founded: 1998
Branch Office(s)
7 Bulfinch, Suite 202, Boston, MA 02114
313A, Zhongguancun Development Bldg, No 12, Shangdi Information Rd, Haidian District, Beijing 100085, China *Tel:* (010) 62961913
8100 Alec Issigonis Way, Oxford OX4 2HU, United Kingdom (headquarters), Sales Mgr: Claire Milburn *Tel:* (01865) 397800 *Fax:* (01865) 397801

Innodata Inc
55 Challenger Rd, Suite 202, Ridgefield Park, NJ 07660
Tel: 201-371-8000 *Toll Free Tel:* 877-454-8400
E-mail: info@innodata.com; marketing@innodata.com
Web Site: innodata.com
Key Personnel
Pres & CEO: Jack S Abuhoff
EVP & COO: Ashok Kumar Mishra
SVP & Gen Coun: Amy Agress
SVP, Prod Innovation: R Douglas Kemp
Founded: 1988
Membership(s): The Association for Work Process Improvement; Association of American

Publishers Professional & Scholarly Publishing Division; Center for Information Development & Content Management Strategies (CIDM); International Association of Outsourcing Professionals (IAOP); National Federation of Abstracting and Information Services (NFAIS); Society for Technical Communication (STC); Society of Knowledge Based Publishers (SKBP); Software & Information Industry Association (SIIA)

International Business Machines Corp, see IBM Corp

Intex Solutions Inc
110 "A" St, Needham, MA 02494
Tel: 781-449-6222 *Fax:* 781-444-2318
E-mail: sales@intex.com
Web Site: www.intex.com
Key Personnel
VP, Sales: Jim Wilner
Founded: 1985

Intuit Inc
2700 Coast Ave, Mountain View, CA 94043
Tel: 650-944-6000 *Toll Free Tel:* 800-446-8848
E-mail: investor_relations@intuit.com
Web Site: www.intuit.com
Key Personnel
Founder & Chmn, Exec Comm: Scott Cook
Exec Chmn of the Bd: Brad Smith
CEO: Sasan Goodarzi *E-mail:* sasan_goodarzi@intuit.com
Chief Mktg Offr & Gen Mgr, Strategic Partnerships: Lara Balazs *E-mail:* lara_balazs@intuit.com
EVP & CFO: Michelle Clatterbuck *E-mail:* michelle_clatterbuck@intuit.com
EVP & CTO: Marianna Tessel *E-mail:* marianna_tessel@intuit.com
EVP & Chief Corp Strategy & Devt Offr: Anton Hanebrink *E-mail:* anton_hanebrink@intuit.com
EVP & Chief Cust Success Offr: Mark Notarainni *E-mail:* mark_notarainni@intuit.com
EVP & Chief Prod & Design Offr: Diego Rodriguez *E-mail:* diego_rodriguez@intuit.com
EVP & Chief People & Places Offr: Laura Fennell *E-mail:* laura_fennell@intuit.com
EVP & Gen Mgr, Consumer Group: Greg Johnson *E-mail:* greg_johnson@intuit.com
SVP, Gen Coun & Corp Secy: Kerry McLean *E-mail:* kerry_mclean@intuit.com
Sr Communs Mgr: Karen Nolan *Tel:* 650-944-6619 *E-mail:* karen_nolan@intuit.com
Founded: 1983

ISIS Papyrus America
Subsidiary of ISIS Information Systems GmbH
301 Bank St, South Lake, TX 76092
Tel: 817-416-2345 *Fax:* 817-416-1223
E-mail: info@isis-papyrus.com
Web Site: www.isis-papyrus.com
Key Personnel
CEO: Annmarie Pucher
Acct Mgr: Carol A Fiore *E-mail:* carol.fiore@isis-papyrus.com
Branch Office(s)
ISIS Papyrus Europe AG, Papyrus Platz 1, Brunn am Gebirge, 2345 Vienna, Austria (intl headquarters)
ISIS Papyrus Asia Pacific Pte Ltd, 29-01 Suntec City Tower 2, 9 Temasek Blvd, Singapore 038989, Singapore

ISOMEDIA Inc
12842 Interurban Ave S, Seattle, WA 98168
Tel: 425-869-5411 *Toll Free Tel:* 866-838-4389 (sales); 877-638-9277 (support) *Fax:* 425-869-9437
E-mail: sales@isomedia.com
Web Site: www.isomedia.com

Key Personnel
Pres & Chmn: Bruce Straughan
CEO & CTO: Steve Milton
Dir, Internet Opers: Dan Sivils
Founded: 1991

Itzhack Shelomi Design
25 Cushman Rd, Scarsdale, NY 10583
Tel: 212-689-7469
E-mail: studio@ishelomi.com; studio@serifes.
  com
Web Site: www.ishelomi.com
Key Personnel
Owner & Creative Dir: Itzhack Shelomi
Founded: 1987

JF Language LLC, see Unitype LLC

Kelmscott, a Fuse LLC company
5656 McDermott Dr, Berkeley, IL 60163
Tel: 630-898-4261
Web Site: www.kelmscott.com
Key Personnel
Principal: Bill Barta
Pres: Scott Voris
EVP: Jason Tews *E-mail:* jtews@kelmscott.com
VP, Strategy & Client Servs: Jennifer Cox
Dir, Opers: Ketan Shah
Founded: 1936

Kensington Technology Group
Division of ACCO Brands Inc
1500 Fashion Island Blvd, Suite 300, San Mateo,
  CA 94404-1595
Toll Free Tel: 800-535-4242
E-mail: globalmarketing@kensington.com
Web Site: www.kensington.com
Key Personnel
VP & Global Gen Mgr: Ben Thacker
Dir, US Mktg: Jeff Smith
Founded: 1981

Knovel Corp
Division of Elsevier Inc
230 Park Ave, 8th fl, New York, NY 10169
Tel: 212-309-8100
Web Site: www.knovel.com; app.novel.com
Founded: 1880
Membership(s): Special Libraries Association
  (SLA)

Kontron America Inc
Division of Kontron S&T AG
9477 Waples St, San Diego, CA 92121
Toll Free Tel: 888-294-4558 (sales); 800-480-
  0044 (cust serv, US only) *Fax:* 858-677-0898
E-mail: info@kontron.com
Web Site: www.kontron.com
Branch Office(s)
5020 Brandin Ct, Fremont, CA 94538 *Tel:* 510-
  284-1100 *Fax:* 510-284-1111
4555 Rue Ambroise-Lafortune, Boisbriand, QC
  J7H 0A4, Canada *Tel:* 450-437-5682 *Toll Free
  Tel:* 800-387-4222 *Fax:* 450-437-8053

Kroy LLC
3830 Kelley Ave, Cleveland, OH 44114
Tel: 216-426-5600 *Toll Free Fax:* 800-523-2881
E-mail: info@kroy.com; support@kroy.com
Web Site: www.kroy.com

KyTek Inc
PO Box 338, Weare, NH 03281
Tel: 603-529-2512
E-mail: sales@kytek.com
Web Site: www.kytek.com
Key Personnel
Pres: Keith Erf

Labrecque Creative Sound
2825 Main St, Becket, MA 01223
Key Personnel
Owner & Prodr: David Labrecque
  Tel: 520-240-6001 (cell) *E-mail:* dave@
  labrecquecreativesound.com
Founded: 1993

Lachina Precision Graphics Services
3791 S Green Rd, Cleveland, OH 44122
Tel: 216-292-7959
E-mail: info@lachina.com
Web Site: www.lachina.com
Key Personnel
Pres: Jeff Lachina *E-mail:* jeff@lachina.com
Dir, Prodn Servs: Whitney Philipp
  E-mail: wphilipp@lachina.com
Dir, Proj Mgmt Off: Shawn Vazinski
  E-mail: svazinski@lachina.com
Founded: 1978

LanternMedia
Division of Lantern Publishing & Media
128 Second Place, Garden Suite, Brooklyn, NY
  11231
Tel: 212-414-2275
Web Site: www.lanternmedia.net
Key Personnel
Pres & Publr: Martin Rowe *E-mail:* martin@
  lanternbooks.com

Laplink Software Inc
600 108 Ave NE, Suite 610, Bellevue, WA 98004
Tel: 425-952-6000 *Toll Free Tel:* 800-LAPLINK
  (527-5465)
E-mail: info@laplink.com; sales@laplink.com
Web Site: web.laplink.com
Key Personnel
Chmn of the Bd & CEO: Thomas Koll
VP, Fin & COO: Randy Clark
VP & CTO: Jack Wilson
Founded: 1983

Leverage Technologies Inc
9519 Greystone Pkwy, Cleveland, OH 44141-
  2939
Tel: 440-838-1203 *Toll Free Tel:* 888-838-1203
  Fax: 440-838-1203
E-mail: info@levtechinc.com
Web Site: www.levtechinc.com
Key Personnel
Pres: David K Ream *E-mail:* daveream@
  levtechinc.com
Founded: 1990
Membership(s): American Society for Indexing
  (ASI)

LexisNexis®
Division of RELX Group PLC
9443 Springboro Pike, Dayton, OH 45342
Toll Free Tel: 800-227-9597
E-mail: information@lexisnexis.com
Web Site: www.lexisnexis.com

LG Electronics USA
Division of LG Electronics Inc
1000 Sylvan Ave, Englewood Cliffs, NJ 07632
Tel: 201-816-2000 *Toll Free Tel:* 800-243-0000
  (cust serv)
Web Site: www.lg.com/us
Key Personnel
Pres & CEO: Thomas Yoon
Founded: 1958

Lightning Source LLC
Subsidiary of Ingram Content Group LLC
1246 Heil Quaker Blvd, La Vergne, TN 37086
Tel: 615-793-5000 (Ingram) *Toll Free Tel:* 800-
  378-5508; 800-509-4156 (cust serv)
E-mail: lsicustomersupport@ingramcontent.com

Web Site: www.ingramcontent.com/publishers/
  print
Key Personnel
Chief Content Offr: Phil Ollila
CFO: Brian Dauphin
Chief Logistics Offr, Global Opers: John F Se-
  crest
Supv, Content Acq Sales: Bailey Davis
Founded: 1997

Linguistic Systems Inc (LSI)
260 Franklin St, Suite 230, Boston, MA 02110
Tel: 617-528-7410 *Toll Free Tel:* 800-654-5006
E-mail: clientservice@linguist.com
Web Site: www.linguist.com
Key Personnel
Founder & Pres: Martin Roberts *Tel:* 617-528-
  7412 *E-mail:* mroberts@linguist.com
VP: Mark Ettinger
VP, Engg: Boris Katsevman
VP, Lang Serv Progs: Jean-Paul Fandel
Founded: 1967
Membership(s): American Translation Association
  Accredited; Association of Language Com-
  panies (ALC); Globalization & Localization
  Association (GALA)

Linguist's Software Inc
844 Alder St, Edmonds, WA 98020-3301
Tel: 425-775-1130
E-mail: sales@linguistsoftware.com
Web Site: www.linguistsoftware.com
Key Personnel
Pres: Philip B Payne *E-mail:* phil@
  linguistsoftware.com
Founded: 1988

Live'N'Loud
PO Box 86, Van Buren, AR 72957
Tel: 479-216-6727
Web Site: nahteboy.tripod.com
Key Personnel
Owner, Dir, Ed & Writer: Ethan Nahte
  E-mail: nahteboy@livenloud.net
Founded: 1992

Love & Logic Institute Inc
2207 Jackson St, Suite 102, Golden, CO 80401-
  2300
Tel: 303-278-7552 *Toll Free Tel:* 800-338-4065
  Fax: 303-278-3894 *Toll Free Fax:* 800-455-
  7557
E-mail: cservice@loveandlogic.com
Web Site: www.loveandlogic.com
Key Personnel
Opers Mgr: Kelly Borden *E-mail:* kellyb@
  loveandlogic.com
Founded: 1977

Lumina Datamatics Inc
Affiliate of Datamatics Global Services (Mumbai)
4 Collins Ave, Plymouth, MA 02360
Tel: 508-746-0300 *Fax:* 508-746-3233
Web Site: luminadatamatics.com
Key Personnel
SVP: Jack Mitchell *Tel:* 508-746-0300 ext 203
  E-mail: jack.mitchell@luminad.com
SVP, Content Technol: John Wheeler
  E-mail: john.wheeler@luminad.com
SVP, Prod Devt: Gordon Laws *E-mail:* gordon.
  laws@luminad.com
SVP, Sales: Prashant Prabhu *E-mail:* prashant.
  prabhu@luminad.com
VP, Fin & Acctg: John Chappell *E-mail:* john.
  chappell@luminad.com
Branch Office(s)
31572 Industrial Rd, Suite 400, Livonia, MI
  48150 *Toll Free Tel:* 800-717-9153 *Fax:* 734-
  525-4455
510 Thornall St Metropark, Suite 100, Edison,
  NJ 08837 (sales) *Toll Free Tel:* 888-772-5532
  Fax: 732-635-0600

345 Seventh Ave, 4th fl, New York, NY 10001
Tel: 646-453-1000 *Fax:* 212-564-8285
1797 Seddon Ct, Ashland, OH 44805 *Tel:* 419-289-0558 *Fax:* 419-289-8923
3265 Farmtrail Rd, York, PA 17406 *Tel:* 717-764-4000
Datamatics Global Services GmbH doo, Gunduliceva br 33, 78000 Banja Luka, Bosnia and Herzegovina *Tel:* 51304120
Im Leuschner, Park 3, 64347 Griesheim, Germany *Tel:* (06155) 862 99-0 *Fax:* (06155) 862 99-19
Ascendas International Tech Park, Taramani Rd, 12th fl, Phase II, Chennai 600 113, India *Tel:* (044) 6604 6000; (044) 6604 6001; (044) 6604 6002 *Fax:* (044) 6604 6098
Knowledge Ctr, St No 17, MIDC, Andheri (E), Mumbai 400 093, India *Tel:* (022) 6102 0000 *Fax:* (022) 2834 3669
Suyojit Datamatics Knowledge Center, Suyojit IT Park, Survey No 804, Unit No S1-S3, Nashik-Mumbai Hwy, Nashik 422 002, India *Tel:* (0253) 610 2222 *Fax:* (0253) 610 2271
Off No 5, 2nd fl, Tower 1, Stellar IT Park, C-25, Sector 62, Noida 201 301, India *Tel:* (0120) 494 0999
Plot No 29-34, East Coast Rd, Saram Revenue Village, Oulgaret Municipality, Lawspet Post, Puducherry 605 008, India *Tel:* (0413) 660 4500; (0413) 660 4501

Lynch Communications
525 Loma Vista Terr, Pacifica, CA 94044
Tel: 678-939-1212 *Fax:* 480-287-9401
Web Site: www.lynchcommunications.com
Key Personnel
Pres: Paul Lynch *E-mail:* paul@lynchcommunications.com
Founded: 1980
BISAC compatible software

Lynx Media Inc
13654 Victory Blvd, No 282, Valley Glen, CA 91401
Tel: 818-761-5859 *Toll Free Tel:* 800-451-5969 *Fax:* 818-761-7099
E-mail: sales@lynxmedia.com
Web Site: www.lynxmedia.com
Key Personnel
Pres: Len Latimer
Founded: 1987

Map Resources
151 N Union St, No 4, Lambertville, NJ 08530
Mailing Address: PO Box 334, Lambertville, NJ 08530
Tel: 609-397-1611 *Toll Free Tel:* 800-334-4291 *Fax:* 609-751-9378
E-mail: info@mapresources.com; support@mapresources.com
Web Site: www.mapresources.com
Key Personnel
Owner: Barbara Fordyce
Founded: 1985

Maps.com
120 Cremona Dr, Suite 260, Santa Barbara, CA 93117
Tel: 805-685-3100 *Toll Free Tel:* 800-430-7532 *Fax:* 805-699-7550
E-mail: info@maps.com
Web Site: www.maps.com
Key Personnel
Pres & CEO: John Glanville
Dir, Busn Devt: Eric Sanborn
Dir, Opers: Bryan Wilby
Founded: 1991
Membership(s): Association of American Publishers PreK-12 Learning Group; Association of Directory Publishers (ADP); Better Business Bureau (BBB); International Map Industry Association (IMIA); National Council for the Social Studies (NCSS); News Media Alliance; North American Cartography Information Society (NACIS); Yellow Pages Publishers Association (YPPA)

Masque Publishing Inc
8400 Park Meadows Dr, Lonetree, CO 80124
Tel: 303-290-9853 *Fax:* 303-290-6303
E-mail: support@masque.com
Web Site: www.masque.com
Key Personnel
Off Mgr: Beverly Scott *Tel:* 303-290-9853 ext 114
Founded: 1986

Master Books®
Imprint of New Leaf Publishing Group Inc
3142 Hwy 103 N, Green Forest, AR 72638
Mailing Address: PO Box 726, Green Forest, AR 72638
Tel: 870-438-5288 *Toll Free Tel:* 800-999-3777
E-mail: nlp@nlpg.com; sales@masterbooks.com
Web Site: www.masterbooks.com; www.nlpg.com/imprint/master-books
Key Personnel
Pres, New Leaf Publishing Group: Tim Dudley
Ed-in-Chief: Laura Welch
Edit Asst: Craig Froman
Founded: 1976

Matrox Graphics Inc
Division of Matrox
1055 Saint Regis Blvd, Dorval, QC H9P 2T4, Canada
Tel: 514-822-6000 *Toll Free Tel:* 800-361-1408 (sales) *Fax:* 514-822-6363
Web Site: www.matrox.com/graphics
Key Personnel
Busn Devt Mgr: Ron Berty
Founded: 1976

Maverick Publications Inc
63324 Nels Anderson Rd, Bend, OR 97701
Mailing Address: PO Box 5007, Bend, OR 97708
Tel: 541-382-6978
E-mail: moreinfo@maverickbooks.com
Web Site: www.maverickbooks.com; www.mavbooks.com
Key Personnel
Owner: Gary Asher
Founded: 1967

Meadows Publishing Solutions
1305 Remington Rd, Suite G, Schaumburg, IL 60173
Tel: 847-882-8202 *Toll Free Tel:* 888-983-6746 *Fax:* 847-882-9494
E-mail: sales@meadowsps.com
Web Site: www.meadowsps.com
Key Personnel
Founder & Pres: John Kriho *E-mail:* jkriho@meadowsps.com
Busn Opers Admin: Pat Druger
Founded: 1991 (as Meadows Information Systems Inc)

Media Cybernetics Inc
1700 Rockville Pike, Suite 240, Rockville, MD 20852
Tel: 301-495-3305 *Toll Free Tel:* 800-263-2088
E-mail: support@mediacy.com; marketing@mediacy.com
Web Site: www.mediacy.com
Key Personnel
Pres: Nick Beavers
Founded: 1981

Media Supply Inc
208 Philips Rd, Exton, PA 19341
Tel: 610-884-4400 *Toll Free Tel:* 800-944-4237 *Fax:* 610-884-4500
E-mail: info@mediasupply.com
Web Site: www.mediasupply.com
Key Personnel
VP: Frank Quinlisk
Founded: 1986

Medina Software Inc
1441 Oberlin Terr, Suite 1010, Lake Mary, FL 32746
Tel: 407-227-4112
Web Site: www.medinasoft.com
Key Personnel
CEO & Dir, Mktg: Carmen Medina
CFO: Jorge Medina *E-mail:* jm@medinasoft.com
Founded: 1985
Membership(s): Institute of Electrical and Electronics Engineers Inc (IEEE)

Megavision Inc
PO Box 60158, Santa Barbara, CA 93160
Tel: 805-964-1400 *Toll Free Tel:* 888-324-2580
E-mail: info@mega-vision.com
Web Site: www.mega-vision.com
Key Personnel
Pres: Ken Boydston
Sales & Mktg: Richard Chang *E-mail:* rchang@mega-vision.com
Founded: 1983

Micro Focus
One Irvington Ctr, 700 King Farm Blvd, Suite 125, Rockville, MD 20850-5736
Tel: 301-838-5000 *Toll Free Tel:* 877-686-9637
Web Site: www.microfocus.com
Founded: 1981

Microboards Technology Inc
8150 Mallory Ct, Chanhassen, MN 55317
Tel: 952-556-1600; 952-556-1639 (tech support) *Toll Free Tel:* 800-646-8881 *Fax:* 952-556-1620
E-mail: sales@microboards.com
Web Site: www.microboards.com
Key Personnel
Dir, Opers: Dean Ditty
Sales Mgr: Brian Towey *E-mail:* briant@microboards.com
Founded: 1989

Microsearch Corp
5 Broadway, Suite 3, Saugus, MA 01906
Tel: 781-231-9991 *Toll Free Tel:* 800-895-0212 *Fax:* 781-231-9996
E-mail: info@microsearch.net
Web Site: www.microsearchcorporation.com
Key Personnel
CEO: Charles J Kelly *Tel:* 781-231-9991 ext 5 *E-mail:* chuck.kelly@microsearch.net
Pres & Mktg Dir: Susan Kelly *Tel:* 781-231-9991 ext 4
Dir, Electronic Publg: Josephine Sacco *Tel:* 781-231-9991 ext 3
Founded: 1995

Miles 33 International LLC
Subsidiary of Miles 33 Ltd
40 Richards Ave, Norwalk, CT 06854
Tel: 203-838-2333 *Fax:* 203-838-4473
E-mail: info@miles33.com
Web Site: www.miles33.com
Key Personnel
VP, US Opers: Jeff Malik

Monotype Imaging Inc
600 Unicorn Park Dr, Woburn, MA 01801
Tel: 781-970-6000
Web Site: www.monotype.com
Key Personnel
Pres & CEO: Scott Landers
Dir, Sales Opers: Kyle Jacobson
Branch Office(s)
12655 W Jefferson Blvd, Los Angeles, CA 90066

600 California St, San Francisco, CA 94108

6309 Monarch Park Place, Suite 102, Niwot, CO
80503

National Bldg, 125 S Clark St, Chicago, IL
60603

1370 Broadway, Suite 1450, New York, NY
10018

Corrientes 161, 2nd fl, Cordoba, Argentina

Monotype China, 16 XiXia Rd, FuHui Bldg,
Suite 5-115, Shanghai 200120, China

Monotype GmbH, Spichernstr 2, 10777 Berlin,
Germany

Prius Global & Universal, Tower-B, 2nd, 3rd &
4th fl, Plot No A-3, 4 & 5, Sector-125, Noida
201 301, India

Monotype KK, MG Ichigaya Bldg, 5th fl, 1-9
Gobancho, Chiyoda-ku, Tokyo 102-0076, Japan

Monotype Korea, 805 Seongji Heights 3-Cha
Bldg, Yeoksam-dong, Gangnam-gu, Seoul 135-
717, South Korea

The Tea Bldg, Unit 2.05, 56 Shoreditch High St,
London E1 6JJ, United Kingdom

MPS North America LLC
Subsidiary of MPS Ltd
5728 Major Blvd, Suite 528, Orlando, FL 32819
Tel: 407-472-1280 *Toll Free Tel:* 866-978-1008
    Fax: 212-981-2983
E-mail: marketing@mpslimited.com
Web Site: www.mpslimited.com
Founded: 1973
Branch Office(s)
1901 S Fourth St, Suite 222, Effingham, IL 62401
477 Madison Ave, 6th fl, New York, NY 10022
    Tel: 407-472-1280
1822 E NC Hwy 54, Suite 120, Durham, NC
27713-3210
MPS Ltd, HMG Ambassador, 137 Residency Rd,
Bangalore 560 025, India *Tel:* (080) 4178 4242
    Fax: (080) 4178 4222
MPS Ltd, RR Towers, Super A, 16/17 TVK In-
dustrial Estate, Guindy, Chennai 600 032, India
    Tel: (044) 4916 2222 *Fax:* (044) 4916 2225
MPS Ltd, 33 IT Park, Sahastradhara Rd,
Dehradun 248 001, India *Tel:* (0135) 6677 954
MPS Ltd, 709 DLI Corporate Greens, Sector
74A, Narsinghpur, Gurugram 122 004, India
    Tel: (0124) 661 3134
MPS Interactive Systems, GRM Tech Bldg, 2nd
fl, Plot No DH-6/29, Action Area-1, Rajarhat,
New Town, Kolkata, West Bengal 700 156, In-
dia *Tel:* (033) 66111500
MPS Interactive Systems, The Great Oasis, D-13,
2nd fl, Marol Industrial Estate, Andheri (E),
Mumbai 400 093, India *Tel:* (022) 6643 8100
    Fax: (022) 6643 8800
MPS Ltd, C35, Sector 62, Noida 201 307, In-
dia (corp off) *Tel:* (0120) 4599750 *Fax:* (0120)
4021280
Membership(s): Publishing Professionals Network
(PPN)

MRC Medical Communications
Division of MRC Media Group Co
12 Lincoln Blvd, Suite 103, Emerson, NJ 07630
Tel: 201-986-0247
E-mail: info@mrcmedical.net
Web Site: www.mrcmedical.net
Key Personnel
Pres & CEO: David J Rector
VP, New Busn Devt: Susan Rector
Founded: 1978

Multi-Tech Systems Inc
2205 Woodale Dr, Mounds View, MN 55112
Tel: 763-785-3500 *Toll Free Tel:* 800-328-9717
    Fax: 763-785-9874
E-mail: info@multitech.com; sales@multitech.
    com; mtsmktg@multitech.com
Web Site: www.multitech.com
Key Personnel
Chmn: Patricia Sharma

CEO: Stefan Lindvall
CFO: Patrick Golden
EVP, Strategic Progs: Del Palacheck
VP, Mktg: Sara Brown
VP, Opers: Terry Boe
VP, Strategic Devt: Daniel Quant
Founded: 1970

Naviga
7900 International Dr, Suite 800, Bloomington,
MN 55425
Tel: 651-639-0662
E-mail: info@navigaglobal.com
Web Site: www.navigaglobal.com
Key Personnel
CEO: Jeffrey Shine
Mktg Mgr: Ted Thomason *Tel:* 602-674-5800 ext
104 *E-mail:* ted.thomason@navigaglobal.com
Founded: 1985
Branch Office(s)
1652 Greenview Dr, Suite 220, Rochester, MN
55902 *Tel:* 609-466-5305
14614 N Kierland Blvd, S-270, Scottsdale, AZ
85254 *Tel:* 602-674-5800
6767 N Wickham Rd, Suite 111, Melbourne, FL
32940 *Tel:* 321-254-5559
302 Knights Run Ave, Suite 940, Tampa, FL
33602 *Tel:* 813-221-1600
One Van de Graaff Dr, Suite 205, Burlington,
MA 01803
173 Parkland Plaza, Suite B, Ann Arbor, MI
48103 *Tel:* 734-887-4400
3 Becker Farm Rd, Suite 401, Roseland, NJ
07068 *Tel:* 973-422-0800
5625 FM 1960 Rd W, Suite 503, Houston, TX
77069 *Tel:* 281-537-6060
350 S 400 W, Suite 100, Lindon, UT 84042
    Tel: 801-853-5000
3610 W 2100 S, Salt Lake City, UT 84120
    Tel: 801-746-1542
Visionsvej 51, 9000 Aalborg, Denmark *Tel:* 96 31
42 00
Pieni Roobertinkatu 9, 00130 Helsinki, Finland
    Tel: (040) 0899637
Rheinstr 40-42, 64283 Darmstadt, Germany
    Tel: (06151) 27 76 652
Berga Alle 1, 254 52 Helsingborg, Sweden
    Tel: (042) 25 39 00
Sodra Langgatan 31, 392 32 Kalmar, Sweden
    Tel: (0480) 36 20 00
49-51 Eton St, Suite 5A, Sutherland, NSW 2232,
Australia *Tel:* (02) 9810 6939

NETS
Division of Newgen North America Inc
2714 Bee Caves Rd, Suite 201, Austin, TX
78746-5682
Web Site: www.netype.com
Founded: 1940
Branch Office(s)
60/3 Lattice Bridge Rd, Thiruvanmiyur, Chennai,
India *Tel:* (044) 4348 0800 *Fax:* (044) 2443
0740

New England Typographic Service, see NETS

New Riders Publishing
Division of Pearson Education Ltd
50 California St, 18th fl, San Francisco, CA
94111
Toll Free Tel: 800-428-5331 (cust serv)
E-mail: customer-service@informit.com; press@
    peachpit.com
Web Site: www.peachpit.com
Founded: 1986

New York Legal Publishing Corp
120 Broadway, Menands, NY 12204
Tel: 518-459-1100 *Toll Free Tel:* 800-541-2681
    Fax: 518-459-9718
E-mail: info@nylp.com

Web Site: www.nylp.com
Key Personnel
Pres: Ernest Barvoets
VP: Alex Barvoets

NewTek Inc
5131 Beckwith Blvd, San Antonio, TX 78249
Tel: 210-370-8000 *Toll Free Tel:* 800-368-5441
    Fax: 210-370-8001
E-mail: sales@newtek.com (cust serv)
Web Site: www.newtek.com
Key Personnel
Dir, PR: Scott Carroll *E-mail:* scarroll@newtek.
    com
Founded: 1986

Nissho Electronics USA Corp
The Concourse I, 226 Airport Pkwy, Suite 340,
San Jose, CA 95110
Tel: 408-969-9700
E-mail: info@nelco.com
Web Site: www.nelco.com
Key Personnel
Pres: Mizuki Enomoto
Founded: 1985

Nisus Software Inc
PO Box 1302, Solana Beach, CA 92075-7302
Tel: 858-481-1477 *Fax:* 858-764-0573
E-mail: info@nisus.com; sales@nisus.com;
    customerservice@nisus.com
Web Site: www.nisus.com
Key Personnel
Founder, Pres & CEO: Jerzy Lewak, PhD
PR: Dave Larson *E-mail:* dave@nisus.com
Founded: 1983

North Atlantic Publishing Systems Inc
66 Commonwealth Ave, Concord, MA 01742
Tel: 978-371-8989
E-mail: naps@napsys.com
Web Site: www.napsys.com
Key Personnel
Pres: Peter Baumgartner *E-mail:* pjb@napsys.com
Founded: 1989

Nuance Communications Inc
One Wayside Rd, Burlington, MA 01803
Tel: 781-565-5000 *Toll Free Tel:* 800-654-1187
    (cust serv); 888-372-1908 (orders)
Web Site: www.nuance.com
Key Personnel
CEO: Mark Benjamin
EVP & CFO: Dan Tempesta
EVP & Chief People Offr: Beth Conway
EVP & CTO: Joe Petro
EVP & Gen Mgr, Healthcare Div: Diana Nole
SVP & CIO: Mark Sherwood
SVP, Corp Devt: David Garfinkel
Sr Communs Mgr: Katie Byrne *Tel:* 781-565-
5290 *E-mail:* katie.byrne@nuance.com

NWinds
One Northgate Sq, Greensburg, PA 15601
Mailing Address: PO Box 1760, Greensburg, PA
15601
Tel: 724-838-8993 *Toll Free Fax:* 888-315-3711
E-mail: support@nwinds.com
Web Site: www.nwinds.com
Key Personnel
Pres & Programming Dir: Randolph S Krofick,
PhD
Founded: 1987
Membership(s): American Society of Mechanical
Engineers (ASME)

OBS, see Open Book Systems Inc®

OKI Data Americas Inc
Subsidiary of OKI Data Corp of Japan
8505 Freeport Pkwy, Suite 600, Irving, TX 75063

Tel: 972-815-4800 *Toll Free Tel:* 800-OKI-DATA (654-3282)
E-mail: support@okidata.com
Web Site: www.oki.com/us/printing
Key Personnel
Pres & CEO: Sergio Horikawa
Deputy Pres: Shigeaki Tadokoro
SVP, Fin & CFO: Takehito Katagiri
Dir, Channel Sales: Mark Hansinger
Founded: 1972
Branch Office(s)
2067 Wineridge Place, Suite C, Escondido, CA 92029
5000 Dearborn Circle, Suite 110, Mount Laurel, NJ 08054
5800 Hurontario St, Suite 1020, Mississauga, ON L5R 4B9, Canada *Tel:* 905-755-5800 *Fax:* 905-755-5840 *Web Site:* www.oki.com/ca

OmniUpdate Inc
1320 Flynn Rd, Suite 100, Camarillo, CA 93012
Tel: 805-484-9400 *Toll Free Tel:* 800-362-2605
E-mail: sales@omniupdate.com
Web Site: omniupdate.com
Key Personnel
Pres & CEO: Lance Merker
CFO: Gordon Dyer
Chief Mktg Offr: Owen Savage
COO: Peter DeVries
Chief Prod Architect: Yves Lempereur
Chief Revenue Offr: Mark Triest
VP, Cust Success: Dennis Esguerra
Sr Dir, Prod Mgmt: Kimberly Prieto
Dir, IT: Micah Roark
Dir, Prod Devt: Shahab Lashkari
Founded: 1982

OMRON Microscan Systems Inc
Division of OMRON Corp
700 SW 39 St, Suite 100, Renton, WA 98057
Tel: 425-226-5700 *Toll Free Tel:* 800-762-1149 *Fax:* 425-226-8250
E-mail: info@microscan.com
Web Site: www.microscan.com
Key Personnel
Pres & CEO: Andy Zosel
Founded: 1982
Branch Office(s)
486 Amherst St, Nashua, NH 03063 *Tel:* 603-598-8400 *Fax:* 603-821-6908
Rm 2211, Bank of China Tower, No 200, Yincheng Zhong Rd, Shanghai 200120, China *Tel:* 400 820 4535; (0186) 6621 9571 (cell) *E-mail:* jdeng@microscan.com

OneTouchPoint
1225 Walnut Ridge Dr, Hartland, WI 53029
Tel: 262-369-6000 *Toll Free Tel:* 800-332-2348 *Fax:* 262-369-5647
E-mail: info@1touchpoint.com
Web Site: www.1touchpoint.com
Key Personnel
CEO: Dave Holland
Dir, Mktg & Sales Opers: Carey Howard
Founded: 1982
BISAC compatible software
Branch Office(s)
5241 Voges Rd, Madison, WI 53718 *Tel:* 608-838-9147
525 W Alameda Dr, Suite 101, Tempe, AZ 85282, Contact: James Parker *Tel:* 480-966-4003 *Fax:* 480-966-4016
5280 Joliet St, Denver, CO 80239 *Tel:* 303-227-1400
1441 Western Ave, Cincinnati, OH 45214 *Tel:* 513-421-1600
8410-B Tuscany Way, Austin, TX 78754 *Tel:* 512-454-6874

Open Book Systems Inc®
21 Broadway, Suite 5, Rockport, MA 01966
Tel: 978-546-7346 *Fax:* 978-231-0222

E-mail: info@obs.com
Web Site: www.obs.com
Key Personnel
Pres: Laura Fillmore
Founded: 1982
Membership(s): Book Industry Study Group (BISG); Independent Book Publishers Association (IBPA); Internet Society

Open Text Corp
275 Frank Tompa Dr, Waterloo, ON N2L 0A1, Canada
Tel: 519-888-7111 *Fax:* 519-888-0677
Web Site: opentext.com
Key Personnel
Vice Chair, CEO & CTO: Mark J Barrenechea
Chief HR Offr: Brian Sweeney
EVP & CFO: Madhu Ranganathan
EVP & Chief Prod Offr: Muhi Majzoub
EVP & Gen Mgr, SMB & Consumer: Craig Stilwell
EVP, Chief Legal Offr & Corp Devt: Gordon A Davies
EVP, Cust Opers: James McGourlay
EVP, Worldwide Sales: Simon "Ted" Harrison
SVP & CIO: David Jamieson
SVP & Chief Mktg Offr: Lou Blatt
SVP, Cloud Serv Delivery: Savinay Berry
SVP, Corp Devt: Douglas "Doug" M Parker
SVP, Partners & Alliances: Prentiss Donohue
SVP, Revenue Opers: Paul Duggan
Branch Office(s)
2655 N Sheridan Way, Suites 301 & 300, Mississauga, ON L5K 2N6, Canada
38 Leek Crescent, Richmond Hill, ON L4B 4N8, Canada *Tel:* 905-762-6001
75 Queen St, Suite 4400, Montreal, QC H3C 2N6, Canada *Tel:* 514-908-5406

Oracle America Inc
Unit of Oracle Corp
500 Oracle Pkwy, Redwood Shores, CA 94065
Tel: 650-506-7000 *Toll Free Tel:* 800-392-2999; 800-633-0738 (sales)
Web Site: www.oracle.com
Key Personnel
Exec Chmn of the Bd & CTO: Larry Ellison
VChmn of the Bd: Jeffrey O Henley
CEO: Safra A Catz
Founded: 1982

O'Reilly Media Inc
1005 Gravenstein Hwy N, Sebastopol, CA 95472
Tel: 707-827-7019 (cust support); 707-827-7000 *Toll Free Tel:* 800-889-8969; 800-998-9938 *Fax:* 707-829-0104; 707-824-8268
E-mail: orders@oreilly.com; support@oreilly.com
Web Site: www.oreilly.com
Key Personnel
Founder & CEO: Tim O'Reilly
Founded: 1978
Branch Office(s)
2 Ave de Lafayette, 6th fl, Boston, MA 02111 *Tel:* 617-354-5800 *Fax:* 617-661-1116

Outskirts Press Inc
10940 S Parker Rd, Suite 515, Parker, CO 80134
Toll Free Tel: 888-OP-BOOKS (672-6657) *Toll Free Fax:* 888-208-8601
E-mail: info@outskirtspress.com
Web Site: www.outskirtspress.com
Key Personnel
CEO: Jeanine Sampson
CFO & CTO: Lynn Sampson
Pres & Chief Mktg Offr: Brent Sampson
Founded: 2003
Membership(s): The Association of Publishers for Special Sales (APSS); Better Business Bureau (BBB); Colorado Independent Publishers Association (CIPA); Florida Writers Association; Independent Book Publishers Association (IBPA)

Paulist Press
997 Macarthur Blvd, Mahwah, NJ 07430-9990
SAN: 202-5159
Tel: 201-825-7300 *Toll Free Tel:* 800-218-1903 *Fax:* 201-825-6921 *Toll Free Fax:* 800-836-3161
E-mail: info@paulistpress.com; publicity@paulistpress.com
Web Site: www.paulistpress.com
Key Personnel
Pres & Publr: Mark-David Janus, CSP
Edit Dir: Trace Murphy
Dir, Mktg & Sales: Bob Byrns *E-mail:* bbyrns@paulistpress.com
Dir, Mktg: Gloria Capik
Sr Academic Ed: Donna Crilly
Founded: 1865
Membership(s): Association of Catholic Publishers Inc

Personal TeX Inc
722 Lombard St, Suite 201, San Francisco, CA 94133
Tel: 415-296-7550 *Toll Free Tel:* 800-808-7906 *Fax:* 415-296-7501
E-mail: sales@pctex.com
Web Site: www.pctex.com
Key Personnel
Pres: Lance Carnes
Founded: 1985

Pivar Computing Services Inc
1500 Abbott Ct, Buffalo Grove, IL 60089
Tel: 847-478-8000 *Toll Free Tel:* 800-CONVERT (266-8378) *Fax:* 847-478-8750
Web Site: www.pivar.com
Key Personnel
Prod Mgr: Scott Johnson *E-mail:* scott@pivar.com
Founded: 1982

Planar
Subsidiary of Leyard International
1195 NW Compton Dr, Beaverton, OR 97006-1992
Tel: 503-748-1100 *Toll Free Tel:* 866-475-2627
E-mail: sales@planar.com
Web Site: www.planar.com
Key Personnel
EVP, Sales, Mktg & Prof Servs: Adam Schmidt
VP, Global Opers: Rob Baumgartner
Founded: 1983

Powis Parker Inc
2929 Fifth St, Berkeley, CA 94710
Tel: 510-848-2463 *Toll Free Tel:* 800-321-BIND (321-2463) *Fax:* 510-848-2169
E-mail: customerservice@powis.com
Web Site: www.powis.com
Key Personnel
Founder & Pres: Kevin Powis Parker
US Sales Dir: Bill Lawrence
Founded: 1983

Presstek LLC, see Mark Andy Inc

PrimeArray Systems Inc
1500 District Ave, Burlington, MA 01803
Tel: 978-455-9488 *Toll Free Tel:* 800-433-5133
E-mail: info@primearray.com; sales@primearray.com
Web Site: www.primearray.com
Key Personnel
Pres: Sean D Campbell

Printronix Inc
6440 Oak Canyon, Suite 200, Irvine, CA 92618
Tel: 714-368-2300 *Toll Free Tel:* 800-665-6210
Web Site: www.printronix.com

Key Personnel
CEO: Werner Heid
CFO: Mark Tobin
VP & Gen Mgr, Global Prods: Marlon Woolforde
VP, Americas Sales & Mktg: Ron Gillies
Founded: 1974

Printware LLC
Member of Vanguard Graphics International
2935 Waters Rd, Suite 160, St Paul, MN 55121-1523
Tel: 651-456-1400 *Fax:* 651-454-3684
E-mail: sales@printwarellc.com
Web Site: www.printwarellc.com
Key Personnel
Pres: Tim Murphy *Tel:* 651-456-1404
    E-mail: tim.murphy@printwarellc.com
Dir, Sales Opers: Bill Frederick *Tel:* 651-456-1418 *E-mail:* bill.frederick@printwarellc.com

ProductionPro
246 Park St, Bensenville, IL 60106
Tel: 847-696-1600
E-mail: sales@productionpro.com; graphics@productionpro.com
Web Site: www.productionpro.com
Key Personnel
Owner: Douglas Tello *Tel:* 847-696-1600 ext 101
    E-mail: douglas@productionpro.com
Founded: 1992

Progressive Publishing Services (PPS)
555 Ryan Run Rd, Suite B, York, PA 17404
Tel: 717-764-5908 *Fax:* 717-764-5530
E-mail: info@pps-ace.com
Web Site: www.pps-ace.com
Key Personnel
VP: Darby Jo Campbell *E-mail:* dcampbell@pps-ace.com
Dir: Crystal Clifton *E-mail:* cclifton@pps-ace.com
Founded: 2015

Pronk Media Inc
PO Box 340, Beaverton, ON L0K 1A0, Canada
Tel: 416-441-3760
E-mail: info@pronk.com
Web Site: www.pronk.com
Key Personnel
Pres: Gord Pronk *Tel:* 416-441-3760 ext 203
    E-mail: gord@pronk.com
BISAC compatible software

ProQuest LLC
789 E Eisenhower Pkwy, Ann Arbor, MI 48108
Mailing Address: PO Box 1346, Ann Arbor, MI 48106-1346
Tel: 734-761-4700 *Toll Free Tel:* 800-521-0600; 877-779-6768 (sales)
E-mail: sales@proquest.com
Web Site: www.proquest.com
Key Personnel
Chmn: Andy Snyder
CEO: Matti Shem Tov
Pres & CFO: Robert VanHees
COO: Yair Amsterdam
CTO: Roger Valade
Pres, ProQuest Books & Chief Strategy Offr: Oren Beit-Arie
Gen Coun: Kevin A Noms
SVP & Gen Mgr, ProQuest Information Solutions: Rafael Sidi
SVP, Global Content Alliances: Julie Carroll-Davis
SVP, Global HR: Marian Roberge
SVP, Global Sales & Mktg: James Holmes
Founded: 1872
Branch Office(s)
699 James L Hart Pkwy, Ypsilanti, MI 48197
    Tel: 734-879-5300 *Fax:* 734-879-5301

6413 Congress Ave, Suite 260, Boca Raton, FL 33487
620 S Third St, Suite 500, Louisville, KY 40202
    Tel: 502-583-4111
7500 Old Georgetown Rd, Suite 1400, Bethesda, MD 20814
630 Central Ave, New Providence, NJ 07974
    Tel: 908-795-3500
888 Seventh Ave, 17th fl, New York, NY 10019
    Tel: 212-331-7700
3 Ingram Blvd, La Vergne, TN 37086 *Tel:* 615-793-5000
5252 N Edgewood Dr, Suite 125, Provo, UT 84604 *Tel:* 801-765-1737
99 Canal Center Plaza, Suite 200, Alexandria, VA 22314 *Tel:* 703-212-8520
1501 First Ave S, Suite 400, Seattle, WA 98134
    Tel: 206-336-7510
607 St Kilda Rd, 1st fl, Melbourne, Victoria 3004, Australia *Tel:* (03) 8517 8333 *Fax:* (03) 8517 8399
Unit 804, Tower E1, Beijing Oriental Plaza, No 1 E Chang An Ave, Dong Cheng District, Beijing 100738, China *Tel:* (010) 5977 6010 *Fax:* (010) 8460 8669
Taskoepruestr 1, 22761 Hamburg, Germany
    Tel: (040) 89 809 0 *Fax:* (040) 89 809 250
16A W Sq, 318 Hennessy Rd, Wanchai, Hong Kong *Tel:* 2836 5636 *Fax:* 2834 7133
315, AKD Tower, Near HUDA Off, Sector 14, Gurgaon 122 001, India *Tel:* (0124) 4100615
Mitsubishi Juko Yokohama Bldg, 3-3-1, Minatomirai, Nishi-ku, Yokohama-shi, Kanagawa 220-8401, Japan *Tel:* (045) 342 4780 *Fax:* (045) 342 4784
B909, Phileo Damansara 1, No 9 Jl 16/11, 46350 Petaling Jaya, Selangor, Malaysia *Tel:* (03) 7954 2880 *Fax:* (03) 7958 3446
Regus Kraanspoor, Kraanspoor 50, 1033 SE Amsterdam, Netherlands *Tel:* (020) 6353190 *Fax:* (020) 6337765
Sungil Bldg, 4th fl, 584 Gangnam-daego, Gangnam-gu, Seoul 06043, South Korea
    Tel: (02) 733-5119 *Fax:* (02) 734-5120
Velazquez 100-5º D, 28006 Madrid, Spain *Tel:* 91 575 5597 *Fax:* 91 575 5585
Al-Thurayya II, Off 1304, PO Box 502568, Dubai, United Arab Emirates *Tel:* (04) 4331810 *Fax:* (04) 3697646
The Quorum, Barnwell Rd, Cambridge CB5 8SW, United Kingdom *Tel:* (01223) 215 512 *Fax:* (01223) 215 513
3 Dorset Rise, 5th fl, London EC4Y 8EN, United Kingdom *Tel:* (020) 7832 1700 *Fax:* (020) 7832 1710
Avon House, Headlands Business Park, Salisbury Rd, Ringwood, Hants BH24 3PB, United Kingdom *Tel:* (01425) 471160

PTC
121 Seaport Blvd, Boston, MA 02210
Tel: 781-370-5000 *Fax:* 781-370-6000
Web Site: www.ptc.com
Key Personnel
Pres & CEO: James Heppelman
EVP & CFO: Kristian Talvitie
EVP & Chief Cust Offr: Eduarda Camacho
EVP & Chief HR Offr: Jill Larsen
EVP & Chief Strategy Offr: Kathleen Mitford
EVP & Gen Coun: Aaron Von Staats
EVP & Pres, SaaS: Jon Hirschtick
EVP, Augmented Reality Prods: Mike Campbell
EVP, Prods: Kevin Wrenn
EVP, Sales & Commercial Mktg: Michael Ditullio
VP, Corp Communs: Jack McAvoy
    E-mail: jmcavoy@ptc.com
Dir, Corp Communs: Michelle Hopkins
    E-mail: mihopkins@ptc.com

Publishing Data Management Inc
39 Broadway, 28th fl, New York, NY 10006
Tel: 212-673-3210 *Fax:* 212-673-3390

E-mail: info@pubdata.com
Web Site: www.pubdata.com
Key Personnel
Pres: Addison Roverano *E-mail:* addison@pubdata.com
Founded: 1970

QualityLogic Inc
9576 W Emerald St, Boise, ID 83704
Tel: 208-424-1905
E-mail: info@qualitylogic.com
Web Site: www.qualitylogic.com
Key Personnel
Pres & CEO: Gary James
SVP, Engg: Steve Kang
Gen Mgr, Smart Grid: James Mater
Founded: 1986
Branch Office(s)
2245 First St, Suite 103, Simi Valley, CA 93065
4045 NW 64 St, Suite 120, Oklahoma City, OK 73116

Quark Software Inc
Chrysler Bldg, 405 Lexington Ave, 9th fl, New York, NY 10174
Toll Free Tel: 800-676-4575
Web Site: www.quark.com
Founded: 1981
Branch Office(s)
1600 Beltline Ave NE, Suite 210, Grand Rapids, MI 49525
QuarkXPress Publishing R&D (India) Pvt Ltd, A-45, Industrial Area, Phase-VIII-B, Mohali 160 059, India
5th fl, Block 3, 3 Custom House Plaza, Harbour Master Place, IFSC, Dublin 1 D01 VY76, Ireland

Regent Press Publishers & Printers
2747 Regent St, Berkeley, CA 94705
Tel: 510-845-1196
E-mail: regentpress@mindspring.com
Web Site: www.regentpress.net
Key Personnel
Owner, Publr & Mng Ed: Mark Weiman
Founded: 1978

REX
13431 SW Scotts Bridge Dr, Tigard, OR 97223-1609
Tel: 503-238-4525
E-mail: info@rexpost.com
Web Site: www.rexpost.com
Key Personnel
Pres & Chief Audio Engr: Russell Gorsline
Founded: 1972
Membership(s): Oregon Media Production Association (OMPA); Screen Actors Guild - American Federation of Television & Radio Artists (SAG-AFTRA)

Rex Three Inc
15431 SW 14 St, Sunrise, FL 33326
Tel: 954-388-8708 *Toll Free Tel:* 800-782-6509 *Fax:* 954-452-0569
Web Site: www.rex3.com
Key Personnel
VP, Sales: Alex Steuben
Founded: 1959

Ricoh Americas Corp
Subsidiary of Ricoh Co Ltd (Tokyo, Japan)
300 Eagleview Blvd, Exton, PA 19341
Tel: 610-296-8000 *Toll Free Tel:* 800-333-2679 (prod support); 800-637-4264 (sales)
Web Site: www.ricoh-usa.com
Key Personnel
Pres & CEO: Joji Tokunaga
SVP & CFO: Sven Adler
SVP, Busn Advancement: Dennis Dispenziere

SVP, Commercial & Indus Print: Gavin Jordan-
Smith
SVP, Gen Coun & Secy: George Gowen
SVP, Strategic Planning Off: Shark Samejima
EVP, HR & Deputy Gen Mgr, Shared Servs:
Donna Venable
Founded: 1962

Rimage Corp
Division of Equus Holdings Inc
201 General Mills Blvd, Golden Valley, MN
55427
Tel: 952-944-8144; 952-946-0004 (option 2, tech
support) *Toll Free Tel:* 800-445-8288; 800-553-
8312 (option 2, tech support)
E-mail: sales@rimage.com
Web Site: www.rimage.com
Key Personnel
VP, Sales (Americas): Sean Gaafar
Founded: 1978
Branch Office(s)
Rimage Information Technology (Shanghai)
Co Ltd, Rm No 206, 207, 2F, No 1, FuXing
Zhong Rd, HuangPu District, Shanghai 200025,
China *Tel:* (021) 5887 8905 *E-mail:* enterprise.
sales@rimage.cn
Rimage Europe GmbH, Werner-von-Braun
str 9, 63303 Dreieich-Offenthal, Germany
Tel: (06074) 8521 0 *E-mail:* sales@rimage.de
Rimage Japan Co Ltd, 4F Arai No 38 Bldg, 2-7-1
Hamamatsu-cho, Minato-ku, Tokyo 105-0013,
Japan *Tel:* (03) 6452 8780 *Fax:* (03) 6452 8785
E-mail: jsales@rimage.co.jp
Rimage Taiwan, 2F-1, No 115, sec 2, Keelung
Rd, Taipei 11053, Taiwan *Tel:* (02) 2726 0100
E-mail: asia-sales@rimage.com

RISO Inc
Subsidiary of RISO Kagaku Corp
10 State St, Suite 201, Woburn, MA 01801-2105
Tel: 978-777-7377 *Toll Free Tel:* 800-942-7476
(cust support)
Web Site: us.riso.com
Key Personnel
Pres & CEO: Koji Sonobe
VP & CFO: Alex Olshan
VP, Corp Planning: Sho Fujiwara
Founded: 1986

The Roberts Group
12803 Eastview Curve, Apple Valley, MN 55124
Tel: 952-322-4005
E-mail: info@editorialservice.com
Web Site: www.editorialservice.com
Key Personnel
Owner: Sherry Roberts; Tony Roberts
Founded: 1990

Roland DGA Corp
Subsidiary of Roland Corporation of Japan
15363 Barranca Pkwy, Irvine, CA 92618-2216
Tel: 949-727-2100 *Toll Free Tel:* 800-542-2307
Fax: 949-727-2112
Web Site: www.rolanddga.com
Key Personnel
Pres & CEO: Andrew Oransky
Mktg Dir: Dan Wilson *E-mail:* dwilson@
rolanddga.com
Founded: 1990

Saferock
75 Armour Place, Dumont, NJ 07628
Tel: 646-535-0110
E-mail: info@saferock.com
Web Site: saferockretail.com
Key Personnel
CEO: Shah Karim *E-mail:* shah@saferock.com
Founded: 1997

Samsung Research America (SRA)
Subsidiary of Samsung Electronics Co Ltd

665 Clyde Ave, Mountain View, CA 94043
Tel: 650-210-1001
E-mail: sra-contact-us@samsung.com
Web Site: www.sra.samsung.com
Key Personnel
Pres: Joon Lee
Founded: 1988
Branch Office(s)
18500 Von Karman Ave, Suite 700, Irvine, CA
92612
735 Battery St, San Francisco, CA 94111
27931 Smyth Dr, Valencia, CA 91355
3 Van De Graff Dr, Suite 4, Burlington, MA
01803
123 W 18 St, 7th fl, New York, NY 10011
6625 Excellence Way, Plano, TX 75023
101 College St, Toronto, ON M5G 1L7, Canada
1250 Rene-Levesque Blvd W, 37th fl, Montreal,
QC H3B 4W8, Canada

Sceptre Inc
16800 Gale Ave, City of Industry, CA 91745
Tel: 626-369-3698 *Toll Free Tel:* 800-788-2878
Fax: 626-369-3488
E-mail: sceptrecs@sceptre.com; scp-marketing@
sceptre.com; scp-sales@sceptre.com
Web Site: www.sceptre.com
Founded: 1984

SCREEN Americas
Subsidiary of SCREEN Graphic & Precision So-
lutions
5110 Tollview Dr, Rolling Meadows, IL 60008-
3715
Tel: 847-870-7400 *Toll Free Tel:* 800-372-7737
E-mail: info@screenamericas.com
Web Site: www.screenamericas.com
Key Personnel
Pres: Ken Ingram
Founded: 1967

Scribe Inc
842 S Second St, Philadelphia, PA 19147
Tel: 215-336-5094 *Fax:* 215-336-5092
E-mail: contact@scribenet.com
Web Site: www.scribenet.com
Key Personnel
Pres: David Alan Rech *E-mail:* drech@scribenet.
com
Founded: 1993
BISAC compatible software
Branch Office(s)
7540 Windsor Dr, Suite 200B, Allentown, PA
18195
3758 SW 30 Ave, Fort Lauderdale, FL 33312

SDL
201 Edgewater Dr, Suite 225, Wakefield, MA
01880
Tel: 781-756-4400 *Toll Free Tel:* 800-933-6910
(sales) *Fax:* 781-989-8199
Web Site: www.sdl.com

SENCOR International
445 Park Ave, 9th fl, New York, NY 10022
Tel: 212-980-6726
Web Site: www.sencorinternational.com
Key Personnel
CEO: George Martel *E-mail:* georgemartel@
sencorinternational.com
Founded: 1984

Sharp Electronics Corp
Subsidiary of Sharp Corp
100 Paragon Dr, Montvale, NJ 07645
Tel: 201-529-8200 *Toll Free Tel:* 800-BE-SHARP
(237-4277) *Fax:* 201-529-8425
Web Site: www.sharpusa.com
Key Personnel
Pres, CEO & Chmn: Doug Albregts

COO: Mike Marusic
Founded: 1962

Shepherd Inc
2223 Key Way Dr, Suite B, Dubuque, IA 52002
Tel: 563-584-0500
Web Site: www.shepherd-inc.com
Key Personnel
Prodn Mgr: Deb Leibfried
Founded: 1989

Six Red Marbles LLC
101 Station Landing, Medford, MA 02155
Tel: 857-588-9000
E-mail: info@sixredmarbles.com
Web Site: www.sixredmarbles.com
Key Personnel
CEO: David Goodman
Chief Mktg & Admin Offr: Robin Zaccardo
EVP, Busn Devt: John Kenney
EVP, Opers: Michele Baird
SVP, Fin: Meg Trant
SVP, Prodn: Alexandre Vallette
SVP, Technol: Chris Kaefer
VP, Busn Devt: Cary Drake
VP, Learning Strategy: Kelvin Bentley
Exec Dir, Humanities: Bill Scroggie
Exec Dir, STEM: Joyce Spangler
Founded: 1996
BISAC compatible software
Branch Office(s)
4030 W Braker Lane, Bldg 3, Suite 350, Austin,
TX 78759 *Tel:* 512-372-4800
209 Austine Dr, Suite 115, Brattleboro, VT 05301
Tel: 410-527-1606
Jouve India Pvt Ltd, 1st fl, No 1415, No 283/
1B2, Old Mahabalipuram Rd, Kottivakkam,
Chennai 600 041, India *Tel:* (044) 40205300
The Great Eastern Ctr, 2nd fl, 70, Nehru Place,
Delhi 110 019, India *Tel:* (011) 42636116

Smart Communications Inc
641 Lexington Ave, 13th fl, New York, NY
10022
Tel: 212-486-1894
E-mail: info@smartny.com
Web Site: www.smartny.com
Key Personnel
Pres: John M Smart
BISAC compatible software

Sony DADC US Inc
Division of Sony Corp of America
1800 N Fruitridge Ave, Terre Haute, IN 47804
Tel: 818-462-8100
E-mail: sales@sonydadc.com
Web Site: www.sonydadc.com
Founded: 1983
Branch Office(s)
430 Gibraltar Dr, Bolingbrook, IL 60440
Tel: 630-739-8060
Membership(s): Association of National Adver-
tisers Inc (ANA); Audio Publishers Associ-
ation; Content Delivery & Storage Associa-
tion (CDSA); The Digital Entertainment Group
(DEG)

Sony Electronics Inc
Division of Sony Corp of America
16535 Via Esprillo, San Diego, CA 92127
Tel: 858-942-2400
E-mail: selpr@sony.com
Web Site: www.sony.com/all-electronics
Key Personnel
Head, Corp Communs: Cheryl Goodman

The Sound Lab Inc
3355 Bee Cave Rd, Bldg 7, Suite 705, Austin,
TX 78746
Tel: 512-476-2122 *Fax:* 512-476-2127
E-mail: info@thesoundlabinc.com
Web Site: www.thesoundlabinc.com

Key Personnel
Owner: Steve Metz *E-mail:* steve@
thesoundlabinc.com
Owner & Pres: Phil Mezzetti *E-mail:* phil@
thesoundlabinc.com
Founded: 2002

Square Two Design Inc
2325 Third St, Suite 213, San Francisco, CA
94107
Tel: 415-437-3888
E-mail: info@square2.com
Web Site: www.square2.com
Key Personnel
Pres & Creative Dir: Eddie Lee *Tel:* 415-437-
3888 ext 101
Founded: 1991
Branch Office(s)
No 8 Hua Jia Di Nan Jie, Chao Yang District,
Beijing 100102, China, Pres: Min Wang
Tel: (01350) 1084-543 *E-mail:* mwang@
square2.com

Star Micronics America Inc
Subsidiary of Star Micronics Co Ltd
65 Clyde Rd, Suite G, Somerset, NJ 08873-3485
Tel: 848-216-3300 (sales) *Toll Free Tel:* 800-782-
7636 *Fax:* 848-216-3222 (sales)
E-mail: sales@starmicronics.com
Web Site: www.starmicronics.com
Key Personnel
Busn Devt Dir: Christophe Naasz
Founded: 1976
Membership(s): Association for Retail Technol-
ogy Standards (ARTS); National Retail Federa-
tion (NRF); Retail Solutions Providers Associa-
tion (RSPA)

Stilo Corp
1900 City Park Dr, Suite 504, Ottawa, ON K1J
1A3, Canada
Tel: 613-745-4242 *Fax:* 613-745-5560
E-mail: contact@stilo.com
Web Site: www.stilo.com
Key Personnel
CEO: Bryan Tipper
Branch Office(s)
Stilo International, Windmill Hill Business Park,
Whitehill Way, Swindon SN5 6QR, United
Kingdom (headquarters) *Tel:* (01793) 441 444
Fax: (01793) 441 644

Story Monsters LLC
4696 W Tyson St, Chandler, AZ 85226-2903
Tel: 480-940-8182 *Fax:* 480-940-8787
Web Site: www.StoryMonsters.com; www.
AuthorsandExperts.com; www.SchoolBookings.
com
Key Personnel
Pres: Linda F Radke *E-mail:* Linda@
StoryMonsters.com
Founded: 1985

SumTotal Systems LLC
Division of Skillsoft Co
2850 NW 43 St, Suite 150, Gainesville, FL
32606
Tel: 352-264-2800 *Toll Free Tel:* 866-933-1416
Fax: 352-374-2257
E-mail: customersupport@sumtotalsystems.com
Web Site: www.sumtotalsystems.com
Key Personnel
Exec Chmn: Ronald Hovsepian
Chief Admin Offr: John Frederick
Chief Content Offr: Mark Onisk
CFO: Bobby Jenkins
Chief Mktg Offr: Michelle Boockoff-Bajdek
COO: Mike Pellegrino
CTO: Apratim Purakayastha
SVP, Global Sales: Ted Winslow

Branch Office(s)
1415 28 St, Suite 410, West Des Moines, IA
50266 *Tel:* 515-222-9903 *Fax:* 515-222-5920
10 Post Office Sq, Suite 800N, Boston, MA
02109 *Tel:* 857-317-7700
200 Summit Dr, 2nd fl, Burlington, MA 01803
600 Parsippany Rd, Parsippany, NJ 07054
1110 A Brookdale Ave, Cornwall, ON K6J 4P4,
Canada
Three International Towers, Level 24, 300
Barangaroo Ave, Sydney, NSW 2000, Australia
Tel: (02) 8067 8663
102-116 Rue Victor Hugo, 92300 Levallois Per-
ret, France *Tel:* 01 70 37 53 18 *Fax:* 01 70 37
53 53 *Web Site:* www.sumtotalsystems.fr
SumTotal Systems GmbH, Berliner Allee 59,
40212 Duesseldorf, Germany *Tel:* (061) 55-60
52 91 *Fax:* (061) 55-60 51 00
Two International Finance Ctr, Level 19, 8 Fi-
nance St, Hong Kong, Hong Kong *Tel:* 2251
8926 *Fax:* 2251 8626
Mindspace Raheja IT Park, Maximus Towers,
Bldg 2-B, 7th fl, Cyberabad, Hyderabad 500
081, India *Tel:* (040) 6695 0000
Urbanprem Shibuya Bldg 4F, 1-4-2, Shibuya,
Shibuya-ku, Tokyo 150-0002, Japan *Tel:* (03)
6823 6400 *Fax:* (03) 6823 6401 *Web
Site:* japan.sumtotalsystems.com
Suntec Tower Three, Level 42, 8 Temasek Blvd,
Singapore 038988, Singapore *Tel:* 6866 3788
In der Luberzen 40, 8902 Undorf, Zurich,
Switzerland *Tel:* (044) 744 47 42
5 Arlington Sq, 1st fl, Dawnshire Way, Brack-
nell RG12 1WA, United Kingdom *Tel:* (01276)
401950

Sunny Day Productions Inc, see REX

Systems & Software Services Ltd
830 W Springfield Rd, Bldg A, Suite 2, Springfield, PA 19064
Key Personnel
Pres: William Kreider
Certified Peachtree Acctg Consultant: Bob Spielberger

Tamron USA Inc
10 Austin Blvd, Commack, NY 11725
Tel: 631-858-8400 *Toll Free Tel:* 800-827-8880
Fax: 631-543-5666; 631-858-8462 (cust serv)
E-mail: custserv@tamron.com
Web Site: www.tamron-usa.com
Key Personnel
Pres & CEO: Greg Maniaci
SVP: Hidekazu Suzuki
VP, Mktg & Communs: Stacie Errera
E-mail: errera@tamron.com
Dir, Fin: Hiroaki Katano *E-mail:* katano@tamron.
com
Dir, Opers: Pat Simonetti *E-mail:* simonetti@
tamron.com

Tatung Co of America Inc
Subsidiary of Tatung Co of Tawain
2850 El Presidio St, Long Beach, CA 90810
Tel: 310-637-2105
E-mail: service@tatungusa.com
Web Site: www.tatungusa.com
Key Personnel
CEO: Christina Sun
Founded: 1972

Chip Taylor Communications LLC
2 East View Dr, Derry, NH 03038
Tel: 603-434-9262 *Toll Free Tel:* 800-876-2447
Fax: 603-432-2723
Web Site: www.chiptaylor.com
Key Personnel
Pres: Chip Taylor
Founded: 1985

Taylor Communications Inc
Subsidiary of Taylor Corp
1725 Roe Crest Dr, North Mankato, MN 56003
Toll Free Tel: 866-541-0937
Web Site: www.taylorcommunications.com
Key Personnel
CEO: Glen Taylor

TEACH Services Inc
11 Quartermaster Circle, Fort Oglethorpe, GA
30742-3886
SAN: 246-9863
Tel: 706-504-9192 *Toll Free Tel:* 800-367-1844
(sales) *Toll Free Fax:* 866-757-6023
E-mail: sales@teachservices.com; info@
teachservices.com
Web Site: www.teachservices.com
Key Personnel
Owner & Pres: Timothy Hullquist *E-mail:* t.
hullquist@teachservices.com
Publr & Opers Mgr: Bill Newman *E-mail:* b.
newman@teachservices.com
Founded: 1984
BISAC compatible software
Membership(s): Independent Book Publishers As-
sociation (IBPA)

Teledyne DALSA
Subsidiary of Teledyne Technologies Inc
605 McMurray Rd, Waterloo, ON N2V 2E9,
Canada
Tel: 519-886-6000 *Toll Free Tel:* 800-361-4914
Web Site: www.teledynedalsa.com
Key Personnel
Group Pres: Edwin Roks
Founded: 1979

TeXnology Inc
57 Longwood Ave, Brookline, MA 02446
Tel: 617-738-8029
Web Site: www.texnology.com
Key Personnel
Pres: Amy Hendrickson *E-mail:* amyh@
texnology.com

Thistle Printing Ltd
Division of DATA Communications Management
Corp
35 Mobile Dr, Toronto, ON M4A 2P6, Canada
Tel: 416-288-1288 *Fax:* 416-288-0737
E-mail: sales@thistleprinting.com
Web Site: www.thistleprinting.com
Key Personnel
Gen Mgr: Mike Branov
Founded: 1931

Thomson Reuters
Union Bank Bldg, 50 California St, San Fran-
cisco, CA 94111
Tel: 424-434-7000
E-mail: editorial.booking@tr.com
Web Site: www.thomsonreuters.com

Three D Graphics Inc
11340 W Olympic Blvd, Suite 352, Los Angeles,
CA 90064
Tel: 310-231-3330 *Toll Free Tel:* 800-913-0008
Fax: 310-231-3303
E-mail: info@threedgraphics.com; orders@
threedgraphics.com; sales@threedgraphics.com
Web Site: www.threedgraphics.com
Key Personnel
CEO: Elmer Easton
Founded: 1986

3M Touch Systems Inc
501 Griffin Brook Park Dr, Methuen, MA 01844
Tel: 978-659-9000
Web Site: www.3m.com/3m/en_us/touch-systems-
us

Times-Square Fantasy Theatre
Subsidiary of Cude & Pickens Productions
519 N Halifax Ave, Daytona Beach, FL 32118
Tel: 386-252-0381 *Fax:* 386-252-0381
E-mail: timessquare@bellsouth.net
Web Site: www.broadwaymusicdownload.com;
    www.timessquarefantasytheatre.com
Key Personnel
Owner & CEO: Bobby Lee Cude
Founded: 1948
Membership(s): Broadcast Music Inc (BMI); National Music Publishers' Association (NMPA)

Transparent Language Inc
12 Murphy Dr, Nashua, NH 03062
Tel: 603-262-6300 *Toll Free Tel:* 800-567-9619
    (cust serv & sales)
E-mail: info@transparent.com; support@
    transparent.com (tech support)
Web Site: www.transparent.com
Key Personnel
Founder & CEO: Michael Quinlan
SVP & Gen Mgr: Chuck McGonagle
Founded: 1991

Treacyfaces Inc
43 Maltby Ave, West Haven, CT 06516
Mailing Address: PO Box 26036, West Haven,
    CT 06516-8036
Tel: 203-389-7037
Web Site: www.treacyfaces.com
Key Personnel
Pres & Dir, Typography: Joseph Treacy
    E-mail: jtreacy@treacyfaces.com
Founded: 1984

TRUMATCH Inc
PO Box 501, Water Mill, NY 11976-0501
Tel: 631-204-9100 *Toll Free Tel:* 800-TRU-9100
    (878-9100 US & CN)
E-mail: info@trumatch.com
Web Site: www.trumatch.com
Key Personnel
Pres: Steven J Abramson
VP: Jane E Nichols *E-mail:* janen@trumatch.com
Founded: 1990
Membership(s): PRINTING United Alliance

Ultimate TechnoGraphics
300 Leo Pariseau, Suite 2120, Montreal, QC H2X
    4B3, Canada
Tel: 514-938-9050 *Toll Free Tel:* 800-363-3590
    (North America only) *Fax:* 514-938-5225
E-mail: customerservice@imposition.com
Web Site: www.imposition.com
Key Personnel
Pres & CEO: Julie Watson *Tel:* 514-938-9050 ext
    226 *E-mail:* julie@imposition.com
Founded: 1989
Membership(s): Association for Print Technologies (APTech); Ghent Workgroup; International Cooperation for Integration of Processes in Prepress, Press & Postpress Organization (CIP4); NAGASA

UniNet Imaging Inc
3232 W El Segundo Blvd, Hawthorne, CA 90250
Tel: 424-675-3300 *Fax:* 424-675-3400
E-mail: sales@uninetimaging.com
Web Site: www.uninetimaging.com
Key Personnel
Pres: Nestor Saporiti
Corp Mktg Dir: Marcela Gasanz
    E-mail: marcelag@uninetimaging.com
Inside Sales Mgr: Karen Hughes *Tel:* 424-675-
    3300 ext 1109 *E-mail:* karenh@uninetimaging.
    com
Founded: 1995
Branch Office(s)
UniNet East Coast, 22 Old Dock Rd, Yaphank,

NY 11980, Dir of Sales, North America: Craig
    Spooner *Tel:* 631-590-1040 ext 203 *Fax:* 603-
    218-3285 *E-mail:* craigs@uninetimaging.com

Unisys Corp
801 Lakeview Dr, Suite 100, Blue Bell, PA 19422
Tel: 215-274-2742
Web Site: www.unisys.com
Key Personnel
Chmn & CEO: Peter Altabef
Pres & COO: Eric Hutto
SVP & CFO: Mike Thomson
SVP & Chief HR Offr: Katie Ebrahimi
SVP & Chief Mktg Offr: Ann Sung Ruckstuhl
SVP & Pres, Global Sales: Jeff Renzi
SVP, Gen Coun & Secy: Gerald P Kenney
SVP, Prods & Platforms & CTO: Vishal Gupta
VP & Corp Cont: Erin Mannix
VP & Treas: Shalabh Gupta
Branch Office(s)
4750 Lindle Rd, Harrisburg, PA 17111 *Tel:* 717-
    561-7500
9701 Jeronimo Rd, Irvine, CA 92618 *Tel:* 949-
    380-5000
5451 Great America Pkwy, Suite 125, Santa
    Clara, CA 95054 *Tel:* 408-980-9526
Discovery Plaza, One Seventh St, Suite A, Augusta, GA 30901 *Tel:* 706-842-6191 *Fax:* 706-
    432-0534
Bishop Street Tower, 700 Bishop St, Suite 507,
    Honolulu, HI 96813
3199 Pilot Knob Rd, Eagan, MN 55121 *Tel:* 651-
    846-0006 *Fax:* 651-687-2985
10B Madison Ave Ext, Albany, NY 12203
    Tel: 518-452-6100 *Fax:* 518-452-6196
55 Broad St, 7th fl, New York, NY 10004
2501 N Harwood St, Suite 1501, Dallas, TX
    75201 *Tel:* 469-250-1620
480 N 2200 W, Salt Lake City, UT 84116
    Tel: 801-594-4911 *Fax:* 801-594-5660
44664 Guilford Dr, Ashburn, VA 20147
1051 E Cary St, Suite 610, Richmond, VA 23219

UnitechEDI Inc
220 Winthrop St, Winthrop, MA 02152
Toll Free Tel: 800-330-4094
E-mail: info@unitechedi.com
Web Site: www.unitechedi.com
Key Personnel
Pres: Rich Vettel
Founded: 1995
Membership(s): Book Industry Study Group
    (BISG)

Unitype LLC
116-A Mockingbird Lane, Lockhart, TX 78644
Tel: 512-620-0384 *Toll Free Tel:* 800-697-9186
E-mail: info@unitype.com; sales@unitype.com;
    support@unitype.com
Web Site: www.unitype.com
Key Personnel
Pres: Mike Forgey

US Lithograph Inc
39 Broadway, 28th fl, New York, NY 10006
Tel: 212-673-3210 *Fax:* 917-503-3990
E-mail: info@pubdata.com
Web Site: www.pubdata.com
Key Personnel
Pres: Scott Kelly *E-mail:* scottkelly@uslitho.com
Founded: 1970

US Lynx Inc
Division of Publishing Data Management Inc
39 Broadway, 28th fl, New York, NY 10006
Tel: 212-673-3210 *Fax:* 917-503-3990
E-mail: info@pubdata.com
Web Site: www.pubdata.com
Key Personnel
Pres: Michael Krieger *E-mail:* mak@uslynx.com

Founded: 1985
Membership(s): Xplor International

Vectorworks Inc
Subsidiary of Nemetschek Group
7150 Riverwood Dr, Columbia, MD 21046
Tel: 410-290-5114 *Toll Free Tel:* 888-646-4223
    (sales) *Fax:* 410-290-7266
E-mail: sales@vectorworks.net
Web Site: www.vectorworks.net
Key Personnel
CEO: Dr Biplab Sarkar
CFO: Maria Bible
CIO: Paul Pharr
VP, Mktg: Jeremy Powell
VP, Prod Devt: Steve Johnson
VP, Sales: Nicole Davison
Founded: 1985

Victoria Productions Inc
76 Beaver St, New York, NY 10005
Tel: 212-425-3013 *Fax:* 646-225-7218
E-mail: victoria@vproductions.net
Web Site: www.vproductions.net
Key Personnel
Pres, CEO & Creative Dir: Victoria H Farago
Founded: 2005

Videotex Systems Inc
10255 Miller Rd, Dallas, TX 75238
Tel: 972-231-9200 *Toll Free Tel:* 800-888-4336
    Fax: 972-231-2420
E-mail: info@videotexsystems.com
Web Site: www.videotexsystems.com
Key Personnel
Pres: Bob Gillman *Tel:* 972-231-9200 ext 102
    E-mail: gillman@videotexsystems.com

Videx Inc
1105 NE Circle Blvd, Corvallis, OR 97330
Tel: 541-738-5500; 541-738-0521 *Fax:* 541-752-
    5285
E-mail: sales@videx.com; support@videx.com
Web Site: www.videx.com
Key Personnel
Pres: Tammy Davis
Founded: 1979

Virginia Systems
5509 W Bay Ct, Midlothian, VA 23112
Tel: 804-739-3200 *Fax:* 804-739-8376
E-mail: sales@virginiasystems.com
Web Site: www.virginiasystems.com
Key Personnel
Pres: Philip Van Cleave *E-mail:* philip@
    virginiasystems.com
VP: Margaret Van Cleave
Founded: 1984

VITEC Multimedia
931 Benecia Ave, Sunnyvale, CA 94085
Tel: 650-230-2400 *Toll Free Tel:* 800-451-5101
    Fax: 408-739-1706
E-mail: sunnyvale@vitec.com
Web Site: www.vitec.com
Founded: 1988
Branch Office(s)
3174 Marjan Dr, Atlanta, GA 30340 *Tel:* 404-
    320-0110 *Fax:* 404-320-3132 *E-mail:* atlanta@
    vitec.com

VO2 Mix Audio Post
116 Spadina Ave, Suite 208, Toronto, ON M5V
    2K6, Canada
Tel: 416-603-3954 *Fax:* 416-603-3957
E-mail: info@vo2mix.ca
Web Site: www.vo2mix.ca
Key Personnel
Owner & Pres: Terry Wedel
Founded: 1999

Wasatch Computer Technology LLC
333 S 300 E, Salt Lake City, UT 84111
Tel: 801-575-8043
E-mail: subscription@wasatch.com
Web Site: www.wasatch.com

Western Telematic Inc (WTI)
5 Sterling, Irvine, CA 92618
Tel: 949-586-9950 *Toll Free Tel:* 800-854-7226
E-mail: info@wti.com
Web Site: www.wti.com
Key Personnel
CEO: Dan Morrison
Founded: 1964

WeWrite LLC
11040 Alba Rd, Ben Lomond, CA 95005
Tel: 831-336-3382
E-mail: info@wewrite.net
Web Site: www.wewrite.net
Key Personnel
Pres & CEO: Delores L Palmer
  E-mail: dpalmer@wewrite.net
Dir, Mktg: Rickey Bowen *E-mail:* rbowen@
  wewrite.net
Ed: Jan Hansen *E-mail:* jhansen@wewrite.net
Founded: 1993

Writers' Supercenter
560 Roland Dr, Norfolk, VA 23509
Tel: 757-515-4315
E-mail: writerspage@writerspage.com
Web Site: writersupercenter.com
Key Personnel
Pres: Irwin Berent
Founded: 2003

Xante Corp
2800 Dauphin St, Suite 100, Mobile, AL 36606
Tel: 251-473-6502; 251-473-4920 (tech support)
  Fax: 251-473-6503
Web Site: www.xante.com
Key Personnel
Pres & CEO: Robert C Ross, Jr
COO: Mark Swanzy
CFO: Mary Ann Harris
VP, Worldwide Mktg & Intl Sales: Mark Priede
Founded: 1989
Branch Office(s)
7920 Alta Sunrise Dr, Suite 110, Citrus Heights,
  CA 95610
Xante Europe BV, Ratio 39, 6921 RW Duiven,
  Netherlands *Tel:* (026) 319 3210 *Fax:* (026)
  319 3211

Z-Axis
1916 Rte 96, Phelps, NY 14532
Tel: 315-548-5000 *Fax:* 315-548-5100
E-mail: sales@zaxis.net
Web Site: www.zaxis.net
Key Personnel
Pres: Michael Allen
Founded: 1989

ZyLAB North America LLC
7918 Jones Branch Dr, Suite 230, McLean, VA
  22102-3366
Tel: 703-442-2400 *Toll Free Tel:* 866-995-2262
  Fax: 703-991-2508
E-mail: info@zylab.com
Web Site: www.zylab.com
Key Personnel
EVP, North America: Nils Nugeren
Founded: 1983
Branch Office(s)
ZyLAB Technologies BV, Laarderhoogtweg 25,
  1101 EB Amsterdam, Netherlands *Tel:* (020)
  717 6500 *E-mail:* info@zylab.nl

Employment Agencies

The firms listed below specialize in the book publishing industry.

Aquent LLC
101 W Elm St, Suite 300, Conshohocken, PA 19428-2075
Tel: 610-828-0900 *Toll Free Fax:* 877-303-5224
E-mail: questions@aquent.com
Web Site: aquentstudios.com; aquent.com
Key Personnel
Mgr: Kelly Griffin
Founded: 1986 (as Aquent Inc in Massachusetts)
A professional services firm with a new way of thinking about business. Every service we provide, every solution we advance is driven by a mission to help clients work smarter & more efficiently, achieving greater business results. Our five areas of focus are: marketing & creative services; information technology; healthcare services; financial services; offshore publishing services.
Since 1986, at nearly 70 locations in 15 countries, Aquent has led the way in these fields with a pioneering approach to staffing, consulting, outsourcing & technology. Through more efficient use of people, processes & technology, Aquent partners with clients to optimize resources, improve productivity & maximize financial outcomes.

Association of Writers & Writing Programs (AWP)
University of Maryland, 5245 Greenbelt Rd, Box 246, College Park, MD 20740
Tel: 240-696-7700
E-mail: awp@awpwriter.org; press@awpwriter.org
Web Site: www.awpwriter.org
Founded: 1967
Provides news, information & services for writers & teachers of creative writing. Publishes job list & provides job placement for writers. Advocates on behalf of freedom of expression & professional standards in academia. Conducts an annual competition for the publication of books in poetry, short fiction, creative nonfiction & the novel.
The Writer's Chronicle is published 6 times yearly, 3 times each academic semester. *The Guide to Writing Programs* is the most comprehensive guide to creative writing programs in the US & Canada.

Bert Davis Executive Search Inc
555 Fifth Ave, Suite 302, New York, NY 10017
Tel: 212-838-4000
E-mail: info@bertdavis.com
Web Site: www.bertdavis.com
Key Personnel
Founder & Chmn: Bert Davis
Pres: James Conley
EVP: Jeanne Bertelle
SVP: Lauren Aaron; Kristi Johnston; Linda Rascher; Janine Subel
VP: John Tagler
Founded: 1977
The largest executive search firm handling senior-level recruitment for all areas of book publishing: sales, marketing, editorial, finance, design etc. Longtime history of placements in leading companies nationwide; confidential & thorough. President is a director of National Association of Executive Recruiters.

Choice Associates
501 Fifth Ave, Suite 1601, New York, NY 10017
Tel: 212-679-2434 *Fax:* 212-213-0984
E-mail: info@choicepersonnelinc.com
Web Site: www.choicepersonnelinc.com
Key Personnel
Founder & Principal: Steve Klein; Harold Robbins
Founded: 1974
Specialize in editorial, marketing, production, promotion, designers & sales.
Branch Office(s)
700 Veterans Hwy, Suite CL140, Hauppage, NY 11788 *Tel:* 631-617-6002

Cohesion®
511 W Bay St, Suite 480, Tampa, FL 33606
Tel: 813-999-3111 *Toll Free Tel:* 866-727-6800
Web Site: www.cohesion.com
Key Personnel
CEO: John Owens
Chief Strategy Offr: John Larson
Founded: 1982
Provides complete publications support & training. Places screened publications professionals in temporary & permanent positions. Provides start-to-finish editorial, production & design services on outsourcing/project basis. Offers workshops in print & interactive publications. Offers consulting services such as publications evaluations & electronic publishing. Industries served: computer industry, management & environmental consulting firms, book publishers, banks & government agencies. Geographic area served: US. Small, minority, woman-owned firms.
Branch Office(s)
6760 Alexander Bell Dr, Suite 120, Columbia, MD 21046 *Toll Free Tel:* 800-560-0630
5151 Pfeiffer Rd, Suite 105, Cincinnati, OH 45242 *Tel:* 513-587-7700

The Creative Group (TCG)
Division of Robert Half International Inc
125 High St, 17th fl, Boston, MA 02110
Tel: 617-690-7386; 617-526-8899
   Toll Free Tel: 888-651-8589
E-mail: boston@creativegroup.com
Web Site: www.roberthalf.com/work-with-us/our-services/creativegroup
Key Personnel
VP & Branch Mgr: Kristen Johnson
Placement of temporary & permanent writers, editors, proofreaders, desktop publishing professionals, designers, illustrators, web designers & course developers for all forms of creative & technical communications.

HumanEdge
30 Glenn St, Suite 401, White Plains, NY 10603
Tel: 914-428-2233 *Fax:* 914-428-5547
E-mail: info@humanedge.com
Web Site: www.humanedge.com
Key Personnel
Pres: Paul Schwabe
Founded: 1988
Working to create great hiring experiences for candidates & clients alike by applying our skills, energy, integrity & understanding of both individual needs & market forces to make the right match for all types of positions, including traditional contract assignments, career-changing direct searches & freelance gigs.

Branch Office(s)
144 E 44 St, Suite 705, New York, NY 10017
   Tel: 212-986-6800; 212-779-3333 (client line)
33 Main St, 2nd fl, Newton, CT 06470 *Tel:* 203-792-8500 *Fax:* 203-792-8508
1100 Park Central Blvd S, Suite 3400, Pompano Beach, FL 33064 *Tel:* 954-236-6381 (client line)
201 Rte 17 N, Suite 605, Rutherford, NJ 07070 *Tel:* 201-939-9416 *Fax:* 201-939-0270
Membership(s): American Staffing Association (ASA); Business Council of Westchester (BCW); Staffing Industry Analysts (SIA)

Koller Search Partners
655 Third Ave, 24th fl, New York, NY 10017
Tel: 212-661-5250
E-mail: ksp@kollersearch.com
Web Site: www.kollersearch.com
Key Personnel
Founder & Mng Partner: Edward R Koller, Jr
   E-mail: ekoller@kollersearch.com
Mng Partner: Karen Danziger
   E-mail: kdanziger@kollersearch.com; Edward Koller, III *E-mail:* erkoller3@kollersearch.com
Executive recruitment in all aspects of book publishing, magazine publishing, direct marketing & electronic information publishing, as well as art & creative publishing.
Branch Office(s)
12655 W Jefferson Blvd, Los Angeles, CA 90066
   Tel: 213-377-5664
600 California St, San Francisco, CA 94108
   Tel: 415-964-5688

Management Recruiters of Gramercy Inc
Division of Management Recruiters International (MRI)
287 Burns St, Forest Hills, NY 11375-6129
Tel: 347-709-1250
Web Site: www.managementrecruitersny.com
Key Personnel
Pres: Stephen D Schwartz *E-mail:* steve@mrgnewyork.com
Founded: 1990
Executive search & recruitment specialists.

Lynne Palmer Executive Recruitment Inc
295 Madison Ave, Suite 1700, New York, NY 10017
Tel: 212-883-0203 *Fax:* 212-883-0149
E-mail: careers@lpalmer.com
Web Site: www.lpalmer.com
Key Personnel
Owner & Pres: Susan Gordon
Executive search & recruitment within media/digital/publishing industry: including books, magazines, journals, newsletters & online media. Areas in which we recruit & place include administration, art, circulation, corporate communications, digital, design & production, editorial, finance, human resources, marketing, operations, public relations, sales & technology. Our nationwide clientele include: publishing, online educational, multimedia, medical communications & public relations firms.

Publications Professionals LLC
3603 Chain Bridge Rd, Suite A & B, Fairfax, VA 22030-3244
Tel: 703-934-4499 *Fax:* 703-591-7389
E-mail: info@pubspros.com

Web Site: www.pubspros.com
Key Personnel
Founder & CEO: Barbara B Hart
Pres: Linda L Stringer
Founded: 1988
Recruiters of permanent & temporary publication specialists. Pubs Pros, its staff & a roster of independent contractors handle production tasks for books, journals & reports. Clients are in the Washington, DC, metropolitan area; across the US & around the world.
Branch Office(s)
11215 Willamette Meridian Rd NW, Silverdale, WA 98383
Membership(s): Washington Publishers (WP); Women's National Book Association (WNBA)

Ribolow Associates Inc
1350 Avenue of the Americas, 2nd fl, New York, NY 10019
Tel: 212-575-2700 *Fax:* 646-496-9122
E-mail: ribolowstaffingservices@gmail.com
Web Site: www.ribolow.com
Key Personnel
Pres: Adele Ribolow *E-mail:* adeleribolow@gmail.com
Founded: 1960
Executive search & recruitment in all areas of publishing, advertising & new media: editorial, production, sales, marketing, finance, interactive, desktop & support staff. Permanent placement services.

Winston Personnel
Division of Winston Resources LLC

122 E 42 St, Suite 320, New York, NY 10168
Tel: 212-557-5000
Web Site: www.winstonresources.com
Key Personnel
Chmn: Sy Kaye
Pres: Gregg Kaye; Todd Kaye
Founded: 1967
Senior management, middle & junior level recruitment in magazine & book publishing, corporate communications & public relations; print production & graphics.
Branch Office(s)
1400 Old Country Rd, Suite 418, Westbury, NY 11590 *Tel:* 516-333-3222
50 Main St, 10th fl, White Plains, NY 10606 *Tel:* 914-682-2076
301 Rte 17 N, Main Lobby, Rutherford, NJ 07070 *Tel:* 201-460-9200

Clipping Bureaus

BurrellesLuce
30 B Vreeland Rd, Florham Park, NJ 07932
Mailing Address: PO Box 674, Florham Park, NJ 07932
Tel: 973-992-6600 *Toll Free Tel:* 800-631-1160; 800-368-8070 *Fax:* 973-992-7675
Web Site: www.burrellesluce.com
Key Personnel
Chmn & CEO: Robert Waggoner
 E-mail: rwaggoner@burrellesluce.com
COO, Prodn & IT: Chaz Waggoner
Chief Mktg Offr: Johna Burke
SVP, Content Mgmt: Daniel Schaible
Founded: 1888
So much more than a press clipping service. As the leader in media relations planning, monitoring & measurement, we provide online services to help you maximize your media relations results, complete with all text, photos & graphics. We begin with complete media coverage & analysis, delivered quickly & accurately. Our coverage is the industry's most comprehensive, providing the highest caliber of coverage of news & information available across all media. To find out why leading corporations & PR agencies choose BurrellesLuce, visit www.burrellesluce.com.
Affiliate Regional Clipping Services include: Arizona Clipping Service; Capital Clipping Service; Carolina Clipping Service; Minnesota Clipping Service; Mutual Press Clipping Service (Harrisburg, PA); New England Newsclip Agency Inc (DE, NJ, PA); New Jersey Clipping Service; New York State Clipping Service; Virginia Clipping Service.
Branch Office(s)
44 W First Ave, Mesa, AZ 85210 *Tel:* 480-834-4884 *Toll Free Tel:* 800-528-8226 *Fax:* 480-834-3821
1120 Connecticut Ave NW, Suite 225, Washington, DC 20036 *Tel:* 202-419-1850
212 W Superior St, Suite 503, Chicago, IL 60610 *Tel:* 312-278-8883

912 S Kansas Ave, Topeka, KS 66612 *Tel:* 785-232-0201 *Toll Free Tel:* 800-255-2303 *Fax:* 785-232-1604
589 Eighth Ave, 16th fl, New York, NY 10018 *Tel:* 212-279-4270 *Fax:* 212-279-4275

Magnolia Clipping Service
298 Commerce Park Dr, Suite A, Ridgeland, MS 39157
Tel: 601-856-0911 *Fax:* 601-856-3340
E-mail: mail@magnoliaclips.com
Web Site: magnoliaclips.com
Key Personnel
Owner: Dred Porter, Sr *E-mail:* dredportersr@magnoliaclips.com
VP & Dir, Print Monitoring: Joe Porter
 E-mail: joe@magnoliaclips.com
VP, Broadcast Div: Dred Porter, Jr
 E-mail: dredporterjr@magnoliaclips.com
Regional newspaper & magazine clipping service; broadcast monitoring service.

Metropolitan Newsclips Service Inc
1250 Hanley Industrial Ct, St Louis, MO 63144
Tel: 314-395-8917
E-mail: cheryllm@metronewsclips.com
Web Site: www.metronewsclips.com
Key Personnel
Pres: Cheryll A Meyer
Founded: 1985
Complete Missouri, regional, national print, online, broadcast & social media monitoring.
Membership(s): North American Conference of Press Clipping Services

New England Newsclip Agency
Affiliate of BurrellesLuce Co
30B Vreeland Rd, Suite 110, Florham Park, NJ 07932
Tel: 973-992-6600 *Toll Free Tel:* 800-631-1160
 Toll Free Fax: 800-563-9725
E-mail: inquiry@burrellesluce.com

Web Site: www.burrellesluce.com
Key Personnel
SVP & Dir, Natl Sales: Rick Melchers
BurrellesLuce is so much more than a press clipping service. As the leader in media relations planning, monitoring & measurement, we provide online services to help you maximize your media relations results, complete with all text, photos & graphics. We begin with complete media coverage & analysis, delivered quickly & accurately. Our coverage is the industry's most comprehensive, providing the highest caliber of coverage of news & information available across all media. To find out why leading corporations & PR agencies choose BurrellesLuce, visit www.burrellesluce.com.

New Jersey Clipping Service
Affiliate of BurrellesLuce
30B Vreeland Rd, Suite 110, Florham Park, NJ 07932
Tel: 973-992-6600 *Toll Free Tel:* 800-631-1160
 Toll Free Fax: 800-563-9725
Web Site: www.burrellesluce.com
Key Personnel
SVP & Dir, Natl Sales: Rick Melchers
Offers highly focused & accurate monitoring of the media in New Jersey. In addition to press clippings from 27 daily newspapers, 280 non-daily newspapers & 255 magazines, we offer expert monitoring of the Internet, newswires & broadcast media.

Oklahoma Press Service Inc
Division of Oklahoma Press Association
3601 N Lincoln, Oklahoma City, OK 73105
Tel: 405-499-0020 *Toll Free Tel:* 888-815-2672 *Fax:* 405-499-0048
Web Site: www.okpress.com
Key Personnel
Mgr, Clipping Bureau: Keith Burgin *Tel:* 405-499-0024
Clipping service/news monitoring service.

Typing & Word Processing Services

The firms and individuals listed below provide typing, word processing or transcription services. For related listings, see **Editorial Services** (volume 1).

Archetype Inc
Affiliate of North Market Street Graphics (NMSG)
317 N Market St, Lancaster, PA 17603
Tel: 717-392-7438 *Fax:* 717-397-8037
E-mail: mail@nmsgbooks.com
Web Site: nmsgbooks.com
Key Personnel
Owner: Elizabeth Andes *E-mail:* landes@nmsgbooks.com; LeRoy R Stipe, Jr
Founded: 1983
Double keyboarding/verification of book mss, conversion & coding of disks, typesetting preparation & translation program for all major desktop & conventional front-end systems, large volume capacity. All related Macintosh services specializing in the book publishing market.

Arrow Graphics Inc
PO Box 380291, Cambridge, MA 02238
E-mail: info@arrow1.com
Web Site: www.arrow1.com
Key Personnel
Pres: Alvart Badalian
Sr Graphic/Pubn Designer: Aramais Andonian
Founded: 1988
Complete book production services with state-of-the-art electronic design & publishing capabilities: copy-editing; indexing; typesetting & page composition; typography; design & art direction from concept to finished product; printing; consultation; project management. Novels, poetry, monographs, self-help, how-to, guides, ebooks & children's picture books. From ms to camera-ready to bound book, serving the publishing industry & self-publishing community. Call or write for free information, or visit our web site.

Cynthia Barnhart
141 E 56 St, New York, NY 10022
Tel: 212-759-8037
E-mail: trans.action@verizon.net
Founded: 2000
Word processing mss, academic papers, market research, interviews, reports, legal documents. Transcription from digital audio files, tapes or longhand drafts.

Clotilde's Secretarial & Management Services
PO Box 871926, New Orleans, LA 70187
Tel: 504-242-2912; 504-266-9239 (cell) *Fax:* 504-242-2912
Key Personnel
Owner, Mgr, Writer & ESL Instructor: Elvira C Sylve *E-mail:* elcsy58@att.net
Researcher: Kelly M Sylve
Writer: Lillian Gail Tillman; Brenda Bailey, MLIS
Founded: 1989
Proofread journals, newsletters, research papers & medical documents. Specialize in preparing research papers, medical & legal documents. Write basic legal briefs & transcribe documents. Type reports, proposals & academic papers.
Membership(s): ProLiteracy

Mari Lynch Dehmler, see Fine Wordworking

Fine Wordworking
PO Box 3041, Monterey, CA 93942-3041
Tel: 831-375-6278
E-mail: info@finewordworking.com
Web Site: marilynch.com
Key Personnel
Owner: Mari Lynch Dehmler
Founded: 1981
Services for individuals, publishers & others. Offer editing for accuracy, clarity & effectiveness. Also special assignment writing, proofreading, other help. Confidential. Visit web site for testimonials & other info.

Mari Lynch, see Fine Wordworking

Peace Visions
18850 Vista del Canon, Suite A, Santa Clarita, CA 91321-4512
Tel: 661-251-6669 *Fax:* 661-251-6669
Key Personnel
Contact: Susie V Kaufman
E-mail: susievkaufman@gmail.com
Transcribing. Type/edit TV/film scripts, treatments, mss, theses/dissertations, reports, resumes, newsletters, correspondence. Proofreading (including web site content).

Polylogics Services LLC
Affiliate of Polylogics Consulting Inc
6209 Mid Rivers Mall, Suite 320, St Peters, MO 63304
Tel: 201-670-4242 *Fax:* 201-670-4244
E-mail: info@polylogics.com
Web Site: www.polylogics.com
Key Personnel
Off Mgr & Sales: Amy Brake *E-mail:* amyb@polylogics.com
Founded: 1984
Complete line of computer services for the directory publishing industry. Keying, proofing, online correcting & formatting of magnetic tapes suitable for use with various typesetters or in general database construction. Extensive input capabilities in handling bibliographic material, directories, dictionaries, catalogs, legal & foreign material.
BISAC compatible software

Scribe Inc
842 S Second St, Philadelphia, PA 19147
Tel: 215-336-5094 *Fax:* 215-336-5092
E-mail: contact@scribenet.com
Web Site: www.scribenet.com
Key Personnel
Pres: David Alan Rech *E-mail:* drech@scribenet.com
Founded: 1993
Our company was created to convert old versions of multilingual books into electronic text format. Developed a linguistic-based global approach to verifying text & applying mark-up. Perform data conversion, OCR, typing, word processing & transcription services.
BISAC compatible software
Branch Office(s)
7540 Windsor Dr, Suite 200B, Allentown, PA 18195
3758 SW 30 Ave, Fort Lauderdale, FL 33312

SENCOR International
445 Park Ave, 9th fl, New York, NY 10022
Tel: 212-980-6726
Web Site: www.sencorinternational.com
Key Personnel
CEO: George Martel *E-mail:* georgemartel@sencorinternational.com
Founded: 1984
Litigational & transactional document drafting & editing, contract abstracting, case summary writing, electronic document discovery & legal research & analysis comprise SENCOR's range of LPO capabilities. The company combines the domain knowledge of legal researchers & attorneys with the efficiency of in-house developed data acquisition & management tools to meet the knowledge requirements of clients in the legal industry. Among these are legal publishers & practitioners needing the latest information in case law, statutes or testimonies to win court battles.
Clients engaging in SENCOR BI work with IT & statistics professionals & domain experts in marketing, risk management, operations & finance. Aids companies in problem definition, data preparation, exploratory data analytics, descriptive & predictive modeling & the processing & deployment of results.
Also provides customized end-to-end content development & publishing solutions that span the range of information acquisition via research, content enhancement & publication in various formats including printed publications & electronic media.

Typing Etc
89 Stephen Dr, Plainview, NY 11803
Tel: 516-681-7328 *Fax:* 516-681-7328
Key Personnel
Owner: Doris Ladd
Typing of mss, theses, resumes, term papers, dissertations, business correspondence, editing & proofreading; computer services.
BISAC compatible software

WordPlayJane
21 Harrison St, Suite 3, New York, NY 10013
Tel: 212-925-4130
Key Personnel
Contact: Jane Freeman *E-mail:* wordplayjane@yahoo.com
Founded: 1980
Ms preparation, fiction & nonfiction, ghostwriting, editing, writing coach & book illustration. References available.

Writer's Relief, Inc
18766 John J Williams Hwy, Unit 4, Box 335, Rehoboth Beach, DE 19971
Toll Free Tel: 866-405-3003 *Fax:* 201-641-1253
E-mail: info@writersrelief.com
Web Site: www.WritersRelief.com
Key Personnel
Pres: Ronnie L Smith *E-mail:* ronnie@wrelief.com
Founded: 1994
Don't have time to submit your creative writing? We can help. Submission leads & cover/query letter guidelines. Join the 60,000+ writers who subscribe to *Submit Write Now!*, our free e-publication.

Translators & Interpreters — Source Language Index

Rosanna M Giammanco Frongia
  PhD, pg 1409
Glasnost Communications, pg 1409
Andrew S Gordon, PhD, pg 1409
Regina Gorzkowska-Rossi, pg 1409
Joan E Howard, pg 1410
Inlingua Translation Service,
  pg 1410
InterNation Inc, pg 1410
iProbe Multilingual Solutions Inc,
  pg 1410
IRCO-International Language Bank,
  pg 1410
JLS Language Corp, pg 1410
Bruni Johnson, pg 1410
Solveig Kjok, pg 1411
LangTech International, pg 1411
The Language Center, pg 1411
Linguistic Systems Inc (LSI),
  pg 1411
MEJ Personal Business Services
  Inc, pg 1411
Metro Translation Service, pg 1411
Ohnaka & Associates Inc, pg 1412
Passwords Communications Inc,
  pg 1412
Emmanuel X Pierreuse, pg 1412
Polish National Union of America,
  pg 1412
Polyglot Communications Inc,
  pg 1412
Polyglot Translators, pg 1412
Louise B Popkin, pg 1412
Rennert International, pg 1412
Claudette Roland, pg 1412
Rosemoor House Translations,
  pg 1412
Richard Schneider Language
  Services, pg 1412
School of World Studies, pg 1413
Schreiber Translations Inc (STI),
  pg 1413
Natalia V Sciarini, pg 1413
Boris Mark Silversteyn, pg 1413
Spanish/English Translation &
  Interpreting Services, pg 1413
Spanish Publishing Services,
  pg 1413
Strictly Spanish Translations LLC,
  pg 1413
Szablya Consultants Inc, pg 1413
Johannes Tan, pg 1413
Teneo Linguistics Co LLC, pg 1413
Transimpex Translators, Interpreters,
  Editors, Consultants Inc, pg 1413
TranslateMedia, pg 1414
Translation & Terminology
  Services, pg 1414
Translations.com, pg 1414
Translingua Associates Inc, pg 1414
Universe Technical Translation Inc,
  pg 1414
University Language Services Inc
  (ULS), pg 1414
Liliana Valenzuela, pg 1414
Esther Vitalis, pg 1414
Maria Lidia Wilczewski, pg 1415

ESPERANTO

A WordJourney Translation LLC,
  pg 1407
American Translation Partners Inc
  (ATP), pg 1407
East-West Concepts, pg 1408
InterNation Inc, pg 1410
iProbe Multilingual Solutions Inc,
  pg 1410

ESTONIAN

A WordJourney Translation LLC,
  pg 1407
American Translation Partners Inc
  (ATP), pg 1407
East-West Concepts, pg 1408
InterNation Inc, pg 1410
iProbe Multilingual Solutions Inc,
  pg 1410
JLS Language Corp, pg 1410
Linguistic Systems Inc (LSI),
  pg 1411
Translations.com, pg 1414
Universe Technical Translation Inc,
  pg 1414

FINNISH

A WordJourney Translation LLC,
  pg 1407
American Translation Partners Inc
  (ATP), pg 1407
East-West Concepts, pg 1408
Eriksen Translations Inc, pg 1409
InterNation Inc, pg 1410
iProbe Multilingual Solutions Inc,
  pg 1410
JLS Language Corp, pg 1410
The Language Center, pg 1411
Linguistic Systems Inc (LSI),
  pg 1411
Translations.com, pg 1414
Universe Technical Translation Inc,
  pg 1414

FLEMISH

A WordJourney Translation LLC,
  pg 1407
American Translation Partners Inc
  (ATP), pg 1407
Wanda J Boeke, pg 1408
East-West Concepts, pg 1408
InterNation Inc, pg 1410
iProbe Multilingual Solutions Inc,
  pg 1410
Linguistic Systems Inc (LSI),
  pg 1411
Translations.com, pg 1414
Universe Technical Translation Inc,
  pg 1414

FRENCH

A L S International, pg 1407
A WordJourney Translation LLC,
  pg 1407
AAA Fine Translation &
  Interpretation, pg 1407
Rodelinde Albrecht, pg 1407
Veronika Albrecht-Rodrigues PhD,
  pg 1407
American Language Services Inc,
  pg 1407
American Translation Partners Inc
  (ATP), pg 1407
Auerbach International, pg 1408
Baker & Taylor Publisher Services,
  pg 1408
Bien Fait Translations, pg 1408
Wanda J Boeke, pg 1408
Robert Bononno, pg 1408
Alexandra Chciuk-Celt, pg 1408
Cross Cultural Communication
  Systems Inc, pg 1408
Cross Culture Communications,
  pg 1408
Marcia Nita Doron, pg 1408
East-West Concepts, pg 1408
Catherine C Elverston ELS,
  pg 1409
Eriksen Translations Inc, pg 1409

French and English Communication
  Services LLC, pg 1409
GGP Publishing Inc, pg 1409
Rosanna M Giammanco Frongia
  PhD, pg 1409
Diana Mara Henry, pg 1410
Mark Herman & Ronnie Apter,
  Translators, pg 1410
Joan E Howard, pg 1410
Inlingua Translation Service,
  pg 1410
InterNation Inc, pg 1410
iProbe Multilingual Solutions Inc,
  pg 1410
IRCO-International Language Bank,
  pg 1410
JLS Language Corp, pg 1410
Alicja T Kawecki, pg 1411
Solveig Kjok, pg 1411
LangTech International, pg 1411
The Language Center, pg 1411
Linguistic Systems Inc (LSI),
  pg 1411
Link Translations Inc, pg 1411
MEJ Personal Business Services
  Inc, pg 1411
Donald Nicholson-Smith, pg 1412
Passwords Communications Inc,
  pg 1412
Emmanuel X Pierreuse, pg 1412
Polyglot Communications Inc,
  pg 1412
Polyglot Translators, pg 1412
Rennert International, pg 1412
Claudette Roland, pg 1412
Richard Schneider Language
  Services, pg 1412
School of World Studies, pg 1413
Schreiber Translations Inc (STI),
  pg 1413
Martin Sokolinsky, pg 1413
Szablya Consultants Inc, pg 1413
Joan Wagner Teller PhD, Translator,
  pg 1413
Teneo Linguistics Co LLC, pg 1413
Transimpex Translators, Interpreters,
  Editors, Consultants Inc, pg 1413
TranslateMedia, pg 1414
Translation & Terminology
  Services, pg 1414
Translations.com, pg 1414
Translingua Associates Inc, pg 1414
Elizabeth Uhlig, pg 1414
Universe Technical Translation Inc,
  pg 1414
University Language Services Inc
  (ULS), pg 1414
Glenn E Weisfeld PhD, pg 1415

GAELIC

A WordJourney Translation LLC,
  pg 1407
American Translation Partners Inc
  (ATP), pg 1407
East-West Concepts, pg 1408
InterNation Inc, pg 1410
iProbe Multilingual Solutions Inc,
  pg 1410
Linguistic Systems Inc (LSI),
  pg 1411

GEORGIAN

A WordJourney Translation LLC,
  pg 1407
American Translation Partners Inc
  (ATP), pg 1407
East-West Concepts, pg 1408
InterNation Inc, pg 1410
iProbe Multilingual Solutions Inc,
  pg 1410

Linguistic Systems Inc (LSI),
  pg 1411
Universe Technical Translation Inc,
  pg 1414

GERMAN

A L S International, pg 1407
A WordJourney Translation LLC,
  pg 1407
AAA Fine Translation &
  Interpretation, pg 1407
Rodelinde Albrecht, pg 1407
Veronika Albrecht-Rodrigues PhD,
  pg 1407
American Translation Partners Inc
  (ATP), pg 1407
Auerbach International, pg 1408
Baker & Taylor Publisher Services,
  pg 1408
Wanda J Boeke, pg 1408
Alexandra Chciuk-Celt, pg 1408
Cross Cultural Communication
  Systems Inc, pg 1408
Cross Culture Communications,
  pg 1408
East-West Concepts, pg 1408
Ecegul (AJ) Elterman, pg 1409
Catherine C Elverston ELS,
  pg 1409
Eriksen Translations Inc, pg 1409
German Language Services,
  pg 1409
GGP Publishing Inc, pg 1409
Mark Herman & Ronnie Apter,
  Translators, pg 1410
Inlingua Translation Service,
  pg 1410
InterNation Inc, pg 1410
iProbe Multilingual Solutions Inc,
  pg 1410
IRCO-International Language Bank,
  pg 1410
JLS Language Corp, pg 1410
Bruni Johnson, pg 1410
Solveig Kjok, pg 1411
Kenneth Kronenberg, pg 1411
The Language Center, pg 1411
Linguistic Systems Inc (LSI),
  pg 1411
Link Translations Inc, pg 1411
MEJ Personal Business Services
  Inc, pg 1411
Metro Translation Service, pg 1411
Verne Moberg, pg 1411
Steven T Murray, pg 1412
Polyglot Communications Inc,
  pg 1412
Polyglot Translators, pg 1412
Rennert International, pg 1412
Richard Schneider Language
  Services, pg 1412
School of World Studies, pg 1413
Schreiber Translations Inc (STI),
  pg 1413
Lesley M Schuldt, pg 1413
Monika Shoffman-Graves, pg 1413
Martin Sokolinsky, pg 1413
Szablya Consultants Inc, pg 1413
Joan Wagner Teller PhD, Translator,
  pg 1413
Teneo Linguistics Co LLC, pg 1413
Transimpex Translators, Interpreters,
  Editors, Consultants Inc, pg 1413
TranslateMedia, pg 1414
Translations.com, pg 1414
Translingua Associates Inc, pg 1414
Elizabeth Uhlig, pg 1414
Universe Technical Translation Inc,
  pg 1414
University Language Services Inc
  (ULS), pg 1414
Krishna Winston, pg 1415

GREEK

A WordJourney Translation LLC, pg 1407

AAA Fine Translation & Interpretation, pg 1407

American Translation Partners Inc (ATP), pg 1407

Cross Cultural Communication Systems Inc, pg 1408

East-West Concepts, pg 1408

InterNation Inc, pg 1410

iProbe Multilingual Solutions Inc, pg 1410

JLS Language Corp, pg 1410

Linguistic Systems Inc (LSI), pg 1411

Translations.com, pg 1414

Elizabeth Uhlig, pg 1414

Universe Technical Translation Inc, pg 1414

HEBREW

A WordJourney Translation LLC, pg 1407

AAA Fine Translation & Interpretation, pg 1407

American Translation Partners Inc (ATP), pg 1407

Cross Cultural Communication Systems Inc, pg 1408

Marcia Nita Doron, pg 1408

East-West Concepts, pg 1408

InterNation Inc, pg 1410

iProbe Multilingual Solutions Inc, pg 1410

Linguistic Systems Inc (LSI), pg 1411

Monika Shoffman-Graves, pg 1413

Translations.com, pg 1414

Universe Technical Translation Inc, pg 1414

HINDI

A WordJourney Translation LLC, pg 1407

AAA Fine Translation & Interpretation, pg 1407

American Translation Partners Inc (ATP), pg 1407

Cross Cultural Communication Systems Inc, pg 1408

East-West Concepts, pg 1408

InterNation Inc, pg 1410

iProbe Multilingual Solutions Inc, pg 1410

Linguistic Systems Inc (LSI), pg 1411

Translations.com, pg 1414

Universe Technical Translation Inc, pg 1414

HUNGARIAN

A WordJourney Translation LLC, pg 1407

AAA Fine Translation & Interpretation, pg 1407

American Translation Partners Inc (ATP), pg 1407

East-West Concepts, pg 1408

InterNation Inc, pg 1410

iProbe Multilingual Solutions Inc, pg 1410

JLS Language Corp, pg 1410

The Language Center, pg 1411

Linguistic Systems Inc (LSI), pg 1411

Szablya Consultants Inc, pg 1413

Translations.com, pg 1414

Universe Technical Translation Inc, pg 1414

Esther Vitalis, pg 1414

ICELANDIC

A WordJourney Translation LLC, pg 1407

American Translation Partners Inc (ATP), pg 1407

East-West Concepts, pg 1408

InterNation Inc, pg 1410

iProbe Multilingual Solutions Inc, pg 1410

Linguistic Systems Inc (LSI), pg 1411

Universe Technical Translation Inc, pg 1414

INDONESIAN

A WordJourney Translation LLC, pg 1407

American Translation Partners Inc (ATP), pg 1407

East-West Concepts, pg 1408

InterNation Inc, pg 1410

iProbe Multilingual Solutions Inc, pg 1410

JLS Language Corp, pg 1410

Linguistic Systems Inc (LSI), pg 1411

Johannes Tan, pg 1413

Translations.com, pg 1414

Universe Technical Translation Inc, pg 1414

ITALIAN

A L S International, pg 1407

A WordJourney Translation LLC, pg 1407

AAA Fine Translation & Interpretation, pg 1407

American Translation Partners Inc (ATP), pg 1407

Anne Milano Appel, pg 1408

Auerbach International, pg 1408

Baker & Taylor Publisher Services, pg 1408

Robert Bononno, pg 1408

Cross Cultural Communication Systems Inc, pg 1408

Cross Culture Communications, pg 1408

East-West Concepts, pg 1408

Eriksen Translations Inc, pg 1409

Mayra E Garcia, pg 1409

GGP Publishing Inc, pg 1409

Rosanna M Giammanco Frongia PhD, pg 1409

Mark Herman & Ronnie Apter, Translators, pg 1410

Inlingua Translation Service, pg 1410

InterNation Inc, pg 1410

iProbe Multilingual Solutions Inc, pg 1410

IRCO-International Language Bank, pg 1410

JLS Language Corp, pg 1410

Alicja T Kawecki, pg 1411

LangTech International, pg 1411

The Language Center, pg 1411

Linguistic Systems Inc (LSI), pg 1411

MEJ Personal Business Services Inc, pg 1411

Polyglot Communications Inc, pg 1412

Polyglot Translators, pg 1412

Rennert International, pg 1412

Rosemoor House Translations, pg 1412

Richard Schneider Language Services, pg 1412

School of World Studies, pg 1413

Schreiber Translations Inc (STI), pg 1413

Teneo Linguistics Co LLC, pg 1413

Transimpex Translators, Interpreters, Editors, Consultants Inc, pg 1413

TranslateMedia, pg 1414

Translations.com, pg 1414

Translingua Associates Inc, pg 1414

Elizabeth Uhlig, pg 1414

Universe Technical Translation Inc, pg 1414

University Language Services Inc (ULS), pg 1414

JAPANESE

A WordJourney Translation LLC, pg 1407

AAA Fine Translation & Interpretation, pg 1407

American Translation Partners Inc (ATP), pg 1407

Cross Cultural Communication Systems Inc, pg 1408

East-West Concepts, pg 1408

GGP Publishing Inc, pg 1409

InterNation Inc, pg 1410

iProbe Multilingual Solutions Inc, pg 1410

JLS Language Corp, pg 1410

Wayne P Lammers, pg 1411

The Language Center, pg 1411

Linguistic Systems Inc (LSI), pg 1411

Metro Translation Service, pg 1411

Ohnaka & Associates Inc, pg 1412

Translations.com, pg 1414

Universe Technical Translation Inc, pg 1414

JAVANESE

A WordJourney Translation LLC, pg 1407

American Translation Partners Inc (ATP), pg 1407

East-West Concepts, pg 1408

InterNation Inc, pg 1410

iProbe Multilingual Solutions Inc, pg 1410

Linguistic Systems Inc (LSI), pg 1411

KHMER

A WordJourney Translation LLC, pg 1407

American Translation Partners Inc (ATP), pg 1407

Cross Cultural Communication Systems Inc, pg 1408

East-West Concepts, pg 1408

InterNation Inc, pg 1410

iProbe Multilingual Solutions Inc, pg 1410

Linguistic Systems Inc (LSI), pg 1411

Translations.com, pg 1414

KOREAN

A WordJourney Translation LLC, pg 1407

AAA Fine Translation & Interpretation, pg 1407

American Translation Partners Inc (ATP), pg 1407

Cross Cultural Communication Systems Inc, pg 1408

East-West Concepts, pg 1408

InterNation Inc, pg 1410

iProbe Multilingual Solutions Inc, pg 1410

JLS Language Corp, pg 1410

The Language Center, pg 1411

Linguistic Systems Inc (LSI), pg 1411

Link Translations Inc, pg 1411

Translations.com, pg 1414

Universe Technical Translation Inc, pg 1414

KURDISH

A WordJourney Translation LLC, pg 1407

American Translation Partners Inc (ATP), pg 1407

East-West Concepts, pg 1408

InterNation Inc, pg 1410

iProbe Multilingual Solutions Inc, pg 1410

Universe Technical Translation Inc, pg 1414

LATIN

A WordJourney Translation LLC, pg 1407

AAA Fine Translation & Interpretation, pg 1407

American Translation Partners Inc (ATP), pg 1407

East-West Concepts, pg 1408

GGP Publishing Inc, pg 1409

Rosanna M Giammanco Frongia PhD, pg 1409

Mark Herman & Ronnie Apter, Translators, pg 1410

InterNation Inc, pg 1410

iProbe Multilingual Solutions Inc, pg 1410

Linguistic Systems Inc (LSI), pg 1411

Szablya Consultants Inc, pg 1413

Translations.com, pg 1414

Universe Technical Translation Inc, pg 1414

LATVIAN

A WordJourney Translation LLC, pg 1407

American Translation Partners Inc (ATP), pg 1407

East-West Concepts, pg 1408

InterNation Inc, pg 1410

iProbe Multilingual Solutions Inc, pg 1410

JLS Language Corp, pg 1410

Linguistic Systems Inc (LSI), pg 1411

Universe Technical Translation Inc, pg 1414

LITHUANIAN

A WordJourney Translation LLC, pg 1407

American Translation Partners Inc (ATP), pg 1407

East-West Concepts, pg 1408

InterNation Inc, pg 1410

iProbe Multilingual Solutions Inc, pg 1410

JLS Language Corp, pg 1410

The Language Center, pg 1411

Linguistic Systems Inc (LSI), pg 1411

Universe Technical Translation Inc, pg 1414

MACEDONIAN

A WordJourney Translation LLC, pg 1407
AAA Fine Translation & Interpretation, pg 1407
American Translation Partners Inc (ATP), pg 1407
East-West Concepts, pg 1408
InterNation Inc, pg 1410
iProbe Multilingual Solutions Inc, pg 1410
JLS Language Corp, pg 1410
Linguistic Systems Inc (LSI), pg 1411
Universe Technical Translation Inc, pg 1414

MALAGASY

A WordJourney Translation LLC, pg 1407
American Translation Partners Inc (ATP), pg 1407
East-West Concepts, pg 1408
InterNation Inc, pg 1410
iProbe Multilingual Solutions Inc, pg 1410
Universe Technical Translation Inc, pg 1414

MALAYALAM

A WordJourney Translation LLC, pg 1407
American Translation Partners Inc (ATP), pg 1407
East-West Concepts, pg 1408
InterNation Inc, pg 1410
iProbe Multilingual Solutions Inc, pg 1410
Universe Technical Translation Inc, pg 1414

MALAYSIAN

A WordJourney Translation LLC, pg 1407
American Translation Partners Inc (ATP), pg 1407
East-West Concepts, pg 1408
InterNation Inc, pg 1410
iProbe Multilingual Solutions Inc, pg 1410
JLS Language Corp, pg 1410
Linguistic Systems Inc (LSI), pg 1411
Translations.com, pg 1414
Universe Technical Translation Inc, pg 1414

NEPALI

A WordJourney Translation LLC, pg 1407
American Translation Partners Inc (ATP), pg 1407
East-West Concepts, pg 1408
InterNation Inc, pg 1410
iProbe Multilingual Solutions Inc, pg 1410
Linguistic Systems Inc (LSI), pg 1411

NORWEGIAN

A WordJourney Translation LLC, pg 1407
AAA Fine Translation & Interpretation, pg 1407
American Translation Partners Inc (ATP), pg 1407
East-West Concepts, pg 1408
Eriksen Translations Inc, pg 1409

InterNation Inc, pg 1410
iProbe Multilingual Solutions Inc, pg 1410
JLS Language Corp, pg 1410
Solveig Kjok, pg 1411
The Language Center, pg 1411
Linguistic Systems Inc (LSI), pg 1411
Verne Moberg, pg 1411
Steven T Murray, pg 1412
Tiina Nunnally, pg 1412
Translations.com, pg 1414
Universe Technical Translation Inc, pg 1414

PERSIAN

A WordJourney Translation LLC, pg 1407
AAA Fine Translation & Interpretation, pg 1407
American Translation Partners Inc (ATP), pg 1407
Cross Cultural Communication Systems Inc, pg 1408
East-West Concepts, pg 1408
InterNation Inc, pg 1410
iProbe Multilingual Solutions Inc, pg 1410
Link Translations Inc, pg 1411
Polyglot Translators, pg 1412
Universe Technical Translation Inc, pg 1414

POLISH

A WordJourney Translation LLC, pg 1407
AAA Fine Translation & Interpretation, pg 1407
American Translation Partners Inc (ATP), pg 1407
Alexandra Chciuk-Celt, pg 1408
Cross Cultural Communication Systems Inc, pg 1408
East-West Concepts, pg 1408
Regina Gelb, pg 1409
Regina Gorzkowska-Rossi, pg 1409
InterNation Inc, pg 1410
iProbe Multilingual Solutions Inc, pg 1410
JLS Language Corp, pg 1410
Alicja T Kawecki, pg 1411
The Language Center, pg 1411
Linguistic Systems Inc (LSI), pg 1411
Polish National Union of America, pg 1412
Translations.com, pg 1414
Universe Technical Translation Inc, pg 1414
Maria Lidia Wilczewski, pg 1415

PORTUGUESE

A WordJourney Translation LLC, pg 1407
AAA Fine Translation & Interpretation, pg 1407
American Language Services Inc, pg 1407
American Translation Partners Inc (ATP), pg 1407
Elizabeth Castaldini, pg 1408
Cross Cultural Communication Systems Inc, pg 1408
East-West Concepts, pg 1408
GGP Publishing Inc, pg 1409
InterNation Inc, pg 1410
iProbe Multilingual Solutions Inc, pg 1410
JLS Language Corp, pg 1410
LangTech International, pg 1411

The Language Center, pg 1411
Linguistic Systems Inc (LSI), pg 1411
Link Translations Inc, pg 1411
Metro Translation Service, pg 1411
Translations.com, pg 1414
Elizabeth Uhlig, pg 1414
Universe Technical Translation Inc, pg 1414

PROVENCAL

A WordJourney Translation LLC, pg 1407
American Translation Partners Inc (ATP), pg 1407
East-West Concepts, pg 1408
Mark Herman & Ronnie Apter, Translators, pg 1410
InterNation Inc, pg 1410
iProbe Multilingual Solutions Inc, pg 1410

PUNJABI

A WordJourney Translation LLC, pg 1407
AAA Fine Translation & Interpretation, pg 1407
American Translation Partners Inc (ATP), pg 1407
Cross Cultural Communication Systems Inc, pg 1408
East-West Concepts, pg 1408
InterNation Inc, pg 1410
iProbe Multilingual Solutions Inc, pg 1410
Linguistic Systems Inc (LSI), pg 1411
Universe Technical Translation Inc, pg 1414

ROMANIAN

A WordJourney Translation LLC, pg 1407
AAA Fine Translation & Interpretation, pg 1407
American Translation Partners Inc (ATP), pg 1407
East-West Concepts, pg 1408
InterNation Inc, pg 1410
iProbe Multilingual Solutions Inc, pg 1410
JLS Language Corp, pg 1410
Linguistic Systems Inc (LSI), pg 1411
Translations.com, pg 1414
Universe Technical Translation Inc, pg 1414

RUSSIAN

A WordJourney Translation LLC, pg 1407
AAA Fine Translation & Interpretation, pg 1407
American Translation Partners Inc (ATP), pg 1407
Cross Cultural Communication Systems Inc, pg 1408
East-West Concepts, pg 1408
GGP Publishing Inc, pg 1409
Glasnost Communications, pg 1409
Mark Herman & Ronnie Apter, Translators, pg 1410
InterNation Inc, pg 1410
iProbe Multilingual Solutions Inc, pg 1410
JLS Language Corp, pg 1410
Alicja T Kawecki, pg 1411
The Language Center, pg 1411

Linguistic Systems Inc (LSI), pg 1411
Link Translations Inc, pg 1411
Marian Schwartz, pg 1413
Natalia V Sciarini, pg 1413
Christina Sever, pg 1413
Boris Mark Silversteyn, pg 1413
Martin Sokolinsky, pg 1413
Joan Wagner Teller PhD, Translator, pg 1413
Translations.com, pg 1414
Universe Technical Translation Inc, pg 1414

SERBO-CROATIAN

A WordJourney Translation LLC, pg 1407
AAA Fine Translation & Interpretation, pg 1407
American Translation Partners Inc (ATP), pg 1407
Cross Cultural Communication Systems Inc, pg 1408
InterNation Inc, pg 1410
iProbe Multilingual Solutions Inc, pg 1410
JLS Language Corp, pg 1410
The Language Center, pg 1411
Linguistic Systems Inc (LSI), pg 1411
Translations.com, pg 1414
Universe Technical Translation Inc, pg 1414

SINHALESE

A WordJourney Translation LLC, pg 1407
American Translation Partners Inc (ATP), pg 1407
East-West Concepts, pg 1408
InterNation Inc, pg 1410
iProbe Multilingual Solutions Inc, pg 1410
Linguistic Systems Inc (LSI), pg 1411

SLOVAK

A WordJourney Translation LLC, pg 1407
AAA Fine Translation & Interpretation, pg 1407
American Translation Partners Inc (ATP), pg 1407
East-West Concepts, pg 1408
InterNation Inc, pg 1410
iProbe Multilingual Solutions Inc, pg 1410
JLS Language Corp, pg 1410
The Language Center, pg 1411
Linguistic Systems Inc (LSI), pg 1411
Translations.com, pg 1414
Universe Technical Translation Inc, pg 1414

SLOVENE

A WordJourney Translation LLC, pg 1407
AAA Fine Translation & Interpretation, pg 1407
American Translation Partners Inc (ATP), pg 1407
East-West Concepts, pg 1408
InterNation Inc, pg 1410
iProbe Multilingual Solutions Inc, pg 1410
Linguistic Systems Inc (LSI), pg 1411
Translations.com, pg 1414

Translators & Interpreters — Target Language Index

MALAYSIAN

A WordJourney Translation LLC, pg 1407

American Translation Partners Inc (ATP), pg 1407

East-West Concepts, pg 1408

InterNation Inc, pg 1410

iProbe Multilingual Solutions Inc, pg 1410

JLS Language Corp, pg 1410

Linguistic Systems Inc (LSI), pg 1411

Translations.com, pg 1414

Universe Technical Translation Inc, pg 1414

NEPALI

A WordJourney Translation LLC, pg 1407

American Translation Partners Inc (ATP), pg 1407

East-West Concepts, pg 1408

InterNation Inc, pg 1410

iProbe Multilingual Solutions Inc, pg 1410

Linguistic Systems Inc (LSI), pg 1411

NORWEGIAN

A WordJourney Translation LLC, pg 1407

AAA Fine Translation & Interpretation, pg 1407

American Translation Partners Inc (ATP), pg 1407

East-West Concepts, pg 1408

Eriksen Translations Inc, pg 1409

InterNation Inc, pg 1410

iProbe Multilingual Solutions Inc, pg 1410

JLS Language Corp, pg 1410

Solveig Kjok, pg 1411

The Language Center, pg 1411

Linguistic Systems Inc (LSI), pg 1411

Translations.com, pg 1414

Universe Technical Translation Inc, pg 1414

PERSIAN

A WordJourney Translation LLC, pg 1407

AAA Fine Translation & Interpretation, pg 1407

American Translation Partners Inc (ATP), pg 1407

Cross Cultural Communication Systems Inc, pg 1408

East-West Concepts, pg 1408

InterNation Inc, pg 1410

iProbe Multilingual Solutions Inc, pg 1410

Polyglot Translators, pg 1412

Universe Technical Translation Inc, pg 1414

POLISH

A WordJourney Translation LLC, pg 1407

American Translation Partners Inc (ATP), pg 1407

Cross Cultural Communication Systems Inc, pg 1408

East-West Concepts, pg 1408

Regina Gelb, pg 1409

Regina Gorzkowska-Rossi, pg 1409

InterNation Inc, pg 1410

iProbe Multilingual Solutions Inc, pg 1410

JLS Language Corp, pg 1410

The Language Center, pg 1411

Linguistic Systems Inc (LSI), pg 1411

Polish National Union of America, pg 1412

Translations.com, pg 1414

Universe Technical Translation Inc, pg 1414

Maria Lidia Wilczewski, pg 1415

PORTUGUESE

A WordJourney Translation LLC, pg 1407

AAA Fine Translation & Interpretation, pg 1407

American Language Services Inc, pg 1407

American Translation Partners Inc (ATP), pg 1407

Elizabeth Castaldini, pg 1408

Cross Cultural Communication Systems Inc, pg 1408

East-West Concepts, pg 1408

GGP Publishing Inc, pg 1409

InterNation Inc, pg 1410

iProbe Multilingual Solutions Inc, pg 1410

JLS Language Corp, pg 1410

The Language Center, pg 1411

Linguistic Systems Inc (LSI), pg 1411

Metro Translation Service, pg 1411

School of World Studies, pg 1413

Translations.com, pg 1414

Universe Technical Translation Inc, pg 1414

PROVENCAL

A WordJourney Translation LLC, pg 1407

American Translation Partners Inc (ATP), pg 1407

East-West Concepts, pg 1408

InterNation Inc, pg 1410

iProbe Multilingual Solutions Inc, pg 1410

PUNJABI

A WordJourney Translation LLC, pg 1407

AAA Fine Translation & Interpretation, pg 1407

American Translation Partners Inc (ATP), pg 1407

Cross Cultural Communication Systems Inc, pg 1408

East-West Concepts, pg 1408

InterNation Inc, pg 1410

iProbe Multilingual Solutions Inc, pg 1410

Linguistic Systems Inc (LSI), pg 1411

Universe Technical Translation Inc, pg 1414

ROMANIAN

A WordJourney Translation LLC, pg 1407

AAA Fine Translation & Interpretation, pg 1407

American Translation Partners Inc (ATP), pg 1407

East-West Concepts, pg 1408

InterNation Inc, pg 1410

iProbe Multilingual Solutions Inc, pg 1410

JLS Language Corp, pg 1410

Linguistic Systems Inc (LSI), pg 1411

Translations.com, pg 1414

Universe Technical Translation Inc, pg 1414

RUSSIAN

A WordJourney Translation LLC, pg 1407

AAA Fine Translation & Interpretation, pg 1407

American Translation Partners Inc (ATP), pg 1407

Cross Cultural Communication Systems Inc, pg 1408

East-West Concepts, pg 1408

GGP Publishing Inc, pg 1409

Glasnost Communications, pg 1409

InterNation Inc, pg 1410

iProbe Multilingual Solutions Inc, pg 1410

JLS Language Corp, pg 1410

The Language Center, pg 1411

Linguistic Systems Inc (LSI), pg 1411

School of World Studies, pg 1413

Natalia V Sciarini, pg 1413

Boris Mark Silversteyn, pg 1413

Translations.com, pg 1414

Universe Technical Translation Inc, pg 1414

SERBO-CROATIAN

A WordJourney Translation LLC, pg 1407

AAA Fine Translation & Interpretation, pg 1407

American Translation Partners Inc (ATP), pg 1407

Cross Cultural Communication Systems Inc, pg 1408

InterNation Inc, pg 1410

iProbe Multilingual Solutions Inc, pg 1410

JLS Language Corp, pg 1410

The Language Center, pg 1411

Linguistic Systems Inc (LSI), pg 1411

Translations.com, pg 1414

Universe Technical Translation Inc, pg 1414

SINHALESE

A WordJourney Translation LLC, pg 1407

American Translation Partners Inc (ATP), pg 1407

East-West Concepts, pg 1408

InterNation Inc, pg 1410

iProbe Multilingual Solutions Inc, pg 1410

Linguistic Systems Inc (LSI), pg 1411

SLOVAK

A WordJourney Translation LLC, pg 1407

AAA Fine Translation & Interpretation, pg 1407

American Translation Partners Inc (ATP), pg 1407

East-West Concepts, pg 1408

InterNation Inc, pg 1410

iProbe Multilingual Solutions Inc, pg 1410

JLS Language Corp, pg 1410

The Language Center, pg 1411

Linguistic Systems Inc (LSI), pg 1411

Translations.com, pg 1414

Universe Technical Translation Inc, pg 1414

SLOVENE

A WordJourney Translation LLC, pg 1407

AAA Fine Translation & Interpretation, pg 1407

American Translation Partners Inc (ATP), pg 1407

East-West Concepts, pg 1408

InterNation Inc, pg 1410

iProbe Multilingual Solutions Inc, pg 1410

Linguistic Systems Inc (LSI), pg 1411

Translations.com, pg 1414

SPANISH

A L S International, pg 1407

A WordJourney Translation LLC, pg 1407

AAA Fine Translation & Interpretation, pg 1407

Marvelia Alpizar, pg 1407

American Language Services Inc, pg 1407

American Translation Partners Inc (ATP), pg 1407

Auerbach International, pg 1408

Baker & Taylor Publisher Services, pg 1408

Calaf Communications, pg 1408

Cross Cultural Communication Systems Inc, pg 1408

Cross Culture Communications, pg 1408

East-West Concepts, pg 1408

Eriksen Translations Inc, pg 1409

Mayra E Garcia, pg 1409

GGP Publishing Inc, pg 1409

Andrew S Gordon, PhD, pg 1409

Inlingua Translation Service, pg 1410

InterNation Inc, pg 1410

iProbe Multilingual Solutions Inc, pg 1410

IRCO-International Language Bank, pg 1410

JLS Language Corp, pg 1410

The Language Center, pg 1411

Linguistic Systems Inc (LSI), pg 1411

Link Translations Inc, pg 1411

MEJ Personal Business Services Inc, pg 1411

Metro Translation Service, pg 1411

Passwords Communications Inc, pg 1412

Polyglot Communications Inc, pg 1412

Polyglot Translators, pg 1412

Louise B Popkin, pg 1412

Rennert International, pg 1412

Richard Schneider Language Services, pg 1412

School of World Studies, pg 1413

Schreiber Translations Inc (STI), pg 1413

Spanish/English Translation & Interpreting Services, pg 1413

Spanish Publishing Services, pg 1413

Strictly Spanish Translations LLC, pg 1413

Teneo Linguistics Co LLC, pg 1413

Transimpex Translators, Interpreters, Editors, Consultants Inc, pg 1413

TranslateMedia, pg 1414

Translations.com, pg 1414

Translators & Interpreters

The two indexes preceding this section identify the source and target languages translated or interpreted by the entrants.

The American Translators Association (225 Reinekers Lane, Suite 590, Alexandria, VA 22314) publishes the *Directory of Translators and Interpreters* (online), which contains information about the association's members and their specialties.

A L S International
18 John St, Suite 300, New York, NY 10038
Tel: 212-766-4111 *Toll Free Tel:* 800-322-0284
Fax: 212-349-0964 *Toll Free Fax:* 888-662-8048
E-mail: rastefanous@alsintl.com
Web Site: www.alsintl.com
Key Personnel
Pres: Victor Hertz
VP: Gail M Finger
Founded: 1983
Translation, interpreting, transcription, voice-overs, subtitling, DTP/graphics, typesetting, conference services, litigation service, localization & multimedia services.
Source Language(s): English, French, German, Italian, Spanish
Target Language(s): English, French, German, Italian, Spanish
Membership(s): American Translators Association (ATA); Association of Language Companies (ALC); National Court Reporters Association (NCRA)

A WordJourney Translation LLC
PO Box 3181, Humble, TX 77347-3181
Tel: 281-813-1827 *Fax:* 832-213-2777
E-mail: word@wjtranslation.com
Web Site: www.awordjourneytranslation.com
Key Personnel
Head, Prodn: Virginia Potcoava *E-mail:* virginia@wjtranslation.com
Founded: 2013
Multilingual staff & linguists worldwide. Virginia Potcoava has years of experience in the translation industry with a multitude of resources for translators worldwide. Certified translators for over 100 different languages. Expertise includes the following industries: energy/oil & gas, legal, technical, compliance, human resources, business & economy/finance, marketing & health. Services include: certified translations, translation/editing of documents, web translations, localization services, video & audio translation, safety compliance translations. E-mail for quote. Sample translation (up to 300 words) can be provided. Also work with Translation Memory.
Source Language(s): Afrikaans, Albanian, Arabic, Armenian, Belarussian, Bengali, Bulgarian, Burmese, Catalan, Chinese, Czech, Danish, Dutch, English, Esperanto, Estonian, Finnish, Flemish, French, Gaelic, Georgian, German, Greek, Hebrew, Hindi, Hungarian, Icelandic, Indonesian, Italian, Japanese, Javanese, Khmer, Korean, Kurdish, Latin, Latvian, Lithuanian, Macedonian, Malagasy, Malayalam, Malaysian, Nepali, Norwegian, Persian, Polish, Portuguese, Provencal, Punjabi, Romanian, Russian, Serbo-Croatian, Sinhalese, Slovak, Slovene, Spanish, Swahili, Swedish, Tagalog, Tamil, Telugu, Thai, Turkish, Ukrainian, Urdu, Vietnamese, Welsh, Yiddish
Target Language(s): Afrikaans, Albanian, Arabic, Armenian, Belarussian, Bengali, Bulgarian, Burmese, Catalan, Chinese, Czech, Danish, Dutch, English, Esperanto, Estonian, Finnish, Flemish, French, Gaelic, Georgian, German, Greek, Hebrew, Hindi, Hungarian, Icelandic, Indonesian, Italian, Japanese, Javanese, Khmer, Korean, Kurdish, Latin, Latvian, Lithuanian, Macedonian, Malagasy, Malayalam, Malaysian, Nepali, Norwegian, Persian, Polish, Portuguese, Provencal, Punjabi, Romanian, Russian, Serbo-Croatian, Sinhalese, Slovak, Slovene, Spanish, Swahili, Swedish, Tagalog, Tamil, Telugu, Thai, Turkish, Ukrainian, Urdu, Vietnamese, Welsh, Yiddish
Membership(s): International Chamber of Commerce–Texas

AAA Fine Translation & Interpretation
162-31 Ninth Ave, Flushing, NY 11357-2010
Tel: 917-582-7456 (contact phone); 718-767-7455 (busn phone) *Fax:* 718-767-0474
Key Personnel
Proj Dir: Prof David Schultz
E-mail: davidtrans123@gmail.com
Speedy translation & live interpretation at very reasonable rates.
Source Language(s): Albanian, Arabic, Belarussian, Bengali, Bulgarian, Catalan, Chinese, Czech, Danish, Dutch, English, French, German, Greek, Hebrew, Hindi, Hungarian, Italian, Japanese, Korean, Latin, Macedonian, Norwegian, Persian, Polish, Portuguese, Punjabi, Romanian, Russian, Serbo-Croatian, Slovak, Slovene, Spanish, Swedish, Thai, Turkish, Ukrainian, Urdu, Yiddish
Target Language(s): Albanian, Arabic, Belarussian, Bengali, Bulgarian, Catalan, Chinese, Czech, Danish, Dutch, English, French, German, Greek, Hebrew, Hindi, Hungarian, Italian, Japanese, Korean, Latin, Macedonian, Norwegian, Persian, Portuguese, Punjabi, Romanian, Russian, Serbo-Croatian, Slovak, Slovene, Spanish, Swedish, Thai, Turkish, Ukrainian, Urdu, Yiddish
Membership(s): American Literary Translators Association (ALTA); Chicago Area Translators & Interpreters Association (CHICATA)

Rodelinde Albrecht
PO Box 444, Lenox Dale, MA 01242-0444
Tel: 413-243-4350
E-mail: rodelinde@gmail.com
Founded: 1979
Source Language(s): French, German
Target Language(s): English

Veronika Albrecht-Rodrigues PhD
PO Box 44, Lovell, ME 04051-0044
Tel: 207-925-3117
E-mail: vroni@fairpoint.net
Translator/cultural consultant. General fiction & nonfiction; arts, humanities, medicine, business, legal & general correspondence & documents. Specialize in translating literary & musical subjects & in editing/proofreading foreign language teaching materials, including software, edit CD-ROMs.
Source Language(s): English, French, German
Target Language(s): English, German

Marvelia Alpizar
PO Box 4013, Burbank, CA 91503
Tel: 213-986-8207
Dependable & accurate service in the following areas of specialization: medicine, entertainment, arts & humanities, social sciences, business, natural sciences, pure sciences & media.
Source Language(s): English, Spanish
Target Language(s): English, Spanish
Membership(s): American Translators Association (ATA); National Association of Hispanic Journalists (NAHJ); Society of Professional Journalists

American Language Services Inc
110 Otis St, Cambridge, MA 02141
Tel: 617-876-0833 *Fax:* 617-876-0853
Web Site: www.americanlanguageservices.us
Key Personnel
Pres: Gema M Schaff *E-mail:* gs@alsiweb.us
Translate from English to Spanish, Portuguese, Haitian Creole, French, Cape Verdean & vice versa; also American Sign Language (ASL).
Source Language(s): English, French, Portuguese, Spanish
Target Language(s): English, French, Portuguese, Spanish
Membership(s): American Translators Association (ATA); International Medical Interpreters Association (IMIA); National Association of Judiciary Interpreters & Translators (NAJIT); New England Translators Association (NETA)

American Translation Partners Inc (ATP)
175 Paramount Dr, Raynham, MA 02767
Tel: 508-823-8892 *Toll Free Tel:* 888-443-2376
Fax: 508-823-8854
E-mail: info@americantranslationpartners.com
Web Site: www.americantranslationpartners.com
Key Personnel
VP & Sr Proj Mgr: Scott M Crystal
E-mail: scott@americantranslationpartners.com
Founded: 1998
Interpretation & translation in over 200 language pairs.
Source Language(s): Afrikaans, Albanian, Arabic, Armenian, Belarussian, Bengali, Bulgarian, Burmese, Catalan, Chinese, Czech, Danish, Dutch, English, Esperanto, Estonian, Finnish, Flemish, French, Gaelic, Georgian, German, Greek, Hebrew, Hindi, Hungarian, Icelandic, Indonesian, Italian, Japanese, Javanese, Khmer, Korean, Kurdish, Latin, Latvian, Lithuanian, Macedonian, Malagasy, Malayalam, Malaysian, Nepali, Norwegian, Persian, Polish, Portuguese, Provencal, Punjabi, Romanian, Russian, Serbo-Croatian, Sinhalese, Slovak, Slovene, Spanish, Swahili, Swedish, Tagalog, Tamil, Telugu, Thai, Turkish, Ukrainian, Urdu, Vietnamese, Welsh, Yiddish
Target Language(s): Afrikaans, Albanian, Arabic, Armenian, Belarussian, Bengali, Bulgarian, Burmese, Catalan, Chinese, Czech, Danish, Dutch, English, Esperanto, Estonian, Finnish, Flemish, French, Gaelic, Georgian, German, Greek, Hebrew, Hindi, Hungarian, Icelandic, Indonesian, Italian, Japanese, Javanese, Khmer, Korean, Kurdish, Latin, Latvian, Lithuanian, Macedonian, Malagasy, Malayalam, Malaysian, Nepali, Norwegian, Persian, Polish, Portuguese, Provencal, Punjabi, Romanian, Russian, Serbo-Croatian, Sinhalese, Slovak, Slovene, Spanish, Swahili, Swedish, Tagalog, Tamil, Telugu, Thai, Turkish, Ukrainian, Urdu, Vietnamese, Welsh, Yiddish

Membership(s): American Translators Association (ATA); Federation of International Translators; Institute of Translation & Interpreting (ITI); International Association of Conference Interpreters (AIIC); Localization Industry Standards Association (LISA); National Association of Judiciary Interpreters & Translators (NAJIT); New England Translators Association (NETA)

Anne Milano Appel
1364 Virginia St, Alamo, CA 94507
Tel: 925-837-5203
E-mail: annemilanoappel@gmail.com; amappel@pacbell.net
Web Site: www.annemilanoappel.com
Founded: 1996
Literary translation.
Source Language(s): Italian
Target Language(s): English
Membership(s): American Literary Translators Association (ALTA); American Translators Association (ATA); The Authors Guild; Northern California Translators Association; PEN America; PEN Center USA West

Apter, Ronnie, see Mark Herman & Ronnie Apter, Translators

Auerbach International
2137 Otis Dr, Suite 306, Alameda, CA 94501
Tel: 415-592-0042 *Fax:* 415-592-0043
E-mail: translations@auerbach-intl.com
Web Site: www.auerbach-intl.com
Key Personnel
Pres & Quoting Mgr: Philip B Auerbach
Tel: 415-592-0042 ext 107
Founded: 1989
25 years of experience translating into 80 languages. Special prices available for publishers.
Source Language(s): English, French, German, Italian, Spanish
Target Language(s): English, French, German, Italian, Spanish

Baker & Taylor Publisher Services
30 Amberwood Pkwy, Ashland, OH 44805
Tel: 567-215-0030 *Toll Free Tel:* 888-814-0208
E-mail: info@btpubservices.com; orders@btpubservices.com
Web Site: www.btpubservices.com
Key Personnel
SVP, Sales & Client Servs: Mark Suchomel
SVP, Opers: Bob Gospodarek
Founded: 2017
Baker & Taylor Publisher Services offers translation services for all major languages, specializing in English-to-Spanish & Spanish-to-English translation.
Source Language(s): English, French, German, Italian, Spanish
Target Language(s): English, French, German, Italian, Spanish

Bien Fait Translations
183 Vernon St, 1st fl, Norword, MA 02062
Tel: 781-769-1637 *Toll Free Tel:* 866-243-6324
E-mail: inquiries@bien-fait.com
Web Site: www.bien-fait.com
Key Personnel
Translator: Bruce D Popp, PhD *E-mail:* bdpopp@bien-fait.com
Founded: 2002
Translate general interest & technical books in astronomy & astrophysics & shorter documents in other scientific & technical areas.
Source Language(s): French
Target Language(s): English
Membership(s): American Astronomical Society; American Translators Association (ATA); New England Translators Association (NETA)

Wanda J Boeke
50 Richmond Ave, Pittsfield, MA 01201-3329
Tel: 413-997-2108 *Fax:* 413-997-2108
E-mail: wjboeke@gmail.com
Translation & copy-editing since 1979: book-length works, articles, reviews; young adult fiction & nonfiction, poetry; publicity texts; reader's reports; AV scripts. Specializing in arts & humanities, accounting, finance, health & medicine, natural sciences, social sciences, tourism & travel. Published NEA translation grant recipient; ATA & TTIG certified. Wide experience, quick turnaround, great result. Contact information updated at www.atanet.org.
Source Language(s): Afrikaans, Dutch, Flemish, French, German
Target Language(s): English
Membership(s): American Literary Translators Association (ALTA); American Translators Association (ATA); Society for the Study of the Short Story (SSSS); The Translators & Interpreters Guild (TTIG)

Robert Bononno
109 E Second St, Apt 5, New York, NY 10009
Tel: 646-673-6102
E-mail: rbononno@twc.com
Web Site: www.robert-bononno.com
Fiction & nonfiction translation from the French by published translator & language consultant. NEA translation grant winner. Over 20 years experience. Nonfiction topics covered include fine art, philosophy, film & television, history & fashion. Experience in marketing & advertising texts. Free price quote on request.
Source Language(s): French, Italian
Target Language(s): English
Membership(s): American Literary Translators Association (ALTA); American Translators Association (ATA); PEN America

Calaf Communications
Affiliate of Cambridge Brick House
10 Warwick Ct, Lawrence, MA 01841
Tel: 978-314-3125 *Fax:* 978-686-5960
Web Site: www.calafcommunications.com
Key Personnel
Principal Consultant: Dolores C Calaf
E-mail: dcalaf@calafcommunications.com
Founded: 1995
Marketing, community relations & media production specialized in reaching Latino/Hispanic/Spanish & the speaking market, cultural adapted campaigns. Special areas/topics include health, education & arts/culture.
Source Language(s): English, Spanish
Target Language(s): Spanish
Membership(s): New England Translators Association (NETA)

Elizabeth Castaldini
32-18 100 St, Apt 2, East Elmhurst, NY 11369
Tel: 646-247-3190
E-mail: eranhec@yahoo.com
Source Language(s): English, Portuguese
Target Language(s): English, Portuguese
Membership(s): National Language Service Corps (NLSC)

CCCS, see Cross Cultural Communication Systems Inc

Alexandra Chciuk-Celt
392 Maple St, West Hempstead, NY 11552
Tel: 516-485-5531
E-mail: languagelady@juno.com
Translating, consecutive & simultaneous interpreting. Specialize in law, poetry, social & artistic subjects, linguistics, psychology.

Source Language(s): French, German, Polish, Spanish
Target Language(s): English

Cross Cultural Communication Systems Inc
227 Garfield Ave, Suite B, Woburn, MA 01801
Mailing Address: PO Box 2308, Woburn, MA 01888-0508
Tel: 781-729-3736 *Toll Free Tel:* 888-678-CCCS (678-2227 out of state only) *Fax:* 781-729-1217
Web Site: www.cccsorg.com; www.embracingculture.com
Key Personnel
Pres & Owner: Zarita Araujo-Lane
E-mail: zaraujo_lane@embracingculture.com
Founded: 1996
Source Language(s): Arabic, Armenian, Bengali, Chinese, English, French, German, Greek, Hebrew, Hindi, Italian, Japanese, Khmer, Korean, Persian, Polish, Portuguese, Punjabi, Russian, Serbo-Croatian, Spanish, Swahili, Tagalog, Thai, Turkish, Urdu, Vietnamese
Target Language(s): Arabic, Armenian, Bengali, Chinese, English, French, German, Greek, Hebrew, Hindi, Italian, Japanese, Khmer, Korean, Persian, Polish, Portuguese, Punjabi, Russian, Serbo-Croatian, Spanish, Swahili, Tagalog, Thai, Turkish, Urdu, Vietnamese
Membership(s): American Translators Association (ATA); Association for Talent Development (ATD); California Healthcare Interpreters Association (CHIA); Conference of Interpreter Trainers (CIT); Florida Chapter of the American Translators Association (FLATA); Massachusetts Medical Interpreters Association (MMIA); Michigan Translators Interpreters Network; National Council on Interpreting in Health Care (NCIHC); New England Translators Association (NETA); New Hampshire Interpreters & Translators Organization (NHITO)

Cross Culture Communications
PO Box 141263, Dallas, TX 75214
Tel: 214-394-3000
E-mail: info@crossculturecommunications.com
Web Site: crossculturecommunications.com
Key Personnel
Co-Founder: Edward Retta *E-mail:* eretta@crossculturecommunications.com;
Marilyn Retta *E-mail:* mretta@crossculturecommunications.com
Founded: 1994
Cross cultural training & language services.
Source Language(s): English, French, German, Italian, Spanish
Target Language(s): English, French, German, Italian, Spanish
Membership(s): American Translators Association (ATA); National Association of Judiciary Interpreters & Translators (NAJIT)

Marcia Nita Doron
6 Glenbrook Lane, Worcester, MA 01609
Tel: 508-755-6642 *Fax:* 508-755-6642
E-mail: mdoron@charter.net
Translating & editing.
Source Language(s): French, Hebrew
Target Language(s): English
Membership(s): National Capital Area Chapter/American Translators Association

East-West Concepts
PO Box 1435, Kapaa, HI 96746
Tel: 808-938-8410 *Fax:* 808-441-8121
Web Site: www.eastwestconcepts.com
Key Personnel
Opers Mgr: Krisztina Samu *E-mail:* krisztina@eastwestconcepts.com
Founded: 1989
Translation company, 260 different Source & Target languages. Also translates to & from

Chamorro, Chuukese, Divehi, Dzongkha, Fijian, Hawaiian, Karen, Kongri, Luxembourgish, Marshallese, Samoan, Shan, Tibetan, Tongan, Yapese, Yi, Yupik & Zulu languages.

Source Language(s): Afrikaans, Albanian, Arabic, Armenian, Belarussian, Bengali, Bulgarian, Burmese, Catalan, Chinese, Czech, Danish, Dutch, English, Esperanto, Estonian, Finnish, Flemish, French, Gaelic, Georgian, German, Greek, Hebrew, Hindi, Hungarian, Icelandic, Indonesian, Italian, Japanese, Javanese, Khmer, Korean, Kurdish, Latin, Latvian, Lithuanian, Macedonian, Malagasy, Malayalam, Malaysian, Nepali, Norwegian, Persian, Polish, Portuguese, Provencal, Punjabi, Romanian, Russian, Sinhalese, Slovak, Slovene, Spanish, Swahili, Swedish, Tagalog, Tamil, Telugu, Thai, Turkish, Ukrainian, Urdu, Vietnamese, Welsh, Yiddish

Target Language(s): Afrikaans, Albanian, Arabic, Armenian, Belarussian, Bengali, Bulgarian, Burmese, Catalan, Chinese, Czech, Danish, Dutch, English, Esperanto, Estonian, Finnish, Flemish, French, Gaelic, Georgian, German, Greek, Hebrew, Hindi, Hungarian, Icelandic, Indonesian, Italian, Japanese, Javanese, Khmer, Korean, Kurdish, Latin, Latvian, Lithuanian, Macedonian, Malagasy, Malayalam, Malaysian, Nepali, Norwegian, Persian, Polish, Portuguese, Provencal, Punjabi, Romanian, Russian, Sinhalese, Slovak, Slovene, Spanish, Swahili, Swedish, Tagalog, Tamil, Telugu, Thai, Turkish, Ukrainian, Urdu, Vietnamese, Welsh, Yiddish

Ecegul (AJ) Elterman
18 Sixteenth St, Bayville, NY 11709
Tel: 516-628-3075; 516-661-6525 (cell)
E-mail: ajelterman@mindspring.com
Translating & interpreting, proofreading, copy-editing, transcribing, narrating & voice-over.
Source Language(s): English, German, Turkish
Target Language(s): English, German, Turkish
Membership(s): American Translators Association (ATA); National Association of Judiciary Interpreters & Translators (NAJIT); New York Circle of Translators

Catherine C Elverston ELS
3242 NW 5 St, Gainesville, FL 32609
Tel: 352-222-0625 (cell)
E-mail: celverston@gmail.com
Source Language(s): French, German, Spanish
Target Language(s): English
Membership(s): American Medical Writers Association (AMWA); Board of Editors in the Life Sciences

Eriksen Translations Inc
50 Court St, Suite 700, Brooklyn, NY 11201
Tel: 718-802-9010 *Fax:* 718-802-0041
Web Site: www.eriksen.com
Key Personnel
Pres & CEO: Vigdis Eriksen *E-mail:* vigdis.eriksen@eriksen.com
Dir, Sales: Will Lach
Founded: 1986
Translation, proofreading, layout & production, web & multimedia localization, cultural consulting, voice-over & subtitling services in over 100 languages.
Source Language(s): Arabic, Chinese, Danish, English, Finnish, French, German, Italian, Norwegian, Spanish, Swedish
Target Language(s): Arabic, Chinese, Danish, English, Finnish, French, German, Italian, Norwegian, Spanish, Swedish
Membership(s): American Translators Association (ATA); Globalization & Localization Association (GALA); New York Circle of Translators

French and English Communication Services LLC
3104 E Camelback Rd, No 124, Phoenix, AZ 85016-4502
Tel: 602-870-1000
E-mail: RequestFAECS2008@cox.net
Web Site: www.FrenchAndEnglish.com
Key Personnel
Owner: Diane Goullard
Founded: 1984
French to English & English to French translation, proofreading, narrating.
Source Language(s): English, French
Target Language(s): English, French

Frongia, Rosanna M, see Rosanna M Giammanco Frongia PhD

Mayra E Garcia
332 Greenwood Hwy, Saluda, SC 29138
Tel: 803-422-5903
E-mail: mayra.garcia11@gmail.com
Speedy & accurate translation with areas of specialization in psychology, psychiatry, education, business, travel & general topics.
Source Language(s): English, Italian
Target Language(s): Spanish
Membership(s): American Translators Association (ATA)

Regina Gelb
900 W 190 St, Suite 4-O, New York, NY 10040
Tel: 212-795-6925
Translating, interpreting, abstracting & editing, literary consulting, proofreading & rewriting.
Source Language(s): English, Polish
Target Language(s): English, Polish

German Language Services
4752 41 Ave SW, Suite B, Seattle, WA 98116
Tel: 206-938-3600 *Fax:* 206-938-8308
E-mail: info@germanlanguageservices.com
Web Site: www.germanlanguageservices.com
Key Personnel
Founder: Courtney Searls-Ridge
    E-mail: courtney@germanlanguageservices.com
Founded: 1979
Translation, readers reports, content editing, copy-editing & proofreading.
Source Language(s): English, German
Target Language(s): English, German
Membership(s): American Translators Association (ATA); Northwest Translators & Interpreters Society (NOTIS)

GGP Publishing Inc
105 Calvert St, Suite 201, Harrison, NY 10528-3138
Tel: 914-834-8896 *Fax:* 914-834-7566
Web Site: www.GGPPublishing.com
Key Personnel
Pres & Publg Dir: Generosa Gina Protano
    E-mail: GGProtano@GGPPublishing.com
Founded: 1991
Packager for trade & educational publishers. All editorial, art & design, production & printing services—from concept to bound books or any segment(s) of this publishing process. Trade (fiction & nonfiction) & children's books, textbooks (el-hi, college & adult education), professional, reference & how-to books, cookbooks, audiotapes, videotapes & CDs. Specialize in the development of materials for the study of foreign languages (such as French, German, Italian, Japanese, Latin, Portuguese, Russian & Spanish) & ESL, as well as in the development of materials for bilingual education & language arts. In addition, we translate complete or partial programs from & into the various languages & act as literary agents & foreign publisher representatives.

Source Language(s): English, French, German, Italian, Japanese, Latin, Portuguese, Russian, Spanish
Target Language(s): English, French, German, Italian, Japanese, Latin, Portuguese, Russian, Spanish

Rosanna M Giammanco Frongia PhD
Affiliate of Verbum Linguistic Services Inc
PO Box 810422, Boca Raton, FL 33481-0422
Tel: 718-619-2637 (cell)
E-mail: giammancorm@gmail.com
Translation, editing, consulting, abstracting, coordinating, research. Ability to handle large multi-language projects. All subjects; broad experience in academic texts, social sciences, Italy, legal, financial. Equipment: PC, laser printer, fax, modem, e-mail.
Source Language(s): English, French, Italian, Latin, Spanish
Target Language(s): English, Italian
Membership(s): American Translators Association (ATA); National Association of Judiciary Interpreters & Translators (NAJIT); New York Circle of Translators

Glasnost Communications
1316 Tallberry Business Plaza, Suite 404, Cincinnati, OH 45230
Tel: 513-231-3599 *Fax:* 513-231-3599
E-mail: glasnost@att.net
Key Personnel
Interpreter/Translator: Alexander (Sasha) Etlin
Founded: 1995
Extensive translation & interpretation experience in many fields including business; manufacturing; agriculture; government, city services, urban planning; health care, public health, domestic violence, substance abuse; NGOs, social services; law, law enforcement; education; religion; environment; arts & culture; mass media. Proofreading, editing of fiction & nonfiction. Many references available. Associates include award-winning writer, native English speaker, available for editing/proofreading of English materials.
Source Language(s): English, Russian, Ukrainian
Target Language(s): English, Russian, Ukrainian

Andrew S Gordon, PhD
1230 23 St NW, No 804, Washington, DC 20037
E-mail: andgordon@yahoo.com
Advertising, law, literature & politics. Certified interpreter/translator with 30 plus years experience. Professor Emeritus of Spanish language, literature & translation.
Source Language(s): English, Spanish
Target Language(s): English, Spanish
Membership(s): Modern Language Association of America (MLA)

Regina Gorzkowska-Rossi
3349 E Thompson St, Philadelphia, PA 19134
Tel: 267-535-1691
E-mail: proarterg@yahoo.com
Source Language(s): English, Polish
Target Language(s): English, Polish
Membership(s): American Literary Translators Association (ALTA)

Diane Goullard, see French and English Communication Services LLC

Rita Granda
466 Cambridge St, Peterborough, ON K9H 4T3, Canada
Tel: 705-748-0943
E-mail: rita@ritagranda.com
Web Site: www.ritagranda.com
Source Language(s): Spanish

Target Language(s): English
Membership(s): American Translators Association (ATA); Association of Translators & Interpreters of Ontario (ATIO)

Diana Mara Henry
187 Prospect St, Newport, VT 05855
Tel: 802-334-7054
E-mail: dmh@dianamarahenry.com
Web Site: www.natzweiler-struthof.com
Founded: 2000
Literary & historical translations; certificates; medical & general transcription & translation of conferences; interpretation for immigration hearings, legal & medical proceedings.
Source Language(s): French
Target Language(s): English

Mark Herman & Ronnie Apter, Translators
2222 Westview Dr, Nashville, TN 37212-4123
Tel: 615-942-8462
E-mail: mnh18@columbia.edu
Key Personnel
Partner: Ronnie Apter; Mark Herman
Founded: 1975
Translation into English of opera & drama for performance & poetry, ancient & modern.
Source Language(s): Catalan, Czech, French, German, Italian, Latin, Provencal, Russian, Spanish
Target Language(s): English
Membership(s): American Literary Translators Association (ALTA); American Translators Association (ATA)

Joan E Howard
51 Congress St, Augusta, ME 04330
Tel: 207-622-0580
E-mail: petiteplaisance@acadia.net
Founded: 1991
Translation & copy-editing.
Source Language(s): English, French
Target Language(s): English, French
Membership(s): Modern Language Association of America (MLA)

Indexing by the Book
PO Box 12513, Tucson, AZ 85732-2513
Tel: 520-750-8439
E-mail: indextran@cox.net
Web Site: www.indexingbythebook.com
Key Personnel
Indexer: Cynthia J Coan
Founded: 2003
Provide both indexing & translation services. Specialties in the translation field include medicine & law/patents.
Source Language(s): Spanish, Swedish
Target Language(s): English
Membership(s): American Society for Indexing (ASI); American Translators Association (ATA); National Council on Interpreting in Health Care (NCIHC)

Inlingua Translation Service
Division of Development & Training International
171 E Ridgewood Ave, Ridgewood, NJ 07450
Tel: 201-444-9500 *Fax:* 201-444-0116
E-mail: ridgewood@inlingua.com
Web Site: www.inlingua.com; www.inlinguametrony.com
Key Personnel
Exec Dir: Deborah Hinckley
Translation & interpreting services to corporations & private individuals; provide language & intercultural training.
Source Language(s): English, French, German, Italian, Spanish
Target Language(s): English, French, German, Italian, Spanish

InterNation Inc
299 Broadway, Suite 918, New York, NY 10007
Tel: 212-619-5545 *Toll Free Tel:* 800-222-8799
  Fax: 212-619-5887
E-mail: info@internation.com
Web Site: www.internation.com
Key Personnel
Pres: Erick Derkatsch
Founded: 1990
Translations, voice-overs, subtitles, desktop publishing, editing, proofreading & foreign language typing.
Source Language(s): Afrikaans, Albanian, Arabic, Armenian, Belarussian, Bengali, Bulgarian, Burmese, Catalan, Chinese, Czech, Danish, Dutch, English, Esperanto, Estonian, Finnish, Flemish, French, Gaelic, Georgian, German, Greek, Hebrew, Hindi, Hungarian, Icelandic, Indonesian, Italian, Japanese, Javanese, Khmer, Korean, Kurdish, Latin, Latvian, Lithuanian, Macedonian, Malagasy, Malayalam, Malaysian, Nepali, Norwegian, Persian, Polish, Portuguese, Provencal, Punjabi, Romanian, Russian, Serbo-Croatian, Sinhalese, Slovak, Slovene, Spanish, Swahili, Swedish, Tagalog, Tamil, Telugu, Thai, Turkish, Ukrainian, Urdu, Vietnamese, Welsh, Yiddish
Target Language(s): Afrikaans, Albanian, Arabic, Armenian, Belarussian, Bengali, Bulgarian, Burmese, Catalan, Chinese, Czech, Danish, Dutch, English, Esperanto, Estonian, Finnish, Flemish, French, Gaelic, Georgian, German, Greek, Hebrew, Hindi, Hungarian, Icelandic, Indonesian, Italian, Japanese, Javanese, Khmer, Korean, Kurdish, Latin, Latvian, Lithuanian, Macedonian, Malagasy, Malayalam, Malaysian, Nepali, Norwegian, Persian, Polish, Portuguese, Provencal, Punjabi, Romanian, Russian, Serbo-Croatian, Sinhalese, Slovak, Slovene, Spanish, Swahili, Swedish, Tagalog, Tamil, Telugu, Thai, Turkish, Ukrainian, Urdu, Vietnamese, Welsh, Yiddish
Membership(s): American Translators Association (ATA); New York Circle of Translators

iProbe Multilingual Solutions Inc
20 Jay St, Suite 638, New York, NY 11201
Tel: 212-489-6035 *Toll Free Tel:* 888-489-6035
  Fax: 212-202-4790
E-mail: info@iprobesolutions.com
Web Site: iprobesolutions.com
Key Personnel
Founder & CEO: Julie H Setbon
  E-mail: setbon@iprobesolutions.com
Founded: 2001
iProbe provides pre-production, production, post-production support & foreign language versioning in 6,912 languages for broadcast, corporate, commercial & educational programming. Our specialty is the creation of multilingual media for print, industrial, broadcast, DVD, video tape, Internet & new media use.
Production, Post-Production & Localization Services: DVD authoring, duplication & replication; production; post-production; video & audio encoding; casting, dubbing & voice-overs; subtitling & captioning; transcription; graphic production; typesetting; desktop publishing (DTP) compositioning; interpreting & simultaneous interpretation wireless equipment, rental & sales. Also provide publishers with scanning & OCR services in major languages including Russian (Cyrillic alphabet).
Source Language(s): Afrikaans, Albanian, Arabic, Armenian, Belarussian, Bengali, Bulgarian, Burmese, Catalan, Chinese, Czech, Danish, Dutch, English, Esperanto, Estonian, Finnish, Flemish, French, Gaelic, Georgian, German, Greek, Hebrew, Hindi, Hungarian, Icelandic, Indonesian, Italian, Japanese, Javanese, Khmer, Korean, Kurdish, Latin, Latvian, Lithuanian, Macedonian, Malagasy, Malayalam, Malaysian, Nepali, Norwegian, Persian, Polish, Portuguese,

Provencal, Punjabi, Romanian, Russian, Serbo-Croatian, Sinhalese, Slovak, Slovene, Spanish, Swahili, Swedish, Tagalog, Tamil, Telugu, Thai, Turkish, Ukrainian, Urdu, Vietnamese, Welsh, Yiddish
Target Language(s): Afrikaans, Albanian, Arabic, Armenian, Belarussian, Bengali, Bulgarian, Burmese, Catalan, Chinese, Czech, Danish, Dutch, English, Esperanto, Estonian, Finnish, Flemish, French, Gaelic, Georgian, German, Greek, Hebrew, Hindi, Hungarian, Icelandic, Indonesian, Italian, Japanese, Javanese, Khmer, Korean, Kurdish, Latin, Latvian, Lithuanian, Macedonian, Malagasy, Malayalam, Malaysian, Nepali, Norwegian, Persian, Polish, Portuguese, Provencal, Punjabi, Romanian, Russian, Serbo-Croatian, Sinhalese, Slovak, Slovene, Spanish, Swahili, Swedish, Tagalog, Tamil, Telugu, Thai, Turkish, Ukrainian, Urdu, Vietnamese, Welsh, Yiddish

IRCO-International Language Bank
10301 NE Glisan St, Portland, OR 97220
Tel: 503-234-0068 (interpretation); 503-505-5186 (translation) *Fax:* 503-234-1259
E-mail: info@irco.org; translation@ircoilb.org; interpretation@ircoilb.org
Web Site: www.irco.org/ilb
Key Personnel
Pres: Trinh Tran
VP: Gerry Uba
Exec Dir: Lee Po Cha
Founded: 1976
Provide interpretation & translation services, specializing in refugee languages.
Source Language(s): English, French, German, Italian, Spanish
Target Language(s): English, French, German, Italian, Spanish
Membership(s): American Translators Association (ATA); International Medical Interpreters Association (IMIA); Northwest Translators & Interpreters Society (NOTIS)

JLS Language Corp
135 Willow Rd, Menlo Park, CA 94025
Tel: 650-321-9832 *Fax:* 650-329-9864
E-mail: info@jls.com
Web Site: www.jls.com
Key Personnel
Pres: Rikko Field
Pubns Acct Mgr: Kevin Lenzen *E-mail:* kevin@jls.com
Technical manual preparation, foreign language translation & desktop publishing. Produces technical & marketing publications.
Source Language(s): Bulgarian, Chinese, Czech, Danish, Dutch, English, Estonian, Finnish, French, German, Greek, Hungarian, Indonesian, Italian, Japanese, Korean, Latvian, Lithuanian, Macedonian, Malaysian, Norwegian, Polish, Portuguese, Romanian, Russian, Serbo-Croatian, Slovak, Spanish, Swedish, Thai, Turkish, Vietnamese
Target Language(s): Bulgarian, Chinese, Czech, Danish, Dutch, English, Estonian, Finnish, French, German, Greek, Hungarian, Indonesian, Italian, Japanese, Korean, Latvian, Lithuanian, Macedonian, Malaysian, Norwegian, Polish, Portuguese, Romanian, Russian, Serbo-Croatian, Slovak, Spanish, Swedish, Thai, Turkish, Vietnamese
Membership(s): American Translators Association (ATA)

Bruni Johnson
457 E Colfax St, Palatine, IL 60074
Tel: 847-359-6839 *Fax:* 847-359-7075
E-mail: brunijohnson@sbcglobal.net
Source Language(s): English, German
Target Language(s): English, German
Membership(s): American Translators Association (ATA)

Alicja T Kawecki
4-AD Foxwood Dr, Morris Plains, NJ 07950
Tel: 973-285-1648
E-mail: atkawecki@optonline.net
Technical & specialized material.
Source Language(s): French, Italian, Polish, Russian, Ukrainian
Target Language(s): English
Membership(s): American Translators Association (ATA); The Institute of Linguists (England)

Solveig Kjok
252 Green St, Brooklyn, NY 11222
Tel: 718-389-8228; 917-288-3445 *Fax:* 718-389-8228
E-mail: linguist@art-texts.plus
Web Site: www.art-texts.plus
Founded: 1984
Fine arts, art history, literary translation. Member of STF - The Association of Government Authorized Translators of Norway.
Source Language(s): Danish, English, French, German, Norwegian, Spanish, Swedish
Target Language(s): English, Norwegian
Membership(s): American Translators Association (ATA)

Kenneth Kronenberg
51 Maple Ave, Cambridge, MA 02139
Tel: 617-868-8070
E-mail: mail@kfkronenberg.com
Web Site: www.kfkronenberg.com
Mr Kronenberg specializes in 19th- & 20th-century diaries & letters for publication & private clients; also Holocaust-related materials. His most recent book is the diaries of Willy Cohn *No Justice in Germany: The Breslau Diaries, 1933-1941* (Stanford University Press, 2012). Other translations include Hubert Wolf *Pope & Devil* (Harvard University Press, 2010), Vilem Flusser *The Freedom of the Migrant* (Illinois University Press, 2003), "The Terezin Diary of Alice Ehrmann" in *Salvaged Pages* (Yale University Press, 2002). He is the author & translator of *Lives & Letters of an Immigrant Family* (University of Nebraska Press, 1998). Mr Kronenberg also translates in psychology/psychiatry: Karl Heinz Brisch *Treating Attachment Disorders* (Guilford, 2002, 2012), Mechthild Papousek *Disorders of Behavioral & Emotional Regulation in the First Years of Life* (Zero to Three Press, 2007).
Source Language(s): German
Target Language(s): English
Membership(s): New England Translators Association (NETA); PEN America

Wayne P Lammers
SW 92 Ave, Tigard, OR 97224
Tel: 503-624-2971
E-mail: wlammers@mac.com
Web Site: www.lammerstranslations.com
Literary translations by commission.
Source Language(s): Japanese
Target Language(s): English

LangTech International
5625 SW 170 Ave, Aloha, OR 97007
Tel: 503-649-2478 *Fax:* 503-649-2478 (call first)
E-mail: langtech.international@yahoo.com
Web Site: www.langtechinternational.com
Key Personnel
Owner: Douglas J Foran
Founded: 1995
Multilingual communication, including translation, localization, interpretation & narration.
Source Language(s): English, French, Italian, Portuguese, Spanish
Target Language(s): English, French

Membership(s): American Translators Association (ATA); Northwest Translators & Interpreters Society (NOTIS); Societe Francaise des Traducteurs (SFT)

The Language Center
Division of The Center for Professional Advancement
62 Brunswick Woods Dr, East Brunswick, NJ 08816
Tel: 732-613-4554 *Fax:* 732-238-7659
Web Site: www.thelanguagectr.com
Key Personnel
Dir: Mary Majkowski *E-mail:* marymajkowski@thelanguagectr.com
Proj Mgr: Grace Chio; Brian Vogel
Founded: 1967
Translation, editing, typesetting in all languages & printing services. Specialize in books, manuals, catalogs, brochures, periodicals, patents, correspondence, package inserts. Fields including, but not limited to pharmaceutical, medical, chemistry, technology, engineering, electronics, computers, manufacturing, law, government, politics, civics, publishing, advertising, marketing, travel & tourism. Also provide onsite & phone interpretation services.
Source Language(s): Arabic, Chinese, Czech, Danish, Dutch, English, Finnish, French, German, Hungarian, Italian, Japanese, Korean, Lithuanian, Norwegian, Polish, Portuguese, Russian, Serbo-Croatian, Slovak, Spanish, Swedish, Turkish, Vietnamese
Target Language(s): Arabic, Chinese, Czech, Danish, Dutch, English, Finnish, French, German, Hungarian, Italian, Japanese, Korean, Lithuanian, Norwegian, Polish, Portuguese, Russian, Serbo-Croatian, Slovak, Spanish, Swedish, Turkish, Vietnamese
Membership(s): American Translators Association, Translation Company Division (TCD); Association of Language Companies (ALC)

Linguistic Systems Inc (LSI)
260 Franklin St, Suite 230, Boston, MA 02110
Tel: 617-528-7410 *Toll Free Tel:* 800-654-5006
E-mail: clientservice@linguist.com
Web Site: www.linguist.com
Key Personnel
Founder & Pres: Martin Roberts *Tel:* 617-528-7412 *E-mail:* mroberts@linguist.com
VP: Mark Ettinger
VP, Engg: Boris Katsevman
VP, Lang Serv Progs: Jean-Paul Fandel
Leading language conversion company, specializing in translation of books, periodicals, manuals & catalogs. For over 50 years the company has produced more than 2,000,000 pages of translation, covering 120 languages. LSI maintains a database of 7,500 carefully screened professional translators for expertise in a broad spectrum of industrial & scientific subjects. Foreign language page formatting & narration for video & multimedia programs are also available.
Source Language(s): Afrikaans, Albanian, Arabic, Armenian, Belarussian, Bengali, Bulgarian, Burmese, Catalan, Chinese, Danish, Dutch, English, Estonian, Finnish, Flemish, French, Gaelic, Georgian, German, Greek, Hebrew, Hindi, Hungarian, Icelandic, Indonesian, Italian, Japanese, Javanese, Khmer, Korean, Latin, Latvian, Lithuanian, Macedonian, Malaysian, Nepali, Norwegian, Polish, Portuguese, Punjabi, Romanian, Russian, Serbo-Croatian, Sinhalese, Slovak, Slovene, Spanish, Swahili, Swedish, Tagalog, Tamil, Turkish, Ukrainian, Urdu, Vietnamese, Yiddish
Target Language(s): Afrikaans, Albanian, Arabic, Armenian, Belarussian, Bengali, Bulgarian, Burmese, Catalan, Chinese, Czech, Danish, Dutch, English, Estonian, Finnish, Flemish, French, Gaelic, Georgian, German, Greek,

Hebrew, Hindi, Hungarian, Icelandic, Indonesian, Italian, Japanese, Javanese, Khmer, Korean, Latin, Latvian, Lithuanian, Macedonian, Malaysian, Nepali, Norwegian, Polish, Portuguese, Punjabi, Romanian, Russian, Serbo-Croatian, Sinhalese, Slovak, Slovene, Spanish, Swahili, Swedish, Tagalog, Tamil, Thai, Turkish, Ukrainian, Urdu, Vietnamese, Yiddish
Membership(s): American Translators Association (ATA); Association of Language Companies (ALC); Globalization & Localization Association (GALA)

Link Translations Inc
250 W 57 St, Suite 2001, New York, NY 10107
Tel: 212-792-7520 *Toll Free Tel:* 877-321-3465
E-mail: info@link-translations.com
Web Site: www.link-translations.com
Key Personnel
Owner & Pres: Evren Ay
Translation, interpretation & localization.
Source Language(s): Arabic, Chinese, French, German, Korean, Persian, Portuguese, Russian, Spanish, Turkish
Target Language(s): English, French, German, Italian, Spanish
Membership(s): American Translators Association (ATA)

MEJ Personal Business Services Inc
245 E 116 St, New York, NY 10029
Tel: 212-426-6017 *Toll Free Tel:* 866-557-5336 *Fax:* 646-827-3628
E-mail: support@mejpbs.com
Web Site: www.mejpbs.com
Key Personnel
Pres: Melvin Johnson *E-mail:* mjohnson@mejpbs.com
Contact: Elizabeth Johnson *E-mail:* ejohnson@mejpbs.com
Full service language service provider. Over 140 languages.
Source Language(s): English, French, German, Italian, Spanish
Target Language(s): English, French, German, Italian, Spanish
Membership(s): American Translators Association (ATA)

Metro Translation Service
294 De Kalb Ave, Brooklyn, NY 11205
Tel: 718-789-0430; 917-558-0089 (cell)
E-mail: metrotourservice21@gmail.com
Web Site: metrotourservice.blogspot.com
Key Personnel
Contact: Mauricio Lorence
In business for more than 15 years providing skilled & accurate translations. Work with businesses & service industries. Languages are Spanish, Japanese, Portuguese, German & English. Also does tailored tours for executives & professionals.
Source Language(s): English, German, Japanese, Portuguese, Spanish
Target Language(s): English, German, Japanese, Portuguese, Spanish
Membership(s): Chicago Area Translators & Interpreters Association (CHICATA); Court Interpreters & Translators Association; New York Circle of Translators

Verne Moberg
Five Star Residences of Yonkers, 537 Riverdale Ave, Apt 410, Yonkers, NY 10705-5512
Tel: 646-306-2171
E-mail: vam1@columbia.edu
Founded: 1988
Literature, history, politics & women's studies.
Source Language(s): Danish, German, Norwegian, Swedish
Target Language(s): English

Membership(s): American Swedish Translators and Researchers Association (ASTRA); Norwegian Researchers & Teachers Association of North America (NORTANA); Society for the Advancement of Scandinavian Study (SASS); Swedish Translators in North America (STINA); Swedish Women's Educational Association (SWEA)

Steven T Murray
PO Box 14630, Albuquerque, NM 87191-4630
Tel: 505-515-5843
E-mail: steventmurray@gmail.com
Founded: 1974
Prize-winning fiction & nonfiction book translation for clients worldwide. Works together with Tiina Nunnally.
Source Language(s): Danish, Dutch, German, Norwegian, Swedish
Target Language(s): English
Membership(s): American Literary Translators Association (ALTA); The Authors Guild; PEN Center USA; Society of Authors (UK)

Donald Nicholson-Smith
50 Plaza St E, Apt 1D, Brooklyn, NY 11238
Tel: 718-636-4732
E-mail: mnr.dns@verizon.net
Specialize in humanities, fiction, psychology & psychoanalysis.
Source Language(s): French, Spanish
Target Language(s): English
Membership(s): Translators Association (London)

Tiina Nunnally
PO Box 14630, Albuquerque, NM 87191-4630
Tel: 505-856-2550
E-mail: tiinanunnally@gmail.com
Founded: 1984
Prize-winning fiction & nonfiction book translation for clients worldwide. Works together with Steven T Murray. Lectures on literary translation.
Source Language(s): Danish, Norwegian, Swedish
Target Language(s): English
Membership(s): American Literary Translators Association (ALTA); The Authors Guild; PEN America

Ohnaka & Associates Inc
6040 Kennedy Blvd E, Suite 23-B, West New York, NJ 07093
Tel: 201-255-5796 *Fax:* 201-255-2890
E-mail: info@ohnaka.com
Web Site: www.ohnaka.com
Key Personnel
Dir: Yuko Ohnaka
Founded: 2005
Comprehensive Japanese language services & business/cultural consulting.
Source Language(s): English, Japanese
Target Language(s): English, Japanese
Membership(s): American Translators Association (ATA); Asian American Journalists Association; National Association of Judiciary Interpreters & Translators (NAJIT)

Passwords Communications Inc
1804 21 St N, Arlington, VA 22209
Tel: 703-624-5953
E-mail: paellero@aol.com
Web Site: www.passwords-comm.com
Translation of fiction, nonfiction, poetry, children's literature & technical documentation.
Source Language(s): English, French, Spanish
Target Language(s): English, Spanish
Membership(s): American Literary Translators Association (ALTA); American Translators Association (ATA)

Emmanuel X Pierreuse
1830 Avenida del Mundo, Suite 412, Coronado, CA 92118
Tel: 619-435-3931 *Fax:* 619-435-3931
E-mail: epierreuse@aol.com
Founded: 1998
Source Language(s): English, French
Target Language(s): English, French
Membership(s): American Translators Association (ATA)

Polish National Union of America
1006 Pittston Ave, Scranton, PA 18505
Tel: 570-344-1513 *Toll Free Tel:* 800-724-6352
Fax: 570-961-5961
E-mail: info@pnu.org
Web Site: www.pnu.org
Key Personnel
Pres: Irene Jugan
Translate from Polish to English & English to Polish & publishes insurance newspaper.
Source Language(s): English, Polish
Target Language(s): English, Polish
Membership(s): American Literary Translators Association (ALTA)

Polyglot Communications Inc
PO Box 1962, Laguna Beach, CA 92652
Tel: 949-497-1544
E-mail: info@polyglot.us.com
Web Site: www.polyglot.us.com
Key Personnel
Pres & CEO: Arturo Valdivia
Founded: 1984
Translations, interpreters & voice-over narration.
Source Language(s): English, French, German, Italian, Spanish
Target Language(s): English, French, German, Italian, Spanish
Membership(s): American Translators Association (ATA)

Polyglot Translators
PO Box 30087, Bethesda, MD 20824
Tel: 301-485-9865 *Fax:* 301-907-8707
E-mail: info@polyglottranslators.com
Web Site: polyglottranslators.com
Key Personnel
Pres: Rostam Zahrai
Founded: 1979
Translating from & into Middle-Eastern languages, including Dari/Farsi/Tajik, in all subjects.
Source Language(s): English, French, German, Italian, Persian, Spanish
Target Language(s): English, French, German, Italian, Persian, Spanish
Membership(s): Capitol Area Translators & Interpreters Association

Louise B Popkin
9 Cliff St, Arlington, MA 02476
Tel: 781-643-6957
E-mail: louise@louisebpopkin.com
Freelance literary translating (fiction, poetry, drama); certified English-Spanish & Spanish-English. Can check translations for accuracy & style.
Source Language(s): English, Spanish
Target Language(s): English, Spanish
Membership(s): American Literary Translators Association (ALTA); American Translators Association (ATA); New England Translators Association (NETA)

Pro Arte Associates, see Regina Gorzkowska-Rossi

Generosa Gina Protano Publishing, see GGP Publishing Inc

Rennert International
Division of Wall Street Languages Ltd
211 E 43 St, New York, NY 10017
Tel: 212-867-8700 *Fax:* 212-867-7666
E-mail: info@rennert.com
Web Site: www.rennert.com
Key Personnel
Pres: Cesar Rennert
Founded: 1973
Translate & interpret all languages; simultaneous & consecutive interpreting; voice-overs, subtitling & foreign language narration for film & video; web site localization & transcreation.
Source Language(s): English, French, German, Italian, Spanish
Target Language(s): English, French, German, Italian, Spanish
Membership(s): American Translators Association (ATA)

Claudette Roland
PO Box 24035, Los Angeles, CA 90024
Tel: 310-475-4347 *Fax:* 310-475-0939
E-mail: claudette_roland@verizon.net
Founded: 1983
Source Language(s): English, French
Target Language(s): English, French
Membership(s): American Translators Association (ATA)

Rosemoor House Translations
Rosemoor House, 400 New Bedford Dr, Vallejo, CA 94591
Tel: 707-557-8595 *Fax:* 707-557-5555
Key Personnel
Owner: Kathryn D Marocchino
E-mail: marocchino@sbcglobal.net
Founded: 1988
Translation services; editorial language consultations; proofreading & editing; summaries of foreign language publications; review books for publishers; special assignment writing; professional tutoring in Italian, English & French; dubbing & film voice-overs; book translations, rewriting & indexing; abstracting; contracts & legal depositions; research, review documents for conferences; technical writing; cassette & dictaphone transcribing; audio & video translation. Specialize in: literature, history, banking & finance, electronics & electrotechnology, humanities, sociology & psychology, linguistics, pedagogy, pharmaceutics, psychiatry, biological sciences, commerce, business, law, mechanical engineering, computer science, semantics & philology, advertising & tourism.
Source Language(s): English, Italian
Target Language(s): English, Italian
Membership(s): American Translators Association (ATA); Northern California Translators Association

Richard Schneider Language Services
Division of MediaLocate Inc
1200 Piedmont Ave, Pacific Grove, CA 93950
Tel: 831-622-0554 *Toll Free Tel:* 800-500-5808
Fax: 831-622-0524
E-mail: service@idioms.com
Web Site: www.idioms.com
Key Personnel
CEO: Stephen Lins
CFO: Ilge Karancak-Splane
Founded: 1980
Accurate language interpreting & translating services in over 170 different languages.
Source Language(s): English, French, German, Italian, Spanish
Target Language(s): English, French, German, Italian, Spanish
Membership(s): American Literary Translators Association (ALTA); American Translators Association (ATA); American Wholesale Booksellers Association (AWBA); Association of

Language Companies (ALC); Better Business Bureau (BBB); Business for Social Responsibility (BSR); California Court Interpreters Association (CCIA); California Federation of Interpreters (CFI); Chicago Area Translators & Interpreters Association (CHICATA); Delaware Valley Translators Association (DVTA); Mid-America Chapter of the American Translators Association (MICATA); Northern Ohio Translators Association (NOTA); NYCTA; Society for Photographic Education (SPE); Southern California Area Translators Association (SCATIA)

School of World Studies
Affiliate of Virginia Commonwealth University
312 N Shafer St, Richmond, VA 23284-2021
Tel: 804-827-1111 *Fax:* 804-828-0127
Web Site: www.has.vcu.edu/wld
Key Personnel
Dir: Mark Wood, PhD *E-mail:* mwood@vcu.edu
Translating & interpreting.
Source Language(s): Arabic, Chinese, English, French, German, Italian, Spanish
Target Language(s): English, French, German, Hebrew, Hindi, Italian, Latin, Portuguese, Russian, Spanish

Schreiber Translations Inc (STI)
51 Monroe St, Suite 101, Rockville, MD 20850
Tel: 301-424-7737 *Toll Free Tel:* 800-822-3213
  Fax: 301-424-2336
E-mail: translation@schreibernet.com
Web Site: www.schreibernet.com
Key Personnel
Pres: Marla Schulman *E-mail:* mschulman@
  schreibernet.com
Founded: 1984
Technical, scientific & literary translation into & out of all languages, all subject matters, translator & interpreter services.
Source Language(s): English, French, German, Italian, Spanish
Target Language(s): English, French, German, Italian, Spanish
Membership(s): American Translators Association (ATA); Association of Language Companies (ALC)

Lesley M Schuldt
1647 Natches Way, Steamboat Springs, CO 80487
Tel: 970-879-5144 *Fax:* 970-879-5144
E-mail: stmbt97@aol.com
German translator.
Source Language(s): German
Target Language(s): English
Membership(s): American Literary Translators Association (ALTA); American Translators Association (ATA); American Translators Association, German Language Division (GLD); American Translators Association, Literary Division (LD); Professional Translators Association

Marian Schwartz
1207 Bickler Rd, Austin, TX 78704
Tel: 512-442-5100 *Fax:* 512-442-5100
E-mail: marianschwartz@gmail.com
Russian literary translator: fiction, history, politics, economics, philosophy, fine arts.
Source Language(s): Russian
Target Language(s): English
Membership(s): American Literary Translators Association (ALTA); PEN America

Natalia V Sciarini
219 New England Rd, Guilford, CT 06437
Tel: 203-314-7680
E-mail: natalia@languageandtext.info
Web Site: languageandtext.info
Source Language(s): English, Russian
Target Language(s): English, Russian
Membership(s): American Translators Association (ATA); Linguistics Society of America (LSA)

Christina Sever
PO Box 197, Corvallis, OR 97339
Tel: 541-753-3913 *Fax:* 541-757-0640
E-mail: csever17@yahoo.com
Founded: 1989
Translation, editing & Russian language research.
Source Language(s): Russian
Target Language(s): English
Membership(s): American Translators Association (ATA); Associated Linguists of Oregon

Monika Shoffman-Graves
70 Transylvania Ave, Key Largo, FL 33037
Tel: 305-451-1462 *Fax:* 305-451-1462
E-mail: mograv@gmail.com
Source Language(s): German, Hebrew, Spanish
Target Language(s): English

Boris Mark Silversteyn
700 Cocoanut Ave, Apt 210, Sarasota, FL 34236
Tel: 941-552-8310; 941-284-7282 (cell)
E-mail: bsilversteyn@comcast.net
Russian & Ukrainian translation & interpretation services.
Source Language(s): English, Russian, Ukrainian
Target Language(s): English, Russian, Ukrainian
Membership(s): American Translators Association (ATA)

Martin Sokolinsky
60 Pineapple St, Unit 1-F, Brooklyn, NY 11201
Tel: 718-643-2747
E-mail: cuddys1@verizon.net
Literary subjects, including fiction; interviews & contemporary affairs. Also reading for publishers.
Source Language(s): French, German, Russian, Spanish
Target Language(s): English

Spanish/English Translation & Interpreting Services
5704 SW 86 Dr, Gainesville, FL 32608-8536
Tel: 352-215-7200
Web Site: www.afn.org/~vanessa
Key Personnel
Bilingual Translator & Interpreter: Vanessa M Carbia *E-mail:* vcarbia@hotmail.com
Source Language(s): English, Spanish
Target Language(s): English, Spanish

Spanish Publishing Services
4343 N Clarendon Ave, Suite 1002, Chicago, IL 60613
SAN: 113-6267
Tel: 773-878-2117 *Fax:* 773-388-2265
E-mail: servicioseditoriales@juno.com
Key Personnel
Gen Mgr: Tomas Bissonnette
Services to Spanish language publishers.
Source Language(s): English, Spanish
Target Language(s): English, Spanish

Strictly Spanish Translations LLC
PO Box 476, Milford, OH 45150
Tel: 513-965-1096
E-mail: information@strictlyspanish.com
Web Site: www.strictlyspanish.com
Key Personnel
Sr Mng Dir & Edit Dir: Laura Leonhartsberger
  E-mail: laura@strictlyspanish.com
Founded: 1990
Spanish translation, proofreading & editing.
Source Language(s): English, Spanish
Target Language(s): English, Spanish
Membership(s): American Translators Association (ATA)

Szablya Consultants Inc
2901 NE Blakely St, Unit 510, Seattle, WA 98105

Tel: 206-457-4564; 206-465-0482 (cell)
Web Site: www.szablya.com; www.helenmszablya. com
Key Personnel
Pres: Helen M Szablya *E-mail:* ilona.szablya@ gmail.com
Founded: 1967 (incorporated in 1991)
Translation: books, documents, writing & lectures.
Source Language(s): English, French, German, Hungarian, Latin
Target Language(s): English, Hungarian
Membership(s): American Association of University Women; American Hungarian Federation (AHF); American Translators Association (ATA); The Authors Guild; Northwest Translators & Interpreters Society (NOTIS); Washington Court Interpreters & Translators Society (WITS)

Mrs Toby Talbot
180 Riverside Dr, New York, NY 10024
Tel: 212-362-1243 *Fax:* 212-787-1725
E-mail: rd10024@aol.com
Source Language(s): Spanish
Target Language(s): English
Membership(s): Chicago Area Translators & Interpreters Association (CHICATA)

Johannes Tan
16682 SW Henderson Ct, Beaverton, OR 97007
Tel: 503-642-2586 *Fax:* 503-642-2586
E-mail: jt@indotransnet.com
Web Site: www.indotransnet.com
Founded: 1993
One-stop English-Indonesian translation & interpreting services.
Source Language(s): English, Indonesian
Target Language(s): English, Indonesian
Membership(s): American Translators Association (ATA)

Joan Wagner Teller PhD, Translator
11625 SE Boise St, Unit 106, Portland, OR 97266-2281
Tel: 503-760-1320
E-mail: j-teller-11@alumni.uchicago.edu
Web Site: joantellertranslations.webs.com
Founded: 1976
Translations from Russian, German, French into English, with experience particularly in literature, mathematics, sports medicine & nutrition, education & psychology. Many published translations. Also many years of experience in evaluating & editing translations.
Source Language(s): French, German, Russian
Target Language(s): English

Teneo Linguistics Co LLC
4700 Bryant Irvin Ct, Suite 301, Fort Worth, TX 76107
Tel: 817-441-9974 *Fax:* 817-231-0052
E-mail: info@tlctranslation.com
Web Site: www.tlctranslation.com
Key Personnel
Founder: Hana Laurenzo
Founded: 2005
Source Language(s): English, French, German, Italian, Spanish
Target Language(s): English, French, German, Italian, Spanish
Membership(s): Metroplex Interpreters & Translators Association (MITA); National Association of Women Business Owners (NAWBO)

Transimpex Translators, Interpreters, Editors, Consultants Inc
2300 Main St, 9th fl, Kansas City, MO 64108
Mailing Address: 602 Fairway, Belton, MO 64012

Tel: 816-561-3777 *Toll Free Tel:* 888-877-4679
Fax: 816-561-5515
E-mail: translations@transimpex.com
Web Site: www.transimpex.com
Key Personnel
Owner & Pres: Doris Ganser *E-mail:* doris@
transimpex.com
VP & Exec Asst: Brian White *E-mail:* brian@
transimpex.com
Proj Dir: Aleyois Silcott *E-mail:* aleyois@
transimpex.com
Off Mgr: Petra Rudat
Founded: 1974
Translation, interpreting & international consultancy, editorial services, foreign language desktop publishing, audio, video, exhibits.
Source Language(s): English, French, German, Italian, Spanish
Target Language(s): English, French, German, Italian, Spanish
Membership(s): Alliance Francaise; American Translators Association (ATA); German American Citizens Association (GACA); Germania Club of Greater Kansas City; International Trade Council of Greater Kansas City; Mid-America Chapter of the American Translators Association (MICATA)

TranslateMedia
27 W 24 St, New York, NY 10010
Tel: 212-796-5636
E-mail: web@translatemedia.com
Web Site: www.translatemedia.com
Key Personnel
Dir, Opers: Daniel Crawford
Founded: 1968
Specialize in medical, legal, technical & business translation.
Source Language(s): English, French, German, Italian, Spanish
Target Language(s): English, French, German, Italian, Spanish
Membership(s): American Translators Association (ATA); Association of Language Companies (ALC); Austin Area Translators & Interpreters Association; Society for Technical Communication (STC); Special Libraries Association (SLA)

Translation & Terminology Services
2090 Lorne Terr, Victoria, BC V8S 2H8, Canada
Tel: 778-265-8869; 604-349-8858 (cell)
Web Site: www.focalpoint.org
Key Personnel
Owner & Chief Translator: Joelle Lake
E-mail: jlake66@gmail.com
Founded: 1986
Translation, adaptation, proofreading & editing.
Source Language(s): English, French
Target Language(s): English, French
Membership(s): American Translators Association (ATA); Society of Translators & Interpreters of British Columbia (STIBC)

Translations.com
3 Park Ave, 39th fl, New York, NY 10016
Tel: 212-689-5555 *Fax:* 212-689-1059
E-mail: newyork@transperfect.com; info@
translations.com
Web Site: www.translations.com
Key Personnel
Co-CEO: Elizabeth Elting; Phil Shawe
CTO: Mark Hagerty
COO: Roy B Trujillo
VP, Sales: Tim Coughlin
Founded: 1999
Specialize in one-stop shopping for multilingual publishing solutions: print, software & web. Specialize in educational publishing localization needs. Extensive project experience from small ancillaries to multimillion dollar adoption: literature resourcing; glossary develop-

ment; creative/technical writing, content development, translation, editing, linguistic proofreading, design desktop publishing, reprint QA services, multimedia adaptation, software internationalization, online help development, web assessment & design.
Source Language(s): Afrikaans, Albanian, Arabic, Armenian, Bengali, Bulgarian, Chinese, Czech, Danish, Dutch, English, Estonian, Finnish, Flemish, French, German, Greek, Hebrew, Hindi, Hungarian, Indonesian, Italian, Japanese, Khmer, Korean, Latin, Malaysian, Norwegian, Polish, Portuguese, Romanian, Russian, Serbo-Croatian, Slovak, Slovene, Spanish, Swedish, Tagalog, Tamil, Thai, Turkish, Ukrainian, Vietnamese, Yiddish
Target Language(s): Afrikaans, Albanian, Arabic, Armenian, Bengali, Bulgarian, Chinese, Czech, Danish, Dutch, English, Estonian, Finnish, Flemish, French, German, Greek, Hebrew, Hindi, Indonesian, Italian, Japanese, Khmer, Korean, Latin, Lithuanian, Malaysian, Norwegian, Polish, Portuguese, Romanian, Russian, Serbo-Croatian, Slovak, Slovene, Spanish, Swedish, Tagalog, Tamil, Thai, Turkish, Ukrainian, Vietnamese, Yiddish

Translingua Associates Inc
630 Ninth Ave, Suite 708, New York, NY 10036
Tel: 212-697-2020 *Fax:* 212-697-2891
Web Site: www.translingua.com
Key Personnel
Pres & Mng Dir: Nicole Cee *E-mail:* nicole.cee@
translingua.com
Founded: 1972
Translating & interpreting services in all languages.
Source Language(s): English, French, German, Italian, Spanish
Target Language(s): English, French, German, Italian, Spanish

TransPerfect, see Translations.com

Elizabeth Uhlig
96-09 66 Ave, Suite 1-D, Rego Park, NY 11374
Tel: 718-896-4186
E-mail: elizabeth.uhlig@yahoo.com
Web Site: home.earthlink.net/~marble.house.
editions
Founded: 1998
Translation of literature, children's books, poetry, nontechnical articles & educational materials.
Source Language(s): French, German, Greek, Italian, Portuguese, Spanish
Target Language(s): English
Membership(s): American Literary Translators Association (ALTA); American Translators Association (ATA); New York Circle of Translators

Universe Technical Translation Inc
9225 Katy Fwy, Suite 400, Houston, TX 77024
Tel: 713-827-8800 *Fax:* 713-464-5511
E-mail: universe@universe.us
Web Site: www.universetranslation.com
Key Personnel
Pres: Marion Rifkind
Founded: 1981
Translation, typesetting, desktop publishing, translation of web pages, printing & simultaneous telephone & consecutive interpreting in more than 60 languages. Also simultaneous interpreting equipment rental.
Source Language(s): Afrikaans, Albanian, Arabic, Armenian, Belarussian, Bengali, Bulgarian, Catalan, Chinese, Czech, Danish, Dutch, English, Estonian, Finnish, Flemish, French, Georgian, German, Greek, Hebrew, Hindi, Hungarian, Icelandic, Indonesian, Italian, Japanese, Korean, Kurdish, Latin, Latvian, Lithuanian, Macedonian, Malagasy, Malayalam,

Malaysian, Norwegian, Persian, Polish, Portuguese, Punjabi, Romanian, Russian, Serbo-Croatian, Slovak, Spanish, Swahili, Swedish, Tagalog, Tamil, Thai, Turkish, Ukrainian, Urdu, Vietnamese, Welsh, Yiddish
Target Language(s): Afrikaans, Albanian, Arabic, Armenian, Belarussian, Bengali, Bulgarian, Catalan, Chinese, Czech, Danish, Dutch, English, Estonian, Finnish, Flemish, French, Georgian, German, Greek, Hebrew, Hindi, Hungarian, Icelandic, Indonesian, Italian, Japanese, Korean, Kurdish, Latin, Latvian, Lithuanian, Macedonian, Malagasy, Malayalam, Malaysian, Norwegian, Persian, Polish, Portuguese, Punjabi, Romanian, Russian, Serbo-Croatian, Slovak, Spanish, Swahili, Swedish, Tagalog, Tamil, Thai, Turkish, Ukrainian, Urdu, Vietnamese, Welsh, Yiddish
Membership(s): American Translators Association (ATA); Greater Houston Partnership; Houston Interpreters & Translators Association (HITA); US-Russia Chamber of Commerce (USRCC)

University Language Services Inc (ULS)
Division of ALS International Inc
15 Maiden Lane, Suite 300, New York, NY 10038
Tel: 212-766-4111 *Toll Free Tel:* 800-419-4601
Fax: 212-571-7155 *Toll Free Fax:* 800-662-8048
E-mail: service@universitylanguage.com
Web Site: www.universitylanguage.com
Key Personnel
Pres: Victor Hertz
VP: Gail M Finger *E-mail:* gfinger@alsintl.com
Founded: 1984
Translation, interpreting, teaching, voice-overs, tape transcription, DTP/graphics, typesetting & conferencing services.
Source Language(s): English, French, German, Italian, Spanish
Target Language(s): English, French, German, Italian, Spanish
Membership(s): American Translators Association (ATA); Chicago Area Translators & Interpreters Association (CHICATA); New York Circle of Translators; Society for Technical Communication (STC); Software & Information Industry Association (SIIA)

Liliana Valenzuela
1103 Maufrais St, Austin, TX 78703
Tel: 512-804-8141
E-mail: reporterliliana@gmail.com
Web Site: www.lilianavalenzuela.com
Key Personnel
Agent: Stuart Bernstein
Founded: 1991
Literary translation services. Specialities include fiction, poetry, museum exhibitions & art catalogues. ATA certified.
Source Language(s): English
Target Language(s): Spanish
Membership(s): American Literary Translators Association (ALTA); American Translators Association (ATA); Austin Area Translators & Interpreters Association

Esther Vitalis
1717 W 13 Ave, Unit 301, Vancouver, BC V6J 2H2, Canada
Tel: 604-738-6869 *Fax:* 604-738-6805 (call first)
E-mail: evital@shaw.ca
Web Site: www.evitalis.com
Founded: 1997
Freelancer, translator & interpreter. Occasional exam marker.
Source Language(s): English, Hungarian
Target Language(s): English, Hungarian
Membership(s): Canadian Translators, Terminologists and Interpreters Council (CTTIC); Fed-

eration of International Translators; Society of Translators & Interpreters of British Columbia (STIBC)

Glenn E Weisfeld PhD
Affiliate of Wayne State University, Dept of Psychology
c/o Wayne State University, Dept of Psychology, Suite 7908, 5057 Woodward, Detroit, MI 48202
Tel: 313-577-2835 *Fax:* 313-577-7636
E-mail: ad4297@wayne.edu
Web Site: www.clas.wayne.edu
Medical, biological & behavioral science literature.

Source Language(s): French
Target Language(s): English

Maria Lidia Wilczewski
228 SW Fernleaf Trail, Port St Lucie, FL 34953
Tel: 772-873-9803 *Fax:* 772-873-9803
E-mail: lidiaw@bellsouth.net
Translating, interpreting, editing, proofreading. Specialize in literary & technical material, natural sciences, computer application, business, legal.
Source Language(s): English, Polish
Target Language(s): English, Polish
Membership(s): American Translators Association (ATA); Colorado Translators Association

Krishna Winston
655 Bow Lane, Middletown, CT 06457
Tel: 860-347-0329; 860-685-3378 *Fax:* 860-685-2511
E-mail: kwinston@wesleyan.edu
Non-technical translation.
Source Language(s): German
Target Language(s): English
Membership(s): American Association of Teachers of German (AATG); American Literary Translators Association (ALTA); Modern Language Association of America (MLA); PEN International

Artists & Art Services — Activity Index

ELECTRONIC LAYOUT

FILM ANIMATION

ICON DESIGN

ILLUSTRATION

JACKET DESIGN

Artists & Art Services

See also **Promotional Printing & Allied Services** for producers of promotional materials.

A & A
Division of Abramson & Abramson
PO Box 543, Hazelwood, MO 63042-0543
Tel: 314-786-5046
E-mail: aaartwork@aol.com; aaauthor@aol.com
Web Site: www.elaineabramson.com
Key Personnel
Pres: Elaine Sandra Abramson
EVP: Martin Stanley Abramson
Founded: 1967
Book design, cartoons, illustrations, character creation, licensing, jacket design, layout, paste-up, poster design & spot drawings. Also provide special assignment writing. All books are via mail order. Packages: Book, t-shirt, greeting card & plush toy, advertising art. Artwork by award-winning artist/author. Licensing fine art & cartoon characters. Also, art & contest judge, t-shirt, plush toy, greeting card & jewelry package design. Absolutely no unagented submissions. Submissions are not returned.
Membership(s): American Advertising Association; Best of Missouri Hands; Chesterfield Writers Guild; Composers, Authors & Artists of America; Creative Coalition; Electronically Published Internet Connection (EPIC); Graphic Artists Guild; Greater St Louis Art Association (GSLAA); Greater St Louis Artists Guild; Maryland Art League; Midwest Independent Booksellers Association (MIBA); Mystery Writers of America (MWA); National Association of Memoir Writers (NAMW); National Association of Television Program Executives Inc (NATPE); National League of American Pen Women; National Writers Association (NWA); National Writers Union (NWU); New Mexico Book Co-op; North Texas Writers Group; Publishers Association of the West (PubWest); Romance Writers of America (RWA); Romance Writers of America (RWA), Kiss of Death Chapter; St Louis Artists' Guild; St Louis Writers Guild; Sisters in Crime; Society of Children's Book Writers & Illustrators (SCBWI); Southern Independent Booksellers Alliance (SIBA); SouthWest Writers; Texas Association of Motion Media Professionals (TAMMP); Thriller Writers of America; Writers Under the Arch

A Good Thing Inc
PO Box 20482, New York, NY 10021-0068
Tel: 212-687-8155 *Fax:* 212-687-8292
Web Site: agoodthingink.com
Key Personnel
Pres: Aaron J Richman *E-mail:* arichman@agoodthingink.com
VP: Howard Petlack *E-mail:* hpetlack@agoodthingink.com
Book, illustration, jacket & poster design, layout, letterheads, spot drawings, packaging; trademarks; computer art.
Membership(s): Book Industry Guild of New York

A-R Editions Inc
1600 Aspen Commons, Suite 100, Middleton, WI 53562
Tel: 608-836-9000 *Fax:* 608-831-8200
E-mail: info@areditions.com
Web Site: www.areditions.com
Key Personnel
Pres & CEO: Patrick Wall *Tel:* 608-203-2575
  E-mail: patrick.wall@areditions.com

Dir, Spec Projs: James Zychowicz *Tel:* 608-203-2580 *E-mail:* james.zychowicz@areditions.com
Mng Ed: Pamela Whitcomb *Tel:* 608-203-2565
  E-mail: pamela.whitcomb@areditions.com
Founded: 1962
Complete production services & project management from editorial & design through typesetting, printing, art creation, indexing, printing & mailing for journal, book & magazine publishers; specialize in computerized music engraving; integration of music & text; foreign language, scientific & non-Roman alphabet. Typesetting on Mac/Quark systems. Disk conversion; automatic pagination; PostScript & PDF output; customized music engraving software for publishers; music typesetting.
Membership(s): American Musicological Society (AMS); Audio Engineering Society (AES); Music Library Association; Music Publishers Association (MPA)

A-Type Marketing + Design
79 Fiddlers Circle, Hyannis, MA 02601
Tel: 508-957-2887
E-mail: info@a-type.com
Web Site: www.a-type.com
Key Personnel
Pres & Creative Dir: Angela Rutzick
  E-mail: angela@a-type.com
Founded: 1992
Driving business growth through marketing & technology.

Abacus Graphics LLC
15179 Hunger Creek Lane, Bigfork, MT 59911-8313
Tel: 406-837-5776
Web Site: www.abacusgraphics.com
Key Personnel
Principal & Creative Dir: John R Webster
  E-mail: jrw@abacusgraphics.com
Designer & Prodn Mgr & Off Mgr: Francesca Droll
Founded: 1979
Creative design specialists of award-winning, eye-catching image & marketing content. Web site design for businesses of all sizes. Hosting, search engine optimization (SEO), databases, exhibit booths, branding, business cards, flyers, Web hosting, etc. Traditional print materials & collateral.
Membership(s): Independent Book Publishers Association (IBPA)

J Adel Art & Design
586 Ramapo Rd, Teaneck, NJ 07666
Tel: 201-836-2606
E-mail: jadelnj@aol.com
Key Personnel
Creative Dir: Judith Adel
Founded: 1985
Complete graphic design services; book & jacket design, posters, letterheads & magazine design; fine art paintings-watercolors & oils.
Membership(s): Middletown Art Group; New Jersey Water Color Society

AFJ Graphics
903 20 Ave, Tuscaloosa, AL 35401-2306
Tel: 205-349-3702 *Fax:* 205-758-2279

Key Personnel
Owner: Anna Jacobs Singer
  E-mail: annajsinger@hotmail.com
Book design, calligraphy, jacket design, layout & letterheads.

Fernando Agudelo
550 SW 138 Ave, Suite K-109, Pembroke Pines, FL 33027-1535
Tel: 954-668-9122
E-mail: fernandoart2014@gmail.com
Web Site: www.creativehotlist.com/profile/fagudelo
Founded: 1980
Creative illustration for book covers & children's picture books.

Rodelinde Albrecht
PO Box 444, Lenox Dale, MA 01242-0444
Tel: 413-243-4350
E-mail: rodelinde@gmail.com
Founded: 1979
Complete design & production services including text & cover design; direct mail brochures, catalogs, promotional pieces. Typesetting & production on PageMaker. Publishing consultation.

Barbara S Anderson
706 W Davis Ave, Ann Arbor, MI 48103-4855
Tel: 734-995-0125; 734-846-3864
E-mail: bsa@watercolorbarbara.com
Commissioned watercolor illustrations—houses, places; portraits in pencil. Newsletter design & page layout. Additional editorial services offered.
Membership(s): Ann Arbor Women Artists

Andrews McMeel Syndication
1130 Walnut St, Kansas City, MO 64106-2109
Tel: 816-581-7300 *Toll Free Tel:* 800-255-6734
Web Site: syndication.andrewsmcmeel.com
Key Personnel
Pres & CEO: Andy Sareyan *E-mail:* asareyan@amuniversal.com
VP & Mng Ed: Sue Roush *Tel:* 816-581-7320
  E-mail: sroush@amuniversal.com
VP, Sales: John Vivona *Tel:* 816-581-7350
  E-mail: salesdirector@amuniversal.com
Founded: 1970
Provide a searchable database of popular cartoons such as Doonesbury, Garfield, For Better or For Worse, Non Sequitur, Marmaduke & Pearls Before Swine for reprinting in books, magazines & newsletters.

Antler Designworks
93 Concession Oak Dr, Bluffton, SC 29909
Tel: 843-705-6695 *Fax:* 843-705-6445
E-mail: antlerdw@aol.com
Key Personnel
Owner & Pres: Bob Antler
Complete graphic design; book, jacket & poster design, charts, graphs, learning materials, letterheads, logos, catalogs, multimedia kits & promotional brochures, point of purchase & complete packaging.

Aptara Inc
Subsidiary of iEnergizer

2901 Telestar Ct, Suite 522, Falls Church, VA 22042
Tel: 703-352-0001
E-mail: moreinfo@aptaracorp.com
Web Site: www.aptaracorp.com
Key Personnel
Pres: Samir Kakar
EVP, Fin & Cont: Prashant Kapoor
SVP, Busn & Contact Ctr Opers: Ashish Madan
Busn Devt: Michael Scott *E-mail:* michael.scott@aptaracorp.com
Founded: 1988
Liaison for complete or any combination of production services, ranging from simple 1-color to complex 4-color projects. Copy-editing.
Branch Office(s)
150 California St, Suite 301, Newton, MA 02458
Tel: 617-423-7755
11009 Metric Blvd, Bldg J, Suite 150, Austin, TX 78758 *Tel:* 512-876-5997
299 Elizabeth St, Level 1, Sydney 2000, Australia *Tel:* (02) 8251 0070
Tower 1 & 2, 8/100, Acharya Thulasi Rd (Shandy Rd), Pallavaram, Chennai 600 043, India *Tel:* (044) 22640676
No 2310, Doon Express Business Park, Saharanpur Rd, Bldg 2000, Dehradun 248 002, India *Tel:* (0135) 2644055
7B, Leela Infopark, Technopark, Trivandrum, Kerala 695 581, India *Tel:* (047) 14063370
A-37, Sector-60, Noida 201 301, India *Tel:* (0120) 7182424
D-10, Sector-2, Noida 201 301, India *Tel:* (0120) 24423678
SEZ Bldg 4A, 1st fl, S P Infocity, Pune Saswad Rd, Phursungi, Pune 412 308, India *Tel:* (020) 66728000

Arbor Books

244 Madison Ave, Box 254, New York, NY 10016
Tel: 212-956-0950 *Toll Free Tel:* 877-822-2500
Fax: 914-401-9385
E-mail: info@arborbooks.com; editorial@arborbooks.net
Web Site: www.arborbooks.com; www.arborservices.co
Key Personnel
Owner: Joel Hochman *Tel:* 877-822-2502 *E-mail:* arborbooksjoel@aol.com; Larry Leichman *Tel:* 877-822-2504 *E-mail:* arborbookslarry@aol.com
Mktg Dir: Olga Vladi
Founded: 1992
Full service book production from ghostwriting & editing to cover design, printing, publishing & marketing. Arbor Books works for both 1) corporations (business books, corporate histories, CEO bios) & 2) individuals: novels (all genres), memoirs, children's books, biz books, etc. Services include supervised (& insured) ghostwriting, copy-editing, translation, proofreading, design (even the most complex, including model shoots, illustrations, photo reconstruction & manipulation, book jacket design, album cover & magazine design), word processing (including transcription), scanning, layout, typesetting, obtaining registrations & endorsements, B&W & 4-color printing, marketing, promotion & advertising. We also create logos, letterheads, annual reports, posters & promotional flyers. We can be hired for part of the job or all of the job. Personal attention & quality are guaranteed. Fully insured, including media insurance. Writers include Pulitzer Prize winners & "NY Times" best-selling authors; listed with Dun & Bradstreet; firm is featured regularly in "The New York Times Book Review." Our self-publishing services include: press kits, press releases, booking TV & radio programs, speaking tours & book signings & negotiating with producers & agents.

Arbor Services, see Arbor Books

Arrow Graphics Inc

PO Box 380291, Cambridge, MA 02238
E-mail: info@arrow1.com
Web Site: www.arrow1.com
Key Personnel
Pres: Alvart Badalian
Sr Graphic/Pubn Designer: Aramais Andonian
Founded: 1988
Complete book production services with state-of-the-art electronic design & publishing capabilities: copy-editing; indexing; typesetting & page composition; typography; design & art direction from concept to finished product; printing; consultation; project management. Novels, poetry, monographs, self-help, how-to, guides, ebooks & children's picture books. From ms to camera-ready to bound book, serving the publishing industry & self-publishing community. Call or write for information, or visit our web site.

The Association of Medical Illustrators (AMI)

201 E Main St, Suite 1405, Lexington, KY 40507
Toll Free Tel: 866-393-4264 *Fax:* 859-514-9166
E-mail: hq@ami.org; info@ami.org
Web Site: www.ami.org
Key Personnel
Exec Dir: Melanie Bowzer *E-mail:* mbowzer@amrms.com
Conferences & Events Mgr: Glen Ellwood *E-mail:* gellwood@amrms.com
Prog Mgr: Sara Zach *E-mail:* szach@amrms.com
Proj Coord: Whitney Wilgus *E-mail:* wwilgus@amrms.com
Film animation, illustration, layout, letterheads, logos & corporate identity, poster design, retouching & technical illustration.

Baker & Taylor Publisher Services

30 Amberwood Pkwy, Ashland, OH 44805
Tel: 567-215-0030 *Toll Free Tel:* 888-814-0208
E-mail: info@btpubservices.com; orders@btpubservices.com
Web Site: www.btpubservices.com
Key Personnel
SVP, Sales & Client Servs: Mark Suchomel
SVP, Opers: Bob Gospodarek
Founded: 2017
Whether print or ebook, Baker & Taylor Publisher Services provides interior & exterior art services, including cover design, interior design, layout & typesetting. Our designers are US based, formally trained in fine & commercial art, & specialize in everything from children's books to college texts. In addition, Baker & Taylor Publisher Services offers distribution & sales, warehousing & fulfillment.

Carol Bancroft & Friends

PO Box 2030, Danbury, CT 06813
Tel: 203-730-8270 *Fax:* 203-730-8275
E-mail: cbfriends@sbcglobal.net
Web Site: www.carolbancroft.com
Key Personnel
Owner: Joy Elton Tricarico
Founded: 1972
Represents many fine illustrators specializing in art for children of all ages. Servicing the publishing industry including, but not limited to: picture/mass market books & educational materials.
We work with packagers, studios, toy companies & corporations in addition to licensing art to related products. Promotional packets sent upon request.
Art services include illustration, full color & black line. Digital art also available.

Unsol artwork not accepted.
Membership(s): Graphic Artists Guild; Society of Children's Book Writers & Illustrators (SCBWI); Society of Illustrators

Karin Batten

463 West St, Suite C-617, New York, NY 10014
Tel: 212-352-8622
E-mail: karin.batten@gmail.com
Web Site: karinbatten.com
Logos & corporate identity, book, jacket & poster design, illustration, letterheads, spot drawings, trademarks.

Benoit & Associates

744 Stockton Heights Ct, Bourbonnais, IL 60914
Tel: 815-932-2582 *Fax:* 815-932-2594
Web Site: www.benoit-associates.com
Key Personnel
Pres: Michael J Benoit *E-mail:* mbenoit@benoit-associates.com
Full service design & advertising studio. Specialize in technical & color airbrush illustration & computer-generated art (Mac & IBM) design, art direction, in-house photography, elementary through college textbook cover & interior design, newsletters, brochures, letterheads & annual reports. High volume, high quality, quick turnaround, satisfaction guaranteed.

Berg Design

15 Francis Ave, Albany, NY 12203
Tel: 518-495-9409
Web Site: edatkeson.com/bpages/berg.htm
Key Personnel
Owner: Ed Atkeson *E-mail:* edatkeson@gmail.com
Founded: 1985
Cover & jacket design specialists. Fine typography & handlettering. Illustration: drawing, linocuts, scans, photoshop retouch & computer graphics. Interior book design: illustrations, maps, diagrams, redraws. Shootable full color comps, camera ready mechanicals, separations, mechanicals on disk. Call for brochure or portfolio on disk.
Membership(s): AIGA, the professional association for design; Graphic Artists Guild

BH Communications

115 E Ninth St, Unit 17-F, New York, NY 10003
Tel: 212-982-6502
Web Site: www.bhcommunications.com
Key Personnel
Principal: Brice Hammack *E-mail:* brice@bhcommunications.com
Freelance art & design. Design & layout of publications, books, periodicals & advertising pieces, jackets & promotional brochures, web graphics & web sites.
Membership(s): AIGA, the professional association for design; American Association of University Presses (AAUP); American Copy Editors Society (ACES)

Big Vision Art + Design

251 Hwy 179, Creekside Plaza A1, Sedona, AZ 86336
Mailing Address: PO Box 1297, Sedona, AZ 86339
Tel: 928-202-6320
Web Site: www.bigvisionarts.com
Key Personnel
Illustrator & Designer: Pamela Becker *E-mail:* pamela@bigvisionarts.com
Founded: 2012
Children's book illustrator & designer, print broker & fine artist.
Membership(s): Society of Children's Book Writers & Illustrators (SCBWI)

Blitz Media-Direct
Subsidiary of The Linick Group Inc
Linick Bldg, 7 Putter Lane, Middle Island, NY 11953
Mailing Address: PO Box 102, Middle Island, NY 11953-0102
Tel: 631-924-3888; 631-924-8555; 630-604-8599
E-mail: blitz4pr@gmail.com; linickgroup@gmail.com
Key Personnel
Pres: Andrew S Linick, PhD
EVP: Roger Dextor
VP: Gaylen Andrews
Graphic Artist: Keith Yates
Specialize in complete book production, graphic & creative services, copy, design, type & layout for all kinds of printed matter. Art & graphic design services include concept through camera-ready copy, attention-getting book, jacket & poster design, cartoons, illustrations & spot drawings. Integrated effective graphic & copy design for Internet & direct mail packages, direct response ads, advertising, marketing & sales promotion materials, catalogs, brochures-broadsides, annual reports, trademark search/creation/approval, logos & corporate identity, slide-video presentations, trade show exhibits & high visibility signs. Satisfaction guaranteed. Provides comprehensive graphic redesign/new web site content development, interactive services with web site marketing makeover advice for first-time authors, self-publishers, professionals & entrepreneurs. Specializes in flash, animation, online advertising/PR, links to top search engines, consulting on a 100% satisfaction guarantee. Free site evaluation marketing checklist (a $250 value) for LMP readers. Web site design, web site critique & web site marketing makeovers.
Branch Office(s)
7 Lincoln Ave, Smithtown, NY 11787
Membership(s): The Association of Publishers for Special Sales (APSS); The Imaging Alliance

The Blue Mouse Studio
26829 37 St, Gobles, MI 49055
Tel: 269-628-5160
E-mail: frogville@earthlink.net
Key Personnel
Illus: Rex Schneider
Writer & Designer: Chris Buchman
Illustration, book design, cartoons, film animation, jacket design, layout, letterheads & lettering, logos & corporate identity, poster & cover design, spot drawings & trademarks; also storyboards, copywriting, research; film history, film presentation, computer graphics & coloring, photograph restoration, PowerPoint presentation, graphics for PowerPoint/DVD programs, DVD production & computer animation.

Bookcovers.com
Subsidiary of Archer Ellison Inc
c/o Archer Ellison Inc, 7025 CR 46-A, Suite 1071, Lake Mary, FL 32746
Toll Free Tel: 800-449-4095 (ext 702)
Toll Free Fax: 800-366-4086
E-mail: info@bookcovers.com
Web Site: bookcovers.com
Key Personnel
Pres: Allen D'Angelo *E-mail:* allen@bookcovers.com
Founded: 1994
Book cover marketing expertise that translates into more book marketing methods.
Membership(s): Independent Book Publishers Association (IBPA)

theBookDesigners
769 Center Blvd, No 22, Fairfax, CA 94930
Tel: 415-491-5426
E-mail: info@bookdesigners.com
Web Site: www.bookdesigners.com
Key Personnel
Co-Founder, Mgr & Cust Rel: Alan Hebel
Co-Founder & Creative Dir: Ian Koviak
Founded: 2008
Help in every aspect of creating your book. Services include design (cover, jacket, interiors), concept development, visualizations, full editorial services, photography & custom illustrations.

BookWise Design
29089 SW Costa Circle W, Wilsonville, OR 97070
Tel: 503-542-3551 *Toll Free Tel:* 800-697-9833
Web Site: bookwisedesign.com
Key Personnel
Partner & Art Dir: Shannon Bodie
 E-mail: shannon@bookwisedesign.com
Partner & Creative Consultant: Bob Swingle
 Tel: 503-542-3550
Proj Mgr: Jann Armstrong *Tel:* 509-675-3440
 E-mail: jann@bookwisedesign.com
Founded: 1992
Offer a full range of book services for every level of the publishing industry bringing years of experience, innovative design skills & personal attention to every project. Services include book covers & interiors, editorial services, web sites, flyers, brochures, bookmarks, postcards, advertisements, CD or audio packages, corporate identity & web design services.
Membership(s): Independent Book Publishers Association (IBPA)

James F Brisson Book Design & Production
PO Box 85, Williamsville, VT 05362-0085
Tel: 802-348-7802 *Fax:* 802-348-7802
Founded: 1982
Complete design & production services; trade books, covers & jackets, illustration, advertising & marketing materials.

Cecile Brunswick
315 W 39 St, No 1306, New York, NY 10018
Tel: 212-222-2088
E-mail: cbrunswick@nyc.rr.com
Web Site: www.cecilebrunswicknyc.com
Creator of original oil paintings on canvas, copper & gouache on paper.
Membership(s): Artists Talk on Art; New York Artists Circle; New York Artists Equity Association

Burmar Technical Corp
106 Ransom Ave, Sea Cliff, NY 11579
Tel: 516-484-6000 *Fax:* 516-484-6356
Web Site: burmar.net
Key Personnel
Pres: Norma Novotny *E-mail:* norma.novotny@burmar.net
VP: Christine Jensen *E-mail:* christine.jensen@burmar.net
Technical & illustrative illustrations; charts, graphs, maps & spot art using Macintosh systems. Complete desktop publishing service with full book experience. Math & other technical subjects a specialty. Design, art direction & production. Scanning, laser & color proofs. Special expertise in the el-hi & college publishing areas. Specialties: composition, desktop publishing & CD-ROM.

By Design Communications
144 W 27 St, 3rd fl (rear), New York, NY 10001
Tel: 212-366-1740
Key Personnel
Principal: Joelle Silverman Miller
Founded: 1990
A full service studio specializing in catalogs, brochures, newsletters, ads, annual reports, posters & other collateral pieces. Complete design, production, writing, editing & printing services provided.

Leila Cabib
8601 Buckhannon Dr, Potomac, MD 20854
Tel: 301-299-2659 *Fax:* 301-299-0513
E-mail: leila@leilacabib.com
Web Site: www.leilacabib.com
Cartoons, humorous illustrations & spot drawings.
Membership(s): Graphic Artists Guild

Carto-Graphics
184 Starr Wood, Hudson, WI 54016
Tel: 715-386-5989
Key Personnel
Owner: Alice B Thiede *E-mail:* athiede@baldwin-telecom.net
Electronic production of maps for textbooks, periodicals & other publications. Specialize in cartographic research, compilation & design. Provide digital topography.

The Cartoon Bank, A New Yorker Magazine Company
One World Trade Center, 42nd fl, New York, NY 10007
Tel: 212-286-2860 *Toll Free Tel:* 800-897-8666
E-mail: image_licensing@condenast.com; licensing@cartoonbank.com; licensing@condenast.com
Web Site: www.cartoonbank.com
Database of over 120,000 New Yorker cartoons.

Cartoon Images for Licensing
PO Box 410, Chassell, MI 49916
Tel: 906-482-6234
Web Site: www.danscartoons.com
Key Personnel
Cartoonist: Dan Rosandich *E-mail:* dan@danscartoons.com
Founded: 1976
Thousands of categorized cartoons available by subject matter on the web site. Fees to license images are based upon circulation or usage. Also offer "custom" cartooning/humorous illustration services.
Membership(s): Graphic Artists Guild

Cenveo Publisher Services
5457 Twin Knolls Rd, Suite 200, Columbia, MD 21045
Tel: 410-850-0500 *Toll Free Tel:* 800-257-5529
E-mail: info.psg@cenveo.com
Web Site: www.cenveopublisherservices.com
Founded: 2009
Provides solutions & services to journal, book, educational, media & trade publishers. Serving the publishing industry for more than 125 years, we deliver a full-range of technology, content & delivery solutions that escalate revenue & delivery solutions while ensuring editorial integrity. Cenveo Publisher Services is an industry leader in XML-early workflow solutions, copy-editing, digital outputs, automated transformations, author services, print & fulfillment services & more.
Branch Office(s)
555 Virginia Dr, Fort Washington, PA 19034
 Tel: 267-470-1590 *Fax:* 215-591-9093
3575 Hempland Rd, Lancaster, PA 17601
 Tel: 717-285-9095
2905 Byrdhill Rd, Richmond, VA 23228
No 31 Kempapura, Hebbal, Bangalore 560 024, India *Tel:* (080) 4000 4888
36 Barnaby Rd, Kilpauk, Chennai, Tamil Nadu 600 010, India *Tel:* (044) 4205 8888
Marwah Ctr, 5th fl, Krishanlal Marwah Marg, Andheri East, Mumbai *Tel:* (022) 4098 5200
Steller IT Park, Tower I, 3rd fl, C 25, Sector 62, Noida 201 301, India *Tel:* (0120) 461 3700
One Mulgrave Chambers, 26-28 Mulgrave Rd, Sutton, Surrey SM2 6LE, United Kingdom

Cenveo Publisher Services
555 Virginia Dr, Fort Washington, PA 19034
Tel: 267-470-1590 *Fax:* 215-591-9093
E-mail: info.psg@cenveo.com
Web Site: www.cenveopublisherservices.com
Key Personnel
CFO: John Pennie
Pres: Atul Goel
VP, Journal Publg Servs: Debbie McClanahan
VP, Learning Solutions: Waseem Andrabi
VP, Media & Intl Delivery Ctr: Dwayne Reed
Dir, Mktg: Mike Groth *E-mail:* mike.groth@
cenveo.com
Founded: 1998
We offer full art, design & production capabilities
for the educational publishing market including
PreK-12 & higher education. Our full service,
in-house creative department includes book designers, illustrators & prepress specialists. We
provide a complete range of creative services
including interior & cover design, instructional
design & art rendition from concept to finished,
prepress product. We specialize in illustrative
art, graphs, charts, maps, technical illustrations
& photo research/shoots. We also provide creation of art specs & art mss, scanning sources
for existing line art +/or photographs & mod-
ification +/or design overhaul of existing art
programs.
Branch Office(s)
3575 Hempland Rd, Lancaster, PA 17601
Tel: 717-285-9095
5457 Twin Knolls Rd, Suite 200, Columbia, MD
21045 *Tel:* 410-850-0500 *Toll Free Tel:* 800-
257-5529
2905 Byrdhill Rd, Richmond, VA 23228
No 31 Kempapura, Hebbal, Bangalore 560 024,
India *Tel:* (080) 4000 4888
36 Barnaby Rd, Kilpauk, Chennai, Tamil Nadu
600 010, India *Tel:* (044) 4205 8888
Marwah Ctr, 5th fl, Krishanlal Marwah Marg,
Andheri East, Mumbai 400 072, India
Tel: (022) 4098 5200
Steller IT Park, Tower I, 3rd fl, C 25, Sector 62,
Noida 201 301, India *Tel:* (0120) 461 3700
One Mulgrave Chambers, 26-28 Mulgrave Rd,
Sutton, Surrey SM2 6LE, United Kingdom

Paul Chevannes
529 Eighth St, Suite 1B, Brooklyn, NY 11215
Tel: 718-788-3550
Book design, jacket design, logos & corporate
identity, poster design.
Membership(s): American Copy Editors Society
(ACES)

Colour Technologies
Division of CJ Graphics Inc
134 Park Lawn Rd, Toronto, ON M8Y 3H9,
Canada
Tel: 416-588-0808 *Fax:* 416-588-5015
E-mail: info@colourtec.com
Web Site: www.colourtec.com
Key Personnel
Owner: Jay Mandarino
Prepress, wide format & color specialists.

Robert Cooney Graphic Design
2813 Naples Ave, Half Moon Bay, CA 94019
Mailing Address: PO Box 362, Half Moon Bay,
CA 94019
Tel: 650-712-4400
Founded: 1979
Art direction, graphic design, photo research &
complete production services for books, publi-
cations & special projects.

Copywriters' Council of America™ (CCA)
Division of The Linick Group Inc
CCA Bldg, 7 Putter Lane, Middle Island, NY
11953-1920

Mailing Address: PO Box 102, Middle Island,
NY 11953-0102
Tel: 631-924-3888; 631-924-8555; 631-604-8599
Key Personnel
Pres: Gaylen Andrews
EVP: Roger Dextor
Dir, Spec Projs: Barbara Deal
Art Dir: Barbara Lande
Graphic Artist: Keith Yates
Complete art, publishing/copywriting services
include: name, URL, slogan & logo design,
editorial, production, all direct response marketing & mail order promotions. Worldwide
clients. Specialize in digital marketing, online
marketing campaigns, sales letters, test mailings, list selection, booklets, premium offers,
bouncebacks, FSI, statement stuffers & inserts for co-op mailings. Retainer & per project
basis. Request free Company Services Market & Industry Specialties Checklist. Provides
comprehensive graphic redesign/new web site
content development, interactive services with
web site marketing makeover advice for first-
time authors, self-publishers, professionals &
entrepreneurs. Specializes in online advertis-
ing/PR, links to top search engines, consulting on a 100% satisfaction guarantee. Free site
evaluation marketing checklist (a $250 value)
for LMP readers.
Branch Office(s)
7 Lincoln Ave, Smithtown, NY 11787

Cornell & Co LLC
44 Jog Hill Rd, Trumbull, CT 06611
Tel: 203-454-4210
Web Site: www.cornellandco.com
Key Personnel
Owner: Merial Cornell *E-mail:* merial@
cornellandco.com
Founded: 1989
Professional illustrators specializing in children's
book markets; educational, trade & mass mar-
ket. Representing over 35 artists with a variety
of styles & techniques.
Membership(s): Graphic Artists Guild; Soci-
ety of Children's Book Writers & Illustrators
(SCBWI)

Cox-King Multimedia
PO Box 909, Geneva, NY 14456
Tel: 315-719-0141
E-mail: info@ckmm.com
Web Site: www.ckmm.com
Key Personnel
Owner & Pres: Charles King
Founded: 1999
Editorial, proofreading, typesetting, book design
& prepress services meeting the needs of a
wide variety of fiction & nonfiction books. Tra-
ditional & on-demand workflows supported.
Self-publishers need not inquire.

Crawshaw Design
120 Bayview Dr, San Rafael, CA 94901
Tel: 415-456-5544 *Fax:* 415-456-4319
Web Site: www.crawshawdesign.com
Key Personnel
Founder & Owner: Todd Crawshaw
E-mail: todd@crawshawdesign.com
Founded: 1975
Book jacket & poster design, letterheads, logos &
trademarks, web site design & development.
Membership(s): Executives Association of San
Francisco (EASF)

Creative Freelancers Inc
PO Box 366, Tallevast, FL 34270
Toll Free Tel: 800-398-9544
Web Site: www.illustratorsonline.com
Key Personnel
Pres: Marilyn Howard
Illustration, design & copy services.

The Creative Group (TCG)
Division of Robert Half International Inc
125 High St, 17th fl, Boston, MA 02110
Tel: 617-690-7386; 617-526-8899
Toll Free Tel: 888-651-8589
E-mail: boston@creativegroup.com
Web Site: www.roberthalf.com/work-with-us/our-
services/creativegroup
Key Personnel
VP & Branch Mgr: Kristen Johnson
Placement of temporary & permanent designers,
illustrators, typographers, desktop publishing
professionals & project managers for publishing, publications, marketing & all aspects of
communications. Creative resource for concept development, writing, designing & project
management through to final production.

CRW Graphics Communications
9100 Pennsauken Hwy, Pennsauken, NJ 08110
Tel: 856-662-9111 *Toll Free Tel:* 800-820-3000
Fax: 856-665-1789
E-mail: info@crwgraphics.com
Web Site: www.crwgraphics.com
Key Personnel
Pres: David Carpenter
EVP: George Slater
VP, Sales & Mktg: Will Glassman
E-mail: wglassman@crwgraphics.com
Cust Serv Mgr: Rich Quigley *E-mail:* rquigley@
crwgraphics.com
Founded: 1964
Highest quality commercial print services, fulfill-
ment & direct mail. Includes database work,
variable imaging, digital prepress & produc-
tions as well as conventional lithography. Work
with artists & designers to refine their work to
a commercially acceptable quality level.

Cypress House
Imprint of Comp-Type Inc
155 Cypress St, Fort Bragg, CA 95437
Tel: 707-964-9520 *Toll Free Tel:* 800-773-7782
Fax: 707-964-7531
Web Site: www.cypresshouse.com
Key Personnel
Pres: Cynthia Frank *E-mail:* cynthia@
cypresshouse.com
Mng Ed: Joe Shaw *E-mail:* joeshaw@
cypresshouse.com
Founded: 1986
Provide complete editorial, design, production,
marketing & promotion services to indepen-
dent publishers. Editorial services include ms
evaluation, editing, rewriting, copymarking &
proofreading. Production services include book,
cover & page design & make-up to camera-
ready. Marketing & promotion services for se-
lected titles.
Membership(s): American Booksellers Association (ABA); Bay Area Independent Publishers
Association (BAIPA); California Independent
Booksellers Alliance (CALIBA); Independent
Book Publishers Association (IBPA); Pacific
Northwest Booksellers Association (PNBA)

Dan Daly
23 Limerock St, Camden, ME 04843-2116
Tel: 207-236-8834
E-mail: dan@dalyart.com
Web Site: www.dalyart.com
Expert based B&W, full color drawings & paint-
ings of wildlife, fly-fishing, hunting & skiing.
Commissioned portraits-house, people, places
in oil or watercolor. Cover illustration services.

D&D Sales & Printing
840 12 St NW, Mason City, IA 50401
Tel: 641-423-9487 *Toll Free Tel:* 800-325-5308
Fax: 641-423-3068
E-mail: ddsales.service@gmail.com
Web Site: www.ddsalesonline.com

Key Personnel
Owner: Dale Helgeland; Sue Helgeland; Dave Lane; Lisa Lane
Founded: 2005
Embossing dies, prepress camera work, stripping, screen printing, embroidery, offset printing (sheetfed).

De Muth Design
59 Chenango St, Cazenovia, NY 13035
Tel: 315-655-8599
Web Site: www.demuthdesign.com
Key Personnel
Pres & CEO: Roger T De Muth *Tel:* 315-415-8599 (cell) *E-mail:* rdemuth@syr.edu
Illustration, including package design, magazine/editorial & advertising illustration & children's books.

Decode, Inc
625 First Ave, Suite 300, Seattle, WA 98104
Tel: 206-343-9101
E-mail: books@decodebooks.com
Web Site: www.decodeinc.com; www.decodebooks.com
Key Personnel
Owner & Pres: John Jenkins, III
Owner & Partner: Stephen Lyons
Founded: 1991
Publish fine art photography monographs; providing innovative graphic & information design services for the educational publishing market.

Delgado & Co Inc
3900 Greystone Ave, Suite 21A, Riverdale, NY 10463
Tel: 718-708-4419
E-mail: mail@delgadoandcompany.com
Web Site: www.delgadoandcompany.com
Key Personnel
Founder & Pres: Lisa Delgado *E-mail:* lisa@delgadoandcompany.com
Founded: 1981
Total design & production service, including copy-editing, proofreading, layout, mechanicals, art direction & prepress.

Desktop Miracles Inc
112 S Main St, Suite 294, Stowe, VT 05672
Tel: 802-253-7900 *Toll Free Fax:* 888-293-2676
E-mail: info@desktopmiracles.com
Web Site: www.desktopmiracles.com
Key Personnel
Pres & CEO: Barry T Kerrigan *E-mail:* barry@desktopmiracles.com
VP: Virginia Kerrigan *E-mail:* virginia@desktopmiracles.com
Full service publishing design & production firm providing interior typesetting & jacket/cover design to publishing clients nationwide.

diacriTech Inc
4 S Market St, 4th fl, Boston, MA 02109
Tel: 617-600-3366 *Fax:* 617-848-2938
Web Site: www.diacritech.com
Key Personnel
EVP: Madhu Rajamani *E-mail:* madhu@diacritech.com
Dir, Prodn & Edit Servs: Maureen Ross *E-mail:* m.ross@diacritech.com
Founded: 1997
Art & design services for K-12, college, STM & trade publishers. Facilities in Boston, MA, Manchester, NH & in Chennai, Madurai & Kottayam in India.

Didona Design
160 Grandview Rd, Ardmore, PA 19003
Tel: 610-649-3110
E-mail: didona@didonadesign.com
Web Site: www.didonadesign.com

Key Personnel
Pres: Lawrence R Didona
Mktg Mgr: Cathy Didona
Founded: 1987
A graphic design studio that specializes in cover design in a wide variety of disciplines for many publishers, large & small. We also design ancillary materials including CD-ROM packaging, brochures & logos. With our strong Photoshop expertise, we also offer digital illustration/collage & photo retouching.

Digital Vista Inc
24 Amity Place, Massapequa, NY 11758
Tel: 516-799-5277
E-mail: info@digitalvista.net
Web Site: www.digitalvista.net
Key Personnel
Owner: Rich Di Silvio
Founded: 1992
Creative cover design, illustration, jacket design, logos, poster design & new media.

Spencer Drate
119 W 80 St, Suite 1-F, New York, NY 10024-7134
Tel: 212-799-0535
E-mail: spencerdrate@yahoo.com
Key Personnel
Owner & Creative Dir: Spencer Drate
Creative Dir: Jutka Salavetz
Founded: 1989
Book jacket & book design, poster design, music design, letterheads, logos, promotional design, trademarks, corporate identity, design & other graphic areas.
Membership(s): AIGA, the professional association for design; The Recording Academy (NARAS)

Dunn+Associates Design
Division of Dunn+Associates Design & Creative Services for Advertising Inc
PO Box 870, Hayward, WI 54843-0870
Tel: 715-634-4857 *Fax:* 715-634-5617
E-mail: info@dunn-design.com
Web Site: www.dunn-design.com
Key Personnel
Pres & Sr Designer: Kathi Dunn
Partner & Creative Dir: Ron "Hobie" Hobart
Founded: 1985
Since 1985, complete design services for large & small publishers. Hundreds of brand-building covers designed, many bestsellers. Cover design, audio & video package design & ebook conversion. Promotional materials including brochures, posters, print ads, catalogs, newsletters, logos, identity. Coaching from ms to printed book. Clients include Tony Robbins, Ken Blanchard, Deepak Chopra, Mark Victor Hansen, Prentice-Hall, HarperCollins, Hay House.
Membership(s): Colorado Independent Publishers Association (CIPA); Independent Book Publishers Association (IBPA); Midwest Independent Publishing Association (MIPA)

DWJ BOOKS LLC
14 Hill Side Lane, East Hampton, NY 11937
Tel: 631-267-8270
E-mail: info@dwjbooks.com
Web Site: www.dwjbooks.com
Key Personnel
EVP: Lauren Fedorko *E-mail:* lfedorko@dwjbooks.com
Edit Dir: Darrell Kozlowski
Founded: 1988
Full service content provider with editorial, art & design & production capabilities. Design, illustration & photo research. Electronic production.
Membership(s): American Book Producers Association (ABPA); The American Library Asso-

ciation (ALA); National Council for the Social Studies (NCSS); National Council of Teachers of English (NCTE)

Wendy Edelson Studios
18 E St Louis St, Rapid City, SD 57701
Tel: 206-319-8158
Web Site: www.wendyedelson.com; www.elevenlemons.blogspot.com
Key Personnel
Prop & Illus: Wendy Edelson *E-mail:* wendy@wendyedelson.com
Founded: 1985
Create water & mixed media paintings for general editorial illustration projects such as book covers, interior art, how-to illustrations, product illustration, illuminated letters & children's books, posters & advertising campaigns, art for licensing.
Membership(s): Society of Illustrators

1106 Design LLC
610 E Bell Rd, Suite 2-139, Phoenix, AZ 85022-2393
Tel: 602-866-3226 *Fax:* 602-866-8166
E-mail: md@1106design.com
Web Site: www.1106design.com
Key Personnel
Owner: Michele De Filippo
Founded: 2001
Quality book cover, interior design & production with 30 years experience.

Emerson, Wajdowicz Studios Inc
530 W 25 St, New York, NY 10001
Tel: 212-807-8144 *Fax:* 212-675-0414
E-mail: info@designews.com
Web Site: www.designews.com; Facebook.com/DesignEWS
Key Personnel
Founder & Creative Dir: Jurek Wajdowicz
Sr Art Dir & Principal: Lisa LaRochelle
Sr Designer: Yoko Yoshida-Carrera
Assoc: Manny Mendez; Abigail Watson
Annual report, book, jacket & poster design, magazine & newspaper design & redesign, letterheads, photo editing, photography, trademarks, lettering, layout, corporate identity, art direction, annual reports & marketing & desktop publishing & web design.

Emsworth Design
147 W 24 St, New York, NY 10011
Tel: 212-877-6139; 917-359-9860 (cell)
Web Site: www.emsworthdesign.com
Key Personnel
Owner: Tony Drobinski
Founded: 1983
Book design & production from mss to bound books. Specialize in heavily illustrated books & exhibition catalogs. Exhibition graphics: posters, signage, banners & collateral material.

Entro Communications Inc
33 Harbour Sq, Suite 202, Toronto, ON M5J 2G2, Canada
Tel: 416-368-6988 *Fax:* 416-368-5616
E-mail: toronto@entro.com
Web Site: www.entro.com
Key Personnel
Partner: Andrew Kuzyk
Graphic design & corporate identity, environmental graphics.

Equator Graphics Inc, see International Mapping Associates

Fairfield Marketing Group Inc
Subsidiary of FMG Inc
The Direct Mail Ctr, 830 Sport Hill Rd, Easton, CT 06112-1241

Tel: 203-261-5585 *Fax:* 203-261-0884
E-mail: info@fairfieldmarketing.com
Web Site: www.fairfieldmarketing.com
Key Personnel
Pres & CEO: Edward P Washchilla, Jr
VP, Cust Serv: Mike Lozada *Tel:* 203-261-5585
  ext 204
VP, Fulfillment: Jason Paul Miller *Tel:* 203-261-
  5585 ext 203 *E-mail:* jason@fairfieldmarketing.
  com
Founded: 1986
Book design, cartoons, film animation, illustra-
  tion, jacket design, layout, letterheads, lettering,
  map design, poster design, trademarks & type-
  setting.
Membership(s): American Booksellers Associ-
  ation (ABA); Bridgeport Regional Business
  Council (BRBC); Education Market Association; United States Chamber of Commerce
  (USCC)

fd2s
1634 E Cesar Chavez, Austin, TX 78702
Tel: 512-476-7733
Web Site: www.fd2s.com
Key Personnel
Co-Founder & Principal: Steven L Stamper
  E-mail: sstamper@fd2s.com
Co-Founder: Larry Fuller
Principal: Curtis Roberts
Founded: 1985
Experiential graphic design, wayfinding consult-
  ing, donor recognition, logos & corporate iden-
  tity, branding & messaging.
Membership(s): Society for Experiential Graphic
  Design (SEGD)

Figaro
PO Box 848, Sharon, CT 06069
Tel: 860-248-8989; 860-364-0834
E-mail: design@figro.com
Web Site: www.figro.com
Key Personnel
Co-Pres & Creative Dir: Walter Schwarz
Co-Pres: Linda Swenson *E-mail:* ls@figro.com
Creative, editorial, production, photographic ser-
  vices for books, catalogs, promotional mate-
  rials & packaging. Digital creation of text,
  art, maps, illustration & photos for current &
  out of print books. Consultation, graphic arts
  management & printing supervision. Web site
  development & maintenance. Photography of
  Suzanne Szasz & Ray Schorr.

Leonard Everett Fisher
7 Twin Bridge Acres Rd, Westport, CT 06880-
  1028
Tel: 203-227-0133 *Fax:* 203-227-0133
E-mail: l.e.fisher@sbcglobal.net
Illustration for young readers.
Membership(s): The Authors Guild; Society
  of Children's Book Writers & Illustrators
  (SCBWI); Society of Illustrators

45th Parallel Maps & Infographics
13720 Paragon Ave N, Stillwater, MN 55082
Tel: 651-430-8127
E-mail: info@45thparallelmaps.com
Web Site: 45thparallelmaps.com
Key Personnel
Principal Cartographer: Patricia Isaacs
  E-mail: patti@45thparallelmaps.com
Founded: 1990
Art production & management for digital &
  print applications. Developmental & technical art services, specializing in custom cartography, charts, graphs & diagrams for text &
  trade books, magazines, travel guides, museum
  & visitor center displays. We can take your
  project from research through design & production & can handle jobs from single piece
  to hundreds. Many subject areas: geography,

geology & other earth sciences; history, an-
  thropology & other social sciences; business,
  computer science, foreign languages. Major
  clients include McGraw-Hill, Houghton Mifflin,
  Cengage & university presses.
Membership(s): Bookbuilders of Boston; Minnesota Book Publishers Roundtable; Minnesota
  Bookbuilders; Publishing Professionals Network (PPN)

Foster Covers
1401 Wonder Way, Fairfield, IA 52556
Tel: 641-472-3953 *Toll Free Tel:* 800-472-3953
  Toll Free Fax: 866-837-0544
E-mail: info@fostercovers.com
Web Site: www.fostercovers.com
Key Personnel
Pres: George Foster *E-mail:* george@fostercovers.
  com
Founded: 1982
Book cover design & audio covers.

Leanne Franson
4 Poplar Ave, Martensville, SK S0K 2T0, Canada
Mailing Address: PO Box 1327, Martensville, SK
  S0K 2T0, Canada
Tel: 306-382-1696
E-mail: leanne@leannefranson.com
Web Site: www.leannefranson.com
Founded: 1991
Illustrate children's textbooks & trade books (pic-
  ture books, children's novels) & magazines to
  client's spec, working in pen & ink (B&W) or
  colored acrylic inks & pencil (watercolor tech-
  nique).
Membership(s): Communication-Jeunesse; Illus-
  tration Quebec; Picture Book Artists Associa-
  tion (PBAA)

G & H Soho Inc
413 Market St, Elmwood Park, NJ 07407
Tel: 201-216-9400 *Fax:* 201-216-1778
E-mail: print@ghsoho.com
Web Site: www.ghsoho.com
Key Personnel
Pres: Gerry Burstein
Prodn Mgr: Jason Burstein
Founded: 1985
Complete service, from copy-editing through pro-
  duction editing. Text & cover design, from
  rough layouts to final pages delivered on film
  or disk. Production service through bound
  books. Specialize in computer, technical &
  heavily illustrated books.
Membership(s): Association of Graphic Commu-
  nications; Book Industry Guild of New York;
  Digital Print Industry Association; PRINTING
  United Alliance

Laurence Gartel
PO Box 4114, Deerfield Beach, FL 33442
Tel: 561-302-6774
E-mail: gartel@comcast.net
Web Site: gartelart.com
Multimedia & DVDs, computer graphic designs
  & illustrations, logos & text, digital photogra-
  phy & digital art.

General Cartography Inc
4 Estate Dr, Boynton Beach, FL 33436
Tel: 561-455-4398
E-mail: terradata@aol.com
Web Site: cartographybypaul.com
Key Personnel
Pres: Paul Pugliese
Founded: 1968
Maps.

GEX Inc
2 Industrial Way, Atkinson, NH 03811
Tel: 603-870-9292

Web Site: www.gexinc.com
Key Personnel
Pres: Gary Russell
VP: Jim LaPierre; Karla Russell
Full service educational publishing services company, providing content development, digital
  & production services to the world's foremost
  publishers. With over 30 years of experience,
  GEX designs courses, creates engaging content
  & provides services that deliver content to a
  variety of media with digital & print solutions.

Gary Gore Book Design
1913 Blair Blvd, Nashville, TN 37212
Tel: 615-298-3588
E-mail: garygore@comcast.net
Book & jacket design, layout. Specialize in schol-
  arly books, nonfiction & art books.

Gore Studio Inc
101 Paxton Ct, Brentwood, TN 37027
Tel: 615-519-2262
E-mail: gorestudioinc@gmail.com
Web Site: www.gorestudio.com
Key Personnel
Pres: Bruce Gore
Book & bookcover design, electronic layout, let-
  terheads, logos, trademarks & posters.

GW Illustration & Design
Formerly Graphic World Illustration Studio
Subsidiary of GW Inc
2290 Ball Dr, St Louis, MO 63146
Tel: 314-567-9854
Web Site: www.gwinc.com
Key Personnel
CEO: Kevin Arrow
EVP: Andy Vosburgh; Mike Loomis
VP, Content Opers: Suzanne Kastner
Scanning & art rendering services for technical,
  medical & educational textbook art projects.

Graphic World Illustration Studio, see GW
  Illustration & Design

Graphics International
Division of Illustration Services Inc
20475 Bunker Hill Dr, Cleveland, OH 44126
Tel: 440-333-9988
Key Personnel
Pres: Don Izold *E-mail:* dlozi@aol.com
Founded: 1981
Precision B&W line illustration.

Ann Grifalconi/Greyfalcon House
124 Waverly Place, No 1, New York, NY 10011
Tel: 212-777-9042
Key Personnel
Dir: Ann Grifalconi *E-mail:* anngrifalconi22@
  gmail.com
Bookstore ad promotions, events/high-level large
  art post wood cutouts poster event. Concept
  to finals/art copy photos. Original art, photography, mixed media, full color or B&W -
  book illustrations (juvenile/young adult), book
  & CD covers; editorial full page or spot for
  magazines, the media. Full color photographs:
  recent New York skyline; attractions; Times
  Square/Blues/human interest/interpretive so-
  larized: Coney Island; Chinatown Parade. Full
  color photo portfolios world class art & historical sites: Buddist outdoor sacred art &
  sculptures/temples, scenes (China, Vietnam,
  Cambodia); Maya art, sculpture archeological
  sites in Central America (Honduras, Mexico,
  Guatemala). Also, current Asian, Mayan &
  Mexican peoples, customs, crafts (3,000 Asian
  & 8,000 Maya totals).

Heidelberg Graphics
2 Stansbury Ct, Chico, CA 95928

SAN: 211-5654
Tel: 530-342-6582 *Fax:* 530-342-6582
E-mail: heidelberggraphics@gmail.com; service@
heidelberggraphics.com
Web Site: www.heidelberggraphics.com
Key Personnel
Owner & Pres: Larry S Jackson
Founded: 1972
Book design, layout & book publication. Consultant to self-publishers. Provide editing, word processing/typesetting, bar codes, Internet sales & copyright services.

Hermani & Sorrentino Design
404 Musgrave Rd, Salt Spring Island, BC V8K
1V5, Canada
Tel: 250-653-9350
E-mail: hermani2sorrentino@gmail.com
Web Site: www.hermanisorrentino.com
Key Personnel
Owner: Michela Sorrentino
Founded: 1993
Complete graphic design services including book design, illustrations & web design.

Hespenheide Design
99 Long Ct, Suite 102, Thousand Oaks, CA
91360
Tel: 805-499-8875
Web Site: www.hespenheide.com
Key Personnel
Owner & Pres: Gary Hespenheide *E-mail:* gary@
hespenheide.com
Founded: 1989
Publishing services for trade, college & el-hi including individual & series basal design, cover design, art direction, electronic production, illustration, photo research & assignment photography; specialists in complete project management.
Membership(s): Publishing Professionals Network
(PPN)

Cathy Hull
180 E 79 St, New York, NY 10075
Tel: 212-772-7743 *Fax:* 212-535-1877
E-mail: cathy@cathyhull.com
Web Site: www.cathyhull.com
Freelance illustrator; specializes in conceptual illustration for editorial, advertising, corporate & institutional clients in the US, Europe & Japan. Services include illustration, logos & corporate identity, greeting cards, fun apparel & products.

International Mapping Associates
5300 Dorsey Hall Dr, Suite 201, Ellicott City,
MD 21042
Tel: 443-367-0050 *Toll Free Tel:* 800-761-6944
Fax: 443-367-0045
Web Site: internationalmapping.com
Key Personnel
Founder & Pres: Scott Edmonds
Dir, Cartographic Opers: Vickie Taylor *Tel:* 443-
367-0050 ext 236
Sr Cartographer: Erin Bolton
Founded: 2000
Custom map design services for the publishing industry. Services include research, design, compilation & production of maps & information graphics for both print & electronic publishing. Offering a complete range of products including textbook maps, wall maps, travel guides, 2-D & 3-D maps, 3-D block diagrams, shaded relief, 3-D terrain models, map exhibits, virtual fly-thrus, animated & interactive maps, web maps & graphics.
Membership(s): International Map Industry Association (IMIA)

ITW Foils
Division of Illinois Tool Works

5 Malcolm Hoyt Dr, Newburyport, MA 01950
Tel: 978-225-8200 *Toll Free Tel:* 800-942-9995
Fax: 978-462-0831
E-mail: info@itwsf.com
Web Site: www.itwfoils.com
Founded: 1926
Hotstamping foil.

Itzhack Shelomi Design
25 Cushman Rd, Scarsdale, NY 10583
Tel: 212-689-7469
E-mail: studio@ishelomi.com; studio@serifes.
com
Web Site: www.ishelomi.com
Key Personnel
Owner & Creative Dir: Itzhack Shelomi
Founded: 1987
Design & production from children's to young adult publications: Storybooks, activity books, educational publications & games, packages for games, packages & sleeve cases for books, display cases, brochures, booklets, newsletters, etc. Handling design, pictures & illustrations editing, page composition & word processing for interior & cover, from the ms through full-color dummy-up to the final mechanical, in both English & Hebrew languages. Special custom-made typefaces & fonts for English & Hebrew languages; 3-D color comps for package's presentation. Fully equipped with the latest computer graphic technology.

The Ivy League of Artists Inc
18 Edgemere Rd, Livingston, NJ 07039
Tel: 973-992-4048 *Fax:* 973-992-4049
E-mail: ilartists2@gmail.com
Key Personnel
Owner & Pres: Ivy Mindlin
Illustration, spot drawings, calligraphy, comps, storyboards, design & mechanical art.

Kachergis Book Design Inc
14 Small St N, Pittsboro, NC 27312
Tel: 919-542-3507
E-mail: goodbooks@kachergisbookdesign.com
Web Site: www.kachergisbookdesign.com
Key Personnel
Pres: Anne Kachergis
Founded: 1980
Book & book cover design, electronic layout, letterheads, logos, trademarks & posters.

Dimitri Karetnikov
7 Tennyson Dr, Plainsboro, NJ 08536
Tel: 609-275-6491
E-mail: dkare@aol.com
Founded: 1983
Advising authors on illustration & graphic design. Illustration from concept through press-ready art. Wide variety of subject matter including medical & science illustrations for books, audiovisual presentations, web sites in a wide variety of graphic formats including Adobe Illustrator & PhotoShop.

Karen Karibian
3 Mill River Lane, Apt B206, Ardsley, NY 10502
Tel: 914-478-4070
E-mail: karenesque2@aol.com; karenkaribian@
gmail.com; karenessence@aol.com
Web Site: www.coroflot.com/karenessence/
undercurrent-cartoons; www.karenessence.wix.
com/undercurrentcartoons
Founded: 2000
Cartoons, illustrations & figure drawing; colorful, whimsical, humorous, festive & sublime. Available for licensing & branding.
Membership(s): Art Directors Club; Art on Call;
Women in Animation

Leonard H Kessler
1624 Treehouse Circle, TR-120, Sarasota, FL
34231-6724
Tel: 941-966-2618
E-mail: lenkessler@comcast.net
Book illustration, children/author children's books, editorial consultant, easy reader books.
Membership(s): The Authors Guild; Pelican Cove Art League; Society of Illustrators

Lachina Precision Graphics Services
3791 S Green Rd, Cleveland, OH 44122
Tel: 216-292-7959
E-mail: info@lachina.com
Web Site: www.lachina.com
Key Personnel
Pres: Jeff Lachina *E-mail:* jeff@lachina.com
Dir, Prodn Servs: Whitney Philipp
E-mail: wphilipp@lachina.com
Dir, Proj Mgmt Off: Shawn Vazinski
E-mail: svazinski@lachina.com
Founded: 1978
Full service creative & business consulting agency that helps companies tackle creative, brand & business dilemmas with the right tools, methods & technology.

Ted Lewin
152 Willoughby Ave, Brooklyn, NY 11205
Tel: 718-622-3882
E-mail: betsyandted@aol.com
Web Site: www.tedlewin.com
Children's picture books.

Wayne Lim
2429 Clement St, No 2, San Francisco, CA 94121
Tel: 415-845-2532
E-mail: w_c_lim@yahoo.com
Founded: 1984
Draw cartoons/illustrations & logos for a wide audience.

Linguistic Systems Inc (LSI)
260 Franklin St, Suite 230, Boston, MA 02110
Tel: 617-528-7410 *Toll Free Tel:* 800-654-5006
E-mail: clientservice@linguist.com
Web Site: www.linguist.com
Key Personnel
Founder & Pres: Martin Roberts *Tel:* 617-528-
7412 *E-mail:* mroberts@linguist.com
VP: Mark Ettinger
VP, Engg: Boris Katsevman
VP, Lang Serv Progs: Jean-Paul Fandel
Founded: 1967
Leading language conversion company, specializing in the translation of books, periodicals, manuals & catalogs. For over 50 years the company has produced more than 2,000,000 pages of translation, covering 120 languages. LSI maintains a database of 7,500 carefully screened translators for expertise in a broad spectrum of industrial & scientific subjects. Foreign language typesetting for print, web site & mobile apps & narration for video & multimedia programs are also available.
Membership(s): American Translation Association Accredited; Association of Language Companies (ALC); Globalization & Localization Association (GALA)

LK Advertising Agency
Division of The Linick Group Inc
Linick Bldg, 7 Putter Lane, Middle Island, NY
11953
Mailing Address: PO Box 102, Middle Island,
NY 11953-0102
Tel: 631-924-3888; 631-924-8555; 631-604-8599
E-mail: topmarketingadvisor@gmail.com
Web Site: topmarketingadvisor.com
Key Personnel
EVP & Mktg Res Mgr: Roger Dextor

Complete art & graphic web site design services. General graphic design: ebooks, books, book jackets, textile & product designs; general illustrations, trade publication, book advertising, fashions, technical, comp illustrations; point of purchase, cartoons, AV, graphics, TV storyboards, retouching, lettering, photography, calligraphy, exhibit design, layout, letterheads, map design, pictorial statistics, spot drawings, corporate identity programs, logos, trademarks, advertising, marketing & sales promotion literature, brochures & catalogs. Worldwide consultants on copywriting & graphics; direct response, mail order & advertising, design web sites, e-mail & e-commerce campaigns. Provides comprehensive graphic redesign/new web site content development, interactive services with web site marketing makeover advice for first-time authors, self-publishers, professionals & entrepreneurs. Specializes in online advertising/pr, links to top search engines, consulting on a 100% satisfaction guarantee. Free site evaluation marketing checklist (a $250 value) for LMP readers.

Membership(s): ADA; The Association of Publishers for Special Sales (APSS); The Imaging Alliance; Independent Book Publishers Association (IBPA)

Jack Lucey
84 Crestwood Dr, San Rafael, CA 94901
Tel: 415-453-3172
Courtroom artist, book jackets & poster design, cartoons, illustration, layout, logos & corporate identity, spot drawings, trademarks & aviation art. Full composition & layout service for camera-ready mechanicals, including illustration. Artist member of the US Air Force Art Program.

Lumina Datamatics Inc
Affiliate of Datamatics Global Services (Mumbai)
4 Collins Ave, Plymouth, MA 02360
Tel: 508-746-0300 *Fax:* 508-746-3233
Web Site: luminadatamatics.com
Key Personnel
SVP: Jack Mitchell *Tel:* 508-746-0300 ext 203
  E-mail: jack.mitchell@luminad.com
SVP, Content Technol: John Wheeler
  E-mail: john.wheeler@luminad.com
SVP, Prod Devt: Gordon Laws *E-mail:* gordon.laws@luminad.com
SVP, Sales: Prashant Prabhu *E-mail:* prashant.prabhu@luminad.com
VP, Fin & Acctg: John Chappell *E-mail:* john.chappell@luminad.com
Founded: 1974
Providing full service content creation, design/packaging & media delivery systems to publishers. Services include authoring/writing, editorial research & development, media development & production, editing, photo & text research/permissions, photography/photo shoot direction, indexing, proofreading, fact checking, design/design direction, art direction/editing, technical/illustrative art packages, photo manipulation & page make-up/composition services. Employs over 1,200 US & offshore resources specializing in content/media creation & make-up including file conversions/repurposing & content management & delivery services. All services are offered both in the US & at offshore facilities. Areas of specialization include school, higher education & professional publishing: mathematics (grade school/algebra/calculus/physics), foreign language (French/Spanish/German/Italian), English & English composition, history, political science, science (chemistry/biology/astronomy), social studies, computer science, business (economics/finance/marketing), engineering & technical trades as well as professional/reference material. Products range from simple one-color

ancillaries components to highly complex design & art intensive core content.
Branch Office(s)
31572 Industrial Rd, Suite 400, Livonia, MI 48150 *Toll Free Tel:* 800-717-9153 *Fax:* 734-525-4455
510 Thornall St Metropark, Suite 100, Edison, NJ 08837 (sales) *Toll Free Tel:* 888-772-5532 *Fax:* 732-635-0600
345 Seventh Ave, 4th fl, New York, NY 10001 *Tel:* 646-453-1000 *Fax:* 212-564-8285
1797 Seddon Ct, Ashland, OH 44805 *Tel:* 419-289-0558 *Fax:* 419-289-8923
3265 Farmtrail Rd, York, PA 17406 *Tel:* 717-764-4000
Datamatics Global Services GmbH doo, Gunduliceva br 33, 78000 Banja Luka, Bosnia and Herzegovina *Tel:* 51304120
Im Leuschner, Park 3, 64347 Griesheim, Germany *Tel:* (06155) 862 99-0 *Fax:* (06155) 862 99-19
Ascendas International Tech Park, Taramani Rd, 12th fl, Phase II, Chennai 600 113, India *Tel:* (044) 6604 6000; (044) 6604 6001; (044) 6604 6002 *Fax:* (044) 6604 6098
Knowledge Ctr, St No 17, MIDC, Andheri (E), Mumbai 400 093, India *Tel:* (022) 6102 0000 *Fax:* (022) 2834 3669
Suyojit Datamatics Knowledge Center, Suyojit IT Park, Survey No 804, Unit No S1-S3, Nashik-Mumbai Hwy, Nashik 422 002, India *Tel:* (0253) 610 2222 *Fax:* (0253) 610 2271
Off No 5, 2nd fl, Tower 1, Stellar IT Park, C-25, Sector 62, Noida 201 301, India *Tel:* (0120) 494 0999
Plot No 29-34, East Coast Rd, Saram Revenue Village, Oulgaret Municipality, Lawspet Post, Puducherry 605 008, India

Mapping Specialists Ltd
3000 Cahill Main, Suite 220, Fitchburg, WI 53711
Tel: 608-274-4004 *Toll Free Tel:* 866-525-2298 *Fax:* 608-274-9689
E-mail: msl@mappingspecialists.com
Web Site: www.mappingspecialists.com
Key Personnel
Owner & Pres: David R Knipfer
Founded: 1984
Full service map program development, consultation services using the latest computer & animated techniques. Complete project coordination, design, in-house research, computer base generation, compilation, shaded relief & digital files. PC, Mac & CD-ROM output. Specialize in thematic mapping for textbooks, encyclopedias, reference, trade, travel guides, etc. Strong staff background in cartography, computer graphics, geography, art illustration, charts, graphs, history. In-house editing at every production stage with emphasis on technical, geographic, historical & thematic accuracy. Project manager works as part of client's team.

Maps by Mathison
PO Box 152, Spring Mills, PA 16875
Tel: 814-321-7571
E-mail: jcmaps6@gmail.com
Web Site: mapsbymathison.com
Key Personnel
Owner: Jeff Mathison
Founded: 1980
Create illustrated maps of real or fictional territory in a variety of styles.

Maps.com
120 Cremona Dr, Suite 260, Santa Barbara, CA 93117
Tel: 805-685-3100 *Toll Free Tel:* 800-430-7532 *Fax:* 805-699-7550
E-mail: info@maps.com
Web Site: www.maps.com

Key Personnel
Pres & CEO: John Glanville
Dir, Busn Devt: Eric Sanborn
Dir, Opers: Bryan Wilby
Founded: 1991
Leading mapping solutions company. The company is a supplier of digital maps & other geographic content to a diverse group of publishers. Solutions include digital map licensing, custom mapping, education mapping & published reference map products (atlases, wall & folded maps). Products are used by major Internet sites, schools, colleges, news broadcasters, major newspapers, directory, educational & reference publishers throughout North America.
Membership(s): Association of American Publishers PreK-12 Learning Group; Association of Directory Publishers (ADP); Better Business Bureau (BBB); International Map Industry Association (IMIA); National Council for the Social Studies (NCSS); News Media Alliance; North American Cartography Information Society (NACIS); Yellow Pages Publishers Association (YPPA)

Barbara Marks Graphic Design
15 Flying Point, Stony Creek, CT 06405
Mailing Address: PO Box 3373, Stony Creek, CT 06405
Tel: 203-481-3361
Founded: 1978
Design, project management & production. From concept to bound books. Specialty: large projects/complex projects/heavily illustrated titles/continuity programs/calendars. Subject matter: cookbooks, lifestyle, reference, health, gardening, nature, guidebooks & how-to/do-it-yourself.

Diane Maurer-Hand Marbled Papers
Subsidiary of Hand Marbled Papers
Water St, Spring Mills, PA 16875
Mailing Address: PO Box 78, Spring Mills, PA 16875-0078
Tel: 814-422-8651
E-mail: dkmaurer1@aol.com
Web Site: www.dianemaurer.com
Illustration; jacket design. Specialize in hand-marbled papers, paste papers & handmade books.

Meadows Design Office
3800 Yuma St NW, Washington, DC 20016
Tel: 202-966-6007
E-mail: mdo@mdomedia.com
Key Personnel
Pres & Creative Dir: Marc Meadows
  E-mail: marc@mdomedia.com
Curator & Image Res: Amy Meadows
Founded: 1981
A full service graphic design firm. Design & production of books, book jackets, illustrated books, cookbooks, publications & promotional materials & sidelines; consultation, art direction, design, layout, type specification & mechanical art. Specialize in trade & text books. Conceptualize & prepare mock-up covers, compositions, presentations & blads for publishers. State-of-the-art electronic publishing equipment & software. Typeset & produce multilingual editions of our book designs.
Membership(s): AIGA, the professional association for design; Type Directors Club

Melissa Turk & the Artist Network
9 Babbling Brook Lane, Suffern, NY 10901
Tel: 845-368-8606
E-mail: melissa@melissaturk.com
Web Site: www.melissaturk.com
Key Personnel
Owner & Pres: Melissa Turk
Contact: Dorothy Ziff
Founded: 1986

Represents professional artists supplying quality illustration, calligraphy & cartography. Specialize in children's trade & educational illustration as well as natural science illustration (wildlife, botanical, medical, etc).

Membership(s): Graphic Artists Guild; Society of Children's Book Writers & Illustrators (SCBWI)

Brian Thomas Merrill
40 Vandale St, Putnam, CT 06260
Tel: 860-315-4638
E-mail: zangmerrill@yahoo.com
Desktop publishing, art & design: jackets, interiors, logos & corporate ID, ads, calligraphy, lettering, cartoons, illustration, letterheads, typesetting, photography.

Wendell Minor
15 Old North Rd, Washington, CT 06793
Mailing Address: PO Box 1135, Washington, CT 06793-0135
Tel: 860-868-9101
E-mail: wendell@minorart.com
Web Site: www.minorart.com
Key Personnel
Proj Coord: Florence Minor
Illustration & design for trade & juvenile books, from concept to electronic mechanical; jacket design & illustration; magazine illustration.

MPS North America LLC
Subsidiary of MPS Ltd
5728 Major Blvd, Suite 528, Orlando, FL 32819
Tel: 407-472-1280 *Toll Free Tel:* 866-978-1008
Fax: 212-981-2453
E-mail: marketing@mpslimited.com
Web Site: www.mpslimited.com
Founded: 1973
Technical, medical, situational, scientific & chemistry. We offer high quality art renderings, as well as full service typesetting & book production.
Branch Office(s)
1901 S Fourth St, Suite 222, Effingham, IL 62401
477 Madison Ave, 6th fl, New York, NY 10022
1822 E NC Hwy 54, Suite 120, Durham, NC 27713-3210
MPS Ltd, HMG Ambassador, 137 Residency Rd, Bangalore 560 025, India *Tel:* (080) 4178 4242 *Fax:* (080) 4178 4222
MPS Ltd, RR Towers, Super A, 16/17 TVK Industrial Estate, Guindy, Chennai 600 032, India *Tel:* (044) 4916 2222 *Fax:* (044) 4916 2225
MPS Ltd, 33 IT Park, Sahastradhara Rd, Dehradun 248 001, India *Tel:* (0135) 6677 954
MPS Ltd, 709 DLI Corporate Greens, Sector 74A, Narsinghpur, Gurugram 122 004, India *Tel:* (0124) 661 3134
MPS Interactive Systems, GRM Tech Bldg, 2nd fl, Plot No DH-6/29, Action Area-1, Rajarhat, New Town, Kolkata, West Bengal 700 156, India *Tel:* (033) 66111500
MPS Interactive Systems, The Great Oasis, D-13, 2nd fl, Marol Industrial Estate, Andheri (E), Mumbai 400 093, India *Tel:* (022) 6643 8100 *Fax:* (022) 6643 8800
MPS Ltd, C35, Sector 62, Noida 201 307, India (corp off) *Tel:* (0120) 4599750 *Fax:* (0120) 4021280
Membership(s): Publishing Professionals Network (PPN)

Andrew Newman Design
54 Winding Cove Rd, Marstons Mills, MA 02648-1825
Tel: 508-420-1161
E-mail: newmandesign@gmail.com
Web Site: www.andrewnewmandesign.com
Key Personnel
Owner: Andrew Newman
Founded: 1980

Award-winning graphic design studio knowledgeable in all areas of design & production for logotypes, advertising & promotional materials, web site design, cover design, illustration, art direction, package design, lettering & typeface design.
Membership(s): AIGA, the professional association for design; Cape Cod Technology Council

North Market Street Graphics (NMSG)
Affiliate of Archetype Inc
317 N Market St, Lancaster, PA 17603
Tel: 717-392-7438 *Fax:* 717-397-8037
E-mail: mail@nmsgbooks.com
Web Site: www.nmsgbooks.com
Key Personnel
Owner: Elizabeth Andes; LeRoy R Stipe, Jr
VP of Opers: Vicky Dawes
Art Dir: Tim Weiler
Prepress services for book publishers including book design, double keyboarding/verify, Macintosh composition including creation of ebooks, page assembly, copy-editing, proofreading, PDF files, postscript, extensive art services & Epson proofing. All commonly used media available. ISDN, DSL electronic transmissions; archiving services.
Art services include: color separation with Photoshop adjustment, B&W scanning with Photoshop adjustment, art & output calibrated to printer specifications.

Open Sky Creative
907 North St, Williamsburg, IA 52361
Tel: 630-564-2583
E-mail: mail@openskycreative.com
Web Site: www.openskycreative.com
Key Personnel
Prop & Graphic Designer: Paul Christenson
Founded: 2007
Creative studio providing all aspects of book design, from covers to interiors.

Tom O'Sullivan
202 Riverside Dr, New York, NY 10025
Tel: 212-865-0229
Illustration, jacket & map design, spot drawings, cartoons.

Robert Pizzo Illustration/Design
21 Lonetown Rd, Redding, CT 06896-2004
Tel: 203-938-0663
E-mail: rp@robertpizzo.com
Web Site: www.robertpizzo.com
Corporate, advertising, editorial & stock illustration, children's books.

Pronk Media Inc
PO Box 340, Beaverton, ON L0K 1A0, Canada
Tel: 416-441-3760
E-mail: info@pronk.com
Web Site: www.pronk.com
Key Personnel
Pres: Gord Pronk *Tel:* 416-441-3760 ext 203
E-mail: gord@pronk.com
Print design & production, including product conceptualization & prototypes, design & art direction, photo research & licensing, infographics, charts, graphs, technical art, page design, layout & production.

Publication Design Inc
6449 Meadowview Terr S, Zionsville, PA 18092
Tel: 610-928-1111
E-mail: ayers@publicationdesign.com
Web Site: www.publicationdesign.com
Key Personnel
Pres: Robert Ayers
Founded: 1986
Magazine designer.

The Pushpin Group Inc
38 W 26 St, New York, NY 10010
Tel: 212-529-7590
Web Site: www.pushpininc.com
Key Personnel
Co-Founder, Pres & Dir: Seymour Chwast
E-mail: seymour@pushpininc.com
Founded: 1954
Book jackets, poster design, illustration, letterheads, trademarks, packaging design, graphics, logo & corporate identity.
Membership(s): AIGA, the professional association for design; Art Directors Club of New York; Graphic Artists Guild

QBS Learning
242 W 30 St, Suite 900, New York, NY 10001
Tel: 929-841-5969
E-mail: sales@qbslearning.com
Web Site: www.qbslearning.com
Key Personnel
CEO: Hanut Singh *E-mail:* hanut.singh@qbslearning.com
COO, ADP: Brian Kobberger *E-mail:* brian.kobberger@qbslearning.com
EVP, Content Devt: Jane Petlinski *E-mail:* jane.petlinski@qbslearning.com
VP, Busn Devt: Michael Porter *E-mail:* michael.porter@qbslearning.com
Group HR Dir: Reggie Chua Singh
E-mail: reggie.singh@qbslearning.com
Founded: 1983 (as Bill Smith Group)
Full development services for children's products. Editorial, photography, illustration, interior & cover design & production; web site design. Art buying illustration services, early childhood thru higher education.

QuaraCORE LLC
One E Wacker Dr, Suite 1900, Chicago, IL 60601
Tel: 312-981-2540
E-mail: info@quaracore.com
Web Site: www.quaracore.com
Key Personnel
Pres & Creative Dir: Randi S Brill
E-mail: randi@quaracore.com
CFO: Bob Taylor
Founded: 2014 (1982 as The Quarasan Group Inc)
From concept to completion, QuaraCORE provides planning, product conceptualization, complete customized publishing systems, editorial, design, marketing & product development services including original writing, substantive & content editing, correlations, focus/field testing, visual design, image procurement & all online & print delivery services for educational & edutainment products. Top caliber project management. Specialize in PreK-12 products in reading, literature, language arts, integrated curriculum programs, intervention, science, math, social studies, music, art, test prep & assessment/standardized tests.
Membership(s): ASCD; Association of American Publishers PreK-12 Learning Group; International Literacy Association (ILA); National Council for the Social Studies (NCSS); National Council of Teachers of English (NCTE); National Council of Teachers of Mathematics (NCTM); National Middle School Association (NMSA); National Science Teachers Association (NSTA); TESOL International Association

Patrick Redmond Design
PO Box 40156, St Paul, MN 55104-8156
Tel: 651-646-4254
E-mail: LMP@PatrickRedmondDesign.com
Web Site: www.PatrickRedmondDesign.com
Key Personnel
Owner & Creative Dir: Patrick Michael Redmond, MA
Founded: 1966

Creative concept, creative direction, art direction & design; graphic design, design consultation & education; brand design; creativity advocacy.
Membership(s): AIGA, the professional association for design

Reynolds Design & Management
52 Piedmont Ave, Waltham, MA 02451-3015
Tel: 781-893-7464
E-mail: rdandm@comcast.net
Key Personnel
Owner: Christine Reynolds
Founded: 1986
Design, project management & production of company history books.
Membership(s): Letterpress Guild of New England; New England Museum Association; Society of Printers; Women's National Book Association (WNBA)

The Roberts Group
12803 Eastview Curve, Apple Valley, MN 55124
Tel: 952-322-4005
E-mail: info@editorialservice.com
Web Site: www.editorialservice.com
Key Personnel
Owner: Sherry Roberts; Tony Roberts
Founded: 1990
Book design, production, editorial services & web development. A one-stop creative resource for quality interior book design, typesetting, editing, proofreading & indexing. Serving established presses & self-publishers. Competitive prices. Satisfaction guaranteed. We pay attention to details & will work to meet your deadlines. Visit our web site for a complete description of services.

Rosenthal Represents
23725 Hartland St, West Hills, CA 91307
Tel: 818-430-3850
E-mail: eliselicenses@earthlink.net
Key Personnel
Pres: Elise Rosenthal
Sales & Mktg & Artists Rep: Neil Sandler
Founded: 1979
Illustration, design, cartoons, children's illustrated, calligraphy, lettering, storyboards, poster & map design, technical & architectural illustration & renderings, licensing illustrations.

Round Table Companies
1027 Kenton Rd, Deerfield, IL 60015
Mailing Address: PO Box 511, Highland Park, IL 60035
Tel: 949-375-1006
Web Site: www.roundtablecompanies.com
Key Personnel
CEO: Corey Michael Blake *Tel:* 847-682-3493 *E-mail:* corey@roundtablecompanies.com
Dir, Client Experience: Yolanda Knight *E-mail:* yolanda@roundtablecompanies.com
Founded: 2006
Writing, branding, printing, distribution, coaching & consulting, bringing culture to companies.

Bernard Schleifer Co
200 W 20 St, Suite 212, New York, NY 10011
Tel: 212-675-2615
Key Personnel
Owner: Bernard Schleifer
Book & jacket design, dummying & mechanicals, formatting, complete book production & Quark Express desktop.

Shadow Canyon Graphics
902 S Cascade, La Veta, CO 81055
Mailing Address: PO Box 307, La Veta, CO 81055
Tel: 720-498-4823
Web Site: www.shadowcanyongraphics.com

Key Personnel
Owner: Dianne J Nelson; Adam Phillips; Lindy Kedro Phillips *E-mail:* lindy@shadowcanyon.graphics
Founded: 1978
Typesetting, cover & interior design, jacket design, layout, typesetting, desktop publishing, copy-editing, proofreading, indexing, publishing consultation, author & book marketing, ebook conversions, photography.
Membership(s): Publishers Association of the West (PubWest)

Shepherd Inc
2223 Key Way Dr, Suite B, Dubuque, IA 52002
Tel: 563-584-0500
Web Site: www.shepherd-inc.com
Key Personnel
Prodn Mgr: Deb Leibfried
Founded: 1989
A seasoned book production company that offers state-of-the-art electronic composition, full service project management. Experienced in producing texts in the college, school, professional, trade & reference fields. Shepherd is a schedule-oriented, cost-efficient & quality-conscious vendor.

Snow Lion Graphics
Division of SLG Books
414 Lesser St, Oakland, CA 94601
Mailing Address: PO Box 9465, Berkeley, CA 94709-0465
Tel: 510-525-1134; 510-816-2840 (cell)
E-mail: info@slgbooks.com
Web Site: www.snowliongraphics.com
Key Personnel
Pres & Dir: Roger Dale Williams *E-mail:* roger@slgbooks.com
Prodn Mgr: Frances Williams
Founded: 1986
Book design & illustrations, color separation & printing (books, calendars, posters, cards), publishing, book packaging.
Membership(s): Book Promotion Forum; The Imaging Alliance

Ned Sonntag
Affiliate of King Features Syndicate/Fleischer Studios
2 Englewood Dr, Suite D3, Harwich, MA 02645
Tel: 774-237-0690
E-mail: nedso@comcast.net
Web Site: nedsonntag.com
Founded: 1971
Illustrator, cartoonist.

Square Two Design Inc
2325 Third St, Suite 213, San Francisco, CA 94107
Tel: 415-437-3888
E-mail: info@square2.com
Web Site: www.square2.com
Key Personnel
Pres & Creative Dir: Eddie Lee *Tel:* 415-437-3888 ext 101
Founded: 1991
Corporate identity & web site design. Full service graphic design firm.
Branch Office(s)
No 8 Hua Jia Di Nan Jie, Chao Yang District, Beijing 100102, China, Pres: Min Wang *Tel:* (01350) 1084-543 *E-mail:* mwang@square2.com

Steeleworks
Affiliate of Tide-mark Press
PO Box 4002, Philadelphia, PA 19118
Tel: 215-247-4619
Web Site: www.sarasteele.com

Key Personnel
Principal: Sara Steele *E-mail:* sara@sarasteele.com
Founded: 1983
Artist, art dealer, designer & art publisher.

J B Stewart
1700 Landings Blvd, Sarasota, FL 34231
Tel: 941-929-0262
E-mail: jstewartx2@comcast.net
Web Site: jbstewartfinearts.com
Key Personnel
Owner & Pres: James B Stewart
Contact: Joan Stewart
Founded: 1982
Graphic design & digital layout for magazines, books & catalogs. Advertising concept & design. Digital photo preparation. Conference through distribution.

Story Monsters LLC
4696 W Tyson St, Chandler, AZ 85226-2903
Tel: 480-940-8182 *Fax:* 480-940-8787
Web Site: www.StoryMonsters.com
Key Personnel
Pres: Linda F Radke *E-mail:* Linda@StoryMonsters.com
Founded: 1985
A team of talented graphic designers creating integrated, eye-catching designs to make our books stand out from the rest. Can provide cover design, format for interior pages, typesetting assistance, logo design, business cards or marketing materials. Just let us know what your needs are & we'll promptly provide a plan & an estimate.
Membership(s): Better Business Bureau (BBB); The Children's Book Council (CBC); Independent Book Publishers Association (IBPA); National Federation of Press Women

Studio E Book Production
PO Box 20005, Santa Barbara, CA 93120-0005
Tel: 805-683-6202 *Fax:* 805-683-6202
E-mail: queries@studio-e-books.com
Web Site: www.studio-e-books.com
Key Personnel
Prop: Eric C Larson *E-mail:* eric@studio-e-books.com
Founded: 1999
Book packaging, book design & typesetting.

Stephen Tiano
56 Tyler Dr, Riverhead, NY 11901
Tel: 631-284-3842; 631-764-2487 (cell) *Fax:* 631-284-3842
E-mail: steve@tianobookdesign.com
Web Site: www.tianobookdesign.com
Founded: 1993
Book designer & page composition specialist who specializes in books on technical & scientific subjects filled with math, equations & tabular material. Also does page design & layout on children's picture & storybooks, as well as trade books loaded with photos & other art.
Membership(s): Editorial Freelancers Association (EFA)

Stan Tusan
105 Breckinridge Dr, Phoenix, OR 97535
Tel: 541-535-6791
E-mail: stantoon@charter.net
Web Site: www.stantoon.com
Digital artwork & design: humorous illustrations, children's educational books & materials, spot drawings; licensor.
Membership(s): National Cartoonist Society

Tyler Creative
1300 S Johnstone Ave, Bartlesville, OK 74003-5624

Tel: 918-527-6779
E-mail: info@tylercreative.com
Web Site: tylercreative.com
Key Personnel
Owner: Sherry L Stinson
Founded: 1994
A full service, award-winning graphic design &
photography studio.
Membership(s): Graphic Artists Guild; Na-
tional Association of Photoshop Professionals
(NAPP); Professional Photographers of Amer-
ica (PPA)

Wild West Communications Group
PO Box 346, Homewood, CA 96141
Tel: 530-525-5201 *Fax:* 530-525-4559
Web Site: www.wildwest-tahoe.com
Key Personnel
Principal: Lolly Kupec *E-mail:* lk.wwcg@gmail.
com

Pres: Edward Miller *E-mail:* em@wildwest-tahoe.
com
Founded: 1977
Editorial services, book design jacket & poster
design, layout, letterheads, logos & corporate
identity, sales presentations & typesetting.

Wilkinson Studios Inc
2955 Kelly Dr, Elgin, IL 60124-4349
Tel: 312-286-3683
Web Site: www.wilkinsonstudios.com
Key Personnel
Founder & Pres: Christine Wilkinson
E-mail: chris@wilkinsonstudios.com
Founded: 1999
Represent illustrators & managing art programs
for educational, trade book & mass market
publishing, children's magazines, games & re-
lated fields. Over 100 illustrators offering age
appropriate artwork for PreK-college in a wide

range of styles, techniques & media, both conventional & electronic. Project management
of large volume blackline or color illustration
programs by dedicated staff with art & design
backgrounds, working directly with the publisher or interfacing with design & development house vendors.
Membership(s): Graphic Artists Guild; International Literacy Association (ILA); Society of Children's Book Writers & Illustrators
(SCBWI)

Brice Wood
PO Box A, Jerome, AZ 86331
Tel: 928-634-3238
E-mail: bricewood@yahoo.com
Web Site: www.bricewood.com
Artist: master draftsman. Design, illustration,
photography, typography. Brochures to books.
Computer graphics & electronic delivery.

Photographers

Listed below are photographers available for almost any type of assignment, although many of them are specialists in one field or another. Among these photographers and firms are many who maintain stock files of their own photos, whereas the section **Stock Photo Agencies** lists firms that represent several photographers and maintain stock photo files of their work.

Russell Abraham Photography
Jack London Sq, 309 Fourth St, Suite 108, Oakland, CA 94607
Tel: 510-444-5204
E-mail: ra@russellabraham.com; info@russellabraham.com
Web Site: russellabraham.com
Key Personnel
Owner & Photog: Russell Abraham
Founded: 1978
Membership(s): American Institute of Architects; American Society of Media Photographers (ASMP)

Dean Abramson Photography
PO Box 610, Raymond, ME 04071
Tel: 207-655-7386
Web Site: www.mainephoto.com
Key Personnel
Owner: Dean Abramson *Tel:* 207-838-3542 (cell)
E-mail: dabramso@maine.rr.com
Founded: 1980
Editorial, stock & commercial photography; Maine, life & landscapes, railroad, international travel, boats & many other subjects.
File Begins: 1975
Membership(s): American Society of Media Photographers (ASMP)

Accent Photography Ltd
1842 31 Ave SW, Calgary, AB T2T 1S7, Canada
Tel: 403-271-4120 *Toll Free Tel:* 844-470-4120
E-mail: accentphoto@shaw.ca
Web Site: www.accentphoto.net; www.calgaryphotographer.com
Key Personnel
Owner & Chief Photog: Lawrence De Pape
Founded: 1979
Portrait & commercial photography, photo restoration.
Membership(s): Alberta Professional Photographers Association (APPA); Professional Photographers of America (PPA); Professional Photographers of Canada (PPOC); Wedding & Portrait Photographers International (WPPI)

ActionGrafixPhotography.com
30 Bishop Tutu Blvd, Toronto, ON M5V 2Z7, Canada
Tel: 416-260-0421
Web Site: www.actiongrafixphotography.com
Key Personnel
Chief Photog: Hugh McClean
E-mail: hmcclean@rogers.com
Founded: 1980
Photo digital imaging; corporate & media photography; digital images transferred worldwide.
Branch Office(s)
Peter Jenkins Ltd, 23 Corby Rd, Mapperly, Nottingham NG3 5HF, United Kingdom
E-mail: petej@petejenkins.co.uk

Aerial Archives
495 N Main St, PMB 113, Lake Port, CA 95453
Tel: 415-771-2555
Web Site: aerialarchives.com
Key Personnel
Dir & Photog: Herb Lingl
Founded: 1989

Aerial photography & aerial videography on assignment; large archive of current & historical aerial photography & satellite imagery.
File Begins: 1907
Membership(s): Advertising Photographers of America; American Society of Media Photographers (ASMP); American Society of Picture Professionals (ASPP); Professional Aerial Photography Association (PAPA)

Airphoto
421 N Main, Suite 103, Pueblo, CO 81003
Tel: 719-542-5719
Web Site: www.airphotona.com
Key Personnel
Owner: John Wark *E-mail:* john@johnwark.com
Founded: 1990
Comprehensive aerial stock photography of North America: urban, agricultural, industry, mining, marine, geology, environmental, national parks, transportation & US borders. Seven books on Jim Wark's aerial photography have been published.
Membership(s): American Society of Media Photographers (ASMP); American Society of Picture Professionals (ASPP); AOPA; Professional Aerial Photography Association (PAPA)

Rodelinde Albrecht
PO Box 444, Lenox Dale, MA 01242-0444
Tel: 413-243-4350
E-mail: rodelinde@gmail.com
Founded: 1979
People, scenics, nature closeups, animals, travel; stock & assignment.
Stock: B&W & color

George Ancona
35 Calle Enrique, Santa Fe, NM 87507
Tel: 505-471-8755
E-mail: geoancona@gmail.com
Web Site: georgeancona.com
Assignment photography; photo illustration, design & texts for children's books. Stock file of children, industry, domestic & international subjects.
Membership(s): The Authors Guild

Atlanta Panorama
Division of ALPS Labs
c/o ALPS Labs, 2139 Liddell Dr NE, Atlanta, GA 30324-4132
Tel: 404-872-2577 *Toll Free Tel:* 800-873-2577
Fax: 404-872-0548
E-mail: alps007@mindspring.com
Web Site: www.atlantapanorama.com
Key Personnel
Owner & Photog: George S Pearl
E-mail: george@atlantapanorama.com
Founded: 1978
Professional photography & art.
Membership(s): American Society of Media Photographers (ASMP)

Noella Ballenger & Associates
PO Box 457, La Canada, CA 91012
Tel: 818-954-0933 *Fax:* 818-954-0910
E-mail: noella1b@aol.com
Web Site: www.noellaballenger.com

Key Personnel
Owner & Photog: Noella Ballenger
Founded: 1984
Stock photography, text/photo packages. Provides online classes with one-on-one instruction & portfolio reviews. Contact directly.
Membership(s): American Society of Media Photographers (ASMP)

Frank Balthis Photography
Affiliate of Nature's Design
PO Box 255, Davenport, CA 95017-0255
Tel: 831-426-8205; 805-770-3018
E-mail: frankbalthis@yahoo.com
Web Site: frankbalthis.photoshelter.com
Key Personnel
Owner & Photog: Frank S Balthis
Founded: 1980
Natural history & travel stock photo file. Photograph & publish natural history cards & books. Postcards & note cards published through Nature's Design. Work closely with parks, interpretive associations, museums & galleries. Over 600 designs currently available.
Stock: 150,000 color transparencies; 35mm & medium formats; 20,000 B&W; 500,000 digital capture

Steve Banks Photographer
Subsidiary of Studio 6 Art
14822 Channel Lane, Santa Monica, CA 90402
Tel: 310-998-7062
E-mail: stevestudio@studio6art.com
Web Site: www.studio6art.com
Founded: 2000
Photojournalist & fine art photographer; stock includes music, celebrities, sports, photographic essays & more.
File Begins: 1964
Membership(s): The Recording Academy (NARAS)

Billy E Barnes
313 Severin St, Chapel Hill, NC 27516-1512
Tel: 919-942-6350 *Fax:* 919-942-6350
E-mail: bbarnes218@aol.com
Web Site: www.billybarnes.com
Editorial style photography for magazines, corporations, annual reports, AV; stock has been published in books of 119 major publishers, 200 magazines. Stock & assignment photography, writing. Stock subjects include jobs, medical, education, travel, people & lifestyles. No search fee, 15-day free examination.
File Begins: 1964
Stock: 60,000 35mm B&W & 65,000 35mm color

Tim Barnwell Photography
244 Coxe Ave, Asheville, NC 28801
Mailing Address: 10 Governors Ct, Asheville, NC 28805
Tel: 828-251-0040
E-mail: barnwellphoto@hotmail.com
Web Site: www.barnwellphoto.com
Key Personnel
Owner: Tim Barnwell

Founded: 1980
Professional photography for editorial & advertising clients. Book publishing under imprint; Numinous Editions. Author of fine books.

Tom Bean Photography
Division of Tom & Susan Bean Inc
4680 Lake Mary Rd, Flagstaff, AZ 86001
Mailing Address: PO Box 1567, Flagstaff, AZ 86002-1567
Tel: 928-779-4381 *Fax:* 928-779-9642
E-mail: tom@tombean.com
Web Site: www.tombean.com
Key Personnel
Pres: Tom Bean
Assignment & stock photography. Stock includes travel & outdoor adventure, earth science, wildlife, Western landscapes & natural areas, with an emphasis on natural history.

Morton Beebe Photographer/Author
150 Lombard St, Suite 808, San Francisco, CA 94111-1139
Tel: 415-362-6222; 415-706-0594
E-mail: morton.beebe@gmail.com
Web Site: www.mortonbeebe.com
Key Personnel
Owner & Photog: Morton Beebe
Founded: 1962
Photojournalist, author & film producer.
Membership(s): American Society of Media Photographers (ASMP); Bay Area Travel Writers

Benoit & Associates
744 Stockton Heights Ct, Bourbonnais, IL 60914
Tel: 815-932-2582 *Fax:* 815-932-2594
Web Site: www.benoit-associates.com
Key Personnel
Pres: Michael J Benoit *E-mail:* mbenoit@benoit-associates.com
Full service design & advertising studio. Specialize in technical & color airbrush illustration & computer-generated art (Mac & IBM) design, art direction, in-house photography, elementary through college textbook cover & interior design, newsletters, brochures, letterheads & annual reports. High volume, high quality, quick turnaround, satisfaction guaranteed.

Miriam Berkley Photography
353 W 51 St, Suite 1-A/6, New York, NY 10019-6457
Tel: 212-246-7979
E-mail: miriam.berkley@mac.com; authorpix@aol.com
Web Site: www.PublishersMarketplace.com/members/MiriamBerkley; www.miriamberkley.com
Founded: 1986
Strong author portraits in color & B&W (35mm film & JPEGs). Now shooting entirely digitally. Large stock (approximately 1,500 names) of international author photographs, including Nobel Prize winners; special strengths: writers from Spain & Latin America; Scandinavia; mystery writers; some publishers & literary agents; publishing & literary events; digitally scan & transmit large number of artistic editorial images suitable for cover art or interiors. Also, since 2003, large stock of New York City images, as well as Paris, London, Stockholm, Mexico & Cuba.
File Begins: 1986
Stock: 150,000 B&W; 200,000 35mm color tranparencies & digital images
Membership(s): American Society of Media Photographers (ASMP); American Society of Picture Professionals (ASPP); The Authors Guild; Editorial Photographers (EP); Professional Women Photographers (PWP)

Raymond Bial
208 W Iowa St, Urbana, IL 61801
Tel: 217-328-2665
E-mail: raybial@gmail.com
Web Site: www.raybial.com
Founded: 1974
Assignment photography; photo illustration & text for children's books & nonfiction books for adults. Specialize in advertising & editorial photography; versatile in portraiture, landscape, still life & action photography in both color & B&W. Photographs widely used by major publishers.
File Begins: 1974
Stock: Over 50,000 stock photographs, B&W & color slides. Wide variety of stock photographs in color & B&W available, especially rural, small town & historical subjects, including Amish, Shakers, Cajuns, Native Americans & others, as well as African-American & other ethnic groups

Jennifer Bishop Photography
843 W University Pkwy, Baltimore, MD 21210
Tel: 410-366-6662
Web Site: www.jenniferbishopphotography.com
Key Personnel
Owner & Photog: Jennifer Bishop *E-mail:* jen@jenniferbishopphotography.com
Assignment & stock photography.
Membership(s): American Society of Media Photographers (ASMP)

Bondarenko Photography
Division of Image Hive LLC
210 S 41 St, Birmingham, AL 35222
Tel: 205-592-8319; 205-243-9910 (cell)
E-mail: info@bondarenkophoto.com
Web Site: www.bondarenkophoto.com
Key Personnel
Owner & Photog: Marc Bondarenko
Founded: 1981
Commercial photography studio working both in studio & on location worldwide.
Membership(s): American Advertising Federation (AAF); American Society of Media Photographers (ASMP)

Bradley Ireland Productions
23852 Pacific Coast Hwy, No 110, Malibu, CA 90265
Tel: 310-458-0700
E-mail: earthimag@aol.com
Web Site: www.bradleyireland.com
Key Personnel
Owner & Photog: Georgienne Bradley; Jay Ireland
Founded: 1990
Video & still stock house-natural history/underwater specialty.
Membership(s): American Society of Media Photographers (ASMP); North American Nature Photography Association (NANPA)

Art Brewer Photography
25262 Mainsail Dr, Dana Point, CA 92629
Tel: 949-661-8930 *Fax:* 949-248-2835
E-mail: art@artbrewer.com
Web Site: www.artbrewer.com; artbrewerphoto.com
Key Personnel
Owner & Photog: Art Brewer
Founded: 1981
File Begins: 1969
Agent(s): Jean Gardner & Associates
Membership(s): Advertising Photographers of America; American Society of Media Photographers (ASMP); Professional Photographers of America (PPA)

Tom Brownold Photography
801 W Summit Ave, Flagstaff, AZ 86001

Tel: 928-779-1583 *Fax:* 928-779-1583
E-mail: tbrownold@tombrownold.com
Web Site: www.tombrownold.com
Key Personnel
Owner: Tom Brownold
Founded: 1995
Advertising location, editorial, commercial services.
File Begins: 1980
Stock: Assignment & Stock; 1,000,000 35mm, color, editorial
Membership(s): American Photographic Artists (APA)

Donna Brunet Macro Photography
PO Box 30123, Columbia, MO 65205-3123
Tel: 573-999-2178
Web Site: www.donnabrunet.com
Key Personnel
Owner: Donna Brunet *E-mail:* donna@donnabrunet.com
Founded: 2006
Provide insect photographs to publishers for textbooks, trade books, magazines & paper products. All images are identified to order & family with a significant number identified to genus or species. Images from over 60 insect families in 13 orders. In addition to insects, there are a limited number of plants, crustaceans & reptiles. A complete species list can be found on the web site.
File Begins: 2003

Cecile Brunswick
315 W 39 St, No 1306, New York, NY 10018
Tel: 212-222-2088
E-mail: cbrunswick@nyc.rr.com
Web Site: www.cecilebrunswicknyc.com
Specialize in colorful impressionist-style, pastel-colored polaroid transfers of travel scenes, local color, people, gardens & floral subjects. Color stock file covers food, children cooking, women working, public events, architecture, interiors. Travel includes the US, Canada, England, Scotland, Italy, Israel, France-Provence, Paris. Large file on New York City: store windows, Central Park, botanical gardens, parades, street scenes, designs & abstracts. Colorful abstract paintings in oil on canvas, acrylic & gouache on paper.
File Begins: 1979
Stock: 35mm B&W & color
Membership(s): New York Artists Circle; New York Artists Equity Association

Cactus Clyde Productions
PO Box 3624, St Francisville, LA 70775-3624
Tel: 225-245-5008
E-mail: cactusclyd@aol.com
Web Site: www.cclockwood.com
Key Personnel
Owner: C C Lockwood
Founded: 1971
Available for worldwide natural history assignments; specialize in swamps & coastal marshes; outdoor, wildlife, underwater subjects & astrophotography.
File Begins: 1971
Stock: 100,000 35mm B&W & color transparencies; 34,000 Nikon digital raw images
Membership(s): American Society of Media Photographers (ASMP); North American Nature Photography Association (NANPA)

Michael Carpenter Photography
7704 Carrleigh Pkwy, Springfield, VA 22152-1304
Tel: 703-644-9666 *Fax:* 703-991-2643
E-mail: mike@michaelcarpenterphotography.com
Web Site: www.michaelcarpenterphotography.com
Key Personnel
Photog: Michael Carpenter

Off Mgr: Debra Carpenter
Annual report & assignment photographer, location, editorial, industrial & portrait, architectural photography.

Maxine Cass Photography
PO Box 111, Gold Hill, OR 97525-0111
Tel: 541-855-8975; 415-244-1682 (cell)
E-mail: mcass@pobox.com
Web Site: www.agpix.com/maxinecass; www.maxinecass.com
Travel, business, assignment photo journalist & stock work, writer & author.
File Begins: 1984
Stock: 50,000 color
Membership(s): American Society of Journalists & Authors (ASJA); The Authors Guild; North American Nature Photography Association (NANPA)

Celtic Castle Photography
1319 Hardys Creek Rd, Jonesville, VA 24263
Tel: 276-346-3625
E-mail: celticastlephotography@gmail.com
Web Site: www.celticastlephotography.com
Key Personnel
Pres: Dr John William O'Connor Sr, PhD
Contact: Kirsten O'Connor
Founded: 1982
High fashion, stock, commercial, portraits, industrial, children, digital.
File Begins: 1975
Membership(s): American Society of Media Photographers (ASMP)

Dwight Cendrowski Photography LLC
2870 Easy St, Ann Arbor, MI 48104-6532
Tel: 734-330-5230
Web Site: www.cendrowski.com
Key Personnel
Owner & Photog: Dwight Cendrowski
    E-mail: dwight@cendrowski.com
Founded: 1978
Corporate & editorial photography for national clients. Stock image file including, corporate/industrial, healthcare, lifestyle, academia & travel.
File Begins: 1978
Membership(s): American Society of Media Photographers (ASMP)

Brandon Cole Marine Photography
4917 N Boeing Rd, Spokane Valley, WA 99206
Tel: 509-535-3489
E-mail: brandoncole@msn.com
Web Site: www.brandoncole.com
Marine photographer.
File Begins: 1991
Stock: 80,000 35mm transparencies & digital captures select HD digital file

Bob Daemmrich Photography Inc
914 Congress Ave, 2nd fl, Austin, TX 78701
Tel: 512-469-9700 *Fax:* 512-469-9713
Web Site: www.bobphoto.com
Key Personnel
Owner & Photog: Bob Daemmrich *E-mail:* bob@bobphoto.com
VP, Mktg: Janis Daemmrich *E-mail:* janis@bobphoto.com
Studio Mgr: Marjorie Kamys Cotera
    E-mail: marjorie@bobphoto.com
Founded: 1985
Editorial & stock photography assignment work, multicultural images.
File Begins: 1984
Agent(s): Photoedit Inc, 235 E Broadway St, Suite 1020, Long Beach, CA 90802 *Toll Free Tel:* 800-860-2098 *Toll Free Fax:* 800-804-3707 *E-mail:* research@photoeditinc.com *Web Site:* www.photoeditinc.com; Alamy, 20 Jay St, Suite 848, Brooklyn, NY 11201 *Toll Free Tel:* 866-671-7305 (US); 866-331-4914 (CN) *E-mail:* sales@alamy.com *Web Site:* www.alamy.com; The Image Works, PO Box 443, Woodstock, NY 12498-0443 *Tel:* 845-679-8500 *Toll Free Tel:* 800-475-8801 *Fax:* 845-679-0606 *E-mail:* info@theimageworks.com *Web Site:* www.theimageworks.com; Getty Images, 605 Fifth Ave S, Suite 400, Seattle, WA 98104 *Tel:* 206-925-5000 *Toll Free Tel:* 888-888-5889 *E-mail:* sales@gettyimages.com *Web Site:* www.gettyimages.com
Membership(s): American Society of Media Photographers (ASMP); American Society of Picture Professionals (ASPP)

Kent Dannen
1997 Big Owl Rd, Allenspark, CO 80510
Tel: 303-747-2047 *Fax:* 303-747-2016
E-mail: kent.dannen@yahoo.com
Nature, outdoor recreation, travel, dogs, scenics & energy. Available for assignments.
Stock: 50,000 35mm & 120mm, B&W & color, HD digital
Agent(s): Photo Researchers Inc

DANPHOTO, LLC
408 E Rte 66, Flagstaff, AZ 86001
Tel: 928-779-4556
E-mail: danman@danphoto.com
Web Site: www.danphoto.com
Key Personnel
Owner & Photog: Daniel Snyder

Dan Donovan Photography
15005 Valley Ridge Dr, St Louis, MO 63017
Tel: 314-712-0021
E-mail: dan@dandonovan.com
Web Site: www.dandonovan.com
Key Personnel
Owner & Photog: Dan Donovan
Founded: 1989
Photos of people for advertising, corporate, editorial & entertainment assignments. Stock photos of St Louis & fine art prints are also available.
Membership(s): American Society of Media Photographers (ASMP)

Steven Edson Photography
219 Orchard St, Belmont, MA 02478
Tel: 617-993-3212
E-mail: steve@stevenedson.com
Web Site: www.stevenedson.com
Key Personnel
Owner & Photog: Steven Edson *Tel:* 617-504-4994 (cell)

Eligh Photographs
2544 Forbes St, Victoria, BC V8R 4B8, Canada
Tel: 250-888-0027
Web Site: www.elighphoto.com
Key Personnel
Owner: Gregg Eligh *E-mail:* gregg@elighphoto.com
Founded: 1978
Personality & author photographs for editorial, corporate & publishing.

Elk Photography
3163 Wisconsin St, Oakland, CA 94602
Tel: 510-531-7469 *Fax:* 510-531-7469
E-mail: cjelk@elkphotography.com
Web Site: www.elkphotography.com
Key Personnel
Owner & Photog: John Elk
Owner & Client Servs: Claude Marie Elk

Ron Elmy Photography
353 Eastern Ave, Suite 104, Toronto, ON M4M 1B7, Canada
Tel: 416-469-6711
E-mail: elmyphotovideo@gmail.com
Web Site: www.ronelmy.com
Specialize in jewelry, people, food, corporate, product, events & stock.

Envirovision
2901 W Coast Hwy, Suite 222, Newport Beach, CA 92663
Mailing Address: PO Box 4136, Laguna Beach, CA 92652
Tel: 949-673-2555
E-mail: bfactor@beverlyfactor.com
Web Site: www.beverlyfactor.com
Key Personnel
Owner & Photog: Beverly Factor
Founded: 1990
Wildlife photography specializing in underwater stock library of over 10,000 images worldwide. Includes tropical islands & beaches, boating, sailboat racing, sunsets, underwater, wildlife, indigenous people, children, sports, worldwide, Africa to South Pacific & tropical destinations. Available for assignments.
Stock: 10,000 images
Membership(s): American Society of Media Photographers (ASMP)

Sigrid Estrada
902 Broadway, No 1610, New York, NY 10010
Tel: 212-673-4300 *Fax:* 212-477-8815
E-mail: s.e.photo@mindspring.com
Web Site: www.sigridestrada.com
Photography, portraits of authors & artists. B&W & color stock, also digital photography.
File Begins: 1978
Stock: 2 1/4 format; B&W & color, digital
Membership(s): American Society of Media Photographers (ASMP)

f-stop Fitzgerald Inc
88 James St, Rosendale, NY 12472
E-mail: fstopf@gmail.com
Key Personnel
CEO: Richard Minissali
Author photos, freelance photography, book-packaging, consulting.
Membership(s): American Book Producers Association (ABPA); Professional Photographers of America (PPA)

Lola Troy Fiur
360 E 65 St, Suite 17-A, New York, NY 10065
Tel: 646-247-9044 *Fax:* 212-861-1911
E-mail: ltfoto@yahoo.com
Web Site: www.ltfstudios.com
B&W & color; digital; flowers, scenic landscapes, food, nostalgia, mystery.
Stock: Digital, 35mm; B&W & color
Membership(s): National Association of Photoshop Professionals (NAPP); New York Women in Film & Television (NYWIFT)

Flavin Photography
5401 Cordova St, Suite 305, Anchorage, AK 99514
Mailing Address: PO Box 141172, Anchorage, AK 99514-1172
Tel: 907-561-1606 *Fax:* 907-242-8206
E-mail: flavin@alaska.net
Web Site: www.flavinphotography.com
Key Personnel
Owner & Photog: Frank P Flavin *E-mail:* flavin@alaska.net
Founded: 1972
Commercial & editorial photography.
Stock: Africa, Alaska, Hawaii, Mexico, Nevada, Russia
Membership(s): American Society of Media Photographers (ASMP); Editorial Photographers (EP); Professional Photographers of America (PPA)

Forer Inc

7881 SW 69 Ave, Miami, FL 33143
Tel: 305-495-0838 *Fax:* 786-420-5835
Web Site: www.forer.com
Key Personnel
Owner & Photog: Dan Forer *E-mail:* dan@forer.com
Founded: 1973
Architectural & interior design photography.
Membership(s): American Institute of Architects; American Society of Interior Designers (ASID); American Society of Media Photographers (ASMP); International Interior Design Association (ITDA)

Steven Foster Photography

Subsidiary of Steven Foster Group Inc
PO Box 191, Eureka Springs, AR 72632-0191
Tel: 479-253-2629
E-mail: info@stevenfoster.com
Web Site: www.stevenfoster.com
Key Personnel
Pres: Steven Foster *E-mail:* sfoster@stevenfoster.com
Founded: 1974
Herbs, spices & medicinal plants. Stock.
File Begins: 1974
Stock: 120,000 35mm color slides, 40,000 digital images

Foster Travel Publishing

1623 Martin Luther King Jr Way, Berkeley, CA 94709
Tel: 510-549-2202
Web Site: www.fostertravel.com; stockphotos.fostertravel.com
Key Personnel
Owner & Pres: Lee Foster *E-mail:* lee@fostertravel.com
Founded: 1972
Travel photography (emphasizing 250 worldwide locations, covering attractions, history & nature) especially California, the Western states, then worldwide destinations. Stock or assignment & writing/photography assignments, especially in Western USA (California), Mexico & Europe.
File Begins: 1975
Stock: 250,000 35mm color; 25,000 digital
Membership(s): American Society of Media Photographers (ASMP); Bay Area Independent Publishers Association (BAIPA); Bay Area Travel Writers; Society of American Travel Writers (SATW)

Fotosmith

245 S Plumer Ave, No 6, Tucson, AZ 85719
Tel: 520-882-2033
E-mail: info@fotosmithusa.com
Web Site: www.jeffsmithusa.com
Key Personnel
Owner & Photog: Jeff Smith *E-mail:* jeff@fotosmithusa.com

James Frank Photography Inc

PO Box 3523, Estes Park, CO 80517
Tel: 970-586-3418
E-mail: photos@jamesfrank.com
Web Site: www.jamesfrank.com
Key Personnel
Owner & Photog: James Frank
Founded: 1980
Fine art, stock & travel photographer, publisher & gallery owner with more than 35 years of experience. Specialize in nature & landscape with emphasis on Rocky Mountain National Park.
Stock: Several hundred thousand image library of Colorado & travels
Agent(s): Stock Connection (Cheryl Pickerell DiFrank)

Fresh Air Photo

2203 McKinley Rd, Suite 220, Johnson City, TN 37604
Tel: 423-928-2700 *Fax:* 423-282-2730
Web Site: www.freshairphoto.com
Key Personnel
Founder & Owner: Tom Raymond *E-mail:* tom@freshairphoto.com
Founded: 1983
All commercial.
Membership(s): American Society of Media Photographers (ASMP); American Society of Picture Professionals (ASPP)

Robert Fried Photography

610 Eldridge Ct, Novato, CA 94947
Tel: 415-898-6153 *Fax:* 415-897-0353
E-mail: rob@robertfriedphotography.com
Web Site: www.robertfriedphotography.com
Key Personnel
Owner: Robert Fried
Photographic assignments worldwide for advertising, corporate & editorial clients. Specialize in travel/tourism industry (brochures, catalogs) & editorial markets (magazines, textbooks, religious publishers, calendars); stock photo files include coverage for agriculture, art, cities, ethnic groups, flora & fauna, industry, landmarks, religion, scenics, tourism, underwater.
File Begins: 1983
Stock: 300,000 35mm color & digital files

Bonnie Geller-Geld

2500 Johnson Ave, Bronx, NY 10463
Tel: 347-275-4040
E-mail: bggeld@gmail.com
Portrait, landscape & documentary photography.
Membership(s): Professional Women Photographers (PWP)

Peter Glass Photography

15 Oakwood St, East Hartford, CT 06108
Tel: 860-528-8559 (off); 860-712-7098 (cell)
E-mail: peter@peterglass.com
Web Site: www.peterglass.com
Commercial photography; specialize in corporate, editorial, public relations & industrial photography.
Stock: 35mm B&W & color, digital

Jeff Gnass Photography

3042 Nowell Ave, Juneau, AK 99801
Mailing Address: PO Box 35415, Juneau, AK 99803-5415
Tel: 907-789-2002 *Fax:* 206-577-6419
E-mail: office@jeffgnass.com
Web Site: www.jeffgnass.com
Key Personnel
Pres: Jeff Gnass
Founded: 1978
Specialize in digital original & 4x5 color transparency photography of natural landscapes & natural history for rights-managed commercial, advertising & editorial usage. Available for assignments & documentary projects worldwide. Stock photo library covers many North American places, themes & topics, including arctic, climate-change, clouds, coasts, deserts, environmental impact, flora, forests, geological formations, historic sites, mountains, national parks, Native American ruins, public land use, travel destinations & wilderness areas. Large libraries of Alaska, Hawaii & western US. International coverage of Canada, Patagonia region of Chile & Argentina, Iceland, Czechia, Slovakia, Austria, Australia, Singapore, England & Scotland. Photo coverage emphasizes public lands & travel destinations. Searchable database of stock photo coverage available online. Fulfillment of photo requests via pre-edited lightboxes for convenient online review & selec-

tion of images for consideration in your next project.
File Begins: 1976
Stock: 90,000 digital originals; 85,000 color transparencies, including: 4x5, 8x10, 2-1/4, 35mm, panorama; 15,000 high-resolution images available for online delivery
Agent(s): Stock Agencies: GEOLIGHT

Beryl Goldberg Photographer

309 W 109 St, Suite 4-F, New York, NY 10025
Tel: 212-222-8215
E-mail: berylgphoto@aol.com; berylgnyc@gmail.com
Web Site: www.berylgoldberg.com
Key Personnel
Owner & Photog: Beryl Goldberg
Assignment & stock photography: Africa, Bangladesh, China, Europe, Israel, Latin America & the US. Health international development families, children.
File Begins: 1976
Stock: 60,000 35mm B&W & color & digital files
Membership(s): American Society of Picture Professionals (ASPP)

Gomsak Photography

10428 S Hall Dr, Charlotte, NC 28270
Web Site: www.gomsak.com
Key Personnel
Owner & Photog: Brian Gomsak *Tel:* 704-996-3816 (cell) *E-mail:* brian@gomsak.com
Founded: 1996
Membership(s): American Photographic Artists (APA)

Dan Gotshall Marine Life Photography

4 Sommerset Rise, Monterey, CA 93940
Tel: 831-656-9169
E-mail: seachall@aol.com
Key Personnel
Owner: Dan Gotshall
Underwater photography. Specialize in Pacific coast marine life. Consultant in identifying marine invertebrates & fishes from slides & photographs. File photos of North American Marine & freshwater invertebrates, fishes, birds & mammals.
Stock: 35mm & 70mm color transparencies & digital
Agent(s): Visuals Unlimited, 27 Meadow Dr, Hollis, NH 03049, Contact: Robert Folz *Tel:* 603-465-3340 *Fax:* 603-465-3340 *E-mail:* rfolz@visualsunlimited.com

Audrey Gottlieb

161 York St, Unit 21, York, ME 03909
Tel: 207-641-7490
E-mail: audreyphoto@gmail.com
Web Site: www.audreygottlieb.com
Key Personnel
Photographer: Audrey Gottlieb *Tel:* 207-641-7490 *E-mail:* audreyphoto@gmail.com
Founded: 1985
Photography, includes travel & documentary of Greece, Japan, France, UN Operation in Somalia, multicultural America, ethnic festivals, landscapes, citiscapes, seascapes, lighthouses & agricultural fairs in Maine, flowers & gardens, urban street life, New York City landmarks (Queens), etc. Photographer proficient in English, French, Spanish & Greek, accepts travel assignments.
File Begins: 1973
Stock: 1,000,000 35mm B&W & color digital images
Membership(s): American Society of Media Photographers (ASMP); American Society of Picture Professionals (ASPP); Professional Women Photographers (PWP); Society for Photographic Education (SPE); United Nations Photographic Society

Geoffrey Gove
734 Broad St, Bloomfield, NJ 07003
Tel: 917-370-6400
E-mail: geoffgove@gmail.com
Web Site: www.facebook.com/ggove
Travel, book covers, creative illustration, special effects, graphics, digital imaging. Americana, sports, music, photojournalism, abstractions, architecture, children, urban life, social issues, personalities & technology. PowerPoint presentations.
Stock: 150,000 35mm color

Diane Graham-Henry Photography
2247 N Geneva Terr, Chicago, IL 60614
Tel: 773-327-4493 *Fax:* 773-248-2774
E-mail: dghphoto@gmail.com
Founded: 1979
Writer/photojournalist/videographer. Specialize in travel & editorial, stock & location portrait.
Stock: 35mm B&W & color
Membership(s): American Society of Media Photographers (ASMP); GWAA

Tom Graves Photography
400-A Clipper St, San Francisco, CA 94114
Tel: 415-550-7241
E-mail: tom@tomgraves.com
Web Site: www.tomgraves.com; www.twiceheroes.com
Authors' portraits, photo illustration, advertising photography.
File Begins: 1975
Stock: B&W & color
Membership(s): Advertising Photographers of America; Bay Area Travel Writers; International Association of Business Communicators (IABC); USMC Combat Correspondents Association (USMCCCA)

Greg Johnston Photography
6214 Solstice Loop, Sanford, FL 32773
Tel: 305-258-7070
E-mail: info@gregjohnston.com
Web Site: www.gregjohnston.com
Key Personnel
Owner: Greg Johnston
Founded: 1984
Advertising, editorial, stock photography, lifestyle resort, hotel industry.
Agent(s): Danita Delimont; Getty Images; Stock Photography
Membership(s): Advertising Photographers of America; American Society of Media Photographers (ASMP); Society of American Travel Writers (SATW); Stock Artists Alliance (SAA)

David M Grossman Photography
211 E Seventh St, Brooklyn, NY 11218
Tel: 718-438-5021
E-mail: david@grossmanphotos.com
Web Site: www.grossmanphotos.com
Key Personnel
Owner: David M Grossman
People photography: depicting the human situation birth through old age, photographic assignments, stock photo library, keyword searchable.
File Begins: 1975
Stock: Digital photography; fully digitized photo library

J S Grove Photography
166 Peace Ave, Tavernier, FL 33070
Tel: 305-852-6004
E-mail: jsimages@aol.com
Key Personnel
Photog & Marine Biologist: Jack Stein Grove
Founded: 1990
Membership(s): American Society of Media Photographers (ASMP)

Guy Gurney
55 Turkey Plain Rd, Bethel, CT 06801
Tel: 203-616-5643; 203-434-7337 (cell)
E-mail: guy@guygurney.com
Web Site: www.guygurney.com

Chris Hamilton Photography
652 Bellemeade Ave NW, Atlanta, GA 30318
Tel: 404-355-9411
Web Site: www.hamphoto.com
Key Personnel
Owner: Chris Hamilton *E-mail:* chris@hamphoto.com
Prodr & Rep: Rita Hamilton *E-mail:* rita@hamphoto.com
Founded: 1984
Commercial photography.
Membership(s): American Society of Media Photographers (ASMP)

Harris Photos, see Susie Harris

Susie Harris
282 Whitetail Lane, Hot Springs, AR 71901
Tel: 501-762-2200
E-mail: sales@harrisphotos.com
Web Site: www.neworleansphotos.com; www.harrisphotos.com; www.mardigrasphotos.net
Founded: 1979
Stock photography related to environment, nature & global travel.

Havey Productions
3457 Ringsby Court, Unit 105, Denver, CO 80216
Tel: 303-296-7448
Web Site: www.haveypro.com
Key Personnel
Owner & Photog: Jim Havey *E-mail:* jim@haveypro.com
Ed & Art Dir: Nathan Church *E-mail:* nathan@haveypro.com
Founded: 1979
Commercial & editorial photography.

Milton Heiberg Studios
Subsidiary of Tern Media LLC
1022 Empress Lane, Orlando, FL 32825-8249
Tel: 407-658-4869 *Fax:* 407-658-4869
E-mail: photonat@cfl.rr.com
Web Site: www.miltonheiberg.com
Key Personnel
Owner & Pres: Milton Heiberg
Founded: 1970
Specialize in nature, especially birds (natural history), wildlife & environmental photography.
File Begins: 1970
Stock: 95,000 35mm, 4 x 5 & 2 1/4 B&W & color nature & wildlife, over 1,000,000 digital images
Agent(s): Photo Researchers Inc, New York, NY

Diana Mara Henry
187 Prospect St, Newport, VT 05855
Tel: 802-334-7054
E-mail: dmh@dianamarahenry.com
Web Site: dianamarahenry.com
Founded: 1967
Traveling exhibits of: The First National Woman's Conference, Houston, 1977, One-room Schools & Schoolteachers of Vermont & New York, Vanishing Jews of Alsace & the Natzweiler-Struthof Concentration Camp, Pompadour-Its French National Stud Farm, People & Celebrities, Harvard College & lifestyles, 1965-1969, NYC-Society & Mores, 1969-1987, Malcolm Forbes balloon meets at the Chateau de Balleroy, Normandy, Carmel, CA, Hawaii, Bali, Kathmandu, Europe & the Caribbean. LIBEL, an exhibit of words & pictures that challenges

the acceptance of photographs & captions as truth.
File Begins: 1967
Stock: 100,000 B&W & color

Michal Heron Photography
3806 Easton St, Sarasota, FL 34238
Tel: 941-922-5124
E-mail: michalheronphoto@gmail.com
Web Site: www.michalheron.com
Key Personnel
Owner: Ms Michal Heron
Photojournalism, assignments worldwide. All subjects for general editorial & corporate reportage. Specialize in American Indians; coverage in China, Japan, Mexico, Peru & Spain.
Stock: B&W, color & digital
Membership(s): American Society of Media Photographers (ASMP); American Society of Picture Professionals (ASPP)

Art Holeman Photography
4156 E Cathedral Rock Dr, Phoenix, AZ 85044
Tel: 602-290-7431 (cell)
E-mail: art@artholeman.com; artholeman@cox.net
Web Site: www.artholeman.com; www.fineartholeman.com
Key Personnel
Owner & Photog: Arthur A Holeman *E-mail:* art@artholeman.com
Founded: 1986
Commercial photographer, location, food styling, property, travel, people, interiors, B&W, fine art.
Membership(s): American Society of Media Photographers (ASMP); Through Each Others Eyes (TEOE)

Hollenbeck Productions
19241 Normandy Park Dr SW, Seattle, WA 98166
Tel: 206-592-1800
Web Site: www.hollenbeckproductions.com; www.cliffscoolstuff.com
Key Personnel
Founder & Owner: Cliff Hollenbeck *E-mail:* cliff@hollenbeckproductions.com; Nancy Hollenbeck *E-mail:* nancy@hollenbeckproductions.com
Worldwide photography assignments & stock files; advertising, editorials & travel, especially Alaska, Hawaii, Mexico, the Northwest, Canada, Morocco, Bahamas, Greece, Far East Mediterranean & South Pacific, Italy. Also specialize in the creation of location, destination & corporation books.
Stock: 400,000 color images

Tom Hopkins Studio
2121 Durham Rd, Madison, CT 06443
Tel: 203-421-4644
E-mail: contact@tomhopkinsstudio.com
Web Site: www.tomhopkinsstudio.com
Key Personnel
Owner & Photog: Tom Hopkins
Membership(s): American Society of Media Photographers (ASMP)

David K Horowitz Studio Inc
920 Chestnut St, No 22, Philadelphia, PA 19107
Studio & location photography: books, catalogs, posters, advertising & architecture.

George H H Huey Photography Inc
382 W Butterfield Rd, Suite 115, Chino Valley, AZ 86323
Tel: 928-445-6800
Web Site: www.georgehhhuey.com
Key Personnel
Owner: George H H Huey *E-mail:* george@georgehhhuey.com

Busn Mgr: Lauren Blauert *E-mail:* lauren@
georgehhhuey.com
Assignment & stock photography: landscapes,
wildlife, travel, national parks & monuments,
historic sites, environmental issues in US &
Mexico. Includes Grand Canyon, Arizona, Cal-
ifornia, Colorado, Texas, New Mexico, Utah,
Sonoran desert, Hawaii, Caribbean, all cactus,
reptiles, flowers, prehistoric ruins & rock art.
People engaged in activities with nature.
Stock: Digital, 35mm, 6 x 7, 6 x 9 & 6 x 17;
B&W & color

Richard Hutchings Photography LLC
11 White Well Dr, Rhinebeck, NY 12572
Tel: 914-715-7461
E-mail: richard@hutchingsphotography.com
Web Site: hutchingsphotography.com
Key Personnel
Owner: Richard Hutchings
Contact: Amy Hutchings
   E-mail: amyhutchingscastings@gmail.com
Founded: 1969
Photography for the publishing industry, more
specifically the educational publishing market.
Also write & photograph nonfiction books for
early readers. Extensive file of children, teens,
families, education, multiethnic, diverse popula-
tion.
File Begins: 1970
Agent(s): Getty; Photoeditinc.com; Photore-
searchers.com

Iverson Science Photos
31 Boss Ave, Portsmouth, NH 03801
Tel: 603-433-8484 *Fax:* 603-433-8484
E-mail: iversonarts@gmail.com
Key Personnel
Owner & Photog: Bruce Iverson
Founded: 1980
Stock & assignment photomicrography, science &
medical photographs. Light micrographs, scan-
ning electron micrographs & transmission elec-
tron micrographs, in all subjects from anatomy
to zoology.
File Begins: 1980
Stock: 10,000, 35mm, 4 x 5 color & B&W &
digital

J Brough Schamp Photography
6907 Avondale Rd, Baltimore, MD 21212
Tel: 410-769-8016
E-mail: brough@schamp.com
Web Site: www.broughschampphotography.com
Key Personnel
Owner & Photog: J Brough Schamp
Founded: 1980
Photography of people, architecture & aerial pho-
tography.
Membership(s): American Society of Media Pho-
tographers (ASMP)

Michael Jacobs Photojournalism (MJP)
2105 Vista Oeste NW, Suite 3, No 2057, Albuquerque, NM 87120
Tel: 323-461-0240 *Toll Free Fax:* 866-563-9212
E-mail: michael.mjphoto@gmail.com
Web Site: www.mjphotogallery.com
Key Personnel
Owner: Michael Jacobs
Founded: 1970
Photo assignments accepted worldwide. Editorial, illustrative & general photography for
publication. Proficiency in photographing Hol-
lywood/the entertainment industry including
production & session work. Public relations,
cultural & social events, concerts, international
travel (over 70 countries covered), children, an-
nual reports & politics. Album & book covers.
Feature films, television & videos.

File Begins: 1970
Stock: Over 2 million multi-format B&W, color
& digital; over 1 million 35mm B&W & color

Kerrick James Photography
235 N 22 Place, Unit 560, Mesa, AZ 85213
Mailing Address: PO Box 30639, Mesa, AZ
85275
Tel: 602-276-3111 *Fax:* 480-268-9005
Web Site: www.kerrickjames.com
Key Personnel
Owner & Photog: Kerrick James
   E-mail: kjames5@cox.net
Travel journalism.
Agent(s): ASAblanca; Getty Images
Membership(s): North American Travel Journal-
ists Association (NATJA); Society of American
Travel Writers (SATW); Through Each Others
Eyes (TEOE)

John Johnston
1288 Southlyn Dr, Dayton, OH 45409
Tel: 937-681-4309
E-mail: jejphotos@gmail.com
Web Site: www.johnjohnston.co
Founded: 1999
Provide commercial, editorial, corporate, assign-
ment, stock, travel, portrait, event & location
photography.
Membership(s): National Press Photographers As-
sociation (NPPA)

Johnston Photography, see John Johnston

Lou Jones Studio
44 Breed St, Boston, MA 02128
Tel: 617-561-1194 *Fax:* 617-561-1196
E-mail: fotojones@aol.com
Web Site: www.fotojones.com
Key Personnel
Owner & Photog: Lou Jones
Founded: 1972
Commercial & advertising photography; in studio
& on location; fine art; editorial.
File Begins: 1972
Agent(s): Zuma Press
Membership(s): American Society of Media Pho-
tographers (ASMP)

Wolfgang Kaehler Photography
723 Third St S, Kirkland, WA 98033
Tel: 425-803-0652
E-mail: photos@wkaehlerphoto.com
Web Site: www.wkaehlerphoto.com
Key Personnel
Owner: Wolfgang Kaehler
Founded: 1977
Available for assignment; worldwide stock pho-
tography coverage, diversity of subjects, online
searchable database.
File Begins: 1977
Stock: 500,000 digital files

Tom Keck Photos
13393 Landfair Rd, San Diego, CA 92130
Tel: 858-755-2975
E-mail: tomkeckphotos@gmail.com
Web Site: www.tomkeckphotos.com
Key Personnel
Owner & Photog: Tom Keck
Founded: 1963
Photojournalist for 50+ years; sports, surfing,
travel, editorial. Includes photo stock of Cuba,
Hawaii, Kenya & South Africa. Branch office
in Laguna Beach.
Stock: ZUMA Press
Membership(s): American Society of Media Pho-
tographers (ASMP); National Press Photog-
raphers Association (NPPA); North American
Nature Photography Association (NANPA)

Bruce Kluckhohn Photographer
2608 Webster Ave S, Minneapolis, MN 55416-
1723
Tel: 612-929-6010
E-mail: bruce@bruceckphoto.com
Web Site: www.bruceckphoto.com
Key Personnel
Photog: Bruce Kluckhohn
Location people photography.

William Koechling Photography
1307 E Harrison Ave, Wheaton, IL 60187
Tel: 630-665-4379
E-mail: bill@koechlingphoto.com
Web Site: www.koechlingphoto.com
Key Personnel
Contact: William Koechling
Founded: 1973
Studio & location photography primarily for au-
thor/artist portraits; stock photography.
Agent(s): Glasshouse Images
Membership(s): American Society of Media Pho-
tographers (ASMP)

Dwight R Kuhn
128 Free St, Dexter, ME 04930
Mailing Address: PO Box 54, Dexter, ME 04930
Tel: 207-924-6206 *Fax:* 207-924-6206
E-mail: dkuhn@kuhnphoto.com
Web Site: www.kuhnphoto.net
Slides of natural history & biology subjects cov-
ering much of the animal & plant kingdom.
Macrophotographs & detailed natural history
coverage of difficult & small subjects. Biology
photos including photomicrographs for text-
book & reference uses. Gardening stock also
included. Available for assignments.
Stock: 200,000 35mm color & digital images
Agent(s): DRK Photo
Membership(s): American Society of Media Pho-
tographers (ASMP)

Mary Langenfeld Photography
3817 Euclid Ave, Madison, WI 53711
Tel: 608-233-9938; 608-334-1375 (cell)
E-mail: madisonfoto@att.net
Web Site: www.langenfeld-photo.com
Founded: 1991
Photojournalist; assignment & stock photography;
specialize in education, social issues, sports &
agricultural.
File Begins: 1985
Stock: Digital files, 35mm B&W/color & color
transparencies
Membership(s): National Press Photographers
Association (NPPA); Wisconsin News Photog-
raphers Association (WNPA)

Jess Lee Photography LLC
13316 Skyview St, Nampa, ID 83686
Tel: 208-521-5170
Web Site: www.jessleephotos.com
Key Personnel
Owner: Jess Lee *E-mail:* jess@jessleephotos.com
Natural history, wildlife, scenics, stock & assign-
ment, western lifestyle.
Stock: 200,000 color slides, digital images

Tom & Pat Leeson
PO Box 2498, Vancouver, WA 98668-2498
Tel: 360-256-0436
E-mail: office@leesonphoto.com
Web Site: www.leesonphoto.com
North American wildlife including lots of eagles,
bears, wolves & whales; travel Alaska, Western
Canada & Pacific Northwest. African wildlife,
elephants, pandas & tigers.
Stock: 14,000 digital images online, backed by
over 100,000 transparencies
Agent(s): Photo Researchers Inc, New York, NY;
Orion (Japan)

Steve Leonard Photography
825 W Gunnison St, Chicago, IL 60640-4267
Tel: 312-206-5344
E-mail: steve@steveleonardphoto.com
Web Site: www.steveleonardphoto.com
Founded: 1983
Location photography.
File Begins: 1985
Membership(s): American Society of Media Photographers (ASMP)

David Lissy Photography, see Table Mesa
Productions/David Lissy Photography

LOF Productions
121 Greenwich Rd, Suite 202, Charlotte, NC 28211
Mailing Address: PO Box 11758, Charlotte, NC 28220-1758
Tel: 704-375-8892 *Fax:* 704-375-6316
Web Site: www.lofproductions.com
Key Personnel
Mgr & Photog: John Daughtry
 E-mail: jdaughtry@lofproductions.com
Graphics & Design: Kyle Flory
Founded: 2001
Photography for business to business marketing & communications.

Marc Longwood Photography
3300 Powell St, Suite 336, Emeryville, CA 94608-1776
Tel: 415-251-7585
Web Site: www.longwoodpro.com
Key Personnel
Owner & Photog: Marc Longwood
 E-mail: marc@longwoodpro.com
Founded: 1982
From stringing for UPI, LA Times & Business Week to environmental portraiture for publication since mid-eighties...conceptualized & crafted images to illustrate any story, cover, or book jacket. Studio quality on location - especially people, hospitality, travel (photography & writing).
Membership(s): American Society of Media Photographers (ASMP); Bay Area Travel Writers; Editorial Photographers (EP)

LTF Studios, see Lola Troy Fiur

MagicLight Productions
4935 McConnell Ave, Suite 1, Marina del Rey, CA 90066
Tel: 310-306-3839 *Fax:* 310-283-8772
Web Site: www.magiclight.com
Key Personnel
CEO & Photog: Robert Reiff *E-mail:* robert@magiclight.com
Founded: 1973
Commercial photography with complete studio. Specialize in food, health & fitness, architecture, fashion, books, travel, cars, women & men.
Membership(s): American Photographic Artists (APA); American Society of Media Photographers (ASMP)

Bruce McMillan
PO Box 85, Shapleigh, ME 04076-0085
Tel: 207-324-9453
E-mail: bruce@brucemcmillan.com
Web Site: www.brucemcmillan.com
Photo-illustrated books, book jackets, photo-illustrator/author of more than 45 children's books & 4 adult books, book designer.
Stock: Children & animals (from mice to whales to Antarctic penguins, especially birds), Iceland, wildlife, horses & landscape

Susan Riva Miller-Alpine Photography
20415 150 Ave SE, Monroe, WA 98272
Tel: 206-679-0475
E-mail: susanrivamiller@hotmail.com
Key Personnel
Owner: Susan Riva Miller
Photo assignments & stock photos of aviation, ranching, how-to book illustrations, mountain, aircraft, snow avalanches, aerial photography & snow crystal photography.
File Begins: 1960
Stock: 35mm B&W & color prints, 4 x 5 transparencies, CDs

Clark James Mishler Photography
1815 School St, Calistoga, CA 94515
Tel: 907-351-7863
Web Site: www.mishlerphotos.com
Key Personnel
Owner & Photog: Clark James Mishler
 E-mail: clark@mishlerphotos.com
Founded: 1989
Freelance photographer.
Membership(s): American Society of Media Photographers (ASMP); National Press Photographers Association (NPPA)

Boyd Norton Photography
28344 Tresine Dr, Evergreen, CO 80439
Mailing Address: PO Box 2605, Evergreen, CO 80437
Tel: 303-674-3009 *Fax:* 303-674-3650
E-mail: boydn@earthlink.net
Web Site: www.boydnorton.com
Key Personnel
Pres: Boyd Norton
Founded: 1968
Stock photo & assignment services. Specialize in travel, adventure, remote areas, wilderness, wildlife, natural history, geography, cultures, cities, environmental & social issues; worldwide coverage. North America: Alaska, Rocky Mountains, Southwest, New England; Asia: Malaysia (Borneo), Indonesia (Bali, Komodo Island, Sumbawa), Siberia; Africa: Democratic Republic of the Congo, Botswana, Kenya, Tanzania, Zaire, Rwanda; South America: Ecuador, Peru, Venezuela & Chile; Antarctica. No research fees.
File Begins: 1966
Stock: 400,000 35mm color, 8,000 2 1/4 color transparencies, 80,000 digital files
Membership(s): American Society of Media Photographers (ASMP); International League of Conservation Photographers

Phillip Norton
Subsidiary of County Photographer
4 Chapel St, Picton, ON K0K 2T0, Canada
Tel: 613-827-3214
E-mail: phil@philnorton.com
Web Site: countyphotographer.com; www.countyoutings.com
Founded: 1987
US-Canada issues, Quebec & Ontario Provinces, environment & travel, rural lifestyles. East & West Coast US, Canada, Central Europe & Mexico. Photos accompanied by text (award-winning author). Fluent French & English, web design, teach photojournalism, multimedia, audio & slideshows.
Stock: 100,000 35mm color transparencies & 500,000 digital

Dale O'Dell
1520 Eagle Point Dr, Prescott, AZ 86301
Tel: 928-541-0944 *Toll Free Tel:* 800-390-9435
 Fax: 928-541-0944
E-mail: dale@cybertrails.com
Web Site: www.dalephoto.com
Stock & assignment photography, digital imaging & author of photography related articles. Stock

photography & illustration services specializing in conceptual photography & digital illustration emphasizing story-telling images over simple pictures of things. Stock photographic files also include a wide range of subjects: landscapes, industry, high-tech, medical, computer tech, still life & travel.
Stock: Digital, B&W & color

Arleen Olson Photography
PO Box 550, Redway, CA 95560-0550
Tel: 707-923-1974
Web Site: arleenolsonphotography.com
Key Personnel
Photog & Publr: Arleen Olson *E-mail:* aolson@redwoodcoast.net
People, animals, events, landscapes, plants & foreign travel. Stock list available. Photographer & publisher of "Humboldt Wild" photography book.
File Begins: 1970
Stock: Over 20,000 35mm color slides, 35mm & medium format B&W & color prints & digital
Membership(s): National Association of Photoshop Professionals (NAPP); North American Nature Photography Association (NANPA); Professional Photographers of America (PPA)

Olson Photographic LLC
232 Hunter's Trail, Madison, CT 06443
Tel: 203-245-3752 *Fax:* 203-245-3752
E-mail: info@olsonphotographic.com
Web Site: www.olsonphotographic.com
Key Personnel
Partner: John Olson *E-mail:* john@olsonphotographic.com
Photographically capture the essence of interior spaces, exterior structures & designed landscapes. We bring extensive photographic experience & creativity to each assignment. Clients have used our award-winning images to gain industry recognition & build their client bases. In addition to being used in professional portfolios, countless numbers of our images have appeared in major consumer & industrial periodicals, books & in manufacturers' marketing & promotional materials. From secluded country estates to Manhattan townhouses & from high-end automobile dealerships to local bistros, we professionally capture award winning designs with the highest expertise & professional equipment.
File Begins: 2004
Membership(s): American Society of Media Photographers (ASMP); Association of Independent Architectural Photographers (AIAP); IAAP

Danuta Otfinowski
625 "E" St NE, Washington, DC 20002
Tel: 202-546-5646 (studio); 202-744-0333 (cell)
E-mail: danuta@danuta.us
Web Site: www.danuta.us
Founded: 1985
Photo journalist/photographer, events, environmental portraits.

Tom Pantages
87 Short St, Marlboro, MA 01752
Tel: 508-305-2828 *Fax:* 508-305-2828
E-mail: pantages@comcast.net
Stock photography: science, commerce & government.
File Begins: 1969
Stock: Over 60,000 35mm color transparencies; over 10 GB digital files
Membership(s): American Society of Picture Professionals (ASPP); New England Outdoor Writers Association Inc (NEOWA)

Jerry Pavia
17 Ginger Lane, Bonners Ferry, ID 83805

Mailing Address: PO Box 912, Bonners Ferry, ID 83805-0912
Tel: 208-267-7374 *Fax:* 208-267-7374
E-mail: plantshooter@yahoo.com
Photos of nature, horticulture, gardens & plants (wild & cultivated), US, Canada, England & France. Stock sales & assignments.
Stock: 75,000 35mm & 2 1/4 & 4 x 5 color transparencies

Douglas Peebles Photography
44-527A Kaneohe Bay Dr, Kaneohe, HI 96744
Tel: 808-342-7930
E-mail: douglas@douglaspeebles.com
Web Site: www.douglaspeebles.com
Editorial photography & stock photo file, especially of Hawaii, Mexico, South Pacific & Alaska.

Photographix
1171 Pauline Blvd, Ann Arbor, MI 48103-5319
Tel: 734-476-2068
Key Personnel
Owner: Lance K Burghardt *E-mail:* lkburghardt@comcast.net
Commercial & advertising photography; process or graphic arts photography, copy photography, scientific & technical photography.
Membership(s): American Society of Media Photographers (ASMP)

Photography by Westura
163 Ashland Ct, Stanhope, NJ 07874
Tel: 973-691-2646
Web Site: personalphotojournalism.com
Key Personnel
Owner: Warren Westura *E-mail:* wwestura@optonline.net
Founded: 2000
Local & state news/sports of Northern New Jersey specializing in the Morris/Sussex county areas. Other New Jersey counties on a more limited basis.
File Begins: 2000
Membership(s): National Press Photographers Association (NPPA)

Photography for Communication & Commerce
3931 S Spruce St, Suite 200, Denver, CO 80237-2152
Tel: 303-829-5678
Web Site: www.howardpaulphotography.com
Key Personnel
Photog: Howard Michael Paul *E-mail:* howard@howardpaulphotography.com
Founded: 1985
Specialize in stock & assignment photography for emergency service & public safety personnel & operations. Specialized stock file of mountain search & rescue operations, fire departments & fire scenes, emergency medical services, Haz-Mat, Chem-Bioterrorism & all areas of rescue operations.
File Begins: 1985
Stock: 16,000 35mm color
Membership(s): American Society of Media Photographers (ASMP)

Geoff Reed Photography
7640 N 22 St, Phoenix, AZ 85020
Tel: 602-749-1103
E-mail: geoff@geoffreedphoto.com
Web Site: www.geoffreedphoto.com
Key Personnel
Owner & Photog: Geoff Reed
Founded: 1989
Business to business corporate location portraiture & travel/outdoor adventure photography.
Membership(s): American Society of Media Photographers (ASMP)

James Porter Photography
211 E Columbine Ave, Suite A-1, Santa Ana, CA 92707
Tel: 714-546-4148
E-mail: info@jamesporterphotography.com
Web Site: www.jamesporterphotography.com
Key Personnel
Owner: James Porter *E-mail:* jim@jamesporterphotography.com
Founded: 1975
Digital photography in studio & on location. Specialize in food, product & people. Full service studio with commercial kitchen.

Sarah Putnam
320 Brookline St, Cambridge, MA 02139
Tel: 617-547-3758
E-mail: sarah@sarahputnam.com
Web Site: www.sarahputnam.com
Editorial & corporate photography, stock, author's portraits, digital & film, multimedia & video.
Stock: B&W & color
Membership(s): National Press Photographers Association (NPPA)

Neil Rashba Photography
1174 Neck Rd, Ponte Vedra Beach, FL 32082
Tel: 904-273-0388 *Fax:* 904-273-6203
E-mail: neil@rashba.com
Web Site: www.rashba.com
Key Personnel
Pres: Neil Rashba
Founded: 1979
Architectural & automotive photography.
Membership(s): American Institute of Architects; SMPS

Laszlo Regos Photography
24067 Research Dr, Farmington Hills, MI 48335
Tel: 248-398-3631
E-mail: laszlo@laszlofoto.com
Web Site: www.laszlofoto.com
Key Personnel
Photog: Laszlo Regos *Tel:* 248-421-1222 (cell)
Founded: 1989
Architectural photographer specializing in retail spaces. Extensive stock library of European cities, Detroit & synagogue architecture.
Membership(s): American Society of Media Photographers (ASMP)

Carol A Robinson, Photographer
2012 Aldrich Place, Downers Grove, IL 60516
Tel: 630-222-6286
E-mail: goodpix@zenfolio.com
Web Site: goodpix.zenfolio.com
Founded: 1989
Nature & landscape assignment photography, annual reports & newsletters. Assignments accepted worldwide. Stock images of Ireland, Egypt, Venice, Italy, Hawaii, Beijing, China, Shanghai, Wuhan, China & US cities.
Stock: Digital
Membership(s): National Association of Photoshop Professionals (NAPP)

Ron Rochon
2386 Bernard Rd, Windsor, ON N8W 4R8, Canada
Tel: 519-945-4565
E-mail: ronron@mnsi.net

Ken Ross Photography
PO Box 4517, Scottsdale, AZ 85261
Tel: 602-319-2974
E-mail: kenrossaz@yahoo.com
Web Site: www.kenrossphotography.com
Key Personnel
Owner & Photog: Ken Ross
Founded: 1985

Commercial photography.
Membership(s): American Society of Media Photographers (ASMP); Through Each Others Eyes (TEOE)

Jeff Rotman Photography
53 Green Ave, Lawrenceville, NJ 08648
Tel: 609-219-0040 *Fax:* 609-219-1595
E-mail: contact@jeffrotman.com
Web Site: www.jeffrotman.com
Key Personnel
Photog: Jeff Rotman *E-mail:* jeffrotman@aol.com
Agent: Isabelle Delafosse
Underwater assignments & land photography. Stock of marine life, nature, people & places from around the world.
Stock: Over 100,000 35mm color slides & 5,000 scanned photos
Membership(s): American Society of Media Photographers (ASMP)

Victoria Roza Research
PO Box 881745, San Diego, CA 92168-1745
Tel: 619-295-8082
E-mail: victoriaproza@gmail.com
Photography & photo research.

Sargent Architectural Photography
7675 Steeplechase Dr, Palm Beach Gardens, FL 33418
Tel: 561-881-8887 *Fax:* 561-881-8882
E-mail: sargentphoto@att.net
Web Site: www.sargentphoto.com
Key Personnel
Owner & Photog: Mr Kim Sargent
Founded: 1987
Commercial photography.
Membership(s): American Society of Media Photographers (ASMP)

Joel Schnell Photographer
2081 Seventh St N, North St Paul, MN 55109
Tel: 612-384-0413
E-mail: joel@schnellphoto.com
Web Site: www.schnellphoto.com
Key Personnel
Owner & Photog: Joel Schnell
Founded: 1986
Studio or location commercial assignment photography. Digital image file management & prepress format expert.

Carl Schreier
c/o Homestead Publishing & Book Design, Box 193, Moose, WY 83012-0193
Tel: 307-733-6248
Photography & writing assignments for the western states. Specialize in wilderness, travel, nature, national parks, environment & science. Stock photos & historical photographs also available; 80,000 historical Yellowstone & Grand Teton, Glacier National Park B&W photographs. The largest private collection. Search for any period or topic of historical photographs.
Stock: 500,000 35mm, 6 x 7 & 4 x 5, 95% color transparencies & B&W prints, digital, electronic

Cosimo Scianna, Photographer
23407 Milano Ct, Boca Raton, FL 33433
Tel: 917-763-2927
E-mail: cosimoscianna@mac.com
Web Site: www.cosimoscianna.com
Key Personnel
Photog: Cosimo Scianna
Exec Prodr & Contact: Irene Scianna
E-mail: irenescianna@mac.com
Founded: 1982
Membership(s): American Society of Media Photographers (ASMP); Directors Guild of America (DGA); Society of Illustrators

Lynn Seldon Travel Writer & Photographer
126 NE 25 St, Oak Island, NC 28465
E-mail: lynn@seldonink.com
Web Site: www.seldonink.com
Key Personnel
Co-Owner: Lynn Seldon
Founded: 1986
Travel writing & photography.
File Begins: 1986
Stock: 200,000

John Sexton Photography
PO Box 30, Carmel Valley, CA 93924
Tel: 831-659-3130 *Fax:* 831-659-5509
E-mail: info@johnsexton.com
Web Site: www.johnsexton.com
Key Personnel
Owner & Photog: John Sexton
Assoc Dir: Anne Larsen
Founded: 1974
Fine art photography, stock photography.
Membership(s): American Society of Media Photographers (ASMP); North America Nature Photography Association

David Sharpe Studio
107 Sunshine Court, Beaufort, NC 28516
Tel: 703-509-8042 (cell)
Web Site: www.davidsharpe.com
Key Personnel
Owner & Photog: David Sharpe *E-mail:* david@davidsharpe.com
Advertising, corporate & editorial photography.
Membership(s): AIGA, the professional association for design; American Society of Media Photographers (ASMP); Art Directors Club of Metropolitan Washington (ADCMW)

Ron Sherman Photography
PO Box 2612, Roswell, GA 30077-2612
Tel: 770-355-8700 (cell)
E-mail: ronsphoto@live.com
Web Site: www.ronsherman.com
Founded: 1971
Location photography, stock photo library & computer imaging. Extensive file of Georgia, Atlanta, corporate/industrial & higher education.
Membership(s): American Photographic Artists (APA); American Society of Media Photographers (ASMP); American Society of Picture Professionals (ASPP)

Silver Visions: Robert Kaufman Photography & Design
PO Box 610415, Newton Highlands, MA 02461-0415
Toll Free Tel: 877-249-0207
E-mail: silverv@silvervisions.com
Web Site: www.silvervisions.com
Key Personnel
Pres: Betty Kaufman *E-mail:* bkaufman1@aol.com
Contact: Robert Kaufman
Founded: 1981
Freelance photography (stock & assignment), books, brochures, catalogs, sidelines, printing, book distribution, publishing, commission & fully digital.
Stock: Color & B&W

Barbara Singer Productions
319 E 24 St, Suite 3-A, New York, NY 10010
Tel: 212-689-0395 *Fax:* 212-689-0395
E-mail: barbara@barbarasinger.com
Web Site: www.barbarasinger.com
Large stock of photographs of flowers, animals & posters for interior decoration to retailers in the US & abroad. Many photographs by Nat Herz of the March on Washington, 1963 & of New York City from 1955 to 1964.

Agent(s): The Bridgeman Art Library International Ltd; Getty Images
Membership(s): Advertising Photographers of America; American Society of Media Photographers (ASMP); American Society of Picture Professionals (ASPP)

Frank Siteman Photography
136 Pond St, Winchester, MA 01890
Tel: 781-729-3747
E-mail: frank@franksiteman.com
Web Site: www.franksiteman.com
Advertising & corporate photography; New England scenics & lifestyle.
Stock: 200,000 35mm color transparencies of select stock & digital extensive files
Membership(s): American Society of Media Photographers (ASMP); American Society of Picture Professionals (ASPP); Photographic Resource Center (PRC)

Scott B Smith Imagery
14 Pump St, Newcastle, ME 04533
Tel: 305-586-8698
E-mail: info@scottbsmith.com
Web Site: www.scottbsmith.com
Key Personnel
Owner: Scott B Smith *E-mail:* scott@scottbsmith.com
Founded: 1999
Extensive travel stock, architecture & vintage Miami B&Ws. Orange Bowl Stadium architectural survey. Maine stock.
Agent(s): Getty Images, 605 Fifth Ave, Suite 400, Seattle, WA 98104 *Tel:* 205-925-5000 *Toll Free Fax:* 888-888-5889
Membership(s): American Society of Media Photographers (ASMP)

Southern Images Photography
142 Westlake Dr, Brandon, MS 39047-9020
Tel: 601-992-9488
Web Site: www.southern-images.com
Key Personnel
Owner & Photog: Debra L Ferguson *E-mail:* dferguson@agfax.com
Founded: 1978
Stock & assignment agriculture photography.
File Begins: 1980s
Membership(s): American Society of Media Photographers (ASMP)

Steve Starr Photojournalist Emeritus
720 Arcadia Place, Colorado Springs, CO 80903
Tel: 719-632-8274
E-mail: steve@stevestarr.com
Web Site: www.stevestarr.com
Key Personnel
Owner & Photog: Steven D Starr
Founded: 1973
Photojournalism.
Membership(s): Christians in Photojournalism (CIP); National Press Photographers Association (NPPA)

Dave Starrett Photographer
101 Thursfield Crescent, Toronto, ON M4G 2N4, Canada
Tel: 647-865-8299
E-mail: dave@davestarrett.com
Web Site: www.davestarrett.com
Key Personnel
Contact: Dave Starrett
Commercial & editorial photography for the textbook & educational publishing market.

Table Mesa Productions/David Lissy Photography
7517 S Monaco Way, Centennial, CO 80012
Tel: 303-919-5296 (cell)
E-mail: fstop@earthlink.net

Web Site: www.davidlissy.com
Key Personnel
Owner & Photog: David Lissy
Founded: 1980
Assignment & stock photography, A to Z, emphasis on recreational sports & videography.
Membership(s): American Society of Media Photographers (ASMP)

Todd Tarbox
330 Oakhurst Lane, Colorado Springs, CO 80906
Tel: 719-579-9110
E-mail: t_tarbox@msn.com
Key Personnel
Contact: Shirley Tarbox
Founded: 1975
Specialize in people around the world; available for location shooting.
File Begins: 1965
Stock: B&W & color

Stephen Trimble: Words & Photographs
70 W Apricot Ave, Salt Lake City, UT 84103
Tel: 801-819-2448
E-mail: steve@stephentrimble.net
Web Site: www.stephentrimble.net
Stock includes Arizona & New Mexico Indians. Wilderness, landscapes, parks, nature, geology: Utah, the Southwest, Rockies, Great Basin, California, Great Plains & Hawaii. Travel, people, architecture: New England, Southeast Asia, Nepal, Mexico, Ecuador, Galapagos, Guatemala, Egypt, Kenya, France (Provence), Italy (Tuscany) & Spain. Assignments accepted.
File Begins: 1970
Stock: 40,000 35mm & 6 x 7 color transparencies, most scanned, plus many years of digital files

Alvis Upitis Photography
82-5847 Napo'opo'o Rd, Captain Cook, HI 96704
Tel: 808-328-8531; 808-937-3173 (cell)
E-mail: auphoto@hawaii.rr.com
Web Site: www.alvisupitis.com

Visual Pursuit
168 W 86 St, New York, NY 10024
Tel: 212-362-8234
Key Personnel
Owner: Joan Menschenfreund *E-mail:* joanmensch3@aol.com
Founded: 1980
Formerly with *Time Magazine* & *Time For Kids Magazine* staff. Experienced picture editor offers complete visual research & consulting service for all media; Subject specialties: history, current events, art, culture, personalities, travel; wide knowledge of sources; detail & deadline oriented.
Membership(s): American Society of Picture Professionals (ASPP)

Nancy Warner Photographer
Division of Warner-Cotter Co
10 Vinton Ct, San Francisco, CA 94108-2407
Tel: 415-989-9157 *Fax:* 415-989-9157
E-mail: nancy.warner@gmail.com
Web Site: www.warnerphoto.com
Key Personnel
Partner: Sean Cotter *Tel:* 415-441-4011 *E-mail:* seancotter@gmail.com
Founded: 1980
Portraits - corporate, author or special assignment. Studio or location.

Patrick J Watson
23 Alden Rd, Poughkeepsie, NY 12603
Tel: 845-475-8654
E-mail: info@patrickjwatson.com
Web Site: www.patrickjwatson.com
Founded: 1980

Media production (photography & video), research & management company; utilizing technologies developed for the largest health care publisher.
File Begins: 1979

Jim West Photography
4875 Three Mile Dr, Detroit, MI 48224
E-mail: jim@jimwestphoto.com
Web Site: www.jimwestphoto.com
Key Personnel
Owner & Photog: Jim West
Founded: 1980
Stock & assignment photography, specializing in labor & social issues.
File Begins: 1980
Agent(s): Alamy Images; The Image Works
Membership(s): American Society of Media Photographers (ASMP); International Labor Communications Association (ILCA); National Press Photographers Association (NPPA)

Carol Wien Photography
6969 E White-Pacheco St, Willcox, AZ 85643
Tel: 520-384-2018
E-mail: carol@azwien.com
Web Site: www.azwien.com
Key Personnel
Owner & Photog: Carol Wien
Freelance stock photographer, nature, wildlife, western scenes & scenery.
Membership(s): Media Image Resource Alliance (MIRA)

Richard Wood Photography
50 Boylston St, Brookline, MA 02445
Tel: 617-872-0654
Web Site: www.rwoodphotography.com
Key Personnel
Owner & Photog: Richard Wood
 E-mail: richard@rwoodphotography.com
Founded: 1976

Corporate & editorial photography featuring executive portraits, architecture & interiors.
Membership(s): American Society of Media Photographers (ASMP); Association of Independent Architectural Photographers (AIAP); CIPNE

Chuck Wyrostok
230 Griffith Run Rd, Spencer, WV 25276
Tel: 304-927-2978
E-mail: wyro@appalight.com
Web Site: www.appalight.com
Founded: 1959
Editorial & commercial photography & writing assignments & stock; covering regional, national & international; based near Charleston, WV.
File Begins: 1960
Stock: 22,000 color; 15,000 B&W

Stock Photo Agencies

This section includes agencies whose stock photo files represent the work of many photographers. Individual photographers who maintain and sell their own files of stock and assignment photos are listed in **Photographers**.

Animals Animals/Earth Scenes
17 Railroad Ave, Chatham, NY 12037
Tel: 518-392-5500 *Toll Free Tel:* 800-392-5503
E-mail: info@animalsanimals.com
Web Site: www.animalsanimals.com
Key Personnel
Pres: Nancy Carrizales
Stock of birds, fish, insects, mammals, reptiles, amphibians, etc, in their natural & domestic habitats throughout the world, as well as other outdoor-related subjects, including sports, travel, landscapes, flowers, etc. Photographers' inquiries must be accompanied by SASE.
Number of Photographers Represented: 300
File Begins: 1971
Stock: 1,500,000 color
Availability: Digital & analog
Restrictions: Nothing detrimental to wildlife
Membership(s): Digital Media Licensing Association (DMLA

AP Images
Division of Associated Press (AP)
200 Liberty St, New York, NY 10281
Tel: 212-621-1930 *Fax:* 212-621-1955
E-mail: info@ap.org
Web Site: www.ap.org
Historical, celebrities, sports, special interests & feature photos; assignment photography; digital transmissions, online photo archive.
Stock: 50 million B&W & color
Availability: Walk-in, mail & phone

AppaLight
230 Griffith Run, Spencer, WV 25276
Tel: 304-927-2978
Web Site: www.appalight.com
Key Personnel
Owner & Dir: Chuck Wyrostok *E-mail:* wyro@ appalight.com
Founded: 1988
Photo library with emphasis on the people, natural history, culture, commerce, flora, fauna & travel destinations of the Appalachian Mountain region & Eastern Shore of the US.
Number of Photographers Represented: 16
File Begins: 1960
Stock: 40,000 color; 20,000 B&W
Availability: E-mail, walk-in, mail & phone
Restrictions: Holding fees & some research fees may apply

Art Resource Inc
65 Bleeker St, 12th fl, New York, NY 10012
Tel: 212-505-8700 *Fax:* 212-505-2053
E-mail: requests@artres.com
Web Site: www.artres.com
Key Personnel
Pres: Ted Feder
Gen Mgr: Michael Slade
Founded: 1968
Art Resource functions as the official rights & permissions bureau for approximately 200 of the world's major museums & collections including The Museum of Modern Art, The Art Institute of Chicago, The Guggenheim Museum, The Kimbell Art Museum, The Morgan Library & Museum, Smithsonian American Art Museum, Smithsonian National Portrait Gallery. Also included from abroad are The National Gallery London, Tate Britain, The British Museum as well as all 51 national museums of France, under the aegis of the Reunion des Musees Nationaux, including the Musee du Louvre, the Musee d'Orsay, the Musee Picasso, Centre Georges Pompidou, the Musee & Chateaux of Versailles, & as well as all 21 Berlin State Museums, among them the Egyptian Museum & the Pergamon Museum. In addition, Art Resource represents fine art images from over 6,000 museums, institutions & monuments worldwide on a non-exclusive basis.
Stock: 3 million digital images
Availability: Mail, phone, fax & e-mail

Daniel H Bailey - Outdoor/Adventure Photography
3535 E 19 Ave, Anchorage, AK 99508
Tel: 970-484-1632
E-mail: dan@danbaileyphoto.com
Web Site: danbaileyphoto.com
Founded: 1996
Photography of adventure, extreme sports & active lifestyles for stock & assignment.
Stock: 20,000
Availability: Order from catalog, by phone, mail or web site

The Bergman Medical/Technical/Scientific Collection
Division of Project Masters Inc
c/o Project Masters Inc, 134 Leabrook Lane, Princeton, NJ 08540
Tel: 609-921-0749
E-mail: information@pmiprinceton.com
Web Site: www.pmiprinceton.com
Key Personnel
VP: Vicky Bergman
Founded: 1980
Works from own medical, scientific & technical collection, plus researchers & freelance photographers.
Number of Photographers Represented: 10
File Begins: 1934
Stock: 20,000, including 35mm, 2 1/4, 5 x 7, 8 x 10, color & B&W

Black Star Publishing Co
333 Mamaroneck Ave, Suite 175, White Plains, NY 10605
Tel: 212-679-3288 *Fax:* 212-889-2052
Web Site: www.blackstar.com
Key Personnel
Pres: Benjamin J Chapnick
EVP: John P Chapnick
Represent photographers in the US & 32 foreign countries. Assignment work & stock photographs; picture stories & single pictures; AV & film presentations.
Number of Photographers Represented: 350
Stock: 3 million color transparencies & 1 million B&W prints
Availability: Mail, phone or online

Brown Brothers
100 Bortree Rd, Sterling, PA 18463
Mailing Address: PO Box 50, Sterling, PA 18463-0050
Tel: 570-209-6902; 570-689-2700 *Fax:* 570-689-2709
E-mail: info@brownbrothersusa.com
Web Site: www.brownbrothersusa.com
Key Personnel
Pres: Raymond A Collins
Founded: 1904
From prehistory to present with special emphasis on early New York, immigrants, slums, political movements, rural & urban life, wars, early technology, disasters, politicians, royalty, sports, inventors, science, American fads & celebrities.
Stock: 100,000 B&W
Availability: Mail, phone, e-mail & fax

Camerique Inc International
164 Regency Dr, Eagleville, PA 19403
Mailing Address: PO Box 175, Blue Bell, PA 19422
Tel: 610-272-4000 *Fax:* 610-539-9558
E-mail: info@camerique.com
Web Site: www.camerique.com
Key Personnel
Pres: Christopher C Johnson
Founded: 1972
Photos on all topics except news & personalities. Ask for free picture search.
Number of Photographers Represented: 300
Stock: 600,000 B&W & color
Availability: Mail & phone
Restrictions: As licensed for use

The Canadian Press Images
Division of The Canadian Press/La Presse Canadienne
36 King St E, Toronto, ON M5C 2L9, Canada
Tel: 416-507-2198 (photo archives)
Toll Free Tel: 866-599-0599
E-mail: info@cpimages.com
Web Site: www.cpimages.com; www. thecanadianpress.com
Key Personnel
Gen Mgr: Ron Welch *E-mail:* ron.welch@ cpimages.com
Founded: 1917
National news, picture & broadcast wire, photo assignment service & photo archive.
Number of Photographers Represented: 500
File Begins: 1840
Availability: Online

ChinaStock/WorldViews
Division of Dennis Cox LLC
2506 Country Village, Ann Arbor, MI 48103-6500
Tel: 734-680-4660
E-mail: decoxphoto@gmail.com
Web Site: www.denniscox.com
Key Personnel
Pres: Dennis Cox
Founded: 1978
Specialize in stock & historical photos of China by American & Chinese photographers & world travel.
Number of Photographers Represented: 15
Stock: 400,000 color
Availability: Phone & e-mail

ClassicStock.com/Robertstock.com
Division of H Armstrong Roberts Inc
4203 Locust St, Philadelphia, PA 19104
Tel: 215-386-6300 *Toll Free Tel:* 800-786-6300
Toll Free Fax: 800-786-1920

E-mail: sales@classicstock.com; info@
classicstock.com; info@robertstock.com
Web Site: www.classicstock.com; www.
robertstock.com
Key Personnel
Pres: Bob Roberts
Mgr: Roberta Groves *E-mail:* robertag@
classicstock.com
Vintage stock photos for editorial & advertising
illustration.
Number of Photographers Represented: 200
File Begins: 1920
Stock: All formats, 2,000,000 B&W & 590,000
color with some earlier illustrations prior to
1920
Availability: Walk-in, mail, phone & web site
Membership(s): Digital Media Licensing Associa-
tion (DMLA

CPimages, see The Canadian Press Images

Davis Art Images
Division of Davis Publications Inc
50 Portland St, Worcester, MA 01608
Tel: 508-754-7201 *Toll Free Tel:* 800-533-2847
Fax: 508-753-3834
E-mail: das@davisart.com; contactus@davisart.
com
Web Site: www.davisart.com
Key Personnel
Pres: Julian Davis Wade
Curator, Images: Karl Cole *E-mail:* kcole@
davisart.com
Assoc Curator: Lydia Keene-Kendrick
E-mail: lkeenekendrick@davisart.com
Founded: 1901
Produce digital images of art & architecture from
ancient to contemporary from both old & new
worlds, also images on commission from many
major American museums. Represent 50 muse-
ums.
Stock: 40,000 35mm, 35,000 digital images
Availability: Mail, phone, by appt, web site or fax

Danita Delimont Stock Photography
4911 Somerset Dr SE, Bellevue, WA 98006
Tel: 425-562-1543 *Fax:* 425-373-5316
Web Site: www.danitadelimont.com
Key Personnel
CEO: Danita Delimont *E-mail:* danita@
danitadelimont.com
CTO: Dave Herbig *E-mail:* dherbig@jps.net
Founded: 1982
Photo agency. Travel destination specialist, world-
wide travel, culture, nature & wildlife. 900,000
images online.
Number of Photographers Represented: 300
File Begins: 2000
Availability: Online downloads
Membership(s): American Society of Picture Pro-
fessionals (ASPP); Digital Media Licensing
Association (DMLA; North America Nature
Photography Association

DRK PHOTO
100 Starlight Way, Sedona, AZ 86351
Tel: 928-284-9808
E-mail: info@drkphoto.com
Web Site: www.drkphoto.com
Key Personnel
Prop: Daniel R Krasemann
Founded: 1980
Hundreds of thousands of color images for adver-
tising, editorial, books, calendars & corporate
use. Specialize in wildlife & natural history
& also maintain a large collection of general
stock, analog or digital delivery.
Number of Photographers Represented: 100
Stock: 35mm, 2 1/4 x 2 1/4, 4 x 5, color only
Availability: Online, phone & by appt

eFootage LLC
530 S Lake Ave, Suite 450, Pasadena, CA 91101
Tel: 626-395-9593
E-mail: info@efootage.com
Web Site: www.efootage.com
Key Personnel
Pres: Paul Lisy
Extensive film & video stockshot library.
US/Canada & world stockshot film & video
from 1896 to present. 20,000 hours film &
video, all formats.
Number of Photographers Represented: 32
File Begins: 1896
Stock: B&W & color, 16mm & 35mm; video, all
formats, 22,000 hours
Availability: Mail & phone
Restrictions: Payment

Envision Stock Photography Inc
27 Hoppin Rd, Newport, RI 02840
Tel: 401-619-1500 *Toll Free Tel:* 800-524-8238
E-mail: envision@att.net
Web Site: www.envision-stock.com
Key Personnel
Pres: Sue Pashko
Founded: 1988
Photo library with many large format originals.
Specialize in food, travel & nature subjects.
Number of Photographers Represented: 50
Stock: 150,000 color
Availability: E-mail, phone & fax
Restrictions: Licensing agreement & fees paid
prior to usage; $100 minimum fee for use
Membership(s): Food Photography Association

Esto
222 Valley Place, Mamaroneck, NY 10543
Tel: 914-698-4060
E-mail: esto@esto.com
Web Site: www.esto.com
Key Personnel
Pres: Erica Stoller
Researcher: Christine Cordazzo
Stock photographs of architecture & design.
Availability: Mail, phone, e-mail & web site
Restrictions: Research fee (at times)

eStock Photo
27-28 Thomson Ave, Suite 628, Long Island City,
NY 11101
Tel: 212-689-5580 *Toll Free Tel:* 800-284-3399
Fax: 212-545-1185
E-mail: sales@estockphoto.com; info@
estockphoto.com
Web Site: www.estockphoto.com
Key Personnel
Off Mgr: Laura Diez *E-mail:* laura@estockphoto.
com
Business, lifestyles, travel & much more.
Number of Photographers Represented: 80
Stock: Over 1,000,000
Availability: By appt, mail, Internet & phone

FILM Archives Inc
35 W 35 St, Suite 904, New York, NY 10001-
2238
Tel: 212-696-2616 *Fax:* 503-210-9927
E-mail: info@filmarchivesonline.com
Web Site: www.filmarchivesonline.com
Key Personnel
Founding Partner & Pres: Mark Trost
Founded: 1986
Vintage & contemporary stock footage (archival).
No photographs.

Fish Films Footage World
1060 Camino Real, Sante Fe, NM 87501
Tel: 818-905-1071
E-mail: footageworld@aol.com
Web Site: www.footageworld.com

Key Personnel
Exec Offr & Secy/Treas: Gloria Lopez
Pres: David Fishbein
Stock footage library.
Number of Photographers Represented: 50
Stock: 16mm, 35mm, one-inch videotape, Beta-
cam, D2, HD, all formats
Availability: By appt, phone & fax

Foster Travel Publishing
1623 Martin Luther King Jr Way, Berkeley, CA
94709
Tel: 510-549-2202
Web Site: www.fostertravel.com; stockphotos.
fostertravel.com
Key Personnel
Owner & Pres: Lee Foster *E-mail:* lee@
fostertravel.com
Founded: 1972
Extensive stock photo files of CA & the West,
Mexico & 50 other foreign countries. Total of
250 travel destinations worldwide.
Number of Photographers Represented: 1
File Begins: 1975
Stock: 250,000 35mm color. 25,000 stock photos
also available online on two web sites
Availability: Walk-in, mail, phone & web site
Membership(s): American Society of Media Pho-
tographers (ASMP); Bay Area Independent
Publishers Association (BAIPA); Bay Area
Travel Writers; Society of American Travel
Writers (SATW)

David R Frazier PhotoLibrary Inc
PO Box 5242, Boise, ID 83705-0242
Tel: 208-342-9250 *Fax:* 208-342-2307
Web Site: www.drfphoto.com
Key Personnel
Pres: David R Frazier *E-mail:* dave@drfphoto.
com
Broad-based collection of foreign & domestic
subjects; strong on textbook & editorial im-
ages; transportation, agriculture, people, geog-
raphy, jobs.
Number of Photographers Represented: 10
Stock: 300,000 color
Availability: Mail, phone, fax, e-mail & web site

Fundamental Photographs
210 Forsyth St, Suite 2, New York, NY 10002
Tel: 212-473-5770
E-mail: mail@fphoto.com
Web Site: www.fphoto.com
Key Personnel
Partner: Richard Megna; Kip Peticolas
Founded: 1979
Photographic studio with the background & ex-
pertise to transform difficult science specs into
visually exciting illustrations. Our specialized
collection includes science illustration, chem-
istry principles, physics, optics, magnetism,
earth science & stroboscopic images. Offer a
specialized stock library of over 40,000 fully-
captioned images, with detailed information
on our subjects. We can also shoot photos on
request.
Number of Photographers Represented: 40
File Begins: 1979
Stock: 40,000 digital files
Availability: Upon request, e-mail, phone & mail.
Visit web site to search library
Membership(s): American Society of Picture Professionals (ASPP)

Getty Images Inc
605 Fifth Ave S, Suite 400, Seattle, WA 98104
Tel: 206-925-5000 *Toll Free Tel:* 800-IMAGERY
(462-4379 sales); 888-888-5889
E-mail: enterprisesolutionssales@gettyimages.com
Web Site: www.gettyimages.com
Key Personnel
CEO: Craig Peters

Chief Technol & Prod Offr: Nate Gandert
SVP & Chief Mktg Offr: Gene Foca
SVP, Content: Ken Mainardis
SVP, Creative Content: Andrew Saunders
SVP & Gen Coun: Kjelti Kellough
SVP, Strategic Devt: Peter Orlowsky
VP, Sales (Americas): Katie Calhoun
Founded: 1995
Global digital media company with distribution network in 53 countries. Collection of high-quality creative photography for use in advertising, design & editorial. Stock includes scenes of the US & world, sports, science, technology, business, industry, natural history, human interest, people/lifestyles, animals/wildlife, special effects, etc. B&W includes contemporary images & a large historical collection dating from the 1850s. Over 200,000 images are added each year. Editorial, entertainment, feature & corporate assignments through NY office. Call for free catalog or a selection of images.
Number of Photographers Represented: 250,000
Stock: 3.2 billion thumbnails
Availability: Walk-in, mail, phone, fax & online, digital delivery
Restrictions: Usage fees for reproduction. Usage must be explained prior to actual use. Model releases available on select images
Branch Office(s)
6300 Wilshire Blvd, 16th fl, Los Angeles, CA 90048 Tel: 323-202-4200
55 E Monroe St, 17th fl, Suite 1700, Chicago, IL 60603 Tel: 312-344-4500
195 Broadway, New York, NY 10007 Tel: 646-613-4000
182 Blues Point Rd, Level 6, McMahons Point, NSW 2060, Australia Tel: 1800 500-141 Fax: (02) 9439 0476
Avenida Roque Petroni Junior, 1089 10° andar cj 1016, Jardim das Acacias, Sao Paulo-SP 04707-000, Brazil Tel: 0800 772 2074
UBP (Universal Business Park), Bldg B5, No 10 Jiuxianqiao St, Chaoyang District, Beijing 100015, China Tel: (010) 5795 0333; (010) 5795 0388 Fax: (010) 5692 0112; (010) 5692 0115
Haihang Bldg, Rm 2307-2308, No 8 Lin He Zhong Rd, Tianhe District, Guangzhou 510610, China Tel: (020) 8550 1070; (020) 8550 1955 Fax: (020) 8550 1073 E-mail: info@visualchina.com Web Site: www.gettyimages.cn
HuanZhi International Sq, Rm 901, No 436 Hengfeng Rd, ZhaBei District, Shanghai, China Tel: (021) 5385 0333 Fax: (021) 5385 0628
4, Bd Poissonniere, 75009 Paris, France Tel: 01 55 33 66 00
Auenstr 5, 80469 Munich, Germany Tel: 0800 101 31 35
Rm 611, 6/F, Lee Garden 3, One Sunning Rd, Causeway Bay, Hong Kong Tel: 2832 0900 Fax: 3017 6747
Weesperstr 61, 1018 VN Amsterdam, Netherlands Tel: 0800 020 1532
PO Box 106671, Auckland City, Auckland 1143, New Zealand Tel: 0800 462 431
3 Church St, Level 8, Samsung Hub, Singapore 049483, Singapore Tel: 6410 3300 Fax: 6410 3301
c/o Wework, Paseo de la Castellana N° 77, 28046 Madrid, Spain Tel: 917 870 900 Toll Free Tel: 800 099 250
G Tower, 9 Rama 9 Rd, Level 33, No 3334, Huay Kwang District, Huay Kwang, Bangkok 10310, Thailand Fax: (02) 0260733
101 Bayham St, London NW1 0AG, United Kingdom

Glasshouse Images
161 W 15 St, Suite 1-C, New York, NY 10011
Tel: 212-462-4538 (research queries only)
E-mail: agency@glasshouseimages.com (collection queries only)
Web Site: glasshouseimages.com

Founded: 2002
A boutique stock photo & representation agency that caters to a select group of exceptional & distinctive imagery. Accept only the most inspired & inspiring images with a clear commercial spark. We look for classic quality in combination with fresh vision. Rights managed & royalty free stock photography.
Number of Photographers Represented: 100
Membership(s): American Photographic Artists (APA); American Society of Media Photographers (ASMP); American Society of Picture Professionals (ASPP); Digital Media Licensing Association (DMLA; Young Photographers Alliance (YPA)

Globe Photos LLC
Division of Capital Art LLC
6445 S Tenaya Way, Suite B130, Las Vegas, NV 89113
Tel: 631-661-3131 Fax: 702-442-2747
E-mail: info@globephotos.com
Web Site: www.globephotos.com
Key Personnel
COO: Tucker DiEdwardo
Founded: 1939
Photo features on all subjects; large library on celebrities. Represent assignment photographers in all areas of the US & some foreign countries.
Stock: 20 million B&W & color
Availability: Mail, phone, e-mail & fax

Granger - Historical Picture Archive
25 Chapel St, Suite 605, Brooklyn, NY 11201
Tel: 212-447-1789 Fax: 212-447-1492
E-mail: info@granger.com
Web Site: www.granger.com
Key Personnel
Researcher: Ian Relihan E-mail: research@granger.com
Founded: 1964
Convenient & reliable source for images from prehistoric times through the recent past. Images are available for licensing for professional use. Holdings have grown to encompass millions of engravings, photographs, lithographs & many other forms of illustration. Web site offers instant access to the vast majority of our images, each meticulously keyworded & accurately captioned. In addition to this vast online collection, our archive contains thousands of undigitized images & we represent the collections of a number of institutions & photographers. Any one of our highly-skilled & knowledgeable researchers would be happy to assist you with your search. Granger offers a number of digital services, including custom scans, retouching & custom colorization. For education use, visit GrangerAcademic.com. For personal use, visit GrangerArtonDemand.com.
File Begins: 23,000 BC
Stock: 6,000,000 B&W & 1,000,000 color
Availability: Online
Membership(s): American Society of Picture Professionals (ASPP); Coordination of European Picture Agencies Press Stock Heritage (CEPIC); Digital Media Licensing Association (DMLA

Grant Heilman Photography Inc
506 W Lincoln Ave, Lititz, PA 17543
Mailing Address: PO Box 317, Lititz, PA 17543
Tel: 717-626-0296 Toll Free Tel: 800-622-2046 Fax: 717-626-0971
E-mail: info@heilmanphoto.com
Web Site: www.heilmanphoto.com
Key Personnel
Pres & CEO: Sonia Shaner Wasco E-mail: sw@heilmanphoto.com
Founded: 1948

The world's most complete & up-to-date library of American agriculture imagery. Extensive file coverage in natural science, horticulture, wildlife & landscapes. Also featuring the boutique PhotoNetwork collection of travel & lifestyle imagery. Superior quality digital files. A major supplier to the editorial & advertising markets & to textbooks, encyclopedias, magazines, greeting cards & posters. Complete & thorough captions & sales histories; immediate delivery & downloads. Call or e-mail for more information. A fully rights managed image collection with a price for every category.
Number of Photographers Represented: 150
Stock: Over 1,000,000 images with a large historical B&W collection
Availability: Mail, phone, e-mail
Membership(s): American Agricultural Editors' Association (AAEA); American Society of Media Photographers (ASMP); American Society of Picture Professionals (ASPP); Digital Media Licensing Association (DMLA; NAMA; North American Nature Photography Association (NANPA)

Diana Mara Henry
187 Prospect St, Newport, VT 05855
Tel: 802-334-7054
E-mail: dmh@dianamarahenry.com
Web Site: dianamarahenry.com
Founded: 1967
Traveling exhibits of: The First National Woman's Conference, Houston, 1977, One-room Schools & Schoolteachers of Vermont & New York, Vanishing Jews of Alsace & the Natzweiler-Struthof Concentration Camp, Pompadour-Its French National Stud Farm, People & Celebrities, Harvard College & lifestyles, 1965-1969, NYC-Society & Mores, 1969-1987, Malcolm Forbes Balloon Meets at the Chateau de Balleroy, Normandy, Carmel, CA, Hawaii, Bali, Kathmandu, Europe & the Caribbean. LIBEL, an exhibit of words & pictures that challenges the acceptance of pictures & captions as truth.
Number of Photographers Represented: 1
File Begins: 1967
Stock: 100,000 color slides & B&W prints

Historic Films LLC
211 Third St, Greenport, NY 11944
Tel: 631-477-9700 Toll Free Tel: 800-249-1940 Fax: 631-477-9800
E-mail: info@historicfilms.com
Web Site: www.historicfilms.com
Key Personnel
Owner & Pres: Joe Lauro
Founded: 1991
Primarily historical stock footage library covering the years 1895-2010 with over 50,000 hours of logged, copyright cleared footage of all types available for all uses. Modem access to database is available to qualified researchers. Also have over 45,000 individual performances covering all genres of American music form Blues/Jazz to Classical & Rock clips on demand.
Availability: Phone, walk-in, mail & e-mail

The Image Finders
2570 Superior Ave, Suite 200, Cleveland, OH 44114
Tel: 216-781-7729; 440-413-6104
E-mail: imagefinders@sbcglobal.net; jim@baronphotography.net
Web Site: www.theimagefinders.com
Key Personnel
Owner: Jim Baron E-mail: jim@theimagefinders.com
Cover all US states & 35 foreign countries.
Number of Photographers Represented: 45
Stock: 350,000 digital images; 500,000 35mm. Great file of North American wildlife & travel, over 100,000 images of Ohio

Availability: Phone & e-mail
Membership(s): American Advertising Federation (AAF); American Society of Media Photographers (ASMP)

The Image Works Inc
PO Box 443, Woodstock, NY 12498-0443
Tel: 845-679-8500 *Toll Free Tel:* 800-475-8801
  Fax: 845-679-0606
E-mail: info@theimageworks.com
Web Site: www.theimageworks.com
Key Personnel
Owner, Pres & Dir: Mark Antman
  E-mail: mark@theimageworks.com
Founded: 1983
General contemporary & historical images for editorial & commercial use. Domestic & worldwide subjects in documentary style. Large European historical & personality file.
Number of Photographers Represented: 300
Stock: 20,000,000 B&W & color
Availability: Mail, phone & by appt
Membership(s): American Society of Picture Professionals (ASPP)

Michael Jacobs Photojournalism (MJP)
2105 Vista Oeste NW, Suite 3, No 2057, Albuquerque, NM 87120
Tel: 323-461-0240 *Toll Free Fax:* 866-563-9212
E-mail: michael.mjphoto@gmail.com
Web Site: www.mjphotogallery.com
Key Personnel
Owner: Michael Jacobs
Founded: 1970
Photo assignments accepted worldwide. Editorial, illustrative & general photography for publication. Proficiency in photographing Hollywood/the entertainment industry including production & session work. Public relations, cultural & social events, concerts, international travel (over 70 countries covered), children, annual reports & politics. Album & book covers. Feature films, television & videos.
File Begins: 1970
Stock: Over 2 million multi-format B&W, color & digital; over 1 million 35mm B&W & color
Availability: Mail, phone, fax, e-mail
Restrictions: Research fees apply; model release generally not available

Jeroboam
120 27 St, San Francisco, CA 94110
Tel: 415-312-0198 (cell)
E-mail: jeroboamster@gmail.com
Key Personnel
Owner: Ellen Bunning
Founded: 1972
Stock photographic agency supplying journalistic, documentary & editorial B&W & color transparencies for reproduction; primarily in the educational market. Also available to publishers, art directors, designers & photo researchers.
Number of Photographers Represented: 150
File Begins: 1972
Stock: 200,000 B&W & 200,000 color
Availability: Walk-in, mail, phone & e-mail
Membership(s): American Society of Picture Professionals (ASPP)

Keystone Press Agency Inc
Subsidiary of Zuma Press
412 N El Camino Real, San Clemente, CA 92672
Tel: 949-481-3747 *Fax:* 949-481-3941
E-mail: info@keystonepictures.com
Web Site: www.keystonepictures.com
Key Personnel
Owner: Scott McKiernan *E-mail:* scott@keystonepictures.com
Founded: 1892
News & feature picture service.
Stock: B&W & color
Availability: Mail & phone

Magnum Photos Inc
12 W 31 St, 11th fl, New York, NY 10001
Tel: 212-929-6000 *Fax:* 212-929-9325
E-mail: photography@magnumphotos.com; contact@magnumphotos.com
Web Site: www.magnumphotos.com
Key Personnel
Dir, Publg, Broadcast & Film: Michael Shulman
Dir, Ad Corp Sales: Diane Raimondo
Visual record of the times for editorial, educational or commercial use. B&W & color reportage: nature, science & technology, social & political history, personalities. Selective historical archives.
Number of Photographers Represented: 92
Stock: Over 4 million B&W color photographs
Availability: Mail & phone, library visit by appt only, images available by digital & analog
Branch Office(s)
19 rue Hegesippe Moreau, Paris 75018, France
  Tel: 01 53 42 50 00 *Fax:* 01 53 42 50 01
  E-mail: magnum@magnumphotos.fr
Tokyodo Jimbocho, No 3 Bldg, 7th fl, 1-1-17 Kanda Jimbocho, Chiyoda-Ku, Tokyo 101-0051, Japan, Contact: Junko Ogawa
  Tel: (03) 3219 0771 *Fax:* (03) 3219 3088
  E-mail: tokyo@magnumphotos.co.jp
63 Gee St, London EC1V 3RS, United Kingdom
  Tel: (020) 7490 1771 *Fax:* (020) 7608 0020
  E-mail: london@magnumphotos.com

Medical Images
Division of Diomedia Inc USA
19-C Trolley Sq, Wilmington, DE 19806
Tel: 212-736-2525 *Toll Free Tel:* 800-542-3686
E-mail: sales@medicalimages.com
Web Site: www.medicalimages.com
Key Personnel
CEO: Edwin Redzepagic
Founded: 1982
Medical & health care, biomedical & research, biomedical illustration, science & technology & ideas & effects.
Number of Photographers Represented: 450
Stock: 500,000 35mm, 4 x 5 B&W & color, digital image
Availability: Phone, by appt & online

Lawrence Migdale Photography/PIX
23 White Hall Dr, Orinda, CA 94563
Tel: 510-612-2572
E-mail: photopix@migdale.com
Web Site: www.migdale.com
Key Personnel
Owner & Partner: Lawrence Migdale
Founded: 1981
Ethnic families & children in the US. Special emphasis on ethnic holidays & celebrations, the library is geared towards the textbook & children's magazine industries in the US.
File Begins: 1981
Stock: 92,000 color images
Membership(s): American Society of Picture Professionals (ASPP)

Minden Pictures Inc
9565 Soquel Dr, Suite 202, Aptos, CA 95003
Tel: 831-661-5551 *Fax:* 831-661-5497
E-mail: info@mindenpictures.com
Web Site: www.mindenpictures.com
Key Personnel
Owner: Larry Minden
Founded: 1988
Stock collection includes nature & wildlife of North America (with a special strength in Alaska), Galapagos, Madagascar, Antarctic, Africa & rainforests worldwide; underwater, especially whales, dolphins; North American scenics; picture stories with a specialty; editorial & advertising assignments: nature & travel.
Number of Photographers Represented: 150

Stock: 600,000 images available for high resolution digital delivery
Restrictions: Rights managed
Membership(s): American Society of Picture Professionals (ASPP); Digital Media Licensing Association (DMLA

National Geographic Creative
Division of National Geographic Society
1145 17 St NW, Washington, DC 20036
Tel: 202-857-7537 *Toll Free Tel:* 800-434-2244
E-mail: natgeocreative@natgeo.com
Web Site: www.natgeocreative.com
Key Personnel
VP, Sales & Mktg: Alice Keating *Tel:* 202-857-7237 *E-mail:* alice.keating@natgeo.com
Digital Content Licensing, Global: Tracey J Stewart *Tel:* 202-828-5688 *E-mail:* tracy.stewart@natgeo.com
Content Licensing Mgr: Dorian Romer *Tel:* 202-656-0754 *E-mail:* dorian.romer@natgeo.com
Founded: 1919
One of the most comprehensive & unique collections of photographs & artwork in the world. Showcasing the work of hundreds of award-winning photographers. Stock images that portray our planet's diverse peoples, creatures & landscapes as only National Geographic can.
File Begins: 1890
Stock: 10,000,000 transparencies & B&W prints
Availability: Online
Membership(s): Digital Media Licensing Association (DMLA

New West Agency
Affiliate of environmentalproductions.com
355 Lowell Blvd, Denver, CO 80219
Tel: 303-935-0277
Web Site: environmentalproductions.com
Key Personnel
Principal Architect & Photog: Niccolo Casewit
  E-mail: niccolo@environmentalproductions.com
Outdoor photography: color & B&W collection of international mountain photos, flora, wildlife, geology & other scenics, sports, foreign travel, architectural, transit-oriented development.
Stock: 35mm B&W & slides, digital, HDV, HDTV
Availability: Mail or e-mail
Membership(s): American Institute of Architects

North Wind Picture Archives
Division of North Wind Productions
12 Waterboro Rd, Alfred, ME 04002
Tel: 207-490-1940 *Toll Free Tel:* 800-952-0703
  Fax: 207-490-3627
E-mail: mail@northwindpictures.com
Web Site: www.northwindpictures.com
Key Personnel
Dir: Nancy L Carter
Founded: 1988
Stock photos, pictures & footage of historical subjects from all countries; science, wars, politics, social & family life, humor, natural history, explorations, business & commerce; any picture available B&W or color.
Number of Photographers Represented: 3
Stock: 500,000 B&W & color images, all available digitally
Availability: E-mail, fax, phone & online
Membership(s): American Society of Picture Professionals (ASPP); Coordination of European Picture Agencies Press Stock Heritage (CEPIC); Digital Media Licensing Association (DMLA

Novastock International Photo Agency
1306 Matthews Plantation Dr, Matthews, NC 28105
E-mail: novastock@aol.com
Key Personnel
Pres: Gerard Fritz

Contact: Anne Clark
Founded: 1993
Marketing images worldwide.
Number of Photographers Represented: 50
Stock: Lifestyle, business, family, exercise/fitness, children, medical, concepts, technology, telecommunications

Panoramic Images
4835 Main St, Suite LL001, Skokie, IL 60077
Tel: 847-324-7000 *Toll Free Tel:* 800-543-5250
   Fax: 847-324-7004
E-mail: info@panoramicimages.com
Web Site: www.panoramicimages.com
Key Personnel
Dir: Doug Segal
Large format & panoramic photo library for advertising & graphic design. Professional staff of photo researchers. Ultra Hi res scans from original films, from 100-mb to 2 gig available for immediate download.
Number of Photographers Represented: 150
Stock: 150,000 color & B&W, 8 x 10, 4 x 10, 6 x 12cm, 6 x 17cm
Availability: Phone, fax & e-mail
Restrictions: Rights managed & royalty free

PhotoEdit Inc
3505 Cadillac Ave, Suite P-101, Costa Mesa, CA 92626
Toll Free Tel: 888-450-0946 *Fax:* 714-434-5937
Web Site: www.photoeditinc.com
Key Personnel
Photo Edit Dir: Tashauna Johnson *Tel:* 714-434-5935 *E-mail:* tashauna.johnson@photoeditinc.com
Founded: 1988
Stock photography agency specializes in children, people & families, especially ethnic & social issues for textbook publishers & magazines; some photographers shoot on spec. Color digital images.
Number of Photographers Represented: 100
Stock: 200,000 digital images online
Availability: Walk-in, mail, phone, fax & e-mail
Restrictions: Research fees when applicable, permission fees, one-time use
Membership(s): American Society of Picture Professionals (ASPP)

Photofest
32 E 31 St, 5th fl, New York, NY 10016
Tel: 212-633-6330 *Fax:* 212-366-9062
E-mail: requests@photofestnyc.com
Web Site: www.photofestnyc.com
Key Personnel
Pres: Howard Mandelbaum
VP: Ron Mandelbaum
Photo research; specialize in the performing arts-historic & current.
Stock: 2,000,000 B&W & color
Availability: Phone, fax, mail & e-mail

Purdy Sports Images
Staff of History, PO Box 65454, University Place, WA 98464
Tel: 253-460-0066
E-mail: vcbcmag@comcast.net
Key Personnel
Pres: Dennis Purdy
VP: Kathy Purdy
Founded: 2009
Provide digital images of most major sports, including baseball, football, basketball, hockey, boxing, golf & soccer. Particularly strong in 19th century & early 20th century baseball. Have extensive collections of sports cards dating back to the 1860s. Also have large collections of: memorabilia; game action photos; player advertising; autographs; uniforms; caps; programs; scorecards; game tickets; books & guides; pennants; trophies; awards; rings;

medals; early photography such as tintypes, CDVs, dags, cabinets, etc; equipment; banners; stadium photos; press pins; ephemera; board games; arcade games; figurines; tobacco items; buttons & pins; posters & broadsides; postcards; first-day covers; sheet music; movie lobby cards; toys; bobble heads; unopened packs wrappers; personal items; the rare & unusual; much more.
File Begins: 1823
Stock: 200,000 color & 100,000 B&W; digital only
Availability: Phone & e-mail

Robertstock.com, see
   ClassicStock.com/Robertstock.com

Science Source®
Division of Photo Researchers Inc
307 Fifth Ave, 3rd fl, New York, NY 10016
Tel: 212-758-3420 *Toll Free Tel:* 800-833-9033
E-mail: info@sciencesource.com
Web Site: www.sciencesource.com
Key Personnel
Pres & Fin Dir: Robert L Zentmaier
   Tel: 212-758-3420 ext 129 *E-mail:* bob@photoresearchers.com
VP & Creative Dir: Bug Sutton *Tel:* 212-758-3420 ext 127 *E-mail:* bug@photoresearchers.com
Lib Dir: Steve Gerard *Tel:* 212-758-3420 ext 122 *E-mail:* steve@photoresearchers.com
Rts & Perms: Peter Pagan *Tel:* 212-758-3420 ext 134 *E-mail:* peter@photoresearchers.com
Founded: 1957
Stocks medical, high technology, electron microscopy, astronomy, chemistry & physics. High resolution scans for reproduction use. Coverage available in all categories, including travel & lifestyle, also the Nature Source collection of wildlife & the Science Source collection of medical, high-tech & scientific photography. Searchable database of over 750,000 images.
Number of Photographers Represented: 700
Stock: 750,000 35mm color & 5,000 B&W
Availability: Mail, phone, web & digital delivery

Shooting Star/Travel
1441 N McCadden Place, Hollywood, CA 90028
Tel: 323-469-2020
E-mail: admin@shootingstaragency.com
Key Personnel
Pres: Yoram Kahana
Founded: 1980
Celebrity & travel stock photos.
File Begins: 1970
Stock: 35mm color & digital
Availability: Mail, phone & e-mail

Shutterstock Inc
Empire State Bldg, 350 Fifth Ave, 21st fl, New York, NY 10118
Tel: 646-419-4452 (sales) *Toll Free Tel:* 866-663-3954 *Fax:* 347-402-0710
E-mail: support@shutterstock.com; press@shutterstock.com
Web Site: www.shutterstock.com
Key Personnel
Founder & CEO: Jon Oringer
CFO & COO: Steven Berns
CTO: Marty Brodbeck
CIO: David Giambruno
Chief Mktg Offr: Jeff Weiser
SVP, Edit: Ben Pfeifer
SVP, Enterprise Sales & Acct Mgmt: Nick Flynn
VP, Communs: Siobhan Aalders
Gen Coun: Heidi Garfield
Founded: 2003
Shutterstock is a leading global provider of high-quality licensed photographs, vectors, illustrations, videos & music to businesses, marketing

agencies & media organizations around the world. Working with its growing community of over 225,000 contributors, Shutterstock adds hundreds of thousands of images each week, & currently has more than 125 million images & more than 7 million video clips available.

The Source Stock Footage Library Inc
Subsidiary of The Source Films
140 S Camino Seco Blvd, Suite 308, Tucson, AZ 85710
Tel: 520-298-4810; 212-925-2547
E-mail: sourcestk@aol.com
Web Site: www.sourcefootage.com
Key Personnel
Pres: Rick De Croix *E-mail:* decroix@streamlinefilms.com
Lib Mgr: Don French
Founded: 1982
Stock footage library, assorted film & video originated images transferred to HD & video.
Availability: Mail, phone & e-mail
Restrictions: No still photos, film & video images as digital files

Sovfoto Inc
263 W 20 St, Suite 3, New York, NY 10011
Tel: 212-727-8170 *Fax:* 212-727-8228
E-mail: research@sovfoto.com
Web Site: www.sovfoto.com
Key Personnel
Pres: Vanya Edwards
Founded: 1932
Complete photo coverage of Russia, China, former USSR, Eastern European Republics & former Soviet Republics current & historical. Complete library & current photojournalism from one of the major Russian news agencies, ITAR-TASS, XINHUA & individual photographers.
Number of Photographers Represented: 25
Stock: B&W & color
Availability: E-mail, mail, fax, phone & by appt
Membership(s): American Society of Picture Professionals (ASPP)

Tom Stack & Associates Inc
7135 N Outrigger Terr, Citrus Springs, FL 34433
Tel: 305-852-5520
E-mail: tomstack@earthlink.net
Web Site: www.tomstackassociates.photoshelter.com
Key Personnel
Pres: Therisa Stack
VP: Tom Stack
High resolution images of all subjects, especially wildlife & marine life. Available for assignments; high resolution downloads available same day.
Number of Photographers Represented: 24
Stock: 200,000 images
Availability: Keyword search & high resolution download from web site

Still Media
714 Mission Park Dr, Santa Barbara, CA 93105
Tel: 805-682-2868 *Fax:* 805-682-2659
E-mail: info@stillmedia.com
Web Site: www.stillmedia.com
Key Personnel
Dir: Becky Green Aaronson
Worldwide travel & photojournalism. Extensive stock includes Asia, North & South America, the Arctic, Europe, Africa & Australia. Magazine, annual reports; advertising & photo reportage.
Number of Photographers Represented: 30
Stock: Over 500,000 photographs
Availability: E-mail, mail & phone

Stock Montage
1817 N Mulligan Ave, Chicago, IL 60639

Tel: 773-637-9790 *Toll Free Tel:* 800-404-0425
Fax: 773-637-9794
E-mail: images@stockmontage.com
Web Site: www.stockmontage.com
Key Personnel
Mgr: Tom Neiman
Stock pictures covering a wide variety of historical people, subjects & events, most prior to 1900.
Stock: Prints & digital image, B&W, color & digital
Availability: E-mail, mail, phone & fax, also see gettyimages.com

Streamline Films Inc
2578 Broadway, Suite 157, New York, NY 10025
Tel: 212-925-2547
Web Site: www.streamlinefilms.com
Key Personnel
VP & Dir, Sales: Rick De Croix
  E-mail: decroix@streamlinefilms.com
Founded: 1998
Historical & contemporary stock footage library. Also carries still photos.
Availability: Mail, phone & e-mail

Superstock
6620 Southpoint Dr S, Suite 501, Jacksonville, FL 32216
Tel: 904-565-0066 *Toll Free Tel:* 800-828-4545
E-mail: yourfriends@superstock.com
Web Site: www.superstock.com
Key Personnel
Sales Mgr: Darryl Jacobson *E-mail:* darryl@ superstock.com
Acct Mgr: Tom Sheeter
General stock picture library; also represents numerous photo stock agencies. Travel, scenic, people, movie personalities, art treasures, religious, Americana, historical, recreation, business, domestic & wild animals, European collection, computer & abstract graphics, nostalgia & other miscellaneous stock. Contemporary color photography, vintage, fine art. Royalty free & rights managed images.
Stock: Over 9 million color & 100,000 B&W
Availability: Web site, mail, e-mail & phone
Membership(s): American Society of Picture Professionals (ASPP); Digital Media Licensing Association (DMLA

University of Southern California Library
University of Southern California, Special Collections, Doheny Memorial Library, Rm 206, Los Angeles, CA 90089-0189

Tel: 213-740-5900 *Fax:* 213-740-2343
E-mail: specol@usc.edu
Web Site: www.usc.edu/libraries
Key Personnel
Dir, Spec Collections & Archives: Marje Schuetze-Coburn *Tel:* 213-740-7119
Maintains a large collection of historical photographs relating to all aspects of life in Southern California, with emphasis on Los Angeles & the surrounding area, between the 1870s & 1960s. The collection includes the work of C Pierce, a professional photographer in Los Angeles at the turn of the century, George Wharton James, historian & photographer of Southwest Native American groups & the stock photo collection created by the Los Angeles Area Chamber of Commerce in the 1920s, 30s & 40s, to "sell" Los Angeles to potential investors in the area; includes LA Examiner photograph morgue & the Dick Whittington Collection.
Number of Photographers Represented: 4
Stock: 1.5 million B&W prints, negatives & duplicates
Availability: Mail & phone
Restrictions: User fee for commercial use of photographs

US Naval Institute Photo Archive
291 Wood Rd, Annapolis, MD 21402
Tel: 410-295-1022 *Fax:* 410-295-1049
E-mail: photoservice@usni.org; photoarchive@ usni.org
Web Site: www.usni.org
Key Personnel
Head, Photo Archives: Janis Jorgensen
  E-mail: jjorgensen@usni.org
Color & B&W photographic collection includes "Our Navy," Miller collection & James C Fahey collections, US & foreign ships & aircraft, weapons, combat scenes & personnel photos. One of the world's largest private collection of over 450,000 US Navy ships & aircraft, of which 15,000 images are available online.
Stock: B&W & color, from 8 x 10 up to 20 x 24, prints
Availability: Online, mail & phone
Restrictions: Reproduction fee to make copies & a usage fee if used for commercial purposes

Viesti Associates
361 S Camino Del Rio, Suite 111, Durango, CO 81303
Tel: 970-403-1000 *Fax:* 970-382-2700
E-mail: photos@viestiassociates.com
Web Site: www.viestiphoto.com

Key Personnel
Pres: Joe Viesti
Founded: 1984
International stock photos & assignment photographers available.
Number of Photographers Represented: 110
File Begins: 1973
Stock: 750,000 color B&W
Availability: Internet, phone & mail
Restrictions: Limited rights to certain photos

Visual Artists & Galleries Association Inc (VAGA)
111 Broadway, Suite 1006, New York, NY 10006
Tel: 212-736-6666 *Fax:* 212-736-6767
E-mail: info@vagarights.com
Web Site: vagarights.com
Key Personnel
Exec Dir: Robert Panzer *E-mail:* rpanzer@ vagarights.com
Represent visual artists' (painters, sculptors, photographers) reproduction rights (copyrights). Publishers & advertisers should contact VAGA to obtain reproduction rights clearance when publishing art in books, magazines, posters, postcards, merchandise, film, television, advertising etc. Rights available for the US & overseas.
Number of Photographers Represented: 18,000
Availability: Mail, phone, fax & e-mail

Claire De Vore
133 Washington St, Belmont, MA 02478
Tel: 617-484-6490
E-mail: cdevore@anthrophoto.com
Web Site: www.anthrophoto.com
Founded: 1970
Collection of B&W & color photos of remote peoples, scientists at work & the evolution of mankind.
Number of Photographers Represented: 98
File Begins: 1934
Stock: 10,000
Availability: Mail, phone & e-mail

WPA Film Library of Stock Footage
16101 S 108 Ave, Orland Park, IL 60467
Tel: 708-460-0555 *Toll Free Tel:* 800-323-0442
  Fax: 708-460-0187
E-mail: sales@wpafilmlibrary.com
Web Site: www.wpafilmlibrary.com
Key Personnel
Dir, Sales & Licensing: Diane Paradiso
Founded: 1987
Stock: Stock footage

Company Index

Included in this index are the names, addresses, telecommunication numbers and electronic addresses of the organizations included in this volume of *LMP*. Entries also include the page number(s) on which the listings appear.

Sections not represented in this index are **Serials Featuring Books; Radio, TV & Cable Networks; Radio Programs Featuring Books** and **TV Programs Featuring Books.**

A & A, PO Box 543, Hazelwood, MO 63042-0543 *Tel:* 314-786-5046 *E-mail:* aaartwork@aol.com; aaauthor@aol.com *Web Site:* www.elaineabramson. com, pg 1183, 1423

A B Data Ltd, 600 A B Data Dr, Milwaukee, WI 53217 *Tel:* 414-961-6400 *Toll Free Tel:* 866-217-4470 *Fax:* 414-961-6410 *E-mail:* consulting@abdata.com *Web Site:* www.abdata.com, pg 1105

A Good Thing Inc, PO Box 20482, New York, NY 10021-0068 *Tel:* 212-687-8155 *Fax:* 212-687-8292 *Web Site:* agoodthingink.com, pg 1423

A L S International, 18 John St, Suite 300, New York, NY 10038 *Tel:* 212-766-4111 *Toll Free Tel:* 800-322-0284 *Fax:* 212-349-0964 *Toll Free Fax:* 888-662-8048 *E-mail:* rastefanous@alsintl.com *Web Site:* www. alsintl.com, pg 1407

A-M Church Supply, 3220 Bay Rd, Suite E, Saginaw, MI 48603 *Tel:* 989-249-9174 *Toll Free Tel:* 800-345-4694 *Web Site:* www.am-church.com, pg 1309

A-R Editions Inc, 1600 Aspen Commons, Suite 100, Middleton, WI 53562 *Tel:* 608-836-9000 *Fax:* 608-831-8200 *E-mail:* info@areditions.com *Web Site:* www.areditions.com, pg 1201, 1215, 1273, 1341, 1423

A to Z Indexing & Bibliographic Services, 20 St James Rd, Shrewsbury, MA 01545 *Tel:* 508-842-5602 *Web Site:* sites.google.com/site/atozindexing, pg 1215

A-Type Marketing + Design, 79 Fiddlers Circle, Hyannis, MA 02601 *Tel:* 508-957-2887 *E-mail:* info@ a-type.com *Web Site:* www.a-type.com, pg 1423

A WordJourney Translation LLC, PO Box 3181, Humble, TX 77347-3181 *Tel:* 281-813-1827 *Fax:* 832-213-2777 *E-mail:* word@wjtranslation.com *Web Site:* www.awordjourneytranslation.com, pg 1407

AAA Fine Translation & Interpretation, 162-31 Ninth Ave, Flushing, NY 11357-2010 *Tel:* 917-582-7456 (contact phone); 718-767-7455 (busn phone) *Fax:* 718-767-0474, pg 1407

A&L Express Corp, PO Box 790733, San Antonio, TX 78279-0733 *Tel:* 210-262-6633 *E-mail:* sales@arts-letters.com; support@arts-letters.com *Web Site:* www. arts-letters.com, pg 1371

Aaron Marcus and Associates Inc, 1196 Euclid Ave, Berkeley, CA 94708-1640 *Tel:* 510-599-3195 (cell) *Fax:* 510-527-1994 *Web Site:* www.bamanda.com, pg 1371

Aatrix Software Inc, 2100 Library Circle, Grand Forks, ND 58201 *Tel:* 701-746-6801; 701-746-6814 (Windows); 701-746-6017 (MacIntosh) *Toll Free Tel:* 800-426-0854 (sales) *Fax:* 701-746-4393 *E-mail:* sales@aatrix.com; support@aatrix.com *Web Site:* www.aatrix.com, pg 1371

Abacus Graphics LLC, 15179 Hunger Creek Lane, Bigfork, MT 59911-8313 *Tel:* 406-837-5776 *Web Site:* www.abacusgraphics.com, pg 1423

ABDI Inc, 16 Avenue "A", Leetsdale, PA 15056 *Toll Free Tel:* 800-796-6471 *Fax:* 412-741-4161 *E-mail:* e-fulfillment@abdintl.com *Web Site:* www.abdi-ecommerce10.com/abdintl; www.abdintl.com/abdintl, pg 1109, 1201, 1331

Abraham Associates Inc, 5120-A Cedar Lake Rd, Minneapolis, MN 55416 *Tel:* 952-927-7920 *Toll Free Tel:* 800-701-2489 *Fax:* 952-927-8089 *E-mail:* info@ abrahamassociatesinc.com *Web Site:* www. abrahamassociatesinc.com, pg 1281

Russell Abraham Photography, Jack London Sq, 309 Fourth St, Suite 108, Oakland, CA 94607 *Tel:* 510-444-5204 *E-mail:* ra@russellabraham.com; info@ russellabraham.com *Web Site:* russellabraham.com, pg 1435

Diane Abrams, 71 Faunce Dr, Providence, RI 02906 *Tel:* 401-274-2149 *Web Site:* www.whitegatefeatures. com, pg 1117

Dean Abramson Photography, PO Box 610, Raymond, ME 04071 *Tel:* 207-655-7386 *Web Site:* www. mainephoto.com, pg 1435

Abridged Readers' Guide to Periodical Literature, 4919 Rte 22, Amenia, NY 12501 *Tel:* 518-789-8700 *Toll Free Tel:* 800-562-2139 *Fax:* 518-789-0556 *E-mail:* books@greyhouse.com *Web Site:* greyhouse. com, pg 1123

Absolut Color, 109 W 27 St, New York, NY 10001 *Tel:* 212-868-0404 *E-mail:* info@absolutcolor.com *Web Site:* www.absolutcolor.com, pg 1241

Academic Reviews, 1-A Glenwood Ave, Lynbrook, NY 11563 *Tel:* 516-593-1275 *E-mail:* info@ academicreviews.com *Web Site:* www. academicreviews.com, pg 1123

ACC Distribution Ltd, 6 W 18 St, Suite 4B, New York, NY 10011 *Tel:* 212-645-1111 *Toll Free Tel:* 800-252-5231 *Fax:* 716-242-4911 *E-mail:* ussales@ accpublishinggroup.com *Web Site:* www. accpublishinggroup.com/us, pg 1281

Accent Photography Ltd, 1842 31 Ave SW, Calgary, AB T2T 1S7, Canada *Tel:* 403-271-4120 *Toll Free Tel:* 844-470-4120 *E-mail:* accentphoto@ shaw.ca *Web Site:* www.accentphoto.net; www. calgaryphotographer.com, pg 1435

Access Points Indexing, PO Box 1155, Hood River, OR 97031 *Tel:* 541-806-5436 *Web Site:* www. accesspointsindexing.com, pg 1215

Accurate Writing & More, 16 Barstow Lane, Hadley, MA 01035 *Tel:* 413-586-2388 *Web Site:* frugalmarketing.com, pg 1085

Accurate Writing & More, 16 Barstow Lane, Hadley, MA 01035 *Tel:* 413-586-2388 *Web Site:* frugalmarketing.com; www.accuratewriting. com, pg 1095

Accurate Writing & More, 16 Barstow Lane, Hadley, MA 01035 *Tel:* 413-586-2388 *Web Site:* frugalmarketing.com, pg 1341

AccuWeather Inc, 385 Science Park Rd, State College, PA 16803 *Tel:* 814-235-8600; 814-237-0309 *E-mail:* salesmail@accuweather.com; support@ accuweather.com *Web Site:* www.accuweather.com; corporate.accuweather.com, pg 1371

ACD Systems International Inc, 129-1335 Bear Mountain Pkwy, Victoria, BC V9B 6T9, Canada *Toll Free Tel:* 800-949-1457 *E-mail:* sales@acdsee.com *Web Site:* www.acdsee.com, pg 1371

Alice B Acheson, PO Box 735, Friday Harbor, WA 98250 *Tel:* 360-378-2815 *Fax:* 360-378-2815 *E-mail:* aliceba7@gmail.com, pg 1095, 1341

AcmeBinding, 8844 Mayfield Rd, Chesterland, OH 44026 *Tel:* 440-729-9411 *Toll Free Tel:* 888-485-5415 *Fax:* 440-729-9415 *Web Site:* www.acmebinding.com, pg 1241

ACT ONE Mailing List Services Inc, 237 Washington St, 2nd fl, Marblehead, MA 01945-3334 *Tel:* 781-639-1919 *Toll Free Tel:* 800-ACT-LIST (228-5478) *Fax:* 781-639-2733 *E-mail:* info@act1lists.com *Web Site:* www.act1lists.com, pg 1111

Actar D, 440 Park Ave S, 17th fl, New York, NY 10016 *Tel:* 212-966-2207 *E-mail:* salesnewyork@actar-d.com *Web Site:* www.actar.com, pg 1281

Action Printing, N6637 Rolling Meadows Dr, Fond du Lac, WI 54937 *Tel:* 920-907-7820 *E-mail:* info@ actionprinting.com *Web Site:* www.actionprinting.com, pg 1241

ActionGrafixPhotography.com, 30 Bishop Tutu Blvd, Toronto, ON M5V 2Z7, Canada *Tel:* 416-260-0421 *Web Site:* www.actiongrafixphotography.com, pg 1435

Acxiom, 301 E Dave Ward Dr, Conway, AR 72032 *Toll Free Tel:* 888-322-9466 *Web Site:* www.acxiom.com, pg 1111, 1371

Adair Graphic Communications, 26975 Northline Rd, Taylor, MI 48180 *Tel:* 734-941-6300 *Fax:* 734-942-0920 *E-mail:* adair@printwell.com *Web Site:* www. adairgraphic.com, pg 1201, 1215, 1241, 1273

Adams Book Co Inc, 80 Broad St, 5th fl, New York, NY 10004 *Tel:* 718-875-5464 *Toll Free Tel:* 800-221-0909 *Fax:* 718-852-3212 *Toll Free Fax:* 888-229-2650 *E-mail:* customerservice@adamsbook.com; orders@ adamsbook.com; sales@adamsbook.com; returns@ adamsbook.com *Web Site:* www.adamsbook.com, pg 1309

Adams Design, 4493 Horseshoe Bend, Murrells Inlet, SC 29576 *Tel:* 843-655-7097 *E-mail:* sa@ stephenadamsdesign.com *Web Site:* www. stephenadamsdesign.com, pg 1215

Adams Magnetic Products Co, 888 N Larch Ave, Elmhurst, IL 60126-1133 *Tel:* 630-617-8880 *Toll Free Tel:* 800-747-7543 (sales) *Fax:* 630-617-8881 *Toll Free Fax:* 800-747-1323 *E-mail:* info@adamsmagnetic.com *Web Site:* www.adamsmagnetic.com, pg 1261

Mark A Adams Inc, 425 Riverside Dr, New York, NY 10025 *Tel:* 212-864-0416 *Fax:* 212-316-6496 *E-mail:* mark@markadamsinc.com, pg 1309

Adams Press, 1712 Oakton St, Evanston, IL 60202 *E-mail:* info@adamspress.com, pg 1201, 1215, 1241

J Adel Art & Design, 586 Ramapo Rd, Teaneck, NJ 07666 *Tel:* 201-836-2606 *E-mail:* jadelnj@aol.com, pg 1423

Adler & Robin Books Inc, 3000 Connecticut Ave NW, Washington, DC 20008 *Tel:* 202-986-9275 *E-mail:* adlerrobininfo@my.netmails.net *Web Site:* www.AdlerRobin.com, pg 1355

Adler, Corey, Issac, 71 Faunce Dr, Providence, RI 02906 *Tel:* 401-274-2149 *Web Site:* www.whitegatefeatures. com, pg 1117

Jane Adler, 71 Faunce Dr, Providence, RI 02906 *Tel:* 401-274-2149 *Web Site:* www.whitegatefeatures. com, pg 1117

Adobe Systems Inc, 345 Park Ave, San Jose, CA 95110-2704 *Tel:* 408-536-6000 *Fax:* 408-537-6000 *Web Site:* www.adobe.com, pg 1371

Adoption Book Catalog, 131 John Muir Dr, Amherst, NY 14228 *Tel:* 716-639-3900 *Toll Free Tel:* 866-691-3300 *E-mail:* info@tapestrybooks.com *Web Site:* www.tapestrybooks.com, pg 1139

Les Messageries ADP, 2315, rue de la Province, Longueuil, QC J4G 1G4, Canada *Tel:* 450-640-1234 (commercial); 450-640-1237 (sales) *Toll Free Tel:* 800-771-3022 (commercial); 866-874-1237 (sales) *Fax:* 450-640-1251 (commercial); 450-674-6237 (sales) *Toll Free Fax:* 800-603-0433 (commercial); 866-874-6237 (sales) *E-mail:* adpcommandes@messageries-adp.com *Web Site:* www.messageries-adp.com, pg 1281

Advantage Laser Products Inc, 1840 Marietta Blvd NW, Atlanta, GA 30318 *Tel:* 404-351-2700 *Toll Free Tel:* 800-722-2804 (cust serv) *Fax:* 404-351-0911 *Toll Free Fax:* 800-871-3305 *E-mail:* sales@advlaser.com *Web Site:* www.advlaser.com, pg 1371

AdvantageCS, 3850 Ranchero Dr, Ann Arbor, MI 48108 *Tel:* 734-327-3600 *Fax:* 734-327-3620 *E-mail:* sales-na@advantagecs.com *Web Site:* www.advantagecs.com, pg 1371

The Advertising, Marketing & Sales Promotion Book Club, Book Club Bldg, 7 Putter Lane, Middle Island, NY 11953 *Tel:* 631-924-3888 (ext 100) *E-mail:* amspbookclub@gmail.com; linickgroup@gmail.com, pg 1135

AEI (Atchity Entertainment International Inc), 9601 Wilshire Blvd, Unit 1202, Beverly Hills, CA 90210 *Tel:* 323-932-1685 *Web Site:* www.aeionline.com, pg 1341

Aeon Books/Vishaal, PO Box 396, Accord, NY 12404-0396 *Tel:* 845-658-3068 *Fax:* 845-658-3068 *E-mail:* aeongroup@msn.com *Web Site:* www.aeongroup.com, pg 1281

Aerial Archives, 495 N Main St, PMB 113, Lake Port, CA 95453 *Tel:* 415-771-2555 *Web Site:* aerialarchives.com, pg 1435

AFJ Graphics, 903 20 Ave, Tuscaloosa, AL 35401-2306 *Tel:* 205-349-3702 *Fax:* 205-758-2279, pg 1423

African American Review (AAR), St Louis University, 317 Adorjan Hall, 3800 Lindell Blvd, St Louis, MO 63108 *Tel:* 314-977-3688 *Fax:* 314-977-1514 *Web Site:* aar.slu.edu, pg 1123

Agent Research & Evaluation Inc (AR&E), 44 Park Rd, Woodbury, CT 06798 *Tel:* 203-586-1397 *Web Site:* www.agentresearch.org, pg 1341

Agfa Canada Inc, 5975 Falbourne St, Unit 2, Mississauga, ON L5R 3V8, Canada *Tel:* 905-361-6982 *Toll Free Tel:* 800-540-2432 *Fax:* 905-502-9360 *E-mail:* can.customercare@agfa.com (orders) *Web Site:* www.agfa.com/printing/worldwide/north-south-america/canada, pg 1371

Agfa Graphics, 611 River Dr, Center 3, Elmwood Park, NJ 07407 *Tel:* 201-440-2500 *Toll Free Tel:* 888-274-8626 (cust serv) *E-mail:* customercare.us@agfa.com *Web Site:* agfagraphics.us, pg 1273, 1372

Agincourt Press, 25 Main St, Chatham, NY 12037 *Tel:* 518-392-2898 *E-mail:* aginpress@aol.com, pg 1355

AGS, 4590 Graphics Dr, White Plains, MD 20695 *Tel:* 301-843-1800 *Fax:* 301-843-6339 *E-mail:* info@ags.com *Web Site:* www.ags.com, pg 1201, 1241, 1372

AGS Bookworks, PO Box 460313, San Francisco, CA 94146-0313 *Tel:* 415-285-8799 *Web Site:* www.agsbookworks.com, pg 1355

Fernando Agudelo, 550 SW 138 Ave, Suite K-109, Pembroke Pines, FL 33027-1535 *Tel:* 954-668-9122 *E-mail:* fernandoart2014@gmail.com *Web Site:* www.creativehotlist.com/profile/fagudelo, pg 1423

AIGA, the professional association for design, 222 Broadway, New York, NY 10038 *Tel:* 212-807-1990 *Fax:* 212-807-1799 *E-mail:* general@aiga.org *Web Site:* www.aiga.org, pg 1133

AIMS International Books Inc, 7709 Hamilton Ave, Cincinnati, OH 45231 *Tel:* 513-521-5590 *Fax:* 513-521-5592 *E-mail:* info@aimsbooks.com *Web Site:* www.aimsbooks.com, pg 1281

Airphoto, 421 N Main, Suite 103, Pueblo, CO 81003 *Tel:* 719-542-5719 *Web Site:* www.airphotona.com, pg 1435

AJP Communications Inc, 95 Macdonald Ave, Burnaby, BC V5C 4M4, Canada *Tel:* 604-879-5880 *E-mail:* info@ajpcommunications.com *Web Site:* www.ajpcommunications.com, pg 1215

AK Press Distribution, 370 Ryan Ave, Unit 100, Chico, CA 95973 *Tel:* 510-208-1700 *Fax:* 510-208-1701 *E-mail:* info@akpress.org; orders@akpress.org; sales@akpress.org *Web Site:* www.akpress.org, pg 1325

AKJ Education, 4702 Benson Ave, Halethorpe, MD 21227 *Tel:* 410-242-1602 *Toll Free Tel:* 800-922-6066 *Fax:* 410-242-6107 *Toll Free Fax:* 888-770-2338 *E-mail:* info@akjeducation.com *Web Site:* www.akjeducation.com, pg 1282, 1309

Rodelinde Albrecht, PO Box 444, Lenox Dale, MA 01242-0444 *Tel:* 413-243-4350 *E-mail:* rodelinde@gmail.com, pg 1407, 1423, 1435

Veronika Albrecht-Rodrigues PhD, PO Box 44, Lovell, ME 04051-0044 *Tel:* 207-925-3117 *E-mail:* vroni@fairpoint.net, pg 1407

ALC Inc, 750 College Rd E, Suite 201, Princeton, NJ 08540 *Tel:* 609-580-2800 *Toll Free Tel:* 800-252-5478 *Fax:* 609-580-2888 *E-mail:* info@alc.com *Web Site:* www.alc.com, pg 1111

alfa CTP Systems Inc, 2503 Spring Ridge Dr, Unit D, Spring Grove, IL 60081 *Tel:* 815-474-7634 *E-mail:* info@alfactp.com *Web Site:* www.alfactp.com, pg 1372

All Craft Digital Inc, 289-C Skidmores Rd, Deer Park, NY 11729 *Tel:* 631-254-8495 *Fax:* 631-254-8496, pg 1215

Allard Inc, 4601 50 St, Suite 204, Lubbock, TX 79414 *Tel:* 214-736-4983 *E-mail:* info@allardinc.com *Web Site:* www.allardinc.com, pg 1215

Allex Indexing, 6039 Sunshine Dr, Ferndale, WA 98248-9234 *Tel:* 360-778-1308 *Web Site:* www.indexpert.com, pg 1215

Alliance Storage Technologies Inc (ASTI), 10045 Federal Dr, Colorado Springs, CO 80908 *Tel:* 719-593-7900 *Toll Free Tel:* 888-567-6332 *Fax:* 719-598-3472 *E-mail:* sales@astiusa.com; info@astiusa.com *Web Site:* www.alliancestoragetechnologies.com, pg 1372

Allied Vaughn, 7600 Parklawn Ave, Suite 300, Minneapolis, MN 55435 *Tel:* 952-832-3100 *Toll Free Tel:* 800-323-0281 *Fax:* 952-832-3203 *Web Site:* www.alliedvaughn.com, pg 1372

AllMedia Inc, 1400 Preston Rd, No 400, Plano, TX 75093 *Tel:* 469-467-9100 *Fax:* 214-291-5431 *Web Site:* www.allmediainc.com, pg 1105, 1111

Allusion Studios & Pure Wave Audio, 248 W Elm St, Tucson, AZ 85705 *Tel:* 520-622-3895 *E-mail:* contact@allusionstudios.com *Web Site:* www.allusionstudios.com; www.purewaveaudio.com, pg 1372

AlphaGraphics Inc, 143 Union Blvd, Suite 650, Lakewood, CO 80228 *Toll Free Tel:* 800-955-6246 *Fax:* 801-595-7270 *E-mail:* contactus@alphagraphics.com *Web Site:* www.alphagraphics.com, pg 1372

Marvelia Alpizar, PO Box 4013, Burbank, CA 91503 *Tel:* 213-986-8207, pg 1407

Alps Alpine North America Inc, 3151 Jay St, Suite 101, Santa Clara, CA 95054 *Tel:* 408-361-6400; 408-226-7301 *Fax:* 408-980-9945; 408-226-7301 *E-mail:* alps-pr@jp.alps.com *Web Site:* www.alpsalpine.com/na, pg 1372

Altman Dedicated Direct, 853 Academy St, Rural Hall, NC 27045-9329 *Tel:* 336-969-9538 *Fax:* 336-969-0187 *Web Site:* www.altmandedicateddirect.com, pg 1341

Ambassador Press Inc, 1400 Washington Ave N, Minneapolis, MN 55411 *Tel:* 612-521-0123 *E-mail:* info@ambpress.com *Web Site:* www.ambpress.com, pg 1215, 1241, 1261

Amcorp Ltd, 10 Norden Lane, Huntington Station, NY 11746 *Tel:* 631-271-0548 *Fax:* 631-549-8849 *E-mail:* amcorpltd@aol.com, pg 1325

Amergraph Corp, Rte 15, 520 Lafayette Rd, Sparta, NJ 07871 *Tel:* 973-383-8700 *Fax:* 973-383-9225 *E-mail:* sales@amergraph.com *Web Site:* amergraph.com, pg 1273

American Artist Studio, 1114 W 26 St, Erie, PA 16508-1518 *Tel:* 814-455-4796 *Toll Free Tel:* 888-462-7813 *Web Site:* americanartiststudio.com, pg 1372

American Association for the Advancement of Science (AAAS), 1200 New York Ave NW, Washington, DC 20005 *Tel:* 202-326-6400 *Fax:* 202-371-9526 *E-mail:* media@aaas.org *Web Site:* www.aaas.org, pg 1139

American Association for Vocational Instructional Materials, 220 Smithonia Rd, Winterville, GA 30683 *Tel:* 706-742-5355 *Fax:* 706-742-7005, pg 1273

The American Audio Prose Library Inc, PO Box 842, Columbia, MO 65205 *Tel:* 573-449-7075 *E-mail:* aaplinc@centurytel.net, pg 1372

American Blackguard Inc, PO Box 680686, Franklin, TN 37068-0686 *Tel:* 615-599-4032 *E-mail:* contact@americanblackguard.com *Web Site:* www.americanblackguard.com, pg 1372

American Book Publishing Record® Monthly, 4919 Rte 22, Amenia, NY 12501 *Tel:* 518-789-8700 *Toll Free Tel:* 800-562-2139 *Fax:* 518-789-0556 *E-mail:* books@greyhouse.com *Web Site:* greyhouse.com, pg 1123

American Book Review, University of Houston-Victoria, School of Arts & Sciences, 3007 N Ben Wilson St, Victoria, TX 77901 *Tel:* 361-570-4848 *Fax:* 361-580-5507 *E-mail:* americanbookreview@uhv.org *Web Site:* americanbookreview.org, pg 1123

American BookWorks Corp, 309 Florida Hill Rd, Ridgefield, CT 06877 *Fax:* 203-244-9522 (orders) *E-mail:* info@abwcorporation.com, pg 1355

American Camp Association Inc, 5000 State Rd 67 N, Martinsville, IN 46151-7902 *Tel:* 765-342-8456 *Toll Free Tel:* 800-428-2267 *Fax:* 765-342-2065 *E-mail:* contactus@acacamps.org *Web Site:* www.acacamps.org, pg 1309

The American Collective Stand®, 277 White St, Buchanan, NY 10511 *Tel:* 914-739-7500 *Toll Free Tel:* 800-462-7687 *Fax:* 914-739-7575 *Web Site:* americancollectivestand.com, pg 1133

American International Distribution Corp (AIDC), 82 Winter Sport Lane, Williston, VT 05495 *Tel:* 802-862-0095 *Toll Free Tel:* 800-678-2432 *Fax:* 802-864-7749 *Web Site:* www.aidcvt.com, pg 1105, 1109, 1215, 1282, 1309, 1331

American Journal of Philology, 2715 N Charles St, Baltimore, MD 21218-4363 *Toll Free Tel:* 800-548-1784 (journal orders) *Fax:* 410-516-6968 *E-mail:* jrnlcirc@press.jhu.edu (journal orders) *Web Site:* www.press.jhu.edu/journals/american_journal_of_philology/index.html, pg 1123

American Language Services Inc, 110 Otis St, Cambridge, MA 02141 *Tel:* 617-876-0833 *Fax:* 617-876-0853 *Web Site:* www.americanlanguageservices.us, pg 1407

American Mathematical Society (AMS), 201 Charles St, Providence, RI 02904-2213 *Tel:* 401-455-4000 *Toll Free Tel:* 800-321-4267 *Fax:* 401-331-3842; 401-455-4046 (cust serv) *E-mail:* cust-serv@ams.org; ams@ams.org *Web Site:* www.ams.org, pg 1201, 1215, 1241, 1273

American Press Service & Features Syndicate, PO Box 854, Van Nuys, CA 91408 *Tel:* 818-997-6496 *E-mail:* iscs3assoc@aol.com, pg 1183

American Quarterly, 2715 N Charles St, Baltimore, MD 21218-4363 *Toll Free Tel:* 800-548-1784 (journal orders) *Fax:* 410-516-6968 *E-mail:* jrnlcirc@press.jhu.edu (journal orders) *Web Site:* www.press.jhu.edu/journals/american_quarterly/index.html, pg 1123

American Translation Partners Inc (ATP), 175 Paramount Dr, Raynham, MA 02767 *Tel:* 508-823-8892 *Toll Free Tel:* 888-443-2376 *Fax:* 508-823-8854 *E-mail:* info@americantranslationpartners.com *Web Site:* www.americantranslationpartners.com, pg 1407

American Urban Radio Networks (AURN), 938 Penn Ave, Suite 701, Pittsburgh, PA 15222-3811 *Tel:* 412-456-4099 *Fax:* 412-456-4077 *Web Site:* www.aurn.com, pg 1183

American West Books Inc, 1254 Commerce Way, Sanger, CA 93657 *Tel:* 559-876-2170 *Fax:* 559-876-2180 *E-mail:* info@americanwestbooks.com *Web Site:* www.americanwestbooks.com, pg 1282, 1309

Amgraf Inc, 1501 Oak St, Kansas City, MO 64108-1424 *Tel:* 816-474-4797 *Toll Free Tel:* 800-304-4797 (sales & mktg) *Fax:* 816-842-4477 *E-mail:* support@amgraf.com *Web Site:* www.amgraf.com, pg 1372

Ampersand Inc/Professional Publishing Services, 515 Madison St, New Orleans, LA 70116 *Tel:* 312-280-8905 *Fax:* 312-944-1582 *E-mail:* info@ampersandworks.com *Web Site:* www.ampersandworks.com, pg 1341

an ICON Company LLC, 401 Harper Ave SW, Lenoir, NC 28645 *Tel:* 828-758-7260 *Fax:* 828-754-6353 *E-mail:* info@lenoirprinting.com *Web Site:* lenoirprinting.com, pg 1241

Ancient Healing Ways, PO Box 459, Espanola, NM 87532 *Tel:* 505-747-2860 *Toll Free Tel:* 877-753-5351 *Web Site:* www.a-healing.com, pg 1309

George Ancona, 35 Calle Enrique, Santa Fe, NM 87507 *Tel:* 505-471-8755 *E-mail:* geoancona@gmail.com *Web Site:* georgeancona.com, pg 1435

Anderberg Innovative Print Solutions, 6999 Oxford St, St Louis Park, MN 55426 *Tel:* 952-848-7300 *Toll Free Tel:* 800-231-9777 *Fax:* 952-920-1103 *E-mail:* sales@anderbergprint.com *Web Site:* www.anderbergprint.com, pg 1241

Anderson & Vreeland Inc, 15348 US Hwy 127 EW, Bryan, OH 43506 *Tel:* 419-636-5002 *Toll Free Tel:* 866-282-7697; 888-832-1600 (CN) *Fax:* 419-636-4334 *E-mail:* info@andersonvreeland.com *Web Site:* andersonvreeland.com, pg 1273

Barbara S Anderson, 706 W Davis Ave, Ann Arbor, MI 48103-4855 *Tel:* 734-995-0125; 734-846-3864 *E-mail:* bsa@watercolorbarbara.com, pg 1423

Andrews McMeel Syndication, 1130 Walnut St, Kansas City, MO 64106-2109 *Tel:* 816-581-7300 *Toll Free Tel:* 800-255-6734 *Web Site:* syndication.andrewsmcmeel.com, pg 1183, 1423

Mark Andy Inc, 18081 Chesterfield Airport Rd, Chesterfield, MO 63005 *Tel:* 636-532-4433 *Toll Free Tel:* 800-447-1231 *Toll Free Fax:* 800-447-1231 *Web Site:* www.presstek.com; markandy.com; shop.markandy.com, pg 1372

Angstrom Graphics Print, 4437 E 49 St, Cleveland, OH 44125 *Tel:* 216-271-5300 *Toll Free Tel:* 800-634-1262 *E-mail:* info@angstromgraphics.com *Web Site:* www.angstromgraphics.com, pg 1241

Animals Animals/Earth Scenes, 17 Railroad Ave, Chatham, NY 12037 *Tel:* 518-392-5500 *Toll Free Tel:* 800-392-5503 *E-mail:* info@animalsanimals.com *Web Site:* www.animalsanimals.com, pg 1445

The Annals of The American Academy of Political & Social Science, 2455 Teller Rd, Thousand Oaks, CA 91320 *Toll Free Tel:* 800-818-7243 *Toll Free Fax:* 800-583-2665 *E-mail:* journals@sagepub.com *Web Site:* www.sagepub.com, pg 1123

Anti-Defamation League, 605 Third Ave, New York, NY 10158-3560 *Tel:* 212-885-7700 *Web Site:* www.adl.org, pg 1139

The Antiquarian Bookstore, 1070 Lafayette Rd, US Rte 1, Portsmouth, NH 03801-5408 *Tel:* 603-436-7250 *Web Site:* www.antiquarianbookstore.com, pg 1309

Antler Designworks, 93 Concession Oak Dr, Bluffton, SC 29909 *Tel:* 843-705-6695 *Fax:* 843-705-6445 *E-mail:* antlerdw@aol.com, pg 1423

Antonia Hall Communications, 9663 Santa Monica Blvd, No 1128, Beverly Hills, CA 90210 *Tel:* 707-234-9738 *E-mail:* ahcassociates@gmail.com *Web Site:* www.antoniahallcommunications.com, pg 1095

Any Laminating Service, 13214 Crenshaw Blvd, Gardena, CA 90249 *Tel:* 310-464-8885 *Toll Free Tel:* 800-400-3105 *E-mail:* quoterequest@anylam.com *Web Site:* anylam.com, pg 1241

AP Images, 200 Liberty St, New York, NY 10281 *Tel:* 212-621-1930 *Fax:* 212-621-1955 *E-mail:* info@ap.org *Web Site:* www.ap.org, pg 1091, 1445

Apex CoVantage, 4045 Sheridan Ave, No 266, Miami Beach, FL 33140 *Tel:* 703-709-3000 *Fax:* 703-709-8242 *E-mail:* info@apexcovantage.com *Web Site:* www.apexcovantage.com, pg 1215

Apex Die Corp, 840 Cherry Lane, San Carlos, CA 94070 *Tel:* 650-592-6350 *Fax:* 650-592-5315 *E-mail:* info@apexdie.com *Web Site:* www.apexdie.com, pg 1242

APG Group, 235 Homestead Place, Suite 1A, Park Ridge, NJ 07656 *Tel:* 201-420-8501 *Web Site:* www.apggroupinc.com, pg 1242

APG Sales & Distribution, 1501 County Hospital Rd, Nashville, TN 37218 *Tel:* 615-254-2488 *Toll Free Tel:* 800-327-5113 *Toll Free Fax:* 800-510-3650 *Web Site:* www.apg-sales.com, pg 1282

AppaLight, 230 Griffith Run, Spencer, WV 25276 *Tel:* 304-927-2978 *Web Site:* www.appalight.com, pg 1445

appatura™, A Broadridge Company, 65 Challenger Rd, Suite 400, Ridgefield Park, NJ 07660 *Tel:* 201-508-6000 *Toll Free Tel:* 800-277-2155 *E-mail:* contactus@appatura.com *Web Site:* www.appatura.com, pg 1091, 1105, 1109, 1201, 1215, 1242

Anne Milano Appel, 1364 Virginia St, Alamo, CA 94507 *Tel:* 925-837-5203 *E-mail:* annemilanoappel@gmail.com; amappel@pacbell.net *Web Site:* www.annemilanoappel.com, pg 1408

Apple Inc, One Apple Park Way, Cupertino, CA 95014 *Tel:* 408-996-1010 *Web Site:* www.apple.com, pg 1372

Applied Information Sciences Corp, PO Box 9182, Calabasas, CA 91372-9182 *Tel:* 818-222-0926 *Fax:* 818-222-4329 *E-mail:* sales@aisciences.com *Web Site:* www.aisciences.com, pg 1341

Aptara Inc, 2901 Telestar Ct, Suite 522, Falls Church, VA 22042 *Tel:* 703-352-0001 *E-mail:* moreinfo@aptaracorp.com *Web Site:* www.aptaracorp.com, pg 1201, 1216, 1341, 1355, 1373, 1423

Aquent LLC, 101 W Elm St, Suite 300, Conshohocken, PA 19428-2075 *Tel:* 610-828-0900 *Toll Free Fax:* 877-303-5224 *E-mail:* questions@aquent.com *Web Site:* aquentstudios.com; aquent.com, pg 1216, 1373, 1389

Arbor Books, 244 Madison Ave, Box 254, New York, NY 10016 *Tel:* 212-956-0950 *Toll Free Tel:* 877-822-2500 *Fax:* 914-401-9385 *E-mail:* info@arborbooks.com; editorial@arborbooks.net *Web Site:* www.arborbooks.com; www.arborservices.co, pg 1201, 1216, 1242, 1261, 1341, 1355, 1424

Archetype Inc, 317 N Market St, Lancaster, PA 17603 *Tel:* 717-392-7438 *Fax:* 717-397-8037 *E-mail:* mail@nmsgbooks.com *Web Site:* nmsgbooks.com, pg 1393

Archetype Press Inc, 11272 N Meadow Sage Dr, Oro Valley, AZ 85737-7250 *Tel:* 302-249-5879 *E-mail:* archepress@aol.com, pg 1355

Ariane Editions, 1217 Bernard W, Suite 101, Montreal, QC H2V 1V7, Canada *Tel:* 514-276-2949 *Fax:* 514-276-4121 *E-mail:* info@editions-ariane.com *Web Site:* www.editions-ariane.com, pg 1309

Arizona Library Binding Service, 1337 W McKinley, Phoenix, AZ 85007 *Tel:* 602-253-1861 *E-mail:* info@azlbinding.com, pg 1323

Arrow (grades 4-6), 557 Broadway, New York, NY 10012 *Tel:* 212-343-6100 *Toll Free Tel:* 800-724-6527 (press 1) *Toll Free Fax:* 800-223-4011 *E-mail:* bookclubs@scholastic.com *Web Site:* scholastic.com/bookclubs, pg 1135

Arrow Graphics Inc, PO Box 380291, Cambridge, MA 02238 *E-mail:* info@arrow1.com *Web Site:* www.arrow1.com, pg 1091, 1202, 1216, 1355, 1373, 1393, 1424

Arrow Publications Inc, 5270 N Park Place NE, Suite 114, Cedar Rapids, IA 52402 *Tel:* 319-395-7833 *Toll Free Tel:* 877-363-6889 *Fax:* 319-395-7353 *Web Site:* www.frangipane.org; www.arrowbookstore.com, pg 1282

Art Consulting Scandinavia: Books on Art & Architecture, 25777 Punto de Vista Dr, Monte Nido, CA 91302-2155 *Tel:* 310-456-8762 *Fax:* 310-456-5714 *E-mail:* info@nordicartbooks.com *Web Site:* www.nordicartbooks.com, pg 1309

Art Image Publications, PO Box 160, Derby Line, VT 05830 *Toll Free Tel:* 800-361-2598 *Toll Free Fax:* 800-559-2598 *E-mail:* customer.service@artimagepublications.com *Web Site:* www.artimagepublications.com, pg 1309

Art Media Resources Inc, 1965 W Pershing Rd, Chicago, IL 60605 *Tel:* 312-663-5351 *Fax:* 312-663-5177 *E-mail:* paragon@paragonbook.com *Web Site:* www.artmediaresources.com, pg 1282

Art Related Technology Inc, 4 Brattle St, Rm 305, Cambridge, MA 02138 *Tel:* 617-661-1225 *Fax:* 617-491-0618 *E-mail:* artinc@artrelated.com *Web Site:* www.artrelated.com, pg 1216, 1373

Art Resource Inc, 65 Bleeker St, 12th fl, New York, NY 10012 *Tel:* 212-505-8700 *Fax:* 212-505-2053 *E-mail:* requests@artres.com *Web Site:* www.artres.com, pg 1445

ASC Systems, Mack Place, B-566, St Clair Shores, MI 48080 *Tel:* 313-882-1133 *E-mail:* ascsystemss@live.com *Web Site:* www.sites.google.com/site/ascsystemsusi, pg 1373

Ascend Public Relations, 2629 Second Ave N, Seattle, WA 98109, pg 1095

Ascot Media Group Inc, PO Box 2394, Friendswood, TX 77549 *Tel:* 832-334-2733 *Toll Free Tel:* 800-854-1134 *Toll Free Fax:* 800-854-2207 *Web Site:* www.ascotmedia.com, pg 1095

Asia Marketing & Management (AMM), 2014 Naudain St, Philadelphia, PA 19146-1317 *Tel:* 215-735-7670; 267-324-6227 (cell phone) *Web Site:* www.asiamarketingmanagement.com, pg 1342

Asia Pacific Offset Inc, 1312 "Q" St NW, Suite B, Washington, DC 20009 *Tel:* 202-462-5436 *Toll Free Tel:* 800-756-4344 *Fax:* 202-986-4030 *Web Site:* www.asiapacificoffset.com, pg 1202, 1216, 1242

Associated Press (AP), 200 Liberty St, New York, NY 10281 *Tel:* 212-621-1500 *E-mail:* info@ap.org *Web Site:* www.ap.org, pg 1183

Association for Childhood Education International, 1875 Connecticut Ave NW, 10th fl, Washington, DC 20009 *Tel:* 202-372-9986 *Toll Free Tel:* 800-423-3563 *E-mail:* headquarters@acei.org *Web Site:* acei.org, pg 1139

Association for Library Service to Children (ALSC), 225 N Michigan Ave, Suite 1300, Chicago, IL 60601 *Tel:* 312-280-2163 *Toll Free Tel:* 800-545-2433 *Fax:* 312-280-5271 *E-mail:* alsc@ala.org *Web Site:* www.ala.org/alsc, pg 1139

Association for PRINT Technologies (APTech), 1896 Preston White Dr, Reston, VA 20191 *Tel:* 703-264-7200 *Fax:* 703-620-0994 *E-mail:* aptech@aptech.org *Web Site:* www.printtechnologies.org, pg 1273, 1373

The Association of Medical Illustrators (AMI), 201 E Main St, Suite 1405, Lexington, KY 40507 *Toll Free Tel:* 866-393-4264 *Fax:* 859-514-9166 *E-mail:* hq@ami.org; info@ami.org *Web Site:* www.ami.org, pg 1424

Association of Writers & Writing Programs (AWP), University of Maryland, 5245 Greenbelt Rd, Box 246, College Park, MD 20740 *Tel:* 240-696-7700 *E-mail:* awp@awpwriter.org; press@awpwriter.org *Web Site:* www.awpwriter.org, pg 1389

Athena Productions Inc, 2204 S Ashford Ct, Nashville, TN 37214 *Tel:* 305-807-8607 *E-mail:* atheprod@aol.com, pg 1282

ATLA Catholic Periodical & Literature Index (CPLI), 300 S Wacker Dr, Suite 2100, Chicago, IL 60606-6701 *Tel:* 312-454-5100 *Toll Free Tel:* 888-665-ATLA (665-2852) *Fax:* 312-454-5505 *E-mail:* products@atla.com *Web Site:* www.atla.com, pg 1124

Atlanta Panorama, c/o ALPS Labs, 2139 Liddell Dr NE, Atlanta, GA 30324-4132 *Tel:* 404-872-2577 *Toll Free Tel:* 800-873-2577 *Fax:* 404-872-0548 *E-mail:* alps007@mindspring.com *Web Site:* www.atlantapanorama.com, pg 1435

ATS Mobile, 1150 First Ave, Suite 105, King of Prussia, PA 19406 *Tel:* 610-688-6000 *Toll Free Tel:* 800-247-1287 *Fax:* 610-964-9117 *Web Site:* www.atsmobile.com, pg 1342

Atwood Capital Partners LLC, The DuMont Bldg, 515 Madison Ave, 35th fl, New York, NY 10022 *Tel:* 212-355-1390 *Fax:* 212-355-1391 *E-mail:* info@atwoodcp.com *Web Site:* www.atwoodadvisors.com, pg 1342

Audiobook Department, 6429 N Talman Ave, Chicago, IL 60645 *Tel:* 773-338-8813 *Fax:* 773-338-8813 *Web Site:* www.judithwest.com, pg 1342

AudioFile®, 37 Silver St, Portland, ME 04101 *Tel:* 207-774-7563 *Toll Free Tel:* 800-506-1212 *Fax:* 207-775-3744 *E-mail:* info@audiofilemagazine.com *Web Site:* www.audiofilemagazine.com, pg 1124

Auerbach International, 2137 Otis Dr, Suite 306, Alameda, CA 94501 *Tel:* 415-592-0042 *Fax:* 415-592-0043 *E-mail:* translations@auerbach-intl.com *Web Site:* www.auerbach-intl.com, pg 1408

Augsburg Fortress Publishers, Publishing House of the Evangelical Lutheran Church in America, 510 Marquette Ave S, Minneapolis, MN 55402 *Tel:* 612-330-3300 *Toll Free Tel:* 800-426-0115 (ext 639, subns); 800-328-4648 (orders) *Fax:* 612-330-3455 *Toll Free Fax:* 800-722-7766 (orders) *E-mail:* customercare@augsburgfortress.org; copyright@augsburgfortress.org (reprint permission requests); info@augsburgfortress.org *Web Site:* www.augsburgfortress.org; www.1517.media, pg 1309

Auromere Ayurvedic Inc, 2621 W Hwy 12, Lodi, CA 95242 *Toll Free Tel:* 800-735-4691 *Web Site:* www.auromere.com, pg 1282, 1325

Author Planet Consulting Services, 7741 S Ash Ct, Centennial, CO 80122 *Tel:* 303-253-1702 *Web Site:* authorplanet.org; jodyreinbooks.com, pg 1342

AuthorBytes, PO Box 382103, Cambridge, MA 02238-2103 *Tel:* 617-492-0442 *E-mail:* info@authorbytes.com *Web Site:* www.authorbytes.com, pg 1342

Author's, Writer's & Book Publisher's Advice Line™, Communications Tower, 7 Putter Lane, Middle Island, NY 11953-1920 *Tel:* 631-924-3888; 631-924-8555; 631-604-8599 *E-mail:* topmarketingadvisor@gmail.com; awbpal@gmail.com *Web Site:* TopMarketingAdvisor.com, pg 1342

Autodesk Inc, 111 McInnis Pkwy, San Rafael, CA 94903 *Tel:* 415-507-5000 *Fax:* 415-507-5100 *Web Site:* www.autodesk.com, pg 1373

AutoGraph International Inc (AGI), 2500 Wilcrest Dr, Suite 324, Houston, TX 77042 *Tel:* 713-954-4848 *E-mail:* sales@myeasycopy.com *Web Site:* myeasycopy.com, pg 1373

Avanti Computer Systems Ltd, 251 Consumers Rd, Suite 600, Toronto, ON M2J 4R3, Canada *Tel:* 416-445-1722 *Toll Free Tel:* 800-482-2908 *Fax:* 416-445-6319 *E-mail:* askavanti@avantisystems.com *Web Site:* www.avantisystems.com, pg 1373

Avanti Enterprises Inc, 18901 Springfield Ave, Flossmoor, IL 60422-1071 *Tel:* 630-850-3245 *Toll Free Tel:* 800-799-6464 *Fax:* 708-799-6474 *Toll Free Fax:* 877-799-6474 *E-mail:* sales@avantiusa.com *Web Site:* www.avantiusa.com, pg 1325

Avery Dennison Corp, 207 N Goode Ave, 6th fl, Glendale, CA 91203-1222 *Tel:* 626-304-2000 *Web Site:* www.averydennison.com, pg 1373

AVT Inc, 8601 Dunwoody Place, Bldg 100, Suite 100, Sandy Springs, GA 30350 *Tel:* 770-541-9780 *E-mail:* support@avt-inc.com *Web Site:* www.avt-inc.com, pg 1273

AWT World Trade Inc, 4321 N Knox Ave, Chicago, IL 60641-1906 *Tel:* 773-777-7100 *Fax:* 773-777-0909 *E-mail:* sales@awtworldtrade.com *Web Site:* www.awt-gpi.com, pg 1273

Azalea Software Inc, PO Box 16660, Seattle, WA 98116-0660 *Tel:* 206-341-9500; 206-336-9559 (software support); 206-336-9575 (sales & info) *Fax:* 206-299-5600 *E-mail:* salesinfo@azaleabarcodes.com *Web Site:* www.azaleabarcodes.com, pg 1373

AZTEK Inc, 13765-F Alton Pkwy, Irvine, CA 92618 *Tel:* 949-770-8787 *E-mail:* mail@aztek.com *Web Site:* www.aztek.net, pg 1373

AzureGreen, 16 Bell Rd, Middlefield, MA 01243 *Tel:* 413-623-2155 *Fax:* 413-623-2156 *E-mail:* azuregreen@azuregreen.com *Web Site:* www.azuregreen.net, pg 1282, 1310

B & Z Printing Inc, 1300 E Wakeham Ave, Unit B, Santa Ana, CA 92705 *Tel:* 714-892-2000 *Web Site:* www.bandzprinting.com, pg 1202, 1242

Backe Communications, Radnor Corporate Ctr, Bldg 3, Suite 101, 100 Matson Ford Rd, Radnor, PA 19087 *Tel:* 610-947-6900 *Web Site:* www.backemarketing.com, pg 1085

Baha'i Distribution Service, 401 Greenleaf Ave, Wilmette, IL 60091 *Tel:* 847-425-7950 *Toll Free Tel:* 800-999-9019 *Fax:* 847-425-7951 *E-mail:* bds@usbnc.org *Web Site:* www.bahaibookstore.com, pg 1283

Daniel H Bailey - Outdoor/Adventure Photography, 3535 E 19 Ave, Anchorage, AK 99508 *Tel:* 970-484-1632 *E-mail:* dan@danbaileyphoto.com *Web Site:* danbaileyphoto.com, pg 1445

Baker & Taylor LLC, 2550 W Tyvola Rd, Suite 300, Charlotte, NC 28217 *Tel:* 704-998-3100 *Toll Free Tel:* 800-775-1800 (info servs) *Fax:* 704-998-3319 *Toll Free Fax:* 800-775-2600 *E-mail:* btinfo@baker-taylor.com *Web Site:* www.baker-taylor.com, pg 1139

Baker & Taylor LLC, 2550 W Tyvola Rd, Suite 300, Charlotte, NC 28217 *Tel:* 704-998-3100 *Toll Free Tel:* 800-775-1800 (info servs) *Fax:* 704-998-3319 *E-mail:* btinfo@baker-taylor.com *Web Site:* www.baker-taylor.com, pg 1283, 1310

Baker & Taylor Publisher Services, 30 Amberwood Pkwy, Ashland, OH 44805 *Tel:* 567-215-0030 *Toll Free Tel:* 888-814-0208 *E-mail:* info@btpubservices.com; orders@btpubservices.com *Web Site:* www.btpubservices.com, pg 1283, 1331, 1408, 1424

Noella Ballenger & Associates, PO Box 457, La Canada, CA 91012 *Tel:* 818-954-0933 *Fax:* 818-954-0910 *E-mail:* noella1b@aol.com *Web Site:* www.noellaballenger.com, pg 1435

Balogh International Inc, 1911 N Duncan Rd, Champaign, IL 61822 *Tel:* 217-355-9331 *Fax:* 217-355-9413 *E-mail:* balogh@balogh.com *Web Site:* www.balogh.com, pg 1283

Frank Balthis Photography, PO Box 255, Davenport, CA 95017-0255 *Tel:* 831-426-8205; 805-770-3018 *E-mail:* frankbalthis@yahoo.com *Web Site:* frankbalthis.photoshelter.com, pg 1435

Bamboo Ink, 807 Oliver Hill Way, Richmond, VA 23219 *Tel:* 804-230-4515 *E-mail:* info@bambooink.com *Web Site:* www.bambooink.com, pg 1242

Carol Bancroft & Friends, PO Box 2030, Danbury, CT 06813 *Tel:* 203-730-8270 *Fax:* 203-730-8275 *E-mail:* cbfriends@sbcglobal.net *Web Site:* www.carolbancroft.com, pg 1424

Bang Printing Co Inc, 3323 Oak St, Brainerd, MN 56401 *Tel:* 218-829-2877 *Toll Free Tel:* 800-328-0450 *Fax:* 218-829-7145 *E-mail:* info@bangprinting.com *Web Site:* www.bangprinting.com, pg 1202, 1216, 1242, 1261

Bank Street Book Store, 2780 Broadway, New York, NY 10025 *Tel:* 212-678-1654 *Fax:* 212-316-7026 *E-mail:* books@bankstreet.edu *Web Site:* www.bankstreetbooks.com, pg 1139

Steve Banks Photographer, 14822 Channel Lane, Santa Monica, CA 90402 *Tel:* 310-998-7062 *E-mail:* stevestudio@studio6art.com *Web Site:* www.studio6art.com, pg 1435

Barcode Graphics Inc, 25 Brodie Dr, Unit 5, Richmond Hill, ON L4B 3K7, Canada *Tel:* 905-770-1154 *Toll Free Tel:* 800-263-3669 (orders) *Fax:* 905-787-1575 *E-mail:* info@barcodegraphics.com *Web Site:* www.barcodegraphics.com, pg 1216

Stephanie Barko Literary Publicist, 16100 Crystal Hills, Austin, TX 78737 *Tel:* 512-291-6188 *E-mail:* stephanie@stephaniebarko.com *Web Site:* www.stephaniebarko.com; www.diybookplatform.com, pg 1095

Ted Barkus Co Inc, 8017 Anderson St, Philadelphia, PA 19118, pg 1085, 1095

The Barnabas Agency, PO Box 3113, Corsicana, TX 75151-3113 *Tel:* 903-654-1319 *E-mail:* info@barnabasagency.com *Web Site:* www.barnabasagency.com, pg 1095

Billy E Barnes, 313 Severin St, Chapel Hill, NC 27516-1512 *Tel:* 919-942-6350 *Fax:* 919-942-6350 *E-mail:* bbarnes218@aol.com *Web Site:* www.billybarnes.com, pg 1435

Cynthia Barnhart, 141 E 56 St, New York, NY 10022 *Tel:* 212-759-8037 *E-mail:* trans.action@verizon.net, pg 1393

The Barnhart Dictionary Companion, PO Box 2018, Hyde Park, NY 12538 *Tel:* 845-489-0333 *E-mail:* info@lexikhouse.com *Web Site:* www.lexikhouse.com, pg 1124

Tim Barnwell Photography, 244 Coxe Ave, Asheville, NC 28801 *Tel:* 828-251-0040 *E-mail:* barnwellphoto@hotmail.com *Web Site:* www.barnwellphoto.com, pg 1435

Diana Barth, 535 W 51 St, Suite 3-A, New York, NY 10019 *Tel:* 212-307-5465 *E-mail:* diabarth@juno.com; diabarth99@gmail.com, pg 1117

Bascom Communications LLC, 200 E 72 St, Suite 6-L, New York, NY 10021-4500 *Tel:* 212-988-4212 *E-mail:* bascomllc@aol.com, pg 1355

Bashian & Associates Inc, 28915 S Village Lane, Glenwillow, OH 44139 *E-mail:* adsales@bashian.com *Web Site:* www.bashian.com, pg 1342

Karin Batten, 463 West St, Suite C-617, New York, NY 10014 *Tel:* 212-352-8622 *E-mail:* karin.batten@gmail.com *Web Site:* karinbatten.com, pg 1424

Richard Bauer & Co Inc, 310 Cedar Lane, Teaneck, NJ 07666 *Tel:* 201-692-1005 *Toll Free Tel:* 800-995-7881 *Fax:* 201-692-8626 *E-mail:* info@richardbauer.com *Web Site:* www.richardbauer.com, pg 1261

Baumfolder Corp, 1660 Campbell Rd, Sidney, OH 45365 *Tel:* 937-492-1281 *Toll Free Tel:* 800-543-6107 *Fax:* 937-492-7280 *E-mail:* baumfolder@baumfolder.com *Web Site:* www.baumfolder.com, pg 1273

BC BookWorld, 3516 W 13 Ave, Vancouver, BC V6R 2S3, Canada *Tel:* 604-736-4011 *Fax:* 604-736-4011 *E-mail:* bookworld@telus.net *Web Site:* www.bcbookworld.com, pg 1124

BCC Software Inc, 75 Josons Dr, Rochester, NY 14623-3494 *Toll Free Tel:* 800-453-3130; 800-337-0442 (sales) *E-mail:* marketing@bccsoftware.com *Web Site:* www.bccsoftware.com, pg 1373

BCH Fulfillment & Distribution, 33 Oakland Ave, Harrison, NY 10528 *Tel:* 914-835-0015 *Toll Free Tel:* 800-431-1579 *Fax:* 914-835-0398 *E-mail:* bookch@aol.com *Web Site:* www.bookch.com, pg 1283, 1310

BDT Products Inc, 250 E Rincon St, Suite 101, Corona, CA 92879 *Tel:* 949-263-6363, pg 1373

Beacon Audiobooks, 7075 Cross County Rd, Box 41573, Charleston, SC 29423 *Toll Free Tel:* 800-817-8480 *E-mail:* info@beaconaudiobooks.com *Web Site:* www.beaconaudiobooks.com, pg 1283

Tom Bean Photography, 4680 Lake Mary Rd, Flagstaff, AZ 86001 *Tel:* 928-779-4381 *Fax:* 928-779-9642 *E-mail:* tom@tombean.com *Web Site:* www.tombean. com, pg 1436

The Bear Wallow Publishing Co, 809 S 12 St, La Grande, OR 97850 *Tel:* 541-962-7864 *Web Site:* www. bear-wallow.com, pg 1216, 1274

becker&mayer!, LLC, 11120 NE 33 Place, Suite 101, Bellevue, WA 98004 *Tel:* 425-827-7120 *Fax:* 425-828-9659 *E-mail:* infobm@beckermayer.com, pg 1356

Bedford Printing Co, 1501 S Blount St, Raleigh, NC 27603 *Tel:* 919-832-3973 *Fax:* 919-755-0204 *Web Site:* www.bedfordprinting.com, pg 1242

Morton Beebe Photographer/Author, 150 Lombard St, Suite 808, San Francisco, CA 94111-1139 *Tel:* 415-362-6222; 415-706-0594 *E-mail:* morton.beebe@gmail.com *Web Site:* www.mortonbeebe.com, pg 1436

Beidel Printing House Inc, 225 S Fayette St, Shippensburg, PA 17257 *Tel:* 717-532-5063 *Fax:* 717-532-2502 *E-mail:* customerservice@dreamprint.com *Web Site:* dreamprint.com, pg 1242, 1342

Beijing Book Co Inc, 701 E Linden Ave, Linden, NJ 07036 *Tel:* 908-862-0909 *Fax:* 908-862-4201 *E-mail:* journals@cnpbbci.com, pg 1310, 1325

Bellevue Literary Review, NYU School of Medicine, Dept of Medicine, 550 First Ave, OBV-A612, New York, NY 10016 *Tel:* 212-263-3973 *E-mail:* info@BLReview.org *Web Site:* www.BLReview.org, pg 1124

Benjamin News Group, 1701 Rankin St, Missoula, MT 59808 *Tel:* 406-721-7801 *Toll Free Tel:* 800-823-6397 (MT only); 800-735-8557 (outside MT) *E-mail:* customerservice@bngmsla.com *Web Site:* www.bngmsla.com; www.facebook.com/Benjamin-News-Group-168874803126737/, pg 1310

Hal Zina Bennett, 9827 Irvine Ave, Upper Lake, CA 95485 *Tel:* 707-275-9011 *Toll Free Tel:* 800-738-6721 *E-mail:* halbooks@halzinabennett.com *Web Site:* www.halzinabennett.com, pg 1342

Benoit & Associates, 744 Stockton Heights Ct, Bourbonnais, IL 60914 *Tel:* 815-932-2582 *Fax:* 815-932-2594 *Web Site:* www.benoit-associates.com, pg 1085, 1216, 1424, 1436

Bentley Publishers, 1734 Massachusetts Ave, Cambridge, MA 02138-1804 *Tel:* 617-547-4170 *Toll Free Tel:* 800-423-4595 *Fax:* 617-876-9235 *E-mail:* sales@bentleypublishers.com *Web Site:* www.bentleypublishers.com, pg 1325

Berg Design, 15 Francis Ave, Albany, NY 12203 *Tel:* 518-495-9409 *Web Site:* edatkeson.com/bpages/berg.htm, pg 1424

The Bergman Medical/Technical/Scientific Collection, c/o Project Masters Inc, 134 Leabrook Lane, Princeton, NJ 08540 *Tel:* 609-921-0749 *E-mail:* information@pmiprinceton.com *Web Site:* www.pmiprinceton.com, pg 1445

Miriam Berkley Photography, 353 W 51 St, Suite 1-A/6, New York, NY 10019-6457 *Tel:* 212-246-7979 *E-mail:* miriam.berkley@mac.com; authorpix@aol.com *Web Site:* www.PublishersMarketplace.com/members/MiriamBerkley; www.miriamberkley.com, pg 1436

David Berman Communications, 340 Selby Ave, Ottawa, ON K2A 3X6, Canada *Tel:* 613-728-6777 *Toll Free Tel:* 800-665-1809 *E-mail:* info@davidberman.com *Web Site:* www.wcag2.com, pg 1216

Bernan, 4501 Forbes Blvd, Suite 200, Lanham, MD 20706 *Tel:* 717-794-3800 (cust serv & orders) *Toll Free Tel:* 800-462-6420 (cust serv & orders) *Fax:* 717-794-3803 *Toll Free Fax:* 800-338-4550 *E-mail:* customercare@bernan.com *Web Site:* rowman.com/page/bernan, pg 1283, 1310

Henry Berry, 293 Ellsworth St, No 8D, Bridgeport, CT 06605 *Tel:* 203-332-7629 *E-mail:* henryberryinct@gmail.com, pg 1124

Berryville Graphics, 25 Jack Enders Blvd, Berryville, VA 22611 *Tel:* 540-955-2750 *Fax:* 540-955-2633 *E-mail:* info@bvgraphics.com *Web Site:* www.bpg-usa.com, pg 1202, 1216, 1242

Bert Davis Executive Search Inc, 555 Fifth Ave, Suite 302, New York, NY 10017 *Tel:* 212-838-4000 *E-mail:* info@bertdavis.com *Web Site:* www.bertdavis.com, pg 1389

Best Mailing Lists Inc, 7507 E Tanque Verde Rd, Tucson, AZ 85715 *Toll Free Tel:* 800-692-2378 *Fax:* 520-885-3100 *E-mail:* best@bestmailing.com *Web Site:* www.bestmailing.com, pg 1111

Bethany Press International Inc, 6820 W 115 St, Bloomington, MN 55438 *Tel:* 952-914-7400 *Toll Free Tel:* 888-717-7400 *Fax:* 952-914-7410 *E-mail:* info@bethanypress.com *Web Site:* www.bethanypress.com, pg 1242

BGHT News, Townsend, 4 Gabriel St, Livingston Manor, NY 12758 *Tel:* 845-439-8177 *Fax:* 845-205-4474 *Web Site:* bght.blogspot.com, pg 1183

BH Communications, 115 E Ninth St, Unit 17-F, New York, NY 10003 *Tel:* 212-982-6502 *Web Site:* www.bhcommunications.com, pg 1373, 1424

Raymond Bial, 208 W Iowa St, Urbana, IL 61801 *Tel:* 217-328-2665 *E-mail:* raybial@gmail.com *Web Site:* www.raybial.com, pg 1436

Bible Truth Publishers, 59 Industrial Rd, Addison, IL 60101 *Tel:* 630-543-1441 *Fax:* 630-543-1476 *E-mail:* btporders@bibletruthpublishers.com *Web Site:* www.bibletruthpublishers.com, pg 1325

Biblical Archaeology Society, 4710 41 St NW, Washington, DC 20016-1705 *Tel:* 202-364-3300 *Toll Free Tel:* 800-221-4644 *Fax:* 202-364-2636 *E-mail:* info@biblicalarchaeology.org *Web Site:* www.biblicalarchaeology.org, pg 1373

Bien Fait Translations, 183 Vernon St, 1st fl, Norword, MA 02062 *Tel:* 781-769-1637 *Toll Free Tel:* 866-243-6324 *E-mail:* inquiries@bien-fait.com *Web Site:* www.bien-fait.com, pg 1408

Big Vision Art + Design, 251 Hwy 179, Creekside Plaza A1, Sedona, AZ 86336 *Tel:* 928-202-6320 *Web Site:* www.bigvisionarts.com, pg 1424

Bilingual Educational Services Inc, 2514 S Grand Ave, Los Angeles, CA 90007 *Tel:* 213-749-6213 *Toll Free Tel:* 800-448-6032, pg 1283, 1310

Bindagraphics Inc, 2701 Wilmarco Ave, Baltimore, MD 21223-9922 *Tel:* 410-362-7200 *Toll Free Tel:* 800-326-0300 *Fax:* 410-362-7233 *E-mail:* info@bindagraphics.com *Web Site:* www.bindagraphics.com, pg 1216, 1242

Bindery & Distribution Service Inc, 9 Overbrook Rd, South Barrington, IL 60010 *Tel:* 312-550-7000 *Fax:* 847-842-8800, pg 1274

The Bindery Inc, 8201 Brooklyn Blvd, Brooklyn Park, MN 55445 *Tel:* 763-201-2800 *Toll Free Tel:* 800-851-6598 *Fax:* 763-201-2790 *E-mail:* info@thebinderymn.com *Web Site:* www.thebinderymn.com, pg 1242

Birmingham Printing & Publishing Inc, 3101 Sixth Ave S, Birmingham, AL 35233 *Tel:* 205-251-5113 *Toll Free Tel:* 888-276-1192 *Fax:* 205-251-2222 *E-mail:* sales@bhamprinting.com *Web Site:* bhamprinting.com, pg 1243

Jennifer Bishop Photography, 843 W University Pkwy, Baltimore, MD 21210 *Tel:* 410-366-6662 *Web Site:* www.jenniferbishopphotography.com, pg 1436

BJU Press, 1430 Wade Hampton Blvd, Greenville, SC 29609-5046 *Tel:* 864-546-4600 *Toll Free Tel:* 800-845-5731 *E-mail:* bjupinfo@bjupress.com *Web Site:* www.bjupress.com, pg 1373

Black Star Publishing Co, 333 Mamaroneck Ave, Suite 175, White Plains, NY 10605 *Tel:* 212-679-3288 *Fax:* 212-889-2052 *Web Site:* www.blackstar.com, pg 1445

The Blaine Group Inc, 8665 Wilshire Blvd, No 301, Beverly Hills, CA 90211 *Tel:* 310-360-1499 *Fax:* 310-360-1498 *Web Site:* www.blainegroupinc.com, pg 1095

Blanks Printing & Imaging Inc, 2343 N Beckley Ave, Dallas, TX 75208 *Tel:* 214-741-3905 *Toll Free Tel:* 800-325-7651 *E-mail:* sales@blanks.com *Web Site:* www.blanks.com, pg 1216, 1243

J R Blitman Marketing Inc, 93 Einstein Way, East Windsor, NJ 08512 *Tel:* 609-448-2490; 301-758-2334 *E-mail:* jrblitman@gmail.com, pg 1342

Blitz Media-Direct, Linick Bldg, 7 Putter Lane, Middle Island, NY 11953 *Tel:* 631-924-3888; 631-924-8555; 630-604-8599 *E-mail:* blitz4pr@gmail.com; linickgroup@gmail.com, pg 1085, 1095, 1425

Blitzprint Inc, 1235 64 Ave SE, Suite 1, Calgary, AB T2H 2J7, Canada *Toll Free Tel:* 866-479-3248 *Fax:* 403-253-5642 *E-mail:* books@blitzprint.com *Web Site:* www.blitzprint.com, pg 1243

C Blohm & Associates Inc, 5999 Monona Dr, Monona, WI 53716-3531 *Tel:* 608-216-7300 *E-mail:* hello@cblohm.com *Web Site:* www.cblohm.com, pg 1096

Blue Fox Associates, 9 Barnacle Rd, Hilton Head Island, SC 29928-5518 *Tel:* 843-681-6939 *E-mail:* Island120@aol.com, pg 1343

The Blue Mouse Studio, 26829 37 St, Gobles, MI 49055 *Tel:* 269-628-5160 *E-mail:* frogville@earthlink.net, pg 1425

Blue Note Publications Inc, 721 North Dr, Suite D, Melbourne, FL 32934 *Tel:* 321-799-2583; 321-622-6289 *Toll Free Tel:* 800-624-0401 (orders) *Fax:* 321-799-1942; 321-622-6830 *E-mail:* bluenotebooks@gmail.com *Web Site:* www.bluenotepublications.com, pg 1202, 1216, 1243, 1274

Blue Ridge Printing Co, 544 Haywood Rd, Asheville, NC 28806 *Tel:* 828-254-1000 *Toll Free Tel:* 800-633-4298 *Fax:* 828-252-6455 *E-mail:* info@brprinting.com *Web Site:* www.brprinting.com, pg 1243

BMI Educational Services Inc, 26 Haypress Rd, Cranbury, NJ 08512 *Tel:* 732-329-6991 *Toll Free Tel:* 800-222-8100 (orders only) *Fax:* 732-329-6994 *Toll Free Fax:* 800-986-9393 (orders only) *E-mail:* info@bmionline.com *Web Site:* bmionline.com, pg 1310, 1323

BMI Global-OMS, 100 Beard Sawmill Rd, Suite 360, Shelton, CT 06484-6150 *Tel:* 203-546-5581 *Fax:* 203-546-5575 *E-mail:* info@BMIGlobalOMS.com *Web Site:* www.BMIGlobalOMS.com, pg 1105

BMR Associates, 60 Corte Amado, Greenbrae, CA 94904 *Tel:* 415-927-1564 *E-mail:* info@bmrassoc.com *Web Site:* www.bmrassoc.com, pg 1343

Wanda J Boeke, 50 Richmond Ave, Pittsfield, MA 01201-3329 *Tel:* 413-997-2108 *Fax:* 413-997-2108 *E-mail:* wjboeke@gmail.com, pg 1408

Bolger Vision Beyond Print, 3301 Como Ave SE, Minneapolis, MN 55414-2809 *Tel:* 651-645-6311 *Toll Free Tel:* 866-264-3287 *E-mail:* contact@bolgerinc.com *Web Site:* www.bolgerinc.com, pg 1091

Bondarenko Photography, 210 S 41 St, Birmingham, AL 35222 *Tel:* 205-592-8319; 205-243-9910 (cell) *E-mail:* info@bondarenkophoto.com *Web Site:* www.bondarenkophoto.com, pg 1436

Robert Bononno, 109 E Second St, Apt 5, New York, NY 10009 *Tel:* 646-673-6102 *E-mail:* rbononno@twc.com *Web Site:* www.robert-bononno.com, pg 1408

Book Automation Inc, 458 Danbury Rd, Unit B10, New Milford, CT 06776 *Tel:* 860-354-7900 *Toll Free Tel:* 800-429-6305 *E-mail:* info@bookautomation.com *Web Site:* www.bookautomation.com, pg 1274

Book Club for the Martial Arts Inc, 7 Putter Lane, Middle Island, NY 11953 *Tel:* 631-924-3888 *E-mail:* bcma@gmail.com; okmagads@gmail.com, pg 1135

Book Creations Inc, 5075 56 Place, Vero Beach, FL 32967 *Tel:* 518-366-4636 (cell), pg 1356

Book Express, 2440 Viking Way, Richmond, BC V6V 1N2, Canada *Tel:* 604-448-7100 *Toll Free Tel:* 800-663-5714 *Fax:* 604-270-7161 *Toll Free Fax:* 800-565-3770 *E-mail:* info@raincoast.com *Web Site:* www.raincoast.com, pg 1310

Book Machine Sales Inc, PO Box 297, Hamlin, PA 18427 *Tel:* 570-647-9111 *Web Site:* bookmachinesales. com, pg 1274

Book Publishers Network, 817 238 St SE, Suite G, Bothell, WA 98021 *Tel:* 425-483-3040 *Fax:* 425-483-3098 *Web Site:* www.bookpublishersnetwork.com, pg 1096

Book Review Index, 27500 Drake Rd, Farmington Hills, MI 48331-3535 *Tel:* 248-699-4253 *Toll Free Tel:* 800-877-4253; 248-699-8074 *Toll Free Fax:* 800-414-5043 (orders); 800-414-5045 *E-mail:* gale.galeord@cengage.com *Web Site:* www.gale.com, pg 1124

Book Sales, 142 W 36 St, 4th fl, New York, NY 10018 *Tel:* 212-779-4971; 212-779-4972 *Fax:* 212-779-6058 *Web Site:* www.quartoknows.com, pg 1310

Book Travelers West, 3614A California Ave SW, No 228, Seattle, WA 98116 *Tel:* 206-932-7865 *Toll Free Fax:* 800-440-0818 *Web Site:* www.booktravelerswest. com, pg 1283

Book Vine for Children, 3980 Albany St, Suite 7, McHenry, IL 60050-8397 *Tel:* 815-363-8880 *Toll Free Tel:* 800-772-4220 *Fax:* 815-363-8883 *E-mail:* info@bookvine.com *Web Site:* www.bookvine.com, pg 1283

Bookazine Co Inc, 75 Hook Rd, Bayonne, NJ 07002 *Tel:* 201-339-7777 *Toll Free Tel:* 800-221-8112 *Fax:* 201-339-7778 *E-mail:* info@bookazine.com *Web Site:* www.bookazine.com, pg 1310, 1325

BookComp Inc, 6124 Belmont Ave NE, Belmont, MI 49306 *Tel:* 616-774-9700 *E-mail:* production@bookcomp.com *Web Site:* www.bookcomp.com, pg 1217, 1356

Bookcovers.com, c/o Archer Ellison Inc, 7025 CR 46-A, Suite 1071, Lake Mary, FL 32746 *Toll Free Tel:* 800-449-4095 (ext 702) *Toll Free Fax:* 800-366-4086 *E-mail:* info@bookcovers.com *Web Site:* bookcovers. com, pg 1425

theBookDesigners, 769 Center Blvd, No 22, Fairfax, CA 94930 *Tel:* 415-491-5426 *E-mail:* info@bookdesigners.com *Web Site:* www.bookdesigners.com, pg 1425

BookFactory, 2302 S Edwin C Moses Blvd, Dayton, OH 45417 *Tel:* 937-226-7100 *Toll Free Tel:* 877-431-2665 *Fax:* 614-388-5635 *E-mail:* sales@bookfactory.com *Web Site:* www.bookfactory.com, pg 1243

Bookforum, 350 Seventh Ave, New York, NY 10001 *Tel:* 212-475-4000 *Fax:* 212-529-1257 *E-mail:* info@bookforum.com; editors@bookforum. com *Web Site:* www.bookforum.com, pg 1124

Booklist, 225 N Michigan Ave, Suite 1300, Chicago, IL 60601 *Tel:* 312-944-6780 *Toll Free Tel:* 800-545-2433 *Fax:* 312-440-9374 *E-mail:* info@booklistonline.com; ala@ala.org *Web Site:* www.booklistonline.com; www. ala.org, pg 1124

BookLogix, 1264 Old Alpharetta Rd, Alpharetta, GA 30005 *Tel:* 470-239-8547 *Toll Free Tel:* 888-564-7890 *E-mail:* publishing@booklogix.com *Web Site:* www. booklogix.com, pg 1202

Bookmasters, 30 Amberwood Pkwy, Ashland, OH 44805 *Tel:* 419-281-5100 *Toll Free Tel:* 800-537-6727 *Fax:* 419-281-0200 *E-mail:* info@btpubservices.com *Web Site:* www.btpubservices.com, pg 1202, 1217, 1243, 1261, 1274

BookMobile, 5120 Cedar Lake Rd, Minneapolis, MN 55416 *Tel:* 763-398-0030 *Toll Free Tel:* 844-488-4477 *Fax:* 763-398-0198 *Web Site:* www.bookmobile.com, pg 1243

BookPage®, 2143 Belcourt Ave, Nashville, TN 37212 *Tel:* 615-292-8926 *Fax:* 615-292-8249 *Web Site:* bookpage.com, pg 1121

Books International Inc, 22883 Quicksilver Dr, Dulles, VA 20166 *Tel:* 703-661-1500 *Fax:* 703-661-1501 *E-mail:* hdqtrs@booksintl.com *Web Site:* booksintl. presswarehouse.com, pg 1331

Bookshelf Bindery Ltd, 22 Secord Dr, Unit 16, St Catharines, ON L2N 1K8, Canada *Tel:* 905-934-2801 *E-mail:* bookshelfbindery@bellnet.ca, pg 1243

The Booksource Inc, 1230 Macklind Ave, St Louis, MO 63110 *Tel:* 314-647-0600 *Toll Free Tel:* 800-444-0435 *Fax:* 314-647-6850 *Toll Free Fax:* 800-647-1923 *E-mail:* service@booksource.com *Web Site:* www. booksource.com, pg 1311

BookWise Design, 29089 SW Costa Circle W, Wilsonville, OR 97070 *Tel:* 503-542-3551 *Toll Free Tel:* 800-697-9833 *Web Site:* bookwisedesign.com, pg 1217, 1425

Bookwrights Design, 1060 Old Ridge Rd, Lovingston, VA 22949 *Tel:* 434-263-4818 *E-mail:* design@bookwrights.com *Web Site:* www.bookwrights.com, pg 1356

Boston Review, PO Box 425786, Cambridge, MA 02142 *Tel:* 617-324-1360 *Toll Free Tel:* 877-406-2443 (cust serv) *Fax:* 617-452-3356 *E-mail:* review@bostonreview.net *Web Site:* bostonreview.net, pg 1124

David Bouchier, PO Box 763, Stony Brook, NY 11790 *Tel:* 631-751-2660 *E-mail:* bouchier@wshu. org *Web Site:* wshu.org/people/david-bouchier; davidbouchier.com, pg 1117

Bound to Stay Bound Books Inc, 1880 W Morton Rd, Jacksonville, IL 62650 *Tel:* 217-245-5191 *Toll Free Tel:* 800-637-6586 *Fax:* 217-245-0424 *Toll Free Fax:* 800-747-7872 *E-mail:* btsb@btsb.com *Web Site:* www.btsb.com, pg 1311, 1323

Bowen Books LLC, 971 First Ave, New York, NY 10022 *Tel:* 212-421-5797 *E-mail:* bowenbooks@aol. com, pg 1356

BR Printers, 665 Lenfest Rd, San Jose, CA 95133 *Tel:* 408-278-7711 *Fax:* 408-929-8062 *E-mail:* info@brprinters.com *Web Site:* www.brprinters.com, pg 1091, 1243

Brackett Inc, 7115 SE Forbes Ave, Topeka, KS 66619 *Tel:* 785-862-2205 *Toll Free Tel:* 800-255-3506 *Fax:* 785-862-1127 *E-mail:* brackett@brackett-inc. com; sales@brackett-inc.com *Web Site:* brackett-inc. com, pg 1274

Bradford & Bigelow Inc, 3 Perkins Way, Newburyport, MA 01950-4007 *Tel:* 978-904-3100 *E-mail:* sales@bradford-bigelow.com *Web Site:* www.bradford-bigelow.com, pg 1202, 1243

Bradley Ireland Productions, 23852 Pacific Coast Hwy, No 110, Malibu, CA 90265 *Tel:* 310-458-0700 *E-mail:* earthmag@aol.com *Web Site:* www. bradleyireland.com, pg 1436

Brainworks Software, 100 S Main St, Sayville, NY 11782 *Tel:* 631-563-5000 *Toll Free Tel:* 800-755-1111 *Fax:* 631-563-6320 *E-mail:* info@brainworks.com; sales@brainworks.com; support@brainworks.com *Web Site:* www.brainworks.com, pg 1373

Brandtjen & Kluge LLC, 539 Blanding Woods Rd, St Croix Falls, WI 54024 *Tel:* 715-483-3265 *Toll Free Tel:* 800-826-7320 *Fax:* 715-483-1640 *E-mail:* sales@kluge.biz *Web Site:* www.kluge.biz, pg 1274

Art Brewer Photography, 25262 Mainsail Dr, Dana Point, CA 92629 *Tel:* 949-661-8930 *Fax:* 949-248-2835 *E-mail:* art@artbrewer.com *Web Site:* www. artbrewer.com; artbrewerphoto.com, pg 1436

Brickman Marketing, 395 Del Monte Ctr, No 250, Monterey, CA 93940 *Tel:* 831-594-1500 *E-mail:* brickman@brickmanmarketing.com *Web Site:* www.brickmanmarketing.com, pg 1096

Bridgeport National Bindery Inc, 662 Silver St, Agawam, MA 01001 *Tel:* 413-789-1981 *Toll Free Tel:* 800-223-5083 *E-mail:* info@bnbindery.com *Web Site:* www.bnbindery.com, pg 1243, 1323

Ashleigh Brilliant Enterprises, 117 W Valerio St, Santa Barbara, CA 93101 *Tel:* 805-682-0531 *Web Site:* www.ashleighbrilliant.com, pg 1183

James F Brisson Book Design & Production, PO Box 85, Williamsville, VT 05362-0085 *Tel:* 802-348-7802 *Fax:* 802-348-7802, pg 1425

Broadcast Wire & Audio, c/o The Canadian Press, 36 King St E, Toronto, ON M5C 2L9, Canada *Tel:* 416-507-2126 *Toll Free Tel:* 800-434-7578

(CN only) *Fax:* 416-364-1325 *E-mail:* broadcast@thecanadianpress.com *Web Site:* www. thecanadianpress.com, pg 1183

BroadVision, 460 Seaport Ct, Suite 102, Redwood City, CA 94063 *Tel:* 650-331-1000 *Web Site:* www. broadvision.com, pg 1373

Brodart Books & Library Services, 500 Arch St, Williamsport, PA 17701 *Tel:* 570-326-2461 *Toll Free Tel:* 800-233-8467 *Fax:* 570-651-1639 *Toll Free Fax:* 800-999-6799 *E-mail:* support@brodart.com *Web Site:* www.brodartbooks.com, pg 1311

Brodart Books & Library Services, 500 Arch St, Williamsport, PA 17701 *Tel:* 570-326-2461 *Toll Free Tel:* 800-474-9816 *Fax:* 570-651-1639 *Toll Free Fax:* 800-999-6799 *E-mail:* support@brodart.com *Web Site:* www.brodartbooks.com, pg 1323

Brody Public Relations, 145 Kingwood Stockton Rd, Stockton, NJ 08559-1711 *Tel:* 908-295-0600 *Web Site:* www.brodypr.com, pg 1096

Rosalie Brody, 360 E 72 St, New York, NY 10021 *Tel:* 212-988-8951, pg 1096

B Broughton Co Ltd, 322 Consumers Rd, North York, ON M2J 1P8, Canada *Tel:* 416-690-4777 *Toll Free Tel:* 800-268-4449 *Fax:* 416-690-5357 *E-mail:* sales@bbroughton.com *Web Site:* www.bbroughton.com, pg 1283, 1311

Brown Book Co Ltd, 65 Crockford Blvd, Toronto, ON M1R 3B7, Canada *Tel:* 416-504-9696 *Fax:* 416-504-9393 *E-mail:* bbc@brownbook.ca *Web Site:* www. brownbook.ca, pg 1202

Brown Brothers, 100 Bortree Rd, Sterling, PA 18463 *Tel:* 570-209-6902; 570-689-2700 *Fax:* 570-689-2709 *E-mail:* info@brownbrothersusa.com *Web Site:* www. brownbrothersusa.com, pg 1445

Tom Brownold Photography, 801 W Summit Ave, Flagstaff, AZ 86001 *Tel:* 928-779-1583 *Fax:* 928-779-1583 *E-mail:* tbrownold@tombrownold.com *Web Site:* www.tombrownold.com, pg 1436

Donna Brunet Macro Photography, PO Box 30123, Columbia, MO 65205-3123 *Tel:* 573-999-2178 *Web Site:* www.donnabrunet.com, pg 1436

Brunswick Books, 14 Afton Ave, Toronto, ON M6J 1R7, Canada *Tel:* 416-703-3598 *Fax:* 416-703-6561 *E-mail:* info@brunswickbooks.ca; orders@brunswickbooks.ca *Web Site:* brunswickbooks.ca, pg 1284

Cecile Brunswick, 315 W 39 St, No 1306, New York, NY 10018 *Tel:* 212-222-2088 *E-mail:* cbrunswick@nyc.rr.com *Web Site:* www.cecilebrunswicknyc.com, pg 1425, 1436

J B Bryans Literary, 7 Meetinghouse Ct, Indian Mills, NJ 08088 *Tel:* 609-922-0369 *E-mail:* info@brylit.com *Web Site:* brylit.com, pg 1343

Bulkley Dunton, One Penn Plaza, Suite 2814, 250 W 34 St, New York, NY 10119 *Tel:* 212-863-1800 *Toll Free Tel:* 800-347-9279 *Fax:* 212-863-1872 *Web Site:* www. bulkleydunton.com, pg 1261

Bulletin of the American Schools of Oriental Research (BASOR), Boston University, 656 Beacon St, 5th fl, Boston, MA 02215 *Tel:* 617-353-6570 *Fax:* 617-353-6575 *E-mail:* asor@bu.edu; asorpubs@bu.edu *Web Site:* www.asor.org (print only subns); www.jstor. org (electronic only & print plus electronic subns), pg 1125

Bulletin of the History of Medicine, 2715 N Charles St, Baltimore, MD 21218-4363 *Toll Free Tel:* 800-548-1784 (journal orders) *Fax:* 410-516-6968 *E-mail:* jrnlcirc@press.jhu.edu (journal orders) *Web Site:* www.press.jhu.edu/journals/bulletin_of_the_history_of_medicine/index.html, pg 1125

Bunting Magnetics Co, 500 S Spencer Rd, Newton, KS 67114 *Tel:* 316-284-2020 *Toll Free Tel:* 800-835-2526; 877-576-0156 *Fax:* 316-283-4975 *E-mail:* bmc@buntingmagnetics.com *Web Site:* www. buntingmagnetics.com, pg 1274

The Bureau, 2354 English St, Maplewood, MN 55109 *Tel:* 612-788-1000; 612-432-3516 (sales) *Toll Free Tel:* 800-788-9536 *Fax:* 612-788-7792 *E-mail:* sales@ thebureau.com *Web Site:* www.thebureau.com, pg 1217, 1243

Burlington News Agency Inc, 382 Hercules Dr, Suite 2, Colchester, VT 05446 *Tel:* 802-655-7000 *Fax:* 802-655-7002 *E-mail:* burlnews@aol.com, pg 1311

Burmar Technical Corp, 106 Ransom Ave, Sea Cliff, NY 11579 *Tel:* 516-484-6000 *Fax:* 516-484-6356 *Web Site:* burmar.net, pg 1217, 1374, 1425

BurrellesLuce, 30 B Vreeland Rd, Florham Park, NJ 07932 *Tel:* 973-992-6600 *Toll Free Tel:* 800-631-1160; 800-368-8070 *Fax:* 973-992-7675 *Web Site:* www.burrellesluce.com, pg 1391

Busch LLC, 516 Viking Dr, Virginia Beach, VA 23452 *Tel:* 757-463-7800 *Toll Free Tel:* 800-USA-PUMP (872-7867) *Fax:* 757-463-7407 *E-mail:* info@buschusa.com; marketing@buschusa.com *Web Site:* www.buschvacuum.com/us, pg 1274

Business Wire, 101 California St, 20th fl, San Francisco, CA 94111 *Tel:* 415-986-4422 *Toll Free Tel:* 800-227-0845 *E-mail:* info@businesswire.com *Web Site:* www.businesswire.com, pg 1183

BW&A Books Inc, 112 W McClanahan St, Oxford, NC 27565 *Tel:* 919-956-9111 *Fax:* 919-956-9112 *E-mail:* bwa@bwabooks.com *Web Site:* www.bwabooks.com, pg 1217

By Design Communications, 144 W 27 St, 3rd fl (rear), New York, NY 10001 *Tel:* 212-366-1740, pg 1425

C & C Offset Printing Co USA Inc, 70 W 36 St, Unit 10C, New York, NY 10018 *Tel:* 212-431-4210 *Toll Free Tel:* 866-540-4134 *Web Site:* www.ccoffset.com, pg 1202, 1217, 1243

C J Traders Inc, 555 Second Ave, Suite C700, Collegeville, PA 19426 *Tel:* 484-902-8057 *Fax:* 484-902-8093 *E-mail:* cjtraders714@gmail.com, pg 1311

Leila Cabib, 8601 Buckhannon Dr, Potomac, MD 20854 *Tel:* 301-299-2659 *Fax:* 301-299-0513 *E-mail:* leila@ leilacabib.com *Web Site:* www.leilacabib.com, pg 1425

Cactus Clyde Productions, PO Box 3624, St Francisville, LA 70775-3624 *Tel:* 225-245-5008 *E-mail:* cactusclyd@aol.com *Web Site:* www.cclockwood.com, pg 1436

Calaf Communications, 10 Warwick Ct, Lawrence, MA 01841 *Tel:* 978-314-3125 *Fax:* 978-686-5960 *Web Site:* www.calafcommunications.com, pg 1408

California Offset Printers Inc, 620 W Elk Ave, Glendale, CA 91204 *Tel:* 818-291-1100 *Toll Free Tel:* 800-280-6446 *Fax:* 818-291-1192 *E-mail:* info@copcomms.com *Web Site:* www.copprints.com, pg 1244

Callaloo, 2715 N Charles St, Baltimore, MD 21218-4363 *Toll Free Tel:* 800-548-1784 (journal orders) *Fax:* 410-516-6968 *E-mail:* jrnlcirc@press.jhu.edu (journal orders) *Web Site:* www.press.jhu.edu/journals/callaloo/index.html, pg 1125

Calvary Distribution, 3232 W MacArthur Blvd, Santa Ana, CA 92704 *Tel:* 714-545-6548 *Toll Free Tel:* 800-444-7664 *Fax:* 714-641-8201 *E-mail:* info@calvaryd.org *Web Site:* www.calvaryd.org, pg 1284

Camerique Inc International, 164 Regency Dr, Eagleville, PA 19403 *Tel:* 610-272-4000 *Fax:* 610-539-9558 *E-mail:* info@camerique.com *Web Site:* www.camerique.com, pg 1445

The Campbell-Logan Bindery Inc, 7615 Baker St NE, Fridley, MN 55432 *Tel:* 612-332-1313 *Toll Free Tel:* 800-942-6224 *E-mail:* info@campbell-logan.com *Web Site:* www.campbell-logan.com, pg 1323

Canadian Manda Group, 664 Annette St, Toronto, ON M6S 2C8, Canada *Tel:* 416-516-0911 *Fax:* 416-516-0917 *Toll Free Fax:* 888-563-8327 (CN only) *E-mail:* general@mandagroup.com; info@mandagroup.com *Web Site:* www.mandagroup.com, pg 1284

The Canadian Press Images, 36 King St E, Toronto, ON M5C 2L9, Canada *Tel:* 416-507-2198 (photo archives) *Toll Free Tel:* 866-599-0599 *E-mail:* info@cpimages.com *Web Site:* www.cpimages.com; www.thecanadianpress.com, pg 1445

The Canadian Press/La Presse Canadienne, 36 King St E, Toronto, ON M5C 2L9, Canada *Tel:* 416-364-0321 *Fax:* 416-364-0207 (newsroom) *E-mail:* sales@thecanadianpress.com *Web Site:* www.thecanadianpress.com, pg 1183

Canon Business Process Services, 460 W 34 St, 6th fl, New York, NY 10001 *Tel:* 212-502-2100 *Toll Free Tel:* 800-937-2724; 888-623-2668 (ext 108) *E-mail:* info@cbps.canon.com *Web Site:* cbps.canon.com, pg 1331

Canon USA Inc, One Canon Park, Milville, NY 11747 *Tel:* 516-328-5000; 631-330-5000 *Web Site:* www.usa.canon.com, pg 1374

Canterbury Press, 120 Interstate N Pkwy E, Suite 200, Atlanta, GA 30339 *Tel:* 770-952-8309 *Fax:* 770-952-4623 *E-mail:* sales@canterburypress.net *Web Site:* canterburypress.net, pg 1244

Canvys® Visual Technology Solutions, 40W267 Keslinger Rd, LaFox, IL 60147 *Toll Free Tel:* 888-735-7373 *Fax:* 630-208-2350 *Web Site:* www.canvys.com, pg 1374

Cape Cod Compositors Inc, 811 Washington St, Suite 2, Pembroke, MA 02359-2333 *Tel:* 781-826-2100, pg 1217

Capitol News Service, 530 Bercut Dr, Suite E, Sacramento, CA 95811 *Tel:* 916-445-6336 *E-mail:* sacramentobulletin@gmail.com *Web Site:* www.mnc.net/capitol.htm, pg 1183

Cardinal Publishers Group, 2402 N Shadeland Ave, Suite A, Indianapolis, IN 46219 *Tel:* 317-352-8200 *Toll Free Tel:* 800-296-0481 (cust serv) *Fax:* 317-352-8202 *E-mail:* customerservice@cardinalpub.com *Web Site:* cardinalpub.com, pg 1284

Carolina Biological Supply Co, 2700 York Rd, Burlington, NC 27215-3398 *Tel:* 336-586-4399 (intl sales); 336-538-6211 *Toll Free Tel:* 800-334-5551 *Fax:* 336-584-7686 (intl sales) *Toll Free Fax:* 800-222-7112 *E-mail:* quotations@carolina.com; product@carolina.com *Web Site:* www.carolina.com, pg 1311

Michael Carpenter Photography, 7704 Carrleigh Pkwy, Springfield, VA 22152-1304 *Tel:* 703-644-9666 *Fax:* 703-991-2643 *E-mail:* mike@michaelcarpenterphotography.com *Web Site:* www.michaelcarpenterphotography.com, pg 1436

R E Carsch, MS-Consultant, 1453 Rhode Island St, San Francisco, CA 94107-3248 *Tel:* 415-533-8356 *E-mail:* recarsch@mzinfo.com, pg 1343

Carto-Graphics, 184 Starr Wood, Hudson, WI 54016 *Tel:* 715-386-5989, pg 1425

The Cartoon Bank, A New Yorker Magazine Company, One World Trade Center, 42nd fl, New York, NY 10007 *Tel:* 212-286-2860 *Toll Free Tel:* 800-897-8666 *E-mail:* image_licensing@condenast.com; licensing@cartoonbank.com; licensing@condenast.com *Web Site:* www.cartoonbank.com, pg 1425

Cartoon Images for Licensing, PO Box 410, Chassell, MI 49916 *Tel:* 906-482-6234 *Web Site:* www.danscartoons.com, pg 1425

Casemate | academic, 1950 Lawrence Rd, Havertown, PA 19083 *Tel:* 610-853-9131 *Fax:* 610-853-9146 *E-mail:* info@casemateacademic.com *Web Site:* www.oxbowbooks.com/dbbc, pg 1284

Casemate | IPM, 1950 Lawrence Rd, Havertown, PA 19083 *Tel:* 610-853-9131 *Fax:* 610-853-9146 *E-mail:* casemate@casematepublishers.com *Web Site:* www.casemateipm.com, pg 1096, 1105, 1284, 1343

Wilson Casey, "Trivia" Guinness World Record Holder, 282 Spring Dr, Spartanburg, SC 29302 *Tel:* 864-621-7129 *E-mail:* trivguy@bellsouth.net; wc@triviaguy.com *Web Site:* triviaguy.com, pg 1117

Maxine Cass Photography, PO Box 111, Gold Hill, OR 97525-0111 *Tel:* 541-855-8975; 415-244-1682 (cell) *E-mail:* mcass@pobox.com *Web Site:* www.agpix.com/maxinecass; www.maxinecass.com, pg 1437

Elizabeth Castaldini, 32-18 100 St, Apt 2, East Elmhurst, NY 11369 *Tel:* 646-247-3190 *E-mail:* eranhec@yahoo.com, pg 1408

Catholic Books & Tapes, PO Box 350333, Fort Lauderdale, FL 33335-0333 *Tel:* 954-583-5108 *Fax:* 954-583-5108 *E-mail:* mascmen7@yahoo.com *Web Site:* www.catholicbook.com, pg 1325

Catholic News Service (CNS), 3211 Fourth St NE, Washington, DC 20017-1100 *Tel:* 202-541-3250 *Fax:* 202-541-3117 *E-mail:* cns@catholicnews.com *Web Site:* www.catholicnews.com, pg 1121, 1184

Cat's Eye Consultancy, 4120 Durham Ct, Eagan, MN 55122 *Tel:* 651-270-3190, pg 1343

Wm Caxton Ltd - Bookseller & Publisher, 12037 Hwy 42, Ellison Bay, WI 54210 *Tel:* 920-854-2955, pg 1311

CC1 Inc, 170 West Rd, Suite 7, Portsmouth, NH 03801 *Tel:* 603-319-2000 *Fax:* 603-319-2200 *E-mail:* customerservice@cc1inc.com *Web Site:* www.cc1inc.com, pg 1274

CD ROM Inc, 3131 E Riverside Dr, Fort Myers, FL 33916 *Tel:* 239-332-2800 *Toll Free Tel:* 866-66-CDROM (662-3766) *Fax:* 239-332-2808 *E-mail:* sales@cdrominc.com *Web Site:* www.cdrominc.com, pg 1374

CD Solutions Inc, 100 W Monument St, Pleasant Hill, OH 45359 *Tel:* 937-676-2376 *Toll Free Tel:* 800-860-2376 *Fax:* 937-676-2478 *E-mail:* contact@cds.com *Web Site:* www.cds.com, pg 1374

CD/Works, 30 Doaks Lane, Marblehead, MA 01945 *Tel:* 978-922-4990 *Toll Free Tel:* 800-CDWORKS (239-6757) *Fax:* 978-922-5110 *Web Site:* www.cdworks.com, pg 1374

CDS Global, 1901 Bell Ave, Des Moines, IA 50315-1099 *Tel:* 515-247-7500 *Toll Free Tel:* 866-897-7987 *E-mail:* salesinfo@cds-global.com *Web Site:* www.cds-global.com, pg 1109, 1111

CeciBooks Editorial & Publishing Consultation, 7057 26 Ave NW, Seattle, WA 98117 *E-mail:* ceci@cecibooks.com *Web Site:* www.cecibooks.com, pg 1343

Cedar Fort Inc, 2373 W 700 S, Springville, UT 84663 *Tel:* 801-489-4084 *Toll Free Tel:* 800-SKY-BOOK (759-2665) *Web Site:* cedarfort.com, pg 1325

Celtic Castle Photography, 1319 Hardys Creek Rd, Jonesville, VA 24263 *Tel:* 276-346-3625 *E-mail:* celticcastlephotography@gmail.com *Web Site:* www.celticcastlephotography.com, pg 1437

Dwight Cendrowski Photography LLC, 2870 Easy St, Ann Arbor, MI 48104-6532 *Tel:* 734-330-5230 *Web Site:* www.cendrowski.com, pg 1437

Century Direct LLC, 15 Enter Lane, Islandia, NY 11749 *Tel:* 212-763-0600 *E-mail:* contact@centurydirect.net *Web Site:* www.centurydirect.net, pg 1091, 1105, 1109, 1274

Cenveo Inc, 200 First Stamford Place, 2nd fl, Stamford, CT 06902 *Tel:* 203-595-3000 *Fax:* 203-595-3070 *E-mail:* info@cenveo.com *Web Site:* www.cenveo.com, pg 1203, 1244, 1261

Cenveo Publisher Services, 555 Virginia Dr, Fort Washington, PA 19034 *Tel:* 267-470-1590 *Fax:* 215-591-9093 *E-mail:* info.psg@cenveo.com *Web Site:* www.cenveopublisherservices.com, pg 1203, 1217, 1356, 1374

Cenveo Publisher Services, 5457 Twin Knolls Rd, Suite 200, Columbia, MD 21045 *Tel:* 410-850-0500 *Toll Free Tel:* 800-257-5529 *E-mail:* info.psg@cenveo.com *Web Site:* www.cenveopublisherservices.com, pg 1425

Cenveo Publisher Services, 555 Virginia Dr, Fort Washington, PA 19034 *Tel:* 267-470-1590 *Fax:* 215-591-9093 *E-mail:* info.psg@cenveo.com *Web Site:* www.cenveopublisherservices.com, pg 1426

Cenveo St Louis, 101 Workman Ct, Eureka, MO 63025 *Tel:* 314-966-2000 *Toll Free Tel:* 800-800-8845 *Fax:* 314-966-4725 *Web Site:* www.cenveo.com, pg 1203, 1217, 1244, 1261

CG Book Printers, 1750 Northway Dr, North Mankato, MN 56003 *Tel:* 507-388-3300 *Toll Free Tel:* 800-729-7575 *Fax:* 507-386-6350 *E-mail:* cgbooks@corpgraph. com *Web Site:* www.corpgraph.com, pg 1091, 1105, 1203, 1217, 1244, 1261, 1274, 1356, 1374

Challenge Machinery Co, 6125 Norton Center Dr, Norton Shores, MI 49441 *Tel:* 231-799-8484 *Fax:* 231-798-1275 *E-mail:* info@challengemachinery. com; sales@challengemachinery.com *Web Site:* www. challengemachinery.com, pg 1274

Champion Printing Inc, 3422 Misty Creek Dr, Erlanger, KY 41018 *Tel:* 859-727-5501 *Toll Free Tel:* 800-543-1957 (US) *Fax:* 859-727-5507 *E-mail:* sales@ championprintinginc.com *Web Site:* www. championprintinginc.com, pg 1091, 1105

Charlesworth Author Services (USA) Inc, c/o Suite 510 Constitution Place, 325 Chestnut St, Philadelphia, PA 19106 *E-mail:* usa@cwauthors.com *Web Site:* www. cwauthors.com, pg 1374

Alexandra Chciuk-Celt, 392 Maple St, West Hempstead, NY 11552 *Tel:* 516-485-5531 *E-mail:* languagelady@ juno.com, pg 1408

Cheneliere Education Inc, 5800, rue St Denis, bureau 900, Montreal, QC H2S 3L5, Canada *Tel:* 514-273-1066 *Toll Free Tel:* 800-565-5531 *Fax:* 514-276-0324 *Toll Free Fax:* 800-814-0324 *E-mail:* info@cheneliere. ca *Web Site:* www.cheneliere.ca, pg 1311

Cheng & Tsui Co Inc, 25 West St, 2nd fl, Boston, MA 02111-1213 *Tel:* 617-988-2400 *Toll Free Tel:* 800-554-1963 *Fax:* 617-426-3669 *E-mail:* service@cheng-tsui. com; orders@cheng-tsui.com *Web Site:* www.cheng-tsui.com, pg 1311

Chernow Editorial Services Inc, 16 W 16 St, Suite 2DS, New York, NY 10011 *Tel:* 212-675-0605, pg 1356

Chesapeake & Hudson Inc, 115 W Potomac St, Brunswick, MD 21716 *Tel:* 301-834-7170 *Toll Free Tel:* 800-231-4469 *Toll Free Fax:* 800-307-5163 *E-mail:* office@cheshud.com *Web Site:* www.cheshud. com, pg 1285

Paul Chevannes, 529 Eighth St, Suite 1B, Brooklyn, NY 11215 *Tel:* 718-788-3550, pg 1426

Chicago Distribution Center (CDC), 11030 S Langley Ave, Chicago, IL 60628 *Tel:* 773-702-7010 *Toll Free Fax:* 800-621-8476 *Web Site:* press.uchicago.edu/cdc, pg 1285

The Children's Book Council (CBC), 54 W 39 St, 14th fl, New York, NY 10018 *Tel:* 212-966-1990 *E-mail:* cbc.info@cbcbooks.org *Web Site:* www. cbcbooks.org, pg 1139

The Children's Book Store Distribution (CBSD), 23 Griffin St, Waterdown, ON L0R 2H0, Canada *Tel:* 905-690-9397 (ext 237) *Toll Free Tel:* 800-757-8372 (cust serv, CN & US) *Fax:* 905-690-3419 *E-mail:* info@childrensgroup.com; sales@idla.ca *Web Site:* www.childrensgroup.com, pg 1311

The Bulletin of the Center for Children's Books, 2715 N Charles St, Baltimore, MD 21218 (USA) *Tel:* 410-516-6900; 410-516-6987 (journal orders outside US & CN); 217-244-0324 (bulletin info) *Toll Free Tel:* 800-548-1784 (journal orders) *Fax:* 410-516-6968; 410-516-3866 (journal orders) *E-mail:* bccb@illinois.edu; jlorder@jhupress.jhu.edu *Web Site:* www.press.jhu. edu/journals/bulletin-center-childrens-books, pg 1125

Children's Books USA Inc, 425 Boardman Ave, Traverse City, MI 49684 *Tel:* 231-933-3699 *E-mail:* info@childrensbooksusa.com *Web Site:* childrensbooksusa.com, pg 1133

Children's Bookwatch, 278 Orchard Dr, Oregon, WI 53575-1129 *Tel:* 608-835-7937 *E-mail:* mbr@execpc. com *Web Site:* www.midwestbookreview.com, pg 1125

Children's Braille Book Club, 88 Saint Stephen St, Boston, MA 02115-4312 *Tel:* 617-266-6160 *Toll Free Tel:* 800-548-7323 (cust serv) *Fax:* 617-437-0456 *E-mail:* contact@nbp.org *Web Site:* www.nbp.org, pg 1135

China Books, 360 Swift Ave, Suite 48, South San Francisco, CA 94080 *Fax:* 650-872-7808 *E-mail:* editor.sinomedia@gmail.com, pg 1311, 1325

China Institute in America, 100 Washington St, New York, NY 10006 *Tel:* 212-744-8181 *Fax:* 212-628-4159 *E-mail:* gallery@chinainstitute.org *Web Site:* www.chinainstitute.org, pg 1311

ChinaStock/WorldViews, 2506 Country Village, Ann Arbor, MI 48103-6500 *Tel:* 734-680-4660 *E-mail:* decoxphoto@gmail.com *Web Site:* www. denniscox.com, pg 1445

Chinese Christian Mission Bookroom, 1269 N McDowell Blvd, Petaluma, CA 94954-1133 *Tel:* 707-762-2688; 707-762-1314 *Fax:* 707-762-1713 *E-mail:* bookroom@ ccmusa.org; ccm@ccmusa.org *Web Site:* www.ccmusa. org; www.ccmbookroom.org, pg 1311

CHOICE, 575 Main St, Suite 300, Middletown, CT 06457 *Tel:* 860-347-6933; 860-347-1387 (ad); 240-646-7027 (subn); 818-487-4555 *E-mail:* acrlsubscriptions@pubservice.com; support@ acrlchoice.freshdesk.com *Web Site:* www.ala.org/acrl/ choice; www.choice360.org, pg 1125

Choice Associates, 501 Fifth Ave, Suite 1601, New York, NY 10017 *Tel:* 212-679-2434 *Fax:* 212-213-0984 *E-mail:* info@choicepersonnelinc.com *Web Site:* www.choicepersonnelinc.com, pg 1389

Choice Books, 2387 Grace Chapel Rd, Harrisonburg, VA 22801 *Tel:* 540-434-1827 *Fax:* 540-434-9894 *E-mail:* info@choicebooks.org *Web Site:* www. choicebooks.org, pg 1312

Christianbook Inc, 140 Summit St, Peabody, MA 01960-5156 *Tel:* 978-977-5060; 978-977-5000 (intl calls) *Toll Free Tel:* 800-CHRISTIAN (247-4784) *Fax:* 978-977-5010 *E-mail:* customer.service@christianbook.com *Web Site:* www.christianbook.com, pg 1312

Chronicles: A Magazine of American Culture, 8011 34 Ave S, Suite C11, Bloomington, MN 55425 *Web Site:* www.chroniclesmagazine.org, pg 1125

Cimarron Design, 8285 Kincross Dr, Boulder, CO 80301-4228 *Tel:* 303-530-1785 *Web Site:* www. cimarrondesign.com, pg 1217

Circle Graphics Inc, 316 Main St, Suite 1C, Reisters Town, MD 21136 *Tel:* 410-833-2200 *E-mail:* production@circleusa.com *Web Site:* www. circleusa.com, pg 1218

Citation Box & Paper Co, 4700 W Augusta Blvd, Chicago, IL 60651-3397 *Tel:* 773-378-1400 *E-mail:* info@citationbox.com *Web Site:* www. citationbox.com, pg 1335

Citizen Systems America Corp, 363 Van Ness Way, Suite 404, Torrance, CA 90501 *Tel:* 310-781-1460 *Toll Free Tel:* 800-421-6516 *Web Site:* www.citizen-systems.com, pg 1374

City Diecutting, One Cory Rd, Morristown, NJ 07960 *Tel:* 973-270-0370 *Fax:* 973-270-0369 *E-mail:* sales@ bookdisplays.com *Web Site:* www.bookdisplays.com, pg 1091, 1343

CJK, 3962 Virginia Ave, Cincinnati, OH 45227 *Tel:* 513-271-6035 *Toll Free Tel:* 800-598-7808 *Fax:* 513-271-6082 *E-mail:* info@cjkusa.com *Web Site:* www.cjkusa. com, pg 1244

Clamco Corp, 775 Berea Industrial Pkwy, Berea, OH 44017 *Tel:* 216-267-1911 *Toll Free Tel:* 800-985-9570 (headquarters) *Fax:* 216-267-8713 *E-mail:* info@ clamcopackaging.com *Web Site:* www.pacmachinery. com/clamcopackaging, pg 1274

Clare Printing, 206 S Keystone Ave, Sayre, PA 18840 *Tel:* 570-888-2244 *E-mail:* hr@clareprint.com *Web Site:* www.clareprint.com, pg 1218, 1244, 1274

Claris International Inc, 5201 Patrick Henry Dr, Santa Clara, CA 95054 *Tel:* 408-727-8227 (sales & cust support) *Toll Free Tel:* 800-725-2747 (sales); 800-325-2747 (cust support) *Fax:* 408-987-7447 *E-mail:* claris_sales@claris.com *Web Site:* www.claris. com, pg 1374

Claritas LLC, 8044 Montgomery Rd, Suite 455, Cincinnati, OH 45236 *Toll Free Tel:* 888-981-0040 *E-mail:* findcustomers@claritas.com; marketing@ claritas.com *Web Site:* www.claritas.com, pg 1374

Clark Distribution Systems (CDS), 3705 Quakerbridge Rd, Suite 116, Hamilton, NJ 08169 *Tel:* 609-528-7660 *Fax:* 609-528-4526 *Web Site:* www.clarkdistribution. net, pg 1331

The Clark Group Inc, 3705 Quakerbridge Rd, Suite 116, Hamilton, NJ 08619 *Tel:* 609-528-7660 *Fax:* 609-528-7710 *E-mail:* service@clarkworldwide.com *Web Site:* www.clarkgroupinc.com, pg 1331

Classics of Golf, 120 Research Dr, Stratford, CT 06615 *Tel:* 845-765-6050 *Toll Free Tel:* 800-483-6449 *E-mail:* info@classicsofgolf.com; customerservice@ classicsofgolf.com *Web Site:* www.classicsofgolf.com, pg 1135

ClassicStock.com/Robertstock.com, 4203 Locust St, Philadelphia, PA 19104 *Tel:* 215-386-6300 *Toll Free Tel:* 800-786-6300 *Toll Free Fax:* 800-786-1920 *E-mail:* sales@classicstock.com; info@classicstock. com; info@robertstock.com *Web Site:* www. classicstock.com; www.robertstock.com, pg 1445

CLC Ministries, 701 Pennsylvania Ave, Fort Washington, PA 19034 *Tel:* 215-542-1240 *Toll Free Tel:* 800-659-1240 *Fax:* 215-542-7580 *E-mail:* orders@ clcpublications.com *Web Site:* www.clcpublications. com, pg 1312

Clear Concepts, 1329 Federal Ave, Suite 6, Los Angeles, CA 90025 *Tel:* 323-285-0325, pg 1096, 1312, 1343

Clear Print, 9025 Fullbright Ave, Chatsworth, CA 91311 *Tel:* 818-709-1220 *Fax:* 818-709-1320 *E-mail:* info@ clearprint.com; sales@clearprint.com *Web Site:* www. clearprint.com, pg 1244

Clerical Plus, 97 Blueberry Lane, Shelton, CT 06484 *Tel:* 203-225-0879 *Fax:* 203-225-0879 *E-mail:* clericalplus@aol.com *Web Site:* www. clericalplus.net, pg 1374

The Cleveland Vibrator Co, 2828 Clinton Ave, Cleveland, OH 44113 *Tel:* 216-241-7157 *Toll Free Tel:* 800-221-3298 *Fax:* 216-241-3480 *E-mail:* sales@clevelandvibrator.com *Web Site:* www. clevelandvibrator.com, pg 1274

Cliff Digital, 14700 S Main St, Gardena, CA 90248 *Tel:* 310-323-5600 *Toll Free Tel:* 866-429-2242 *Fax:* 310-400-3090 *E-mail:* cliff@cliffdigital.com *Web Site:* www.cliffdigital.com, pg 1091

Clotilde's Secretarial & Management Services, PO Box 871926, New Orleans, LA 70187 *Tel:* 504-242-2912; 504-266-9239 (cell) *Fax:* 504-242-2912, pg 1393

Dwight Clough, W7502 County Rd "G", Pardeeville, WI 53954 *Tel:* 608-429-1440 *E-mail:* lmp@dwightclough. com *Web Site:* dwightclough.com, pg 1343, 1374

Club Leo (Spanish & bilingual books for all grades), 557 Broadway, New York, NY 10012 *Tel:* 212-343-6100 *Toll Free Tel:* 800-724-6527 (press 1) *Toll Free Fax:* 800-223-4011 *E-mail:* bookclubs@scholastic.com *Web Site:* scholastic.com/bookclubs, pg 1135

Coach House Printing, 80 bpNichol Lane, Toronto, ON M5S 3J4, Canada *Tel:* 416-979-2217 *Toll Free Tel:* 800-367-6360 (outside Toronto) *Fax:* 416-977-1158 *E-mail:* mail@chbooks.com *Web Site:* www. chbooks.com, pg 1218, 1244

Codra Enterprises Inc, 17692 Cowan, Suite 200, Irvine, CA 92614 *Tel:* 949-756-8400 *Toll Free Tel:* 888-992-6372 *Fax:* 949-756-8484 *E-mail:* codra@codra.com; sales@codra.com *Web Site:* www.codra.com, pg 1203, 1244

Herbert J Cohen, 281 Hicks St, Brooklyn Heights, NY 11201 *Tel:* 718-875-4092 *Fax:* 718-875-5065 *E-mail:* herbertjcohen@aol.com, pg 1343

Cohesion®, 511 W Bay St, Suite 480, Tampa, FL 33606 *Tel:* 813-999-3111 *Toll Free Tel:* 866-727-6800 *Web Site:* www.cohesion.com, pg 1343, 1374, 1389

The Colad Group LLC, 693 Seneca St, 5th fl, Buffalo, NY 14210 *Tel:* 716-961-1776 *Toll Free Tel:* 800-950-1755 *Fax:* 716-961-1753 *E-mail:* info@colad.com *Web Site:* www.colad.com, pg 1091

Brandon Cole Marine Photography, 4917 N Boeing Rd, Spokane Valley, WA 99206 *Tel:* 509-535-3489 *E-mail:* brandoncole@msn.com *Web Site:* www.brandoncole.com, pg 1437

Leon Collins, 71 Faunce Dr, Providence, RI 02906 *Tel:* 401-274-2149 *Web Site:* www.whitegatefeatures.com, pg 1117

Color Graphic Press Inc, 42 Main St, Nyack, NY 10960 *Tel:* 845-535-3444 *Fax:* 845-535-3446 *E-mail:* info@cgpny.com *Web Site:* www.cgpny.com, pg 1244

Color House Graphics Inc, 3505 Eastern Ave SE, Grand Rapids, MI 49508 *Toll Free Tel:* 800-454-1916 *Fax:* 616-245-5494 *Web Site:* www.colorhousegraphics.com, pg 1203, 1244, 1343

ColorPage, 81 Ten Broeck Ave, Kingston, NY 12401 *Tel:* 845-331-7581 *Toll Free Tel:* 800-836-7581 *Fax:* 845-331-1571 *E-mail:* sales@colorpageonline.com *Web Site:* www.colorpageonline.com, pg 1203, 1218, 1244, 1261

Colour Technologies, 134 Park Lawn Rd, Toronto, ON M8Y 3H9, Canada *Tel:* 416-588-0808 *Fax:* 416-588-5015 *E-mail:* info@colourtec.com *Web Site:* www.colourtec.com, pg 1426

Columbia Finishing Mills Inc, 135 Boundary Rd, Cornwall, ON K6H 5T3, Canada *Tel:* 613-933-1462 *Toll Free Tel:* 800-267-9174 *Fax:* 613-933-7717 *Toll Free Fax:* 800-242-9174 *E-mail:* info@columbiafinishingmills.com *Web Site:* www.columbiafinishingmills.com, pg 1262

Comag Marketing Group LLC (CMG), 155 Village Blvd, Suite 300, Princeton, NJ 08540 *Tel:* 609-524-1800 *Fax:* 609-524-1629 *Web Site:* www.i-cmg.com, pg 1312

The Combined Book Exhibit®, 277 White St, Buchanan, NY 10511 *Tel:* 914-739-7500 *Toll Free Tel:* 800-462-7687 *Fax:* 914-739-7575 *E-mail:* info@combinedbook.com *Web Site:* www.combinedbook.com; www.cbedatabase.com, pg 1133

Communication Abstracts, 10 Estes St, Ipswich, MA 01938 *Tel:* 978-356-6500 *Toll Free Tel:* 800-653-2726 *Fax:* 978-356-6565 *E-mail:* information@ebscohost.com *Web Site:* www.ebscohost.com, pg 1125

Communication Matters, 48 Aylmer Ave, Ottawa, ON K1S 2X1, Canada *Tel:* 613-233-5423 *Web Site:* www.communicationmatters.ca, pg 1096

Communicorp Inc, 1001 Lockwood Ave, Columbus, GA 31999 *Tel:* 706-324-1182 *E-mail:* mktech@communicorp.com *Web Site:* www.communicorp.com, pg 1218, 1244

Compassion Books, 7036 Hwy 80 S, Burnsville, NC 28714 *Tel:* 828-675-5909 *Toll Free Tel:* 800-970-4220 *Fax:* 828-675-9687 *E-mail:* orders@compassionbooks.com *Web Site:* www.compassionbooks.com, pg 1135

Computer Analytics Corp, 999 E Touhy Ave, Suite 130, Des Plaines, IL 60018-2736 *Tel:* 847-297-5290 *Fax:* 847-297-8680 *Web Site:* www.cacorp.com, pg 1374

Concierge Marketing Inc, 4822 S 133 St, Omaha, NE 68137 *Tel:* 402-884-5995 *Fax:* 413-669-8870 *Web Site:* www.conciergemarketing.com, pg 1343

Concord Editorial & Design LLC, 9450 SW Gemini Dr, Suite 68669, Beaverton, OR 97008 *Tel:* 616-827-7537 *Fax:* 616-825-6048 *E-mail:* info@concordeditorial.com *Web Site:* www.concordeditorial.com, pg 1218, 1356

Conrad Direct Inc, 300 Knickerbocker Rd, Cresskill, NJ 07626 *Tel:* 201-567-3200 *Fax:* 201-567-1530 *E-mail:* listinfo@conraddirect.com *Web Site:* www.conraddirect.com, pg 1105

C Harrison Conroy Co Inc, 501 Penman St, Charlotte, NC 28203 *Tel:* 704-358-0459 *Toll Free Tel:* 800-242-2789 *Fax:* 704-358-0459 *E-mail:* chcphoto@charrisonconroy.com *Web Site:* www.charrisonconroy.com, pg 1203, 1245

Conservation Resources International LLC, 7350 Lockport Place, Suite A, Lorton, VA 22079 *Tel:* 703-321-7730 *Toll Free Tel:* 800-634-6932 *Fax:* 703-321-0629 *E-mail:* sales@conservationresources.com *Web Site:* www.conservationresources.com, pg 1262

Conservative Book Club, 300 New Jersey Ave NW, Suite 500, Washington, DC 20001 *Tel:* 202-216-0601 *Fax:* 202-216-0614 *Web Site:* www.conservativebookclub.com, pg 1135

Consolidated Printers Inc, 2630 Eighth St, Berkeley, CA 94710 *Tel:* 510-495-3113 (sales); 510-843-8565 (admin) *Web Site:* www.consoprinters.com, pg 1203, 1245

Consortium Book Sales & Distribution, an Ingram brand, The Keg House, Suite 101, 34 13 Ave NE, Minneapolis, MN 55413-1007 *Tel:* 612-746-2600 *Toll Free Tel:* 800-283-3572 (cust serv, Jackson, TN) *Fax:* 612-746-2606 *E-mail:* info@cbsd.com *Web Site:* www.cbsd.com, pg 1285

Conspire Creative, PO Box 1524, Milwaukee, WI 53201 *Tel:* 312-226-8400 *Fax:* 312-226-8420 *Web Site:* www.conspirecreative.com, pg 1344

CONTECH (Converting Technologies), 1756 S 151 St W, Goddard, KS 67052 *Tel:* 316-722-6907 *Fax:* 316-722-2976 *E-mail:* info@contechusa.com *Web Site:* www.contechusa.com, pg 1274

Content Critical Solutions, 121 Moonachi Ave, Moonachi, NJ 07074 *Tel:* 201-528-2777 *E-mail:* sales_info@contentcritical.com *Web Site:* www.contentcritical.com, pg 1105

Continental Book Co Inc, 7000 Broadway, Suite 102, Denver, CO 80221-2913 *Tel:* 303-289-1761 *Toll Free Fax:* 800-279-1764 *E-mail:* cbc@continentalbook.com *Web Site:* www.continentalbook.com, pg 1285, 1312, 1325

Continental Features/Continental News Service, 501 W Broadway, Plaza A, PMB 265, San Diego, CA 92101 *Tel:* 858-492-8696 *E-mail:* info@continentalnewsservice.com; continentalnewstime@gmail.com *Web Site:* www.continentalnewsservice.com, pg 1184

Continental Sales Inc, 213 W Main St, Barrington, IL 60010 *Tel:* 847-381-6530 *Fax:* 847-382-0385; 847-382-0419 *Web Site:* www.continentalsalesinc.com, pg 1285

Continental Web Press Inc, 1430 Industrial Dr, Itasca, IL 60143-1858 *Tel:* 630-773-1903 *E-mail:* inquiries@continentalweb.com *Web Site:* www.continentalweb.com, pg 1245

Conway Greene Co, 1400 E 30 St, Suite 402, Cleveland, OH 44114 *Tel:* 216-965-3195 *Web Site:* www.conwaygreene.com, pg 1374

Cook Public Relations, 3251 Spear Ave, Arcata, CA 95521 *Tel:* 707-630-3597; 415-302-1752 (cell) *Web Site:* www.cookpr.com, pg 1096

Cookbook Publishers Inc, 11633 W 83 Terr, Lenexa, KS 66285 *Tel:* 913-492-5900 *Toll Free Tel:* 800-227-7282 *Fax:* 913-492-5947 *E-mail:* info@cookbookpublishers.com *Web Site:* www.cookbookpublishers.com, pg 1218, 1245

Robert Cooney Graphic Design, 2813 Naples Ave, Half Moon Bay, CA 94019 *Tel:* 650-712-4400, pg 1426

Cooperative Etudiante de Polytechnique, Pavillon Principal Local C-220, 2900 Edouard Mont Petit, Montreal, QC H3T 1J4, Canada *Tel:* 514-340-4851 *Fax:* 514-340-4543 *E-mail:* andre.daneau@polymtl.ca *Web Site:* www.coopoly.ca, pg 1312

Copycats, 216 E 45 St, 10th fl, New York, NY 10017 *Tel:* 212-557-2111 *Toll Free Tel:* 800-404-2679 *Fax:* 212-557-2039 *E-mail:* client@copycats.com *Web Site:* www.copycats.com, pg 1245

Copyright Clearance Center Inc (CCC), 222 Rosewood Dr, Danvers, MA 01923 *Tel:* 978-750-8400 (sales); 978-646-2600 (cust serv) *E-mail:* info@copyright.com *Web Site:* www.copyright.com, pg 1344

Copywriters' Council of America™ (CCA), CCA Bldg, 7 Putter Lane, Middle Island, NY 11953-1920 *Tel:* 631-924-3888; 631-924-8555; 631-604-8599, pg 1086

Copywriters' Council of America™ (CCA), CCA Bldg, 7 Putter Lane, Middle Island, NY 11953-1920 *Tel:* 631-924-3888; 631-604-8599; 631-924-8555, pg 1096

Copywriters' Council of America™ (CCA), CCA Bldg, 7 Putter Lane, Middle Island, NY 11953-1920 *Tel:* 631-924-3888; 631-924-8555; 631-604-8599, pg 1105, 1344, 1356, 1375, 1426

Coral Graphic Services Inc, 840 S Broadway, Hicksville, NY 11801 *Tel:* 516-576-2100 *Fax:* 516-576-2168 *E-mail:* info@coralgraphics.com *Web Site:* www.bpg-usa.com, pg 1218, 1245, 1262

Corder Associates Inc, 2602 W Baseline Rd, Suite 22, Mesa, AZ 85202 *Tel:* 480-752-8533 *Toll Free Tel:* 877-303-7575 *Fax:* 480-752-8534 *E-mail:* info@cordernet.com *Web Site:* cordernet.com, pg 1375

Corel Corp, 1600 Carling Ave, Ottawa, ON K1Z 8R7, Canada *Tel:* 613-728-8200 (PR) *Toll Free Tel:* 877-582-6735 *Web Site:* www.corel.com, pg 1375

Steve Corey, 71 Faunce Dr, Providence, RI 02906 *Tel:* 401-274-2149 *Web Site:* www.whitegatefeatures.com, pg 1117

Cornell & Co LLC, 44 Jog Hill Rd, Trumbull, CT 06611 *Tel:* 203-454-4210 *Web Site:* www.cornellandco.com, pg 1426

Coronet Books Inc, 33 Ashley Dr, Schwenksville, PA 19473 *Tel:* 215-925-2762 *Fax:* 215-925-1912 *Web Site:* www.coronetbooks.com, pg 1312

The Corporate Communications Group (CCG), 14 Henderson Dr, West Caldwell, NJ 07006 *Tel:* 973-808-0009 *Fax:* 973-808-9740 *E-mail:* info@corpcomm.com *Web Site:* home.corpcomm.com, pg 1106

Corporate Disk Co, 4610 Prime Pkwy, McHenry, IL 60050-7005 *Tel:* 815-331-6000 *Toll Free Tel:* 800-634-3475 *Fax:* 815-331-6030 *E-mail:* info@disk.com *Web Site:* www.disk.com, pg 1218, 1245, 1375

Cosmos Communications Inc, 11-05 44 Dr, Long Island City, NY 11101 *Tel:* 718-482-1800 *Toll Free Tel:* 800-223-5751 *Fax:* 718-482-1968 *Web Site:* www.cosmoscommunications.com, pg 1375

The Country Press Inc, One Commercial Dr, Lakeville, MA 02347 *Tel:* 508-947-4485 *Toll Free Tel:* 888-343-2227 *Fax:* 508-947-8989 *E-mail:* info@countrypressinc.com *Web Site:* www.countrypressprinting.com, pg 1203, 1245

Courier Printing, One Courier Place, Smyrna, TN 37167 *Tel:* 615-355-4000 *Toll Free Tel:* 800-467-0444 *Fax:* 615-355-4088 *Web Site:* www.courierprinting.com, pg 1218, 1245

Courier Systems Inc, 180 Pulaski St, Bayonne, NJ 07002 *Tel:* 201-432-0550 *Toll Free Tel:* 800-252-0353 *Fax:* 201-432-9686 *E-mail:* sales@csweb.biz *Web Site:* www.csweb.biz, pg 1331

Course Crafters Inc, 243 Greenleaf Rd, Anson, ME 04911 *Tel:* 207-696-4050 *E-mail:* info@coursecrafters.com *Web Site:* www.coursecrafters.com, pg 1357

Courter Films LLC, 1145 N Stoney Point, Crystal River, FL 34429 *Tel:* 352-563-7888 (cell) *Fax:* 352-795-3889 *E-mail:* info@courterfilms.com *Web Site:* www.courterfilms.com, pg 1375

Coverline Inc, 13 Spruce Pond Rd, Franklin, MA 02038 *Tel:* 508-528-8511 *Fax:* 508-528-6838, pg 1262

Cox-King Multimedia, PO Box 909, Geneva, NY 14456 *Tel:* 315-719-0141 *E-mail:* info@ckmm.com *Web Site:* www.ckmm.com, pg 1426

CQ Roll Call, 1201 Pennsylvania Ave NW, Suite 600, Washington, DC 20004 *Tel:* 202-650-6500; 202-650-6511 (subns); 202-650-6621 (cust serv) *Toll Free Tel:* 800-432-2250; 800-678-8511 (subns) *E-mail:* customerservice@cqrollcall.com *Web Site:* cqrollcall.com; www.rollcall.com, pg 1184

Crafter's Choice®, 34 W 27 St, 10th fl, New York, NY 10001 *Tel:* 716-250-5700 (cust serv) *E-mail:* customer.service@crafterschoice.com *Web Site:* www.crafterschoice.com, pg 1135

Craftsmen Machinery Co Inc, 1257 Worcester Rd, Unit 167, Framingham, MA 01701 *Tel:* 508-376-2001 *Fax:* 508-376-2003 *E-mail:* sales@craftsmenmachinery.com *Web Site:* www.craftsmenmachinery.com, pg 1275

Crain Communications Inc, 1155 Gratiot Ave, Detroit, MI 48207-2732 *Tel:* 313-446-6000 *Fax:* 313-446-0383 *E-mail:* info@crain.com *Web Site:* crain.com, pg 1184

Cranbury International LLC, 7 Clarendon Ave, Suite 2, Montpelier, VT 05602 *Tel:* 802-223-6565 *Fax:* 802-223-6824 *E-mail:* inquiries@cranburyinternational.com *Web Site:* www.cranburyinternational.com, pg 1325

Crane Duplicating Service Inc, 4915 Rattlesnake Hammock Rd, Suite 207, Naples, FL 34113 *Tel:* 305-280-6742 (help desk) *Tel:* 239-732-8415 *E-mail:* info@craneduplicating.com *Web Site:* www.craneduplicating.com, pg 1203, 1245

Crawshaw Design, 120 Bayview Dr, San Rafael, CA 94901 *Tel:* 415-456-5544 *Fax:* 415-456-4319 *Web Site:* www.crawshawdesign.com, pg 1426

Creative Direct Marketing Group Inc (CDMG), 21171 S Western, Suite 260, Torrance, CA 90501 *Tel:* 310-212-5727 *Fax:* 310-212-5773 *Web Site:* www.cdminc.com, pg 1344

Creative Freelancers Inc, PO Box 366, Tallevast, FL 34270 *Toll Free Tel:* 800-398-9544 *Web Site:* www.illustratorsonline.com, pg 1426

The Creative Group (TCG), 125 High St, 17th fl, Boston, MA 02110 *Tel:* 617-690-7386; 617-526-8899 *Toll Free Tel:* 888-651-8589 *E-mail:* boston@creativegroup.com *Web Site:* www.roberthalf.com/work-with-us/our-services/creativegroup, pg 1389, 1426

The Creative Spark, 7010 85 Street Ct E, Bradenton, FL 34202 *Tel:* 941-356-2514 *E-mail:* info@creativespark.com *Web Site:* www.creativespark.com, pg 1357

Creative Trust Inc, 210 Jamestown Park Dr, Suite 200, Brentwood, TN 37027 *Tel:* 615-297-5010 *Fax:* 615-297-5020 *E-mail:* info@creativetrust.com *Web Site:* creativetrust.com, pg 1344

Creators Syndicate, 737 Third St, Hermosa Beach, CA 90254 *Tel:* 310-337-7003 *E-mail:* info@creators.com *Web Site:* www.creators.com, pg 1184

Crescent Imports, PO Box 721, Union City, CA 94587 *Tel:* 734-665-3492 *Toll Free Tel:* 800-521-9744 *Fax:* 734-677-1717 *E-mail:* message@crescentimports.com *Web Site:* www.crescentimports.com; www.crescentcatalog.com, pg 1312, 1326

The Cricket Letter Inc, PO Box 527, Ardmore, PA 19003-0527 *Tel:* 610-924-9158 *Fax:* 610-924-9159 *E-mail:* crcktinc@aol.com, pg 1184

The Criterion Collection, 215 Park Ave S, 5th fl, New York, NY 10003 *Tel:* 212-756-8822 *E-mail:* suggestions@criterion.com *Web Site:* www.criterion.com, pg 1375

Cromwell Leather, 147 Palmer Ave, Mamaroneck, NY 10543 *Tel:* 914-381-0100 *Fax:* 914-381-0046 *E-mail:* sales@cromwellgroup.com *Web Site:* www.cromwellgroup.com, pg 1262

Cross Country Computer Corp, 250 Carleton Ave, East Islip, NY 11730-1240 *Tel:* 631-334-1810 *E-mail:* inquiry@crosscountrycomputer.com *Web Site:* www.crosscountrycomputer.com, pg 1111

Cross Cultural Communication Systems Inc, 227 Garfield Ave, Suite B, Woburn, MA 01801 *Tel:* 781-729-3736 *Toll Free Tel:* 888-678-CCCS (678-2227 out of state only) *Fax:* 781-729-1217 *Web Site:* www.cccsorg.com; www.embracingculture.com, pg 1408

Cross-Cultural Communications, 239 Wynsum Ave, Merrick, NY 11566-4725 *Tel:* 516-868-5635 *Fax:* 516-379-1901 *E-mail:* cccpoetry@aol.com; cccbarkan@optonline.net *Web Site:* www.facebook.com/CrossCulturalCommunications.NY/, pg 1375

Cross Culture Communications, PO Box 141263, Dallas, TX 75214 *Tel:* 214-394-3000 *E-mail:* info@crossculturecommunications.com *Web Site:* crossculturecommunications.com, pg 1408

The Crowley Co, 5111 Pegasus Ct, Suite M, Frederick, MD 21704 *Tel:* 240-215-0224 *Fax:* 240-215-0234 *E-mail:* webrequest@thecrowleycompany.com *Web Site:* www.thecrowleycompany.com, pg 1375

Crown Connect, 250 W Rialto Ave, San Bernadino, CA 92408 *Tel:* 909-888-7531 *Fax:* 909-889-1639 *E-mail:* sales@crownconnect.com *Web Site:* www.crownconnect.com, pg 1203, 1218, 1275

Crown Roll Leaf Inc, 91 Illinois Ave, Paterson, NJ 07503 *Tel:* 973-742-4000 *Toll Free Tel:* 800-631-3831 *Fax:* 973-742-0219 *Web Site:* www.crownrollleaf.com, pg 1245

CRW Graphics Communications, 9100 Pennsauken Hwy, Pennsauken, NJ 08110 *Tel:* 856-662-9111 *Toll Free Tel:* 800-820-3000 *Fax:* 856-665-1789 *E-mail:* info@crwgraphics.com *Web Site:* www.crwgraphics.com, pg 1092, 1375, 1426

CS International Literary Agency, 43 W 39 St, New York, NY 10018 *Tel:* 212-921-1610; 212-391-9208 *E-mail:* query@csliterary.com; csliterary08@gmail.com *Web Site:* www.csliterary.com, pg 1344

Dr Mildred L Culp, 24541 S Wildwood Trail, Crete, IL 60417-3735 *E-mail:* workwise@comcast.net *Web Site:* knoxne.ws/mildred-culp, pg 1117

Current Biography, 4919 Rte 22, Amenia, NY 12501 *Tel:* 518-789-8700 *Toll Free Tel:* 800-562-2139 *Fax:* 518-789-0556 *E-mail:* books@greyhouse.com *Web Site:* greyhouse.com, pg 1125

Ralph Curtis Books, 16956 McGregor Blvd, Suite 9, Fort Myers, FL 33908 *Tel:* 239-454-0010 *Fax:* 239-395-2727 *E-mail:* rcurtisbks@yahoo.com *Web Site:* www.ralphcurtisbooks.com, pg 1312, 1326

Cushing-Malloy Inc, 1350 N Main St, Ann Arbor, MI 48104-1045 *Tel:* 734-663-8554 *Fax:* 734-663-5731 *Web Site:* www.cushing-malloy.com; www.c-mbooks.com, pg 1203, 1245

Custom Studios, 77 Main St, Tappan, NY 10983 *Tel:* 845-365-0414 *Toll Free Tel:* 800-631-1362 *Fax:* 845-365-0864 *E-mail:* customusa@aol.com *Web Site:* customstudios.com, pg 1218

CVI Capital, 165 Annursnac Hill Rd, Concord, MA 01742 *Tel:* 978-371-0995 *Fax:* 978-287-5869 *E-mail:* admin@cvicapital.com *Web Site:* www.cvicapital.com, pg 1344

CyberWolf® Inc, 1596 Pacheco, Suite 203, Santa Fe, NM 87505 *Tel:* 505-983-6463 *E-mail:* sales@cyberwolf.com *Web Site:* www.cyberwolf.com; www.accumenbook.com; www.ebookdownloadservice.com, pg 1375

Cypress House, 155 Cypress St, Fort Bragg, CA 95437 *Tel:* 707-964-9520 *Toll Free Tel:* 800-773-7782 *Fax:* 707-964-7531 *Web Site:* www.cypresshouse.com, pg 1092, 1218, 1275, 1344, 1426

D C Graphics Inc, 59 Central Ave, Suite 15, Farmingdale, NY 11735 *Tel:* 631-777-3100 *Fax:* 631-777-7899 *E-mail:* prepress@dcgraphicsinc.com *Web Site:* www.dcgraphicsinc.com, pg 1245

Bob Daemmrich Photography Inc, 914 Congress Ave, 2nd fl, Austin, TX 78701 *Tel:* 512-469-9700 *Fax:* 512-469-9713 *Web Site:* www.bobphoto.com, pg 1437

Dan Daly, 23 Limerock St, Camden, ME 04843-2116 *Tel:* 207-236-8834 *E-mail:* dan@dalyart.com *Web Site:* www.dalyart.com, pg 1426

D&D Sales & Printing, 840 12 St NW, Mason City, IA 50401 *Tel:* 641-423-9487 *Toll Free Tel:* 800-325-5308 *Fax:* 641-423-3068 *E-mail:* ddsales.service@gmail.com *Web Site:* www.ddsalesonline.com, pg 1426

D&K Group Inc, 1795 Commerce Dr, Elk Grove Village, IL 60007 *Tel:* 847-956-0160; 847-956-4757 (tech support) *Toll Free Tel:* 800-632-2314 *Fax:* 847-956-8214 *E-mail:* info@dkgroup.net *Web Site:* www.dkgroup.com, pg 1245, 1262, 1275

Kent Dannen, 1997 Big Owl Rd, Allenspark, CO 80510 *Tel:* 303-747-2047 *Fax:* 303-747-2016 *E-mail:* kent.dannen@yahoo.com, pg 1437

DANPHOTO, LLC, 408 E Rte 66, Flagstaff, AZ 86001 *Tel:* 928-779-4556 *E-mail:* danman@danphoto.com *Web Site:* www.danphoto.com, pg 1437

Darwill, 11900 W Roosevelt Rd, Hillside, IL 60162 *Tel:* 708-236-4900 *Fax:* 708-236-5820 *E-mail:* info@darwill.com *Web Site:* www.darwill.com, pg 1218

Data Axle, 13155 Noel Rd, Suite 1750, Dallas, TX 75240 *Toll Free Tel:* 866-DATAXLE (328-2953) *E-mail:* sales@data-axle.com; corporate.communications@data-axle.com *Web Site:* www.data-axle.com, pg 1111

Data Connect/RelComm Inc, 4868 Hwy 4, Suite G, Angels Camp, CA 95222 *Tel:* 301-924-7400 (ext 17) *Fax:* 301-924-7403 *E-mail:* sales@relcomm.com *Web Site:* www.relcomm.com, pg 1375

Data Conversion Laboratory Inc (DCL), 61-18 190 St, Suite 205, Fresh Meadows, NY 11365 *Tel:* 718-357-8700 *Toll Free Tel:* 800-321-2816 (provider problems) *E-mail:* info@dclab.com *Web Site:* www.dataconversionlaboratory.com, pg 1218, 1375

Data Index Inc, 13713 NW Indian Springs Dr, Vancouver, WA 98685 *Tel:* 425-760-9193 *Web Site:* www.dataindex.com, pg 1218

Data Reproductions Corp, 4545 Glenmeade Lane, Auburn Hills, MI 48326 *Tel:* 248-371-3700 *Toll Free Tel:* 800-242-3114 *Fax:* 248-371-3710 *Web Site:* datarepro.com, pg 1203, 1245

Datacolor, 5 Princess Rd, Lawrenceville, NJ 08648 *Tel:* 609-924-2189 *Toll Free Tel:* 800-982-6496 (support) *Fax:* 609-895-7414 *E-mail:* marketing@datacolor.com *Web Site:* www.datacolor.com, pg 1218

Datalogic USA Inc, 959 Terry St, Eugene, OR 97402-9150 *Tel:* 541-683-5700 *Toll Free Tel:* 800-227-2633 *Web Site:* www.datalogic.com, pg 1275

Datalogics Inc, 101 N Wacker, Suite 1800, Chicago, IL 60606 *Tel:* 312-853-8200 *Fax:* 312-853-8282 *E-mail:* sales@datalogics.com; marketing@datalogics.com *Web Site:* www.datalogics.com, pg 1375

Jeff Davidson MBA, CMC, Breathing Space Institute, 3202 Ruffin St, Raleigh, NC 27607 *Tel:* 919-932-1996 *Web Site:* www.breathingspace.com; www.ghostwiththemost.com, pg 1344

Davis Art Images, 50 Portland St, Worcester, MA 01608 *Tel:* 508-754-7201 *Toll Free Tel:* 800-533-2847 *Fax:* 508-753-3834 *E-mail:* das@davisart.com; contactus@davisart.com *Web Site:* www.davisart.com, pg 1446

Jerilyn Glenn Davis, Cathedral Sta, Box 1712, New York, NY 10025 *Tel:* 212-889-2239 *E-mail:* jdavisbook@gmail.com, pg 1245

Dayton Daily News, 4805 Meredith Rd, Yellow Springs, OH 45387 *Tel:* 937-767-1396, pg 1125

DCA Inc, 1515 E Pine St, Cushing, OK 74023 *Tel:* 918-225-0346 *Fax:* 918-225-1113 *E-mail:* sales@dcainc.com *Web Site:* www.dcainc.com, pg 1375

De Muth Design, 59 Chenango St, Cazenovia, NY 13035 *Tel:* 315-655-8599 *Web Site:* www.demuthdesign.com, pg 1427

De Ru's Fine Art, 9100 E Artesia Blvd, Bellflower, CA 90706-6205 *Tel:* 562-920-1312 *Fax:* 562-920-3077 *E-mail:* derusgal@aol.com *Web Site:* www.derusfinearts.com, pg 1312

Decker Intellectual Properties Inc, 372 Richmond St W, Toronto, ON M5V 2L7, Canada *Tel:* 905-522-8526 *Toll Free Tel:* 855-647-6511 *E-mail:* customercare@deckermed.com *Web Site:* www.deckerip.com, pg 1375

Decode, Inc, 625 First Ave, Suite 300, Seattle, WA 98104 *Tel:* 206-343-9101 *E-mail:* books@decodebooks.com *Web Site:* www.decodeinc.com; www.decodebooks.com, pg 1427

Peter L DeGiglio, 6 Overlook Dr, Washingtonville, NY 10992 *Tel:* 914-850-3803 *E-mail:* pdegiglio@gmail.com, pg 1344

DeHART's Media Services Inc, 6586 Whitbourne Dr, San Jose, CA 95120 *Tel:* 408-768-1575 *Web Site:* www.deharts.com, pg 1245

DeHoff Christian Bookstore, 749 NW Broad St, Murfreesboro, TN 37129 *Tel:* 615-893-8322 *Toll Free Tel:* 800-695-5385 *Fax:* 615-896-7447 *E-mail:* dehoffbooks@gmail.com *Web Site:* www. dehoffpublications.com, pg 1312

Dekker Bookbinding Inc, 2941 Clydon Ave SW, Grand Rapids, MI 49519 *Tel:* 616-538-5160 *Toll Free Tel:* 800-299-BIND (299-2463) *E-mail:* hello@ dekkerbook.com *Web Site:* www.dekkerbook.com, pg 1245, 1262

Del Commune Enterprises Inc, 307 Seventh Ave, Suite 807, New York, NY 10001 *Tel:* 212-226-6664 *E-mail:* mail@dcescouts.com *Web Site:* www. dcescouts.com, pg 1344

Delgado & Co Inc, 3900 Greystone Ave, Suite 21A, Riverdale, NY 10463 *Tel:* 718-708-4419 *E-mail:* mail@delgadoandcompany.com *Web Site:* www.delgadoandcompany.com, pg 1357, 1427

Danita Delimont Stock Photography, 4911 Somerset Dr SE, Bellevue, WA 98006 *Tel:* 425-562-1543 *Fax:* 425-373-5316 *Web Site:* www.danitadelimont.com, pg 1446

Dell EMC, 176 South St, Hopkinton, MA 01748 *Tel:* 508-435-1000 *Toll Free Tel:* 866-438-3622 *Web Site:* www.delltechnologies.com, pg 1375

Dell Magazines, 44 Wall St, Suite 904, New York, NY 10005-2401 *Tel:* 212-686-7188 *Toll Free Tel:* 800-220-7443 (corp sales) *Fax:* 212-480-5751 *E-mail:* customerservice@pennydellpuzzles.com *Web Site:* www.pennydellpuzzles.com, pg 1357

Dell Wyse, One Dell Way, Round Rock, TX 78682 *Toll Free Tel:* 866-438-3622 (sales) *Web Site:* www. delltechnologies.com, pg 1376

Delmas Typesetting Inc, 461 Hilldale Dr, Ann Arbor, MI 48105 *Tel:* 734-662-8899 *E-mail:* delmastype@ comcast.net *Web Site:* www.delmastype.com, pg 1219

Delphax Solutions Inc, 2810 Argentia Rd, Unit 6, Mississauga, ON L5N 8L2, Canada *Toll Free Tel:* 833-DELPHAX (335-7429) *Web Site:* www. delphaxsolutions.com, pg 1376

Demand Marketing, 377 Fisher Rd, Suite D, Grosse Pointe, MI 48230 *Tel:* 313-823-8598 *Toll Free Tel:* 888-977-2256 *Fax:* 313-823-8598 *E-mail:* info@ create-demand.com *Web Site:* www.create-demand. com, pg 1106

Carla Demers, 71 Faunce Dr, Providence, RI 02906 *Tel:* 401-274-2149 *Web Site:* www.whitegatefeatures. com, pg 1117

Democrat Printing & Lithographing Co, 6401 Lindsey Rd, Little Rock, AR 72206 *Toll Free Tel:* 800-622-2216 *Fax:* 501-907-7953 *Web Site:* democratprinting. com, pg 1246

Denver Bookbinding Co Inc, 1401 W 47 Ave, Denver, CO 80211 *Tel:* 303-455-5521 *E-mail:* dbbc@ denverbook.com; info@denverbook.com *Web Site:* www.denverbook.com, pg 1323

Design Plus, 1086 Main Rd, Aquebogue, NY 11931 *Tel:* 631-722-4384 *E-mail:* designplusonline@yahoo. com, pg 1376

Design Science Inc (DSI), 444 W Ocean Blvd, Suite 800, Long Beach, CA 90802 *Tel:* 562-432-2920 *Toll Free Tel:* 800-827-0685 (US sales only) *Fax:* 562-624-2859 *E-mail:* info@wiris.com; sales@wiris. com; support@wiris.com *Web Site:* www.dessci.com, pg 1376

Desktop Miracles Inc, 112 S Main St, Suite 294, Stowe, VT 05672 *Tel:* 802-253-7900 *Toll Free Fax:* 888-293-2676 *E-mail:* info@desktopmiracles.com *Web Site:* www.desktopmiracles.com, pg 1204, 1219, 1262, 1275, 1357, 1427

Devin-Adair Publishers, 9 Lafayette Ct, Suite 3, Greenwich, CT 06830 *Tel:* 203-622-1010 *Fax:* 718-359-8568, pg 1312

DeVorss & Co, 553 Constitution Ave, Camarillo, CA 93012-8510 *Tel:* 805-322-9010 *Toll Free Tel:* 800-843-5743 *Fax:* 805-322-9011 *E-mail:* service@devorss.com *Web Site:* www.devorss.com, pg 1139, 1312

DFI Technologies LLC, 5501 Monte Claire Lane, Loomis, CA 95650 *Tel:* 916-568-1234 *Web Site:* dfitech.com, pg 1376

diacriTech Inc, 4 S Market St, 4th fl, Boston, MA 02109 *Tel:* 617-600-3366 *Fax:* 617-848-2938 *Web Site:* www. diacritech.com, pg 1219, 1357, 1427

Diacritics, 2715 N Charles St, Baltimore, MD 21218-4363 *Toll Free Tel:* 800-548-1784 (journal orders) *Fax:* 410-516-6968 *E-mail:* jrnlcirc@press.jhu.edu (journal orders) *Web Site:* www.press.jhu.edu/journals/ diacritics/index.html, pg 1125

Steven Diamond Inc, 104 W 17 St, Suite 3-E, New York, NY 10011 *Tel:* 212-675-0723 *Fax:* 212-675-0762 *E-mail:* steven.diamond@verizon.net, pg 1344

Didona Design, 160 Grandview Rd, Ardmore, PA 19003 *Tel:* 610-649-3110 *E-mail:* didona@didonadesign.com *Web Site:* www.didonadesign.com, pg 1219, 1427

Diecrafters Inc, 1349 S 55 Ct, Cicero, IL 60804-1211 *Tel:* 708-656-3336 *Fax:* 708-656-3386 *E-mail:* info@ diecrafters.com *Web Site:* www.diecrafters.com, pg 1246

Diffusion Inter-Livres, 1701 Belleville, Lemoyne, QC J4P 3M2, Canada *Tel:* 450-465-0037 *Toll Free Tel:* 866-465-5579 *E-mail:* interlivres@llbquebec.ca *Web Site:* www.inter-livres.ca, pg 1286

Digimage Arts, 100 S Eighth Ave, Winterset, IA 50273 *Tel:* 515-462-1874 *E-mail:* geninfo@digimagearts.com *Web Site:* www.digimagearts.com, pg 1376

Digital Vista Inc, 24 Amity Place, Massapequa, NY 11758 *Tel:* 516-799-5277 *E-mail:* info@digitalvista.net *Web Site:* www.digitalvista.net, pg 1427

Digital Wisdom Inc, PO Box 11, Tappahannock, VA 22560-0011 *Tel:* 804-443-9000 *Toll Free Tel:* 800-800-8560 *E-mail:* info@digitalwisdom.net *Web Site:* www. digiwis.com; www.mountainhighmaps.com, pg 1376

Dikeman Laminating Corp, 181 Sargeant Ave, Clifton, NJ 07013 *Tel:* 973-473-5696 *Fax:* 973-473-2540 *E-mail:* office@dikemanlaminating.com *Web Site:* dikemanlaminating.com, pg 1262

The Dingley Press, 119 Lisbon St, Lisbon, ME 04250 *Tel:* 207-353-4151 *Toll Free Tel:* 800-317-4574 *Fax:* 207-353-9886 *E-mail:* info@dingley.com *Web Site:* www.dingley.com, pg 1246

Direct Link™ Worldwide Inc, 700 Dowd Ave, Elizabeth, NJ 07201 *Tel:* 908-289-0703 *Toll Free Tel:* 800-223-7967 *Fax:* 908-289-0705 *E-mail:* infousa@directlink. com *Web Site:* www.directlink.com, pg 1331

Direct Marketing Solutions Inc, 1275 Fairfax Ave, San Francisco, CA 94124 *Tel:* 415-642-8600 *Fax:* 415-642-8640 *E-mail:* dmsi@directmailing.com *Web Site:* www.directmailing.com, pg 1106, 1345

Disc Makers, 7905 N Crescent Blvd, Pennsauken, NJ 08110-1402 *Tel:* 856-663-9030 *Toll Free Tel:* 800-468-9353 *Fax:* 856-661-3450 *E-mail:* info@discmakers. com *Web Site:* www.discmakers.com, pg 1376

DisplayMate Technologies Corp, PO Box 550, Amherst, NH 03031 *Tel:* 603-672-8500 *Toll Free Tel:* 800-932-6323 (orders) *E-mail:* info.dm@displaymate.com *Web Site:* www.displaymate.com, pg 1376

Disticor Magazine Distribution Services, 1000 Thornton Rd S, Oshawa, ON L1J 7E2, Canada *Tel:* 905-619-6565 *Toll Free Tel:* 800-668-7724 (CN only) *Fax:* 905-619-2903 *Web Site:* www.disticor.com; www. magamall.com, pg 1331

Distribooks Inc, 8154 N Ridgeway Ave, Skokie, IL 60076-2911 *Tel:* 847-676-1596 *Toll Free Fax:* 888-266-5713 *E-mail:* info@distribooks.com, pg 1286

Distribooks Inc, 8154 N Ridgeway Ave, Skokie, IL 60076-2911 *Tel:* 847-676-1596 *Fax:* 847-676-1195 *Toll Free Fax:* 888-266-5713 *E-mail:* info@ distribooks.com; info@schoenhofs.com *Web Site:* www.schoenhofs.com, pg 1313

Distributed Art Publishers (DAP), 75 Broad St, Suite 630, New York, NY 10004 *Tel:* 212-627-1999 *Toll Free Tel:* 800-338-2665 (cust serv) *Fax:* 212-627-9484 *Toll Free Fax:* 800-478-3128 *E-mail:* orders@dapinc. com *Web Site:* www.artbook.com, pg 1286

District Administration Magazine, 35 Nutmeg Dr, Suite 205, Trumbull, CT 06611 *Tel:* 203-663-0100 *E-mail:* circulation@promediagrp.com *Web Site:* www. districtadministration.com, pg 1126

Diversified Printing Services Inc, 3425 Cherokee Ave, Columbus, GA 31906 *Tel:* 706-323-2759 *Toll Free Fax:* 888-410-5502 *Web Site:* www.1dps.com, pg 1246

dix! Digital Prepress Inc, 8462 Wayfarer Dr, Cicero, NY 13039 *Tel:* 315-288-5888 *Fax:* 315-288-5898 *E-mail:* info@dixtype.com *Web Site:* www.dixtype. com, pg 1219, 1246

DJD/Golden Advertising, 145 W 28 St, 12th fl, New York, NY 10001 *Tel:* 212-366-5033 *Fax:* 212-243-5044 *E-mail:* call@djdgolden.com *Web Site:* www. djdgolden.com, pg 1086

DNP America LLC, 335 Madison Ave, 3rd fl, New York, NY 10017 *Tel:* 212-503-1060 *E-mail:* gps@dnp-g.com *Web Site:* www.dnpamerica.com, pg 1204, 1219, 1246, 1262

Docunet Corp, 2435 Xenium Lane N, Plymouth, MN 55441 *Tel:* 763-475-9600 *Toll Free Tel:* 800-936-2863 *Fax:* 763-475-1516 *E-mail:* print@docunetworks.com *Web Site:* www.docunetworks.com, pg 1246

DocuWare Corp, 4 Crotty Lane, Suite 200, New Windsor, NY 12553 *Tel:* 845-563-9045 *Toll Free Tel:* 888-565-5907 *Fax:* 845-563-9046 *E-mail:* dwsales@docuware.com; support.americas@ docuware.com *Web Site:* www.docuware.com, pg 1376

Domtar Paper Co LLC, 234 Kingsley Park Dr, Fort Mill, SC 29715 *Tel:* 803-802-7500 *Toll Free Tel:* 877-877-4685 *E-mail:* communications@domtar.com; commercialprinting@domtar.com *Web Site:* www. domtar.com, pg 1262

RR Donnelley, 35 W Wacker Dr, Chicago, IL 60601 *Toll Free Tel:* 800-742-4455 *Web Site:* www.rrd.com, pg 1204, 1219, 1246, 1262, 1275

RR Donnelley & Sons Company, 35 W Wacker Dr, Chicago, IL 60601 *Tel:* 312-326-8000 *Toll Free Tel:* 800-742-4455 *Web Site:* www.rrd.com, pg 1332

RR Donnelley Marketing Solutions, 35 W Wacker Dr, Chicago, IL 60601 *Toll Free Tel:* 800-742-4455 *Web Site:* www.rrd.com/services/marketing, pg 1092

Dan Donovan Photography, 15005 Valley Ridge Dr, St Louis, MO 63017 *Tel:* 314-712-0021 *E-mail:* dan@ dandonovan.com *Web Site:* www.dandonovan.com, pg 1437

Marcia Nita Doron, 6 Glenbrook Lane, Worcester, MA 01609 *Tel:* 508-755-6642 *Fax:* 508-755-6642 *E-mail:* mdoron@charter.net, pg 1408

Dotronix Technology Inc, 2420 Oakgreen Ave N, West Lakeland, MN 55082 *Tel:* 651-633-1742 *Fax:* 651-633-2152 *E-mail:* sales@dotronix.com *Web Site:* dotronix.com, pg 1376

Double Play, 303 Hillcrest Rd, Belton, MO 64012-1852 *Tel:* 816-651-7118, pg 1345

Doubleday Book Club®, 34 W 27 St, 10th fl, New York, NY 10001 *Tel:* 716-250-5700 (cust serv) *Toll Free Tel:* 866-250-3166 *E-mail:* customer. service@doubledaybookclub.com; member. services@doubledaybookclub.com *Web Site:* www. doubledaybookclub.com, pg 1135

Doubleday Large Print Book Club®, 34 W 27 St, 10th fl, New York, NY 10001 *Tel:* 716-250-5700 (cust serv) *E-mail:* customer.service@doubledaylargeprint.com *Web Site:* www.doubledaylargeprint.com, pg 1136

Dougherty and Associates Public Relations, 1303 Caldwell Mountain Rd, Hot Springs, NC 28743 *Tel:* 828-622-3285 *Fax:* 828-622-3285 *E-mail:* dougherty1515@gmail.com *Web Site:* doughertyandassociatespr.com, pg 1097

Douthitt Corp, 245 Adair St, Detroit, MI 48207-4287 *Tel:* 313-259-1565 *Toll Free Tel:* 800-368-8448 *Fax:* 313-259-6806 *E-mail:* em@douthittcorp.com *Web Site:* www.douthittcorp.com, pg 1275

W R Draper Co, 162 Norfinch Dr, Toronto, ON M3N 1X6, Canada *Tel:* 416-663-6001 *Fax:* 416-663-6043 *E-mail:* info@arthurpress.com *Web Site:* www.arthurpress.com, pg 1204, 1219, 1246, 1262

Spencer Drate, 119 W 80 St, Suite 1-F, New York, NY 10024-7134 *Tel:* 212-799-0535 *E-mail:* spencerdrate@yahoo.com, pg 1427

DRK PHOTO, 100 Starlight Way, Sedona, AZ 86351 *Tel:* 928-284-9808 *E-mail:* info@drkphoto.com *Web Site:* www.drkphoto.com, pg 1446

Drummond, 5664 New Peachtree Rd, Atlanta, GA 30341 *Tel:* 678-597-1050 *Fax:* 678-597-1051 *E-mail:* info@drummond.com *Web Site:* pgc-atl.com, pg 1246

DSCS LLC, 5000 College Ave, Suite 4100, College Park, MD 20742 *Tel:* 301-405-2883 *Fax:* 301-314-2799 *E-mail:* info@dscs.com *Web Site:* www.dscs.com, pg 1219, 1376

DSM Producers Inc, PO Box 1160, Marco Island, FL 34146-1160 *Tel:* 212-245-0006, pg 1376

D3Logic Inc, 89 Commercial Way, East Providence, RI 02915 *Tel:* 401-435-4300 *Toll Free Tel:* 844-385-5388 *E-mail:* contact@d3-inc.com *Web Site:* www.d3-inc.com, pg 1246

Dual Graphics, 370 Cliffwood Park, Brea, CA 92821 *Tel:* 714-990-3700 *Fax:* 714-990-6818 *Web Site:* www.dualgraphics.com, pg 1219, 1246

Eileen Duhne Public Relations, 203-B Picnic Ave, San Rafael, CA 94901 *Tel:* 415-459-2573 *Fax:* 415-459-2573 *E-mail:* eduhne@comcast.net *Web Site:* eduhne.com, pg 1097

Dukane Corp, Audio Visual Products Division, 2900 Dukane Dr, St Charles, IL 60174 *Tel:* 630-584-2300 *Toll Free Tel:* 888-245-1966; 800-676-2487 (tech support) *Fax:* 630-584-5156 *E-mail:* avsales@dukane.com *Web Site:* dukaneav.com, pg 1376

Dunhill International List Co Inc, 6400 Congress Ave, Suite 1750, Boca Raton, FL 33487-2898 *Tel:* 561-998-7800 *Toll Free Tel:* 800-DUNHILL (386-4455) *Fax:* 561-998-7880 *E-mail:* dunhill@dunhillintl.com *Web Site:* www.dunhills.com, pg 1112

Dunn & Co Inc, 75 Green St, Clinton, MA 01510 *Tel:* 978-368-8505 *Fax:* 978-368-7867 *E-mail:* info@booktrauma.com *Web Site:* www.booktrauma.com, pg 1204, 1246, 1263

Dunn+Associates Design, PO Box 870, Hayward, WI 54843-0870 *Tel:* 715-634-4857 *Fax:* 715-634-5617 *E-mail:* info@dunn-design.com *Web Site:* www.dunn-design.com, pg 1427

Dupli Envelope & Graphics Corp, 6761 Thompson Rd N, Syracuse, NY 13211 *Tel:* 315-472-1316 *Toll Free Tel:* 800-724-2477 *E-mail:* sales@duplionline.com; orders@duplionline.com *Web Site:* www.duplionline.com, pg 1246

Durr MEGTEC LLC, 830 Prosper St, DePere, WI 54115 *Tel:* 920-336-5715 *E-mail:* megtecinquiries@megtec.com *Web Site:* www.durr-megtec.com, pg 1275

DWJ BOOKS LLC, 14 Hill Side Lane, East Hampton, NY 11937 *Tel:* 631-267-8270 *E-mail:* info@dwjbooks.com *Web Site:* www.dwjbooks.com, pg 1357, 1427

Dynabook Americas Inc, 5241 California Ave, Suite 100, Irvine, CA 92617 *Tel:* 949-583-3000 *Web Site:* us.dynabook.com, pg 1376

Dynamic Graphic Finishing, 945 Horsham Rd, Horsham, PA 19044 *Tel:* 215-441-8880 *E-mail:* info@dgfinc.com *Web Site:* www.bpg-usa.com, pg 1247

Dynaric Inc, 5740 Bayside Rd, Virginia Beach, VA 23455 *Tel:* 757-363-5850 *Toll Free Tel:* 800-526-0827 *Fax:* 757-363-8016 *E-mail:* gd@dynaric.com; order@dynaric.com *Web Site:* www.dynaric.com, pg 1275

E L H (English Literary History), 2715 N Charles St, Baltimore, MD 21218-4363 *Toll Free Tel:* 800-548-1784 (journal orders) *Fax:* 410-516-3866 (journal orders) *E-mail:* jrnlcirc@press.jhu.edu (journal orders) *Web Site:* www.press.jhu.edu/journals/english_literary_history/index.html, pg 1126

Eaglecrafts Inc, 168 W 12 St, Ogden, UT 84404 *Tel:* 801-393-3991 *Fax:* 801-393-4647 *E-mail:* sales@eaglefeathertrading.com *Web Site:* www.eaglefeathertrading.com, pg 1313

East Mountain Editing Services, PO Box 1895, Tijeras, NM 87059-1895 *Tel:* 505-281-8422 *Web Site:* www.spanishindexing.com, pg 1219

East-West Concepts, PO Box 1435, Kapaa, HI 96746 *Tel:* 808-938-8410 *Fax:* 808-441-8121 *Web Site:* www.eastwestconcepts.com, pg 1408

East-West Health Arts, 45 Academy Circle, Oakland, NJ 07436-0945 *Tel:* 201-337-8787, pg 1313

Eastern Book Co, 7 Lincoln Ave, Scarborough, ME 04074 *Tel:* 207-856-1370 *Toll Free Tel:* 800-937-0331 *Toll Free Fax:* 800-214-3895 *E-mail:* info@ebc.com; sales@ebc.com *Web Site:* www.ebc.com, pg 1313

Eastgate Systems Inc, 134 Main St, Watertown, MA 02472 *Tel:* 617-924-9044 *Toll Free Tel:* 800-562-1638 *E-mail:* info@eastgate.com *Web Site:* www.eastgate.com, pg 1376

Eastman Kodak Co, 343 State St, Rochester, NY 14650 *Tel:* 585-724-4000 *Toll Free Tel:* 866-563-2533 *Web Site:* www.kodak.com, pg 1275

Eastwind Books & Arts Inc, 1435 Stockton St, San Francisco, CA 94133 *Tel:* 415-772-5888 *Fax:* 415-772-5885 *E-mail:* contact@eastwindbooks.com *Web Site:* www.eastwindbooks.com, pg 1313, 1326

Eckhart & Co Inc, 4011 W 54 St, Indianapolis, IN 46254 *Tel:* 317-347-2665 *Toll Free Tel:* 800-443-3791 *Fax:* 317-347-2666 *E-mail:* info@eckhartandco.com *Web Site:* www.eckhartandco.com, pg 1247

Ecological Fibers Inc, 40 Pioneer Dr, Lunenburg, MA 01462 *Tel:* 978-537-0003 *Fax:* 978-537-2238 *E-mail:* info@ecofibers.com *Web Site:* www.ecofibers.com, pg 1204, 1263

ECRM Imaging Systems, 25 Commerce Way, North Andover, MA 01845-1002 *Tel:* 978-851-0207 *Toll Free Tel:* 800-537-ECRM (537-3276) *E-mail:* sales@ecrm.com *Web Site:* www.ecrm.com, pg 1376

Wendy Edelson Studios, 18 E St Louis St, Rapid City, SD 57701 *Tel:* 206-319-8158 *Web Site:* www.wendyedelson.com; www.elevenlemons.blogspot.com, pg 1427

Edipresse Inc, 945, ave Beaumont, Montreal, QC H3N 1W3, Canada *Tel:* 514-273-6141 *Toll Free Tel:* 800-361-1043 *Fax:* 514-273-7021 *E-mail:* information@edipresse.ca *Web Site:* www.edipresse.ca, pg 1313

Edison Lithograph & Printing Corp, 3725 Tonnelle Ave, North Bergen, NJ 07047-2421 *Tel:* 201-902-9191 *Fax:* 201-902-0475 *E-mail:* info@edisonlitho.com *Web Site:* www.edisonlitho.com, pg 1219, 1247, 1263

Les Editions Themis, Faculte de droit, Universite de Montreal, CP 6128, Succursale Centreville, Montreal, QC H3C 3J7, Canada *Tel:* 514-343-6627 *Fax:* 514-343-6779 *E-mail:* info@editionsthemis.com *Web Site:* ssl.editionsthemis.com, pg 1313

Steven Edson Photography, 219 Orchard St, Belmont, MA 02478 *Tel:* 617-993-3212 *E-mail:* steve@stevenedson.com *Web Site:* www.stevenedson.com, pg 1437

eFootage LLC, 530 S Lake Ave, Suite 450, Pasadena, CA 91101 *Tel:* 626-395-9593 *E-mail:* info@efootage.com *Web Site:* www.efootage.com, pg 1446

eFulfillment Service Inc, 807 Airport Access Rd, Traverse City, MI 49686 *Tel:* 231-276-5057 *Toll Free Tel:* 866-922-6783 *Web Site:* www.efulfillmentservice.com, pg 1332

Eizo Inc, 5710 Warland Dr, Cypress, CA 90630 *Tel:* 562-431-5011 *Toll Free Tel:* 800-800-5202 *Fax:* 562-431-4811 *E-mail:* orders@eizo.com *Web Site:* www.eizo.com, pg 1376

The Lisa Ekus Group LLC, 57 North St, Hatfield, MA 01038 *Tel:* 413-247-9325 *Fax:* 413-247-9873 *E-mail:* info@lisaekus.com *Web Site:* lisaekus.com, pg 1097

Elder's Bookstore, 101 White Bridge Rd, Nashville, TN 37209 *Tel:* 615-352-1562 *E-mail:* info@eldersbookstore.com *Web Site:* eldersbookstore.com, pg 1313

Electronics for Imaging Inc (EFI), 6750 Dumbarton Circle, Fremont, CA 94555 *Tel:* 650-357-3500 *Toll Free Tel:* 800-568-1917; 800-875-7117 (sales) *Fax:* 650-357-3907 *E-mail:* info@efi.com *Web Site:* www.efi.com, pg 1376

1106 Design LLC, 610 E Bell Rd, Suite 2-139, Phoenix, AZ 85022-2393 *Tel:* 602-866-3226 *Fax:* 602-866-8166 *E-mail:* md@1106design.com *Web Site:* www.1106design.com, pg 1427

Eligh Photographs, 2544 Forbes St, Victoria, BC V8R 4B8, Canada *Tel:* 250-888-0027 *Web Site:* www.elighphoto.com, pg 1437

Elixir Technologies Corp, 1314 E Ojai Ave, Ojai, CA 93023 *Tel:* 805-641-5900 *Fax:* 805-648-9151 *E-mail:* info_us@elixir.com *Web Site:* www.elixir.com, pg 1377

Elk Photography, 3163 Wisconsin St, Oakland, CA 94602 *Tel:* 510-531-7469 *Fax:* 510-531-7469 *E-mail:* cjelk@elkphotography.com *Web Site:* www.elkphotography.com, pg 1437

Ron Elmy Photography, 353 Eastern Ave, Suite 104, Toronto, ON M4M 1B7, Canada *Tel:* 416-469-6711 *E-mail:* elmyphotovideo@gmail.com *Web Site:* www.ronelmy.com, pg 1437

Ecegul (AJ) Elterman, 18 Sixteenth St, Bayville, NY 11709 *Tel:* 516-628-3075; 516-661-6525 (cell) *E-mail:* ajelterman@mindspring.com, pg 1409

Catherine C Elverston ELS, 3242 NW 5 St, Gainesville, FL 32609 *Tel:* 352-222-0625 (cell) *E-mail:* celverston@gmail.com, pg 1409

Emerson, Wajdowicz Studios Inc, 530 W 25 St, New York, NY 10001 *Tel:* 212-807-8144 *Fax:* 212-675-0414 *E-mail:* info@designews.com *Web Site:* www.designews.com; Facebook.com/DesignEWS, pg 1427

Emery-Pratt Co, 1966 W M 21, Owosso, MI 48867-1397 *Tel:* 989-723-5291 *Toll Free Tel:* 800-762-5683 (orders); 800-248-3887 (cust serv) *Fax:* 989-723-4677 *Toll Free Fax:* 800-523-6379 (cust serv) *E-mail:* customer.service@emery-pratt.com *Web Site:* www.emery-pratt.com, pg 1313

Empire Publishing Service, PO Box 1344, Studio City, CA 91614-0344 *Tel:* 818-784-8918 *Fax:* 818-990-2477 *E-mail:* empirepubsvc@att.net, pg 1286

Emprint®, 5425 Florida Blvd, Baton Rouge, LA 70806 *Tel:* 225-923-2550 *Toll Free Tel:* 800-211-8335 *Web Site:* emprint.com, pg 1204, 1219, 1247

Emsworth Design, 147 W 24 St, New York, NY 10011 *Tel:* 212-877-6139; 917-359-9860 (cell) *Web Site:* www.emsworthdesign.com, pg 1427

EMT International Inc, 780 Centerline Dr, Hobart, WI 54155 *Tel:* 920-468-5475 *Fax:* 920-468-7991 *E-mail:* info@emtinternational.com *Web Site:* www.emtinternational.com, pg 1276

Encyclopaedia Britannica Inc, 325 N La Salle St, Suite 200, Chicago, IL 60654 *Tel:* 312-347-7000 (all other countries) *Toll Free Tel:* 800-323-1229 (US & CN) *Fax:* 312-294-2104 *E-mail:* contact@eb.com *Web Site:* www.britannica.com, pg 1313

Energy Psychology Press, 3340 Fulton Rd, No 442, Fulton, CA 95439 *Tel:* 707-525-9292 *Toll Free Fax:* 800-330-9798 *E-mail:* energypsychologypress@gmail.com *Web Site:* www.energypsychologypress.com, pg 1345

Engineered Software™, PO Box 408, Grafton, MA 01519-0408 *Tel:* 336-299-4843 *E-mail:* info@engsw.com; sales@engsw.com *Web Site:* www.engsw.com, pg 1377

Entertainment News Service, PO Box 6123, West Caldwell, NJ 07007-6123 *Tel:* 973-227-4433, pg 1184

Entro Communications Inc, 33 Harbour Sq, Suite 202, Toronto, ON M5J 2G2, Canada *Tel:* 416-368-6988 *Fax:* 416-368-5616 *E-mail:* toronto@entro.com *Web Site:* www.entro.com, pg 1427

Envirovision, 2901 W Coast Hwy, Suite 222, Newport Beach, CA 92663 *Tel:* 949-673-2555 *E-mail:* bfactor@beverlyfactor.com *Web Site:* www.beverlyfactor.com, pg 1437

Envision Peripherals Inc (EPI), 490 N McCarthy Blvd, Suite 120, Milpitas, CA 95035 *Web Site:* us.aoc.com, pg 1377

Envision Stock Photography Inc, 27 Hoppin Rd, Newport, RI 02840 *Tel:* 401-619-1500 *Toll Free Tel:* 800-524-8238 *E-mail:* envision@att.net *Web Site:* www.envision-stock.com, pg 1446

EP Graphics, 169 S Jefferson St, Berne, IN 46711 *Tel:* 260-589-2145 *Toll Free Tel:* 877-589-2145 *Fax:* 260-589-2810 *Web Site:* www.epgraphics.com, pg 1247

Bob Erdmann, 1116 Oakmont Dr, No 6, Walnut Creek, CA 94595 *Tel:* 925-451-8201 *E-mail:* info@bob-erdmann.com *Web Site:* www.columbinecommunications.com, pg 1345

Eriako Associates, 1380 Morningside Way, Venice, CA 90291 *Tel:* 310-392-6537 *Fax:* 310-392-6537 *E-mail:* eriakoassociates@gmail.com, pg 1357

Eriksen Translations Inc, 50 Court St, Suite 700, Brooklyn, NY 11201 *Tel:* 718-802-9010 *Fax:* 718-802-0041 *Web Site:* www.eriksen.com, pg 1409

Eska USA BV Inc, 1910 Campostella Rd, Chesapeake, VA 23324 *Tel:* 757-494-7330 *E-mail:* usa@eska.com *Web Site:* www.eska.com, pg 1263

Esko USA, 8535 Gander Creek Dr, Miamisburg, OH 45342 *Tel:* 937-454-1721 *Toll Free Tel:* 800-743-7131 *Fax:* 937-454-1522 *E-mail:* info.usa@esko.com *Web Site:* www.esko.com, pg 1377

Essex Products Group, 30 Industrial Park Rd, Centerbrook, CT 06409-0307 *Tel:* 860-767-7130 *Toll Free Tel:* 800-394-7130 *Fax:* 860-767-9137 *E-mail:* sales@epg-inc.com *Web Site:* www.epg-inc.com, pg 1276

Esto, 222 Valley Place, Mamaroneck, NY 10543 *Tel:* 914-698-4060 *E-mail:* esto@esto.com *Web Site:* www.esto.com, pg 1446

eStock Photo, 27-28 Thomson Ave, Suite 628, Long Island City, NY 11101 *Tel:* 212-689-5580 *Toll Free Tel:* 800-284-3399 *Fax:* 212-545-1185 *E-mail:* sales@estockphoto.com; info@estockphoto.com *Web Site:* www.estockphoto.com, pg 1446

Sigrid Estrada, 902 Broadway, No 1610, New York, NY 10010 *Tel:* 212-673-4300 *Fax:* 212-477-8815 *E-mail:* s.e.photo@mindspring.com *Web Site:* www.sigridestrada.com, pg 1437

European Books & Media, 6600 Shattuck Ave, Oakland, CA 94609 *Tel:* 510-922-9157 *E-mail:* europeanbook.com *Web Site:* www.europeanbook.com, pg 1313, 1326

Evergreen Engravers, 1819 S Central Ave, Suite 24, Kent, WA 98032 *Tel:* 253-852-6766 *Toll Free Tel:* 800-852-6766 *Fax:* 253-850-3944 *E-mail:* emboss@evergreenengravers.com *Web Site:* www.evergreenengravers.com, pg 1276

Evolution Computing Inc, 4228 E Andrea Dr, Cave Creek, AZ 85331 *Tel:* 602-299-1949 *E-mail:* support@fastcad.com; order_request@fastcad.com *Web Site:* www.fastcad.com, pg 1377

Exhibit Promotions Plus Inc, 11620 Vixens Path, Ellicott City, MD 21042-1539 *Tel:* 410-997-0763 *Fax:* 410-997-0764 *E-mail:* exhibit@epponline.com *Web Site:* www.epponline.com, pg 1133, 1345

f-stop Fitzgerald Inc, 88 James St, Rosendale, NY 12472 *E-mail:* fstopf@gmail.com, pg 1357, 1437

Taryn Fagerness Agency, 4810 Point Fosdick Dr NW, PMB 34, Gig Harbor, WA 98335 *Tel:* 858-254-7711 *E-mail:* taryn.fagerness@gmail.com *Web Site:* tarynfagernessagency.com, pg 1345

Faherty & Associates Inc, 6665 SW Hampton St, Suite 100, Portland, OR 97223 *Tel:* 503-639-3113 *Toll Free Tel:* 800-824-2888 *Fax:* 503-598-9850 *Web Site:* fahertybooks.com, pg 1286

The Fairfield Chronicle, PO Box 6123, West Caldwell, NJ 07007-6123 *Tel:* 973-227-4433, pg 1184

Fairfield Marketing Group Inc, The Direct Mail Ctr, 830 Sport Hill Rd, Easton, CT 06112-1241 *Tel:* 203-261-5585 *Fax:* 203-261-0884 *E-mail:* info@fairfieldmarketing.com *Web Site:* www.fairfieldmarketing.com, pg 1092, 1097, 1106, 1109, 1112, 1219, 1247, 1276, 1345, 1377, 1427

Falcon Safety Products Inc, 25 Imclone Dr, Branchburg, NJ 08876 *Tel:* 908-707-4900 *Toll Free Tel:* 800-332-5266 *E-mail:* marketing@falconsafety.com *Web Site:* www.falconsafety.com, pg 1377

Fall River News Co Inc, 144 Robeson St, Fall River, MA 02720 *Tel:* 508-679-5266 *E-mail:* frnewco@gmail.com, pg 1313

Far Eastern Books, 250 Cochrane Dr, Suite 14, Markham, ON L3R 8E5, Canada *Tel:* 905-477-2900 *Toll Free Tel:* 800-291-8886 *Fax:* 905-479-2988 *E-mail:* books@febonline.com *Web Site:* fareasternbooks.com, pg 1286

Publicaciones Faro de Gracia (PFG), 1317 Railroad St, Burlington, NC 27217 *Tel:* 336-792-2690 *E-mail:* oficina@farodegracia.org *Web Site:* www.farodegracia.org, pg 1287

Amy E Farrar, 4638 Manchester Rd, Mound, MN 55364 *Tel:* 952-451-5982 *Fax:* 952-472-6874 (call first) *E-mail:* amyfarrar@mchsi.com *Web Site:* www.writeandedit.net, pg 1117

Bryan Farrish Marketing, 1828 Broadway, 2nd fl, Santa Monica, CA 90404 *Tel:* 310-998-8305 *E-mail:* airplay@radio-media.com *Web Site:* www.radio-media.com, pg 1097

FCI Digital, 2032 S Alex Rd, Suite A, West Carrollton, OH 45449 *Tel:* 937-859-9701 *Web Site:* www.fcidigital.com, pg 1220

fd2s, 1634 E Cesar Chavez, Austin, TX 78702 *Tel:* 512-476-7733 *Web Site:* www.fd2s.com, pg 1428

FedEx Ground, 1000 FedEx Dr, Coraopolis, PA 15108 *Tel:* 412-269-1000 *Toll Free Tel:* 800-762-3725 *Web Site:* www.fedex.com, pg 1332

FedEx Supply Chain, 6700 Cranberry Woods Dr, Cranberry Township, PA 16066 *Toll Free Tel:* 800-677-3110 *E-mail:* solution@fedex.com *Web Site:* supplychain.fedex.com, pg 1332

Feigenbaum Publishing Consultants Inc, 61 Bounty Lane, Jericho, NY 11753 *Tel:* 516-647-8314 (cell), pg 1345

Karen Feld, 304 E 65 St, Unit 26-C, New York, NY 10065-6785 *Tel:* 212-327-1067; 202-236-0047 *E-mail:* news@karenfeld.com; karen@karenfeld.com *Web Site:* www.karenfeld.com, pg 1117

Feldheim Publishers, 208 Airport Executive Park, Nanuet, NY 10954 *Tel:* 845-356-2282 *Toll Free Tel:* 800-237-7149 (orders) *Fax:* 845-425-1908 *E-mail:* sales@feldheim.com *Web Site:* www.feldheim.com, pg 1313

Gayle Feldman, 131 E 74 St, New York, NY 10021 *Tel:* 212-772-8265 *Fax:* 212-517-4020 *E-mail:* feldmangayle@gmail.com *Web Site:* www.gaylefeldman.com; www.thebookseller.com, pg 1117

Reginald F Fennell Subscription Service Inc, 1002 W Michigan Ave, Jackson, MI 49202 *Tel:* 517-782-3132 *Toll Free Tel:* 800-603-5557 *Fax:* 517-782-1109 *E-mail:* fennellss@acd.net, pg 1313

Fenway Group, 870 Commonwealth Ave, Boston, MA 02215 *Tel:* 617-226-1900 *Fax:* 617-226-1901 *E-mail:* info@fenwaycommunications.com *Web Site:* www.fenway-group.com, pg 1247

Ferry Associates Inc, 49 Fostertown Rd, Medford, NJ 08055 *Tel:* 609-953-1233 *Toll Free Tel:* 800-257-5258 *Fax:* 609-953-8637 *Web Site:* www.ferryassociates.com, pg 1204, 1220, 1247, 1276

5th Grade Book Club, 557 Broadway, New York, NY 10012 *Tel:* 212-343-6100 *Toll Free Tel:* 800-724-6527 (press 1) *Toll Free Fax:* 800-223-4011 *E-mail:* bookclubs@scholastic.com *Web Site:* scholastic.com/bookclubs, pg 1136

Figaro, PO Box 848, Sharon, CT 06069 *Tel:* 860-248-8989; 860-364-0834 *E-mail:* design@figro.com *Web Site:* www.figro.com, pg 1345, 1357, 1377, 1428

FILM Archives Inc, 35 W 35 St, Suite 904, New York, NY 10001-2238 *Tel:* 212-696-2616 *Fax:* 503-210-9927 *E-mail:* info@filmarchivesonline.com *Web Site:* www.filmarchivesonline.com, pg 1446

Film Quarterly, Journals & Digital Publishing, 155 Grand Ave, Suite 400, Oakland, CA 94612-3758 *Tel:* 510-883-8326 (fulfillment) *Fax:* 510-836-8910 (fulfillment) *E-mail:* customerservice@ucpress.edu *Web Site:* www.filmquarterly.org; fq.ucpress.edu, pg 1126

Filmet Inc, 1051 Russellton Rd, Cheswick, PA 15024-1045 *Toll Free Tel:* 800-255-9000 *Fax:* 724-275-1704 *Web Site:* www.filmet.com; www.profilmet.com, pg 1220, 1247

FIM, 18 Central Blvd, South Hackensack, NJ 07606 *Tel:* 201-549-1037 *Web Site:* www.fimheadbands.com, pg 1263

Finch Paper LLC, One Glen St, Glens Falls, NY 12801 *Tel:* 518-793-2541 *Toll Free Tel:* 800-833-9983 *Fax:* 518-743-9656 *E-mail:* info@finchpaper.com *Web Site:* www.finchpaper.com, pg 1263

Fine Wordworking, PO Box 3041, Monterey, CA 93942-3041 *Tel:* 831-375-6278 *E-mail:* info@finewordworking.com *Web Site:* marilynch.com, pg 1393

Fire Engineering Books & Videos, 1421 S Sheridan Rd, Tulsa, OK 74112 *Tel:* 918-831-9421 *Toll Free Tel:* 800-752-9764 *Fax:* 918-831-9555 *E-mail:* sales@pennwell.com *Web Site:* www.pennwellbooks.com, pg 1287

Firebrand Technologies, 44 Merrimac St, Newburyport, MA 01950 *Tel:* 978-465-7755 *Toll Free Tel:* 800-779-7345 *Fax:* 978-465-7759 *E-mail:* askburnie@firebrandtech.com *Web Site:* www.firebrandtech.com, pg 1345, 1377

Firefly (PreK-K), 557 Broadway, New York, NY 10012 *Tel:* 212-343-6100 *Toll Free Tel:* 800-724-6527 (press 1) *Toll Free Fax:* 800-223-4011 *E-mail:* bookclubs@scholastic.com *Web Site:* scholastic.com/bookclubs, pg 1136

Firefly Books Ltd, 50 Staples Ave, Unit 1, Richmond Hill, ON L4B 0A7, Canada *Tel:* 416-499-8412 *Toll Free Tel:* 800-387-6192 (CN); 800-387-5085 (US) *Fax:* 416 499-8313 *Toll Free Fax:* 800-450-0391 (CN); 800-565-6034 (US) *E-mail:* service@fireflybooks.com *Web Site:* www.fireflybooks.com, pg 1287

First Choice Copy, 5208 Grand Ave, Maspeth, NY 11378 *Tel:* 718-381-1480 (ext 200) *Toll Free Tel:* 800-222-COPY (222-2679) *Web Site:* www.firstchoice-copy.com, pg 1109, 1204, 1247, 1377

1st Grade Book Club, 557 Broadway, New York, NY 10012 *Tel:* 212-343-6100 *Toll Free Tel:* 800-724-6527 (press 1) *Toll Free Fax:* 800-223-4011 *E-mail:* bookclubs@scholastic.com *Web Site:* scholastic.com/bookclubs, pg 1136

First Things: A Journal of Religion, Culture & Public Life, 35 E 21 St, 6th fl, New York, NY 10010 *Tel:* 212-627-1985 *Fax:* 212-627-2184 *E-mail:* ft@firstthings.com *Web Site:* www.firstthings.com, pg 1126

Fish Films Footage World, 1060 Camino Real, Sante Fe, NM 87501 *Tel:* 818-905-1071 *E-mail:* footageworld@aol.com *Web Site:* www.footageworld.com, pg 1446

The Fisher Company, PO Box 89578, Tucson, AZ 85752-9578 *Tel:* 520-547-2460 *Web Site:* www.thefishercompany.com, pg 1345

Leonard Everett Fisher, 7 Twin Bridge Acres Rd, Westport, CT 06880-1028 *Tel:* 203-227-0133 *Fax:* 203-227-0133 *E-mail:* l.e.fisher@sbcglobal.net, pg 1428

Lola Troy Fiur, 360 E 65 St, Suite 17-A, New York, NY 10065 *Tel:* 646-247-9044 *Fax:* 212-861-1911 *E-mail:* ltfoto@yahoo.com *Web Site:* www.ltfstudios.com, pg 1437

Flannery Book Service, 20258 Hwy 18, No 430-436, Apple Valley, CA 92307 *Toll Free Tel:* 800-456-3400 *Toll Free Fax:* 800-284-5600 *E-mail:* contact@fbs-now.com *Web Site:* www.fbs-now.com, pg 1345

Flavin Photography, 5401 Cordova St, Suite 305, Anchorage, AK 99514 *Tel:* 907-561-1606 *Fax:* 907-242-8206 *E-mail:* flavin@alaska.net *Web Site:* www.flavinphotography.com, pg 1437

Flock Tex Inc, 200 Founders Dr, Woonsocket, RI 02895 *Tel:* 401-765-2340 *Toll Free Tel:* 800-556-7286 *Fax:* 401-765-4915 *Web Site:* www.flocktex.com, pg 1263

Flottman Co Inc, 720 Centre View Blvd, Crestview Hills, KY 41017 *Tel:* 859-331-6636 *Fax:* 859-344-7085 *E-mail:* info@flottmanco.com *Web Site:* www.flottmanco.com, pg 1204

Fluke Networks, 6920 Seaway Blvd, Everett, WA 98203 *Tel:* 425-446-5500; 425-446-4519 (sales & support) *Toll Free Tel:* 800-283-5853 *E-mail:* info@flukenetworks.com *Web Site:* www.flukenetworks.com, pg 1377

Flynn Media, 1233 Fitzwater St, Philadelphia, PA 19147 *Tel:* 215-772-3048 *Web Site:* www.flynnmedia.com, pg 1097

Focus Strategic Communications Inc, 15 Hunter Way, Brantford, ON N3T 6S3, Canada *Tel:* 519-756-3265 *E-mail:* info@focussc.com *Web Site:* www.focussc.com, pg 1357

Follett Higher Education Group, 3 Westbrook Corporate Ctr, Suite 200, Westchester, IL 60154 *Tel:* 708-884-0000 *Toll Free Tel:* 800-FOLLETT (365-5388) *Web Site:* www.follett.com/higher-ed, pg 1314

Follett School Solutions Inc, 1340 Ridgeview Dr, McHenry, IL 60050 *Tel:* 815-759-1700 *Toll Free Tel:* 888-511-5114 (cust serv); 877-899-8550 (sales) *Fax:* 815-759-9831 *Toll Free Fax:* 800-852-5458 *E-mail:* info@follettlearning.com; customerservice@follett.com *Web Site:* www.follettlearning.com; www.follett.com/prek12; www.titlewave.com, pg 1287, 1377

The Font Bureau Inc, 151 Beach Rd, Vineyard Haven, MA 02568 *E-mail:* info@fontbureau.com *Web Site:* fontbureau.typenetwork.com, pg 1220

Fontlab Ltd, 403 S Lincoln St, Suite 4-51, Port Angeles, WA 98362 *Tel:* 301-560-3208 *Toll Free Tel:* 866-571-5039 *E-mail:* orders@fontlab.com; contact@fontlab.com *Web Site:* www.fontlab.com, pg 1377

Forecast, 2550 W Tyvola Rd, Suite 300, Charlotte, NC 28217 *Tel:* 704-998-3100 *Toll Free Tel:* 800-775-1800 (info servs); 800-775-1700 (cust serv) *Toll Free Fax:* 866-557-3396 (cust serv) *E-mail:* btinfo@baker-taylor.com *Web Site:* www.baker-taylor.com, pg 1126

Forer Inc, 7881 SW 69 Ave, Miami, FL 33143 *Tel:* 305-495-0838 *Fax:* 786-420-5835 *Web Site:* www.forer.com, pg 1438

Forest Sales & Distributing Co, 139 Jean Marie St, Reserve, LA 70084 *E-mail:* forestsales@juno.com, pg 1314

Foreword Reviews, 413 E Eighth St, Traverse City, MI 49686 *Tel:* 231-933-3699 *Web Site:* www.forewordreviews.com, pg 1126

Forthcoming Books™, 4919 Rte 22, Amenia, NY 12501 *Tel:* 518-789-8700 *Toll Free Tel:* 800-562-2139 *Fax:* 518-789-0556 *E-mail:* books@greyhouse.com *Web Site:* greyhouse.com, pg 1126

Fortunato Book Packaging, 500 Angell St, No 203, Providence, RI 02906 *Tel:* 845-826-3675 *Web Site:* twitter.com/chrisfortunato, pg 1358

45th Parallel Maps & Infographics, 13720 Paragon Ave N, Stillwater, MN 55082 *Tel:* 651-430-8127 *E-mail:* info@45thparallelmaps.com *Web Site:* 45thparallelmaps.com, pg 1428

Foster Covers, 1401 Wonder Way, Fairfield, IA 52556 *Tel:* 641-472-3953 *Toll Free Tel:* 800-472-3953 *Toll Free Fax:* 866-837-0544 *E-mail:* info@fostercovers.com *Web Site:* www.fostercovers.com, pg 1428

Steven Foster Photography, PO Box 191, Eureka Springs, AR 72632-0191 *Tel:* 479-253-2629 *E-mail:* info@stevenfoster.com *Web Site:* www.stevenfoster.com, pg 1438

Foster Travel Publishing, 1623 Martin Luther King Jr Way, Berkeley, CA 94709 *Tel:* 510-549-2202 *Web Site:* www.fostertravel.com, 1117, 1377

Foster Travel Publishing, 1623 Martin Luther King Jr Way, Berkeley, CA 94709 *Tel:* 510-549-2202 *Web Site:* www.fostertravel.com; stockphotos.fostertravel.com, pg 1438, 1446

Fotofolio, 561 Broadway, New York, NY 10012 *Tel:* 212-226-0923 *Toll Free Tel:* 800-955-FOTO (955-3686) *E-mail:* contact@fotofolio.com *Web Site:* www.fotofolio.com, pg 1287

Fotosmith, 245 S Plumer Ave, No 6, Tucson, AZ 85719 *Tel:* 520-882-2033 *E-mail:* info@fotosmithusa.com *Web Site:* www.jeffsmithusa.com, pg 1438

Four Colour Print Group, 2410 Frankfort Ave, Louisville, KY 40206 *Tel:* 502-896-9644 *Fax:* 502-896-9594 *E-mail:* sales@fourcolour.com *Web Site:* www.fourcolour.com, pg 1204, 1247, 1276

Fournies Associates, 1226 NW 19 Terr, Delray Beach, FL 33445 *Tel:* 561-445-5102, pg 1345

4th Grade Book Club, 557 Broadway, New York, NY 10012 *Tel:* 212-343-6100 *Toll Free Tel:* 800-724-6527 (press 1) *Toll Free Fax:* 800-223-4011 *E-mail:* bookclubs@scholastic.com *Web Site:* scholastic.com/bookclubs, pg 1136

James Frank Photography Inc, PO Box 3523, Estes Park, CO 80517 *Tel:* 970-586-3418 *E-mail:* photos@jamesfrank.com *Web Site:* www.jamesfrank.com, pg 1438

The Frank Promotion Corp, 10860 Green Valley Walk, Boynton Beach, FL 33437 *Tel:* 561-737-2325 *E-mail:* frankpromo@aol.com, pg 1097

Franklin Advertising Associates Inc, 441 Main St, Yarmouth Port, MA 02675 *Tel:* 508-362-7472 *E-mail:* contact@franklinad.com *Web Site:* www.franklinad.com, pg 1086

Franklin & Siegal Associates Inc, 1350 Broadway, Suite 2015, New York, NY 10018 *Tel:* 212-868-6311 *Fax:* 212-868-6312 *Web Site:* www.franklinandsiegal.com, pg 1345

Leanne Franson, 4 Poplar Ave, Martensville, SK S0K 2T0, Canada *Tel:* 306-382-1696 *E-mail:* leanne@leannefranson.com *Web Site:* www.leannefranson.com, pg 1220, 1428

David R Frazier PhotoLibrary Inc, PO Box 5242, Boise, ID 83705-0242 *Tel:* 208-342-9250 *Fax:* 208-342-2307 *Web Site:* www.drfphoto.com, pg 1446

Frederic Printing, 14701 E 38 Ave, Aurora, CO 80011-1215 *Tel:* 303-371-7990 *Fax:* 303-371-7959 *Web Site:* www.fredericprinting.com, pg 1220, 1247

Freestyle Software, 9 Campus Dr, Parsippany, NJ 07054 *Toll Free Tel:* 800-474-5760 *Fax:* 973-237-9043 *E-mail:* info@freestylesolutions.com *Web Site:* www.freestylesolutions.com, pg 1377

French and English Communication Services LLC, 3104 E Camelback Rd, No 124, Phoenix, AZ 85016-4502 *Tel:* 602-870-1000 *E-mail:* RequestFAECS2008@cox.net *Web Site:* www.FrenchAndEnglish.com, pg 1409

French & European Publications Inc, 425 E 58 St, Suite 27-D, New York, NY 10022 *Tel:* 212-581-8810 *Fax:* 212-202-4356 *E-mail:* livresny@gmail.com; frenchbookstore@aol.com *Web Site:* www.frencheuropean.com, pg 1326

French Paper, 100 French St, Niles, MI 49120 *Tel:* 269-683-1100 *Toll Free Tel:* 800-253-5952 *E-mail:* frenchassetorders@frenchpaper.com; frenchpaperco@gmail.com *Web Site:* www.frenchpaper.com, pg 1263

French Publishers' Agency, 30 Vandam St, Suite 5A, New York, NY 10013 *Tel:* 212-254-4540 *Web Site:* www.frenchpubagency.com, pg 1346

Samuel French Inc, 235 Park Ave S, 5th fl, New York, NY 10003 *Tel:* 212-206-8990 *Toll Free Tel:* 866-598-8449 *Fax:* 212-206-1429 *E-mail:* info@samuelfrench.com *Web Site:* www.samuelfrench.com, pg 1314

Fresh Air Photo, 2203 McKinley Rd, Suite 220, Johnson City, TN 37604 *Tel:* 423-928-2700 *Fax:* 423-282-2730 *Web Site:* www.freshairphoto.com, pg 1438

Robert Fried Photography, 610 Eldridge Ct, Novato, CA 94947 *Tel:* 415-898-6153 *Fax:* 415-897-0353 *E-mail:* rob@robertfriedphotography.com *Web Site:* www.robertfriedphotography.com, pg 1438

Friesens Corp, One Printers Way, Altona, MB R0G 0B0, Canada *Tel:* 204-324-6401 *Fax:* 204-324-1333 *E-mail:* book_info@friesens.com *Web Site:* www.friesens.com, pg 1205, 1247

Rita Berman Frischer, 450 NE 100 St, Suite 426, Seattle, WA 98125 *Tel:* 206-361-9772; 818-469-0535 (cell) *Fax:* 206-361-9772 *E-mail:* rcfrischer@aol.com, pg 1117

Fry Communications Inc, 800 W Church Rd, Mechanicsburg, PA 17055 *Tel:* 717-766-0211 *Toll Free Tel:* 800-334-1429 *Fax:* 717-691-0341 *E-mail:* info@frycomm.com *Web Site:* www.frycomm.com, pg 1205, 1220, 1247, 1276

Fujifilm North America Corporation, Graphic Systems Division, 850 Central Ave, Hanover Park, IL 60133 *Tel:* 630-259-7200 *Toll Free Tel:* 800-877-0555 *Fax:* 630-259-7078 *Web Site:* www.fujifilmusa.com/products/graphic_arts_printing/index.html; www.fujifilmusa.com, pg 1276

Fujii Associates Inc, 75 Sunny Hill Dr, Troy, MO 63379 *Tel:* 636-528-2546 *Fax:* 636-600-5153 *Web Site:* www.fujiiassociates.com, pg 1287

Fujitsu Computer Products of America Inc, 1250 E Arques Ave, Sunnyvale, CA 94085-4701 *Tel:* 408-746-6000 *Toll Free Tel:* 800-626-4686 *E-mail:* scanner-sales@us.fujitsu.com *Web Site:* www.fujitsu.com/us, pg 1377

Fulfillment by Amazon (FBA), 440 Terry Ave N, Seattle, WA 98109 *Web Site:* services.amazon.com; www.amazon.com/advantage, pg 1287

H B Fuller Co, 1200 Willow Lake Blvd, St Paul, MN 55110-5146 *Tel:* 651-236-5900 *Toll Free Tel:* 888-423-8553 *E-mail:* inquiry@hbfuller.com *Web Site:* www.hbfuller.com, pg 1263, 1276

Fundamental Photographs, 210 Forsyth St, Suite 2, New York, NY 10002 *Tel:* 212-473-5770 *E-mail:* mail@fphoto.com *Web Site:* www.fphoto.com, pg 1446

Fundcraft Publishing, 410 Hwy 72 W, Collierville, TN 38017 *Tel:* 901-853-7070 *Toll Free Tel:* 800-853-1363 *Fax:* 901-853-6196 *E-mail:* info@fundcraft.com *Web Site:* www.fundcraft.com, pg 1205

Fuse Graphics, 1800 Sandy Plains Pkwy, Suite 124, Marietta, GA 30066 *Tel:* 770-499-7777 *Fax:* 770-499-7778 *E-mail:* info@fusegraphicsatlanta.com *Web Site:* www.fusegraphicsatlanta.com, pg 1247

G & H Soho Inc, 413 Market St, Elmwood Park, NJ 07407 *Tel:* 201-216-9400 *Fax:* 201-216-1778 *E-mail:* print@ghsoho.com *Web Site:* www.ghsoho.com, pg 1205, 1220, 1248, 1263, 1346, 1358, 1428

Gail Leondar Public Relations, 21 Belknap St, Arlington, MA 02474 *Tel:* 781-648-1658 *E-mail:* gail@glprbooks.com *Web Site:* www.glprbooks.com, pg 1097

Gallus Group, One Ivybrook Blvd, Suite 180, Ivyland, PA 18974 *Tel:* 215-677-9600 *Fax:* 215-677-9700 *E-mail:* info@gallus-group.com *Web Site:* gallus.contento.ch, pg 1276

Gane Brothers & Lane Inc, 1400 Greenleaf Ave, Elk Grove Village, IL 60007 *Tel:* 847-593-3364 *Toll Free Tel:* 800-323-0596 *Toll Free Fax:* 800-784-2464 *E-mail:* sales@ganebrothers.com *Web Site:* www.ganebrothers.com, pg 1263

Gannett News Service, 7950 Jones Branch Dr, McLean, VA 22107-0150 Tel: 703-854-6000 E-mail: pr@gannett.com Web Site: www.gannett.com, pg 1184

Mayra E Garcia, 332 Greenwood Hwy, Saluda, SC 29138 Tel: 803-422-5903 E-mail: mayra.garcia11@gmail.com, pg 1409

Garcia Publishing Services, 919 Tappan St, Woodstock, IL 60098 Tel: 815-338-5512 Fax: 815-338-5512 Web Site: www.gpsdesign.net, pg 1358

Garlich Printing Co, 525 Rudder Rd, St Louis, MO 63026 Tel: 636-349-8000 Toll Free Tel: 844-449-4752 Fax: 636-349-8080 E-mail: customerservice@garlich.com Web Site: www.garlich.com, pg 1248

Laurence Gartel, PO Box 4114, Deerfield Beach, FL 33442 Tel: 561-302-6774 E-mail: gartel@comcast.net Web Site: gartelart.com, pg 1428

Garvan Media, Management & Marketing Inc, PO Box 737, Sandpoint, ID 83864 Tel: 208-265-1718 Web Site: facebook.com/stephen.b.garvan, pg 1346

The Gate Worldwide, 71 Fifth Ave, 8th fl, New York, NY 10003 Tel: 212-508-3400 Fax: 212-508-3402 (cgi) E-mail: contact@thegateworldwide.com Web Site: thegateworldwide.com, pg 1086

Gaunt Inc, Gaunt Bldg, 3011 Gulf Dr, Holmes Beach, FL 34217 Tel: 941-778-5211 Toll Free Tel: 800-WGAUNT3 (942-8683) Fax: 941-778-5252 E-mail: info@gaunt.com Web Site: www.gaunt.com, pg 1287

GBS Books, 11226 N 23 Ave, Suite 103, Phoenix, AZ 85029 Tel: 602-863-6000 Toll Free Tel: 800-851-6001 E-mail: gbsbooks@gbsbooks.com Web Site: www.gbsbooks.com, pg 1314

GEI WideFormat, A Visual Edge Technology Company, 3874 Highland Park NW, North Canton, OH 44720 Toll Free Tel: 800-842-8448 (serv); 888-722-6434 (sales) E-mail: sales@geiwideformat.com Web Site: www.geiwideformat.com; www.visualedgetechnology.com, pg 1378

Regina Gelb, 900 W 190 St, Suite 4-O, New York, NY 10040 Tel: 212-795-6925, pg 1409

Bonnie Geller-Geld, 2500 Johnson Ave, Bronx, NY 10463 Tel: 347-275-4040 E-mail: bggeld@gmail.com, pg 1438

Gem Guides Book Co, 1155 W Ninth St, Upland, CA 91786 Tel: 626-855-1611 Toll Free Tel: 800-824-5118 (orders) Fax: 626-855-1610 E-mail: info@gemguidesbooks.com; sales@gemguidesbooks.com (orders) Web Site: www.gemguidesbooks.com, pg 1314

General Cartography Inc, 4 Estate Dr, Boynton Beach, FL 33436 Tel: 561-455-4398 E-mail: terradata@aol.com Web Site: cartographybypaul.com, pg 1428

Genesis Marketing Group Inc, 850 Wade Hampton Blvd, Bldg A, Suite 100, Greenville, SC 29609 Tel: 864-233-2651 Toll Free Tel: 800-627-2651 Toll Free Fax: 800-849-4363 E-mail: orders@genesislink.com Web Site: www.genesislink.com, pg 1287

German Language Services, 4752 41 Ave SW, Suite B, Seattle, WA 98116 Tel: 206-938-3600 Fax: 206-938-8308 E-mail: info@germanlanguageservices.com Web Site: www.germanlanguageservices.com, pg 1409

Get Rich Book Club, 7 Putter Lane, Middle Island, NY 11953 Tel: 631-924-3888 (ext 202) E-mail: grbookclub@gmail.com; linickgroup@gmail.com, pg 1136

Getty Images Inc, 605 Fifth Ave S, Suite 400, Seattle, WA 98104 Tel: 206-925-5000 Toll Free Tel: 800-IMAGERY (462-4379 sales); 888-888-5889 E-mail: enterprisesolutionssales@gettyimages.com Web Site: www.gettyimages.com, pg 1378, 1446

GEX Inc, 2 Industrial Way, Atkinson, NH 03811 Tel: 603-870-9292 Web Site: www.gexinc.com, pg 1205, 1220, 1358, 1378, 1428

GGP Publishing Inc, 105 Calvert St, Suite 201, Harrison, NY 10528-3138 Tel: 914-834-8896 Fax: 914-834-7566 Web Site: www.GGPPublishing.com, pg 1346, 1358, 1409

GHP, 475 Heffernan Dr, West Haven, CT 06516 Tel: 203-479-7500 Fax: 203-479-7575 Web Site: www.ghpmedia.com, pg 1220, 1248

Rosanna M Giammanco Frongia PhD, PO Box 810422, Boca Raton, FL 33481-0422 Tel: 718-619-2637 (cell) E-mail: giammancorm@gmail.com, pg 1409

Giant Horse Printing Inc, 1336 San Mateo Ave, South San Francisco, CA 94080 Tel: 650-875-7137 Fax: 650-875-7194 E-mail: info@gianthorse.com Web Site: www.gianthorse.com, pg 1205

Dot Gibson Publications, PO Box 117, Waycross, GA 31502 Tel: 912-285-2848 Toll Free Tel: 800-336-8095 (for orders) Fax: 912-285-2848 E-mail: info@dotgibson.com Web Site: www.dotgibson.com, pg 1314

Gilman's LRC (Lost River Caverns), 726 Durham St, Hellertown, PA 18055 Tel: 610-838-8767 Toll Free Tel: 888-529-1907 Fax: 610-838-2961 E-mail: info.lostcave@gmail.com Web Site: www.lostcave.com, pg 1314

Girol Books Inc, PO Box 5473, LCD Merivale, Ottawa, ON K2C 3M1, Canada Tel: 613-233-9044 Fax: 613-233-9044 E-mail: info@girol.com Web Site: www.girol.com, pg 1287, 1314, 1326

Glasnost Communications, 1316 Tallberry Business Plaza, Suite 404, Cincinnati, OH 45230 Tel: 513-231-3599 Fax: 513-231-3599 E-mail: glasnost@att.net, pg 1409

Peter Glass Photography, 15 Oakwood St, East Hartford, CT 06108 Tel: 860-528-8559 (off); 860-712-7098 (cell) E-mail: peter@peterglass.com Web Site: www.peterglass.com, pg 1438

Glasshouse Images, 161 W 15 St, Suite 1-C, New York, NY 10011 Tel: 212-462-4538 (research queries only) E-mail: agency@glasshouseimages.com (collection queries only) Web Site: glasshouseimages.com, pg 1447

Glatfelter, Capitol Towers South, 4350 Congress St, Suite 600, Charlotte, NC 28209 Tel: 717-850-0170 Toll Free Tel: 866-744-7380 E-mail: info@glatfelter.com Web Site: www.glatfelter.com, pg 1263

Glenbow Museum Shop, 130 Ninth Ave SE, Calgary, AB T2G 0P3, Canada Tel: 403-268-4119 Fax: 403-262-4045 E-mail: shop@glenbow.org Web Site: www.glenbow.org, pg 1314

Global Graphics Software Inc, 5996 Clark Center Ave, Sarasota, FL 34238 Tel: 941-925-1303 E-mail: info@globalgraphics.com; sales@globalgraphics.com Web Site: www.globalgraphics.com/globalgraphics-software, pg 1378

Global Horizons, 1330 New Hampshire Ave NW, Unit 609, Washington, DC 20036, pg 1184

Global Information Network Ltd, 6040 Boulevard E, No 21-H, West New York, NJ 07093 Tel: 212-244-3123 E-mail: newsdesk@mindspring.com Web Site: www.indepthnews.net, pg 1184

Global Interprint Inc, 800 Warrington Rd, Santa Rosa, CA 95403 Tel: 707-545-1220 Fax: 707-545-1210 Web Site: www.globalinterprint.com, pg 1248

Globe Photos LLC, 6445 S Tenaya Way, Suite B130, Las Vegas, NV 89113 Tel: 631-661-3131 Fax: 702-442-2747 E-mail: info@globephotos.com Web Site: www.globephotos.com, pg 1447

GLS Companies, 1280 Energy Park Dr, St Paul, MN 55108-5106 Tel: 651-644-3000 Toll Free Tel: 800-655-9405 Web Site: www.glsmn.com, pg 1220, 1248

The Gluefast Co Inc, 3535 State Rte 66, Bldg No 1, Neptune, NJ 07753 Tel: 732-918-4600 Toll Free Tel: 800-242-7318 Fax: 732-918-4646 E-mail: info@gluefast.com Web Site: www.gluefast.com, pg 1335

Jeff Gnass Photography, 3042 Nowell Ave, Juneau, AK 99801 Tel: 907-789-2002 Fax: 206-577-6419 E-mail: office@jeffgnass.com Web Site: www.jeffgnass.com, pg 1438

GoalsGuy Learning Systems, 36181 E Lake Rd, Suite 139, Palm Harbor, FL 34685 Toll Free Tel: 877-462-5748 Fax: 813-435-2022 Toll Free Fax: 877-903-2284 E-mail: info@goalsguy.com Web Site: www.100daychallenge.com, pg 1314

GOBI® Library Solutions from EBSCO, 999 Maple St, Contoocook, NH 03229 Tel: 603-746-3102 Toll Free Tel: 800-258-3774 (US & CN) Fax: 603-746-5628 E-mail: information@ebsco.com Web Site: gobi.ebsco.com, pg 1314

Celia Godkin, Mod 6, Comp 12, 10 James St, Frankville, ON K0E 1H0, Canada Tel: 613-275-7204 E-mail: celia@godkin.ca Web Site: www.celiagodkin.com, pg 1220

Beryl Goldberg Photographer, 309 W 109 St, Suite 4-F, New York, NY 10025 Tel: 212-222-8215 E-mail: berylgphoto@aol.com; berylgnyc@gmail.com Web Site: www.berylgoldberg.com, pg 1438

Louis Goldberg Library Book Supplier, 45 Belvidere St, Nazareth, PA 18064 Tel: 610-759-9458 E-mail: orders@goldberg-books.com Web Site: www.goldberg-books.com, pg 1314

Goldberg McDuffie Communications, 250 Park Ave, 7th fl, New York, NY 10177 Tel: 212-705-4211 E-mail: bookpr@goldbergmcduffie.com Web Site: www.goldbergmcduffie.com, pg 1097, 1346

Gomsak Photography, 10428 S Hall Dr, Charlotte, NC 28270 Web Site: www.gomsak.com, pg 1438

The Good Cook®, 34 W 27 St, 10th fl, New York, NY 10001 Tel: 212-250-5700 (cust serv) E-mail: customer.service@thegoodcook.com Web Site: www.thegoodcook.com, pg 1136

GoodMinds.com, Six Nations of the Grand River Territory, 188 Mohawk St, Brantford, ON N3S 2X2, Canada Tel: 519-753-1185 Toll Free Tel: 877-862-8483 (CN & US) Fax: 519-751-3136 E-mail: helpme@goodminds.com Web Site: www.goodminds.com, pg 1287

Dave Goodwin & Associates, 721 86 St, Miami Beach, FL 33141-1115 Tel: 305-865-0158 E-mail: davegoodwi@aol.com Web Site: davegoodwin.weebly.com, pg 1184

Goose River Press, 3400 Friendship Rd, Waldoboro, ME 04572-6337 Tel: 207-832-6665 E-mail: gooseriverpress@gmail.com Web Site: gooseriverpress.com, pg 1220, 1248

Andrew S Gordon, PhD, 1230 23 St NW, No 804, Washington, DC 20037 E-mail: andgordon@yahoo.com, pg 1409

Gordon Management Inc (GMI), 305 Churchill Ave, Somerset, NJ 08873 Tel: 732-846-4800 Fax: 732-846-4709 E-mail: info@gmidistribution.com Web Site: www.gmidistribution.com, pg 1332, 1346

P M Gordon Associates Inc, 2115 Wallace St, Philadelphia, PA 19130 Tel: 215-769-2525 Web Site: www.pmgordonassociates.com, pg 1358

Gary Gore Book Design, 1913 Blair Blvd, Nashville, TN 37212 Tel: 615-298-3588 E-mail: garygore@comcast.net, pg 1428

Gore Studio Inc, 101 Paxton Ct, Brentwood, TN 37027 Tel: 615-519-2262 E-mail: gorestudioinc@gmail.com Web Site: www.gorestudio.com, pg 1428

Gorham Printing, 3718 Mahoney Dr, Centralia, WA 98531 Tel: 360-623-1323 Toll Free Tel: 800-837-0970 E-mail: info@gorhamprinting.com Web Site: www.gorhamprinting.com, pg 1248

Sandra Goroff & Associates, 42 Waterfall Dr, Suite L, Canton, MA 02021 Tel: 617-750-0555 E-mail: sgma@aol.com Web Site: www.sandragoroff.com, pg 1097

Regina Gorzkowska-Rossi, 3349 E Thompson St, Philadelphia, PA 19134 Tel: 267-535-1691 E-mail: proarterg@yahoo.com, pg 1409

Dan Gotshall Marine Life Photography, 4 Sommerset Rise, Monterey, CA 93940 Tel: 831-656-9169 E-mail: seachall@aol.com, pg 1438

Audrey Gottlieb, 161 York St, Unit 21, York, ME 03909 *Tel:* 207-641-7490 *E-mail:* audreyphoto@gmail.com *Web Site:* www.audreygottlieb.com, pg 1438

Gould Paper Corp, 99 Park Ave, 10th fl, New York, NY 10016 *Tel:* 212-301-0000 *Toll Free Tel:* 800-221-3043 *Fax:* 212-481-0067 *E-mail:* info@gouldpaper.com *Web Site:* www.gouldpaper.com, pg 1263

Stephen Gould Corp, 35 S Jefferson Rd, Whippany, NJ 07981 *Tel:* 973-428-1500; 973-428-1510 *E-mail:* info@stephengould.com *Web Site:* www.stephengould.com, pg 1092, 1335

Joseph C Goulden, 1534 29 St NW, Washington, DC 20007 *Tel:* 202-965-4757 *E-mail:* josephg894@aol.com, pg 1118

Geoffrey Gove, 734 Broad St, Bloomfield, NJ 07003 *Tel:* 917-370-6400 *E-mail:* geoffgove@gmail.com *Web Site:* www.facebook.com/ggove, pg 1439

Gracenote, a Nielsen Company, 2000 Powell St, Suite 1500, Emeryville, CA 94608 *Tel:* 510-428-7200 *Web Site:* www.gracenote.com, pg 1184

Joe & Teresa Graedon, 300 W 57 St, 41st fl, New York, NY 10019 *Tel:* 212-969-7550 *Toll Free Tel:* 800-526-5464; 800-708-7311 (FL edit) *Fax:* 646-280-1550 *Web Site:* www.kingfeatures.com; www.peoplespharmacy.org, pg 1118

Diane Graham-Henry Photography, 2247 N Geneva Terr, Chicago, IL 60614 *Tel:* 773-327-4493 *Fax:* 773-248-2774 *E-mail:* dghphoto@gmail.com, pg 1439

Rita Granda, 466 Cambridge St, Peterborough, ON K9H 4T3, Canada *Tel:* 705-748-0943 *E-mail:* rita@ritagranda.com *Web Site:* www.ritagranda.com, pg 1409

Granger - Historical Picture Archive, 25 Chapel St, Suite 605, Brooklyn, NY 11201 *Tel:* 212-447-1789 *Fax:* 212-447-1492 *E-mail:* info@granger.com *Web Site:* www.granger.com, pg 1447

Michael Grant, 115 Carthage Rd, Scarsdale, NY 10583 *Tel:* 914-821-8315 *E-mail:* michael@michaelgrantdirect.com; michaelgrant12@optonline.net *Web Site:* www.michaelgrantdirect.com, pg 1346

Graphic Composition Inc, N1246 Technical Dr, Greenville, WI 54942 *Tel:* 920-757-6977 *Toll Free Tel:* 800-262-8973 *Fax:* 920-757-9266 *E-mail:* socialmedia@graphiccomp.com *Web Site:* www.graphiccomp.com, pg 1248

Graphic Connections Group LLC, 174 Chesterfield Industrial Blvd, Chesterfield, MO 63005 *Tel:* 636-519-8320 *Toll Free Tel:* 800-378-0378 *Fax:* 636-519-8310 *Web Site:* www.gcfrog.com, pg 1205

GW Illustration & Design, 2290 Ball Dr, St Louis, MO 63146 *Tel:* 314-567-9854 *Web Site:* www.gwinc.com, pg 1428

Graphic Litho, 130 Shepard St, Lawrence, MA 01843 *Tel:* 978-683-2766 *Fax:* 978-681-7588 *E-mail:* sales@graphiclitho.com *Web Site:* www.graphiclitho.com, pg 1092, 1206, 1248

GraphiColor Corp, 3490 N Mill Rd, Vineland, NJ 08360 *Tel:* 856-691-2507 *Toll Free Tel:* 800-552-2507 *Fax:* 856-696-3229 *Web Site:* www.graphicolorcorp.com, pg 1220, 1248

Graphics International, 20475 Bunker Hill Dr, Cleveland, OH 44126 *Tel:* 440-333-9988, pg 1428

Graphics Two, 819 S Main St, Burbank, CA 91506 *Tel:* 818-841-4922, pg 1220, 1276

Tom Graves Photography, 400-A Clipper St, San Francisco, CA 94114 *Tel:* 415-550-7241 *E-mail:* tom@tomgraves.com *Web Site:* www.tomgraves.com; www.twiceheroes.com, pg 1439

Great Lakes Bindery Inc, 3741 Linden Ave SE, Wyoming, MI 49548 *Tel:* 616-245-5264 *Fax:* 616-245-5883 *E-mail:* jeremy@greatlakesbindery.com *Web Site:* www.greatlakesbindery.com, pg 1248

Susanna Greenberg Public Relations, 41 Old Brook Rd, Dix Hills, NY 11746 *Tel:* 646-801-7477 *E-mail:* publicity@bookbuzz.com *Web Site:* bookbuzz.com; linkedin.com/in/susannahgreenberg; www.facebook.com/SusannahGreenbergPublicRelations; twitter.com/SueGreenbergPR, pg 1097

Greenleaf Book Group LLC, 3 Park Place, 4005 Banister Lane, Suite B, Austin, TX 78704 *Tel:* 512-891-6100 *Fax:* 512-891-6150 *E-mail:* contact@greenleafbookgroup.com *Web Site:* www.greenleafbookgroup.com, pg 1288, 1358

Greg Johnston Photography, 6214 Solstice Loop, Sanford, FL 32773 *Tel:* 305-258-7070 *E-mail:* info@gregjohnston.com *Web Site:* www.gregjohnston.com, pg 1439

Ann Grifalconi/Greyfalcon House, 124 Waverly Place, No 1, New York, NY 10011 *Tel:* 212-777-9042, pg 1428

Gropen Associates, 9 Clubview Dr, Birmingham, AL 35223 *Toll Free Tel:* 888-3GROPEN (347-6736) *Toll Free Fax:* 888-347-6736 *Web Site:* www.gropenassoc.com, pg 1346

David M Grossman Photography, 211 E Seventh St, Brooklyn, NY 11218 *Tel:* 718-438-5021 *E-mail:* david@grossmanphotos.com *Web Site:* www.grossmanphotos.com, pg 1439

J S Grove Photography, 166 Peace Ave, Tavernier, FL 33070 *Tel:* 305-852-6004 *E-mail:* jsimages@aol.com, pg 1439

GSB Digital, 33-01 Hunters Point Ave, Long Island City, NY 11101 *Tel:* 212-684-3600 *Fax:* 212-684-3613 *E-mail:* questions@gsbdigital.com *Web Site:* www.gsbdigital.com, pg 1378

GTCO Calcomp, 14557 N 82 St, Scottsdale, AZ 85260 *Tel:* 480-443-2264 *Toll Free Tel:* 800-220-1137 *Fax:* 480-948-1751 *E-mail:* sales@gtcocalcomp.com *Web Site:* www.gtcocalcomp.com, pg 1378

GTI Graphic Technology Inc, 211 Dupont Ave, Newburgh, NY 12550 *Tel:* 845-562-7066 *Fax:* 845-562-2543 *E-mail:* sales@gtilite.com *Web Site:* www.gtilite.com, pg 1276, 1378

GTxcel Inc, 144 Turnpike Rd, Suite 130, Southborough, MA 01772-2104 *Toll Free Tel:* 800-609-8994 *Web Site:* www.gtxcel.com, pg 1378

Guardian Book Co, 7019 Edinburgh Dr, Lambertville, MI 48144 *Tel:* 734-856-1765 *Toll Free Tel:* 800-560-6697 *Fax:* 734-854-7638 *Web Site:* guardianbookcompany.com; gbcbooks.com, pg 1314

Polly Guerin, 15 Park Ave, No 14A, New York, NY 10016-4348 *Tel:* 212-725-0977 *E-mail:* pollytalknyc@gmail.com *Web Site:* www.pollytalk.com, pg 1118

Gulotta Communications Inc, 321 Walnut St, Newton, MA 02460 *Tel:* 617-630-9286 *Fax:* 978-733-6162 *Web Site:* www.booktours.com, pg 1097

Gurarys Israeli Trading Co Inc, 724 Eastern Pkwy, Brooklyn, NY 11213 *Tel:* 718-493-5225 *E-mail:* hebbook@gmail.com, pg 1326

Guy Gurney, 55 Turkey Plain Rd, Bethel, CT 06801 *Tel:* 203-616-5643; 203-434-7337 (cell) *E-mail:* guy@guygurney.com *Web Site:* www.guygurney.com, pg 1439

GW Inc, 2290 Ball Dr, St Louis, MO 63146 *Tel:* 314-567-9854 *Web Site:* www.gwinc.com, pg 1220, 1378

Kathryn Hall, Publicist, PO Box 1486, Ukiah, CA 95482 *Tel:* 707-468-8201 *E-mail:* khpbooks@gmail.com *Web Site:* www.kathrynhallpublicist.com; estrellacatarina.com, pg 1098

Molly Hall, 4338 Mitchell St, Philadelphia, PA 19128 *Tel:* 215-970-1837 *E-mail:* mollyhallindexer@hotmail.com, pg 1220

Anita Halton Associates, 559 Alta Vista Way, Laguna Beach, CA 92651 *Tel:* 415-640-5486 (cell) *E-mail:* ahapub@aol.com *Web Site:* anitahaltonassociates.com, pg 1098

Chris Hamilton Photography, 652 Bellemeade Ave NW, Atlanta, GA 30318 *Tel:* 404-355-9411 *Web Site:* www.hamphoto.com, pg 1439

Hannecke Display Systems Inc, 210 Grove St, Franklin, MA 02038 *Tel:* 774-235-2329 *E-mail:* info@hannecke.com *Web Site:* www.hannecke.com, pg 1092

Hanser Publications LLC, 414 Walnut St, Suite 323, Cincinnati, OH 45202 *Toll Free Tel:* 800-950-8977; 888-558-2632 (orders) *E-mail:* info@hanserpublications.com *Web Site:* www.hanserpublications.com, pg 1288

Susie Harris, 282 Whitetail Lane, Hot Springs, AR 71901 *Tel:* 501-762-2200 *E-mail:* sales@harrisphotos.com *Web Site:* www.neworleansphotos.com; www.harrisphotos.com; www.mardigrasphotos.net, pg 1439

Hartnett Inc, 2308 Mount Vernon Ave, Suite 817, Alexandria, VA 22301 *Tel:* 703-660-6799 *Web Site:* www.hartnettinc.com, pg 1346

Harty Integrated Solutions, 25 James St, New Haven, CT 06513 *Tel:* 203-562-5112 *Toll Free Tel:* 800-654-0562 *Fax:* 203-782-9168 *Web Site:* www.hartynet.com, pg 1092

Harvard Art Museums, 32 Quincy St, Cambridge, MA 02138 *Tel:* 617-495-9400 *Fax:* 617-495-9985 *Web Site:* www.harvardartmuseums.org, pg 1314

Harvard Educational Review, 8 Story St, 1st fl, Cambridge, MA 02138 *Tel:* 617-495-3432 *Toll Free Tel:* 888-437-1437 (orders) *Fax:* 617-496-3584; 978-348-1233 (orders) *Web Site:* hepg.org/her-home/home, pg 1126

Hassett Express, 18W100 22 St, Suite 109, Oakbrook Terrace, IL 60181 *Tel:* 630-530-6515 *Toll Free Tel:* 800-323-9422 *Fax:* 630-530-6538 *Web Site:* www.hassettexpress.com, pg 1332

Havey Productions, 3457 Ringsby Court, Unit 105, Denver, CO 80216 *Tel:* 303-296-7448 *Web Site:* www.haveypro.com, pg 1439

Haynes North America Inc, 859 Lawrence Dr, Newbury Park, CA 91320-1514 *Tel:* 805-498-6703 *Toll Free Tel:* 800-4-HAYNES (442-9637) *Fax:* 805-498-2867 *E-mail:* cstn@haynes.com *Web Site:* www.haynes.com, pg 1326

HBG Productions/International Publishers Alliance, PO Box 5560, Chico, CA 95927-5560 *Tel:* 530-893-4699 *Web Site:* www.hbgproductions.com, pg 1288

HBP Inc, 952 Frederick St, Hagerstown, MD 21740 *Tel:* 301-733-2000 *Toll Free Tel:* 800-638-3508 *Fax:* 301-733-6586 *E-mail:* contactus@hbp.com *Web Site:* www.hbp.com, pg 1220, 1248, 1276

Hearst Newspapers, 300 W 57 St, New York, NY 10019 *Tel:* 212-649-2000 *Web Site:* www.hearst.com/newspapers, pg 1185

Hedquist Productions Inc, PO Box 1475, Fairfield, IA 52556-1475 *Tel:* 641-472-6708 *Toll Free Fax:* 855-510-5726 *Web Site:* www.hedquist.com, pg 1378

Milton Heiberg Studios, 1022 Empress Lane, Orlando, FL 32825-8249 *Tel:* 407-658-4869 *Fax:* 407-658-4869 *E-mail:* photonat@cfl.rr.com *Web Site:* www.miltonheiberg.com, pg 1439

Heidelberg Graphics, 2 Stansbury Ct, Chico, CA 95928 *Tel:* 530-342-6582 *Fax:* 530-342-6582 *E-mail:* heidelberggraphics@gmail.com; service@heidelberggraphics.com *Web Site:* www.heidelberggraphics.com, pg 1221, 1248, 1276, 1346, 1378, 1428

Heidelberg USA Inc, 1000 Gutenberg Dr, Kennesaw, GA 30144 *Tel:* 770-419-6500 *Toll Free Tel:* 800-437-7388 *E-mail:* info@heidelberg.com *Web Site:* www.heidelberg.com/us, pg 1276

Grant Heilman Photography Inc, 506 W Lincoln Ave, Lititz, PA 17543 *Tel:* 717-626-0296 *Toll Free Tel:* 800-622-2046 *Fax:* 717-626-0971 *E-mail:* info@heilmanphoto.com *Web Site:* www.heilmanphoto.com, pg 1447

William S Hein & Co Inc, 2350 N Forest Rd, Getzville, NY 14068 *Tel:* 716-882-2600 *Toll Free Tel:* 800-828-7571 *Fax:* 716-883-8100 *E-mail:* mail@wshein.com; marketing@wshein.com *Web Site:* www.wshein.com, pg 1314

Albert Henderson, 655 West Ave, Milford, CT 06461-3003 *Tel:* 203-301-0791 *E-mail:* 70244.1532@compuserve.com, pg 1346

The Hendra Agency Inc, 142 Sterling Place, Brooklyn, NY 11217-3307 *Tel:* 718-622-3232; 212-947-9898 *Fax:* 718-622-3322, pg 1098

Henkel Corp, One Henkel Way, Rocky Hill, CT 06067 *Tel:* 860-571-5100 *Fax:* 860-571-5465 *E-mail:* corp.info@henkel.com *Web Site:* www.henkel-northamerica.com; www.henkel-adhesives.com, pg 1264

Hennegan Co, 7455 Empire Dr, Florence, KY 41042 *Tel:* 859-282-3600 *Fax:* 859-282-3601 *Web Site:* www.hennegan.com, pg 1221, 1248

Diana Mara Henry, 187 Prospect St, Newport, VT 05855 *Tel:* 802-334-7054 *E-mail:* dmh@dianamarahenry.com *Web Site:* www.natzweiler-struthof.com, pg 1410

Diana Mara Henry, 187 Prospect St, Newport, VT 05855 *Tel:* 802-334-7054 *E-mail:* dmh@dianamarahenry.com *Web Site:* dianamarahenry.com, pg 1439, 1447

The Henry James Review, 2715 N Charles St, Baltimore, MD 21218-4363 *Tel:* 410-516-6987 (journal orders outside US & CN) *Toll Free Tel:* 800-548-1784 (journal orders) *Fax:* 410-516-8600 *E-mail:* jrnlcirc@press.jhu.edu (journal orders) *Web Site:* www.press.jhu.edu/journals/henry_james_review/index.html, pg 1126

Heraeus Noblelight America LLC, 910 Clopper Rd, Gaithersburg, MD 20878-1361 *Tel:* 301-527-2660 *Toll Free Tel:* 888-276-8600 *Fax:* 301-527-2661 *E-mail:* info.hna.uvp@heraeus.com *Web Site:* www.heraeus-noblelight.com/uvamericas, pg 1276

Mark Herman & Ronnie Apter, Translators, 2222 Westview Dr, Nashville, TN 37212-4123 *Tel:* 615-942-8462 *E-mail:* mnh18@columbia.edu, pg 1410

Hermani & Sorrentino Design, 404 Musgrave Rd, Salt Spring Island, BC V8K 1V5, Canada *Tel:* 250-653-9350 *E-mail:* hermani2sorrentino@gmail.com *Web Site:* www.hermanisorrentino.com, pg 1429

Michal Heron Photography, 3806 Easton St, Sarasota, FL 34238 *Tel:* 941-922-5124 *E-mail:* michalheronphoto@gmail.com *Web Site:* www.michalheron.com, pg 1439

Herr's Indexing Service, 76-340 Kealoha St, Kailua Kona, HI 96740-2915 *Tel:* 808-365-4348 *Web Site:* www.herrsindexing.com, pg 1221

Hespenheide Design, 99 Long Ct, Suite 102, Thousand Oaks, CA 91360 *Tel:* 805-499-8875 *Web Site:* www.hespenheide.com, pg 1429

Hess Print Solutions, 3765 Sunnybrook Rd, Brimfield, OH 44240 *Toll Free Tel:* 800-678-1222 *E-mail:* info@hessprintsolutions.com *Web Site:* www.hessprintsolutions.com, pg 1206, 1248

HF Group LLC, 8844 Mayfield Rd, Chesterland, OH 44026 *Tel:* 440-729-2445; 440-729-9411 (bindery) *E-mail:* custservice-oh@hfgroup.com *Web Site:* www.hfgroup.com, pg 1248, 1264, 1323

HFS, 2715 N Charles St, Baltimore, MD 21218 *Tel:* 410-516-6965 *Toll Free Tel:* 800-537-5487 (US & CN) *Fax:* 410-516-6998 *E-mail:* hfscustserv@press.jhu.edu *Web Site:* hfs.jhu.edu; www.hfsbooks.com, pg 1288

The Hibbert Group, 400 Pennington Ave, Trenton, NJ 08650 *Tel:* 609-394-7500 *Toll Free Tel:* 888-HIBBERT (442-2378) *E-mail:* info@hibbertgroup.com *Web Site:* hibbert.com, pg 1092, 1106, 1109

HID Global, 611 Center Ridge Dr, Austin, TX 78753 *Tel:* 512-776-9000 *Toll Free Tel:* 800-872-5359 (cust serv) *Fax:* 512-776-9930 *E-mail:* customerservice@hidglobal.com *Web Site:* www.hidglobal.com, pg 1378

HID Ultraviolet LLC, 520 Lafayette Rd, Sparta, NJ 07871 *Tel:* 973-383-8535 *Fax:* 973-383-1606 *E-mail:* sales@hid.com *Web Site:* www.hid.com, pg 1277

Worth Higgins & Associates Inc, 8770 Park Central Dr, Richmond, VA 23227-1146 *Tel:* 804-264-2304 *Toll Free Tel:* 800-883-7768 *Fax:* 804-264-5733 *E-mail:* contact@whaprint.com *Web Site:* www.worthhiggins.com, pg 1221, 1249

Hignell Book Printing Ltd, 488 Burnell St, Winnipeg, MB R3G 2B4, Canada *Tel:* 204-784-1030 *Toll Free Tel:* 800-304-5553 *Fax:* 204-774-4053 *E-mail:* books@hignell.mb.ca *Web Site:* www.hignell.mb.ca, pg 1206, 1249

Hill+Knowlton Strategies, 237 Park Ave, 4th fl, New York, NY 10017 *Tel:* 212-885-0300 *Web Site:* www.hkstrategies.com, pg 1098

Hilsinger-Mendelson West Inc, 8916 Ashcroft Ave, Los Angeles, CA 90048 *Tel:* 310-659-7930 *E-mail:* hmiwest@aol.com *Web Site:* www.hilsingermendelson.com, pg 1098

Historic Aviation Books, 640 Taft St NE, Minneapolis, MN 55413-2815 *Tel:* 612-206-3200 *Toll Free Tel:* 800-225-5575 *Fax:* 612-877-3160 *E-mail:* info@historicaviation.com; customerservice@historicaviation.com *Web Site:* www.historicaviation.com, pg 1315

Historic Cherry Hill, 523 1/2 S Pearl St, Albany, NY 12202 *Tel:* 518-434-4791 *Fax:* 518-434-4806 *E-mail:* info@historiccherryhill.org *Web Site:* historiccherryhill.org, pg 1315

Historic Films LLC, 211 Third St, Greenport, NY 11944 *Tel:* 631-477-9700 *Toll Free Tel:* 800-249-1940 *Fax:* 631-477-9800 *E-mail:* info@historicfilms.com *Web Site:* www.historicfilms.com, pg 1447

The Historical Novels Review, 400 Dark Star Ct, Fairbanks, AK 99709 *Tel:* 217-581-7538 *Fax:* 217-581-7534 *E-mail:* reviews@historicalnovelsociety.org *Web Site:* historicalnovelsociety.org, pg 1126

History Book Club®, 34 W 27 St, 10th fl, New York, NY 10001 *Tel:* 716-250-5700 (cust serv) *E-mail:* customer.service@historybookclub.com *Web Site:* www.historybookclub.com, pg 1136

History: Reviews of New Books, 530 Walnut St, Suite 850, Philadelphia, PA 19106 *Tel:* 215-625-8900 (ext 4) *Toll Free Tel:* 800-354-1420 *Fax:* 215-207-0050; 215-207-0046 (cust serv) *E-mail:* historyreviews@taylorandfrancis.com; support@tandfonline.com *Web Site:* www.tandfonline.com, pg 1127

HJMT Public Relations Inc, 78 E Park Ave, Long Beach, NY 11561 *Tel:* 347-696-0220 *E-mail:* info@hjmt.com *Web Site:* www.hjmt.com, pg 1098

Bruce Hoffman, 71 Faunce Dr, Providence, RI 02906 *Tel:* 401-274-2149 *Web Site:* www.whitegatefeatures.com, pg 1118

Art Holeman Photography, 4156 E Cathedral Rock Dr, Phoenix, AZ 85044 *Tel:* 602-290-7431 (cell) *E-mail:* art@artholeman.com; artholeman@cox.net *Web Site:* www.artholeman.com; www.fineartholeman.com, pg 1439

Hollenbeck Productions, 19241 Normandy Park Dr SW, Seattle, WA 98166 *Tel:* 206-592-1800 *Web Site:* www.hollenbeckproductions.com; www.cliffscoolstuff.com, pg 1439

Hollinger Metal Edge Inc, 9401 Northeast Dr, Fredricksburg, VA 22408 *Tel:* 540-898-7300 *Toll Free Tel:* 800-634-0491 *Toll Free Fax:* 800-947-8814 *E-mail:* info@hollingermetaledge.com *Web Site:* www.hollingermetaledge.com, pg 1264

Holliston Holdings LLC, 905 Holliston Mills Rd, Church Hill, TN 37642 *Tel:* 423-357-6141 *Toll Free Tel:* 800-251-0451; 800-251-0251 (cust serv) *Fax:* 423-357-8840 *Toll Free Fax:* 800-325-0351 (cust serv) *E-mail:* custserv@holliston.com *Web Site:* holliston.com, pg 1264

Holmberg Co Inc, 4155 Berkshire Lane N, Minneapolis, MN 55446-3814 *Tel:* 763-559-4155 *Toll Free Tel:* 800-328-5101 *E-mail:* customerservice@holmberg.com *Web Site:* www.holmberg.com, pg 1249

Henry Holmes Literary Agent/Book Publicist/Marketing Consultant, Mitchell Heights, Apt 205, 2100 S Main St, Fall River, MA 02724 *Tel:* 508-672-2258; 508-415-4062 (cell), pg 1086, 1098, 1346

Holo Image Technology Inc, 101 William Leigh Dr, Tullytown, PA 19007 *Tel:* 215-946-2190 *Fax:* 215-946-2129 *E-mail:* info@holoimagetechnology.com *Web Site:* www.holoimagetechnology.com, pg 1277

Homestead Publishing, Box 193, Moose, WY 83012-0193 *Tel:* 307-733-6248 *Fax:* 415-621-5039, pg 1358

Honeybee (ages 2-4), 557 Broadway, New York, NY 10012 *Tel:* 212-343-6100 *Toll Free Tel:* 800-724-6527 (press 1) *Toll Free Fax:* 800-223-4011 *E-mail:* bookclubs@scholastic.com *Web Site:* scholastic.com/bookclubs, pg 1136

Tom Hopkins Studio, 2121 Durham Rd, Madison, CT 06443 *Tel:* 203-421-4644 *E-mail:* contact@tomhopkinsstudio.com *Web Site:* www.tomhopkinsstudio.com, pg 1439

The Horah Group, 351 Manville Rd, Suite 105, Pleasantville, NY 10570 *Tel:* 914-495-3200 *Fax:* 914-769-8802 *Web Site:* www.horah.com, pg 1092

Horizon Paper Co Inc, 1010 Washington Blvd, Stamford, CT 06901 *Tel:* 203-358-0855 *Toll Free Tel:* 866-358-0855 *E-mail:* info@horizonpaper.com *Web Site:* www.horizonpaper.com, pg 1264

The Horn Book Guide, 300 The Fenway, Suite P-311, Palace Road Bldg, Boston, MA 02115 *Tel:* 617-278-0225 *Toll Free Tel:* 888-628-0225 *Fax:* 617-278-6062 *E-mail:* info@hbook.com *Web Site:* www.hbook.com, pg 1127

Horn Book Inc, 300 The Fenway, Suite P-311, Palace Road Bldg, Boston, MA 02115 *Tel:* 617-278-0225 *Toll Free Tel:* 888-628-0225 *Fax:* 617-278-6062 *E-mail:* info@hbook.com *Web Site:* www.hbook.com, pg 1140

The Horn Book Magazine, 300 The Fenway, Suite P-311, Palace Road Bldg, Boston, MA 02115 *Tel:* 617-278-0225 *Toll Free Tel:* 888-628-0225 *Fax:* 617-278-6062 *E-mail:* info@hbook.com *Web Site:* www.hbook.com, pg 1127

Alice Hornbaker, 11050 Springfield Pike, No F-508, Cincinnati, OH 45246 *Tel:* 513-772-3506 *Fax:* 513-772-3506 *E-mail:* ajhornbaker@yahoo.com *Web Site:* www.wmkvfm.org, pg 1118

Shirley Horner, 535 Mountain Ave, New Providence, NJ 07974 *Tel:* 908-795-2512 *E-mail:* sjhorner@comcast.net, pg 1118

David K Horowitz Studio Inc, 920 Chestnut St, No 22, Philadelphia, PA 19107, pg 1439

Houchen Bindery Ltd, 340 First St, Utica, NE 68456 *Tel:* 402-534-2261 *Toll Free Tel:* 800-869-0420 *Fax:* 402-534-2761 *E-mail:* email@houchenbindery.com *Web Site:* www.houchenbindery.com, pg 1323

Hourglass Press LLC, 39 W 32 St, Suite 1404, New York, NY 10001 *Tel:* 917-449-3707 *Web Site:* www.hourglasspress.com, pg 1358

Joan E Howard, 51 Congress St, Augusta, ME 04330 *Tel:* 207-622-0580 *E-mail:* petiteplaisance@acadia.net, pg 1410

HP Inc, 1501 Paige Mill Rd, Palo Alto, CA 94304-1112 *Tel:* 650-857-1501 *Toll Free Tel:* 800-282-6672 *Web Site:* www.hp.com, pg 1378

The Hubbard Co, 612 Clinton St, Defiance, OH 43512 *Tel:* 419-784-4455 *Toll Free Tel:* 888-448-2227 *Web Site:* www.hubbardcompany.com, pg 1315

George H H Huey Photography Inc, 382 W Butterfield Rd, Suite 115, Chino Valley, AZ 86323 *Tel:* 928-445-6800 *Web Site:* www.georgehhhuey.com, pg 1439

Cathy Hull, 180 E 79 St, New York, NY 10075 *Tel:* 212-772-7743 *Fax:* 212-535-1877 *E-mail:* cathy@cathyhull.com *Web Site:* www.cathyhull.com, pg 1429

Human Rights Quarterly, 2715 N Charles St, Baltimore, MD 21218-4363 *Tel:* 410-516-6987 (journal orders outside US & CN) *Toll Free Tel:* 800-548-1784 (journal orders) *Fax:* 410-516-3866 (journal orders) *E-mail:* jrnlcirc@press.jhu.edu (journal orders) *Web Site:* www.press.jhu.edu/journals/human_rights_quarterly, pg 1127

HumanEdge, 30 Glenn St, Suite 401, White Plains, NY 10603 *Tel:* 914-428-2233 *Fax:* 914-428-5547 *E-mail:* info@humanedge.com *Web Site:* www. humanedge.com, pg 1389

Nancy Humphreys Wordmaps, 600 Humboldt St, Richmond, CA 94805 *Tel:* 510-215-9960 *Web Site:* authormaps.com, pg 1346

HurleyMedia LLC, 1477 Canyon Rd, Santa Fe, NM 87501 *Tel:* 505-603-6392 *Web Site:* www.hurleymedia. com, pg 1098, 1346

Richard Hutchings Photography LLC, 11 White Well Dr, Rhinebeck, NY 12572 *Tel:* 914-715-7461 *E-mail:* richard@hutchingsphotography.com *Web Site:* hutchingsphotography.com, pg 1440

The P A Hutchison Co, 400 Penn Ave, Mayfield, PA 18433 *Tel:* 570-876-4560 *Toll Free Tel:* 800-USA-PRNT (872-7768) *Fax:* 570-876-4561 *E-mail:* sales@ pahutch.com *Web Site:* www.pahutch.com, pg 1206, 1221, 1249, 1264, 1277

I-Web, 175 Bodwell St, Avon, MA 02322 *Tel:* 508-580-5809 *Fax:* 508-580-5632 *E-mail:* info@iwebus.com *Web Site:* iwebus.com, pg 1277

IBM Corp, One New Orchard Rd, Armonk, NY 10504 *Tel:* 914-499-1900 *Toll Free Tel:* 800-426-4968 *E-mail:* askibm@vnet.ibm.com *Web Site:* www.ibm. com, pg 1378

iCAD Inc, 98 Spit Brook Rd, Suite 100, Nashua, NH 03062 *Tel:* 603-882-5200 *Toll Free Tel:* 866-280-2239 *E-mail:* sales@icadmed.com; support@icamed.com *Web Site:* www.icadmed.com, pg 1379

ICSID Review: Foreign Investment Law Journal, 2001 Evans Rd, Cary, NC 27513 *Tel:* 919-677-0977 *Toll Free Tel:* 800-852-7323 *Fax:* 919-677-1714 *Web Site:* academic.oup.org, pg 1127

Idea Architects, 523 Swift St, Santa Cruz, CA 95060 *Tel:* 831-465-9565 *Web Site:* www.ideaarchitects.com, pg 1347

The Idea Logical Co Inc, 300 E 51 St, Apt 17C, New York, NY 10022 *Tel:* 212-758-5670 *E-mail:* info@ idealog.com *Web Site:* www.idealog.com, pg 1347

Ideal Foreign Books LLC, 132-10 Hillside Ave, Richmond Hill, NY 11418 *Tel:* 718-297-7477 *Toll Free Tel:* 800-284-2490 *Fax:* 718-297-7645 *E-mail:* idealforeignbooks@att.net, pg 1315

The Image Finders, 2570 Superior Ave, Suite 200, Cleveland, OH 44114 *Tel:* 216-781-7729; 440-413-6104 *E-mail:* imagefinders@sbcglobal.net; jim@ baronphotography.net *Web Site:* www.theimagefinders. com, pg 1447

The Image Works Inc, PO Box 443, Woodstock, NY 12498-0443 *Tel:* 845-679-8500 *Toll Free Tel:* 800-475-8801 *Fax:* 845-679-0606 *E-mail:* info@ theimageworks.com *Web Site:* www.theimageworks. com, pg 1448

Imago, 110 W 40 St, New York, NY 10018 *Tel:* 212-921-4411 *Fax:* 212-921-8226 *E-mail:* sales@ imagousa.com *Web Site:* www.imagousa.com, pg 1206, 1221, 1249, 1264, 1277, 1347, 1379

Impressions Inc, 1050 Westgate Dr, St Paul, MN 55114 *Tel:* 651-646-1050 *Toll Free Tel:* 800-251-4285 *Fax:* 651-646-7228 *E-mail:* info@i-i.com *Web Site:* www.i-i.com, pg 1249

Imprint Group West, 2070 Cherry St, Denver, CO 80207 *Toll Free Tel:* 800-738-3961 *Toll Free Fax:* 888-867-3869 *Web Site:* imprintgroupwest.com, pg 1288

IMSI/Design LLC, 384 Bel Marin Keys Blvd, No 150, Novato, CA 94949 *Tel:* 415-483-8000 *Toll Free Tel:* 800-833-8082 (sales) *E-mail:* sales@imsidesign. com; support@imsidesign.com *Web Site:* www. imsidesign.com, pg 1379

Inchworm (ages 3-5), 557 Broadway, New York, NY 10012 *Tel:* 212-343-6100 *Toll Free Tel:* 800-724-6527 (press 1) *Toll Free Fax:* 800-223-4011 *E-mail:* bookclubs@scholastic.com *Web Site:* scholastic.com/bookclubs, pg 1136

The Independent Book Publishers Association (IBPA), 1020 Manhattan Beach Blvd, Suite 204, Manhattan Beach, CA 90266 *Tel:* 310-546-1818 *E-mail:* info@ ibpa-online.org *Web Site:* www.ibpa-online.org, pg 1106

Independent Publishers Group (IPG), 814 N Franklin St, Chicago, IL 60610 *Tel:* 312-337-0747 *Toll Free Tel:* 800-888-4741 (orders) *Fax:* 312-337-5985 *E-mail:* frontdesk@ipgbook.com; orders@ipgbook.com *Web Site:* www.ipgbook.com, pg 1288, 1326

Indexing by the Book, PO Box 12513, Tucson, AZ 85732-2513 *Tel:* 520-750-8439 *E-mail:* indextran@ cox.net *Web Site:* www.indexingbythebook.com, pg 1410

Indexing Research, 620 Park Ave, Suite 183, Rochester, NY 14607 *Tel:* 585-413-1819 *E-mail:* info@indexres. com *Web Site:* www.indexres.com, pg 1379

indiCo, 528 E Lorain St, Oberlin, OH 44074-1298 *Toll Free Tel:* 800-622-7498; 800-321-3883 (orders) *E-mail:* cs@goindico.com; info@goindico.com; orders@goindico.com; service@goindico.com *Web Site:* www.goindico.com, pg 1315

Indigo Books & Music Inc, 468 King St W, Suite 500, Toronto, ON M5V 1L8, Canada *Tel:* 416-364-4499 *E-mail:* cisales@indigo.ca *Web Site:* www.chapters. indigo.ca, pg 1290

InfinitPrint Solutions Inc, 14 N Tenth St, Richmond, IN 47374 *Tel:* 765-962-1507 *Toll Free Tel:* 800-478-4885 *Fax:* 765-962-4997 *E-mail:* info@infinitprint.com *Web Site:* infinitprint.com, pg 1206, 1249

Infinity Graphics, 2277 Science Pkwy, Suite 5, Okemos, MI 48864 *Tel:* 517-349-4635 *Toll Free Tel:* 800-292-2633 *Fax:* 517-349-7608 *E-mail:* barcode@ infinitygraphics.com *Web Site:* www.infinitygraphics. com, pg 1221, 1249, 1379

Infocus® Corp, 13190 SW 68 Pkwy, Suite 120, Portland, OR 97223-8368 *Tel:* 503-207-4700 *Toll Free Tel:* 877-388-8360 (cust serv) *E-mail:* salessupport@infocus. com *Web Site:* www.infocus.com, pg 1379

Ingenta, 317 George St, New Brunswick, NJ 08901 *Tel:* 732-563-9292 *Fax:* 732-563-9044 *Web Site:* www. ingenta.com, pg 1379

Ingram Content Group LLC, One Ingram Blvd, La Vergne, TN 37086-1986 *Tel:* 615-793-5000 *Toll Free Tel:* 800-937-8000 (retailers); 800-937-5300 (ext 1, libs) *E-mail:* customerservice@ingramcontent.com *Web Site:* www.ingramcontent.com, pg 1290, 1315

Ingram Micro Inc, 3351 Michelson Dr, Suite 100, Irvin, CA 92612 *Tel:* 714-566-1000 *E-mail:* customerexperience@ingrammicro.com *Web Site:* www.ingrammicro.com, pg 1315

Ingram Publisher Services, an Ingram brand, One Ingram Blvd, La Vergne, TN 37086 *Tel:* 615-793-5000 *Toll Free Tel:* 866-400-5351 (cust serv) *E-mail:* ips@ ingramcontent.com *Web Site:* www.ingramcontent.com, pg 1290

Inland Press, 2001 W Lafayette Blvd, Detroit, MI 48216 *Tel:* 313-961-6000 *Web Site:* www.inlandpress.com, pg 1092

Inlingua Translation Service, 171 E Ridgewood Ave, Ridgewood, NJ 07450 *Tel:* 201-444-9500 *Fax:* 201-444-0116 *E-mail:* ridgewood@inlingua.com *Web Site:* www.inlingua.com; www.inlinguametrony. com, pg 1410

Inman, 75 N Woodward Ave, Suite 80368, Tallahassee, FL 32313 *Tel:* 510-658-9252 *E-mail:* customerservice@inman.com *Web Site:* www. inman.com, pg 1185

Innodata Inc, 55 Challenger Rd, Suite 202, Ridgefield Park, NJ 07660 *Tel:* 201-371-8000 *Toll Free Tel:* 877-454-8400 *E-mail:* info@innodata.com; marketing@ innodata.com *Web Site:* innodata.com, pg 1221, 1347, 1379

Innovative Design & Graphics, 1327 Greenleaf St, Evanston, IL 60202 *Tel:* 847-475-7772 *Fax:* 847-475-7784 *E-mail:* info@idgevanston.com *Web Site:* www. idgevanston.com, pg 1221

Institute for the Study of Human Knowledge (ISHK), 1702-L Meridian Ave, No 266, San Jose, CA 95125-5586 *Tel:* 617-497-4124 *Toll Free Tel:* 800-222-4745 (orders) *Fax:* 617-500-0268 *Toll Free Fax:* 800-223-4200 (orders) *E-mail:* ishkadm@aol.com; ishkbooks@ aol.com (orders) *Web Site:* www.ishk.com, pg 1291

Institute of Intergovernmental Relations, Queen's University, Robert Sutherland Hall, Rm 301, Kingston, ON K7L 3N6, Canada *Tel:* 613-533-2080 *E-mail:* iigr@queensu.ca *Web Site:* www.queensu. ca/iigr, pg 1315

Integra Software Services Inc, 1110 Jorie Blvd, Suite 200, Oak Brook, IL 60523 *Tel:* 630-586-2579 *Fax:* 630-586-2599 *E-mail:* marketing@integra.co.in *Web Site:* www.integra.co.in, pg 1347, 1358

Integrated Distribution Services (IDS), 9431 AllPoints Pkwy, Plainfield, IN 46168 *Toll Free Tel:* 866-232-6533 *E-mail:* adale@idsfulfillment.com *Web Site:* www.idsfulfillment.com, pg 1332

Integrated PR Agency (IPR), Penthouse, 9025 Wilshire Blvd, Suite 500, Beverly Hills, CA 90211 *Tel:* 310-858-8230 *Web Site:* www.integrated-pr.com, pg 1098

Intellicor Communications LLC, 330 Eden Rd, Lancaster, PA 17601 *Toll Free Tel:* 800-233-0107 *Web Site:* www.intellicor.com, pg 1092

The Intermarketing Group-Art Licensing Agency, 29 Holt Rd, Amherst, NH 03031 *Tel:* 603-672-0499, pg 1347

InterNation Inc, 299 Broadway, Suite 918, New York, NY 10007 *Tel:* 212-619-5545 *Toll Free Tel:* 800-222-8799 *Fax:* 212-619-5887 *E-mail:* info@internation. com *Web Site:* www.internation.com, pg 1410

International Book Centre Inc, 2391 Auburn Rd, Shelby Township, MI 48317 *Tel:* 586-254-7230 *Fax:* 586-254-7230 *E-mail:* ibc@ibcbooks.com *Web Site:* www. ibcbooks.com, pg 1315

International Book Import Service Inc, 161 Main St, Lynchburg, TN 37352-8300 *Tel:* 931-759-7400 *Toll Free Tel:* 800-277-4247 *Fax:* 931-759-7555 *Toll Free Fax:* 866-277-2722 *E-mail:* ibis@ibiservice.com *Web Site:* www.ibiservice.com, pg 1326

International Institute of Reflexology Inc, PO Box 12642, St Petersburg, FL 33733-2642 *Tel:* 727-343-4811 *E-mail:* info@reflexology-usa.net; orderdept@ reflexology-usa.net *Web Site:* reflexology-usa.net, pg 1315, 1326

International Leads (IL), 225 N Michigan Ave, Suite 1300, Chicago, IL 60601 *Tel:* 312-944-6780 *Toll Free Tel:* 800-545-2433 *Fax:* 312-440-9374 *E-mail:* ala. intl.leads@gmail.com; ala@ala.org *Web Site:* www. ala.org/rt/irrt/intlleads/internationalleads; www.ala. org/rt/irrt; www.ala.org, pg 1127

International Mapping Associates, 5300 Dorsey Hall Dr, Suite 201, Ellicott City, MD 21042 *Tel:* 443-367-0050 *Toll Free Tel:* 800-761-6944 *Fax:* 443-367-0045 *Web Site:* internationalmapping.com, pg 1429

International Paper Co, 6400 Poplar Ave, Memphis, TN 38197 *Tel:* 901-419-9000 *Toll Free Tel:* 800-207-4003 *Web Site:* www.internationalpaper.com; facebook.com/ internationalpaper; twitter.com/intlpaperco, pg 1264

International Press Publication Inc, Spadina Rd, Richmond Hill, ON L4B 3C5, Canada *Tel:* 905-883-0343 *E-mail:* sales@ippbooks.com *Web Site:* www. ippbooks.com; www.facebook.com/ippbooks; twitter. com/ippbooks2, pg 1221, 1277, 1291, 1315

International Service Co, International Service Bldg, 333 Fourth Ave, Indialantic, FL 32903-4295 *Tel:* 321-724-1443 *Fax:* 321-724-1443, pg 1316, 1323, 1326, 1329

International Transactions Inc, 28 Alope Way, Gila, NM 88038 *Tel:* 845-373-9696 *Fax:* 480-393-5162 *E-mail:* info@internationaltransactions.us *Web Site:* www.intltrans.com, pg 1347

Internet Bookwatch, 278 Orchard Dr, Oregon, WI 53575-1129 *Tel:* 608-835-7937 *E-mail:* mbr@execpc. com *Web Site:* www.midwestbookreview.com, pg 1127

Keister-Williams Newspaper Services Inc, PO Box 8187, Charlottesville, VA 22906 *Tel:* 434-293-4709 *Toll Free Tel:* 800-293-4709 *E-mail:* kw@kwnews.com *Web Site:* www.kwnews.com, pg 1185

Kelley & Hall Book Publicity, 5 Briar Lane, Marblehead, MA 01945 *Tel:* 617-680-1976 *Fax:* 781-631-5959 *Web Site:* www.kelleyandhall.com, pg 1099

Kelmscott, a Fuse LLC company, 5656 McDermott Dr, Berkeley, IL 60163 *Tel:* 630-898-4261 *Web Site:* www.kelmscott.com, pg 1206, 1222, 1380

Kensai International Ltd, 75 Nottingham Rd, Malverne, NY 11565 *Tel:* 516-593-0480 *E-mail:* info@kensai.net *Web Site:* www.kensai.net, pg 1348

Kensington Technology Group, 1500 Fashion Island Blvd, Suite 300, San Mateo, CA 94404-1595 *Toll Free Tel:* 800-535-4242 *E-mail:* globalmarketing@kensington.com *Web Site:* www.kensington.com, pg 1380

Leonard H Kessler, 1624 Treehouse Circle, TR-120, Sarasota, FL 34231-6724 *Tel:* 941-966-2618 *E-mail:* lenkessler@comcast.net, pg 1429

Ketab Corp, 12701 Van Nuys Blvd, Unit H, Pacoima, CA 91331 *Tel:* 310-477-7477 *Toll Free Tel:* 800-FOR-IRAN (367-4726) *Fax:* 818-908-1457 *E-mail:* ketab1@ketab.com *Web Site:* www.ketab.com, pg 1316

Keystone Press Agency Inc, 412 N El Camino Real, San Clemente, CA 92672 *Tel:* 949-481-3747 *Fax:* 949-481-3941 *E-mail:* info@keystonepictures.com *Web Site:* www.keystonepictures.com, pg 1185, 1448

Kindergarten Book Club, 557 Broadway, New York, NY 10012 *Tel:* 212-343-6100 *Toll Free Tel:* 800-724-6527 (press 1) *Toll Free Fax:* 800-223-4011 *E-mail:* bookclubs@scholastic.com *Web Site:* scholastic.com/bookclubs, pg 1136

King Features Syndicate, 300 W 57 St, New York, NY 10019-5238 *Tel:* 212-969-7550 *Toll Free Tel:* 800-526-5464 *Web Site:* www.kingfeatures.com, pg 1185

Linda King, 71 Faunce Dr, Providence, RI 02906 *Tel:* 401-274-2149 *Web Site:* www.whitegatefeatures.com, pg 1118

King Printing, 181 Industrial Ave E, Lowell, MA 01852-5147 *Tel:* 978-458-2345 *Fax:* 978-458-1441 *E-mail:* inquiries@kingprinting.com *Web Site:* www.kingprinting.com; www.adibooks.com, pg 1206

Kinokuniya Bookstores of America Co Ltd, 1581 Webster St, San Francisco, CA 94115 *Tel:* 415-567-6787 *Fax:* 415-567-4109 *E-mail:* sales@kinokuniya.com; san_francisco@kinokuniya.com; bookwebusa@kinokuniya.com (cust serv) *Web Site:* usa.kinokuniya.com, pg 1316, 1326

Kinokuniya Publications Service of New York (KPS-NY), 1073 Avenue of the Americas, New York, NY 10018-3701 *Tel:* 212-765-1465 *Fax:* 212-307-5593 *E-mail:* nyinfo@kinokuniya.com *Web Site:* www.kinokuniya.co.jp; www.kinokuniya.com, pg 1348

Kiplinger's Personal Finance/The Kiplinger Washington Editors Inc, 1100 13 St NW, Suite 750, Washington, DC 20005-4364 *Tel:* 202-887-6400 *Toll Free Tel:* 800-544-0155 (cust serv) *E-mail:* feedback@kiplinger.com *Web Site:* www.kiplinger.com, pg 1185

Kirkus, 65 W 36 St, Suite 700, New York, NY 10018 *E-mail:* customercare@kirkus.com *Web Site:* www.kirkusreviews.com, pg 1128

Kitzmiller Sales & Marketing Co, 35 Flint St, Suite 304, Salem, MA 01970-3264 *Tel:* 978-985-1144 (cell) *Fax:* 978-744-0232 *E-mail:* dnd.kitzmiller@gmail.com, pg 1291

Solveig Kjok, 252 Green St, Brooklyn, NY 11222 *Tel:* 718-389-8228; 917-288-3445 *Fax:* 718-389-8228 *E-mail:* linguist@art-texts.plus *Web Site:* www.art-texts.plus, pg 1411

Klopotek North America Inc, 2001 Rte 46, Suite 203, Parsippany, NJ 07054 *Tel:* 973-331-1010 *Toll Free Tel:* 800-239-9254 *Fax:* 973-331-0042 *E-mail:* info@klopotek.com *Web Site:* www.klopotek.com; www.gtsystems.com, pg 1348

Bruce Kluckhohn Photographer, 2608 Webster Ave S, Minneapolis, MN 55416-1723 *Tel:* 612-929-6010 *E-mail:* bruce@bruceekphoto.com *Web Site:* www.bruceekphoto.com, pg 1440

Knepper Press Corp, 2251 Sweeney Dr, Clinton, PA 15026 *Tel:* 724-899-4200 *Fax:* 724-899-1331 *Web Site:* www.knepperpress.com, pg 1206, 1222, 1249

knk Software LP, 89 Headquarters Plaza N, No 1478, Morristown, NJ 07960 *Tel:* 908-206-4599 *E-mail:* info@knk.com *Web Site:* www.knkpublishingsoftware.com, pg 1348

Knovel Corp, 230 Park Ave, 8th fl, New York, NY 10169 *Tel:* 212-309-8100 *Web Site:* www.knovel.com; app.novel.com, pg 1380

William Koechling Photography, 1307 E Harrison Ave, Wheaton, IL 60187 *Tel:* 630-665-4379 *E-mail:* bill@koechlingphoto.com *Web Site:* www.koechlingphoto.com, pg 1440

David W Koehser Attorney at Law, 322 First Ave N, Suite 402, Minneapolis, MN 55401 *Tel:* 612-910-6468 *E-mail:* dk@dklex.com *Web Site:* www.dklex.com, pg 1348

Koenig & Bauer (US) Inc, 2555 Regent Blvd, Dallas, TX 75229 *Tel:* 469-532-8000 *Fax:* 469-532-8190 *Web Site:* us.koenig-bauer.com, pg 1277

Koller Search Partners, 655 Third Ave, 24th fl, New York, NY 10017 *Tel:* 212-661-5250 *E-mail:* ksp@kollersearch.com *Web Site:* www.kollersearch.com, pg 1389

Kontron America Inc, 9477 Waples St, San Diego, CA 92121 *Toll Free Tel:* 888-294-4558 (sales); 800-480-0044 (cust serv, US only) *Fax:* 858-677-0898 *E-mail:* info@kontron.com *Web Site:* www.kontron.com, pg 1380

Jill Kramer - Best of Books, 71 Faunce Dr, Providence, RI 02906 *Tel:* 401-274-2149 *Web Site:* www.whitegatefeatures.com, pg 1118

Kreab, House of Sweden, Suite 504, 2900 "K" St NW, Washington, DC 20007 *Tel:* 202-536-1590 *E-mail:* washingtondc@kreab.com *Web Site:* www.kreab.com/washington-dc, pg 1099

Krishnamurti Publications of America, 1070 McAndrew Rd, Ojai, CA 93023 *Tel:* 805-646-2726 *E-mail:* kfa@kfa.org *Web Site:* www.kfa.org, pg 1327

Kromar Printing Ltd, 725 Portage Ave, Winnipeg, MB R3G 0M8, Canada *Tel:* 204-775-8721 *Fax:* 204-783-8985 *E-mail:* info@kromar.com *Web Site:* www.kromar.com, pg 1206, 1250

Kenneth Kronenberg, 51 Maple Ave, Cambridge, MA 02139 *Tel:* 617-868-8070 *E-mail:* mail@kfkronenberg.com *Web Site:* www.kfkronenberg.com, pg 1411

Kroy LLC, 3830 Kelley Ave, Cleveland, OH 44114 *Tel:* 216-426-5600 *Toll Free Fax:* 800-523-2881 *E-mail:* info@kroy.com; support@kroy.com *Web Site:* www.kroy.com, pg 1380

KT Public Relations & Literary Services, 1905 Cricklewood Cove, Fogelsville, PA 18051 *Tel:* 610-395-6298 *Web Site:* www.ktpublicrelations.com, pg 1099

Dwight R Kuhn, 128 Free St, Dexter, ME 04930 *Tel:* 207-924-6206 *Fax:* 207-924-6206 *E-mail:* dkuhn@kuhnphoto.com *Web Site:* www.kuhnphoto.net, pg 1440

Kwikprint Manufacturing Co Inc, 4868 Victor St, Jacksonville, FL 32207 *Tel:* 904-737-3755 *Toll Free Tel:* 904-940-5945 *Fax:* 904-730-0349 *E-mail:* info@kwikprint.net *Web Site:* www.kwik-print.com, pg 1264

KyTek Inc, PO Box 338, Weare, NH 03281 *Tel:* 603-529-2512 *E-mail:* sales@kytek.com *Web Site:* www.kytek.com, pg 1380

La Crosse Graphics Inc, 3025 East Ave S, La Crosse, WI 54601 *Tel:* 608-788-2500 *Toll Free Tel:* 800-832-2503 *Fax:* 608-788-2660 *Web Site:* www.lacrossegraphics.com, pg 1250

Labels Inc, 10 Merrill Industrial Dr, Hampton, NH 03842 *Tel:* 603-929-3088 *Toll Free Tel:* 800-852-2357 *Fax:* 603-929-7305 *E-mail:* sales@labelsinc.com *Web Site:* www.labelsinc.com, pg 1250

Labrecque Creative Sound, 2825 Main St, Becket, MA 01223, pg 1380

Lachina Precision Graphics Services, 3791 S Green Rd, Cleveland, OH 44122 *Tel:* 216-292-7959 *E-mail:* info@lachina.com *Web Site:* www.lachina.com, pg 1222, 1359, 1380, 1429

Laissez Faire Club, 808 St Paul St, Baltimore, MD 21202 *Toll Free Tel:* 877-453-1177 *E-mail:* contact@lfb.org; feedback@lfb.org *Web Site:* www.lfb.org, pg 1137

Julie A Laitin Enterprises Inc, 160 West End Ave, Suite 23N, New York, NY 10023 *Tel:* 917-841-8566 *E-mail:* info@julielaitin.com *Web Site:* www.julielaitin.com, pg 1086

Lake Book Manufacturing Inc, 2085 N Cornell Ave, Melrose Park, IL 60160 *Tel:* 708-345-7000 *E-mail:* info@lakebook.com *Web Site:* www.lakebook.com, pg 1206, 1222, 1250, 1264, 1277

Lake Group Media Inc, One Byram Brook Place, Armonk, NY 10504 *Tel:* 914-925-2400 *Fax:* 914-925-2499 *Web Site:* www.lakegroupmedia.com, pg 1112

Lambda Literary, PO Box 20186, New York, NY 10014 *Tel:* 213-277-5755 *Fax:* 323-643-4281 *E-mail:* admin@lambdaliterary.org *Web Site:* www.lambdaliterary.org, pg 1128

Wayne P Lammers, SW 92 Ave, Tigard, OR 97224 *Tel:* 503-624-2971 *E-mail:* wlammers@mac.com *Web Site:* www.lammerstranslations.com, pg 1411

L+L Printers, 6200 Yarrow Dr, Carlsbad, CA 92011 *Tel:* 760-438-3456; 760-477-0321 *Fax:* 760-929-0853 *E-mail:* info@llprinters.com *Web Site:* www.llprinters.com, pg 1250

Anthony Lane, One World Trade Center, New York, NY 10007 *Tel:* 212-286-2860 *Web Site:* www.newyorker.com, pg 1118

The Lane Press Inc, 87 Meadowland Dr, South Burlington, VT 05403 *Tel:* 802-863-5555 *Toll Free Tel:* 877-300-5933 *Fax:* 802-264-1485 *E-mail:* sales@lanepress.com *Web Site:* www.lanepress.com, pg 1222, 1250

Mary Langenfeld Photography, 3817 Euclid Ave, Madison, WI 53711 *Tel:* 608-233-9938; 608-334-1375 (cell) *E-mail:* madisonfoto@att.net *Web Site:* www.langenfeld-photo.com, pg 1440

LangTech International, 5625 SW 170 Ave, Aloha, OR 97007 *Tel:* 503-649-2478 *Fax:* 503-649-2478 (call first) *E-mail:* langtech.international@yahoo.com *Web Site:* www.langtechinternational.com, pg 1411

The Language Center, 62 Brunswick Woods Dr, East Brunswick, NJ 08816 *Tel:* 732-613-4554 *Fax:* 732-238-7659 *Web Site:* www.thelanguagectr.com, pg 1411

LanternMedia, 128 Second Place, Garden Suite, Brooklyn, NY 11231 *Tel:* 212-414-2275 *Web Site:* www.lanternmedia.net, pg 1380

Laplink Software Inc, 600 108 Ave NE, Suite 610, Bellevue, WA 98004 *Tel:* 425-952-6000 *Toll Free Tel:* 800-LAPLINK (527-5465) *E-mail:* info@laplink.com; sales@laplink.com *Web Site:* web.laplink.com, pg 1380

LARB Quarterly Journal, 6671 Sunset Blvd, Suite 1521, Los Angeles, CA 90028 *Tel:* 323-952-3950 *E-mail:* info@lareviewofbooks.org; editorial@lareviewofbooks.org *Web Site:* lareviewofbooks.org, pg 1128

Larson Texts Inc, 1762 Norcross Rd, Erie, PA 16510 *Tel:* 814-824-6365 *Toll Free Tel:* 800-530-2355 *Fax:* 814-824-6377 *Web Site:* www.larsontexts.com, pg 1222, 1265, 1359

Lassco-Wizer Equipment & Supplies, 485 Hague St, Rochester, NY 14606-1296 *Tel:* 585-436-1934 *Toll Free Tel:* 800-854-6595 *Fax:* 585-464-8665 *E-mail:* info@lasscowizer.com; sales@lasscowizer.com *Web Site:* www.lasscowizer.com, pg 1277

Login Canada, 300 Saulteaux Crescent, Winnipeg, MB R3J 3T2, Canada *Tel:* 204-837-2987 *Toll Free Tel:* 800-665-1148 (CN only) *Fax:* 204-837-3116 *Toll Free Fax:* 800-665-0103 *E-mail:* sales@lb.ca *Web Site:* www.lb.ca, pg 1317

Long's Roullet Bookbinders Inc, 2800 Monticello Ave, Norfolk, VA 23504 *Tel:* 757-623-4244 *Fax:* 757-627-1404 *E-mail:* bindlrbi@gmail.com *Web Site:* longsroullet.com, pg 1250, 1323

Marc Longwood Photography, 3300 Powell St, Suite 336, Emeryville, CA 94608-1776 *Tel:* 415-251-7585 *Web Site:* www.longwoodpro.com, pg 1441

Lorimer Literary Consulting, 1033 SW Yamhill St, Suite 205, Portland, OR 97205 *Tel:* 503-481-5847 *E-mail:* lorimerliterary@yahoo.com, pg 1349

Love & Logic Institute Inc, 2207 Jackson St, Suite 102, Golden, CO 80401-2300 *Tel:* 303-278-7552 *Toll Free Tel:* 800-338-4065 *Fax:* 303-278-3894 *Toll Free Fax:* 800-455-7557 *E-mail:* cservice@loveandlogic.com *Web Site:* www.loveandlogic.com, pg 1380

Lowe Graphics & Printing, 220 Great Circle Rd, Suite 122, Nashville, TN 37228 *Tel:* 615-242-6649 *Fax:* 615-254-8867 *Web Site:* www.etlowe.com, pg 1222

Jack Lucey, 84 Crestwood Dr, San Rafael, CA 94901 *Tel:* 415-453-3172, pg 1430

LuciaMarquand, 1400 Second Ave, Seattle, WA 98101 *Tel:* 206-624-2030 *Fax:* 206-624-1821 *Web Site:* luciamarquand.com, pg 1359

Lucky (grades 2-3), 557 Broadway, New York, NY 10012 *Tel:* 212-343-6100 *Toll Free Tel:* 800-724-6527 (press 1) *Toll Free Fax:* 800-223-4011 *E-mail:* bookclubs@scholastic.com *Web Site:* scholastic.com/bookclubs, pg 1137

Lumina Datamatics Inc, 4 Collins Ave, Plymouth, MA 02360 *Tel:* 508-746-0300 *Fax:* 508-746-3233 *Web Site:* luminadatamatics.com, pg 1207, 1222, 1349, 1359, 1380, 1430

Lushena Books Inc, 607 Country Club Dr, Unit E, Bensenville, IL 60106 *Tel:* 630-238-8708 *Toll Free Tel:* 800-785-1545 *Fax:* 630-238-8824 *E-mail:* lushenabks@yahoo.com *Web Site:* lushenabks.com, pg 1317

Lynch Communications, 525 Loma Vista Terr, Pacifica, CA 94044 *Tel:* 678-939-1212 *Fax:* 480-287-9401 *Web Site:* www.lynchcommunications.com, pg 1381

Lynx Media Inc, 13654 Victory Blvd, No 282, Valley Glen, CA 91401 *Tel:* 818-761-5859 *Toll Free Tel:* 800-451-5969 *Fax:* 818-761-7099 *E-mail:* sales@lynxmedia.com *Web Site:* www.lynxmedia.com, pg 1381

M L N (Modern Language Notes), 2715 N Charles St, Baltimore, MD 21218-4363 *Toll Free Tel:* 800-548-1784 (journal orders) *Fax:* 410-516-6968 *E-mail:* jrnlcirc@press.jhu.edu (journal orders) *Web Site:* www.press.jhu.edu/journals/modern_language_notes/index.html, pg 1128

MacDermid Graphics Solutions LLC, 5210 Phillip Lee Dr, Atlanta, GA 30336 *Tel:* 404-696-4565 *Toll Free Tel:* 800-348-7201 *E-mail:* mpsproductinfo@macdermid.com *Web Site:* graphics.macdermid.com, pg 1277

Mackin Educational Resources, 3505 County Rd 42 W, Burnsville, MN 55306 *Tel:* 952-895-9540 *Toll Free Tel:* 800-245-9540 *Fax:* 952-894-8806 *Toll Free Fax:* 800-369-5490 *E-mail:* mackin@mackin.com *Web Site:* www.mackin.com, pg 1317

MagicLight Productions, 4935 McConnell Ave, Suite 1, Marina del Rey, CA 90066 *Tel:* 310-306-3839 *Fax:* 310-283-8772 *Web Site:* www.magiclight.com, pg 1441

Magna Visual Inc, 28271 Cedar Park Blvd, Perrysburg, OH 43551 *Tel:* 314-843-9000 *Toll Free Tel:* 800-843-3399 *Fax:* 314-843-0000 *E-mail:* magna@magnavisual.com; mvsales@magnavisual.com *Web Site:* www.magnavisual.com, pg 1277

Magnolia Clipping Service, 298 Commerce Park Dr, Suite A, Ridgeland, MS 39157 *Tel:* 601-856-0911 *Fax:* 601-856-3340 *E-mail:* mail@magnoliaclips.com *Web Site:* magnoliaclips.com, pg 1391

Magnum Book Services, 180 Raritan Center Pkwy, Suite 105, Edison, NJ 07737 *Tel:* 908-349-2300 *Fax:* 732-225-2037 *E-mail:* sales@magnumbookservices.com *Web Site:* www.magnumbookservices.com; www.linkedin.com/company/magnum-book-services; www.facebook.com/magnumbookservices, pg 1332

Magnum Photos Inc, 12 W 31 St, 11th fl, New York, NY 10001 *Tel:* 212-929-6000 *Fax:* 212-929-9325 *E-mail:* photography@magnumphotos.com; contact@magnumphotos.com *Web Site:* www.magnumphotos.com, pg 1448

Susan Magrino Agency, 352 Park Ave S, 6th fl, New York, NY 10010 *Tel:* 212-957-3005 *Fax:* 212-957-4071 *E-mail:* info@smapr.com *Web Site:* www.smapr.com, pg 1099

Mail Order Media & Marketing Inc, 5500 Linkside Ct, Suite 2-A, Fuquay Varina, NC 27526-8499 *Tel:* 203-254-9390 *Fax:* 203-254-3253 *E-mail:* mailordermedia2000@yahoo.com, pg 1087

Maison de l'Education Inc, 10840 Ave Millen, Montreal, QC H2C 0A5, Canada *Tel:* 514-384-4401 *Fax:* 514-384-4844 *E-mail:* librairie@maisondeleducation.com *Web Site:* maisondeleducation.com, pg 1317

Management Communication Quarterly: An International Journal, 2455 Teller Rd, Thousand Oaks, CA 91320 *Toll Free Tel:* 800-818-7243 *Toll Free Fax:* 800-583-2665 *E-mail:* journals@sagepub.com *Web Site:* www.sagepub.com, pg 1129

Management Recruiters of Gramercy Inc, 287 Burns St, Forest Hills, NY 11375-6129 *Tel:* 347-709-1250 *Web Site:* www.managementrecruitersny.com, pg 1389

Mandel Graphic Solution, 727 W Glendale Ave, Suite 100, Milwaukee, WI 53209 *Tel:* 414-271-6970 *Fax:* 414-386-4660 *E-mail:* info@mandelcompany.com *Web Site:* www.mandelcompany.com, pg 1223, 1250

Scott Manning & Associates, 433 Broadway, Suite 433, New York, NY 10013 *Tel:* 646-661-6665 *Web Site:* www.scottmanningpr.com, pg 1099

Manning's Book & Prints, 580-M Crespi Dr, Pacifica, CA 94044 *Tel:* 415-621-3565 *Toll Free Tel:* 800-TRY-MAPS (879-6277) *Fax:* 650-355-1851 *E-mail:* staff@printsoldandrare.com; manningsbk@aol.com *Web Site:* www.printsoldandrare.com, pg 1317

manroland Goss web systems Americas LLC, 121 Technology Dr, Durham, NH 03824 *Tel:* 603-749-6600 *Toll Free Tel:* 800-323-1200 (parts & serv) *Fax:* 603-750-6860 *E-mail:* info@manrolandgoss.com *Web Site:* www.manrolandgoss.com, pg 1277

Manroland Inc, 800 E Oak Hill Dr, Westmont, IL 60559 *Tel:* 630-920-2000 *E-mail:* info.us@manrolandsheetfed.com *Web Site:* manrolandsheetfed.com, pg 1250, 1277

Map Resources, 151 N Union St, No 4, Lambertville, NJ 08530 *Tel:* 609-397-1611 *Toll Free Tel:* 800-334-4291 *Fax:* 609-751-9378 *E-mail:* info@mapresources.com; support@mapresources.com *Web Site:* www.mapresources.com, pg 1381

Maple Logistics Solutions, 60 Grumbacher Rd, York, PA 17406 *Tel:* 717-764-4596 *Fax:* 717-764-4494 *E-mail:* info@maplesoln.com *Web Site:* www.maplelogisticssolutions.com, pg 1291, 1332

Maple Press, 480 Willow Springs Lane, York, PA 17406 *Tel:* 717-764-5911 *Toll Free Tel:* 800-999-5911 *Fax:* 717-764-4702 *E-mail:* sales@maplepress.com *Web Site:* www.maplepress.com, pg 1207, 1250, 1277

Mapping Specialists Ltd, 3000 Cahill Main, Suite 220, Fitchburg, WI 53711 *Tel:* 608-274-4004 *Toll Free Tel:* 866-525-2298 *Fax:* 608-274-9689 *E-mail:* msl@mappingspecialists.com *Web Site:* www.mappingspecialists.com, pg 1430

Maps by Mathison, PO Box 152, Spring Mills, PA 16875 *Tel:* 814-321-7571 *E-mail:* jcmaps6@gmail.com *Web Site:* mapsbymathison.com, pg 1430

Maps.com, 120 Cremona Dr, Suite 260, Santa Barbara, CA 93117 *Tel:* 805-685-3100 *Toll Free Tel:* 800-430-7532 *Fax:* 805-699-7550 *Web Site:* www.maps.com, pg 1251, 1381, 1430

Maracle Inc, 1156 King St E, Oshawa, ON L1H 1H8, Canada *Tel:* 905-723-3438 *Toll Free Tel:* 800-558-8604 *Fax:* 905-723-1759 *E-mail:* hello@maracleinc.com *Web Site:* www.maracleinc.com, pg 1207, 1223, 1251

March Tenth Inc, 24 Hillside Terr, Montvale, NJ 07645 *Tel:* 201-387-6551 *Fax:* 201-387-6552 *Web Site:* www.march10th.com, pg 1360

Market Partners International Inc, 232 Madison Ave, Suite 1400, New York, NY 10016 *Tel:* 212-447-0855 *Fax:* 212-447-0785 *E-mail:* info@marketpartnersinternational.com *Web Site:* www.marketpartnersinternational.com, pg 1349

Marketry Inc, 1420 NW Gilman Blvd, No 2558, Issaquah, WA 98027 *Tel:* 425-451-1262 *Toll Free Tel:* 800-346-2013 *Web Site:* www.marketry.com, pg 1112

Barbara Marks Graphic Design, 15 Flying Point, Stony Creek, CT 06405 *Tel:* 203-481-3361, pg 1430

Markwith Tool Co Inc, 5261 State Rte 49 S, Greenville, OH 45331 *Tel:* 937-548-6808 *Fax:* 937-548-7051 *Web Site:* markwithtool.com, pg 1277

Marquis Book Printing Inc, 350, rue des Entrepreneurs, Montmagny, QC G5V 4T1, Canada *Tel:* 418-246-5666 *Toll Free Tel:* 855-566-1937; 800-246-2468 *E-mail:* marquis@marquisbook.com *Web Site:* www.marquislivre.com; www.marquisbook.com, pg 1251

Marrakech Express Inc, 720 Wesley Ave, No 10, Tarpon Springs, FL 34689 *Tel:* 727-942-2218 *Toll Free Tel:* 800-940-6566 *Fax:* 727-937-4758 *E-mail:* print@marrak.com *Web Site:* www.marrak.com, pg 1207, 1251, 1278

Judith Martin, 1130 Walnut St, Kansas City, MO 64106-2109 *Tel:* 816-581-7300 *Toll Free Tel:* 800-255-6734 *Web Site:* syndication.andrewsmcmeel.com, pg 1118

Martin Printing Co Inc, 1765 Powdersville Rd, Easley, SC 29642 *Toll Free Tel:* 888-985-7330 *Fax:* 864-859-8620 *E-mail:* info@martinprinting.com *Web Site:* www.martinprinting.com, pg 1251

Connie Martinson Talks Books, 2288 Coldwater Canyon, Beverly Hills, CA 90210 *Tel:* 310-271-4127 *E-mail:* talksbks@aol.com *Web Site:* www.conniemartinson.com, pg 1118

Maryheart Crusaders Inc, 531 W Main St, Meriden, CT 06451-2707 *Tel:* 203-238-9735 *Toll Free Tel:* 800-879-1957 (orders only) *Fax:* 203-235-0059 *E-mail:* maryheart@msn.com *Web Site:* www.maryheartcrusaders.com, pg 1137

Masque Publishing Inc, 8400 Park Meadows Dr, Lonetree, CO 80124 *Tel:* 303-290-9853 *Fax:* 303-290-6303 *E-mail:* support@masque.com *Web Site:* www.masque.com, pg 1381

Master Books®, 3142 Hwy 103 N, Green Forest, AR 72638 *Tel:* 870-438-5288 *Toll Free Tel:* 800-999-3777 *E-mail:* nlp@nlpg.com; sales@masterbooks.com *Web Site:* www.masterbooks.com; www.nlpg.com/imprint/master-books, pg 1381

Master Flo Technology Inc, 154 Seale Rd, Wentworth, QC J8H 0G9, Canada *Tel:* 450-533-0088 *Fax:* 450-533-4597 *E-mail:* info@mflo.com; sales@mflo.com *Web Site:* www.mflo.com, pg 1278

The Master's Press, 14550 Midway Rd, Dallas, TX 75244 *Tel:* 972-387-0046 *Fax:* 972-404-0317 *Web Site:* www.themasterspress.com, pg 1251

Matrox Graphics Inc, 1055 Saint Regis Blvd, Dorval, QC H9P 2T4, Canada *Tel:* 514-822-6000 *Toll Free Tel:* 800-361-1408 (sales) *Fax:* 514-822-6363 *Web Site:* www.matrox.com/graphics, pg 1381

Matthews Book Co, 11559 Rock Island Ct, Maryland Heights, MO 63043 *Tel:* 314-432-1400 *Toll Free Tel:* 800-633-2665 *Fax:* 314-432-7044 *Toll Free Fax:* 800-421-8816 *E-mail:* orders@mattmccoy.com *Web Site:* www.matthewsbooks.com, pg 1291

Diane Maurer-Hand Marbled Papers, Water St, Spring Mills, PA 16875 *Tel:* 814-422-8651 *E-mail:* dkmaurer1@aol.com *Web Site:* www. dianemaurer.com, pg 1430

Maverick Publications Inc, 63324 Nels Anderson Rd, Bend, OR 97701 *Tel:* 541-382-6978 *E-mail:* moreinfo@maverickbooks.com *Web Site:* www.maverickbooks.com; www.mavbooks. com, pg 1207, 1360, 1381

Maxcess International, 222 W Memorial Rd, Oklahoma City, OK 73114 *Tel:* 405-755-1600 *Toll Free Tel:* 800-639-3433 *Fax:* 405-755-8425 *E-mail:* sales@ maxcessintl.com *Web Site:* www.maxcessintl.com, pg 1278

The Mazel Co, 31000 Aurora Rd, Solon, OH 44139-2769 *Tel:* 440-248-5200 *Toll Free Tel:* 800-443-4789 *Fax:* 440-349-1931 *Web Site:* www.themazelcompany. com, pg 1317

MBA Computer Service, 1920 Lookout Dr, North Mankato, MN 56003 *Tel:* 507-625-3797, pg 1223

MBR Bookwatch, 278 Orchard Dr, Oregon, WI 53575-1129 *Tel:* 608-835-7937 *E-mail:* mbr@execpc.com *Web Site:* www.midwestbookreview.com, pg 1129

MBS Textbook Exchange Inc, 2711 W Ash, Columbia, MO 65203 *Tel:* 573-445-2243 *Toll Free Tel:* 800-325-0530 (textbook solutions); 800-325-4138 (bookstore systems) *Fax:* 573-446-5256 *E-mail:* cserv@ mbsbooks.com *Web Site:* www.mbsbooks.com, pg 1317

McCarthy Digital, 15 Mountain Trail, Croton-on-Hudson, NY 10520 *Tel:* 914-334-0408 *Toll Free Fax:* 866-618-8605 *Web Site:* www.mccarthy-digital.com, pg 1349

McClain Printing Co, 212 Main St, Parsons, WV 26287-1033 *Tel:* 304-478-2881 *Toll Free Tel:* 800-654-7179 *Fax:* 304-478-4658 *E-mail:* mcclain@mcclainprinting. com *Web Site:* www.mcclainprinting.com, pg 1207, 1223, 1251, 1265, 1278

Anita D McClellan Associates, 464 Common St, Suite 142, Belmont, MA 02478-2704 *Tel:* 617-575-9203 *E-mail:* adm@anitamcclellan.com *Web Site:* www. anitamcclellan.com, pg 1349

Virginia McCullough, 2527 Telluride Trail, Suite D, Green Bay, WI 54313 *Tel:* 920-662-9633 *E-mail:* vemccullough@earthlink.net *Web Site:* www. virginiamccullough.com, pg 1350

McGarr & Associates, 5692 Heathwood Ct, Covington, KY 41015 *Tel:* 859-356-9295 *Fax:* 859-356-7804, pg 1292

MCH Strategic Data, 601 E Marshall St, Sweet Springs, MO 65351 *Toll Free Tel:* 800-776-6373 *E-mail:* sales@mchdata.com *Web Site:* www.mchdata. com, pg 1112

John B McHugh Publishing Consultant, PO Box 170665, Milwaukee, WI 53217-8056 *Tel:* 414-351-3056 *E-mail:* jack@johnbmchugh.com *Web Site:* www. johnbmchugh.com, pg 1350

McManus & Morgan, 2506 W Seventh St, Los Angeles, CA 90057 *Tel:* 213-387-4433 *Web Site:* www. mcmanusandmorgan.com, pg 1265

Michael J McManus, 9311 Harrington Dr, Potomac, MD 20854 *Tel:* 301-978-3105 *E-mail:* mike@ marriagesavers.com *Web Site:* www.ethicsandreligion. com, pg 1118

Bruce McMillan, PO Box 85, Shapleigh, ME 04076-0085 *Tel:* 207-324-9453 *E-mail:* bruce@ brucemcmillan.com *Web Site:* www.brucemcmillan. com, pg 1441

McNaughton & Gunn Inc, Plant: 960 Woodland Dr, Saline, MI 48176 *Tel:* 734-429-5411 *Toll Free Fax:* 800-677-BOOK (677-2665) *Web Site:* www. bookprinters.com, pg 1207, 1251

MDR, A D&B Co, 6 Armstrong Rd, Suite 301, Shelton, CT 06484 *Tel:* 203-926-4800 *Toll Free Tel:* 800-333-8802 *Fax:* 203-225-4603 *Toll Free Fax:* 866-532-7097 *E-mail:* mdrinfo@dnb.com *Web Site:* mdreducation. com, pg 1107, 1112

Meadows Design Office, 3800 Yuma St NW, Washington, DC 20016 *Tel:* 202-966-6007 *E-mail:* mdo@mdomedia.com, pg 1208, 1223, 1360, 1430

Meadows Publishing Solutions, 1305 Remington Rd, Suite G, Schaumburg, IL 60173 *Tel:* 847-882-8202 *Toll Free Tel:* 888-983-6746 *Fax:* 847-882-9494 *E-mail:* sales@meadowsps.com *Web Site:* www. meadowsps.com, pg 1381

Media Connect, 301 E 57 St, 4th fl, New York, NY 10022 *Tel:* 212-583-2718 *Web Site:* www.media-connect.com, pg 1099

Media Cybernetics Inc, 1700 Rockville Pike, Suite 240, Rockville, MD 20852 *Tel:* 301-495-3305 *Toll Free Tel:* 800-263-2088 *E-mail:* support@mediacy.com; marketing@mediacy.com *Web Site:* www.mediacy. com, pg 1381

Media Masters Publicity, 61 Depot St, Tryon, NC 28782 *Tel:* 828-859-9456 *E-mail:* info@mmpublicity.com *Web Site:* www.mmpublicity.com, pg 1099, 1350

Media Relations Agency, 350 W Burnsville Pkwy, Suite 350, Burnsville, MN 55337 *Tel:* 952-697-5220 *Fax:* 952-697-3256 *Web Site:* www.publicity.com, pg 1099

Media Supply Inc, 208 Philips Rd, Exton, PA 19341 *Tel:* 610-884-4400 *Toll Free Tel:* 800-944-4237 *Fax:* 610-884-4500 *E-mail:* info@mediasupply.com *Web Site:* www.mediasupply.com, pg 1381

Medical Images, 19-C Trolley Sq, Wilmington, DE 19806 *Tel:* 212-736-2525 *Toll Free Tel:* 800-542-3686 *E-mail:* sales@medicalimages.com *Web Site:* www. medicalimages.com, pg 1448

Medievalia et Humanistica: Studies in Medieval & Renaissance Culture, 4501 Forbes Blvd, Suite 200, Lanham, MD 20706 *Tel:* 301-459-3366; 717-794-3800 (cust serv) *Toll Free Tel:* 800-462-6420 (ext 3024, cust serv) *Fax:* 301-429-5748; 717-794-3803 (cust serv) *Toll Free Fax:* 800-338-4550 (cust serv) *E-mail:* customercare@rowman.com *Web Site:* rowman.com, pg 1129

Medina Software Inc, 1441 Oberlin Terr, Suite 1010, Lake Mary, FL 32746 *Tel:* 407-227-4112 *Web Site:* www.medinasoft.com, pg 1381

Megavision Inc, PO Box 60158, Santa Barbara, CA 93160 *Tel:* 805-964-1400 *Toll Free Tel:* 888-324-2580 *E-mail:* info@mega-vision.com *Web Site:* www.mega-vision.com, pg 1381

MEJ Personal Business Services Inc, 245 E 116 St, New York, NY 10029 *Tel:* 212-426-6017 *Toll Free Tel:* 866-557-5336 *Fax:* 646-827-3628 *E-mail:* support@mejpbs.com *Web Site:* www.mejpbs. com, pg 1411

Mekatronics Inc, 85 Channel Dr, Port Washington, NY 11050 *Tel:* 516-883-6805 *Fax:* 516-883-6948 *E-mail:* office@mekatronicsinc.com *Web Site:* mekatronicsinc.com, pg 1265

Donya Melanson Associates, 5 Bisson Lane, Merrimac, MA 01860 *Tel:* 978-346-9240 *Fax:* 978-346-8345 *E-mail:* dmelanson@dmelanson.com *Web Site:* www. dmelanson.com, pg 1087, 1107

Melcher Media Inc, 124 W 13 St, New York, NY 10011 *Tel:* 212-727-2322 *Fax:* 212-627-1973 *E-mail:* info@ melcher.com *Web Site:* www.melcher.com, pg 1360

Melissa Data Corp, 22382 Avenida Empresa, Rancho Santa Margarita, CA 92688-2112 *Tel:* 949-858-3000 *Toll Free Tel:* 800-800-6245 *E-mail:* info@ melissadata.com *Web Site:* www.melissadata.com, pg 1223

Melissa Turk & the Artist Network, 9 Babbling Brook Lane, Suffern, NY 10901 *Tel:* 845-368-8606 *E-mail:* melissa@melissaturk.com *Web Site:* www. melissaturk.com, pg 1430

Tom Mellers Publishing Services (TMPS), 60 Second Ave, Suite 8, New York, NY 10003 *Tel:* 212-254-4958 *E-mail:* tmps71@yahoo.com, pg 1350

Melman-Moster Associates Inc, 48 Post Ave, Hawthorne, NJ 07506 *Tel:* 862-452-6196 *Fax:* 973-304-4923 *E-mail:* books@melman-moster.com, pg 1292

Mendon Associates Inc, 4195 Dundas St W, Suite 346, Toronto, ON M8X 1Y4, Canada *Tel:* 416-239-9661 *Toll Free Tel:* 800-361-1325 *Fax:* 416-239-1076 *E-mail:* info@mendon.com *Web Site:* www.mendon. com, pg 1350

MEP Education, 8154 N Ridgeway Ave, Skokie, IL 60076 *Tel:* 847-676-1596 *Fax:* 847-676-1195 *E-mail:* info@mep-inc.net *Web Site:* www. mepeducation.net, pg 1350

Merrell Enterprises, 3542 E State Rte 73, Waynesville, OH 45068 *Tel:* 202-265-1925 *Fax:* 513-855-4277 *Web Site:* www.merrellenterprises.com, pg 1185

Brian Thomas Merrill, 40 Vandale St, Putnam, CT 06260 *Tel:* 860-315-4638 *E-mail:* zangmerrill@yahoo.com, pg 1431

Le Messager Chretien (The Christian Messenger), 185 Gatineau Ave, Gatineau, QC J8T 4J7, Canada *Tel:* 819-243-8880 *Toll Free Tel:* 800-263-8086 *Fax:* 819-243-1220 *E-mail:* info@messagerchretien. com *Web Site:* www.messagerchretien.com, pg 1317

MetaComet Systems, 29 College St, South Hadley, MA 01075 *Tel:* 413-536-5989 *Web Site:* www.metacomet. com, pg 1350

Metaphysical Book Club, 18340 Sonoma Hwy, Sonoma, CA 95476 *Tel:* 707-939-9212 *Fax:* 707-938-3515 *E-mail:* warwick@vom.com *Web Site:* www. warwickassociates.com, pg 1137

Metro Editorial Services, 519 Eighth Ave, New York, NY 10018 *Tel:* 212-947-5100 (ext 253, outside US & CN) *Toll Free Tel:* 800-223-1600 *E-mail:* service@metro-email.com *Web Site:* www. mcg.metrocreativeconnection.com, pg 1185

Metro 360, 120 Sinnott Rd, Scarborough, ON M1L 4N1, Canada *Tel:* 416-752-8720 *Toll Free Tel:* 888-260-2208 *Web Site:* www.metro360.ca, pg 1317

Metro Translation Service, 294 De Kalb Ave, Brooklyn, NY 11205 *Tel:* 718-789-0430; 917-558-0089 (cell) *E-mail:* metrotourservice21@gmail.com *Web Site:* metrotourservice.blogspot.com, pg 1411

Metropolitan Newsclips Service Inc, 1250 Hanley Industrial Ct, St Louis, MO 63144 *Tel:* 314-395-8917 *E-mail:* cheryllm@metronewsclips.com *Web Site:* www.metronewsclips.com, pg 1391

MGP Direct Inc, 17814 Shotley Bridge Place, Olney, MD 20832 *Tel:* 240-755-6976 *Web Site:* www. mgpdirect.com, pg 1350

Miami Wabash Paper LLC, 301 Wedcor Ave, Wabash, IN 46992 *Tel:* 260-563-4181 *Toll Free Tel:* 800-842-9112 *Fax:* 219-563-2724 *E-mail:* miamivalley@ mafcote.com *Web Site:* www.mafcote.com, pg 1265

Vick Mickunas, 4805 Meredith Rd, Yellow Springs, OH 45387 *Tel:* 937-767-1396 *E-mail:* vick@vickmickunas. com *Web Site:* www.wyso.org/programs/book-nook, pg 1118

Micro Focus, One Irvington Ctr, 700 King Farm Blvd, Suite 125, Rockville, MD 20850-5736 *Tel:* 301-838-5000 *Toll Free Tel:* 877-686-9637 *Web Site:* www. microfocus.com, pg 1381

Microboards Technology Inc, 8150 Mallory Ct, Chanhassen, MN 55317 *Tel:* 952-556-1600; 952-556-1639 (tech support) *Toll Free Tel:* 800-646-8881 *Fax:* 952-556-1620 *E-mail:* sales@microboards.com *Web Site:* www.microboards.com, pg 1381

Microsearch Corp, 5 Broadway, Suite 3, Saugus, MA 01906 *Tel:* 781-231-9991 *Toll Free Tel:* 800-895-0212 *Fax:* 781-231-9996 *E-mail:* info@microsearch.net *Web Site:* www.microsearchcorporation.com, pg 1381

Midland Paper, Packaging & Supplies, 101 E Palatine Rd, Wheeling, IL 60090 *Tel:* 847-777-2700 *Toll Free Tel:* 800-323-8522; 888-564-3526 (cust serv) *Fax:* 847-403-6320 (cust serv) *E-mail:* whl@ midlandpaper.com; sales@midlandpaper.com; custservice@midlandpaper.com *Web Site:* www. midlandpaper.com, pg 1265

Midpoint National Inc, 1263 Southwest Blvd, Kansas City, KS 66103 *Tel:* 913-362-7400 *Toll Free Tel:* 800-228-4321 *E-mail:* info@midpt.com *Web Site:* www.midpt.com, pg 1292

Midpoint Trade Books, 814 N Franklin St, Suite 100, Chicago, IL 60610 *Tel:* 312-337-0747 *Fax:* 312-337-5985 *E-mail:* orders@ipgbook.com *Web Site:* www.midpointtrade.com, pg 1292

The Midwest Book Review, 278 Orchard Dr, Oregon, WI 53575-1129 *Tel:* 608-835-7937 *E-mail:* mbr@execpc.com; mwbookrevw@aol.com *Web Site:* www.midwestbookreview.com, pg 1129

Midwest Library Service, 11443 Saint Charles Rock Rd, Bridgeton, MO 63044 *Tel:* 314-739-3100 *Fax:* 314-739-1326 *E-mail:* mail@midwestls.com *Web Site:* www.midwestls.com, pg 1317

Midwest Paper Group, 540 Prospect St, Combined Locks, WI 54113 *Tel:* 920-788-3550 *Toll Free Tel:* 800-828-1987 *Fax:* 920-968-3950 *Web Site:* mwpaper.com, pg 1266

Lawrence Migdale Photography/PIX, 23 White Hall Dr, Orinda, CA 94563 *Tel:* 510-612-2572 *E-mail:* photopix@migdale.com *Web Site:* www.migdale.com, pg 1448

Miles 33 International LLC, 40 Richards Ave, Norwalk, CT 06854 *Tel:* 203-838-2333 *Fax:* 203-838-4473 *E-mail:* info@miles33.com *Web Site:* www.miles33.com, pg 1223, 1278, 1381

The Military Book Club®, 34 W 27 St, 10th fl, New York, NY 10001 *Tel:* 716-250-5700 (cust serv) *E-mail:* customer.service@militarybookclub.com *Web Site:* www.militarybookclub.com, pg 1137

Military Update, PO Box 231111, Centreville, VA 20120-1111 *Tel:* 703-830-6863 *E-mail:* milupdate@aol.com *Web Site:* www.militaryupdate.com, pg 1185

S J Miller Communications, PO Box 834, Randolph, MA 02368-0834 *Tel:* 781-986-0732 *E-mail:* bookpromotion@gmail.com *Web Site:* bookpr.com, pg 1099

Susan Riva Miller-Alpine Photography, 20415 150 Ave SE, Monroe, WA 98272 *Tel:* 206-679-0475 *E-mail:* susanrivamiller@hotmail.com, pg 1441

Miller Trade Book Marketing Inc, 1426 W Carmen Ave, Chicago, IL 60640 *Tel:* 773-307-3446, pg 1293

Minden Pictures Inc, 9565 Soquel Dr, Suite 202, Aptos, CA 95003 *Tel:* 831-661-5551 *Fax:* 831-661-5497 *E-mail:* info@mindenpictures.com *Web Site:* www.mindenpictures.com, pg 1448

Wendell Minor, 15 Old North Rd, Washington, CT 06793 *Tel:* 860-868-9101 *E-mail:* wendell@minorart.com *Web Site:* www.minorart.com, pg 1431

Clark James Mishler Photography, 1815 School St, Calistoga, CA 94515 *Tel:* 907-351-7863 *Web Site:* www.mishlerphotos.com, pg 1441

MMoCA Museum Store, 227 State St, Madison, WI 53703 *Tel:* 608-257-3222 *Fax:* 608-257-1219 *E-mail:* store@mmoca.org *Web Site:* www.mmoca.org, pg 1317

Verne Moberg, Five Star Residences of Yonkers, 537 Riverdale Ave, Apt 410, Yonkers, NY 10705-5512 *Tel:* 646-306-2171 *E-mail:* vam1@columbia.edu, pg 1411

Mobium Creative Group, 200 S Michigan Ave, 17th fl, Chicago, IL 60604 *Tel:* 312-422-8950; 312-422-5995 *Fax:* 312-422-5901 *Web Site:* www.mobium.com, pg 1350

Mohawk Fine Papers Inc, 465 Saratoga St, Cohoes, NY 12047 *Tel:* 518-237-1740 *Toll Free Tel:* 800-THE-MILL (843-6455) *Fax:* 518-237-7394 *Web Site:* www.mohawkconnects.com, pg 1266

Monadnock Paper Mills Inc, 117 Antrim Rd, Bennington, NH 03442-4205 *Tel:* 603-588-3311 *Toll Free Tel:* 800-221-2159 (cust serv) *Fax:* 603-588-3158 *E-mail:* info@mpm.com *Web Site:* www.mpm.com, pg 1266

Monotype Imaging Inc, 600 Unicorn Park Dr, Woburn, MA 01801 *Tel:* 781-970-6000 *Web Site:* www.monotype.com, pg 1381

Monteiro & Co Inc, 301 E 57 St, 4th fl, New York, NY 10022 *Tel:* 212-832-8183 *Web Site:* www.monteiroandco.com, pg 1099

Montfort Publications, 26 S Saxon Ave, Bay Shore, NY 11706-8993 *Tel:* 631-665-0726; 631-666-7500 *Fax:* 631-665-0726 *E-mail:* info@montfortpublications.com *Web Site:* www.montfortpublications.com, pg 1317

Morris Press Cookbooks®, 3212 E Hwy 30, Kearney, NE 68847 *Tel:* 308-236-7888; 308-234-1385 *Toll Free Tel:* 800-445-6621 *Fax:* 308-234-3969 *E-mail:* cookbook@morriscookbooks.com *Web Site:* www.morriscookbooks.com, pg 1208

Morris Printing Group Inc, 3212 E Hwy 30, Kearney, NE 68847 *Tel:* 308-236-7888 *Toll Free Tel:* 800-650-7888 *Fax:* 308-237-0263 *Web Site:* www.morrisprintinggroup.com, pg 1251

Morris Publishing®, 3212 E Hwy 30, Kearney, NE 68847 *Tel:* 308-236-7888 *Toll Free Tel:* 800-650-7888 *Fax:* 308-237-0263 *E-mail:* publish@morrispublishing.com *Web Site:* www.morrispublishing.com, pg 1251

The Morristown News, PO Box 6123, West Caldwell, NJ 07007-6123 *Tel:* 973-227-4433, pg 1185

Motor News Media Corp, 3710 Capitol Circle, Suite F, Grimes, IA 50111-5046 *Tel:* 515-986-1155 *E-mail:* motornewsmedia@live.com *Web Site:* www.motornewsmedia.com, pg 1185

Motorbooks, 100 Cummings Ctr, Suite 265D, Beverly, MA 01915 *Tel:* 978-282-9590 *Toll Free Tel:* 800-759-0190 (orders) *Web Site:* www.quartoknows.com/motorbooks, pg 1317, 1327

Mount Ida Press, 111 Washington Ave, Albany, NY 12210-2203 *Tel:* 518-426-5935 *Fax:* 518-426-4116 *E-mail:* info@mountidapress.com *Web Site:* www.mountidapress.com, pg 1317

Mountain Lion Inc, 9 Voorhees Ct, Pennington, NJ 08534 *Tel:* 609-730-1665 *E-mail:* mtlion@me.com *Web Site:* www.mtlioninc.net, pg 1360

MPS North America LLC, 5728 Major Blvd, Suite 528, Orlando, FL 32819 *Tel:* 407-472-1280 *Toll Free Tel:* 866-978-1008 *Fax:* 212-981-2983 *E-mail:* marketing@mpslimited.com *Web Site:* www.mpslimited.com, pg 1223, 1382, 1431

MRC Medical Communications, 12 Lincoln Blvd, Suite 103, Emerson, NJ 07630 *Tel:* 201-986-0247 *E-mail:* info@mrcmedical.net *Web Site:* www.mrcmedical.net, pg 1382

MSC Lists, PO Box 32510, Minneapolis, MN 55432 *Tel:* 763-502-8819 *Fax:* 763-571-8292, pg 1112

Mary Mueller, 516 Bartram Rd, Moorestown, NJ 08057 *Tel:* 856-778-4769 *E-mail:* mamam49@aol.com, pg 1118

Muller Martini Corp, 456 Wheeler Rd, Hauppauge, NY 11788 *Tel:* 631-582-4343 *Toll Free Tel:* 888-268-5537 *Fax:* 631-348-1961 *E-mail:* info@us.mullermartini.com *Web Site:* www.mullermartiniusa.com, pg 1278

Multi-Reliure, 2112 Ave de la Transmission, Shawinigan, QC G9N 8N8, Canada *Tel:* 819-537-6008 *Toll Free Tel:* 888-735-4873 *Fax:* 819-537-4598 *E-mail:* info@multi-reliure.com; administration@multi-reliure.com *Web Site:* www.multireliure.com, pg 1251

Multi-Tech Systems Inc, 2205 Woodale Dr, Mounds View, MN 55112 *Tel:* 763-785-3500 *Toll Free Tel:* 800-328-9717 *Fax:* 763-785-9874 *E-mail:* info@multitech.com; sales@multitech.com; mtsmktg@multitech.com *Web Site:* www.multitech.com, pg 1382

Multicultural Marketing Resources Inc, 720 Greenwich St, No 7T, New York, NY 10014 *Tel:* 212-242-3351 *Web Site:* www.multicultural.com, pg 1099

Steven T Murray, PO Box 14630, Albuquerque, NM 87191-4630 *Tel:* 505-515-5843 *E-mail:* steventmurray@gmail.com, pg 1412

Music City Arts Network, PO Box 843, Brentwood, TN 37024 *Toll Free Tel:* 888-80-SHINE (807-4463) *E-mail:* info@musiccityarts.net *Web Site:* www.musiccityartsupdate.com; www.shinetimebooks.com, pg 1099

Mystery Guild®, 34 W 27 St, 10th fl, New York, NY 10001 *Tel:* 716-250-5700 (cust serv) *E-mail:* customer.service@mysteryguild.com *Web Site:* www.mysteryguild.com, pg 1137

Mystery Readers Journal, 7155 Marlborough Terr, Berkeley, CA 94705 *Tel:* 510-845-3600 *Web Site:* www.mysteryreaders.org, pg 1129

NameBank International, 1001 Cathedral St, Baltimore, MD 21201 *Tel:* 410-864-0854 *Fax:* 410-864-0837 *E-mail:* lists@namebank.com *Web Site:* www.namebank.com, pg 1140

NAPCO Inc, 120 Trojan Ave, Sparta, NC 28675 *Tel:* 336-372-5228 *Toll Free Tel:* 800-854-8621 *Fax:* 336-372-8602 *E-mail:* info@napcousa.com *Web Site:* www.napcousa.com, pg 1251

National Association of Book Entrepreneurs (NABE), PO Box 606, Cottage Grove, OR 97424 *Tel:* 541-942-7455 *Fax:* 541-942-7455 *E-mail:* nabe@bookmarketingprofits.com *Web Site:* www.bookmarketingprofits.com, pg 1133, 1293

National Book Co Inc, Keystone Industrial Park, Dunmore, PA 18512 *Tel:* 570-346-2029 *Toll Free Tel:* 800-233-4830, pg 1318

National Book Network (NBN), 4501 Forbes Blvd, Suite 200, Lanham, MD 20706 *Tel:* 301-459-3366 *Toll Free Tel:* 800-462-6420 (orders only) *Fax:* 301-429-5746 *Toll Free Fax:* 800-338-4550 (orders only) *E-mail:* customercare@nbnbooks.com *Web Site:* www.nbnbooks.com, pg 1293, 1318

National Council of Teachers of English (NCTE), 340 N Neil St, Suite 104, Champaign, IL 61820 *Tel:* 217-328-3870 *Toll Free Tel:* 877-369-6283 (cust serv) *Fax:* 217-328-9645 *E-mail:* customerservice@ncte.org; permissions@ncte.org *Web Site:* ncte.org, pg 1140

National Geographic Creative, 1145 17 St NW, Washington, DC 20036 *Tel:* 202-857-7537 *Toll Free Tel:* 800-434-2244 *E-mail:* natgeocreative@natgeo.com *Web Site:* www.natgeocreative.com, pg 1448

National Learning Corp, 212 Michael Dr, Syosset, NY 11791 *Tel:* 516-921-8888 *Toll Free Tel:* 800-632-8888 *Fax:* 516-921-8743 *E-mail:* info@passbooks.com *Web Site:* www.passbooks.com, pg 1318

National Library Bindery Co of Indiana Inc (NLBCo), 55 S State Ave, Suite 100, Indianapolis, IN 46201 *Tel:* 317-636-5606 *E-mail:* nlbco@nlbco.com *Web Site:* www.nlbco.com, pg 1323

Naviga, 7900 International Dr, Suite 800, Bloomington, MN 55425 *Tel:* 651-639-0662 *E-mail:* info@navigaglobal.com *Web Site:* www.navigaglobal.com, pg 1382

NCS Inc, 149 N Railroad St, Selmer, TN 38375 *Tel:* 731-645-4496 *E-mail:* service@ncsmags.com, pg 1332

Near Eastern Archaeology, Boston University, 656 Beacon St, 5th fl, Boston, MA 02215 *Tel:* 617-353-6570 *Fax:* 617-353-6575 *E-mail:* asor@bu.edu; asorpubs@bu.edu *Web Site:* www.asor.org (print only subns); www.jstor.org (electronic only & print plus electronic subns), pg 1129

Neenah Inc, 3460 Preston Ridge Rd, Suite 600, Alpharetta, GA 30005 *Toll Free Tel:* 800-344-5287 *E-mail:* publishing.team@neenah.com *Web Site:* www.neenahperformance.com/products/neenah-performance/publishing-products, pg 1266, 1278

Mrs Nelson's Library Services, 1650 W Orange Grove Ave, Pomona, CA 91768 *Tel:* 909-397-7820 *Toll Free Tel:* 800-875-9911 *Fax:* 909-397-7833 *E-mail:* bookcompany@mrsnelsons.com *Web Site:* www.mrsnelsons.com, pg 1318

NETS, 2714 Bee Caves Rd, Suite 201, Austin, TX 78746-5682 *Web Site:* www.netype.com, pg 1223, 1382

Omnipress, 2600 Anderson St, Madison, WI 53704 *Tel:* 608-246-2600 *Toll Free Tel:* 800-828-0305 *E-mail:* justask@omnipress.com *Web Site:* www.omnipress.com, pg 1208, 1252

OmniUpdate Inc, 1320 Flynn Rd, Suite 100, Camarillo, CA 93012 *Tel:* 805-484-9400 *Toll Free Tel:* 800-362-2605 *E-mail:* sales@omniupdate.com *Web Site:* omniupdate.com, pg 1383

OMRON Microscan Systems Inc, 700 SW 39 St, Suite 100, Renton, WA 98057 *Tel:* 425-226-5700 *Toll Free Tel:* 800-762-1149 *Fax:* 425-226-8250 *E-mail:* info@microscan.com *Web Site:* www.microscan.com, pg 1383

On Demand Machinery, 150 Broadway, Elizabeth, NJ 07206 *Tel:* 908-351-6906 *Fax:* 908-351-7156 *E-mail:* info@odmachinery.com *Web Site:* www.odmachinery.com, pg 1278

One Potata Productions Inc, 80 E 11 St, Suite 301-A, New York, NY 10003 *Tel:* 212-353-3478 *Fax:* 212-353-9667 *E-mail:* onepotata@gmail.com *Web Site:* onepotata.com, pg 1100

One Spirit®, 34 W 27 St, 10th fl, New York, NY 10001 *Tel:* 716-250-5700 (cust serv) *E-mail:* customer.service@onespirit.com *Web Site:* www.onespirit.com, pg 1137

O'Neil Digital Solutions LLC, 12655 Beatrice St, Los Angeles, CA 90066 *Tel:* 310-448-6400 *E-mail:* sales@oneildata.com *Web Site:* www.oneildata.com, pg 1224, 1252, 1266, 1278

OneTouchPoint, 1225 Walnut Ridge Dr, Hartland, WI 53029 *Tel:* 262-369-6000 *Toll Free Tel:* 800-332-2348 *Fax:* 262-369-5647 *E-mail:* info@1touchpoint.com *Web Site:* www.1touchpoint.com, pg 1093, 1208, 1252, 1383

Online Training Solutions Inc (OTSI), 16794 Santanella St, San Diego, CA 92127 *Toll Free Tel:* 888-308-6874 *E-mail:* biz@otsi.com *Web Site:* www.otsi.com, pg 1360

Open Book Systems Inc®, 21 Broadway, Suite 5, Rockport, MA 01966 *Tel:* 978-546-7346 *Fax:* 978-231-0222 *E-mail:* info@obs.com *Web Site:* www.obs.com, pg 1350, 1383

Open Horizons Publishing Co, PO Box 2887, Taos, NM 87571 *Tel:* 575-751-3398 *E-mail:* books@bookmarketingbestsellers.com *Web Site:* bookmarketingbestsellers.com, pg 1350

Open Sky Creative, 907 North St, Williamsburg, IA 52361 *Tel:* 630-564-2583 *E-mail:* mail@openskycreative.com *Web Site:* www.openskycreative.com, pg 1431

Open Text Corp, 275 Frank Tompa Dr, Waterloo, ON N2L 0A1, Canada *Tel:* 519-888-7111 *Fax:* 519-888-0677 *Web Site:* opentext.com, pg 1383

Oracle America Inc, 500 Oracle Pkwy, Redwood Shores, CA 94065 *Tel:* 650-506-7000 *Toll Free Tel:* 800-392-2999; 800-633-0738 (sales) *Web Site:* www.oracle.com, pg 1383

The Order Fulfillment Group, 7313 Mayflower Park Dr, Zionsville, IN 46077 *Tel:* 317-733-7755 *Fax:* 317-733-8799 *Web Site:* www.tofg.com, pg 1332

O'Reilly Media Inc, 1005 Gravenstein Hwy N, Sebastopol, CA 95472 *Tel:* 707-827-7019 (cust support); 707-827-7000 *Toll Free Tel:* 800-889-8969; 800-998-9938 *Fax:* 707-829-0104; 707-824-8268 *E-mail:* orders@oreilly.com; support@oreilly.com *Web Site:* www.oreilly.com, pg 1383

Orobora Inc, 644 Greenville Ave, Suite 234, Staunton, VA 24401 *Tel:* 540-324-7023 *E-mail:* info@orobora.com *Web Site:* orobora.com, pg 1350

Osa's Ark Museum Shop, 111 N Lincoln Ave, Chanute, KS 66720 *Tel:* 620-431-2730 *Fax:* 620-431-2730 *E-mail:* osajohns@safarimuseum.com; osasark@yahoo.com *Web Site:* www.safarimuseum.com, pg 1318

Tom O'Sullivan, 202 Riverside Dr, New York, NY 10025 *Tel:* 212-865-0229, pg 1431

Danuta Otfinowski, 625 "E" St NE, Washington, DC 20002 *Tel:* 202-546-5646 (studio); 202-744-0333 (cell) *E-mail:* danuta@danuta.us *Web Site:* www.danuta.us, pg 1441

OTTN Publishing, 16 Risler St, Stockton, NJ 08559 *Tel:* 609-397-4005 *Toll Free Tel:* 866-356-6886 *Fax:* 609-397-4007 *E-mail:* inquiries@ottnpublishing.com; sales@ottnpublishing.com *Web Site:* www.ottnpublishing.com, pg 1360

Outskirts Press Inc, 10940 S Parker Rd, Suite 515, Parker, CO 80134 *Toll Free Tel:* 888-OP-BOOKS (672-6657) *Toll Free Fax:* 888-208-8601 *E-mail:* info@outskirtspress.com *Web Site:* www.outskirtspress.com, pg 1252, 1383

Over the River Public Relations LLC, 116 Gladwin Ave, Leonia, NJ 07605 *Tel:* 201-503-1321 *Fax:* 201-503-0952 *E-mail:* info@otrpr.com *Web Site:* www.otrpr.com, pg 1100

OverDrive Inc, One OverDrive Way, Cleveland, OH 44125 *Tel:* 216-573-6886 *Fax:* 216-573-6888 *E-mail:* info@overdrive.com *Web Site:* www.overdrive.com, pg 1294

Overseas Printing Corporation, 4040 Civic Center Dr, Suite 200, San Rafael, CA 94903 *Tel:* 415-500-8331 *Fax:* 415-835-9899 *Web Site:* www.overseasprinting.com, pg 1208, 1224, 1252, 1266, 1278

The Ovid Bell Press Inc, 1201 Bluff St, Fulton, MO 65251 *Tel:* 573-642-2256 *Toll Free Tel:* 800-835-8919 *E-mail:* sales@ovidbell.com *Web Site:* ovidbell.com, pg 1224, 1252, 1266, 1278

Oyster River Press, 36 Oyster River Rd, Durham, NH 03824-3029 *Tel:* 603-868-5006 *E-mail:* oysterriverpress@comcast.net *Web Site:* www.oysterriverbooks.com; www.facebook.com/OysterRiverPress, pg 1318

Pacific Publishing Co Inc, 636 Alaska St S, Seattle, WA 98108 *Tel:* 206-461-1300 *E-mail:* ppcprint@nwlink.com; ppccirc@nwlink.com; ppcbind@nwlink.com *Web Site:* pacificpublishingcompany.com, pg 1252

PadillaCRT, 1101 W River Pkwy, Suite 400, Minneapolis, MN 55415 *Tel:* 612-455-1700 *Fax:* 612-455-1060 *Web Site:* www.padillacrt.com, pg 1100

Page Turner Publicity, 8785 SW 28 St, Miami, FL 33165 *Tel:* 949-254-3214 *E-mail:* pgturnerpub@aol.com *Web Site:* www.pageturnerpublicity.com, pg 1100

Lynne Palmer Executive Recruitment Inc, 295 Madison Ave, Suite 1700, New York, NY 10017 *Tel:* 212-883-0203 *Fax:* 212-883-0149 *E-mail:* careers@lpalmer.com *Web Site:* www.lpalmer.com, pg 1389

Panaprint Inc, 7979 NE Industrial Blvd, Macon, GA 31216 *Tel:* 478-788-0676 *Toll Free Tel:* 800-622-0676 *Fax:* 478-788-4276 *Web Site:* www.panaprint.com, pg 1252

Pannonia Bookstore, 300 Sainte Clair Ave W, Suite 103, Toronto, ON M4V 1S4, Canada *Tel:* 416-966-5156 *E-mail:* info@pannonia.ca *Web Site:* www.pannonia.ca, pg 1318, 1327

Panoramic Images, 4835 Main St, Suite LL001, Skokie, IL 60077 *Tel:* 847-324-7000 *Toll Free Tel:* 800-543-5250 *Fax:* 847-324-7004 *E-mail:* info@panoramicimages.com *Web Site:* www.panoramicimages.com, pg 1449

Tom Pantages, 87 Short St, Marlboro, MA 01752 *Tel:* 508-305-2828 *Fax:* 508-305-2828 *E-mail:* pantages@comcast.net, pg 1441

Pantagraph Printing, 217 W Jefferson St, Bloomington, IL 61701 *Tel:* 309-829-1071 *E-mail:* queries1@pantagraphprinting.com *Web Site:* www.pantagraphprinting.com, pg 1224

Pantone Inc, 590 Commerce Blvd, Carlstadt, NJ 07072-3098 *Tel:* 201-935-5500 *Toll Free Tel:* 866-PANTONE (726-8663) *Fax:* 201-896-0242 *E-mail:* pantoneorders@pantone.com *Web Site:* www.pantone.com, pg 1278

Paper Brigade, 520 Eighth Ave, 4th fl, New York, NY 10018 *Tel:* 212-201-2920 *Fax:* 212-532-4952 *E-mail:* info@jewishbooks.org *Web Site:* www.jewishbookcouncil.org, pg 1130

Paperbacks For Educators, 426 W Front St, Washington, MO 63090 *Tel:* 314-960-3015 *E-mail:* paperbacks@usmo.com *Web Site:* www.any-book-in-print.com, pg 1318

Parachute Publishing LLC, 157 Columbus Ave, Suite 518, New York, NY 10023 *Tel:* 212-691-1422, pg 1360

Paraclete Press Inc, 36 Southern Eagle Cartway, Brewster, MA 02631 *Tel:* 508-255-4685 *Toll Free Tel:* 800-451-5006 *Fax:* 508-255-5705 *E-mail:* customerservice@paracletepress.com *Web Site:* www.paracletepress.com, pg 1208, 1224

Parasource Marketing & Distribution Ltd, 55 Woodslee Ave, Paris, ON N3L 3E5, Canada *Tel:* 519-442-7853 *Toll Free Tel:* 800-263-2664 *Fax:* 519-442-1303 *Toll Free Fax:* 800-461-8575 *E-mail:* custserv@parasource.com *Web Site:* parasource.com, pg 1294, 1318

Mel Parker Books LLC, 75 Prospect Park West, 6B, Brooklyn, NY 11215 *Tel:* 212-982-8215 *E-mail:* info@melparkerbooks.com *Web Site:* melparkerbooks.com, pg 1360

Parkhurst Communications Inc, 11 Riverside Dr, Suite 1-TW, New York, NY 10023 *Tel:* 212-362-9722 *Web Site:* www.parkhurstcommunications.com, pg 1100

The Parsippany News, PO Box 6123, West Caldwell, NJ 07007-6123 *Tel:* 973-227-4433, pg 1185

Parson Weems' Publisher Services LLC, 3811 Canterbury Rd, No 707, Baltimore, MD 21218 *Tel:* 914-948-4259 *Toll Free Fax:* 866-861-0337 *E-mail:* office@parsonweems.com *Web Site:* www.parsonweems.com, pg 1294

Passwords Communications Inc, 1804 21 St N, Arlington, VA 22209 *Tel:* 703-624-5953 *E-mail:* paellero@aol.com *Web Site:* www.passwords-comm.com, pg 1412

Pathway Book Service, 34 Production Ave, Keene, NH 03431 *Tel:* 603-357-0236 *Toll Free Tel:* 800-345-6665 *Fax:* 603-965-2181 *E-mail:* pbs@pathwaybook.com *Web Site:* www.pathwaybook.com, pg 1319

Patterson Printing Co, 1550 Territorial Rd, Benton Harbor, MI 49022 *Tel:* 269-925-2177 *Toll Free Tel:* 800-848-8826 *Fax:* 269-925-6057 *E-mail:* sales@patterson-printing.com *Web Site:* www.patterson-printing.com, pg 1208, 1252, 1266, 1278

Paulist Press, 997 Macarthur Blvd, Mahwah, NJ 07430-9990 *Tel:* 201-825-7300 *Toll Free Tel:* 800-218-1903 *Fax:* 201-825-6921 *Toll Free Fax:* 800-836-3161 *E-mail:* info@paulistpress.com *Web Site:* www.paulistpress.com, pg 1319

Paulist Press, 997 Macarthur Blvd, Mahwah, NJ 07430-9990 *Tel:* 201-825-7300 *Toll Free Tel:* 800-218-1903 *Fax:* 201-825-6921 *Toll Free Fax:* 800-836-3161 *E-mail:* info@paulistpress.com; publicity@paulistpress.com *Web Site:* www.paulistpress.com, pg 1383

Jerry Pavia, 17 Ginger Lane, Bonners Ferry, ID 83805 *Tel:* 208-267-7374 *Fax:* 208-267-7374 *E-mail:* plantshooter@yahoo.com, pg 1441

Paz & Associates: The Bookstore Training & Consulting Group, 1417 Sadler Rd, No 274, Fernandina Beach, FL 32034 *Tel:* 904-277-2664 *Fax:* 904-261-6742 *Web Site:* www.pazbookbiz.com, pg 1350

PBD Worldwide Inc, 1650 Bluegrass Lakes Pkwy, Alpharetta, GA 30004 *Tel:* 470-769-1000 *Toll Free Tel:* 866-998-4PBD (998-4723) *E-mail:* sales.marketing@pbd.com; customerservice@pbd.com *Web Site:* www.pbd.com, pg 1333

PBM Graphics Inc, an RR Donnelley Co, 3700 S Miami Blvd, Durham, NC 27703 *Tel:* 919-544-6222 *Toll Free Tel:* 800-849-8100 *Fax:* 919-544-6695 *E-mail:* info@pbmgraphics.com *Web Site:* pbmgraphics.com, pg 1252

Peace Visions, 18850 Vista del Canon, Suite A, Santa Clarita, CA 91321-4512 *Tel:* 661-251-6669 *Fax:* 661-251-6669, pg 1393

Douglas Peebles Photography, 44-527A Kaneohe Bay Dr, Kaneohe, HI 96744 *Tel:* 808-342-7930 *E-mail:* douglas@douglaspeebles.com *Web Site:* www.douglaspeebles.com, pg 1442

Penfield Books, 215 Brown St, Iowa City, IA 52245 *Tel:* 319-337-9998 *Toll Free Tel:* 800-728-9998 *Fax:* 319-351-6846 *E-mail:* penfield@penfieldbooks.com; orders@penfieldbooks.com *Web Site:* www.penfieldbooks.com, pg 1319

Penguin Random House Canada, 320 Front St W, Suite 1400, Toronto, ON M5V 3B6, Canada *Tel:* 416-364-4449 *Toll Free Tel:* 888-523-9292 (cust serv) *Fax:* 416-598-7764 *Web Site:* www.penguinrandomhouse.ca, pg 1295

Pennsylvania Literary Journal (PLJ), 1108 W Third St, Quanah, TX 79252 *Tel:* 470-289-6395 *Web Site:* anaphoraliterary.com, pg 1130

The Penworthy Company LLC, 219 N Milwaukee St, 4th fl, Milwaukee, WI 53202 *Tel:* 414-287-4600 *Toll Free Tel:* 800-262-2665 *Fax:* 414-287-4602 *E-mail:* info@penworthy.com *Web Site:* www.penworthy.com, pg 1319, 1324

Peregrine Arts Bindery, 7 Avenida Vista Grande, Suite B-7 119, Santa Fe, NM 87508 *Tel:* 505-466-0490 *Web Site:* www.peregrineartsbindery.etsy.com, pg 1266

Perma-Bound Books, 617 E Vandalia Rd, Jacksonville, IL 62650 *Tel:* 217-243-5451 *Toll Free Tel:* 800-637-6581 *Fax:* 217-243-7505 *Toll Free Fax:* 800-551-1169 *E-mail:* books@perma-bound.com *Web Site:* www.perma-bound.com, pg 1319, 1324

Perma Graphics, 1356 S Jason St, Denver, CO 80223 *Tel:* 303-477-2070 *E-mail:* info@perma-graphics.com *Web Site:* www.perma-graphics.com, pg 1252

The Permissions Group Inc, 401 S Milwaukee Ave, Suite 180, Wheeling, IL 60090 *Tel:* 847-635-6550 *Toll Free Tel:* 800-374-7985 *Fax:* 847-635-6968 *E-mail:* info@permissionsgroup.com *Web Site:* www.permissionsgroup.com, pg 1350

Personal TeX Inc, 722 Lombard St, Suite 201, San Francisco, CA 94133 *Tel:* 415-296-7550 *Toll Free Tel:* 800-808-7906 *Fax:* 415-296-7501 *E-mail:* sales@pctex.com *Web Site:* www.pctex.com, pg 1383

Philosophy & Literature, 2715 N Charles St, Baltimore, MD 21218-4363 *Toll Free Tel:* 800-548-1784 (journal orders) *Fax:* 410-516-6968 *E-mail:* jrnlcirc@press.jhu.cdu (journal orders) *Web Site:* www.press.jhu.edu/journals/philosophy_and_literature/index.html, pg 1130

Phoenix Media, 29 Miriam Dr, Matawan, NJ 07747 *Tel:* 732-441-1519 *Fax:* 732-566-1913 *Web Site:* www.phoenixmediapr.com, pg 1100

PhotoEdit Inc, 3505 Cadillac Ave, Suite P-101, Costa Mesa, CA 92626 *Toll Free Tel:* 888-450-0946 *Fax:* 714-434-5937 *Web Site:* www.photoeditinc.com, pg 1449

Photofest, 32 E 31 St, 5th fl, New York, NY 10016 *Tel:* 212-633-6330 *Fax:* 212-366-9062 *E-mail:* requests@photofestnyc.com *Web Site:* www.photofestnyc.com, pg 1449

Photographix, 1171 Pauline Blvd, Ann Arbor, MI 48103-5319 *Tel:* 734-476-2068, pg 1442

Photography by Westura, 163 Ashland Ct, Stanhope, NJ 07874 *Tel:* 973-691-2646 *Web Site:* personalphotojournalism.com, pg 1442

Photography for Communication & Commerce, 3931 S Spruce St, Suite 200, Denver, CO 80237-2152 *Tel:* 303-829-5678 *Web Site:* www.howardpaulphotography.com, pg 1442

Geoff Reed Photography, 7640 N 22 St, Phoenix, AZ 85020 *Tel:* 602-749-1103 *E-mail:* geoff@geoffreedphoto.com *Web Site:* www.geoffreedphoto.com, pg 1442

Emmanuel X Pierreuse, 1830 Avenida del Mundo, Suite 412, Coronado, CA 92118 *Tel:* 619-435-3931 *Fax:* 619-435-3931 *E-mail:* epierreuse@aol.com, pg 1412

Law Office of Robert G Pimm Attorney at Law, 2977 Ygnacio Valley Rd, Suite 265, Walnut Creek, CA 94598-3535 *Tel:* 925-374-1442 *Fax:* 925-281-2888 *Web Site:* www.rgpimm.com, pg 1351

Pint Size Productions LLC, 5745 Main St, Amherst, NY 14221 *Tel:* 716-204-3353 *E-mail:* sales@pintsizeproductions.com *Web Site:* www.pintsizeproductions.com, pg 1252

Pivar Computing Services Inc, 1500 Abbott Ct, Buffalo Grove, IL 60089 *Tel:* 847-478-8000 *Toll Free Tel:* 800-CONVERT (266-8378) *Fax:* 847-478-8750 *Web Site:* www.pivar.com, pg 1383

Robert Pizzo Illustration/Design, 21 Lonetown Rd, Redding, CT 06896-2004 *Tel:* 203-938-0663 *E-mail:* rp@robertpizzo.com *Web Site:* www.robertpizzo.com, pg 1431

Planar, 1195 NW Compton Dr, Beaverton, OR 97006-1992 *Tel:* 503-748-1100 *Toll Free Tel:* 866-475-2627 *E-mail:* sales@planar.com *Web Site:* www.planar.com, pg 1383

PMSI Direct, 242 Old New Brunswick Rd, Suite 350, Piscataway, NJ 08854 *Tel:* 732-465-1570 *Toll Free Tel:* 800-238-1316 *Web Site:* www.pmsidirect.com, pg 1109

POD Print, 2012 E Northern St, Wichita, KS 67216 *Tel:* 316-522-5599 *Toll Free Tel:* 800-767-6066 *E-mail:* info@podprint.com *Web Site:* www.podprint.com, pg 1208, 1224, 1252

Poetry Flash, 1450 Fourth St, Suite 4, Berkeley, CA 94710 *Tel:* 510-525-5476 *Fax:* 510-525-6752 *E-mail:* editor@poetryflash.org *Web Site:* www.poetryflash.org, pg 1130

Polish National Union of America, 1006 Pittston Ave, Scranton, PA 18505 *Tel:* 570-344-1513 *Toll Free Tel:* 800-724-6352 *Fax:* 570-961-5961 *E-mail:* info@pnu.org *Web Site:* www.pnu.org, pg 1412

Polybook Distributors, 501 Mamaroneck Ave, White Plains, NY 10605 *Tel:* 914-328-6346 *Fax:* 914-328-6348, pg 1319

Polyglot Communications Inc, PO Box 1962, Laguna Beach, CA 92652 *Tel:* 949-497-1544 *E-mail:* info@polyglot.us.com *Web Site:* www.polyglot.us.com, pg 1412

Polyglot Translators, PO Box 30087, Bethesda, MD 20824 *Tel:* 301-485-9865 *Fax:* 301-907-8707 *E-mail:* info@polyglottranslators.com *Web Site:* polyglottranslators.com, pg 1412

Polylogics Services LLC, 6209 Mid Rivers Mall, Suite 320, St Peters, MO 63304 *Tel:* 201-670-4242 *Fax:* 201-670-4244 *E-mail:* info@polylogics.com *Web Site:* www.polylogics.com, pg 1393

Louise B Popkin, 9 Cliff St, Arlington, MA 02476 *Tel:* 781-643-6957 *E-mail:* louise@louisebpopkin.com, pg 1412

James Porter Photography, 211 E Columbine Ave, Suite A-1, Santa Ana, CA 92707 *Tel:* 714-546-4148 *E-mail:* info@jamesporterphotography.com *Web Site:* www.jamesporterphotography.com, pg 1442

Porter Novelli, 195 Broadway, 17th fl, New York, NY 10007 *Tel:* 212-601-8000 *Web Site:* www.porternovelli.com, pg 1100

Post Bulletin Co LLC, 18 First Ave SE, Rochester, MN 55903 *Tel:* 507-285-7600 *Toll Free Tel:* 800-562-1758 *E-mail:* news@postbulletin.com *Web Site:* www.postbulletin.com, pg 1186

Power Engineering Books Ltd, 7 Perron St, St Albert, AB T8N 1E3, Canada *Tel:* 780-458-3155; 780-459-2525 *Toll Free Tel:* 800-667-3155 *Fax:* 780-460-2530 *E-mail:* power@nucleus.com *Web Site:* www.powerengbooks.com, pg 1295

Powis Parker Inc, 2929 Fifth St, Berkeley, CA 94710 *Tel:* 510-848-2463 *Toll Free Tel:* 800-321-BIND (321-2463) *Fax:* 510-848-2169 *E-mail:* customerservice@powis.com *Web Site:* www.powis.com, pg 1383

PR by the Book LLC, PO Box 6226, Round Rock, TX 78683 *Tel:* 512-501-4399 *Fax:* 512-501-4399 *E-mail:* info@prbythebook.com *Web Site:* www.prbythebook.com, pg 1100

PR Newswire, 350 Hudson St, Suite 300, New York, NY 10014-4504 *Toll Free Tel:* 888-776-0942; 800-776-8090 *Toll Free Fax:* 800-793-9313 *E-mail:* mediainquiries@prnewswire.com *Web Site:* www.prnewswire.com, pg 1101

PR/PR Public Relations, 2301 Hickory Lane, Orlando, FL 32803 *Tel:* 407-895-8800 *Web Site:* www.prpr.net, pg 1101

PrairieView Press, 625 Seventh St, Gretna, MB R0G 0V0, Canada *Tel:* 204-327-6543 *Toll Free Tel:* 800-477-7377 *Toll Free Fax:* 866-480-0253 *Web Site:* prairieviewpress.com, pg 1224, 1252, 1266, 1278

Pratt Paper Company LLC, 20 Davis Rd, Marblehead, MA 01945 *Tel:* 781-639-9450 *Fax:* 781-639-9452, pg 1266

Premier Graphics, 860 Honeyspot Rd, Stratford, CT 06615 *Tel:* 203-378-6200 *Toll Free Tel:* 800-414-1624 *Fax:* 203-386-1624 *E-mail:* info@premieruplink.com *Web Site:* www.premieruplink.com, pg 1107, 1109

PremierIMS Inc, 11101 Ella Blvd, Houston, TX 77067 *Tel:* 832-608-6400 *Fax:* 832-608-6420 *E-mail:* info@premier-ims.com *Web Site:* www.premier-ims.com, pg 1110

Press Associates Union News Service, 4000 Cathedral Ave NW, No 535B, Washington, DC 20016 *Tel:* 312-806-4825 *E-mail:* paiunionnews@gmail.com, pg 1186

Press Box Publicity, 3920 Duncan Dr, Boca Raton, FL 33434 *Tel:* 912-658-7860 *E-mail:* sportspr@smithpublicity.com *Web Site:* pressboxpublicity-smithpublicity.com, pg 1101

Presskits, PO Box 71, East Walpole, MA 02032 *Toll Free Tel:* 800-472-3497 *E-mail:* files@presskits.com; team@presskits.com *Web Site:* presskits.com, pg 1093

Preston Kelly, 222 First Ave NE, Minneapolis, MN 55413 *Tel:* 612-843-4000 *Fax:* 612-843-3900 *E-mail:* iconicideas@prestonkelly.com *Web Site:* prestonkelly.com, pg 1087

PrimeArray Systems Inc, 1500 District Ave, Burlington, MA 01803 *Tel:* 978-455-9488 *Toll Free Tel:* 800-433-5133 *E-mail:* info@primearray.com; sales@primearray.com *Web Site:* www.primearray.com, pg 1383

Print It Plus, 11420 Okeechobee Blvd, Royal Palm Beach, FL 33411 *Tel:* 561-790-0884 *Fax:* 561-790-9378 *E-mail:* info@printitplus.com *Web Site:* printitplus.com, pg 1253

Printed Matter Inc, 231 11 Ave, Ground fl, New York, NY 10001 *Tel:* 212-925-0325 *Fax:* 212-925-0464 *E-mail:* info@printedmatter.org *Web Site:* www.printedmatter.org, pg 1295

The Printer, 2810 Cowell Blvd, Davis, CA 95618 *Tel:* 530-753-2519 *Fax:* 530-753-2528 *E-mail:* info@the-printer.net *Web Site:* the-printer.net, pg 1093, 1253

Printer's Repair Parts, 2706 Edgington St, Franklin Park, IL 60131-3438 *Tel:* 847-288-9000 *Toll Free Tel:* 800-444-4338 *Fax:* 847-288-9010 *E-mail:* prpsales@printersrepairparts.com *Web Site:* www.printersrepairparts.com, pg 1278

Printing Corporation of the Americas Inc, 620 SW 12 Ave, Pompano Beach, FL 33069 *Tel:* 954-781-8100 *Toll Free Tel:* 866-721-1PCA (721-1722) *Web Site:* pcaprintingplus.com, pg 1208, 1224, 1253, 1266

Printing Research Inc (PRI), 10760 Shady Trail, Suite 300, Dallas, TX 75220 *Tel:* 214-353-9000 *Toll Free Tel:* 800-627-5537 (US only) *Fax:* 214-357-5847 *E-mail:* info@superblue.net *Web Site:* www.printingresearch.com; www.superblue.net, pg 1278

Printronix Inc, 6440 Oak Canyon, Suite 200, Irvine, CA 92618 *Tel:* 714-368-2300 *Toll Free Tel:* 800-665-6210 *Web Site:* www.printronix.com, pg 1383

Printware LLC, 2935 Waters Rd, Suite 160, St Paul, MN 55121-1523 *Tel:* 651-456-1400 *Fax:* 651-454-3684 *E-mail:* sales@printwarellc.com *Web Site:* www.printwarellc.com, pg 1384

PrintWest, 1111 Eighth Ave, Regina, SK S4R 1C9, Canada *Tel:* 306-525-2304 *Toll Free Tel:* 800-236-6438 *Fax:* 306-757-2439 *E-mail:* general@printwest. com *Web Site:* www.printwest.com, pg 1208, 1224, 1266, 1278

Pro-Composition Inc, 2501 Catherine St, Suite 3, York, PA 17408 *Tel:* 717-965-9872 *Web Site:* www.pro-composition.com, pg 1224

Pro Laminators, 1511 Avco Blvd, Sellersburg, IN 47172 *Tel:* 812-246-0900 *Toll Free Tel:* 800-357-6812 *Fax:* 812-246-1900 *E-mail:* customerservice@ prolaminators.com *Web Site:* prolaminators.com, pg 1253

Product Identification & Processing Systems Inc, 10 Midland Ave, Suite M-02, Port Chester, NY 10573-5911 *Tel:* 212-996-6000 *Toll Free Tel:* 888-783-7439 *Fax:* 212-410-7477 *Toll Free Fax:* 800-241-PIPS (241-7477) *E-mail:* info@pips.com *Web Site:* www.pips. com, pg 1224

ProductionPro, 246 Park St, Bensenville, IL 60106 *Tel:* 847-696-1600 *E-mail:* sales@productionpro. com; graphics@productionpro.com *Web Site:* www. productionpro.com, pg 1253, 1384

ProFAX Inc, 20 Max Ave, Hicksville, NY 11801-1419 *Toll Free Tel:* 877-942-8100 *E-mail:* sales@profax. com *Web Site:* www.profax.com, pg 1110

Progress Printing Plus, 2677 Waterlick Rd, Lynchburg, VA 24502 *Tel:* 434-239-9213 *Toll Free Tel:* 800-572-7804 *Fax:* 434-832-7573 *E-mail:* info@progressprintplus.com *Web Site:* www. progressprintplus.com, pg 1093, 1208, 1224, 1253

Progressive Publishing Services (PPS), 555 Ryan Run Rd, Suite B, York, PA 17404 *Tel:* 717-764-5908 *Fax:* 717-764-5530 *E-mail:* info@pps-ace.com *Web Site:* www.pps-ace.com, pg 1224, 1384

Prologue Inc, 1650 Blvd Lionel-Bertrand, Boisbriand, QC J7H 1N7, Canada *Tel:* 450-434-0306 (ext 231) *Toll Free Tel:* 800-363-2864 *Fax:* 450-434-2627 *Toll Free Fax:* 800-361-8088 (cust serv) *E-mail:* prologue@prologue.ca *Web Site:* www. prologue.ca; www.prologuenumerique.ca, pg 1295

Promote A Book, 591 Mantua Blvd, Sewell, NJ 08080 *Tel:* 512-586-6073 *Web Site:* promoteabook.media, pg 1351

Promotion in Motion, 714 Crescent Dr, Beverly Hills, CA 90210 *Tel:* 323-461-3921; 310-497-4001 (cell) *Fax:* 323-461-0917 *E-mail:* irwinzuckerpr@aol. com *Web Site:* www.promotioninmotion.net; www. bookpublicists.org, pg 1101

Promotional Book Co, 12 Cranfield Rd, No 100, Toronto, ON M4B 3G8, Canada *Tel:* 416-759-2226 *Fax:* 416-759-2150, pg 1319

Pronk Media Inc, PO Box 340, Beaverton, ON L0K 1A0, Canada *Tel:* 416-441-3760 *E-mail:* info@pronk. com *Web Site:* www.pronk.com, pg 1224, 1384, 1431

ProQuest LLC, 789 E Eisenhower Pkwy, Ann Arbor, MI 48108 *Tel:* 734-761-4700 *Toll Free Tel:* 800-521-0600; 877-779-6768 (sales) *E-mail:* sales@proquest.com *Web Site:* www.proquest.com, pg 1384

Jennifer Prost Public Relations, 51 Christopher St, Montclair, NJ 07042 *Tel:* 973-746-8723 *E-mail:* jprostpr@comcast.net *Web Site:* www. jenniferprost.com, pg 1101

ProtoView, 7515 NE Ambassador Place, Suite A, Portland, OR 97220 *Tel:* 503-281-9230 *E-mail:* info@ protoview.com *Web Site:* www.protoview.com, pg 1130, 1140

ps ink LLC, 857 Post Rd, Suite 367, Fairfield, CT 06824 *Tel:* 203-255-9789 *Web Site:* www.ps-ink.com, pg 1351

PsycCRITIQUES™, 750 First St NE, Washington, DC 20002-4242 *Tel:* 202-336-5500 *Fax:* 202-336-5502 *E-mail:* subscriptions@apa.org *Web Site:* www.apa.org, pg 1130

PTC, 121 Seaport Blvd, Boston, MA 02210 *Tel:* 781-370-5000 *Fax:* 781-370-6000 *Web Site:* www.ptc.com, pg 1384

Publication Design Inc, 6449 Meadowview Terr S, Zionsville, PA 18092 *Tel:* 610-928-1111 *E-mail:* ayers@publicationdesign.com *Web Site:* www. publicationdesign.com, pg 1431

Publication Identification & Processing Systems, 10 Midland Ave, Suite M-02, Port Chester, NY 10573 *Tel:* 212-996-6000 *Toll Free Tel:* 888-783-7439 *Fax:* 212-410-7477 *Toll Free Fax:* 800-241-7477 *E-mail:* info@pips.com *Web Site:* www.pips.com, pg 1224

Publications Professionals LLC, 3603 Chain Bridge Rd, Suite A & B, Fairfax, VA 22030-3244 *Tel:* 703-934-4499 *Fax:* 703-591-7389 *E-mail:* info@pubspros.com *Web Site:* www.pubspros.com, pg 1389

Publicis North America, 1675 Broadway, New York, NY 10009 *Tel:* 212-474-5000 *Web Site:* www.publicisna. com, pg 1101

Publishers Book Bindery (NY), 250 W 16 St, 4th fl, New York, NY 10011 *Tel:* 917-497-2950, pg 1208, 1253, 1278

Publishers' Feature Service, 4013 Coyte Ct, Marietta, GA 30062 *Tel:* 561-247-5533 *E-mail:* pfssyndicate@ gmail.com *Web Site:* publishersfeatureservice.com, pg 1186

Publishers' Graphics LLC, 131 Fremont St, Chicago, IL 60185 *Tel:* 630-221-1850 *E-mail:* contactpg@ pubgraphics.com *Web Site:* pubgraphics.com, pg 1208, 1253, 1279

Publishers Group West (PGW), an Ingram brand, 1700 Fourth St, Berkeley, CA 94710 *Tel:* 510-809-3700 *Toll Free Tel:* 866-400-5351 (cust serv) *Fax:* 510-809-3777 *E-mail:* info@pgw.com *Web Site:* www.pgw.com, pg 1295

Publishers Storage & Shipping Corp, 46 Development Rd, Fitchburg, MA 01420 *Tel:* 978-345-2121 *Fax:* 978-348-1233 *Web Site:* www.pssc.com, pg 1333

Publishers Weekly, 71 W 23 St, Suite 1608, New York, NY 10010 *Tel:* 212-377-5500 *Fax:* 212-377-2733 *Web Site:* www.publishersweekly.com, pg 1130

Publishing Data Management Inc, 39 Broadway, 28th fl, New York, NY 10006 *Tel:* 212-673-3210 *Fax:* 212-673-3390 *E-mail:* info@pubdata.com *Web Site:* www. pubdata.com, pg 1224, 1253, 1384

Publishing Management Associates Inc, 129 S Phelps Ave, Suite 312, Rockford, IL 61108 *Tel:* 815-398-8569 *Fax:* 815-398-8579 *E-mail:* pma@pma-inc.net *Web Site:* www.pma-inc.net, pg 1351

Publishing Resources Inc, 425 Carr 693, PMB 160, Dorado, PR 00646 *Tel:* 787-647-9342 *E-mail:* pri@ chevako.net, pg 1225, 1361

Publishing Trends, 232 Madison Ave, Suite 1400, New York, NY 10016 *Tel:* 212-447-0855 *Fax:* 212-447-0785 *E-mail:* info@publishingtrends.com *Web Site:* www.marketpartnersinternational.com; www. publishingtrends.com, pg 1130

Purdy Sports Images, Staff of History, PO Box 65454, University Place, WA 98464 *Tel:* 253-460-0066 *E-mail:* vcbcmag@comcast.net, pg 1449

Puritan Press Inc, 95 Runnells Bridge Rd, Hollis, NH 03049-6565 *Tel:* 603-889-4500 *Toll Free Tel:* 800-635-6302 *Fax:* 603-889-6551 *E-mail:* print@puritancapital. com *Web Site:* www.puritanpress.com, pg 1253

The Pushpin Group Inc, 38 W 26 St, New York, NY 10010 *Tel:* 212-529-7590 *Web Site:* www.pushpininc. com, pg 1361, 1431

Sarah Putnam, 320 Brookline St, Cambridge, MA 02139 *Tel:* 617-547-3758 *E-mail:* sarah@sarahputnam.com *Web Site:* www.sarahputnam.com, pg 1442

QBR The Black Book Review, 591 Warburton Ave, Unit 170, Hastings-on-Hudson, NY 10706 *Tel:* 914-231-6778 *Web Site:* www.qbr.com, pg 1130

QBS Learning, 242 W 30 St, Suite 900, New York, NY 10001 *Tel:* 929-841-5969 *E-mail:* sales@qbslearning. com *Web Site:* www.qbslearning.com, pg 1361, 1431

Quadrata Inc, 15 Byron St, Wakefield, MA 01880 *Tel:* 781-245-1183 *Fax:* 781-246-9040, pg 1361

Quality Bindery Services Inc, 501 Amherst St, Buffalo, NY 14207 *Tel:* 716-883-5185 *Toll Free Tel:* 888-883-1266 *Fax:* 716-883-1598 *E-mail:* info@qualitybindery. com *Web Site:* www.qualitybindery.com, pg 1253

QualityLogic Inc, 9576 W Emerald St, Boise, ID 83704 *Tel:* 208-424-1905 *E-mail:* info@qualitylogic.com *Web Site:* www.qualitylogic.com, pg 1384

Quantum Group, 6511 Oakton St, Morton Grove, IL 60053 *Tel:* 847-967-3600 *Fax:* 847-967-3610 *E-mail:* info@quantumgroup.com *Web Site:* www. quantumgroup.com, pg 1253

QuaraCORE LLC, One E Wacker Dr, Suite 1900, Chicago, IL 60601 *Tel:* 312-981-2540 *E-mail:* info@ quaracore.com *Web Site:* www.quaracore.com, pg 1431

Quark Software Inc, Chrysler Bldg, 405 Lexington Ave, 9th fl, New York, NY 10174 *Toll Free Tel:* 800-676-4575 *Web Site:* www.quark.com, pg 1384

Quarto Distribution Services (QDS), 100 Cummings Ctr, Suite 265D, Beverly, MA 01915 *Tel:* 978-282-9590 *E-mail:* qds@quarto.com *Web Site:* www.quartoknows. com/qds, pg 1296

Quiz Features, PO Box 42222, Northwest Sta, Washington, DC 20015-0822 *Tel:* 202-966-0025 *Fax:* 202-966-0025, pg 1186

R & R Book Co LLC, 666 Godwin Ave, Suite 120-C, Midland Park, NJ 07432 *Tel:* 201-337-3400 *Web Site:* www.rrbookcompany.com, pg 1296

R J Promotions & Advertising, 120 Holton Ave S, Hamilton, ON L8M 2L5, Canada *Tel:* 905-548-0389 *E-mail:* rjpromo@cogeco.ca, pg 1351

Raab Associates Inc, 730 Yale Ave, Swarthmore, PA 19081 *Tel:* 914-241-2117 *E-mail:* info@raabassociates. com *Web Site:* www.raabassociates.com, pg 1101, 1351

Rainbo Electronic Reviews, 5405 Cumberland Rd, Minneapolis, MN 55410 *Tel:* 612-408-4057 *Web Site:* www.rainboreviews.com, pg 1121

Raincoast Books Distribution Ltd, 2440 Viking Way, Richmond, BC V6V 1N2, Canada *Tel:* 604-448-7100 *Toll Free Tel:* 800-663-5714 (CN only) *Fax:* 604-270-7161 *Toll Free Fax:* 800-565-3770 *E-mail:* info@ raincoast.com; customerservice@raincoast.com *Web Site:* www.raincoast.com, pg 1296

RAM Publications & Distribution Inc, 2525 Michigan Ave, Bldg A2, Santa Monica, CA 90404 *Tel:* 310-453-0043 *Fax:* 310-264-4888 *E-mail:* info@rampub.com; orders@rampub.com *Web Site:* www.rampub.com, pg 1296

RAmEx Ars Medica Inc, 1714 S Westgate Ave, No 2, Los Angeles, CA 90025-3852 *Tel:* 310-826-4964 *Toll Free Tel:* 800-633-9281 *Fax:* 310-826-9674 *E-mail:* ars.medica@ramex.com *Web Site:* www. ramex.com, pg 1296

Neil Rashba Photography, 1174 Neck Rd, Ponte Vedra Beach, FL 32082 *Tel:* 904-273-0388 *Fax:* 904-273-6203 *E-mail:* neil@rashba.com *Web Site:* www.rashba. com, pg 1442

Rayonier Advanced Materials, 1301 Riverplace Blvd, Suite 2300, Jacksonville, FL 32207 *Tel:* 904-357-4600 *Web Site:* rayonieram.com, pg 1266

Readerlink Distribution Services LLC, 1420 Kensington Rd, Suite 300, Oakbrook, IL 60523-2164 *Tel:* 708-547-4400 *Toll Free Tel:* 800-549-5389 *E-mail:* info@ readerlink.com; marketingservices@readerlink.com *Web Site:* www.readerlink.com, pg 1297

Readers' Guide to Periodical Literature, 4919 Rte 22, Amenia, NY 12501 *Tel:* 518-789-8700 *Toll Free Tel:* 800-562-2139 *Fax:* 518-789-0556 *E-mail:* books@greyhouse.com *Web Site:* greyhouse. com, pg 1130

Patrick Redmond Design, PO Box 40156, St Paul, MN 55104-8156 *Tel:* 651-646-4254 *E-mail:* LMP@ PatrickRedmondDesign.com *Web Site:* www. PatrickRedmondDesign.com, pg 1431

Redwing Book Co, 202 Bendix St, Taos, NM 87571 *Tel:* 575-758-7758 *Toll Free Tel:* 800-873-3946 (US); 888-873-3947 (CN) *Fax:* 575-758-7768 *E-mail:* info@ redwingbooks.com; custsrv@redwingbooks.com *Web Site:* www.redwingbooks.com, pg 1319, 1327

V G Reed & Sons Inc, 1002 S 12 St, Louisville, KY 40210-1302 *Toll Free Tel:* 800-635-9788 *Fax:* 502-560-0197 *Web Site:* www.vgreed.com, pg 1093, 1253

Reference & User Services Quarterly (RUSQ), 225 N Michigan Ave, Suite 1300, Chicago, IL 60601 *Tel:* 312-280-4395 *Toll Free Tel:* 800-545-2433 *Fax:* 312-280-5273 *E-mail:* rusa@ala.org *Web Site:* www.ala.org/rusa, pg 1131

Regal Press, 79 Astor Ave, Norwood, MA 02062 *Tel:* 781-769-3900 *Toll Free Tel:* 800-447-3425 *Fax:* 781-769-7361 *E-mail:* info@regalpress.com *Web Site:* www.regalpress.com, pg 1093, 1253

Regent Book Co, PO Box 37, Liberty Corner, NJ 07938 *Tel:* 973-574-7600 *Toll Free Tel:* 800-999-9554 *Fax:* 973-944-5073 *Toll Free Fax:* 888-597-3661 *E-mail:* info@regentbook.com *Web Site:* www.regentbook.com, pg 1319

Regent Press Publishers & Printers, 2747 Regent St, Berkeley, CA 94705 *Tel:* 510-845-1196 *E-mail:* regentpress@mindspring.com *Web Site:* www.regentpress.net, pg 1384

Laszlo Regos Photography, 24067 Research Dr, Farmington Hills, MI 48335 *Tel:* 248-398-3631 *E-mail:* laszlo@laszlofoto.com *Web Site:* www.laszlofoto.com, pg 1442

Reichhold Inc, 1035 Swabia Ct, Durham, NC 27703 *Tel:* 919-990-7500 *Toll Free Tel:* 800-448-3482 *Fax:* 919-990-7749 *Web Site:* www.reichhold.com, pg 1267

Reindl Bindery Co Inc, W194 N11381 McCormick Dr, Germantown, WI 53022 *Tel:* 262-293-1444 *Toll Free Tel:* 800-878-1121 *Fax:* 262-293-1445 *E-mail:* info@ reindlbindery.com *Web Site:* www.reindlbindery.com, pg 1253

Ruth & Robert Reld, 71 Faunce Dr, Providence, RI 02906 *Tel:* 401-274-2149 *Web Site:* www.whitegatefeatures.com, pg 1118

Religion News Service, c/o University of Missouri's Journalism School, 30 Neff Annex, Columbia, MO 65211 *Tel:* 573-884-1327 *E-mail:* info@religionnews.com *Web Site:* www.religionnews.com, pg 1186

Renaissance Consultations, PO Box 561, Auburn, CA 95604 *Tel:* 530-362-1339 *E-mail:* info@ marketingandpr.com *Web Site:* www.MarketingAndPR.com, pg 1101

Renaissance House, 465 Westview Ave, Englewood, NJ 07631 *Tel:* 201-408-4048 *Web Site:* www.renaissancehouse.net, pg 1361

Rennert International, 211 E 43 St, New York, NY 10017 *Tel:* 212-867-8700 *Fax:* 212-867-7666 *E-mail:* info@rennert.com *Web Site:* www.rennert.com, pg 1412

Reno Typographers, 1020 S Rock Blvd, Suite C, Reno, NV 89502 *Tel:* 775-852-8800 *E-mail:* info@renotype.com; work@renotype.com *Web Site:* www.renotype.com, pg 1225

Renouf Publishing Co Ltd, 22-1010 Polytek St, Ottawa, ON K1J 9J1, Canada *Tel:* 613-745-2665 *Toll Free Tel:* 866-767-6766; 888-551-7470 (North America) *Fax:* 613-745-7660 *E-mail:* order.dept@renoufbooks.com *Web Site:* www.renoufbooks.com, pg 1297

The Renton Printery Inc, 315 S Third St, Renton, WA 98057-2028 *Tel:* 425-235-1776 *E-mail:* info@ rentonprintery.com *Web Site:* www.rentonprintery.com, pg 1225, 1253

Resolute Forest Products, 111 Robert-Bourassa Blvd, Suite 5000, Montreal, QC H3C 2M1, Canada *Tel:* 514-875-2160 *Toll Free Tel:* 800-361-2888 *E-mail:* info@resolutefp.com *Web Site:* www.resolutefp.com, pg 1267

Retailing Insight, 119 N Commercial St, Suite 560, Bellingham, WA 98225 *Tel:* 360-676-0789 *Toll Free Tel:* 800-463-9243 *E-mail:* info@retailinginsight.com *Web Site:* retailinginsight.com, pg 1131

Reviewer Bookwatch, 278 Orchard Dr, Oregon, WI 53575-1129 *Tel:* 608-835-7937 *E-mail:* mbr@execpc.com *Web Site:* www.midwestbookreview.com, pg 1131

Reviews in American History, 2715 N Charles St, Baltimore, MD 21218-4363 *Toll Free Tel:* 800-548-1784 (journal orders) *Fax:* 410-516-6968 *E-mail:* jrnlcirc@press.jhu.edu (journal orders) *Web Site:* www.press.jhu.edu/journals/reviews_in_american_history/index.html, pg 1131

REX, 13431 SW Scotts Bridge Dr, Tigard, OR 97223-1609 *Tel:* 503-238-4525 *E-mail:* info@rexpost.com *Web Site:* www.rexpost.com, pg 1384

Rex Three Inc, 15431 SW 14 St, Sunrise, FL 33326 *Tel:* 954-388-8708 *Toll Free Tel:* 800-782-6509 *Fax:* 954-452-0569 *Web Site:* www.rex3.com, pg 1384

Reynolds Design & Management, 52 Piedmont Ave, Waltham, MA 02451-3015 *Tel:* 781-893-7464 *E-mail:* rdandm@comcast.net, pg 1432

Nina J Reznick Esq, 28 E Tenth St, New York, NY 10003 *Tel:* 212-473-6279 *E-mail:* ninarezesq@icloud.com, pg 1351

Ribolow Associates Inc, 1350 Avenue of the Americas, 2nd fl, New York, NY 10019 *Tel:* 212-575-2700 *Fax:* 646-496-9122 *E-mail:* ribolowstaffingservices@ gmail.com *Web Site:* www.ribolow.com, pg 1390

Law Offices of Lloyd L Rich, 1163 Vine St, Denver, CO 80206 *Tel:* 303-388-5215 *E-mail:* rich@ publishingattorney.com *Web Site:* www.publaw.com, pg 1351

Ricoh Americas Corp, 300 Eagleview Blvd, Exton, PA 19341 *Tel:* 610-296-8000 *Toll Free Tel:* 800-333-2679 (prod support); 800-637-4264 (sales) *Web Site:* www.ricoh-usa.com, pg 1384

Jan Riggenbach, 2319 S 105 Ave, Omaha, NE 68124 *Tel:* 402-502-4367 *Web Site:* midwestgardening.com, pg 1118

Rights & Distribution Inc, 7519 LaPaz Blvd, Suite C303, Boca Raton, FL 33433 *Tel:* 954-925-5242 *E-mail:* rightsinc@aol.com, pg 1297

Rimage Corp, 201 General Mills Blvd, Golden Valley, MN 55427 *Tel:* 952-944-8144; 952-946-0004 (option 2, tech support) *Toll Free Tel:* 800-445-8288; 800-553-8312 (option 2, tech support) *E-mail:* sales@rimage.com *Web Site:* www.rimage.com, pg 1385

Rising Sun Book Co, 1424 Stony Brook Rd, Stony Brook, NY 11790 *Tel:* 631-473-7000 *Fax:* 631-473-7447 *Web Site:* risingsunbook.com, pg 1319, 1327

RISO Inc, 10 State St, Suite 201, Woburn, MA 01801-2105 *Tel:* 978-777-7377 *Toll Free Tel:* 800-942-7476 (cust support) *Web Site:* us.riso.com, pg 1253, 1385

Judith Riven Literary Agent LLC, 250 W 16 St, Suite 4F, New York, NY 10011 *Tel:* 212-255-1009 *Fax:* 212-255-8547 *E-mail:* rivenlitqueries@gmail.com *Web Site:* rivenlit.com, pg 1351

Rivendell Media Inc, 1248 Rte 22 W, Mountainside, NJ 07092 *Tel:* 908-232-2021 ext 200 *Fax:* 908-232-0521 *E-mail:* info@rivendellmedia.com; sales@ rivendellmedia.com *Web Site:* www.rivendellmedia.com, pg 1101

Riverside Book Co Inc, PO Box 237043, New York, NY 10023-0028 *Tel:* 212-595-0700 *Fax:* 212-595-0700 *Web Site:* www.riversidebook.com, pg 1319

Rizzoli Bookstores, 1133 Broadway, New York, NY 10010 *Tel:* 212-759-2424 *Toll Free Tel:* 800-52-BOOKS (522-6657) *Fax:* 212-826-9754 *Web Site:* rizzolibookstore.com; www.rizzoliusa.com, pg 1319

The Roberts Group, 12803 Eastview Curve, Apple Valley, MN 55124 *Tel:* 952-322-4005 *E-mail:* info@ editorialservice.com *Web Site:* www.editorialservice.com, pg 1225, 1385, 1432

The John Roberts Company, 9687 East River Rd NW, Minneapolis, MN 55433 *Tel:* 763-755-5500 *Toll Free Tel:* 800-551-1534 *Fax:* 763-755-0394 *E-mail:* success@johnroberts.com *Web Site:* www.johnroberts.com; www.facebook.com/TheJohnRobertsCompany, pg 1093

Richard Owen Roberts, Booksellers & Publishers, 139 N Washington St, Wheaton, IL 60189 *Tel:* 630-752-4122 *E-mail:* sales@rorbooks.com *Web Site:* www.rorbooks.com, pg 1319

Carol A Robinson, Photographer, 2012 Aldrich Place, Downers Grove, IL 60516 *Tel:* 630-222-6286 *E-mail:* goodpix@zenfolio.com *Web Site:* goodpix.zenfolio.com, pg 1442

Ron Rochon, 2386 Bernard Rd, Windsor, ON N8W 4R8, Canada *Tel:* 519-945-4565 *E-mail:* ronron@mnsi.net, pg 1442

Stephanie Rogers & Associates, 8737 Carlitas Joy Ct, Las Vegas, NV 89117 *Tel:* 702-255-9999 *E-mail:* sjrlion@aol.com; write2wow@aol.com *Web Site:* www.write2wow.com, pg 1351

Claudette Roland, PO Box 24035, Los Angeles, CA 90024 *Tel:* 310-475-4347 *Fax:* 310-475-0939 *E-mail:* claudette_roland@verizon.net, pg 1412

Roland DGA Corp, 15363 Barranca Pkwy, Irvine, CA 92618-2216 *Tel:* 949-727-2100 *Toll Free Tel:* 800-542-2307 *Fax:* 949-727-2112 *Web Site:* www.rolanddga.com, pg 1385

Rolland Enterprises, 256 JB Rolland W, St-Jerome, QC J7Y 0L6, Canada *Toll Free Tel:* 800-567-9872 (CN); 800-388-0882 (US) *E-mail:* media@rollandinc.com; marketing@rollandinc.com *Web Site:* www.rollandinc.com, pg 1267

Roosevelt Paper Co, One Roosevelt Dr, Mount Laurel, NJ 08054 *Tel:* 856-303-4100 *Toll Free Tel:* 800-523-3470 *Fax:* 856-642-1949 *E-mail:* marketing@ rooseveltpaper.com *Web Site:* www.rooseveltpaper.com, pg 1267

Roots & Rhythm Inc, PO Box 837, El Cerrito, CA 94530 *Tel:* 510-965-9503 *Toll Free Tel:* 888-ROOTS-66 (766-8766) *Fax:* 510-526-9001 *E-mail:* roots@ toast.net *Web Site:* www.rootsandrhythm.com, pg 1137

Rosemoor House Translations, Rosemoor House, 400 New Bedford Dr, Vallejo, CA 94591 *Tel:* 707-557-8595 *Fax:* 707-557-5555, pg 1412

Sherri Rosen Publicity Intl NYC, 454 Manhattan Ave, Suite 3-J, New York, NY 10026 *Tel:* 212-222-1183 *E-mail:* sherri@sherrirosen.com *Web Site:* www.sherrirosen.com, pg 1101, 1351

Rosenthal Represents, 23725 Hartland St, West Hills, CA 91307 *Tel:* 818-430-3850 *E-mail:* eliselicenses@ earthlink.net, pg 1432

Alex Ross, One World Trade Center, New York, NY 10007 *Tel:* 212-286-2860 *Web Site:* www.newyorker.com; www.therestisnoise.com, pg 1118

Ross Gage Inc, 8502 Brookville Rd, Indianapolis, IN 46239 *Tel:* 317-283-2323 *Toll Free Tel:* 800-799-2323 *Fax:* 317-931-2108 *E-mail:* info@rossgage.com *Web Site:* www.rossgage.com, pg 1225, 1253

Ken Ross Photography, PO Box 4517, Scottsdale, AZ 85261 *Tel:* 602-319-2974 *E-mail:* kenrossaz@yahoo.com *Web Site:* www.kenrossphotography.com, pg 1442

Roswell Bookbinding, 2614 N 29 Ave, Phoenix, AZ 85009 *Tel:* 602-272-9338 *Toll Free Tel:* 888-803-8883 *Fax:* 602-272-9786 *Web Site:* www.roswellbookbinding.com, pg 1253, 1324

Roth Advertising Inc, PO Box 96, Sea Cliff, NY 11579 *Tel:* 516-674-8603 *Fax:* 516-368-3885 *Web Site:* www.rothadvertising.com, pg 1087

Jeff Rotman Photography, 53 Green Ave, Lawrenceville, NJ 08648 *Tel:* 609-219-0040 *Fax:* 609-219-1595 *E-mail:* contact@jeffrotman.com *Web Site:* www.jeffrotman.com, pg 1442

Round Table Companies, 1027 Kenton Rd, Deerfield, IL 60015 *Tel:* 949-375-1006 *Web Site:* www.roundtablecompanies.com, pg 1432

Roundtable Press Inc, 20 E Ninth St, New York, NY 10003 *Tel:* 917-597-2183 *Web Site:* www. roundtablepressinc.com, pg 1361

Dick Rowson, 4701 Connecticut Ave NW, Suite 503, Washington, DC 20008 *Tel:* 202-244-8104 *E-mail:* rcrowson2@aol.com, pg 1351

Royalty Review LLC, 485 Madison Ave, 9th fl, New York, NY 10022 *Tel:* 212-792-6300 *Fax:* 212-792-6350 *E-mail:* info@janoverllc.com *Web Site:* www. jrllc.com, pg 1351

Victoria Roza Research, PO Box 881745, San Diego, CA 92168-1745 *Tel:* 619-295-8082 *E-mail:* victoriaproza@gmail.com, pg 1442

RRD Manchester, 151 Red Stone Rd, Manchester, CT 06042 *Tel:* 860-649-5570 *Fax:* 860-649-7800 *Web Site:* www.rrdonnelley.com/commercial-print/location/rr-donnelley-manchester, pg 1093

Ruder Finn Inc, 425 E 53 St, New York, NY 10022 *Tel:* 212-593-6400 *E-mail:* info@ruderfinn.com *Web Site:* www.ruderfinn.com, pg 1101

Rushmore News Inc, 924 E Saint Andrew, Rapid City, SD 57701 *Tel:* 605-342-2617 *Toll Free Tel:* 800-423-0501, pg 1319

Ryukyu Books & Periodicals Inc, PO Box 535, Olathe, KS 66051 *Tel:* 913-782-3920 *Toll Free Tel:* 800-383-4017 *Fax:* 913-780-1750 *E-mail:* info@ryukyubooks. com *Web Site:* www.ryukyu.com, pg 1319

Ryukyu Books & Periodicals Inc, 5005 Merriam Dr, Merriam, KS 66203 *Tel:* 913-782-3920 *Toll Free Tel:* 800-383-4017 *Fax:* 913-780-1750 *Web Site:* www. ryukyu.com, pg 1327

S & L Sales Co Inc, 2165 Industrial Blvd, Waycross, GA 31503 *Tel:* 912-283-0210 *Toll Free Tel:* 800-243-3699 *Fax:* 912-283-0261 *Toll Free Fax:* 800-736-7329 *E-mail:* sales@slsales.com *Web Site:* slsales.com, pg 1319

Saferock, 75 Armour Place, Dumont, NJ 07628 *Tel:* 646-535-0110 *E-mail:* info@saferock.com *Web Site:* saferockretail.com, pg 1385

St Armand Paper Mill, 3700 St Patrick, Montreal, QC H4E 1A2, Canada *Tel:* 514-931-8338 *Fax:* 514-931-5953 *Web Site:* www.st-armand.com, pg 1267

St Catharines Museum, 1932 Welland Canals Pkwy, RR 6, St Catharines, ON L2R 7K6, Canada *Tel:* 905-984-8880 *Toll Free Tel:* 800-305-5134 *Fax:* 905-984-6910 *E-mail:* museum@stcatharines.ca *Web Site:* www. stcatharines.ca, pg 1297

St Joseph Communications-Print Group, 50 Macintosh Blvd, Concord, ON L4K 4P3, Canada *Tel:* 905-660-3111 *E-mail:* marketing@stjoseph.com *Web Site:* stjoseph.com, pg 1093, 1254

Sakurai USA Inc, 1700 N Basswood Rd, Schaumburg, IL 60173 *Tel:* 847-490-9400 *Toll Free Tel:* 800-458-4720 *Fax:* 847-490-4200 *E-mail:* inquiry@sakurai.com *Web Site:* www.sakurai.com, pg 1279

Samsung Research America (SRA), 665 Clyde Ave, Mountain View, CA 94043 *Tel:* 650-210-1001 *E-mail:* sra-contact-us@samsung.com *Web Site:* www. sra.samsung.com, pg 1385

Samuel Packaging Systems, 4020 Gault Ave S, Fort Payne, AL 35967 *Tel:* 256-845-1928 *Web Site:* www. samuel.com, pg 1279

San Diego Museum of Art, Balboa Park, 1450 El Prado, San Diego, CA 92112 *Tel:* 619-232-7931 *Fax:* 619-232-9367 *Web Site:* www.sdmart.org, pg 1320

Sandhill Book Marketing Ltd, Millcreek Industrial Park, Unit 4, 3308 Appaloosa Rd, Kelowna, BC V1V 2W5, Canada *Tel:* 250-491-1446 *Toll Free Tel:* 800-667-3848 (CN only) *Fax:* 250-491-4066 *E-mail:* info@sandhillbooks.com *Web Site:* www.sandhillbooks.com, pg 1320

Santec Corp, 84 Old Gate Lane, Milford, CT 06460 *Tel:* 203-878-1379 *Fax:* 203-876-0949 *E-mail:* info@santeccorp.com *Web Site:* www.santeccorp.com, pg 1279

Sappi Fine Paper North America, 255 State St, Boston, MA 02109 *Tel:* 617-423-7300 *Toll Free Tel:* 800-882-4332 *E-mail:* webqueriesna@sappi.com *Web Site:* www.sappi.com/na, pg 1267

Sargent Architectural Photography, 7675 Steeplechase Dr, Palm Beach Gardens, FL 33418 *Tel:* 561-881-8887 *Fax:* 561-881-8882 *E-mail:* sargentphoto@att.net *Web Site:* www.sargentphoto.com, pg 1442

Saunders Book Co, PO Box 308, Collingwood, ON L9Y 3Z7, Canada *Tel:* 705-445-4777 *Toll Free Tel:* 800-461-9120 *Fax:* 705-445-9569 *Toll Free Fax:* 800-561-1763 *E-mail:* info@saundersbook.ca *Web Site:* librarybooks.com, pg 1297

Scarf Press, 1385 Baptist Church Rd, Yorktown Heights, NY 10598 *Tel:* 914-245-7811, pg 1361

SCB Distributors, 15608 S New Century Dr, Gardena, CA 90248 *Tel:* 310-532-9400 *Toll Free Tel:* 800-729-6423 *Fax:* 310-532-7001 *E-mail:* scb@scbdistributors. com *Web Site:* www.scbdistributors.com, pg 1297

Sceptre Inc, 16800 Gale Ave, City of Industry, CA 91745 *Tel:* 626-369-3698 *Toll Free Tel:* 800-788-2878 *Fax:* 626-369-3488 *E-mail:* sceptrecs@sceptre.com; scp-marketing@sceptre.com; scp-sales@sceptre.com *Web Site:* www.sceptre.com, pg 1385

Schaefer Machine Co Inc, 200 Commercial Dr, Deep River, CT 06417 *Tel:* 860-526-4000 *Toll Free Tel:* 800-243-5143 *Fax:* 860-526-4654 *E-mail:* schaefer@schaeferco.com *Web Site:* www. schaeferco.com, pg 1279

Schenkman Books Inc, 145 Bethel Mountain Rd, Rochester, VT 05767 *Tel:* 802-767-3104 *E-mail:* schenkmanbooks@gmail.com *Web Site:* www. schenkmanbooks.com, pg 1361

Bernard Schleifer Co, 200 W 20 St, Suite 212, New York, NY 10011 *Tel:* 212-675-2615, pg 1351, 1432

Richard Schneider Language Services, 1200 Piedmont Ave, Pacific Grove, CA 93950 *Tel:* 831-622-0554 *Toll Free Tel:* 800-500-5808 *Fax:* 831-622-0524 *E-mail:* service@idioms.com *Web Site:* www.idioms. com, pg 1412

Joel Schnell Photographer, 2081 Seventh St N, North St Paul, MN 55109 *Tel:* 612-384-0413 *E-mail:* joel@schnellphoto.com *Web Site:* www.schnellphoto.com, pg 1442

Schnoll Media Consulting, 1253 Springfield Ave, PMB 338, New Providence, NJ 07974 *Tel:* 908-522-3190 *Fax:* 908-273-2667 *Web Site:* www.schnollconsult. com, pg 1351

Schoenhof's Foreign Books Inc, 76 A Mount Auburn St, Cambridge, MA 02138 *Tel:* 617-547-8855 *E-mail:* info@schoenhofs.com *Web Site:* www. schoenhofs.com, pg 1320, 1327

Scholarly Book Services Inc, 289 Bridgeland Ave, Unit 105, Toronto, ON M6A 1Z6, Canada *Toll Free Tel:* 800-847-9736 *Toll Free Fax:* 800-220-9895 *E-mail:* customerservice@sbookscan.com *Web Site:* www.sbookscan.com, pg 1297

The Scholar's Choice, 6300 W Port Bay Rd, Suite 101, Wolcott, NY 14590 *Tel:* 315-905-4208 *E-mail:* information@scholarschoice.com *Web Site:* www.scholarschoice.com, pg 1133

Scholar's Choice Ltd, 2323 Trafalgar St, London, ON N5Y 5S7, Canada *Tel:* 519-453-7470 *Toll Free Tel:* 800-265-1095 *Fax:* 519-455-2853 *Toll Free Fax:* 800-363-3398 (CN only) *E-mail:* sales@scholarschoice.ca *Web Site:* www.scholarschoice.ca, pg 1298

Scholastic Book Fairs®, 1080 Greenwood Blvd, Lake Mary, FL 32746 *Tel:* 407-829-8000 *Fax:* 407-829-2600 *E-mail:* custservbf@scholasticbookfairs.com *Web Site:* www.scholastic.com/bookfairs, pg 1298, 1320

School Library Journal, 123 William St, Suite 802, New York, NY 10038 *Tel:* 646-380-0752 *Toll Free Tel:* 800-595-1066 *Fax:* 646-380-0756 *E-mail:* slj@mediasourceinc.com; sljsubs@pcspublink.com *Web Site:* www.slj.com; www.facebook.com/schoollibraryjournal; twitter.com/sljournal, pg 1131

School of World Studies, 312 N Shafer St, Richmond, VA 23284-2021 *Tel:* 804-827-1111 *Fax:* 804-828-0127 *Web Site:* www.has.vcu.edu/wld, pg 1413

Schoolhouse Indexing, 10-B Parade Ground Rd, Etna, NH 03750 *Tel:* 603-643-1617 *Web Site:* schoolhouseindexing.com, pg 1225

Schreiber Translations Inc (STI), 51 Monroe St, Suite 101, Rockville, MD 20850 *Tel:* 301-424-7737 *Toll Free Tel:* 800-822-3213 *Fax:* 301-424-2336 *E-mail:* translation@schreibernet.com *Web Site:* www. schreibernet.com, pg 1413

Carl Schreier, c/o Homestead Publishing & Book Design, Box 193, Moose, WY 83012-0193 *Tel:* 307-733-6248, pg 1442

Bettina Schrewe Literary Scouting, 220 E 23 St, Suite 409, New York, NY 10010 *Tel:* 212-414-2515 *Fax:* 212-414-2516 *E-mail:* bschrewe@bschrewe.com *Web Site:* www.bschrewe.com, pg 1351

Schroeder Indexing Services, 23 Camilla Pink Ct, Bluffton, SC 29909 *Tel:* 843-705-9779; 843-415-3900 (cell) *E-mail:* sanindex@schroederindexing.com *Web Site:* www.schroederindexing.com, pg 1225

Schroeder's Book Haven, 104 Michigan Ave, League City, TX 77573 *Tel:* 281-332-5226 *E-mail:* info@bookhaventexas.com *Web Site:* www.bookhaventexas. com, pg 1320

Lesley M Schuldt, 1647 Natches Way, Steamboat Springs, CO 80487 *Tel:* 970-879-5144 *Fax:* 970-879-5144 *E-mail:* stmbt97@aol.com, pg 1413

E C Schultz & Company Inc, 333 Crossen Ave, Elk Grove Village, IL 60007-2001 *Tel:* 847-640-1190 *E-mail:* jobfiles@ecschultz.com *Web Site:* www. ecschultz.com, pg 1279

Marian Schwartz, 1207 Bickler Rd, Austin, TX 78704 *Tel:* 512-442-5100 *Fax:* 512-442-5100 *E-mail:* marianschwartz@gmail.com, pg 1413

Susan Schwartzman Public Relations, 88 Kings Way, Pawling, NY 12564 *Toll Free Tel:* 877-833-4276 *Toll Free Fax:* 877-833-4276 *E-mail:* susan@susanschwartzmanpublicity.com *Web Site:* www. susanschwartzmanpublicity.com, pg 1102

Cosimo Scianna, Photographer, 23407 Milano Ct, Boca Raton, FL 33433 *Tel:* 917-763-2927 *E-mail:* cosimoscianna@mac.com *Web Site:* www. cosimoscianna.com, pg 1442

Natalia V Sciarini, 219 New England Rd, Guilford, CT 06437 *Tel:* 203-314-7680 *E-mail:* natalia@languageandtext.info *Web Site:* languageandtext.info, pg 1413

Science Books & Films, 1200 New York Ave NW, Washington, DC 20005 *Tel:* 202-326-6400 *Fax:* 202-371-9526 *E-mail:* media@aaas.org *Web Site:* www. aaas.org, pg 1131

Science Fiction Book Club®, 34 W 27 St, 10th fl, New York, NY 10001 *Tel:* 716-250-5700 (cust serv) *E-mail:* customer.service@sfbc.com *Web Site:* www. sfbc.com, pg 1137

Science Source®, 307 Fifth Ave, 3rd fl, New York, NY 10016 *Tel:* 212-758-3420 *Toll Free Tel:* 800-833-9033 *E-mail:* info@sciencesource.com *Web Site:* www. sciencesource.com, pg 1449

Scientific Bindery Inc, 8052 Monticello Ave, Suite 206, Skokie, IL 60076 *Tel:* 847-329-0510 *Fax:* 847-329-0608 *E-mail:* info@scientificbindery.com *Web Site:* www.scientificbindery.com, pg 1254

Scott Publications Inc, 2145 W Sherman Blvd, Norton Shores, MI 49441 *Tel:* 231-755-2200 *Toll Free Tel:* 866-733-9382 *Fax:* 231-755-1003 *E-mail:* contactus@scottpublications.com *Web Site:* scottpublications.com, pg 1093

SCREEN Americas, 5110 Tollview Dr, Rolling Meadows, IL 60008-3715 *Tel:* 847-870-7400 *Toll Free Tel:* 800-372-7737 *E-mail:* info@screenamericas.com *Web Site:* www.screenamericas.com, pg 1279, 1385

Sony DADC US Inc, 1800 N Fruitridge Ave, Terre Haute, IN 47804 *Tel:* 818-462-8100 *E-mail:* sales@sonydadc.com *Web Site:* www.sonydadc.com, pg 1385

Sony Electronics Inc, 16535 Via Esprillo, San Diego, CA 92127 *Tel:* 858-942-2400 *E-mail:* selpr@sony.com *Web Site:* www.sony.com/all-electronics, pg 1385

The Sound Lab Inc, 3355 Bee Cave Rd, Bldg 7, Suite 705, Austin, TX 78746 *Tel:* 512-476-2122 *Fax:* 512-476-2127 *E-mail:* info@thesoundlabinc.com *Web Site:* www.thesoundlabinc.com, pg 1385

The Source Stock Footage Library Inc, 140 S Camino Seco Blvd, Suite 308, Tucson, AZ 85710 *Tel:* 520-298-4810; 212-925-2547 *E-mail:* sourcestk@aol.com *Web Site:* www.sourcefootage.com, pg 1449

Southeastern Book Co, 2001 SW 31 Ave, Pembroke Park, FL 33009 *Tel:* 954-985-9400 *Toll Free Tel:* 800-223-3251 *Fax:* 954-987-2200 *E-mail:* staff@sebcobooks.com *Web Site:* www.sebcobooks.com, pg 1320

Southeastern Printing Co, 3601 SE Dixie Hwy, Stuart, FL 34997 *Tel:* 772-287-2141 *Toll Free Tel:* 800-226-8221 *Fax:* 772-288-3988 *E-mail:* sales@seprint.com *Web Site:* www.seprint.com, pg 1226, 1254, 1268, 1279

Southern Book Service, 4360 NW 135 St, Opa-locka, FL 33054 *Tel:* 305-681-3424 *Fax:* 305-681-8427, pg 1320

Southern California Focus, 1720 Oak St, Santa Monica, CA 90405 *Tel:* 310-452-3918 *Web Site:* www.californiafocus.net, pg 1186

Southern Images Photography, 142 Westlake Dr, Brandon, MS 39047-9020 *Tel:* 601-992-9488 *Web Site:* www.southern-images.com, pg 1443

Southern Territory Associates, 4508 64 St, Lubbock, TX 79414 *E-mail:* sta77@suddenlink.net *Web Site:* www.southernterritory.com, pg 1299

Southern Tier News Company, Inc, 353 Upper Oakwood Ave, Elmira Heights, NY 14903 *Tel:* 607-734-7108 *Toll Free Tel:* 888-287-4786 *Fax:* 607-734-6825 *Web Site:* www.southerntiernews.com, pg 1320

Southern Wisconsin News Co, 58 Artisan Dr, Edgerton, WI 53534 *Tel:* 608-884-2600 *Fax:* 608-884-2636 *Web Site:* www.southernwisconsinnews.com, pg 1320

Southwest Book Co, 13003 Murphy Rd, Suite H1, Stafford, TX 77477-3934 *Tel:* 281-498-2603 *Fax:* 281-498-7566, pg 1299

Southwestern Publishing House Inc, 2451 Atrium Way, Nashville, TN 37214 *Toll Free Tel:* 800-358-0560 *Fax:* 615-391-2815 *E-mail:* info@swpublishinggroup.com *Web Site:* www.swpublishinggroup.com, pg 1362

Bruce E Southworth Reviews, 1621 Lafond Ave, St Paul, MN 55104-2212 *Tel:* 651-808-1099 *E-mail:* mnbookcritic@yahoo.com, pg 1118

The Souza Agency Inc, PO Box 128, Annapolis, MD 21401-0128 *Tel:* 410-573-1300 *Fax:* 410-573-1305 *E-mail:* info@souza.com *Web Site:* www.souza.com, pg 1087

Sovfoto Inc, 263 W 20 St, Suite 3, New York, NY 10011 *Tel:* 212-727-8170 *Fax:* 212-727-8228 *E-mail:* research@sovfoto.com *Web Site:* www.sovfoto.com, pg 1449

Spanish/English Translation & Interpreting Services, 5704 SW 86 Dr, Gainesville, FL 32608-8536 *Tel:* 352-215-7200 *Web Site:* www.afn.org/~vanessa, pg 1413

Spanish Publishing Services, 4343 N Clarendon Ave, Suite 1002, Chicago, IL 60613 *Tel:* 773-878-2117 *Fax:* 773-388-2265 *E-mail:* servicioseditoriales@juno.com, pg 1413

Special Libraries Association (SLA), 7918 Jones Branch Dr, Suite 300, McLean, VA 22102 *Tel:* 703-647-4900 *Fax:* 703-506-3266 *E-mail:* sla@sla.org *Web Site:* www.sla.org, pg 1112

Specialist Marketing Services Inc, 777 Terrace Ave, Suite 401, Hasbrouck Heights, NJ 07604 *Tel:* 201-865-5800 *E-mail:* info@sms-inc.com *Web Site:* www.sms-inc.com, pg 1112

Specialty Book Marketing Inc, 87-80 115 St, Richmond Hill, NY 11418 *Tel:* 212-696-0415 *Fax:* 718-849-5131 *Web Site:* www.specialtybooks.com, pg 1352

Specialty Finishing Group, 1401 Kirk St, Elk Grove Village, IL 60007 *Tel:* 847-290-0110 *Fax:* 847-290-9404 *Web Site:* www.sfgrp.com, pg 1254

Specialty Product Technologies, 2100 W Broad St, Elizabethtown, NC 28337 *Tel:* 910-862-2511 *Toll Free Tel:* 800-390-6405 *Fax:* 910-879-5486 *E-mail:* customer.service@sptech.com *Web Site:* www.specialtyproducttechnologies.com, pg 1279

Spectrum PrintGroup Inc, 1535 Farmer's Lane, Suite 254, Santa Rosa, CA 95405 *Tel:* 707-542-6044 *Toll Free Tel:* 888-340-6049 *Fax:* 707-542-6045 *E-mail:* sales@spectrumprintgroup.com *Web Site:* www.spectrumprintgroup.com, pg 1209, 1254, 1268

Spicers Paper, 12310 E Slauson Ave, Santa Fe Springs, CA 90670 *Toll Free Tel:* 800-774-2377 *Fax:* 562-693-8339 *Web Site:* www.spicers.com, pg 1268

Spiral Binding LLC, One Maltese Dr, Totowa, NJ 07511 *Tel:* 973-256-0666 *Toll Free Tel:* 800-631-3572 *Fax:* 973-256-5981 *E-mail:* customerservice@spiralbinding.com; international@spiralbinding.com (outside US) *Web Site:* spiralbinding.com, pg 1255

Spraymation Inc, 4180 NW Tenth Ave, Fort Lauderdale, FL 33309 *Tel:* 954-484-9700 *Toll Free Tel:* 800-327-4985 *Fax:* 954-301-0842 *E-mail:* orders@spraymation.com *Web Site:* www.spraymation.com, pg 1279

Spring Arbor Distributors Inc, One Ingram Blvd, La Vergne, TN 37086-1986 *Toll Free Tel:* 800-395-4340 *Toll Free Fax:* 800-876-0186 *E-mail:* customerservice@ingramcontent.com *Web Site:* www.ingramcontent.com, pg 1279, 1299, 1320

Springdale Bindery LLC, 11411 Landan Lane, Cincinnati, OH 45246 *Tel:* 513-772-8500 *E-mail:* info@springdalebindery.com *Web Site:* www.springdalebindery.com, pg 1255

Barbara Spurll Illustration, 160 Browning Ave, Toronto, ON M4K 1W5, Canada *Tel:* 416-594-6594 *Toll Free Tel:* 800-989-3123 *Web Site:* www.barbaraspurll.com, pg 1226

Square Deal Records Book Department, 303 Higuera St, San Luis Obispo, CA 93401-1002 *Tel:* 805-543-3636 *Toll Free Tel:* 800-235-4114 *Fax:* 805-543-3938 *E-mail:* web@squaredealonline.com *Web Site:* www.squaredealonline.com, pg 1327

Square Two Design Inc, 2325 Third St, Suite 213, San Francisco, CA 94107 *Tel:* 415-437-3888 *E-mail:* info@square2.com *Web Site:* www.square2.com, pg 1226, 1386, 1432

SSPR LLC, One Northfield Plaza, Suite 400, Northfield, IL 60093 *Toll Free Tel:* 800-287-2279 *Web Site:* www.sspr.com, pg 1102

Tom Stack & Associates Inc, 7135 N Outrigger Terr, Citrus Springs, FL 34433 *Tel:* 305-852-5520 *E-mail:* tomstack@earthlink.net *Web Site:* www.tomstackassociates.photoshelter.com, pg 1449

Standard Finishing Systems, 10 Connector Rd, Andover, MA 01810 *Tel:* 978-470-1920 *Toll Free Tel:* 877-404-4460 *Fax:* 978-470-0819 *E-mail:* marketing@sdmc.com *Web Site:* www.sdmc.com, pg 1279

Staplex® Electric Stapler Division, 777 Fifth Ave, Brooklyn, NY 11232-1626 *Tel:* 718-768-3333 *Toll Free Tel:* 800-221-0822 *Fax:* 718-965-0750 *E-mail:* info@staplex.com *Web Site:* www.staplex.com, pg 1279

Star Micronics America Inc, 65 Clyde Rd, Suite G, Somerset, NJ 08873-3485 *Tel:* 848-216-3300 (sales) *Toll Free Tel:* 800-782-7636 *Fax:* 848-216-3222 (sales) *E-mail:* sales@starmicronics.com *Web Site:* www.starmicronics.com, pg 1386

StarGroup International Inc, 1194 Old Dixie Hwy, Suite 201, West Palm Beach, FL 33413 *Tel:* 561-547-0667 *E-mail:* info@stargroupinternational.com *Web Site:* stargroupinternational.com, pg 1102

Jane Starr Literary Scouts, 1350 Avenue of the Americas, Suite 1205, New York, NY 10019 *Tel:* 212-421-0777 *E-mail:* jane@janestarr.com, pg 1352

Steve Starr Photojournalist Emeritus, 720 Arcadia Place, Colorado Springs, CO 80903 *Tel:* 719-632-8274 *E-mail:* steve@stevestarr.com *Web Site:* www.stevestarr.com, pg 1443

Dave Starrett Photographer, 101 Thursfield Crescent, Toronto, ON M4G 2N4, Canada *Tel:* 647-865-8299 *E-mail:* dave@davestarrett.com *Web Site:* www.davestarrett.com, pg 1443

Steeleworks, PO Box 4002, Philadelphia, PA 19118 *Tel:* 215-247-4619 *Web Site:* www.sarasteele.com, pg 1432

Stephenson Printing, 5731 General Washington Dr, Alexandria, VA 22312 *Tel:* 703-642-9000 *Toll Free Tel:* 800-336-4637 *Fax:* 703-354-0384 *Web Site:* www.stephensonprinting.com, pg 1255

Sterling Pierce Co Inc, 395 Atlantic Ave, East Rockaway, NY 11518 *Tel:* 516-593-1170 *Fax:* 516-593-1401 *Web Site:* www.sterlingpierce.com, pg 1209, 1255

J B Stewart, 1700 Landings Blvd, Sarasota, FL 34231 *Tel:* 941-929-0262 *E-mail:* jstewartx2@comcast.net *Web Site:* jbstewartfinearts.com, pg 1432

Matt Stewart, 71 Faunce Dr, Providence, RI 02906 *Tel:* 401-274-2149 *Web Site:* www.whitegatefeatures.com, pg 1118

Still Media, 714 Mission Park Dr, Santa Barbara, CA 93105 *Tel:* 805-682-2868 *Fax:* 805-682-2659 *E-mail:* info@stillmedia.com *Web Site:* www.stillmedia.com, pg 1449

Stilo Corp, 1900 City Park Dr, Suite 504, Ottawa, ON K1J 1A3, Canada *Tel:* 613-745-4242 *Fax:* 613-745-5560 *E-mail:* contact@stilo.com *Web Site:* www.stilo.com, pg 1386

Stock Montage, 1817 N Mulligan Ave, Chicago, IL 60639 *Tel:* 773-637-9790 *Toll Free Tel:* 800-404-0425 *Fax:* 773-637-9794 *E-mail:* images@stockmontage.com *Web Site:* www.stockmontage.com, pg 1449

Stoesser Register Systems, 610 Whitetail Blvd, River Falls, WI 54022 *Tel:* 715-425-1900 *Toll Free Tel:* 888-407-4808 *Fax:* 715-425-1901 *E-mail:* info@nela-usa.com *Web Site:* www.nela-usa.com, pg 1279

Stonesong, 270 W 39 St, Suite 201, New York, NY 10018 *Tel:* 212-929-4600 *E-mail:* editors@stonesong.com *Web Site:* www.stonesong.com, pg 1362

StoraEnso North American Sales Inc, Canterbury Green, 201 Broad St, Stamford, CT 06901 *Tel:* 203-541-5100 *Fax:* 203-353-1143 *Web Site:* www.storaenso.com, pg 1268

Story Monsters LLC, 4696 W Tyson St, Chandler, AZ 85226-2903 *Tel:* 480-940-8182 *Fax:* 480-940-8787 *Web Site:* www.StoryMonsters.com; www.AuthorsandExperts.com; www.SchoolBookings.com; www.partnershippublishing.com; www.fivestarpublishingsecrets.com; www.eStarPublish.com; www.DragonflyBookAwards.com, pg 1102

Story Monsters LLC, 4696 W Tyson St, Chandler, AZ 85226-2903 *Tel:* 480-940-8182 *Fax:* 480-940-8787 *Web Site:* www.StoryMonsters.com, pg 1352, 1362

Story Monsters LLC, 4696 W Tyson St, Chandler, AZ 85226-2903 *Tel:* 480-940-8182 *Fax:* 480-940-8787 *Web Site:* www.StoryMonsters.com; www.AuthorsandExperts.com; www.SchoolBookings.com, pg 1386

Story Monsters LLC, 4696 W Tyson St, Chandler, AZ 85226-2903 *Tel:* 480-940-8182 *Fax:* 480-940-8787 *Web Site:* www.StoryMonsters.com, pg 1432

Streamline Films Inc, 2578 Broadway, Suite 157, New York, NY 10025 *Tel:* 212-925-2547 *Web Site:* www.streamlinefilms.com, pg 1450

Streem Communications LLC, 4949 Harrison Ave, Rockford, IL 61107 *Tel:* 815-282-7695 *Toll Free Tel:* 800-325-7732 *Fax:* 815-639-8931 *Toll Free Fax:* 888-435-2348 *E-mail:* streemsales@cleo.com; sales@cleo.com *Web Site:* www.streem.net, pg 1110

Strictly Spanish Translations LLC, PO Box 476, Milford, OH 45150 *Tel:* 513-965-1096 *E-mail:* information@ strictlyspanish.com *Web Site:* www.strictlyspanish.com, pg 1413

Hope Strong, 71 Faunce Dr, Providence, RI 02906 *Tel:* 401-274-2149 *Web Site:* www.whitegatefeatures. com, pg 1118

Studio E Book Production, PO Box 20005, Santa Barbara, CA 93120-0005 *Tel:* 805-683-6202 *Fax:* 805-683-6202 *E-mail:* queries@studio-e-books.com *Web Site:* www.studio-e-books.com, pg 1432

Studio 31 Inc, 2740 SW Martin Downs Blvd, Suite 358, Palm City, FL 34990 *Tel:* 772-781-7195 *Fax:* 772-781-6044 *Web Site:* www.studio31.com, pg 1226, 1362

The Studley Press Inc, 151 E Housatonic St, Dalton, MA 01226 *Tel:* 413-684-0441 *Toll Free Tel:* 877-684-0441 *Fax:* 413-684-0220 *Web Site:* thestudleypress.com, pg 1255, 1268

Styled Packaging LLC, PO Box 30299, Philadelphia, PA 19103-8299 *Tel:* 610-529-4122 *Fax:* 610-520-9662 *Web Site:* www.taylorbox.com, pg 1255, 1268, 1279, 1333, 1335

Stylus Publishing LLC, 22883 Quicksilver Dr, Sterling, VA 20166-2019 *Tel:* 703-661-1504 (edit & sales); 703-661-1581 (orders & cust serv); 703-996-1036 *Toll Free Tel:* 800-232-0223 (orders & cust serv) *Fax:* 703-661-1547; 703-661-1501 (orders & cust serv) *E-mail:* stylusinfo@styluspub.com; stylusmail@styluspub.com (orders & cust serv) *Web Site:* styluspub.presswarehouse.com, pg 1299

SumTotal Systems LLC, 2850 NW 43 St, Suite 150, Gainesville, FL 32606 *Tel:* 352-264-2800 *Toll Free Tel:* 866-933-1416 *Fax:* 352-374-2257 *E-mail:* customersupport@sumtotalsystems.com *Web Site:* www.sumtotalsystems.com, pg 1386

Sun Chemical Corp, 35 Waterview Blvd, Parsippany, NJ 07054-1285 *Tel:* 973-404-6000 *E-mail:* globalmarketing@sunchemical.com *Web Site:* www.sunchemical.com, pg 1268

Sun Graphics LLC, 1818 Broadway, Parsons, KS 67357 *Toll Free Tel:* 800-835-0588 *Fax:* 620-421-2089 *E-mail:* info@sun-graphics.com *Web Site:* www.sun-graphics.com, pg 1209, 1226, 1255

Sunbelt Publications Inc, 1250 Fayette St, El Cajon, CA 92020-1511 *Tel:* 619-258-4911 *Toll Free Tel:* 800-626-6579 (cust serv) *Fax:* 619-258-4916 *E-mail:* info@ sunbeltpublications.com; sunbeltbook@sunbeltpub.com *Web Site:* sunbeltpublications.com, pg 1321

Sunday San Francisco Chronicle Book Review, 901 Mission St, San Francisco, CA 94103 *Tel:* 415-777-1111 *Toll Free Tel:* 866-732-4766 *Web Site:* www. sfgate.com, pg 1131

Superior Printing Ink Co Inc, 100 North St, Teterboro, NJ 07608 *Tel:* 201-478-5600 *Fax:* 201-478-5650 *Web Site:* www.superiorink.com, pg 1268

Superstock, 6620 Southpoint Dr S, Suite 501, Jacksonville, FL 32216 *Tel:* 904-565-0066 *Toll Free Tel:* 800-828-4545 *E-mail:* yourfriends@superstock. com *Web Site:* www.superstock.com, pg 1450

The Supreme Co, 1909 Lagneaux Rd, Lafayette, LA 70506 *Tel:* 337-453-1028 *Toll Free Fax:* 888-600-4180 *E-mail:* information@supremebooks.com *Web Site:* www.supremebooks.com, pg 1321

Suspension Feeder, 631 E Washington St, St Henry, OH 45883 *Tel:* 419-763-1377 *Fax:* 888-210-9654 *Web Site:* www.suspensionfeeder.com, pg 1279

Margaret Swaine, 2 Hawthorn Gardens, Unit 4, Toronto, ON M4W 1P3, Canada *Tel:* 416-961-5328 *E-mail:* m. swaine@rogers.com *Web Site:* www.margaretswaine. com, pg 1119

Swan Packaging Fulfillment Inc, 415 Hamburg Tpke, Wayne, NJ 07470 *Tel:* 973-790-8417 *Fax:* 973-790-0216 *Web Site:* www.swanpackaging.com, pg 1107, 1333, 1335

Swedenborg Foundation, 320 N Church St, West Chester, PA 19380 *Tel:* 610-430-3222 *Toll Free Tel:* 800-355-3222 (cust serv) *Fax:* 610-430-7982 *E-mail:* info@ swedenborg.com *Web Site:* swedenborg.com, pg 1321

Sweetgrass Books, 2750 Broadway Ave, Helena, MT 59602 *Tel:* 406-422-1255 *Toll Free Tel:* 800-821-3874 *Web Site:* sweetgrassbooks.com, pg 1362

John S Swift Co Inc, 999 Commerce Ct, Buffalo Grove, IL 60089 *Tel:* 847-465-3300 *Fax:* 847-465-3309 *Web Site:* www.johnswiftprint.com, pg 1209, 1226, 1255

Swordsmith Productions, PO Box 242, Pomfret, CT 06258 *Tel:* 860-208-4829 *E-mail:* information@ swordsmith.com *Web Site:* www.swordsmith.com, pg 1226

Symbology Inc, 7351 Kirkwood Lane N, Suite 126, Maple Grove, MN 55369 *Tel:* 763-315-8080 *Toll Free Tel:* 800-328-2612 *Fax:* 763-315-8088 *E-mail:* clientservices@symbology.com; sales@ symbology.com *Web Site:* www.symbology.com, pg 1226

Symmetry Creative Production, 1300 S Grove Ave, Suite 103, Barrington, IL 60010 *Tel:* 847-382-8750 *E-mail:* information@symmetrycp.com *Web Site:* www.symmetrycp.com, pg 1226

Systems & Software Services Ltd, 830 W Springfield Rd, Bldg A, Suite 2, Springfield, PA 19064, pg 1386

Szablya Consultants Inc, 2901 NE Blakely St, Unit 510, Seattle, WA 98105 *Tel:* 206-457-4564; 206-465-0482 (cell) *Web Site:* www.szablya.com; www. helenmszablya.com, pg 1413

T C Public Relations, One N La Salle St, Suite 600, Chicago, IL 60602 *Tel:* 312-422-1333 *Web Site:* www. tcpr.net, pg 1102

TAB (grades 6 & up), 557 Broadway, New York, NY 10012 *Tel:* 212-343-6100 *Toll Free Tel:* 800-724-6527 (press 1) *Toll Free Fax:* 800-223-4011 *E-mail:* bookclubs@scholastic.com *Web Site:* scholastic.com/bookclubs, pg 1137

Tabby House, PO Box 544, Mineral, VA 23117 *Tel:* 540-895-5355 *E-mail:* tabbyhouse@gmail.com *Web Site:* www.tabbyhouse.com, pg 1362

Table Mesa Productions/David Lissy Photography, 7517 S Monaco Way, Centennial, CO 80012 *Tel:* 303-919-5296 (cell) *E-mail:* fstop@earthlink.net *Web Site:* www.davidlissy.com, pg 1443

Taconic Wire, 250 Totoket Rd, North Branford, CT 06471 *Tel:* 203-484-2863 *Toll Free Tel:* 800-253-1450 *Fax:* 203-484-2865 *E-mail:* sales@taconicwire. com; taconicwiresales@gmail.com *Web Site:* www. taconicwire.com, pg 1279

Talas, 330 Morgan Ave, Brooklyn, NY 11211 *Tel:* 212-219-0770 *E-mail:* info@talasonline.com; support@ talasonline.com *Web Site:* www.talasonline.com, pg 1268, 1321

Mrs Toby Talbot, 180 Riverside Dr, New York, NY 10024 *Tel:* 212-362-1243 *Fax:* 212-787-1725 *E-mail:* rd10024@aol.com, pg 1413

Tamron USA Inc, 10 Austin Blvd, Commack, NY 11725 *Tel:* 631-858-8400 *Toll Free Tel:* 800-827-8880 *Fax:* 631-543-5666; 631-858-8462 (cust serv) *E-mail:* custserv@tamron.com *Web Site:* www.tamron-usa.com, pg 1386

Johannes Tan, 16682 SW Henderson Ct, Beaverton, OR 97007 *Tel:* 503-642-2586 *Fax:* 503-642-2586 *E-mail:* jt@indotransnet.com *Web Site:* www. indotransnet.com, pg 1413

Tandem Literary, 28 Clinton Rd, Glen Ridge, NJ 07028 *Tel:* 212-629-1990 *Fax:* 212-629-1990 *Web Site:* www.tandemliterary.com, pg 1102

Tanenbaum International Literary Agency Ltd (TILA), 1035 Fifth Ave, Suite 15D, New York, NY 10028 *Tel:* 212-371-4120 *Fax:* 212-988-0457 *E-mail:* tips001@aol.com *Web Site:* www. tanenbauminternational.com, pg 1352

Todd Tarbox, 330 Oakhurst Lane, Colorado Springs, CO 80906 *Tel:* 719-579-9110 *E-mail:* t_tarbox@msn.com, pg 1443

Tatung Co of America Inc, 2850 El Presidio St, Long Beach, CA 90810 *Tel:* 310-637-2105 *E-mail:* service@tatungusa.com *Web Site:* www. tatungusa.com, pg 1386

Chip Taylor Communications LLC, 2 East View Dr, Derry, NH 03038 *Tel:* 603-434-9262 *Toll Free Tel:* 800-876-2447 *Fax:* 603-432-2723 *Web Site:* www. chiptaylor.com, pg 1299, 1386

Taylor Communications Inc, 1725 Roe Crest Dr, North Mankato, MN 56003 *Toll Free Tel:* 866-541-0937 *Web Site:* www.taylorcommunications.com, pg 1255, 1386

Taylor Specialty Books, 1550 W Mockingbird Lane, Dallas, TX 75235 *Tel:* 214-819-8588 (cust serv) *Fax:* 214-819-5051 (cust serv) *Toll Free Fax:* 800-203-9778 *E-mail:* rfq@taylorpub.com (estimates) *Web Site:* www.taylorspecialtybooks.com, pg 1209, 1226, 1255, 1268, 1362

TEACH Services Inc, 11 Quartermaster Circle, Fort Oglethorpe, GA 30742-3886 *Tel:* 706-504-9192 *Toll Free Tel:* 800-367-1844 (sales) *Toll Free Fax:* 866-757-6023 *E-mail:* sales@teachservices.com; info@ teachservices.com *Web Site:* www.teachservices.com, pg 1321, 1386

Teacher's Discovery®, 2741 Paldan Dr, Auburn Hills, MI 48326 *Toll Free Tel:* 800-TEACHER (832-2437) *Toll Free Fax:* 800-287-4509 *E-mail:* help@ teachersdiscovery.com; orders@teachersdiscovery.com *Web Site:* www.teachersdiscovery.com, pg 1299, 1321

Tecnau Inc, 4 Suburban Park Dr, Billerica, MA 01821 *Tel:* 978-608-0500 *Fax:* 978-608-0558 *E-mail:* info. us@tecnau.com *Web Site:* www.tecnau.com, pg 1279

TEENS (grades 7 & up), 557 Broadway, New York, NY 10012 *Tel:* 212-343-6100 *Toll Free Tel:* 800-724-6527 (press 1) *Toll Free Fax:* 800-223-4011 *E-mail:* bookclubs@scholastic.com *Web Site:* scholastic.com/bookclubs, pg 1138

Teledyne DALSA, 605 McMurray Rd, Waterloo, ON N2V 2E9, Canada *Tel:* 519-886-6000 *Toll Free Tel:* 800-361-4914 *Web Site:* www.teledynedalsa.com, pg 1386

Joan Wagner Teller PhD, Translator, 11625 SE Boise St, Unit 106, Portland, OR 97266-2281 *Tel:* 503-760-1320 *E-mail:* j-teller-11@alumni.uchicago.edu *Web Site:* joantellertranslations.webs.com, pg 1413

Teneo Linguistics Co LLC, 4700 Bryant Irvin Ct, Suite 301, Fort Worth, TX 76107 *Tel:* 817-441-9974 *Fax:* 817-231-0052 *E-mail:* info@tlctranslation.com *Web Site:* www.tlctranslation.com, pg 1413

Tennessee Book Co, 1550 Heil Quaker Blvd, La Vergne, TN 37086 *Tel:* 615-793-5040 *Toll Free Tel:* 800-456-0418 *Fax:* 615-213-9545 *Web Site:* www. tennesseebook.com, pg 1321

Terry & Read LLC, 4471 Dean Martin Dr, The Martin 3302, Las Vegas, NV 89103 *Tel:* 510-813-9854 *Toll Free Fax:* 866-214-4762, pg 1300

Texas Art Supply, 2001 Montrose Blvd, Houston, TX 77006 *Tel:* 713-526-5221 *E-mail:* customerservice@ texasart.com *Web Site:* www.texasart.com, pg 1321

Texas Book Co, 8501 Technology Circle, Greenville, TX 75402 *Tel:* 903-455-6969 *Toll Free Tel:* 800-527-1016 *E-mail:* customerservice@texasbook.com *Web Site:* www.texasbook.com, pg 1321

Texas Bookman, 2700 Lone Star Dr, Dallas, TX 75212 *Tel:* 214-678-6680 *Toll Free Tel:* 800-566-2665 *Fax:* 214-678-6699 *E-mail:* orders@texasbookman. com *Web Site:* www.texasbookman.com, pg 1321

Texas Graphic Resource Inc, 1234 Round Table Dr, Dallas, TX 75247 *Tel:* 214-630-2800 *Fax:* 214-630-0713 *E-mail:* info@texasgraphics.com *Web Site:* www. texasgraphics.com, pg 1226

TeXnology Inc, 57 Longwood Ave, Brookline, MA 02446 *Tel:* 617-738-8029 *Web Site:* www.texnology. com, pg 1386

Theatre Journal, 2715 N Charles St, Baltimore, MD 21218-4363 *Toll Free Tel:* 800-548-1784 (journal orders) *Fax:* 410-516-6968 *E-mail:* jrnlcirc@press. jhu.edu (journal orders) *Web Site:* www.press.jhu. edu/journals/theatre_journal/index.html, pg 1131

Thinkers' Press Inc, 1524 Le Claire St, Davenport, IA 52803 Tel: 563-271-6657 E-mail: info@chessbutler. com Web Site: www.thinkerspressinc.com, pg 1328

3rd Grade Book Club, 557 Broadway, New York, NY 10012 Tel: 212-343-6100 Toll Free Tel: 800-724-6527 (press 1) Toll Free Fax: 800-223-4011 E-mail: bookclubs@scholastic.com Web Site: scholastic.com/bookclubs, pg 1138

Thistle Printing Ltd, 35 Mobile Dr, Toronto, ON M4A 2P6, Canada Tel: 416-288-1288 Fax: 416-288-0737 E-mail: sales@thistleprinting.com Web Site: www. thistleprinting.com, pg 1227, 1255, 1386

Thomas Allen & Son Ltd, 195 Allstate Pkwy, Markham, ON L3R 4T8, Canada Tel: 905-475-9126 Toll Free Tel: 800-387-4333 Fax: 905-475-6747 Toll Free Fax: 800-458-5504 E-mail: info@t-allen.com Web Site: www.thomasallen.ca, pg 1300

The Thomas Tape & Supply Co Inc, 1713 Sheridan Ave, Springfield, OH 45505 Tel: 937-325-6414 Fax: 937-325-2850 Web Site: www.thomastape.com, pg 1269

Thomson Reuters, 3 Times Sq, New York, NY 10036 Tel: 646-223-4000; 646-223-6100 (edit); 646-223-6000 (newsroom) Web Site: www.thomsonreuters.com, pg 1186

Thomson Reuters, Union Bank Bldg, 50 California St, San Francisco, CA 94111 Tel: 424-434-7000 E-mail: editorial.booking@tr.com Web Site: www. thomsonreuters.com, pg 1386

Three D Graphics Inc, 11340 W Olympic Blvd, Suite 352, Los Angeles, CA 90064 Tel: 310-231-3330 Toll Free Tel: 800-913-0008 Fax: 310-231-3303 E-mail: info@threedgraphics.com; orders@threedgraphics.com; sales@threedgraphics.com Web Site: www.threedgraphics.com, pg 1386

3M Touch Systems Inc, 501 Griffin Brook Park Dr, Methuen, MA 01844 Tel: 978-659-9000 Web Site: www.3m.com/3m/en_us/touch-systems-us, pg 1386

Stephen Tiano, 56 Tyler Dr, Riverhead, NY 11901 Tel: 631-284-3842; 631-764-2487 (cell) Fax: 631-284-3842 E-mail: steve@tianobookdesign.com Web Site: www.tianobookdesign.com, pg 1432

Times Citizen Communication Inc, 406 Stevens St, Iowa Falls, IA 50126 Tel: 641-648-2521 Toll Free Tel: 800-798-2691 Fax: 641-648-4765 E-mail: tcc@iafalls.com Web Site: timescitizen.com, pg 1227

Times Printing LLC, 100 Industrial Dr, Random Lake, WI 53075 Tel: 920-994-4396 Toll Free Tel: 800-236-4396 (sales) E-mail: info@kappapma.com Web Site: www.kappapma.com, pg 1227, 1255, 1269, 1280

Times-Square Fantasy Theatre, 519 N Halifax Ave, Daytona Beach, FL 32118 Tel: 386-252-0381 Fax: 386-252-0381 E-mail: timessquare@bellsouth.net Web Site: www.broadwaymusicdownload.com; www. timessquarefantasytheatre.com, pg 1387

Timsons Inc, 385 Crossen Ave, Elk Grove Village, IL 60007 Tel: 847-884-8611 Fax: 847-884-8676 E-mail: sales@timsonsinc.com Web Site: www. timsonsinc.com, pg 1280

TNG, 3320 S Service Rd, Burlington, ON L7N 3M6, Canada Toll Free Tel: 800-201-8127 Toll Free Fax: 877-664-9732 E-mail: cs@tng.com Web Site: www.tng.com, pg 1321

To Press & Beyond, 825 E Pedregosa St, Suite 2, Santa Barbara, CA 93103 Tel: 805-898-2263 E-mail: info@topressandbeyond.com Web Site: www. topressandbeyond.com, pg 1102, 1352, 1363

Tobias Associates Inc, 50 Industrial Dr, Ivyland, PA 18974 Tel: 215-322-1500 Toll Free Tel: 800-877-3367 Fax: 215-322-1504 E-mail: sales@tobiasinc.com Web Site: www.densitometer.com, pg 1280

Tompkins Printing Equipment Co, 5050 N Rose St, Schiller Park, IL 60176 Tel: 847-671-5050 Fax: 847-671-5538 E-mail: sales@tompkins.com Web Site: www.tompkins.com, pg 1280

Toni Werbell Public Relations, 5900 Arlington Ave, 9P, Riverdale, NY 10471 Tel: 929-222-4209 E-mail: twprbooks@aol.com, pg 1102

Toof American Digital, 4222 Pilot Dr, Memphis, TN 38118 Tel: 901-274-3632 Toll Free Tel: 800-722-4772 Web Site: www.toofamericandigital.com, pg 1209, 1227, 1255, 1269

TOP Engraving, 106 Windsor Way, Berkeley Heights, NJ 07922 Tel: 212-239-9170; 201-223-4800, pg 1255

Total Printing Systems, 201 S Gregory Dr, Newton, IL 62448 Tel: 618-783-2978 Toll Free Tel: 800-465-5200 Fax: 618-783-8407 E-mail: sales@tps1.com Web Site: www.tps1.com, pg 1255

TotalWorks™ Inc, 420 W Huron St, Chicago, IL 60654 Tel: 773-489-4313 E-mail: production@totalworks.net Web Site: www.totalworks.net, pg 1227, 1255

Townsend Communications Inc, 20 E Gregory Blvd, Kansas City, MO 64114 Tel: 816-361-0616 Web Site: www.townsendcommunications.com; www. townsendprint.com, pg 1227, 1255, 1280

Trade Commission in Miami, Embassy of Spain in the US, 2655 Le Juene Rd, Suite 1114, Miami, FL 33134 Tel: 305-446-4387 Fax: 305-446-2602 E-mail: info@newspanishbooks.com Web Site: www. newspanishbooks.us, pg 1140

Transimpex Translators, Interpreters, Editors, Consultants Inc, 2300 Main St, 9th fl, Kansas City, MO 64108 Tel: 816-561-3777 Toll Free Tel: 888-877-4679 Fax: 816-561-5515 E-mail: translations@transimpex. com Web Site: www.transimpex.com, pg 1413

TranslateMedia, 27 W 24 St, New York, NY 10010 Tel: 212-796-5636 E-mail: web@translatemedia.com Web Site: www.translatemedia.com, pg 1414

Translation & Terminology Services, 2090 Lorne Terr, Victoria, BC V8S 2H8, Canada Tel: 778-265-8869; 604-349-8858 (cell) Web Site: www.focalpoint.org, pg 1414

Translations.com, 3 Park Ave, 39th fl, New York, NY 10016 Tel: 212-689-5555 Fax: 212-689-1059 E-mail: newyork@transperfect.com; info@translations. com Web Site: www.translations.com, pg 1414

Translingua Associates Inc, 630 Ninth Ave, Suite 708, New York, NY 10036 Tel: 212-697-2020 Fax: 212-697-2891 Web Site: www.translingua.com, pg 1414

Transparent Language Inc, 12 Murphy Dr, Nashua, NH 03062 Tel: 603-262-6300 Toll Free Tel: 800-567-9619 (cust serv & sales) E-mail: info@transparent. com; support@transparent.com (tech support) Web Site: www.transparent.com, pg 1387

Treacyfaces Inc, 43 Maltby Ave, West Haven, CT 06516 Tel: 203-389-7037 Web Site: www.treacyfaces.com, pg 1387

Trend Offset Printing Services, 3791 Catalina St, Los Alamitos, CA 90720 Tel: 562-598-2446 Fax: 562-493-6840 (sales); 562-430-2373 E-mail: salesca@trendoffset.com Web Site: www.trendoffset.com, pg 1256

Tri-Fold Books, PO Box 534, King City, ON L7B 1A7, Canada Tel: 905-726-0142 Fax: 905-727-1068 E-mail: info@trifoldbooks.com, pg 1300

Tri-Media Integrated Marketing Technologies Inc, 1027 Pelham St, Unit 2, Fonthill, ON L0S 1E0, Canada E-mail: think@tri-media.com Web Site: tri-media.com, pg 1087

Tribal Print Source, 36146 Pala Temecula Rd, Bldg J, Pala, CA 92059 Tel: 760-597-2650 E-mail: sales@tribalprintsource.com Web Site: www.tribalprintsource. com, pg 1093, 1107, 1256

The Tribune News Service, 160 N Stetson Ave, Chicago, IL 60601 Tel: 312-222-4131 E-mail: tcanews@trbpub.com Web Site: www.mctdirect.com; tribunecontentagency.com/tribune-news-service, pg 1186

Stephen Trimble: Words & Photographs, 70 W Apricot Ave, Salt Lake City, UT 84103 Tel: 801-819-2448 E-mail: steve@stephentrimble.net Web Site: www. stephentrimble.net, pg 1443

Trophy Room Books, PO Box 3041, Agoura, CA 91301 Tel: 818-889-2469 Fax: 818-889-4849 E-mail: info@trophyroombooks.com Web Site: www. trophyroombooks.com, pg 1328

TRUMATCH Inc, PO Box 501, Water Mill, NY 11976-0501 Tel: 631-204-9100 Toll Free Tel: 800-TRU-9100 (878-9100 US & CN) E-mail: info@trumatch.com Web Site: www.trumatch.com, pg 1387

TSO General Corp, 79 Emjay Blvd, Brentwood, NY 11717 Tel: 631-952-5320 Fax: 631-952-5315 Web Site: www.tsogeneral.com, pg 1256, 1269

Tukaiz LLC, 2917 N Latoria Lane, Franklin Park, IL 60131 Tel: 847-455-1588; 847-288-4968 (sales) Toll Free Tel: 800-543-2674 E-mail: contacttukaiz@tukaiz. com Web Site: www.tukaiz.com, pg 1227, 1256, 1269, 1280

Turtleback Books, 1000 N Second Ave, Logan, IA 51546-0500 Toll Free Tel: 800-831-4190 Toll Free Fax: 800-543-2745 E-mail: turtleback@perfectionlearning.com Web Site: turtleback. perfectionlearning.com, pg 1256, 1324

Stan Tusan, 105 Breckinridge Dr, Phoenix, OR 97535 Tel: 541-535-6791 E-mail: stantoon@charter.net Web Site: www.stantoon.com, pg 1432

TWIG One Stop, 10444 White Pinto Ct, Lake Worth, FL 33449 Tel: 561-588-0244 Toll Free Tel: 855-894-4178 E-mail: info@twigonestop.com Web Site: www. twigonestop.com, pg 1093

Twin Rivers Paper Co, 82 Bridge Ave, Madawaska, ME 04756 Tel: 207-728-3321 Toll Free Tel: 800-920-9988 Fax: 207-728-8701 E-mail: info@twinriverspaper.com Web Site: www.twinriverspaper.com, pg 1269

Two Rivers Distribution, an Ingram brand, 1400 Broadway, Suite 520, New York, NY 10018 Toll Free Tel: 866-400-5351 E-mail: ips@ingramcontent. com (orders, independent bookstores & gift accts) Web Site: www.tworiversdistribution.com, pg 1300

Tyler Creative, 1300 S Johnstone Ave, Bartlesville, OK 74003-5624 Tel: 918-527-6779 E-mail: info@tylercreative.com Web Site: tylercreative.com, pg 1432

Typing Etc, 89 Stephen Dr, Plainview, NY 11803 Tel: 516-681-7328 Fax: 516-681-7328, pg 1393

P Tyrrell Associates, 321 Monica Crescent, Burlington, ON L7N 1Z5, Canada Tel: 289-937-6436 Fax: 905-639-2640 E-mail: pgtyrrell@cogeco.ca, pg 1300

Eric Tyson, 300 W 57 St, 15th fl, New York, NY 10019-5238 Tel: 212-969-7550 Toll Free Tel: 800-526-5464 Fax: 646-280-1550 E-mail: eric@erictyson.com Web Site: www.erictyson.com, pg 1119

Elizabeth Uhlig, 96-09 66 Ave, Suite 1-D, Rego Park, NY 11374 Tel: 718-896-4186 E-mail: elizabeth. uhlig@yahoo.com Web Site: home.earthlink.net/~marble.house.editions, pg 1414

Ulster Linen Co Inc, 383 Moffit Blvd, Islip, NY 11751 Tel: 631-859-5244 Fax: 631-859-4990 E-mail: sales@ulsterlinen.com Web Site: www.ulsterlinen.com, pg 1269

Ultimate TechnoGraphics, 300 Leo Pariseau, Suite 2120, Montreal, QC H2X 4B3, Canada Tel: 514-938-9050 Toll Free Tel: 800-363-3590 (North America only) Fax: 514-938-5225 E-mail: customerservice@imposition.com Web Site: www.imposition.com, pg 1387

Ulverscroft Large Print (USA) Inc, 950A Union Rd, Suite 427, West Seneca, NY 14224 Tel: 716-674-4270; 905-637-8734 (CN) Toll Free Tel: 800-955-9659; 888-860-3365 (CN) Fax: 716-674-4195; 905-333-6788 (CN) E-mail: sales@ulverscroftusa.com; sales@ulverscroftcanada.com (CN) Web Site: www. ulverscroft.com, pg 1300

UniNet Imaging Inc, 3232 W El Segundo Blvd, Hawthorne, CA 90250 Tel: 424-675-3300 Fax: 424-675-3400 E-mail: sales@uninetimaging.com Web Site: www.uninetimaging.com, pg 1387

Unisys Corp, 801 Lakeview Dr, Suite 100, Blue Bell, PA 19422 Tel: 215-274-2742 Web Site: www.unisys.com, pg 1387

UnitechEDI Inc, 220 Winthrop St, Winthrop, MA 02152 *Toll Free Tel:* 800-330-4094 *E-mail:* info@unitechedi. com *Web Site:* www.unitechedi.com, pg 1387

United Library Services Inc, 7140 Fairmount Dr SE, Calgary, AB T2H 0X4, Canada *Tel:* 403-252-4426 *Toll Free Tel:* 888-342-5857 (CN only) *Fax:* 403-258-3426 *Toll Free Fax:* 800-661-2806 (CN only) *E-mail:* info@ uls.com *Web Site:* www.uls.com, pg 1321

United Press International (UPI), 1133 19 St NW, Suite 800, Washington, DC 20036 *Tel:* 202-898-8000 *E-mail:* media@upi.com *Web Site:* www.upi.com, pg 1121, 1186

Unitype LLC, 116-A Mockingbird Lane, Lockhart, TX 78644 *Tel:* 512-620-0384 *Toll Free Tel:* 800-697-9186 *E-mail:* info@unitype.com; sales@unitype.com; support@unitype.com *Web Site:* www.unitype.com, pg 1387

Universal Bindery (Sask) Ltd, 516-A Duchess St, Saskatoon, SK S7K 0R1, Canada *Tel:* 306-652-8313 *Toll Free Tel:* 888-JOE-MENU (563-6368) *Fax:* 306-244-2994 *E-mail:* gib@unibindery.com, pg 1093

Universal Bookbindery Inc, 1200 N Colorado, San Antonio, TX 78207 *Tel:* 210-734-9502 *Toll Free Tel:* 800-594-2015 *Fax:* 210-736-0867 *E-mail:* service@universalbookbindery.com *Web Site:* www.universalbookbindery.com, pg 1256

UniversalWilde, 26 Dartmouth St, Westwood, MA 02090 *Tel:* 781-251-2700 *Fax:* 781-251-2613 *Web Site:* www.universalwilde.com, pg 1093, 1107, 1227, 1256

Universe Technical Translation Inc, 9225 Katy Fwy, Suite 400, Houston, TX 77024 *Tel:* 713-827-8800 *Fax:* 713-464-5511 *E-mail:* universe@universe.us *Web Site:* www.universetranslation.com, pg 1414

University Language Services Inc (ULS), 15 Maiden Lane, Suite 300, New York, NY 10038 *Tel:* 212-766-4111 *Toll Free Tel:* 800-419-4601 *Fax:* 212-571-7155 *Toll Free Fax:* 800-662-8048 *E-mail:* service@universitylanguage.com *Web Site:* www.universitylanguage.com, pg 1414

University of Southern California Library, University of Southern California, Special Collections, Doheny Memorial Library, Rm 206, Los Angeles, CA 90089-0189 *Tel:* 213-740-5900 *Fax:* 213-740-2343 *E-mail:* specol@usc.edu *Web Site:* www.usc.edu/libraries, pg 1450

University of Toronto Press Guidance Centre, 5201 Dufferin St, Toronto, ON M3H 5T8, Canada *Tel:* 416-667-7791 *Toll Free Tel:* 800-565-9523 *Fax:* 416-667-7832 *Toll Free Fax:* 800-221-9985 *E-mail:* utpbooks@ utpress.utoronto.ca *Web Site:* www.utpguidancecentre. com, pg 1300

University Products Inc, 517 Main St, Holyoke, MA 01040 *Tel:* 413-532-3372 *Toll Free Tel:* 800-628-1912 (orders) *Fax:* 413-533-4743 *Toll Free Fax:* 800-532-9281 *E-mail:* info@universityproducts.com *Web Site:* www.universityproducts.com, pg 1269

Alvis Upitis Photography, 82-5847 Napo'opo'o Rd, Captain Cook, HI 96704 *Tel:* 808-328-8531; 808-937-3173 (cell) *E-mail:* auphoto@hawaii.rr.com *Web Site:* www.alvisupitis.com, pg 1443

Upper Access Inc, 87 Upper Access Rd, Hinesburg, VT 05461 *Tel:* 802-482-2988 *E-mail:* upperaccessbooks@ gmail.com *Web Site:* www.upperaccess.com, pg 1102, 1352

UPS Supply Chain Solutions, 12380 Morris Rd, Alpharetta, GA 30005 *Tel:* 913-693-6151 (outside US & CN) *Toll Free Tel:* 800-742-5727 (US & CN) *Web Site:* upsscs.com, pg 1333

Upstart Books™, PO Box 7488, Madison, WI 53707 *Tel:* 608-241-1201 *Toll Free Tel:* 800-356-1200 (orders); 800-962-4463 (cust serv) *Toll Free Fax:* 800-245-1329 (orders) *E-mail:* custserv@demco.com; order@demco.com *Web Site:* www.demco.com/upstart, pg 1140, 1322

US Lithograph Inc, 39 Broadway, 28th fl, New York, NY 10006 *Tel:* 212-673-3210 *Fax:* 917-503-3990 *E-mail:* info@pubdata.com *Web Site:* www.pubdata. com, pg 1387

US Lynx Inc, 39 Broadway, 28th fl, New York, NY 10006 *Tel:* 212-673-3210 *Fax:* 917-503-3990 *E-mail:* info@pubdata.com *Web Site:* www.pubdata. com, pg 1387

US Naval Institute Photo Archive, 291 Wood Rd, Annapolis, MD 21402 *Tel:* 410-295-1022 *Fax:* 410-295-1049 *E-mail:* photoservice@usni.org; photoarchive@usni.org *Web Site:* www.usni.org, pg 1450

US Postal Service Global Business, 475 L'Enfant Plaza SW, Rm 5100, Washington, DC 20260-4016 *Tel:* 202-268-2178 *Web Site:* www.usps.com, pg 1333

USCIB International Bookstore, 1212 Avenue of the Americas, 21st fl, New York, NY 10036 *Tel:* 212-703-5066 *Fax:* 212-944-0012 *E-mail:* bookstore@uscib.org *Web Site:* store.internationaltradebooks.org, pg 1300

UTA News & Broadcast, 888 Seventh Ave, 7th fl, New York, NY 10106 *Tel:* 212-765-3040 *Fax:* 212-757-6411 *E-mail:* nsb@nsbtalent.com *Web Site:* bienstock. unitedtalent.com, pg 1352

Liliana Valenzuela, 1103 Maufrais St, Austin, TX 78703 *Tel:* 512-804-8141 *E-mail:* reporterliliana@gmail.com *Web Site:* www.lilianavalenzuela.com, pg 1414

Valid USA, 1011 Warrenville Rd, Suite 450, Lisle, IL 60532 *Tel:* 630-852-8200 *Toll Free Tel:* 800-773-1588 (cust serv); 855-825-4387 (sales) *Web Site:* www.valid. com, pg 1110

Valley News Co, 1305 Stadium Rd, Mankato, MN 56001 *Tel:* 507-345-4819 *Fax:* 507-345-6793 *Web Site:* www. valleynewscompany.com, pg 1322

Value Added Resources, 7900 Rockville Rd, Indianapolis, IN 46214 *Tel:* 317-899-1000 *Fax:* 317-899-2259 *E-mail:* info@valueaddedres.com *Web Site:* www.valueaddedres.com, pg 1333

VanDam Inc, The VanDam Bldg, 121 W 27 St, New York, NY 10001 *Tel:* 212-929-0416 *Toll Free Tel:* 800-UNFOLDS (863-6537) *Fax:* 212-929-0426 *E-mail:* info@vandam.com *Web Site:* www.vandam. com, pg 1363

Vectorworks, 7150 Riverwood Dr, Columbia, MD 21046 *Tel:* 410-290-5114 *Toll Free Tel:* 888-646-4223 (sales) *Fax:* 410-290-7266 *E-mail:* sales@vectorworks. net *Web Site:* www.vectorworks.net, pg 1387

Vedanta Book Center, 14630 S Lemont Rd, Homer Glen, IL 60491 *Tel:* 708-301-9062 *Fax:* 708-301-9063 *Web Site:* www.vedantabooks.com, pg 1322, 1328

Veritiv™ Corporation, 400 Northpark Town Ctr, 1000 Abernathy Rd, Suite 1700, Atlanta, GA 30328 *Tel:* 770-391-8200 *Toll Free Tel:* 844-VERITIV (837-4848); 800-864-7687 (cust serv) *E-mail:* contactus@ veritivcorp.com *Web Site:* www.veritivcorp.com, pg 1269

VeronaLibri, 124 Willowbrook Ave, Stamford, CT 06902 *Tel:* 203-614-8335 *Web Site:* www.veronalibri.com, pg 1256

Versa Press Inc, 1465 Spring Bay Rd, East Peoria, IL 61611-9788 *Tel:* 309-822-8272 *Toll Free Tel:* 800-447-7829 *Fax:* 309-822-8141 *Web Site:* www.versapress. com, pg 1209, 1227, 1256, 1269

Verso Advertising Inc, 50 W 17 St, 5th fl, New York, NY 10011 *Tel:* 212-292-2990 *Fax:* 212-557-2592 *Web Site:* www.versoadvertising.com, pg 1087

ViaTech Publishing Solutions Inc, 11935 N Stemmons Fwy, Dallas, TX 75234 *Tel:* 214-827-8151 *E-mail:* marketing@viatechpub.com *Web Site:* www. viatech.io, pg 1227, 1256

Vicks Lithograph & Printing Corp, 5166 Commercial Dr, Yorkville, NY 13495 *Tel:* 315-736-9344 *E-mail:* info@vicks.biz *Web Site:* www.vicks.biz, pg 1209, 1256

Victoria Productions Inc, 76 Beaver St, New York, NY 10005 *Tel:* 212-425-3013 *Fax:* 646-225-7218 *E-mail:* victoria@vproductions.net *Web Site:* www. vproductions.net, pg 1387

Victory Productions Inc, 55 Linden St, Worcester, MA 01609 *Tel:* 508-755-0051 *E-mail:* victory@victoryprd. com *Web Site:* www.victoryprd.com, pg 1363

Videojet Technologies Inc, 1500 N Mittel Blvd, Wood Dale, IL 60191-1073 *Tel:* 630-860-7300 *Toll Free Tel:* 800-843-3610 *Toll Free Fax:* 800-582-1343 *E-mail:* info@videojet.com *Web Site:* www.videojet. com, pg 1280

Videotex Systems Inc, 10255 Miller Rd, Dallas, TX 75238 *Tel:* 972-231-9200 *Toll Free Tel:* 800-888-4336 *Fax:* 972-231-2420 *E-mail:* info@videotexsystems. com *Web Site:* www.videotexsystems.com, pg 1387

Videx Inc, 1105 NE Circle Blvd, Corvallis, OR 97330 *Tel:* 541-738-5500; 541-738-0521 *Fax:* 541-752-5285 *E-mail:* sales@videx.com; support@videx.com *Web Site:* www.videx.com, pg 1387

Viesti Associates, 361 S Camino Del Rio, Suite 111, Durango, CO 81303 *Tel:* 970-403-1000 *Fax:* 970-382-2700 *E-mail:* photos@viestiassociates.com *Web Site:* www.viestiphoto.com, pg 1450

VillageSoup®, 91 Camden St, Suite 403, Rockland, ME 04841 *Tel:* 207-594-4401 *Fax:* 207-594-1679 *E-mail:* info@villagesoup.com *Web Site:* www. villagesoup.com, pg 1352

VIP Digital Print Center, 200 Circle Dr N, Piscataway, NJ 08854 *Tel:* 732-469-5400 *Fax:* 732-469-8414 *E-mail:* info@vipcopycenter.com *Web Site:* www. vipcopycenter.com, pg 1256

Virginia Publications, 4930A Eisenhower Ave, Alexandria, VA 22304 *Tel:* 703-212-9113 *Toll Free Tel:* 800-699-9113 *Fax:* 703-212-9114 *E-mail:* vapub@msn.com *Web Site:* www. washingtonbk.com, pg 1322

Virginia Systems, 5509 W Bay Ct, Midlothian, VA 23112 *Tel:* 804-739-3200 *Fax:* 804-739-8376 *E-mail:* sales@virginiasystems.com *Web Site:* www. virginiasystems.com, pg 1387

Viridiam LLC, 3030 Lowell Dr, Green Bay, WI 54311 *Tel:* 920-465-3030 *Toll Free Tel:* 800-829-6555 *Web Site:* www.viridiam.com, pg 1094, 1227, 1256

VisionWorks, PO Box 92, Greenfield, MA 01302 *Tel:* 413-772-6569 *Toll Free Tel:* 800-933-7326 (orders) *Fax:* 413-772-6559 *E-mail:* dreaming@ changingworld.com *Web Site:* www.changingworld. com, pg 1322

VistaBooks LLC, 637 Blue Ridge Rd, Silverthorne, CO 80498-8931 *Tel:* 970-468-7673 *Fax:* 970-468-7673 *E-mail:* email@vistabooks.com *Web Site:* www. vistabooks.com, pg 1322

Visual Artists & Galleries Association Inc (VAGA), 111 Broadway, Suite 1006, New York, NY 10006 *Tel:* 212-736-6666 *Fax:* 212-736-6767 *E-mail:* info@vagarights. com *Web Site:* vagarights.com, pg 1352, 1450

Visual Pursuit, 168 W 86 St, New York, NY 10024 *Tel:* 212-362-8234, pg 1443

Esther Vitalis, 1717 W 13 Ave, Unit 301, Vancouver, BC V6J 2H2, Canada *Tel:* 604-738-6869 *Fax:* 604-738-6805 (call first) *E-mail:* evital@shaw.ca *Web Site:* www.evitalis.com, pg 1414

VITEC Multimedia, 931 Benecia Ave, Sunnyvale, CA 94085 *Tel:* 650-230-2400 *Toll Free Tel:* 800-451-5101 *Fax:* 408-739-1706 *E-mail:* sunnyvale@vitec.com *Web Site:* www.vitec.com, pg 1387

VKH Media Resources, 122 S Oneida Ave, Rhinelander, WI 54501 *Tel:* 715-369-4535 *Web Site:* www. victoriahouston.com, pg 1363

Voice of Youth Advocates, 16211 Oxford Ct, Bowie, MD 20715 *Tel:* 301-805-2191 *Fax:* 301-805-2192 *Web Site:* www.voyamagazine.com, pg 1131

Claire De Vore, 133 Washington St, Belmont, MA 02478 *Tel:* 617-484-6490 *E-mail:* cdevore@anthrophoto.com *Web Site:* www.anthrophoto.com, pg 1450

VO2 Mix Audio Post, 116 Spadina Ave, Suite 208, Toronto, ON M5V 2K6, Canada *Tel:* 416-603-3954 *Fax:* 416-603-3957 *E-mail:* info@vo2mix.ca *Web Site:* www.vo2mix.ca, pg 1387

Brice Wood, PO Box A, Jerome, AZ 86331 *Tel:* 928-634-3238 *E-mail:* bricewood@yahoo.com *Web Site:* www.bricewood.com, pg 1433

Richard Wood Photography, 50 Boylston St, Brookline, MA 02445 *Tel:* 617-872-0654 *Web Site:* www.rwoodphotography.com, pg 1444

Woodcrafters Lumber Sales Inc, 212 NE Sixth Ave, Portland, OR 97232-2976 *Tel:* 503-231-0226 *Toll Free Tel:* 800-777-3709 *Fax:* 503-232-0511 *Web Site:* www.woodcrafters.us, pg 1322

Fred Woolf List Co Inc, 60 Newtown Rd, PMB 132, Danbury, CT 06810 *Tel:* 203-456-6239 *Toll Free Tel:* 800-431-1557 *Fax:* 914-694-1710 *E-mail:* info@woolflist.com *Web Site:* www.woolflist.com, pg 1113

Word-Wise Advertising, 3500 Virginia Beach Blvd, Suite 611, Virginia Beach, VA 23452 *Tel:* 757-455-5020, pg 1353

WordCo Indexing Services Inc, 66 Franklin St, Norwich, CT 06360 *E-mail:* office@wordco.com *Web Site:* www.wordco.com, pg 1228

WordPlayJane, 21 Harrison St, Suite 3, New York, NY 10013 *Tel:* 212-925-4130, pg 1393

World Exonumia Press, PO Box 4143, Rockford, IL 61110-0643 *Tel:* 815-226-0771 *Web Site:* www.exonumia.com, pg 1322

World Literature Today, 630 Parrington Oval, Suite 110, Norman, OK 73019-4033 *Tel:* 405-325-4531 *E-mail:* wlt@ou.edu *Web Site:* www.worldliteraturetoday.org, pg 1132

Worldata, 3000 N Military Trail, Boca Raton, FL 33431-6321 *Tel:* 561-393-8200 *Toll Free Tel:* 800-331-8102 *E-mail:* hello@worldata.com *Web Site:* www.worldata.com, pg 1113

Worldwide Books, 1001 W Seneca St, Ithaca, NY 14850-3342 *Tel:* 607-272-9200 *Toll Free Tel:* 800-473-8146 (US/CN orders only) *Fax:* 607-272-0239 *E-mail:* info@worldwide-artbooks.com *Web Site:* www.worldwide-artbooks.com, pg 1300

Worzalla, 3535 Jefferson St, Stevens Point, WI 54481 *Tel:* 715-344-9608 *Fax:* 715-344-2578 *Web Site:* www.worzalla.com, pg 1210, 1228, 1257

WPA Film Library of Stock Footage, 16101 S 108 Ave, Orland Park, IL 60467 *Tel:* 708-460-0555 *Toll Free Tel:* 800-323-0442 *Fax:* 708-460-0187 *E-mail:* sales@wpafilmlibrary.com *Web Site:* www.wpafilmlibrary.com, pg 1450

The Writer's Lifeline Inc, 400 S Burnside Ave, Suite 11B, Los Angeles, CA 90036 *Tel:* 323-932-1685 *Web Site:* www.thewriterslifeline.com, pg 1353

Writer's Relief, Inc, 18766 John J Williams Hwy, Unit 4, Box 335, Rehoboth Beach, DE 19971 *Toll Free Tel:* 866-405-3003 *Fax:* 201-641-1253 *E-mail:* info@writersrelief.com *Web Site:* www.WritersRelief.com, pg 1228, 1353, 1393

Writers' Supercenter, 560 Roland Dr, Norfolk, VA 23509 *Tel:* 757-515-4315 *E-mail:* writerspage@writerspage.com *Web Site:* writersupercenter.com, pg 1388

Wunderman, 3 Columbus Circle, New York, NY 10019 *Tel:* 212-941-3000 *Web Site:* www.wunderman.com, pg 1087

Wybel Marketing Group Inc, 213 W Main St, Barrington, IL 60010 *Tel:* 847-382-0384; 847-382-0382 *Toll Free Tel:* 800-323-5297 *Fax:* 847-382-0385 *Toll Free Fax:* 800-595-5252 *E-mail:* bookreps@wybel.com, pg 1301

Chuck Wyrostok, 230 Griffith Run Rd, Spencer, WV 25276 *Tel:* 304-927-2978 *E-mail:* wyro@appalight.com *Web Site:* www.appalight.com, pg 1444

X-Height Studio, 83 High St, Milford, MA 01757 *Tel:* 508-478-3897 *Toll Free Tel:* 888-474-8973 *E-mail:* info@x-heightstudio.com *Web Site:* www.x-heightstudio.com, pg 1228

X-Rite Inc, 4300 44 St SE, Grand Rapids, MI 49512 *Tel:* 616-803-2100 *Toll Free Tel:* 800-248-9748; 888-800-9580 (sales) *E-mail:* info@xrite.com *Web Site:* www.xrite.com, pg 1280

Xante Corp, 2800 Dauphin St, Suite 100, Mobile, AL 36606 *Tel:* 251-473-6502; 251-473-4920 (tech support) *Fax:* 251-473-6503 *Web Site:* www.xante.com, pg 1388

Xerox Corp, 26600 SW Parkway Ave, Wilsonville, OR 97070 *Toll Free Tel:* 800-835-6100 (cust serv) *Web Site:* www.office.xerox.com, pg 1269

Yeck Brothers Co, 2222 Arbor Blvd, Dayton, OH 45439 *Tel:* 937-294-4000 *Toll Free Tel:* 800-417-2767 *Fax:* 937-294-6985 *Web Site:* www.yeck.com, pg 1107

Yurchak Printing Inc, 920 Links Ave, Landisville, PA 17538 *Tel:* 717-399-0209 *E-mail:* ypi.info@yurchak.com *Web Site:* www.yurchak.com, pg 1210, 1257, 1280

Z-Axis, 1916 Rte 96, Phelps, NY 14532 *Tel:* 315-548-5000 *Fax:* 315-548-5100 *E-mail:* sales@zaxis.net *Web Site:* www.zaxis.net, pg 1388

Meryl Zegarek Public Relations Inc, 255 W 108 St, Suite 9D1, New York, NY 10025 *Tel:* 917-493-3601 *Web Site:* www.mzpr.com, pg 1103

ZyLAB North America LLC, 7918 Jones Branch Dr, Suite 230, McLean, VA 22102-3366 *Tel:* 703-442-2400 *Toll Free Tel:* 866-995-2262 *Fax:* 703-991-2508 *E-mail:* info@zylab.com *Web Site:* www.zylab.com, pg 1388

Personnel Index

Included in this index are the personnel included in the entries in this volume of *LMP*, along with the page number(s) on which they appear. Not included in this index are those individuals associated with listings in the **Serials Featuring Books; Radio, TV & Cable Networks; Radio Programs Featuring Books** and **TV Programs Featuring Books** sections. Also, personnel associated with secondary addresses within listings (such as branch offices, sales offices, editorial offices, etc.) are not included.

Aalders, Siobhan, Shutterstock Inc, Empire State Bldg, 350 Fifth Ave, 21st fl, New York, NY 10118 *Tel:* 646-419-4452 (sales) *Toll Free Tel:* 866-663-3954 *Fax:* 347-402-0710 *E-mail:* support@shutterstock.com; press@shutterstock.com *Web Site:* www.shutterstock.com, pg 1449

Aaron, Lauren, Bert Davis Executive Search Inc, 555 Fifth Ave, Suite 302, New York, NY 10017 *Tel:* 212-838-4000 *E-mail:* info@bertdavis.com *Web Site:* www.bertdavis.com, pg 1389

Aaronson, Becky Green, Still Media, 714 Mission Park Dr, Santa Barbara, CA 93105 *Tel:* 805-682-2868 *Fax:* 805-682-2659 *E-mail:* info@stillmedia.com *Web Site:* www.stillmedia.com, pg 1449

Abboud, Dennis, Readerlink Distribution Services LLC, 1420 Kensington Rd, Suite 300, Oakbrook, IL 60523-2164 *Tel:* 708-547-4400 *Toll Free Tel:* 800-549-5389 *E-mail:* info@readerlink.com; marketingservices@readerlink.com *Web Site:* www.readerlink.com, pg 1297

Abfier, Mel, StarGroup International Inc, 1194 Old Dixie Hwy, Suite 201, West Palm Beach, FL 33413 *Tel:* 561-547-0667 *E-mail:* info@stargroupinternational.com *Web Site:* stargroupinternational.com, pg 1102

Ableman, Brian, The Learning Source Ltd, 644 Tenth St, Brooklyn, NY 11215 *E-mail:* info@learningsourceltd.com *Web Site:* www.learningsourceltd.com, pg 1359

Abraham, Russell, Russell Abraham Photography, Jack London Sq, 309 Fourth St, Suite 108, Oakland, CA 94607 *Tel:* 510-444-5204 *E-mail:* ra@russellabraham.com; info@russellabraham.com *Web Site:* russellabraham.com, pg 1435

Abraham, Stu, Abraham Associates Inc, 5120-A Cedar Lake Rd, Minneapolis, MN 55416 *Tel:* 952-927-7920 *Toll Free Tel:* 800-701-2489 *Fax:* 952-927-8089 *E-mail:* info@abrahamassociatesinc.com *Web Site:* www.abrahamassociatesinc.com, pg 1281

Abramek, Brian, Flock Tex Inc, 200 Founders Dr, Woonsocket, RI 02895 *Tel:* 401-765-2340 *Toll Free Tel:* 800-556-7286 *Fax:* 401-765-4915 *Web Site:* www.flocktex.com, pg 1263

Abramek, Edward T Jr, Flock Tex Inc, 200 Founders Dr, Woonsocket, RI 02895 *Tel:* 401-765-2340 *Toll Free Tel:* 800-556-7286 *Fax:* 401-765-4915 *Web Site:* www.flocktex.com, pg 1263

Abramek, Gary, Flock Tex Inc, 200 Founders Dr, Woonsocket, RI 02895 *Tel:* 401-765-2340 *Toll Free Tel:* 800-556-7286 *Fax:* 401-765-4915 *Web Site:* www.flocktex.com, pg 1263

Abrams, Douglas Carlton, Idea Architects, 523 Swift St, Santa Cruz, CA 95060 *Tel:* 831-465-9565 *Web Site:* www.ideaarchitects.com, pg 1347

Abramson, Dean, Dean Abramson Photography, PO Box 610, Raymond, ME 04071 *Tel:* 207-655-7386 *Web Site:* www.mainephoto.com, pg 1435

Abramson, Elaine Sandra, A & A, PO Box 543, Hazelwood, MO 63042-0543 *Tel:* 314-786-5046 *E-mail:* aaartwork@aol.com; aaauthor@aol.com *Web Site:* www.elaineabramson.com, pg 1183, 1423

Abramson, Martin Stanley, A & A, PO Box 543, Hazelwood, MO 63042-0543 *Tel:* 314-786-5046 *E-mail:* aaartwork@aol.com; aaauthor@aol.com *Web Site:* www.elaineabramson.com, pg 1183, 1423

Abramson, Steven J, TRUMATCH Inc, PO Box 501, Water Mill, NY 11976-0501 *Tel:* 631-204-9100 *Toll Free Tel:* 800-TRU-9100 (878-9100 US & CN) *E-mail:* info@trumatch.com *Web Site:* www.trumatch.com, pg 1387

Abuhoff, Jack S, Innodata Inc, 55 Challenger Rd, Suite 202, Ridgefield Park, NJ 07660 *Tel:* 201-371-8000 *Toll Free Tel:* 877-454-8400 *E-mail:* info@innodata.com; marketing@innodata.com *Web Site:* innodata.com, pg 1221, 1347, 1379

Acquarola, Amy, Swedenborg Foundation, 320 N Church St, West Chester, PA 19380 *Tel:* 610-430-3222 *Toll Free Tel:* 800-355-3222 (cust serv) *Fax:* 610-430-7982 *E-mail:* info@swedenborg.com *Web Site:* swedenborg.com, pg 1321

Acree, Cat, BookPage®, 2143 Belcourt Ave, Nashville, TN 37212 *Tel:* 615-292-8926 *Fax:* 615-292-8249 *Web Site:* bookpage.com, pg 1121

Adair, Dennis, Adair Graphic Communications, 26975 Northline Rd, Taylor, MI 48180 *Tel:* 734-941-6300 *Fax:* 734-942-0920 *E-mail:* adair@printwell.com *Web Site:* www.adairgraphic.com, pg 1201, 1215, 1241, 1273

Adams, Joanne, Specialist Marketing Services Inc, 777 Terrace Ave, Suite 401, Hasbrouck Heights, NJ 07604 *Tel:* 201-865-5800 *E-mail:* info@sms-inc.com *Web Site:* www.sms-inc.com, pg 1112

Adams, Katherine, Apple Inc, One Apple Park Way, Cupertino, CA 95014 *Tel:* 408-996-1010 *Web Site:* www.apple.com, pg 1372

Adams, Simon, Gracenote, a Nielsen Company, 2000 Powell St, Suite 1500, Emeryville, CA 94608 *Tel:* 510-428-7200 *Web Site:* www.gracenote.com, pg 1184

Adams, Stephen, Adams Design, 4493 Horseshoe Bend, Murrells Inlet, SC 29576 *Tel:* 843-655-7097 *E-mail:* sa@stephenadamsdesign.com *Web Site:* www.stephenadamsdesign.com, pg 1215

Adanalian, Verjine, Human Rights Quarterly, 2715 N Charles St, Baltimore, MD 21218-4363 *Tel:* 410-516-6987 (journal orders outside US & CN) *Toll Free Tel:* 800-548-1784 (journal orders) *Fax:* 410-516-3866 (journal orders) *E-mail:* jrnlcirc@press.jhu.edu/journals/human_rights_quarterly, pg 1127

Adel, Judith, J Adel Art & Design, 586 Ramapo Rd, Teaneck, NJ 07666 *Tel:* 201-836-2606 *E-mail:* jadelnj@aol.com, pg 1423

Adler, Bill Jr, Adler & Robin Books Inc, 3000 Connecticut Ave NW, Washington, DC 20008 *Tel:* 202-986-9275 *E-mail:* adlerrobininfo@my.netmails.net *Web Site:* www.AdlerRobin.com, pg 1355

Adler, Stephen J, Thomson Reuters, 3 Times Sq, New York, NY 10036 *Tel:* 646-223-4000; 646-223-6100 (edit); 646-223-6000 (newsroom) *Web Site:* www.thomsonreuters.com, pg 1186

Adler, Sven, Ricoh Americas Corp, 300 Eagleview Blvd, Exton, PA 19341 *Tel:* 610-296-8000 *Toll Free Tel:* 800-333-2679 (prod support); 800-637-4264 (sales) *Web Site:* www.ricoh-usa.com, pg 1384

Agress, Amy, Innodata Inc, 55 Challenger Rd, Suite 202, Ridgefield Park, NJ 07660 *Tel:* 201-371-8000 *Toll Free Tel:* 877-454-8400 *E-mail:* info@innodata.com; marketing@innodata.com *Web Site:* innodata.com, pg 1221, 1347, 1379

Ajamian, Vartan, Books International Inc, 22883 Quicksilver Dr, Dulles, VA 20166 *Tel:* 703-661-1500 *Fax:* 703-661-1501 *E-mail:* hdqtrs@booksintl.com *Web Site:* booksintl.presswarehouse.com, pg 1331

Akins, Jeanna, PBD Worldwide Inc, 1650 Bluegrass Lakes Pkwy, Alpharetta, GA 30004 *Tel:* 470-769-1000 *Toll Free Tel:* 866-998-4PBD (998-4723) *E-mail:* sales.marketing@pbd.com; customerservice@pbd.com *Web Site:* www.pbd.com, pg 1333

Akoury-Ross, Lisa, SDP Publishing Solutions LLC, 36 Captain's Way, East Bridgewater, MA 02333 *Tel:* 617-775-0656 *E-mail:* info@sdppublishing.com *Web Site:* sdppublishing.com, pg 1352

Albanese, Andrew R, Publishers Weekly, 71 W 23 St, Suite 1608, New York, NY 10010 *Tel:* 212-377-5500 *Fax:* 212-377-2733 *Web Site:* www.publishersweekly.com, pg 1130

Albregts, Doug, Sharp Electronics Corp, 100 Paragon Dr, Montvale, NJ 07645 *Tel:* 201-529-8200 *Toll Free Tel:* 800-BE-SHARP (237-4277) *Fax:* 201-529-8425 *Web Site:* www.sharpusa.com, pg 1385

Albright, Nicole, Crown Connect, 250 W Rialto Ave, San Bernardino, CA 92408 *Tel:* 909-888-7531 *Fax:* 909-889-1639 *E-mail:* sales@crownconnect.com *Web Site:* www.crownconnect.com, pg 1203, 1218, 1275

Alcorn, Pete, BMR Associates, 60 Corte Amado, Greenbrae, CA 94904 *Tel:* 415-927-1564 *E-mail:* info@bmrassoc.com *Web Site:* www.bmrassoc.com, pg 1343

Aldacushion, Richard, Washington Post News Service with Bloomberg News, 1301 "K" St NW, Washington, DC 20071 *Tel:* 202-334-7666 *E-mail:* syndication@washpost.com *Web Site:* www.washingtonpost.com/syndication, pg 1186

Alden, John, Avanti Computer Systems Ltd, 251 Consumers Rd, Suite 600, Toronto, ON M2J 4R3, Canada *Tel:* 416-445-1722 *Toll Free Tel:* 800-482-2908 *Fax:* 416-445-6319 *E-mail:* askavanti@avantisystems.com *Web Site:* www.avantisystems.com, pg 1373

Aldred, Nadene D, Maracle Inc, 1156 King St E, Oshawa, ON L1H 1H8, Canada *Tel:* 905-723-3438 *Toll Free Tel:* 800-558-8604 *Fax:* 905-723-1759 *E-mail:* hello@maracleinc.com *Web Site:* www.maracleinc.com, pg 1207, 1223, 1251

Alexander, Gary R, The Advertising, Marketing & Sales Promotion Book Club, Book Club Bldg, 7 Putter Lane, Middle Island, NY 11953 *Tel:* 631-924-3888 (ext 100) *E-mail:* amspbookclub@gmail.com; linickgroup@gmail.com, pg 1135

Alexander, Lara, Independent Publishers Group (IPG), 814 N Franklin St, Chicago, IL 60610 *Tel:* 312-337-0747 *Toll Free Tel:* 800-888-4741 (orders) *Fax:* 312-337-5985 *E-mail:* frontdesk@ipgbook.com; orders@ipgbook.com *Web Site:* www.ipgbook.com, pg 1288, 1326

Alexander, Mary Lou, Spring Arbor Distributors Inc, One Ingram Blvd, La Vergne, TN 37086-1986 *Toll Free Tel:* 800-395-4340 *Toll Free Fax:* 800-876-0186 *E-mail:* customerservice@ingramcontent.com *Web Site:* www.ingramcontent.com, pg 1279, 1299, 1320

Alfano, Carm, TNG, 3320 S Service Rd, Burlington, ON L7N 3M6, Canada *Toll Free Tel:* 800-201-8127 *Toll Free Fax:* 877-664-9732 *E-mail:* cs@tng.com *Web Site:* www.tng.com, pg 1321

Ali, Liaquat, Kazi Publications Inc, 3023 W Belmont Ave, Chicago, IL 60618 *Tel:* 773-267-7001 *Fax:* 773-267-7002 *E-mail:* info@kazi.org *Web Site:* www.kazi.org, pg 1316, 1326

Alleger, Dave, The Clark Group Inc, 3705 Quakerbridge Rd, Suite 116, Hamilton, NJ 08619 *Tel:* 609-528-7660 *Fax:* 609-528-7710 *E-mail:* service@clarkworldwide.com *Web Site:* www.clarkgroupinc.com, pg 1331

Allen, Jennifer, Fujii Associates Inc, 75 Sunny Hill Dr, Troy, MO 63379 *Tel:* 636-528-2546 *Fax:* 636-600-5153 *Web Site:* www.fujiiassociates.com, pg 1287

Allen, Michael, Z-Axis, 1916 Rte 96, Phelps, NY 14532 *Tel:* 315-548-5000 *Fax:* 315-548-5100 *E-mail:* sales@zaxis.net *Web Site:* www.zaxis.net, pg 1388

Allen, Pete, JMW Group Inc, 347 Rte 6, No 867, Mahopac, NY 10541 *Tel:* 914-841-7105 *Fax:* 914-248-8861 *E-mail:* jmwgroup@jmwgroup.net *Web Site:* jmwforlife.com, pg 1348

Allen, T James, Thomas Allen & Son Ltd, 195 Allstate Pkwy, Markham, ON L3R 4T8, Canada *Tel:* 905-475-9126 *Toll Free Tel:* 800-387-4333 *Fax:* 905-475-6747 *Toll Free Fax:* 800-458-5504 *E-mail:* info@t-allen.com *Web Site:* www.thomasallen.ca, pg 1300

Allex, Wendy, Allex Indexing, 6039 Sunshine Dr, Ferndale, WA 98248-9234 *Tel:* 360-778-1308 *Web Site:* www.indexpert.com, pg 1215

Allouche, Danny, Avery Dennison Corp, 207 N Goode Ave, 6th fl, Glendale, CA 91203-1222 *Tel:* 626-304-2000 *Web Site:* www.averydennison.com, pg 1373

Allred, Julie, BW&A Books Inc, 112 W McClanahan St, Oxford, NC 27565 *Tel:* 919-956-9111 *Fax:* 919-956-9112 *E-mail:* bwa@bwabooks.com *Web Site:* www.bwabooks.com, pg 1217

Almeter, Rebecca L, Whitman Printing & Creative Services LLC, PO Box 1681, Batavia, NY 14020 *Tel:* 516-294-5350 *Fax:* 516-294-5239 *E-mail:* info@whitmanprinting.com *Web Site:* www.whitmanprinting.com, pg 1094

Alperen, Jennifer, The Nolan/Lehr Group Inc, 214 W 29 St, Suite 1002, New York, NY 10001 *Tel:* 212-967-8200 *E-mail:* dblehr@cs.com *Web Site:* www.nolanlehrgroup.com, pg 1100

Altabef, Peter, Unisys Corp, 801 Lakeview Dr, Suite 100, Blue Bell, PA 19422 *Tel:* 215-274-2742 *Web Site:* www.unisys.com, pg 1387

Altman, Amy, The Gluefast Co Inc, 3535 State Rte 66, Bldg No 1, Neptune, NJ 07753 *Tel:* 732-918-4600 *Toll Free Tel:* 800-242-7318 *Fax:* 732-918-4646 *E-mail:* info@gluefast.com *Web Site:* www.gluefast.com, pg 1335

Altman, Shari, Altman Dedicated Direct, 853 Academy St, Rural Hall, NC 27045-9329 *Tel:* 336-969-9538 *Fax:* 336-969-0187 *Web Site:* www.altmandedicateddirect.com, pg 1341

Ambrose, Albert E Jr, Lowe Graphics & Printing, 220 Great Circle Rd, Suite 122, Nashville, TN 37228 *Tel:* 615-242-6649 *Fax:* 615-254-8867 *Web Site:* www.etlowe.com, pg 1222

Ambrosi, Leigh Ann, Susan Magrino Agency, 352 Park Ave S, 6th fl, New York, NY 10010 *Tel:* 212-957-3005 *Fax:* 212-957-4071 *E-mail:* info@smapr.com *Web Site:* www.smapr.com, pg 1099

Ames, Michael, Puritan Press Inc, 95 Runnells Bridge Rd, Hollis, NH 03049-6565 *Tel:* 603-889-4500 *Toll Free Tel:* 800-635-6302 *Fax:* 603-889-6551 *E-mail:* print@puritancapital.com *Web Site:* www.puritanpress.com, pg 1253

Amick, W Michael Jr, International Paper Co, 6400 Poplar Ave, Memphis, TN 38197 *Tel:* 901-419-9000 *Toll Free Tel:* 800-207-4003 *Web Site:* www.internationalpaper.com; facebook.com/internationalpaper; twitter.com/intlpaperco, pg 1264

Amorese, Cynthia, Julie A Laitin Enterprises Inc, 160 West End Ave, Suite 23N, New York, NY 10023 *Tel:* 917-841-8566 *E-mail:* info@julielaitin.com *Web Site:* www.julielaitin.com, pg 1086

Amsterdam, Yair, ProQuest LLC, 789 E Eisenhower Pkwy, Ann Arbor, MI 48108 *Tel:* 734-761-4700 *Toll Free Tel:* 800-521-0600; 877-779-6768 (sales) *E-mail:* sales@proquest.com *Web Site:* www.proquest.com, pg 1384

Amundson, Sandy, Augsburg Fortress Publishers, Publishing House of the Evangelical Lutheran Church in America, 510 Marquette Ave S, Minneapolis, MN 55402 *Tel:* 612-330-3300 *Toll Free Tel:* 800-426-0115 (ext 639, subns); 800-328-4648 (orders) *Fax:* 612-330-3455 *Toll Free Fax:* 800-722-7766 (orders) *E-mail:* customercare@augsburgfortress.org; copyright@augsburgfortress.org (reprint permission requests); info@augsburgfortress.org *Web Site:* www.augsburgfortress.org; www.1517.media, pg 1309

Anagnost, Andrew, Autodesk Inc, 111 McInnis Pkwy, San Rafael, CA 94903 *Tel:* 415-507-5000 *Fax:* 415-507-5100 *Web Site:* www.autodesk.com, pg 1373

Anderberg, Greg, Anderberg Innovative Print Solutions, 6999 Oxford St, St Louis Park, MN 55426 *Tel:* 952-848-7300 *Toll Free Tel:* 800-231-9777 *Fax:* 952-920-1103 *E-mail:* sales@anderbergprint.com *Web Site:* www.anderbergprint.com, pg 1241

Anderberg, Paul, Anderberg Innovative Print Solutions, 6999 Oxford St, St Louis Park, MN 55426 *Tel:* 952-848-7300 *Toll Free Tel:* 800-231-9777 *Fax:* 952-920-1103 *E-mail:* sales@anderbergprint.com *Web Site:* www.anderbergprint.com, pg 1241

Andersen, R Wayne, Publicaciones Faro de Gracia (PFG), 1317 Railroad St, Burlington, NC 27217 *Tel:* 336-792-2690 *E-mail:* oficina@farodegracia.org *Web Site:* www.farodegracia.org, pg 1287

Andersen, Sheila K, Leading Edge Review, 3651 Robin Lane, Minnetonka, MN 55503 *Tel:* 952-217-4665 *Web Site:* www.leadingedgereview.com, pg 1128

Anderson, Bill, L+L Printers, 6200 Yarrow Dr, Carlsbad, CA 92011 *Tel:* 760-438-3456; 760-477-0321 *Fax:* 760-929-0853 *E-mail:* info@llprinters.com *Web Site:* www.llprinters.com, pg 1250

Anderson, Jennifer, Holliston Holdings LLC, 905 Holliston Mills Rd, Church Hill, TN 37642 *Tel:* 423-357-6141 *Toll Free Tel:* 800-251-0451; 800-251-0251 (cust serv) *Fax:* 423-357-8840 *Toll Free Fax:* 800-325-0351 (cust serv) *E-mail:* custserv@holliston.com *Web Site:* holliston.com, pg 1264

Anderson, Joseph, Anderson & Vreeland Inc, 15348 US Hwy 127 EW, Bryan, OH 43506 *Tel:* 419-636-5002 *Toll Free Tel:* 866-282-7697; 888-832-1600 (CN) *Fax:* 419-636-4334 *E-mail:* info@andersonvreeland.com *Web Site:* www.andersonvreeland.com, pg 1273

Anderson, Rick, Spicers Paper, 12310 E Slauson Ave, Santa Fe Springs, CA 90670 *Toll Free Tel:* 800-774-2377 *Fax:* 562-693-8339 *Web Site:* www.spicers.com, pg 1268

Anderson, Ryan, St Joseph Communications-Print Group, 50 Macintosh Blvd, Concord, ON L4K 4P3, Canada *Tel:* 905-660-3111 *E-mail:* marketing@stjoseph.com *Web Site:* stjoseph.com, pg 1093, 1254

Andes, Elizabeth, Archetype Inc, 317 N Market St, Lancaster, PA 17603 *Tel:* 717-392-7438 *Fax:* 717-397-8037 *E-mail:* mail@nmsgbooks.com *Web Site:* nmsgbooks.com, pg 1393

Andes, Elizabeth, North Market Street Graphics (NMSG), 317 N Market St, Lancaster, PA 17603 *Tel:* 717-392-7438 *Fax:* 717-397-8037 *E-mail:* mail@nmsgbooks.com *Web Site:* www.nmsgbooks.com, pg 1223, 1431

Andonian, Aramais, Arrow Graphics Inc, PO Box 380291, Cambridge, MA 02238 *E-mail:* info@arrow1.com *Web Site:* www.arrow1.com, pg 1091, 1202, 1216, 1355, 1373, 1393, 1424

Andrabi, Waseem, Cenveo Publisher Services, 555 Virginia Dr, Fort Washington, PA 19034 *Tel:* 267-470-1590 *Fax:* 215-591-9093 *E-mail:* info.psg@cenveo.com *Web Site:* www.cenveopublisherservices.com, pg 1203, 1217, 1356, 1374, 1426

Andrew, Jan, The Hendra Agency Inc, 142 Sterling Place, Brooklyn, NY 11217-3307 *Tel:* 718-622-3232; 212-947-9898 *Fax:* 718-622-3322, pg 1098

Andrews, Gaylen, Blitz Media-Direct, Linick Bldg, 7 Putter Lane, Middle Island, NY 11953 *Tel:* 631-924-3888; 631-924-8555; 630-604-8599 *E-mail:* blitz4pr@gmail.com; linickgroup@gmail.com, pg 1085, 1095, 1425

Andrews, Gaylen, Copywriters' Council of America™ (CCA), CCA Bldg, 7 Putter Lane, Middle Island, NY 11953-1920 *Tel:* 631-924-3888; 631-604-8599; 631-924-8555, pg 1096

Andrews, Gaylen, Copywriters' Council of America™ (CCA), CCA Bldg, 7 Putter Lane, Middle Island, NY 11953-1920 *Tel:* 631-924-3888; 631-924-8555; 631-604-8599, pg 1106, 1344, 1375, 1426

Angstrom, Mark, Angstrom Graphics Print, 4437 E 49 St, Cleveland, OH 44125 *Tel:* 216-271-5300 *Toll Free Tel:* 800-634-1262 *E-mail:* info@angstromgraphics.com *Web Site:* www.angstromgraphics.com, pg 1241

Angstrom, Wayne, Angstrom Graphics Print, 4437 E 49 St, Cleveland, OH 44125 *Tel:* 216-271-5300 *Toll Free Tel:* 800-634-1262 *E-mail:* info@angstromgraphics.com *Web Site:* www.angstromgraphics.com, pg 1241

Anson, Matt, Bindagraphics Inc, 2701 Wilmarco Ave, Baltimore, MD 21223-9922 *Tel:* 410-362-7200 *Toll Free Tel:* 800-326-0300 *Fax:* 410-362-7233 *E-mail:* info@bindagraphics.com *Web Site:* www.bindagraphics.com, pg 1216, 1242

Anson, Todd, The Colad Group LLC, 693 Seneca St, 5th fl, Buffalo, NY 14210 *Tel:* 716-961-1776 *Toll Free Tel:* 800-950-1755 *Fax:* 716-961-1753 *E-mail:* info@colad.com *Web Site:* www.colad.com, pg 1091

Ansorge, Jessica, Sheridan MI, 613 E Industrial Dr, Chelsea, MI 48118 *Tel:* 734-475-9145 *Web Site:* www.sheridan.com, pg 1209, 1254, 1267

Antler, Bob, Antler Designworks, 93 Concession Oak Dr, Bluffton, SC 29909 *Tel:* 843-705-6695 *Fax:* 843-705-6445 *E-mail:* antlerdw@aol.com, pg 1423

Antman, Mark, The Image Works Inc, PO Box 443, Woodstock, NY 12498-0443 *Tel:* 845-679-8500 *Toll Free Tel:* 800-475-8801 *Fax:* 845-679-0606 *E-mail:* info@theimageworks.com *Web Site:* www.theimageworks.com, pg 1448

Antone, Peter, Ingram Publisher Services, an Ingram brand, One Ingram Blvd, La Vergne, TN 37086 *Tel:* 615-793-5000 *Toll Free Tel:* 866-400-5351 (cust serv) *E-mail:* ips@ingramcontent.com *Web Site:* www.ingramcontent.com, pg 1290

Apelian, Bill, BJU Press, 1430 Wade Hampton Blvd, Greenville, SC 29609-5046 *Tel:* 864-546-4600 *Toll Free Tel:* 800-845-5731 *E-mail:* bjupinfo@bjupress.com *Web Site:* www.bjupress.com, pg 1373

Appelbaum, Judith, Sensible Solutions Inc, 500 Croton Lake Rd, Mount Kisco, NY 10549 *Tel:* 914-241-4749 *Fax:* 914-241-1942 *Web Site:* www.happilypublished.com, pg 1352

Apter, Ronnie, Mark Herman & Ronnie Apter, Translators, 2222 Westview Dr, Nashville, TN 37212-4123 *Tel:* 615-942-8462 *E-mail:* mnh18@columbia.edu, pg 1410

Aragone, Augusto P, Ingram Micro Inc, 3351 Michelson Dr, Suite 100, Irvin, CA 92612 *Tel:* 714-566-1000 *E-mail:* customerexperience@ingrammicro.com *Web Site:* www.ingrammicro.com, pg 1315

Arambarri, Yolanda, United Library Services Inc, 7140 Fairmount Dr SE, Calgary, AB T2H 0X4, Canada *Tel:* 403-252-4426 *Toll Free Tel:* 888-342-5857 (CN only) *Fax:* 403-258-3426 *Toll Free Fax:* 800-661-2806 (CN only) *E-mail:* info@uls.com *Web Site:* www.uls.com, pg 1321

Araujo-Lane, Zarita, Cross Cultural Communication Systems Inc, 227 Garfield Ave, Suite B, Woburn, MA 01801 *Tel:* 781-729-3736 *Toll Free Tel:* 888-678-CCCS (678-2227 out of state only) *Fax:* 781-729-1217 *Web Site:* www.cccsorg.com; www.embracingculture.com, pg 1408

Baxter, Nicole, BookMobile, 5120 Cedar Lake Rd, Minneapolis, MN 55416 *Tel:* 763-398-0030 *Toll Free Tel:* 844-488-4477 *Fax:* 763-398-0198 *Web Site:* www. bookmobile.com, pg 1243

Bean, Mike, Allard Inc, 4601 50 St, Suite 204, Lubbock, TX 79414 *Tel:* 214-736-4983 *E-mail:* info@allardinc. com *Web Site:* www.allardinc.com, pg 1215

Bean, Tom, Tom Bean Photography, 4680 Lake Mary Rd, Flagstaff, AZ 86001 *Tel:* 928-779-4381 *Fax:* 928-779-9642 *E-mail:* tom@tombean.com *Web Site:* www. tombean.com, pg 1436

Beard, Morgan, Swedenborg Foundation, 320 N Church St, West Chester, PA 19380 *Tel:* 610-430-3222 *Toll Free Tel:* 800-355-3222 (cust serv) *Fax:* 610-430-7982 *E-mail:* info@swedenborg.com *Web Site:* swedenborg. com, pg 1321

Beauregard, Sue-Ellen, Booklist, 225 N Michigan Ave, Suite 1300, Chicago, IL 60601 *Tel:* 312-944-6780 *Toll Free Tel:* 800-545-2433 *Fax:* 312-440-9374 *E-mail:* info@booklistonline.com; ala@ala.org *Web Site:* www.booklistonline.com; www.ala.org, pg 1124

Beavers, Nick, Media Cybernetics Inc, 1700 Rockville Pike, Suite 240, Rockville, MD 20852 *Tel:* 301-495-3305 *Toll Free Tel:* 800-263-2088 *E-mail:* support@mediacy.com; marketing@mediacy. com *Web Site:* www.mediacy.com, pg 1381

Becerra, Nannette, Gem Guides Book Co, 1155 W Ninth St, Upland, CA 91786 *Tel:* 626-855-1611 *Toll Free Tel:* 800-824-5118 (orders) *Fax:* 626-855-1610 *E-mail:* info@gemguidesbooks.com; sales@ gemguidesbooks.com (orders) *Web Site:* www. gemguidesbooks.com, pg 1314

Beck, Eileen L, Glatfelter, Capitol Towers South, 4350 Congress St, Suite 600, Charlotte, NC 28209 *Tel:* 717-850-0170 *Toll Free Tel:* 866-744-7380 *E-mail:* info@ glatfelter.com *Web Site:* www.glatfelter.com, pg 1263

Becker, Brian, Widen Enterprises Inc, 6911 Mangrove Lane, Madison, WI 53713 *Tel:* 608-222-1296 *Toll Free Tel:* 800-444-2828 *E-mail:* marketing@widen.com *Web Site:* www.widen.com, pg 1228

Becker, Pamela, Big Vision Art + Design, 251 Hwy 179, Creekside Plaza A1, Sedona, AZ 86336 *Tel:* 928-202-6320 *Web Site:* www.bigvisionarts.com, pg 1424

Becker, Rick, AllMedia Inc, 1400 Preston Rd, No 400, Plano, TX 75093 *Tel:* 469-467-9100 *Fax:* 214-291 5431 *Web Site:* www.allmediainc.com, pg 1105, 1111

Beckerich, Michael P, Classics of Golf, 120 Research Dr, Stratford, CT 06615 *Tel:* 845-765-6050 *Toll Free Tel:* 800-483-6449 *E-mail:* info@classicsofgolf.com; customerservice@classicsofgolf.com *Web Site:* www. classicsofgolf.com, pg 1135

Beebe, Morton, Morton Beebe Photographer/Author, 150 Lombard St, Suite 808, San Francisco, CA 94111-1139 *Tel:* 415-362-6222; 415-706-0594 *E-mail:* morton.beebe@gmail.com *Web Site:* www. mortonbeebe.com, pg 1436

Beer, Tom, Kirkus, 65 W 36 St, Suite 700, New York, NY 10018 *E-mail:* customercare@kirkus.com *Web Site:* www.kirkusreviews.com, pg 1128

Begley, Christine, Dell Magazines, 44 Wall St, Suite 904, New York, NY 10005-2401 *Tel:* 212-686-7188 *Toll Free Tel:* 800-220-7443 (corp sales) *Fax:* 212-480-5751 *E-mail:* customerservice@pennydellpuzzles. com *Web Site:* www.pennydellpuzzles.com, pg 1357

Beit-Arie, Oren, ProQuest LLC, 789 E Eisenhower Pkwy, Ann Arbor, MI 48108 *Tel:* 734-761-4700 *Toll Free Tel:* 800-521-0600; 877-779-6768 (sales) *E-mail:* sales@proquest.com *Web Site:* www.proquest. com, pg 1384

Bell, E, Haynes North America Inc, 859 Lawrence Dr, Newbury Park, CA 91320-1514 *Tel:* 805-498-6703 *Toll Free Tel:* 800-4-HAYNES (442-9637) *Fax:* 805-498-2867 *E-mail:* cstn@haynes.com *Web Site:* www. haynes.com, pg 1326

Bell, Michael, Ingram Content Group LLC, One Ingram Blvd, La Vergne, TN 37086-1986 *Tel:* 615-793-5000 *Toll Free Tel:* 800-937-8000 (retailers); 800-937-5300

(ext 1, libs) *E-mail:* customerservice@ingramcontent. com *Web Site:* www.ingramcontent.com, pg 1290, 1315

Bell, Robin, Chesapeake & Hudson Inc, 115 W Potomac St, Brunswick, MD 21716 *Tel:* 301-834-7170 *Toll Free Tel:* 800-231-4469 *Toll Free Fax:* 800-307-5163 *E-mail:* office@cheshud.com *Web Site:* www.cheshud. com, pg 1285

Belling, Catherine, Literature & Medicine, 2715 N Charles St, Baltimore, MD 21218-4363 *Toll Free Tel:* 800-548-1784 (journal orders) *Fax:* 410-516-6968 *E-mail:* jrnlcirc@press.jhu.edu (journal orders) *Web Site:* www.press.jhu.edu/journals/ literature_and_medicine/index.html, pg 1128

Belsky, Scott, Adobe Systems Inc, 345 Park Ave, San Jose, CA 95110-2704 *Tel:* 408-536-6000 *Fax:* 408-537-6000 *Web Site:* www.adobe.com, pg 1371

Benanzer, Janice, Baumfolder Corp, 1660 Campbell Rd, Sidney, OH 45365 *Tel:* 937-492-1281 *Toll Free Tel:* 800-543-6107 *Fax:* 937-492-7280 *E-mail:* baumfolder@baumfolder.com *Web Site:* www. baumfolder.com, pg 1273

Benatar, Raquel, Renaissance House, 465 Westview Ave, Englewood, NJ 07631 *Tel:* 201-408-4048 *Web Site:* www.renaissancehouse.net, pg 1361

Bendror, Jack, Mekatronics Inc, 85 Channel Dr, Port Washington, NY 11050 *Tel:* 516-883-6805 *Fax:* 516-883-6948 *E-mail:* office@mekatronicsinc.com *Web Site:* mekatronicsinc.com, pg 1265

Benedict, Jim, GLS Companies, 1280 Energy Park Dr, St Paul, MN 55108-5106 *Tel:* 651-644-3000 *Toll Free Tel:* 800-655-9405 *Web Site:* www.glsmn.com, pg 1220, 1248

Benenati, Joe, The Gluefast Co Inc, 3535 State Rte 66, Bldg No 1, Neptune, NJ 07753 *Tel:* 732-918-4600 *Toll Free Tel:* 800-242-7318 *Fax:* 732-918-4646 *E-mail:* info@gluefast.com *Web Site:* www.gluefast. com, pg 1335

Bengard, Jamie, Dual Graphics, 370 Cliffwood Park, Brea, CA 92821 *Tel:* 714-990-3700 *Fax:* 714-990-6818 *Web Site:* www.dualgraphics.com, pg 1219, 1246

Bengel, Tricia Racke, Ingram Content Group LLC, One Ingram Blvd, La Vergne, TN 37086-1986 *Tel:* 615-793-5000 *Toll Free Tel:* 800-937-8000 (rctailers), 800-937-5300 (ext 1, libs) *E-mail:* customerservice@ ingramcontent.com *Web Site:* www.ingramcontent.com, pg 1290, 1315

Benjamin, Mark, Nuance Communications Inc, One Wayside Rd, Burlington, MA 01803 *Tel:* 781-565-5000 *Toll Free Tel:* 800-654-1187 (cust serv); 888-372-1908 (orders) *Web Site:* www.nuance.com, pg 1382

Benner, Deborah J, Goose River Press, 3400 Friendship Rd, Waldoboro, ME 04572-6337 *Tel:* 207-832-6665 *E-mail:* gooseriverpress@gmail.com *Web Site:* gooseriverpress.com, pg 1220, 1248

Benner, Whitney, PR Newswire, 350 Hudson St, Suite 300, New York, NY 10014-4504 *Toll Free Tel:* 888-776-0942; 800-776-8090 *Toll Free Fax:* 800-793-9313 *E-mail:* mediainquiries@prnewswire.com *Web Site:* www.prnewswire.com, pg 1101

Bennett, Stephen, Esko USA, 8535 Gander Creek Dr, Miamisburg, OH 45342 *Tel:* 937-454-1721 *Toll Free Tel:* 800-743-7131 *Fax:* 937-454-1522 *E-mail:* info. usa@esko.com *Web Site:* www.esko.com, pg 1377

Bennett, Steve, AuthorBytes, PO Box 382103, Cambridge, MA 02238-2103 *Tel:* 617-492-0442 *E-mail:* info@authorbytes.com *Web Site:* www. authorbytes.com, pg 1342

Benoit, Michael J, Benoit & Associates, 744 Stockton Heights Ct, Bourbonnais, IL 60914 *Tel:* 815-932-2582 *Fax:* 815-932-2594 *Web Site:* www.benoit-associates. com, pg 1085, 1216, 1424, 1436

Benson, Barry, Promotion in Motion, 714 Crescent Dr, Beverly Hills, CA 90210 *Tel:* 323-461-3921; 310-497-4001 (cell) *Fax:* 323-461-0917

E-mail: irwinzuckerpr@aol.com *Web Site:* www. promotioninmotion.net; www.bookpublicists.org, pg 1101

Benson, Ingrid, Integra Software Services Inc, 1110 Jorie Blvd, Suite 200, Oak Brook, IL 60523 *Tel:* 630-586-2579 *Fax:* 630-586-2599 *E-mail:* marketing@integra. co.in *Web Site:* www.integra.co.in, pg 1347, 1358

Benson, Ken, PrintWest, 1111 Eighth Ave, Regina, SK S4R 1C9, Canada *Tel:* 306-525-2304 *Toll Free Tel:* 800-236-6438 *Fax:* 306-757-2439 *E-mail:* general@printwest.com *Web Site:* www. printwest.com, pg 1208, 1224, 1266, 1278

Benson, Scot, MacDermid Graphics Solutions LLC, 5210 Phillip Lee Dr, Atlanta, GA 30336 *Tel:* 404-696-4565 *Toll Free Tel:* 800-348-7201 *E-mail:* mpsproductinfo@macdermid.com *Web Site:* graphics.macdermid.com, pg 1277

Bentley, Kelvin, Six Red Marbles LLC, 101 Station Landing, Medford, MA 02155 *Tel:* 857-588-9000 *E-mail:* info@sixredmarbles.com *Web Site:* www. sixredmarbles.com, pg 1226, 1385

Bentley, Michael, Bentley Publishers, 1734 Massachusetts Ave, Cambridge, MA 02138-1804 *Tel:* 617-547-4170 *Toll Free Tel:* 800-423-4595 *Fax:* 617-876-9235 *E-mail:* sales@bentleypublishers. com *Web Site:* www.bentleypublishers.com, pg 1325

Bentz, Bob, ATS Mobile, 1150 First Ave, Suite 105, King of Prussia, PA 19406 *Tel:* 610-688-6000 *Toll Free Tel:* 800-247-1287 *Fax:* 610-964-9117 *Web Site:* www.atsmobile.com, pg 1342

Benyovszky, Chris, Maple Logistics Solutions, 60 Grumbacher Rd, York, PA 17406 *Tel:* 717-764-4596 *Fax:* 717-764-4494 *E-mail:* info@maplesoln.com *Web Site:* www.maplelogisticssolutions.com, pg 1291, 1332

Benyovszky, Chris, Maple Press, 480 Willow Springs Lane, York, PA 17406 *Tel:* 717-764-5911 *Toll Free Tel:* 800-999-5911 *Fax:* 717-764-4702 *E-mail:* sales@ maplepress.com *Web Site:* www.maplepress.com, pg 1207, 1250, 1277

Berchenko, Dan, Publishers Weekly, 71 W 23 St, Suite 1608, New York, NY 10010 *Tel:* 212-377-5500 *Fax:* 212-377-2733 *Web Site:* www.publishersweekly. com, pg 1130

Berent, Irwin, Writers' Supercenter, 560 Roland Dr, Norfolk, VA 23509 *Tel:* 757-515-4315 *E-mail:* writerspage@writerspage.com *Web Site:* writersupercenter.com, pg 1388

Berg, Susan M, Next Chapter Book Club (NCBC), 125 Woodside Park Dr, Amelia, OH 45102 *Tel:* 614-404-6060 *Web Site:* nextchapterbookclub.org, pg 1137

Bergenholtz, Tom, ViaTech Publishing Solutions Inc, 11935 N Stemmons Fwy, Dallas, TX 75234 *Tel:* 214-827-8151 *E-mail:* marketing@viatechpub.com *Web Site:* www.viatech.io, pg 1227, 1256

Berger, Corey, Readerlink Distribution Services LLC, 1420 Kensington Rd, Suite 300, Oakbrook, IL 60523-2164 *Tel:* 708-547-4400 *Toll Free Tel:* 800-549-5389 *E-mail:* info@readerlink.com; marketingservices@ readerlink.com *Web Site:* www.readerlink.com, pg 1297

Berger, Dick, Cross Country Computer Corp, 250 Carleton Ave, East Islip, NY 11730-1240 *Tel:* 631-334-1810 *E-mail:* inquiry@crosscountrycomputer.com *Web Site:* www.crosscountrycomputer.com, pg 1111

Berger, Elisa PhD, Cross Country Computer Corp, 250 Carleton Ave, East Islip, NY 11730-1240 *Tel:* 631-334-1810 *E-mail:* inquiry@crosscountrycomputer.com *Web Site:* www.crosscountrycomputer.com, pg 1111

Berger, Thomas, Cross Country Computer Corp, 250 Carleton Ave, East Islip, NY 11730-1240 *Tel:* 631-334-1810 *E-mail:* inquiry@crosscountrycomputer.com *Web Site:* www.crosscountrycomputer.com, pg 1111

Berghaum, Lisa, Monadnock Paper Mills Inc, 117 Antrim Rd, Bennington, NH 03442-4205 *Tel:* 603-588-3311 *Toll Free Tel:* 800-221-2159 (cust serv) *Fax:* 603-588-3158 *E-mail:* info@mpm.com *Web Site:* www.mpm.com, pg 1266

Bergkamp, Will, Augsburg Fortress Publishers, Publishing House of the Evangelical Lutheran Church in America, 510 Marquette Ave S, Minneapolis, MN 55402 *Tel:* 612-330-3300 *Toll Free Tel:* 800-426-0115 (ext 639, subns); 800-328-4648 (orders) *Fax:* 612-330-3455 *Toll Free Fax:* 800-722-7766 (orders) *E-mail:* customercare@augsburgfortress.org; copyright@augsburgfortress.org (reprint permission requests); info@augsburgfortress.org *Web Site:* www.augsburgfortress.org; www.1517.media, pg 1309

Berglind, Debra, Book Express, 2440 Viking Way, Richmond, BC V6V 1N2, Canada *Tel:* 604-448-7100 *Toll Free Tel:* 800-663-5714 *Fax:* 604-270-7161 *Toll Free Fax:* 800-565-3770 *E-mail:* info@raincoast.com *Web Site:* www.raincoast.com, pg 1310

Bergman, Vicky, The Bergman Medical/Technical/ Scientific Collection, c/o Project Masters Inc, 134 Leabrook Lane, Princeton, NJ 08540 *Tel:* 609-921-0749 *E-mail:* information@pmiprinceton.com *Web Site:* www.pmiprinceton.com, pg 1445

Bergstrom, Gerald, Morris Publishing®, 3212 E Hwy 30, Kearney, NE 68847 *Tel:* 308-236-7888 *Toll Free Tel:* 800-650-7888 *Fax:* 308-237-0263 *E-mail:* publish@morrispublishing.com *Web Site:* www.morrispublishing.com, pg 1251

Berkowitz, David H, Gould Paper Corp, 99 Park Ave, 10th fl, New York, NY 10016 *Tel:* 212-301-0000 *Toll Free Tel:* 800-221-3043 *Fax:* 212-481-0067 *E-mail:* info@gouldpaper.com *Web Site:* www.gouldpaper.com, pg 1263

Berkowitz, Jay, Circle Graphics Inc, 316 Main St, Suite 1C, Reisters Town, MD 21136 *Tel:* 410-833-2200 *E-mail:* production@circleusa.com *Web Site:* www.circleusa.com, pg 1218

Berkowitz, Richard, Circle Graphics Inc, 316 Main St, Suite 1C, Reisters Town, MD 21136 *Tel:* 410-833-2200 *E-mail:* production@circleusa.com *Web Site:* www.circleusa.com, pg 1218

Berlow, David, The Font Bureau Inc, 151 Beach Rd, Vineyard Haven, MA 02568 *E-mail:* info@fontbureau.com *Web Site:* fontbureau.typenetwork.com, pg 1220

Berlow, Sam, The Font Bureau Inc, 151 Beach Rd, Vineyard Haven, MA 02568 *E-mail:* info@fontbureau.com *Web Site:* fontbureau.typenetwork.com, pg 1220

Berman, David, David Berman Communications, 340 Selby Ave, Ottawa, ON K2A 3X6, Canada *Tel:* 613-728-6777 *Toll Free Tel:* 800-665-1809 *E-mail:* info@davidberman.com *Web Site:* www.wcag2.com, pg 1216

Bernard, Peter, Pacific Publishing Co Inc, 636 Alaska St S, Seattle, WA 98108 *Tel:* 206-461-1300 *E-mail:* ppcprint@nwlink.com; ppccirc@nwlink.com; ppcbind@nwlink.com *Web Site:* pacificpublishingcompany.com, pg 1252

Bernhardt, Phil, Scholastic Book Fairs®, 1080 Greenwood Blvd, Lake Mary, FL 32746 *Tel:* 407-829-8000 *Fax:* 407-829-2600 *E-mail:* custservbf@scholasticbookfairs.com *Web Site:* www.scholastic.com/bookfairs, pg 1298, 1320

Berns, Steven, Shutterstock Inc, Empire State Bldg, 350 Fifth Ave, 21st fl, New York, NY 10118 *Tel:* 646-419-4452 (sales) *Toll Free Tel:* 866-663-3954 *Fax:* 347-402-0710 *E-mail:* support@shutterstock.com; press@shutterstock.com *Web Site:* www.shutterstock.com, pg 1449

Bernstein, David, The Gate Worldwide, 71 Fifth Ave, 8th fl, New York, NY 10003 *Tel:* 212-508-3400 *Fax:* 212-508-3402 (cgi) *E-mail:* contact@thegateworldwide.com *Web Site:* thegateworldwide.com, pg 1086

Bernstein, Mark, Eastgate Systems Inc, 134 Main St, Watertown, MA 02472 *Tel:* 617-924-9044 *Toll Free Tel:* 800-562-1638 *E-mail:* info@eastgate.com *Web Site:* www.eastgate.com, pg 1376

Bernstein, Stuart, Liliana Valenzuela, 1103 Maufrais St, Austin, TX 78703 *Tel:* 512-804-8141 *E-mail:* reporterliliana@gmail.com *Web Site:* www.lilianavalenzuela.com, pg 1414

Berry, Nerry, Bryan Farrish Marketing, 1828 Broadway, 2nd fl, Santa Monica, CA 90404 *Tel:* 310-998-8305 *E-mail:* airplay@radio-media.com *Web Site:* www.radio-media.com, pg 1097

Berry, Savinay, Open Text Corp, 275 Frank Tompa Dr, Waterloo, ON N2L 0A1, Canada *Tel:* 519-888-7111 *Fax:* 519-888-0677 *Web Site:* opentext.com, pg 1383

Bertelle, Jeanne, Bert Davis Executive Search Inc, 555 Fifth Ave, Suite 302, New York, NY 10017 *Tel:* 212-838-4000 *E-mail:* info@bertdavis.com *Web Site:* www.bertdavis.com, pg 1389

Bertelli, Eileen, Parson Weems' Publisher Services LLC, 3811 Canterbury Rd, No 707, Baltimore, MD 21218 *Tel:* 914-948-4259 *Toll Free Fax:* 866-861-0337 *E-mail:* office@parsonweems.com *Web Site:* www.parsonweems.com, pg 1294

Berthiaume, Denise, Verso Advertising Inc, 50 W 17 St, 5th fl, New York, NY 10011 *Tel:* 212-292-2990 *Fax:* 212-557-2592 *Web Site:* www.versoadvertising.com, pg 1087

Bertuch, Michael, ViaTech Publishing Solutions Inc, 11935 N Stemmons Fwy, Dallas, TX 75234 *Tel:* 214-827-8151 *E-mail:* marketing@viatechpub.com *Web Site:* www.viatech.io, pg 1227, 1256

Berty, Ron, Matrox Graphics Inc, 1055 Saint Regis Blvd, Dorval, QC H9P 2T4, Canada *Tel:* 514-822-6000 *Toll Free Tel:* 800-361-1408 (sales) *Fax:* 514-822-6363 *Web Site:* www.matrox.com/graphics, pg 1381

Bethke, Darwin, Action Printing, N6637 Rolling Meadows Dr, Fond du Lac, WI 54937 *Tel:* 920-907-7820 *E-mail:* info@actionprinting.com *Web Site:* www.actionprinting.com, pg 1241

Bethune, Bob, Maple Press, 480 Willow Springs Lane, York, PA 17406 *Tel:* 717-764-5911 *Toll Free Tel:* 800-999-5911 *Fax:* 717-764-4702 *E-mail:* sales@maplepress.com *Web Site:* www.maplepress.com, pg 1207, 1250, 1277

Bevington, Stan, Coach House Printing, 80 bpNichol Lane, Toronto, ON M5S 3J4, Canada *Tel:* 416-979-2217 *Toll Free Tel:* 800-367-6360 (outside Toronto) *Fax:* 416-977-1158 *E-mail:* mail@chbooks.com *Web Site:* www.chbooks.com, pg 1218, 1244

Beyer, Rodger, Worzalla, 3535 Jefferson St, Stevens Point, WI 54481 *Tel:* 715-344-9608 *Fax:* 715-344-2578 *Web Site:* www.worzalla.com, pg 1210, 1228, 1257

Bible, Maria, Vectorworks Inc, 7150 Riverwood Dr, Columbia, MD 21046 *Tel:* 410-290-5114 *Toll Free Tel:* 888-646-4223 (sales) *Fax:* 410-290-7266 *E-mail:* sales@vectorworks.net *Web Site:* www.vectorworks.net, pg 1387

Bick, Israel I, American Press Service & Features Syndicate, PO Box 854, Van Nuys, CA 91408 *Tel:* 818-997-6496 *E-mail:* iscs3assoc@aol.com, pg 1183

Bicksler, Dennis, North Market Street Graphics (NMSG), 317 N Market St, Lancaster, PA 17603 *Tel:* 717-392-7438 *Fax:* 717-397-8037 *E-mail:* mail@nmsgbooks.com *Web Site:* www.nmsgbooks.com, pg 1223

Biegel, Brian, D&K Group Inc, 1795 Commerce Dr, Elk Grove Village, IL 60007 *Tel:* 847-956-0160; 847-956-4757 (tech support) *Toll Free Tel:* 800-632-2314 *Fax:* 847-956-8214 *E-mail:* info@dkgroup.net *Web Site:* www.dkgroup.com, pg 1245, 1262, 1275

Biesiadecki, Paul J, Mohawk Fine Papers Inc, 465 Saratoga St, Cohoes, NY 12047 *Tel:* 518-237-1740 *Toll Free Tel:* 800-THE-MILL (843-6455) *Fax:* 518-237-7394 *Web Site:* www.mohawkconnects.com, pg 1266

Biggins, Eric, Sheridan PA, 450 Fame Ave, Hanover, PA 17331 *Tel:* 717-632-3535 *Toll Free Tel:* 800-352-2210 *Fax:* 717-633-8900 *Web Site:* www.sheridan.com, pg 1254

Bilitzky, Tammy, Data Conversion Laboratory Inc (DCL), 61-18 190 St, Suite 205, Fresh Meadows, NY 11365 *Tel:* 718-357-8700 *Toll Free Tel:* 800-321-2816 (provider problems) *E-mail:* info@dclab.com *Web Site:* www.dataconversionlaboratory.com, pg 1218, 1375

Bilyard, Celeste, Westchester Publishing Services, 4 Old Newtown Rd, Danbury, CT 06810 *Tel:* 203-791-0080 *Fax:* 203-791-9286 *E-mail:* info@westchesterpubsvcs.com *Web Site:* www.westchesterpublishingservices.com, pg 1227

Binder, Fred, Smith-Edwards-Dunlap Co, 2867 E Allegheny Ave, Philadelphia, PA 19134 *Tel:* 215-425-8800 *Toll Free Tel:* 800-829-0020 *Fax:* 215-425-9715 *E-mail:* sales@sed.com *Web Site:* www.sed.com, pg 1226, 1254, 1268

Bindseil, Heather, Library Bound Inc, 100 Bathurst Dr, Unit 2, Waterloo, ON N2V 1V6, Canada *Tel:* 519-885-3233 *Toll Free Tel:* 800-363-4728 *Fax:* 519-885-2662 *Web Site:* www.librarybound.com, pg 1316

Bird, Andy, Publicis North America, 1675 Broadway, New York, NY 10009 *Tel:* 212-474-5000 *Web Site:* www.publicisna.com, pg 1101

Biscanti, John, Bulkley Dunton, One Penn Plaza, Suite 2814, 250 W 34 St, New York, NY 10119 *Tel:* 212-863-1800 *Toll Free Tel:* 800-347-9279 *Fax:* 212-863-1872 *Web Site:* www.bulkleydunton.com, pg 1261

Biscanti, John, Veritiv™ Corporation, 400 Northpark Town Ctr, 1000 Abernathy Rd, Suite 1700, Atlanta, GA 30328 *Tel:* 770-391-8200 *Toll Free Tel:* 844-VERITIV (837-4848); 800-864-7687 (cust serv) *E-mail:* contactus@veritivcorp.com *Web Site:* www.veritivcorp.com, pg 1269

Bishop, Jennifer, Jennifer Bishop Photography, 843 W University Pkwy, Baltimore, MD 21210 *Tel:* 410-366-6662 *Web Site:* www.jenniferbishopphotography.com, pg 1436

Bissonnette, Tomas, Spanish Publishing Services, 4343 N Clarendon Ave, Suite 1002, Chicago, IL 60613 *Tel:* 773-878-2117 *Fax:* 773-388-2265 *E-mail:* servicioseditoriales@juno.com, pg 1413

Black, Alison, Ingram Publisher Services, an Ingram brand, One Ingram Blvd, La Vergne, TN 37086 *Tel:* 615-793-5000 *Toll Free Tel:* 866-400-5351 (cust serv) *E-mail:* ips@ingramcontent.com *Web Site:* www.ingramcontent.com, pg 1290

Black, Chris, Rayonier Advanced Materials, 1301 Riverplace Blvd, Suite 2300, Jacksonville, FL 32207 *Tel:* 904-357-4600 *Web Site:* rayonieram.com, pg 1266

Black, Norm, Guardian Book Co, 7019 Edinburgh Dr, Lambertville, MI 48144 *Tel:* 734-856-1765 *Toll Free Tel:* 800-560-6697 *Fax:* 734-854-7638 *Web Site:* guardianbookcompany.com; gbcbooks.com, pg 1314

Black, Roger, The Font Bureau Inc, 151 Beach Rd, Vineyard Haven, MA 02568 *E-mail:* info@fontbureau.com *Web Site:* fontbureau.typenetwork.com, pg 1220

Blackwell, Taylor, Walker360, 2501 Fifth Ave E, Montgomery, AL 36107 *Tel:* 334-832-4975 *E-mail:* info@walker360.com *Web Site:* walker360.com, pg 1209, 1256

Blaine, Devon, The Blaine Group Inc, 8665 Wilshire Blvd, No 301, Beverly Hills, CA 90211 *Tel:* 310-360-1499 *Fax:* 310-360-1498 *Web Site:* www.blainegroupinc.com, pg 1095

Blair, Gary Ryan, GoalsGuy Learning Systems, 36181 E Lake Rd, Suite 139, Palm Harbor, FL 34685 *Toll Free Tel:* 877-462-5748 *Fax:* 813-435-2022 *Toll Free Fax:* 877-903-2284 *E-mail:* info@goalsguy.com *Web Site:* www.100daychallenge.com, pg 1314

Blair, Jennifer, World Literature Today, 630 Parrington Oval, Suite 110, Norman, OK 73019-4033 *Tel:* 405-325-4531 *E-mail:* wlt@ou.edu *Web Site:* www.worldliteraturetoday.org, pg 1132

Blake, Corey Michael, Round Table Companies, 1027 Kenton Rd, Deerfield, IL 60015 *Tel:* 949-375-1006 *Web Site:* www.roundtablecompanies.com, pg 1432

Blanchett, Brian, Canvys® Visual Technology Solutions, 40W267 Keslinger Rd, LaFox, IL 60147 *Toll Free Tel:* 888-735-7373 *Fax:* 630-208-2350 *Web Site:* www.canvys.com, pg 1374

755-0394 *E-mail:* success@johnroberts.com *Web Site:* www.johnroberts.com; www.facebook. com/TheJohnRobertsCompany, pg 1093

Boydston, Ken, Megavision Inc, PO Box 60158, Santa Barbara, CA 93160 *Tel:* 805-964-1400 *Toll Free Tel:* 888-324-2580 *E-mail:* info@mega-vision.com *Web Site:* www.mega-vision.com, pg 1381

Boyer, Randy, Yurchak Printing Inc, 920 Links Ave, Landisville, PA 17538 *Tel:* 717-399-0209 *E-mail:* ypi. info@yurchak.com *Web Site:* www.yurchak.com, pg 1210, 1257, 1280

Boylan, Anne, Boston Review, PO Box 425786, Cambridge, MA 02142 *Tel:* 617-324-1360 *Toll Free Tel:* 877-406-2443 (cust serv) *Fax:* 617-452-3356 *E-mail:* review@bostonreview.net *Web Site:* bostonreview.net, pg 1124

Boyles, Kelly, Copywriters' Council of America™ (CCA), CCA Bldg, 7 Putter Lane, Middle Island, NY 11953-1920 *Tel:* 631-924-3888; 631-924-8555; 631-604-8599, pg 1086

Boyles, Kelly, Copywriters' Council of America™ (CCA), CCA Bldg, 7 Putter Lane, Middle Island, NY 11953-1920 *Tel:* 631-924-3888; 631-604-8599; 631-924-8555, pg 1096

Boyles, Kelly, Copywriters' Council of America™ (CCA), CCA Bldg, 7 Putter Lane, Middle Island, NY 11953-1920 *Tel:* 631-924-3888; 631-924-8555; 631-604-8599, pg 1106, 1344, 1356, 1375

Boyles, Kelly, Andrew S Linick PhD, The Copyologist®, Linick Bldg, 7 Putter Lane, Middle Island, NY 11953 *Tel:* 631-924-3888; 631-924-8555; 631-604-8599 *E-mail:* linickgroup@gmail.com *Web Site:* topmarketingadvisor.com, pg 1106, 1348

Boyles, Kelly, Linick International Inc, Linick Bldg, 7 Putter Lane, Middle Island, NY 11953 *Tel:* 631-924-3888; 631-924-8555; 631-604-8599 *E-mail:* topmarketingadvisor@gmail.com *Web Site:* topmarketingadvisor.com, pg 1349

Boyles, Kelly, LK Advertising Agency, Linick Bldg, 7 Putter Lane, Middle Island, NY 11953 *Tel:* 631-924-3888; 631-924-8555; 631-604-8599 *E-mail:* topmarketingadvisor@gmail.com *Web Site:* topmarketingadvisor.com, pg 1087, 1107

Boynton, Paul G, Rayonier Advanced Materials, 1301 Riverplace Blvd, Suite 2300, Jacksonville, FL 32207 *Tel:* 904-357-4600 *Web Site:* rayonieram.com, pg 1266

Bozuwa, Paul, Sheridan MI, 613 E Industrial Dr, Chelsea, MI 48118 *Tel:* 734-475-9145 *Web Site:* www. sheridan.com, pg 1209, 1254, 1267

Bozuwa, Paul, Sheridan NH, 69 Lyme Rd, Hanover, NH 03755 *Tel:* 603-643-2220 *Web Site:* www.sheridan. com, pg 1254

Bozuwa, Paul, Sheridan PA, 450 Fame Ave, Hanover, PA 17331 *Tel:* 717-632-3535 *Toll Free Tel:* 800-352-2210 *Fax:* 717-633-8900 *Web Site:* www.sheridan.com, pg 1254

Bradley, Bob, Bradford & Bigelow Inc, 3 Perkins Way, Newburyport, MA 01950-4007 *Tel:* 978-904-3100 *E-mail:* sales@bradford-bigelow.com *Web Site:* www. bradford-bigelow.com, pg 1202, 1243

Bradley, Chris, Fundcraft Publishing, 410 Hwy 72 W, Collierville, TN 38017 *Tel:* 901-853-7070 *Toll Free Tel:* 800-853-1363 *Fax:* 901-853-6196 *E-mail:* info@ fundcraft.com *Web Site:* www.fundcraft.com, pg 1205

Bradley, David, Fundcraft Publishing, 410 Hwy 72 W, Collierville, TN 38017 *Tel:* 901-853-7070 *Toll Free Tel:* 800-853-1363 *Fax:* 901-853-6196 *E-mail:* info@ fundcraft.com *Web Site:* www.fundcraft.com, pg 1205

Bradley, Georgienne, Bradley Ireland Productions, 23852 Pacific Coast Hwy, No 110, Malibu, CA 90265 *Tel:* 310-458-0700 *E-mail:* earthimag@aol.com *Web Site:* www.bradleyireland.com, pg 1436

Bradley, Lynda, BMI Educational Services Inc, 26 Haypress Rd, Cranbury, NJ 08512 *Tel:* 732-329-6991 *Toll Free Tel:* 800-222-8100 (orders only) *Fax:* 732-

329-6994 *Toll Free Fax:* 800-986-9393 (orders only) *E-mail:* info@bmionline.com *Web Site:* bmionline. com, pg 1310, 1323

Brake, Amy, Polylogics Services LLC, 6209 Mid Rivers Mall, Suite 320, St Peters, MO 63304 *Tel:* 201-670-4242 *Fax:* 201-670-4244 *E-mail:* info@polylogics.com *Web Site:* www.polylogics.com, pg 1393

Brakel-Schutt, Nina, Widen Enterprises Inc, 6911 Mangrove Lane, Madison, WI 53713 *Tel:* 608-222-1296 *Toll Free Tel:* 800-444-2828 *E-mail:* marketing@ widen.com *Web Site:* www.widen.com, pg 1228

Braman, Carol, Publishers Storage & Shipping Corp, 46 Development Rd, Fitchburg, MA 01420 *Tel:* 978-345-2121 *Fax:* 978-348-1233 *Web Site:* www.pssc.com, pg 1333

Bramson, Scott B, Magnum Book Services, 180 Raritan Center Pkwy, Suite 105, Edison, NJ 07737 *Tel:* 908-349-2300 *Fax:* 732-225-2037 *E-mail:* sales@ magnumbookservices.com *Web Site:* www. magnumbookservices.com; www.linkedin.com/ company/magnum-book-services; www.facebook. com/magnumbookservices, pg 1332

Brancati, John, ACC Distribution Ltd, 6 W 18 St, Suite 4B, New York, NY 10011 *Tel:* 212-645-1111 *Toll Free Tel:* 800-252-5231 *Fax:* 716-242-4911 *E-mail:* ussales@accpublishinggroup.com *Web Site:* www.accpublishinggroup.com/us, pg 1281

Branch, Justin, Greenleaf Book Group LLC, 3 Park Place, 4005 Banister Lane, Suite B, Austin, TX 78704 *Tel:* 512-891-6100 *Fax:* 512-891-6150 *E-mail:* contact@greenleafbookgroup.com *Web Site:* www.greenleafbookgroup.com, pg 1288, 1358

Brandon, Christine, D C Graphics Inc, 59 Central Ave, Suite 15, Farmingdale, NY 11735 *Tel:* 631-777-3100 *Fax:* 631-777-7899 *E-mail:* prepress@dcgraphicsinc. com *Web Site:* www.dcgraphicsinc.com, pg 1245

Brandt, Suzanne, Feldheim Publishers, 208 Airport Executive Park, Nanuet, NY 10954 *Tel:* 845-356-2282 *Toll Free Tel:* 800-237-7149 (orders) *Fax:* 845-425-1908 *E-mail:* sales@feldheim.com *Web Site:* www. feldheim.com, pg 1313

Branov, Mike, Thistle Printing Ltd, 35 Mobile Dr, Toronto, ON M4A 2P6, Canada *Tel:* 416-288-1288 *Fax:* 416-288-0737 *E-mail:* sales@thistleprinting.com *Web Site:* www.thistleprinting.com, pg 1227, 1255, 1386

Brash, Brian, Actar D, 440 Park Ave S, 17th fl, New York, NY 10016 *Tel:* 212-966-2207 *E-mail:* salesnewyork@actar-d.com *Web Site:* www. actar.com, pg 1281

Brassell, Robert F, Comag Marketing Group LLC (CMG), 155 Village Blvd, Suite 300, Princeton, NJ 08540 *Tel:* 609-524-1800 *Fax:* 609-524-1629 *Web Site:* www.i-cmg.com, pg 1312

Bratton, Jim, AcmeBinding, 8844 Mayfield Rd, Chesterland, OH 44026 *Tel:* 440-729-9411 *Toll Free Tel:* 888-485-5415 *Fax:* 440-729-9415 *Web Site:* www. acmebinding.com, pg 1241

Bratton, Jim, HF Group LLC, 8844 Mayfield Rd, Chesterland, OH 44026 *Tel:* 440-729-2445; 440-729-9411 (bindery) *E-mail:* custservice-oh@hfgroup.com *Web Site:* www.hfgroup.com, pg 1248, 1264, 1323

Breier, Davida, HFS, 2715 N Charles St, Baltimore, MD 21218 *Tel:* 410-516-6965 *Toll Free Tel:* 800-537-5487 (US & CN) *Fax:* 410-516-6998 *E-mail:* hfscustserv@ press.jhu.edu *Web Site:* hfs.jhu.edu; www.hfsbooks. com, pg 1288

Brenner, Jodi, Pro-Composition Inc, 2501 Catherine St, Suite 3, York, PA 17408 *Tel:* 717-965-9872 *Web Site:* www.pro-composition.com, pg 1224

Brewer, Art, Art Brewer Photography, 25262 Mainsail Dr, Dana Point, CA 92629 *Tel:* 949-661-8930 *Fax:* 949-248-2835 *E-mail:* art@artbrewer.com *Web Site:* www.artbrewer.com; artbrewerphoto.com, pg 1436

Brian, Dean, North Market Street Graphics (NMSG), 317 N Market St, Lancaster, PA 17603 *Tel:* 717-392-7438 *Fax:* 717-397-8037 *E-mail:* mail@nmsgbooks. com *Web Site:* www.nmsgbooks.com, pg 1223

Brickman, Ravelle, Julie A Laitin Enterprises Inc, 160 West End Ave, Suite 23N, New York, NY 10023 *Tel:* 917-841-8566 *E-mail:* info@julielaitin.com *Web Site:* www.julielaitin.com, pg 1086

Brickman, Wendy, Brickman Marketing, 395 Del Monte Ctr, No 250, Monterey, CA 93940 *Tel:* 831-594-1500 *E-mail:* brickman@brickmanmarketing.com *Web Site:* www.brickmanmarketing.com, pg 1096

Bridge, Patti, Mobium Creative Group, 200 S Michigan Ave, 17th fl, Chicago, IL 60604 *Tel:* 312-422-8950; 312-422-5995 *Fax:* 312-422-5901 *Web Site:* www. mobium.com, pg 1350

Briggs, Marian, PadillaCRT, 1101 W River Pkwy, Suite 400, Minneapolis, MN 55415 *Tel:* 612-455-1700 *Fax:* 612-455-1060 *Web Site:* www.padillacrt.com, pg 1100

Brill, Randi S, QuaraCORE LLC, One E Wacker Dr, Suite 1900, Chicago, IL 60601 *Tel:* 312-981-2540 *E-mail:* info@quaracore.com *Web Site:* www. quaracore.com, pg 1431

Brilliant, Ashleigh, Ashleigh Brilliant Enterprises, 117 W Valerio St, Santa Barbara, CA 93101 *Tel:* 805-682-0531 *Web Site:* www.ashleighbrilliant.com, pg 1183

Brilliant, Dorothy, Ashleigh Brilliant Enterprises, 117 W Valerio St, Santa Barbara, CA 93101 *Tel:* 805-682-0531 *Web Site:* www.ashleighbrilliant.com, pg 1183

Broad, David M, Digital Wisdom Inc, PO Box 11, Tappahannock, VA 22560-0011 *Tel:* 804-443-9000 *Toll Free Tel:* 800-800-8560 *E-mail:* info@ digitalwisdom.net *Web Site:* www.digiwis.com; www. mountainhighmaps.com, pg 1376

Broadhurst, Jamie, Raincoast Books Distribution Ltd, 2440 Viking Way, Richmond, BC V6V 1N2, Canada *Tel:* 604-448-7100 *Toll Free Tel:* 800-663-5714 (CN only) *Fax:* 604-270-7161 *Toll Free Fax:* 800-565-3770 *E-mail:* info@raincoast.com; customerservice@ raincoast.com *Web Site:* www.raincoast.com, pg 1296

Brockman, Seth, Academic Reviews, 1-A Glenwood Ave, Lynbrook, NY 11563 *Tel:* 516-593-1275 *E-mail:* info@academicreviews.com *Web Site:* www. academicreviews.com, pg 1123

Brockwell, Jason, National Book Network (NBN), 4501 Forbes Blvd, Suite 200, Lanham, MD 20706 *Tel:* 301-459-3366 *Toll Free Tel:* 800-462-6420 (orders only) *Fax:* 301-429-5746 *Toll Free Fax:* 800-338-4550 (orders only) *E-mail:* customercare@nbnbooks.com *Web Site:* www.nbnbooks.com, pg 1293, 1318

Brodbeck, Marty, Shutterstock Inc, Empire State Bldg, 350 Fifth Ave, 21st fl, New York, NY 10118 *Tel:* 646-419-4452 (sales) *Toll Free Tel:* 866-663-3954 *Fax:* 347-402-0710 *E-mail:* support@shutterstock.com; press@shutterstock.com *Web Site:* www.shutterstock. com, pg 1449

Broderick, Tracy, C & C Offset Printing Co USA Inc, 70 W 36 St, Unit 10C, New York, NY 10018 *Tel:* 212-431-4210 *Toll Free Fax:* 866-540-4134 *Web Site:* www.ccoffset.com, pg 1202, 1217, 1243

Brody, Beth, Brody Public Relations, 145 Kingwood Stockton Rd, Stockton, NJ 08559-1711 *Tel:* 908-295-0600 *Web Site:* www.brodypr.com, pg 1096

Brody, Louisa, Ingram Content Group LLC, One Ingram Blvd, La Vergne, TN 37086-1986 *Tel:* 615-793-5000 *Toll Free Tel:* 800-937-8000 (retailers); 800-937-5300 (ext 1, libs) *E-mail:* customerservice@ingramcontent. com *Web Site:* www.ingramcontent.com, pg 1290, 1315

Brody, Louisa, Two Rivers Distribution, an Ingram brand, 1400 Broadway, Suite 520, New York, NY 10018 *Toll Free Tel:* 866-400-5351 *E-mail:* ips@ ingramcontent.com (orders, independent bookstores & gift accts) *Web Site:* www.tworiversdistribution.com, pg 1300

Brokering, Mark, BMR Associates, 60 Corte Amado, Greenbrae, CA 94904 *Tel:* 415-927-1564 *E-mail:* info@bmrassoc.com *Web Site:* www.bmrassoc. com, pg 1343

Burstein, Jason, G & H Soho Inc, 413 Market St, Elmwood Park, NJ 07407 *Tel:* 201-216-9400 *Fax:* 201-216-1778 *E-mail:* print@ghsoho.com *Web Site:* www.ghsoho.com, pg 1205, 1220, 1248, 1263, 1346, 1358, 1428

Burt, Madelyn, Stonesong, 270 W 39 St, Suite 201, New York, NY 10018 *Tel:* 212-929-4600 *E-mail:* editors@ stonesong.com *Web Site:* www.stonesong.com, pg 1362

Burton, Michael, Cenveo Inc, 200 First Stamford Place, 2nd fl, Stamford, CT 06902 *Tel:* 203-595-3000 *Fax:* 203-595-3070 *E-mail:* info@cenveo.com *Web Site:* www.cenveo.com, pg 1203, 1244, 1261

Burton, Robert G Jr, Cenveo Inc, 200 First Stamford Place, 2nd fl, Stamford, CT 06902 *Tel:* 203-595-3000 *Fax:* 203-595-3070 *E-mail:* info@cenveo.com *Web Site:* www.cenveo.com, pg 1203, 1244, 1261

Buser, Jason, All Craft Digital Inc, 289-C Skidmores Rd, Deer Park, NY 11729 *Tel:* 631-254-8495 *Fax:* 631-254-8496, pg 1215

Bush, Nora, Specialist Marketing Services Inc, 777 Terrace Ave, Suite 401, Hasbrouck Heights, NJ 07604 *Tel:* 201-865-5800 *E-mail:* info@sms-inc.com *Web Site:* www.sms-inc.com, pg 1112

Bushell, Ginger, Gracenote, a Nielsen Company, 2000 Powell St, Suite 1500, Emeryville, CA 94608 *Tel:* 510-428-7200 *Web Site:* www.gracenote.com, pg 1184

Butcher, Chantelle, The John Roberts Company, 9687 East River Rd NW, Minneapolis, MN 55433 *Tel:* 763-755-5500 *Toll Free Tel:* 800-551-1534 *Fax:* 763-755-0394 *E-mail:* success@johnroberts. com *Web Site:* www.johnroberts.com; www.facebook. com/TheJohnRobertsCompany, pg 1093

Butier, Mitch, Avery Dennison Corp, 207 N Goode Ave, 6th fl, Glendale, CA 91203-1222 *Tel:* 626-304-2000 *Web Site:* www.averydennison.com, pg 1373

Butler, Butch, StarGroup International Inc, 1194 Old Dixie Hwy, Suite 201, West Palm Beach, FL 33413 *Tel:* 561-547-0667 *E-mail:* info@stargroupinternational.com *Web Site:* stargroupinternational.com, pg 1102

Butler, Doug, Staplex® Electric Stapler Division, 777 Fifth Ave, Brooklyn, NY 11232-1626 *Tel:* 718-768-3333 *Toll Free Tel:* 800-221-0822 *Fax:* 718-965-0750 *E-mail:* info@staplex.com *Web Site:* www.staplex.com, pg 1279

Butler, Rob, Viridiam LLC, 3030 Lowell Dr, Green Bay, WI 54311 *Tel:* 920-465-3030 *Toll Free Tel:* 800-829-6555 *Web Site:* www.viridiam.com, pg 1094, 1227, 1256

Byatt, Lucinda, The Historical Novels Review, 400 Dark Star Ct, Fairbanks, AK 99709 *Tel:* 217-581-7538 *Fax:* 217-581-7534 *E-mail:* reviews@historicalnovelsociety.org *Web Site:* historicalnovelsociety.org, pg 1126

Byers, Gail, International Institute of Reflexology Inc, PO Box 12642, St Petersburg, FL 33733-2642 *Tel:* 727-343-4811 *E-mail:* info@reflexology-usa.net; orderdept@reflexology-usa.net *Web Site:* reflexology-usa.net, pg 1315, 1326

Byrne, Katie, Nuance Communications Inc, One Wayside Rd, Burlington, MA 01803 *Tel:* 781-565-5000 *Toll Free Tel:* 800-654-1187 (cust serv); 888-372-1908 (orders) *Web Site:* www.nuance.com, pg 1382

Byrns, Bob, Paulist Press, 997 Macarthur Blvd, Mahwah, NJ 07430-9990 *Tel:* 201-825-7300 *Toll Free Tel:* 800-218-1903 *Fax:* 201-825-6921 *Toll Free Fax:* 800-836-3161 *E-mail:* info@paulistpress.com *Web Site:* www. paulistpress.com, pg 1319

Byrns, Bob, Paulist Press, 997 Macarthur Blvd, Mahwah, NJ 07430-9990 *Tel:* 201-825-7300 *Toll Free Tel:* 800-218-1903 *Fax:* 201-825-6921 *Toll Free Fax:* 800-836-3161 *E-mail:* info@paulistpress.com; publicity@ paulistpress.com *Web Site:* www.paulistpress.com, pg 1383

Cafarella, Adair, AzureGreen, 16 Bell Rd, Middlefield, MA 01243 *Tel:* 413-623-2155 *Fax:* 413-623-2156 *E-mail:* azuregreen@azuregreen.com *Web Site:* www. azuregreen.net, pg 1282, 1310

Caglioni, Manrico, Book Automation Inc, 458 Danbury Rd, Unit B10, New Milford, CT 06776 *Tel:* 860-354-7900 *Toll Free Tel:* 800-429-6305 *E-mail:* info@ bookautomation.com *Web Site:* www.bookautomation. com, pg 1274

Cai, Liting, Infocus® Corp, 13190 SW 68 Pkwy, Suite 120, Portland, OR 97223-8368 *Tel:* 503-207-4700 *Toll Free Tel:* 877-388-8360 (cust serv) *E-mail:* salessupport@infocus.com *Web Site:* www. infocus.com, pg 1379

Calabra, Christopher, Tukaiz LLC, 2917 N Latoria Lane, Franklin Park, IL 60131 *Tel:* 847-455-1588; 847-288-4968 (sales) *Toll Free Tel:* 800-543-2674 *E-mail:* contacttukaiz@tukaiz.com *Web Site:* www. tukaiz.com, pg 1227, 1256, 1269, 1280

Calaf, Dolores C, Calaf Communications, 10 Warwick Ct, Lawrence, MA 01841 *Tel:* 978-314-3125 *Fax:* 978-686-5960 *Web Site:* www. calafcommunications.com, pg 1408

Caldwell, Tom, Southern Territory Associates, 4508 64 St, Lubbock, TX 79414 *E-mail:* sta77@suddenlink.net *Web Site:* www.southernterritory.com, pg 1299

Calhoun, Katie, Getty Images Inc, 605 Fifth Ave S, Suite 400, Seattle, WA 98104 *Tel:* 206-925-5000 *Toll Free Tel:* 800-IMAGERY (462-4379 sales); 888-888-5889 *E-mail:* enterprisesolutionssales@gettyimages.com *Web Site:* www.gettyimages.com, pg 1378, 1447

Calkins, Melanie, Neenah Inc, 3460 Preston Ridge Rd, Suite 600, Alpharetta, GA 30005 *Toll Free Tel:* 800-344-5287 *E-mail:* publishing.team@neenah.com *Web Site:* www.neenahperformance.com/products/ neenah-performance/publishing-products, pg 1266, 1278

Callison, Kay, The American Audio Prose Library Inc, PO Box 842, Columbia, MO 65205 *Tel:* 573-449-7075 *E-mail:* aaplinc@centurytel.net, pg 1372

Camacho, Eduarda, PTC, 121 Seaport Blvd, Boston, MA 02210 *Tel:* 781-370-5000 *Fax:* 781-370-6000 *Web Site:* www.ptc.com, pg 1384

Campagna, Frank J II, ColorPage, 81 Ten Broeck Ave, Kingston, NY 12401 *Tel:* 845-331-7581 *Toll Free Tel:* 800-836-7581 *Fax:* 845-331-1571 *E-mail:* sales@ colorpageonline.com *Web Site:* www.colorpageonline. com, pg 1203, 1218, 1244, 1261

Campbell, Darby Jo, Progressive Publishing Services (PPS), 555 Ryan Run Rd, Suite B, York, PA 17404 *Tel:* 717-764-5908 *Fax:* 717-764-5530 *E-mail:* info@ pps-ace.com *Web Site:* www.pps-ace.com, pg 1224, 1384

Campbell, Duncan, The Campbell-Logan Bindery Inc, 7615 Baker St NE, Fridley, MN 55432 *Tel:* 612-332-1313 *Toll Free Tel:* 800-942-6224 *E-mail:* info@ campbell-logan.com *Web Site:* www.campbell-logan. com, pg 1323

Campbell, Greg, The Campbell-Logan Bindery Inc, 7615 Baker St NE, Fridley, MN 55432 *Tel:* 612-332-1313 *Toll Free Tel:* 800-942-6224 *E-mail:* info@campbell-logan.com *Web Site:* www.campbell-logan.com, pg 1323

Campbell, Kathy, Gorham Printing, 3718 Mahoney Dr, Centralia, WA 98531 *Tel:* 360-623-1323 *Toll Free Tel:* 800-837-0970 *E-mail:* info@gorhamprinting.com *Web Site:* www.gorhamprinting.com, pg 1248

Campbell, Mike, PTC, 121 Seaport Blvd, Boston, MA 02210 *Tel:* 781-370-5000 *Fax:* 781-370-6000 *Web Site:* www.ptc.com, pg 1384

Campbell, Sean D, PrimeArray Systems Inc, 1500 District Ave, Burlington, MA 01803 *Tel:* 978-455-9488 *Toll Free Tel:* 800-433-5133 *E-mail:* info@primearray.com; sales@primearray.com *Web Site:* www.primearray.com, pg 1383

Campoli, Leila, Stonesong, 270 W 39 St, Suite 201, New York, NY 10018 *Tel:* 212-929-4600 *E-mail:* editors@ stonesong.com *Web Site:* www.stonesong.com, pg 1362

Candelora, Anthony, Taconic Wire, 250 Totoket Rd, North Branford, CT 06471 *Tel:* 203-484-2863 *Toll Free Tel:* 800-253-1450 *Fax:* 203-484-2865 *E-mail:* sales@taconicwire.com; taconicwiresales@ gmail.com *Web Site:* www.taconicwire.com, pg 1279

Cann, Jay D Jr, Kwikprint Manufacturing Co Inc, 4868 Victor St, Jacksonville, FL 32207 *Tel:* 904-737-3755 *Toll Free Tel:* 800-940-5945 *Fax:* 904-730-0349 *E-mail:* info@kwikprint.net *Web Site:* www.kwik-print.com, pg 1264

Cannon, Peter, Publishers Weekly, 71 W 23 St, Suite 1608, New York, NY 10010 *Tel:* 212-377-5500 *Fax:* 212-377-2733 *Web Site:* www.publishersweekly. com, pg 1130

Capellan, Dr Angel, LEA Libros de Espana y America, 170-23 83 Ave, Jamaica, NY 11432 *Tel:* 718-291-9891 *Fax:* 718-291-9830 *E-mail:* lea@leabooks.com; orders@leabooks.com *Web Site:* www.leabooks.com, pg 1327

Capen, Christopher, Southwestern Publishing House Inc, 2451 Atrium Way, Nashville, TN 37214 *Toll Free Tel:* 800-358-0560 *Fax:* 615-391-2815 *E-mail:* info@swpublishinggroup.com *Web Site:* www. swpublishinggroup.com, pg 1362

Capik, Gloria, Paulist Press, 997 Macarthur Blvd, Mahwah, NJ 07430-9990 *Tel:* 201-825-7300 *Toll Free Tel:* 800-218-1903 *Fax:* 201-825-6921 *Toll Free Fax:* 800-836-3161 *E-mail:* info@paulistpress.com *Web Site:* www.paulistpress.com, pg 1319

Capik, Gloria, Paulist Press, 997 Macarthur Blvd, Mahwah, NJ 07430-9990 *Tel:* 201-825-7300 *Toll Free Tel:* 800-218-1903 *Fax:* 201-825-6921 *Toll Free Fax:* 800-836-3161 *E-mail:* info@paulistpress. com; publicity@paulistpress.com *Web Site:* www. paulistpress.com, pg 1383

Capwell, Ross, NCS Inc, 149 N Railroad St, Selmer, TN 38375 *Tel:* 731-645-4496 *E-mail:* service@ncsmags. com, pg 1332

Carbia, Vanessa M, Spanish/English Translation & Interpreting Services, 5704 SW 86 Dr, Gainesville, FL 32608-8536 *Tel:* 352-215-7200 *Web Site:* www.afn. org/~vanessa, pg 1413

Carey, Tyler M, Westchester Publishing Services, 4 Old Newtown Rd, Danbury, CT 06810 *Tel:* 203-791-0080 *Fax:* 203-791-9286 *E-mail:* info@westchesterpubsvcs. com *Web Site:* www.westchesterpublishingservices. com, pg 1227

Cargill, Robert R, Biblical Archaeology Society, 4710 41 St NW, Washington, DC 20016-1705 *Tel:* 202-364-3300 *Toll Free Tel:* 800-221-4644 *Fax:* 202-364-2636 *E-mail:* info@biblicalarchaeology.org *Web Site:* www. biblicalarchaeology.org, pg 1373

Carlin, James J, Fuse Graphics, 1800 Sandy Plains Pkwy, Suite 124, Marietta, GA 30066 *Tel:* 770-499-7777 *Fax:* 770-499-7778 *E-mail:* info@ fusegraphicsatlanta.com *Web Site:* www. fusegraphicsatlanta.com, pg 1248

Carlin, Kelly, Fuse Graphics, 1800 Sandy Plains Pkwy, Suite 124, Marietta, GA 30066 *Tel:* 770-499-7777 *Fax:* 770-499-7778 *E-mail:* info@fusegraphicsatlanta. com *Web Site:* www.fusegraphicsatlanta.com, pg 1248

Carling, Thomas J, Shoreline Publishing Group LLC, 125 Santa Rosa Place, Santa Barbara, CA 93109 *Tel:* 805-564-1004 *Toll Free Fax:* 800-840-6713 *Web Site:* shorelinepublishing.com, pg 1361

Carlini, Matt, Javelin Group, 203 S Union St, Suite 200, Alexandria, VA 22314 *Tel:* 703-490-8845 *E-mail:* hello@javelindc.com *Web Site:* javelindc.com, pg 1347

Carlson, Lisa, Upper Access Inc, 87 Upper Access Rd, Hinesburg, VT 05461 *Tel:* 802-482-2988 *E-mail:* upperaccessbooks@gmail.com *Web Site:* www.upperaccess.com, pg 1352

Carlson, Mark, The John Roberts Company, 9687 East River Rd NW, Minneapolis, MN 55433 *Tel:* 763-755-5500 *Toll Free Tel:* 800-551-1534 *Fax:* 763-755-0394 *E-mail:* success@johnroberts. com *Web Site:* www.johnroberts.com; www.facebook. com/TheJohnRobertsCompany, pg 1093

Carlson, Stephen T, Upper Access Inc, 87 Upper Access Rd, Hinesburg, VT 05461 *Tel:* 802-482-2988 *E-mail:* upperaccessbooks@gmail.com *Web Site:* www.upperaccess.com, pg 1102, 1352

Carnes, Lance, Personal TeX Inc, 722 Lombard St, Suite 201, San Francisco, CA 94133 *Tel:* 415-296-7550 *Toll Free Tel:* 800-808-7906 *Fax:* 415-296-7501 *E-mail:* sales@pctex.com *Web Site:* www.pctex.com, pg 1383

Carney, Dennis, Roosevelt Paper Co, One Roosevelt Dr, Mount Laurel, NJ 08054 *Tel:* 856-303-4100 *Toll Free Tel:* 800-523-3470 *Fax:* 856-642-1949 *E-mail:* marketing@rooseveltpaper.com *Web Site:* www.rooseveltpaper.com, pg 1267

Carpenter, David, CRW Graphics Communications, 9100 Pennsauken Hwy, Pennsauken, NJ 08110 *Tel:* 856-662-9111 *Toll Free Tel:* 800-820-3000 *Fax:* 856-665-1789 *E-mail:* info@crwgraphics.com *Web Site:* www.crwgraphics.com, pg 1092, 1375, 1426

Carpenter, Debra, Michael Carpenter Photography, 7704 Carrleigh Pkwy, Springfield, VA 22152-1304 *Tel:* 703-644-9666 *Fax:* 703-991-2643 *E-mail:* mike@michaelcarpenterphotography.com *Web Site:* www.michaelcarpenterphotography.com, pg 1437

Carpenter, Michael, Michael Carpenter Photography, 7704 Carrleigh Pkwy, Springfield, VA 22152-1304 *Tel:* 703-644-9666 *Fax:* 703-991-2643 *E-mail:* mike@michaelcarpenterphotography.com *Web Site:* www.michaelcarpenterphotography.com, pg 1436

Carr, Chris, Alliance Storage Technologies Inc (ASTI), 10045 Federal Dr, Colorado Springs, CO 80908 *Tel:* 719-593-7900 *Toll Free Tel:* 888-567-6332 *Fax:* 719-598-3472 *E-mail:* sales@astiusa.com; info@astiusa.com *Web Site:* www.alliancestoragetechnologies.com, pg 1372

Carreiro, Scotty, Azalea Software Inc, PO Box 16660, Seattle, WA 98116-0660 *Tel:* 206-341-9500; 206-336-9559 (software support); 206-336-9575 (sales & info) *Fax:* 206-299-5600 *E-mail:* salesinfo@azaleabarcodes.com *Web Site:* www.azaleabarcodes.com, pg 1373

Carrizales, Nancy, Animals Animals/Earth Scenes, 17 Railroad Ave, Chatham, NY 12037 *Tel:* 518-392-5500 *Toll Free Tel:* 800-392-5503 *E-mail:* info@animalsanimals.com *Web Site:* www.animalsanimals.com, pg 1445

Carroll, Scott, NewTek Inc, 5131 Beckwith Blvd, San Antonio, TX 78249 *Tel:* 210-370-8000 *Toll Free Tel:* 800-368-5441 *Fax:* 210-370-8001 *E-mail:* sales@newtek.com (cust serv) *Web Site:* www.newtek.com, pg 1382

Carroll-Davis, Julie, ProQuest LLC, 789 E Eisenhower Pkwy, Ann Arbor, MI 48108 *Tel:* 734-761-4700 *Toll Free Tel:* 800-521-0600; 877-779-6768 (sales) *E-mail:* sales@proquest.com *Web Site:* www.proquest.com, pg 1384

Carruthers, David, St Armand Paper Mill, 3700 St Patrick, Montreal, QC H4E 1A2, Canada *Tel:* 514-931-8338 *Fax:* 514-931-5953 *Web Site:* www.st-armand.com, pg 1267

Carson, Doug, DCA Inc, 1515 E Pine St, Cushing, OK 74023 *Tel:* 918-225-0346 *Fax:* 918-225-1113 *E-mail:* sales@dcainc.com *Web Site:* www.dcainc.com, pg 1375

Carter, Barbara, Cardinal Publishers Group, 2402 N Shadeland Ave, Suite A, Indianapolis, IN 46219 *Tel:* 317-352-8200 *Toll Free Tel:* 800-296-0481 (cust serv) *Fax:* 317-352-8202 *E-mail:* customerservice@cardinalpub.com *Web Site:* cardinalpub.com, pg 1284

Carter, Brian, Scholastic Book Fairs®, 1080 Greenwood Blvd, Lake Mary, FL 32746 *Tel:* 407-829-8000 *Fax:* 407-829-2600 *E-mail:* custservbf@scholasticbookfairs.com *Web Site:* www.scholastic.com/bookfairs, pg 1298, 1320

Carter, Nancy L, North Wind Picture Archives, 12 Waterboro Rd, Alfred, ME 04002 *Tel:* 207-490-1940 *Toll Free Tel:* 800-952-0703 *Fax:* 207-490-3627 *E-mail:* mail@northwindpictures.com *Web Site:* www.northwindpictures.com, pg 1448

Cary, Britt, Challenge Machinery Co, 6125 Norton Center Dr, Norton Shores, MI 49441 *Tel:* 231-799-8484 *Fax:* 231-798-1275 *E-mail:* info@challengemachinery.com; sales@challengemachinery.com *Web Site:* www.challengemachinery.com, pg 1274

Casewit, Niccolo, New West Agency, 355 Lowell Blvd, Denver, CO 80219 *Tel:* 303-935-0277 *Web Site:* environmentalproductions.com, pg 1448

Casey, Lynn, PadillaCRT, 1101 W River Pkwy, Suite 400, Minneapolis, MN 55415 *Tel:* 612-455-1700 *Fax:* 612-455-1060 *Web Site:* www.padillacrt.com, pg 1100

Cashin, Michael, Consortium Book Sales & Distribution, an Ingram brand, The Keg House, Suite 101, 34 13 Ave NE, Minneapolis, MN 55413-1007 *Tel:* 612-746-2600 *Toll Free Tel:* 800-283-3572 (cust serv, Jackson, TN) *Fax:* 612-746-2606 *E-mail:* info@cbsd.com *Web Site:* www.cbsd.com, pg 1285

Cassidy, Christi, Publishers Weekly, 71 W 23 St, Suite 1608, New York, NY 10010 *Tel:* 212-377-5500 *Fax:* 212-377-2733 *Web Site:* www.publishersweekly.com, pg 1130

Castle, Sara, JMW Group Inc, 347 Rte 6, No 867, Mahopac, NY 10541 *Tel:* 914-841-7105 *Fax:* 914-248-8861 *E-mail:* jmwgroup@jmwgroup.net *Web Site:* jmwforlife.com, pg 1348

Castomguay, Genevieve, Socadis Inc, 420 rue Stinson, Ville St-Laurent, QC H4N 3L7, Canada *Tel:* 514-331-3300 *Toll Free Tel:* 800-361-2847 (CN only) *Fax:* 514-745-3282 *Toll Free Fax:* 866-803-5422 *E-mail:* socinfo@socadis.com; direction@socadis.com *Web Site:* www.socadis.com, pg 1299

Catz, Safra A, Oracle America Inc, 500 Oracle Pkwy, Redwood Shores, CA 94065 *Tel:* 650-506-7000 *Toll Free Tel:* 800-392-2999; 800-633-0738 (sales) *Web Site:* www.oracle.com, pg 1383

Cauley, Leslie, Hill+Knowlton Strategies, 237 Park Ave, 4th fl, New York, NY 10017 *Tel:* 212-885-0300 *Web Site:* www.hkstrategies.com, pg 1098

Caurant, Jeanette, Aeon Books/Vishaal, PO Box 396, Accord, NY 12404-0396 *Tel:* 845-658-3068 *Fax:* 845-658-3068 *E-mail:* aeongroup@msn.com *Web Site:* www.aeongroup.com, pg 1281

Cee, Nicole, Translingua Associates, 630 Ninth Ave, Suite 708, New York, NY 10036 *Tel:* 212-697-2020 *Fax:* 212-697-2891 *Web Site:* www.translingua.com, pg 1414

Cendrowski, Dwight, Dwight Cendrowski Photography LLC, 2870 Easy St, Ann Arbor, MI 48104-6532 *Tel:* 734-330-5230 *Web Site:* www.cendrowski.com, pg 1437

Ceraso, Melissa, CHOICE, 575 Main St, Suite 300, Middletown, CT 06457 *Tel:* 860-347-6933; 860-347-1387 (ad); 240-646-7027 (subn); 818-487-4555 *E-mail:* acrlsubscriptions@pubservice.com; support@acrlchoice.freshdesk.com *Web Site:* www.ala.org/acrl/choice; www.choice360.org, pg 1125

Cerda, Jessy, VanDam Inc, The VanDam Bldg, 121 W 27 St, New York, NY 10001 *Tel:* 212-929-0416 *Toll Free Tel:* 800-UNFOLDS (863-6537) *Fax:* 212-929-0426 *E-mail:* info@vandam.com *Web Site:* www.vandam.com, pg 1363

Cha, Lee Po, IRCO-International Language Bank, 10301 NE Glisan St, Portland, OR 97220 *Tel:* 503-234-0068 (interpretation); 503-505-5186 (translation) *Fax:* 503-234-1259 *E-mail:* info@irco.org; translation@ircoilb.org; interpretation@ircoilb.org *Web Site:* www.irco.org/ilb, pg 1410

Chakravarthy, Anil, Adobe Systems Inc, 345 Park Ave, San Jose, CA 95110-2704 *Tel:* 408-536-6000 *Fax:* 408-537-6000 *Web Site:* www.adobe.com, pg 1371

Challenger, Sheena, Renouf Publishing Co Ltd, 22-1010 Polytek St, Ottawa, ON K1J 9J1, Canada *Tel:* 613-745-2665 *Toll Free Tel:* 866-767-6766; 888-551-7470 (North America) *Fax:* 613-745-7660 *E-mail:* order.dept@renoufbooks.com *Web Site:* www.renoufbooks.com, pg 1297

Chamaillard, Pascal, Edipresse Inc, 945, ave Beaumont, Montreal, QC H3N 1W3, Canada *Tel:* 514-273-6141 *Toll Free Tel:* 800-361-1043 *Fax:* 514-273-7021 *E-mail:* information@edipresse.ca *Web Site:* www.edipresse.ca, pg 1313

Chambers, Joe, Townsend Communications Inc, 20 E Gregory Blvd, Kansas City, MO 64114 *Tel:* 816-361-0616 *Web Site:* www.townsendcommunications.com; www.townsendprint.com, pg 1227, 1256, 1280

Champagne, Mark, Login Canada, 300 Saulteaux Crescent, Winnipeg, MB R3J 3T2, Canada *Tel:* 204-837-2987 *Toll Free Tel:* 800-665-1148 (CN only) *Fax:* 204-837-3116 *Toll Free Fax:* 800-665-0103 *E-mail:* sales@lb.ca *Web Site:* www.lb.ca, pg 1317

Champine, Heather, Media Relations Agency, 350 W Burnsville Pkwy, Suite 350, Burnsville, MN 55337 *Tel:* 952-697-5220 *Fax:* 952-697-3256 *Web Site:* www.publicity.com, pg 1099

Chan, James W PhD, Asia Marketing & Management (AMM), 2014 Naudain St, Philadelphia, PA 19146-1317 *Tel:* 215-735-7670; 267-324-6227 (cell phone) *Web Site:* www.asiamarketingmanagement.com, pg 1342

Chan, Simon, C & C Offset Printing Co USA Inc, 70 W 36 St, Unit 10C, New York, NY 10018 *Tel:* 212-431-4210 *Toll Free Fax:* 866-540-4134 *Web Site:* www.ccoffset.com, pg 1202, 1217, 1243

Chan, Terry, O'Neil Digital Solutions LLC, 12655 Beatrice St, Los Angeles, CA 90066 *Tel:* 310-448-6400 *E-mail:* sales@oneildata.com *Web Site:* www.oneildata.com, pg 1224, 1252, 1266, 1278

Chan, Yuk, BroadVision, 460 Seaport Ct, Suite 102, Redwood City, CA 94063 *Tel:* 650-331-1000 *Web Site:* www.broadvision.com, pg 1374

Chaney, Brian, Advantage Laser Products Inc, 1840 Marietta Blvd NW, Atlanta, GA 30318 *Tel:* 404-351-2700 *Toll Free Tel:* 800-722-2804 (cust serv) *Fax:* 404-351-0911 *Toll Free Fax:* 800-871-3305 *E-mail:* sales@advlaser.com *Web Site:* www.advlaser.com, pg 1371

Chang, Beth, Fujii Associates Inc, 75 Sunny Hill Dr, Troy, MO 63379 *Tel:* 636-528-2546 *Fax:* 636-600-5153 *Web Site:* www.fujiiassociates.com, pg 1287

Chang, Richard, Megavision Inc, PO Box 60158, Santa Barbara, CA 93160 *Tel:* 805-964-1400 *Toll Free Tel:* 888-324-2580 *E-mail:* info@mega-vision.com *Web Site:* www.mega-vision.com, pg 1381

Chapman, Amy, AIGA, the professional association for design, 222 Broadway, New York, NY 10038 *Tel:* 212-807-1990 *Fax:* 212-807-1799 *E-mail:* general@aiga.org *Web Site:* www.aiga.org, pg 1133

Chapman, Kristen, Indigo Books & Music Inc, 468 King St W, Suite 500, Toronto, ON M5V 1L8, Canada *Tel:* 416-364-4499 *E-mail:* cisales@indigo.ca *Web Site:* www.chapters.indigo.ca, pg 1290

Chapnick, Benjamin J, Black Star Publishing Co, 333 Mamaroneck Ave, Suite 175, White Plains, NY 10605 *Tel:* 212-679-3288 *Fax:* 212-889-2052 *Web Site:* www.blackstar.com, pg 1445

Chapnick, John P, Black Star Publishing Co, 333 Mamaroneck Ave, Suite 175, White Plains, NY 10605 *Tel:* 212-679-3288 *Fax:* 212-889-2052 *Web Site:* www.blackstar.com, pg 1445

Chappell, John, Lumina Datamatics Inc, 4 Collins Ave, Plymouth, MA 02360 *Tel:* 508-746-0300 *Fax:* 508-746-3233 *Web Site:* luminadatamatics.com, pg 1207, 1222, 1349, 1359, 1380, 1430

Chappo, Louis, GTI Graphic Technology Inc, 211 Dupont Ave, Newburgh, NY 12550 *Tel:* 845-562-7066 *Fax:* 845-562-2543 *E-mail:* sales@gtilite.com *Web Site:* www.gtilite.com, pg 1276, 1378

Charlebois, Rob, Corel Corp, 1600 Carling Ave, Ottawa, ON K1Z 8R7, Canada *Tel:* 613-728-8200 (PR) *Toll Free Tel:* 877-582-6735 *Web Site:* www.corel.com, pg 1375

Corder, Jennifer D, Corder Associates Inc, 2602 W Baseline Rd, Suite 22, Mesa, AZ 85202 *Tel:* 480-752-8533 *Toll Free Tel:* 877-303-7575 *Fax:* 480-752-8534 *E-mail:* info@cordernet.com *Web Site:* cordernet.com, pg 1375

Corder, Kelly, Corder Associates Inc, 2602 W Baseline Rd, Suite 22, Mesa, AZ 85202 *Tel:* 480-752-8533 *Toll Free Tel:* 877-303-7575 *Fax:* 480-752-8534 *E-mail:* info@cordernet.com *Web Site:* cordernet.com, pg 1375

Coreno, Annie, Publishers Weekly, 71 W 23 St, Suite 1608, New York, NY 10010 *Tel:* 212-377-5500 *Fax:* 212-377-2733 *Web Site:* www.publishersweekly.com, pg 1130

Corey, Steve, Whitegate Features Syndicate, 71 Faunce Dr, Providence, RI 02906 *Tel:* 401-274-2149 *Web Site:* www.whitegatefeatures.com, pg 1186

Corkrean, John, H B Fuller Co, 1200 Willow Lake Blvd, St Paul, MN 55110-5146 *Tel:* 651-236-5900 *Toll Free Tel:* 888-423-8553 *E-mail:* inquiry@hbfuller.com *Web Site:* www.hbfuller.com, pg 1263, 1276

Cormier, Beth, Sappi Fine Paper North America, 255 State St, Boston, MA 02109 *Tel:* 617-423-7300 *Toll Free Tel:* 800-882-4332 *E-mail:* webqueriesna@sappi.com *Web Site:* www.sappi.com/na, pg 1267

Cornell, Merial, Cornell & Co LLC, 44 Jog Hill Rd, Trumbull, CT 06611 *Tel:* 203-454-4210 *Web Site:* www.cornellandco.com, pg 1426

Cornell, Mike, National Book Network (NBN), 4501 Forbes Blvd, Suite 200, Lanham, MD 20706 *Tel:* 301-459-3366 *Toll Free Tel:* 800-462-6420 (orders only) *Fax:* 301-429-5746 *Toll Free Fax:* 800-338-4550 (orders only) *E-mail:* customercare@nbnbooks.com *Web Site:* www.nbnbooks.com, pg 1293, 1318

Correa, Alex, Lectorum Publications Inc, 205 Chubb Ave, Lyndhurst, NJ 07071 *Tel:* 201-559-2200 *Toll Free Tel:* 800-345-5946 *Fax:* 201-559-2201 *Toll Free Fax:* 877-532-8676 *E-mail:* lectorum@lectorum.com *Web Site:* www.lectorum.com, pg 1316

Corrette, George, Pathway Book Service, 34 Production Ave, Keene, NH 03431 *Tel:* 603-357-0236 *Toll Free Tel:* 800-345-6665 *Fax:* 603-965-2181 *E-mail:* pbs@pathwaybook.com *Web Site:* www.pathwaybook.com, pg 1319

Corsa, Bill, Studio 31 Inc, 2740 SW Martin Downs Blvd, Suite 358, Palm City, FL 34990 *Tel:* 772-781-7195 *Fax:* 772-781-6044 *Web Site:* www.studio31.com, pg 1226, 1362

Corsa, William L, Specialty Book Marketing Inc, 87-80 115 St, Richmond Hill, NY 11418 *Tel:* 212-696-0415 *Fax:* 718-849-5131 *Web Site:* www.specialtybooks.com, pg 1352

Corsi, Mark, PMSI Direct, 242 Old New Brunswick Rd, Suite 350, Piscataway, NJ 08854 *Tel:* 732-465-1570 *Toll Free Tel:* 800-238-1316 *Web Site:* www.pmsidirect.com, pg 1109

Cosentino, Jay, Computer Analytics Corp, 999 E Touhy Ave, Suite 130, Des Plaines, IL 60018-2736 *Tel:* 847-297-5290 *Fax:* 847-297-8680 *Web Site:* www.cacorp.com, pg 1374

Cotera, Marjorie Kamys, Bob Daemmrich Photography Inc, 914 Congress Ave, 2nd fl, Austin, TX 78701 *Tel:* 512-469-9700 *Fax:* 512-469-9713 *Web Site:* www.bobphoto.com, pg 1437

Cotter, Sean, Nancy Warner Photographer, 10 Vinton Ct, San Francisco, CA 94108-2407 *Tel:* 415-989-9157 *Fax:* 415-989-9157 *E-mail:* nancy.warner@gmail.com *Web Site:* www.warnerphoto.com, pg 1443

Cottle, Aaron, The Master's Press, 14550 Midway Rd, Dallas, TX 75244 *Tel:* 972-387-0046 *Fax:* 972-404-0317 *Web Site:* www.themasterspress.com, pg 1251

Coughlin, Tim, Translations.com, 3 Park Ave, 39th fl, New York, NY 10016 *Tel:* 212-689-5555 *Fax:* 212-689-1059 *E-mail:* newyork@transperfect.com; info@translations.com *Web Site:* www.translations.com, pg 1414

Courter, Gay, Courter Films LLC, 1145 N Stoney Point, Crystal River, FL 34429 *Tel:* 352-563-7888 (cell) *Fax:* 352-795-3889 *E-mail:* info@courterfilms.com *Web Site:* www.courterfilms.com, pg 1375

Courter, Philip R, Courter Films LLC, 1145 N Stoney Point, Crystal River, FL 34429 *Tel:* 352-563-7888 (cell) *Fax:* 352-795-3889 *E-mail:* info@courterfilms.com *Web Site:* www.courterfilms.com, pg 1375

Couturier, Greg, Arizona Library Binding Service, 1337 W McKinley, Phoenix, AZ 85007 *Tel:* 602-253-1861 *E-mail:* info@azlbinding.com, pg 1323

Couturier, Tom, Arizona Library Binding Service, 1337 W McKinley, Phoenix, AZ 85007 *Tel:* 602-253-1861 *E-mail:* info@azlbinding.com, pg 1323

Covas, Laura, Copywriters' Council of America™ (CCA), CCA Bldg, 7 Putter Lane, Middle Island, NY 11953-1920 *Tel:* 631-924-3888; 631-924-8555; 631-604-8599, pg 1344

Cowles, Gregory, The New York Times Book Review, 620 Eighth Ave, 5th fl, New York, NY 10018 *Tel:* 212-556-1234 *Toll Free Tel:* 800-631-2580 (subns) *E-mail:* bookreview@nytimes.com; books@nytimes.com *Web Site:* www.nytimes.com, pg 1129

Cox, Bryan A, ABDI Inc, 16 Avenue "A", Leetsdale, PA 15056 *Toll Free Tel:* 800-796-6471 *Fax:* 412-741-4161 *E-mail:* e-fulfillment@abdintl.com *Web Site:* www.abdi-ecommerce10.com/abdintl; www.abdintl.com/abdintl, pg 1109, 1201, 1331

Cox, Dennis, ChinaStock/WorldViews, 2506 Country Village, Ann Arbor, MI 48103-6500 *Tel:* 734-680-4660 *E-mail:* decoxphoto@gmail.com *Web Site:* www.denniscox.com, pg 1445

Cox, James A, Children's Bookwatch, 278 Orchard Dr, Oregon, WI 53575-1129 *Tel:* 608-835-7937 *E-mail:* mbr@execpc.com *Web Site:* www.midwestbookreview.com, pg 1125

Cox, James A, Internet Bookwatch, 278 Orchard Dr, Oregon, WI 53575-1129 *Tel:* 608-835-7937 *E-mail:* mbr@execpc.com *Web Site:* www.midwestbookreview.com, pg 1127

Cox, James A, Library Bookwatch, 278 Orchard Dr, Oregon, WI 53575-1129 *Tel:* 608-835-7937 *E-mail:* mbr@execpc.com *Web Site:* www.midwestbookreview.com, pg 1128

Cox, James A, MBR Bookwatch, 278 Orchard Dr, Oregon, WI 53575-1129 *Tel:* 608-835-7937 *E-mail:* mbr@execpc.com *Web Site:* www.midwestbookreview.com, pg 1129

Cox, James A, The Midwest Book Review, 278 Orchard Dr, Oregon, WI 53575-1129 *Tel:* 608-835-7937 *E-mail:* mbr@execpc.com; mwbookrevw@aol.com *Web Site:* www.midwestbookreview.com, pg 1129

Cox, James A, Reviewer Bookwatch, 278 Orchard Dr, Oregon, WI 53575-1129 *Tel:* 608-835-7937 *E-mail:* mbr@execpc.com *Web Site:* www.midwestbookreview.com, pg 1131

Cox, James A, Small Press Bookwatch, 278 Orchard Dr, Oregon, WI 53575-1129 *Tel:* 608-835-7937 *E-mail:* mbr@execpc.com *Web Site:* www.midwestbookreview.com, pg 1131

Cox, James A, Wisconsin Bookwatch, 278 Orchard Dr, Oregon, WI 53575-1129 *Tel:* 608-835-7937 *E-mail:* mbr@execpc.com *Web Site:* www.midwestbookreview.com, pg 1132

Cox, Jennifer, Kelmscott, a Fuse LLC company, 5656 McDermott Dr, Berkeley, IL 60163 *Tel:* 630-898-4261 *Web Site:* www.kelmscott.com, pg 1206, 1222, 1380

Cox, Joseph A, National Library Bindery Co of Indiana Inc (NLBCo), 55 S State Ave, Suite 100, Indianapolis, IN 46201 *Tel:* 317-636-5606 *E-mail:* nlbco@nlbco.com *Web Site:* www.nlbco.com, pg 1324

Cox, Laura, ProtoView, 7515 NE Ambassador Place, Suite A, Portland, OR 97220 *Tel:* 503-281-9230 *E-mail:* info@protoview.com *Web Site:* www.protoview.com, pg 1140

Coyne, Stephen P, Eastern Book Co, 7 Lincoln Ave, Scarborough, ME 04074 *Tel:* 207-856-1370 *Toll Free Tel:* 800-937-0331 *Toll Free Fax:* 800-214-3895 *E-mail:* info@ebc.com; sales@ebc.com *Web Site:* www.ebc.com, pg 1313

Cozzi-James, Christine, Copyright Clearance Center Inc (CCC), 222 Rosewood Dr, Danvers, MA 01923 *Tel:* 978-750-8400 (sales); 978-646-2600 (cust serv) *E-mail:* info@copyright.com *Web Site:* www.copyright.com, pg 1344

Craig, David L, Paperbacks For Educators, 426 W Front St, Washington, MO 63090 *Tel:* 314-960-3015 *E-mail:* paperbacks@usmo.com *Web Site:* www.any-book-in-print.com, pg 1318

Craig, Sean, Maxcess International, 222 W Memorial Rd, Oklahoma City, OK 73114 *Tel:* 405-755-1600 *Toll Free Tel:* 800-639-3433 *Fax:* 405-755-8425 *E-mail:* sales@maxcessintl.com *Web Site:* www.maxcessintl.com, pg 1278

Crain, Christopher, Crain Communications Inc, 1155 Gratiot Ave, Detroit, MI 48207-2732 *Tel:* 313-446-6000 *Fax:* 313-446-0383 *E-mail:* info@crain.com *Web Site:* crain.com, pg 1184

Crain, K C, Crain Communications Inc, 1155 Gratiot Ave, Detroit, MI 48207-2732 *Tel:* 313-446-6000 *Fax:* 313-446-0383 *E-mail:* info@crain.com *Web Site:* crain.com, pg 1184

Crain, Keith, Crain Communications Inc, 1155 Gratiot Ave, Detroit, MI 48207-2732 *Tel:* 313-446-6000 *Fax:* 313-446-0383 *E-mail:* info@crain.com *Web Site:* crain.com, pg 1184

Cramer, Phoebe, Publishers Weekly, 71 W 23 St, Suite 1608, New York, NY 10010 *Tel:* 212-377-5500 *Fax:* 212-377-2733 *Web Site:* www.publishersweekly.com, pg 1130

Crawford, Daniel, TranslateMedia, 27 W 24 St, New York, NY 10010 *Tel:* 212-796-5636 *E-mail:* web@translatemedia.com *Web Site:* www.translatemedia.com, pg 1414

Crawford, Sterling, Ingram Content Group LLC, One Ingram Blvd, La Vergne, TN 37086-1986 *Tel:* 615-793-5000 *Toll Free Tel:* 800-937-8000 (retailers); 800-937-5300 (ext 1, libs) *E-mail:* customerservice@ingramcontent.com *Web Site:* www.ingramcontent.com, pg 1290, 1315

Crawshaw, Todd, Crawshaw Design, 120 Bayview Dr, San Rafael, CA 94901 *Tel:* 415-456-5544 *Fax:* 415-456-4319 *Web Site:* www.crawshawdesign.com, pg 1426

Creasy, Sally, Specialty Product Technologies, 2100 W Broad St, Elizabethtown, NC 28337 *Tel:* 910-862-2511 *Toll Free Tel:* 800-390-6405 *Fax:* 910-879-5486 *E-mail:* customer.service@sptech.com *Web Site:* www.specialtyproducttechnologies.com, pg 1279

Crecca, Paul J, Westchester Publishing Services, 4 Old Newtown Rd, Danbury, CT 06810 *Tel:* 203-791-0080 *Fax:* 203-791-9286 *E-mail:* info@westchesterpubsvcs.com *Web Site:* www.westchesterpublishingservices.com, pg 1227

Crilly, Donna, Paulist Press, 997 Macarthur Blvd, Mahwah, NJ 07430-9990 *Tel:* 201-825-7300 *Toll Free Tel:* 800-218-1903 *Fax:* 201-825-6921 *Toll Free Fax:* 800-836-3161 *E-mail:* info@paulistpress.com *Web Site:* www.paulistpress.com, pg 1319

Crilly, Donna, Paulist Press, 997 Macarthur Blvd, Mahwah, NJ 07430-9990 *Tel:* 201-825-7300 *Toll Free Tel:* 800-218-1903 *Fax:* 201-825-6921 *Toll Free Fax:* 800-836-3161 *E-mail:* info@paulistpress.com; publicity@paulistpress.com *Web Site:* www.paulistpress.com, pg 1383

Cripps, Paul, Electronics for Imaging Inc (EFI), 6750 Dumbarton Circle, Fremont, CA 94555 *Tel:* 650-357-3500 *Toll Free Tel:* 800-568-1917; 800-875-7117 (sales) *Fax:* 650-357-3907 *E-mail:* info@efi.com *Web Site:* www.efi.com, pg 1377

Crochetiere, Chris, BW&A Books Inc, 112 W McClanahan St, Oxford, NC 27565 *Tel:* 919-956-9111 *Fax:* 919-956-9112 *E-mail:* bwa@bwabooks.com *Web Site:* www.bwabooks.com, pg 1217

Crockett, Samuel, Worzalla, 3535 Jefferson St, Stevens Point, WI 54481 *Tel:* 715-344-9608 *Fax:* 715-344-2578 *Web Site:* www.worzalla.com, pg 1210, 1228, 1257

Cronshaw, Francine, East Mountain Editing Services, PO Box 1895, Tijeras, NM 87059-1895 *Tel:* 505-281-8422 *Web Site:* www.spanishindexing.com, pg 1219

Croom, Darren, Texas Book Co, 8501 Technology Circle, Greenville, TX 75402 *Tel:* 903-455-6969 *Toll Free Tel:* 800-527-1016 *E-mail:* customerservice@texasbook.com *Web Site:* www.texasbook.com, pg 1321

Cross, Tim, Westchester Publishing Services, 4 Old Newtown Rd, Danbury, CT 06810 *Tel:* 203-791-0080 *Fax:* 203-791-9286 *E-mail:* info@westchesterpubsvcs.com *Web Site:* www.westchesterpublishingservices.com, pg 1227

Crowell, David, AIMS International Books Inc, 7709 Hamilton Ave, Cincinnati, OH 45231 *Tel:* 513-521-5590 *Fax:* 513-521-5592 *E-mail:* info@aimsbooks.com *Web Site:* www.aimsbooks.com, pg 1282

Crowell, Georgia W, AIMS International Books Inc, 7709 Hamilton Ave, Cincinnati, OH 45231 *Tel:* 513-521-5590 *Fax:* 513-521-5592 *E-mail:* info@aimsbooks.com *Web Site:* www.aimsbooks.com, pg 1282

Crowley, Alex, Publishers Weekly, 71 W 23 St, Suite 1608, New York, NY 10010 *Tel:* 212-377-5500 *Fax:* 212-377-2733 *Web Site:* www.publishersweekly.com, pg 1130

Crowley, Kevin, The Crowley Co, 5111 Pegasus Ct, Suite M, Frederick, MD 21704 *Tel:* 240-215-0224 *Fax:* 240-215-0234 *E-mail:* webrequest@thecrowleycompany.com *Web Site:* www.thecrowleycompany.com, pg 1375

Crowley, Pat, The Crowley Co, 5111 Pegasus Ct, Suite M, Frederick, MD 21704 *Tel:* 240-215-0224 *Fax:* 240-215-0234 *E-mail:* webrequest@thecrowleycompany.com *Web Site:* www.thecrowleycompany.com, pg 1375

Croy, Michael, Consortium Book Sales & Distribution, an Ingram brand, The Keg House, Suite 101, 34 13 Ave NE, Minneapolis, MN 55413-1007 *Tel:* 612-746-2600 *Toll Free Tel:* 800-283-3572 (cust serv, Jackson, TN) *Fax:* 612-746-2606 *E-mail:* info@cbsd.com *Web Site:* www.cbsd.com, pg 1285

Crystal, Scott M, American Translation Partners Inc (ATP), 175 Paramount Dr, Raynham, MA 02767 *Tel:* 508-823-8892 *Toll Free Tel:* 888-443-2376 *Fax:* 508-823-8854 *E-mail:* info@americantranslationpartners.com *Web Site:* www.americantranslationpartners.com, pg 1407

Cucciniello, John, Direct Link™ Worldwide Inc, 700 Dowd Ave, Elizabeth, NJ 07201 *Tel:* 908-289-0703 *Toll Free Tel:* 800-223-7967 *Fax:* 908-289-0705 *E-mail:* infousa@directlink.com *Web Site:* www.directlink.com, pg 1331

Cude, Bobby Lee, Times-Square Fantasy Theatre, 519 N Halifax Ave, Daytona Beach, FL 32118 *Tel:* 386-252-0381 *Fax:* 386-252-0381 *E-mail:* timessquare@bellsouth.net *Web Site:* www.broadwaymusicdownload.com; www.timessquarefantasytheatre.com, pg 1387

Cue, Eddy, Apple Inc, One Apple Park Way, Cupertino, CA 95014 *Tel:* 408-996-1010 *Web Site:* www.apple.com, pg 1372

Cullen, Teddee, Apex Die Corp, 840 Cherry Lane, San Carlos, CA 94070 *Tel:* 650-592-6350 *Fax:* 650-592-5315 *E-mail:* info@apexdie.com *Web Site:* www.apexdie.com, pg 1242

Culver, Russ, Whitehots Inc, 205 Industrial Pkwy N, Unit 3, Aurora, ON L4G 4C4, Canada *Tel:* 905-727-9188 *Toll Free Tel:* 888-567-9188 *Fax:* 905-727-8756 *Toll Free Fax:* 888-563-0020 *E-mail:* admin@whitehots.com *Web Site:* www.whitehots.com, pg 1322

Culver, Sharon, Whitehots Inc, 205 Industrial Pkwy N, Unit 3, Aurora, ON L4G 4C4, Canada *Tel:* 905-727-9188 *Toll Free Tel:* 888-567-9188 *Fax:* 905-727-8756 *Toll Free Fax:* 888-563-0020 *E-mail:* admin@whitehots.com *Web Site:* www.whitehots.com, pg 1322

Cummings, Eva, Apex Die Corp, 840 Cherry Lane, San Carlos, CA 94070 *Tel:* 650-592-6350 *Fax:* 650-592-5315 *E-mail:* info@apexdie.com *Web Site:* www.apexdie.com, pg 1242

Cummings, Mark, CHOICE, 575 Main St, Suite 300, Middletown, CT 06457 *Tel:* 860-347-6933; 860-347-1387 (ad); 240-646-7027 (subn); 818-487-4555 *E-mail:* acrlsubscriptions@pubservice.com; support@acrlchoice.freshdesk.com *Web Site:* www.ala.org/acrl/choice; www.choice360.org, pg 1125

Cunningham, Brent, Small Press Distribution Inc, 1341 Seventh St, Berkeley, CA 94710-1409 *Tel:* 510-524-1668 *Toll Free Tel:* 800-869-7553 (within the US) *Fax:* 510-524-0852 *E-mail:* spd@spdbooks.org *Web Site:* www.spdbooks.org, pg 1298

Curley, Sandra, The Supreme Co, 1909 Lagneaux Rd, Lafayette, LA 70506 *Tel:* 337-453-1028 *Toll Free Tel:* 888-600-4180 *E-mail:* information@supremebooks.com *Web Site:* www.supremebooks.com, pg 1321

Curran, Kevin, SITMA USA Inc, 45 Empire Dr, St Paul, MN 55103-1856 *Tel:* 651-222-2324 *Fax:* 651-222-4652 *E-mail:* sales@sitma.com *Web Site:* www.sitma.it, pg 1279

Curtis, Ralph C, Ralph Curtis Books, 16956 McGregor Blvd, Suite 9, Fort Myers, FL 33908 *Tel:* 239-454-0010 *Fax:* 239-395-2727 *E-mail:* rcurtisbks@yahoo.com *Web Site:* www.ralphcurtisbooks.com, pg 1312, 1326

Curva, Laure, Bashian & Associates Inc, 28915 S Village Lane, Glenwillow, OH 44139 *E-mail:* adsales@bashian.com *Web Site:* www.bashian.com, pg 1342

Cushing, Connie M, Cushing-Malloy Inc, 1350 N Main St, Ann Arbor, MI 48104-1045 *Tel:* 734-663-8554 *Fax:* 734-663-5731 *Web Site:* www.cushing-malloy.com; www.c-mbooks.com, pg 1203, 1245

Cushinsky, Steven M, ACT ONE Mailing List Services Inc, 237 Washington St, 2nd fl, Marblehead, MA 01945-3334 *Tel:* 781-639-1919 *Toll Free Tel:* 800-ACT-LIST (228-5478) *Fax:* 781-639-2733 *E-mail:* info@act1lists.com *Web Site:* www.act1lists.com, pg 1111

Cushman, Tori, Ingram Content Group LLC, One Ingram Blvd, La Vergne, TN 37086-1986 *Tel:* 615-793-5000 *Toll Free Tel:* 800-937-8000 (retailers); 800-937-5300 (ext 1, libs) *E-mail:* customerservice@ingramcontent.com *Web Site:* www.ingramcontent.com, pg 1290, 1315

Cusick, Kate, Porter Novelli, 195 Broadway, 17th fl, New York, NY 10007 *Tel:* 212-601-8000 *Web Site:* www.porternovelli.com, pg 1100

Cusson, Charles, Les Messageries ADP, 2315, rue de la Province, Longueuil, QC J4G 1G4, Canada *Tel:* 450-640-1234 (commercial); 450-640-1237 (sales) *Toll Free Tel:* 800-771-3022 (commercial); 866-874-1237 (sales) *Fax:* 450-640-1251 (commercial); 450-674-6237 (sales) *Toll Free Fax:* 800-603-0433 (commercial); 866-874-6237 (sales) *E-mail:* adpcommandes@messageries-adp.com *Web Site:* www.messageries-adp.com, pg 1281

Custard, Jill, The Ovid Bell Press Inc, 1201 Bluff St, Fulton, MO 65251 *Tel:* 573-642-2256 *Toll Free Tel:* 800-835-8919 *E-mail:* sales@ovidbell.com *Web Site:* ovidbell.com, pg 1224, 1252, 1266, 1278

Czerwinski, Diane, Scientific Bindery Inc, 8052 Monticello Ave, Suite 206, Skokie, IL 60076 *Tel:* 847-329-0510 *Fax:* 847-329-0608 *E-mail:* info@scientificbindery.com *Web Site:* www.scientificbindery.com, pg 1254

D'Angelo, Allen, Bookcovers.com, c/o Archer Ellison Inc, 7025 CR 46-A, Suite 1071, Lake Mary, FL 32746 *Toll Free Tel:* 800-449-4095 (ext 702) *Toll Free Fax:* 800-366-4086 *E-mail:* info@bookcovers.com *Web Site:* bookcovers.com, pg 1425

D'Angelo, Louise, Maryheart Crusaders Inc, 531 W Main St, Meriden, CT 06451-2707 *Tel:* 203-238-9735 *Toll Free Tel:* 800-879-1957 (orders only) *Fax:* 203-235-0059 *E-mail:* maryheart@msn.com *Web Site:* www.maryheartcrusaders.com, pg 1137

D'Angelo, Michael, Maryheart Crusaders Inc, 531 W Main St, Meriden, CT 06451-2707 *Tel:* 203-238-9735 *Toll Free Tel:* 800-879-1957 (orders only) *Fax:* 203-235-0059 *E-mail:* maryheart@msn.com *Web Site:* www.maryheartcrusaders.com, pg 1137

D'Antonio, Ray, St Joseph Communications-Print Group, 50 Macintosh Blvd, Concord, ON L4K 4P3, Canada *Tel:* 905-660-3111 *E-mail:* marketing@stjoseph.com *Web Site:* stjoseph.com, pg 1093, 1254

D'Aquila, Greg, Dunhill International List Co Inc, 6400 Congress Ave, Suite 1750, Boca Raton, FL 33487-2898 *Tel:* 561-998-7800 *Toll Free Tel:* 800-DUNHILL (386-4455) *Fax:* 561-998-7880 *E-mail:* dunhill@dunhillintl.com *Web Site:* www.dunhills.com, pg 1112

D'Onofrio, Joe, Chicago Distribution Center (CDC), 11030 S Langley Ave, Chicago, IL 60628 *Tel:* 773-702-7010 *Toll Free Tel:* 800-621-8476 *Web Site:* press.uchicago.edu/cdc, pg 1285

Daemmrich, Bob, Bob Daemmrich Photography Inc, 914 Congress Ave, 2nd fl, Austin, TX 78701 *Tel:* 512-469-9700 *Fax:* 512-469-9713 *Web Site:* www.bobphoto.com, pg 1437

Daemmrich, Janis, Bob Daemmrich Photography Inc, 914 Congress Ave, 2nd fl, Austin, TX 78701 *Tel:* 512-469-9700 *Fax:* 512-469-9713 *Web Site:* www.bobphoto.com, pg 1437

Daigneault, Yves, Cooperative Etudiante de Polytechnique, Pavillon Principal Local C-220, 2900 Edouard Mont Petit, Montreal, QC H3T 1J4, Canada *Tel:* 514-340-4851 *Fax:* 514-340-4543 *E-mail:* andre.daneau@polymtl.ca *Web Site:* www.coopoly.ca, pg 1312

Daniels, Tracey, Media Masters Publicity, 61 Depot St, Tryon, NC 28782 *Tel:* 828-859-9456 *E-mail:* info@mmpublicity.com *Web Site:* www.mmpublicity.com, pg 1099, 1350

Danziger, Karen, Koller Search Partners, 655 Third Ave, 24th fl, New York, NY 10017 *Tel:* 212-661-5250 *E-mail:* ksp@kollersearch.com *Web Site:* www.kollersearch.com, pg 1389

Daubert, Fred, Universal Bookbindery Inc, 1200 N Colorado, San Antonio, TX 78207 *Tel:* 210-734-9502 *Toll Free Tel:* 800-594-2015 *Fax:* 210-736-0867 *E-mail:* service@universalbookbindery.com *Web Site:* www.universalbookbindery.com, pg 1256

Daughtry, John, LOF Productions, 121 Greenwich Rd, Suite 202, Charlotte, NC 28211 *Tel:* 704-375-8892 *Fax:* 704-375-6316 *Web Site:* www.lofproductions.com, pg 1441

Dauphin, Brian, Ingram Content Group LLC, One Ingram Blvd, La Vergne, TN 37086-1986 *Tel:* 615-793-5000 *Toll Free Tel:* 800-937-8000 (retailers); 800-937-5300 (ext 1, libs) *E-mail:* customerservice@ingramcontent.com *Web Site:* www.ingramcontent.com, pg 1290, 1315

Dauphin, Brian, Lightning Source LLC, 1246 Heil Quaker Blvd, La Vergne, TN 37086 *Tel:* 615-793-5000 (Ingram) *Toll Free Tel:* 800-378-5508; 800-509-4156 (cust serv) *E-mail:* lsicustomersupport@ingramcontent.com; contentacquisitioninquiries@ingramcontent.com *Web Site:* www.ingramcontent.com/publishers/print, pg 1207

Dauphin, Brian, Lightning Source LLC, 1246 Heil Quaker Blvd, La Vergne, TN 37086 *Tel:* 615-793-5000 (Ingram) *Toll Free Tel:* 800-378-5508; 800-509-4156 (cust serv) *E-mail:* lsicustomersupport@ingramcontent.com *Web Site:* www.ingramcontent.com/publishers/print, pg 1250, 1380

Davey, Kate, Chicago Distribution Center (CDC), 11030 S Langley Ave, Chicago, IL 60628 *Tel:* 773-702-7010 *Toll Free Fax:* 800-621-8476 *Web Site:* press.uchicago.edu/cdc, pg 1285

Davidson, Brian, Wood & Associates Direct Marketing Services Ltd, 9-1410 Bayly St, Pickering, ON L1W 3R3, Canada *Tel:* 416-293-2511 *Fax:* 416-293-2594 *E-mail:* clientservices@wood-and-associates.com *Web Site:* www.wood-and-associates.com, pg 1333

Defino, Frank Sr, Tukaiz LLC, 2917 N Latoria Lane, Franklin Park, IL 60131 *Tel:* 847-455-1588; 847-288-4968 (sales) *Toll Free Tel:* 800-543-2674 *E-mail:* contacttukaiz@tukaiz.com *Web Site:* www.tukaiz.com, pg 1227

Defino, Frank Jr, Tukaiz LLC, 2917 N Latoria Lane, Franklin Park, IL 60131 *Tel:* 847-455-1588; 847-288-4968 (sales) *Toll Free Tel:* 800-543-2674 *E-mail:* contacttukaiz@tukaiz.com *Web Site:* www.tukaiz.com, pg 1256

Defino, Frank Sr, Tukaiz LLC, 2917 N Latoria Lane, Franklin Park, IL 60131 *Tel:* 847-455-1588; 847-288-4968 (sales) *Toll Free Tel:* 800-543-2674 *E-mail:* contacttukaiz@tukaiz.com *Web Site:* www.tukaiz.com, pg 1256

Defino, Frank Jr, Tukaiz LLC, 2917 N Latoria Lane, Franklin Park, IL 60131 *Tel:* 847-455-1588; 847-288-4968 (sales) *Toll Free Tel:* 800-543-2674 *E-mail:* contacttukaiz@tukaiz.com *Web Site:* www.tukaiz.com, pg 1269

Defino, Frank Sr, Tukaiz LLC, 2917 N Latoria Lane, Franklin Park, IL 60131 *Tel:* 847-455-1588; 847-288-4968 (sales) *Toll Free Tel:* 800-543-2674 *E-mail:* contacttukaiz@tukaiz.com *Web Site:* www.tukaiz.com, pg 1269

Defino, Frank Jr, Tukaiz LLC, 2917 N Latoria Lane, Franklin Park, IL 60131 *Tel:* 847-455-1588; 847-288-4968 (sales) *Toll Free Tel:* 800-543-2674 *E-mail:* contacttukaiz@tukaiz.com *Web Site:* www.tukaiz.com, pg 1280

Defino, Frank Sr, Tukaiz LLC, 2917 N Latoria Lane, Franklin Park, IL 60131 *Tel:* 847-455-1588; 847-288-4968 (sales) *Toll Free Tel:* 800-543-2674 *E-mail:* contacttukaiz@tukaiz.com *Web Site:* www.tukaiz.com, pg 1280

Deger, Dave, Twin Rivers Paper Co, 82 Bridge Ave, Madawaska, ME 04756 *Tel:* 207-728-3321 *Toll Free Tel:* 800-920-9988 *Fax:* 207-728-8701 *E-mail:* info@twinriverspaper.com *Web Site:* www.twinriverspaper.com, pg 1269

DeHamer, Steve, Springdale Bindery LLC, 11411 Landan Lane, Cincinnati, OH 45246 *Tel:* 513-772-8500 *E-mail:* info@springdalebindery.com *Web Site:* www.springdalebindery.com, pg 1255

DeHart, Don, DeHART's Media Services Inc, 6586 Whitbourne Dr, San Jose, CA 95120 *Tel:* 408-768-1575 *Web Site:* www.deharts.com, pg 1245

Dehmler, Mari Lynch, Fine Wordworking, PO Box 3041, Monterey, CA 93942-3041 *Tel:* 831-375-6278 *E-mail:* info@finewordworking.com *Web Site:* marilynch.com, pg 1393

Dekker, Chris, Dekker Bookbinding Inc, 2941 Clydon Ave SW, Grand Rapids, MI 49519 *Tel:* 616-538-5160 *Toll Free Tel:* 800-299-BIND (299-2463) *E-mail:* hello@dekkerbook.com *Web Site:* www.dekkerbook.com, pg 1245, 1262

Dekker, Corbin, Dekker Bookbinding Inc, 2941 Clydon Ave SW, Grand Rapids, MI 49519 *Tel:* 616-538-5160 *Toll Free Tel:* 800-299-BIND (299-2463) *E-mail:* hello@dekkerbook.com *Web Site:* www.dekkerbook.com, pg 1245, 1262

del Commune, Lauri, Del Commune Enterprises Inc, 307 Seventh Ave, Suite 807, New York, NY 10001 *Tel:* 212-226-6664 *E-mail:* mail@dcescouts.com *Web Site:* www.dcescouts.com, pg 1344

Delafosse, Isabelle, Jeff Rotman Photography, 53 Green Ave, Lawrenceville, NJ 08648 *Tel:* 609-219-0040 *Fax:* 609-219-1595 *E-mail:* contact@jeffrotman.com *Web Site:* www.jeffrotman.com, pg 1442

Delanoy, Randy, ColorPage, 81 Ten Broeck Ave, Kingston, NY 12401 *Tel:* 845-331-7581 *Toll Free Tel:* 800-836-7581 *Fax:* 845-331-1571 *E-mail:* sales@colorpageonline.com *Web Site:* www.colorpageonline.com, pg 1203, 1218, 1244, 1261

DeLetto, Ralph, Midland Paper, Packaging & Supplies, 101 E Palatine Rd, Wheeling, IL 60090 *Tel:* 847-777-2700 *Toll Free Tel:* 800-323-8522; 888-564-3526 (cust serv) *Fax:* 847-403-6320 (cust serv)

E-mail: whl@midlandpaper.com; sales@midlandpaper.com; custservice@midlandpaper.com *Web Site:* www.midlandpaper.com, pg 1265

Delgado, Lisa, Delgado & Co Inc, 3900 Greystone Ave, Suite 21A, Riverdale, NY 10463 *Tel:* 718-708-4419 *E-mail:* mail@delgadoandcompany.com *Web Site:* www.delgadoandcompany.com, pg 1357, 1427

Delimont, Danita, Danita Delimont Stock Photography, 4911 Somerset Dr SE, Bellevue, WA 98006 *Tel:* 425-562-1543 *Fax:* 425-373-5316 *Web Site:* www.danitadelimont.com, pg 1446

Dell, Michael S, Dell Wyse, One Dell Way, Round Rock, TX 78682 *Toll Free Tel:* 866-438-3622 (sales) *Web Site:* www.delltechnologies.com, pg 1376

Delmonico, Ralph R Jr, D3Logic Inc, 89 Commercial Way, East Providence, RI 02915 *Tel:* 401-435-4300 *Toll Free Tel:* 844-385-5388 *E-mail:* contact@d3-inc.com *Web Site:* www.d3-inc.com, pg 1246

Delquie, Emilie, Copyright Clearance Center Inc (CCC), 222 Rosewood Dr, Danvers, MA 01923 *Tel:* 978-750-8400 (sales); 978-646-2600 (cust serv) *E-mail:* info@copyright.com *Web Site:* www.copyright.com, pg 1344

DeLuca, Mike, Hearst Newspapers, 300 W 57 St, New York, NY 10019 *Tel:* 212-649-2000 *Web Site:* www.hearst.com/newspapers, pg 1185

DeMaestri, Adam, BR Printers, 665 Lenfest Rd, San Jose, CA 95133 *Tel:* 408-278-7711 *Fax:* 408-929-8062 *E-mail:* info@brprinters.com *Web Site:* www.brprinters.com, pg 1091, 1243

DeMatteo, Patti, JMW Group Inc, 347 Rte 6, No 867, Mahopac, NY 10541 *Tel:* 914-841-7105 *Fax:* 914-248-8861 *E-mail:* jmwgroup@jmwgroup.net *Web Site:* jmwforlife.com, pg 1348

Dembowski, Robert, City Diecutting, One Cory Rd, Morristown, NJ 07960 *Tel:* 973-270-0370 *Fax:* 973-270-0369 *E-mail:* sales@bookdisplays.com *Web Site:* www.bookdisplays.com, pg 1091, 1343

Deng, Cat, Eastwind Books & Arts Inc, 1435 Stockton St, San Francisco, CA 94133 *Tel:* 415-772-5888 *Fax:* 415-772-5885 *E-mail:* contact@eastwindbooks.com *Web Site:* www.eastwindbooks.com, pg 1313, 1326

Dennewitz-Hobson, Denise, GEI WideFormat, A Visual Edge Technology Company, 3874 Highland Park NW, North Canton, OH 44720 *Toll Free Tel:* 800-842-8448 (serv); 888-722-6434 (sales) *E-mail:* sales@geiwideformat.com *Web Site:* www.geiwideformat.com; www.visualedgetechnology.com, pg 1378

Dennis, Gil, Indigo Books & Music Inc, 468 King St W, Suite 500, Toronto, ON M5V 1L8, Canada *Tel:* 416-364-4499 *E-mail:* cisales@indigo.ca *Web Site:* chapters.indigo.ca, pg 1290

Dennys, Louise, Penguin Random House Canada, 320 Front St W, Suite 1400, Toronto, ON M5V 3B6, Canada *Tel:* 416-364-4449 *Toll Free Tel:* 888-523-9292 (cust serv) *Fax:* 416-598-7764 *Web Site:* www.penguinrandomhouse.ca, pg 1295

Deos, Tim, Copywriters' Council of America™ (CCA), CCA Bldg, 7 Putter Lane, Middle Island, NY 11953-1920 *Tel:* 631-924-3888; 631-924-8555; 631-604-8599, pg 1344

Derie, Kate, Mystery Readers Journal, 7155 Marlborough Terr, Berkeley, CA 94705 *Tel:* 510-845-3600 *Web Site:* www.mysteryreaders.org, pg 1129

Derkatsch, Erick, InterNation Inc, 299 Broadway, Suite 918, New York, NY 10007 *Tel:* 212-619-5545 *Toll Free Tel:* 800-222-8799 *Fax:* 212-619-5887 *E-mail:* info@internation.com *Web Site:* www.internation.com, pg 1410

Derosa, Peter, ALC Inc, 750 College Rd E, Suite 201, Princeton, NJ 08540 *Tel:* 609-580-2800 *Toll Free Tel:* 800-252-5478 *Fax:* 609-580-2888 *E-mail:* info@alc.com *Web Site:* www.alc.com, pg 1111

Dertien, Jon F, BookComp Inc, 6124 Belmont Ave NE, Belmont, MI 49306 *Tel:* 616-774-9700 *E-mail:* production@bookcomp.com *Web Site:* www.bookcomp.com, pg 1217, 1356

Deschenes, Luc, Le Messager Chretien (The Christian Messenger), 185 Gatineau Ave, Gatineau, QC J8T 4J7, Canada *Tel:* 819-243-8880 *Toll Free Tel:* 800-263-8086 *Fax:* 819-243-1220 *E-mail:* info@messagerchretien.com *Web Site:* www.messagerchretien.com, pg 1317

Desharnais, Jacques, Cooperative Etudiante de Polytechnique, Pavillon Principal Local C-220, 2900 Edouard Mont Petit, Montreal, QC H3T 1J4, Canada *Tel:* 514-340-4851 *Fax:* 514-340-4543 *E-mail:* andre.daneau@polymtl.ca *Web Site:* www.coopoly.ca, pg 1312

Desjardins, Francoise, Art Image Publications, PO Box 160, Derby Line, VT 05830 *Toll Free Tel:* 800-361-2598 *Toll Free Fax:* 800-559-2598 *E-mail:* customer.service@artimagepublications.com *Web Site:* www.artimagepublications.com, pg 1309

Deuel, Kim, Worzalla, 3535 Jefferson St, Stevens Point, WI 54481 *Tel:* 715-344-9608 *Fax:* 715-344-2578 *Web Site:* www.worzalla.com, pg 1210, 1228, 1257

Devereaux, Dorothy, Bascom Communications LLC, 200 E 72 St, Suite 6-L, New York, NY 10021-4500 *Tel:* 212-988-4212 *E-mail:* bascomllc@aol.com, pg 1355

Devereaux, William, Bascom Communications LLC, 200 E 72 St, Suite 6-L, New York, NY 10021-4500 *Tel:* 212-988-4212 *E-mail:* bascomllc@aol.com, pg 1355

DeVries, Peter, OmniUpdate Inc, 1320 Flynn Rd, Suite 100, Camarillo, CA 93012 *Tel:* 805-484-9400 *Toll Free Tel:* 800-362-2605 *E-mail:* sales@omniupdate.com *Web Site:* omniupdate.com, pg 1383

Dew, Allison, Dell Wyse, One Dell Way, Round Rock, TX 78682 *Toll Free Tel:* 866-438-3622 (sales) *Web Site:* www.delltechnologies.com, pg 1376

DeWeerd, Steve, Sheridan GR, 5100 33 St SE, Grand Rapids, MI 49512 *Tel:* 616-957-5100 *Web Site:* www.sheridan.com, pg 1209, 1254

DeWester, Nanette, Parkhurst Communications Inc, 11 Riverside Dr, Suite 1-TW, New York, NY 10023 *Tel:* 212-362-9722 *Web Site:* www.parkhurstcommunications.com, pg 1100

Dextor, Roger, Author's, Writer's & Book Publisher's Advice Line™, Communications Tower, 7 Putter Lane, Middle Island, NY 11953-1920 *Tel:* 631-924-3888; 631-924-8555; 631-604-8599 *E-mail:* topmarketingadvisor@gmail.com; awbpal@gmail.com *Web Site:* TopMarketingAdvisor.com, pg 1342

Dextor, Roger, Blitz Media-Direct, Linick Bldg, 7 Putter Lane, Middle Island, NY 11953 *Tel:* 631-924-3888; 631-924-8555; 630-604-8599 *E-mail:* blitz4pr@gmail.com; linickgroup@gmail.com, pg 1085, 1095, 1425

Dextor, Roger, Copywriters' Council of America™ (CCA), CCA Bldg, 7 Putter Lane, Middle Island, NY 11953-1920 *Tel:* 631-924-3888; 631-924-8555; 631-604-8599, pg 1086

Dextor, Roger, Copywriters' Council of America™ (CCA), CCA Bldg, 7 Putter Lane, Middle Island, NY 11953-1920 *Tel:* 631-924-3888; 631-604-8599; 631-924-8555, pg 1096

Dextor, Roger, Copywriters' Council of America™ (CCA), CCA Bldg, 7 Putter Lane, Middle Island, NY 11953-1920 *Tel:* 631-924-3888; 631-924-8555; 631-604-8599, pg 1106, 1344, 1356, 1375, 1426

Dextor, Roger, Andrew S Linick PhD, The Copyologist®, Linick Bldg, 7 Putter Lane, Middle Island, NY 11953 *Tel:* 631-924-3888; 631-924-8555; 631-604-8599 *E-mail:* linickgroup@gmail.com *Web Site:* topmarketingadvisor.com, pg 1106, 1348

Dextor, Roger, Linick International Inc, Linick Bldg, 7 Putter Lane, Middle Island, NY 11953 *Tel:* 631-924-3888; 631-924-8555; 631-604-8599 *E-mail:* topmarketingadvisor@gmail.com *Web Site:* topmarketingadvisor.com, pg 1222, 1349

1505

Dextor, Roger, LK Advertising Agency, Linick Bldg, 7 Putter Lane, Middle Island, NY 11953 *Tel:* 631-924-3888; 631-924-8555; 631-604-8599 *E-mail:* topmarketingadvisor@gmail.com *Web Site:* topmarketingadvisor.com, pg 1087, 1106, 1429

Dextor, Roger, LK Litho, Linick Bldg, 7 Putter Lane, Middle Island, NY 11953 *Tel:* 631-924-3888; 631-924-8555; 631-604-8599 *E-mail:* lklitho@mail.com; linickgroup@gmail.com *Web Site:* topmarketingadvisor.com, pg 1222

DeYoung, Christina, Harvard Educational Review, 8 Story St, 1st fl, Cambridge, MA 02138 *Tel:* 617-495-3432 *Toll Free Tel:* 888-437-1437 (orders) *Fax:* 617-496-3584; 978-348-1233 (orders) *Web Site:* hepg.org/her-home/home, pg 1126

Dhamee, Saleem, Chicago Distribution Center (CDC), 11030 S Langley Ave, Chicago, IL 60628 *Tel:* 773-702-7010 *Toll Free Fax:* 800-621-8476 *Web Site:* press.uchicago.edu/cdc, pg 1285

Di Leo, Jeffrey R, American Book Review, University of Houston-Victoria, School of Arts & Sciences, 3007 N Ben Wilson St, Victoria, TX 77901 *Tel:* 361-570-4848 *Fax:* 361-580-5507 *E-mail:* americanbookreview@uhv.org *Web Site:* americanbookreview.org, pg 1123

Di Silvio, Rich, Digital Vista Inc, 24 Amity Place, Massapequa, NY 11758 *Tel:* 516-799-5277 *E-mail:* info@digitalvista.net *Web Site:* www.digitalvista.net, pg 1427

Diamond, Steven, Steven Diamond Inc, 104 W 17 St, Suite 3-E, New York, NY 10011 *Tel:* 212-675-0723 *Fax:* 212-675-0762 *E-mail:* steven.diamond@verizon.net, pg 1345

Diarra, Alpha, appatura™, A Broadridge Company, 65 Challenger Rd, Suite 400, Ridgefield Park, NJ 07660 *Tel:* 201-508-6000 *Toll Free Tel:* 800-277-2155 *E-mail:* contactus@appatura.com *Web Site:* www.appatura.com, pg 1091, 1105, 1109, 1201, 1215, 1242

DiCanio, Theresa, Videojet Technologies Inc, 1500 N Mittel Blvd, Wood Dale, IL 60191-1073 *Tel:* 630-860-7300 *Toll Free Tel:* 800-843-3610 *Toll Free Fax:* 800-582-1343 *E-mail:* info@videojet.com *Web Site:* www.videojet.com, pg 1280

Dick, George C, Four Colour Print Group, 2410 Frankfort Ave, Louisville, KY 40206 *Tel:* 502-896-9644 *Fax:* 502-896-9594 *E-mail:* sales@fourcolour.com *Web Site:* www.fourcolour.com, pg 1204, 1247, 1276

Dick, Jason, CQ Roll Call, 1201 Pennsylvania Ave NW, Suite 600, Washington, DC 20004 *Tel:* 202-650-6500; 202-650-6511 (subns); 202-650-6621 (cust serv) *Toll Free Tel:* 800-432-2250; 800-678-8511 (subns) *E-mail:* customerservice@cqrollcall.com *Web Site:* cqrollcall.com; www.rollcall.com, pg 1184

Dickey, Bob, Gannett News Service, 7950 Jones Branch Dr, McLean, VA 22107-0150 *Tel:* 703-854-6000 *E-mail:* pr@gannett.com *Web Site:* www.gannett.com, pg 1184

Dickie, Matthew, Ingram Publisher Services, an Ingram brand, One Ingram Blvd, La Vergne, TN 37086 *Tel:* 615-793-5000 *Toll Free Tel:* 866-400-5351 (cust serv) *E-mail:* ips@ingramcontent.com *Web Site:* www.ingramcontent.com, pg 1290

Didona, Cathy, Didona Design, 160 Grandview Rd, Ardmore, PA 19003 *Tel:* 610-649-3110 *E-mail:* didona@didonadesign.com *Web Site:* www.didonadesign.com, pg 1219, 1427

Didona, Lawrence R, Didona Design, 160 Grandview Rd, Ardmore, PA 19003 *Tel:* 610-649-3110 *E-mail:* didona@didonadesign.com *Web Site:* www.didonadesign.com, pg 1219, 1427

Dieckman, Tom, Finch Paper LLC, One Glen St, Glens Falls, NY 12801 *Tel:* 518-793-2541 *Toll Free Tel:* 800-833-9983 *Fax:* 518-743-9656 *E-mail:* info@finchpaper.com *Web Site:* www.finchpaper.com, pg 1263

DiEdwardo, Tucker, Globe Photos LLC, 6445 S Tenaya Way, Suite B130, Las Vegas, NV 89113 *Tel:* 631-661-3131 *Fax:* 702-442-2747 *E-mail:* info@globephotos.com *Web Site:* www.globephotos.com, pg 1447

Dietz, Jeff, Koenig & Bauer (US) Inc, 2555 Regent Blvd, Dallas, TX 75229 *Tel:* 469-532-8000 *Fax:* 469-532-8190 *Web Site:* us.koenig-bauer.com, pg 1277

Diez, Laura, eStock Photo, 27-28 Thomson Ave, Suite 628, Long Island City, NY 11101 *Tel:* 212-689-5580 *Toll Free Tel:* 800-284-3399 *Fax:* 212-545-1185 *E-mail:* sales@estockphoto.com; info@estockphoto.com *Web Site:* www.estockphoto.com, pg 1446

Dill, Richard, Brodart Books & Library Services, 500 Arch St, Williamsport, PA 17701 *Tel:* 570-326-2461 *Toll Free Tel:* 800-233-8467 *Fax:* 570-651-1639 *Toll Free Fax:* 800-999-6799 *E-mail:* support@brodart.com *Web Site:* www.brodartbooks.com, pg 1311

Dill, Richard, Brodart Books & Library Services, 500 Arch St, Williamsport, PA 17701 *Tel:* 570-326-2461 *Toll Free Tel:* 800-474-9816 *Fax:* 570-651-1639 *Toll Free Fax:* 800-999-6799 *E-mail:* support@brodart.com *Web Site:* www.brodartbooks.com, pg 1323

Dillon, Cecile, The Library Services Centre, 131 Shoemaker St, Kitchener, ON N2E 3B5, Canada *Tel:* 519-746-4420 *Toll Free Tel:* 800-265-3360 (CN only) *Fax:* 519-746-4425 *Web Site:* www.lsc.on.ca, pg 1317

Dion, Danielle, Maison de l'Education Inc, 10840 Ave Millen, Montreal, QC H2C 0A5, Canada *Tel:* 514-384-4401 *Fax:* 514-384-4844 *E-mail:* librairie@maisondeleducation.com *Web Site:* maisondeleducation.com, pg 1317

Diponio, Anthony, Crain Communications Inc, 1155 Gratiot Ave, Detroit, MI 48207-2732 *Tel:* 313-446-6000 *Fax:* 313-446-0383 *E-mail:* info@crain.com *Web Site:* crain.com, pg 1184

Dirks, Paul, Valley News Co, 1305 Stadium Rd, Mankato, MN 56001 *Tel:* 507-345-4819 *Fax:* 507-345-6793 *Web Site:* www.valleynewscompany.com, pg 1322

Dispenziere, Dennis, Ricoh Americas Corp, 300 Eagleview Blvd, Exton, PA 19341 *Tel:* 610-296-8000 *Toll Free Tel:* 800-333-2679 (prod support); 800-637-4264 (sales) *Web Site:* www.ricoh-usa.com, pg 1384

Ditty, Dean, Microboards Technology Inc, 8150 Mallory Ct, Chanhassen, MN 55317 *Tel:* 952-556-1600; 952-556-1639 (tech support) *Toll Free Tel:* 800-646-8881 *Fax:* 952-556-1620 *E-mail:* sales@microboards.com *Web Site:* www.microboards.com, pg 1381

Ditullio, Michael, PTC, 121 Seaport Blvd, Boston, MA 02210 *Tel:* 781-370-5000 *Fax:* 781-370-6000 *Web Site:* www.ptc.com, pg 1384

Dobiel, Maryrita, Historic Cherry Hill, 523 1/2 S Pearl St, Albany, NY 12202 *Tel:* 518-434-4791 *Fax:* 518-434-4806 *E-mail:* info@historiccherryhill.org *Web Site:* www.historiccherryhill.org, pg 1315

Dobratz, Tim, The Bureau, 2354 English St, Maplewood, MN 55109 *Tel:* 612-788-1000; 612-432-3516 (sales) *Toll Free Tel:* 800-788-9536 *Fax:* 612-788-7792 *E-mail:* sales@thebureau.com *Web Site:* www.thebureau.com, pg 1217, 1243

Dockter, Gregory R, PBD Worldwide Inc, 1650 Bluegrass Lakes Pkwy, Alpharetta, GA 30004 *Tel:* 470-769-1000 *Toll Free Tel:* 866-998-4PBD (998-4723) *E-mail:* sales.marketing@pbd.com; customerservice@pbd.com *Web Site:* www.pbd.com, pg 1333

Dockter, Scott A, PBD Worldwide Inc, 1650 Bluegrass Lakes Pkwy, Alpharetta, GA 30004 *Tel:* 470-769-1000 *Toll Free Tel:* 866-998-4PBD (998-4723) *E-mail:* sales.marketing@pbd.com; customerservice@pbd.com *Web Site:* www.pbd.com, pg 1333

Dodds, Lucy, Renouf Publishing Co Ltd, 22-1010 Polytek St, Ottawa, ON K1J 9J1, Canada *Tel:* 613-745-2665 *Toll Free Tel:* 866-767-6766; 888-551-7470 (North America) *Fax:* 613-745-7660 *E-mail:* order.dept@renoufbooks.com *Web Site:* www.renoufbooks.com, pg 1297

Dodge, Elizabeth K, AudioFile®, 37 Silver St, Portland, ME 04101 *Tel:* 207-774-7563 *Toll Free Tel:* 800-506-1212 *Fax:* 207-775-3744 *E-mail:* info@audiofilemagazine.com *Web Site:* www.audiofilemagazine.com, pg 1124

Doherty, Adriane, Cardinal Publishers Group, 2402 N Shadeland Ave, Suite A, Indianapolis, IN 46219 *Tel:* 317-352-8200 *Toll Free Tel:* 800-296-0481 (cust serv) *Fax:* 317-352-8202 *E-mail:* customerservice@cardinalpub.com *Web Site:* cardinalpub.com, pg 1284

Dolan, Mike, Pantagraph Printing, 217 W Jefferson St, Bloomington, IL 61701 *Tel:* 309-829-1071 *E-mail:* queries1@pantagraphprinting.com *Web Site:* www.pantagraphprinting.com, pg 1224

Donohue, Mike, AGS, 4590 Graphics Dr, White Plains, MD 20695 *Tel:* 301-843-1800 *Fax:* 301-843-6339 *E-mail:* info@ags.com *Web Site:* www.ags.com, pg 1201, 1241, 1372

Donohue, Prentiss, Open Text Corp, 275 Frank Tompa Dr, Waterloo, ON N2L 0A1, Canada *Tel:* 519-888-7111 *Toll Free Tel:* 519-888-0677 *Web Site:* opentext.com, pg 1383

Donovan, Dan, Dan Donovan Photography, 15005 Valley Ridge Dr, St Louis, MO 63017 *Tel:* 314-712-0021 *E-mail:* dan@dandonovan.com *Web Site:* www.dandonovan.com, pg 1437

Doornbos, Scott, Dukane Corp, Audio Visual Products Division, 2900 Dukane Dr, St Charles, IL 60174 *Tel:* 630-584-2300 *Toll Free Tel:* 888-245-1966; 800-676-2487 (tech support) *Fax:* 630-584-5156 *E-mail:* avsales@dukane.com *Web Site:* dukaneav.com, pg 1376

Dotson, David, ALC Inc, 750 College Rd E, Suite 201, Princeton, NJ 08540 *Tel:* 609-580-2800 *Toll Free Tel:* 800-252-5478 *Fax:* 609-580-2888 *E-mail:* info@alc.com *Web Site:* www.alc.com, pg 1111

Doucet, Marc, Webcom Inc, 3480 Pharmacy Ave, Toronto, ON M1W 2S7, Canada *Tel:* 416-496-1000 *Toll Free Tel:* 800-665-9322 *Fax:* 416-496-1537 *E-mail:* webcom@webcomlink.com *Web Site:* www.webcomlink.com, pg 1210, 1257, 1280

Dougherty, Michael J, Dougherty and Associates Public Relations, 1303 Caldwell Mountain Rd, Hot Springs, NC 28743 *Tel:* 828-622-3285 *Fax:* 828-622-3285 *E-mail:* dougherty1515@gmail.com *Web Site:* doughertyandassociatespr.com, pg 1097

Douglas, James A, The Advertising, Marketing & Sales Promotion Book Club, Book Club Bldg, 7 Putter Lane, Middle Island, NY 11953 *Tel:* 631-924-3888 (ext 100) *E-mail:* amspbookclub@gmail.com; linickgroup@gmail.com, pg 1135

Douglass, Roy, Electronics for Imaging Inc (EFI), 6750 Dumbarton Circle, Fremont, CA 94555 *Tel:* 650-357-3500 *Toll Free Tel:* 800-568-1917; 800-875-7117 (sales) *Fax:* 650-357-3907 *E-mail:* info@efi.com *Web Site:* www.efi.com, pg 1376

Dove, Veronica M, Bernan, 4501 Forbes Blvd, Suite 200, Lanham, MD 20706 *Tel:* 717-794-3800 (cust serv & orders) *Toll Free Tel:* 800-462-6420 (cust serv & orders) *Fax:* 717-794-3803 *Toll Free Fax:* 800-338-4550 *E-mail:* customercare@bernan.com *Web Site:* rowman.com/page/bernan, pg 1283, 1310

Dowdell, Chris, Devin-Adair Publishers, 9 Lafayette Ct, Suite 3, Greenwich, CT 06830 *Tel:* 203-622-1010 *Fax:* 718-359-8568, pg 1312

Dowell, Jennifer M, AudioFile®, 37 Silver St, Portland, ME 04101 *Tel:* 207-774-7563 *Toll Free Tel:* 800-506-1212 *Fax:* 207-775-3744 *E-mail:* info@audiofilemagazine.com *Web Site:* www.audiofilemagazine.com, pg 1124

Downes, Debbie, ColorPage, 81 Ten Broeck Ave, Kingston, NY 12401 *Tel:* 845-331-7581 *Toll Free Tel:* 800-836-7581 *Fax:* 845-331-1571 *E-mail:* sales@colorpageonline.com *Web Site:* www.colorpageonline.com, pg 1203, 1218, 1244, 1262

Drake, Cary, Six Red Marbles LLC, 101 Station Landing, Medford, MA 02155 *Tel:* 857-588-9000 *E-mail:* info@sixredmarbles.com *Web Site:* www.sixredmarbles.com, pg 1226, 1385

Dralyuk, Boris, LARB Quarterly Journal, 6671 Sunset Blvd, Suite 1521, Los Angeles, CA 90028 Tel: 323-952-3950 E-mail: info@ lareviewofbooks.org; editorial@lareviewofbooks.org Web Site: lareviewofbooks.org, pg 1128

Drate, Spencer, Spencer Drate, 119 W 80 St, Suite 1-F, New York, NY 10024-7134 Tel: 212-799-0535 E-mail: spencerdrate@yahoo.com, pg 1427

Dreshfield, Richard, Koenig & Bauer (US) Inc, 2555 Regent Blvd, Dallas, TX 75229 Tel: 469-532-8000 Fax: 469-532-8190 Web Site: us.koenig-bauer.com, pg 1277

Drew, Michael R, Promote A Book, 591 Mantua Blvd, Sewell, NJ 08080 Tel: 512-586-6073 Web Site: promoteabook.media, pg 1351

Drinkwater, Simone, Casemate | academic, 1950 Lawrence Rd, Havertown, PA 19083 Tel: 610-853-9131 Fax: 610-853-9146 E-mail: info@ casemateacademic.com Web Site: www.oxbowbooks.com/dbbc, pg 1284

Drinkwater, Simone, Casemate | IPM, 1950 Lawrence Rd, Havertown, PA 19083 Tel: 610-853-9131 Fax: 610-853-9146 E-mail: casemate@ casematepublishers.com Web Site: www.casemateipm.com, pg 1096, 1105, 1284, 1343

Driscoll, Jim, EMT International Inc, 780 Centerline Dr, Hobart, WI 54155 Tel: 920-468-5475 Fax: 920-468-7991 E-mail: info@emtinternational.com Web Site: www.emtinternational.com, pg 1276

Drobinski, Tony, Emsworth Design, 147 W 24 St, New York, NY 10011 Tel: 212-877-6139; 917-359-9860 (cell) Web Site: www.emsworthdesign.com, pg 1427

Droll, Francesca, Abacus Graphics LLC, 15179 Hunger Creek Lane, Bigfork, MT 59911-8313 Tel: 406-837-5776 Web Site: www.abacusgraphics.com, pg 1423

Druger, Pat, Meadows Publishing Solutions, 1305 Remington Rd, Suite G, Schaumburg, IL 60173 Tel: 847-882-8202 Toll Free Tel: 888-983-6746 Fax: 847-882-9494 E-mail: sales@meadowsps.com Web Site: www.meadowsps.com, pg 1381

Dryl, Mariel, Northeast Publishers Reps, Montville Chase, 20 Davenport Rd, Montville, NJ 07045 Tel: 973-299-0085 Fax: 973-263-2363 E-mail: siraksirak@aol.com Web Site: www.nepubreps.com, pg 1294

Dubin, Jordan, Association for Library Service to Children (ALSC), 225 N Michigan Ave, Suite 1300, Chicago, IL 60601 Tel: 312-280-2163 Toll Free Tel: 800-545-2433 Fax: 312-280-5271 E-mail: alsc@ ala.org Web Site: www.ala.org/alsc, pg 1139

Dubreuil, Laurent, Diacritics, 2715 N Charles St, Baltimore, MD 21218-4363 Toll Free Tel: 800-548-1784 (journal orders) Fax: 410-516-6968 E-mail: jrnlcirc@press.jhu.edu (journal orders) Web Site: www.press.jhu.edu/journals/diacritics/index.html, pg 1125

Dubuque, Don, Standard Finishing Systems, 10 Connector Rd, Andover, MA 01810 Tel: 978-470-1920 Toll Free Tel: 877-404-4460 Fax: 978-470-0819 E-mail: marketing@sdmc.com Web Site: www.sdmc.com, pg 1279

Dudley, Tim, Master Books®, 3142 Hwy 103 N, Green Forest, AR 72638 Tel: 870-438-5288 Toll Free Tel: 800-999-3777 E-mail: nlp@nlpg.com; sales@ masterbooks.com Web Site: www.masterbooks.com; www.nlpg.com/imprint/master-books, pg 1381

Duffes, Melissa, Lucia|Marquand, 1400 Second Ave, Seattle, WA 98101 Tel: 206-624-2030 Fax: 206-624-1821 Web Site: luciamarquand.com, pg 1359

Duffy, Tim, Master Flo Technology Inc, 154 Seale Rd, Wentworth, QC J8H 0G9, Canada Tel: 450-533-0088 Fax: 450-533-4597 E-mail: info@mflo.com; sales@ mflo.com Web Site: www.mflo.com, pg 1278

Dufour, Michelle, Data Index Inc, 13713 NW Indian Springs Dr, Vancouver, WA 98685 Tel: 425-760-9193 Web Site: www.dataindex.com, pg 1218

Duggan, Paul, Open Text Corp, 275 Frank Tompa Dr, Waterloo, ON N2L 0A1, Canada Tel: 519-888-7111 Fax: 519-888-0677 Web Site: opentext.com, pg 1383

Duignam, Dianne, Louis Goldberg Library Book Supplier, 45 Belvidere St, Nazareth, PA 18064 Tel: 610-759-9458 E-mail: orders@goldberg-books.com Web Site: www.goldberg-books.com, pg 1314

Dumas, Kellie, Tennessee Book Co, 1550 Heil Quaker Blvd, La Vergne, TN 37086 Tel: 615-793-5040 Toll Free Tel: 800-456-0418 Fax: 615-213-9545 Web Site: www.tennesseebook.com, pg 1321

Dunbar, Lori, Ingram Content Group LLC, One Ingram Blvd, La Vergne, TN 37086-1986 Tel: 615-793-5000 Toll Free Tel: 800-937-8000 (ext 1, libs) E-mail: customerservice@ingramcontent.com Web Site: www.ingramcontent.com, pg 1290, 1315

Dunham, Joe, LBS, 1801 Thompson Ave, Des Moines, IA 50316-2751 Tel: 515-262-3191 Toll Free Tel: 800-247-5323 Toll Free Fax: 800-262-4091 E-mail: info@ lbsbind.com Web Site: www.lbsbind.com, pg 1265

Dunhill, Candy, Dunhill International List Co Inc, 6400 Congress Ave, Suite 1750, Boca Raton, FL 33487-2898 Tel: 561-998-7800 Toll Free Tel: 800-DUNHILL (386-4455) Fax: 561-998-7880 E-mail: dunhill@ dunhillintl.com Web Site: www.dunhills.com, pg 1112

Dunhill, Cindy, Dunhill International List Co Inc, 6400 Congress Ave, Suite 1750, Boca Raton, FL 33487-2898 Tel: 561-998-7800 Toll Free Tel: 800-DUNHILL (386-4455) Fax: 561-998-7880 E-mail: dunhill@ dunhillintl.com Web Site: www.dunhills.com, pg 1112

Dunhill, Robert, Dunhill International List Co Inc, 6400 Congress Ave, Suite 1750, Boca Raton, FL 33487-2898 Tel: 561-998-7800 Toll Free Tel: 800-DUNHILL (386-4455) Fax: 561-998-7880 E-mail: dunhill@ dunhillintl.com Web Site: www.dunhills.com, pg 1112

Dunn, David M, Dunn & Co Inc, 75 Green St, Clinton, MA 01510 Tel: 978-368-8505 Fax: 978-368-7867 E-mail: info@booktrauma.com Web Site: www.booktrauma.com, pg 1204, 1246, 1263

Dunn, Frank, Circle Graphics Inc, 316 Main St, Suite 1C, Reisters Town, MD 21136 Tel: 410-833-2200 E-mail: production@circleusa.com Web Site: www.circleusa.com, pg 1218

Dunn, Kathi, Dunn+Associates Design, PO Box 870, Hayward, WI 54843-0870 Tel: 715-634-4857 Fax: 715-634-5617 E-mail: info@dunn-design.com Web Site: www.dunn-design.com, pg 1427

Dunphy, John A, University Products Inc, 517 Main St, Holyoke, MA 01040 Tel: 413-532-3372 Toll Free Tel: 800-628-1912 (orders) Fax: 413-533-4743 Toll Free Fax: 800-532-9281 E-mail: info@universityproducts.com Web Site: www.universityproducts.com, pg 1269

Dupuis, Tom, Dual Graphics, 370 Cliffwood Park, Brea, CA 92821 Tel: 714-990-3700 Fax: 714-990-6818 Web Site: www.dualgraphics.com, pg 1219, 1246

Dupuis-Jones, Trish, Falcon Safety Products Inc, 25 Imclone Dr, Branchburg, NJ 08876 Tel: 908-707-4900 Toll Free Tel: 800-332-5266 E-mail: marketing@ falconsafety.com Web Site: www.falconsafety.com, pg 1377

Duran, Victor, SCB Distributors, 15608 S New Century Dr, Gardena, CA 90248 Tel: 310-532-9400 Toll Free Tel: 800-729-6423 Fax: 310-532-7001 E-mail: scb@ scbdistributors.com Web Site: www.scbdistributors.com, pg 1297

Durham, Rusty, StarGroup International Inc, 1194 Old Dixie Hwy, Suite 201, West Palm Beach, FL 33413 Tel: 561-547-0667 E-mail: info@stargroupinternational.com Web Site: stargroupinternational.com, pg 1102

Durkee, Jim, Tri-Media Integrated Marketing Technologies Inc, 1027 Pelham St, Unit 2, Fonthill, ON L0S 1E0, Canada E-mail: think@tri-media.com Web Site: tri-media.com, pg 1087

Dutton, Denis, Philosophy & Literature, 2715 N Charles St, Baltimore, MD 21218-4363 Toll Free Tel: 800-548-1784 (journal orders) Fax: 410-516-6968 E-mail: jrnlcirc@press.jhu.edu (journal orders) Web Site: www.press.jhu.edu/journals/philosophy_and_literature/index.html, pg 1130

Dutton, Doris, The Karel/Dutton Group, 3145 Geary Blvd, PMB 619, San Francisco, CA 94118 Tel: 415-668-0829 Fax: 415-668-2463, pg 1291

Duvieusart, Guillaume, Diffusion Inter-Livres, 1701 Belleville, Lemoyne, QC J4P 3M2, Canada Tel: 450-465-0037 Toll Free Tel: 866-465-5579 E-mail: interlivres@llbquebec.ca Web Site: www.inter-livres.ca, pg 1286

Dyer, C Brent, Texas Book Co, 8501 Technology Circle, Greenville, TX 75402 Tel: 903-455-6969 Toll Free Tel: 800-527-1016 E-mail: customerservice@ texasbook.com Web Site: www.texasbook.com, pg 1321

Dyer, Gordon, OmniUpdate Inc, 1320 Flynn Rd, Suite 100, Camarillo, CA 93012 Tel: 805-484-9400 Toll Free Tel: 800-362-2605 E-mail: sales@omniupdate.com Web Site: omniupdate.com, pg 1383

Dyer, Stacy, Texas Book Co, 8501 Technology Circle, Greenville, TX 75402 Tel: 903-455-6969 Toll Free Tel: 800-527-1016 E-mail: customerservice@ texasbook.com Web Site: www.texasbook.com, pg 1321

Dykhouse, Clarence, Wallaceburg Bookbinding & Mfg Co Ltd, 95 Arnold St, Wallaceburg, ON N8A 3P3, Canada Tel: 519-627-3552 Toll Free Tel: 800-214-BIND (214-2463) Fax: 519-627-6922 E-mail: helpdesk@wbmbindery.com Web Site: www.wbmbindery.com, pg 1256, 1324

Dykhouse, Gerrit, Wallaceburg Bookbinding & Mfg Co Ltd, 95 Arnold St, Wallaceburg, ON N8A 3P3, Canada Tel: 519-627-3552 Toll Free Tel: 800-214-BIND (214-2463) Fax: 519-627-6922 E-mail: helpdesk@wbmbindery.com Web Site: www.wbmbindery.com, pg 1256, 1324

Dziesietnik, Ghilad, Electronics for Imaging Inc (EFI), 6750 Dumbarton Circle, Fremont, CA 94555 Tel: 650-357-3500 Toll Free Tel: 800-568-1917; 800-875-7117 (sales) Fax: 650-357-3907 E-mail: info@efi.com Web Site: www.efi.com, pg 1376

Eads, Carol, Ross Gage Inc, 8502 Brookville Rd, Indianapolis, IN 46239 Tel: 317-283-2323 Toll Free Tel: 800-799-2323 Fax: 317-931-2108 E-mail: info@ rossgage.com Web Site: www.rossgage.com, pg 1225, 1253

Eakin, Emily, The New York Times Book Review, 620 Eighth Ave, 5th fl, New York, NY 10018 Tel: 212-556-1234 Toll Free Tel: 800-631-2580 (subns) E-mail: bookreview@nytimes.com; books@nytimes.com Web Site: www.nytimes.com, pg 1129

Ealy, C Cato, International Paper Co, 6400 Poplar Ave, Memphis, TN 38197 Tel: 901-419-9000 Toll Free Tel: 800-207-4003 Web Site: www.internationalpaper.com; facebook.com/internationalpaper; twitter.com/intlpaperco, pg 1264

Earls, G Scott, Simon Miller Paper & Packaging, 3409 W Chester Pike, Suite 204, Newton Square, PA 19073 Tel: 215-923-3600 Toll Free Tel: 800-642-1899 Fax: 610-355-9330 E-mail: info@simonmiller.com Web Site: www.simonmiller.com, pg 1267

Eastman, Daniel, Distribooks Inc, 8154 N Ridgeway Ave, Skokie, IL 60076-2911 Tel: 847-676-1596 Toll Free Fax: 888-266-5713 E-mail: info@distribooks.com, pg 1286

Eastman, Daniel, Distribooks Inc, 8154 N Ridgeway Ave, Skokie, IL 60076-2911 Tel: 847-676-1596 Fax: 847-676-1195 Toll Free Fax: 888-266-5713 E-mail: info@distribooks.com; info@schoenhofs.com Web Site: www.schoenhofs.com, pg 1313

Eastman, Daniel, Schoenhof's Foreign Books Inc, 76 A Mount Auburn St, Cambridge, MA 02138 Tel: 617-547-8855 E-mail: info@schoenhofs.com Web Site: www.schoenhofs.com, pg 1320, 1327

Easton, Elmer, Three D Graphics Inc, 11340 W Olympic Blvd, Suite 352, Los Angeles, CA 90064 Tel: 310-231-3330 Toll Free Tel: 800-913-0008 Fax: 310-231-

3303 E-mail: info@threedgraphics.com; orders@ threedgraphics.com; sales@threedgraphics.com Web Site: www.threedgraphics.com, pg 1386

Eastwood, Mike, Thomson Reuters, 3 Times Sq, New York, NY 10036 Tel: 646-223-4000; 646-223-6100 (edit); 646-223-6000 (newsroom) Web Site: www. thomsonreuters.com, pg 1186

Eberle, Adam, OverDrive Inc, One OverDrive Way, Cleveland, OH 44125 Tel: 216-573-6886 Fax: 216-573-6888 E-mail: info@overdrive.com Web Site: www.overdrive.com, pg 1294

Ebrahimi, Katie, Unisys Corp, 801 Lakeview Dr, Suite 100, Blue Bell, PA 19422 Tel: 215-274-2742 Web Site: www.unisys.com, pg 1387

Eck, Caitlin, Independent Publishers Group (IPG), 814 N Franklin St, Chicago, IL 60610 Tel: 312-337-0747 Toll Free Tel: 800-888-4741 (orders) Fax: 312-337-5985 E-mail: frontdesk@ipgbook.com; orders@ipgbook.com Web Site: www.ipgbook.com, pg 1288, 1326

Eckhart, Chris, Eckhart & Co Inc, 4011 W 54 St, Indianapolis, IN 46254 Tel: 317-347-2665 Toll Free Tel: 800-443-3791 Fax: 317-347-2666 E-mail: info@ eckhartandco.com Web Site: www.eckhartandco.com, pg 1247

Eckmair, Hans G, Academic Reviews, 1-A Glenwood Ave, Lynbrook, NY 11563 Tel: 516-593-1275 E-mail: info@academicreviews.com Web Site: www. academicreviews.com, pg 1123

Eckstein, Meyer, Listco Direct Marketing, 1276 46 St, Brooklyn, NY 11219 Tel: 718-871-8400 Fax: 718-871-7692 E-mail: info@listcodirect.com Web Site: www.listcodirect.com, pg 1112

Eckstein, Shlomo, Listco Direct Marketing, 1276 46 St, Brooklyn, NY 11219 Tel: 718-871-8400 Fax: 718-871-7692 E-mail: info@listcodirect.com Web Site: www.listcodirect.com, pg 1112

Edelboim, Jason, PR Newswire, 350 Hudson St, Suite 300, New York, NY 10014-4504 Toll Free Tel: 888-776-0942; 800-776-8090 Toll Free Fax: 800-793-9313 E-mail: mediainquiries@prnewswire.com Web Site: www.prnewswire.com, pg 1101

Edelson, Wendy, Wendy Edelson Studios, 18 E St Louis St, Rapid City, SD 57701 Tel: 206-319-8158 Web Site: www.wendyedelson.com; www. elevenlemons.blogspot.com, pg 1427

Edmonds, Scott, International Mapping Associates, 5300 Dorsey Hall Dr, Suite 201, Ellicott City, MD 21042 Tel: 443-367-0050 Toll Free Tel: 800-761-6944 Fax: 443-367-0045 Web Site: internationalmapping. com, pg 1429

Edson, Durga, Amcorp Ltd, 10 Norden Lane, Huntington Station, NY 11746 Tel: 631-271-0548 Fax: 631-549-8849 E-mail: amcorpltd@aol.com, pg 1325

Edson, Steven, Steven Edson Photography, 219 Orchard St, Belmont, MA 02478 Tel: 617-993-3212 E-mail: steve@stevenedson.com Web Site: www. stevenedson.com, pg 1437

Edwards, Adrianna, Focus Strategic Communications Inc, 15 Hunter Way, Brantford, ON N3T 6S3, Canada Tel: 519-756-3265 E-mail: info@focussc.com Web Site: www.focussc.com, pg 1357

Edwards, Melissa, Stonesong, 270 W 39 St, Suite 201, New York, NY 10018 Tel: 212-929-4600 E-mail: editors@stonesong.com Web Site: www. stonesong.com, pg 1362

Edwards, Ron, Focus Strategic Communications Inc, 15 Hunter Way, Brantford, ON N3T 6S3, Canada Tel: 519-756-3265 E-mail: info@focussc.com Web Site: www.focussc.com, pg 1357

Edwards, Vanya, Sovfoto Inc, 263 W 20 St, Suite 3, New York, NY 10011 Tel: 212-727-8170 Fax: 212-727-8228 E-mail: research@sovfoto.com Web Site: www.sovfoto.com, pg 1449

Egan, Dean T, Roosevelt Paper Co, One Roosevelt Dr, Mount Laurel, NJ 08054 Tel: 856-303-4100 Toll Free Tel: 800-523-3470 Fax: 856-642-1949 E-mail: marketing@rooseveltpaper.com Web Site: www.rooseveltpaper.com, pg 1267

Egan, Elisabeth, The New York Times Book Review, 620 Eighth Ave, 5th fl, New York, NY 10018 Tel: 212-556-1234 Toll Free Tel: 800-631-2580 (subns) E-mail: bookreview@nytimes.com; books@ nytimes.com Web Site: www.nytimes.com, pg 1129

Ehrlich, Serena, Business Wire, 101 California St, 20th fl, San Francisco, CA 94111 Tel: 415-986-4422 Toll Free Tel: 800-227-0845 E-mail: info@businesswire. com Web Site: www.businesswire.com, pg 1183

Ekus, Lisa, The Lisa Ekus Group LLC, 57 North St, Hatfield, MA 01038 Tel: 413-247-9325 Fax: 413-247-9873 E-mail: info@lisaekus.com Web Site: lisaekus. com, pg 1097

Ekus, Sally, The Lisa Ekus Group LLC, 57 North St, Hatfield, MA 01038 Tel: 413-247-9325 Fax: 413-247-9873 E-mail: info@lisaekus.com Web Site: lisaekus. com, pg 1097

Elancheran, Maran, Newgen North America Inc, 2714 Bee Cave Rd, Suite 201, Austin, TX 78746 Tel: 512-478-5341 Fax: 512-476-4756 E-mail: sales@newgen. co Web Site: www.newgen.co, pg 1223

Elder, David C, Glatfelter, Capitol Towers South, 4350 Congress St, Suite 600, Charlotte, NC 28209 Tel: 717-850-0170 Toll Free Tel: 866-744-7380 E-mail: info@ glatfelter.com Web Site: www.glatfelter.com, pg 1263

Elder, Randy, Elder's Bookstore, 101 White Bridge Rd, Nashville, TN 37209 Tel: 615-352-1562 E-mail: info@eldersbookstore.com Web Site: eldersbookstore.com, pg 1313

Eldon, Bonnie, Melcher Media Inc, 124 W 13 St, New York, NY 10011 Tel: 212-727-2322 Fax: 212-627-1973 E-mail: info@melcher.com Web Site: www. melcher.com, pg 1360

Eldred, Tanya, Sheridan GR, 5100 33 St SE, Grand Rapids, MI 49512 Tel: 616-957-5100 Web Site: www. sheridan.com, pg 1209, 1254

Elias, Thomas D, Southern California Focus, 1720 Oak St, Santa Monica, CA 90405 Tel: 310-452-3918 Web Site: www.californiafocus.net, pg 1186

Eligh, Gregg, Eligh Photographs, 2544 Forbes St, Victoria, BC V8R 4B8, Canada Tel: 250-888-0027 Web Site: www.elighphoto.com, pg 1437

Elizalde, Steve, Greenleaf Book Group LLC, 3 Park Place, 4005 Banister Lane, Suite B, Austin, TX 78704 Tel: 512-891-6100 Fax: 512-891-6150 E-mail: contact@greenleafbookgroup.com Web Site: www.greenleafbookgroup.com, pg 1288, 1358

Elk, Claude Marie, Elk Photography, 3163 Wisconsin St, Oakland, CA 94602 Tel: 510-531-7469 Fax: 510-531-7469 E-mail: cjelk@elkphotography.com Web Site: www.elkphotography.com, pg 1437

Elk, John, Elk Photography, 3163 Wisconsin St, Oakland, CA 94602 Tel: 510-531-7469 Fax: 510-531-7469 E-mail: cjelk@elkphotography.com Web Site: www.elkphotography.com, pg 1437

Elkalai, Khalid, MetaComet Systems, 29 College St, South Hadley, MA 01075 Tel: 413-536-5989 Web Site: www.metacomet.com, pg 1350

Ellis, Duncan, Avanti Computer Systems Ltd, 251 Consumers Rd, Suite 600, Toronto, ON M2J 4R3, Canada Tel: 416-445-1722 Toll Free Tel: 800-482-2908 Fax: 416-445-6319 E-mail: askavanti@ avantisystems.com Web Site: www.avantisystems.com, pg 1373

Ellison, Larry, Oracle America Inc, 500 Oracle Pkwy, Redwood Shores, CA 94065 Tel: 650-506-7000 Toll Free Tel: 800-392-2999; 800-633-0738 (sales) Web Site: www.oracle.com, pg 1383

Ellwood, Glen, The Association of Medical Illustrators (AMI), 201 E Main St, Suite 1405, Lexington, KY 40507 Toll Free Tel: 866-393-4264 Fax: 859-514-9166 E-mail: hq@ami.org; info@ami.org Web Site: www. ami.org, pg 1424

Elmore, Tina, Ingram Content Group LLC, One Ingram Blvd, La Vergne, TN 37086-1986 Tel: 615-793-5000 Toll Free Tel: 800-937-8000 (retailers); 800-937-5300

(ext 1, libs) E-mail: customerservice@ingramcontent. com Web Site: www.ingramcontent.com, pg 1290, 1315

Elting, Elizabeth, Translations.com, 3 Park Ave, 39th fl, New York, NY 10016 Tel: 212-689-5555 Fax: 212-689-1059 E-mail: newyork@transperfect.com; info@ translations.com Web Site: www.translations.com, pg 1414

Embury, Emily, C Blohm & Associates Inc, 5999 Monona Dr, Monona, WI 53716-3531 Tel: 608-216-7300 E-mail: hello@cblohm.com Web Site: www. cblohm.com, pg 1096

Endugesick, Sharon, Brown Book Co Ltd, 65 Crockford Blvd, Toronto, ON M1R 3B7, Canada Tel: 416-504-9696 Fax: 416-504-9393 E-mail: bbc@brownbook.ca Web Site: www.brownbook.ca, pg 1202

Engel, George S, Book Creations Inc, 5075 56 Place, Vero Beach, FL 32967 Tel: 518-366-4636 (cell), pg 1356

Engelgau, Chad, Acxiom, 301 E Dave Ward Dr, Conway, AR 72032 Toll Free Tel: 888-322-9466 Web Site: www.acxiom.com, pg 1371

Engle, Harold, Ambassador Press Inc, 1400 Washington Ave N, Minneapolis, MN 55411 Tel: 612-521-0123 E-mail: info@ambpress.com Web Site: www.ambpress. com, pg 1215, 1241, 1261

Engle-Fieldman, Candice, Ambassador Press Inc, 1400 Washington Ave N, Minneapolis, MN 55411 Tel: 612-521-0123 E-mail: info@ambpress.com Web Site: www.ambpress.com, pg 1215, 1241, 1261

Enomoto, Mizuki, Nissho Electronics USA Corp, The Concourse I, 226 Airport Pkwy, Suite 340, San Jose, CA 95110 Tel: 408-969-9700 E-mail: info@nelco.com Web Site: www.nelco.com, pg 1382

Epping, Robert, GTxcel Inc, 144 Turnpike Rd, Suite 130, Southborough, MA 01772-2104 Toll Free Tel: 800-609-8994 Web Site: www.gtxcel.com, pg 1378

Erf, Keith, KyTek Inc, PO Box 338, Weare, NH 03281 Tel: 603-529-2512 E-mail: sales@kytek.com Web Site: www.kytek.com, pg 1380

Eriksen, Vigdis, Eriksen Translations Inc, 50 Court St, Suite 700, Brooklyn, NY 11201 Tel: 718-802-9010 Fax: 718-802-0041 Web Site: www.eriksen.com, pg 1409

Ermelino, Louisa, Publishers Weekly, 71 W 23 St, Suite 1608, New York, NY 10010 Tel: 212-377-5500 Fax: 212-377-2733 Web Site: www.publishersweekly. com, pg 1130

Errera, Stacie, Tamron USA Inc, 10 Austin Blvd, Commack, NY 11725 Tel: 631-858-8400 Toll Free Tel: 800-827-8880 Fax: 631-543-5666; 631-858-8462 (cust serv) E-mail: custserv@tamron.com Web Site: www.tamron-usa.com, pg 1386

Errico, Joe, VIP Digital Print Center, 200 Circle Dr N, Piscataway, NJ 08854 Tel: 732-469-5400 Fax: 732-469-8414 E-mail: info@vipcopycenter.com Web Site: www.vipcopycenter.com, pg 1256

Esguerra, Dennis, OmniUpdate Inc, 1320 Flynn Rd, Suite 100, Camarillo, CA 93012 Tel: 805-484-9400 Toll Free Tel: 800-362-2605 E-mail: sales@ omniupdate.com Web Site: omniupdate.com, pg 1383

Eskenazi, Brian, Riverside Book Co Inc, PO Box 237043, New York, NY 10023-0028 Tel: 212-595-0700 Fax: 212-595-0700 Web Site: www. riversidebook.com, pg 1319

Eskenazi, Brian, Skylark Co Inc, PO Box 237043, New York, NY 10023-0028 Tel: 212-595-0700 Fax: 212-595-0700, pg 1327

Eskenazi, Victor, Riverside Book Co Inc, PO Box 237043, New York, NY 10023-0028 Tel: 212-595-0700 Fax: 212-595-0700 Web Site: www. riversidebook.com, pg 1319

Esterly, Flora, Bettina Schrewe Literary Scouting, 220 E 23 St, Suite 409, New York, NY 10010 *Tel:* 212-414-2515 *Fax:* 212-414-2516 *E-mail:* bschrewe@bschrewe.com *Web Site:* www.bschrewe.com, pg 1351

Ethier, Melanie, Multi-Reliure, 2112 Ave de la Transmission, Shawinigan, QC G9N 8N8, Canada *Tel:* 819-537-6008 *Toll Free Tel:* 888-735-4873 *Fax:* 819-537-4598 *E-mail:* info@multi-reliure.com; administration@multi-reliure.com *Web Site:* www.multireliure.com, pg 1251

Etlin, Alexander (Sasha), Glasnost Communications, 1316 Tallberry Business Plaza, Suite 404, Cincinnati, OH 45230 *Tel:* 513-231-3599 *Fax:* 513-231-3599 *E-mail:* glasnost@att.net, pg 1409

Ettinger, Mark, Linguistic Systems Inc (LSI), 260 Franklin St, Suite 230, Boston, MA 02110 *Tel:* 617-528-7410 *Toll Free Tel:* 800-654-5006 *E-mail:* clientservice@linguist.com *Web Site:* www.linguist.com, pg 1222, 1380, 1411, 1429

Evans, Craig, Dual Graphics, 370 Cliffwood Park, Brea, CA 92821 *Tel:* 714-990-3700 *Fax:* 714-990-6818 *Web Site:* www.dualgraphics.com, pg 1219, 1246

Evans, Daryl, Miami Wabash Paper LLC, 301 Wedcor Ave, Wabash, IN 46992 *Tel:* 260-563-4181 *Toll Free Tel:* 800-842-9112 *Fax:* 219-563-2724 *E-mail:* miamivalley@mafcote.com *Web Site:* www.mafcote.com, pg 1265

Evans, Todd, Rivendell Media Inc, 1248 Rte 22 W, Mountainside, NJ 07092 *Tel:* 908-232-2021 ext 200 *Fax:* 908-232-0521 *E-mail:* info@rivendellmedia.com; sales@rivendellmedia.com *Web Site:* www.rivendellmedia.com, pg 1101

Eveleigh, Douglas, Encyclopaedia Britannica Inc, 325 N La Salle St, Suite 200, Chicago, IL 60654 *Tel:* 312-347-7000 (all other countries) *Toll Free Tel:* 800-323-1229 (US & CN) *Fax:* 312-294-2104 *E-mail:* contact@eb.com *Web Site:* www.britannica.com, pg 1313

Everson, Shawn, Ingram Content Group LLC, One Ingram Blvd, La Vergne, TN 37086-1986 *Tel:* 615-793-5000 *Toll Free Tel:* 800-937-8000 (retailers); 800-937-5300 (ext 1, libs) *E-mail:* customerservice@ingramcontent.com *Web Site:* www.ingramcontent.com, pg 1290, 1315

Eykemans, Tom, Lucia|Marquand, 1400 Second Ave, Seattle, WA 98101 *Tel:* 206-624-2030 *Fax:* 206-624-1821 *Web Site:* luciamarquand.com, pg 1359

Fabian, Erika, Eriako Associates, 1380 Morningside Way, Venice, CA 90291 *Tel:* 310-392-6537 *Fax:* 310-392-6537 *E-mail:* eriakoassociates@gmail.com, pg 1357

Fackert, H Mason III, CVI Capital, 165 Annursnac Hill Rd, Concord, MA 01742 *Tel:* 978-371-0995 *Fax:* 978-287-5869 *E-mail:* admin@cvicapital.com *Web Site:* www.cvicapital.com, pg 1344

Factor, Beverly, Envirovision, 2901 W Coast Hwy, Suite 222, Newport Beach, CA 92663 *Tel:* 949-673-2555 *E-mail:* bfactor@beverlyfactor.com *Web Site:* www.beverlyfactor.com, pg 1437

Fager, Edwin, Kensai International Ltd, 75 Nottingham Rd, Malverne, NY 11565 *Tel:* 516-593-0480 *E-mail:* info@kensai.net *Web Site:* www.kensai.net, pg 1348

Faherty, Kevin L, Lorimer Literary Consulting, 1033 SW Yamhill St, Suite 205, Portland, OR 97205 *Tel:* 503-481-5847 *E-mail:* lorimerliterary@yahoo.com, pg 1349

Fahr, Jean, Crane Duplicating Service Inc, 4915 Rattlesnake Hammock Rd, Suite 207, Naples, FL 34113 *Tel:* 305-280-6742 (help desk) *Fax:* 239-732-8415 *E-mail:* info@craneduplicating.com *Web Site:* www.craneduplicating.com, pg 1203, 1245

Fairfield, Jay, HF Group LLC, 8844 Mayfield Rd, Chesterland, OH 44026 *Tel:* 440-729-2445; 440-729-9411 (hindery) *E-mail:* custservice-oh@hfgroup.com *Web Site:* www.hfgroup.com, pg 1248, 1264, 1323

Fakeris, Edward G, The Ohio Blow Pipe Co, 446 E 131 St, Cleveland, OH 44108-1684 *Tel:* 216-681-7379 *Fax:* 216-681-7713 *E-mail:* sales@obpairsystems.com *Web Site:* www.obpairsystems.com, pg 1278

Fakes, Bonnie, DeHoff Christian Bookstore, 749 NW Broad St, Murfreesboro, TN 37129 *Tel:* 615-893-8322 *Toll Free Tel:* 800-695-5385 *Fax:* 615-896-7447 *E-mail:* dehoffbooks@gmail.com *Web Site:* www.dehoffpublications.com, pg 1312

Faktorovich, Dr Anna, Pennsylvania Literary Journal (PLJ), 1108 W Third St, Quanah, TX 79252 *Tel:* 470-289-6395 *Web Site:* anaphoraliterary.com, pg 1130

Falcon, Laura, Conservative Book Club, 300 New Jersey Ave NW, Suite 500, Washington, DC 20001 *Tel:* 202-216-0601 *Fax:* 202-216-0614 *Web Site:* www.conservativebookclub.com, pg 1135

Fancher, Chris, Adoption Book Catalog, 131 John Muir Dr, Amherst, NY 14228 *Tel:* 716-639-3900 *Toll Free Tel:* 866-691-3300 *E-mail:* info@tapestrybooks.com *Web Site:* www.tapestrybooks.com, pg 1139

Fandel, Jean-Paul, Linguistic Systems Inc (LSI), 260 Franklin St, Suite 230, Boston, MA 02110 *Tel:* 617-528-7410 *Toll Free Tel:* 800-654-5006 *E-mail:* clientservice@linguist.com *Web Site:* www.linguist.com, pg 1222, 1380, 1411, 1429

Farago, Victoria H, Victoria Productions Inc, 76 Beaver St, New York, NY 10005 *Tel:* 212-425-3013 *Fax:* 646-225-7218 *E-mail:* victoria@vproductions.net *Web Site:* www.vproductions.net, pg 1387

Fareed, Faisal, appatura™, A Broadridge Company, 65 Challenger Rd, Suite 400, Ridgefield Park, NJ 07660 *Tel:* 201-508-6000 *Toll Free Tel:* 800-277-2155 *E-mail:* contactus@appatura.com *Web Site:* www.appatura.com, pg 1091, 1105, 1109, 1201, 1215, 1242

Fargis, Alison, Stonesong, 270 W 39 St, Suite 201, New York, NY 10018 *Tel:* 212-929-4600 *E-mail:* editors@stonesong.com *Web Site:* www.stonesong.com, pg 1362

Farley, Kelly, dix! Digital Prepress Inc, 8462 Wayfarer Dr, Cicero, NY 13039 *Tel:* 315-288-5888 *Fax:* 315-288-5898 *E-mail:* info@dixtype.com *Web Site:* www.dixtype.com, pg 1219, 1246

Farmer, Gary, American Association for Vocational Instructional Materials, 220 Smithonia Rd, Winterville, GA 30683 *Tel:* 706-742-5355 *Fax:* 706-742-7005, pg 1273

Farmer, Greg, OverDrive Inc, One OverDrive Way, Cleveland, OH 44125 *Tel:* 216-573-6886 *Fax:* 216-573-6888 *E-mail:* info@overdrive.com *Web Site:* www.overdrive.com, pg 1294

Farmer, Tessin, BookFactory, 2302 S Edwin C Moses Blvd, Dayton, OH 45417 *Tel:* 937-226-7100 *Toll Free Tel:* 877-431-2665 *Fax:* 614-388-5635 *E-mail:* sales@bookfactory.com *Web Site:* www.bookfactory.com, pg 1243

Farnham, Kyle, Porter Novelli, 195 Broadway, 17th fl, New York, NY 10007 *Tel:* 212-601-8000 *Web Site:* www.porternovelli.com, pg 1100

Farris, Ryan, AlphaGraphics Inc, 143 Union Blvd, Suite 650, Lakewood, CO 80228 *Toll Free Tel:* 800-955-6246 *Fax:* 801-595-7270 *E-mail:* contactus@alphagraphics.com *Web Site:* www.alphagraphics.com, pg 1372

Farrish, Bryan, Bryan Farrish Marketing, 1828 Broadway, 2nd fl, Santa Monica, CA 90404 *Tel:* 310-998-8305 *E-mail:* airplay@radio-media.com *Web Site:* www.radio-media.com, pg 1097

Fasching, Bernadette, Linick International Inc, Linick Bldg, 7 Putter Lane, Middle Island, NY 11953 *Tel:* 631-924-3888; 631-924-8555; 631-604-8599 *E-mail:* topmarketingadvisor@gmail.com *Web Site:* topmarketingadvisor.com, pg 1349

Faulkner, Cassandra, Cat's Eye Consultancy, 4120 Durham Ct, Eagan, MN 55122 *Tel:* 651-270-3190, pg 1343

Fazakerley, Richard, Pacific Publishing Co Inc, 636 Alaska St S, Seattle, WA 98108 *Tel:* 206-461-1300 *E-mail:* ppcprint@nwlink.com; ppccirc@nwlink.com; ppcbind@nwlink.com *Web Site:* pacificpublishingcompany.com, pg 1252

Fazekas, Zsolt Bede, Pannonia Bookstore, 300 Sainte Clair Ave W, Suite 103, Toronto, ON M4V 1S4, Canada *Tel:* 416-966-5156 *E-mail:* info@pannonia.ca *Web Site:* www.pannonia.ca, pg 1318, 1327

Febus, Fernando, Lectorum Publications Inc, 205 Chubb Ave, Lyndhurst, NJ 07071 *Tel:* 201-559-2200 *Toll Free Tel:* 800-345-5946 *Fax:* 201-559-2201 *Toll Free Fax:* 877-532-8676 *E-mail:* lectorum@lectorum.com *Web Site:* www.lectorum.com, pg 1316

Feder, Rosalie Brody, Rosalie Brody, 360 E 72 St, New York, NY 10021 *Tel:* 212-988-8951, pg 1096

Feder, Ted, Art Resource Inc, 65 Bleeker St, 12th fl, New York, NY 10012 *Tel:* 212-505-8700 *Fax:* 212-505-2053 *E-mail:* requests@artres.com *Web Site:* www.artres.com, pg 1445

Federighi, Craig, Apple Inc, One Apple Park Way, Cupertino, CA 95014 *Tel:* 408-996-1010 *Web Site:* www.apple.com, pg 1372

Fedorko, Lauren, DWJ BOOKS LLC, 14 Hill Side Lane, East Hampton, NY 11937 *Tel:* 631-267-8270 *E-mail:* info@dwjbooks.com *Web Site:* www.dwjbooks.com, pg 1357, 1427

Fedorko, Paul, UTA News & Broadcast, 888 Seventh Ave, 7th fl, New York, NY 10106 *Tel:* 212-765-3040 *Fax:* 212-757-6411 *E-mail:* nsb@nsbtalent.com *Web Site:* bienstock.unitedtalent.com, pg 1352

Feeney, Maggie, Retailing Insight, 119 N Commercial St, Suite 560, Bellingham, WA 98225 *Tel:* 360-676-0789 *Toll Free Tel:* 800-463-9243 *E-mail:* info@retailinginsight.com *Web Site:* retailinginsight.com, pg 1131

Feigenbaum, Laurie, Feigenbaum Publishing Consultants Inc, 61 Bounty Lane, Jericho, NY 11753 *Tel:* 516-647-8314 (cell), pg 1345

Feinblum, Brian, Media Connect, 301 E 57 St, 4th fl, New York, NY 10022 *Tel:* 212-583-2718 *Web Site:* www.media-connect.com, pg 1099

Feldheim, Yitzchak, Feldheim Publishers, 208 Airport Executive Park, Nanuet, NY 10954 *Tel:* 845-356-2282 *Toll Free Tel:* 800-237-7149 (orders) *Fax:* 845-425-1908 *E-mail:* sales@feldheim.com *Web Site:* www.feldheim.com, pg 1313

Felgenbaum, Laurie, Linick International Inc, Linick Bldg, 7 Putter Lane, Middle Island, NY 11953 *Tel:* 631-924-3888; 631-924-8555; 631-604-8599 *E-mail:* topmarketingadvisor@gmail.com *Web Site:* topmarketingadvisor.com, pg 1349

Felski, Rita, New Literary History: A Journal of Theory & Interpretation, 2715 N Charles St, Baltimore, MD 21218-4363 *Tel:* 410-516-6987 (journal orders outside US & CN) *Toll Free Tel:* 800-548-1784 (journal orders) *Fax:* 410-516-6968 *E-mail:* jrnlcirc@press.jhu.edu (journal orders) *Web Site:* www.press.jhu.edu/journals/new_literary_history/index.html, pg 1129

Felt, Robert, Redwing Book Co, 202 Bendix St, Taos, NM 87571 *Tel:* 575-758-7758 *Toll Free Tel:* 800-873-3946 (US); 888-873-3947 (CN) *Fax:* 575-758-7768 *E-mail:* info@redwingbooks.com; custsrv@redwingbooks.com *Web Site:* www.redwingbooks.com, pg 1319, 1327

Felts, James W, Comag Marketing Group LLC (CMG), 155 Village Blvd, Suite 300, Princeton, NJ 08540 *Tel:* 609-524-1800 *Fax:* 609-524-1629 *Web Site:* www.i-cmg.com, pg 1312

Feng, Kelly, China Books, 360 Swift Ave, Suite 48, South San Francisco, CA 94080 *Fax:* 650-872-7808 *E-mail:* editor.sinomedia@gmail.com, pg 1311, 1325

Fenkel, William R, Styled Packaging LLC, PO Box 30299, Philadelphia, PA 19103-8299 *Tel:* 610-529-4122 *Fax:* 610-520-9662 *Web Site:* www.taylorbox.com, pg 1255, 1268, 1279, 1333, 1335

Fennell, Laura, Intuit Inc, 2700 Coast Ave, Mountain View, CA 94043 *Tel:* 650-944-6000 *Toll Free Tel:* 800-446-8848 *E-mail:* investor_relations@intuit.com *Web Site:* www.intuit.com, pg 1379

Fennell, Reg, Reginald F Fennell Subscription Service Inc, 1002 W Michigan Ave, Jackson, MI 49202 *Tel:* 517-782-3132 *Toll Free Tel:* 800-603-5557 *Fax:* 517-782-1109 *E-mail:* fennellss@acd.net, pg 1313

Fenton-Hathaway, Anna, Literature & Medicine, 2715 N Charles St, Baltimore, MD 21218-4363 *Toll Free Tel:* 800-548-1784 (journal orders) *Fax:* 410-516-6968 *E-mail:* jrnlcirc@press.jhu.edu (journal orders) *Web Site:* www.press.jhu.edu/journals/literature_and_medicine/index.html, pg 1128

Ferguson, David S, PBD Worldwide Inc, 1650 Bluegrass Lakes Pkwy, Alpharetta, GA 30004 *Tel:* 470-769-1000 *Toll Free Tel:* 866-998-4PBD (998-4723) *E-mail:* sales.marketing@pbd.com; customerservice@pbd.com *Web Site:* www.pbd.com, pg 1333

Ferguson, Debra L, Southern Images Photography, 142 Westlake Dr, Brandon, MS 39047-9020 *Tel:* 601-992-9488 *Web Site:* www.southern-images.com, pg 1443

Ferreyra, Gonzalo, Ingram Publisher Services, an Ingram brand, One Ingram Blvd, La Vergne, TN 37086 *Tel:* 615-793-5000 *Toll Free Tel:* 866-400-5351 (cust serv) *E-mail:* ips@ingramcontent.com *Web Site:* www.ingramcontent.com, pg 1290

Ferris, Kjerstin, Square Deal Records Book Department, 303 Higuera St, San Luis Obispo, CA 93401-1002 *Tel:* 805-543-3636 *Toll Free Tel:* 800-235-4114 *Fax:* 805-543-3938 *E-mail:* web@squaredealonline.com *Web Site:* www.squaredealonline.com, pg 1328

Ferris, R W, Square Deal Records Book Department, 303 Higuera St, San Luis Obispo, CA 93401-1002 *Tel:* 805-543-3636 *Toll Free Tel:* 800-235-4114 *Fax:* 805-543-3938 *E-mail:* web@squaredealonline.com *Web Site:* www.squaredealonline.com, pg 1328

Ferry, Kevin, Ferry Associates Inc, 49 Fostertown Rd, Medford, NJ 08055 *Tel:* 609-953-1233 *Toll Free Tel:* 800-257-5258 *Fax:* 609-953-8637 *Web Site:* www.ferryassociates.com, pg 1204, 1220, 1247, 1276

Fetaya, Alain, Ideal Foreign Books LLC, 132-10 Hillside Ave, Richmond Hill, NY 11418 *Tel:* 718-297-7477 *Toll Free Tel:* 800-284-2490 *Fax:* 718-297-7645 *E-mail:* idealforeignbooks@att.net, pg 1315

Fetherston, James, Worzalla, 3535 Jefferson St, Stevens Point, WI 54481 *Tel:* 715-344-9608 *Fax:* 715-344-2578 *Web Site:* www.worzalla.com, pg 1210, 1228, 1257

Fideler, David PhD, Concord Editorial & Design LLC, 9450 SW Gemini Dr, Suite 68669, Beaverton, OR 97008 *Tel:* 616-827-7537 *Fax:* 616-825-6048 *E-mail:* info@concordeditorial.com *Web Site:* www.concordeditorial.com, pg 1218, 1356

Fiegas, Barbara, Academic Reviews, 1-A Glenwood Ave, Lynbrook, NY 11563 *Tel:* 516-593-1275 *E-mail:* info@academicreviews.com *Web Site:* www.academicreviews.com, pg 1123

Field, David C, Separa Color, 6951 Oran Circle, Buena Park, CA 90621 *Tel:* 818-988-2882 *Toll Free Tel:* 800-859-0629 *Fax:* 818-988-3882 *E-mail:* sales@separacolor.com *Web Site:* www.separacolor.com; www.simplybrochures.com; www.simplycatalogs.com; www.simplypostcards.com, pg 1093

Field, Diane, Continental Web Press Inc, 1430 Industrial Dr, Itasca, IL 60143-1858 *Tel:* 630-773-1903 *E-mail:* inquiries@continentalweb.com *Web Site:* www.continentalweb.com, pg 1245

Field, Ken Jr, Continental Web Press Inc, 1430 Industrial Dr, Itasca, IL 60143-1858 *Tel:* 630-773-1903 *E-mail:* inquiries@continentalweb.com *Web Site:* www.continentalweb.com, pg 1245

Field, Ken Sr, Continental Web Press Inc, 1430 Industrial Dr, Itasca, IL 60143-1858 *Tel:* 630-773-1903 *E-mail:* inquiries@continentalweb.com *Web Site:* www.continentalweb.com, pg 1245

Field, Rikko, JLS Language Corp, 135 Willow Rd, Menlo Park, CA 94025 *Tel:* 650-321-9832 *Fax:* 650-329-9864 *E-mail:* info@jls.com *Web Site:* www.jls.com, pg 1410

Fields, Marty, Interstate Books4School, 201 E Badger Rd, Madison, WI 53713 *Tel:* 608-277-2407 *Toll Free Tel:* 800-752-3131 *Fax:* 608-277-2410 *E-mail:* sales@books4school.com *Web Site:* www.books4school.com, pg 1316

Fieler, Steve, HP Inc, 1501 Paige Mill Rd, Palo Alto, CA 94304-1112 *Tel:* 650-857-1501 *Toll Free Tel:* 800-282-6672 *Web Site:* www.hp.com, pg 1378

Figurniak, Jim, Linick International Inc, Linick Bldg, 7 Putter Lane, Middle Island, NY 11953 *Tel:* 631-924-3888; 631-924-8555; 631-604-8599 *E-mail:* topmarketingadvisor@gmail.com *Web Site:* topmarketingadvisor.com, pg 1349

Fillmore, Laura, Open Book Systems Inc®, 21 Broadway, Suite 5, Rockport, MA 01966 *Tel:* 978-546-7346 *Fax:* 978-231-0222 *E-mail:* info@obs.com *Web Site:* www.obs.com, pg 1350, 1383

Finger, Gail M, A L S International, 18 John St, Suite 300, New York, NY 10038 *Tel:* 212-766-4111 *Toll Free Tel:* 800-322-0284 *Fax:* 212-349-0964 *Toll Free Fax:* 888-662-8048 *E-mail:* rastefanous@alsintl.com *Web Site:* www.alsintl.com, pg 1407

Finger, Gail M, University Language Services Inc (ULS), 15 Maiden Lane, Suite 300, New York, NY 10038 *Tel:* 212-766-4111 *Toll Free Tel:* 800-419-4601 *Fax:* 212-571-7155 *Toll Free Fax:* 800-662-8048 *E-mail:* service@universitylanguage.com *Web Site:* www.universitylanguage.com, pg 1414

Finger, Lea, Lucia|Marquand, 1400 Second Ave, Seattle, WA 98101 *Tel:* 206-624-2030 *Fax:* 206-624-1821 *E-mail:* luciamarquand.com, pg 1359

Finken, Zach, The Tribune News Service, 160 N Stetson Ave, Chicago, IL 60601 *Tel:* 312-222-4131 *E-mail:* tcanews@trbpub.com *Web Site:* www.mctdirect.com; tribunecontentagency.com/tribune-news-service, pg 1186

Fiore, Carol A, ISIS Papyrus America, 301 Bank St, South Lake, TX 76092 *Tel:* 817-416-2345 *Fax:* 817-416-1223 *E-mail:* info@isis-papyrus.com *Web Site:* www.isis-papyrus.com, pg 1379

Fiorelli, Paolo, AlphaGraphics Inc, 143 Union Blvd, Suite 650, Lakewood, CO 80228 *Toll Free Tel:* 800-955-6246 *Fax:* 801-595-7270 *E-mail:* contactus@alphagraphics.com *Web Site:* www.alphagraphics.com, pg 1372

Firestone-Teeter, Naomi, Jewish Book Council, 520 Eighth Ave, 4th fl, New York, NY 10018 *Tel:* 212-201-2920 *Fax:* 212-532-4952 *E-mail:* info@jewishbooks.org *Web Site:* www.jewishbookcouncil.org, pg 1140

Firestone-Teeter, Naomi, Paper Brigade, 520 Eighth Ave, 4th fl, New York, NY 10018 *Tel:* 212-201-2920 *Fax:* 212-532-4952 *E-mail:* info@jewishbooks.org *Web Site:* www.jewishbookcouncil.org, pg 1130

Fischer, Charles H "Skip" III, The Clark Group Inc, 3705 Quakerbridge Rd, Suite 116, Hamilton, NJ 08619 *Tel:* 609-528-7660 *Fax:* 609-528-7710 *E-mail:* service@clarkworldwide.com *Web Site:* www.clarkgroupinc.com, pg 1331

Fish, Thomas PhD, Next Chapter Book Club (NCBC), 125 Woodside Park Dr, Amelia, OH 45102 *Tel:* 614-404-6060 *Web Site:* nextchapterbookclub.org, pg 1137

Fishbein, David, Fish Films Footage World, 1060 Camino Real, Sante Fe, NM 87501 *Tel:* 818-905-1071 *E-mail:* footageworld@aol.com *Web Site:* www.footageworld.com, pg 1446

Fisher, Cory, Krishnamurti Publications of America, 1070 McAndrew Rd, Ojai, CA 93023 *Tel:* 805-646-2726 *E-mail:* kfa@kfa.org *Web Site:* www.kfa.org, pg 1327

Fisher, Howard W, The Fisher Company, PO Box 89578, Tucson, AZ 85752-9578 *Tel:* 520-547-2460 *Web Site:* www.thefishercompany.com, pg 1345

Fiske, Mr Kelly M, Worldwide Books, 1001 W Seneca St, Ithaca, NY 14850-3342 *Tel:* 607-272-9200 *Toll Free Tel:* 800-473-8146 (US/CN orders only) *Fax:* 607-272-0239 *E-mail:* info@worldwide-artbooks.com *Web Site:* www.worldwide-artbooks.com, pg 1300

Fissell, Mary, Bulletin of the History of Medicine, 2715 N Charles St, Baltimore, MD 21218-4363 *Toll Free Tel:* 800-548-1784 (journal orders) *Fax:* 410-516-6968 *E-mail:* jrnlcirc@press.jhu.edu (journal orders) *Web Site:* www.press.jhu.edu/journals/bulletin_of_the_history_of_medicine/index.html, pg 1125

Fitzmaurice, Eamonn, VanDam Inc, The VanDam Bldg, 121 W 27 St, New York, NY 10001 *Tel:* 212-929-0416 *Toll Free Tel:* 800-UNFOLDS (863-6537) *Fax:* 212-929-0426 *E-mail:* info@vandam.com *Web Site:* www.vandam.com, pg 1363

Fitzwilliam, Grant, Spraymation Inc, 4180 NW Tenth Ave, Fort Lauderdale, FL 33309 *Tel:* 954-484-9700 *Toll Free Tel:* 800-327-4985 *Fax:* 954-301-0842 *E-mail:* orders@spraymation.com *Web Site:* www.spraymation.com, pg 1279

Flatow, Bob, Lake Book Manufacturing Inc, 2085 N Cornell Ave, Melrose Park, IL 60160 *Tel:* 708-345-7000 *E-mail:* info@lakebook.com *Web Site:* www.lakebook.com, pg 1206, 1222, 1250, 1264, 1277

Flatt, Doug, PR by the Book LLC, PO Box 6226, Round Rock, TX 78683 *Tel:* 512-501-4399 *Fax:* 512-501-4399 *E-mail:* info@prbythebook.com *Web Site:* www.prbythebook.com, pg 1101

Flatt, Marika, PR by the Book LLC, PO Box 6226, Round Rock, TX 78683 *Tel:* 512-501-4399 *Fax:* 512-501-4399 *E-mail:* info@prbythebook.com *Web Site:* www.prbythebook.com, pg 1101

Flattau, Ed, Global Horizons, 1330 New Hampshire Ave NW, Unit 609, Washington, DC 20036, pg 1184

Flavin, Bill, Lake Book Manufacturing Inc, 2085 N Cornell Ave, Melrose Park, IL 60160 *Tel:* 708-345-7000 *E-mail:* info@lakebook.com *Web Site:* www.lakebook.com, pg 1207, 1222, 1250, 1265, 1277

Flavin, Frank P, Flavin Photography, 5401 Cordova St, Suite 305, Anchorage, AK 99514 *Tel:* 907-561-1606 *Fax:* 907-242-8206 *E-mail:* flavin@alaska.net *Web Site:* www.flavinphotography.com, pg 1437

Flax, Shoshana, The Horn Book Magazine, 300 The Fenway, Suite P-311, Palace Road Bldg, Boston, MA 02115 *Tel:* 617-278-0225 *Toll Free Tel:* 888-628-0225 *Fax:* 617-278-6062 *E-mail:* info@hbook.com *Web Site:* www.hbook.com, pg 1127

Fleeman, Mark, Fujii Associates Inc, 75 Sunny Hill Dr, Troy, MO 63379 *Tel:* 636-528-2546 *Fax:* 636-600-5153 *Web Site:* www.fujiiassociates.com, pg 1287

Fleisch, Thomas, Cromwell Leather, 147 Palmer Ave, Mamaroneck, NY 10543 *Tel:* 914-381-0100 *Fax:* 914-381-0046 *E-mail:* sales@cromwellgroup.com *Web Site:* www.cromwellgroup.com, pg 1262

Fleming, Tom, ALC Inc, 750 College Rd E, Suite 201, Princeton, NJ 08540 *Tel:* 609-580-2800 *Toll Free Tel:* 800-252-5478 *Fax:* 609-580-2888 *E-mail:* info@alc.com *Web Site:* www.alc.com, pg 1111

Flint, Alan, AGS, 4590 Graphics Dr, White Plains, MD 20695 *Tel:* 301-843-1800 *Fax:* 301-843-6339 *E-mail:* info@ags.com *Web Site:* www.ags.com, pg 1201, 1241, 1372

Flood, Stephen, Universal|Wilde, 26 Dartmouth St, Westwood, MA 02090 *Tel:* 781-251-2700 *Fax:* 781-251-2613 *Web Site:* www.universalwilde.com, pg 1093, 1107, 1227, 1256

Flory, Kyle, LOF Productions, 121 Greenwich Rd, Suite 202, Charlotte, NC 28211 *Tel:* 704-375-8892 *Fax:* 704-375-6316 *Web Site:* www.lofproductions.com, pg 1441

Flottman, Peter, Flottman Co Inc, 720 Centre View Blvd, Crestview Hills, KY 41017 *Tel:* 859-331-6636 *Fax:* 859-344-7085 *E-mail:* info@flottmanco.com *Web Site:* www.flottmanco.com, pg 1204

Flynn, Kathleen, Indigo Books & Music Inc, 468 King St W, Suite 500, Toronto, ON M5V 1L8, Canada *Tel:* 416-364-4499 *E-mail:* cisales@indigo.ca *Web Site:* www.chapters.indigo.ca, pg 1290

Freeman, Kent, Ingram Content Group LLC, One Ingram Blvd, La Vergne, TN 37086-1986 *Tel:* 615-793-5000 *Toll Free Tel:* 800-937-8000 (retailers); 800-937-5300 (ext 1, libs) *E-mail:* customerservice@ingramcontent.com *Web Site:* www.ingramcontent.com, pg 1290, 1315

Freeman, Nancy, VeronaLibri, 124 Willowbrook Ave, Stamford, CT 06902 *Tel:* 203-614-8335 *Web Site:* www.veronalibri.com, pg 1256

Freese, Michael, Rushmore News Inc, 924 E Saint Andrew, Rapid City, SD 57701 *Tel:* 605-342-2617 *Toll Free Tel:* 800-423-0501, pg 1319

Freitag, Brad, Claris International Inc, 5201 Patrick Henry Dr, Santa Clara, CA 95054 *Tel:* 408-727-8227 (sales & cust support) *Toll Free Tel:* 800-725-2747 (sales); 800-325-2747 (cust support) *Fax:* 408-987-7447 *E-mail:* claris_sales@claris.com *Web Site:* www.claris.com, pg 1374

French, Don, The Source Stock Footage Library Inc, 140 S Camino Seco Blvd, Suite 308, Tucson, AZ 85710 *Tel:* 520-298-4810; 212-925-2547 *E-mail:* sourcestk@aol.com *Web Site:* www.sourcefootage.com, pg 1449

Frerichs, Darold D, Versa Press Inc, 1465 Spring Bay Rd, East Peoria, IL 61611-9788 *Tel:* 309-822-8272 *Toll Free Tel:* 800-447-7829 *Fax:* 309-822-8141 *Web Site:* www.versapress.com, pg 1209, 1227, 1256, 1269

Freund, Ron, Midpoint National Inc, 1263 Southwest Blvd, Kansas City, KS 66103 *Tel:* 913-362-7400 *Toll Free Tel:* 800-228-4321 *E-mail:* info@midpt.com *Web Site:* www.midpt.com, pg 1292

Frew, Lena, C & C Offset Printing Co USA Inc, 70 W 36 St, Unit 10C, New York, NY 10018 *Tel:* 212-431-4210 *Toll Free Fax:* 866-540-4134 *Web Site:* www.ccoffset.com, pg 1202, 1217, 1243

Freydank, Gabriele, Tri-Fold Books, PO Box 534, King City, ON L7B 1A7, Canada *Tel:* 905-726-0142 *Fax:* 905-727-1068 *E-mail:* info@trifoldbooks.com, pg 1300

Fried, Robert, Robert Fried Photography, 610 Eldridge Ct, Novato, CA 94947 *Tel:* 415-898-6153 *Fax:* 415-897-0353 *E-mail:* rob@robertfriedphotography.com *Web Site:* www.robertfriedphotography.com, pg 1438

Friedenberg, Michael, Thomson Reuters, 3 Times Sq, New York, NY 10036 *Tel:* 646-223-4000; 646-223-6100 (edit); 646-223-6000 (newsroom) *Web Site:* www.thomsonreuters.com, pg 1186

Friedman, Dina, Accurate Writing & More, 16 Barstow Lane, Hadley, MA 01035 *Tel:* 413-586-2388 *Web Site:* frugalmarketing.com, pg 1085

Friedman, Dina, Accurate Writing & More, 16 Barstow Lane, Hadley, MA 01035 *Tel:* 413-586-2388 *Web Site:* frugalmarketing.com; www.accuratewriting.com, pg 1095

Friedman, Dina, Accurate Writing & More, 16 Barstow Lane, Hadley, MA 01035 *Tel:* 413-586-2388 *Web Site:* frugalmarketing.com, pg 1341

Friel, Emily, Integra Software Services Inc, 1110 Jorie Blvd, Suite 200, Oak Brook, IL 60523 *Tel:* 630-586-2579 *Fax:* 630-586-2599 *E-mail:* marketing@integra.co.in *Web Site:* www.integra.co.in, pg 1347, 1358

Friesen, Chad, Friesens Corp, One Printers Way, Altona, MB R0G 0B0, Canada *Tel:* 204-324-6401 *Fax:* 204-324-1333 *E-mail:* book_info@friesens.com *Web Site:* www.friesens.com, pg 1205, 1247

Friesen, Russell, Login Canada, 300 Saulteaux Crescent, Winnipeg, MB R3J 3T2, Canada *Tel:* 204-837-2987 *Toll Free Tel:* 800-665-1148 (CN only) *Fax:* 204-837-3116 *Toll Free Fax:* 800-665-0103 *E-mail:* sales@lb.ca *Web Site:* www.lb.ca, pg 1317

Fritsch, Janet, The American Collective Stand®, 277 White St, Buchanan, NY 10511 *Tel:* 914-739-7500 *Toll Free Tel:* 800-462-7687 *Fax:* 914-739-7575 *Web Site:* www.americancollectivestand.com, pg 1133

Fritz, Gerard, Novastock International Photo Agency, 1306 Matthews Plantation Dr, Matthews, NC 28105 *E-mail:* novastock@aol.com, pg 1448

Fritz, Thomas M, Beidel Printing House Inc, 225 S Fayette St, Shippensburg, PA 17257 *Tel:* 717-532-5063 *Fax:* 717-532-2502 *E-mail:* customerservice@dreamprint.com *Web Site:* dreamprint.com, pg 1242, 1342

Froehlich, Conrad G, Osa's Ark Museum Shop, 111 N Lincoln Ave, Chanute, KS 66720 *Tel:* 620-431-2730 *Fax:* 620-431-2730 *E-mail:* osajohns@safarimuseum.com; osasark@yahoo.com *Web Site:* www.safarimuseum.com, pg 1318

Froman, Craig, Master Books®, 3142 Hwy 103 N, Green Forest, AR 72638 *Tel:* 870-438-5288 *Toll Free Tel:* 800-999-3777 *E-mail:* nlp@nlpg.com; sales@masterbooks.com *Web Site:* www.masterbooks.com; www.nlpg.com/imprint/master-books, pg 1381

Fry, David S, Fry Communications Inc, 800 W Church Rd, Mechanicsburg, PA 17055 *Tel:* 717-766-0211 *Toll Free Tel:* 800-334-1429 *Fax:* 717-691-0341 *E-mail:* info@frycomm.com *Web Site:* www.frycomm.com, pg 1205, 1220, 1247, 1276

Fry, Henry, Fry Communications Inc, 800 W Church Rd, Mechanicsburg, PA 17055 *Tel:* 717-766-0211 *Toll Free Tel:* 800-334-1429 *Fax:* 717-691-0341 *E-mail:* info@frycomm.com *Web Site:* www.frycomm.com, pg 1205, 1220, 1247, 1276

Fujiwara, Sho, RISO Inc, 10 State St, Suite 201, Woburn, MA 01801-2105 *Tel:* 978-777-7377 *Toll Free Tel:* 800-942-7476 (cust support) *Web Site:* us.riso.com, pg 1253, 1385

Fuller, Larry, fd2s, 1634 E Cesar Chavez, Austin, TX 78702 *Tel:* 512-476-7733 *Web Site:* www.fd2s.com, pg 1428

Furtak, Shannon, William S Hein & Co Inc, 2350 N Forest Rd, Getzville, NY 14068 *Tel:* 716-882-2600 *Toll Free Tel:* 800-828-7571 *Fax:* 716-883-8100 *E-mail:* mail@wshein.com; marketing@wshein.com *Web Site:* www.wshein.com, pg 1315

Gaafar, Sean, Rimage Corp, 201 General Mills Blvd, Golden Valley, MN 55427 *Tel:* 952-944-8144; 952-946-0004 (option 2, tech support) *Toll Free Tel:* 800-445-8288; 800-553-8312 (option 2, tech support) *E-mail:* sales@rimage.com *Web Site:* www.rimage.com, pg 1385

Gagliano, John, St Joseph Communications-Print Group, 50 Macintosh Blvd, Concord, ON L4K 4P3, Canada *Tel:* 905-660-3111 *E-mail:* marketing@stjoseph.com *Web Site:* stjoseph.com, pg 1093, 1254

Gaither, John, Reichhold Inc, 1035 Swabia Ct, Durham, NC 27703 *Tel:* 919-990-7500 *Toll Free Tel:* 800-448-3482 *Fax:* 919-990-7749 *Web Site:* www.reichhold.com, pg 1267

Galasso, Al, National Association of Book Entrepreneurs (NABE), PO Box 606, Cottage Grove, OR 97424 *Tel:* 541-942-7455 *Fax:* 541-942-7455 *E-mail:* nabe@bookmarketingprofits.com *Web Site:* www.bookmarketingprofits.com, pg 1133, 1293

Galbreath, Howard, The Printer, 2810 Cowell Blvd, Davis, CA 95618 *Tel:* 530-753-2519 *Fax:* 530-753-2528 *E-mail:* info@the-printer.net *Web Site:* the-printer.net, pg 1093, 1253

Gall, David, BR Printers, 665 Lenfest Rd, San Jose, CA 95133 *Tel:* 408-278-7711 *Fax:* 408-929-8062 *E-mail:* info@brprinters.com *Web Site:* www.brprinters.com, pg 1091, 1243

Gallagher, Bill, Alliance Storage Technologies Inc (ASTI), 10045 Federal Dr, Colorado Springs, CO 80908 *Tel:* 719-593-7900 *Toll Free Tel:* 888-567-6332 *Fax:* 719-598-3472 *E-mail:* sales@astiusa.com; info@astiusa.com *Web Site:* www.alliancestoragetechnologies.com, pg 1372

Gallagher, Jim, OTTN Publishing, 16 Risler St, Stockton, NJ 08559 *Tel:* 609-397-4005 *Toll Free Tel:* 866-356-6886 *Fax:* 609-397-4007 *E-mail:* inquiries@ottnpublishing.com; sales@ottnpublishing.com *Web Site:* www.ottnpublishing.com, pg 1360

Gallagher, Kelly, Ingram Content Group LLC, One Ingram Blvd, La Vergne, TN 37086-1986 *Tel:* 615-793-5000 *Toll Free Tel:* 800-937-8000 (retailers); 800-937-5300 (ext 1, libs) *E-mail:* customerservice@ingramcontent.com *Web Site:* www.ingramcontent.com, pg 1290, 1315

Gallagher, Sharon, Distributed Art Publishers (DAP), 75 Broad St, Suite 630, New York, NY 10004 *Tel:* 212-627-1999 *Toll Free Tel:* 800-338-2665 (cust serv) *Fax:* 212-627-9484 *Toll Free Fax:* 800-478-3128 *E-mail:* orders@dapinc.com *Web Site:* www.artbook.com, pg 1286

Gallagher, Thomas L, Religion News Service, c/o University of Missouri's Journalism School, 30 Neff Annex, Columbia, MO 65211 *Tel:* 573-884-1327 *E-mail:* info@religionnews.com *Web Site:* www.religionnews.com, pg 1186

Gallant, Barry, Penguin Random House Canada, 320 Front St W, Suite 1400, Toronto, ON M5V 3B6, Canada *Tel:* 416-364-4449 *Toll Free Tel:* 888-523-9292 (cust serv) *Fax:* 416-598-7764 *Web Site:* www.penguinrandomhouse.ca, pg 1295

Gallant, Thomas W, Journal of Modern Greek Studies, 2715 N Charles St, Baltimore, MD 21218-4363 *Toll Free Tel:* 800-548-1784 (journal orders) *Fax:* 410-516-6968 *E-mail:* jrnlcirc@press.jhu.edu (journal orders) *Web Site:* www.press.jhu.edu/journals/journal_of_modern_greek_studies/index.html, pg 1128

Galletta, Gregg, ALC Inc, 750 College Rd E, Suite 201, Princeton, NJ 08540 *Tel:* 609-580-2800 *Toll Free Tel:* 800-252-5478 *Fax:* 609-580-2888 *E-mail:* info@alc.com *Web Site:* www.alc.com, pg 1111

Galligan, John, Bradford & Bigelow Inc, 3 Perkins Way, Newburyport, MA 01950-4007 *Tel:* 978-904-3100 *E-mail:* sales@bradford-bigelow.com *Web Site:* www.bradford-bigelow.com, pg 1202, 1243

Gallo, Jamie, Wunderman, 3 Columbus Circle, New York, NY 10019 *Tel:* 212-941-3000 *Web Site:* www.wunderman.com, pg 1087

Gallo, Jim, Specialty Finishing Group, 1401 Kirk St, Elk Grove Village, IL 60007 *Tel:* 847-290-0110 *Fax:* 847-290-9404 *Web Site:* www.sfgrp.com, pg 1254

Gallup, Stuart, Mark Andy Inc, 18081 Chesterfield Airport Rd, Chesterfield, MO 63005 *Tel:* 636-532-4433 *Toll Free Tel:* 800-447-1231 *Toll Free Fax:* 800-447-1231 *Web Site:* www.presstek.com; markandy.com; shop.markandy.com, pg 1372

Gamache, Genevieve, Prologue Inc, 1650 Blvd Lionel-Bertrand, Boisbriand, QC J7H 1N7, Canada *Tel:* 450-434-0306 (ext 231) *Toll Free Tel:* 800-363-2864 *Fax:* 450-434-2627 *Toll Free Fax:* 800-361-8088 (cust serv) *E-mail:* prologue@prologue.ca *Web Site:* www.prologue.ca; www.prologuenumerique.ca, pg 1295

Gammons, Robert, Schaefer Machine Co Inc, 200 Commercial Dr, Deep River, CT 06417 *Tel:* 860-526-4000 *Toll Free Tel:* 800-243-5143 *Fax:* 860-526-4654 *E-mail:* schaefer@schaeferco.com *Web Site:* www.schaeferco.com, pg 1279

Gandert, Nate, Getty Images Inc, 605 Fifth Ave S, Suite 400, Seattle, WA 98104 *Tel:* 206-925-5000 *Toll Free Tel:* 800-IMAGERY (462-4379 sales); 888-888-5889 *E-mail:* enterprisesolutionssales@gettyimages.com *Web Site:* www.gettyimages.com, pg 1378, 1447

Ganesan, Prasannaa, Corel Corp, 1600 Carling Ave, Ottawa, ON K1Z 8R7, Canada *Tel:* 613-728-8200 (PR) *Toll Free Tel:* 877-582-6735 *Web Site:* www.corel.com, pg 1375

Ganser, Doris, Transimpex Translators, Interpreters, Editors, Consultants Inc, 2300 Main St, 9th fl, Kansas City, MO 64108 *Tel:* 816-561-3777 *Toll Free Tel:* 888-877-4679 *Fax:* 816-561-5515 *E-mail:* translations@transimpex.com *Web Site:* www.transimpex.com, pg 1414

Garcia, Cesar, Premier Graphics, 860 Honeyspot Rd, Stratford, CT 06615 *Tel:* 203-378-6200 *Toll Free Tel:* 800-414-1624 *Fax:* 203-386-1624 *E-mail:* info@premieruplink.com *Web Site:* www.premieruplink.com, pg 1107, 1110

Garcia, Michael, Domtar Paper Co LLC, 234 Kingsley Park Dr, Fort Mill, SC 29715 *Tel:* 803-802-7500 *Toll Free Tel:* 877-877-4685 *E-mail:* communications@domtar.com; commercialprinting@domtar.com *Web Site:* www.domtar.com, pg 1262

Gordon, Peter, Absolut Color, 109 W 27 St, New York, NY 10001 *Tel:* 212-868-0404 *E-mail:* info@absolutcolor.com *Web Site:* www.absolutcolor.com, pg 1241

Gordon, Susan, Lynne Palmer Executive Recruitment Inc, 295 Madison Ave, Suite 1700, New York, NY 10017 *Tel:* 212-883-0203 *Fax:* 212-883-0149 *E-mail:* careers@lpalmer.com *Web Site:* www.lpalmer.com, pg 1389

Gore, Bruce, Gore Studio Inc, 101 Paxton Ct, Brentwood, TN 37027 *Tel:* 615-519-2262 *E-mail:* gorestudioinc@gmail.com *Web Site:* www.gorestudio.com, pg 1428

Gorham, Kurt, Gorham Printing, 3718 Mahoney Dr, Centralia, WA 98531 *Tel:* 360-623-1323 *Toll Free Tel:* 800-837-0970 *E-mail:* info@gorhamprinting.com *Web Site:* www.gorhamprinting.com, pg 1248

Gorham, Norma, Gorham Printing, 3718 Mahoney Dr, Centralia, WA 98531 *Tel:* 360-623-1323 *Toll Free Tel:* 800-837-0970 *E-mail:* info@gorhamprinting.com *Web Site:* www.gorhamprinting.com, pg 1248

Goroff, Sandra, Sandra Goroff & Associates, 42 Waterfall Dr, Suite L, Canton, MA 02021 *Tel:* 617-750-0555 *E-mail:* sgma@aol.com *Web Site:* www.sandragoroff.com, pg 1097

Gorowsky, John, Symbology Inc, 7351 Kirkwood Lane N, Suite 126, Maple Grove, MN 55369 *Tel:* 763-315-8080 *Toll Free Tel:* 800-328-2612 *Fax:* 763-315-8088 *E-mail:* clientservices@symbology.com; sales@symbology.com *Web Site:* www.symbology.com, pg 1226

Gorsline, Russell, REX, 13431 SW Scotts Bridge Dr, Tigard, OR 97223-1609 *Tel:* 503-238-4525 *E-mail:* info@rexpost.com *Web Site:* www.rexpost.com, pg 1384

Gospodarek, Bob, Baker & Taylor Publisher Services, 30 Amberwood Pkwy, Ashland, OH 44805 *Tel:* 567-215-0030 *Toll Free Tel:* 888-814-0208 *E-mail:* info@btpubservices.com; orders@btpubservices.com *Web Site:* www.btpubservices.com, pg 1283, 1331, 1408, 1424

Gossen, Jeff, Symbology Inc, 7351 Kirkwood Lane N, Suite 126, Maple Grove, MN 55369 *Tel:* 763-315-8080 *Toll Free Tel:* 800-328-2612 *Fax:* 763-315-8088 *E-mail:* clientservices@symbology.com; sales@symbology.com *Web Site:* www.symbology.com, pg 1226

Gotshall, Dan, Dan Gotshall Marine Life Photography, 4 Sommerset Rise, Monterey, CA 93940 *Tel:* 831-656-9169 *E-mail:* seachall@aol.com, pg 1438

Gottesman, Jan, Spicers Paper, 12310 E Slauson Ave, Santa Fe Springs, CA 90670 *Toll Free Tel:* 800-774-2377 *Fax:* 562-693-8339 *Web Site:* www.spicers.com, pg 1268

Gottlieb, Audrey, Audrey Gottlieb, 161 York St, Unit 21, York, ME 03909 *Tel:* 207-641-7490 *E-mail:* audreyphoto@gmail.com *Web Site:* www.audreygottlieb.com, pg 1438

Gougherty, Dan, Capitol News Service, 530 Bercut Dr, Suite E, Sacramento, CA 95811 *Tel:* 916-445-6336 *E-mail:* sacramentobulletin@gmail.com *Web Site:* www.mnc.net/capitol.htm, pg 1184

Gould, Donna, Phoenix Media, 29 Miriam Dr, Matawan, NJ 07747 *Tel:* 732-441-1519 *Fax:* 732-566-1913 *Web Site:* www.phoenixmediapr.com, pg 1100

Goullard, Diane, French and English Communication Services LLC, 3104 E Camelback Rd, No 124, Phoenix, AZ 85016-4502 *Tel:* 602-870-1000 *E-mail:* RequestFAECS2008@cox.net *Web Site:* www.FrenchAndEnglish.com, pg 1409

Gourley, Michael, Chesapeake & Hudson Inc, 115 W Potomac St, Brunswick, MD 21716 *Tel:* 301-834-7170 *Toll Free Tel:* 800-231-4469 *Toll Free Fax:* 800-307-5163 *E-mail:* office@cheshud.com *Web Site:* www.cheshud.com, pg 1285

Gow, Val, Penguin Random House Canada, 320 Front St W, Suite 1400, Toronto, ON M5V 3B6, Canada *Tel:* 416-364-4449 *Toll Free Tel:* 888-523-9292 (cust serv) *Fax:* 416-598-7764 *Web Site:* www.penguinrandomhouse.ca, pg 1295

Gowen, George, Ricoh Americas Corp, 300 Eagleview Blvd, Exton, PA 19341 *Tel:* 610-296-8000 *Toll Free Tel:* 800-333-2679 (prod support); 800-637-4264 (sales) *Web Site:* www.ricoh-usa.com, pg 1385

Grab, Alex K, Electronics for Imaging Inc (EFI), 6750 Dumbarton Circle, Fremont, CA 94555 *Tel:* 650-357-3500 *Toll Free Tel:* 800-568-1917; 800-875-7117 (sales) *Fax:* 650-357-3907 *E-mail:* info@efi.com *Web Site:* www.efi.com, pg 1376

Graf, Jane R, Casemate | IPM, 1950 Lawrence Rd, Havertown, PA 19083 *Tel:* 610-853-9131 *Fax:* 610-853-9146 *E-mail:* casemate@casematepublishers.com *Web Site:* www.casemateipm.com, pg 1096, 1105, 1284, 1343

Graf, Michael, Letterhead Press Inc (LPI), 16800 W Ryerson Rd, New Berlin, WI 53151 *Tel:* 262-787-1717 *Fax:* 262-787-1710; 262-787-7315 (estimating) *E-mail:* contact@letterhead-press.com *Web Site:* www.letterheadpress.com, pg 1250

Grahame, Brigid, Renouf Publishing Co Ltd, 22-1010 Polytek St, Ottawa, ON K1J 9J1, Canada *Tel:* 613-745-2665 *Toll Free Tel:* 866-767-6766; 888-551-7470 (North America) *Fax:* 613-745-7660 *E-mail:* order.dept@renoufbooks.com *Web Site:* www.renoufbooks.com, pg 1297

Grahame, Gordon, Renouf Publishing Co Ltd, 22-1010 Polytek St, Ottawa, ON K1J 9J1, Canada *Tel:* 613-745-2665 *Toll Free Tel:* 866-767-6766; 888-551-7470 (North America) *Fax:* 613-745-7660 *E-mail:* order.dept@renoufbooks.com *Web Site:* www.renoufbooks.com, pg 1297

Grant, Nathan L, African American Review (AAR), St Louis University, 317 Adorjan Hall, 3800 Lindell Blvd, St Louis, MO 63108 *Tel:* 314-977-3688 *Fax:* 314-977-1514 *Web Site:* aar.slu.edu, pg 1123

Grant, Patricia, VanDam Inc, The VanDam Bldg, 121 W 27 St, New York, NY 10001 *Tel:* 212-929-0416 *Toll Free Tel:* 800-UNFOLDS (863-6537) *Fax:* 212-929-0426 *E-mail:* info@vandam.com *Web Site:* www.vandam.com, pg 1363

Grantz, Peter, Crain Communications Inc, 1155 Gratiot Ave, Detroit, MI 48207-2732 *Tel:* 313-446-6000 *Fax:* 313-446-0383 *E-mail:* info@crain.com *Web Site:* crain.com, pg 1184

Graves, Mike, Midland Paper, Packaging & Supplies, 101 E Palatine Rd, Wheeling, IL 60090 *Tel:* 847-777-2700 *Toll Free Tel:* 800-323-8522; 888-564-3526 (cust serv) *Fax:* 847-403-6320 (cust serv) *E-mail:* whl@midlandpaper.com; sales@midlandpaper.com; custservice@midlandpaper.com *Web Site:* www.midlandpaper.com, pg 1265

Grayson, Fred N, American BookWorks Corp, 309 Florida Hill Rd, Ridgefield, CT 06877 *Tel:* 203-244-9522 (orders) *E-mail:* info@abwcorporation.com, pg 1355

Green, Brandy, Electronics for Imaging Inc (EFI), 6750 Dumbarton Circle, Fremont, CA 94555 *Tel:* 650-357-3500 *Toll Free Tel:* 800-568-1917; 800-875-7117 (sales) *Fax:* 650-357-3907 *E-mail:* info@efi.com *Web Site:* www.efi.com, pg 1376

Green, Eve, Whitegate Features Syndicate, 71 Faunce Dr, Providence, RI 02906 *Tel:* 401-274-2149 *Web Site:* www.whitegatefeatures.com, pg 1186

Green, Fran, ALC Inc, 750 College Rd E, Suite 201, Princeton, NJ 08540 *Tel:* 609-580-2800 *Toll Free Tel:* 800-252-5478 *Fax:* 609-580-2888 *E-mail:* info@alc.com *Web Site:* www.alc.com, pg 1111

Green, Heidi, Upstart Books™, PO Box 7488, Madison, WI 53707 *Tel:* 608-241-1201 *Toll Free Tel:* 800-356-1200 (orders); 800-962-4463 (cust serv) *Toll Free Fax:* 800-245-1329 (orders) *E-mail:* custserv@demco.com; order@demco.com *Web Site:* www.demco.com/upstart, pg 1140, 1322

Green, Joel, L+L Printers, 6200 Yarrow Dr, Carlsbad, CA 92011 *Tel:* 760-438-3456; 760-477-0321 *Fax:* 760-929-0853 *E-mail:* info@llprinters.com *Web Site:* www.llprinters.com, pg 1250

Green, Michael, AWT World Trade Inc, 4321 N Knox Ave, Chicago, IL 60641-1906 *Tel:* 773-777-7100 *Fax:* 773-777-0909 *E-mail:* sales@awtworldtrade.com *Web Site:* www.awt-gpi.com, pg 1273

Green, Victoria, Dell Magazines, 44 Wall St, Suite 904, New York, NY 10005-2401 *Tel:* 212-686-7188 *Toll Free Tel:* 800-220-7443 (corp sales) *Fax:* 212-480-5751 *E-mail:* customerservice@pennydellpuzzles.com *Web Site:* www.pennydellpuzzles.com, pg 1357

Greenberg, Karen Matsu, Hourglass Press LLC, 39 W 32 St, Suite 1404, New York, NY 10001 *Tel:* 917-449-3707 *Web Site:* www.hourglasspress.com, pg 1358

Greenberg, Susannah, Susannah Greenberg Public Relations, 41 Old Brook Rd, Dix Hills, NY 11746 *Tel:* 646-801-7477 *E-mail:* publicity@bookbuzz.com *Web Site:* bookbuzz.com; linkedin.com/in/susannahgreenberg; www.facebook.com/SusannahGreenbergPublicRelations; twitter.com/SueGreenbergPR, pg 1097

Greenblatt, Jonathan, Anti-Defamation League, 605 Third Ave, New York, NY 10158-3560 *Tel:* 212-885-7700 *Web Site:* www.adl.org, pg 1139

Greene, Bruce, Compassion Books, 7036 Hwy 80 S, Burnsville, NC 28714 *Tel:* 828-675-5909 *Toll Free Tel:* 800-970-4220 *Fax:* 828-675-9687 *E-mail:* orders@compassionbooks.com *Web Site:* www.compassionbooks.com, pg 1135

Greenleaf, Clint, Greenleaf Book Group LLC, 3 Park Place, 4005 Banister Lane, Suite B, Austin, TX 78704 *Tel:* 512-891-6100 *Fax:* 512-891-6150 *E-mail:* contact@greenleafbookgroup.com *Web Site:* www.greenleafbookgroup.com, pg 1288, 1358

Greer, Derrick, Tennessee Book Co, 1550 Heil Quaker Blvd, La Vergne, TN 37086 *Tel:* 615-793-5040 *Toll Free Tel:* 800-456-0418 *Fax:* 615-213-9545 *Web Site:* www.tennesseebook.com, pg 1321

Gregory, Cam, Bookshelf Bindery Ltd, 22 Secord Dr, Unit 16, St Catharines, ON L2N 1K8, Canada *Tel:* 905-934-2801 *E-mail:* bookshelfbindery@bellnet.ca, pg 1243

Grifalconi, Ann, Ann Grifalconi/Greyfalcon House, 124 Waverly Place, No 1, New York, NY 10011 *Tel:* 212-777-9042, pg 1428

Griffin, Andrew, Metro Editorial Services, 519 Eighth Ave, New York, NY 10018 *Tel:* 212-947-5100 (ext 253, outside US & CN) *Toll Free Tel:* 800-223-1600 *E-mail:* service@metro-email.com *Web Site:* www.mcg.metrocreativeconnection.com, pg 1185

Griffin, Kelly, Aquent LLC, 101 W Elm St, Suite 300, Conshohocken, PA 19428-2075 *Tel:* 610-828-0900 *Toll Free Fax:* 877-303-5224 *E-mail:* questions@aquent.com *Web Site:* aquentstudios.com; aquent.com, pg 1216, 1373, 1389

Griffin, Peter, Essex Products Group, 30 Industrial Park Rd, Centerbrook, CT 06409-0307 *Tel:* 860-767-7130 *Toll Free Tel:* 800-394-7130 *Fax:* 860-767-9137 *E-mail:* sales@epg-inc.com *Web Site:* www.epg-inc.com, pg 1276

Griffin, Susan M, The Henry James Review, 2715 N Charles St, Baltimore, MD 21218-4363 *Tel:* 410-516-6987 (journal orders outside US & CN) *Toll Free Tel:* 800-548-1784 (journal orders) *Fax:* 410-516-6968 *E-mail:* jrnlcirc@press.jhu.edu (journal orders) *Web Site:* www.press.jhu.edu/journals/henry_james_review/index.html, pg 1126

Griffith, Mike, DCA Inc, 1515 E Pine St, Cushing, OK 74023 *Tel:* 918-225-0346 *Fax:* 918-225-1113 *E-mail:* sales@dcainc.com *Web Site:* www.dcainc.com, pg 1375

Grima, Tony, Children's Braille Book Club, 88 Saint Stephen St, Boston, MA 02115-4312 *Tel:* 617-266-6160 *Toll Free Tel:* 800-548-7323 (cust serv) *Fax:* 617-437-0456 *E-mail:* contact@nbp.org *Web Site:* www.nbp.org, pg 1135

Haney, Mike, Allied Vaughn, 7600 Parklawn Ave, Suite 300, Minneapolis, MN 55435 *Tel:* 952-832-3100 *Toll Free Tel:* 800-323-0281 *Fax:* 952-832-3203 *Web Site:* www.alliedvaughn.com, pg 1372

Hanger, Nancy C, Windhaven®, 466 Rte 10, Orford, NH 03777 *Tel:* 603-512-9251 (cell) *E-mail:* info@windhavenpress.com *Web Site:* www.windhavenpress.com, pg 1228

Hannigan, Deece, Sappi Fine Paper North America, 255 State St, Boston, MA 02109 *Tel:* 617-423-7300 *Toll Free Tel:* 800-882-4332 *E-mail:* webqueriesna@sappi.com *Web Site:* www.sappi.com/na, pg 1267

Hansen, Jan, WeWrite LLC, 11040 Alba Rd, Ben Lomond, CA 95005 *Tel:* 831-336-3382 *E-mail:* info@wewrite.net *Web Site:* www.wewrite.net, pg 1322, 1388

Hansen, Jeffrey, Horizon Paper Co Inc, 1010 Washington Blvd, Stamford, CT 06901 *Tel:* 203-358-0855 *Toll Free Tel:* 866-358-0855 *E-mail:* info@horizonpaper.com *Web Site:* www.horizonpaper.com, pg 1264

Hansen, Lena Torslow, Art Consulting Scandinavia: Books on Art & Architecture, 25777 Punto de Vista Dr, Monte Nido, CA 91302-2155 *Tel:* 310-456-8762 *Fax:* 310-456-5714 *E-mail:* info@nordicartbooks.com *Web Site:* www.nordicartbooks.com, pg 1309

Hansinger, Mark, OKI Data Americas Inc, 8505 Freeport Pkwy, Suite 600, Irving, TX 75063 *Tel:* 972-815-4800 *Toll Free Tel:* 800-OKI-DATA (654-3282) *E-mail:* support@okidata.com *Web Site:* www.oki.com/us/printing, pg 1383

Hara, Sheryn, Book Publishers Network, 817 238 St SE, Suite G, Bothell, WA 98021 *Tel:* 425-483-3040 *Fax:* 425-483-3098 *Web Site:* www.bookpublishersnetwork.com, pg 1096

Hardell, Joyce, Ecological Fibers Inc, 40 Pioneer Dr, Lunenburg, MA 01462 *Tel:* 978-537-0003 *Fax:* 978-537-2238 *E-mail:* info@ecofibers.com *Web Site:* www.ecofibers.com, pg 1204, 1263

Hardin, Lara Love, Idea Architects, 523 Swift St, Santa Cruz, CA 95060 *Tel:* 831-465-9565 *Web Site:* www.ideaarchitects.com, pg 1347

Harding, Peter, Lindenmeyr Book Publishing Papers, 3 Manhattanville Rd, Purchase, NY 10577 *Tel:* 914-696-9300 *Web Site:* www.lindenmeyrbook.com, pg 1265

Hargest, Scott, Ironmark, 9040 Junction Dr, Annapolis Junction, MD 20701 *Toll Free Tel:* 888-775-3737 *E-mail:* marketing@ironmarkusa.com *Web Site:* ironmarkusa.com, pg 1206, 1221, 1249, 1264, 1277

Harkness, Frances, C & C Offset Printing Co USA Inc, 70 W 36 St, Unit 10C, New York, NY 10018 *Tel:* 212-431-4210 *Toll Free Fax:* 866-540-4134 *Web Site:* www.ccoffset.com, pg 1202, 1217, 1243

Harper, Bill, Foreword Reviews, 413 E Eighth St, Traverse City, MI 49686 *Tel:* 231-933-3699 *Web Site:* www.forewordreviews.com, pg 1126

Harper, Mary, Access Points Indexing, PO Box 1155, Hood River, OR 97031 *Tel:* 541-806-5436 *Web Site:* www.accesspointsindexing.com, pg 1215

Harrington, Dr Robert M, American Mathematical Society (AMS), 201 Charles St, Providence, RI 02904-2213 *Tel:* 401-455-4000 *Toll Free Tel:* 800-321-4267 *Fax:* 401-331-3842; 401-455-4046 (cust serv) *E-mail:* cust-serv@ams.org; ams@ams.org *Web Site:* www.ams.org, pg 1201, 1215, 1241, 1273

Harris, Debbie, The Crowley Co, 5111 Pegasus Ct, Suite M, Frederick, MD 21704 *Tel:* 240-215-0224 *Fax:* 240-215-0234 *E-mail:* webrequest@thecrowleycompany.com *Web Site:* www.thecrowleycompany.com, pg 1375

Harris, Mary Ann, Xante Corp, 2800 Dauphin St, Suite 100, Mobile, AL 36606 *Tel:* 251-473-6502; 251-473-4920 (tech support) *Fax:* 251-473-6503 *Web Site:* www.xante.com, pg 1388

Harrison, Margaret, Ingram Content Group LLC, One Ingram Blvd, La Vergne, TN 37086-1986 *Tel:* 615-793-5000 *Toll Free Tel:* 800-937-8000 (retailers);

800-937-5300 (ext 1, libs) *E-mail:* customerservice@ingramcontent.com *Web Site:* www.ingramcontent.com, pg 1290, 1315

Harrison, Simon "Ted", Open Text Corp, 275 Frank Tompa Dr, Waterloo, ON N2L 0A1, Canada *Tel:* 519-888-7111 *Fax:* 519-888-0677 *Web Site:* opentext.com, pg 1383

Harrison, Ted, Fontlab Ltd, 403 S Lincoln St, Suite 4-51, Port Angeles, WA 98362 *Tel:* 301-560-3208 *Toll Free Tel:* 866-571-5039 *E-mail:* orders@fontlab.com; contact@fontlab.com *Web Site:* www.fontlab.com, pg 1377

Harry, Tarek, Elixir Technologies Corp, 1314 E Ojai Ave, Ojai, CA 93023 *Tel:* 805-641-5900 *Fax:* 805-648-9151 *E-mail:* info_us@elixir.com *Web Site:* www.elixir.com, pg 1377

Hart, Barbara B, Publications Professionals LLC, 3603 Chain Bridge Rd, Suite A & B, Fairfax, VA 22030-3244 *Tel:* 703-934-4499 *Fax:* 703-591-7389 *E-mail:* info@pubspros.com *Web Site:* www.pubspros.com, pg 1390

Hartford, Charles, Victory Productions Inc, 55 Linden St, Worcester, MA 01609 *Tel:* 508-755-0051 *E-mail:* victory@victoryprd.com *Web Site:* www.victoryprd.com, pg 1363

Hartley, Robert, Integrated Distribution Services (IDS), 9431 AllPoints Pkwy, Plainfield, IN 46168 *Toll Free Tel:* 866-232-6533 *E-mail:* adale@idsfulfillment.com *Web Site:* www.idsfulfillment.com, pg 1332

Hartmans, Kathleen, Quality Bindery Services Inc, 501 Amherst St, Buffalo, NY 14207 *Tel:* 716-883-5185 *Toll Free Tel:* 888-883-1266 *Fax:* 716-883-1598 *E-mail:* info@qualitybindery.com *Web Site:* www.qualitybindery.com, pg 1253

Hartnett, Kate, GOBI® Library Solutions from EBSCO, 999 Maple St, Contoocook, NH 03229 *Tel:* 603-746-3102 *Toll Free Tel:* 800-258-3774 (US & CN) *Fax:* 603-746-5628 *E-mail:* information@ebsco.com *Web Site:* gobi.ebsco.com, pg 1314

Hartnett, Teresa, Hartnett Inc, 2308 Mount Vernon Ave, Suite 817, Alexandria, VA 22301 *Tel:* 703-660-6799 *Web Site:* www.hartnettinc.com, pg 1346

Hartzog, Rich, World Exonumia Press, PO Box 4143, Rockford, IL 61110-0643 *Tel:* 815-226-0771 *Web Site:* www.exonumia.com, pg 1322

Harwood, Josh, Bookazine Co Inc, 75 Hook Rd, Bayonne, NJ 07002 *Tel:* 201-339-7777 *Toll Free Tel:* 800-221-8112 *Fax:* 201-339-7778 *E-mail:* info@bookazine.com *Web Site:* www.bookazine.com, pg 1310, 1325

Hasker, Steve, Thomson Reuters, 3 Times Sq, New York, NY 10036 *Tel:* 646-223-4000; 646-223-6100 (edit); 646-223-6000 (newsroom) *Web Site:* www.thomsonreuters.com, pg 1186

Hatfill, Scott, Independent Publishers Group (IPG), 814 N Franklin St, Chicago, IL 60610 *Tel:* 312-337-0747 *Toll Free Tel:* 800-888-4741 (orders) *Fax:* 312-337-5985 *E-mail:* frontdesk@ipgbook.com; orders@ipgbook.com *Web Site:* www.ipgbook.com, pg 1288, 1326

Havemeyer, Craig, BMR Associates, 60 Corte Amado, Greenbrae, CA 94904 *Tel:* 415-927-1564 *E-mail:* info@bmrassoc.com *Web Site:* www.bmrassoc.com, pg 1343

Havey, Jim, Havey Productions, 3457 Ringsby Court, Unit 105, Denver, CO 80216 *Tel:* 303-296-7448 *Web Site:* www.haveypro.com, pg 1439

Hawkins, Lawrence A, Consolidated Printers Inc, 2630 Eighth St, Berkeley, CA 94710 *Tel:* 510-495-3113 (sales); 510-843-8565 (admin) *Web Site:* www.consoprinters.com, pg 1203, 1245

Hawkinson, Lynnette, Holmberg Co Inc, 4155 Berkshire Lane N, Minneapolis, MN 55446-3814 *Tel:* 763-559-4155 *Toll Free Tel:* 800-328-5101 *E-mail:* customerservice@holmberg.com *Web Site:* www.holmberg.com, pg 1249

Hawley, Kim, Taylor Specialty Books, 1550 W Mockingbird Lane, Dallas, TX 75235 *Tel:* 214-819-8588 (cust serv) *Fax:* 214-819-5051 (cust serv) *Toll Free Fax:* 800-203-9778 *E-mail:* rfq@taylorpub.com (estimates) *Web Site:* www.taylorspecialtybooks.com, pg 1209, 1226, 1255, 1268, 1362

Haws, Mike, Sappi Fine Paper North America, 255 State St, Boston, MA 02109 *Tel:* 617-423-7300 *Toll Free Tel:* 800-882-4332 *E-mail:* webqueriesna@sappi.com *Web Site:* www.sappi.com/na, pg 1267

Hayat, Linette, Continental Book Co Inc, 7000 Broadway, Suite 102, Denver, CO 80221-2913 *Tel:* 303-289-1761 *Toll Free Fax:* 800-279-1764 *E-mail:* cbc@continentalbook.com *Web Site:* www.continentalbook.com, pg 1285, 1312, 1325

Hayes, Trish, The Library Services Centre, 131 Shoemaker St, Kitchener, ON N2E 3B5, Canada *Tel:* 519-746-4420 *Toll Free Tel:* 800-265-3360 (CN only) *Fax:* 519-746-4425 *Web Site:* www.lsc.on.ca, pg 1317

Haywood, Jack, Pro Laminators, 1511 Avco Blvd, Sellersburg, IN 47172 *Tel:* 812-246-0900 *Toll Free Tel:* 800-357-6812 *Fax:* 812-246-1900 *E-mail:* customerservice@prolaminators.com *Web Site:* prolaminators.com, pg 1253

Haywood, Karen, Pro Laminators, 1511 Avco Blvd, Sellersburg, IN 47172 *Tel:* 812-246-0900 *Toll Free Tel:* 800-357-6812 *Fax:* 812-246-1900 *E-mail:* customerservice@prolaminators.com *Web Site:* prolaminators.com, pg 1253

Hazaert, Jenna, Impressions Inc, 1050 Westgate Dr, St Paul, MN 55114 *Tel:* 651-646-1050 *Toll Free Tel:* 800-251-4285 *Fax:* 651-646-7228 *E-mail:* info@i-i.com *Web Site:* www.i-i.com, pg 1249

Healy, Michael, Copyright Clearance Center Inc (CCC), 222 Rosewood Dr, Danvers, MA 01923 *Tel:* 978-750-8400 (sales); 978-646-2600 (cust serv) *E-mail:* info@copyright.com *Web Site:* www.copyright.com, pg 1344

Hearley, Randy, JP Graphics Inc, 3001 E Venture Dr, Appleton, WI 54911 *Tel:* 920-733-4483 *Fax:* 920-733-1700 *E-mail:* support@jpinc.com *Web Site:* www.jpinc.com; www.print.jpinc.com, pg 1206, 1222, 1249

Hebel, Alan, theBookDesigners, 769 Center Blvd, No 22, Fairfax, CA 94930 *Tel:* 415-491-5426 *E-mail:* info@bookdesigners.com *Web Site:* www.bookdesigners.com, pg 1425

Hecht, Michael, Graphic Connections Group LLC, 174 Chesterfield Industrial Blvd, Chesterfield, MO 63005 *Tel:* 636-519-8320 *Toll Free Tel:* 800-378-0378 *Fax:* 636-519-8310 *Web Site:* www.gcfrog.com, pg 1206

Hedeen, Katrina, The Horn Book Guide, 300 The Fenway, Suite P-311, Palace Road Bldg, Boston, MA 02115 *Tel:* 617-278-0225 *Toll Free Tel:* 888-628-0225 *Fax:* 617-278-6062 *E-mail:* info@hbook.com *Web Site:* www.hbook.com, pg 1127

Hedquist, Jeffrey P, Hedquist Productions Inc, PO Box 1475, Fairfield, IA 52556-1475 *Tel:* 641-472-6708 *Toll Free Fax:* 855-510-5726 *Web Site:* www.hedquist.com, pg 1378

Heelan, Peter R, Dunn & Co Inc, 75 Green St, Clinton, MA 01510 *Tel:* 978-368-8505 *Fax:* 978-368-7867 *E-mail:* info@booktrauma.com *Web Site:* www.booktrauma.com, pg 1204, 1246, 1263

Heffernan, Daniel D, AdvantageCS, 3850 Ranchero Dr, Ann Arbor, MI 48108 *Tel:* 734-327-3600 *Fax:* 734-327-3620 *E-mail:* sales-na@advantagecs.com *Web Site:* www.advantagecs.com, pg 1371

Heffner, Donna, Forecast, 2550 W Tyvola Rd, Suite 300, Charlotte, NC 28217 *Tel:* 704-998-3100 *Toll Free Tel:* 800-775-1800 (info servs); 800-775-1700 (cust serv) *Toll Free Fax:* 866-557-3396 (cust serv) *E-mail:* btinfo@baker-taylor.com *Web Site:* www.baker-taylor.com, pg 1126

Heiberg, Milton, Milton Heiberg Studios, 1022 Empress Lane, Orlando, FL 32825-8249 *Tel:* 407-658-4869 *Fax:* 407-658-4869 *E-mail:* photonat@cfl.rr.com *Web Site:* www.miltonheiberg.com, pg 1439

Heid, Werner, Printronix Inc, 6440 Oak Canyon, Suite 200, Irvine, CA 92618 *Tel:* 714-368-2300 *Toll Free Tel:* 800-665-6210 *Web Site:* www.printronix.com, pg 1384

Heidemann, Eric, Fujii Associates Inc, 75 Sunny Hill Dr, Troy, MO 63379 *Tel:* 636-528-2546 *Fax:* 636-600-5153 *Web Site:* www.fujiiassociates.com, pg 1287

Heidt, Eleanor, Whitehots Inc, 205 Industrial Pkwy N, Unit 3, Aurora, ON L4G 4C4, Canada *Tel:* 905-727-9188 *Toll Free Tel:* 888-567-9188 *Fax:* 905-727-8756 *Toll Free Fax:* 888-563-0020 *E-mail:* admin@whitehots.com *Web Site:* www.whitehots.com, pg 1322

Heimann, Gail, Weber Shandwick, 909 Third Ave, New York, NY 10022 *Tel:* 212-445-8000 *Fax:* 212-445-8001 *Web Site:* www.webershandwick.com, pg 1103

Hein, W Shannon, William S Hein & Co Inc, 2350 N Forest Rd, Getzville, NY 14068 *Tel:* 716-882-2600 *Toll Free Tel:* 800-828-7571 *Fax:* 716-883-8100 *E-mail:* mail@wshein.com; marketing@wshein.com *Web Site:* www.wshein.com, pg 1315

Hein, William S Jr, William S Hein & Co Inc, 2350 N Forest Rd, Getzville, NY 14068 *Tel:* 716-882-2600 *Toll Free Tel:* 800-828-7571 *Fax:* 716-883-8100 *E-mail:* mail@wshein.com; marketing@wshein.com *Web Site:* www.wshein.com, pg 1314

Heitzenrater, Stacey, FedEx Supply Chain, 6700 Cranberry Woods Dr, Cranberry Township, PA 16066 *Toll Free Tel:* 800-677-3110 *E-mail:* solution@fedex.com *Web Site:* supplychain.fedex.com, pg 1332

Helgeland, Dale, D&D Sales & Printing, 840 12 St NW, Mason City, IA 50401 *Tel:* 641-423-9487 *Toll Free Tel:* 800-325-5308 *Fax:* 641-423-3068 *E-mail:* ddsales.service@gmail.com *Web Site:* www.ddsalesonline.com, pg 1427

Helgeland, Sue, D&D Sales & Printing, 840 12 St NW, Mason City, IA 50401 *Tel:* 641-423-9487 *Toll Free Tel:* 800-325-5308 *Fax:* 641-423-3068 *E-mail:* ddsales.service@gmail.com *Web Site:* www.ddsalesonline.com, pg 1427

Heller, Robert J, Publishers' Feature Service, 4013 Coyte Ct, Marietta, GA 30062 *Tel:* 561-247-5533 *E-mail:* pfssyndicate@gmail.com *Web Site:* publishersfeatureservice.com, pg 1186

Helmer, Jim, The Bindery Inc, 8201 Brooklyn Blvd, Brooklyn Park, MN 55445 *Tel:* 763-201-2800 *Toll Free Tel:* 800-851-6598 *Fax:* 763-201-2790 *E-mail:* info@thebinderymn.com *Web Site:* www.thebinderymn.com, pg 1242

Helmers, Kathryn A, Creative Trust Inc, 210 Jamestown Park Dr, Suite 200, Brentwood, TN 37027 *Tel:* 615-297-5010 *Fax:* 615-297-5020 *E-mail:* info@creativetrust.com *Web Site:* creativetrust.com, pg 1344

Helton, John, CQ Roll Call, 1201 Pennsylvania Ave NW, Suite 600, Washington, DC 20004 *Tel:* 202-650-6500; 202-650-6511 (subns); 202-650-6621 (cust serv) *Toll Free Tel:* 800-432-2250; 800-678-8511 (subns) *E-mail:* customerservice@cqrollcall.com *Web Site:* cqrollcall.com; www.rollcall.com, pg 1184

Henderson, Bob, Hollinger Metal Edge Inc, 9401 Northeast Dr, Fredricksburg, VA 22408 *Tel:* 540-898-7300 *Toll Free Tel:* 800-634-0491 *Toll Free Fax:* 800-947-8814 *E-mail:* info@hollingermetaledge.com *Web Site:* www.hollingermetaledge.com, pg 1264

Henderson, John, The Bureau, 2354 English St, Maplewood, MN 55109 *Tel:* 612-788-1000; 612-432-3516 (sales) *Toll Free Tel:* 800-788-9536 *Fax:* 612-788-7792 *E-mail:* sales@thebureau.com *Web Site:* www.thebureau.com, pg 1217, 1243

Henderson, Mark, MBS Textbook Exchange Inc, 2711 W Ash, Columbia, MO 65203 *Tel:* 573-445-2243 *Toll Free Tel:* 800-325-0530 (textbook solutions); 800-325-4138 (bookstore systems) *Fax:* 573-446-5256 *E-mail:* cserv@mbsbooks.com *Web Site:* www.mbsbooks.com, pg 1317

Hendra, Barbara J, The Hendra Agency Inc, 142 Sterling Place, Brooklyn, NY 11217-3307 *Tel:* 718-622-3232; 212-947-9898 *Fax:* 718-622-3322, pg 1098

Hendrick, Rachel, CHOICE, 575 Main St, Suite 300, Middletown, CT 06457 *Tel:* 860-347-6933; 860-347-1387 (ad); 240-646-7027 (subn); 818-487-4555 *E-mail:* acrlsubscriptions@pubservice.com; support@acrlchoice.freshdesk.com *Web Site:* www.ala.org/acrl/choice; www.choice360.org, pg 1125

Hendrickson, Amy, TeXnology Inc, 57 Longwood Ave, Brookline, MA 02446 *Tel:* 617-738-8029 *Web Site:* www.texnology.com, pg 1386

Hendrickson, Kevin, Christianbook Inc, 140 Summit St, Peabody, MA 01960-5156 *Tel:* 978-977-5060; 978-977-5000 (intl calls) *Toll Free Tel:* 800-CHRISTIAN (247-4784) *Fax:* 978-977-5010 *E-mail:* customer.service@christianbook.com *Web Site:* www.christianbook.com, pg 1312

Hendrickson, Ray, Christianbook Inc, 140 Summit St, Peabody, MA 01960-5156 *Tel:* 978-977-5060; 978-977-5000 (intl calls) *Toll Free Tel:* 800-CHRISTIAN (247-4784) *Fax:* 978-977-5010 *E-mail:* customer.service@christianbook.com *Web Site:* www.christianbook.com, pg 1312

Henley, Jeffrey O, Oracle America Inc, 500 Oracle Pkwy, Redwood Shores, CA 94065 *Tel:* 650-506-7000 *Toll Free Tel:* 800-392-2999; 800-633-0738 (sales) *Web Site:* www.oracle.com, pg 1383

Hennicke, Erin, Franklin & Siegal Associates Inc, 1350 Broadway, Suite 2015, New York, NY 10018 *Tel:* 212-868-6311 *Fax:* 212-868-6312 *Web Site:* www.franklinandsiegal.com, pg 1345

Henning, Robert D, FedEx Ground, 1000 FedEx Dr, Coraopolis, PA 15108 *Tel:* 412-269-1000 *Toll Free Tel:* 800-762-3725 *Web Site:* www.fedex.com, pg 1332

Henrie, Sam, Wheatmark Inc, 2030 E Speedway Blvd, Suite 106, Tucson, AZ 85719 *Tel:* 520-798-0888 *Toll Free Tel:* 888-934-0888 *Fax:* 520-798-3394 *E-mail:* info@wheatmark.com *Web Site:* www.wheatmark.com, pg 1353

Henry, Jay, ProtoView, 7515 NE Ambassador Place, Suite A, Portland, OR 97220 *Tel:* 503-281-9230 *E-mail:* info@protoview.com *Web Site:* www.protoview.com, pg 1140

Henzell, Peter, Marrakech Express Inc, 720 Wesley Ave, No 10, Tarpon Springs, FL 34689 *Tel:* 727-942-2218 *Toll Free Tel:* 800-940-6566 *Fax:* 727-937-4758 *E-mail:* print@marrak.com *Web Site:* www.marrak.com, pg 1207, 1251, 1278

Heppelman, James, PTC, 121 Seaport Blvd, Boston, MA 02210 *Tel:* 781-370-5000 *Fax:* 781-370-6000 *Web Site:* www.ptc.com, pg 1384

Herbig, Dave, Danita Delimont Stock Photography, 4911 Somerset Dr SE, Bellevue, WA 98006 *Tel:* 425-562-1543 *Fax:* 425-373-5316 *Web Site:* www.danitadelimont.com, pg 1446

Herman, Chacho, San Diego Museum of Art, Balboa Park, 1450 El Prado, San Diego, CA 92112 *Tel:* 619-232-7931 *Fax:* 619-232-9367 *Web Site:* www.sdmart.org, pg 1320

Herman, Gretchen, Brodart Books & Library Services, 500 Arch St, Williamsport, PA 17701 *Tel:* 570-326-2461 *Toll Free Tel:* 800-233-8467 *Fax:* 570-651-1639 *Toll Free Fax:* 800-999-6799 *E-mail:* support@brodart.com *Web Site:* www.brodartbooks.com, pg 1311

Herman, Gretchen, Brodart Books & Library Services, 500 Arch St, Williamsport, PA 17701 *Tel:* 570-326-2461 *Toll Free Tel:* 800-474-9816 *Fax:* 570-651-1639 *Toll Free Fax:* 800-999-6799 *E-mail:* support@brodart.com *Web Site:* www.brodartbooks.com, pg 1323

Herman, Mark, Mark Herman & Ronnie Apter, Translators, 2222 Westview Dr, Nashville, TN 37212-4123 *Tel:* 615-942-8462 *E-mail:* mnh18@columbia.edu, pg 1410

Hermann, Kathy, Specialist Marketing Services Inc, 777 Terrace Ave, Suite 401, Hasbrouck Heights, NJ 07604 *Tel:* 201-865-5800 *E-mail:* info@sms-inc.com *Web Site:* www.sms-inc.com, pg 1112

Hernandez, Johnny, Small Press Distribution Inc, 1341 Seventh St, Berkeley, CA 94710-1409 *Tel:* 510-524-1668 *Toll Free Tel:* 800-869-7553 (within the US) *Fax:* 510-524-0852 *E-mail:* spd@spdbooks.org *Web Site:* www.spdbooks.org, pg 1298

Herndon, Rick, Lee Publications, 1100 W Broadway, Louisville, KY 40203 *Tel:* 502-587-6804 *Toll Free Tel:* 800-626-8247 *Fax:* 502-587-6822 *E-mail:* info@leemagicpen.com *Web Site:* www.leemagicpen.com, pg 1250

Heron, Ms Michal, Michal Heron Photography, 3806 Easton St, Sarasota, FL 34238 *Tel:* 941-922-5124 *E-mail:* michalheronphoto@gmail.com *Web Site:* www.michalheron.com, pg 1439

Herrick, Greg E, Historic Aviation Books, 640 Taft St NE, Minneapolis, MN 55413-2815 *Tel:* 612-206-3200 *Toll Free Tel:* 800-225-5575 *Fax:* 612-877-3160 *E-mail:* info@historicaviation.com; customerservice@historicaviation.com *Web Site:* www.historicaviation.com, pg 1315

Herrin, Ann, MSC Lists, PO Box 32510, Minneapolis, MN 55432 *Tel:* 763-502-8819 *Fax:* 763-571-8292, pg 1112

Herring, Ellen, Trophy Room Books, PO Box 3041, Agoura, CA 91301 *Tel:* 818-889-2469 *Fax:* 818-889-4849 *E-mail:* info@trophyroombooks.com *Web Site:* www.trophyroombooks.com, pg 1328

Herring, Jim, Trophy Room Books, PO Box 3041, Agoura, CA 91301 *Tel:* 818-889-2469 *Fax:* 818-889-4849 *E-mail:* info@trophyroombooks.com *Web Site:* www.trophyroombooks.com, pg 1328

Herrington, Michael P, Comag Marketing Group LLC (CMG), 155 Village Blvd, Suite 300, Princeton, NJ 08540 *Tel:* 609-524-1800 *Fax:* 609-524-1629 *Web Site:* www.i-cmg.com, pg 1312

Herrold, Kelly, Scott Publications Inc, 2145 W Sherman Blvd, Norton Shores, MI 49441 *Tel:* 231-755-2200 *Toll Free Tel:* 866-733-9382 *Fax:* 231-755-1003 *E-mail:* contactus@scottpublications.com *Web Site:* scottpublications.com, pg 1093

Hershberg, Neil, Business Wire, 101 California St, 20th fl, San Francisco, CA 94111 *Tel:* 415-986-4422 *Toll Free Tel:* 800-227-0845 *E-mail:* info@businesswire.com *Web Site:* www.businesswire.com, pg 1183

Hershberger, John, BMR Associates, 60 Corte Amado, Greenbrae, CA 94904 *Tel:* 415-927-1564 *E-mail:* info@bmrassoc.com *Web Site:* www.bmrassoc.com, pg 1343

Hertz, Victor, A L S International, 18 John St, Suite 300, New York, NY 10038 *Tel:* 212-766-4111 *Toll Free Tel:* 800-322-0284 *Fax:* 212-349-0964 *Toll Free Fax:* 888-662-8048 *E-mail:* rastefanous@alsintl.com *Web Site:* www.alsintl.com, pg 1407

Hertz, Victor, University Language Services Inc (ULS), 15 Maiden Lane, Suite 300, New York, NY 10038 *Tel:* 212-766-4111 *Toll Free Tel:* 800-419-4601 *Fax:* 212-571-7155 *Toll Free Fax:* 800-662-8048 *E-mail:* service@universitylanguage.com *Web Site:* www.universitylanguage.com, pg 1414

Herzig, John, Barcode Graphics Inc, 25 Brodie Dr, Unit 5, Richmond Hill, ON L4B 3K7, Canada *Tel:* 905-770-1154 *Toll Free Tel:* 800-263-3669 (orders) *Fax:* 905-787-1575 *E-mail:* info@barcodegraphics.com *Web Site:* www.barcodegraphics.com, pg 1216

Hespenheide, Gary, Hespenheide Design, 99 Long Ct, Suite 102, Thousand Oaks, CA 91360 *Tel:* 805-499-8875 *Web Site:* www.hespenheide.com, pg 1429

Hettler, Kurt, Ingram Content Group LLC, One Ingram Blvd, La Vergne, TN 37086-1986 *Tel:* 615-793-5000 *Toll Free Tel:* 800-937-8000 (retailers); 800-937-5300 (ext 1, libs) *E-mail:* customerservice@ingramcontent.com *Web Site:* www.ingramcontent.com, pg 1290, 1315

Heyerdahl, Doug, Blanks Printing & Imaging Inc, 2343 N Beckley Ave, Dallas, TX 75208 *Tel:* 214-741-3905 *Toll Free Tel:* 800-325-7651 *E-mail:* sales@blanks.com *Web Site:* www.blanks.com, pg 1216, 1243

Hieber, Adam, Cushing-Malloy Inc, 1350 N Main St, Ann Arbor, MI 48104-1045 *Tel:* 734-663-8554 *Fax:* 734-663-5731 *Web Site:* www.cushing-malloy.com; www.c-mbooks.com, pg 1203, 1245

Hilberer, David, McNaughton & Gunn Inc, Plant: 960 Woodland Dr, Saline, MI 48176 *Tel:* 734-429-5411 *Toll Free Fax:* 800-677-BOOK (677-2665) *Web Site:* www.bookprinters.com, pg 1207, 1251

Hill, Anne, Avery Dennison Corp, 207 N Goode Ave, 6th fl, Glendale, CA 91203-1222 *Tel:* 626-304-2000 *Web Site:* www.averydennison.com, pg 1373

Hill, Devra, Promotion in Motion, 714 Crescent Dr, Beverly Hills, CA 90210 *Tel:* 323-461-3921; 310-497-4001 (cell) *Fax:* 323-461-0917 *E-mail:* irwinzuckerpr@aol.com *Web Site:* www.promotioninmotion.net; www.bookpublicists.org, pg 1101

Hill, Jeffrey A, Horizon Paper Co Inc, 1010 Washington Blvd, Stamford, CT 06901 *Tel:* 203-358-0855 *Toll Free Tel:* 866-358-0855 *E-mail:* info@horizonpaper.com *Web Site:* www.horizonpaper.com, pg 1264

Hillard, Samuel L, Glatfelter, Capitol Towers South, 4350 Congress St, Suite 600, Charlotte, NC 28209 *Tel:* 717-850-0170 *Toll Free Tel:* 866-744-7380 *E-mail:* info@glatfelter.com *Web Site:* www.glatfelter.com, pg 1263

Hilsinger, Judy, Hilsinger-Mendelson West Inc, 8916 Ashcroft Ave, Los Angeles, CA 90048 *Tel:* 310-659-7930 *E-mail:* hmiwest@aol.com *Web Site:* www.hilsingermendelson.com, pg 1098

Hilton, Jeff, Evergreen Engravers, 1819 S Central Ave, Suite 24, Kent, WA 98032 *Tel:* 253-852-6766 *Toll Free Tel:* 800-852-6766 *Fax:* 253-850-3944 *E-mail:* emboss@evergreenengravers.com *Web Site:* www.evergreenengravers.com, pg 1276

Hiltwein, Mark, Cenveo Inc, 200 First Stamford Place, 2nd fl, Stamford, CT 06902 *Tel:* 203-595-3000 *Fax:* 203-595-3070 *E-mail:* info@cenveo.com *Web Site:* www.cenveo.com, pg 1203, 1244, 1261

Hinckley, Deborah, Inlingua Translation Service, 171 E Ridgewood Ave, Ridgewood, NJ 07450 *Tel:* 201-444-9500 *Fax:* 201-444-0116 *E-mail:* ridgewood@inlingua.com *Web Site:* www.inlingua.com; www.inlinguametrony.com, pg 1410

Hindman, Gene, Drummond, 5664 New Peachtree Rd, Atlanta, GA 30341 *Tel:* 678-597-1050 *Fax:* 678-597-1051 *E-mail:* info@drummond.com *Web Site:* pgc-atl.com, pg 1246

Hirsch, Emil G, Whitehall Printing Co, 4244 Corporate Sq, Naples, FL 34104 *Tel:* 239-643-6464 *Toll Free Tel:* 800-321-9290 *Fax:* 239-643-6439 *E-mail:* info@whitehallprinting.com *Web Site:* www.whitehallprinting.com, pg 1210, 1227, 1257, 1269

Hirsch, Jeff, Whitehall Printing Co, 4244 Corporate Sq, Naples, FL 34104 *Tel:* 239-643-6464 *Toll Free Tel:* 800-321-9290 *Fax:* 239-643-6439 *E-mail:* info@whitehallprinting.com *Web Site:* www.whitehallprinting.com, pg 1210, 1227, 1257, 1269

Hirsch, Mike, Whitehall Printing Co, 4244 Corporate Sq, Naples, FL 34104 *Tel:* 239-643-6464 *Toll Free Tel:* 800-321-9290 *Fax:* 239-643-6439 *E-mail:* info@whitehallprinting.com *Web Site:* www.whitehallprinting.com, pg 1210, 1227, 1257, 1269

Hirschtick, Jon, PTC, 121 Seaport Blvd, Boston, MA 02210 *Tel:* 781-370-5000 *Fax:* 781-370-6000 *Web Site:* www.ptc.com, pg 1384

Hischar, Mark, Koenig & Bauer (US) Inc, 2555 Regent Blvd, Dallas, TX 75229 *Tel:* 469-532-8000 *Fax:* 469-532-8190 *Web Site:* us.koenig-bauer.com, pg 1277

Hite, Robyn, Wimmer Cookbooks, 4650 Shelby Air Dr, Memphis, TN 38118 *Toll Free Tel:* 800-548-2537 *Fax:* 901-363-1771 *Web Site:* www.wimmerco.com, pg 1210, 1257, 1300, 1322, 1353

Ho, Edward, OCS America Inc, 195 Anderson Ave, Moonachie, NJ 07074 *Tel:* 201-460-2888 *Toll Free Tel:* 800-367-3405 *E-mail:* info@ocsworld.com *Web Site:* www.ocsworld.com, pg 1327

Ho, Francis, C & C Offset Printing Co USA Inc, 70 W 36 St, Unit 10C, New York, NY 10018 *Tel:* 212-431-4210 *Toll Free Fax:* 866-540-4134 *Web Site:* www.ccoffset.com, pg 1202, 1217, 1243

Hoadley, Katherine, Louis Goldberg Library Book Supplier, 45 Belvidere St, Nazareth, PA 18064 *Tel:* 610-759-9458 *E-mail:* orders@goldberg-books.com *Web Site:* www.goldberg-books.com, pg 1314

Hoar, Bill, Chesapeake & Hudson Inc, 115 W Potomac St, Brunswick, MD 21716 *Tel:* 301-834-7170 *Toll Free Tel:* 800-231-4469 *Toll Free Fax:* 800-307-5163 *E-mail:* office@cheshud.com *Web Site:* www.cheshud.com, pg 1285

Hobart, Ron "Hobie", Dunn+Associates Design, PO Box 870, Hayward, WI 54843-0870 *Tel:* 715-634-4857 *Fax:* 715-634-5617 *E-mail:* info@dunn-design.com *Web Site:* www.dunn-design.com, pg 1427

Hober, Rosemary Mengel, The Hibbert Group, 400 Pennington Ave, Trenton, NJ 08650 *Tel:* 609-394-7500 *Toll Free Tel:* 888-HIBBERT (442-2378) *E-mail:* info@hibbertgroup.com *Web Site:* hibbert.com, pg 1092, 1106, 1109

Hochman, Joel, Arbor Books, 244 Madison Ave, Box 254, New York, NY 10016 *Tel:* 212-956-0950 *Toll Free Tel:* 877-822-2500 *Fax:* 914-401-9385 *E-mail:* info@arborbooks.com; editorial@arborbooks.net *Web Site:* www.arborbooks.com; www.arborservices.co, pg 1201, 1216, 1242, 1261, 1342, 1355, 1424

Hockenbury, Don, Garlich Printing Co, 525 Rudder Rd, St Louis, MO 63026 *Tel:* 636-349-8000 *Toll Free Tel:* 844-449-4752 *Fax:* 636-349-8080 *E-mail:* customerservice@garlich.com *Web Site:* www.garlich.com, pg 1248

Hodge, Camden, AlphaGraphics Inc, 143 Union Blvd, Suite 650, Lakewood, CO 80228 *Toll Free Tel:* 800-955-6246 *Fax:* 801-595-7270 *E-mail:* contactus@alphagraphics.com *Web Site:* www.alphagraphics.com, pg 1372

Hoesly, Sherry, The Permissions Group Inc, 401 S Milwaukee Ave, Suite 180, Wheeling, IL 60090 *Tel:* 847-635-6550 *Toll Free Tel:* 800-374-7985 *Fax:* 847-635-6968 *E-mail:* info@permissionsgroup.com *Web Site:* www.permissionsgroup.com, pg 1351

Hoey, Charlene, Linick International Inc, Linick Bldg, 7 Putter Lane, Middle Island, NY 11953 *Tel:* 631-924-3888; 631-924-8555; 631-604-8599 *E-mail:* topmarketingadvisor@gmail.com *Web Site:* topmarketingadvisor.com, pg 1349

Hoffman, Carol, Academic Reviews, 1-A Glenwood Ave, Lynbrook, NY 11563 *Tel:* 516-593-1275 *E-mail:* info@academicreviews.com *Web Site:* www.academicreviews.com, pg 1123

Hogan, Bruce M, Mohawk Fine Papers Inc, 465 Saratoga St, Cohoes, NY 12047 *Tel:* 518-237-1740 *Toll Free Tel:* 800-THE-MILL (843-6455) *Fax:* 518-237-7394 *Web Site:* www.mohawkconnects.com, pg 1266

Hoge, Kurt, Reno Typographers, 1020 S Rock Blvd, Suite C, Reno, NV 89502 *Tel:* 775-852-8800 *E-mail:* info@renotype.com; work@renotype.com *Web Site:* www.renotype.com, pg 1225

Hoggan, Kathy D, K H Marketing Communications, 16205 NE Sixth St, Bellevue, WA 98008 *Tel:* 425-269-7411 (cell), pg 1098

Hohenshell, John, Sun Graphics LLC, 1818 Broadway, Parsons, KS 67357 *Toll Free Tel:* 800-835-0588 *Fax:* 620-421-2089 *E-mail:* info@sun-graphics.com *Web Site:* www.sun-graphics.com, pg 1209, 1226, 1255

Holcomb, Andy, Fujii Associates Inc, 75 Sunny Hill Dr, Troy, MO 63379 *Tel:* 636-528-2546 *Fax:* 636-600-5153 *Web Site:* www.fujiiassociates.com, pg 1287

Holden, Oliver, knk Software LP, 89 Headquarters Plaza N, No 1478, Morristown, NJ 07960 *Tel:* 908-206-4599 *E-mail:* info@knk.com *Web Site:* www.knkpublishingsoftware.com, pg 1348

Holder, Kelly, MCH Strategic Data, 601 E Marshall St, Sweet Springs, MO 65351 *Toll Free Tel:* 800-776-6373 *E-mail:* sales@mchdata.com *Web Site:* www.mchdata.com, pg 1112

Holeman, Arthur A, Art Holeman Photography, 4156 E Cathedral Rock Dr, Phoenix, AZ 85044 *Tel:* 602-290-7431 (cell) *E-mail:* art@artholeman.com; artholeman@cox.net *Web Site:* www.artholeman.com; www.fineartholeman.com, pg 1439

Holland, Dave, OneTouchPoint, 1225 Walnut Ridge Dr, Hartland, WI 53029 *Tel:* 262-369-6000 *Toll Free Tel:* 800-332-2348 *Fax:* 262-369-5647 *E-mail:* info@1touchpoint.com *Web Site:* www.1touchpoint.com, pg 1093, 1208, 1252, 1383

Hollander, Eli M, Feldheim Publishers, 208 Airport Executive Park, Nanuet, NY 10954 *Tel:* 845-356-2282 *Toll Free Tel:* 800-237-7149 (orders) *Fax:* 845-425-1908 *E-mail:* sales@feldheim.com *Web Site:* www.feldheim.com, pg 1313

Hollenbeck, Cliff, Hollenbeck Productions, 19241 Normandy Park Dr SW, Seattle, WA 98166 *Tel:* 206-592-1800 *Web Site:* www.hollenbeckproductions.com; www.cliffscoolstuff.com, pg 1439

Hollenbeck, Nancy, Hollenbeck Productions, 19241 Normandy Park Dr SW, Seattle, WA 98166 *Tel:* 206-592-1800 *Web Site:* www.hollenbeckproductions.com; www.cliffscoolstuff.com, pg 1439

Hollinger, Catherine, Conservation Resources International LLC, 7350 Lockport Place, Suite A, Lorton, VA 22079 *Tel:* 703-321-7730 *Toll Free Tel:* 800-634-6932 *Fax:* 703-321-0629 *E-mail:* sales@conservationresources.com *Web Site:* www.conservationresources.com, pg 1262

Hollinger, Lavonia, Conservation Resources International LLC, 7350 Lockport Place, Suite A, Lorton, VA 22079 *Tel:* 703-321-7730 *Toll Free Tel:* 800-634-6932 *Fax:* 703-321-0629 *E-mail:* sales@conservationresources.com *Web Site:* www.conservationresources.com, pg 1262

Hollinger, William K Jr, Conservation Resources International LLC, 7350 Lockport Place, Suite A, Lorton, VA 22079 *Tel:* 703-321-7730 *Toll Free Tel:* 800-634-6932 *Fax:* 703-321-0629 *E-mail:* sales@conservationresources.com *Web Site:* www.conservationresources.com, pg 1262

Holmberg, Steve, The Islander Group, 269 Palii St, Mililani, HI 96789 *Tel:* 808-676-0116 *Toll Free Tel:* 877-828-4852 *Fax:* 808-676-5156 *E-mail:* customerservice@islandergroup.com *Web Site:* www.islandergroup.com, pg 1316, 1326

Holmes, Henry, Henry Holmes Literary Agent/Book Publicist/Marketing Consultant, Mitchell Heights, Apt 205, 2100 S Main St, Fall River, MA 02724 *Tel:* 508-672-2258; 508-415-4062 (cell), pg 1086, 1098, 1346

Holmes, James, ProQuest LLC, 789 E Eisenhower Pkwy, Ann Arbor, MI 48108 *Tel:* 734-761-4700 *Toll Free Tel:* 800-521-0600; 877-779-6768 (sales) *E-mail:* sales@proquest.com *Web Site:* www.proquest.com, pg 1384

Holzschuh, Douglas, Hess Print Solutions, 3765 Sunnybrook Rd, Brimfield, OH 44240 *Toll Free Tel:* 800-678-1222 *E-mail:* info@hessprintsolutions.com *Web Site:* www.hessprintsolutions.com, pg 1206, 1248

Hoogwerf, Robin, United Library Services Inc, 7140 Fairmount Dr SE, Calgary, AB T2H 0X4, Canada *Tel:* 403-252-4426 *Toll Free Tel:* 888-342-5857 (CN only) *Fax:* 403-258-3426 *Toll Free Fax:* 800-661-2806 (CN only) *E-mail:* info@uls.com *Web Site:* www.uls.com, pg 1321

Hook, Ruth Alden, R & R Book Co LLC, 666 Godwin Ave, Suite 120-C, Midland Park, NJ 07432 *Tel:* 201-337-3400 *Web Site:* www.rrbookcompany.com, pg 1296

Hoover, Jane, Lifland et al., Bookmakers, 442 William St, 2nd fl, Williamsport, PA 17701 *Tel:* 570-326-4100 *E-mail:* liflandh@comcast.net, pg 1359

Hopkins, Michelle, PTC, 121 Seaport Blvd, Boston, MA 02210 *Tel:* 781-370-5000 *Fax:* 781-370-6000 *Web Site:* www.ptc.com, pg 1384

Hopkins, Tom, Tom Hopkins Studio, 2121 Durham Rd, Madison, CT 06443 *Tel:* 203-421-4644 *E-mail:* contact@tomhopkinsstudio.com *Web Site:* www.tomhopkinsstudio.com, pg 1439

Horikawa, Sergio, OKI Data Americas Inc, 8505 Freeport Pkwy, Suite 600, Irving, TX 75063 *Tel:* 972-815-4800 *Toll Free Tel:* 800-OKI-DATA (654-3282) *E-mail:* support@okidata.com *Web Site:* www.oki.com/us/printing, pg 1383

Hornyak, Kim, Jenkins Group Inc, 1129 Woodmere Ave, Suite B, Traverse City, MI 49686 *Tel:* 231-933-0445 *Toll Free Tel:* 800-706-4636 *Fax:* 231-933-0448 *E-mail:* info@bookpublishing.com *Web Site:* www.bookpublishing.com, pg 1347

Horowitz, Devoiry, Listco Direct Marketing, 1276 46 St, Brooklyn, NY 11219 *Tel:* 718-871-8400 *Fax:* 718-871-7692 *E-mail:* info@listcodirect.com *Web Site:* www.listcodirect.com, pg 1112

Horowitz, Eileen S, Exhibit Promotions Plus Inc, 11620 Vixens Path, Ellicott City, MD 21042-1539 *Tel:* 410-997-0763 *Fax:* 410-997-0764 *E-mail:* exhibit@epponline.com *Web Site:* www.epponline.com, pg 1133, 1345

Horowitz, Harve C Esq, Exhibit Promotions Plus Inc, 11620 Vixens Path, Ellicott City, MD 21042-1539 *Tel:* 410-997-0763 *Fax:* 410-997-0764 *E-mail:* exhibit@epponline.com *Web Site:* www.epponline.com, pg 1133, 1345

Horowitz, Shel, Accurate Writing & More, 16 Barstow Lane, Hadley, MA 01035 *Tel:* 413-586-2388 *Web Site:* frugalmarketing.com, pg 1085

Horowitz, Shel, Accurate Writing & More, 16 Barstow Lane, Hadley, MA 01035 *Tel:* 413-586-2388 *Web Site:* frugalmarketing.com; www.accuratewriting.com, pg 1095

Horowitz, Shel, Accurate Writing & More, 16 Barstow Lane, Hadley, MA 01035 *Tel:* 413-586-2388 *Web Site:* frugalmarketing.com, pg 1341

Hoskin, Christine, Schoolhouse Indexing, 10-B Parade Ground Rd, Etna, NH 03750 *Tel:* 603-643-1617 *Web Site:* schoolhouseindexing.com, pg 1225

Houston, Victoria, VKH Media Resources, 122 S Oneida Ave, Rhinelander, WI 54501 *Tel:* 715-369-4535 *Web Site:* www.victoriahouston.com, pg 1363

Hoving, Morgen Anne, Academic Reviews, 1-A Glenwood Ave, Lynbrook, NY 11563 *Tel:* 516-593-1275 *E-mail:* info@academicreviews.com *Web Site:* www.academicreviews.com, pg 1123

Hovsepian, Ronald, SumTotal Systems LLC, 2850 NW 43 St, Suite 150, Gainesville, FL 32606 *Tel:* 352-264-2800 *Toll Free Tel:* 866-933-1416 *Fax:* 352-374-2257 *E-mail:* customersupport@sumtotalsystems.com *Web Site:* www.sumtotalsystems.com, pg 1386

Howard, Carey, OneTouchPoint, 1225 Walnut Ridge Dr, Hartland, WI 53029 *Tel:* 262-369-6000 *Toll Free Tel:* 800-332-2348 *Fax:* 262-369-5647 *E-mail:* info@1touchpoint.com *Web Site:* www.1touchpoint.com, pg 1093, 1208, 1252, 1383

Howard, Mari, Diane Abrams, 71 Faunce Dr, Providence, RI 02906 *Tel:* 401-274-2149 *Web Site:* www.whitegatefeatures.com, pg 1117

Howard, Mari, Adler, Corey, Issac, 71 Faunce Dr, Providence, RI 02906 *Tel:* 401-274-2149 *Web Site:* www.whitegatefeatures.com, pg 1117

Howard, Mari, Jane Adler, 71 Faunce Dr, Providence, RI 02906 *Tel:* 401-274-2149 *Web Site:* www.whitegatefeatures.com, pg 1117

Howard, Mari, Leon Collins, 71 Faunce Dr, Providence, RI 02906 *Tel:* 401-274-2149 *Web Site:* www.whitegatefeatures.com, pg 1117

Howard, Mari, Steve Corey, 71 Faunce Dr, Providence, RI 02906 *Tel:* 401-274-2149 *Web Site:* www.whitegatefeatures.com, pg 1117

Howard, Mari, Carla Demers, 71 Faunce Dr, Providence, RI 02906 *Tel:* 401-274-2149 *Web Site:* www.whitegatefeatures.com, pg 1117

Howard, Mari, Bruce Hoffman, 71 Faunce Dr, Providence, RI 02906 *Tel:* 401-274-2149 *Web Site:* www.whitegatefeatures.com, pg 1118

Howard, Mari, Linda King, 71 Faunce Dr, Providence, RI 02906 *Tel:* 401-274-2149 *Web Site:* www.whitegatefeatures.com, pg 1118

Howard, Mari, Jill Kramer - Best of Books, 71 Faunce Dr, Providence, RI 02906 *Tel:* 401-274-2149 *Web Site:* www.whitegatefeatures.com, pg 1118

Howard, Mari, Ruth & Robert Reld, 71 Faunce Dr, Providence, RI 02906 *Tel:* 401-274-2149 *Web Site:* www.whitegatefeatures.com, pg 1118

Howard, Mari, Matt Stewart, 71 Faunce Dr, Providence, RI 02906 *Tel:* 401-274-2149 *Web Site:* www.whitegatefeatures.com, pg 1118

Howard, Mari, Hope Strong, 71 Faunce Dr, Providence, RI 02906 *Tel:* 401-274-2149 *Web Site:* www.whitegatefeatures.com, pg 1119

Howard, Mari, Whitegate Features Syndicate, 71 Faunce Dr, Providence, RI 02906 *Tel:* 401-274-2149 *Web Site:* www.whitegatefeatures.com, pg 1186

Howard, Marilyn, Creative Freelancers Inc, PO Box 366, Tallevast, FL 34270 *Toll Free Tel:* 800-398-9544 *Web Site:* www.illustratorsonline.com, pg 1426

Howe, Aaron, Independent Publishers Group (IPG), 814 N Franklin St, Chicago, IL 60610 *Tel:* 312-337-0747 *Toll Free Tel:* 800-888-4741 (orders) *Fax:* 312-337-5985 *E-mail:* frontdesk@ipgbook.com; orders@ipgbook.com *Web Site:* www.ipgbook.com, pg 1288, 1326

Hoxsie, Fred, GHP, 475 Heffernan Dr, West Haven, CT 06516 *Tel:* 203-479-7500 *Fax:* 203-479-7575 *Web Site:* www.ghpmedia.com, pg 1220, 1248

Hreha, Bob, Knepper Press Corp, 2251 Sweeney Dr, Clinton, PA 15026 *Tel:* 724-899-4200 *Fax:* 724-899-1331 *Web Site:* www.knepperpress.com, pg 1206, 1222, 1249

Hu, Huver, Amgraf Inc, 1501 Oak St, Kansas City, MO 64108-1424 *Tel:* 816-474-4797 *Toll Free Tel:* 800-304-4797 (sales & mktg) *Fax:* 816-842-4477 *E-mail:* support@amgraf.com *Web Site:* www.amgraf.com, pg 1372

Hubbard, Greg, Omnipress, 2600 Anderson St, Madison, WI 53704 *Tel:* 608-246-2600 *Toll Free Tel:* 800-828-0305 *E-mail:* justask@omnipress.com *Web Site:* www.omnipress.com, pg 1208, 1252

Hubbard, Thomas K, The Hubbard Co, 612 Clinton St, Defiance, OH 43512 *Tel:* 419-784-4455 *Toll Free Tel:* 888-448-2227 *Web Site:* www.hubbardcompany.com, pg 1315

Hudson, Scott, Worth Higgins & Associates Inc, 8770 Park Central Dr, Richmond, VA 23227-1146 *Tel:* 804-264-2304 *Toll Free Tel:* 800-883-7768 *Fax:* 804-264-5733 *E-mail:* contact@whaprint.com *Web Site:* www.worthhiggins.com, pg 1221, 1249

Huey, Craig, Creative Direct Marketing Group Inc (CDMG), 21171 S Western, Suite 260, Torrance, CA 90501 *Tel:* 310-212-5727 *Fax:* 310-212-5773 *Web Site:* www.cdmginc.com, pg 1344

Huey, George H H, George H H Huey Photography Inc, 382 W Butterfield Rd, Suite 115, Chino Valley, AZ 86323 *Tel:* 928-445-6800 *Web Site:* www.georgehhhuey.com, pg 1439

Hughes, Annette, Midpoint Trade Books, 814 N Franklin St, Suite 100, Chicago, IL 60610 *Tel:* 312-337-0747 *Fax:* 312-337-5985 *E-mail:* orders@ipgbook.com *Web Site:* www.midpointtrade.com, pg 1292

Hughes, Karen, UniNet Imaging Inc, 3232 W El Segundo Blvd, Hawthorne, CA 90250 *Tel:* 424-675-3300 *Fax:* 424-675-3400 *E-mail:* sales@uninetimaging.com *Web Site:* www.uninetimaging.com, pg 1387

Hughes, Tony, The Order Fulfillment Group, 7313 Mayflower Park Dr, Zionsville, IN 46077 *Tel:* 317-733-7755 *Fax:* 317-733-8799 *Web Site:* www.tofg.com, pg 1332

Huhn, William, Midpoint Trade Books, 814 N Franklin St, Suite 100, Chicago, IL 60610 *Tel:* 312-337-0747 *Fax:* 312-337-5985 *E-mail:* orders@ipgbook.com *Web Site:* www.midpointtrade.com, pg 1292

Hullquist, Timothy, TEACH Services Inc, 11 Quartermaster Circle, Fort Oglethorpe, GA 30742-3886 *Tel:* 706-504-9192 *Toll Free Tel:* 800-367-1844 (sales) *Toll Free Fax:* 866-757-6023 *E-mail:* sales@teachservices.com; info@teachservices.com *Web Site:* www.teachservices.com, pg 1321, 1386

Humphreys, Nancy K, Nancy Humphreys Wordmaps, 600 Humboldt St, Richmond, CA 94805 *Tel:* 510-215-9960 *Web Site:* authormaps.com, pg 1346

Humrich, Rebecca, Sheridan MI, 613 E Industrial Dr, Chelsea, MI 48118 *Tel:* 734-475-9145 *Web Site:* www.sheridan.com, pg 1209, 1254, 1267

Hurd, Charlie, CLC Ministries, 701 Pennsylvania Ave, Fort Washington, PA 19034 *Tel:* 215-542-1240 *Toll Free Tel:* 800-659-1240 *Fax:* 215-542-7580 *E-mail:* orders@clcpublications.com *Web Site:* www.clcpublications.com, pg 1312

Hurley, Joanna Thorne, HurleyMedia LLC, 1477 Canyon Rd, Santa Fe, NM 87501 *Tel:* 505-603-6392 *Web Site:* www.hurleymedia.com, pg 1098, 1346

Hurley, Michael P, Horizon Paper Co Inc, 1010 Washington Blvd, Stamford, CT 06901 *Tel:* 203-358-0855 *Toll Free Tel:* 866-358-0855 *E-mail:* info@horizonpaper.com *Web Site:* www.horizonpaper.com, pg 1264

Hussey, John, Ingram Content Group LLC, One Ingram Blvd, La Vergne, TN 37086-1986 *Tel:* 615-793-5000 *Toll Free Tel:* 800-937-8000 (retailers); 800-937-5300 (ext 1, libs) *E-mail:* customerservice@ingramcontent.com *Web Site:* www.ingramcontent.com, pg 1290, 1315

Hutcheson, Deborah, Agfa Graphics, 611 River Dr, Center 3, Elmwood Park, NJ 07407 *Tel:* 201-440-2500 *Toll Free Tel:* 888-274-8626 (cust serv) *E-mail:* customercare.us@agfa.com *Web Site:* agfagraphics.us, pg 1273, 1372

Hutchings, Amy, Richard Hutchings Photography LLC, 11 White Well Dr, Rhinebeck, NY 12572 *Tel:* 914-715-7461 *E-mail:* richard@hutchingsphotography.com *Web Site:* hutchingsphotography.com, pg 1440

Hutchings, Richard, Richard Hutchings Photography LLC, 11 White Well Dr, Rhinebeck, NY 12572 *Tel:* 914-715-7461 *E-mail:* richard@hutchingsphotography.com *Web Site:* hutchingsphotography.com, pg 1440

Hutchison, Chris, The P A Hutchison Co, 400 Penn Ave, Mayfield, PA 18433 *Tel:* 570-876-4560 *Toll Free Tel:* 800-USA-PRNT (872-7768) *Fax:* 570-876-4561 *E-mail:* sales@pahutch.com *Web Site:* www.pahutch.com, pg 1206, 1221, 1249, 1264, 1277

Hutchison, Roger, CD ROM Inc, 3131 E Riverside Dr, Fort Myers, FL 33916 *Tel:* 239-332-2800 *Toll Free Tel:* 866-66-CDROM (662-3766) *Fax:* 239-332-2808 *E-mail:* sales@cdrominc.com *Web Site:* www.cdrominc.com, pg 1374

Hutto, Eric, Unisys Corp, 801 Lakeview Dr, Suite 100, Blue Bell, PA 19422 *Tel:* 215-274-2742 *Web Site:* www.unisys.com, pg 1387

Hyde, Jen, Bellevue Literary Review, NYU School of Medicine, Dept of Medicine, 550 First Ave, OBV-A612, New York, NY 10016 *Tel:* 212-263-3973 *E-mail:* info@BLReview.org *Web Site:* www.BLReview.org, pg 1124

Hynes, Johanna, Ingram Publisher Services, an Ingram brand, One Ingram Blvd, La Vergne, TN 37086 *Tel:* 615-793-5000 *Toll Free Tel:* 866-400-5351 (cust serv) *E-mail:* ips@ingramcontent.com *Web Site:* www.ingramcontent.com, pg 1290

Hyzy, Karen, Chicago Distribution Center (CDC), 11030 S Langley Ave, Chicago, IL 60628 *Tel:* 773-702-7010 *Toll Free Tel:* 800-621-8476 *Web Site:* press.uchicago.edu/cdc, pg 1285

Iannantuono, Albert, Tri-Media Integrated Marketing Technologies Inc, 1027 Pelham St, Unit 2, Fonthill, ON L0S 1E0, Canada *E-mail:* think@tri-media.com *Web Site:* tri-media.com, pg 1087

Jenkins, Jerrold R, Jenkins Group Inc, 1129 Woodmere Ave, Suite B, Traverse City, MI 49686 *Tel:* 231-933-0445 *Toll Free Tel:* 800-706-4636 *Fax:* 231-933-0448 *E-mail:* info@bookpublishing.com *Web Site:* www.bookpublishing.com, pg 1221, 1347, 1359

Jenkins, John III, Decode, Inc, 625 First Ave, Suite 300, Seattle, WA 98104 *Tel:* 206-343-9101 *E-mail:* books@decodebooks.com *Web Site:* www.decodeinc.com; www.decodebooks.com, pg 1427

Jenkins, Joyce, Poetry Flash, 1450 Fourth St, Suite 4, Berkeley, CA 94710 *Tel:* 510-525-5476 *Fax:* 510-525-6752 *E-mail:* info@poetryflash.org *Web Site:* www.poetryflash.org, pg 1130

Jenkins, Ralph, Mark Andy Inc, 18081 Chesterfield Airport Rd, Chesterfield, MO 63005 *Tel:* 636-532-4433 *Toll Free Tel:* 800-447-1231 *Toll Free Fax:* 800-447-1231 *Web Site:* www.presstek.com; markandy.com; shop.markandy.com, pg 1372

Jennette, Alyssa, Stonesong, 270 W 39 St, Suite 201, New York, NY 10018 *Tel:* 212-929-4600 *E-mail:* editors@stonesong.com *Web Site:* www.stonesong.com, pg 1362

Jensen, Bruce, TotalWorks™ Inc, 420 W Huron St, Chicago, IL 60654 *Tel:* 773-489-4313 *E-mail:* production@totalworks.net *Web Site:* www.totalworks.net, pg 1227, 1255

Jensen, Christine, Burmar Technical Corp, 106 Ransom Ave, Sea Cliff, NY 11579 *Tel:* 516-484-6000 *Fax:* 516-484-6356 *Web Site:* burmar.net, pg 1217, 1374, 1425

Jensen, Janine, Chesapeake & Hudson Inc, 115 W Potomac St, Brunswick, MD 21716 *Tel:* 301-834-7170 *Toll Free Tel:* 800-231-4469 *Toll Free Fax:* 800-307-5163 *E-mail:* office@cheshud.com *Web Site:* www.cheshud.com, pg 1285

Jensen, Michael Jon, Westchester Publishing Services, 4 Old Newtown Rd, Danbury, CT 06810 *Tel:* 203-791-0080 *Fax:* 203-791-9286 *E-mail:* info@westchesterpubsvcs.com *Web Site:* www.westchesterpublishingservices.com, pg 1227

Jernigan, Ms S A "Sam", Renaissance Consultations, PO Box 561, Auburn, CA 95604 *Tel:* 530-362-1339 *E-mail:* info@marketingandpr.com *Web Site:* www.MarketingAndPR.com, pg 1101

Jesse, Joanne, Cape Cod Compositors Inc, 811 Washington St, Suite 2, Pembroke, MA 02359-2333 *Tel:* 781-826-2100, pg 1217

Jessen, Dale C, Computer Analytics Corp, 999 E Touhy Ave, Suite 130, Des Plaines, IL 60018-2736 *Tel:* 847-297-5290 *Fax:* 847-297-8680 *Web Site:* www.cacorp.com, pg 1374

Jewett, Brad, Corel Corp, 1600 Carling Ave, Ottawa, ON K1Z 8R7, Canada *Tel:* 613-728-8200 (PR) *Toll Free Tel:* 877-582-6735 *Web Site:* www.corel.com, pg 1375

Jillens, Allison, PsycCRITIQUES™, 750 First St NE, Washington, DC 20002-4242 *Tel:* 202-336-5500 *Fax:* 202-336-5502 *E-mail:* subscriptions@apa.org *Web Site:* www.apa.org, pg 1130

Jobson, Leslie, Ingram Publisher Services, an Ingram brand, One Ingram Blvd, La Vergne, TN 37086 *Tel:* 615-793-5000 *Toll Free Tel:* 866-400-5351 (cust serv) *E-mail:* ips@ingramcontent.com *Web Site:* www.ingramcontent.com, pg 1290

Joesel, Kevin, Heraeus Noblelight America LLC, 910 Clopper Rd, Gaithersburg, MD 20878-1361 *Tel:* 301-527-2660 *Toll Free Tel:* 888-276-8600 *Fax:* 301-527-2661 *E-mail:* info.hna.uvp@heraeus.com *Web Site:* www.heraeus-noblelight.com/uvamericas, pg 1276

Johansson, Kay, Gracenote, a Nielsen Company, 2000 Powell St, Suite 1500, Emeryville, CA 94608 *Tel:* 510-428-7200 *Web Site:* www.gracenote.com, pg 1184

Johnson, Bennie F, AIGA, the professional association for design, 222 Broadway, New York, NY 10038 *Tel:* 212-807-1990 *Fax:* 212-807-1799 *E-mail:* general@aiga.org *Web Site:* www.aiga.org, pg 1133

Johnson, Bert, Graphics Two, 819 S Main St, Burbank, CA 91506 *Tel:* 818-841-4922, pg 1220, 1276

Johnson, Christopher C, Camerique Inc International, 164 Regency Dr, Eagleville, PA 19403 *Tel:* 610-272-4000 *Fax:* 610-539-9558 *E-mail:* info@camerique.com *Web Site:* www.camerique.com, pg 1445

Johnson, Connie, Double Play, 303 Hillcrest Rd, Belton, MO 64012-1852 *Tel:* 816-651-7118, pg 1345

Johnson, Elizabeth, MEJ Personal Business Services Inc, 245 E 116 St, New York, NY 10029 *Tel:* 212-426-6017 *Toll Free Tel:* 866-557-5336 *Fax:* 646-827-3628 *E-mail:* support@mejpbs.com *Web Site:* www.mejpbs.com, pg 1411

Johnson, Emily, Abraham Associates Inc, 5120-A Cedar Lake Rd, Minneapolis, MN 55416 *Tel:* 952-927-7920 *Toll Free Tel:* 800-701-2489 *Fax:* 952-927-8089 *E-mail:* info@abrahamassociatesinc.com *Web Site:* www.abrahamassociatesinc.com, pg 1281

Johnson, Greg, Intuit Inc, 2700 Coast Ave, Mountain View, CA 94043 *Tel:* 650-944-6000 *Toll Free Tel:* 800-446-8848 *E-mail:* investor_relations@intuit.com *Web Site:* www.intuit.com, pg 1379

Johnson, Jeffrey M, Hearst Newspapers, 300 W 57 St, New York, NY 10019 *Tel:* 212-649-2000 *Web Site:* www.hearst.com/newspapers, pg 1185

Johnson, Kristen, The Creative Group (TCG), 125 High St, 17th fl, Boston, MA 02110 *Tel:* 617-690-7386; 617-526-8899 *Toll Free Tel:* 888-651-8589 *E-mail:* boston@creativegroup.com *Web Site:* www.roberthalf.com/work-with-us/our-services/creativegroup, pg 1389, 1426

Johnson, Lloyd, Double Play, 303 Hillcrest Rd, Belton, MO 64012-1852 *Tel:* 816-651-7118, pg 1345

Johnson, Melvin, MEJ Personal Business Services Inc, 245 E 116 St, New York, NY 10029 *Tel:* 212-426-6017 *Toll Free Tel:* 866-557-5336 *Fax:* 646-827-3628 *E-mail:* support@mejpbs.com *Web Site:* www.mejpbs.com, pg 1411

Johnson, Michelle, World Literature Today, 630 Parrington Oval, Suite 110, Norman, OK 73019-4033 *Tel:* 405-325-4531 *E-mail:* wlt@ou.edu *Web Site:* www.worldliteraturetoday.org, pg 1132

Johnson, Paolo, Cliff Digital, 14700 S Main St, Gardena, CA 90248 *Tel:* 310-323-5600 *Toll Free Tel:* 866-429-2242 *Fax:* 310-400-3090 *E-mail:* cliff@cliffdigital.com *Web Site:* www.cliffdigital.com, pg 1091

Johnson, Peter H, Book Machine Sales Inc, PO Box 297, Hamlin, PA 18427 *Tel:* 570-647-9111 *Web Site:* bookmachinesales.com, pg 1274

Johnson, Sarah, The Historical Novels Review, 400 Dark Star Ct, Fairbanks, AK 99709 *Tel:* 217-581-7538 *Fax:* 217-581-7534 *E-mail:* reviews@historicalnovelsociety.org *Web Site:* historicalnovelsociety.org, pg 1126

Johnson, Scott, Pivar Computing Services Inc, 1500 Abbott Ct, Buffalo Grove, IL 60089 *Tel:* 847-478-8000 *Toll Free Tel:* 800-CONVERT (266-8378) *Fax:* 847-478-8750 *Web Site:* www.pivar.com, pg 1383

Johnson, Stephanie, AlphaGraphics Inc, 143 Union Blvd, Suite 650, Lakewood, CO 80228 *Toll Free Tel:* 800-955-6246 *Fax:* 801-595-7270 *E-mail:* contactus@alphagraphics.com *Web Site:* www.alphagraphics.com, pg 1372

Johnson, Steve, Vectorworks Inc, 7150 Riverwood Dr, Columbia, MD 21046 *Tel:* 410-290-5114 *Toll Free Tel:* 888-646-4223 (sales) *Fax:* 410-290-7266 *E-mail:* sales@vectorworks.net *Web Site:* www.vectorworks.net, pg 1387

Johnson, Tashauna, PhotoEdit Inc, 3505 Cadillac Ave, Suite P-101, Costa Mesa, CA 92626 *Toll Free Tel:* 888-450-0946 *Fax:* 714-434-5937 *Web Site:* www.photoeditinc.com, pg 1449

Johnson, William, Lambda Literary, PO Box 20186, New York, NY 10014 *Tel:* 213-277-5755 *Fax:* 323-643-4281 *E-mail:* admin@lambdaliterary.org *Web Site:* www.lambdaliterary.org, pg 1128

Johnston, Charidy, Penguin Random House Canada, 320 Front St W, Suite 1400, Toronto, ON M5V 3B6, Canada *Tel:* 416-364-4449 *Toll Free Tel:* 888-523-9292 (cust serv) *Fax:* 416-598-7764 *Web Site:* www.penguinrandomhouse.ca, pg 1295

Johnston, Greg, Greg Johnston Photography, 6214 Solstice Loop, Sanford, FL 32773 *Tel:* 305-258-7070 *E-mail:* info@gregjohnston.com *Web Site:* www.gregjohnston.com, pg 1439

Johnston, Kristi, Bert Davis Executive Search Inc, 555 Fifth Ave, Suite 302, New York, NY 10017 *Tel:* 212-838-4000 *E-mail:* info@bertdavis.com *Web Site:* www.bertdavis.com, pg 1389

Jones, Carla, Thomson Reuters, 3 Times Sq, New York, NY 10036 *Tel:* 646-223-4000; 646-223-6100 (edit); 646-223-6000 (newsroom) *Web Site:* www.thomsonreuters.com, pg 1186

Jones, Carrie, Greenleaf Book Group LLC, 3 Park Place, 4005 Banister Lane, Suite B, Austin, TX 78704 *Tel:* 512-891-6100 *Fax:* 512-891-6150 *E-mail:* contact@greenleafbookgroup.com *Web Site:* www.greenleafbookgroup.com, pg 1288, 1358

Jones, Christopher, Chicago Distribution Center (CDC), 11030 S Langley Ave, Chicago, IL 60628 *Tel:* 773-702-7010 *Toll Free Fax:* 800-621-8476 *Web Site:* press.uchicago.edu/cdc, pg 1285

Jones, Cindy, Four Colour Print Group, 2410 Frankfort Ave, Louisville, KY 40206 *Tel:* 502-896-9644 *Fax:* 502-896-9594 *E-mail:* sales@fourcolour.com *Web Site:* www.fourcolour.com, pg 1204, 1247, 1276

Jones, Erin, The P A Hutchison Co, 400 Penn Ave, Mayfield, PA 18433 *Tel:* 570-876-4560 *Toll Free Tel:* 800-USA-PRNT (872-7768) *Fax:* 570-876-4561 *E-mail:* sales@pahutch.com *Web Site:* www.pahutch.com, pg 1206, 1221, 1249, 1264, 1277

Jones, Everett, Publishers Weekly, 71 W 23 St, Suite 1608, New York, NY 10010 *Tel:* 212-377-5500 *Fax:* 212-377-2733 *Web Site:* www.publishersweekly.com, pg 1130

Jones, Howard J Sr, The Advertising, Marketing & Sales Promotion Book Club, Book Club Bldg, 7 Putter Lane, Middle Island, NY 11953 *Tel:* 631-924-3888 (ext 100) *E-mail:* amspbookclub@gmail.com; linickgroup@gmail.com, pg 1135

Jones, Jan, PBD Worldwide Inc, 1650 Bluegrass Lakes Pkwy, Alpharetta, GA 30004 *Tel:* 470-769-1000 *Toll Free Tel:* 866-998-4PBD (998-4723) *E-mail:* sales.marketing@pbd.com; customerservice@pbd.com *Web Site:* www.pbd.com, pg 1333

Jones, Lou, Lou Jones Studio, 44 Breed St, Boston, MA 02128 *Tel:* 617-561-1194 *Fax:* 617-561-1196 *E-mail:* fotojones@aol.com *Web Site:* www.fotojones.com, pg 1440

Jones, Mike, Integrated Distribution Services (IDS), 9431 AllPoints Pkwy, Plainfield, IN 46168 *Toll Free Tel:* 866-232-6533 *E-mail:* adale@idsfulfillment.com *Web Site:* www.idsfulfillment.com, pg 1332

Jones, Phillip, Printing Research Inc (PRI), 10760 Shady Trail, Suite 300, Dallas, TX 75220 *Tel:* 214-353-9000 *Toll Free Tel:* 800-627-5537 (US only) *Fax:* 214-357-5847 *E-mail:* info@superblue.net *Web Site:* www.printingresearch.com; www.superblue.net, pg 1278

Jones, Roger L, Bedford Printing Co, 1501 S Blount St, Raleigh, NC 27603 *Tel:* 919-832-3973 *Fax:* 919-755-0204 *Web Site:* www.bedfordprinting.com, pg 1242

Jones, Stephanie, Cookbook Publishers Inc, 11633 W 83 Terr, Lenexa, KS 66285 *Tel:* 913-492-5900 *Toll Free Tel:* 800-227-7282 *Fax:* 913-492-5947 *E-mail:* info@cookbookpublishers.com *Web Site:* www.cookbookpublishers.com, pg 1218, 1245

Jones, Steve, Roswell Bookbinding, 2614 N 29 Ave, Phoenix, AZ 85009 *Tel:* 602-272-9338 *Toll Free Tel:* 888-803-8883 *Fax:* 602-272-9786 *Web Site:* www.roswellbookbinding.com, pg 1254, 1324

Jones, Suzanne, International Service Co, International Service Bldg, 333 Fourth Ave, Indialantic, FL 32903-4295 *Tel:* 321-724-1443 *Fax:* 321-724-1443, pg 1316, 1323, 1326, 1329

Jones, William R, VistaBooks LLC, 637 Blue Ridge Rd, Silverthorne, CO 80498-8931 *Tel:* 970-468-7673 *Fax:* 970-468-7673 *E-mail:* email@vistabooks.com *Web Site:* www.vistabooks.com, pg 1322

Jordan, Tina, The New York Times Book Review, 620 Eighth Ave, 5th fl, New York, NY 10018 *Tel:* 212-556-1234 *Toll Free Tel:* 800-631-2580 (subns) *E-mail:* bookreview@nytimes.com; books@nytimes.com *Web Site:* www.nytimes.com, pg 1129

Jordan-Smith, Gavin, Ricoh Americas Corp, 300 Eagleview Blvd, Exton, PA 19341 *Tel:* 610-296-8000 *Toll Free Tel:* 800-333-2679 (prod support); 800-637-4264 (sales) *Web Site:* www.ricoh-usa.com, pg 1385

Jorgensen, Janis, US Naval Institute Photo Archive, 291 Wood Rd, Annapolis, MD 21402 *Tel:* 410-295-1022 *Fax:* 410-295-1049 *E-mail:* photoservice@usni.org; photoarchive@usni.org *Web Site:* www.usni.org, pg 1450

Jorgensen, Mike, Impressions Inc, 1050 Westgate Dr, St Paul, MN 55114 *Tel:* 651-646-1050 *Toll Free Tel:* 800-251-4285 *Fax:* 651-646-7228 *E-mail:* info@i-i.com *Web Site:* www.i-i.com, pg 1249

Jose, Laura, ICSID Review: Foreign Investment Law Journal, 2001 Evans Rd, Cary, NC 27513 *Tel:* 919-677-0977 *Toll Free Tel:* 800-852-7323 *Fax:* 919-677-1714 *Web Site:* academic.oup.org, pg 1127

Joseph, Miles, Solar-Screen Co Inc, 53-11 105 St, Corona, NY 11368 *Tel:* 718-592-8222 *Toll Free Tel:* 800-347-6527 *Toll Free Fax:* 888-271-0891 *E-mail:* solarscreen@prodigy.net *Web Site:* www.solar-screen.com, pg 1268

Joseph, Tommy S, International Paper Co, 6400 Poplar Ave, Memphis, TN 38197 *Tel:* 901-419-9000 *Toll Free Tel:* 800-207-4003 *Web Site:* www.internationalpaper.com; facebook.com/internationalpaper; twitter.com/intlpaperco, pg 1264

Joyce, Jim, Dual Graphics, 370 Cliffwood Park, Brea, CA 92821 *Tel:* 714-990-3700 *Fax:* 714-990-6818 *Web Site:* www.dualgraphics.com, pg 1219, 1246

Judge, Amrit, Hilsinger-Mendelson West Inc, 8916 Ashcroft Ave, Los Angeles, CA 90048 *Tel:* 310-659-7930 *E-mail:* hmiwest@aol.com *Web Site:* www.hilsingermendelson.com, pg 1098

Jugan, Irene, Polish National Union of America, 1006 Pittston Ave, Scranton, PA 18505 *Tel:* 570-344-1513 *Toll Free Tel:* 800-724-6352 *Fax:* 570-961-5961 *E-mail:* info@pnu.org *Web Site:* www.pnu.org, pg 1412

Jungen, Mark, Graphic Composition Inc, N1246 Technical Dr, Greenville, WI 54942 *Tel:* 920-757-6977 *Toll Free Tel:* 800-262-8973 *Fax:* 920-757-9266 *E-mail:* socialmedia@graphiccomp.com *Web Site:* www.graphiccomp.com, pg 1248

Juris, Carolyn, Publishers Weekly, 71 W 23 St, Suite 1608, New York, NY 10010 *Tel:* 212-377-5500 *Fax:* 212-377-2733 *Web Site:* www.publishersweekly.com, pg 1130

Jutkowitz, Alexander, Hill+Knowlton Strategies, 237 Park Ave, 4th fl, New York, NY 10017 *Tel:* 212-885-0300 *Web Site:* www.hkstrategies.com, pg 1098

Kachergis, Anne, Kachergis Book Design Inc, 14 Small St N, Pittsboro, NC 27312 *Tel:* 919-542-3507 *E-mail:* goodbooks@kachergisbookdesign.com *Web Site:* www.kachergisbookdesign.com, pg 1222, 1429

Kaefer, Chris, Six Red Marbles LLC, 101 Station Landing, Medford, MA 02155 *Tel:* 857-588-9000 *E-mail:* info@sixredmarbles.com *Web Site:* www.sixredmarbles.com, pg 1226, 1385

Kaehler, Wolfgang, Wolfgang Kaehler Photography, 723 Third St S, Kirkland, WA 98033 *Tel:* 425-803-0652 *E-mail:* photos@wkaehlerphoto.com *Web Site:* www.wkaehlerphoto.com, pg 1440

Kahana, Yoram, Shooting Star/Travel, 1441 N McCadden Place, Hollywood, CA 90028 *Tel:* 323-469-2020 *E-mail:* admin@shootingstaragency.com, pg 1449

Kahanec, Cheryl, Quantum Group, 6511 Oakton St, Morton Grove, IL 60053 *Tel:* 847-967-3600 *Fax:* 847-967-3610 *E-mail:* info@quantumgroup.com *Web Site:* www.quantumgroup.com, pg 1253

Kahn, Karen, HP Inc, 1501 Paige Mill Rd, Palo Alto, CA 94304-1112 *Tel:* 650-857-1501 *Toll Free Tel:* 800-282-6672 *Web Site:* www.hp.com, pg 1378

Kaiman, Athena Millas, Athena Productions Inc, 2204 S Ashford Ct, Nashville, TN 37214 *Tel:* 305-807-8607 *E-mail:* atheprod@aol.com, pg 1282

Kaiman, Ken, Athena Productions Inc, 2204 S Ashford Ct, Nashville, TN 37214 *Tel:* 305-807-8607 *E-mail:* atheprod@aol.com, pg 1282

Kakar, Samir, Aptara Inc, 2901 Telestar Ct, Suite 522, Falls Church, VA 22042 *Tel:* 703-352-0001 *E-mail:* moreinfo@aptaracorp.com *Web Site:* www.aptaracorp.com, pg 1201, 1216, 1341, 1355, 1373, 1424

Kalajian, James, Jenkins Group Inc, 1129 Woodmere Ave, Suite B, Traverse City, MI 49686 *Tel:* 231-933-0445 *Toll Free Tel:* 800-706-4636 *Fax:* 231-933-0448 *E-mail:* info@bookpublishing.com *Web Site:* www.bookpublishing.com, pg 1221, 1347, 1359

Kallek, Nikki, Crain Communications Inc, 1155 Gratiot Ave, Detroit, MI 48207-2732 *Tel:* 313-446-6000 *Fax:* 313-446-0383 *E-mail:* info@crain.com *Web Site:* crain.com, pg 1184

Kallman, Richard, Bookazine Co Inc, 75 Hook Rd, Bayonne, NJ 07002 *Tel:* 201-339-7777 *Toll Free Tel:* 800-221-8112 *Fax:* 201-339-7778 *E-mail:* info@bookazine.com *Web Site:* www.bookazine.com, pg 1310, 1325

Kallman, Robert, Bookazine Co Inc, 75 Hook Rd, Bayonne, NJ 07002 *Tel:* 201-339-7777 *Toll Free Tel:* 800-221-8112 *Fax:* 201-339-7778 *E-mail:* info@bookazine.com *Web Site:* www.bookazine.com, pg 1310, 1325

Kalvin, William, Delmas Typesetting Inc, 461 Hilldale Dr, Ann Arbor, MI 48105 *Tel:* 734-662-8899 *E-mail:* delmastype@comcast.net *Web Site:* www.delmastype.com, pg 1219

Kampmann, Alex, Independent Publishers Group (IPG), 814 N Franklin St, Chicago, IL 60610 *Tel:* 312-337-0747 *Toll Free Tel:* 800-888-4741 (orders) *Fax:* 312-337-5985 *E-mail:* frontdesk@ipgbook.com; orders@ipgbook.com *Web Site:* www.ipgbook.com, pg 1288, 1326

Kampmann, Alex, Midpoint Trade Books, 814 N Franklin St, Suite 100, Chicago, IL 60610 *Tel:* 312-337-0747 *Fax:* 312-337-5985 *E-mail:* orders@ipgbook.com *Web Site:* www.midpointtrade.com, pg 1292

Kampmann, Alison, Midpoint Trade Books, 814 N Franklin St, Suite 100, Chicago, IL 60610 *Tel:* 312-337-0747 *Fax:* 312-337-5985 *E-mail:* orders@ipgbook.com *Web Site:* www.midpointtrade.com, pg 1292

Kampmann, Eric, Midpoint Trade Books, 814 N Franklin St, Suite 100, Chicago, IL 60610 *Tel:* 312-337-0747 *Fax:* 312-337-5985 *E-mail:* orders@ipgbook.com *Web Site:* www.midpointtrade.com, pg 1292

Kang, Steve, QualityLogic Inc, 9576 W Emerald St, Boise, ID 83704 *Tel:* 208-424-1905 *E-mail:* info@qualitylogic.com *Web Site:* www.qualitylogic.com, pg 1384

Kanter, Peter, Dell Magazines, 44 Wall St, Suite 904, New York, NY 10005-2401 *Tel:* 212-686-7188 *Toll Free Tel:* 800-220-7443 (corp sales) *Fax:* 212-480-5751 *E-mail:* customerservice@pennydellpuzzles.com *Web Site:* www.pennydellpuzzles.com, pg 1357

Kantor, Becca, Paper Brigade, 520 Eighth Ave, 4th fl, New York, NY 10018 *Tel:* 212-201-2920 *Fax:* 212-532-4952 *E-mail:* info@jewishbooks.org *Web Site:* www.jewishbookcouncil.org, pg 1130

Kantor, Emma, Publishers Weekly, 71 W 23 St, Suite 1608, New York, NY 10010 *Tel:* 212-377-5500 *Fax:* 212-377-2733 *Web Site:* www.publishersweekly.com, pg 1130

Kaplan, Linda, Kaplan/DeFiore Rights, 47 E 19 St, 3rd fl, New York, NY 10003 *Tel:* 212-925-7244 *Web Site:* kaplanrights.com, pg 1348

Kaplan, Robert, Linick International Inc, Linick Bldg, 7 Putter Lane, Middle Island, NY 11953 *Tel:* 631-924-3888; 631-924-8555; 631-604-8599 *E-mail:* topmarketingadvisor@gmail.com *Web Site:* topmarketingadvisor.com, pg 1349

Kapolnek, Paul, Western Printing Machinery Co (WPM), 9228 Ivanhoe St, Schiller Park, IL 60176 *Tel:* 847-678-1740 *Fax:* 847-678-6176 *E-mail:* info@wpm.com *Web Site:* www.wpm.com, pg 1280

Kapoor, Prashant, Aptara Inc, 2901 Telestar Ct, Suite 522, Falls Church, VA 22042 *Tel:* 703-352-0001 *E-mail:* moreinfo@aptaracorp.com *Web Site:* www.aptaracorp.com, pg 1201, 1216, 1341, 1355, 1373, 1424

Karabots, Nick, Kappa Graphics LLP, 50 Rock St, Hughestown, PA 18640 *Tel:* 570-655-9681 *Toll Free Tel:* 800-236-4396 (sales) *E-mail:* weborders@kappapma.com *Web Site:* www.kappapma.com/kappagraphics; kappapuzzles.com, pg 1222, 1249

Karamsetty, Pardha, Apex CoVantage, 4045 Sheridan Ave, No 266, Miami Beach, FL 33140 *Tel:* 703-709-3000 *Fax:* 703-709-8242 *E-mail:* info@apexcovantage.com *Web Site:* www.apexcovantage.com, pg 1215

Karancak-Splane, Ilge, Richard Schneider Language Services, 1200 Piedmont Ave, Pacific Grove, CA 93950 *Tel:* 831-622-0554 *Toll Free Tel:* 800-500-5808 *Fax:* 831-622-0524 *E-mail:* service@idioms.com *Web Site:* www.idioms.com, pg 1412

Karel, Howard, The Karel/Dutton Group, 3145 Geary Blvd, PMB 619, San Francisco, CA 94118 *Tel:* 415-668-0829 *Fax:* 415-668-2463, pg 1291

Karim, Shah, Saferock, 75 Armour Place, Dumont, NJ 07628 *Tel:* 646-535-0110 *E-mail:* info@saferock.com *Web Site:* saferockretail.com, pg 1385

Karmelich, Robert, Design Science Inc (DSI), 444 W Ocean Blvd, Suite 800, Long Beach, CA 90802 *Tel:* 562-432-2920 *Toll Free Tel:* 800-827-0685 (US sales only) *Fax:* 562-624-2859 *E-mail:* info@wiris.com; sales@wiris.com; support@wiris.com *Web Site:* www.dessci.com, pg 1376

Kass, David, Hilsinger-Mendelson West Inc, 8916 Ashcroft Ave, Los Angeles, CA 90048 *Tel:* 310-659-7930 *E-mail:* hmiwest@aol.com *Web Site:* www.hilsingermendelson.com, pg 1098

Kastner, Suzanne, GW Illustration & Design, 2290 Ball Dr, St Louis, MO 63146 *Tel:* 314-567-9854 *Web Site:* www.gwinc.com, pg 1428

Kastner, Suzanne, GW Inc, 2290 Ball Dr, St Louis, MO 63146 *Tel:* 314-567-9854 *Web Site:* www.gwinc.com, pg 1220, 1378

Katagiri, Takehito, OKI Data Americas Inc, 8505 Freeport Pkwy, Suite 600, Irving, TX 75063 *Tel:* 972-815-4800 *Toll Free Tel:* 800-OKI-DATA (654-3282) *E-mail:* support@okidata.com *Web Site:* www.oki.com/us/printing, pg 1383

Katano, Hiroaki, Tamron USA Inc, 10 Austin Blvd, Commack, NY 11725 *Tel:* 631-858-8400 *Toll Free Tel:* 800-827-8880 *Fax:* 631-543-5666; 631-858-8462 (cust serv) *E-mail:* custserv@tamron.com *Web Site:* www.tamron-usa.com, pg 1386

Katsevman, Boris, Linguistic Systems Inc (LSI), 260 Franklin St, Suite 230, Boston, MA 02110 *Tel:* 617-528-7410 *Toll Free Tel:* 800-654-5006 *E-mail:* clientservice@linguist.com *Web Site:* www.linguist.com, pg 1222, 1380, 1411, 1429

Katzenberger, Amy, American Camp Association Inc, 5000 State Rd 67 N, Martinsville, IN 46151-7902 *Tel:* 765-342-8456 *Toll Free Tel:* 800-428-2267 *Fax:* 765-342-2065 *E-mail:* contactus@acacamps.org *Web Site:* www.acacamps.org, pg 1309

Kaufman, Betty, Silver Visions: Robert Kaufman Photography & Design, PO Box 610415, Newton Highlands, MA 02461-0415 *Toll Free Tel:* 877-249-0207 *E-mail:* silverv@silvervisions.com *Web Site:* www.silvervisions.com, pg 1443

Kaufman, Carol E, Paper Brigade, 520 Eighth Ave, 4th fl, New York, NY 10018 *Tel:* 212-201-2920 *Fax:* 212-532-4952 *E-mail:* info@jewishbooks.org *Web Site:* www.jewishbookcouncil.org, pg 1130

Kaufman, Cecile, X-Height Studio, 83 High St, Milford, MA 01757 *Tel:* 508-478-3897 *Toll Free Tel:* 888-474-8973 *E-mail:* info@x-heightstudio.com *Web Site:* www.x-heightstudio.com, pg 1228

Kaufman, Donna Paz, Paz & Associates: The Bookstore Training & Consulting Group, 1417 Sadler Rd, No 274, Fernandina Beach, FL 32034 *Tel:* 904-277-2664 *Fax:* 904-261-6742 *Web Site:* www.pazbookbiz.com, pg 1350

Kaufman, Doris, DSM Producers Inc, PO Box 1160, Marco Island, FL 34146-1160 *Tel:* 212-245-0006, pg 1376

Kaufman, Mark, Paz & Associates: The Bookstore Training & Consulting Group, 1417 Sadler Rd, No 274, Fernandina Beach, FL 32034 *Tel:* 904-277-2664 *Fax:* 904-261-6742 *Web Site:* www.pazbookbiz.com, pg 1350

Kaufman, Robert, Silver Visions: Robert Kaufman Photography & Design, PO Box 610415, Newton Highlands, MA 02461-0415 *Toll Free Tel:* 877-249-0207 *E-mail:* silverv@silvervisions.com *Web Site:* www.silvervisions.com, pg 1443

Kaufman, Roy S, Copyright Clearance Center Inc (CCC), 222 Rosewood Dr, Danvers, MA 01923 *Tel:* 978-750-8400 (sales); 978-646-2600 (cust serv) *E-mail:* info@copyright.com *Web Site:* www.copyright.com, pg 1344

Kaufman, Susie V, Peace Visions, 18850 Vista del Canon, Suite A, Santa Clarita, CA 91321-4512 *Tel:* 661-251-6669 *Fax:* 661-251-6669, pg 1393

Kavanagh, Dennis, Data Reproductions Corp, 4545 Glenmeade Lane, Auburn Hills, MI 48326 *Tel:* 248-371-3700 *Toll Free Tel:* 800-242-3114 *Fax:* 248-371-3710 *Web Site:* datarepro.com, pg 1204, 1245

Kavanagh, Kimberly, Data Reproductions Corp, 4545 Glenmeade Lane, Auburn Hills, MI 48326 *Tel:* 248-371-3700 *Toll Free Tel:* 800-242-3114 *Fax:* 248-371-3710 *Web Site:* datarepro.com, pg 1204, 1245

Kavanaugh, James J, IBM Corp, One New Orchard Rd, Armonk, NY 10504 *Tel:* 914-499-1900 *Toll Free Tel:* 800-426-4968 *E-mail:* askibm@vnet.ibm.com *Web Site:* www.ibm.com, pg 1379

Kaye, Gregg, Winston Personnel, 122 E 42 St, Suite 320, New York, NY 10168 *Tel:* 212-557-5000 *Web Site:* www.winstonresources.com, pg 1390

Kaye, Sy, Winston Personnel, 122 E 42 St, Suite 320, New York, NY 10168 *Tel:* 212-557-5000 *Web Site:* www.winstonresources.com, pg 1390

Kaye, Todd, Winston Personnel, 122 E 42 St, Suite 320, New York, NY 10168 *Tel:* 212-557-5000 *Web Site:* www.winstonresources.com, pg 1390

Kazan, Michael, Verso Advertising Inc, 50 W 17 St, 5th fl, New York, NY 10011 *Tel:* 212-292-2990 *Fax:* 212-557-2592 *Web Site:* www.versoadvertising.com, pg 1087

Kean, Carla, Penguin Random House Canada, 320 Front St W, Suite 1400, Toronto, ON M5V 3B6, Canada *Tel:* 416-364-4449 *Toll Free Tel:* 888-523-9292 (cust serv) *Fax:* 416-598-7764 *Web Site:* www.penguinrandomhouse.ca, pg 1295

Kearney, Louisa Daniels, Boston Review, PO Box 425786, Cambridge, MA 02142 *Tel:* 617-324-1360 *Toll Free Tel:* 877-406-2443 (cust serv) *Fax:* 617-452-3356 *E-mail:* review@bostonreview.net *Web Site:* bostonreview.net, pg 1124

Kearns, Gail M, To Press & Beyond, 825 E Pedregosa St, Suite 2, Santa Barbara, CA 93103 *Tel:* 805-898-2263 *E-mail:* info@topressandbeyond.com *Web Site:* www.topressandbeyond.com, pg 1102, 1352, 1363

Keating, Alice, National Geographic Creative, 1145 17 St NW, Washington, DC 20036 *Tel:* 202-857-7537 *Toll Free Tel:* 800-434-2244 *E-mail:* natgeocreative@natgeo.com *Web Site:* www.natgeocreative.com, pg 1448

Keck, Tom, Tom Keck Photos, 13393 Landfair Rd, San Diego, CA 92130 *Tel:* 858-755-2975 *E-mail:* tomkeckphotos@gmail.com *Web Site:* www.tomkeckphotos.com, pg 1440

Kecskemethy, Thomas A, The Annals of The American Academy of Political & Social Science, 2455 Teller Rd, Thousand Oaks, CA 91320 *Toll Free Tel:* 800-818-7243 *Toll Free Fax:* 800-583-2665 *E-mail:* journals@sagepub.com *Web Site:* www.sagepub.com, pg 1123

Keegan, Wayne, Ingram Content Group LLC, One Ingram Blvd, La Vergne, TN 37086-1986 *Tel:* 615-793-5000 *Toll Free Tel:* 800-937-8000 (retailers); 800-937-5300 (ext 1, libs) *E-mail:* customerservice@ingramcontent.com *Web Site:* www.ingramcontent.com, pg 1290, 1315

Keenan, Aileen M, African American Review (AAR), St Louis University, 317 Adorjan Hall, 3800 Lindell Blvd, St Louis, MO 63108 *Tel:* 314-977-3688 *Fax:* 314-977-1514 *Web Site:* aar.slu.edu, pg 1123

Keenan, Timothy, H B Fuller Co, 1200 Willow Lake Blvd, St Paul, MN 55110-5146 *Tel:* 651-236-5900 *Toll Free Tel:* 888-423-8553 *E-mail:* inquiry@hbfuller.com *Web Site:* www.hbfuller.com, pg 1263, 1276

Keene, Michael, The John Roberts Company, 9687 East River Rd NW, Minneapolis, MN 55433 *Tel:* 763-755-5500 *Toll Free Tel:* 800-551-1534 *Fax:* 763-755-0394 *E-mail:* success@johnroberts.com *Web Site:* www.johnroberts.com; www.facebook.com/TheJohnRobertsCompany, pg 1093

Keene-Kendrick, Lydia, Davis Art Images, 50 Portland St, Worcester, MA 01608 *Tel:* 508-754-7201 *Toll Free Tel:* 800-533-2847 *Fax:* 508-753-3834 *E-mail:* das@davisart.com; contactus@davisart.com *Web Site:* www.davisart.com, pg 1446

Keessen, Robert H, Scott Publications Inc, 2145 W Sherman Blvd, Norton Shores, MI 49441 *Tel:* 231-755-2200 *Toll Free Tel:* 866-733-9382 *Fax:* 231-755-1003 *E-mail:* contactus@scottpublications.com *Web Site:* scottpublications.com, pg 1093

Keessen, Ruth M, Scott Publications Inc, 2145 W Sherman Blvd, Norton Shores, MI 49441 *Tel:* 231-755-2200 *Toll Free Tel:* 866-733-9382 *Fax:* 231-755-1003 *E-mail:* contactus@scottpublications.com *Web Site:* scottpublications.com, pg 1093

Kelley, Gloria, Kelley & Hall Book Publicity, 5 Briar Lane, Marblehead, MA 01945 *Tel:* 617-680-1976 *Fax:* 781-631-5959 *Web Site:* www.kelleyandhall.com, pg 1099

Kelley, Jocelyn, Kelley & Hall Book Publicity, 5 Briar Lane, Marblehead, MA 01945 *Tel:* 617-680-1976 *Fax:* 781-631-5959 *Web Site:* www.kelleyandhall.com, pg 1099

Kelley, Sarah, Jane Wesman Public Relations Inc, 322 Eighth Ave, Suite 1702, New York, NY 10001 *Tel:* 212-620-4080 *Fax:* 212-620-0370 *Web Site:* www.wesmanpr.com, pg 1098

Kellough, Kjelti, Getty Images Inc, 605 Fifth Ave S, Suite 400, Seattle, WA 98104 *Tel:* 206-925-5000 *Toll Free Tel:* 800-IMAGERY (462-4379 sales); 888-888-5889 *E-mail:* enterprisesolutionssales@gettyimages.com *Web Site:* www.gettyimages.com, pg 1378, 1447

Kelly, Charles J, Microsearch Corp, 5 Broadway, Suite 3, Saugus, MA 01906 *Tel:* 781-231-9991 *Toll Free Tel:* 800-895-0212 *Fax:* 781-231-9996 *E-mail:* info@microsearch.net *Web Site:* www.microsearchcorporation.com, pg 1381

Kelly, Chuck, Preston Kelly, 222 First Ave NE, Minneapolis, MN 55413 *Tel:* 612-843-4000 *Fax:* 612-843-3900 *E-mail:* iconicideas@prestonkelly.com *Web Site:* prestonkelly.com, pg 1087

Kelly, David, The New York Times Book Review, 620 Eighth Ave, 5th fl, New York, NY 10018 *Tel:* 212-556-1234 *Toll Free Tel:* 800-631-2580 (subns) *E-mail:* bookreview@nytimes.com; books@nytimes.com *Web Site:* www.nytimes.com, pg 1129

Kelly, Heather, SSPR LLC, One Northfield Plaza, Suite 400, Northfield, IL 60093 *Toll Free Tel:* 800-287-2279 *Web Site:* www.sspr.com, pg 1102

Kelly, Henry Boon, DCA Inc, 1515 E Pine St, Cushing, OK 74023 *Tel:* 918-225-0346 *Fax:* 918-225-1113 *E-mail:* sales@dcainc.com *Web Site:* www.dcainc.com, pg 1375

Kelly, Ryan, FedEx Supply Chain, 6700 Cranberry Woods Dr, Cranberry Township, PA 16066 *Toll Free Tel:* 800-677-3110 *E-mail:* solution@fedex.com *Web Site:* supplychain.fedex.com, pg 1332

Kelly, Scott, US Lithograph Inc, 39 Broadway, 28th fl, New York, NY 10006 *Tel:* 212-673-3210 *Fax:* 917-503-3990 *E-mail:* info@pubdata.com *Web Site:* www.pubdata.com, pg 1387

Kelly, Susan, Microsearch Corp, 5 Broadway, Suite 3, Saugus, MA 01906 *Tel:* 781-231-9991 *Toll Free Tel:* 800-895-0212 *Fax:* 781-231-9996 *E-mail:* info@microsearch.net *Web Site:* www.microsearchcorporation.com, pg 1381

Kelty, John, Andrew S Linick PhD, The Copyologist®, Linick Bldg, 7 Putter Lane, Middle Island, NY 11953 *Tel:* 631-924-3888; 631-924-8555; 631-604-8599 *E-mail:* linickgroup@gmail.com *Web Site:* topmarketingadvisor.com, pg 1106

Kemp, R Douglas, Innodata Inc, 55 Challenger Rd, Suite 202, Ridgefield Park, NJ 07660 *Tel:* 201-371-8000 *Toll Free Tel:* 877-454-8400 *E-mail:* info@innodata.com; marketing@innodata.com *Web Site:* innodata.com, pg 1221, 1347, 1379

Kempf, Adam, Action Printing, N6637 Rolling Meadows Dr, Fond du Lac, WI 54937 *Tel:* 920-907-7820 *E-mail:* info@actionprinting.com *Web Site:* www.actionprinting.com, pg 1241

Kendziora, Laurie, Wybel Marketing Group Inc, 213 W Main St, Barrington, IL 60010 *Tel:* 847-382-0384; 847-382-0382 *Toll Free Tel:* 800-323-5297 *Fax:* 847-382-0385 *Toll Free Fax:* 800-595-5252 *E-mail:* bookreps@wybel.com, pg 1301

Kennedy, Kyle, The John Roberts Company, 9687 East River Rd NW, Minneapolis, MN 55433 *Tel:* 763-755-5500 *Toll Free Tel:* 800-551-1534 *Fax:* 763-755-0394 *E-mail:* success@johnroberts.com *Web Site:* www.johnroberts.com; www.facebook.com/TheJohnRobertsCompany, pg 1093

Kennedy, Mary, Institute of Intergovernmental Relations, Queen's University, Robert Sutherland Hall, Rm 301, Kingston, ON K7L 3N6, Canada *Tel:* 613-533-2080 *E-mail:* iigr@queensu.ca *Web Site:* www.queensu.ca/iigr, pg 1315

Kennedy, Tom, AlphaGraphics Inc, 143 Union Blvd, Suite 650, Lakewood, CO 80228 *Toll Free Tel:* 800-955-6246 *Fax:* 801-595-7270 *E-mail:* contactus@alphagraphics.com *Web Site:* www.alphagraphics.com, pg 1372

Kennell, Joseph F, Versa Press Inc, 1465 Spring Bay Rd, East Peoria, IL 61611-9788 *Tel:* 309-822-8272 *Toll Free Tel:* 800-447-7829 *Fax:* 309-822-8141 *Web Site:* www.versapress.com, pg 1209, 1227, 1256, 1269

Kennell, Steven J, Versa Press Inc, 1465 Spring Bay Rd, East Peoria, IL 61611-9788 *Tel:* 309-822-8272 *Toll Free Tel:* 800-447-7829 *Fax:* 309-822-8141 *Web Site:* www.versapress.com, pg 1209, 1227, 1256, 1269

Kenney, Elaine, Communication Matters, 48 Aylmer Ave, Ottawa, ON K1S 2X1, Canada *Tel:* 613-233-5423 *Web Site:* www.communicationmatters.ca, pg 1096

Kenney, Gerald P, Unisys Corp, 801 Lakeview Dr, Suite 100, Blue Bell, PA 19422 *Tel:* 215-274-2742 *Web Site:* www.unisys.com, pg 1387

Koffler, Lionel, Firefly Books Ltd, 50 Staples Ave, Unit 1, Richmond Hill, ON L4B 0A7, Canada *Tel:* 416-499-8412 *Toll Free Tel:* 800-387-6192 (CN); 800-387-5085 (US) *Fax:* 416-499-8313 *Toll Free Fax:* 800-450-0391 (CN); 800-565-6034 (US) *E-mail:* service@fireflybooks.com *Web Site:* www.fireflybooks.com, pg 1287

Kohan, Deborah, Media Connect, 301 E 57 St, 4th fl, New York, NY 10022 *Tel:* 212-583-2718 *Web Site:* www.media-connect.com, pg 1099

Kolatch, David, Jonathan David Publishers Inc, 52 Tuscan Way, Suite 202-371, St Augustine, FL 32092 *Tel:* 718-456-8611 *E-mail:* customerservice@jdbooks.com *Web Site:* www.jdbooks.com, pg 1291

Koll, Thomas, Laplink Software Inc, 600 108 Ave NE, Suite 610, Bellevue, WA 98004 *Tel:* 425-952-6000 *Toll Free Tel:* 800-LAPLINK (527-5465) *E-mail:* info@laplink.com; sales@laplink.com *Web Site:* web.laplink.com, pg 1380

Koller, Edward III, Koller Search Partners, 655 Third Ave, 24th fl, New York, NY 10017 *Tel:* 212-661-5250 *E-mail:* ksp@kollersearch.com *Web Site:* www.kollersearch.com, pg 1389

Koller, Edward R Jr, Koller Search Partners, 655 Third Ave, 24th fl, New York, NY 10017 *Tel:* 212-661-5250 *E-mail:* ksp@kollersearch.com *Web Site:* www.kollersearch.com, pg 1389

Konecky, Steven, Printing Corporation of the Americas Inc, 620 SW 12 Ave, Pompano Beach, FL 33069 *Tel:* 954-781-8100 *Toll Free Tel:* 866-721-1PCA (721-1722) *Web Site:* pcaprintingplus.com, pg 1208, 1224, 1253, 1266

Koon, Tyler, Lawton Connect, 649 Triumph Ct, Orlando, FL 32805 *Tel:* 407-260-0400 *Toll Free Tel:* 877-330-1900 *Fax:* 407-260-1321 *E-mail:* hello@lawtonconnect.com *Web Site:* www.lawtonconnect.com, pg 1250

Koonse, Emma, Publishers Weekly, 71 W 23 St, Suite 1608, New York, NY 10010 *Tel:* 212-377-5500 *Fax:* 212-377-2733 *Web Site:* www.publishersweekly.com, pg 1130

Kopp, Bill, Champion Printing Inc, 3422 Misty Creek Dr, Erlanger, KY 41018 *Tel:* 859-727-5501 *Toll Free Tel:* 800-543-1957 (US) *Fax:* 859-727-5507 *E-mail:* sales@championprintinginc.com *Web Site:* www.championprintinginc.com, pg 1091, 1105

Kopp, Darby, GOBI® Library Solutions from EBSCO, 999 Maple St, Contoocook, NH 03229 *Tel:* 603-746-3102 *Toll Free Tel:* 800-258-3774 (US & CN) *Fax:* 603-746-5628 *E-mail:* information@ebsco.com *Web Site:* gobi.ebsco.com, pg 1314

Kosloff, David, Roosevelt Paper Co, One Roosevelt Dr, Mount Laurel, NJ 08054 *Tel:* 856-303-4100 *Toll Free Tel:* 800-523-3470 *Fax:* 856-642-1949 *E-mail:* marketing@rooseveltpaper.com *Web Site:* www.rooseveltpaper.com, pg 1267

Kosloff, Ted, Roosevelt Paper Co, One Roosevelt Dr, Mount Laurel, NJ 08054 *Tel:* 856-303-4100 *Toll Free Tel:* 800-523-3470 *Fax:* 856-642-1949 *E-mail:* marketing@rooseveltpaper.com *Web Site:* www.rooseveltpaper.com, pg 1267

Kosnik, Kenneth R, Computer Analytics Corp, 999 E Touhy Ave, Suite 130, Des Plaines, IL 60018-2736 *Tel:* 847-297-5290 *Fax:* 847-297-8680 *Web Site:* www.cacorp.com, pg 1374

Koss, Gretchen, Tandem Literary, 28 Clinton Rd, Glen Ridge, NJ 07028 *Tel:* 212-629-1990 *Fax:* 212-629-1990 *Web Site:* tandemliterary.com, pg 1102

Kostiuk, Tony, Citation Box & Paper Co, 4700 W Augusta Blvd, Chicago, IL 60651-3397 *Tel:* 773-378-1400 *E-mail:* info@citationbox.com *Web Site:* www.citationbox.com, pg 1335

Koviak, Ian, theBookDesigners, 769 Center Blvd, No 22, Fairfax, CA 94930 *Tel:* 415-491-5426 *E-mail:* info@bookdesigners.com *Web Site:* www.bookdesigners.com, pg 1425

Kowkabany, Bob, Theatre Journal, 2715 N Charles St, Baltimore, MD 21218-4363 *Toll Free Tel:* 800-548-1784 (journal orders) *Fax:* 410-516-6968 *E-mail:* jrnlcirc@press.jhu.edu (journal orders) *Web Site:* www.press.jhu.edu/journals/theatre_journal/index.html, pg 1131

Koza, Kate, Bookforum, 350 Seventh Ave, New York, NY 10001 *Tel:* 212-475-4000 *Fax:* 212-529-1257 *E-mail:* info@bookforum.com; editors@bookforum.com *Web Site:* www.bookforum.com, pg 1124

Kozlowski, Darrell, DWJ BOOKS LLC, 14 Hill Side Lane, East Hampton, NY 11937 *Tel:* 631-267-8270 *E-mail:* info@dwjbooks.com *Web Site:* www.dwjbooks.com, pg 1357, 1427

Krasemann, Daniel R, DRK PHOTO, 100 Starlight Way, Sedona, AZ 86351 *Tel:* 928-284-9808 *E-mail:* info@drkphoto.com *Web Site:* www.drkphoto.com, pg 1446

Kraus, Dennis, Chicago Distribution Center (CDC), 11030 S Langley Ave, Chicago, IL 60628 *Tel:* 773-702-7010 *Toll Free Tel:* 800-621-8476 *Web Site:* press.uchicago.edu/cdc, pg 1285

Krause, Rayner, Southern Territory Associates, 4508 64 St, Lubbock, TX 79414 *E-mail:* sta77@suddenlink.net *Web Site:* www.southernterritory.com, pg 1299

Kravitz, Scott, Ironmark, 9040 Junction Dr, Annapolis Junction, MD 20701 *Toll Free Tel:* 888-775-3737 *E-mail:* marketing@ironmarkusa.com *Web Site:* ironmarkusa.com, pg 1206, 1221, 1249, 1264, 1277

Kravtin, Teresa Rolfe, Southern Territory Associates, 4508 64 St, Lubbock, TX 79414 *E-mail:* sta77@suddenlink.net *Web Site:* www.southernterritory.com, pg 1299

Kreider, William, Systems & Software Services Ltd, 830 W Springfield Rd, Bldg A, Suite 2, Springfield, PA 19064, pg 1386

Kremer, John, Open Horizons Publishing Co, PO Box 2887, Taos, NM 87571 *Tel:* 575-751-3398 *E-mail:* books@bookmarketingbestsellers.com *Web Site:* bookmarketingbestsellers.com, pg 1350

Krickett, J D, The Cricket Letter Inc, PO Box 527, Ardmore, PA 19003-0527 *Tel:* 610-924-9158 *Fax:* 610-924-9159 *E-mail:* crcktinc@aol.com, pg 1184

Krieger, Michael, US Lynx Inc, 39 Broadway, 28th fl, New York, NY 10006 *Tel:* 212-673-3210 *Fax:* 917-503-3990 *E-mail:* info@pubdata.com *Web Site:* www.pubdata.com, pg 1387

Kriho, John, Meadows Publishing Solutions, 1305 Remington Rd, Suite G, Schaumburg, IL 60173 *Tel:* 847-882-8202 *Toll Free Tel:* 888-983-6746 *Fax:* 847-882-9494 *E-mail:* sales@meadowsps.com *Web Site:* www.meadowsps.com, pg 1381

Krinsky, Santosh, New Leaf Distributing Co, 401 Thornton Rd, Lithia Springs, GA 30122-1557 *Tel:* 770-948-7845 *Toll Free Tel:* 800-326-2665 (orders) *Fax:* 770-944-2313 *Toll Free Fax:* 800-326-1066 (orders) *E-mail:* customerservice@newleaf-dist.com *Web Site:* newleafdist.com, pg 1294, 1318

Krise, Matthew, Encyclopaedia Britannica Inc, 325 N La Salle St, Suite 200, Chicago, IL 60654 *Tel:* 312-347-7000 (all other countries) *Toll Free Tel:* 800-323-1229 (US & CN) *Fax:* 312-294-2104 *E-mail:* contact@eb.com *Web Site:* www.britannica.com, pg 1313

Krishna, Arvind, IBM Corp, One New Orchard Rd, Armonk, NY 10504 *Tel:* 914-499-1900 *Toll Free Tel:* 800-426-4968 *E-mail:* askibm@vnet.ibm.com *Web Site:* www.ibm.com, pg 1379

Krishnan, Karthik, Encyclopaedia Britannica Inc, 325 N La Salle St, Suite 200, Chicago, IL 60654 *Tel:* 312-347-7000 (all other countries) *Toll Free Tel:* 800-323-1229 (US & CN) *Fax:* 312-294-2104 *E-mail:* contact@eb.com *Web Site:* www.britannica.com, pg 1313

Kriz, Rebecca, Sunbelt Publications Inc, 1250 Fayette St, El Cajon, CA 92020-1511 *Tel:* 619-258-4911 *Toll Free Tel:* 800-626-6579 (cust serv) *Fax:* 619-258-4916 *E-mail:* info@sunbeltpublications.com; sunbeltbook@sunbeltpub.com *Web Site:* sunbeltpublications.com, pg 1321

Krofick, Randolph S PhD, NWinds, One Northgate Sq, Greensburg, PA 15601 *Tel:* 724-838-8993 *Toll Free Fax:* 888-315-3711 *E-mail:* support@nwinds.com *Web Site:* www.nwinds.com, pg 1382

Krueger, Ray, The New York Times Licensing Group, 620 Eighth Ave, 20th fl, New York, NY 10018 *Tel:* 212-556-1927 *E-mail:* nytlg-sales@nytimes.com *Web Site:* nytlicensing.com, pg 1185

Kruk, Ondrej, X-Rite Inc, 4300 44 St SE, Grand Rapids, MI 49512 *Tel:* 616-803-2100 *Toll Free Tel:* 800-248-9748; 888-800-9580 (sales) *E-mail:* info@xrite.com *Web Site:* www.xrite.com, pg 1280

Kubinec, Jessica, LARB Quarterly Journal, 6671 Sunset Blvd, Suite 1521, Los Angeles, CA 90028 *Tel:* 323-952-3950 *E-mail:* info@lareviewofbooks.org; editorial@lareviewofbooks.org *Web Site:* lareviewofbooks.org, pg 1128

Kucharski, Matt, PadillaCRT, 1101 W River Pkwy, Suite 400, Minneapolis, MN 55415 *Tel:* 612-455-1700 *Fax:* 612-455-1060 *Web Site:* www.padillacrt.com, pg 1100

Kuehn, Meg LaBorde, Kirkus, 65 W 36 St, Suite 700, New York, NY 10018 *E-mail:* customercare@kirkus.com *Web Site:* www.kirkusreviews.com, pg 1128

Kuhne, Chris, The Writer's Lifeline Inc, 400 S Burnside Ave, Suite 11B, Los Angeles, CA 90036 *Tel:* 323-932-1685 *Web Site:* www.thewriterslifeline.com, pg 1353

Kui, Barnabas, Hearst Newspapers, 300 W 57 St, New York, NY 10019 *Tel:* 212-649-2000 *Web Site:* www.hearst.com/newspapers, pg 1185

Kulick, Kim, Entertainment News Service, PO Box 6123, West Caldwell, NJ 07007-6123 *Tel:* 973-227-4433, pg 1184

Kumar, Nilima, Avanti Enterprises Inc, 18901 Springfield Ave, Flossmoor, IL 60422-1071 *Tel:* 630-850-3245 *Toll Free Tel:* 800-799-6464 *Fax:* 708-799-6474 *Toll Free Fax:* 877-799-6474 *E-mail:* sales@avantiusa.com *Web Site:* www.avantiusa.com, pg 1325

Kupec, Lolly, Wild West Communications Group, PO Box 346, Homewood, CA 96141 *Tel:* 530-525-5201 *Fax:* 530-525-4559 *Web Site:* www.wildwest-tahoe.com, pg 1433

Kurdyla, Edward, Voice of Youth Advocates, 16211 Oxford Ct, Bowie, MD 20715 *Tel:* 301-805-2191 *Fax:* 301-805-2192 *Web Site:* www.voyamagazine.com, pg 1131

Kurdyla, Lisa, Voice of Youth Advocates, 16211 Oxford Ct, Bowie, MD 20715 *Tel:* 301-805-2191 *Fax:* 301-805-2192 *Web Site:* www.voyamagazine.com, pg 1131

Kuriyqua, Toshihiro, Alps Alpine North America Inc, 3151 Jay St, Suite 101, Santa Clara, CA 95054 *Tel:* 408-361-6400; 408-226-7301 *Fax:* 408-980-9945; 408-226-7301 *E-mail:* alps-pr@jp.alps.com *Web Site:* www.alpsalpine.com/na, pg 1372

Kurtis, Matthew, Ware-Pak LLC, 2427 Bond St, University Park, IL 60484 *Tel:* 708-534-2600 *Fax:* 708-534-7803 *Web Site:* www.ware-pak.com, pg 1333

Kurtzman, Chris, Webcrafters Inc, 2211 Fordem Ave, Madison, WI 53704 *Tel:* 608-244-3561 *Toll Free Tel:* 800-356-8200 *Fax:* 608-244-5120 *E-mail:* info@webcrafters-inc.com *Web Site:* www.webcrafters-inc.com, pg 1210, 1257, 1280

Kurz, Dave, Stoesser Register Systems, 610 Whitetail Blvd, River Falls, WI 54022 *Tel:* 715-425-1900 *Toll Free Tel:* 888-407-4808 *Fax:* 715-425-1901 *E-mail:* info@nela-usa.com *Web Site:* www.nela-usa.com, pg 1279

Kushnick, Hannah, Publishers Weekly, 71 W 23 St, Suite 1608, New York, NY 10010 *Tel:* 212-377-5500 *Fax:* 212-377-2733 *Web Site:* www.publishersweekly.com, pg 1130

Larson, Kent, Bridgeport National Bindery Inc, 662 Silver St, Agawam, MA 01001 *Tel:* 413-789-1981 *Toll Free Tel:* 800-223-5083 *E-mail:* info@bnbindery.com *Web Site:* www.bnbindery.com, pg 1243, 1323

Larson, Pete, Bethany Press International Inc, 6820 W 115 St, Bloomington, MN 55438 *Tel:* 952-914-7400 *Toll Free Tel:* 888-717-7400 *Fax:* 952-914-7410 *E-mail:* info@bethanypress.com *Web Site:* www. bethanypress.com, pg 1242

Larson, Tim, Larson Texts Inc, 1762 Norcross Rd, Erie, PA 16510 *Tel:* 814-824-6365 *Toll Free Tel:* 800-530-2355 *Fax:* 814-824-6377 *Web Site:* www.larsontexts. com, pg 1222, 1265, 1359

Laschinger, Mary A, Veritiv™ Corporation, 400 Northpark Town Ctr, 1000 Abernathy Rd, Suite 1700, Atlanta, GA 30328 *Tel:* 770-391-8200 *Toll Free Tel:* 844-VERITIV (837-4848); 800-864-7687 (cust serv) *E-mail:* contactus@veritivcorp.com *Web Site:* www.veritivcorp.com, pg 1269

Lashkari, Shahab, OmniUpdate Inc, 1320 Flynn Rd, Suite 100, Camarillo, CA 93012 *Tel:* 805-484-9400 *Toll Free Tel:* 800-362-2605 *E-mail:* sales@ omniupdate.com *Web Site:* omniupdate.com, pg 1383

Latham, Bethany, The Historical Novels Review, 400 Dark Star Ct, Fairbanks, AK 99709 *Tel:* 217-581-7538 *Fax:* 217-581-7534 *E-mail:* reviews@historicalnovelsociety.org *Web Site:* historicalnovelsociety.org, pg 1126

Latimer, Len, Lynx Media Inc, 13654 Victory Blvd, No 282, Valley Glen, CA 91401 *Tel:* 818-761-5859 *Toll Free Tel:* 800-451-5969 *Fax:* 818-761-7099 *E-mail:* sales@lynxmedia.com *Web Site:* www. lynxmedia.com, pg 1381

Latimer, Matt, Javelin Group, 203 S Union St, Suite 200, Alexandria, VA 22314 *Tel:* 703-490-8845 *E-mail:* hello@javelindc.com *Web Site:* javelindc.com, pg 1347

Lau, Victoria, Jane Wesman Public Relations Inc, 322 Eighth Ave, Suite 1702, New York, NY 10001 *Tel:* 212-620-4080 *Fax:* 212-620-0370 *Web Site:* www. wesmanpr.com, pg 1098

Lauer, Valerie, Hanser Publications LLC, 414 Walnut St, Suite 323, Cincinnati, OH 45202 *Toll Free Tel:* 800-950-8977; 888-558-2632 (orders) *E-mail:* info@hanserpublications.com *Web Site:* www. hanserpublications.com, pg 1288

Laurenzo, Hana, Teneo Linguistics Co LLC, 4700 Bryant Irvin Ct, Suite 301, Fort Worth, TX 76107 *Tel:* 817-441-9974 *Fax:* 817-231-0052 *E-mail:* info@ tlctranslation.com *Web Site:* www.tlctranslation.com, pg 1413

Laures, Wolfgang, Glatfelter, Capitol Towers South, 4350 Congress St, Suite 600, Charlotte, NC 28209 *Tel:* 717-850-0170 *Toll Free Tel:* 866-744-7380 *E-mail:* info@glatfelter.com *Web Site:* www.glatfelter. com, pg 1263

Lauro, Joe, Historic Films LLC, 211 Third St, Greenport, NY 11944 *Tel:* 631-477-9700 *Toll Free Tel:* 800-249-1940 *Fax:* 631-477-9800 *E-mail:* info@ historicfilms.com *Web Site:* www.historicfilms.com, pg 1447

Law, Sandra, Abraham Associates Inc, 5120-A Cedar Lake Rd, Minneapolis, MN 55416 *Tel:* 952-927-7920 *Toll Free Tel:* 800-701-2489 *Fax:* 952-927-8089 *E-mail:* info@abrahamassociatesinc.com *Web Site:* www.abrahamassociatesinc.com, pg 1281

Lawlor, Owen, Victory Productions Inc, 55 Linden St, Worcester, MA 01609 *Tel:* 508-755-0051 *E-mail:* victory@victoryprd.com *Web Site:* www. victoryprd.com, pg 1363

Lawrance, Heidy, WeMakeBooks.ca, 238 Willowdale Ave, North York, ON M2N 4Z5, Canada *Tel:* 416-733-1827 *Fax:* 416-733-7663 *Web Site:* www. wemakebooks.ca, pg 1227

Lawrence, Bill, Powis Parker Inc, 2929 Fifth St, Berkeley, CA 94710 *Tel:* 510-848-2463 *Toll Free Tel:* 800-321-BIND (321-2463) *Fax:* 510-848-2169 *E-mail:* customerservice@powis.com *Web Site:* www. powis.com, pg 1383

Lawrence, Derek, Imprint Group West, 2070 Cherry St, Denver, CO 80207 *Toll Free Tel:* 800-738-3961 *Toll Free Fax:* 888-867-3869 *Web Site:* imprintgroupwest. com, pg 1288

Lawrence, Ron, Upper Access Inc, 87 Upper Access Rd, Hinesburg, VT 05461 *Tel:* 802-482-2988 *E-mail:* upperaccessbooks@gmail.com *Web Site:* www.upperaccess.com, pg 1352

Laws, Gordon, Lumina Datamatics Inc, 4 Collins Ave, Plymouth, MA 02360 *Tel:* 508-746-0300 *Fax:* 508-746-3233 *Web Site:* luminadatamatics.com, pg 1207, 1222, 1349, 1359, 1380, 1430

Lawton-Koon, Kimberly, Lawton Connect, 649 Triumph Ct, Orlando, FL 32805 *Tel:* 407-260-0400 *Toll Free Tel:* 877-330-1900 *Fax:* 407-260-1321 *E-mail:* hello@ lawtonconnect.com *Web Site:* www.lawtonconnect. com, pg 1250

Lazzaro, Erica, OverDrive Inc, One OverDrive Way, Cleveland, OH 44125 *Tel:* 216-573-6886 *Fax:* 216-573-6888 *E-mail:* info@overdrive.com *Web Site:* www.overdrive.com, pg 1294

Leah, Deanna, HBG Productions/International Publishers Alliance, PO Box 5560, Chico, CA 95927-5560 *Tel:* 530-893-4699 *Web Site:* www.hbgproductions. com, pg 1288

Leathem, Jane, Stylus Publishing LLC, 22883 Quicksilver Dr, Sterling, VA 20166-2019 *Tel:* 703-661-1504 (edit & sales); 703-661-1581 (orders & cust serv); 703-996-1036 *Toll Free Tel:* 800-232-0223 (orders & cust serv) *Fax:* 703-661-1547; 703-661-1501 (orders & cust serv) *E-mail:* stylusinfo@ styluspub.com; stylusmail@styluspub.com (orders & cust serv) *Web Site:* styluspub.presswarehouse.com, pg 1299

Lebrun, Denise, Design Plus, 1086 Main Rd, Aquebogue, NY 11931 *Tel:* 631-722-4384 *E-mail:* designplusonline@yahoo.com, pg 1376

Lee, Amy, Art Media Resources Inc, 1965 W Pershing Rd, Chicago, IL 60605 *Tel:* 312-663-5351 *Fax:* 312-663-5177 *E-mail:* paragon@paragonbook.com *Web Site:* www.artmediaresources.com, pg 1282

Lee, Eddie, Square Two Design Inc, 2325 Third St, Suite 213, San Francisco, CA 94107 *Tel:* 415-437-3888 *E-mail:* info@square2.com *Web Site:* www.square2. com, pg 1226, 1386, 1432

Lee, Jess, Jess Lee Photography LLC, 13316 Skyview St, Nampa, ID 83686 *Tel:* 208-521-5170 *Web Site:* www.jessleephotos.com, pg 1440

Lee, Joon, Samsung Research America (SRA), 665 Clyde Ave, Mountain View, CA 94043 *Tel:* 650-210-1001 *E-mail:* sra-contact-us@samsung.com *Web Site:* www.sra.samsung.com, pg 1385

Lee, Richard, Delphax Solutions Inc, 2810 Argentia Rd, Unit 6, Mississauga, ON L5N 8L2, Canada *Toll Free Tel:* 833-DELPHAX (335-7429) *Web Site:* www. delphaxsolutions.com, pg 1376

Lee, Richard, The Historical Novels Review, 400 Dark Star Ct, Fairbanks, AK 99709 *Tel:* 217-581-7538 *Fax:* 217-581-7534 *E-mail:* reviews@historicalnovelsociety.org *Web Site:* historicalnovelsociety.org, pg 1126

Lee, Roger, Ingram Content Group LLC, One Ingram Blvd, La Vergne, TN 37086-1986 *Tel:* 615-793-5000 *Toll Free Tel:* 800-937-8000 (retailers); 800-937-5300 (ext 1, libs) *E-mail:* customerservice@ingramcontent. com *Web Site:* www.ingramcontent.com, pg 1290, 1315

Leeper, Don, BookMobile, 5120 Cedar Lake Rd, Minneapolis, MN 55416 *Tel:* 763-398-0030 *Toll Free Tel:* 844-488-4477 *Fax:* 763-398-0198 *Web Site:* www. bookmobile.com, pg 1243

Lehr, Donald B, The Nolan/Lehr Group Inc, 214 W 29 St, Suite 1002, New York, NY 10001 *Tel:* 212-967-8200 *E-mail:* dblehr@cs.com *Web Site:* www. nolanlehrgroup.com, pg 1100

Leibfried, Deb, Shepherd Inc, 2223 Key Way Dr, Suite B, Dubuque, IA 52002 *Tel:* 563-584-0500 *Web Site:* www.shepherd-inc.com, pg 1226, 1254, 1385, 1432

Leibner, Jonathan, UTA News & Broadcast, 888 Seventh Ave, 7th fl, New York, NY 10106 *Tel:* 212-765-3040 *Fax:* 212-757-6411 *E-mail:* nsb@nsbtalent.com *Web Site:* bienstock.unitedtalent.com, pg 1352

Leibner, Richard, UTA News & Broadcast, 888 Seventh Ave, 7th fl, New York, NY 10106 *Tel:* 212-765-3040 *Fax:* 212-757-6411 *E-mail:* nsb@nsbtalent.com *Web Site:* bienstock.unitedtalent.com, pg 1352

Leichman, Larry, Arbor Books, 244 Madison Ave, Box 254, New York, NY 10016 *Tel:* 212-956-0950 *Toll Free Tel:* 877-822-2500 *Fax:* 914-401-9385 *E-mail:* info@arborbooks.com; editorial@ arborbooks.net *Web Site:* www.arborbooks.com; www. arborservices.co, pg 1202, 1216, 1242, 1261, 1342, 1355, 1424

Leiferman, Troy, Valley News Co, 1305 Stadium Rd, Mankato, MN 56001 *Tel:* 507-345-4819 *Fax:* 507-345-6793 *Web Site:* www.valleynewscompany.com, pg 1322

Leisner, Debby, Widen Enterprises Inc, 6911 Mangrove Lane, Madison, WI 53713 *Tel:* 608-222-1296 *Toll Free Tel:* 800-444-2828 *E-mail:* marketing@widen.com *Web Site:* www.widen.com, pg 1228

Leland, David, Print It Plus, 11420 Okeechobee Blvd, Royal Palm Beach, FL 33411 *Tel:* 561-790-0884 *Fax:* 561-790-9378 *E-mail:* info@printitplus.com *Web Site:* printitplus.com, pg 1253

Leland, Kimberly, Print It Plus, 11420 Okeechobee Blvd, Royal Palm Beach, FL 33411 *Tel:* 561-790-0884 *Fax:* 561-790-9378 *E-mail:* info@printitplus.com *Web Site:* printitplus.com, pg 1253

Lemieux, Drew J, Pratt Paper Company LLC, 20 Davis Rd, Marblehead, MA 01945 *Tel:* 781-639-9450 *Fax:* 781-639-9452, pg 1266

Lempereur, Yves, OmniUpdate Inc, 1320 Flynn Rd, Suite 100, Camarillo, CA 93012 *Tel:* 805-484-9400 *Toll Free Tel:* 800-362-2605 *E-mail:* sales@ omniupdate.com *Web Site:* omniupdate.com, pg 1383

Lennertz, Carl, The Children's Book Council (CBC), 54 W 39 St, 14th fl, New York, NY 10018 *Tel:* 212-966-1990 *E-mail:* cbc.info@cbcbooks.org *Web Site:* www. cbcbooks.org, pg 1139

Lennie, Frances S, Indexing Research, 620 Park Ave, Suite 183, Rochester, NY 14607 *Tel:* 585-413-1819 *E-mail:* info@indexres.com *Web Site:* www.indexres. com, pg 1379

Lenzen, Kevin, JLS Language Corp, 135 Willow Rd, Menlo Park, CA 94025 *Tel:* 650-321-9832 *Fax:* 650-329-9864 *E-mail:* info@jls.com *Web Site:* www.jls. com, pg 1410

Leondar-Wright, Gail, Gail Leondar Public Relations, 21 Belknap St, Arlington, MA 02474 *Tel:* 781-648-1658 *E-mail:* gail@glprbooks.com *Web Site:* www. glprbooks.com, pg 1097

Leonhartsberger, Laura, Strictly Spanish Translations LLC, PO Box 476, Milford, OH 45150 *Tel:* 513-965-1096 *E-mail:* information@strictlyspanish.com *Web Site:* www.strictlyspanish.com, pg 1413

Leontis, Artemis, Journal of Modern Greek Studies, 2715 N Charles St, Baltimore, MD 21218-4363 *Toll Free Tel:* 800-548-1784 (journal orders) *Fax:* 410-516-6968 *E-mail:* jrnlcirc@press.jhu.edu (journal orders) *Web Site:* www.press.jhu.edu/journals/ journal_of_modern_greek_studies/index.html, pg 1128

Lepore, Bernie, Electronics for Imaging Inc (EFI), 6750 Dumbarton Circle, Fremont, CA 94555 *Tel:* 650-357-3500 *Toll Free Tel:* 800-568-1917; 800-875-7117 (sales) *Fax:* 650-357-3907 *E-mail:* info@efi.com *Web Site:* www.efi.com, pg 1377

Lerner, Ilene, HBP Inc, 952 Frederick St, Hagerstown, MD 21740 *Tel:* 301-733-2000 *Toll Free Tel:* 800-638-3508 *Fax:* 301-733-6586 *E-mail:* contactus@hbp.com *Web Site:* www.hbp.com, pg 1220, 1248, 1276

Linick, Andrew S PhD, LK Advertising Agency, Linick Bldg, 7 Putter Lane, Middle Island, NY 11953 Tel: 631-924-3888; 631-924-8555; 631-604-8599 E-mail: topmarketingadvisor@gmail.com Web Site: topmarketingadvisor.com, pg 1087, 1106

Lins, Stephen, Richard Schneider Language Services, 1200 Piedmont Ave, Pacific Grove, CA 93950 Tel: 831-622-0554 Toll Free Tel: 800-500-5808 Fax: 831-622-0524 E-mail: service@idioms.com Web Site: www.idioms.com, pg 1412

Lippenholz, Michael, National Book Network (NBN), 4501 Forbes Blvd, Suite 200, Lanham, MD 20706 Tel: 301-459-3366 Toll Free Tel: 800-462-6420 (orders only) Fax: 301-429-5746 Toll Free Fax: 800-338-4550 (orders only) E-mail: customercare@nbnbooks.com Web Site: www.nbnbooks.com, pg 1293, 1318

Lissy, David, Table Mesa Productions/David Lissy Photography, 7517 S Monaco Way, Centennial, CO 80012 Tel: 303-919-5296 (cell) E-mail: fstop@earthlink.net Web Site: www.davidlissy.com, pg 1443

Lisy, Paul, eFootage LLC, 530 S Lake Ave, Suite 450, Pasadena, CA 91101 Tel: 626-395-9593 E-mail: info@efootage.com Web Site: www.efootage.com, pg 1446

Litty, Tedd, Cushing-Malloy Inc, 1350 N Main St, Ann Arbor, MI 48104-1045 Tel: 734-663-8554 Fax: 734-663-5731 Web Site: www.cushing-malloy.com; www.c-mbooks.com, pg 1203, 1245

Lizza, Fred, Freestyle Software, 9 Campus Dr, Parsippany, NJ 07054 Toll Free Tel: 800-474-5760 Fax: 973-237-9043 E-mail: info@freestylesolutions.com Web Site: www.freestylesolutions.com, pg 1377

Lloyd-Sgambati, Vanesse, The Literary Media & Publishing Consultants, 1815 Wynnewood Rd, Philadelphia, PA 19151 Tel: 215-877-2012, pg 1099

Lo Gatto, Michael, Lo Gatto Bookbinding, 390 Paterson Ave, East Rutherford, NJ 07073 Tel: 201-438-4344 Fax: 201-438-1775 E-mail: bookbindin@aol.com Web Site: www.logattobookbinding.com, pg 1207, 1250

Locascio, James, Dukane Corp, Audio Visual Products Division, 2900 Dukane Dr, St Charles, IL 60174 Tel: 630-584-2300 Toll Free Tel: 888-245-1966; 800-676-2487 (tech support) Fax: 630-584-5156 E-mail: avsales@dukane.com Web Site: dukaneav.com, pg 1376

Lochner, Lindsey, Firebrand Technologies, 44 Merrimac St, Newburyport, MA 01950 Tel: 978-465-7755 Toll Free Tel: 800-779-7345 Fax: 978-465-7759 E-mail: askburnie@firebrandtech.com Web Site: www.firebrandtech.com, pg 1345, 1377

Lockley, Beth, Penguin Random House Canada, 320 Front St W, Suite 1400, Toronto, ON M5V 3B6, Canada Tel: 416-364-4449 Toll Free Tel: 888-523-9292 (cust serv) Fax: 416-598-7764 Web Site: www.penguinrandomhouse.ca, pg 1295

Lockwood, Bert, Human Rights Quarterly, 2715 N Charles St, Baltimore, MD 21218-4363 Tel: 410-516-6987 (journal orders outside US & CN) Toll Free Tel: 800-548-1784 (journal orders) Fax: 410-516-3866 (journal orders) E-mail: jrnlcirc@press.jhu.edu (journal orders) Web Site: www.press.jhu.edu/journals/human_rights_quarterly, pg 1127

Lockwood, C C, Cactus Clyde Productions, PO Box 3624, St Francisville, LA 70775-3624 Tel: 225-245-5008 E-mail: cactusclyd@aol.com Web Site: www.cclockwood.com, pg 1436

Loeffler, Katherine, Peregrine Arts Bindery, 7 Avenida Vista Grande, Suite B-7 119, Santa Fe, NM 87508 Tel: 505-466-0490 Web Site: www.peregrineartsbindery.etsy.com, pg 1266

Loerke, Ellen, Books International Inc, 22883 Quicksilver Dr, Dulles, VA 20166 Tel: 703-661-1500 Fax: 703-661-1501 E-mail: hdqtrs@booksintl.com Web Site: booksintl.presswarehouse.com, pg 1331

Loewen-Young, Anais, Penguin Random House Canada, 320 Front St W, Suite 1400, Toronto, ON M5V 3B6, Canada Tel: 416-364-4449 Toll Free Tel: 888-523-9292 (cust serv) Fax: 416-598-7764 Web Site: www.penguinrandomhouse.ca, pg 1295

Logan, George, Klopotek North America Inc, 2001 Rte 46, Suite 203, Parsippany, NJ 07054 Tel: 973-331-1010 Toll Free Tel: 800-239-9254 Fax: 973-331-0042 E-mail: info@klopotek.com Web Site: www.klopotek.com; www.gtsystems.com, pg 1348

Lohwater, Tiffany, American Association for the Advancement of Science (AAAS), 1200 New York Ave NW, Washington, DC 20005 Tel: 202-326-6400 Fax: 202-371-9526 E-mail: media@aaas.org Web Site: www.aaas.org, pg 1139

Lombardo, Laura M, Santec Corp, 84 Old Gate Lane, Milford, CT 06460 Tel: 203-878-1379 Fax: 203-876-0949 E-mail: info@santeccorp.com Web Site: www.santeccorp.com, pg 1279

Lombardo, Vito, Santec Corp, 84 Old Gate Lane, Milford, CT 06460 Tel: 203-878-1379 Fax: 203-876-0949 E-mail: info@santeccorp.com Web Site: www.santeccorp.com, pg 1279

Long, Bob, Thinkers' Press Inc, 1524 Le Claire St, Davenport, IA 52803 Tel: 563-271-6657 E-mail: info@chessbutler.com Web Site: www.thinkerspressinc.com, pg 1328

Long, Mayapriya, Bookwrights Design, 1060 Old Ridge Rd, Lovingston, VA 22949 Tel: 434-263-4818 E-mail: design@bookwrights.com Web Site: www.bookwrights.com, pg 1356

Long, Peter, MCH Strategic Data, 601 E Marshall St, Sweet Springs, MO 65351 Toll Free Tel: 800-776-6373 E-mail: sales@mchdata.com Web Site: www.mchdata.com, pg 1112

Long, Thayer, Association for PRINT Technologies (APTech), 1896 Preston White Dr, Reston, VA 20191 Tel: 703-264-7200 Fax: 703-620-0994 E-mail: aptech@aptech.org Web Site: www.printtechnologies.org, pg 1273, 1373

Long, William S, Maple Logistics Solutions, 60 Grumbacher Rd, York, PA 17406 Tel: 717-764-4596 Fax: 717-764-4494 E-mail: info@maplesoln.com Web Site: www.maplelogisticssolutions.com, pg 1291, 1332

Longo, Regina, Film Quarterly, Journals & Digital Publishing, 155 Grand Ave, Suite 400, Oakland, CA 94612-3758 Tel: 510-883-8326 (fulfillment) Fax: 510-836-8910 (fulfillment) E-mail: customerservice@ucpress.edu Web Site: www.filmquarterly.org; fq.ucpress.edu, pg 1126

Longwood, Marc, Marc Longwood Photography, 3300 Powell St, Suite 336, Emeryville, CA 94608-1776 Tel: 415-251-7585 Web Site: www.longwoodpro.com, pg 1441

Longworth, Jo-Ann, Resolute Forest Products, 111 Robert-Bourassa Blvd, Suite 5000, Montreal, QC H3C 2M1, Canada Tel: 514-875-2160 Toll Free Tel: 800-361-2888 E-mail: info@resolutefp.com Web Site: www.resolutefp.com, pg 1267

Loomis, Dan, Omnipress, 2600 Anderson St, Madison, WI 53704 Tel: 608-246-2600 Toll Free Tel: 800-828-0305 E-mail: justask@omnipress.com Web Site: www.omnipress.com, pg 1208, 1252

Loomis, Mike, GW Illustration & Design, 2290 Ball Dr, St Louis, MO 63146 Tel: 314-567-9854 Web Site: www.gwinc.com, pg 1428

Loomis, Mike, GW Inc, 2290 Ball Dr, St Louis, MO 63146 Tel: 314-567-9854 Web Site: www.gwinc.com, pg 1220, 1378

Lopez, Gloria, Fish Films Footage World, 1060 Camino Real, Sante Fe, NM 87501 Tel: 818-905-1071 E-mail: footageworld@aol.com Web Site: www.footageworld.com, pg 1446

Lorence, Mauricio, Metro Translation Service, 294 De Kalb Ave, Brooklyn, NY 11205 Tel: 718-789-0430; 917-558-0089 (cell) E-mail: metrotourservice21@gmail.com Web Site: metrotourservice.blogspot.com, pg 1411

Lorenz, Scott, Westwind Communications, 1310 Maple St, Plymouth, MI 48170 Tel: 734-667-2090 Web Site: www.book-marketing-expert.com, pg 1353

Lores, Enrique, HP Inc, 1501 Paige Mill Rd, Palo Alto, CA 94304-1112 Tel: 650-857-1501 Toll Free Tel: 800-282-6672 Web Site: www.hp.com, pg 1378

Lory, Irene, Cross Country Computer Corp, 250 Carleton Ave, East Islip, NY 11730-1240 Tel: 631-334-1810 E-mail: inquiry@crosscountrycomputer.com Web Site: www.crosscountrycomputer.com, pg 1111

Losch, Brian, Worth Higgins & Associates Inc, 8770 Park Central Dr, Richmond, VA 23227-1146 Tel: 804-264-2304 Toll Free Tel: 800-883-7768 Fax: 804-264-5733 E-mail: contact@whaprint.com Web Site: www.worthhiggins.com, pg 1221, 1249

Loubier, Serge, Marquis Book Printing Inc, 350, rue des Entrepreneurs, Montmagny, QC G5V 4T1, Canada Tel: 418-246-5666 Toll Free Tel: 855-566-1937; 800-246-2468 E-mail: marquis@marquisbook.com Web Site: www.marquislivre.com; www.marquisbook.com, pg 1251

Lourie, Roger H, Devin-Adair Publishers, 9 Lafayette Ct, Suite 3, Greenwich, CT 06830 Tel: 203-622-1010 Fax: 718-359-8568, pg 1312

Love, Brian, DocuWare Corp, 4 Crotty Lane, Suite 200, New Windsor, NY 12553 Tel: 845-563-9045 Toll Free Tel: 888-565-5907 Fax: 845-563-9046 E-mail: dwsales@docuware.com; support.americas@docuware.com Web Site: www.docuware.com, pg 1376

Love, Cody, Idea Architects, 523 Swift St, Santa Cruz, CA 95060 Tel: 831-465-9565 Web Site: www.ideaarchitects.com, pg 1347

Love, Dave, Cross Country Computer Corp, 250 Carleton Ave, East Islip, NY 11730-1240 Tel: 631-334-1810 E-mail: inquiry@crosscountrycomputer.com Web Site: www.crosscountrycomputer.com, pg 1111

Love, Ty Gideon, Idea Architects, 523 Swift St, Santa Cruz, CA 95060 Tel: 831-465-9565 Web Site: www.ideaarchitects.com, pg 1347

Lovins, Greg, Avery Dennison Corp, 207 N Goode Ave, 6th fl, Glendale, CA 91203-1222 Tel: 626-304-2000 Web Site: www.averydennison.com, pg 1373

Low, Carey, Canadian Manda Group, 664 Annette St, Toronto, ON M6S 2C8, Canada Tel: 416-516-0911 Fax: 416-516-0917 Toll Free Fax: 888-563-8327 (CN only) E-mail: general@mandagroup.com; info@mandagroup.com Web Site: www.mandagroup.com, pg 1284

Low, Trisha, Small Press Distribution Inc, 1341 Seventh St, Berkeley, CA 94710-1409 Tel: 510-524-1668 Toll Free Tel: 800-869-7553 (within the US) Fax: 510-524-0852 E-mail: spd@spdbooks.org Web Site: www.spdbooks.org, pg 1298

Lowe, Kurtis, Book Travelers West, 3614A California Ave SW, No 228, Seattle, WA 98116 Tel: 206-932-7865 Toll Free Fax: 800-440-0818 Web Site: www.booktravelerswest.com, pg 1283

Lowenstein, Dr Jerome, Bellevue Literary Review, NYU School of Medicine, Dept of Medicine, 550 First Ave, OBV-A612, New York, NY 10016 Tel: 212-263-3973 E-mail: info@BLReview.org Web Site: www.BLReview.org, pg 1124

Loy, Paul, Sheridan MI, 613 E Industrial Dr, Chelsea, MI 48118 Tel: 734-475-9145 Web Site: www.sheridan.com, pg 1209, 1254, 1267

Loy, Paul, Sheridan NH, 69 Lyme Rd, Hanover, NH 03755 Tel: 603-643-2220 Web Site: www.sheridan.com, pg 1254

Loy, Paul, Sheridan PA, 450 Fame Ave, Hanover, PA 17331 Tel: 717-632-3535 Toll Free Tel: 800-352-2210 Fax: 717-633-8900 Web Site: www.sheridan.com, pg 1254

Lozada, Avery, Distributed Art Publishers (DAP), 75 Broad St, Suite 630, New York, NY 10004 Tel: 212-627-1999 Toll Free Tel: 800-338-2665 (cust serv) Fax: 212-627-9484 Toll Free Tel: 800-478-3128 E-mail: orders@dapinc.com Web Site: www.artbook.com, pg 1286

Malagisi, Christopher N, Conservative Book Club, 300 New Jersey Ave NW, Suite 500, Washington, DC 20001 *Tel:* 202-216-0601 *Fax:* 202-216-0614 *Web Site:* www.conservativebookclub.com, pg 1135

Malandrakis, Kirk, TSO General Corp, 79 Emjay Blvd, Brentwood, NY 11717 *Tel:* 631-952-5320 *Fax:* 631-952-5315 *Web Site:* www.tsogeneral.com, pg 1256, 1269

Malen, Ms Michal Hoschander, Paper Brigade, 520 Eighth Ave, 4th fl, New York, NY 10018 *Tel:* 212-201-2920 *Fax:* 212-532-4952 *E-mail:* info@jewishbooks.org *Web Site:* www.jewishbookcouncil.org, pg 1130

Malik, Jeff, Miles 33 International LLC, 40 Richards Ave, Norwalk, CT 06854 *Tel:* 203-838-2333 *Fax:* 203-838-4473 *E-mail:* info@miles33.com *Web Site:* www.miles33.com, pg 1223, 1278, 1381

Malik, Virender, Far Eastern Books, 250 Cochrane Dr, Suite 14, Markham, ON L3R 8E5, Canada *Tel:* 905-477-2900 *Toll Free Tel:* 800-291-8886 *Fax:* 905-479-2988 *E-mail:* books@febonline.com *Web Site:* fareasternbooks.com, pg 1287

Malinowski, Chris, The Combined Book Exhibit®, 277 White St, Buchanan, NY 10511 *Tel:* 914-739-7500 *Toll Free Tel:* 800-462-7687 *Fax:* 914-739-7575 *E-mail:* info@combinedbook.com *Web Site:* www.combinedbook.com; www.cbedatabase.com, pg 1133

Malinowski, Jon, The American Collective Stand®, 277 White St, Buchanan, NY 10511 *Tel:* 914-739-7500 *Toll Free Tel:* 800-462-7687 *Fax:* 914-739-7575 *Web Site:* www.americancollectivestand.com, pg 1133

Malinowski, Jon, The Combined Book Exhibit®, 277 White St, Buchanan, NY 10511 *Tel:* 914-739-7500 *Toll Free Tel:* 800-462-7687 *Fax:* 914-739-7575 *E-mail:* info@combinedbook.com *Web Site:* www.combinedbook.com; www.cbedatabase.com, pg 1133

Mallet, Lester, The Gluefast Co Inc, 3535 State Rte 66, Bldg No 1, Neptune, NJ 07753 *Tel:* 732-918-4600 *Toll Free Tel:* 800-242-7318 *Fax:* 732-918-4646 *E-mail:* info@gluefast.com *Web Site:* www.gluefast.com, pg 1335

Mallozzi, Frank, Electronics for Imaging Inc (EFI), 6750 Dumbarton Circle, Fremont, CA 94555 *Tel:* 650-357-3500 *Toll Free Tel:* 800-568-1917; 800-875-7117 (sales) *Fax:* 650-357-3907 *E-mail:* info@efi.com *Web Site:* www.efi.com, pg 1376

Maluccio, Paul, Blue Note Publications Inc, 721 North Dr, Suite D, Melbourne, FL 32934 *Tel:* 321-799-2583; 321-622-6289 *Toll Free Tel:* 800-624-0401 (orders) *Fax:* 321-799-1942; 321-622-6830 *E-mail:* bluenotebooks@gmail.com *Web Site:* bluenotepublications.com, pg 1202, 1217, 1243, 1274

Mancher, Diane, One Potata Productions Inc, 80 E 11 St, Suite 301-A, New York, NY 10003 *Tel:* 212-353-3478 *Fax:* 212-353-9667 *E-mail:* onepotata@gmail.com *Web Site:* onepotata.com, pg 1100

Manchester, Sarah, Sappi Fine Paper North America, 255 State St, Boston, MA 02109 *Tel:* 617-423-7300 *Toll Free Tel:* 800-882-4332 *E-mail:* webqueriesna@sappi.com *Web Site:* www.sappi.com/na, pg 1267

Mandarino, Jay, Colour Technologies, 134 Park Lawn Rd, Toronto, ON M8Y 3H9, Canada *Tel:* 416-588-0808 *Fax:* 416-588-5015 *E-mail:* info@colourtec.com *Web Site:* www.colourtec.com, pg 1426

Mandel, Rick, Mandel Graphic Solution, 727 W Glendale Ave, Suite 100, Milwaukee, WI 53209 *Tel:* 414-271-6970 *Fax:* 414-386-4660 *E-mail:* info@mandelcompany.com *Web Site:* www.mandelcompany.com, pg 1223, 1250

Mandelbaum, Howard, Photofest, 32 E 31 St, 5th fl, New York, NY 10016 *Tel:* 212-633-6330 *Fax:* 212-366-9062 *E-mail:* requests@photofestnyc.com *Web Site:* www.photofestnyc.com, pg 1449

Mandelbaum, Ron, Photofest, 32 E 31 St, 5th fl, New York, NY 10016 *Tel:* 212-633-6330 *Fax:* 212-366-9062 *E-mail:* requests@photofestnyc.com *Web Site:* www.photofestnyc.com, pg 1449

Mandell, Lon, Specialist Marketing Services Inc, 777 Terrace Ave, Suite 401, Hasbrouck Heights, NJ 07604 *Tel:* 201-865-5800 *E-mail:* info@sms-inc.com *Web Site:* www.sms-inc.com, pg 1112

Maniaci, Greg, Tamron USA Inc, 10 Austin Blvd, Commack, NY 11725 *Tel:* 631-858-8400 *Toll Free Tel:* 800-827-8880 *Fax:* 631-543-5666; 631-858-8462 (cust serv) *E-mail:* custserv@tamron.com *Web Site:* www.tamron-usa.com, pg 1386

Mann, Jim, BCC Software Inc, 75 Josons Dr, Rochester, NY 14623-3494 *Toll Free Tel:* 800-453-3130; 800-337-0442 (sales) *E-mail:* marketing@bccsoftware.com *Web Site:* www.bccsoftware.com, pg 1373

Manning, Kathleen, Manning's Book & Prints, 580-M Crespi Dr, Pacifica, CA 94044 *Tel:* 415-621-3565 *Toll Free Tel:* 800-TRY-MAPS (879-6277) *Fax:* 650-355-1851 *E-mail:* staff@printsoldandrare.com; manningsbk@aol.com *Web Site:* www.printsoldandrare.com, pg 1317

Manning, Scott, Scott Manning & Associates, 433 Broadway, Suite 433, New York, NY 10013 *Tel:* 646-661-6665 *Web Site:* www.scottmanningpr.com, pg 1099

Mannix, Erin, Unisys Corp, 801 Lakeview Dr, Suite 100, Blue Bell, PA 19422 *Tel:* 215-274-2742 *Web Site:* www.unisys.com, pg 1387

Manoliu, Connie, Walker360, 2501 Fifth Ave E, Montgomery, AL 36107 *Tel:* 334-832-4975 *E-mail:* info@walker360.com *Web Site:* walker360.com, pg 1209, 1256

Mansoor, Leah, Encyclopaedia Britannica Inc, 325 N La Salle St, Suite 200, Chicago, IL 60654 *Tel:* 312-347-7000 (all other countries) *Toll Free Tel:* 800-323-1229 (US & CN) *Fax:* 312-294-2104 *E-mail:* contact@eb.com *Web Site:* www.britannica.com, pg 1313

Mantilla, Antonio, Busch LLC, 516 Viking Dr, Virginia Beach, VA 23452 *Tel:* 757-463-7800 *Toll Free Tel:* 800-USA-PUMP (872-7867) *Fax:* 757-463-7407 *E-mail:* info@buschusa.com; marketing@buschusa.com *Web Site:* www.buschvacuum.com/us, pg 1274

Manwiller, Jeffrey, The Crowley Co, 5111 Pegasus Ct, Suite M, Frederick, MD 21704 *Tel:* 240-215-0224 *Fax:* 240-215-0234 *E-mail:* webrequest@thecrowleycompany.com *Web Site:* www.thecrowleycompany.com, pg 1375

Manzer, William R, Rayonier Advanced Materials, 1301 Riverplace Blvd, Suite 2300, Jacksonville, FL 32207 *Tel:* 904-357-4600 *Web Site:* rayonieram.com, pg 1266

Mao, Douglas, E L H (English Literary History), 2715 N Charles St, Baltimore, MD 21218-4363 *Toll Free Tel:* 800-548-1784 (journal orders) *Fax:* 410-516-3866 (journal orders) *E-mail:* jrnlcirc@press.jhu.edu (journal orders) *Web Site:* www.press.jhu.edu/journals/english_literary_history/index.html, pg 1126

Marciano, Joseph R, Canon Business Process Services, 460 W 34 St, 6th fl, New York, NY 10001 *Tel:* 212-502-2100 *Toll Free Tel:* 800-937-2724; 888-623-2668 (ext 108) *E-mail:* info@cbps.canon.com *Web Site:* cbps.canon.com, pg 1331

Marcus, Aaron, Aaron Marcus and Associates Inc, 1196 Euclid Ave, Berkeley, CA 94708-1640 *Tel:* 510-599-3195 (cell) *Fax:* 510-527-1994 *Web Site:* www.bamanda.com, pg 1371

Mariniello, Debra, Copyright Clearance Center Inc (CCC), 222 Rosewood Dr, Danvers, MA 01923 *Tel:* 978-750-8400 (sales); 978-646-2600 (cust serv) *E-mail:* info@copyright.com *Web Site:* www.copyright.com, pg 1344

Marino, Pamela, CHOICE, 575 Main St, Suite 300, Middletown, CT 06457 *Tel:* 860-347-6933; 860-347-1387 (ad); 240-646-7027 (subn); 818-487-4555 *E-mail:* acrlsubscriptions@pubservice.com; support@acrlchoice.freshdesk.com *Web Site:* www.ala.org/acrl/choice; www.choice360.org, pg 1125

Markfield, Sarah, Association for PRINT Technologies (APTech), 1896 Preston White Dr, Reston, VA 20191 *Tel:* 703-264-7200 *Fax:* 703-620-0994 *E-mail:* aptech@aptech.org *Web Site:* www.printtechnologies.org, pg 1273, 1373

Markley, Chris, Tecnau Inc, 4 Suburban Park Dr, Billerica, MA 01821 *Tel:* 978-608-0500 *Fax:* 978-608-0558 *E-mail:* info.us@tecnau.com *Web Site:* www.tecnau.com, pg 1279

Marks, Meredith, Hill+Knowlton Strategies, 237 Park Ave, 4th fl, New York, NY 10017 *Tel:* 212-885-0300 *Web Site:* www.hkstrategies.com, pg 1098

Marks, Sherwin, Craftsmen Machinery Co Inc, 1257 Worcester Rd, Unit 167, Framingham, MA 01701 *Tel:* 508-376-2001 *Fax:* 508-376-2003 *E-mail:* sales@craftsmenmachinery.com *Web Site:* www.craftsmenmachinery.com, pg 1275

Marlin, David, MetaComet Systems, 29 College St, South Hadley, MA 01075 *Tel:* 413-536-5989 *Web Site:* www.metacomet.com, pg 1350

Marmanis, Haralambos "Babis", Copyright Clearance Center Inc (CCC), 222 Rosewood Dr, Danvers, MA 01923 *Tel:* 978-750-8400 (sales); 978-646-2600 (cust serv) *E-mail:* info@copyright.com *Web Site:* www.copyright.com, pg 1344

Marmion, Shane P, William S Hein & Co Inc, 2350 N Forest Rd, Getzville, NY 14068 *Tel:* 716-882-2600 *Toll Free Tel:* 800-828-7571 *Fax:* 716-883-8100 *E-mail:* mail@wshein.com; marketing@wshein.com *Web Site:* www.wshein.com, pg 1314

Marocchino, Kathryn D, Rosemoor House Translations, Rosemoor House, 400 New Bedford Dr, Vallejo, CA 94591 *Tel:* 707-557-8595 *Fax:* 707-557-5555, pg 1412

Maroney, Kevin, The New York Review of Science Fiction, 206 Valentine St, Yonkers, NY 10704-1814 *Tel:* 914-965-4861 *Web Site:* www.nyrsf.com, pg 1129

Marquand, Ed, Lucia/Marquand, 1400 Second Ave, Seattle, WA 98101 *Tel:* 206-624-2030 *Fax:* 206-624-1821 *Web Site:* luciamarquand.com, pg 1359

Marsh, Robert S, National Book Network (NBN), 4501 Forbes Blvd, Suite 200, Lanham, MD 20706 *Tel:* 301-459-3366 *Toll Free Tel:* 800-462-6420 (orders only) *Fax:* 301-429-5746 *Toll Free Fax:* 800-338-4550 (orders only) *E-mail:* customercare@nbnbooks.com *Web Site:* www.nbnbooks.com, pg 1293, 1318

Marshall, Caitlin, Author Planet Consulting Services, 7741 S Ash Ct, Centennial, CO 80122 *Tel:* 303-253-1702 *Web Site:* authorplanet.org; jodyreinbooks.com, pg 1342

Marshall, Kelly K, Exhibit Promotions Plus Inc, 11620 Vixens Path, Ellicott City, MD 21042-1539 *Tel:* 410-997-0763 *Fax:* 410-997-0764 *E-mail:* exhibit@epponline.com *Web Site:* www.epponline.com, pg 1133, 1345

Marshall, Steve, Ingram Content Group LLC, One Ingram Blvd, La Vergne, TN 37086-1986 *Tel:* 615-793-5000 *Toll Free Tel:* 800-937-8000 (retailers); 800-937-5300 (ext 1, libs) *E-mail:* customerservice@ingramcontent.com *Web Site:* www.ingramcontent.com, pg 1290, 1315

Marston, Susan, Junior Library Guild, 7858 Industrial Pkwy, Plain City, OH 43064 *Tel:* 614-733-0312 *Toll Free Tel:* 800-491-0174 *Fax:* 614-733-0501 *Toll Free Fax:* 800-827-3080 *E-mail:* editorial@juniorlibraryguild.com *Web Site:* www.juniorlibraryguild.com, pg 1136

Martel, George, SENCOR International, 445 Park Ave, 9th fl, New York, NY 10022 *Tel:* 212-980-6726 *Web Site:* www.sencorinternational.com, pg 1385, 1393

Martin, Alice, Adams Magnetic Products Co, 888 N Larch Ave, Elmhurst, IL 60126-1133 *Tel:* 630-617-8880 *Toll Free Tel:* 800-747-7543 (sales) *Fax:* 630-617-8881 *Toll Free Fax:* 800-747-1323 *E-mail:* info@adamsmagnetic.com *Web Site:* www.adamsmagnetic.com, pg 1261

Martin, Amy, Four Colour Print Group, 2410 Frankfort Ave, Louisville, KY 40206 *Tel:* 502-896-9644 *Fax:* 502-896-9594 *E-mail:* sales@fourcolour.com *Web Site:* www.fourcolour.com, pg 1204, 1247, 1276

Martin, Beth, Northeast Publishers Reps, Montville Chase, 20 Davenport Rd, Montville, NJ 07045 *Tel:* 973-299-0085 *Fax:* 973-263-2363 *E-mail:* siraksirak@aol.com *Web Site:* www.nepubreps.com, pg 1294

Martin, Beverly Swerling, Agent Research & Evaluation Inc (AR&E), 44 Park Rd, Woodbury, CT 06798 *Tel:* 203-586-1397 *Web Site:* www.agentresearch.org, pg 1341

Martin, Jack, Hill+Knowlton Strategies, 237 Park Ave, 4th fl, New York, NY 10017 *Tel:* 212-885-0300 *Web Site:* www.hkstrategies.com, pg 1098

Martin, Jan, Domtar Paper Co LLC, 234 Kingsley Park Dr, Fort Mill, SC 29715 *Tel:* 803-802-7500 *Toll Free Tel:* 877-877-4685 *E-mail:* communications@domtar.com; commercialprinting@domtar.com *Web Site:* www.domtar.com, pg 1262

Martin, Ken, Crown Connect, 250 W Rialto Ave, San Bernadino, CA 92408 *Tel:* 909-888-7531 *Fax:* 909-889-1639 *E-mail:* sales@crownconnect.com *Web Site:* www.crownconnect.com, pg 1203, 1218, 1275

Martin, Peter B, Signature Print Services, 3565 Sierra Rd, San Jose, CA 95132 *Tel:* 408-213-3393 *Fax:* 408-213-3399 *Web Site:* www.signatureprint.com, pg 1254

Martin, R, ASC Systems, Mack Place, B-566, St Clair Shores, MI 48080 *Tel:* 313-882-1133 *E-mail:* ascsystemss@live.com *Web Site:* www.sites.google.com/site/ascsystemsusi, pg 1373

Martinelli, Rob, Tri-Media Integrated Marketing Technologies Inc, 1027 Pelham St, Unit 2, Fonthill, ON L0S 1E0, Canada *E-mail:* think@tri-media.com *Web Site:* tri-media.com, pg 1087

Martinez, Joseph, Dynaric Inc, 5740 Bayside Rd, Virginia Beach, VA 23455 *Tel:* 757-363-5850 *Toll Free Tel:* 800-526-0827 *Fax:* 757-363-8016 *E-mail:* gd@dynaric.com; order@dynaric.com *Web Site:* www.dynaric.com, pg 1275

Martino, Lisa, Dunhill International List Co Inc, 6400 Congress Ave, Suite 1750, Boca Raton, FL 33487-2898 *Tel:* 561-998-7800 *Toll Free Tel:* 800-DUNHILL (386-4455) *Fax:* 561-998-7880 *E-mail:* dunhill@dunhillintl.com *Web Site:* www.dunhills.com, pg 1112

Martinson, Connie, Connie Martinson Talks Books, 2288 Coldwater Canyon, Beverly Hills, CA 90210 *Tel:* 310-271-4127 *E-mail:* talksbks@aol.com *Web Site:* www.conniemartinson.com, pg 1118

Martsching, Robert, H B Fuller Co, 1200 Willow Lake Blvd, St Paul, MN 55110-5146 *Tel:* 651-236-5900 *Toll Free Tel:* 888-423-8553 *E-mail:* inquiry@hbfuller.com *Web Site:* www.hbfuller.com, pg 1263, 1276

Marty, Jeff, Scholastic Book Fairs®, 1080 Greenwood Blvd, Lake Mary, FL 32746 *Tel:* 407-829-8000 *Fax:* 407-829-2600 *E-mail:* custservbf@scholasticbookfairs.com *Web Site:* www.scholastic.com/bookfairs, pg 1298, 1320

Marusic, Mike, Sharp Electronics Corp, 100 Paragon Dr, Montvale, NJ 07645 *Tel:* 201-529-8200 *Toll Free Tel:* 800-BE-SHARP (237-4277) *Fax:* 201-529-8425 *Web Site:* www.sharpusa.com, pg 1385

Marx, Kyle, Readerlink Distribution Services LLC, 1420 Kensington Rd, Suite 300, Oakbrook, IL 60523-2164 *Tel:* 708-547-4400 *Toll Free Tel:* 800-549-5389 *E-mail:* info@readerlink.com; marketingservices@readerlink.com *Web Site:* www.readerlink.com, pg 1297

Marzullo, Chris, Ironmark, 9040 Junction Dr, Annapolis Junction, MD 20701 *Toll Free Tel:* 888-775-3737 *E-mail:* marketing@ironmarkusa.com *Web Site:* ironmarkusa.com, pg 1206, 1221, 1249, 1264, 1277

Marzullo, Matt, Ironmark, 9040 Junction Dr, Annapolis Junction, MD 20701 *Toll Free Tel:* 888-775-3737 *E-mail:* marketing@ironmarkusa.com *Web Site:* ironmarkusa.com, pg 1206, 1221, 1249, 1264, 1277

Masaaki, Yamamoto, C & C Offset Printing Co USA Inc, 70 W 36 St, Unit 10C, New York, NY 10018 *Tel:* 212-431-4210 *Toll Free Fax:* 866-540-4134 *Web Site:* www.ccoffset.com, pg 1202, 1217, 1243

Masco, Linda, CyberWolf® Inc, 1596 Pacheco, Suite 203, Santa Fe, NM 87505 *Tel:* 505-983-6463 *E-mail:* sales@cyberwolf.com *Web Site:* www.cyberwolf.com; www.accumenbook.com; www.ebookdownloadservice.com, pg 1375

Massari, Kristina, Book Review Index, 27500 Drake Rd, Farmington Hills, MI 48331-3535 *Tel:* 248-699-4253 *Toll Free Tel:* 800-877-4253 *Fax:* 248-699-8074 *Toll Free Fax:* 800-414-5043 (orders); 800-414-5045 *E-mail:* gale.galeord@cengage.com *Web Site:* www.gale.com, pg 1124

Massik, Peter, BMR Associates, 60 Corte Amado, Greenbrae, CA 94904 *Tel:* 415-927-1564 *E-mail:* info@bmrassoc.com *Web Site:* www.bmrassoc.com, pg 1343

Mast, E Dale, Choice Books, 2387 Grace Chapel Rd, Harrisonburg, VA 22801 *Tel:* 540-434-1827 *Fax:* 540-434-9894 *E-mail:* info@choicebooks.org *Web Site:* www.choicebooks.org, pg 1312

Mastantuono, Gina, Ingram Micro Inc, 3351 Michelson Dr, Suite 100, Irvin, CA 92612 *Tel:* 714-566-1000 *E-mail:* customerexperience@ingrammicro.com *Web Site:* www.ingrammicro.com, pg 1315

Masterson, Neil, Thomson Reuters, 3 Times Sq, New York, NY 10036 *Tel:* 646-223-4000; 646-223-6100 (edit); 646-223-6000 (newsroom) *Web Site:* www.thomsonreuters.com, pg 1186

Mater, James, QualityLogic Inc, 9576 W Emerald St, Boise, ID 83704 *Tel:* 208-424-1905 *E-mail:* info@qualitylogic.com *Web Site:* www.qualitylogic.com, pg 1384

Mateski, Kristin, Walsworth, 306 N Kansas Ave, Marceline, MO 64658 *Toll Free Tel:* 800-265-6795 *Web Site:* www.walsworth.com; www.walsworthhistorybooks.com, pg 1209, 1227, 1256

Mathison, Jeff, Maps by Mathison, PO Box 152, Spring Mills, PA 16875 *Tel:* 814-321-7571 *E-mail:* jcmaps6@gmail.com *Web Site:* mapsbymathison.com, pg 1430

Matlock, Trevin, Faherty & Associates Inc, 6665 SW Hampton St, Suite 100, Portland, OR 97223 *Tel:* 503-639-3113 *Toll Free Tel:* 800-824-2888 *Fax:* 503-598-9850 *Web Site:* www.fahertybooks.com, pg 1286

Matsliach, Gaby, Electronics for Imaging Inc (EFI), 6750 Dumbarton Circle, Fremont, CA 94555 *Tel:* 650-357-3500 *Toll Free Tel:* 800-568-1917; 800-875-7117 (sales) *Fax:* 650-357-3907 *E-mail:* info@efi.com *Web Site:* www.efi.com, pg 1377

Matt, J Kemper Jr, Dupli Envelope & Graphics Corp, 6761 Thompson Rd N, Syracuse, NY 13211 *Tel:* 315-472-1316 *Toll Free Tel:* 800-724-2477 *E-mail:* sales@duplionline.com; orders@duplionline.com *Web Site:* www.duplionline.com, pg 1246

Matthews, Bradley, Conservative Book Club, 300 New Jersey Ave NW, Suite 500, Washington, DC 20001 *Tel:* 202-216-0601 *Fax:* 202-216-0614 *Web Site:* www.conservativebookclub.com, pg 1135

Matthews, Clark, Independent Publishers Group (IPG), 814 N Franklin St, Chicago, IL 60610 *Tel:* 312-337-0747 *Toll Free Tel:* 800-888-4741 (orders) *Fax:* 312-337-5985 *E-mail:* frontdesk@ipgbook.com; orders@ipgbook.com *Web Site:* www.ipgbook.com, pg 1288, 1326

Matthews, Joe, Independent Publishers Group (IPG), 814 N Franklin St, Chicago, IL 60610 *Tel:* 312-337-0747 *Toll Free Tel:* 800-888-4741 (orders) *Fax:* 312-337-5985 *E-mail:* frontdesk@ipgbook.com; orders@ipgbook.com *Web Site:* www.ipgbook.com, pg 1288, 1326

Mattina, Nick, Cross Country Computer Corp, 250 Carleton Ave, East Islip, NY 11730-1240 *Tel:* 631-334-1810 *E-mail:* inquiry@crosscountrycomputer.com *Web Site:* www.crosscountrycomputer.com, pg 1111

Mattscheck, Karen, National Book Network (NBN), 4501 Forbes Blvd, Suite 200, Lanham, MD 20706 *Tel:* 301-459-3366 *Toll Free Tel:* 800-462-6420 (orders only) *Fax:* 301-429-5746 *Toll Free Fax:* 800-338-4550 (orders only) *E-mail:* customercare@nbnbooks.com *Web Site:* www.nbnbooks.com, pg 1293, 1318

Mattsson, Jay, Hedquist Productions Inc, PO Box 1475, Fairfield, IA 52556-1475 *Tel:* 641-472-6708 *Toll Free Fax:* 855-510-5726 *Web Site:* www.hedquist.com, pg 1378

Matuska, Todd, GLS Companies, 1280 Energy Park Dr, St Paul, MN 55108-5106 *Tel:* 651-644-3000 *Toll Free Tel:* 800-655-9405 *Web Site:* www.glsmn.com, pg 1220, 1248

Mauritz, Rob, LBS, 1801 Thompson Ave, Des Moines, IA 50316-2751 *Tel:* 515-262-3191 *Toll Free Tel:* 800-247-5323 *Toll Free Fax:* 800-262-4091 *E-mail:* info@lbsbind.com *Web Site:* www.lbsbind.com, pg 1265

Mauro, JoAnn, GTxcel Inc, 144 Turnpike Rd, Suite 130, Southborough, MA 01772-2104 *Toll Free Tel:* 800-609-8994 *Web Site:* www.gtxcel.com, pg 1378

Mayer, Robert, IMSI/Design LLC, 384 Bel Marin Keys Blvd, No 150, Novato, CA 94949 *Tel:* 415-483-8000 *Toll Free Tel:* 800-833-8082 (sales) *E-mail:* sales@imsidesign.com; support@imsidesign.com *Web Site:* www.imsidesign.com, pg 1379

Mayers, Glen, Kiplinger's Personal Finance/The Kiplinger Washington Editors Inc, 1100 13 St NW, Suite 750, Washington, DC 20005-4364 *Tel:* 202-887-6400 *Toll Free Tel:* 800-544-0155 (cust serv) *E-mail:* feedback@kiplinger.com *Web Site:* www.kiplinger.com, pg 1185

Mayland, Chris, Encyclopaedia Britannica Inc, 325 N La Salle St, Suite 200, Chicago, IL 60654 *Tel:* 312-347-7000 (all other countries) *Toll Free Tel:* 800-323-1229 (US & CN) *Fax:* 312-294-2104 *E-mail:* contact@eb.com *Web Site:* www.britannica.com, pg 1313

Maylander, Heather, Lake Group Media Inc, One Byram Brook Place, Armonk, NY 10504 *Tel:* 914-925-2400 *Fax:* 914-925-2499 *Web Site:* www.lakegroupmedia.com, pg 1112

Mazer, Norm, Applied Information Sciences Corp, PO Box 9182, Calabasas, CA 91372-9182 *Tel:* 818-222-0926 *Fax:* 818-222-4329 *E-mail:* sales@aisciences.com *Web Site:* www.aisciences.com, pg 1341

Mazzolini, Anna, Bashian & Associates Inc, 28915 S Village Lane, Glenwillow, OH 44139 *E-mail:* adsales@bashian.com *Web Site:* www.bashian.com, pg 1342

McAndrew, Karen, alfa CTP Systems Inc, 2503 Spring Ridge Dr, Unit D, Spring Grove, IL 60081 *Tel:* 815-474-7634 *E-mail:* info@alfactp.com *Web Site:* www.alfactp.com, pg 1372

McAuley, Pat, Mobium Creative Group, 200 S Michigan Ave, 17th fl, Chicago, IL 60604 *Tel:* 312-422-8950; 312-422-5995 *Fax:* 312-422-5901 *Web Site:* www.mobium.com, pg 1350

McAvoy, Jack, PTC, 121 Seaport Blvd, Boston, MA 02210 *Tel:* 781-370-5000 *Fax:* 781-370-6000 *Web Site:* www.ptc.com, pg 1384

McCabe, Matthew, The Crowley Co, 5111 Pegasus Ct, Suite M, Frederick, MD 21704 *Tel:* 240-215-0224 *Fax:* 240-215-0234 *E-mail:* webrequest@thecrowleycompany.com *Web Site:* www.thecrowleycompany.com, pg 1375

McCafferty, Jim, Ecological Fibers Inc, 40 Pioneer Dr, Lunenburg, MA 01462 *Tel:* 978-537-0003 *Fax:* 978-537-2238 *E-mail:* info@ecofibers.com *Web Site:* www.ecofibers.com, pg 1204, 1263

McCaffrey, Kalah, Franklin & Siegal Associates Inc, 1350 Broadway, Suite 2015, New York, NY 10018 *Tel:* 212-868-6311 *Fax:* 212-868-6312 *Web Site:* www.franklinandsiegal.com, pg 1345

McCall, Dewitt C, De Ru's Fine Art, 9100 E Artesia Blvd, Bellflower, CA 90706-6205 *Tel:* 562-920-1312 *Fax:* 562-920-3077 *E-mail:* derusgal@aol.com *Web Site:* www.derusfinearts.com, pg 1312

McCall, Kim, Ascot Media Group Inc, PO Box 2394, Friendswood, TX 77549 *Tel:* 832-334-2733 *Toll Free Tel:* 800-854-1134 *Toll Free Fax:* 800-854-2207 *Web Site:* www.ascotmedia.com, pg 1095

McCallum, Duncan, Spectrum PrintGroup Inc, 1535 Farmer's Lane, Suite 254, Santa Rosa, CA 95405 *Tel:* 707-542-6044 *Toll Free Tel:* 888-340-6049 *Fax:* 707-542-6045 *E-mail:* sales@spectrumprintgroup. com *Web Site:* www.spectrumprintgroup.com, pg 1209, 1255, 1268

McCann, Ryan, Claris International Inc, 5201 Patrick Henry Dr, Santa Clara, CA 95054 *Tel:* 408-727-8227 (sales & cust support) *Toll Free Tel:* 800-725-2747 (sales); 800-325-2747 (cust support) *Fax:* 408-987-7447 *E-mail:* claris_sales@claris.com *Web Site:* www.claris.com, pg 1374

McCarthy, Peter, McCarthy Digital, 15 Mountain Trail, Croton-on-Hudson, NY 10520 *Tel:* 914-334-0408 *Toll Free Fax:* 866-618-8605 *Web Site:* www.mccarthy-digital.com, pg 1349

McCarthy, Rob, SGS International LLC, 626 W Main St, Suite 500, Louisville, KY 40202 *Tel:* 502-637-5443 *E-mail:* info@sgsco.com *Web Site:* www.sgsintl.com, pg 1225

McCarthy, Sabrina, Ingram Content Group LLC, One Ingram Blvd, La Vergne, TN 37086-1986 *Tel:* 615-793-5000 *Toll Free Tel:* 800-937-8000 (retailers); 800-937-5300 (ext 1, libs) *E-mail:* customerservice@ingramcontent.com *Web Site:* www.ingramcontent.com, pg 1290, 1315

McCarthy, Sabrina, Ingram Publisher Services, an Ingram brand, One Ingram Blvd, La Vergne, TN 37086 *Tel:* 615-793-5000 *Toll Free Tel:* 866-400-5351 (cust serv) *E-mail:* ips@ingramcontent.com *Web Site:* www.ingramcontent.com, pg 1290

McCarthy, Sabrina, Two Rivers Distribution, an Ingram brand, 1400 Broadway, Suite 520, New York, NY 10018 *Toll Free Tel:* 866-400-5351 *E-mail:* ips@ingramcontent.com (orders, independent bookstores & gift accts) *Web Site:* www.tworiversdistribution.com, pg 1300

McClanahan, Debbie, Cenveo Publisher Services, 555 Virginia Dr, Fort Washington, PA 19034 *Tel:* 267-470-1590 *Fax:* 215-591-9093 *E-mail:* info.psg@cenveo.com *Web Site:* www.cenveopublisherservices.com, pg 1203, 1217, 1356, 1374, 1426

McClean, Hugh, ActionGrafixPhotography.com, 30 Bishop Tutu Blvd, Toronto, ON M5V 2Z7, Canada *Tel:* 416-260-0421 *Web Site:* www.actiongrafixphotography.com, pg 1435

McCloat, Keith, King Features Syndicate, 300 W 57 St, New York, NY 10019-5238 *Tel:* 212-969-7550 *Toll Free Tel:* 800-526-5464 *Web Site:* www.kingfeatures.com, pg 1185

McCloat, Keith, Eric Tyson, 300 W 57 St, 15th fl, New York, NY 10019-5238 *Tel:* 212-969-7550 *Toll Free Tel:* 800-526-5464 *Fax:* 646-280-1550 *E-mail:* eric@erictyson.com *Web Site:* www.erictyson.com, pg 1119

McCombs, Mark, Taylor Specialty Books, 1550 W Mockingbird Lane, Dallas, TX 75235 *Tel:* 214-819-8588 (cust serv) *Fax:* 214-819-5051 (cust serv) *Toll Free Fax:* 800-203-9778 *E-mail:* rfq@taylorpub.com (estimates) *Web Site:* www.taylorspecialtybooks.com, pg 1209, 1226, 1255, 1268, 1362

McConnell, Danielle, Bookforum, 350 Seventh Ave, New York, NY 10001 *Tel:* 212-475-4000 *Fax:* 212-529-1257 *E-mail:* info@bookforum.com; editors@bookforum.com *Web Site:* www.bookforum.com, pg 1124

McConnell, Marilyn, American International Distribution Corp (AIDC), 82 Winter Sport Lane, Williston, VT 05495 *Tel:* 802-862-0095 *Toll Free Tel:* 800-678-2432 *Fax:* 802-864-7749 *Web Site:* www.aidcvt.com, pg 1105, 1109, 1215, 1282, 1309, 1331

McConnell, Suzanne, Bellevue Literary Review, NYU School of Medicine, Dept of Medicine, 550 First Ave, OBV-A612, New York, NY 10016 *Tel:* 212-263-3973 *E-mail:* info@BLReview.org *Web Site:* www.BLReview.org, pg 1124

McCourtney, Carolynn, Walter's Publishing, 1750 Northway Dr, North Mankato, MN 56003 *Toll Free Tel:* 800-447-3274 *E-mail:* info@walterspublishing.com *Web Site:* www.walterspublishing.com, pg 1210

McCracken, Leah Rex, Ingram Publisher Services, an Ingram brand, One Ingram Blvd, La Vergne, TN 37086 *Tel:* 615-793-5000 *Toll Free Tel:* 866-400-5351 (cust serv) *E-mail:* ips@ingramcontent.com *Web Site:* www.ingramcontent.com, pg 1290

McCurdy, Robert, GTI Graphic Technology Inc, 211 Dupont Ave, Newburgh, NY 12550 *Tel:* 845-562-7066 *Fax:* 845-562-2543 *E-mail:* sales@gtilite.com *Web Site:* www.gtilite.com, pg 1276, 1378

McDonough, Judy, PR by the Book LLC, PO Box 6226, Round Rock, TX 78683 *Tel:* 512-501-4399 *Fax:* 512-501-4399 *E-mail:* info@prbythebook.com *Web Site:* www.prbythebook.com, pg 1101

McEvoy, Kathleen, Communication Abstracts, 10 Estes St, Ipswich, MA 01938 *Tel:* 978-356-6500 *Toll Free Tel:* 800-653-2726 *Fax:* 978-356-6565 *E-mail:* information@ebscohost.com *Web Site:* www.ebscohost.com, pg 1125

McFadden, Stillman, Toof American Digital, 4222 Pilot Dr, Memphis, TN 38118 *Tel:* 901-274-3632 *Toll Free Tel:* 800-722-4772 *Web Site:* www.toofamericandigital.com, pg 1209, 1227, 1255, 1269

McFarland, Julie, McNaughton & Gunn Inc, Plant: 960 Woodland Dr, Saline, MI 48176 *Tel:* 734-429-5411 *Toll Free Fax:* 800-677-BOOK (677-2665) *Web Site:* www.bookprinters.com, pg 1207, 1251

McGarr, Bill, Wybel Marketing Group Inc, 213 W Main St, Barrington, IL 60010 *Tel:* 847-382-0384; 847-382-0382 *Toll Free Tel:* 800-323-5297 *Fax:* 847-382-0385 *Toll Free Fax:* 800-595-5252 *E-mail:* bookreps@wybel.com, pg 1301

McGarr, William D, McGarr & Associates, 5692 Heathwood Ct, Covington, KY 41015 *Tel:* 859-356-9295 *Fax:* 859-356-7804, pg 1292

McGarrity, Andrew, Tennessee Book Co, 1550 Heil Quaker Blvd, La Vergne, TN 37086 *Tel:* 615-793-5040 *Toll Free Tel:* 800-456-0418 *Fax:* 615-213-9545 *Web Site:* www.tennesseebook.com, pg 1321

McGavic, Mary Francis, The Creative Spark, 7010 85 Street Ct E, Bradenton, FL 34202 *Tel:* 941-356-2514 *E-mail:* info@creativespark.com *Web Site:* www.creativespark.com, pg 1357

McGee, Adam, Boston Review, PO Box 425786, Cambridge, MA 02142 *Tel:* 617-324-1360 *Toll Free Tel:* 877-406-2443 (cust serv) *Fax:* 617-452-3356 *E-mail:* review@bostonreview.net *Web Site:* bostonreview.net, pg 1124

McGee, Thomas, Horizon Paper Co Inc, 1010 Washington Blvd, Stamford, CT 06901 *Tel:* 203-358-0855 *Toll Free Tel:* 866-358-0855 *E-mail:* info@horizonpaper.com *Web Site:* www.horizonpaper.com, pg 1264

McGonagle, Chuck, Transparent Language Inc, 12 Murphy Dr, Nashua, NH 03062 *Tel:* 603-262-6300 *Toll Free Tel:* 800-567-9619 (cust serv & sales) *E-mail:* info@transparent.com; support@transparent.com (tech support) *Web Site:* www.transparent.com, pg 1387

McGough, Jim, JPMC Associates, 7037 Snapdragon Dr, Carlsbad, CA 92011 *Tel:* 916-203-3693 *Fax:* 760-931-6878 *E-mail:* jpmcaso@aol.com, pg 1348

McGourlay, James, Open Text Corp, 275 Frank Tompa Dr, Waterloo, ON N2L 0A1, Canada *Tel:* 519-888-7111 *Fax:* 519-888-0677 *Web Site:* opentext.com, pg 1383

McHugh, John B, John B McHugh Publishing Consultant, PO Box 170665, Milwaukee, WI 53217-8056 *Tel:* 414-351-3056 *E-mail:* jack@johnbmchugh.com *Web Site:* www.johnbmchugh.com, pg 1350

McInerney, Linda, University Products Inc, 517 Main St, Holyoke, MA 01040 *Tel:* 413-532-3372 *Toll Free Tel:* 800-628-1912 (orders) *Fax:* 413-533-4743 *Toll Free Fax:* 800-532-9281 *E-mail:* info@universityproducts.com *Web Site:* www.universityproducts.com, pg 1269

McKee, Jeff, X-Rite Inc, 4300 44 St SE, Grand Rapids, MI 49512 *Tel:* 616-803-2100 *Toll Free Tel:* 800-248-9748; 888-800-9580 (sales) *E-mail:* info@xrite.com *Web Site:* www.xrite.com, pg 1280

McKenna, Graham, Gracenote, a Nielsen Company, 2000 Powell St, Suite 1500, Emeryville, CA 94608 *Tel:* 510-428-7200 *Web Site:* www.gracenote.com, pg 1184

McKeon, John C, Hearst Newspapers, 300 W 57 St, New York, NY 10019 *Tel:* 212-649-2000 *Web Site:* www.hearst.com/newspapers, pg 1185

McKiernan, Scott, Keystone Press Agency Inc, 412 N El Camino Real, San Clemente, CA 92672 *Tel:* 949-481-3747 *Fax:* 949-481-3941 *E-mail:* info@keystonepictures.com *Web Site:* www.keystonepictures.com, pg 1185, 1448

McKinley, Brian, Ingram Content Group LLC, One Ingram Blvd, La Vergne, TN 37086-1986 *Tel:* 615-793-5000 *Toll Free Tel:* 800-937-8000 (retailers); 800-937-5300 (ext 1, libs) *E-mail:* customerservice@ingramcontent.com *Web Site:* www.ingramcontent.com, pg 1290, 1315

McKinnie, Michelle, McClain Printing Co, 212 Main St, Parsons, WV 26287-1033 *Tel:* 304-478-2881 *Toll Free Tel:* 800-654-7179 *Fax:* 304-478-4658 *E-mail:* mcclain@mcclainprinting.com *Web Site:* www.mcclainprinting.com, pg 1207, 1223, 1251, 1265, 1278

McKown-Finken, Amber, Independent Publishers Group (IPG), 814 N Franklin St, Chicago, IL 60610 *Tel:* 312-337-0747 *Toll Free Tel:* 800-888-4741 (orders) *Fax:* 312-337-5985 *E-mail:* frontdesk@ipgbook.com; orders@ipgbook.com *Web Site:* www.ipgbook.com, pg 1288

McLachlan, Campbell, ICSID Review: Foreign Investment Law Journal, 2001 Evans Rd, Cary, NC 27513 *Tel:* 919-677-0977 *Toll Free Tel:* 800-852-7323 *Fax:* 919-677-1714 *Web Site:* academic.oup.org, pg 1127

McLaughlin, Carolyn, Bulletin of the History of Medicine, 2715 N Charles St, Baltimore, MD 21218-4363 *Toll Free Tel:* 800-548-1784 (journal orders) *Fax:* 410-516-6968 *E-mail:* jrnlcirc@press.jhu.edu (journal orders) *Web Site:* www.press.jhu.edu/journals/bulletin_of_the_history_of_medicine/index.html, pg 1125

McLaughlin, Paul V, CVI Capital, 165 Annursnac Hill Rd, Concord, MA 01742 *Tel:* 978-371-0995 *Fax:* 978-287-5869 *E-mail:* admin@cvicapital.com *Web Site:* www.cvicapital.com, pg 1344

McLean, Kerry, Intuit Inc, 2700 Coast Ave, Mountain View, CA 94043 *Tel:* 650-944-6000 *Toll Free Tel:* 800-446-8848 *E-mail:* investor_relations@intuit.com *Web Site:* www.intuit.com, pg 1379

McLean, Thomas, Cardinal Publishers Group, 2402 N Shadeland Ave, Suite A, Indianapolis, IN 46219 *Tel:* 317-352-8200 *Toll Free Tel:* 800-296-0481 (cust serv) *Fax:* 317-352-8202 *E-mail:* customerservice@cardinalpub.com *Web Site:* cardinalpub.com, pg 1284

McLeester, Dick, VisionWorks, PO Box 92, Greenfield, MA 01302 *Tel:* 413-772-6569 *Toll Free Tel:* 800-933-7326 (orders) *Fax:* 413-772-6559 *E-mail:* dreaming@changingworld.com *Web Site:* www.changingworld.com, pg 1322

McLoraine, Jack, Gane Brothers & Lane Inc, 1400 Greenleaf Ave, Elk Grove Village, IL 60007 *Tel:* 847-593-3364 *Toll Free Tel:* 800-323-0596 *Toll Free Fax:* 800-784-2464 *E-mail:* sales@ganebrothers.com *Web Site:* www.ganebrothers.com, pg 1263

McManus, Brian, Worzalla, 3535 Jefferson St, Stevens Point, WI 54481 *Tel:* 715-344-9608 *Fax:* 715-344-2578 *Web Site:* www.worzalla.com, pg 1210, 1228, 1257

McMillen, Jim, Spraymation Inc, 4180 NW Tenth Ave, Fort Lauderdale, FL 33309 *Tel:* 954-484-9700 *Toll Free Tel:* 800-327-4985 *Fax:* 954-301-0842 *E-mail:* orders@spraymation.com *Web Site:* www.spraymation.com, pg 1279

McMurtrie, John, Sunday San Francisco Chronicle Book Review, 901 Mission St, San Francisco, CA 94103 *Tel:* 415-777-1111 *Toll Free Tel:* 866-732-4766 *Web Site:* www.sfgate.com, pg 1131

McNamee, A Miles, Copyright Clearance Center Inc (CCC), 222 Rosewood Dr, Danvers, MA 01923 *Tel:* 978-750-8400 (sales); 978-646-2600 (cust serv) *E-mail:* info@copyright.com *Web Site:* www.copyright.com, pg 1344

McNeace, Richard, Faherty & Associates Inc, 6665 SW Hampton St, Suite 100, Portland, OR 97223 *Tel:* 503-639-3113 *Toll Free Tel:* 800-824-2888 *Fax:* 503-598-9850 *Web Site:* www.fahertybooks.com, pg 1286

McNeill, Kevin, Datalogics Inc, 101 N Wacker, Suite 1800, Chicago, IL 60606 *Tel:* 312-853-8200 *Fax:* 312-853-8282 *E-mail:* sales@datalogics.com; marketing@datalogics.com *Web Site:* www.datalogics.com, pg 1375

McNulty, Timothy, C & C Offset Printing Co USA Inc, 70 W 36 St, Unit 10C, New York, NY 10018 *Tel:* 212-431-4210 *Toll Free Fax:* 866-540-4134 *Web Site:* www.ccoffset.com, pg 1202, 1217, 1243

McNutty, Aidan, The New York Times Licensing Group, 620 Eighth Ave, 20th fl, New York, NY 10018 *Tel:* 212-556-1927 *E-mail:* nytlg-sales@nytimes.com *Web Site:* nytlicensing.com, pg 1185

McPhate, Chris, Crown Connect, 250 W Rialto Ave, San Bernadino, CA 92408 *Tel:* 909-888-7531 *Fax:* 909-889-1639 *E-mail:* sales@crownconnect.com *Web Site:* www.crownconnect.com, pg 1203, 1218, 1275

McPherson, Bill, AlphaGraphics Inc, 143 Union Blvd, Suite 650, Lakewood, CO 80228 *Toll Free Tel:* 800-955-6246 *Fax:* 801-595-7270 *E-mail:* contactus@alphagraphics.com *Web Site:* www.alphagraphics.com, pg 1372

McWilliams, Skip, Teacher's Discovery®, 2741 Paldan Dr, Auburn Hills, MI 48326 *Toll Free Tel:* 800-TEACHER (832-2437) *Toll Free Fax:* 800-287-4509 *E-mail:* help@teachersdiscovery.com; orders@teachersdiscovery.com *Web Site:* www.teachersdiscovery.com, pg 1299, 1321

Mead, Jim, Walsworth, 306 N Kansas Ave, Marceline, MO 64658 *Toll Free Tel:* 800-265-6795 *Web Site:* www.walsworth.com; www.walsworthhistorybooks.com, pg 1209, 1227, 1256

Meadows, Amy, Meadows Design Office, 3800 Yuma St NW, Washington, DC 20016 *E-mail:* mdo@mdomedia.com, pg 1208, 1223, 1360, 1430

Meadows, Marc, Meadows Design Office, 3800 Yuma St NW, Washington, DC 20016 *Tel:* 202-966-6007 *E-mail:* mdo@mdomedia.com, pg 1208, 1223, 1360, 1430

Medeiros, George, The Country Press Inc, One Commercial Dr, Lakeville, MA 02347 *Tel:* 508-947-4485 *Toll Free Tel:* 888-343-2227 *Fax:* 508-947-8989 *E-mail:* info@countrypressinc.com *Web Site:* www.countrypressprinting.com, pg 1203, 1245

Medina, Carmen, Medina Software Inc, 1441 Oberlin Terr, Suite 1010, Lake Mary, FL 32746 *Tel:* 407-227-4112 *Web Site:* www.medinasoft.com, pg 1381

Medina, Jorge, Medina Software Inc, 1441 Oberlin Terr, Suite 1010, Lake Mary, FL 32746 *Tel:* 407-227-4112 *Web Site:* www.medinasoft.com, pg 1381

Megna, Richard, Fundamental Photographs, 210 Forsyth St, Suite 2, New York, NY 10002 *Tel:* 212-473-5770 *E-mail:* mail@fphoto.com *Web Site:* www.fphoto.com, pg 1446

Meisner, Joe, First Choice Copy, 5208 Grand Ave, Maspeth, NY 11378 *Tel:* 718-381-1480 (ext 200) *Toll Free Tel:* 800-222-COPY (222-2679) *Web Site:* www.firstchoice-copy.com, pg 1109, 1204, 1247, 1377

Melanson, Donya, Donya Melanson Associates, 5 Bisson Lane, Merrimac, MA 01860 *Tel:* 978-346-9240 *Fax:* 978-346-8345 *E-mail:* dmelanson@dmelanson.com *Web Site:* www.dmelanson.com, pg 1087, 1107

Melcher, Charles, Melcher Media Inc, 124 W 13 St, New York, NY 10011 *Tel:* 212-727-2322 *Fax:* 212-627-1973 *E-mail:* info@melcher.com *Web Site:* www.melcher.com, pg 1360

Melchers, Rick, New England Newsclip Agency, 30B Vreeland Rd, Suite 110, Florham Park, NJ 07932 *Tel:* 973-992-6600 *Toll Free Tel:* 800-631-1160 *Toll Free Fax:* 800-563-9725 *E-mail:* inquiry@burrellesluce.com *Web Site:* www.burrellesluce.com, pg 1391

Melchers, Rick, New Jersey Clipping Service, 30B Vreeland Rd, Suite 110, Florham Park, NJ 07932 *Tel:* 973-992-6600 *Toll Free Tel:* 800-631-1160 *Toll Free Fax:* 800-563-9725 *Web Site:* www.burrellesluce.com, pg 1391

Melendez, John, RAM Publications & Distribution Inc, 2525 Michigan Ave, Bldg A2, Santa Monica, CA 90404 *Tel:* 310-453-0043 *Fax:* 310-264-4888 *E-mail:* info@rampub.com; orders@rampub.com *Web Site:* www.rampub.com, pg 1296

Melissa, Raymond F, Melissa Data Corp, 22382 Avenida Empresa, Rancho Santa Margarita, CA 92688-2112 *Tel:* 949-858-3000 *Toll Free Tel:* 800-800-6245 *E-mail:* info@melissadata.com *Web Site:* www.melissadata.com, pg 1223

Mellers, Tom, Tom Mellers Publishing Services (TMPS), 60 Second Ave, Suite 8, New York, NY 10003 *Tel:* 212-254-4958 *E-mail:* tmps71@yahoo.com, pg 1350

Melnick, Marsha, Roundtable Press Inc, 20 E Ninth St, New York, NY 10003 *Tel:* 917-597-2183 *Web Site:* www.roundtablepressinc.com, pg 1361

Melvin, Terrence, HFS, 2715 N Charles St, Baltimore, MD 21218 *Tel:* 410-516-6965 *Toll Free Tel:* 800-537-5487 (US & CN) *Fax:* 410-516-6998 *E-mail:* hfscustserv@press.jhu.edu *Web Site:* hfs.jhu.edu; www.hfsbooks.com, pg 1288

Mendelson, Sandi, Hilsinger-Mendelson West Inc, 8916 Ashcroft Ave, Los Angeles, CA 90048 *Tel:* 310-659-7930 *E-mail:* hmiwest@aol.com *Web Site:* www.hilsingermendelson.com, pg 1098

Mendez, Manny, Emerson, Wajdowicz Studios Inc, 530 W 25 St, New York, NY 10001 *Tel:* 212-807-8144 *Fax:* 212-675-0414 *E-mail:* info@designews.com *Web Site:* www.designews.com; Facebook.com/DesignEWS, pg 1427

Menezes, Andrew, CQ Roll Call, 1201 Pennsylvania Ave NW, Suite 600, Washington, DC 20004 *Tel:* 202-650-6500; 202-650-6511 (subns); 202-650-6621 (cust serv) *Toll Free Tel:* 800-432-2250; 800-678-8511 (subns) *E-mail:* customerservice@cqrollcall.com *Web Site:* cqrollcall.com; www.rollcall.com, pg 1184

Mengin, Nicolas, Distribooks Inc, 8154 N Ridgeway Ave, Skokie, IL 60076-2911 *Tel:* 847-676-1596 *Toll Free Fax:* 888-266-5713 *E-mail:* info@distribooks.com, pg 1286

Mengin, Nicolas, Distribooks Inc, 8154 N Ridgeway Ave, Skokie, IL 60076-2911 *Tel:* 847-676-1596 *Fax:* 847-676-1195 *Toll Free Fax:* 888-266-5713 *E-mail:* info@distribooks.com; info@schoenhofs.com *Web Site:* www.schoenhofs.com, pg 1313

Mengin, Nicolas, Schoenhof's Foreign Books Inc, 76 A Mount Auburn St, Cambridge, MA 02138 *Tel:* 617-547-8855 *E-mail:* info@schoenhofs.com *Web Site:* www.schoenhofs.com, pg 1320, 1327

Menke, Jim, Roswell Bookbinding, 2614 N 29 Ave, Phoenix, AZ 85009 *Tel:* 602-272-9338 *Toll Free Tel:* 888-803-8883 *Fax:* 602-272-9786 *Web Site:* www.roswellbookbinding.com, pg 1254, 1324

Menoudakos, Toni, Mail Order Media & Marketing Inc, 5500 Linkside Ct, Suite 2-A, Fuquay Varina, NC 27526-8499 *Tel:* 203-254-9390 *Fax:* 203-254-3253 *E-mail:* mailordermedia2000@yahoo.com, pg 1087

Menschenfreund, Joan, Visual Pursuit, 168 W 86 St, New York, NY 10024 *Tel:* 212-362-8234, pg 1443

Mercer, Rachel, ALC Inc, 750 College Rd E, Suite 201, Princeton, NJ 08540 *Tel:* 609-580-2800 *Toll Free Tel:* 800-252-5478 *Fax:* 609-580-2888 *E-mail:* info@alc.com *Web Site:* www.alc.com, pg 1111

Merker, Lance, OmniUpdate Inc, 1320 Flynn Rd, Suite 100, Camarillo, CA 93012 *Tel:* 805-484-9400 *Toll Free Tel:* 800-362-2605 *E-mail:* sales@omniupdate.com *Web Site:* omniupdate.com, pg 1383

Merrell, Jesse H, Merrell Enterprises, 3542 E State Rte 73, Waynesville, OH 45068 *Tel:* 202-265-1925 *Fax:* 513-855-4277 *Web Site:* www.merrellenterprises.com, pg 1185

Mersmann, Peter, StoraEnso North American Sales Inc, Canterbury Green, 201 Broad St, Stamford, CT 06901 *Tel:* 203-541-5100 *Fax:* 203-353-1143 *Web Site:* www.storaenso.com, pg 1268

Mesjak, John, Abraham Associates Inc, 5120-A Cedar Lake Rd, Minneapolis, MN 55416 *Tel:* 952-927-7920 *Toll Free Tel:* 800-701-2489 *Fax:* 952-927-8089 *E-mail:* info@abrahamassociatesinc.com *Web Site:* www.abrahamassociatesinc.com, pg 1281

Messenger, Jeff, EMT International Inc, 780 Centerline Dr, Hobart, WI 54155 *Tel:* 920-468-5475 *Fax:* 920-468-7991 *E-mail:* info@emtinternational.com *Web Site:* www.emtinternational.com, pg 1276

Metrailler, Gerard, Corel Corp, 1600 Carling Ave, Ottawa, ON K1Z 8R7, Canada *Tel:* 613-728-8200 (PR) *Toll Free Tel:* 877-582-6735 *Web Site:* www.corel.com, pg 1375

Metz, Steve, The Sound Lab Inc, 3355 Bee Cave Rd, Bldg 7, Suite 705, Austin, TX 78746 *Tel:* 512-476-2122 *Fax:* 512-476-2127 *E-mail:* info@thesoundlabinc.com *Web Site:* www.thesoundlabinc.com, pg 1386

Metzger, Heather, Biblical Archaeology Society, 4710 41 St NW, Washington, DC 20016-1705 *Tel:* 202-364-3300 *Toll Free Tel:* 800-221-4644 *Fax:* 202-364-2636 *E-mail:* info@biblicalarchaeology.org *Web Site:* www.biblicalarchaeology.org, pg 1373

Meurice, Stephen, The Canadian Press/La Presse Canadienne, 36 King St E, Toronto, ON M5C 2L9, Canada *Tel:* 416-364-0321 *Fax:* 416-364-0207 (newsroom) *E-mail:* sales@thecanadianpress.com *Web Site:* www.thecanadianpress.com, pg 1183

Meyer, Cheryll A, Metropolitan Newsclips Service Inc, 1250 Hanley Industrial Ct, St Louis, MO 63144 *Tel:* 314-395-8917 *E-mail:* cheryllm@metronewsclips.com *Web Site:* www.metronewsclips.com, pg 1391

Mezzetti, Phil, The Sound Lab Inc, 3355 Bee Cave Rd, Bldg 7, Suite 705, Austin, TX 78746 *Tel:* 512-476-2122 *Fax:* 512-476-2127 *E-mail:* info@thesoundlabinc.com *Web Site:* www.thesoundlabinc.com, pg 1386

Micaelian, Fadi, BroadVision, 460 Seaport Ct, Suite 102, Redwood City, CA 94063 *Tel:* 650-331-1000 *Web Site:* www.broadvision.com, pg 1374

Michaels, Joanne, JMB Associates, PO Box 425, Woodstock, NY 12498 *Tel:* 845-679-5719 *E-mail:* contact@joannemichaels.com *Web Site:* www.joannemichaels.com, pg 1348

Michailidis, Parisa, Firefly Books Ltd, 50 Staples Ave, Unit 1, Richmond Hill, ON L4B 0A7, Canada *Tel:* 416-499-8412 *Toll Free Tel:* 800-387-6192 (CN); 800-387-5085 (US) *Fax:* 416-499-8313 *Toll Free Fax:* 800-450-0391 (CN); 800-565-6034 (US) *E-mail:* service@fireflybooks.com *Web Site:* www.fireflybooks.com, pg 1287

Michalowski, Piotr, Journal of Cuneiform Studies (JCS), Boston University, 656 Beacon St, 5th fl, Boston, MA 02215 *Tel:* 617-353-6570 *Fax:* 617-353-6575 *E-mail:* asor@bu.edu; asorpubs@bu.edu *Web Site:* www.asor.org (print only subns); www.jstor.org (electronic only & print plus electronic subns), pg 1128

Michaud, Ann, Association for Library Service to Children (ALSC), 225 N Michigan Ave, Suite 1300, Chicago, IL 60601 *Tel:* 312-280-2163 *Toll Free Tel:* 800-545-2433 *Fax:* 312-280-5271 *E-mail:* alsc@ala.org *Web Site:* www.ala.org/alsc, pg 1139

Mickey, Bill, CHOICE, 575 Main St, Suite 300, Middletown, CT 06457 *Tel:* 860-347-6933; 860-347-1387 (ad); 240-646-7027 (subn); 818-487-4555 *E-mail:* acrlsubscriptions@pubservice.com; support@acrlchoice.freshdesk.com *Web Site:* www.ala.org/acrl/choice; www.choice360.org, pg 1125

Mickunas, Vick, Dayton Daily News, 4805 Meredith Rd, Yellow Springs, OH 45387 *Tel:* 937-767-1396, pg 1125

Migdale, Lawrence, Lawrence Migdale Photography/PIX, 23 White Hall Dr, Orinda, CA 94563 *Tel:* 510-612-2572 *E-mail:* photopix@migdale.com *Web Site:* www.migdale.com, pg 1448

Mihaley, Jackie, Ulster Linen Co Inc, 383 Moffit Blvd, Islip, NY 11751 *Tel:* 631-859-5244 *Fax:* 631-859-4990 *E-mail:* sales@ulsterlinen.com *Web Site:* www.ulsterlinen.com, pg 1269

Mikos, Peter, North 49 Books, 35 Prince Andrew Place, Toronto, ON M3C 2H2, Canada *Tel:* 416-449-4000 *Toll Free Tel:* 800-490-4049 *Fax:* 416-449-9924 *Toll Free Fax:* 888-349-2221 *E-mail:* sales@north49books.com *Web Site:* www.north49books.com, pg 1318

Milano, Chrissi, Dunhill International List Co Inc, 6400 Congress Ave, Suite 1750, Boca Raton, FL 33487-2898 *Tel:* 561-998-7800 *Toll Free Tel:* 800-DUNHILL (386-4455) *Fax:* 561-998-7880 *E-mail:* dunhill@dunhillintl.com *Web Site:* www.dunhills.com, pg 1112

Miller, Bruce, Miller Trade Book Marketing Inc, 1426 W Carmen Ave, Chicago, IL 60640 *Tel:* 773-307-3446, pg 1293

Miller, Ceci, CeciBooks Editorial & Publishing Consultation, 7057 26 Ave NW, Seattle, WA 98117 *E-mail:* ceci@cecibooks.com *Web Site:* www.cecibooks.com, pg 1343

Miller, Edward, Wild West Communications Group, PO Box 346, Homewood, CA 96141 *Tel:* 530-525-5201 *Fax:* 530-525-4559 *Web Site:* www.wildwest-tahoe.com, pg 1433

Miller, Jason Paul, Fairfield Marketing Group Inc, The Direct Mail Ctr, 830 Sport Hill Rd, Easton, CT 06112-1241 *Tel:* 203-261-5585 *Fax:* 203-261-0884 *E-mail:* info@fairfieldmarketing.com *Web Site:* www.fairfieldmarketing.com, pg 1092, 1097, 1106, 1109, 1112, 1220, 1247, 1276, 1345, 1377, 1428

Miller, Jeff, MBS Textbook Exchange Inc, 2711 W Ash, Columbia, MO 65203 *Tel:* 573-445-2243 *Toll Free Tel:* 800-325-0530 (textbook solutions); 800-325-4138 (bookstore systems) *Fax:* 573-446-5256 *E-mail:* cserv@mbsbooks.com *Web Site:* www.mbsbooks.com, pg 1317

Miller, Joelle Silverman, By Design Communications, 144 W 27 St, 3rd fl (rear), New York, NY 10001 *Tel:* 212-366-1740, pg 1425

Miller, John, Advantage Laser Products Inc, 1840 Marietta Blvd NW, Atlanta, GA 30318 *Tel:* 404-351-2700 *Toll Free Tel:* 800-722-2804 (cust serv) *Fax:* 404-351-0911 *Toll Free Fax:* 800-871-3305 *E-mail:* sales@advlaser.com *Web Site:* www.advlaser.com, pg 1371

Miller, Merlin, Markwith Tool Co Inc, 5261 State Rte 49 S, Greenville, OH 45331 *Tel:* 937-548-6808 *Fax:* 937-548-7051 *Web Site:* markwithtool.com, pg 1278

Miller, Rebecca, International Leads (IL), 225 N Michigan Ave, Suite 1300, Chicago, IL 60601 *Tel:* 312-944-6780 *Toll Free Tel:* 800-545-2433 *Fax:* 312-440-9374 *E-mail:* ala.intl.leads@gmail.com; ala@ala.org *Web Site:* www.ala.org/rt/irrt/intlleads/internationalleads; www.ala.org/rt/irrt; www.ala.org, pg 1127

Miller, Rebecca T, The Horn Book Guide, 300 The Fenway, Suite P-311, Palace Road Bldg, Boston, MA 02115 *Tel:* 617-278-0225 *Toll Free Tel:* 888-628-0225 *Fax:* 617-278-6062 *E-mail:* info@hbook.com *Web Site:* www.hbook.com, pg 1127

Miller, Rebecca T, Horn Book Inc, 300 The Fenway, Suite P-311, Palace Road Bldg, Boston, MA 02115 *Tel:* 617-278-0225 *Toll Free Tel:* 888-628-0225 *Fax:* 617-278-6062 *E-mail:* info@hbook.com *Web Site:* www.hbook.com, pg 1140

Miller, Rebecca T, The Horn Book Magazine, 300 The Fenway, Suite P-311, Palace Road Bldg, Boston, MA 02115 *Tel:* 617-278-0225 *Toll Free Tel:* 888-628-0225 *Fax:* 617-278-6062 *E-mail:* info@hbook.com *Web Site:* www.hbook.com, pg 1127

Miller, Rebecca T, Library Journal, 123 William St, Suite 802, New York, NY 10038 *Tel:* 646-380-0700 *Toll Free Tel:* 800-588-1030 *Fax:* 646-380-0756 *E-mail:* ljinfo@mediasourceinc.com *Web Site:* www.libraryjournal.com, pg 1128

Miller, Rebecca T, School Library Journal, 123 William St, Suite 802, New York, NY 10038 *Tel:* 646-380-0752 *Toll Free Tel:* 800-595-1066 *Fax:* 646-380-0756 *E-mail:* slj@mediasourceinc.com; sljsubs@pcspublink.com *Web Site:* www.slj.com; www.facebook.com/schoollibraryjournal; twitter.com/sljournal, pg 1131

Miller, Samuel, The Morristown News, PO Box 6123, West Caldwell, NJ 07007-6123 *Tel:* 973-227-4433, pg 1185

Miller, Stacey J, S J Miller Communications, PO Box 834, Randolph, MA 02368-0834 *Tel:* 781-986-0732 *E-mail:* bookpromotion@gmail.com *Web Site:* bookpr.com, pg 1099

Miller, Sue, Avery Dennison Corp, 207 N Goode Ave, 6th fl, Glendale, CA 91203-1222 *Tel:* 626-304-2000 *Web Site:* www.averydennison.com, pg 1373

Miller, Susan Riva, Susan Riva Miller-Alpine Photography, 20415 150 Ave SE, Monroe, WA 98272 *Tel:* 206-679-0475 *E-mail:* susanrivamiller@hotmail.com, pg 1441

Miller, Zack, Motorbooks, 100 Cummings Ctr, Suite 265D, Beverly, MA 01915 *Tel:* 978-282-9590 *Toll Free Tel:* 800-759-0190 (orders) *Web Site:* www.quartoknows.com/motorbooks, pg 1317, 1327

Milliot, Jim, Publishers Weekly, 71 W 23 St, Suite 1608, New York, NY 10010 *Tel:* 212-377-5500 *Fax:* 212-377-2733 *Web Site:* www.publishersweekly.com, pg 1130

Milton, Steve, ISOMEDIA Inc, 12842 Interurban Ave S, Seattle, WA 98168 *Tel:* 425-869-5411 *Toll Free Tel:* 866-838-4389 (sales); 877-638-9277 (support) *Fax:* 425-869-9437 *E-mail:* sales@isomedia.com *Web Site:* www.isomedia.com, pg 1380

Minden, Larry, Minden Pictures Inc, 9565 Soquel Dr, Suite 202, Aptos, CA 95003 *Tel:* 831-661-5551 *Fax:* 831-661-5497 *E-mail:* info@mindenpictures.com *Web Site:* www.mindenpictures.com, pg 1448

Mindlin, Ivy, The Ivy League of Artists Inc, 18 Edgemere Rd, Livingston, NJ 07039 *Tel:* 973-992-4048 *Fax:* 973-992-4049 *E-mail:* ilartists2@gmail.com, pg 1429

Minguez, Patrice, Resolute Forest Products, 111 Robert-Bourassa Blvd, Suite 5000, Montreal, QC H3C 2M1, Canada *Tel:* 514-875-2160 *Toll Free Tel:* 800-361-2888 *E-mail:* info@resolutefp.com *Web Site:* www.resolutefp.com, pg 1267

Minissali, Richard, f-stop Fitzgerald Inc, 88 James St, Rosendale, NY 12472 *E-mail:* fstopf@gmail.com, pg 1357, 1437

Minor, Florence, Wendell Minor, 15 Old North Rd, Washington, CT 06793 *Tel:* 860-868-9101 *E-mail:* wendell@minorart.com *Web Site:* www.minorart.com, pg 1431

Mishler, Clark James, Clark James Mishler Photography, 1815 School St, Calistoga, CA 94515 *Tel:* 907-351-7863 *Web Site:* www.mishlerphotos.com, pg 1441

Mishra, Ashok Kumar, Innodata Inc, 55 Challenger Rd, Suite 202, Ridgefield Park, NJ 07660 *Tel:* 201-371-8000 *Toll Free Tel:* 877-454-8400 *E-mail:* info@innodata.com; marketing@innodata.com *Web Site:* innodata.com, pg 1221, 1347, 1379

Misiewicz, Megan, The Philip Lief Group (PLG) Inc, 2976 Pleasant Ridge Rd, Wingdale, NY 12594 *Tel:* 609-430-1000 *Fax:* 845-724-7139 *E-mail:* info@plg.us.com *Web Site:* plg.us.com, pg 1359

Mitchell, Jack, Lumina Datamatics Inc, 4 Collins Ave, Plymouth, MA 02360 *Tel:* 508-746-0300 *Fax:* 508-746-3233 *Web Site:* luminadatamatics.com, pg 1207, 1222, 1349, 1359, 1380, 1430

Mitford, Kathleen, PTC, 121 Seaport Blvd, Boston, MA 02210 *Tel:* 781-370-5000 *Fax:* 781-370-6000 *Web Site:* www.ptc.com, pg 1384

Mittelsdorf, Carol, Fred Weidner & Daughter Printers, 99 Hudson St, 5th fl, New York, NY 10013 *Tel:* 646-706-5180 *E-mail:* info@fwdprinters.com *Web Site:* www.fwdprinters.com, pg 1227, 1257, 1269, 1280, 1353

Mitten, Lisa, CHOICE, 575 Main St, Suite 300, Middletown, CT 06457 *Tel:* 860-347-6933; 860-347-1387 (ad); 240-646-7027 (subn); 818-487-4555 *E-mail:* acrlsubscriptions@pubservice.com; support@acrlchoice.freshdesk.com *Web Site:* www.ala.org/acrl/choice; www.choice360.org, pg 1125

Mittendorf, Christoph, Berryville Graphics, 25 Jack Enders Blvd, Berryville, VA 22611 *Tel:* 540-955-2750 *Fax:* 540-955-2633 *E-mail:* info@bvgraphics.com *Web Site:* www.bpg-usa.com, pg 1202, 1216, 1242

Mittendorf, Christoph, Coral Graphic Services Inc, 840 S Broadway, Hicksville, NY 11801 *Tel:* 516-576-2100 *Fax:* 516-576-2168 *E-mail:* info@coralgraphics.com *Web Site:* www.bpg-usa.com, pg 1218, 1245, 1262

Mittendorf, Christoph, Dynamic Graphic Finishing, 945 Horsham Rd, Horsham, PA 19044 *Tel:* 215-441-8880 *E-mail:* info@dgfinc.com *Web Site:* www.bpg-usa.com, pg 1247

Mittendorf, Christoph, Offset Paperback Manufacturers Inc, 2211 Memorial Hwy, Dallas, PA 18612 *Tel:* 570-675-5261 *Fax:* 570-675-8714 *Web Site:* www.bpg-usa.com, pg 1208, 1223, 1252

Mo, David, Envision Peripherals Inc (EPI), 490 N McCarthy Blvd, Suite 120, Milpitas, CA 95035 *Web Site:* us.aoc.com, pg 1377

Mockler, Bill, Consortium Book Sales & Distribution, an Ingram brand, The Keg House, Suite 101, 34 13 Ave NE, Minneapolis, MN 55413-1007 *Tel:* 612-746-2600 *Toll Free Tel:* 800-283-3572 (cust serv, Jackson, TN) *Fax:* 612-746-2606 *E-mail:* info@cbsd.com *Web Site:* www.cbsd.com, pg 1285

Molho, Emanuel, French & European Publications Inc, 425 E 58 St, Suite 27-D, New York, NY 10022 *Tel:* 212-581-8810 *Fax:* 212-202-4356 *E-mail:* livresny@gmail.com; frenchbookstore@aol.com *Web Site:* www.frencheuropean.com, pg 1326

Monahan, Michael, The Library Services Centre, 131 Shoemaker St, Kitchener, ON N2E 3B5, Canada *Tel:* 519-746-4420 *Toll Free Tel:* 800-265-3360 (CN only) *Fax:* 519-746-4425 *Web Site:* www.lsc.on.ca, pg 1317

Monie, Alain, Ingram Micro Inc, 3351 Michelson Dr, Suite 100, Irvin, CA 92612 *Tel:* 714-566-1000 *E-mail:* customerexperience@ingrammicro.com *Web Site:* www.ingrammicro.com, pg 1315

Monteiro, Barbara, Monteiro & Co Inc, 301 E 57 St, 4th fl, New York, NY 10022 *Tel:* 212-832-8183 *Web Site:* www.monteiroandco.com, pg 1099

Monteleone, John J, Mountain Lion Inc, 9 Voorhees Ct, Pennington, NJ 08534 *Tel:* 609-730-1665 *E-mail:* mtlion@me.com *Web Site:* www.mtlioninc.net, pg 1360

Moonan, Thomas J, The Hibbert Group, 400 Pennington Ave, Trenton, NJ 08650 *Tel:* 609-394-7500 *Toll Free Tel:* 888-HIBBERT (442-2378) *E-mail:* info@hibbertgroup.com *Web Site:* hibbert.com, pg 1092, 1106, 1109

Moonan, Timothy J, The Hibbert Group, 400 Pennington Ave, Trenton, NJ 08650 *Tel:* 609-394-7500 *Toll Free Tel:* 888-HIBBERT (442-2378) *E-mail:* info@hibbertgroup.com *Web Site:* hibbert.com, pg 1092, 1106, 1109

Moore, Erica, Follett School Solutions Inc, 1340 Ridgeview Dr, McHenry, IL 60050 *Tel:* 815-759-1700 *Toll Free Tel:* 888-511-5114 (cust serv); 877-899-8550 (sales) *Fax:* 815-759-9831 *Toll Free Fax:* 800-852-5458 *E-mail:* info@follettlearning.com; customerservice@follett.com *Web Site:* www.follettlearning.com; www.follett.com/prek12; www.titlewave.com, pg 1287, 1377

Moore, Marc, McNaughton & Gunn Inc, Plant: 960 Woodland Dr, Saline, MI 48176 *Tel:* 734-429-5411 *Toll Free Fax:* 800-677-BOOK (677-2665) *Web Site:* www.bookprinters.com, pg 1207, 1251

Moore, Michael, Augsburg Fortress Publishers, Publishing House of the Evangelical Lutheran Church in America, 510 Marquette Ave S, Minneapolis, MN 55402 *Tel:* 612-330-3300 *Toll Free Tel:* 800-426-0115 (ext 639, subns); 800-328-4648 (orders) *Fax:* 612-330-3455 *Toll Free Fax:* 800-722-7766 (orders) *E-mail:* customercare@augsburgfortress.org; copyright@augsburgfortress.org (reprint permission requests); info@augsburgfortress.org *Web Site:* www.augsburgfortress.org; www.1517.media, pg 1309

Morales, Jessica, Two Rivers Distribution, an Ingram brand, 1400 Broadway, Suite 520, New York, NY 10018 *Toll Free Tel:* 866-400-5351 *E-mail:* ips@ingramcontent.com (orders, independent bookstores & gift accts) *Web Site:* www.tworiversdistribution.com, pg 1300

Moran, Kevin, Parson Weems' Publisher Services LLC, 3811 Canterbury Rd, No 707, Baltimore, MD 21218 *Tel:* 914-948-4259 *Toll Free Fax:* 866-861-0337 *E-mail:* office@parsonweems.com *Web Site:* www.parsonweems.com, pg 1294

Moran, Michael, Gem Guides Book Co, 1155 W Ninth St, Upland, CA 91786 *Tel:* 626-855-1611 *Toll Free Tel:* 800-824-5118 (orders) *Fax:* 626-855-1610 *E-mail:* info@gemguidesbooks.com; sales@gemguidesbooks.com (orders) *Web Site:* www.gemguidesbooks.com, pg 1314

Moran, Michael, Spraymation Inc, 4180 NW Tenth Ave, Fort Lauderdale, FL 33309 *Tel:* 954-484-9700 *Toll Free Tel:* 800-327-4985 *Fax:* 954-301-0842 *E-mail:* orders@spraymation.com *Web Site:* www.spraymation.com, pg 1279

Morcom, David, Hignell Book Printing Ltd, 488 Burnell St, Winnipeg, MB R3G 2B4, Canada *Tel:* 204-784-1030 *Toll Free Tel:* 800-304-5553 *Fax:* 204-774-4053 *E-mail:* books@hignell.mb.ca *Web Site:* www.hignell.mb.ca, pg 1206, 1249

Morehead, Tod, Indigo Books & Music Inc, 468 King St W, Suite 500, Toronto, ON M5V 1L8, Canada *Tel:* 416-364-4499 *E-mail:* cisales@indigo.ca *Web Site:* www.chapters.indigo.ca, pg 1290

Morgan, Emmanuelle, Stonesong, 270 W 39 St, Suite 201, New York, NY 10018 *Tel:* 212-929-4600 *E-mail:* editors@stonesong.com *Web Site:* www.stonesong.com, pg 1362

Morgan, Tim, Genesis Marketing Group Inc, 850 Wade Hampton Blvd, Bldg A, Suite 100, Greenville, SC 29609 *Tel:* 864-233-2651 *Toll Free Tel:* 800-627-2651 *Toll Free Fax:* 800-849-4363 *E-mail:* orders@genesislink.com *Web Site:* www.genesislink.com, pg 1287

Morgan, Tim, La Crosse Graphics Inc, 3025 East Ave S, La Crosse, WI 54601 *Tel:* 608-788-2500 *Toll Free Tel:* 800-832-2503 *Fax:* 608-788-2660 *Web Site:* www.lacrossegraphics.com, pg 1250

Moriarty, Amy, WordCo Indexing Services Inc, 66 Franklin St, Norwich, CT 06360 *E-mail:* office@wordco.com *Web Site:* www.wordco.com, pg 1228

Morical, Wendy, Docunet Corp, 2435 Xenium Lane N, Plymouth, MN 55441 *Tel:* 763-475-9600 *Toll Free Tel:* 800-936-2863 *Fax:* 763-475-1516 *E-mail:* print@docunetworks.com *Web Site:* www.docunetworks.com, pg 1246

Morin, Michel, Les Editions Themis, Faculte de droit, Universite de Montreal, CP 6128, Succursale Centreville, Montreal, QC H3C 3J7, Canada *Tel:* 514-343-6627 *Fax:* 514-343-6779 *E-mail:* info@editionsthemis.com *Web Site:* ssl.editionsthemis.com, pg 1313

Morin, Shawn, Ingram Content Group LLC, One Ingram Blvd, La Vergne, TN 37086-1986 *Tel:* 615-793-5000 *Toll Free Tel:* 800-937-8000 (retailers); 800-937-5300 (ext 1, libs) *E-mail:* customerservice@ingramcontent.com *Web Site:* www.ingramcontent.com, pg 1290, 1315

Morong, Martha, Quadrata Inc, 15 Byron St, Wakefield, MA 01880 *Tel:* 781-245-1183 *Fax:* 781-246-9040, pg 1361

Morris, Jamie, Specialty Finishing Group, 1401 Kirk St, Elk Grove Village, IL 60007 *Tel:* 847-290-0110 *Fax:* 847-290-9404 *Web Site:* www.sfgrp.com, pg 1254

Morris, Melody, Sun Graphics LLC, 1818 Broadway, Parsons, KS 67357 *Toll Free Tel:* 800-835-0588 *Fax:* 620-421-2089 *E-mail:* info@sun-graphics.com *Web Site:* www.sun-graphics.com, pg 1209, 1226, 1255

Morris, Ryan, Morris Printing Group Inc, 3212 E Hwy 30, Kearney, NE 68847 *Tel:* 308-236-7888 *Toll Free Tel:* 800-650-7888 *Fax:* 308-237-0263 *Web Site:* www.morrisprintinggroup.com, pg 1251

Morris, Scott, Morris Printing Group Inc, 3212 E Hwy 30, Kearney, NE 68847 *Tel:* 308-236-7888 *Toll Free Tel:* 800-650-7888 *Fax:* 308-237-0263 *Web Site:* www.morrisprintinggroup.com, pg 1251

Morrison, Beth, Symmetry Creative Production, 1300 S Grove Ave, Suite 103, Barrington, IL 60010 *Tel:* 847-382-8750 *E-mail:* information@symmetrycp.com *Web Site:* www.symmetrycp.com, pg 1226

Morrison, Dan, Western Telematic Inc (WTI), 5 Sterling, Irvine, CA 92618 *Tel:* 949-586-9950 *Toll Free Tel:* 800-854-7226 *E-mail:* info@wti.com *Web Site:* www.wti.com, pg 1388

Morrissey, Caitlyn, Bank Street Book Store, 2780 Broadway, New York, NY 10025 *Tel:* 212-678-1654 *Fax:* 212-316-7026 *E-mail:* books@bankstreet.edu *Web Site:* www.bankstreetbooks.com, pg 1139

Morrissey, Patrick, Electronics for Imaging Inc (EFI), 6750 Dumbarton Circle, Fremont, CA 94555 *Tel:* 650-357-3500 *Toll Free Tel:* 800-568-1917; 800-875-7117 (sales) *Fax:* 650-357-3907 *E-mail:* info@efi.com *Web Site:* www.efi.com, pg 1377

Morrow, Dee, New England Book Service Inc, 7000 Vt Rte 17 W, Addison, VT 05491 *Tel:* 802-759-3000 *Toll Free Tel:* 800-356-5772 *Fax:* 802-759-3220 *E-mail:* nebs@together.net *Web Site:* www.nebooks.com, pg 1318

Morrow, Diane, The Barnabas Agency, PO Box 3113, Corsicana, TX 75151-3113 *Tel:* 903-654-1319 *E-mail:* info@barnabasagency.com *Web Site:* www.barnabasagency.com, pg 1095

Morrow, Fred, New England Book Service Inc, 7000 Vt Rte 17 W, Addison, VT 05491 *Tel:* 802-759-3000 *Toll Free Tel:* 800-356-5772 *Fax:* 802-759-3220 *E-mail:* nebs@together.net *Web Site:* www.nebooks.com, pg 1318

Mortee, Marvin, Art Related Technology Inc, 4 Brattle St, Rm 305, Cambridge, MA 02138 *Tel:* 617-661-1225 *Fax:* 617-491-0618 *E-mail:* artinc@artrelated.com *Web Site:* www.artrelated.com, pg 1216, 1373

Morten, Scott J, Interprint Web Printing, 12350 US 19 N, Clearwater, FL 33764 *Tel:* 727-531-8957 *Toll Free Tel:* 800-749-5152 *Fax:* 727-536-0647 *E-mail:* info@interprintwebprinting.com *Web Site:* www.interprintwebprinting.com, pg 1092

Mortimer, Bryce, Cedar Fort Inc, 2373 W 700 S, Springville, UT 84663 *Tel:* 801-489-4084 *Toll Free Tel:* 800-SKY-BOOK (759-2665) *Web Site:* cedarfort.com, pg 1325

Moss, Monique, Integrated PR Agency (IPR), Penthouse, 9025 Wilshire Blvd, Suite 500, Beverly Hills, CA 90211 *Tel:* 310-858-8230 *Web Site:* www.integrated-pr.com, pg 1098

Moster, Meg, Melman-Moster Associates Inc, 48 Post Ave, Hawthorne, NJ 07506 *Tel:* 862-452-6196 *Fax:* 973-304-4923 *E-mail:* books@melman-moster.com, pg 1292

Moster, Nancy, Melman-Moster Associates Inc, 48 Post Ave, Hawthorne, NJ 07506 *Tel:* 862-452-6196 *Fax:* 973-304-4923 *E-mail:* books@melman-moster.com, pg 1292

Muchnick, Laurie, Kirkus, 65 W 36 St, Suite 700, New York, NY 10018 *E-mail:* customercare@kirkus.com *Web Site:* www.kirkusreviews.com, pg 1128

Mueller, Felix, Heidelberg USA Inc, 1000 Gutenberg Dr, Kennesaw, GA 30144 *Tel:* 770-419-6500 *Toll Free Tel:* 800-437-7388 *E-mail:* info@heidelberg.com *Web Site:* www.heidelberg.com/us, pg 1276

Mugambi, Florence, International Leads (IL), 225 N Michigan Ave, Suite 1300, Chicago, IL 60601 *Tel:* 312-944-6780 *Toll Free Tel:* 800-545-2433 *Fax:* 312-440-9374 *E-mail:* ala.intl.leads@gmail.com; ala@ala.org *Web Site:* www.ala.org/rt/irrt/intlleads/internationalleads; www.ala.org/rt/irrt; www.ala.org, pg 1127

Mukalla, Doris, International Book Centre Inc, 2391 Auburn Rd, Shelby Township, MI 48317 *Tel:* 586-254-7230 *Fax:* 586-254-7230 *E-mail:* ibc@ibcbooks.com *Web Site:* www.ibcbooks.com, pg 1315

Mukherjee, Debabrata, Finch Paper LLC, One Glen St, Glens Falls, NY 12801 *Tel:* 800-833-9983 *Toll Free Tel:* 518-743-9656 *E-mail:* info@finchpaper.com *Web Site:* www.finchpaper.com, pg 1263

Muller, Soren, Direct Link™ Worldwide Inc, 700 Dowd Ave, Elizabeth, NJ 07201 *Tel:* 908-289-0703 *Toll Free Tel:* 800-223-7967 *Fax:* 908-289-0705 *E-mail:* infousa@directlink.com *Web Site:* www.directlink.com, pg 1331

Mulvaney, Jon, The Criterion Collection, 215 Park Ave S, 5th fl, New York, NY 10003 *Tel:* 212-756-8822 *E-mail:* suggestions@criterion.com *Web Site:* www.criterion.com, pg 1375

Mummert, Nicole, Sheridan MI, 613 E Industrial Dr, Chelsea, MI 48118 *Tel:* 734-475-9145 *Web Site:* www.sheridan.com, pg 1209, 1254, 1267

Mummert, Nicole, Sheridan NH, 69 Lyme Rd, Hanover, NH 03755 *Tel:* 603-643-2220 *Web Site:* www.sheridan.com, pg 1254

Mummert, Nicole, Sheridan PA, 450 Fame Ave, Hanover, PA 17331 *Tel:* 717-632-3535 *Toll Free Tel:* 800-352-2210 *Fax:* 717-633-8900 *Web Site:* www.sheridan.com, pg 1254

Munford, Robert, Pacific Publishing Co Inc, 636 Alaska St S, Seattle, WA 98108 *Tel:* 206-461-1300 *E-mail:* ppcprint@nwlink.com; ppccirc@nwlink.com; ppcbind@nwlink.com *Web Site:* pacificpublishingcompany.com, pg 1252

Murad, Richard, Courier Systems Inc, 180 Pulaski St, Bayonne, NJ 07002 *Tel:* 201-432-0550 *Toll Free Tel:* 800-252-0353 *Fax:* 201-432-9686 *E-mail:* sales@csweb.biz *Web Site:* www.csweb.biz, pg 1331

Murphy, Brian T, Burlington News Agency Inc, 382 Hercules Dr, Suite 2, Colchester, VT 05446 *Tel:* 802-655-7000 *Fax:* 802-655-7002 *E-mail:* burlnews@aol.com, pg 1311

Murphy, Cynthia, Independent Publishers Group (IPG), 814 N Franklin St, Chicago, IL 60610 *Tel:* 312-337-0747 *Toll Free Tel:* 800-888-4741 (orders) *Fax:* 312-337-5985 *E-mail:* frontdesk@ipgbook.com; orders@ipgbook.com *Web Site:* www.ipgbook.com, pg 1288, 1326

Murphy, Glenn E, Burlington News Agency Inc, 382 Hercules Dr, Suite 2, Colchester, VT 05446 *Tel:* 802-655-7000 *Fax:* 802-655-7002 *E-mail:* burlnews@aol.com, pg 1311

Murphy, John, Adobe Systems Inc, 345 Park Ave, San Jose, CA 95110-2704 *Tel:* 408-536-6000 *Fax:* 408-537-6000 *Web Site:* www.adobe.com, pg 1371

Murphy, Paul, Independent Publishers Group (IPG), 814 N Franklin St, Chicago, IL 60610 *Tel:* 312-337-0747 *Toll Free Tel:* 800-888-4741 (orders) *Fax:* 312-337-5985 *E-mail:* frontdesk@ipgbook.com; orders@ipgbook.com *Web Site:* www.ipgbook.com, pg 1288, 1326

Murphy, Tim, Printware LLC, 2935 Waters Rd, Suite 160, St Paul, MN 55121-1523 *Tel:* 651-456-1400 *Fax:* 651-454-3684 *E-mail:* sales@printwarellc.com *Web Site:* www.printwarellc.com, pg 1384

Murphy, Trace, Paulist Press, 997 Macarthur Blvd, Mahwah, NJ 07430-9990 *Tel:* 201-825-7300 *Toll Free Tel:* 800-218-1903 *Fax:* 201-825-6921 *Toll Free Fax:* 800-836-3161 *E-mail:* info@paulistpress.com *Web Site:* www.paulistpress.com, pg 1319

Murphy, Trace, Paulist Press, 997 Macarthur Blvd, Mahwah, NJ 07430-9990 *Tel:* 201-825-7300 *Toll Free Tel:* 800-218-1903 *Fax:* 201-825-6921 *Toll Free Fax:* 800-836-3161 *E-mail:* info@paulistpress. com; publicity@paulistpress.com *Web Site:* www. paulistpress.com, pg 1383

Murray, J M "Mike", Brackett Inc, 7115 SE Forbes Ave, Topeka, KS 66619 *Tel:* 785-862-2205 *Toll Free Tel:* 800-255-3506 *Fax:* 785-862-1127 *E-mail:* brackett@brackett-inc.com; sales@brackett-inc.com *Web Site:* brackett-inc.com, pg 1274

Murray, Sharon, Login Canada, 300 Saulteaux Crescent, Winnipeg, MB R3J 3T2, Canada *Tel:* 204-837-2987 *Toll Free Tel:* 800-665-1148 (CN only) *Fax:* 204-837-3116 *Toll Free Fax:* 800-665-0103 *E-mail:* sales@lb.ca *Web Site:* www.lb.ca, pg 1317

Musanti, Joe, Universal/Wilde, 26 Dartmouth St, Westwood, MA 02090 *Tel:* 781-251-2700 *Fax:* 781-251-2613 *Web Site:* www.universalwilde.com, pg 1093, 1107, 1227, 1256

Musk, Howard, Imago, 110 W 40 St, New York, NY 10018 *Tel:* 212-921-4411 *Fax:* 212-921-8226 *E-mail:* sales@imagousa.com *Web Site:* www. imagousa.com, pg 1206, 1221, 1249, 1264, 1277, 1347, 1379

Musto, Diane, BCH Fulfillment & Distribution, 33 Oakland Ave, Harrison, NY 10528 *Tel:* 914-835-0015 *Toll Free Tel:* 800-431-1579 *Fax:* 914-835-0398 *E-mail:* bookch@aol.com *Web Site:* www.bookch.com, pg 1283, 1310

Muzzarelli, Linda, Women's Publications, 13326 SW 28 St, Suite 102, Fort Lauderdale, FL 33330-1102 *Tel:* 954-370-9153 *Fax:* 954-472-1008 (orders only) *E-mail:* info@consumerpress.com *Web Site:* www. consumerpress.com, pg 1113

Myers, Cindy, Small Press Distribution Inc, 1341 Seventh St, Berkeley, CA 94710-1409 *Tel:* 510-524-1668 *Toll Free Tel:* 800-869-7553 (within the US) *Fax:* 510-524-0852 *E-mail:* spd@spdbooks.org *Web Site:* www.spdbooks.org, pg 1298

Myers, Evan, AccuWeather Inc, 385 Science Park Rd, State College, PA 16803 *Tel:* 814-235-8600; 814-237-0309 *E-mail:* salesmail@accuweather.com; support@accuweather.com *Web Site:* www.accuweather.com; corporate.accuweather.com, pg 1371

Myers, Jason, DSCS LLC, 5000 College Ave, Suite 4100, College Park, MD 20742 *Tel:* 301-405-2883 *Fax:* 301-314-2799 *E-mail:* info@dscs.com *Web Site:* www.dscs.com, pg 1219, 1376

Myers, Dr Joel N, AccuWeather Inc, 385 Science Park Rd, State College, PA 16803 *Tel:* 814-235-8600; 814-237-0309 *E-mail:* salesmail@accuweather. com; support@accuweather.com *Web Site:* www. accuweather.com; corporate.accuweather.com, pg 1371

Myhren, Tor, Apple Inc, One Apple Park Way, Cupertino, CA 95014 *Tel:* 408-996-1010 *Web Site:* www.apple.com, pg 1372

Naasz, Christophe, Star Micronics America Inc, 65 Clyde Rd, Suite G, Somerset, NJ 08873-3485 *Tel:* 848-216-3300 (sales) *Toll Free Tel:* 800-782-7636 *Fax:* 848-216-3222 (sales) *E-mail:* sales@starmicronics.com *Web Site:* www.starmicronics.com, pg 1386

Naegeli, Werner, Muller Martini Corp, 456 Wheeler Rd, Hauppauge, NY 11788 *Tel:* 631-582-4343 *Toll Free Tel:* 888-268-5537 *Fax:* 631-348-1961 *E-mail:* info@us.mullermartini.com *Web Site:* www.mullermartiniusa. com, pg 1278

Nagaoka, Yasuhiko, Fujitsu Computer Products of America Inc, 1250 E Arques Ave, Sunnyvale, CA 94085-4701 *Tel:* 408-746-6000 *Toll Free Tel:* 800-626-4686 *E-mail:* scanner-sales@us.fujitsu.com *Web Site:* www.fujitsu.com/us, pg 1378

Nahte, Ethan, Live'N'Loud, PO Box 86, Van Buren, AR 72957 *Tel:* 479-216-6727 *Web Site:* nahteboy.tripod. com, pg 1380

Nakamura, Norikatsu, DNP America LLC, 335 Madison Ave, 3rd fl, New York, NY 10017 *Tel:* 212-503-1060 *E-mail:* gps@dnp-g.com *Web Site:* www.dnpamerica. com, pg 1204, 1219, 1246, 1262

Nanzetta, Phil, Signature Book Printing Inc, 8041 Cessna Ave, Gaithersburg, MD 20879 *Tel:* 301-258-8353 *Fax:* 301-670-4147 *E-mail:* book@sbpbooks.com *Web Site:* sbpbooks.com, pg 1209, 1226, 1254

Narasimhan, Lavanya, Penguin Random House Canada, 320 Front St W, Suite 1400, Toronto, ON M5V 3B6, Canada *Tel:* 416-364-4449 *Toll Free Tel:* 888-523-9292 (cust serv) *Fax:* 416-598-7764 *Web Site:* www. penguinrandomhouse.ca, pg 1295

Narayen, Shantanu, Adobe Systems Inc, 345 Park Ave, San Jose, CA 95110-2704 *Tel:* 408-536-6000 *Fax:* 408-537-6000 *Web Site:* www.adobe.com, pg 1371

Narowski, Eric, BCC Software Inc, 75 Josons Dr, Rochester, NY 14623-3494 *Toll Free Tel:* 800-453-3130; 800-337-0442 (sales) *E-mail:* marketing@bccsoftware.com *Web Site:* www.bccsoftware.com, pg 1373

Nash, Douglas, Spiral Binding LLC, One Maltese Dr, Totowa, NJ 07511 *Tel:* 973-256-0666 *Toll Free Tel:* 800-631-3572 *Fax:* 973-256-5981 *E-mail:* customerservice@spiralbinding.com; international@spiralbinding.com (outside US) *Web Site:* spiralbinding.com, pg 1255

Nash, Linda, Matthews Book Co, 11559 Rock Island Ct, Maryland Heights, MO 63043 *Tel:* 314-432-1400 *Toll Free Tel:* 800-633-2665 *Fax:* 314-432-7044 *Toll Free Fax:* 800-421-8816 *E-mail:* orders@mattmccoy.com *Web Site:* www.matthewsbooks.com, pg 1283

Nason, Charles, Worzalla, 3535 Jefferson St, Stevens Point, WI 54481 *Tel:* 715-344-9608 *Fax:* 715-344-2578 *Web Site:* www.worzalla.com, pg 1210, 1228, 1257

Nathan, Lauren, Melcher Media Inc, 124 W 13 St, New York, NY 10011 *Tel:* 212-727-2322 *Fax:* 212-627-1973 *E-mail:* info@melcher.com *Web Site:* www. melcher.com, pg 1360

Nathan, Terry, The Independent Book Publishers Association (IBPA), 1020 Manhattan Beach Blvd, Suite 204, Manhattan Beach, CA 90266 *Tel:* 310-546-1818 *E-mail:* info@ibpa-online.org *Web Site:* www. ibpa-online.org, pg 1106

Naughton, Kevin, Cookbook Publishers Inc, 11633 W 83 Terr, Lenexa, KS 66285 *Tel:* 913-492-5900 *Toll Free Tel:* 800-227-7282 *Fax:* 913-492-5947 *E-mail:* info@cookbookpublishers.com *Web Site:* www.cookbookpublishers.com, pg 1218, 1245

Navin, Jennifer, OEC Graphics Inc, 555 W Waukau Ave, Oshkosh, WI 54902 *Tel:* 920-235-7770 *Fax:* 920-235-2252 *Web Site:* www.oecgraphics.com, pg 1223

Nawotka, Ed, Publishers Weekly, 71 W 23 St, Suite 1608, New York, NY 10010 *Tel:* 212-377-5500 *Fax:* 212-377-2733 *Web Site:* www.publishersweekly. com, pg 1130

Nay, Meta L, Keister-Williams Newspaper Services Inc, PO Box 8187, Charlottesville, VA 22906 *Tel:* 434-293-4709 *Toll Free Tel:* 800-293-4709 *E-mail:* kw@kwnews.com *Web Site:* www.kwnews.com, pg 1185

Nazzaro, Mike, Claritas LLC, 8044 Montgomery Rd, Suite 455, Cincinnati, OH 45236 *Toll Free Tel:* 888-981-0040 *E-mail:* findcustomers@claritas.com; marketing@claritas.com *Web Site:* www.claritas.com, pg 1374

Neesemann, Cynthia, CS International Literary Agency, 43 W 39 St, New York, NY 10018 *Tel:* 212-921-1610; 212-391-9208 *E-mail:* query@csliterary.com; csliterary08@gmail.com *Web Site:* www.csliterary. com, pg 1344

Neiman, Tom, Stock Montage, 1817 N Mulligan Ave, Chicago, IL 60639 *Tel:* 773-637-9790 *Toll Free Tel:* 800-404-0425 *Fax:* 773-637-9794 *E-mail:* images@stockmontage.com *Web Site:* www. stockmontage.com, pg 1450

Nelson, Brant, Docunet Corp, 2435 Xenium Lane N, Plymouth, MN 55441 *Tel:* 763-475-9600 *Toll Free Tel:* 800-936-2863 *Fax:* 763-475-1516 *E-mail:* print@docunetworks.com *Web Site:* www.docunetworks.com, pg 1246

Nelson, Dianne J, Shadow Canyon Graphics, 902 S Cascade, La Veta, CO 81055 *Tel:* 720-498-4823 *Web Site:* www.shadowcanyongraphics.com, pg 1432

Nelson, Jason, Sheridan GR, 5100 33 St SE, Grand Rapids, MI 49512 *Tel:* 616-957-5100 *Web Site:* www. sheridan.com, pg 1209, 1254

Nelson, Judy, Mrs Nelson's Library Services, 1650 W Orange Grove Ave, Pomona, CA 91768 *Tel:* 909-397-7820 *Toll Free Tel:* 800-875-9911 *Fax:* 909-397-7833 *E-mail:* bookcompany@mrsnelsons.com *Web Site:* www.mrsnelsons.com, pg 1318

Nelson, Patrick, Mrs Nelson's Library Services, 1650 W Orange Grove Ave, Pomona, CA 91768 *Tel:* 909-397-7820 *Toll Free Tel:* 800-875-9911 *Fax:* 909-397-7833 *E-mail:* bookcompany@mrsnelsons.com *Web Site:* www.mrsnelsons.com, pg 1318

Nelson, Peter, Claris International Inc, 5201 Patrick Henry Dr, Santa Clara, CA 95054 *Tel:* 408-727-8227 (sales & cust support) *Toll Free Tel:* 800-725-2747 (sales); 800-325-2747 (cust support) *Fax:* 408-987-7447 *E-mail:* claris_sales@claris.com *Web Site:* www. claris.com, pg 1374

Nelson, Todd, Trend Offset Printing Services, 3791 Catalina St, Los Alamitos, CA 90720 *Tel:* 562-598-2446 *Fax:* 562-493-6840 (sales); 562-430-2373 *E-mail:* salesca@trendoffset.com *Web Site:* www. trendoffset.com, pg 1256

Nelson, Tony, LBS, 1801 Thompson Ave, Des Moines, IA 50316-2751 *Tel:* 515-262-3191 *Toll Free Tel:* 800-247-5323 *Toll Free Fax:* 800-262-4091 *E-mail:* info@lbsbind.com *Web Site:* www.lbsbind.com, pg 1265

Netburn, Malcolm, CDS Global, 1901 Bell Ave, Des Moines, IA 50315-1099 *Tel:* 515-247-7500 *Toll Free Tel:* 866-897-7987 *E-mail:* salesinfo@cds-global.com *Web Site:* www.cds-global.com, pg 1109, 1111

Neumann, Rachel, Idea Architects, 523 Swift St, Santa Cruz, CA 95060 *Tel:* 831-465-9565 *Web Site:* www. ideaarchitects.com, pg 1347

Never, Peter August, Academic Reviews, 1-A Glenwood Ave, Lynbrook, NY 11563 *Tel:* 516-593-1275 *E-mail:* info@academicreviews.com *Web Site:* www. academicreviews.com, pg 1123

Nevins, Iris, Iris Nevins Decorative Papers, PO Box 429, Johnsonburg, NJ 07846-0429 *Tel:* 908-813-8617 *E-mail:* irisnevins@verizon.net *Web Site:* www. marblingpaper.com, pg 1266

Newborn, Barry, Newborn Enterprises Inc (Altoona News Agency), 808 Green Ave, Altoona, PA 16601 *Tel:* 814-944-3593, pg 1318

Newcomb, Doug, Special Libraries Association (SLA), 7918 Jones Branch Dr, Suite 300, McLean, VA 22102 *Tel:* 703-647-4900 *Fax:* 703-506-3266 *E-mail:* sla@sla.org *Web Site:* www.sla.org, pg 1112

Newcombe, Jack, Creators Syndicate, 737 Third St, Hermosa Beach, CA 90254 *Tel:* 310-337-7003 *E-mail:* info@creators.com *Web Site:* www.creators. com, pg 1184

Newcombe, Rick, Creators Syndicate, 737 Third St, Hermosa Beach, CA 90254 *Tel:* 310-337-7003 *E-mail:* info@creators.com *Web Site:* www.creators. com, pg 1184

Newman, Andrew, Andrew Newman Design, 54 Winding Cove Rd, Marstons Mills, MA 02648-1825 *Tel:* 508-420-1161 *E-mail:* newmandesign@gmail.com *Web Site:* www.andrewnewmandesign.com, pg 1431

Newman, Bill, TEACH Services Inc, 11 Quartermaster Circle, Fort Oglethorpe, GA 30742-3886 *Tel:* 706-504-9192 *Toll Free Tel:* 800-367-1844 (sales) *Toll Free Fax:* 866-757-6023 *E-mail:* sales@teachservices.com; info@teachservices.com *Web Site:* www.teachservices. com, pg 1321, 1386

Newman, Helen, Custom Studios, 77 Main St, Tappan, NY 10983 *Tel:* 845-365-0414 *Toll Free Tel:* 800-631-1362 *Fax:* 845-365-0864 *E-mail:* customusa@aol.com *Web Site:* customstudios.com, pg 1218

O'Connor, Thomas D Jr, Mohawk Fine Papers Inc, 465 Saratoga St, Cohoes, NY 12047 *Tel:* 518-237-1740 *Toll Free Tel:* 800-THE-MILL (843-6455) *Fax:* 518-237-7394 *Web Site:* www.mohawkconnects.com, pg 1266

O'Donley, David, The Ovid Bell Press Inc, 1201 Bluff St, Fulton, MO 65251 *Tel:* 573-642-2256 *Toll Free Tel:* 800-835-8919 *E-mail:* sales@ovidbell.com *Web Site:* ovidbell.com, pg 1224, 1252, 1266, 1278

O'Donnell, Paul, Religion News Service, c/o University of Missouri's Journalism School, 30 Neff Annex, Columbia, MO 65211 *Tel:* 573-884-1327 *E-mail:* info@religionnews.com *Web Site:* www. religionnews.com, pg 1186

O'Grady, John, Eastman Kodak Co, 343 State St, Rochester, NY 14650 *Tel:* 585-724-4000 *Toll Free Tel:* 866-563-2533 *Web Site:* www.kodak.com, pg 1275

O'Keefe, Steve, Orobora Inc, 644 Greenville Ave, Suite 234, Staunton, VA 24401 *Tel:* 540-324-7023 *E-mail:* info@orobora.com *Web Site:* orobora.com, pg 1350

O'Leyne, Eithne, ProtoView, 7515 NE Ambassador Place, Suite A, Portland, OR 97220 *Tel:* 503-281-9230 *E-mail:* info@protoview.com *Web Site:* www. protoview.com, pg 1130, 1140

O'Meara, Kelvin, Western Printing Machinery Co (WPM), 9228 Ivanhoe St, Schiller Park, IL 60176 *Tel:* 847-678-1740 *Fax:* 847-678-6176 *E-mail:* info@wpm.com *Web Site:* www.wpm.com, pg 1280

O'Reilly, Tim, O'Reilly Media Inc, 1005 Gravenstein Hwy N, Sebastopol, CA 95472 *Tel:* 707-827-7019 (cust support); 707-827-7000 *Toll Free Tel:* 800-889-8969; 800-998-9938 *Fax:* 707-829-0104; 707-824-8268 *E-mail:* orders@oreilly.com; support@oreilly. com *Web Site:* www.oreilly.com, pg 1383

O'Toole, Jim, Midland Paper, Packaging & Supplies, 101 E Palatine Rd, Wheeling, IL 60090 *Tel:* 847-777-2700 *Toll Free Tel:* 800-323-8522; 888-564-3526 (cust serv) *Fax:* 847-403-6320 (cust serv) *E-mail:* whl@midlandpaper.com; sales@midlandpaper. com; custservice@midlandpaper.com *Web Site:* www. midlandpaper.com, pg 1265

Obernier, Robert B, Horizon Paper Co Inc, 1010 Washington Blvd, Stamford, CT 06901 *Tel:* 203-358-0855 *Toll Free Tel:* 866-358-0855 *E-mail:* info@horizonpaper.com *Web Site:* www.horizonpaper.com, pg 1264

Ocher, Medaya, LARB Quarterly Journal, 6671 Sunset Blvd, Suite 1521, Los Angeles, CA 90028 *Tel:* 323-952-3950 *E-mail:* info@lareviewofbooks.org; editorial@lareviewofbooks.org *Web Site:* lareviewofbooks.org, pg 1128

Ochs, Brenda, Total Printing Systems, 201 S Gregory Dr, Newton, IL 62448 *Tel:* 618-783-2978 *Toll Free Tel:* 800-465-5200 *Fax:* 618-783-8407 *E-mail:* sales@tps1.com *Web Site:* www.tps1.com, pg 1255

Ofri, Dr Danielle, Bellevue Literary Review, NYU School of Medicine, Dept of Medicine, 550 First Ave, OBV-A612, New York, NY 10016 *Tel:* 212-263-3973 *E-mail:* info@BLReview.org *Web Site:* www. BLReview.org, pg 1124

Ogawa, Kazuto, Canon USA Inc, One Canon Park, Milville, NY 11747 *Tel:* 516-328-5000; 631-330-5000 *Web Site:* www.usa.canon.com, pg 1374

Ogden, Max, CONTECH (Converting Technologies), 1756 S 151 St W, Goddard, KS 67052 *Tel:* 316-722-6907 *Fax:* 316-722-2976 *E-mail:* info@contechusa. com *Web Site:* www.contechusa.com, pg 1275

Oglesby, John, Data Index Inc, 13713 NW Indian Springs Dr, Vancouver, WA 98685 *Tel:* 425-760-9193 *Web Site:* www.dataindex.com, pg 1218

Ogushwitz, Mary Blanton, Susan Magrino Agency, 352 Park Ave S, 6th fl, New York, NY 10010 *Tel:* 212-957-3005 *Fax:* 212-957-4071 *E-mail:* info@smapr.com *Web Site:* www.smapr.com, pg 1099

Ohnaka, Yuko, Ohnaka & Associates Inc, 6040 Kennedy Blvd E, Suite 23-B, West New York, NJ 07093 *Tel:* 201-255-5796 *Fax:* 201-255-2890 *E-mail:* info@ohnaka.com *Web Site:* www.ohnaka.com, pg 1412

Okhai, Adam, Learning World Inc, 287 Wycliffe Ave, Vaughan, ON L4L 3N7, Canada, pg 1316

Olin, Marc, Electronics for Imaging Inc (EFI), 6750 Dumbarton Circle, Fremont, CA 94555 *Tel:* 650-357-3500 *Toll Free Tel:* 800-568-1917; 800-875-7117 (sales) *Fax:* 650-357-3907 *E-mail:* info@efi.com *Web Site:* www.efi.com, pg 1376

Olinsky, David, Disc Makers, 7905 N Crescent Blvd, Pennsauken, NJ 08110-1402 *Tel:* 856-663-9030 *Toll Free Tel:* 800-468-9353 *Fax:* 856-661-3450 *E-mail:* info@discmakers.com *Web Site:* www. discmakers.com, pg 1376

Oliver, Kirk, The Library Services Centre, 131 Shoemaker St, Kitchener, ON N2E 3B5, Canada *Tel:* 519-746-4420 *Toll Free Tel:* 800-265-3360 (CN only) *Fax:* 519-746-4425 *Web Site:* www.lsc.on.ca, pg 1317

Oliver, Matthew J, Dupli Envelope & Graphics Corp, 6761 Thompson Rd N, Syracuse, NY 13211 *Tel:* 315-472-1316 *Toll Free Tel:* 800-724-2477 *E-mail:* sales@duplionline.com; orders@duplionline. com *Web Site:* www.duplionline.com, pg 1246

Olko, Steve, Data Reproductions Corp, 4545 Glenmeade Lane, Auburn Hills, MI 48326 *Tel:* 248-371-3700 *Toll Free Tel:* 800-242-3114 *Fax:* 248-371-3710 *Web Site:* datarepro.com, pg 1204, 1245

Ollila, Phil, Ingram Content Group LLC, One Ingram Blvd, La Vergne, TN 37086-1986 *Tel:* 615-793-5000 *Toll Free Tel:* 800-937-8000 (retailers); 800-937-5300 (ext 1, libs) *E-mail:* customerservice@ingramcontent. com *Web Site:* www.ingramcontent.com, pg 1290, 1315

Ollila, Phil, Lightning Source LLC, 1246 Heil Quaker Blvd, La Vergne, TN 37086 *Tel:* 615-793-5000 (Ingram) *Toll Free Tel:* 800-378-5508; 800-509-4156 (cust serv) *E-mail:* lsicustomersupport@ingramcontent. com; contentacquisitioninquiries@ingramcontent.com *Web Site:* www.ingramcontent.com/publishers/print, pg 1207

Ollila, Phil, Lightning Source LLC, 1246 Heil Quaker Blvd, La Vergne, TN 37086 *Tel:* 615-793-5000 (Ingram) *Toll Free Tel:* 800-378-5508; 800-509-4156 (cust serv) *E-mail:* lsicustomersupport@ingramcontent. com *Web Site:* www.ingramcontent.com/publishers/ print, pg 1250, 1380

Ollis, Kenneth R, Ollis Book Co, 28 E 35 St, Steger, IL 60475 *Tel:* 708-755-5151 *Toll Free Tel:* 800-323-0343 (natl) *Fax:* 708-755-5153, pg 1318

Olshan, Alex, RISO Inc, 10 State St, Suite 201, Woburn, MA 01801-2105 *Tel:* 978-777-7377 *Toll Free Tel:* 800-942-7476 (cust support) *Web Site:* us.riso. com, pg 1253, 1385

Olson, Arleen, Arleen Olson Photography, PO Box 550, Redway, CA 95560-0550 *Tel:* 707-923-1974 *Web Site:* arleenolsonphotography.com, pg 1441

Olson, Georgine, The Historical Novels Review, 400 Dark Star Ct, Fairbanks, AK 99709 *Tel:* 217-581-7538 *Fax:* 217-581-7534 *E-mail:* reviews@historicalnovelsociety.org *Web Site:* historicalnovelsociety.org, pg 1126

Olson, John, Olson Photographic LLC, 232 Hunter's Trail, Madison, CT 06443 *Tel:* 203-245-3752 *Fax:* 203-245-3752 *E-mail:* info@olsonphotographic. com *Web Site:* www.olsonphotographic.com, pg 1441

Olson, Peter, TNG, 3320 S Service Rd, Burlington, ON L7N 3M6, Canada *Toll Free Tel:* 800-201-8127 *Toll Free Fax:* 877-664-9732 *E-mail:* cs@tng.com *Web Site:* www.tng.com, pg 1321

Olzenak, Doug, Allied Vaughn, 7600 Parklawn Ave, Suite 300, Minneapolis, MN 55435 *Tel:* 952-832-3100 *Toll Free Tel:* 800-323-0281 *Fax:* 952-832-3203 *Web Site:* www.alliedvaughn.com, pg 1372

Omerefendic, Inda, Bulletin of the American Schools of Oriental Research (BASOR), Boston University, 656 Beacon St, 5th fl, Boston, MA 02215 *Tel:* 617-

353-6570 *Fax:* 617-353-6575 *E-mail:* asor@bu.edu; asorpubs@bu.edu *Web Site:* www.asor.org (print only subns); www.jstor.org (electronic only & print plus electronic subns), pg 1125

Omerefendic, Inda, Journal of Cuneiform Studies (JCS), Boston University, 656 Beacon St, 5th fl, Boston, MA 02215 *Tel:* 617-353-6570 *Fax:* 617-353-6575 *E-mail:* asor@bu.edu; asorpubs@bu.edu *Web Site:* www.asor.org (print only subns); www.jstor. org (electronic only & print plus electronic subns), pg 1128

Omerefendic, Inda, Near Eastern Archaeology, Boston University, 656 Beacon St, 5th fl, Boston, MA 02215 *Tel:* 617-353-6570 *Fax:* 617-353-6575 *E-mail:* asor@bu.edu; asorpubs@bu.edu *Web Site:* www.asor.org (print only subns); www.jstor.org (electronic only & print plus electronic subns), pg 1129

Onisk, Mark, SumTotal Systems LLC, 2850 NW 43 St, Suite 150, Gainesville, FL 32606 *Tel:* 352-264-2800 *Toll Free Tel:* 866-933-1416 *Fax:* 352-374-2257 *E-mail:* customersupport@sumtotalsystems.com *Web Site:* www.sumtotalsystems.com, pg 1386

Ono, Shigeharu, Kinokuniya Publications Service of New York (KPS-NY), 1073 Avenue of the Americas, New York, NY 10018-3701 *Tel:* 212-765-1465 *Fax:* 212-307-5593 *E-mail:* nyinfo@kinokuniya.com *Web Site:* www.kinokuniya.co.jp; www.kinokuniya. com, pg 1348

Oransky, Andrew, Roland DGA Corp, 15363 Barranca Pkwy, Irvine, CA 92618-2216 *Tel:* 949-727-2100 *Toll Free Tel:* 800-542-2307 *Fax:* 949-727-2112 *Web Site:* www.rolanddga.com, pg 1385

Orf, Steve, FCI Digital, 2032 S Alex Rd, Suite A, West Carrollton, OH 45449 *Tel:* 937-859-9701 *Web Site:* www.fcidigital.com, pg 1220

Oringer, Jon, Shutterstock Inc, Empire State Bldg, 350 Fifth Ave, 21st fl, New York, NY 10118 *Tel:* 646-419-4452 (sales) *Toll Free Tel:* 866-663-3954 *Fax:* 347-402-0710 *E-mail:* support@shutterstock.com; press@shutterstock.com *Web Site:* www.shutterstock.com, pg 1449

Orlowsky, Peter, Getty Images Inc, 605 Fifth Ave S, Suite 400, Seattle, WA 98104 *Tel:* 206-925-5000 *Toll Free Tel:* 800-IMAGERY (462-4379 sales); 888-888-5889 *E-mail:* enterprisesolutionssales@gettyimages. com *Web Site:* www.gettyimages.com, pg 1378, 1447

Ornstein, Robert PhD, Institute for the Study of Human Knowledge (ISHK), 1702-L Meridian Ave, No 266, San Jose, CA 95125-5586 *Tel:* 617-497-4124 *Toll Free Tel:* 800-222-4745 (orders) *Fax:* 617-500-0268 *Toll Free Fax:* 800-223-4200 (orders) *E-mail:* ishkadm@aol.com; ishkbooks@aol.com (orders) *Web Site:* www. ishk.com, pg 1291

Orr, James, Perma-Bound Books, 617 E Vandalia Rd, Jacksonville, IL 62650 *Tel:* 217-243-5451 *Toll Free Tel:* 800-637-6581 *Fax:* 217-243-7505 *Toll Free Fax:* 800-551-1169 *E-mail:* books@perma-bound.com *Web Site:* www.perma-bound.com, pg 1319, 1324

Ortega, Claribel, The Combined Book Exhibit®, 277 White St, Buchanan, NY 10511 *Tel:* 914-739-7500 *Toll Free Tel:* 800-462-7687 *Fax:* 914-739-7575 *E-mail:* info@combinedbook.com *Web Site:* www. combinedbook.com; www.cbedatabase.com, pg 1133

Ortolani, Terry, Pint Size Productions LLC, 5745 Main St, Amherst, NY 14221 *Tel:* 716-204-3353 *E-mail:* sales@pintsizeproductions.com *Web Site:* www.pintsizeproductions.com, pg 1252

Osborne, H Damon, Houchen Bindery Ltd, 340 First St, Utica, NE 68456 *Tel:* 402-534-2261 *Toll Free Tel:* 800-869-0420 *Fax:* 402-534-2761 *E-mail:* email@houchenbindery.com *Web Site:* www.houchenbindery. com, pg 1323

Oshinsky, David, Bellevue Literary Review, NYU School of Medicine, Dept of Medicine, 550 First Ave, OBV-A612, New York, NY 10016 *Tel:* 212-263-3973 *E-mail:* info@BLReview.org *Web Site:* www. BLReview.org, pg 1124

Osman, Dr A, Learning World Inc, 287 Wycliffe Ave, Vaughan, ON L4L 3N7, Canada, pg 1316

Parsons, Walter, BMR Associates, 60 Corte Amado, Greenbrae, CA 94904 *Tel:* 415-927-1564 *E-mail:* info@bmrassoc.com, pg 1343

Parzival, Robert, BMR Associates, 60 Corte Amado, Greenbrae, CA 94904 *Tel:* 415-927-1564 *E-mail:* info@bmrassoc.com *Web Site:* www.bmrassoc.com, pg 1343

Pasanen, Jennifer, Verso Advertising Inc, 50 W 17 St, 5th fl, New York, NY 10011 *Tel:* 212-292-2990 *Fax:* 212-557-2592 *Web Site:* www.versoadvertising.com, pg 1087

Pashko, Sue, Envision Stock Photography Inc, 27 Hoppin Rd, Newport, RI 02840 *Tel:* 401-619-1500 *Toll Free Tel:* 800-524-8238 *E-mail:* envision@att.net *Web Site:* www.envision-stock.com, pg 1446

Pasqua, Dominique, DJD/Golden Advertising, 145 W 28 St, 12th fl, New York, NY 10001 *Tel:* 212-366-5033 *Fax:* 212-243-5044 *E-mail:* call@djdgolden.com *Web Site:* www.djdgolden.com, pg 1086

Patil, Galina, Business Wire, 101 California St, 20th fl, San Francisco, CA 94111 *Tel:* 415-986-4422 *Toll Free Tel:* 800-227-0845 *E-mail:* info@businesswire.com *Web Site:* www.businesswire.com, pg 1183

Patten, Barbara L, International Book Import Service Inc, 161 Main St, Lynchburg, TN 37352-8300 *Tel:* 931-759-7400 *Toll Free Tel:* 800-277-4247 *Fax:* 931-759-7555 *Toll Free Fax:* 866-277-2722 *E-mail:* ibis@ibiservice.com *Web Site:* www.ibiservice.com, pg 1326

Patterson, Leroy, Patterson Printing Co, 1550 Territorial Rd, Benton Harbor, MI 49022 *Tel:* 269-925-2177 *Toll Free Tel:* 800-848-8826 *Fax:* 269-925-6057 *E-mail:* sales@patterson-printing.com *Web Site:* www.patterson-printing.com, pg 1208, 1252, 1266, 1278

Patterson, William, Demand Marketing, 377 Fisher Rd, Suite D, Grosse Pointe, MI 48230 *Tel:* 313-823-8598 *Toll Free Tel:* 888-977-2256 *Fax:* 313-823-8598 *E-mail:* info@create-demand.com *Web Site:* www.create-demand.com, pg 1106

Patti, Chris, AccuWeather Inc, 385 Science Park Rd, State College, PA 16803 *Tel:* 814-235-8600; 814-237-0309 *E-mail:* salesmail@accuweather.com; support@accuweather.com *Web Site:* www.accuweather.com; corporate.accuweather.com, pg 1371

Patton, Rob, Clamco Corp, 775 Berea Industrial Pkwy, Berea, OH 44017 *Tel:* 216-267-1911 *Toll Free Tel:* 800-985-9570 (headquarters) *Fax:* 216-267-8713 *E-mail:* info@clamcopackaging.com *Web Site:* www.pacmachinery.com/clamcopackaging, pg 1274

Paul, Howard Michael, Photography for Communication & Commerce, 3931 S Spruce St, Suite 200, Denver, CO 80237-2152 *Tel:* 303-829-5678 *Web Site:* www.howardpaulphotography.com, pg 1442

Paul, Pamela, The New York Times Book Review, 620 Eighth Ave, 5th fl, New York, NY 10018 *Tel:* 212-556-1234 *Toll Free Tel:* 800-631-2580 (subns) *E-mail:* bookreview@nytimes.com; books@nytimes.com *Web Site:* www.nytimes.com, pg 1129

Paul, Tammy, Chicago Distribution Center (CDC), 11030 S Langley Ave, Chicago, IL 60628 *Tel:* 773-702-7010 *Toll Free Tel:* 800-621-8476 *Web Site:* press.uchicago.edu/cdc, pg 1285

Paulsen, Eric, Dynabook Americas Inc, 5241 California Ave, Suite 100, Irvine, CA 92617 *Tel:* 949-583-3000 *Web Site:* us.dynabook.com, pg 1376

Paulson, Tim, Augsburg Fortress Publishers, Publishing House of the Evangelical Lutheran Church in America, 510 Marquette Ave S, Minneapolis, MN 55402 *Tel:* 612-330-3300 *Toll Free Tel:* 800-426-0115 (ext 639, subns); 800-328-4648 (orders) *Fax:* 612-330-3455 *Toll Free Fax:* 800-722-7766 (orders) *E-mail:* customercare@augsburgfortress.org; copyright@augsburgfortress.org (reprint permission requests); info@augsburgfortress.org *Web Site:* www.augsburgfortress.org; www.1517.media, pg 1309

Pauly, Louise, TotalWorks™ Inc, 420 W Huron St, Chicago, IL 60654 *Tel:* 773-489-4313 *E-mail:* production@totalworks.net *Web Site:* www.totalworks.net, pg 1227, 1255

Pautz, Michael, E C Schultz & Company Inc, 333 Crossen Ave, Elk Grove Village, IL 60007-2001 *Tel:* 847-640-1190 *E-mail:* jobfiles@ecschultz.com *Web Site:* www.ecschultz.com, pg 1279

Pavett, Jim, Allusion Studios & Pure Wave Audio, 248 W Elm St, Tucson, AZ 85705 *Tel:* 520-622-3895 *E-mail:* contact@allusionstudios.com *Web Site:* www.allusionstudios.com; www.purewaveaudio.com, pg 1372

Pavlin, Maryanne, Datalogics Inc, 101 N Wacker, Suite 1800, Chicago, IL 60606 *Tel:* 312-853-8200 *Fax:* 312-853-8282 *E-mail:* sales@datalogics.com; marketing@datalogics.com *Web Site:* www.datalogics.com, pg 1375

Paxson, Chris, LBS, 1801 Thompson Ave, Des Moines, IA 50316-2751 *Tel:* 515-262-3191 *Toll Free Tel:* 800-247-5323 *Toll Free Fax:* 800-262-4091 *E-mail:* info@lbsbind.com *Web Site:* www.lbsbind.com, pg 1265

Payne, Philip B, Linguist's Software Inc, 844 Alder St, Edmonds, WA 98020-3301 *Tel:* 425-775-1130 *E-mail:* sales@linguistsoftware.com *Web Site:* www.linguistsoftware.com, pg 1380

Peacock, Bradley R, FedEx Supply Chain, 6700 Cranberry Woods Dr, Cranberry Township, PA 16066 *Toll Free Tel:* 800-677-3110 *E-mail:* solution@fedex.com *Web Site:* supplychain.fedex.com, pg 1332

Pearce, Jerry, NAPCO Inc, 120 Trojan Ave, Sparta, NC 28675 *Tel:* 336-372-5228 *Toll Free Tel:* 800-854-8621 *Fax:* 336-372-8602 *E-mail:* info@napcousa.com *Web Site:* www.napcousa.com, pg 1251

Pearl, George S, Atlanta Panorama, c/o ALPS Labs, 2139 Liddell Dr NE, Atlanta, GA 30324-4132 *Tel:* 404-872-2577 *Toll Free Tel:* 800-873-2577 *Fax:* 404-872-0548 *E-mail:* alps007@mindspring.com *Web Site:* www.atlantapanorama.com, pg 1435

Peattie, Gary R, DeVorss & Co, 553 Constitution Ave, Camarillo, CA 93012-8510 *Tel:* 805-322-9010 *Toll Free Tel:* 800-843-5743 *Fax:* 805-322-9011 *E-mail:* service@devorss.com *Web Site:* www.devorss.com, pg 1139, 1313

Pecaric, John, RR Donnelley, 35 W Wacker Dr, Chicago, IL 60601 *Toll Free Tel:* 800-742-4455 *Web Site:* www.rrd.com, pg 1204, 1219, 1246, 1262, 1275

Pecaric, John, RR Donnelley & Sons Company, 35 W Wacker Dr, Chicago, IL 60601 *Tel:* 312-326-8000 *Toll Free Tel:* 800-742-4455 *Web Site:* www.rrd.com, pg 1332

Peccarelli, Brian, Thomson Reuters, 3 Times Sq, New York, NY 10036 *Tel:* 646-223-4000; 646-223-6100 (edit); 646-223-6000 (newsroom) *Web Site:* www.thomsonreuters.com, pg 1186

Peck, Tom, Ingram Micro Inc, 3351 Michelson Dr, Suite 100, Irvin, CA 92612 *Tel:* 714-566-1000 *E-mail:* customerexperience@ingrammicro.com *Web Site:* www.ingrammicro.com, pg 1315

Peel, Alan, L+L Printers, 6200 Yarrow Dr, Carlsbad, CA 92011 *Tel:* 760-438-3456; 760-477-0321 *Fax:* 760-929-0853 *E-mail:* info@llprinters.com *Web Site:* www.llprinters.com, pg 1250

Pegram, Norm, PremierIMS Inc, 11101 Ella Blvd, Houston, TX 77067 *Tel:* 832-608-6400 *Fax:* 832-608-6420 *E-mail:* info@premier-ims.com *Web Site:* www.premier-ims.com, pg 1110

Pelczar, Anne H, Conservative Book Club, 300 New Jersey Ave NW, Suite 500, Washington, DC 20001 *Tel:* 202-216-0601 *Fax:* 202-216-0614 *Web Site:* www.conservativebookclub.com, pg 1135

Pelikan, Karl, Horizon Paper Co Inc, 1010 Washington Blvd, Stamford, CT 06901 *Tel:* 203-358-0855 *Toll Free Tel:* 866-358-0855 *E-mail:* info@horizonpaper.com *Web Site:* www.horizonpaper.com, pg 1264

Pelland, Michael, American International Distribution Corp (AIDC), 82 Winter Sport Lane, Williston, VT 05495 *Tel:* 802-862-0095 *Toll Free Tel:* 800-678-2432 *Fax:* 802-864-7749 *Web Site:* www.aidcvt.com, pg 1105, 1109, 1215, 1282, 1309, 1331

Pellegrino, Mike, SumTotal Systems LLC, 2850 NW 43 St, Suite 150, Gainesville, FL 32606 *Tel:* 352-264-2800 *Toll Free Tel:* 866-933-1416 *Fax:* 352-374-2257 *E-mail:* customersupport@sumtotalsystems.com *Web Site:* www.sumtotalsystems.com, pg 1386

Pellerin, Nicolas, European Books & Media, 6600 Shattuck Ave, Oakland, CA 94609 *Tel:* 510-922-9157 *E-mail:* info@europeanbook.com *Web Site:* www.europeanbook.com, pg 1313, 1326

Pelto, Lisa K, Concierge Marketing Inc, 4822 S 133 St, Omaha, NE 68137 *Tel:* 402-884-5995 *Fax:* 413-669-8870 *Web Site:* www.conciergemarketing.com, pg 1343

Peluso, Michelle, IBM Corp, One New Orchard Rd, Armonk, NY 10504 *Tel:* 914-499-1900 *Toll Free Tel:* 800-426-4968 *E-mail:* askibm@vnet.ibm.com *Web Site:* www.ibm.com, pg 1379

Penberthy, Stephen, Woodcrafters Lumber Sales Inc, 212 NE Sixth Ave, Portland, OR 97232-2976 *Tel:* 503-231-0226 *Toll Free Tel:* 800-777-3709 *Fax:* 503-232-0511 *Web Site:* www.woodcrafters.us, pg 1322

Penichet, Jeff, Bilingual Educational Services Inc, 2514 S Grand Ave, Los Angeles, CA 90007 *Tel:* 213-749-6213 *Toll Free Tel:* 800-448-6032, pg 1283, 1310

Pennie, John, Cenveo Publisher Services, 555 Virginia Dr, Fort Washington, PA 19034 *Tel:* 267-470-1590 *Fax:* 215-591-9093 *E-mail:* info.psg@cenveo.com *Web Site:* www.cenveopublisherservices.com, pg 1203, 1217, 1356, 1374, 1426

Perez, Amilcar, Gracenote, a Nielsen Company, 2000 Powell St, Suite 1500, Emeryville, CA 94608 *Tel:* 510-428-7200 *Web Site:* www.gracenote.com, pg 1184

Perez, Javier, Page Turner Publicity, 8785 SW 28 St, Miami, FL 33165 *Tel:* 949-254-3214 *E-mail:* pgturnerpub@aol.com *Web Site:* www.pageturnerpublicity.com, pg 1100

Perez, McKenzie, AlphaGraphics Inc, 143 Union Blvd, Suite 650, Lakewood, CO 80228 *Toll Free Tel:* 800-955-6246 *Fax:* 801-595-7270 *E-mail:* contactus@alphagraphics.com *Web Site:* www.alphagraphics.com, pg 1372

Perica, Adrian, Apple Inc, One Apple Park Way, Cupertino, CA 95014 *Tel:* 408-996-1010 *Web Site:* www.apple.com, pg 1372

Pernu, Dennis, Motorbooks, 100 Cummings Ctr, Suite 265D, Beverly, MA 01915 *Tel:* 978-282-9590 *Toll Free Tel:* 800-759-0190 (orders) *Web Site:* www.quartoknows.com/motorbooks, pg 1317, 1327

Perritt, Rickey L, S & L Sales Co Inc, 2165 Industrial Blvd, Waycross, GA 31503 *Tel:* 912-283-0210 *Toll Free Tel:* 800-243-3699 *Fax:* 912-283-0261 *Toll Free Fax:* 800-736-7329 *E-mail:* sales@slsales.com *Web Site:* slsales.com, pg 1319

Perron, Michel Carl, Cheneliere Education Inc, 5800, rue St Denis, bureau 900, Montreal, QC H2S 3L5, Canada *Tel:* 514-273-1066 *Toll Free Tel:* 800-565-5531 *Fax:* 514-276-0324 *Toll Free Fax:* 800-814-0324 *E-mail:* info@cheneliere.ca *Web Site:* www.cheneliere.ca, pg 1311

Perrotti, Theresa, Maryheart Crusaders Inc, 531 W Main St, Meriden, CT 06451-2707 *Tel:* 203-238-9735 *Toll Free Tel:* 800-879-1957 (orders only) *Fax:* 203-235-0059 *E-mail:* maryheart@msn.com *Web Site:* www.maryheartcrusaders.com, pg 1137

Perry, Brian, Infinity Graphics, 2277 Science Pkwy, Suite 5, Okemos, MI 48864 *Tel:* 517-349-4635 *Toll Free Tel:* 800-292-2633 *Fax:* 517-349-7608 *E-mail:* barcode@infinitygraphics.com *Web Site:* www.infinitygraphics.com, pg 1221, 1249, 1379

Perry, Connie, Monteiro & Co Inc, 301 E 57 St, 4th fl, New York, NY 10022 *Tel:* 212-832-8183 *Web Site:* www.monteiroandco.com, pg 1099

Perry, Glynn, RR Donnelley, 35 W Wacker Dr, Chicago, IL 60601 *Toll Free Tel:* 800-742-4455 *Web Site:* www.rrd.com, pg 1204, 1219, 1246, 1262, 1275

Perry, Glynn, RR Donnelley & Sons Company, 35 W Wacker Dr, Chicago, IL 60601 *Tel:* 312-326-8000 *Toll Free Tel:* 800-742-4455 *Web Site:* www.rrd.com, pg 1332

Perry, Russell, The Horn Book Guide, 300 The Fenway, Suite P-311, Palace Road Bldg, Boston, MA 02115 *Tel:* 617-278-0225 *Toll Free Tel:* 888-628-0225 *Fax:* 617-278-6062 *E-mail:* info@hbook.com *Web Site:* www.hbook.com, pg 1127

Perry, Suzette, Infinity Graphics, 2277 Science Pkwy, Suite 5, Okemos, MI 48864 *Tel:* 517-349-4635 *Toll Free Tel:* 800-292-2633 *Fax:* 517-349-7608 *E-mail:* barcode@infinitygraphics.com *Web Site:* www. infinitygraphics.com, pg 1221, 1249, 1379

Persaud, Leah, Penguin Random House Canada, 320 Front St W, Suite 1400, Toronto, ON M5V 3B6, Canada *Tel:* 416-364-4449 *Toll Free Tel:* 888-523-9292 (cust serv) *Fax:* 416-598-7764 *Web Site:* www. penguinrandomhouse.ca, pg 1295

Peters, Craig, Getty Images Inc, 605 Fifth Ave S, Suite 400, Seattle, WA 98104 *Tel:* 206-925-5000 *Toll Free Tel:* 800-IMAGERY (462-4379 sales); 888-888-5889 *E-mail:* enterprisesolutionssales@gettyimages.com *Web Site:* www.gettyimages.com, pg 1378, 1446

Peterson, Kurt A, Puritan Press Inc, 95 Runnells Bridge Rd, Hollis, NH 03049-6565 *Tel:* 603-889-4500 *Toll Free Tel:* 800-635-6302 *Fax:* 603-889-6551 *E-mail:* print@puritancapital.com *Web Site:* www. puritanpress.com, pg 1253

Peterson, Terry D, RR Donnelley, 35 W Wacker Dr, Chicago, IL 60601 *Toll Free Tel:* 800-742-4455 *Web Site:* www.rrd.com, pg 1204, 1219, 1246, 1262, 1275

Peterson, Terry D, RR Donnelley & Sons Company, 35 W Wacker Dr, Chicago, IL 60601 *Tel:* 312-326-8000 *Toll Free Tel:* 800-742-4455 *Web Site:* www.rrd.com, pg 1332

Peticolas, Kip, Fundamental Photographs, 210 Forsyth St, Suite 2, New York, NY 10002 *Tel:* 212-473-5770 *E-mail:* mail@fphoto.com *Web Site:* www.fphoto.com, pg 1446

Petlack, Howard, A Good Thing Inc, PO Box 20482, New York, NY 10021-0068 *Tel:* 212-687-8155 *Fax:* 212-687-8292 *Web Site:* agoodthingink.com, pg 1423

Petlinski, Jane, QBS Learning, 242 W 30 St, Suite 900, New York, NY 10001 *Tel:* 929-841-5969 *E-mail:* sales@qbslearning.com *Web Site:* www. qbslearning.com, pg 1361, 1431

Petriw, Les, National Book Network (NBN), 4501 Forbes Blvd, Suite 200, Lanham, MD 20706 *Tel:* 301-459-3366 *Toll Free Tel:* 800-462-6420 (orders only) *Fax:* 301-429-5746 *Toll Free Fax:* 800-338-4550 (orders only) *E-mail:* customercare@nbnbooks.com *Web Site:* www.nbnbooks.com, pg 1293, 1318

Petro, Joe, Nuance Communications Inc, One Wayside Rd, Burlington, MA 01803 *Tel:* 781-565-5000 *Toll Free Tel:* 800-654-1187 (cust serv); 888-372-1908 (orders) *Web Site:* www.nuance.com, pg 1382

Petrook, Malcolm, DJD/Golden Advertising, 145 W 28 St, 12th fl, New York, NY 10001 *Tel:* 212-366-5033 *Fax:* 212-243-5044 *E-mail:* call@djdgolden.com *Web Site:* www.djdgolden.com, pg 1086

Petrucci, Anthony, HID Global, 611 Center Ridge Dr, Austin, TX 78753 *Tel:* 512-776-9000 *Toll Free Tel:* 800-872-5359 (cust serv) *Fax:* 512-776-9930 *E-mail:* customerservice@hidglobal.com *Web Site:* www.hidglobal.com, pg 1378

Petruch, Myron, Sun Chemical Corp, 35 Waterview Blvd, Parsippany, NJ 07054-1285 *Tel:* 973-404-6000 *E-mail:* globalmarketing@sunchemical.com *Web Site:* www.sunchemical.com, pg 1268

Petty, Shea, Faherty & Associates Inc, 6665 SW Hampton St, Suite 100, Portland, OR 97223 *Tel:* 503-639-3113 *Toll Free Tel:* 800-824-2888 *Fax:* 503-598-9850 *Web Site:* www.fahertybooks.com, pg 1286

Pfeifer, Ben, Shutterstock Inc, Empire State Bldg, 350 Fifth Ave, 21st fl, New York, NY 10118 *Tel:* 646-419-4452 (sales) *Toll Free Tel:* 866-663-3954 *Fax:* 347-402-0710 *E-mail:* support@shutterstock.com; press@shutterstock.com *Web Site:* www.shutterstock.com, pg 1449

Pfister, Erin, Perma Graphics, 1356 S Jason St, Denver, CO 80223 *Tel:* 303-477-2070 *E-mail:* info@perma-graphics.com *Web Site:* www.perma-graphics.com, pg 1252

Phadnis, Atul, Gracenote, a Nielsen Company, 2000 Powell St, Suite 1500, Emeryville, CA 94608 *Tel:* 510-428-7200 *Web Site:* www.gracenote.com, pg 1184

Pharr, Paul, Vectorworks Inc, 7150 Riverwood Dr, Columbia, MD 21046 *Tel:* 410-290-5114 *Toll Free Tel:* 888-646-4223 (sales) *Fax:* 410-290-7266 *E-mail:* sales@vectorworks.net *Web Site:* www. vectorworks.net, pg 1387

Philipp, Whitney, Lachina Precision Graphics Services, 3791 S Green Rd, Cleveland, OH 44122 *Tel:* 216-292-7959 *E-mail:* info@lachina.com *Web Site:* www. lachina.com, pg 1222, 1359, 1380, 1429

Phillips, Adam, Shadow Canyon Graphics, 902 S Cascade, La Veta, CO 81055 *Tel:* 720-498-4823 *Web Site:* www.shadowcanyongraphics.com, pg 1432

Phillips, Andrew V, Windhaven®, 466 Rte 10, Orford, NH 03777 *Tel:* 603-512-9251 (cell) *E-mail:* info@ windhavenpress.com *Web Site:* www.windhavenpress. com, pg 1228

Phillips, Burt, Hess Print Solutions, 3765 Sunnybrook Rd, Brimfield, OH 44240 *Toll Free Tel:* 800-678-1222 *E-mail:* info@hessprintsolutions.com *Web Site:* www. hessprintsolutions.com, pg 1206, 1248

Phillips, Lindy Kedro, Shadow Canyon Graphics, 902 S Cascade, La Veta, CO 81055 *Tel:* 720-498-4823 *Web Site:* www.shadowcanyongraphics.com, pg 1432

Philpott, Tom, Military Update, PO Box 231111, Centreville, VA 20120-1111 *Tel:* 703-830-6863 *E-mail:* milupdate@aol.com *Web Site:* www. militaryupdate.com, pg 1185

Pick, Geoffrey, Clear Print, 9025 Fullbright Ave, Chatsworth, CA 91311 *Tel:* 818-709-1220 *Fax:* 818-709-1320 *E-mail:* info@clearprint.com; sales@ clearprint.com *Web Site:* www.clearprint.com, pg 1244

Pickert, Jeffrey, GOBI® Library Solutions from EBSCO, 999 Maple St, Contoocook, NH 03229 *Tel:* 603-746-3102 *Toll Free Tel:* 800-258-3774 (US & CN) *Fax:* 603-746-5628 *E-mail:* information@ebsco.com *Web Site:* gobi.ebsco.com, pg 1314

Pidgeon, Tom, D&K Group Inc, 1795 Commerce Dr, Elk Grove Village, IL 60007 *Tel:* 847-956-0160; 847-956-4757 (tech support) *Toll Free Tel:* 800-632-2314 *Fax:* 847-956-8214 *E-mail:* info@dkgroup.net *Web Site:* www.dkgroup.com, pg 1245, 1262, 1275

Pieters, Jeff, Post Bulletin Co LLC, 18 First Ave SE, Rochester, MN 55903 *Tel:* 507-285-7600 *Toll Free Tel:* 800-562-1758 *E-mail:* news@postbulletin.com *Web Site:* www.postbulletin.com, pg 1186

Pimm, Robert G, Law Office of Robert G Pimm Attorney at Law, 2977 Ygnacio Valley Rd, Suite 265, Walnut Creek, CA 94598-3535 *Tel:* 925-374-1442 *Fax:* 925-281-2888 *Web Site:* www.rgpimm.com, pg 1351

Pinero, Miranda, Azalea Software Inc, PO Box 16660, Seattle, WA 98116-0660 *Tel:* 206-341-9500; 206-336-9559 (software support); 206-336-9575 (sales & info) *Fax:* 206-299-5600 *E-mail:* salesinfo@azaleabarcodes. com *Web Site:* www.azaleabarcodes.com, pg 1373

Ping, Trisha, BookPage®, 2143 Belcourt Ave, Nashville, TN 37212 *Tel:* 615-292-8926 *Fax:* 615-292-8249 *Web Site:* bookpage.com, pg 1121

Pinkin, Jeff, The Corporate Communications Group (CCG), 14 Henderson Dr, West Caldwell, NJ 07006 *Tel:* 973-808-0009 *Fax:* 973-808-9740 *E-mail:* info@ corpcomm.com *Web Site:* home.corpcomm.com, pg 1106

Pinto, Mike, The Country Press Inc, One Commercial Dr, Lakeville, MA 02347 *Tel:* 508-947-4485 *Toll Free Tel:* 888-343-2227 *Fax:* 508-947-8989 *E-mail:* info@countrypressinc.com *Web Site:* www. countrypressprinting.com, pg 1203, 1245

Pirosko, Lauren, American Book Review, University of Houston-Victoria, School of Arts & Sciences, 3007 N Ben Wilson St, Victoria, TX 77901 *Tel:* 361-570-4848 *Fax:* 361-580-5507 *E-mail:* americanbookreview@uhv. org *Web Site:* americanbookreview.org, pg 1123

Pistone, Dennis, Westchester Publishing Services, 4 Old Newtown Rd, Danbury, CT 06810 *Tel:* 203-791-0080 *Fax:* 203-791-9286 *E-mail:* info@westchesterpubsvcs. com *Web Site:* www.westchesterpublishingservices. com, pg 1227

Pitman, Jim, CLC Ministries, 701 Pennsylvania Ave, Fort Washington, PA 19034 *Tel:* 215-542-1240 *Toll Free Tel:* 800-659-1240 *Fax:* 215-542-7580 *E-mail:* orders@clcpublications.com *Web Site:* www. clcpublications.com, pg 1312

Pizar, Charles, Forecast, 2550 W Tyvola Rd, Suite 300, Charlotte, NC 28217 *Tel:* 704-998-3100 *Toll Free Tel:* 800-775-1800 (info servs); 800-775-1700 (cust serv) *Toll Free Fax:* 866-557-3396 (cust serv) *E-mail:* btinfo@baker-taylor.com *Web Site:* www. baker-taylor.com, pg 1126

Plantz, Julie, The Penworthy Company LLC, 219 N Milwaukee St, 4th fl, Milwaukee, WI 53202 *Tel:* 414-287-4600 *Toll Free Tel:* 800-262-2665 *Fax:* 414-287-4602 *E-mail:* info@penworthy.com *Web Site:* www. penworthy.com, pg 1319, 1324

Plath, Thomas J, International Paper Co, 6400 Poplar Ave, Memphis, TN 38197 *Tel:* 901-419-9000 *Toll Free Tel:* 800-207-4003 *Web Site:* www.internationalpaper. com; facebook.com/internationalpaper; twitter.com/ intlpaperco, pg 1264

Platt, George R, Harty Integrated Solutions, 25 James St, New Haven, CT 06513 *Tel:* 203-562-5112 *Toll Free Tel:* 800-654-0562 *Fax:* 203-782-9168 *Web Site:* www. hartynet.com, pg 1092

Platt, Kevin, Harty Integrated Solutions, 25 James St, New Haven, CT 06513 *Tel:* 203-562-5112 *Toll Free Tel:* 800-654-0562 *Fax:* 203-782-9168 *Web Site:* www. hartynet.com, pg 1092

Plotka, Richard, appatura™, A Broadridge Company, 65 Challenger Rd, Suite 400, Ridgefield Park, NJ 07660 *Tel:* 201-508-6000 *Toll Free Tel:* 800-277-2155 *E-mail:* contactus@appatura.com *Web Site:* www. appatura.com, pg 1091, 1105, 1109, 1201, 1215, 1242

Plourde, Dan, Columbia Finishing Mills Inc, 135 Boundary Rd, Cornwall, ON K6H 5T3, Canada *Tel:* 613-933-1462 *Toll Free Tel:* 800-267-9174 *Fax:* 613-933-7717 *Toll Free Fax:* 800-242-9174 *E-mail:* info@columbiafinishingmills.com *Web Site:* www.columbiafinishingmills.com, pg 1262

Polansky, Andy, Weber Shandwick, 909 Third Ave, New York, NY 10022 *Tel:* 212-445-8000 *Fax:* 212-445-8001 *Web Site:* www.webershandwick.com, pg 1103

Polich, Ryan, LucialMarquand, 1400 Second Ave, Seattle, WA 98101 *Tel:* 206-624-2030 *Fax:* 206-624-1821 *Web Site:* luciamarquand.com, pg 1359

Poll, Debra, Amgraf Inc, 1501 Oak St, Kansas City, MO 64108-1424 *Tel:* 816-474-4797 *Toll Free Tel:* 800-304-4797 (sales & mktg) *Fax:* 816-842-4477 *E-mail:* support@amgraf.com *Web Site:* www.amgraf. com, pg 1372

Pollard, Scott, Hill+Knowlton Strategies, 237 Park Ave, 4th fl, New York, NY 10017 *Tel:* 212-885-0300 *Web Site:* www.hkstrategies.com, pg 1098

Polley, Kevin, Hignell Book Printing Ltd, 488 Burnell St, Winnipeg, MB R3G 2B4, Canada *Tel:* 204-784-1030 *Toll Free Tel:* 800-304-5553 *Fax:* 204-774-4053 *E-mail:* books@hignell.mb.ca *Web Site:* www.hignell. mb.ca, pg 1206, 1249

Pollock, Ian, Mark Andy Inc, 18081 Chesterfield Airport Rd, Chesterfield, MO 63005 *Tel:* 636-532-4433 *Toll Free Tel:* 800-447-1231 *Toll Free Fax:* 800-447-1231 *Web Site:* www.presstek.com; markandy.com; shop. markandy.com, pg 1372

Pollock, Michele, Taconic Wire, 250 Totoket Rd, North Branford, CT 06471 *Tel:* 203-484-2863 *Toll Free Tel:* 800-253-1450 *Fax:* 203-484-2865 *E-mail:* sales@taconicwire.com; taconicwiresales@gmail.com *Web Site:* www.taconicwire.com, pg 1279

Polus, Paul, CDS Global, 1901 Bell Ave, Des Moines, IA 50315-1099 *Tel:* 515-247-7500 *Toll Free Tel:* 866-897-7987 *E-mail:* salesinfo@cds-global.com *Web Site:* www.cds-global.com, pg 1109, 1111

Pon, Amy, AJP Communications Inc, 95 Macdonald Ave, Burnaby, BC V5C 4M4, Canada *Tel:* 604-879-5880 *E-mail:* info@ajpcommunications.com *Web Site:* www.ajpcommunications.com, pg 1215

Poos, Shannon, Penguin Random House Canada, 320 Front St W, Suite 1400, Toronto, ON M5V 3B6, Canada *Tel:* 416-364-4449 *Toll Free Tel:* 888-523-9292 (cust serv) *Fax:* 416-598-7764 *Web Site:* www.penguinrandomhouse.ca, pg 1295

Pope, Jennifer, AEI (Atchity Entertainment International Inc), 9601 Wilshire Blvd, Unit 1202, Beverly Hills, CA 90210 *Tel:* 323-932-1685 *Web Site:* www.aeionline.com, pg 1341

Popp, Bruce D PhD, Bien Fait Translations, 183 Vernon St, 1st fl, Norword, MA 02062 *Tel:* 781-769-1637 *Toll Free Tel:* 866-243-6324 *E-mail:* inquiries@bien-fait.com *Web Site:* www.bien-fait.com, pg 1408

Popp, Jonny, Omnipress, 2600 Anderson St, Madison, WI 53704 *Tel:* 608-246-2600 *Toll Free Tel:* 800-828-0305 *E-mail:* justask@omnipress.com *Web Site:* www.omnipress.com, pg 1208, 1252

Porras, Raul, Victory Productions Inc, 55 Linden St, Worcester, MA 01609 *Tel:* 508-755-0051 *E-mail:* victory@victoryprd.com *Web Site:* www.victoryprd.com, pg 1363

Porras, Victoria, Victory Productions Inc, 55 Linden St, Worcester, MA 01609 *Tel:* 508-755-0051 *E-mail:* victory@victoryprd.com *Web Site:* www.victoryprd.com, pg 1363

Portales, Ingeborg, Lectorum Publications Inc, 205 Chubb Ave, Lyndhurst, NJ 07071 *Tel:* 201-559-2200 *Toll Free Tel:* 800-345-5946 *Fax:* 201-559-2201 *Toll Free Fax:* 877-532-8676 *E-mail:* lectorum@lectorum.com *Web Site:* www.lectorum.com, pg 1316

Porter, Dred Jr, Magnolia Clipping Service, 298 Commerce Park Dr, Suite A, Ridgeland, MS 39157 *Tel:* 601-856-0911 *Fax:* 601-856-3340 *E-mail:* mail@magnoliaclips.com *Web Site:* magnoliaclips.com, pg 1391

Porter, Dred Sr, Magnolia Clipping Service, 298 Commerce Park Dr, Suite A, Ridgeland, MS 39157 *Tel:* 601-856-0911 *Fax:* 601-856-3340 *E-mail:* mail@magnoliaclips.com *Web Site:* magnoliaclips.com, pg 1391

Porter, James, James Porter Photography, 211 E Columbine Ave, Suite A-1, Santa Ana, CA 92707 *Tel:* 714-546-4148 *E-mail:* info@jamesporterphotography.com *Web Site:* www.jamesporterphotography.com, pg 1442

Porter, Joe, Magnolia Clipping Service, 298 Commerce Park Dr, Suite A, Ridgeland, MS 39157 *Tel:* 601-856-0911 *Fax:* 601-856-3340 *E-mail:* mail@magnoliaclips.com *Web Site:* magnoliaclips.com, pg 1391

Porter, Jonathan, AccuWeather Inc, 385 Science Park Rd, State College, PA 16803 *Tel:* 814-235-8600; 814-237-0309 *E-mail:* salesmail@accuweather.com; support@accuweather.com *Web Site:* www.accuweather.com; corporate.accuweather.com, pg 1371

Porter, Michael, QBS Learning, 242 W 30 St, Suite 900, New York, NY 10001 *Tel:* 929-841-5969 *E-mail:* sales@qbslearning.com *Web Site:* www.qbslearning.com, pg 1361, 1431

Poston, Neal, The Dingley Press, 119 Lisbon St, Lisbon, ME 04250 *Tel:* 207-353-4151 *Toll Free Tel:* 800-317-4574 *Fax:* 207-353-9886 *E-mail:* info@dingley.com *Web Site:* www.dingley.com, pg 1246

Potash, Steve, OverDrive Inc, One OverDrive Way, Cleveland, OH 44125 *Tel:* 216-573-6886 *Fax:* 216-573-6888 *E-mail:* info@overdrive.com *Web Site:* www.overdrive.com, pg 1294

Potcoava, Virginia, A WordJourney Translation LLC, PO Box 3181, Humble, TX 77347-3181 *Tel:* 281-813-1827 *Fax:* 832-213-2777 *E-mail:* word@wjtranslation.com *Web Site:* www.awordjourneytranslation.com, pg 1407

Potente, Ralph, ProFAX Inc, 20 Max Ave, Hicksville, NY 11801-1419 *Toll Free Tel:* 877-942-8100 *E-mail:* sales@profax.com *Web Site:* www.profax.com, pg 1110

Potesky, Ron, Pantone Inc, 590 Commerce Blvd, Carlstadt, NJ 07072-3098 *Tel:* 201-935-5500 *Toll Free Tel:* 866-PANTONE (726-8663) *Fax:* 201-896-0242 *E-mail:* pantoneorders@pantone.com *Web Site:* www.pantone.com, pg 1278

Poticny, Carol, Steven Diamond Inc, 104 W 17 St, Suite 3-E, New York, NY 10011 *Tel:* 212-675-0723 *Fax:* 212-675-0762 *E-mail:* steven.diamond@verizon.net, pg 1345

Powell, Frank, GLS Companies, 1280 Energy Park Dr, St Paul, MN 55108-5106 *Tel:* 651-644-3000 *Toll Free Tel:* 800-655-9405 *Web Site:* www.glsmn.com, pg 1220, 1248

Powell, Jeremy, Vectorworks Inc, 7150 Riverwood Dr, Columbia, MD 21046 *Tel:* 410-290-5114 *Toll Free Tel:* 888-646-4223 (sales) *Fax:* 410-290-7266 *E-mail:* sales@vectorworks.net *Web Site:* www.vectorworks.net, pg 1387

Powell, Kathleen, St Catharines Museum, 1932 Welland Canals Pkwy, RR 6, St Catharines, ON L2R 7K6, Canada *Tel:* 905-984-8880 *Toll Free Tel:* 800-305-5134 *Fax:* 905-984-6910 *E-mail:* museum@stcatharines.ca *Web Site:* www.stcatharines.ca, pg 1297

Powers, Marcia, Wilshire Book Co, 22647 Ventura Blvd, Suite 314, Woodland Hills, CA 91364 *Tel:* 818-700-1522 *E-mail:* sales@mpowers.com *Web Site:* www.mpowers.com, pg 1322

Prabhu, Prashant, Lumina Datamatics Inc, 4 Collins Ave, Plymouth, MA 02360 *Tel:* 508-746-0300 *Fax:* 508-746-3233 *Web Site:* luminadatamatics.com, pg 1207, 1222, 1349, 1359, 1380, 1430

Pratt, Jane, Association for PRINT Technologies (APTech), 1896 Preston White Dr, Reston, VA 20191 *Tel:* 703-264-7200 *Fax:* 703-620-0994 *E-mail:* aptech@aptech.org *Web Site:* www.printtechnologies.org, pg 1273, 1373

Prazuch, Ron, Continental Sales Inc, 213 W Main St, Barrington, IL 60010 *Tel:* 847-381-6530 *Fax:* 847-382-0385; 847-382-0419 *Web Site:* www.continentalsalesinc.com, pg 1286

Prazuch, Ronald J, Wybel Marketing Group Inc, 213 W Main St, Barrington, IL 60010 *Tel:* 847-382-0384; 847-382-0382 *Toll Free Tel:* 800-323-5297 *Fax:* 847-382-0385 *Toll Free Fax:* 800-595-5252 *E-mail:* bookreps@wybel.com, pg 1301

Prentiss, Winnie, Motorbooks, 100 Cummings Ctr, Suite 265D, Beverly, MA 01915 *Tel:* 978-282-9590 *Toll Free Tel:* 800-759-0190 (orders) *Web Site:* www.quartoknows.com/motorbooks, pg 1317, 1327

Preston, Chris, Preston Kelly, 222 First Ave NE, Minneapolis, MN 55413 *Tel:* 612-843-4000 *Fax:* 612-843-3900 *E-mail:* iconicideas@prestonkelly.com *Web Site:* prestonkelly.com, pg 1087

Previn, Fletcher, IBM Corp, One New Orchard Rd, Armonk, NY 10504 *Tel:* 914-499-1900 *Toll Free Tel:* 800-426-4968 *E-mail:* askibm@vnet.ibm.com *Web Site:* www.ibm.com, pg 1379

Price, Bruce, Word-Wise Advertising, 3500 Virginia Beach Blvd, Suite 611, Virginia Beach, VA 23452 *Tel:* 757-455-5020, pg 1353

Price, Karen, New Leaf Distributing Co, 401 Thornton Rd, Lithia Springs, GA 30122-1557 *Tel:* 770-948-7845 *Toll Free Tel:* 800-326-2665 (orders) *Fax:* 770-944-2313 *Toll Free Fax:* 800-326-1066 (orders) *E-mail:* customerservice@newleaf-dist.com *Web Site:* newleafdist.com, pg 1294, 1318

Price, Richard W, Crane Duplicating Service Inc, 4915 Rattlesnake Hammock Rd, Suite 207, Naples, FL 34113 *Tel:* 305-280-6742 (help desk) *Fax:* 239-732-8415 *E-mail:* info@craneduplicating.com *Web Site:* www.craneduplicating.com, pg 1203, 1245

Prickett, Byron, Panaprint Inc, 7979 NE Industrial Blvd, Macon, GA 31216 *Tel:* 478-788-0676 *Toll Free Tel:* 800-622-0676 *Fax:* 478-788-4276 *Web Site:* www.panaprint.com, pg 1252

Priede, Mark, Xante Corp, 2800 Dauphin St, Suite 100, Mobile, AL 36606 *Tel:* 251-473-6502; 251-473-4920 (tech support) *Fax:* 251-473-6503 *Web Site:* www.xante.com, pg 1388

Prieto, Kimberly, OmniUpdate Inc, 1320 Flynn Rd, Suite 100, Camarillo, CA 93012 *Tel:* 805-484-9400 *Toll Free Tel:* 800-362-2605 *E-mail:* sales@omniupdate.com *Web Site:* omniupdate.com, pg 1383

Primo, Jim, Douthitt Corp, 245 Adair St, Detroit, MI 48207-4287 *Tel:* 313-259-1565 *Toll Free Tel:* 800-368-8448 *Fax:* 313-259-6806 *E-mail:* em@douthittcorp.com *Web Site:* www.douthittcorp.com, pg 1275

Prince, Boo, Idea Architects, 523 Swift St, Santa Cruz, CA 95060 *Tel:* 831-465-9565 *Web Site:* www.ideaarchitects.com, pg 1347

Prins, Thomas, The Scholar's Choice, 6300 W Port Bay Rd, Suite 101, Wolcott, NY 14590 *Tel:* 315-905-4208 *E-mail:* information@scholarschoice.com *Web Site:* www.scholarschoice.com, pg 1133

Pritzkat, Carl, Publishers Weekly, 71 W 23 St, Suite 1608, New York, NY 10010 *Tel:* 212-377-5500 *Fax:* 212-377-2733 *Web Site:* www.publishersweekly.com, pg 1130

Proffit, James R, NAPCO Inc, 120 Trojan Ave, Sparta, NC 28675 *Tel:* 336-372-5228 *Toll Free Tel:* 800-854-8621 *Fax:* 336-372-8602 *E-mail:* info@napcousa.com *Web Site:* www.napcousa.com, pg 1251

Prohaske, Eugene, D C Graphics Inc, 59 Central Ave, Suite 15, Farmingdale, NY 11735 *Tel:* 631-777-3100 *Fax:* 631-777-7899 *E-mail:* prepress@dcgraphicsinc.com *Web Site:* www.dcgraphicsinc.com, pg 1245

Pronk, Gord, Pronk Media Inc, PO Box 340, Beaverton, ON L0K 1A0, Canada *Tel:* 416-441-3760 *E-mail:* info@pronk.com *Web Site:* www.pronk.com, pg 1224, 1384, 1431

Protano, Generosa Gina, GGP Publishing Inc, 105 Calvert St, Suite 201, Harrison, NY 10528-3138 *Tel:* 914-834-8896 *Fax:* 914-834-7566 *Web Site:* www.GGPPublishing.com, pg 1346, 1358, 1409

Pruitt, Charles, A B Data Ltd, 600 A B Data Dr, Milwaukee, WI 53217 *Tel:* 414-961-6400 *Toll Free Tel:* 866-217-4470 *Fax:* 414-961-6410 *E-mail:* consulting@abdata.com *Web Site:* www.abdata.com, pg 1105

Pruitt, Gary, Associated Press (AP), 200 Liberty St, New York, NY 10281 *Tel:* 212-621-1500 *E-mail:* info@ap.org *Web Site:* www.ap.org, pg 1183

Pucher, Annmarie, ISIS Papyrus America, 301 Bank St, South Lake, TX 76092 *Tel:* 817-416-2345 *Fax:* 817-416-1223 *E-mail:* info@isis-papyrus.com *Web Site:* www.isis-papyrus.com, pg 1379

Pugliese, Paul, General Cartography Inc, 4 Estate Dr, Boynton Beach, FL 33436 *Tel:* 561-455-4398 *E-mail:* terradata@aol.com *Web Site:* cartographybypaul.com, pg 1428

Purakayastha, Apratim, SumTotal Systems LLC, 2850 NW 43 St, Suite 150, Gainesville, FL 32606 *Tel:* 352-264-2800 *Toll Free Tel:* 866-933-1416 *Fax:* 352-374-2257 *E-mail:* customersupport@sumtotalsystems.com *Web Site:* www.sumtotalsystems.com, pg 1386

Purdy, Dennis, Purdy Sports Images, Staff of History, PO Box 65454, University Place, WA 98464 *Tel:* 253-460-0066 *E-mail:* vcbcmag@comcast.net, pg 1449

Purdy, Judy, Saunders Book Co, PO Box 308, Collingwood, ON L9Y 3Z7, Canada *Tel:* 705-445-4777 *Toll Free Tel:* 800-461-9120 *Fax:* 705-445-9569 *Toll Free Fax:* 800-561-1763 *E-mail:* info@saundersbook.ca *Web Site:* librarybooks.com, pg 1297

Purdy, Kathy, Purdy Sports Images, Staff of History, PO Box 65454, University Place, WA 98464 *Tel:* 253-460-0066 *E-mail:* vcbcmag@comcast.net, pg 1449

Purnell, Thomas, Southern Wisconsin News Co, 58 Artisan Dr, Edgerton, WI 53534 *Tel:* 608-884-2600 *Fax:* 608-884-2636 *Web Site:* www.southernwisconsinnews.com, pg 1320

Quagliato, Steve, Lake Book Manufacturing Inc, 2085 N Cornell Ave, Melrose Park, IL 60160 *Tel:* 708-345-7000 *E-mail:* info@lakebook.com *Web Site:* www.lakebook.com, pg 1207, 1222, 1250, 1265, 1277

Quant, Daniel, Multi-Tech Systems Inc, 2205 Woodale Dr, Mounds View, MN 55112 *Tel:* 763-785-3500 *Toll Free Tel:* 800-328-9717 *Fax:* 763-785-9874 *E-mail:* info@multitech.com; sales@multitech.com; mtsmktg@multitech.com *Web Site:* www.multitech.com, pg 1382

Quental, Carla, National Book Network (NBN), 4501 Forbes Blvd, Suite 200, Lanham, MD 20706 *Tel:* 301-459-3366 *Toll Free Tel:* 800-462-6420 (orders only) *Fax:* 301-429-5746 *Toll Free Fax:* 800-338-4550 (orders only) *E-mail:* customercare@nbnbooks.com *Web Site:* www.nbnbooks.com, pg 1293, 1318

Quigley, Rich, CRW Graphics Communications, 9100 Pennsauken Hwy, Pennsauken, NJ 08110 *Tel:* 856-662-9111 *Toll Free Tel:* 800-820-3000 *Fax:* 856-665-1789 *E-mail:* info@crwgraphics.com *Web Site:* www.crwgraphics.com, pg 1092, 1375, 1426

Quill, John A, Ecological Fibers Inc, 40 Pioneer Dr, Lunenburg, MA 01462 *Tel:* 978-537-0003 *Fax:* 978-537-2238 *E-mail:* info@ecofibers.com *Web Site:* www.ecofibers.com, pg 1204, 1263

Quinlan, Michael, Transparent Language Inc, 12 Murphy Dr, Nashua, NH 03062 *Tel:* 603-262-6300 *Toll Free Tel:* 800-567-9619 (cust serv & sales) *E-mail:* info@transparent.com; support@transparent.com (tech support) *Web Site:* www.transparent.com, pg 1387

Quinlisk, Frank, Media Supply Inc, 208 Philips Rd, Exton, PA 19341 *Tel:* 610-884-4400 *Toll Free Tel:* 800-944-4237 *Fax:* 610-884-4500 *E-mail:* info@mediasupply.com *Web Site:* www.mediasupply.com, pg 1381

Quinn, Kevin, Fry Communications Inc, 800 W Church Rd, Mechanicsburg, PA 17055 *Tel:* 717-766-0211 *Toll Free Tel:* 800-334-1429 *Fax:* 717-691-0341 *E-mail:* info@frycomm.com *Web Site:* www.frycomm.com, pg 1205, 1220, 1247, 1276

Quinton, Sasha, Scholastic Book Fairs®, 1080 Greenwood Blvd, Lake Mary, FL 32746 *Tel:* 407-829-8000 *Fax:* 407-829-2600 *E-mail:* custservbf@scholasticbookfairs.com *Web Site:* www.scholastic.com/bookfairs, pg 1298, 1320

Raab, Susan Salzman, Raab Associates Inc, 730 Yale Ave, Swarthmore, PA 19081 *Tel:* 914-241-2117 *E-mail:* info@raabassociates.com *Web Site:* www.raabassociates.com, pg 1101, 1351

Rada, James Jr, Linick International Inc, Linick Bldg, 7 Putter Lane, Middle Island, NY 11953 *Tel:* 631-924-3888; 631-924-8555; 631-604-8599 *E-mail:* topmarketingadvisor@gmail.com *Web Site:* topmarketingadvisor.com, pg 1349

Radke, Linda F, Story Monsters LLC, 4696 W Tyson St, Chandler, AZ 85226-2903 *Tel:* 480-940-8182 *Fax:* 480-940-8787 *Web Site:* www.StoryMonsters.com; www.AuthorsandExperts.com; www.SchoolBookings.com; www.partnershippublishing.com; www.fivestarpublishingsecrets.com; www.eStarPublish.com; www.DragonflyBookAwards.com, pg 1102

Radke, Linda F, Story Monsters LLC, 4696 W Tyson St, Chandler, AZ 85226-2903 *Tel:* 480-940-8182 *Fax:* 480-940-8787 *Web Site:* www.StoryMonsters.com, pg 1352, 1362

Radke, Linda F, Story Monsters LLC, 4696 W Tyson St, Chandler, AZ 85226-2903 *Tel:* 480-940-8182 *Fax:* 480-940-8787 *Web Site:* www.StoryMonsters.com; www.AuthorsandExperts.com; www.SchoolBookings.com, pg 1386

Radke, Linda F, Story Monsters LLC, 4696 W Tyson St, Chandler, AZ 85226-2903 *Tel:* 480-940-8182 *Fax:* 480-940-8787 *Web Site:* www.StoryMonsters.com, pg 1432

Ragan, Lise B, Course Crafters Inc, 243 Greenleaf Rd, Anson, ME 04911 *Tel:* 207-696-4050 *E-mail:* info@coursecrafters.com *Web Site:* www.coursecrafters.com, pg 1357

Ragsdale, Craig, Martin Printing Co Inc, 1765 Powdersville Rd, Easley, SC 29642 *Toll Free Tel:* 888-985-7330 *Fax:* 864-859-8620 *E-mail:* info@martinprinting.com *Web Site:* www.martinprinting.com, pg 1251

Ragsdale, William, Martin Printing Co Inc, 1765 Powdersville Rd, Easley, SC 29642 *Toll Free Tel:* 888-985-7330 *Fax:* 864-859-8620 *E-mail:* info@martinprinting.com *Web Site:* www.martinprinting.com, pg 1251

Rahja, John, Augsburg Fortress Publishers, Publishing House of the Evangelical Lutheran Church in America, 510 Marquette Ave S, Minneapolis, MN 55402 *Tel:* 612-330-3300 *Toll Free Tel:* 800-426-0115 (ext 639, subns); 800-328-4648 (orders) *Fax:* 612-330-3455 *Toll Free Fax:* 800-722-7766 (orders) *E-mail:* customercare@augsburgfortress.org; copyright@augsburgfortress.org (reprint permission requests); info@augsburgfortress.org *Web Site:* www.augsburgfortress.org; www.1517.media, pg 1309

Raimondo, Diane, Magnum Photos Inc, 12 W 31 St, 11th fl, New York, NY 10001 *Tel:* 212-929-6000 *Fax:* 212-929-9325 *E-mail:* photography@magnumphotos.com; contact@magnumphotos.com *Web Site:* www.magnumphotos.com, pg 1448

Raines, Daniel, Creative Trust Inc, 210 Jamestown Park Dr, Suite 200, Brentwood, TN 37027 *Tel:* 615-297-5010 *Fax:* 615-297-5020 *E-mail:* info@creativetrust.com *Web Site:* creativetrust.com, pg 1344

Raiton, Cindy, Bookazine Co Inc, 75 Hook Rd, Bayonne, NJ 07002 *Tel:* 201-339-7777 *Toll Free Tel:* 800-221-8112 *Fax:* 201-339-7778 *E-mail:* info@bookazine.com *Web Site:* www.bookazine.com, pg 1310, 1325

Rajamani, Madhu, diacriTech Inc, 4 S Market St, 4th fl, Boston, MA 02109 *Tel:* 617-600-3366 *Fax:* 617-848-2938 *Web Site:* www.diacritech.com, pg 1219, 1357, 1427

Rajasekharan, Mahesh PhD, Streem Communications LLC, 4949 Harrison Ave, Rockford, IL 61107 *Tel:* 815-282-7695 *Toll Free Tel:* 800-325-7732 *Fax:* 815-639-8931 *Toll Free Fax:* 888-435-2348 *E-mail:* streemsales@cleo.com; sales@cleo.com *Web Site:* www.streem.net, pg 1110

Rambo, Amy, MCH Strategic Data, 601 E Marshall St, Sweet Springs, MO 65351 *Toll Free Tel:* 800-776-6373 *E-mail:* sales@mchdata.com *Web Site:* www.mchdata.com, pg 1112

Rameau, Ms Leone Giannone, Edipresse Inc, 945, ave Beaumont, Montreal, QC H3N 1W3, Canada *Tel:* 514-273-6141 *Toll Free Tel:* 800-361-1043 *Fax:* 514-273-7021 *E-mail:* information@edipresse.ca *Web Site:* www.edipresse.ca, pg 1313

Rampertab, Ramesh, RAmEx Ars Medica Inc, 1714 S Westgate Ave, No 2, Los Angeles, CA 90025-3852 *Tel:* 310-826-4964 *Toll Free Tel:* 800-633-9281 *Fax:* 310-826-9674 *E-mail:* ars.medica@ramex.com *Web Site:* www.ramex.com, pg 1296

Randles, Peter M, Southwest Book Co, 13003 Murphy Rd, Suite H1, Stafford, TX 77477-3934 *Tel:* 281-498-2603 *Fax:* 281-498-7566, pg 1299

Ranganathan, Madhu, Open Text Corp, 275 Frank Tompa Dr, Waterloo, ON N2L 0A1, Canada *Tel:* 519-888-7111 *Fax:* 519-888-0677 *Web Site:* opentext.com, pg 1383

Rangel, Nicholas, Eastman Kodak Co, 343 State St, Rochester, NY 14650 *Tel:* 585-724-4000 *Toll Free Tel:* 866-563-2533 *Web Site:* www.kodak.com, pg 1275

Rao, Dana, Adobe Systems Inc, 345 Park Ave, San Jose, CA 95110-2704 *Tel:* 408-536-6000 *Fax:* 408-537-6000 *Web Site:* www.adobe.com, pg 1371

Rao, Karthik, Gracenote, a Nielsen Company, 2000 Powell St, Suite 1500, Emeryville, CA 94608 *Tel:* 510-428-7200 *Web Site:* www.gracenote.com, pg 1184

Rapin-Klopp, Karrie, A-M Church Supply, 3220 Bay Rd, Suite E, Saginaw, MI 48603 *Tel:* 989-249-9174 *Toll Free Tel:* 800-345-4694 *Web Site:* www.am-church.com, pg 1309

Rapp, Ken, Sheridan MI, 613 E Industrial Dr, Chelsea, MI 48118 *Tel:* 734-475-9145 *Web Site:* www.sheridan.com, pg 1209, 1254, 1267

Rapp, Ken, Sheridan NH, 69 Lyme Rd, Hanover, NH 03755 *Tel:* 603-643-2220 *Web Site:* www.sheridan.com, pg 1254

Rappaport, Donn, ALC Inc, 750 College Rd E, Suite 201, Princeton, NJ 08540 *Tel:* 609-580-2800 *Toll Free Tel:* 800-252-5478 *Fax:* 609-580-2888 *E-mail:* info@alc.com *Web Site:* www.alc.com, pg 1111

Rappaport, Jennifer, Falcon Safety Products Inc, 25 Imclone Dr, Branchburg, NJ 08876 *Tel:* 908-707-4900 *Toll Free Tel:* 800-332-5266 *E-mail:* marketing@falconsafety.com *Web Site:* www.falconsafety.com, pg 1377

Rappaport, Susan Rice, ALC Inc, 750 College Rd E, Suite 201, Princeton, NJ 08540 *Tel:* 609-580-2800 *Toll Free Tel:* 800-252-5478 *Fax:* 609-580-2888 *E-mail:* info@alc.com *Web Site:* www.alc.com, pg 1111

Rascher, Linda, Bert Davis Executive Search Inc, 555 Fifth Ave, Suite 302, New York, NY 10017 *Tel:* 212-838-4000 *E-mail:* info@bertdavis.com *Web Site:* www.bertdavis.com, pg 1389

Rashba, Neil, Neil Rashba Photography, 1174 Neck Rd, Ponte Vedra Beach, FL 32082 *Tel:* 904-273-0388 *Fax:* 904-273-6203 *E-mail:* neil@rashba.com *Web Site:* www.rashba.com, pg 1442

Rauppius, Lawrence H Jr, B W Wilson Paper Co Inc, 2501 Brittons Hill Rd, Richmond, VA 23230 *Tel:* 804-358-6715 *Toll Free Tel:* 800-868-2868 *Fax:* 804-358-4742 *E-mail:* info@bwwilson.com; sales@bwwilson.com *Web Site:* www.bwwilson.com, pg 1269

Ray, Luanne, Get Rich Book Club, 7 Putter Lane, Middle Island, NY 11953 *Tel:* 631-924-3888 (ext 202) *E-mail:* grbookclub@gmail.com; linickgroup@gmail.com, pg 1136

Raymond, Tom, Fresh Air Photo, 2203 McKinley Rd, Suite 220, Johnson City, TN 37604 *Tel:* 423-928-2700 *Fax:* 423-282-2730 *Web Site:* www.freshairphoto.com, pg 1438

Rayner, Terry, Wimmer Cookbooks, 4650 Shelby Air Dr, Memphis, TN 38118 *Toll Free Tel:* 800-548-2537 *Fax:* 901-363-1771 *Web Site:* www.wimmerco.com, pg 1210, 1257, 1300, 1322, 1353

Read, Alan, Terry & Read LLC, 4471 Dean Martin Dr, The Martin 3302, Las Vegas, NV 89103 *Tel:* 510-813-9854 *Toll Free Fax:* 866-214-4762, pg 1300

Ream, David K, Leverage Technologies Inc, 9519 Greystone Pkwy, Cleveland, OH 44141-2939 *Tel:* 440-838-1203 *Toll Free Tel:* 888-838-1203 *Fax:* 440-838-1203 *E-mail:* info@levtechinc.com *Web Site:* www.levtechinc.com, pg 1380

Reboli, John A, Entertainment News Service, PO Box 6123, West Caldwell, NJ 07007-6123 *Tel:* 973-227-4433, pg 1184

Reboli, John A, The Fairfield Chronicle, PO Box 6123, West Caldwell, NJ 07007-6123 *Tel:* 973-227-4433, pg 1184

Reboli, John A, The Morristown News, PO Box 6123, West Caldwell, NJ 07007-6123 *Tel:* 973-227-4433, pg 1185

Reboli, John A, The Parsippany News, PO Box 6123, West Caldwell, NJ 07007-6123 *Tel:* 973-227-4433, pg 1186

Recchia, Bob, Crain Communications Inc, 1155 Gratiot Ave, Detroit, MI 48207-2732 *Tel:* 313-446-6000 *Fax:* 313-446-0383 *E-mail:* info@crain.com *Web Site:* crain.com, pg 1184

Rech, David Alan, Scribe Inc, 842 S Second St, Philadelphia, PA 19147 *Tel:* 215-336-5094 *Fax:* 215-336-5092 *E-mail:* contact@scribenet.com *Web Site:* www.scribenet.com, pg 1225, 1352, 1361, 1385, 1393

Reckamp, Renee, Western Printing Machinery Co (WPM), 9228 Ivanhoe St, Schiller Park, IL 60176 *Tel:* 847-678-1740 *Fax:* 847-678-6176 *E-mail:* info@wpm.com *Web Site:* www.wpm.com, pg 1280

Reckinger, Michael, ALC Inc, 750 College Rd E, Suite 201, Princeton, NJ 08540 *Tel:* 609-580-2800 *Toll Free Tel:* 800-252-5478 *Fax:* 609-580-2888 *E-mail:* info@alc.com *Web Site:* www.alc.com, pg 1111

Rector, David J, MRC Medical Communications, 12 Lincoln Blvd, Suite 103, Emerson, NJ 07630 *Tel:* 201-986-0247 *E-mail:* info@mrcmedical.net *Web Site:* www.mrcmedical.net, pg 1382

Rector, Susan, MRC Medical Communications, 12 Lincoln Blvd, Suite 103, Emerson, NJ 07630 *Tel:* 201-986-0247 *E-mail:* info@mrcmedical.net *Web Site:* www.mrcmedical.net, pg 1382

Redmond, Patrick Michael MA, Patrick Redmond Design, PO Box 40156, St Paul, MN 55104-8156 *Tel:* 651-646-4254 *E-mail:* LMP@PatrickRedmondDesign.com *Web Site:* www.PatrickRedmondDesign.com, pg 1431

Redwood, Joan, Cross Country Computer Corp, 250 Carleton Ave, East Islip, NY 11730-1240 *Tel:* 631-334-1810 *E-mail:* inquiry@crosscountrycomputer.com *Web Site:* www.crosscountrycomputer.com, pg 1111

Redzepagic, Edwin, Medical Images, 19-C Trolley Sq, Wilmington, DE 19806 *Tel:* 212-736-2525 *Toll Free Tel:* 800-542-3686 *E-mail:* sales@medicalimages.com *Web Site:* www.medicalimages.com, pg 1448

Reed, Bobby Sr, V G Reed & Sons Inc, 1002 S 12 St, Louisville, KY 40210-1302 *Toll Free Tel:* 800-635-9788 *Fax:* 502-560-0197 *Web Site:* www.vgreed.com, pg 1093, 1253

Reed, Dwayne, Cenveo Publisher Services, 555 Virginia Dr, Fort Washington, PA 19034 *Tel:* 267-470-1590 *Fax:* 215-591-9093 *E-mail:* info.psg@cenveo.com *Web Site:* www.cenveopublisherservices.com, pg 1203, 1217, 1356, 1374, 1426

Reed, Geoff, Geoff Reed Photography, 7640 N 22 St, Phoenix, AZ 85020 *Tel:* 602-749-1103 *E-mail:* geoff@geoffreedphoto.com *Web Site:* www.geoffreedphoto.com, pg 1442

Reed, Mary, Dunhill International List Co Inc, 6400 Congress Ave, Suite 1750, Boca Raton, FL 33487-2898 *Tel:* 561-998-7800 *Toll Free Tel:* 800-DUNHILL (386-4455) *Fax:* 561-998-7880 *E-mail:* dunhill@dunhillintl.com *Web Site:* www.dunhills.com, pg 1112

Reed, Scott W, V G Reed & Sons Inc, 1002 S 12 St, Louisville, KY 40210-1302 *Toll Free Tel:* 800-635-9788 *Fax:* 502-560-0197 *Web Site:* www.vgreed.com, pg 1093, 1253

Reeves, Chuck, Book Club for the Martial Arts Inc, 7 Putter Lane, Middle Island, NY 11953 *Tel:* 631-924-3888 *E-mail:* bcma@gmail.com; okmagads@gmail.com, pg 1135

Rego, Martin A, Century Direct LLC, 15 Enter Lane, Islandia, NY 11749 *Tel:* 212-763-0600 *E-mail:* contact@centurydirect.net *Web Site:* www.centurydirect.net, pg 1091, 1105, 1109, 1274

Regos, Laszlo, Laszlo Regos Photography, 24067 Research Dr, Farmington Hills, MI 48335 *Tel:* 248-398-3631 *E-mail:* laszlo@laszlofoto.com *Web Site:* www.laszlofoto.com, pg 1442

Reid, Calvin, Publishers Weekly, 71 W 23 St, Suite 1608, New York, NY 10010 *Tel:* 212-377-5500 *Fax:* 212-377-2733 *Web Site:* www.publishersweekly.com, pg 1130

Reid, Jessica, Penguin Random House Canada, 320 Front St W, Suite 1400, Toronto, ON M5V 3B6, Canada *Tel:* 416-364-4449 *Toll Free Tel:* 888-523-9292 (cust serv) *Fax:* 416-598-7764 *Web Site:* www.penguinrandomhouse.ca, pg 1295

Reid, Tracy, Library Bound Inc, 100 Bathurst Dr, Unit 2, Waterloo, ON N2V 1V6, Canada *Tel:* 519-885-3233 *Toll Free Tel:* 800-363-4728 *Fax:* 519-885-2662 *Web Site:* www.librarybound.com, pg 1317

Reiff, Robert, MagicLight Productions, 4935 McConnell Ave, Suite 1, Marina del Rey, CA 90066 *Tel:* 310-306-3839 *Fax:* 310-283-8772 *Web Site:* www.magiclight.com, pg 1441

Rein, Jody, Author Planet Consulting Services, 7741 S Ash Ct, Centennial, CO 80122 *Tel:* 303-253-1702 *Web Site:* authorplanet.org; jodyreinbooks.com, pg 1342

Reindl, David C, Reindl Bindery Co Inc, W194 N11381 McCormick Dr, Germantown, WI 53022 *Tel:* 262-293-1444 *Toll Free Tel:* 800-878-1121 *Fax:* 262-293-1445 *E-mail:* info@reindlbindery.com *Web Site:* www.reindlbindery.com, pg 1253

Reindl, Dick, Letterhead Press Inc (LPI), 16800 W Ryerson Rd, New Berlin, WI 53151 *Tel:* 262-787-1717 *Fax:* 262-787-1710; 262-787-7315 (estimating) *E-mail:* contact@letterhead-press.com *Web Site:* www.letterheadpress.com, pg 1250

Reinhard, Cordell, Universal Bookbindery Inc, 1200 N Colorado, San Antonio, TX 78207 *Tel:* 210-734-9502 *Toll Free Tel:* 800-594-2015 *Fax:* 210-736-0867 *E-mail:* service@universalbookbindery.com *Web Site:* www.universalbookbindery.com, pg 1256

Reisman, Heather, Indigo Books & Music Inc, 468 King St W, Suite 500, Toronto, ON M5V 1L8, Canada *Tel:* 416-364-4499 *E-mail:* cisales@indigo.ca *Web Site:* www.chapters.indigo.ca, pg 1290

Relihan, Ian, Granger - Historical Picture Archive, 25 Chapel St, Suite 605, Brooklyn, NY 11201 *Tel:* 212-447-1789 *Fax:* 212-447-1492 *E-mail:* info@granger.com *Web Site:* www.granger.com, pg 1447

Remington, Paul, DocuWare Corp, 4 Crotty Lane, Suite 200, New Windsor, NY 12553 *Tel:* 845-563-9045 *Toll Free Tel:* 888-565-5907 *Fax:* 845-563-9046 *E-mail:* dwsales@docuware.com; support.americas@docuware.com *Web Site:* www.docuware.com, pg 1376

Renaud, Beth, The Lane Press Inc, 87 Meadowland Dr, South Burlington, VT 05403 *Tel:* 802-863-5555 *Toll Free Tel:* 877-300-5933 *Fax:* 802-264-1485 *E-mail:* sales@lanepress.com *Web Site:* www.lanepress.com, pg 1222, 1250

Renner, Randy, Omeda, 555 Huehl Rd, Northbrook, IL 60062 *Tel:* 847-564-8900 *Fax:* 847-559-7555 *E-mail:* sales@omeda.com *Web Site:* ww3.omeda.com, pg 1332

Rennert, Cesar, Rennert International, 211 E 43 St, New York, NY 10017 *Tel:* 212-867-8700 *Fax:* 212-867-7666 *E-mail:* info@rennert.com *Web Site:* www.rennert.com, pg 1412

Reno, R R, First Things: A Journal of Religion, Culture & Public Life, 35 E 21 St, 6th fl, New York, NY 10010 *Tel:* 212-627-1985 *Fax:* 212-627-2184 *E-mail:* ft@firstthings.com *Web Site:* www.firstthings.com, pg 1126

Renzi, Jeff, Unisys Corp, 801 Lakeview Dr, Suite 100, Blue Bell, PA 19422 *Tel:* 215-274-2742 *Web Site:* www.unisys.com, pg 1387

Resk, Patrick, Porter Novelli, 195 Broadway, 17th fl, New York, NY 10007 *Tel:* 212-601-8000 *Web Site:* www.porternovelli.com, pg 1100

Resnik, Josh, CQ Roll Call, 1201 Pennsylvania Ave NW, Suite 600, Washington, DC 20004 *Tel:* 202-650-6500; 202-650-6511 (subns); 202-650-6621 (cust serv) *Toll Free Tel:* 800-432-2250; 800-678-8511 (subns) *E-mail:* customerservice@cqrollcall.com *Web Site:* cqrollcall.com; www.rollcall.com, pg 1184

Retta, Edward, Cross Culture Communications, PO Box 141263, Dallas, TX 75214 *Tel:* 214-394-3000 *E-mail:* info@crossculturecommunications.com *Web Site:* crossculturecommunications.com, pg 1408

Retta, Marilyn, Cross Culture Communications, PO Box 141263, Dallas, TX 75214 *Tel:* 214-394-3000 *E-mail:* info@crossculturecommunications.com *Web Site:* crossculturecommunications.com, pg 1408

Reyes, Crystal, Texas Bookman, 2700 Lone Star Dr, Dallas, TX 75212 *Tel:* 214-678-6680 *Toll Free Tel:* 800-566-2665 *Fax:* 214-678-6699 *E-mail:* orders@texasbookman.com *Web Site:* www.texasbookman.com, pg 1321

Reynolds, Christine, Reynolds Design & Management, 52 Piedmont Ave, Waltham, MA 02451-3015 *Tel:* 781-893-7464 *E-mail:* rdandm@comcast.net, pg 1432

Reynolds, Mike, Eckhart & Co Inc, 4011 W 54 St, Indianapolis, IN 46254 *Tel:* 317-347-2665 *Toll Free Tel:* 800-443-3791 *Fax:* 317-347-2666 *E-mail:* info@eckhartandco.com *Web Site:* www.eckhartandco.com, pg 1247

Rhodes, Amy, Market Partners International Inc, 232 Madison Ave, Suite 1400, New York, NY 10016 *Tel:* 212-447-0855 *Fax:* 212-447-0785 *E-mail:* info@marketpartnersinternational.com *Web Site:* www.marketpartnersinternational.com, pg 1349

Rhodes, Amy, Publishing Trends, 232 Madison Ave, Suite 1400, New York, NY 10016 *Tel:* 212-447-0855 *Fax:* 212-447-0785 *E-mail:* info@publishingtrends.com *Web Site:* www.marketpartnersinternational.com; www.publishingtrends.com, pg 1130

Rhodes, Brooke, Bamboo Ink, 807 Oliver Hill Way, Richmond, VA 23219 *Tel:* 804-230-4515 *E-mail:* info@bambooink.com *Web Site:* www.bambooink.com, pg 1242

Rhodes, Robert, Bamboo Ink, 807 Oliver Hill Way, Richmond, VA 23219 *Tel:* 804-230-4515 *E-mail:* info@bambooink.com *Web Site:* www.bambooink.com, pg 1242

Ribas, Maria, Stonesong, 270 W 39 St, Suite 201, New York, NY 10018 *Tel:* 212-929-4600 *E-mail:* editors@stonesong.com *Web Site:* www.stonesong.com, pg 1362

Ribolow, Adele, Ribolow Associates Inc, 1350 Avenue of the Americas, 2nd fl, New York, NY 10019 *Tel:* 212-575-2700 *Fax:* 646-496-9122 *E-mail:* ribolowstaffingservices@gmail.com *Web Site:* www.ribolow.com, pg 1390

Riccio, Dan, Apple Inc, One Apple Park Way, Cupertino, CA 95014 *Tel:* 408-996-1010 *Web Site:* www.apple.com, pg 1372

Rich, B Ruby, Film Quarterly, Journals & Digital Publishing, 155 Grand Ave, Suite 400, Oakland, CA 94612-3758 *Tel:* 510-883-8326 (fulfillment) *Fax:* 510-836-8910 (fulfillment) *E-mail:* customerservice@ucpress.edu *Web Site:* www.filmquarterly.org; fq.ucpress.edu, pg 1126

Rich, Lloyd L, Law Offices of Lloyd L Rich, 1163 Vine St, Denver, CO 80206 *Tel:* 303-388-5215 *E-mail:* rich@publishingattorney.com *Web Site:* www.publaw.com, pg 1351

Richard, Brent, Penguin Random House Canada, 320 Front St W, Suite 1400, Toronto, ON M5V 3B6, Canada *Tel:* 416-364-4449 *Toll Free Tel:* 888-523-9292 (cust serv) *Fax:* 416-598-7764 *Web Site:* www.penguinrandomhouse.ca, pg 1295

Richards, Bill, Lake Book Manufacturing Inc, 2085 N Cornell Ave, Melrose Park, IL 60160 *Tel:* 708-345-7000 *E-mail:* info@lakebook.com *Web Site:* www.lakebook.com, pg 1207, 1222, 1250, 1264, 1277

Richards, Jennifer, Over the River Public Relations LLC, 116 Gladwin Ave, Leonia, NJ 07605 *Tel:* 201-503-1321 *Fax:* 201-503-0952 *E-mail:* info@otrpr.com *Web Site:* www.otrpr.com, pg 1100

Richardson, Scott, GLS Companies, 1280 Energy Park Dr, St Paul, MN 55108-5106 *Tel:* 651-644-3000 *Toll Free Tel:* 800-655-9405 *Web Site:* www.glsmn.com, pg 1220, 1248

Richman, Aaron J, A Good Thing Inc, PO Box 20482, New York, NY 10021-0068 *Tel:* 212-687-8155 *Fax:* 212-687-8292 *Web Site:* agoodthingink.com, pg 1423

Richter, Barbara Basbanes, Literary Features Syndicate, 88 Briarcliff Rd, Larchmont, NY 10538 *Tel:* 914-834-7480, pg 1121

Rickerby, Joan, Promotional Book Co, 12 Cranfield Rd, No 100, Toronto, ON M4B 3G8, Canada *Tel:* 416-759-2226 *Fax:* 416-759-2150, pg 1319

Riddle, Michael, Evolution Computing Inc, 4228 E Andrea Dr, Cave Creek, AZ 85331 *Tel:* 602-299-1949 *E-mail:* support@fastcad.com; order_request@fastcad.com *Web Site:* www.fastcad.com, pg 1377

Ridpath, Angela, MCH Strategic Data, 601 E Marshall St, Sweet Springs, MO 65351 *Toll Free Tel:* 800-776-6373 *E-mail:* sales@mchdata.com *Web Site:* www.mchdata.com, pg 1112

Riemenschneider, Jennifer, Sheridan MI, 613 E Industrial Dr, Chelsea, MI 48118 *Tel:* 734-475-9145 *Web Site:* www.sheridan.com, pg 1209, 1254, 1267

Rifenberick, Adam, Press Box Publicity, 3920 Duncan Dr, Boca Raton, FL 33434 *Tel:* 912-658-7860 *E-mail:* sportspr@smithpublicity.com *Web Site:* pressboxpublicity-smithpublicity.com, pg 1101

Rifkind, Marion, Universe Technical Translation Inc, 9225 Katy Fwy, Suite 400, Houston, TX 77024 *Tel:* 713-827-8800 *Fax:* 713-464-5511 *E-mail:* universe@universe.us *Web Site:* www.universetranslation.com, pg 1414

Rigelman, Tony, Twin Rivers Paper Co, 82 Bridge Ave, Madawaska, ME 04756 *Tel:* 207-728-3321 *Toll Free Tel:* 800-920-9988 *Fax:* 207-728-8701 *E-mail:* info@twinriverspaper.com *Web Site:* www.twinriverspaper.com, pg 1269

Riggenbach, Jan, Jandon Features, 2319 S 105 Ave, Omaha, NE 68124 *Tel:* 402-502-4367 *Web Site:* midwestgardening.com, pg 1185

Riggins, Kathy, ColorPage, 81 Ten Broeck Ave, Kingston, NY 12401 *Tel:* 845-331-7581 *Toll Free Tel:* 800-836-7581 *Fax:* 845-331-1571 *E-mail:* sales@colorpageonline.com *Web Site:* www.colorpageonline.com, pg 1203, 1218, 1244, 1261

Riley, Estella, Walker360, 2501 Fifth Ave E, Montgomery, AL 36107 *Tel:* 334-832-4975 *E-mail:* info@walker360.com *Web Site:* walker360.com, pg 1209, 1256

Riley, Michael, Independent Publishers Group (IPG), 814 N Franklin St, Chicago, IL 60610 *Tel:* 312-337-0747 *Toll Free Tel:* 800-888-4741 (orders) *Fax:* 312-337-5985 *E-mail:* frontdesk@ipgbook.com; orders@ipgbook.com *Web Site:* www.ipgbook.com, pg 1288, 1326

Rishel, Grace, POD Print, 2012 E Northern St, Wichita, KS 67216 *Tel:* 316-522-5599 *Toll Free Tel:* 800-767-6066 *E-mail:* info@podprint.com *Web Site:* www.podprint.com, pg 1208, 1224, 1252

Rishel, Jim, POD Print, 2012 E Northern St, Wichita, KS 67216 *Tel:* 316-522-5599 *Toll Free Tel:* 800-767-6066 *E-mail:* info@podprint.com *Web Site:* www.podprint.com, pg 1208, 1224, 1252

Ritchie, Ken, Finch Paper LLC, One Glen St, Glens Falls, NY 12801 *Tel:* 518-793-2541 *Toll Free Tel:* 800-833-9983 *Fax:* 518-743-9656 *E-mail:* info@finchpaper.com *Web Site:* www.finchpaper.com, pg 1263

Rithcreek, Chris, King Features Syndicate, 300 W 57 St, New York, NY 10019-5238 *Tel:* 212-969-7550 *Toll Free Tel:* 800-526-5464 *Web Site:* www.kingfeatures.com, pg 1185

Ritter, Cynthia K, The Horn Book Guide, 300 The Fenway, Suite P-311, Palace Road Bldg, Boston, MA 02115 *Tel:* 617-278-0225 *Toll Free Tel:* 888-628-0225 *Fax:* 617-278-6062 *E-mail:* info@hbook.com *Web Site:* www.hbook.com, pg 1127

Rittwage, William, California Offset Printers Inc, 620 W Elk Ave, Glendale, CA 91204 *Tel:* 818-291-1100 *Toll Free Tel:* 800-280-6446 *Fax:* 818-291-1192 *E-mail:* info@copcomms.com *Web Site:* www.copprints.com, pg 1244

Ritz, Holly, The Penworthy Company LLC, 219 N Milwaukee St, 4th fl, Milwaukee, WI 53202 *Tel:* 414-287-4600 *Toll Free Tel:* 800-262-2665 *Fax:* 414-287-4602 *E-mail:* info@penworthy.com *Web Site:* www.penworthy.com, pg 1319, 1324

Riva, Peter, International Transactions Inc, 28 Alope Way, Gila, NM 88038 *Tel:* 845-373-9696 *Fax:* 480-393-5162 *E-mail:* info@internationaltransactions.us *Web Site:* www.intltrans.com, pg 1347

Riven, Judith, Judith Riven Literary Agent LLC, 250 W 16 St, Suite 4F, New York, NY 10011 *Tel:* 212-255-1009 *Fax:* 212-255-8547 *E-mail:* rivenlitqueries@gmail.com *Web Site:* rivenlit.com, pg 1351

Rivera, Kim M, HP Inc, 1501 Paige Mill Rd, Palo Alto, CA 94304-1112 *Tel:* 650-857-1501 *Toll Free Tel:* 800-282-6672 *Web Site:* www.hp.com, pg 1378

Rivers, Alena, Association for Library Service to Children (ALSC), 225 N Michigan Ave, Suite 1300, Chicago, IL 60601 *Tel:* 312-280-2163 *Toll Free Tel:* 800-545-2433 *Fax:* 312-280-5271 *E-mail:* alsc@ala.org *Web Site:* www.ala.org/alsc, pg 1139

Rizzo, Geoff, Southern Territory Associates, 4508 64 St, Lubbock, TX 79414 *E-mail:* sta77@suddenlink.net *Web Site:* www.southernterritory.com, pg 1299

Roark, Micah, OmniUpdate Inc, 1320 Flynn Rd, Suite 100, Camarillo, CA 93012 *Tel:* 805-484-9400 *Toll Free Tel:* 800-362-2605 *E-mail:* sales@omniupdate.com *Web Site:* omniupdate.com, pg 1383

Roback, Diane, Publishers Weekly, 71 W 23 St, Suite 1608, New York, NY 10010 *Tel:* 212-377-5500 *Fax:* 212-377-2733 *Web Site:* www.publishersweekly.com, pg 1130

Robbins, Christopher, American West Books Inc, 1254 Commerce Way, Sanger, CA 93657 *Tel:* 559-876-2170 *Fax:* 559-876-2180 *E-mail:* info@americanwestbooks.com *Web Site:* www.americanwestbooks.com, pg 1282, 1309

Robbins, Dave, Ecological Fibers Inc, 40 Pioneer Dr, Lunenburg, MA 01462 *Tel:* 978-537-0003 *Fax:* 978-537-2238 *E-mail:* info@ecofibers.com *Web Site:* www.ecofibers.com, pg 1204, 1263

Robbins, Harold, Choice Associates, 501 Fifth Ave, Suite 1601, New York, NY 10017 *Tel:* 212-679-2434 *Fax:* 212-213-0984 *E-mail:* info@choicepersonnelinc.com *Web Site:* www.choicepersonnelinc.com, pg 1389

Roberge, Marian, ProQuest LLC, 789 E Eisenhower Pkwy, Ann Arbor, MI 48108 *Tel:* 734-761-4700 *Toll Free Tel:* 800-521-0600; 877-779-6768 (sales) *E-mail:* sales@proquest.com *Web Site:* www.proquest.com, pg 1384

Roberson, Rick, The Barnabas Agency, PO Box 3113, Corsicana, TX 75151-3113 *Tel:* 903-654-1319 *E-mail:* info@barnabasagency.com *Web Site:* www.barnabasagency.com, pg 1095

Roberts, Bill, The Ohio Blow Pipe Co, 446 E 131 St, Cleveland, OH 44108-1684 *Tel:* 216-681-7379 *Fax:* 216-681-7713 *E-mail:* sales@obpairsystems.com *Web Site:* www.obpairsystems.com, pg 1278

Roberts, Bob, ClassicStock.com/Robertstock.com, 4203 Locust St, Philadelphia, PA 19104 *Tel:* 215-386-6300 *Toll Free Tel:* 800-786-6300 *Toll Free Fax:* 800-786-1920 *E-mail:* sales@classicstock.com; info@classicstock.com; info@robertstock.com *Web Site:* www.classicstock.com; www.robertstock.com, pg 1446

Roberts, Dr Catherine A, American Mathematical Society (AMS), 201 Charles St, Providence, RI 02904-2213 *Tel:* 401-455-4000 *Toll Free Tel:* 800-321-4267 *Fax:* 401-331-3842; 401-455-4046 (cust serv) *E-mail:* cust-serv@ams.org; ams@ams.org *Web Site:* www.ams.org, pg 1201, 1215, 1241, 1273

Roberts, Curtis, fd2s, 1634 E Cesar Chavez, Austin, TX 78702 *Tel:* 512-476-7733 *Web Site:* www.fd2s.com, pg 1428

Roberts, Gillian, CQ Roll Call, 1201 Pennsylvania Ave NW, Suite 600, Washington, DC 20004 *Tel:* 202-650-6500; 202-650-6511 (subns); 202-650-6621 (cust serv) *Toll Free Tel:* 800-432-2250; 800-678-8511 (subns) *E-mail:* customerservice@cqrollcall.com *Web Site:* cqrollcall.com; www.rollcall.com, pg 1184

Roberts, Margaret J, Richard Owen Roberts, Booksellers & Publishers, 139 N Washington St, Wheaton, IL 60189 *Tel:* 630-752-4122 *E-mail:* sales@rorbooks.com *Web Site:* www.rorbooks.com, pg 1319

Roberts, Martin, Linguistic Systems Inc (LSI), 260 Franklin St, Suite 230, Boston, MA 02110 *Tel:* 617-528-7410 *Toll Free Tel:* 800-654-5006 *E-mail:* clientservice@linguist.com *Web Site:* www.linguist.com, pg 1222, 1380, 1411, 1429

Roberts, Richard Owen, Richard Owen Roberts, Booksellers & Publishers, 139 N Washington St, Wheaton, IL 60189 *Tel:* 630-752-4122 *E-mail:* sales@rorbooks.com *Web Site:* www.rorbooks.com, pg 1319

Roberts, Sherry, The Roberts Group, 12803 Eastview Curve, Apple Valley, MN 55124 *Tel:* 952-322-4005 *E-mail:* info@editorialservice.com *Web Site:* www.editorialservice.com, pg 1225, 1385, 1432

Roberts, Tony, The Roberts Group, 12803 Eastview Curve, Apple Valley, MN 55124 *Tel:* 952-322-4005 *E-mail:* info@editorialservice.com *Web Site:* www.editorialservice.com, pg 1225, 1385, 1432

Robertson, Nicholle, BookComp Inc, 6124 Belmont Ave NE, Belmont, MI 49306 *Tel:* 616-774-9700 *E-mail:* production@bookcomp.com *Web Site:* www.bookcomp.com, pg 1217

Robin, Peggy, Adler & Robin Books Inc, 3000 Connecticut Ave NW, Washington, DC 20008 *Tel:* 202-986-9275 *E-mail:* adlerrobininfo@my.netmails.net *Web Site:* www.AdlerRobin.com, pg 1355

Robinson, Catherine, Ingram Content Group LLC, One Ingram Blvd, La Vergne, TN 37086-1986 *Tel:* 615-793-5000 *Toll Free Tel:* 800-937-8000 (retailers); 800-937-5300 (ext 1, libs) *E-mail:* customerservice@ingramcontent.com *Web Site:* www.ingramcontent.com, pg 1290, 1315

Robinson, Joe, Lake Group Media Inc, One Byram Brook Place, Armonk, NY 10504 *Tel:* 914-925-2400 *Fax:* 914-925-2499 *Web Site:* www.lakegroupmedia.com, pg 1112

Robinson, John, GHP, 475 Heffernan Dr, West Haven, CT 06516 *Tel:* 203-479-7500 *Fax:* 203-479-7575 *Web Site:* www.ghpmedia.com, pg 1220, 1248

Robinson, Lolly, The Horn Book Guide, 300 The Fenway, Suite P-311, Palace Road Bldg, Boston, MA 02115 *Tel:* 617-278-0225 *Toll Free Tel:* 888-628-0225 *Fax:* 617-278-6062 *E-mail:* info@hbook.com *Web Site:* www.hbook.com, pg 1127

Robinson, Lolly, The Horn Book Magazine, 300 The Fenway, Suite P-311, Palace Road Bldg, Boston, MA 02115 *Tel:* 617-278-0225 *Toll Free Tel:* 888-628-0225 *Fax:* 617-278-6062 *E-mail:* info@hbook.com *Web Site:* www.hbook.com, pg 1127

Robitaille, Lyne, Les Messageries ADP, 2315, rue de la Province, Longueuil, QC J4G 1G4, Canada *Tel:* 450-640-1234 (commercial); 450-640-1237 (sales) *Toll Free Tel:* 800-771-3022 (commercial); 866-874-1237 (sales) *Fax:* 450-640-1251 (commercial); 450-674-6237 (sales) *Toll Free Fax:* 800-603-0433 (commercial); 866-874-6237 (sales) *E-mail:* adpcommandes@messageries-adp.com *Web Site:* www.messageries-adp.com, pg 1281

Robyn, Chris, China Books, 360 Swift Ave, Suite 48, South San Francisco, CA 94080 *Fax:* 650-872-7808 *E-mail:* editor.sinomedia@gmail.com, pg 1311, 1325

Roche, Bonnie, Crain Communications Inc, 1155 Gratiot Ave, Detroit, MI 48207-2732 *Tel:* 313-446-6000 *Fax:* 313-446-0383 *E-mail:* info@crain.com *Web Site:* crain.com, pg 1184

Rocheleau, Kathleen, A to Z Indexing & Bibliographic Services, 20 St James Rd, Shrewsbury, MA 01545 *Tel:* 508-842-5602 *Web Site:* sites.google.com/site/atozindexing, pg 1215

Rochman, Paul, Color Graphic Press Inc, 42 Main St, Nyack, NY 10960 *Tel:* 845-535-3444 *Fax:* 845-535-3446 *E-mail:* info@ogpny.com *Web Site:* www.cgpny.com, pg 1244

Rock, Britta Meyer, Claris International Inc, 5201 Patrick Henry Dr, Santa Clara, CA 95054 *Tel:* 408-727-8227 (sales & cust support) *Toll Free Tel:* 800-725-2747 (sales); 800-325-2747 (cust support) *Fax:* 408-987-7447 *E-mail:* claris_sales@claris.com *Web Site:* www.claris.com, pg 1374

Rodriguez, Diego, Intuit Inc, 2700 Coast Ave, Mountain View, CA 94043 *Tel:* 650-944-6000 *Toll Free Tel:* 800-446-8848 *E-mail:* investor_relations@intuit.com *Web Site:* www.intuit.com, pg 1379

Rodriguez, Max, QBR The Black Book Review, 591 Warburton Ave, Unit 170, Hastings-on-Hudson, NY 10706 *Tel:* 914-231-6778 *Web Site:* www.qbr.com, pg 1130

Roeske, Keith, alfa CTP Systems Inc, 2503 Spring Ridge Dr, Unit D, Spring Grove, IL 60081 *Tel:* 815-474-7634 *E-mail:* info@alfactp.com *Web Site:* www.alfactp.com, pg 1372

Roessner, Jeff, Suspension Feeder, 631 E Washington St, St Henry, OH 45883 *Tel:* 419-763-1377 *Toll Free Fax:* 888-210-9654 *Web Site:* www.suspensionfeeder.com, pg 1279

Rogalski, Margaret, Hilsinger-Mendelson West Inc, 8916 Ashcroft Ave, Los Angeles, CA 90048 *Tel:* 310-659-7930 *E-mail:* hmiwest@aol.com *Web Site:* www.hilsingermendelson.com, pg 1098

Rogers, Fran, Alliance Storage Technologies Inc (ASTI), 10045 Federal Dr, Colorado Springs, CO 80908 *Tel:* 719-593-7900 *Toll Free Tel:* 888-567-6332 *Fax:* 719-598-3472 *E-mail:* sales@astiusa.com; info@astiusa.com *Web Site:* www.alliancestoragetechnologies.com, pg 1372

Rogers, Stephanie, Stephanie Rogers & Associates, 8737 Carlitas Joy Ct, Las Vegas, NV 89117 *Tel:* 702-255-9999 *E-mail:* sjrlion@aol.com; write2wow@aol.com *Web Site:* www.write2wow.com, pg 1351

Rogers-Naff, Shirley, Osa's Ark Museum Shop, 111 N Lincoln Ave, Chanute, KS 66720 *Tel:* 620-431-2730 *Fax:* 620-431-2730 *E-mail:* osajohns@safarimuseum.com; osasark@yahoo.com *Web Site:* www.safarimuseum.com, pg 1318

Roks, Edwin, Teledyne DALSA, 605 McMurray Rd, Waterloo, ON N2V 2E9, Canada *Tel:* 519-886-6000 *Toll Free Tel:* 800-361-4914 *Web Site:* www.teledynedalsa.com, pg 1386

Roland, David, Ingram Content Group LLC, One Ingram Blvd, La Vergne, TN 37086-1986 *Tel:* 615-793-5000 *Toll Free Tel:* 800-937-8000 (retailers); 800-937-5300 (ext 1, libs) *E-mail:* customerservice@ingramcontent.com *Web Site:* www.ingramcontent.com, pg 1290, 1315

Rollston, Christopher A, Bulletin of the American Schools of Oriental Research (BASOR), Boston University, 656 Beacon St, 5th fl, Boston, MA 02215 *Tel:* 617-353-6570 *Fax:* 617-353-6575 *E-mail:* asor@bu.edu; asorpubs@bu.edu *Web Site:* www.asor.org (print only subns); www.jstor.org (electronic only & print plus electronic subns), pg 1125

Romano, Jen, Casemate | academic, 1950 Lawrence Rd, Havertown, PA 19083 *Tel:* 610-853-9131 *Fax:* 610-853-9146 *E-mail:* info@casemateacademic.com *Web Site:* www.oxbowbooks.com/dbbc, pg 1284

Romer, Dorian, National Geographic Creative, 1145 17 St NW, Washington, DC 20036 *Tel:* 202-857-7537 *Toll Free Tel:* 800-434-2244 *E-mail:* natgeocreative@natgeo.com *Web Site:* www.natgeocreative.com, pg 1448

Rosado, Adrienne, Stonesong, 270 W 39 St, Suite 201, New York, NY 10018 *Tel:* 212-929-4600 *E-mail:* editors@stonesong.com *Web Site:* www.stonesong.com, pg 1362

Rosandich, Dan, Cartoon Images for Licensing, PO Box 410, Chassell, MI 49916 *Tel:* 906-482-6234 *Web Site:* www.danscartoons.com, pg 1425

Rosario, Jason, Stephen Gould Corp, 35 S Jefferson Rd, Whippany, NJ 07981 *Tel:* 973-428-1500; 973-428-1510 *E-mail:* info@stephengould.com *Web Site:* www.stephengould.com, pg 1092, 1335

Rosati, Daniel P, William S Hein & Co Inc, 2350 N Forest Rd, Getzville, NY 14068 *Tel:* 716-882-2600 *Toll Free Tel:* 800-828-7571 *Fax:* 716-883-8100 *E-mail:* mail@wshein.com; marketing@wshein.com *Web Site:* www.wshein.com, pg 1315

Rosato, Steve, OverDrive Inc, One OverDrive Way, Cleveland, OH 44125 *Tel:* 216-573-6886 *Fax:* 216-573-6888 *E-mail:* info@overdrive.com *Web Site:* www.overdrive.com, pg 1294

Rose, David, Sakurai USA Inc, 1700 N Basswood Rd, Schaumburg, IL 60173 *Tel:* 847-490-9400 *Toll Free Tel:* 800-458-4720 *Fax:* 847-490-4200 *E-mail:* inquiry@sakurai.com *Web Site:* www.sakurai.com, pg 1279

Roseman, Donald, Ingram Content Group LLC, One Ingram Blvd, La Vergne, TN 37086-1986 *Tel:* 615-793-5000 *Toll Free Tel:* 800-937-8000 (retailers); 800-937-5300 (ext 1, libs) *E-mail:* customerservice@ingramcontent.com *Web Site:* www.ingramcontent.com, pg 1290, 1315

Rosen, Jamie, Publicis North America, 1675 Broadway, New York, NY 10009 *Tel:* 212-474-5000 *Web Site:* www.publicisna.com, pg 1101

Rosen, Sherri, Sherri Rosen Publicity Intl NYC, 454 Manhattan Ave, Suite 3-J, New York, NY 10026 *Tel:* 212-222-1183 *E-mail:* sherri@sherrirosen.com *Web Site:* www.sherrirosen.com, pg 1101, 1351

Rosenbaum, Emily, The Tribune News Service, 160 N Stetson Ave, Chicago, IL 60601 *Tel:* 312-222-4131 *E-mail:* tcanews@trbpub.com *Web Site:* www.mctdirect.com; tribunecontentagency.com/tribune-news-service, pg 1186

Rosenbaum, Nanette, Stephen Gould Corp, 35 S Jefferson Rd, Whippany, NJ 07981 *Tel:* 973-428-1500; 973-428-1510 *E-mail:* info@stephengould.com *Web Site:* www.stephengould.com, pg 1092, 1335

Rosenberg, Roberta, MGP Direct Inc, 17814 Shotley Bridge Place, Olney, MD 20832 *Tel:* 240-755-6976 *Web Site:* www.mgpdirect.com, pg 1350

Rosenberger, Jim, Any Laminating Service, 13214 Crenshaw Blvd, Gardena, CA 90249 *Tel:* 310-464-8885 *Toll Free Tel:* 800-400-3105 *E-mail:* quoterequest@anylam.com *Web Site:* anylam.com, pg 1241

Rosenthal, Elise, Rosenthal Represents, 23725 Hartland St, West Hills, CA 91307 *Tel:* 818-430-3850 *E-mail:* eliselicenses@earthlink.net, pg 1432

Ross, Ken, Ken Ross Photography, PO Box 4517, Scottsdale, AZ 85261 *Tel:* 602-319-2974 *E-mail:* kenrossaz@yahoo.com *Web Site:* www.kenrossphotography.com, pg 1442

Ross, Maureen, diacriTech Inc, 4 S Market St, 4th fl, Boston, MA 02109 *Tel:* 617-600-3366 *Fax:* 617-848-2938 *Web Site:* www.diacritech.com, pg 1219, 1357, 1427

Ross, Robert C Jr, Xante Corp, 2800 Dauphin St, Suite 100, Mobile, AL 36606 *Tel:* 251-473-6502; 251-473-4920 (tech support) *Fax:* 251-473-6503 *Web Site:* www.xante.com, pg 1388

Ross, Sarah, E L H (English Literary History), 2715 N Charles St, Baltimore, MD 21218-4363 *Toll Free Tel:* 800-548-1784 (journal orders) *Fax:* 410-516-3866 (journal orders) *E-mail:* jrnlcirc@press.jhu.edu (journal orders) *Web Site:* www.press.jhu.edu/journals/english_literary_history/index.html, pg 1126

Ross, Thomas W, Ross Gage Inc, 8502 Brookville Rd, Indianapolis, IN 46239 *Tel:* 317-283-2323 *Toll Free Tel:* 800-799-2323 *Fax:* 317-931-2108 *E-mail:* info@rossgage.com *Web Site:* www.rossgage.com, pg 1225, 1253

Rosson, Mark, O'Neil Digital Solutions LLC, 12655 Beatrice St, Los Angeles, CA 90066 *Tel:* 310-448-6400 *E-mail:* sales@oneildata.com *Web Site:* www.oneildata.com, pg 1224, 1252, 1266, 1278

Roster, Leslie, Girol Books Inc, PO Box 5473, LCD Merivale, Ottawa, ON K2C 3M1, Canada *Tel:* 613-233-9044 *Fax:* 613-233-9044 *E-mail:* info@girol.com *Web Site:* www.girol.com, pg 1287, 1326

Roster, Peter, Girol Books Inc, PO Box 5473, LCD Merivale, Ottawa, ON K2C 3M1, Canada *Tel:* 613-233-9044 *Fax:* 613-233-9044 *E-mail:* info@girol.com *Web Site:* www.girol.com, pg 1287, 1314, 1326

Roswell, Michael, Roswell Bookbinding, 2614 N 29 Ave, Phoenix, AZ 85009 *Tel:* 602-272-9338 *Toll Free Tel:* 888-803-8883 *Fax:* 602-272-9786 *Web Site:* www.roswellbookbinding.com, pg 1254, 1324

Rotella, Mark, Publishers Weekly, 71 W 23 St, Suite 1608, New York, NY 10010 *Tel:* 212-377-5500 *Fax:* 212-377-2733 *Web Site:* www.publishersweekly.com, pg 1130

Roth, Charles A, Roth Advertising Inc, PO Box 96, Sea Cliff, NY 11579 *Tel:* 516-674-8603 *Fax:* 516-368-3885 *Web Site:* www.rothadvertising.com, pg 1087

Roth, Daniel J, Roth Advertising Inc, PO Box 96, Sea Cliff, NY 11579 *Tel:* 516-674-8603 *Fax:* 516-368-3885 *Web Site:* www.rothadvertising.com, pg 1087

Roth, Robert, Spiral Binding LLC, One Maltese Dr, Totowa, NJ 07511 *Tel:* 973-256-0666 *Toll Free Tel:* 800-631-3572 *Fax:* 973-256-5981 *E-mail:* customerservice@spiralbinding.com; international@spiralbinding.com (outside US) *Web Site:* spiralbinding.com, pg 1255

Roth, Steve, Motorbooks, 100 Cummings Ctr, Suite 265D, Beverly, MA 01915 *Tel:* 978-282-9590 *Toll Free Tel:* 800-759-0190 (orders) *Web Site:* www.quartoknows.com/motorbooks, pg 1318, 1327

Roth, Tom, Fluke Networks, 6920 Seaway Blvd, Everett, WA 98203 *Tel:* 425-446-5500; 425-446-4519 (sales & support) *Toll Free Tel:* 800-283-5853 *E-mail:* info@flukenetworks.com *Web Site:* www.flukenetworks.com, pg 1377

Rothchild, Susan, The Parsippany News, PO Box 6123, West Caldwell, NJ 07007-6123 *Tel:* 973-227-4433, pg 1186

Rotman, Jeff, Jeff Rotman Photography, 53 Green Ave, Lawrenceville, NJ 08648 *Tel:* 609-219-0040 *Fax:* 609-219-1595 *E-mail:* contact@jeffrotman.com *Web Site:* www.jeffrotman.com, pg 1442

Rotterman, Jacqueline, R J Promotions & Advertising, 120 Holton Ave S, Hamilton, ON L8M 2L5, Canada *Tel:* 905-548-0389 *E-mail:* rjpromo@cogeco.ca, pg 1351

Roukas, Marie, Warehouse Books Inc, 1006 Ballantine Blvd, Norfolk, VA 23504 *Tel:* 757-627-4160 *E-mail:* sales@warehousebooksinc.com *Web Site:* www.warehousebooksinc.com, pg 1322

Roullet, Alain, Long's Roullet Bookbinders Inc, 2800 Monticello Ave, Norfolk, VA 23504 *Tel:* 757-623-4244 *Fax:* 757-627-1404 *E-mail:* bindlrbi@gmail.com *Web Site:* longs-roullet.com, pg 1250, 1323

Roullet, Eileen, Long's Roullet Bookbinders Inc, 2800 Monticello Ave, Norfolk, VA 23504 *Tel:* 757-623-4244 *Fax:* 757-627-1404 *E-mail:* bindlrbi@gmail.com *Web Site:* longs-roullet.com, pg 1250, 1323

Roush, Sue, Andrews McMeel Syndication, 1130 Walnut St, Kansas City, MO 64106-2109 *Tel:* 816-581-7300 *Toll Free Tel:* 800-255-6734 *Web Site:* syndication.andrewsmcmeel.com, pg 1183, 1423

Rousseau, Stephane, Les Editions Themis, Faculte de droit, Universite de Montreal, CP 6128, Succursale Centreville, Montreal, QC H3C 3J7, Canada *Tel:* 514-343-6627 *Fax:* 514-343-6779 *E-mail:* info@editionsthemis.com *Web Site:* ssl.editionsthemis.com, pg 1313

Roverano, Addison, Publishing Data Management Inc, 39 Broadway, 28th fl, New York, NY 10006 *Tel:* 212-673-3210 *Fax:* 212-673-3390 *E-mail:* info@pubdata.com *Web Site:* www.pubdata.com, pg 1224, 1253, 1384

Samper, Marjorie, Lectorum Publications Inc, 205 Chubb Ave, Lyndhurst, NJ 07071 *Tel:* 201-559-2200 *Toll Free Tel:* 800-345-5946 *Fax:* 201-559-2201 *Toll Free Fax:* 877-532-8676 *E-mail:* lectorum@lectorum.com *Web Site:* www.lectorum.com, pg 1316

Sampson, Brent, Outskirts Press Inc, 10940 S Parker Rd, Suite 515, Parker, CO 80134 *Toll Free Tel:* 888-OP-BOOKS (672-6657) *Toll Free Fax:* 888-208-8601 *E-mail:* info@outskirtspress.com *Web Site:* www.outskirtspress.com, pg 1252, 1383

Sampson, Jeanine, Outskirts Press Inc, 10940 S Parker Rd, Suite 515, Parker, CO 80134 *Toll Free Tel:* 888-OP-BOOKS (672-6657) *Toll Free Fax:* 888-208-8601 *E-mail:* info@outskirtspress.com *Web Site:* www.outskirtspress.com, pg 1252, 1383

Sampson, Lynn, Outskirts Press Inc, 10940 S Parker Rd, Suite 515, Parker, CO 80134 *Toll Free Tel:* 888-OP-BOOKS (672-6657) *Toll Free Fax:* 888-208-8601 *E-mail:* info@outskirtspress.com *Web Site:* www.outskirtspress.com, pg 1252, 1383

Samu, Krisztina, East-West Concepts, PO Box 1435, Kapaa, HI 96746 *Tel:* 808-938-8410 *Fax:* 808-441-8121 *Web Site:* www.eastwestconcepts.com, pg 1408

Samuels, Ann C, International Service Co, International Service Bldg, 333 Fourth Ave, Indialantic, FL 32903-4295 *Tel:* 321-724-1443 *Fax:* 321-724-1443, pg 1316, 1323, 1326, 1329

Samuels, Dennis, International Service Co, International Service Bldg, 333 Fourth Ave, Indialantic, FL 32903-4295 *Tel:* 321-724-1443 *Fax:* 321-724-1443, pg 1316, 1323, 1326, 1329

Sanborn, Eric, Maps.com, 120 Cremona Dr, Suite 260, Santa Barbara, CA 93117 *Tel:* 805-685-3100 *Toll Free Tel:* 800-430-7532 *Fax:* 805-699-7550 *E-mail:* info@maps.com *Web Site:* www.maps.com, pg 1251, 1381, 1430

Sander, Brian, Post Bulletin Co LLC, 18 First Ave SE, Rochester, MN 55903 *Tel:* 507-285-7600 *Toll Free Tel:* 800-562-1758 *E-mail:* news@postbulletin.com *Web Site:* www.postbulletin.com, pg 1186

Sandler, Neil, Rosenthal Represents, 23725 Hartland St, West Hills, CA 91307 *Tel:* 818-430-3850 *E-mail:* eliselicenses@earthlink.net, pg 1432

Sands, Rick, Fenway Group, 870 Commonwealth Ave, Boston, MA 02215 *Tel:* 617-226-1900 *Fax:* 617-226-1901 *E-mail:* info@fenwaycommunications.com *Web Site:* www.fenway-group.com, pg 1247

Sandstrom, Pamela, CHOICE, 575 Main St, Suite 300, Middletown, CT 06457 *Tel:* 860-347-6933; 860-347-1387 (ad); 240-646-7027 (subn); 818-487-4555 *E-mail:* acrlsubscriptions@pubservice.com; support@acrlchoice.freshdesk.com *Web Site:* www.ala.org/acrl/choice; www.choice360.org, pg 1125

Saphire-Bernstein, Evie, Jewish Book Council, 520 Eighth Ave, 4th fl, New York, NY 10018 *Tel:* 212-201-2920 *Fax:* 212-532-4952 *E-mail:* info@jewishbooks.org *Web Site:* www.jewishbookcouncil.org, pg 1140

Saporiti, Nestor, UniNet Imaging Inc, 3232 W El Segundo Blvd, Hawthorne, CA 90250 *Tel:* 424-675-3300 *Fax:* 424-675-3400 *E-mail:* sales@uninetimaging.com *Web Site:* www.uninetimaging.com, pg 1387

Sappenfield, Darrin, Total Printing Systems, 201 S Gregory Dr, Newton, IL 62448 *Tel:* 618-783-2978 *Toll Free Tel:* 800-465-5200 *Fax:* 618-783-8407 *E-mail:* sales@tps1.com *Web Site:* www.tps1.com, pg 1255

Sareyan, Andy, Andrews McMeel Syndication, 1130 Walnut St, Kansas City, MO 64106-2109 *Tel:* 816-581-7300 *Toll Free Tel:* 800-255-6734 *Web Site:* syndication.andrewsmcmeel.com, pg 1183, 1423

Sargent, Mr Kim, Sargent Architectural Photography, 7675 Steeplechase Dr, Palm Beach Gardens, FL 33418 *Tel:* 561-881-8887 *Fax:* 561-881-8882 *E-mail:* sargentphoto@att.net *Web Site:* www.sargentphoto.com, pg 1442

Sarkar, Dr Biplab, Vectorworks Inc, 7150 Riverwood Dr, Columbia, MD 21046 *Tel:* 410-290-5114 *Toll Free Tel:* 888-646-4223 (sales) *Fax:* 410-290-7266 *E-mail:* sales@vectorworks.net *Web Site:* www.vectorworks.net, pg 1387

Sartain, Jeff, American Book Review, University of Houston-Victoria, School of Arts & Sciences, 3007 N Ben Wilson St, Victoria, TX 77901 *Tel:* 361-570-4848 *Fax:* 361-580-5507 *E-mail:* americanbookreview@uhv.org *Web Site:* americanbookreview.org, pg 1123

Sass, Brian, Champion Printing Inc, 3422 Misty Creek Dr, Erlanger, KY 41018 *Tel:* 859-727-5501 *Toll Free Tel:* 800-543-1957 (US) *Fax:* 859-727-5507 *E-mail:* sales@championprintinginc.com *Web Site:* www.championprintinginc.com, pg 1091, 1105

Satterlee, Seth, Publishers Weekly, 71 W 23 St, Suite 1608, New York, NY 10010 *Tel:* 212-377-5500 *Fax:* 212-377-2733 *Web Site:* www.publishersweekly.com, pg 1130

Sauer, Scott, Omniafiltra LLC, 9567 Main St, Beaver Falls, NY 13305 *Tel:* 315-346-7300 *Web Site:* www.omniafiltra.it/inglese/default_en.html, pg 1266

Saunders, Andrew, Getty Images Inc, 605 Fifth Ave S, Suite 400, Seattle, WA 98104 *Tel:* 206-925-5000 *Toll Free Tel:* 800-IMAGERY (462-4379 sales); 888-888-5889 *E-mail:* enterprisesolutionssales@gettyimages.com *Web Site:* www.gettyimages.com, pg 1378, 1447

Saunders, Carol, Saunders Book Co, PO Box 308, Collingwood, ON L9Y 3Z7, Canada *Tel:* 705-445-4777 *Toll Free Tel:* 800-461-9120 *Fax:* 705-445-9569 *Toll Free Fax:* 800-561-1763 *E-mail:* info@saundersbook.ca *Web Site:* librarybooks.com, pg 1297

Saunders, James, Saunders Book Co, PO Box 308, Collingwood, ON L9Y 3Z7, Canada *Tel:* 705-445-4777 *Toll Free Tel:* 800-461-9120 *Fax:* 705-445-9569 *Toll Free Fax:* 800-561-1763 *E-mail:* info@saundersbook.ca *Web Site:* librarybooks.com, pg 1297

Saunders, John, Saunders Book Co, PO Box 308, Collingwood, ON L9Y 3Z7, Canada *Tel:* 705-445-4777 *Toll Free Tel:* 800-461-9120 *Fax:* 705-445-9569 *Toll Free Fax:* 800-561-1763 *E-mail:* info@saundersbook.ca *Web Site:* librarybooks.com, pg 1297

Saunders, Neil, Victory Productions Inc, 55 Linden St, Worcester, MA 01609 *Tel:* 508-755-0051 *E-mail:* victory@victoryprd.com *Web Site:* www.victoryprd.com, pg 1363

Sauter, Megan, Biblical Archaeology Society, 4710 41 St NW, Washington, DC 20016-1705 *Tel:* 202-364-3300 *Toll Free Tel:* 800-221-4644 *Fax:* 202-364-2636 *E-mail:* info@biblicalarchaeology.org *Web Site:* www.biblicalarchaeology.org, pg 1373

Sauvageau, Yvon, Multi-Reliure, 2112 Ave de la Transmission, Shawinigan, QC G9N 8N8, Canada *Tel:* 819-537-6008 *Toll Free Tel:* 888-735-4873 *Fax:* 819-537-4598 *E-mail:* info@multi-reliure.com; administration@multi-reliure.com *Web Site:* www.multireliure.com, pg 1251

Savage, Owen, OmniUpdate Inc, 1320 Flynn Rd, Suite 100, Camarillo, CA 93012 *Tel:* 805-484-9400 *Toll Free Tel:* 800-362-2605 *E-mail:* sales@omniupdate.com *Web Site:* omniupdate.com, pg 1383

Savage, Rogue, Get Rich Book Club, 7 Putter Lane, Middle Island, NY 11953 *Tel:* 631-924-3888 (ext 202) *E-mail:* grbookclub@gmail.com; linickgroup@gmail.com, pg 1136

Sawatzki, Cory, AlphaGraphics Inc, 143 Union Blvd, Suite 650, Lakewood, CO 80228 *Toll Free Tel:* 800-955-6246 *Fax:* 801-595-7270 *E-mail:* contactus@alphagraphics.com *Web Site:* www.alphagraphics.com, pg 1372

Sawyer, John, Book Express, 2440 Viking Way, Richmond, BC V6V 1N2, Canada *Tel:* 604-448-7100 *Toll Free Tel:* 800-663-5714 *Fax:* 604-270-7161 *Toll Free Fax:* 800-565-3770 *E-mail:* info@raincoast.com *Web Site:* www.raincoast.com, pg 1310

Sawyer, John, Raincoast Books Distribution Ltd, 2440 Viking Way, Richmond, BC V6V 1N2, Canada *Tel:* 604-448-7100 *Toll Free Tel:* 800-663-5714 (CN only) *Fax:* 604-270-7161 *Toll Free Fax:* 800-565-3770 *E-mail:* info@raincoast.com; customerservice@raincoast.com *Web Site:* www.raincoast.com, pg 1296

Saxe, Dr Karen, American Mathematical Society (AMS), 201 Charles St, Providence, RI 02904-2213 *Tel:* 401-455-4000 *Toll Free Tel:* 800-321-4267 *Fax:* 401-331-3842; 401-455-4046 (cust serv) *E-mail:* cust-serv@ams.org; ams@ams.org *Web Site:* www.ams.org, pg 1201, 1215, 1241, 1273

Scelba, Dave, SGW Integrated Marketing Communications Inc, 219 Changebridge Rd, Montville, NJ 07045 *Tel:* 973-299-8000 *E-mail:* info@sgw.com *Web Site:* www.sgw.com, pg 1110

Schaff, Gema M, American Language Services Inc, 110 Otis St, Cambridge, MA 02141 *Tel:* 617-876-0833 *Fax:* 617-876-0853 *Web Site:* www.americanlanguageservices.us, pg 1407

Schaible, Daniel, BurrellesLuce, 30 B Vreeland Rd, Florham Park, NJ 07932 *Tel:* 973-992-6600 *Toll Free Tel:* 800-631-1160; 800-368-8070 *Fax:* 973-992-7675 *Web Site:* www.burrellesluce.com, pg 1391

Schamp, J Brough, J Brough Schamp Photography, 6907 Avondale Rd, Baltimore, MD 21212 *Tel:* 410-769-8016 *E-mail:* brough@schamp.com *Web Site:* www.broughschampphotography.com, pg 1440

Schaper, Julie, Consortium Book Sales & Distribution, an Ingram brand, The Keg House, Suite 101, 34 13 Ave NE, Minneapolis, MN 55413-1007 *Tel:* 612-746-2600 *Toll Free Tel:* 800-283-3572 (cust serv, Jackson, TN) *Fax:* 612-746-2606 *E-mail:* info@cbsd.com *Web Site:* www.cbsd.com, pg 1285

Schattner, Glen, Adams Book Co Inc, 80 Broad St, 5th fl, New York, NY 10004 *Tel:* 718-875-5464 *Toll Free Tel:* 800-221-0909 *Fax:* 718-852-3212 *Toll Free Fax:* 888-229-2650 *E-mail:* customerservice@adamsbook.com; orders@adamsbook.com; sales@adamsbook.com; returns@adamsbook.com *Web Site:* www.adamsbook.com, pg 1309

Schauer, Justin, SGS International LLC, 626 W Main St, Suite 500, Louisville, KY 40202 *Tel:* 502-637-5443 *E-mail:* info@sgsco.com *Web Site:* www.sgsintl.com, pg 1225

Schauffler, Rob, Forest Sales & Distributing Co, 139 Jean Marie St, Reserve, LA 70084 *E-mail:* forestsales@juno.com, pg 1314

Schelberger, Ken, Printer's Repair Parts, 2706 Edgington St, Franklin Park, IL 60131-3438 *Tel:* 847-288-9000 *Toll Free Tel:* 800-444-4338 *Fax:* 847-288-9010 *E-mail:* prpsales@printersrepairparts.com *Web Site:* www.printersrepairparts.com, pg 1278

Schell, Christopher, HP Inc, 1501 Paige Mill Rd, Palo Alto, CA 94304-1112 *Tel:* 650-857-1501 *Toll Free Tel:* 800-282-6672 *Web Site:* www.hp.com, pg 1378

Schell, Debbie M, Wagner & Schell LLP, 780 Lee St, Suite 102, Des Plaines, IL 60016 *Tel:* 847-759-9833 *Fax:* 847-759-9834 *Web Site:* www.wagneruslaw.com, pg 1352

Schell, Richard E, Wagner & Schell LLP, 780 Lee St, Suite 102, Des Plaines, IL 60016 *Tel:* 847-759-9833 *Fax:* 847-759-9834 *Web Site:* www.wagneruslaw.com, pg 1352

Schenkman, Joe, Schenkman Books Inc, 145 Bethel Mountain Rd, Rochester, VT 05767 *Tel:* 802-767-3104 *E-mail:* schenkmanbooks@gmail.com *Web Site:* www.schenkmanbooks.com, pg 1361

Schenkman, Kathryn, Schenkman Books Inc, 145 Bethel Mountain Rd, Rochester, VT 05767 *Tel:* 802-767-3104 *E-mail:* schenkmanbooks@gmail.com *Web Site:* www.schenkmanbooks.com, pg 1361

Scherba, Nancy, Roswell Bookbinding, 2614 N 29 Ave, Phoenix, AZ 85009 *Tel:* 602-272-9338 *Toll Free Tel:* 888-803-8883 *Fax:* 602-272-9786 *Web Site:* www.roswellbookbinding.com, pg 1254, 1324

Scheuch, Jennylene, Bookwrights Design, 1060 Old Ridge Rd, Lovingston, VA 22949 *Tel:* 434-263-4818 *E-mail:* design@bookwrights.com *Web Site:* www.bookwrights.com, pg 1356

Schiele, Nichole, Motorbooks, 100 Cummings Ctr, Suite 265D, Beverly, MA 01915 *Tel:* 978-282-9590 *Toll Free Tel:* 800-759-0190 (orders) *Web Site:* www. quartoknows.com/motorbooks, pg 1318, 1327

Schiller, Philip W, Apple Inc, One Apple Park Way, Cupertino, CA 95014 *Tel:* 408-996-1010 *Web Site:* www.apple.com, pg 1372

Schingler, Michelle Anne, Foreword Reviews, 413 E Eighth St, Traverse City, MI 49686 *Tel:* 231-933-3699 *Web Site:* www.forewordreviews.com, pg 1126

Schleifer, Bernard, Bernard Schleifer Co, 200 W 20 St, Suite 212, New York, NY 10011 *Tel:* 212-675-2615, pg 1351, 1432

Schloesser, Jack, OEC Graphics Inc, 555 W Waukau Ave, Oshkosh, WI 54902 *Tel:* 920-235-7770 *Fax:* 920-235-2252 *Web Site:* www.oecgraphics.com, pg 1223

Schloesser, Jeff, OEC Graphics Inc, 555 W Waukau Ave, Oshkosh, WI 54902 *Tel:* 920-235-7770 *Fax:* 920-235-2252 *Web Site:* www.oecgraphics.com, pg 1223

Schmidt, Adam, Planar, 1195 NW Compton Dr, Beaverton, OR 97006-1992 *Tel:* 503-748-1100 *Toll Free Tel:* 866-475-2627 *E-mail:* sales@planar.com *Web Site:* www.planar.com, pg 1383

Schmitt, Mike, CG Book Printers, 1750 Northway Dr, North Mankato, MN 56003 *Tel:* 507-388-3300 *Toll Free Tel:* 800-729-7575 *Fax:* 507-386-6350 *E-mail:* cgbooks@corpgraph.com *Web Site:* www. corpgraph.com, pg 1091, 1105, 1203, 1217, 1244, 1261, 1274, 1356, 1374

Schneider, F, International Service Co, International Service Bldg, 333 Fourth Ave, Indialantic, FL 32903-4295 *Tel:* 321-724-1443 *Fax:* 321-724-1443, pg 1316, 1323, 1326, 1329

Schneider, Rex, The Blue Mouse Studio, 26829 37 St, Gobles, MI 49055 *Tel:* 269-628-5160 *E-mail:* frogville@earthlink.net, pg 1425

Schneider, Thomas, Near Eastern Archaeology, Boston University, 656 Beacon St, 5th fl, Boston, MA 02215 *Tel:* 617-353-6570 *Fax:* 617-353-6575 *E-mail:* asor@bu.edu; asorpubs@bu.edu *Web Site:* www.asor.org (print only subns); www.jstor.org (electronic only & print plus electronic subns), pg 1129

Schneiderman, Jason, Bellevue Literary Review, NYU School of Medicine, Dept of Medicine, 550 First Ave, OBV-A612, New York, NY 10016 *Tel:* 212-263-3973 *E-mail:* info@BLReview.org *Web Site:* www. BLReview.org, pg 1124

Schnell, Joel, Joel Schnell Photographer, 2081 Seventh St N, North St Paul, MN 55109 *Tel:* 612-384-0413 *E-mail:* joel@schnellphoto.com *Web Site:* www. schnellphoto.com, pg 1442

Schnoll, Steven, Schnoll Media Consulting, 1253 Springfield Ave, PMB 338, New Providence, NJ 07974 *Tel:* 908-522-3190 *Fax:* 908-273-2667 *Web Site:* www.schnollconsult.com, pg 1351

Schonwald, Barbara, Conrad Direct Inc, 300 Knickerbocker Rd, Cresskill, NJ 07626 *Tel:* 201-567-3200 *Fax:* 201-567-1530 *E-mail:* listinfo@conraddirect.com *Web Site:* www.conraddirect.com, pg 1105

Schreider, Ilene, Independent Publishers Group (IPG), 814 N Franklin St, Chicago, IL 60610 *Tel:* 312-337-0747 *Toll Free Tel:* 800-888-4741 (orders) *Fax:* 312-337-5985 *E-mail:* frontdesk@ipgbook.com; orders@ipgbook.com *Web Site:* www.ipgbook.com, pg 1288, 1326

Schreier, Carl, Homestead Publishing, Box 193, Moose, WY 83012-0193 *Tel:* 307-733-6248 *Fax:* 415-621-5039, pg 1358

Schreiner, Mike, The Bureau, 2354 English St, Maplewood, MN 55109 *Tel:* 612-788-1000; 612-432-3516 (sales) *Toll Free Tel:* 800-788-9536 *Fax:* 612-788-7792 *E-mail:* sales@thebureau.com *Web Site:* www.thebureau.com, pg 1217, 1243

Schrewe, Bettina, Bettina Schrewe Literary Scouting, 220 E 23 St, Suite 409, New York, NY 10010 *Tel:* 212-414-2515 *Fax:* 212-414-2516 *E-mail:* bschrewe@bschrewe.com *Web Site:* www. bschrewe.com, pg 1351

Schriver, Amy, Sheridan PA, 450 Fame Ave, Hanover, PA 17331 *Tel:* 717-632-3535 *Toll Free Tel:* 800-352-2210 *Fax:* 717-633-8900 *Web Site:* www.sheridan. com, pg 1254

Schroeder, Bert, Schroeder's Book Haven, 104 Michigan Ave, League City, TX 77573 *Tel:* 281-332-5226 *E-mail:* info@bookhaventexas.com *Web Site:* www. bookhaventexas.com, pg 1320

Schroeder, Sandi, Schroeder Indexing Services, 23 Camilla Pink Ct, Bluffton, SC 29909 *Tel:* 843-705-9779; 843-415-3900 (cell) *E-mail:* sanindex@schroederindexing.com *Web Site:* www. schroederindexing.com, pg 1225

Schroeder, Yannic, Berryville Graphics, 25 Jack Enders Blvd, Berryville, VA 22611 *Tel:* 540-955-2750 *Fax:* 540-955-2633 *E-mail:* info@bvgraphics.com *Web Site:* www.bpg-usa.com, pg 1202, 1216, 1242

Schroeder, Yannic, Coral Graphic Services Inc, 840 S Broadway, Hicksville, NY 11801 *Tel:* 516-576-2100 *Fax:* 516-576-2168 *E-mail:* info@coralgraphics.com *Web Site:* www.bpg-usa.com, pg 1218, 1245, 1262

Schroeder, Yannic, Dynamic Graphic Finishing, 945 Horsham Rd, Horsham, PA 19044 *Tel:* 215-441-8880 *E-mail:* info@dgfinc.com *Web Site:* www.bpg-usa. com, pg 1247

Schroeder, Yannic, Offset Paperback Manufacturers Inc, 2211 Memorial Hwy, Dallas, PA 18612 *Tel:* 570-675-5261 *Fax:* 570-675-8714 *Web Site:* www.bpg-usa.com, pg 1208, 1223, 1252

Schubert, Michael, Ruder Finn Inc, 425 E 53 St, New York, NY 10022 *Tel:* 212-593-6400 *E-mail:* info@ruderfinn.com *Web Site:* www.ruderfinn.com, pg 1101

Schuetze-Coburn, Marje, University of Southern California Library, University of Southern California, Special Collections, Doheny Memorial Library, Rm 206, Los Angeles, CA 90089-0189 *Tel:* 213-740-5900 *Fax:* 213-740-2343 *E-mail:* specol@usc.edu *Web Site:* www.usc.edu/libraries, pg 1450

Schulman, Marla, Schreiber Translations Inc (STI), 51 Monroe St, Suite 101, Rockville, MD 20850 *Tel:* 301-424-7737 *Toll Free Tel:* 800-822-3213 *Fax:* 301-424-2336 *E-mail:* translation@schreibernet.com *Web Site:* www.schreibernet.com, pg 1413

Schulman, Steven A, Miami Wabash Paper LLC, 301 Wedcor Ave, Wabash, IN 46992 *Tel:* 260-563-4181 *Toll Free Tel:* 800-842-9112 *Fax:* 219-563-2724 *E-mail:* miamivalley@mafcote.com *Web Site:* www. mafcote.com, pg 1265

Schultz, Prof David, AAA Fine Translation & Interpretation, 162-31 Ninth Ave, Flushing, NY 11357-2010 *Tel:* 917-582-7456 (contact phone); 718-767-7455 (busn phone) *Fax:* 718-767-0474, pg 1407

Schultz, Emily, The John Roberts Company, 9687 East River Rd NW, Minneapolis, MN 55433 *Tel:* 763-755-5500 *Toll Free Tel:* 800-551-1534 *Fax:* 763-755-0394 *E-mail:* success@johnroberts. com *Web Site:* www.johnroberts.com; www.facebook. com/TheJohnRobertsCompany, pg 1093

Schultz, Mike, Sappi Fine Paper North America, 255 State St, Boston, MA 02109 *Tel:* 617-423-7300 *Toll Free Tel:* 800-882-4332 *E-mail:* webqueriesna@sappi. com *Web Site:* www.sappi.com/na, pg 1267

Schumacher, Paul, RAM Publications & Distribution Inc, 2525 Michigan Ave, Bldg A2, Santa Monica, CA 90404 *Tel:* 310-453-0043 *Fax:* 310-264-4888 *E-mail:* info@rampub.com; orders@rampub.com *Web Site:* www.rampub.com, pg 1296

Schumann, Max, Printed Matter Inc, 231 11 Ave, Ground fl, New York, NY 10001 *Tel:* 212-925-0325 *Fax:* 212-925-0464 *E-mail:* info@printedmatter.org *Web Site:* www.printedmatter.org, pg 1295

Schutte, Kim, Ingram Content Group LLC, One Ingram Blvd, La Vergne, TN 37086-1986 *Tel:* 615-793-5000 *Toll Free Tel:* 800-937-8000 (retailers); 800-937-5300 (ext 1, libs) *E-mail:* customerservice@ingramcontent. com *Web Site:* www.ingramcontent.com, pg 1290, 1315

Schwabe, Paul, HumanEdge, 30 Glenn St, Suite 401, White Plains, NY 10603 *Tel:* 914-428-2233 *Fax:* 914-428-5547 *E-mail:* info@humanedge.com *Web Site:* www.humanedge.com, pg 1389

Schwartz, Eugene, BMR Associates, 60 Corte Amado, Greenbrae, CA 94904 *Tel:* 415-927-1564 *E-mail:* info@bmrassoc.com *Web Site:* www.bmrassoc. com, pg 1343

Schwartz, Jerry, Associated Press (AP), 200 Liberty St, New York, NY 10281 *Tel:* 212-621-1500 *E-mail:* info@ap.org *Web Site:* www.ap.org, pg 1183

Schwartz, Meredith, Library Journal, 123 William St, Suite 802, New York, NY 10038 *Tel:* 646-380-0700 *Toll Free Tel:* 800-588-1030 *Fax:* 646-380-0756 *E-mail:* ljinfo@mediasourceinc.com *Web Site:* www. libraryjournal.com, pg 1128

Schwartz, Rodney, Durr MEGTEC LLC, 830 Prosper St, DePere, WI 54115 *Tel:* 920-336-5715 *E-mail:* megtecinquiries@megtec.com *Web Site:* www. durr-megtec.com, pg 1275

Schwartz, Stephen D, Management Recruiters of Gramercy Inc, 287 Burns St, Forest Hills, NY 11375-6129 *Tel:* 347-709-1250 *Web Site:* www. managementrecruitersny.com, pg 1389

Schwarz, Walter, Figaro, PO Box 848, Sharon, CT 06069 *Tel:* 860-248-8989; 860-364-0834 *E-mail:* design@figro.com *Web Site:* www.figro.com, pg 1345, 1357, 1377, 1428

Schwedelson, Jay, Worldata, 3000 N Military Trail, Boca Raton, FL 33431-6321 *Tel:* 561-393-8200 *Toll Free Tel:* 800-331-8102 *E-mail:* hello@worldata.com *Web Site:* www.worldata.com, pg 1113

Scianna, Cosimo, Cosimo Scianna, Photographer, 23407 Milano Ct, Boca Raton, FL 33433 *Tel:* 917-763-2927 *E-mail:* cosimoscianna@mac.com *Web Site:* www. cosimoscianna.com, pg 1442

Scianna, Irene, Cosimo Scianna, Photographer, 23407 Milano Ct, Boca Raton, FL 33433 *Tel:* 917-763-2927 *E-mail:* cosimoscianna@mac.com *Web Site:* www. cosimoscianna.com, pg 1442

Scordato, Ellen, Stonesong, 270 W 39 St, Suite 201, New York, NY 10018 *Tel:* 212-929-4600 *E-mail:* editors@stonesong.com *Web Site:* www. stonesong.com, pg 1362

Scorzelli, Frank, L+L Printers, 6200 Yarrow Dr, Carlsbad, CA 92011 *Tel:* 760-438-3456; 760-477-0321 *Fax:* 760-929-0853 *E-mail:* info@llprinters.com *Web Site:* www.llprinters.com, pg 1250

Scott, Beverly, Masque Publishing Inc, 8400 Park Meadows Dr, Lonetree, CO 80124 *Tel:* 303-290-9853 *Fax:* 303-290-6303 *E-mail:* support@masque.com *Web Site:* www.masque.com, pg 1381

Scott, Darryl, Thomas Allen & Son Ltd, 195 Allstate Pkwy, Markham, ON L3R 4T8, Canada *Tel:* 905-475-9126 *Toll Free Tel:* 800-387-4333 *Fax:* 905-475-6747 *Toll Free Fax:* 800-458-5504 *E-mail:* info@t-allen.com *Web Site:* www.thomasallen.ca, pg 1300

Scott, Frank, Roots & Rhythm Inc, PO Box 837, El Cerrito, CA 94530 *Tel:* 510-965-9503 *Toll Free Tel:* 888-ROOTS-66 (766-8766) *Fax:* 510-526-9001 *E-mail:* roots@toast.net *Web Site:* www. rootsandrhythm.com, pg 1137

Scott, Michael, Aptara Inc, 2901 Telestar Ct, Suite 522, Falls Church, VA 22042 *Tel:* 703-352-0001 *E-mail:* moreinfo@aptaracorp.com *Web Site:* www. aptaracorp.com, pg 1201, 1216, 1341, 1355, 1373, 1424

Scott-Noennig, Nancy, Roots & Rhythm Inc, PO Box 837, El Cerrito, CA 94530 *Tel:* 510-965-9503 *Toll Free Tel:* 888-ROOTS-66 (766-8766) *Fax:* 510-526-9001 *E-mail:* roots@toast.net *Web Site:* www. rootsandrhythm.com, pg 1137

Scotti, Chris, Codra Enterprises Inc, 17692 Cowan, Suite 200, Irvine, CA 92614 *Tel:* 949-756-8400 *Toll Free Tel:* 888-992-6372 *Fax:* 949-756-8484 *E-mail:* codra@codra.com; sales@codra.com *Web Site:* www.codra. com, pg 1203, 1244

Scroggie, Bill, Six Red Marbles LLC, 101 Station Landing, Medford, MA 02155 *Tel:* 857-588-9000 *E-mail:* info@sixredmarbles.com *Web Site:* www. sixredmarbles.com, pg 1226, 1385

Scruggs, Jim, Carolina Biological Supply Co, 2700 York Rd, Burlington, NC 27215-3398 *Tel:* 336-586-4399 (intl sales); 336-538-6211 *Toll Free Tel:* 800-334-5551 *Fax:* 336-584-7686 (intl sales) *Toll Free Fax:* 800-222-7112 *E-mail:* quotations@carolina.com; product@carolina.com *Web Site:* www.carolina.com, pg 1311

Seagram, Mike, Publishers Storage & Shipping Corp, 46 Development Rd, Fitchburg, MA 01420 *Tel:* 978-345-2121 *Fax:* 978-348-1233 *Web Site:* www.pssc.com, pg 1333

Seaman, Donna, Booklist, 225 N Michigan Ave, Suite 1300, Chicago, IL 60601 *Tel:* 312-944-6780 *Toll Free Tel:* 800-545-2433 *Fax:* 312-440-9374 *E-mail:* info@booklistonline.com; ala@ala.org *Web Site:* www. booklistonline.com; www.ala.org, pg 1124

Searles, Bradley J, Whitehurst & Clark Book Fulfillment, 1200 County Rd, Rte 523, Flemington, NJ 08822 *Tel:* 908-782-2323 *Toll Free Tel:* 800-488-8040 *Fax:* 908-237-2407 *E-mail:* wcbooks@aol.com *Web Site:* www.wcbks.com, pg 1333

Searls-Ridge, Courtney, German Language Services, 4752 41 Ave SW, Suite B, Seattle, WA 98116 *Tel:* 206-938-3600 *Fax:* 206-938-8308 *E-mail:* info@germanlanguageservices.com *Web Site:* www. germanlanguageservices.com, pg 1409

Secrest, John, Ingram Content Group LLC, One Ingram Blvd, La Vergne, TN 37086-1986 *Tel:* 615-793-5000 *Toll Free Tel:* 800-937-8000 (retailers); 800-937-5300 (ext 1, libs) *E-mail:* customerservice@ingramcontent. com *Web Site:* www.ingramcontent.com, pg 1290

Secrest, John F, Lightning Source LLC, 1246 Heil Quaker Blvd, La Vergne, TN 37086 *Tel:* 615-793-5000 (Ingram) *Toll Free Tel:* 800-378-5508; 800-509-4156 (cust serv) *E-mail:* lsicustomersupport@ingramcontent. com; contentacquisitioninquiries@ingramcontent.com *Web Site:* www.ingramcontent.com/publishers/print, pg 1207

Secrest, John F, Lightning Source LLC, 1246 Heil Quaker Blvd, La Vergne, TN 37086 *Tel:* 615-793-5000 (Ingram) *Toll Free Tel:* 800-378-5508; 800-509-4156 (cust serv) *E-mail:* lsicustomersupport@ingramcontent.com *Web Site:* www.ingramcontent. com/publishers/print, pg 1250, 1380

Segal, Doug, Panoramic Images, 4835 Main St, Suite LL001, Skokie, IL 60077 *Tel:* 847-324-7000 *Toll Free Tel:* 800-543-5250 *Fax:* 847-324-7004 *E-mail:* info@panoramicimages.com *Web Site:* www. panoramicimages.com, pg 1449

Segal, Joseph, Israel's Judaica Center, 441 Clark Ave W, Thornhill, ON L4J 6W7, Canada *Tel:* 905-881-1010 *Toll Free Tel:* 877-511-1010 *Fax:* 905-881-1016 *E-mail:* contact@israelsjudaica.com; thornhill@israelsjudaica.com (retail store) *Web Site:* www. israelsjudaica.com, pg 1316

Segura, Jonathan, Publishers Weekly, 71 W 23 St, Suite 1608, New York, NY 10010 *Tel:* 212-377-5500 *Fax:* 212-377-2733 *Web Site:* www.publishersweekly. com, pg 1130

Sekler, Marvin, Jonathan David Publishers Inc, 52 Tuscan Way, Suite 202-371, St Augustine, FL 32092 *Tel:* 718-456-8611 *E-mail:* customerservice@jdbooks. com *Web Site:* www.jdbooks.com, pg 1291

Selden, Charles J, Selden Associates, 150 S Mountain Ave, Montclair, NJ 07042 *Tel:* 973-746-0421, pg 1352

Seldon, Eric, Communicorp Inc, 1001 Lockwood Ave, Columbus, GA 31999 *Tel:* 706-324-1182 *E-mail:* mktech@communicorp.com *Web Site:* www. communicorp.com, pg 1218, 1244

Seldon, Lynn, Lynn Seldon Travel Writer & Photographer, 126 NE 25 St, Oak Island, NC 28465 *E-mail:* lynn@seldonink.com *Web Site:* www. seldonink.com, pg 1443

Self, Dennis, Acxiom, 301 E Dave Ward Dr, Conway, AR 72032 *Toll Free Tel:* 888-322-9466 *Web Site:* www.acxiom.com, pg 1111

Seltz, Martin, Augsburg Fortress Publishers, Publishing House of the Evangelical Lutheran Church in America, 510 Marquette Ave S, Minneapolis, MN 55402 *Tel:* 612-330-3300 *Toll Free Tel:* 800-426-0115 (ext 639, subns); 800-328-4648 (orders) *Fax:* 612-330-3455 *Toll Free Fax:* 800-722-7766 (orders) *E-mail:* customercare@augsburgfortress.org; copyright@augsburgfortress.org (reprint permission requests); info@augsburgfortress.org *Web Site:* www. augsburgfortress.org; www.1517.media, pg 1309

Sepp, Peter, Sepp Leaf Products Inc, 381 Park Ave S, No 13, New York, NY 10016 *Tel:* 212-683-2840 *Fax:* 212-725-0308 *E-mail:* sales@seppleaf.com *Web Site:* www.seppleaf.com, pg 1267

Serrano, Carla, Publicis North America, 1675 Broadway, New York, NY 10009 *Tel:* 212-474-5000 *Web Site:* www.publicisna.com, pg 1101

Serrano, Elizabeth, Association for Library Service to Children (ALSC), 225 N Michigan Ave, Suite 1300, Chicago, IL 60601 *Tel:* 312-280-2163 *Toll Free Tel:* 800-545-2433 *Fax:* 312-280-5271 *E-mail:* alsc@ala.org *Web Site:* www.ala.org/alsc, pg 1139

Seshadri, Jana, United Library Services Inc, 7140 Fairmount Dr SE, Calgary, AB T2H 0X4, Canada *Tel:* 403-252-4426 *Toll Free Tel:* 888-342-5857 (CN only) *Fax:* 403-258-3426 *Toll Free Fax:* 800-661-2806 (CN only) *E-mail:* info@uls.com *Web Site:* www.uls. com, pg 1321

Setbon, Julie H, iProbe Multilingual Solutions Inc, 20 Jay St, Suite 638, New York, NY 11201 *Tel:* 212-489-6035 *Toll Free Tel:* 888-489-6035 *Fax:* 212-202-4790 *E-mail:* info@iprobesolutions.com *Web Site:* iprobesolutions.com, pg 1410

Sethi, Bali, International Press Publication Inc, Spadina Rd, Richmond Hill, ON L4B 3C5, Canada *Tel:* 905-883-0343 *E-mail:* sales@ippbooks.com *Web Site:* www.ippbooks.com; www.facebook.com/ippbooks; twitter.com/ippbooks2, pg 1221, 1277, 1291, 1316

Sevoz, Philippe, Glatfelter, Capitol Towers South, 4350 Congress St, Suite 600, Charlotte, NC 28209 *Tel:* 717-850-0170 *Toll Free Tel:* 866-744-7380 *E-mail:* info@glatfelter.com *Web Site:* www.glatfelter.com, pg 1263

Sexton, John, John Sexton Photography, PO Box 30, Carmel Valley, CA 93924 *Tel:* 831-659-3130 *Fax:* 831-659-5509 *E-mail:* info@johnsexton.com *Web Site:* www.johnsexton.com, pg 1443

Sexton, Paul, Electronics for Imaging Inc (EFI), 6750 Dumbarton Circle, Fremont, CA 94555 *Tel:* 650-357-3500 *Toll Free Tel:* 800-568-1917; 800-875-7117 (sales) *Fax:* 650-357-3907 *E-mail:* info@efi.com *Web Site:* www.efi.com, pg 1376

Seykora, Ted, Abraham Associates Inc, 5120-A Cedar Lake Rd, Minneapolis, MN 55416 *Tel:* 952-927-7920 *Toll Free Tel:* 800-701-2489 *Fax:* 952-927-8089 *E-mail:* info@abrahamassociatesinc.com *Web Site:* www.abrahamassociatesinc.com, pg 1281

Shaffner, Carol, Shaffner's Bindery, 3305 Pattee Canyon Rd, Missoula, MT 59803 *Tel:* 406-251-2699 *E-mail:* shaffnersbindery@centric.net *Web Site:* shaffnersbindery.com, pg 1324

Shaffner, Jeff, Shaffner's Bindery, 3305 Pattee Canyon Rd, Missoula, MT 59803 *Tel:* 406-251-2699 *E-mail:* shaffnersbindery@centric.net *Web Site:* shaffnersbindery.com, pg 1324

Shah, Ketan, Kelmscott, a Fuse LLC company, 5656 McDermott Dr, Berkeley, IL 60163 *Tel:* 630-898-4261 *Web Site:* www.kelmscott.com, pg 1206, 1222, 1380

Shaifer, Norman, Custom Studios, 77 Main St, Tappan, NY 10983 *Tel:* 845-365-0414 *Toll Free Tel:* 800-631-1362 *Fax:* 845-365-0864 *E-mail:* customusa@aol.com *Web Site:* customstudios.com, pg 1218

Shanbhag, Arun, Rising Sun Book Co, 1424 Stony Brook Rd, Stony Brook, NY 11790 *Tel:* 631-473-7000 *Fax:* 631-473-7447 *Web Site:* risingsunbook.com, pg 1319, 1327

Shanley, Lorraine W, Market Partners International Inc, 232 Madison Ave, Suite 1400, New York, NY 10016 *Tel:* 212-447-0855 *Fax:* 212-447-0785 *E-mail:* info@marketpartnersinternational.com *Web Site:* www. marketpartnersinternational.com, pg 1349

Shanley, Lorraine W, Publishing Trends, 232 Madison Ave, Suite 1400, New York, NY 10016 *Tel:* 212-447-0855 *Fax:* 212-447-0785 *E-mail:* info@publishingtrends.com *Web Site:* www.marketpartnersinternational.com; www. publishingtrends.com, pg 1130

Shapiro, Daniel, Metro 360, 120 Sinnott Rd, Scarborough, ON M1L 4N1, Canada *Tel:* 416-752-8720 *Toll Free Tel:* 888-260-2208 *Web Site:* www. metro360.ca, pg 1317

Shapiro, Ira, AlphaGraphics Inc, 143 Union Blvd, Suite 650, Lakewood, CO 80228 *Toll Free Tel:* 800-955-6246 *Fax:* 801-595-7270 *E-mail:* contactus@alphagraphics.com *Web Site:* www.alphagraphics.com, pg 1372

Shapiro, Jan, Aeon Books/Vishaal, PO Box 396, Accord, NY 12404-0396 *Tel:* 845-658-3068 *Fax:* 845-658-3068 *E-mail:* aeongroup@msn.com *Web Site:* www. aeongroup.com, pg 1281

Shapiro, Jonathan, Smith-Edwards-Dunlap Co, 2867 E Allegheny Ave, Philadelphia, PA 19134 *Tel:* 215-425-8800 *Toll Free Tel:* 800-829-0020 *Fax:* 215-425-9715 *E-mail:* sales@sed.com *Web Site:* www.sed.com, pg 1226, 1254, 1268

Shari, Judi, Promotion in Motion, 714 Crescent Dr, Beverly Hills, CA 90210 *Tel:* 323-461-3921; 310-497-4001 (cell) *Fax:* 323-461-0917 *E-mail:* irwinzuckerpr@aol.com *Web Site:* www. promotioninmotion.net; www.bookpublicists.org, pg 1101

Sharma, Patricia, Multi-Tech Systems Inc, 2205 Woodale Dr, Mounds View, MN 55112 *Tel:* 763-785-3500 *Toll Free Tel:* 800-328-9717 *Fax:* 763-785-9874 *E-mail:* info@multitech.com; sales@multitech.com; mtsmktg@multitech.com *Web Site:* www.multitech. com, pg 1382

Sharp, Brad, Bookmasters, 30 Amberwood Pkwy, Ashland, OH 44805 *Tel:* 419-281-5100 *Toll Free Tel:* 800-537-6727 *Fax:* 419-281-0200 *E-mail:* info@btpubservices.com *Web Site:* www.btpubservices.com, pg 1202, 1217, 1243, 1261, 1274

Sharp, Michael J, RR Donnelley, 35 W Wacker Dr, Chicago, IL 60601 *Toll Free Tel:* 800-742-4455 *Web Site:* www.rrd.com, pg 1204, 1219, 1246, 1262, 1275

Sharp, Michael J, RR Donnelley & Sons Company, 35 W Wacker Dr, Chicago, IL 60601 *Tel:* 312-326-8000 *Toll Free Tel:* 800-742-4455 *Web Site:* www.rrd.com, pg 1332

Sharpe, David, David Sharpe Studio, 107 Sunshine Court, Beaufort, NC 28516 *Tel:* 703-509-8042 (cell) *Web Site:* www.davidsharpe.com, pg 1443

Sharpe, Lindsay, Brunswick Books, 14 Afton Ave, Toronto, ON M6J 1R7, Canada *Tel:* 416-703-3598 *Fax:* 416-703-6561 *E-mail:* info@brunswickbooks.ca; orders@brunswickbooks.ca *Web Site:* brunswickbooks. ca, pg 1284

Shattuck, Byron, Emery-Pratt Co, 1966 W M 21, Owosso, MI 48867-1397 *Tel:* 989-723-5291 *Toll Free Tel:* 800-762-5683 (orders); 800-248-3887 (cust serv) *Fax:* 989-723-4677 *Toll Free Fax:* 800-523-6379 (cust serv) *E-mail:* customer.service@emery-pratt.com *Web Site:* www.emery-pratt.com, pg 1313

Shattuck, Maurie, Emery-Pratt Co, 1966 W M 21, Owosso, MI 48867-1397 *Tel:* 989-723-5291 *Toll Free Tel:* 800-762-5683 (orders); 800-248-3887 (cust serv) *Fax:* 989-723-4677 *Toll Free Fax:* 800-523-6379 (cust serv) *E-mail:* customer.service@emery-pratt.com *Web Site:* www.emery-pratt.com, pg 1313

Shattuck, Mo, Emery-Pratt Co, 1966 W M 21, Owosso, MI 48867-1397 *Tel:* 989-723-5291 *Toll Free Tel:* 800-762-5683 (orders); 800-248-3887 (cust serv) *Fax:* 989-723-4677 *Toll Free Fax:* 800-523-6379 (cust serv) *E-mail:* customer.service@emery-pratt.com *Web Site:* www.emery-pratt.com, pg 1313

Singer, Karl, D&K Group Inc, 1795 Commerce Dr, Elk Grove Village, IL 60007 *Tel:* 847-956-0160; 847-956-4757 (tech support) *Toll Free Tel:* 800-632-2314 *Fax:* 847-956-8214 *E-mail:* info@dkgroup.net *Web Site:* www.dkgroup.com, pg 1245, 1262, 1275

Singh, Hanut, QBS Learning, 242 W 30 St, Suite 900, New York, NY 10001 *Tel:* 929-841-5969 *E-mail:* sales@qbslearning.com *Web Site:* www.qbslearning.com, pg 1361, 1431

Singh, Reggie Chua, QBS Learning, 242 W 30 St, Suite 900, New York, NY 10001 *Tel:* 929-841-5969 *E-mail:* sales@qbslearning.com *Web Site:* www.qbslearning.com, pg 1361, 1431

Singh, Siri Ram, Ancient Healing Ways, PO Box 459, Espanola, NM 87532 *Tel:* 505-747-2860 *Toll Free Tel:* 877-753-5351 *Web Site:* www.a-healing.com, pg 1309

Sirak, James F, Northeast Publishers Reps, Montville Chase, 20 Davenport Rd, Montville, NJ 07045 *Tel:* 973-299-0085 *Fax:* 973-263-2363 *E-mail:* siraksirak@aol.com *Web Site:* www.nepubreps.com, pg 1294

Sirak, Lisa, Northeast Publishers Reps, Montville Chase, 20 Davenport Rd, Montville, NJ 07045 *Tel:* 973-299-0085 *Fax:* 973-263-2363 *E-mail:* siraksirak@aol.com *Web Site:* www.nepubreps.com, pg 1294

Sit, Jenny, Chinese Christian Mission Bookroom, 1269 N McDowell Blvd, Petaluma, CA 94954-1133 *Tel:* 707-762-2688; 707-762-1314 *Fax:* 707-762-1713 *E-mail:* bookroom@ccmusa.org; ccm@ccmusa.org *Web Site:* www.ccmusa.org; www.ccmbookroom.org, pg 1311

Sittlinger, George, Maracle Inc, 1156 King St E, Oshawa, ON L1H 1H8, Canada *Tel:* 905-723-3438 *Toll Free Tel:* 800-558-8604 *Fax:* 905-723-1759 *E-mail:* hello@maracleinc.com *Web Site:* www.maracleinc.com, pg 1207, 1223, 1251

Sivils, Dan, ISOMEDIA Inc, 12842 Interurban Ave S, Seattle, WA 98168 *Tel:* 425-869-5411 *Toll Free Tel:* 866-838-4389 (sales); 877-638-9277 (support) *Fax:* 425-869-9437 *E-mail:* sales@isomedia.com *Web Site:* www.isomedia.com, pg 1380

Skelton, Samantha, The Writer's Lifeline Inc, 400 S Burnside Ave, Suite 11B, Los Angeles, CA 90036 *Tel:* 323-932-1685 *Web Site:* www.thewriterslifeline.com, pg 1353

Skillman, Richard, Allied Vaughn, 7600 Parklawn Ave, Suite 300, Minneapolis, MN 55435 *Tel:* 952-832-3100 *Toll Free Tel:* 800-323-0281 *Fax:* 952-832-3203 *Web Site:* www.alliedvaughn.com, pg 1372

Skriloff, Lisa, Multicultural Marketing Resources Inc, 720 Greenwich St, No 7T, New York, NY 10014 *Tel:* 212-242-3351 *Web Site:* www.multicultural.com, pg 1099

Slade, Michael, Art Resource Inc, 65 Bleeker St, 12th fl, New York, NY 10012 *Tel:* 212-505-8700 *Fax:* 212-505-2053 *E-mail:* requests@artres.com *Web Site:* www.artres.com, pg 1445

Slaney, John, Content Critical Solutions, 121 Moonachi Ave, Moonachi, NJ 07074 *Tel:* 201-528-2777 *E-mail:* sales_info@contentcritical.com *Web Site:* www.contentcritical.com, pg 1105

Slater, George, CRW Graphics Communications, 9100 Pennsauken Hwy, Pennsauken, NJ 08110 *Tel:* 856-662-9111 *Toll Free Tel:* 800-820-3000 *Fax:* 856-665-1789 *E-mail:* info@crwgraphics.com *Web Site:* www.crwgraphics.com, pg 1092, 1375, 1426

Slaughter, Thomas, Reviews in American History, 2715 N Charles St, Baltimore, MD 21218-4363 *Toll Free Tel:* 800-548-1784 (journal orders) *Fax:* 410-516-6968 *E-mail:* jrnlcirc@press.jhu.edu (journal orders) *Web Site:* www.press.jhu.edu/journals/reviews_in_american_history/index.html, pg 1131

Slowik, George Jr, Publishers Weekly, 71 W 23 St, Suite 1608, New York, NY 10010 *Tel:* 212-377-5500 *Fax:* 212-377-2733 *Web Site:* www.publishersweekly.com, pg 1130

Sluijter, Jaap, Krishnamurti Publications of America, 1070 McAndrew Rd, Ojai, CA 93023 *Tel:* 805-646-2726 *E-mail:* kfa@kfa.org *Web Site:* www.kfa.org, pg 1327

Small, Ian, Simply Audiobooks, 935 Sheldon Ct, Burlington, ON L7L 5K6, Canada *Tel:* 905-634-3035 *Toll Free Tel:* 877-554-4332 *Fax:* 905-847-9310 *E-mail:* customerservice@simplyaudiobooks.com *Web Site:* www.simplyaudiobooks.com, pg 1137

Smallwood, John, Smallwood & Stewart Inc, 5 E 20 St, New York, NY 10003 *Tel:* 212-505-3268 *Fax:* 212-505-3624 *Web Site:* www.smallwoodandstewart.com, pg 1362

Smart, John M, Smart Communications Inc, 641 Lexington Ave, 13th fl, New York, NY 10022 *Tel:* 212-486-1894 *E-mail:* info@smartny.com *Web Site:* www.smartny.com, pg 1385

Smietana, Bob, Religion News Service, c/o University of Missouri's Journalism School, 30 Neff Annex, Columbia, MO 65211 *Tel:* 573-884-1327 *E-mail:* info@religionnews.com *Web Site:* www.religionnews.com, pg 1186

Smith, Andy, FedEx Supply Chain, 6700 Cranberry Woods Dr, Cranberry Township, PA 16066 *Toll Free Tel:* 800-677-3110 *E-mail:* solution@fedex.com *Web Site:* supplychain.fedex.com, pg 1332

Smith, Brad, Intuit Inc, 2700 Coast Ave, Mountain View, CA 94043 *Tel:* 650-944-6000 *Toll Free Tel:* 800-446-8848 *E-mail:* investor_relations@intuit.com *Web Site:* www.intuit.com, pg 1379

Smith, Jeff, Fotosmith, 245 S Plumer Ave, No 6, Tucson, AZ 85719 *Tel:* 520-882-2033 *E-mail:* info@fotosmithusa.com *Web Site:* www.jeffsmithusa.com, pg 1438

Smith, Jeff, Kensington Technology Group, 1500 Fashion Island Blvd, Suite 300, San Mateo, CA 94404-1595 *Toll Free Tel:* 800-535-4242 *E-mail:* globalmarketing@kensington.com *Web Site:* www.kensington.com, pg 1380

Smith, Kenneth E, McClain Printing Co, 212 Main St, Parsons, WV 26287-1033 *Tel:* 304-478-2881 *Toll Free Tel:* 800-654-7179 *Fax:* 304-478-4658 *E-mail:* mcclain@mcclainprinting.com *Web Site:* www.mcclainprinting.com, pg 1207, 1223, 1251, 1265, 1278

Smith, Kesley, Greenleaf Book Group LLC, 3 Park Place, 4005 Banister Lane, Suite B, Austin, TX 78704 *Tel:* 512-891-6100 *Fax:* 512-891-6150 *E-mail:* contact@greenleafbookgroup.com *Web Site:* www.greenleafbookgroup.com, pg 1288, 1358

Smith, Kristal, Ingram Publisher Services, an Ingram brand, One Ingram Blvd, La Vergne, TN 37086 *Tel:* 615-793-5000 *Toll Free Tel:* 866-400-5351 (cust serv) *E-mail:* ips@ingramcontent.com *Web Site:* www.ingramcontent.com, pg 1290

Smith, Laura, Sheriar Foundation Bookstore, 603 Briarwood Dr, Myrtle Beach, SC 29572 *Tel:* 843-272-1339 *Fax:* 843-361-1747 *Web Site:* www.sheriarbooks.org, pg 1320

Smith, Megan, Ingram Content Group LLC, One Ingram Blvd, La Vergne, TN 37086-1986 *Tel:* 615-793-5000 *Toll Free Tel:* 800-937-8000 (retailers); 800-937-5300 (ext 1, libs) *E-mail:* customerservice@ingramcontent.com *Web Site:* www.ingramcontent.com, pg 1290, 1315

Smith, Monte, Eaglecrafts Inc, 168 W 12 St, Ogden, UT 84404 *Tel:* 801-393-3991 *Fax:* 801-393-4647 *E-mail:* sales@eaglefeathertrading.com *Web Site:* www.eaglefeathertrading.com, pg 1313

Smith, Nick, Canadian Manda Group, 664 Annette St, Toronto, ON M6S 2C8, Canada *Tel:* 416-516-0911 *Fax:* 416-516-0917 *Toll Free Fax:* 888-563-8327 (CN only) *E-mail:* general@mandagroup.com; info@mandagroup.com *Web Site:* www.mandagroup.com, pg 1284

Smith, Rob, TNG, 3320 S Service Rd, Burlington, ON L7N 3M6, Canada *Toll Free Tel:* 800-201-8127 *Toll Free Fax:* 877-664-9732 *E-mail:* cs@tng.com *Web Site:* www.tng.com, pg 1321

Smith, Ronnie L, Writer's Relief, Inc, 18766 John J Williams Hwy, Unit 4, Box 335, Rehoboth Beach, DE 19971 *Toll Free Tel:* 866-405-3003 *Fax:* 201-641-1253 *E-mail:* info@writersrelief.com *Web Site:* www.WritersRelief.com, pg 1228, 1353, 1393

Smith, Scott B, Scott B Smith Imagery, 14 Pump St, Newcastle, ME 04533 *Tel:* 305-586-8698 *E-mail:* info@scottbsmith.com *Web Site:* www.scottbsmith.com, pg 1443

Smith, Steven, AccuWeather Inc, 385 Science Park Rd, State College, PA 16803 *Tel:* 814-235-8600; 814-237-0309 *E-mail:* salesmail@accuweather.com; support@accuweather.com *Web Site:* www.accuweather.com; corporate.accuweather.com, pg 1371

Smith, Sue, Eaglecrafts Inc, 168 W 12 St, Ogden, UT 84404 *Tel:* 801-393-3991 *Fax:* 801-393-4647 *E-mail:* sales@eaglefeathertrading.com *Web Site:* www.eaglefeathertrading.com, pg 1313

Smith, Vicky, Kirkus, 65 W 36 St, Suite 700, New York, NY 10018 *E-mail:* customercare@kirkus.com *Web Site:* www.kirkusreviews.com, pg 1128

Smits, Angie, Southern Territory Associates, 4508 64 St, Lubbock, TX 79414 *E-mail:* sta77@suddenlink.net *Web Site:* www.southernterritory.com, pg 1299

Smolin, Ronald P, Coronet Books Inc, 33 Ashley Dr, Schwenksville, PA 19473 *Tel:* 215-925-2762 *Fax:* 215-925-1912 *Web Site:* www.coronetbooks.com, pg 1312

Smuck, Art, FedEx Supply Chain, 6700 Cranberry Woods Dr, Cranberry Township, PA 16066 *Toll Free Tel:* 800-677-3110 *E-mail:* solution@fedex.com *Web Site:* supplychain.fedex.com, pg 1332

Smyth, Judy, The Children's Book Store Distribution (CBSD), 23 Griffin St, Waterdown, ON L0R 2H0, Canada *Tel:* 905-690-9397 (ext 237) *Toll Free Tel:* 800-757-8372 (cust serv, CN & US) *Fax:* 905-690-3419 *E-mail:* info@childrensgroup.com; sales@idla.ca *Web Site:* www.childrensgroup.com, pg 1311

Smyth, Sam, StarGroup International Inc, 1194 Old Dixie Hwy, Suite 201, West Palm Beach, FL 33413 *Tel:* 561-547-0667 *E-mail:* info@stargroupinternational.com *Web Site:* stargroupinternational.com, pg 1102

Snell, Heather, Jeunesse: Young People, Texts, Cultures, University of Winnipeg, Centre for Research in Young People's Texts & Cultures, 515 Portage Ave, Winnipeg, MB R3B 2E9, Canada *Tel:* 204-786-9351 *Fax:* 204-774-4134 *E-mail:* jeunesse@uwinnipeg.ca *Web Site:* www.jeunessejournal.ca, pg 1127

Snow, Chris, Labels Inc, 10 Merrill Industrial Dr, Hampton, NH 03842 *Tel:* 603-929-3088 *Toll Free Tel:* 800-852-2357 *Fax:* 603-929-7305 *E-mail:* sales@labelsinc.com *Web Site:* www.labelsinc.com, pg 1250

Snow, Ella, Tanenbaum International Literary Agency Ltd (TILA), 1035 Fifth Ave, Suite 15D, New York, NY 10028 *Tel:* 212-371-4120 *Fax:* 212-988-0457 *E-mail:* tips001@aol.com *Web Site:* www.tanenbauminternational.com, pg 1352

Snyder, Andy, ProQuest LLC, 789 E Eisenhower Pkwy, Ann Arbor, MI 48108 *Tel:* 734-761-4700 *Toll Free Tel:* 800-521-0600; 877-779-6768 (sales) *E-mail:* sales@proquest.com *Web Site:* www.proquest.com, pg 1384

Snyder, Daniel, DANPHOTO, LLC, 408 E Rte 66, Flagstaff, AZ 86001 *Tel:* 928-779-4556 *E-mail:* danman@danphoto.com *Web Site:* www.danphoto.com, pg 1437

Snyder, Jeffrey W, Dikeman Laminating Corp, 181 Sargeant Ave, Clifton, NJ 07013 *Tel:* 973-473-5696 *Fax:* 973-473-2540 *E-mail:* office@dikemanlaminating.com *Web Site:* dikemanlaminating.com, pg 1262

Snyder, John, HBP Inc, 952 Frederick St, Hagerstown, MD 21740 *Tel:* 301-733-2000 *Toll Free Tel:* 800-638-3508 *Fax:* 301-733-6586 *E-mail:* contactus@hbp.com *Web Site:* www.hbp.com, pg 1220, 1248, 1276

Soden, Dave, manroland Goss web systems Americas LLC, 121 Technology Dr, Durham, NH 03824 *Tel:* 603-749-6600 *Toll Free Tel:* 800-323-1200 (parts & serv) *Fax:* 603-750-6860 *E-mail:* info@manrolandgoss.com *Web Site:* www.manrolandgoss.com, pg 1277

Solherm, Mark, Kiplinger's Personal Finance/The Kiplinger Washington Editors Inc, 1100 13 St NW, Suite 750, Washington, DC 20005-4364 *Tel:* 202-887-6400 *Toll Free Tel:* 800-544-0155 (cust serv) *E-mail:* feedback@kiplinger.com *Web Site:* www.kiplinger.com, pg 1185

Solmson, Jim, Canterbury Press, 120 Interstate N Pkwy E, Suite 200, Atlanta, GA 30339 *Tel:* 770-952-8309 *Fax:* 770-952-4623 *E-mail:* sales@canterburypress.net *Web Site:* canterburypress.net, pg 1244

Solomon, J D, District Administration Magazine, 35 Nutmeg Dr, Suite 205, Trumbull, CT 06611 *Tel:* 203-663-0100 *E-mail:* circulation@promediagrp.com *Web Site:* www.districtadministration.com, pg 1126

Solomon, Lisa, The Karel/Dutton Group, 3145 Geary Blvd, PMB 619, San Francisco, CA 94118 *Tel:* 415-668-0829 *Fax:* 415-668-2463, pg 1291

Solyom, Lori, T C Public Relations, One N La Salle St, Suite 600, Chicago, IL 60602 *Tel:* 312-422-1333 *Web Site:* www.tcpr.net, pg 1102

Sonder, Tim, Innovative Design & Graphics, 1327 Greenleaf St, Evanston, IL 60202 *Tel:* 847-475-7772 *Fax:* 847-475-7784 *E-mail:* info@idgevanston.com *Web Site:* www.idgevanston.com, pg 1221

Soneira, Dr Raymond, DisplayMate Technologies Corp, PO Box 550, Amherst, NH 03031 *Tel:* 603-672-8500 *Toll Free Tel:* 800-932-6323 (orders) *E-mail:* info.dm@displaymate.com *Web Site:* www.displaymate.com, pg 1376

Sonobe, Koji, RISO Inc, 10 State St, Suite 201, Woburn, MA 01801-2105 *Tel:* 978-777-7377 *Toll Free Tel:* 800-942-7476 (cust support) *Web Site:* us.riso.com, pg 1253, 1385

Sood, Tej PS, Newgen North America Inc, 2714 Bee Cave Rd, Suite 201, Austin, TX 78746 *Tel:* 512-478-5341 *Fax:* 512-476-4756 *E-mail:* sales@newgen.co *Web Site:* www.newgen.co, pg 1223

Sorrentino, Michela, Hermani & Sorrentino Design, 404 Musgrave Rd, Salt Spring Island, BC V8K 1V5, Canada *Tel:* 250-653-9350 *E-mail:* hermani2sorrentino@gmail.com *Web Site:* www.hermanisorrentino.com, pg 1429

Sosa, Maria, Science Books & Films, 1200 New York Ave NW, Washington, DC 20005 *Tel:* 202-326-6400 *Fax:* 202-371-9526 *E-mail:* media@aaas.org *Web Site:* www.aaas.org, pg 1131

Sosinsky, Milt, Copywriters' Council of America™ (CCA), CCA Bldg, 7 Putter Lane, Middle Island, NY 11953-1920 *Tel:* 631-924-3888; 631-924-8555; 631-604-8599, pg 1344

Souers, Dan, Victory Productions Inc, 55 Linden St, Worcester, MA 01609 *Tel:* 508-755-0051 *E-mail:* victory@victoryprd.com *Web Site:* www.victoryprd.com, pg 1363

Southworth, Bruce E, Bruce E Southworth Reviews, 1621 Lafond Ave, St Paul, MN 55104-2212 *Tel:* 651-808-1099 *E-mail:* mnbookcritic@yahoo.com, pg 1118

Souza, Anthony, The Souza Agency Inc, PO Box 128, Annapolis, MD 21401-0128 *Tel:* 410-573-1300 *Fax:* 410-573-1305 *E-mail:* info@souza.com *Web Site:* www.souza.com, pg 1087

Souza, Roseanne, The Souza Agency Inc, PO Box 128, Annapolis, MD 21401-0128 *Tel:* 410-573-1300 *Fax:* 410-573-1305 *E-mail:* info@souza.com *Web Site:* www.souza.com, pg 1087

Spangler, Joyce, Six Red Marbles LLC, 101 Station Landing, Medford, MA 02155 *Tel:* 857-588-9000 *E-mail:* info@sixredmarbles.com *Web Site:* www.sixredmarbles.com, pg 1226, 1385

Spanos, Jason, knk Software LP, 89 Headquarters Plaza N, No 1478, Morristown, NJ 07960 *Tel:* 908-206-4599 *E-mail:* info@knk.com *Web Site:* www.knkpublishingsoftware.com, pg 1348

Spedding, Michelle, The Hibbert Group, 400 Pennington Ave, Trenton, NJ 08650 *Tel:* 609-394-7500 *Toll Free Tel:* 888-HIBBERT (442-2378) *E-mail:* info@hibbertgroup.com *Web Site:* hibbert.com, pg 1092, 1106, 1109

Speer, Ren, United Library Services Inc, 7140 Fairmount Dr SE, Calgary, AB T2H 0X4, Canada *Tel:* 403-252-4426 *Toll Free Tel:* 888-342-5857 (CN only) *Fax:* 403-258-3426 *Toll Free Fax:* 800-661-2806 (CN only) *E-mail:* info@uls.com *Web Site:* www.uls.com, pg 1321

Spiegel, Tom, Presskits, PO Box 71, East Walpole, MA 02032 *Toll Free Tel:* 800-472-3497 *E-mail:* files@presskits.com; team@presskits.com *Web Site:* presskits.com, pg 1093

Spielberger, Bob, Systems & Software Services Ltd, 830 W Springfield Rd, Bldg A, Suite 2, Springfield, PA 19064, pg 1386

Spielman, Rachel, Ruder Finn Inc, 425 E 53 St, New York, NY 10022 *Tel:* 212-593-6400 *E-mail:* info@ruderfinn.com *Web Site:* www.ruderfinn.com, pg 1101

Spretnjak, Dr Christine, SOM Publishing, 163 Moon Valley Rd, Windyville, MO 65783 *Tel:* 417-345-8411 *Fax:* 417-345-6668 *E-mail:* som@som.org; dreams@dreamschool.org *Web Site:* www.som.org; www.dreamschool.org, pg 1320

Springett, Sean, Manroland Inc, 800 E Oak Hill Dr, Westmont, IL 60559 *Tel:* 630-920-2000 *E-mail:* info.us@manrolandsheetfed.com *Web Site:* manrolandsheetfed.com, pg 1250, 1277

Springmeyer, Kathy, Sweetgrass Books, 2750 Broadway Ave, Helena, MT 59602 *Tel:* 406-422-1255 *Toll Free Tel:* 800-821-3874 *Web Site:* sweetgrassbooks.com, pg 1362

Spurgeon, Heath, Flannery Book Service, 20258 Hwy 18, No 430-436, Apple Valley, CA 92307 *Toll Free Tel:* 800-456-3400 *Toll Free Fax:* 800-284-5600 *E-mail:* contact@fbs-now.com *Web Site:* www.fbs-now.com, pg 1345

Spurll, Barbara, Barbara Spurll Illustration, 160 Browning Ave, Toronto, ON M4K 1W5, Canada *Tel:* 416-594-6594 *Toll Free Tel:* 800-989-3123 *Web Site:* www.barbaraspurll.com, pg 1226

Spurlock, Tammy, Ingram Content Group LLC, One Ingram Blvd, La Vergne, TN 37086-1986 *Tel:* 615-793-5000 *Toll Free Tel:* 800-937-8000 (retailers); 800-937-5300 (ext 1, libs) *E-mail:* customerservice@ingramcontent.com *Web Site:* www.ingramcontent.com, pg 1290, 1315

Srouji, Johnny, Apple Inc, One Apple Park Way, Cupertino, CA 95014 *Tel:* 408-996-1010 *Web Site:* www.apple.com, pg 1372

St Clair, David, BDT Products Inc, 250 E Rincon St, Suite 101, Corona, CA 92879 *Tel:* 949-263-6363, pg 1373

St Clement, Courtney, DJD/Golden Advertising, 145 W 28 St, 12th fl, New York, NY 10001 *Tel:* 212-366-5033 *Fax:* 212-243-5044 *E-mail:* call@djdgolden.com *Web Site:* www.djdgolden.com, pg 1086

St-Jean, Lise, Renouf Publishing Co Ltd, 22-1010 Polytek St, Ottawa, ON K1J 9J1, Canada *Tel:* 613-745-2665 *Toll Free Tel:* 866-767-6766; 888-551-7470 (North America) *Fax:* 613-745-7660 *E-mail:* order.dept@renoufbooks.com *Web Site:* www.renoufbooks.com, pg 1297

Stachowiak, Charles Jr, Quality Bindery Services Inc, 501 Amherst St, Buffalo, NY 14207 *Tel:* 716-883-5185 *Toll Free Tel:* 888-883-1266 *Fax:* 716-883-1598 *E-mail:* info@qualitybindery.com *Web Site:* www.qualitybindery.com, pg 1253

Stack, Therisa, Tom Stack & Associates Inc, 7135 N Outrigger Terr, Citrus Springs, FL 34433 *Tel:* 305-852-5520 *E-mail:* tomstack@earthlink.net *Web Site:* www.tomstackassociates.photoshelter.com, pg 1449

Stack, Tom, Tom Stack & Associates Inc, 7135 N Outrigger Terr, Citrus Springs, FL 34433 *Tel:* 305-852-5520 *E-mail:* tomstack@earthlink.net *Web Site:* www.tomstackassociates.photoshelter.com, pg 1449

Stacy, Laurie, MMoCA Museum Store, 227 State St, Madison, WI 53703 *Tel:* 608-257-3222 *Fax:* 608-257-1219 *E-mail:* store@mmoca.org *Web Site:* www.mmoca.org, pg 1317

Stadnik, Ron, Library Bound Inc, 100 Bathurst Dr, Unit 2, Waterloo, ON N2V 1V6, Canada *Tel:* 519-885-3233 *Toll Free Tel:* 800-363-4728 *Fax:* 519-885-2662 *Web Site:* www.librarybound.com, pg 1317

Stafford, Clay, American Blackguard Inc, PO Box 680686, Franklin, TN 37068-0686 *Tel:* 615-599-4032 *E-mail:* contact@americanblackguard.com *Web Site:* www.americanblackguard.com, pg 1372

Stafford, Jacqueline, American Blackguard Inc, PO Box 680686, Franklin, TN 37068-0686 *Tel:* 615-599-4032 *E-mail:* contact@americanblackguard.com *Web Site:* www.americanblackguard.com, pg 1372

Stahl, Albert, Academic Reviews, 1-A Glenwood Ave, Lynbrook, NY 11563 *Tel:* 516-593-1275 *E-mail:* info@academicreviews.com *Web Site:* www.academicreviews.com, pg 1123

Staley, Rachel, Next Chapter Book Club (NCBC), 125 Woodside Park Dr, Amelia, OH 45102 *Tel:* 614-404-6060 *Web Site:* nextchapterbookclub.org, pg 1137

Stamper, Steven L, fd2s, 1634 E Cesar Chavez, Austin, TX 78702 *Tel:* 512-476-7733 *Web Site:* www.fd2s.com, pg 1428

Stanley, Deirdre, Thomson Reuters, 3 Times Sq, New York, NY 10036 *Tel:* 646-223-4000; 646-223-6100 (edit); 646-223-6000 (newsroom) *Web Site:* www.thomsonreuters.com, pg 1186

Stanley, Todd, Engineered Software™, PO Box 408, Grafton, MA 01519-0408 *Tel:* 336-299-4843 *E-mail:* info@engsw.com; sales@engsw.com *Web Site:* www.engsw.com, pg 1377

Stanton, Maria, ATLA Catholic Periodical & Literature Index (CPLI), 300 S Wacker Dr, Suite 2100, Chicago, IL 60606-6701 *Tel:* 312-454-5100 *Toll Free Tel:* 888-665-ATLA (665-2852) *Fax:* 312-454-5505 *E-mail:* products@atla.com *Web Site:* www.atla.com, pg 1124

Star, Brenda, StarGroup International Inc, 1194 Old Dixie Hwy, Suite 201, West Palm Beach, FL 33413 *Tel:* 561-547-0667 *E-mail:* info@stargroupinternational.com *Web Site:* stargroupinternational.com, pg 1102

Starfield, Jeffrey, CD/Works, 30 Doaks Lane, Marblehead, MA 01945 *Tel:* 978-922-4990 *Toll Free Tel:* 800-CDWORKS (239-6757) *Fax:* 978-922-5110 *Web Site:* www.cdworks.com, pg 1374

Starling, Jaime, Consortium Book Sales & Distribution, an Ingram brand, The Keg House, Suite 101, 34 13 Ave NE, Minneapolis, MN 55413-1007 *Tel:* 612-746-2600 *Toll Free Tel:* 800-283-3572 (cust serv, Jackson, TN) *Fax:* 612-746-2606 *E-mail:* info@cbsd.com *Web Site:* www.cbsd.com, pg 1285

Starr, Jane, Jane Starr Literary Scouts, 1350 Avenue of the Americas, Suite 1205, New York, NY 10019 *Tel:* 212-421-0777 *E-mail:* jane@janestarr.com, pg 1352

Starr, Steven D, Steve Starr Photojournalist Emeritus, 720 Arcadia Place, Colorado Springs, CO 80903 *Tel:* 719-632-8274 *E-mail:* steve@stevestarr.com *Web Site:* www.stevestarr.com, pg 1443

Starrett, Dave, Dave Starrett Photographer, 101 Thursfield Crescent, Toronto, ON M4G 2N4, Canada *Tel:* 647-865-8299 *E-mail:* dave@davestarrett.com *Web Site:* www.davestarrett.com, pg 1443

Stecher, Patricia, ALC Inc, 750 College Rd E, Suite 201, Princeton, NJ 08540 *Tel:* 609-580-2800 *Toll Free Tel:* 800-252-5478 *Fax:* 609-580-2888 *E-mail:* info@alc.com *Web Site:* www.alc.com, pg 1111

Steele, Jennifer, AudioFile®, 37 Silver St, Portland, ME 04101 Tel: 207-774-7563 Toll Free Tel: 800-506-1212 Fax: 207-775-3744 E-mail: info@audiofilemagazine. com Web Site: www.audiofilemagazine.com, pg 1124

Steele, Julia, BookPage®, 2143 Belcourt Ave, Nashville, TN 37212 Tel: 615-292-8926 Fax: 615-292-8249 Web Site: bookpage.com, pg 1121

Steele, Sara, Steeleworks, PO Box 4002, Philadelphia, PA 19118 Tel: 215-247-4619 Web Site: www. sarasteele.com, pg 1432

Steen, John, Evolution Computing Inc, 4228 E Andrea Dr, Cave Creek, AZ 85331 Tel: 602-299-1949 E-mail: support@fastcad.com; order_request@fastcad. com Web Site: www.fastcad.com, pg 1377

Stehle, Causten, Parson Weems' Publisher Services LLC, 3811 Canterbury Rd, No 707, Baltimore, MD 21218 Tel: 914-948-4259 Toll Free Fax: 866-861-0337 E-mail: office@parsonweems.com Web Site: www. parsonweems.com, pg 1294

Stein, Andrea J, Jane Wesman Public Relations Inc, 322 Eighth Ave, Suite 1702, New York, NY 10001 Tel: 212-620-4080 Fax: 212-620-0370 Web Site: www. wesmanpr.com, pg 1098

Stein, Jennifer, Walter's Publishing, 1750 Northway Dr, North Mankato, MN 56003 Toll Free Tel: 800-447-3274 E-mail: info@walterspublishing.com Web Site: www.walterspublishing.com, pg 1210

Stein, Lori, Layla Productions, 370 E 76 St, Apt C-704, New York, NY 10021-2556 Tel: 212-879-6984 E-mail: laylaprod820@gmail.com, pg 1359

Steinbuch, Jack, The Cleveland Vibrator Co, 2828 Clinton Ave, Cleveland, OH 44113 Tel: 216-241-7157 Toll Free Tel: 800-221-3298 Fax: 216-241-3480 E-mail: sales@clevelandvibrator.com Web Site: www. clevelandvibrator.com, pg 1274

Steiner, Deborah, RR Donnelley, 35 W Wacker Dr, Chicago, IL 60601 Toll Free Tel: 800-742-4455 Web Site: www.rrd.com, pg 1204, 1219, 1246, 1262, 1275

Steiner, Deborah, RR Donnelley & Sons Company, 35 W Wacker Dr, Chicago, IL 60601 Tel: 312-326-8000 Toll Free Tel: 800-742-4455 Web Site: www.rrd.com, pg 1332

Steiner, Stephan S, GSB Digital, 33-01 Hunters Point Ave, Long Island City, NY 11101 Tel: 212-684-3600 Fax: 212-684-3613 E-mail: questions@gsbdigital.com Web Site: www.gsbdigital.com, pg 1378

Steller, Sue F, Flottman Co Inc, 720 Centre View Blvd, Crestview Hills, KY 41017 Tel: 859-331-6636 Fax: 859-344-7085 E-mail: info@flottmanco.com Web Site: www.flottmanco.com, pg 1204

Stenger, Robert W Jr, GraphiColor Corp, 3490 N Mill Rd, Vineland, NJ 08360 Tel: 856-691-2507 Toll Free Tel: 800-552-2507 Fax: 856-696-3229 Web Site: www. graphicolorcorp.com, pg 1220, 1248

Stephens, Walter, M L N (Modern Language Notes), 2715 N Charles St, Baltimore, MD 21218-4363 Toll Free Tel: 800-548-1784 (journal orders) Tel: 410-516-6968 E-mail: jrnlcirc@press.jhu.edu (journal orders) Web Site: www.press.jhu.edu/journals/ modern_language_notes/index.html, pg 1129

Stephenson, George W, Stephenson Printing, 5731 General Washington Dr, Alexandria, VA 22312 Tel: 703-642-9000 Toll Free Tel: 800-336-4637 Fax: 703-354-0384 Web Site: www.stephensonprinting. com, pg 1255

Stephenson, Sandy, Stephenson Printing, 5731 General Washington Dr, Alexandria, VA 22312 Tel: 703-642-9000 Toll Free Tel: 800-336-4637 Fax: 703-354-0384 Web Site: www.stephensonprinting.com, pg 1255

Steuben, Alex, Rex Three Inc, 15431 SW 14 St, Sunrise, FL 33326 Tel: 954-388-8708 Toll Free Tel: 800-782-6509 Fax: 954-452-0569 Web Site: www.rex3.com, pg 1384

Stevens, Melissa, Mohawk Fine Papers Inc, 465 Saratoga St, Cohoes, NY 12047 Tel: 518-237-1740 Toll Free Tel: 800-THE-MILL (843-6455) Fax: 518-237-7394 Web Site: www.mohawkconnects.com, pg 1266

Stevens, Stacey, iCAD Inc, 98 Spit Brook Rd, Suite 100, Nashua, NH 03062 Tel: 603-882-5200 Toll Free Tel: 866-280-2239 E-mail: sales@icadmed.com; support@icamed.com Web Site: www.icadmed.com, pg 1379

Stevens, Trish, Ascot Media Group Inc, PO Box 2394, Friendswood, TX 77549 Tel: 832-334-2733 Toll Free Tel: 800-854-1134 Toll Free Fax: 800-854-2207 Web Site: www.ascotmedia.com, pg 1095

Stevenson, Deborah, The Bulletin of the Center for Children's Books, 2715 N Charles St, Baltimore, MD 21218-4363 Tel: 410-516-6900; 410-516-6987 (journal orders outside US & CN); 217-244-0324 (bulletin info) Toll Free Tel: 800-548-1784 (journal orders) Fax: 410-516-6968; 410-516-3866 (journal orders) E-mail: bccb@illinois.edu; jlorder@jhupress.jhu.edu Web Site: www.press.jhu.edu/journals/bulletin-center-childrens-books, pg 1125

Stevenson, Judy, Southern Territory Associates, 4508 64 St, Lubbock, TX 79414 E-mail: sta77@suddenlink.net Web Site: www.southernterritory.com, pg 1299

Stewart, James B, J B Stewart, 1700 Landings Blvd, Sarasota, FL 34231 Tel: 941-929-0262 E-mail: jstewartx2@comcast.net Web Site: jbstewartfinearts.com, pg 1432

Stewart, Jay, Puritan Press Inc, 95 Runnells Bridge Rd, Hollis, NH 03049-6565 Tel: 603-889-4500 Toll Free Tel: 800-635-6302 Fax: 603-889-6551 E-mail: print@ puritancapital.com Web Site: www.puritanpress.com, pg 1253

Stewart, Joan, J B Stewart, 1700 Landings Blvd, Sarasota, FL 34231 Tel: 941-929-0262 E-mail: jstewartx2@comcast.net Web Site: jbstewartfinearts.com, pg 1432

Stewart, Mark, Chicago Distribution Center (CDC), 11030 S Langley Ave, Chicago, IL 60628 Tel: 773-702-7010 Toll Free Fax: 800-621-8476 Web Site: press.uchicago.edu/cdc, pg 1285

Stewart, Tracey J, National Geographic Creative, 1145 17 St NW, Washington, DC 20036 Tel: 202-857-7537 Toll Free Tel: 800-434-2244 E-mail: natgeocreative@ natgeo.com Web Site: www.natgeocreative.com, pg 1448

Stickney, Patricia A, CVI Capital, 165 Annursnac Hill Rd, Concord, MA 01742 Tel: 978-371-0995 Fax: 978-287-5869 E-mail: admin@cvicapital.com Web Site: www.cvicapital.com, pg 1344

Stile, Ted, GTxcel Inc, 144 Turnpike Rd, Suite 130, Southborough, MA 01772-2104 Toll Free Tel: 800-609-8994 Web Site: www.gtxcel.com, pg 1378

Stilson, Peter, GTxcel Inc, 144 Turnpike Rd, Suite 130, Southborough, MA 01772-2104 Toll Free Tel: 800-609-8994 Web Site: www.gtxcel.com, pg 1378

Stilwell, Craig, Open Text Corp, 275 Frank Tompa Dr, Waterloo, ON N2L 0A1, Canada Tel: 519-888-7111 Fax: 519-888-0677 Web Site: opentext.com, pg 1383

Stine, Jane, Parachute Publishing LLC, 157 Columbus Ave, Suite 518, New York, NY 10023 Tel: 212-691-1422, pg 1360

Stinson, Sherry L, Tyler Creative, 1300 S Johnstone Ave, Bartlesville, OK 74003-5624 Tel: 918-527-6779 E-mail: info@tylercreative.com Web Site: tylercreative. com, pg 1433

Stipe, LeRoy R Jr, Archetype Inc, 317 N Market St, Lancaster, PA 17603 Tel: 717-392-7438 Fax: 717-397-8037 E-mail: mail@nmsgbooks.com Web Site: nmsgbooks.com, pg 1393

Stipe, LeRoy R Jr, North Market Street Graphics (NMSG), 317 N Market St, Lancaster, PA 17603 Tel: 717-392-7438 Fax: 717-397-8037 E-mail: mail@ nmsgbooks.com Web Site: www.nmsgbooks.com, pg 1223, 1431

Stire, Rob, The Bindery Inc, 8201 Brooklyn Blvd, Brooklyn Park, MN 55445 Tel: 763-201-2800 Toll Free Tel: 800-851-6598 Fax: 763-201-2790 E-mail: info@thebinderymn.com Web Site: www. thebinderymn.com, pg 1242

Stocking, Derek, LBS, 1801 Thompson Ave, Des Moines, IA 50316-2751 Tel: 515-262-3191 Toll Free Tel: 800-247-5323 Toll Free Fax: 800-262-4091 E-mail: info@lbsbind.com Web Site: www.lbsbind. com, pg 1265

Stoehr, John, CHOICE, 575 Main St, Suite 300, Middletown, CT 06457 Tel: 860-347-6933; 860-347-1387 (ad); 240-646-7027 (subn); 818-487-4555 E-mail: acrlsubscriptions@pubservice.com; support@ acrlchoice.freshdesk.com Web Site: www.ala.org/acrl/ choice; www.choice360.org, pg 1125

Stoffel, Rod, JP Graphics Inc, 3001 E Venture Dr, Appleton, WI 54911 Tel: 920-733-4483 Fax: 920-733-1700 E-mail: support@jpinc.com Web Site: www. jpinc.com; www.print.jpinc.com, pg 1206, 1222, 1249

Stoller, Erica, Esto, 222 Valley Place, Mamaroneck, NY 10543 Tel: 914-698-4060 E-mail: esto@esto.com Web Site: www.esto.com, pg 1446

Stone, Ben, Scholastic Book Fairs®, 1080 Greenwood Blvd, Lake Mary, FL 32746 Tel: 407-829-8000 Fax: 407-829-2600 E-mail: custservbf@ scholasticbookfairs.com Web Site: www.scholastic. com/bookfairs, pg 1298, 1320

Stone, Jenn, Chicago Distribution Center (CDC), 11030 S Langley Ave, Chicago, IL 60628 Tel: 773-702-7010 Toll Free Fax: 800-621-8476 Web Site: press.uchicago. edu/cdc, pg 1285

Stone, Lisa, Faherty & Associates Inc, 6665 SW Hampton St, Suite 100, Portland, OR 97223 Tel: 503-639-3113 Toll Free Tel: 800-824-2888 Fax: 503-598-9850 Web Site: www.fahertybooks.com, pg 1286

Stonebridge, Jason Duncan, Academic Reviews, 1-A Glenwood Ave, Lynbrook, NY 11563 Tel: 516-593-1275 E-mail: info@academicreviews.com Web Site: www.academicreviews.com, pg 1123

Stor, Robert, Copycats, 216 E 45 St, 10th fl, New York, NY 10017 Tel: 212-557-2111 Toll Free Tel: 800-404-2679 Fax: 212-557-2039 E-mail: client@copycats.com Web Site: www.copycats.com, pg 1245

Stradinger, Kristen, Bolger Vision Beyond Print, 3301 Como Ave SE, Minneapolis, MN 55414-2809 Tel: 651-645-6311 Toll Free Tel: 866-264-3287 E-mail: contact@bolgerinc.com Web Site: www. bolgerinc.com, pg 1091

Strang, Ward B, FedEx Ground, 1000 FedEx Dr, Coraopolis, PA 15108 Tel: 412-269-1000 Toll Free Tel: 800-762-3725 Web Site: www.fedex.com, pg 1332

Straughan, Bruce, ISOMEDIA Inc, 12842 Interurban Ave S, Seattle, WA 98168 Tel: 425-869-5411 Toll Free Tel: 866-838-4389 (sales); 877-638-9277 (support) Fax: 425-869-9437 E-mail: sales@isomedia.com Web Site: www.isomedia.com, pg 1380

Straus, Diane, Washington Monthly, 1200 18 St NW, Suite 330, Washington, DC 20036 Tel: 202-955-9010 Fax: 202-955-9011 E-mail: editors@ washingtonmonthly.com Web Site: www. washingtonmonthly.com, pg 1132

Straw, Steve, Chesapeake & Hudson Inc, 115 W Potomac St, Brunswick, MD 21716 Tel: 301-834-7170 Toll Free Tel: 800-231-4469 Toll Free Fax: 800-307-5163 E-mail: office@cheshud.com Web Site: www. cheshud.com, pg 1285

Stringer, Linda L, Publications Professionals LLC, 3603 Chain Bridge Rd, Suite A & B, Fairfax, VA 22030-3244 Tel: 703-934-4499 Fax: 703-591-7389 E-mail: info@pubspros.com Web Site: www.pubspros. com, pg 1390

Strittmatter, Aimee, Association for Library Service to Children (ALSC), 225 N Michigan Ave, Suite 1300, Chicago, IL 60601 Tel: 312-280-2163 Toll Free Tel: 800-545-2433 Fax: 312-280-5271 E-mail: alsc@ ala.org Web Site: www.ala.org/alsc, pg 1139

Strong, Kathi, Emery-Pratt Co, 1966 W M 21, Owosso, MI 48867-1397 Tel: 989-723-5291 Toll Free Tel: 800-762-5683 (orders); 800-248-3887 (cust serv) Fax: 989-

Uchimoto, Dennis, Bindery & Distribution Service Inc, 9 Overbrook Rd, South Barrington, IL 60010 *Tel:* 312-550-7000 *Fax:* 847-842-8800, pg 1274

Uenishi, Hiroyuki, Nissha USA Inc, 1051 Perimeter Dr, Suite 600, Schaumburg, IL 60173 *Tel:* 847-413-2665 *Fax:* 847-413-4085 *Web Site:* www.nissha.com, pg 1208, 1223, 1251

Urbahn, Keith, Javelin Group, 203 S Union St, Suite 200, Alexandria, VA 22314 *Tel:* 703-490-8845 *E-mail:* hello@javelindc.com *Web Site:* javelindc.com, pg 1347

Urey, Jill L, Glatfelter, Capitol Towers South, 4350 Congress St, Suite 600, Charlotte, NC 28209 *Tel:* 717-850-0170 *Toll Free Tel:* 866-744-7380 *E-mail:* info@glatfelter.com *Web Site:* www.glatfelter.com, pg 1263

Uttam, Lal, Amcorp Ltd, 10 Norden Lane, Huntington Station, NY 11746 *Tel:* 631-271-0548 *Fax:* 631-549-8849 *E-mail:* amcorpltd@aol.com, pg 1325

Vachon, Jacques, Resolute Forest Products, 111 Robert-Bourassa Blvd, Suite 5000, Montreal, QC H3C 2M1, Canada *Tel:* 514-875-2160 *Toll Free Tel:* 800-361-2888 *E-mail:* info@resolutefp.com *Web Site:* www.resolutefp.com, pg 1267

Valade, Roger, ProQuest LLC, 789 E Eisenhower Pkwy, Ann Arbor, MI 48108 *Tel:* 734-761-4700 *Toll Free Tel:* 800-521-0600; 877-779-6768 (sales) *E-mail:* sales@proquest.com *Web Site:* www.proquest.com, pg 1384

Valdivia, Arturo, Polyglot Communications Inc, PO Box 1962, Laguna Beach, CA 92652 *Tel:* 949-497-1544 *E-mail:* info@polyglot.us.com *Web Site:* www.polyglot.us.com, pg 1412

Vallee, Marc, Ariane Editions, 1217 Bernard W, Suite 101, Montreal, QC H2V 1V7, Canada *Tel:* 514-276-2949 *Fax:* 514-276-4121 *E-mail:* info@editions-ariane.com *Web Site:* www.editions-ariane.com, pg 1309

Vallette, Alexandre, Six Red Marbles LLC, 101 Station Landing, Medford, MA 02155 *Tel:* 857-588-9000 *E-mail:* info@sixredmarbles.com *Web Site:* www.sixredmarbles.com, pg 1226, 1385

Van Alstyne, Fred, Content Critical Solutions, 121 Moonachi Ave, Moonachi, NJ 07074 *Tel:* 201-528-2777 *E-mail:* sales_info@contentcritical.com *Web Site:* www.contentcritical.com, pg 1105

Van Cleave, Margaret, Virginia Systems, 5509 W Bay Ct, Midlothian, VA 23112 *Tel:* 804-739-3200 *Fax:* 804-739-8376 *E-mail:* sales@virginiasystems.com *Web Site:* www.virginiasystems.com, pg 1387

Van Cleave, Philip, Virginia Systems, 5509 W Bay Ct, Midlothian, VA 23112 *Tel:* 804-739-3200 *Fax:* 804-739-8376 *E-mail:* sales@virginiasystems.com *Web Site:* www.virginiasystems.com, pg 1387

Van Dam, Stephan, VanDam Inc, The VanDam Bldg, 121 W 27 St, New York, NY 10001 *Tel:* 212-929-0416 *Toll Free Tel:* 800-UNFOLDS (863-6537) *Fax:* 212-929-0426 *E-mail:* info@vandam.com *Web Site:* www.vandam.com, pg 1363

Van Dyke, Brandon, Darwill, 11900 W Roosevelt Rd, Hillside, IL 60162 *Tel:* 708-236-4900 *Fax:* 708-236-5820 *E-mail:* info@darwill.com *Web Site:* www.darwill.com, pg 1218

Van Dyke, Troy, Darwill, 11900 W Roosevelt Rd, Hillside, IL 60162 *Tel:* 708-236-4900 *Fax:* 708-236-5820 *E-mail:* info@darwill.com *Web Site:* www.darwill.com, pg 1218

Van Horn, James R, Sun Chemical Corp, 35 Waterview Blvd, Parsippany, NJ 07054-1285 *Tel:* 973-404-6000 *E-mail:* globalmarketing@sunchemical.com *Web Site:* www.sunchemical.com, pg 1268

van Kralingen, Bridget, IBM Corp, One New Orchard Rd, Armonk, NY 10504 *Tel:* 914-499-1900 *Toll Free Tel:* 800-426-4968 *E-mail:* askibm@vnet.ibm.com *Web Site:* www.ibm.com, pg 1379

Van Leeuwen, Mitzi, Reichhold Inc, 1035 Swabia Ct, Durham, NC 27703 *Tel:* 919-990-7500 *Toll Free Tel:* 800-448-3482 *Fax:* 919-990-7749 *Web Site:* www.reichhold.com, pg 1267

Van Sprang, Andrew J, Maple Logistics Solutions, 60 Grumbacher Rd, York, PA 17406 *Tel:* 717-764-4596 *Fax:* 717-764-4494 *E-mail:* info@maplesoln.com *Web Site:* www.maplelogisticssolutions.com, pg 1291, 1332

Van Sprang, Andrew J, Maple Press, 480 Willow Springs Lane, York, PA 17406 *Tel:* 717-764-5911 *Toll Free Tel:* 800-999-5911 *Fax:* 717-764-4702 *E-mail:* sales@maplepress.com *Web Site:* www.maplepress.com, pg 1207, 1250, 1277

Van Wagenen, Jay, JVW Direct, 309 W Hutchinson Ave, Pittsburgh, PA 15218, pg 1086, 1348

Vance, Becky, Emprint®, 5425 Florida Blvd, Baton Rouge, LA 70806 *Tel:* 225-923-2550 *Toll Free Tel:* 800-211-8335 *Web Site:* emprint.com, pg 1204, 1219, 1247

Vanek, Todd, Bang Printing Co Inc, 3323 Oak St, Brainerd, MN 56401 *Tel:* 218-829-2877 *Toll Free Tel:* 800-328-0450 *Fax:* 218-829-7145 *E-mail:* info@bangprinting.com *Web Site:* www.bangprinting.com, pg 1202, 1216, 1242, 1261

VanHees, Robert, ProQuest LLC, 789 E Eisenhower Pkwy, Ann Arbor, MI 48108 *Tel:* 734-761-4700 *Toll Free Tel:* 800-521-0600; 877-779-6768 (sales) *E-mail:* sales@proquest.com *Web Site:* www.proquest.com, pg 1384

Vanzetti, Dakshina, Auromere Ayurvedic Inc, 2621 W Hwy 12, Lodi, CA 95242 *Toll Free Tel:* 800-735-4691 *Web Site:* www.auromere.com, pg 1282, 1325

Varadananda, Swami, Vedanta Book Center, 14630 S Lemont Rd, Homer Glen, IL 60491 *Tel:* 708-301-9062 *Fax:* 708-301-9063 *Web Site:* www.vedantabooks.com, pg 1322, 1328

Varallo, Margie, ATS Mobile, 1150 First Ave, Suite 105, King of Prussia, PA 19406 *Tel:* 610-688-6000 *Toll Free Tel:* 800-247-1287 *Fax:* 610-964-9117 *Web Site:* www.atsmobile.com, pg 1342

Varno, David, Publishers Weekly, 71 W 23 St, Suite 1608, New York, NY 10010 *Tel:* 212-377-5500 *Fax:* 212-377-2733 *Web Site:* www.publishersweekly.com, pg 1130

Varrasso, Rino, OGM USA, 4333 46 St, Suite F2, Sunnyside, NY 11104 *Tel:* 212-964-2430 *Web Site:* www.ogm.it, pg 1208, 1224, 1252, 1266

Vatne, Britt, ALC Inc, 750 College Rd E, Suite 201, Princeton, NJ 08540 *Tel:* 609-580-2800 *Toll Free Tel:* 800-252-5478 *Fax:* 609-580-2888 *E-mail:* info@alc.com *Web Site:* www.alc.com, pg 1111

Vaughan, Richard A, Publishing Management Associates Inc, 129 S Phelps Ave, Suite 312, Rockford, IL 61108 *Tel:* 815-398-8569 *Fax:* 815-398-8579 *E-mail:* pma@pma-inc.net *Web Site:* www.pma-inc.net, pg 1351

Vaughn, Lizanne, Getty Images Inc, 605 Fifth Ave S, Suite 400, Seattle, WA 98104 *Tel:* 206-925-5000 *Toll Free Tel:* 800-IMAGERY (462-4379 sales); 888-888-5889 *E-mail:* enterprisesolutionssales@gettyimages.com *Web Site:* www.gettyimages.com, pg 1378

Vazinski, Shawn, Lachina Precision Graphics Services, 3791 S Green Rd, Cleveland, OH 44122 *Tel:* 216-292-7959 *E-mail:* info@lachina.com *Web Site:* www.lachina.com, pg 1222, 1359, 1380, 1429

Vekony, Atilla, Wheatmark Inc, 2030 E Speedway Blvd, Suite 106, Tucson, AZ 85719 *Tel:* 520-798-0888 *Toll Free Tel:* 888-934-0888 *Fax:* 520-798-3394 *E-mail:* info@wheatmark.com *Web Site:* www.wheatmark.com, pg 1353

Velasco, Jorge, Berryville Graphics, 25 Jack Enders Blvd, Berryville, VA 22611 *Tel:* 540-955-2750 *Fax:* 540-955-2633 *E-mail:* info@bvgraphics.com *Web Site:* www.bpg-usa.com, pg 1202, 1216, 1242

Velasco, Jorge, Coral Graphic Services Inc, 840 S Broadway, Hicksville, NY 11801 *Tel:* 516-576-2100 *Fax:* 516-576-2168 *E-mail:* info@coralgraphics.com *Web Site:* www.bpg-usa.com, pg 1218, 1245, 1262

Velasco, Jorge, Dynamic Graphic Finishing, 945 Horsham Rd, Horsham, PA 19044 *Tel:* 215-441-8880 *E-mail:* info@dgfinc.com *Web Site:* www.bpg-usa.com, pg 1247

Velasco, Jorge, Offset Paperback Manufacturers Inc, 2211 Memorial Hwy, Dallas, PA 18612 *Tel:* 570-675-5261 *Fax:* 570-675-8714 *Web Site:* www.bpg-usa.com, pg 1208, 1223, 1252

Venable, Donna, Ricoh Americas Corp, 300 Eagleview Blvd, Exton, PA 19341 *Tel:* 610-296-8000 *Toll Free Tel:* 800-333-2679 (prod support); 800-637-4264 (sales) *Web Site:* www.ricoh-usa.com, pg 1385

Verant, Cindy, Allied Vaughn, 7600 Parklawn Ave, Suite 300, Minneapolis, MN 55435 *Tel:* 952-832-3100 *Toll Free Tel:* 800-323-0281 *Fax:* 952-832-3203 *Web Site:* www.alliedvaughn.com, pg 1372

Vergoth, Nick, Lake Book Manufacturing Inc, 2085 N Cornell Ave, Melrose Park, IL 60160 *Tel:* 708-345-7000 *E-mail:* info@lakebook.com *Web Site:* www.lakebook.com, pg 1207, 1222, 1250, 1265, 1277

Vettel, Rich, UnitechEDI Inc, 220 Winthrop St, Winthrop, MA 02152 *Toll Free Tel:* 800-330-4094 *E-mail:* info@unitechedi.com *Web Site:* www.unitechedi.com, pg 1387

Vicks, Dwight E III, Vicks Lithograph & Printing Corp, 5166 Commercial Dr, Yorkville, NY 13495 *Tel:* 315-736-9344 *E-mail:* info@vicks.biz *Web Site:* www.vicks.biz, pg 1209, 1256

Viesti, Joe, Viesti Associates, 361 S Camino Del Rio, Suite 111, Durango, CO 81303 *Tel:* 970-403-1000 *Fax:* 970-382-2700 *E-mail:* photos@viestiassociates.com *Web Site:* www.viestiphoto.com, pg 1450

Vijil, Alfonso, The Latin American Book Store Ltd, PO Box 7328, Redlands, CA 92375 *Toll Free Tel:* 800-645-4276 *Fax:* 909-335-9945 *E-mail:* libros@latinamericanbooks.com *Web Site:* www.latinamericanbooks.com, pg 1327

Viktorin, Brian, Greenleaf Book Group LLC, 3 Park Place, 4005 Banister Lane, Suite B, Austin, TX 78704 *Tel:* 512-891-6100 *Fax:* 512-891-6150 *E-mail:* contact@greenleafbookgroup.com *Web Site:* www.greenleafbookgroup.com, pg 1288, 1358

Vitale, Mary Beth, Veritiv™ Corporation, 400 Northpark Town Ctr, 1000 Abernathy Rd, Suite 1700, Atlanta, GA 30328 *Tel:* 770-391-8200 *Toll Free Tel:* 844-VERITIV (837-4848); 800-864-7687 (cust serv) *E-mail:* contactus@veritivcorp.com *Web Site:* www.veritivcorp.com, pg 1269

Vives, Lisa, Global Information Network Ltd, 6040 Boulevard E, No 21-H, West New York, NJ 07093 *Tel:* 212-244-3123 *E-mail:* newsdesk@mindspring.com *Web Site:* www.indepthnews.net, pg 1184

Vivona, John, Andrews McMeel Syndication, 1130 Walnut St, Kansas City, MO 64106-2109 *Tel:* 816-581-7300 *Toll Free Tel:* 800-255-6734 *Web Site:* syndication.andrewsmcmeel.com, pg 1183, 1423

Vladi, Olga, Arbor Books, 244 Madison Ave, Box 254, New York, NY 10016 *Tel:* 212-956-0950 *Toll Free Tel:* 877-822-2500 *Fax:* 914-401-9385 *E-mail:* info@arborbooks.com; editorial@arborbooks.net *Web Site:* www.arborbooks.com; www.arborservices.co, pg 1202, 1216, 1242, 1261, 1342, 1355, 1424

Vlazny, Jeanne, Graphics Two, 819 S Main St, Burbank, CA 91506 *Tel:* 818-841-4922, pg 1220, 1276

Vogel, Brian, The Language Center, 62 Brunswick Woods Dr, East Brunswick, NJ 08816 *Tel:* 732-613-4554 *Fax:* 732-238-7659 *Web Site:* www.thelanguagectr.com, pg 1411

Vollmar, Robert, World Literature Today, 630 Parrington Oval, Suite 110, Norman, OK 73019-4033 *Tel:* 405-325-4531 *E-mail:* wlt@ou.edu *Web Site:* www.worldliteraturetoday.org, pg 1132

von Knorring, John, Stylus Publishing LLC, 22883 Quicksilver Dr, Sterling, VA 20166-2019 *Tel:* 703-661-1504 (edit & sales); 703-661-1581 (orders & cust serv); 703-996-1036 *Toll Free Tel:* 800-232-0223 (orders & cust serv) *Fax:* 703-661-1547; 703-

661-1501 (orders & cust serv) *E-mail:* stylusinfo@ styluspub.com; stylusmail@styluspub.com (orders & cust serv) *Web Site:* styluspub.presswarehouse.com, pg 1299

Von Olenhusen, Cuno, Hannecke Display Systems Inc, 210 Grove St, Franklin, MA 02038 *Tel:* 774-235-2329 *E-mail:* info@hannecke.com *Web Site:* www.hannecke. com, pg 1092

Von Staats, Aaron, PTC, 121 Seaport Blvd, Boston, MA 02210 *Tel:* 781-370-5000 *Fax:* 781-370-6000 *Web Site:* www.ptc.com, pg 1384

Voorhees, Barry, Bunting Magnetics Co, 500 S Spencer Rd, Newton, KS 67114 *Tel:* 316-284-2020 *Toll Free Tel:* 800-835-2526; 877-576-0156 *Fax:* 316-283-4975 *E-mail:* bmc@buntingmagnetics.com *Web Site:* www. buntingmagnetics.com, pg 1274

Voris, Scott, Kelmscott, a Fuse LLC company, 5656 McDermott Dr, Berkeley, IL 60163 *Tel:* 630-898-4261 *Web Site:* www.kelmscott.com, pg 1206, 1222, 1380

Vosburgh, Andy, GW Illustration & Design, 2290 Ball Dr, St Louis, MO 63146 *Tel:* 314-567-9854 *Web Site:* www.gwinc.com, pg 1428

Vosburgh, Andy, GW Inc, 2290 Ball Dr, St Louis, MO 63146 *Tel:* 314-567-9854 *Web Site:* www.gwinc.com, pg 1220, 1378

Votel, Kevin, Publishers Group West (PGW), an Ingram brand, 1700 Fourth St, Berkeley, CA 94710 *Tel:* 510-809-3700 *Toll Free Tel:* 866-400-5351 (cust serv) *Fax:* 510-809-3777 *E-mail:* info@pgw.com *Web Site:* www.pgw.com, pg 1295

Vreeland, Howard Jr, Anderson & Vreeland Inc, 15348 US Hwy 127 EW, Bryan, OH 43506 *Tel:* 419-636-5002 *Toll Free Tel:* 866-282-7697; 888-832-1600 (CN) *Fax:* 419-636-4334 *E-mail:* info@andersonvreeland. com *Web Site:* andersonvreeland.com, pg 1273

Vuicic, Mary Alice, Thomson Reuters, 3 Times Sq, New York, NY 10036 *Tel:* 646-223-4000; 646-223-6100 (edit); 646-223-6000 (newsroom) *Web Site:* www. thomsonreuters.com, pg 1186

Vuolo, Tim, Scholastic Book Fairs®, 1080 Greenwood Blvd, Lake Mary, FL 32746 *Tel:* 407-829-8000 *Fax:* 407-829-2600 *E-mail:* custservbf@ scholasticbookfairs.com *Web Site:* www.scholastic. com/bookfairs, pg 1298, 1320

Wade, Julian Davis, Davis Art Images, 50 Portland St, Worcester, MA 01608 *Tel:* 508-754-7201 *Toll Free Tel:* 800-533-2847 *Fax:* 508-753-3834 *E-mail:* das@ davisart.com; contactus@davisart.com *Web Site:* www. davisart.com, pg 1446

Waggoner, Chaz, BurrellesLuce, 30 B Vreeland Rd, Florham Park, NJ 07932 *Tel:* 973-992-6600 *Toll Free Tel:* 800-631-1160; 800-368-8070 *Fax:* 973-992-7675 *Web Site:* www.burrellesluce.com, pg 1391

Waggoner, Robert, BurrellesLuce, 30 B Vreeland Rd, Florham Park, NJ 07932 *Tel:* 973-992-6600 *Toll Free Tel:* 800-631-1160; 800-368-8070 *Fax:* 973-992-7675 *Web Site:* www.burrellesluce.com, pg 1391

Wagner, Jerry, BMI Educational Services Inc, 26 Haypress Rd, Cranbury, NJ 08512 *Tel:* 732-329-6991 *Toll Free Tel:* 800-222-8100 (orders only) *Fax:* 732-329-6994 *Toll Free Fax:* 800-986-9393 (orders only) *E-mail:* info@bmionline.com *Web Site:* bmionline. com, pg 1310, 1323

Wagner, Kurt A, Wagner & Schell LLP, 780 Lee St, Suite 102, Des Plaines, IL 60016 *Tel:* 847-759-9833 *Fax:* 847-759-9834 *Web Site:* www.wagneruslaw.com, pg 1352

Waite, Diana S, Mount Ida Press, 111 Washington Ave, Albany, NY 12210-2203 *Tel:* 518-426-5935 *Fax:* 518-426-4116 *E-mail:* info@mountidapress.com *Web Site:* www.mountidapress.com, pg 1378

Waitts, George, Crown Roll Leaf Inc, 91 Illinois Ave, Paterson, NJ 07503 *Tel:* 973-742-4000 *Toll Free Tel:* 800-631-3831 *Fax:* 973-742-0219 *Web Site:* www. crownrollleaf.com, pg 1245

Wajdowicz, Jurek, Emerson, Wajdowicz Studios Inc, 530 W 25 St, New York, NY 10001 *Tel:* 212-807-8144 *Fax:* 212-675-0414 *E-mail:* info@designews. com *Web Site:* www.designews.com; Facebook. com/DesignEWS, pg 1427

Wakabayashi, Clark, Welcome Enterprises Inc, 6 W 18 St, Unit 4B, New York, NY 10011 *Tel:* 212-989-3200 *Fax:* 212-989-3205 *E-mail:* info@ welcomeenterprisesinc.com *Web Site:* www. welcomeenterprisesinc.com, pg 1363

Waletzki, Dave, Eizo Inc, 5710 Warland Dr, Cypress, CA 90630 *Tel:* 562-431-5011 *Toll Free Tel:* 800-800-5202 *Fax:* 562-431-4811 *E-mail:* orders@eizo.com *Web Site:* www.eizo.com, pg 1376

Walker, Charles J, Kable Packaging Services, 4275 Thunderbird Lane, Fairfield, OH 45014 *Tel:* 513-671-2800 *E-mail:* info@kable.com *Web Site:* www. kablefulfillment.com, pg 1332

Walker, Jayne, Jayne Walker Editorial, 1406 Euclid Ave, Suite 1, Berkeley, CA 94708 *Tel:* 510-843-8265, pg 1353

Walker, Meg, Tandem Literary, 28 Clinton Rd, Glen Ridge, NJ 07028 *Tel:* 212-629-1990 *Fax:* 212-629-1990 *Web Site:* tandemliterary.com, pg 1102

Walker, Ruth, Datalogics Inc, 101 N Wacker, Suite 1800, Chicago, IL 60606 *Tel:* 312-853-8200 *Fax:* 312-853-8282 *E-mail:* sales@datalogics.com; marketing@ datalogics.com *Web Site:* www.datalogics.com, pg 1375

Wall, Patrick, A-R Editions Inc, 1600 Aspen Commons, Suite 100, Middleton, WI 53562 *Tel:* 608-836-9000 *Fax:* 608-831-8200 *E-mail:* info@areditions.com *Web Site:* www.areditions.com, pg 1201, 1215, 1273, 1341, 1423

Wallman, Marc, The Clark Group Inc, 3705 Quakerbridge Rd, Suite 116, Hamilton, NJ 08619 *Tel:* 609-528-7660 *Fax:* 609-528-7710 *E-mail:* service@clarkworldwide.com *Web Site:* www. clarkgroupinc.com, pg 1331

Walsh, John R, Catholic Books & Tapes, PO Box 350333, Fort Lauderdale, FL 33335-0333 *Tel:* 954-583-5108 *Fax:* 954-583-5108 *E-mail:* mascmen7@ yahoo.com *Web Site:* www.catholicbook.com, pg 1325

Walsworth, Don Jr, Walsworth, 306 N Kansas Ave, Marceline, MO 64658 *Toll Free Tel:* 800-265-6795 *Web Site:* www.walsworth.com; www. walsworthhistorybooks.com, pg 1209, 1227, 1256

Walsworth, Don O, Walsworth, 306 N Kansas Ave, Marceline, MO 64658 *Toll Free Tel:* 800-265-6795 *Web Site:* www.walsworth.com; www. walsworthhistorybooks.com, pg 1209, 1227, 1256

Walters, Doug, Bang Printing Co Inc, 3323 Oak St, Brainerd, MN 56401 *Tel:* 218-829-2877 *Toll Free Tel:* 800-328-0450 *Fax:* 218-829-7145 *E-mail:* info@ bangprinting.com *Web Site:* www.bangprinting.com, pg 1202, 1216, 1242, 1261

Walters, Eric, Crain Communications Inc, 1155 Gratiot Ave, Detroit, MI 48207-2732 *Tel:* 313-446-6000 *Fax:* 313-446-0383 *E-mail:* info@crain.com *Web Site:* crain.com, pg 1184

Ward, Chris, Christopher Ward & Co, 11515 Kruhm Rd, Burtonsville, MD 20866 *Tel:* 860-355-8273 *E-mail:* cwardandco@gmail.com, pg 1300

Warech, Ken, UPS Supply Chain Solutions, 12380 Morris Rd, Alpharetta, GA 30005 *Tel:* 913-693-6151 (outside US & CN) *Toll Free Tel:* 800-742-5727 (US & CN) *Web Site:* upsscs.com, pg 1333

Waricha, Joan, Parachute Publishing LLC, 157 Columbus Ave, Suite 518, New York, NY 10023 *Tel:* 212-691-1422, pg 1360

Wark, John, Airphoto, 421 N Main, Suite 103, Pueblo, CO 81003 *Tel:* 719-542-5719 *Web Site:* www. airphotona.com, pg 1435

Warner, Jerry, CD Solutions Inc, 100 W Monument St, Pleasant Hill, OH 45359 *Tel:* 937-676-2376 *Toll Free Tel:* 800-860-2376 *Fax:* 937-676-2478 *E-mail:* contact@cds.com *Web Site:* www.cds.com, pg 1374

Warner, Luther A, Lushena Books Inc, 607 Country Club Dr, Unit E, Bensenville, IL 60106 *Tel:* 630-238-8708 *Toll Free Tel:* 800-785-1545 *Fax:* 630-238-8824 *E-mail:* lushenabks@yahoo.com *Web Site:* lushenabks. com, pg 1317

Warner, Matt, Gem Guides Book Co, 1155 W Ninth St, Upland, CA 91786 *Tel:* 626-855-1611 *Toll Free Tel:* 800-824-5118 (orders) *Fax:* 626-855-1610 *E-mail:* info@gemguidesbooks.com; sales@ gemguidesbooks.com (orders) *Web Site:* www. gemguidesbooks.com, pg 1314

Warren, Erin, Crown Connect, 250 W Rialto Ave, San Bernadino, CA 92408 *Tel:* 909-888-7531 *Fax:* 909-889-1639 *E-mail:* sales@crownconnect.com *Web Site:* www.crownconnect.com, pg 1203, 1218, 1275

Warwick-Smith, Simon, Metaphysical Book Club, 18340 Sonoma Hwy, Sonoma, CA 95476 *Tel:* 707-939-9212 *Fax:* 707-938-3515 *E-mail:* warwick@vom.com *Web Site:* www.warwickassociates.com, pg 1137

Warwick-Smith, Simon, Warwick Associates, 18340 Sonoma Hwy, Sonoma, CA 95476 *Tel:* 707-939-9212 *Fax:* 707-938-3515 *E-mail:* warwick@vom.com *Web Site:* www.warwickassociates.com, pg 1102, 1353

Wasco, Sonia Shaner, Grant Heilman Photography Inc, 506 W Lincoln Ave, Lititz, PA 17543 *Tel:* 717-626-0296 *Toll Free Tel:* 800-622-2046 *Fax:* 717-626-0971 *E-mail:* info@heilmanphoto.com *Web Site:* www. heilmanphoto.com, pg 1447

Washburne, Mollie H, New Literary History: A Journal of Theory & Interpretation, 2715 N Charles St, Baltimore, MD 21218-4363 *Tel:* 410-516-6987 (journal orders outside US & CN) *Toll Free Tel:* 800-548-1784 (journal orders) *Fax:* 410-516-6968 *E-mail:* jrnlcirc@press.jhu.edu (journal orders) *Web Site:* www.press.jhu.edu/journals/ new_literary_history/index.html, pg 1129

Washchilla, Edward P Jr, Fairfield Marketing Group Inc, The Direct Mail Ctr, 830 Sport Hill Rd, Easton, CT 06112-1241 *Tel:* 203-261-5585 *Fax:* 203-261-0884 *E-mail:* info@fairfieldmarketing.com *Web Site:* www. fairfieldmarketing.com, pg 1092, 1097, 1106, 1109, 1112, 1220, 1247, 1276, 1345, 1377, 1428

Washington, Kaylynn, Essex Products Group, 30 Industrial Park Rd, Centerbrook, CT 06409-0307 *Tel:* 860-767-7130 *Toll Free Tel:* 800-394-7130 *Fax:* 860-767-9137 *E-mail:* sales@epg-inc.com *Web Site:* www.epg-inc.com, pg 1276

Wasserman, James, Studio 31 Inc, 2740 SW Martin Downs Blvd, Suite 358, Palm City, FL 34990 *Tel:* 772-781-7195 *Fax:* 772-781-6044 *Web Site:* www. studio31.com, pg 1226, 1362

Watrous, Angela, Taconic Wire, 250 Totoket Rd, North Branford, CT 06471 *Tel:* 203-484-2863 *Toll Free Tel:* 800-253-1450 *Fax:* 203-484-2865 *E-mail:* sales@ taconicwire.com; taconicwiresales@gmail.com *Web Site:* www.taconicwire.com, pg 1279

Watson, Abigail, Emerson, Wajdowicz Studios Inc, 530 W 25 St, New York, NY 10001 *Tel:* 212-807-8144 *Fax:* 212-675-0414 *E-mail:* info@designews. com *Web Site:* www.designews.com; Facebook. com/DesignEWS, pg 1427

Watson, Amber, Data Conversion Laboratory Inc (DCL), 61-18 190 St, Suite 205, Fresh Meadows, NY 11365 *Tel:* 718-357-8700 *Toll Free Tel:* 800-321-2816 (provider problems) *E-mail:* info@dclab. com *Web Site:* www.dataconversionlaboratory.com, pg 1218, 1375

Watson, Julie, Ultimate TechnoGraphics, 300 Leo Pariseau, Suite 2120, Montreal, QC H2X 4B3, Canada *Tel:* 514-938-9050 *Toll Free Tel:* 800-363-3590 (North America only) *Fax:* 514-938-5225 *E-mail:* customerservice@imposition.com *Web Site:* www.imposition.com, pg 1387

Wawrzyniak, Chris, Fry Communications Inc, 800 W Church Rd, Mechanicsburg, PA 17055 *Tel:* 717-766-0211 *Toll Free Tel:* 800-334-1429 *Fax:* 717-691-0341 *E-mail:* info@frycomm.com *Web Site:* www.frycomm. com, pg 1205, 1220, 1247, 1276

Wheeler, Brad, Diversified Printing Services Inc, 3425 Cherokee Ave, Columbus, GA 31906 *Tel:* 706-323-2759 *Toll Free Fax:* 888-410-5502 *Web Site:* www.1dps.com, pg 1246

Wheeler, John, Lumina Datamatics Inc, 4 Collins Ave, Plymouth, MA 02360 *Tel:* 508-746-0300 *Fax:* 508-746-3233 *Web Site:* luminadatamatics.com, pg 1207, 1222, 1349, 1359, 1380, 1430

Whitcomb, Pamela, A-R Editions Inc, 1600 Aspen Commons, Suite 100, Middleton, WI 53562 *Tel:* 608-836-9000 *Fax:* 608-831-8200 *E-mail:* info@areditions.com *Web Site:* www.areditions.com, pg 1423

White, Brian, Transimpex Translators, Interpreters, Editors, Consultants Inc, 2300 Main St, 9th fl, Kansas City, MO 64108 *Tel:* 816-561-3777 *Toll Free Tel:* 888-877-4679 *Fax:* 816-561-5515 *E-mail:* translations@transimpex.com *Web Site:* www.transimpex.com, pg 1414

White, Steven, Royalty Review LLC, 485 Madison Ave, 9th fl, New York, NY 10022 *Tel:* 212-792-6300 *Fax:* 212-792-6350 *E-mail:* info@janoverllc.com *Web Site:* www.jrllc.com, pg 1351

Whitehead, Diane, Association for Childhood Education International, 1875 Connecticut Ave NW, 10th fl, Washington, DC 20009 *Tel:* 202-372-9986 *Toll Free Tel:* 800-423-3563 *E-mail:* headquarters@acei.org *Web Site:* acei.org, pg 1139

Whitehurst, Jim, IBM Corp, One New Orchard Rd, Armonk, NY 10504 *Tel:* 914-499-1900 *Toll Free Tel:* 800-426-4968 *E-mail:* askibm@vnet.ibm.com *Web Site:* www.ibm.com, pg 1379

Whiting, Chuck, Music City Arts Network, PO Box 843, Brentwood, TN 37024 *Toll Free Tel:* 888-80-SHINE (807-4463) *E-mail:* info@musiccityarts.net *Web Site:* www.musiccityartsupdate.com; www.shinetimebooks.com, pg 1100

Whiting, Jerry, Azalea Software Inc, PO Box 16660, Seattle, WA 98116-0660 *Tel:* 206-341-9500; 206-336-9559 (software support); 206-336-9575 (sales & info) *Fax:* 206-299-5600 *E-mail:* salesinfo@azaleabarcodes.com *Web Site:* www.azaleabarcodes.com, pg 1373

Whitney, Haynes, Democrat Printing & Lithographing Co, 6401 Lindsey Rd, Little Rock, AR 72206 *Toll Free Tel:* 800-622-2216 *Fax:* 501-907-7953 *Web Site:* democratprinting.com, pg 1246

Whitney, Thomas, Democrat Printing & Lithographing Co, 6401 Lindsey Rd, Little Rock, AR 72206 *Toll Free Tel:* 800-622-2216 *Fax:* 501-907-7953 *Web Site:* democratprinting.com, pg 1246

Whitten, Robin F, AudioFile®, 37 Silver St, Portland, ME 04101 *Tel:* 207-774-7563 *Toll Free Tel:* 800-506-1212 *Fax:* 207-775-3744 *E-mail:* info@audiofilemagazine.com *Web Site:* www.audiofilemagazine.com, pg 1124

Whobrey, Larry A, International Service Co, International Service Bldg, 333 Fourth Ave, Indialantic, FL 32903-4295 *Tel:* 321-724-1443 *Fax:* 321-724-1443, pg 1316, 1323, 1326, 1329

Wickersham, John, Atwood Capital Partners LLC, The DuMont Bldg, 515 Madison Ave, 35th fl, New York, NY 10022 *Tel:* 212-355-1390 *Fax:* 212-355-1391 *E-mail:* info@atwoodcp.com *Web Site:* www.atwoodadvisors.com, pg 1342

Wien, Carol, Carol Wien Photography, 6969 E White-Pacheco St, Willcox, AZ 85643 *Tel:* 520-384-2018 *E-mail:* carol@azwien.com *Web Site:* www.azwien.com, pg 1444

Wiese, Kris, Ingram Content Group LLC, One Ingram Blvd, La Vergne, TN 37086-1986 *Tel:* 615-793-5000 *Toll Free Tel:* 800-937-8000 (retailers); 800-937-5300 (ext 1, libs) *E-mail:* customerservice@ingramcontent.com *Web Site:* www.ingramcontent.com, pg 1290, 1315

Wilbur, Ralph E, Graphic Litho, 130 Shepard St, Lawrence, MA 01843 *Tel:* 978-683-2766 *Fax:* 978-681-7588 *E-mail:* sales@graphiclitho.com *Web Site:* www.graphiclitho.com, pg 1092, 1206, 1248

Wilby, Bryan, Maps.com, 120 Cremona Dr, Suite 260, Santa Barbara, CA 93117 *Tel:* 805-685-3100 *Toll Free Tel:* 800-430-7532 *Fax:* 805-699-7550 *E-mail:* info@maps.com *Web Site:* www.maps.com, pg 1251, 1381, 1430

Wilcox, Alana, Coach House Printing, 80 bpNichol Lane, Toronto, ON M5S 3J4, Canada *Tel:* 416-979-2217 *Toll Free Tel:* 800-367-6360 (outside Toronto) *Fax:* 416-977-1158 *E-mail:* mail@chbooks.com *Web Site:* www.chbooks.com, pg 1218, 1244

Wilcox, Bruce, Carolina Biological Supply Co, 2700 York Rd, Burlington, NC 27215-3398 *Tel:* 336-586-4399 (intl sales); 336-538-6211 *Toll Free Tel:* 800-334-5551 *Fax:* 336-584-7686 (intl sales) *Toll Free Fax:* 800-222-7112 *E-mail:* quotations@carolina.com; product@carolina.com *Web Site:* www.carolina.com, pg 1311

Wilgus, Whitney, The Association of Medical Illustrators (AMI), 201 E Main St, Suite 1405, Lexington, KY 40507 *Toll Free Tel:* 866-393-4264 *Fax:* 859-514-9166 *E-mail:* hq@ami.org; info@ami.org *Web Site:* www.ami.org, pg 1424

Wilkinson, Christine, Wilkinson Studios Inc, 2955 Kelly Dr, Elgin, IL 60124-4349 *Tel:* 312-286-3683 *Web Site:* www.wilkinsonstudios.com, pg 1433

Will, Stephen, The Hendra Agency Inc, 142 Sterling Place, Brooklyn, NY 11217-3307 *Tel:* 718-622-3232; 212-947-9898 *Fax:* 718-622-3322, pg 1098

Willemstyn, Brian, Great Lakes Bindery Inc, 3741 Linden Ave SE, Wyoming, MI 49548 *Tel:* 616-245-5264 *Fax:* 616-245-5883 *E-mail:* jeremy@greatlakesbindery.com *Web Site:* www.greatlakesbindery.com, pg 1248

Willen, Georgia, Midwest Library Service, 11443 Saint Charles Rock Rd, Bridgeton, MO 63044 *Tel:* 314-739-3100 *Fax:* 314-739-1326 *E-mail:* mail@midwestls.com *Web Site:* www.midwestls.com, pg 1317

Willette, E David, Allied Vaughn, 7600 Parklawn Ave, Suite 300, Minneapolis, MN 55435 *Tel:* 952-832-3100 *Toll Free Tel:* 800-323-0281 *Fax:* 952-832-3203 *Web Site:* www.alliedvaughn.com, pg 1372

Willette, Emily, Hilsinger-Mendelson West Inc, 8916 Ashcroft Ave, Los Angeles, CA 90048 *Tel:* 310-659-7930 *E-mail:* hmiwest@aol.com *Web Site:* www.hilsingermendelson.com, pg 1098

Williams, Abigail, GBS Books, 11226 N 23 Ave, Suite 103, Phoenix, AZ 85029 *Tel:* 602-863-6000 *Toll Free Tel:* 800-851-6001 *E-mail:* gbsbooks@gbsbooks.com *Web Site:* www.gbsbooks.com, pg 1314

Williams, Amy, Data Conversion Laboratory Inc (DCL), 61-18 190 St, Suite 205, Fresh Meadows, NY 11365 *Tel:* 718-357-8700 *Toll Free Tel:* 800-321-2816 (provider problems) *E-mail:* info@dclab.com *Web Site:* www.dataconversionlaboratory.com, pg 1218, 1375

Williams, Dirk, L+L Printers, 6200 Yarrow Dr, Carlsbad, CA 92011 *Tel:* 760-438-3456; 760-477-0321 *Fax:* 760-929-0853 *E-mail:* info@llprinters.com *Web Site:* www.llprinters.com, pg 1250

Williams, Frances, Snow Lion Graphics, 414 Lesser St, Oakland, CA 94601 *Tel:* 510-525-1134; 510-816-2840 (cell) *E-mail:* info@slgbooks.com *Web Site:* www.snowliongraphics.com, pg 1432

Williams, Jeff, Apple Inc, One Apple Park Way, Cupertino, CA 95014 *Tel:* 408-996-1010 *Web Site:* www.apple.com, pg 1372

Williams, Kathleen, Larson Texts Inc, 1762 Norcross Rd, Erie, PA 16510 *Tel:* 814-824-6365 *Toll Free Tel:* 800-530-2355 *Fax:* 814-824-6377 *Web Site:* www.larsontexts.com, pg 1222, 1265, 1359

Williams, Lenore, American Urban Radio Networks (AURN), 938 Penn Ave, Suite 701, Pittsburgh, PA 15222-3811 *Tel:* 412-456-4099 *Fax:* 412-456-4077 *Web Site:* www.aurn.com, pg 1183

Williams, Lisa, PBD Worldwide Inc, 1650 Bluegrass Lakes Pkwy, Alpharetta, GA 30004 *Tel:* 470-769-1000 *Toll Free Tel:* 866-998-4PBD (998-4723) *E-mail:* sales.marketing@pbd.com; customerservice@pbd.com *Web Site:* www.pbd.com, pg 1333

Williams, Mary K, DocuWare Corp, 4 Crotty Lane, Suite 200, New Windsor, NY 12553 *Tel:* 845-563-9045 *Toll Free Tel:* 888-565-5907 *Fax:* 845-563-9046 *E-mail:* dwsales@docuware.com; support.americas@docuware.com *Web Site:* www.docuware.com, pg 1376

Williams, Matt, Ingenta, 317 George St, New Brunswick, NJ 08901 *Tel:* 732-563-9292 *Fax:* 732-563-9044 *Web Site:* www.ingenta.com, pg 1379

Williams, Melissa, Midwest Library Service, 11443 Saint Charles Rock Rd, Bridgeton, MO 63044 *Tel:* 314-739-3100 *Fax:* 314-739-1326 *E-mail:* mail@midwestls.com *Web Site:* www.midwestls.com, pg 1317

Williams, Richard T, Independent Publishers Group (IPG), 814 N Franklin St, Chicago, IL 60610 *Tel:* 312-337-0747 *Toll Free Tel:* 800-888-4741 (orders) *Fax:* 312-337-5985 *E-mail:* frontdesk@ipgbook.com; orders@ipgbook.com *Web Site:* www.ipgbook.com, pg 1288, 1326

Williams, Robert, I-Web, 175 Bodwell St, Avon, MA 02322 *Tel:* 508-580-5809 *Fax:* 508-580-5632 *E-mail:* info@iwebus.com *Web Site:* iwebus.com, pg 1277

Williams, Roger Dale, Snow Lion Graphics, 414 Lesser St, Oakland, CA 94601 *Tel:* 510-525-1134; 510-816-2840 (cell) *E-mail:* info@slgbooks.com *Web Site:* www.snowliongraphics.com, pg 1432

Williams, Sylvia, National Book Network (NBN), 4501 Forbes Blvd, Suite 200, Lanham, MD 20706 *Tel:* 301-459-3366 *Toll Free Tel:* 800-462-6420 (orders only) *Fax:* 301-429-5746 *Toll Free Fax:* 800-338-4550 (orders only) *E-mail:* customercare@nbnbooks.com *Web Site:* www.nbnbooks.com, pg 1293, 1318

Williams, Troy, GBS Books, 11226 N 23 Ave, Suite 103, Phoenix, AZ 85029 *Tel:* 602-863-6000 *Toll Free Tel:* 800-851-6001 *E-mail:* gbsbooks@gbsbooks.com *Web Site:* www.gbsbooks.com, pg 1314

Williams, Troy, The Ovid Bell Press Inc, 1201 Bluff St, Fulton, MO 65251 *Tel:* 573-642-2256 *Toll Free Tel:* 800-835-8919 *E-mail:* sales@ovidbell.com *Web Site:* ovidbell.com, pg 1224, 1252, 1266, 1278

Willis, Aaron, Social Studies School Service, 10200 Jefferson Blvd, PO Box 802, Culver City, CA 90232 *Tel:* 310-839-2436 *Toll Free Tel:* 800-421-4246 *Fax:* 310-839-2249 *Toll Free Fax:* 800-944-5432 (US & CN) *E-mail:* access@socialstudies.com *Web Site:* www.socialstudies.com, pg 1299, 1320

Wilmoth, Gabriel, SCB Distributors, 15608 S New Century Dr, Gardena, CA 90248 *Tel:* 310-532-9400 *Toll Free Tel:* 800-729-6423 *Fax:* 310-532-7001 *E-mail:* scb@scbdistributors.com *Web Site:* www.scbdistributors.com, pg 1297

Wilner, Jim, Intex Solutions Inc, 110 "A" St, Needham, MA 02494 *Tel:* 781-449-6222 *Fax:* 781-444-2318 *E-mail:* sales@intex.com *Web Site:* www.intex.com, pg 1379

Wilson, Dan, Roland DGA Corp, 15363 Barranca Pkwy, Irvine, CA 92618-2216 *Tel:* 949-727-2100 *Toll Free Tel:* 800-542-2307 *Fax:* 949-727-2112 *Web Site:* www.rolanddga.com, pg 1385

Wilson, Jack, Laplink Software Inc, 600 108 Ave NE, Suite 610, Bellevue, WA 98004 *Tel:* 425-952-6000 *Toll Free Tel:* 800-LAPLINK (527-5465) *E-mail:* info@laplink.com; sales@laplink.com *Web Site:* web.laplink.com, pg 1380

Wilson, Scott, Value Added Resources, 7900 Rockville Rd, Indianapolis, IN 46214 *Tel:* 317-899-1000 *Fax:* 317-899-2259 *E-mail:* info@valueaddedres.com *Web Site:* www.valueaddedres.com, pg 1333

Wilson, Stacy, Progress Printing Plus, 2677 Waterlick Rd, Lynchburg, VA 24502 *Tel:* 434-239-9213 *Toll Free Tel:* 800-572-7804 *Fax:* 434-832-7573 *E-mail:* info@progressprintplus.com *Web Site:* www.progressprintplus.com, pg 1224

Wilson, Steven, Book Sales, 142 W 36 St, 4th fl, New York, NY 10018 *Tel:* 212-779-4971; 212-779-4972 *Fax:* 212-779-6058 *Web Site:* www.quartoknows.com, pg 1310

Winchester, Dawn, Publicis North America, 1675 Broadway, New York, NY 10009 Tel: 212-474-5000 Web Site: www.publicisna.com, pg 1101

Windler, Robert, Diecrafters Inc, 1349 S 55 Ct, Cicero, IL 60804-1211 Tel: 708-656-3336 Fax: 708-656-3386 E-mail: info@diecrafters.com Web Site: www.diecrafters.com, pg 1246

Windover, Rocco, Dunn & Co Inc, 75 Green St, Clinton, MA 01510 Tel: 978-368-8505 Fax: 978-368-7867 E-mail: info@booktrauma.com Web Site: www.booktrauma.com, pg 1204, 1246, 1263

Wineberg, Ronna, Bellevue Literary Review, NYU School of Medicine, Dept of Medicine, 550 First Ave, OBV-A612, New York, NY 10016 Tel: 212-263-3973 E-mail: info@BLReview.org Web Site: www.BLReview.org, pg 1124

Wingate, Donna, LucialMarquand, 1400 Second Ave, Seattle, WA 98101 Tel: 206-624-2030 Fax: 206-624-1821 Web Site: luciamarquand.com, pg 1359

Winkleman, Mark, Kirkus, 65 W 36 St, Suite 700, New York, NY 10018 E-mail: customercare@kirkus.com Web Site: www.kirkusreviews.com, pg 1128

Winkler, Simon, Listco Direct Marketing, 1276 46 St, Brooklyn, NY 11219 Tel: 718-871-8400 Fax: 718-871-7692 E-mail: info@listcodirect.com Web Site: www.listcodirect.com, pg 1112

Winner, Scott, Ingenta, 317 George St, New Brunswick, NJ 08901 Tel: 732-563-9292 Fax: 732-563-9044 Web Site: www.ingenta.com, pg 1379

Winslow, Ted, SumTotal Systems LLC, 2850 NW 43 St, Suite 150, Gainesville, FL 32606 Tel: 352-264-2800 Toll Free Tel: 866-933-1416 Fax: 352-374-2257 E-mail: customersupport@sumtotalsystems.com Web Site: www.sumtotalsystems.com, pg 1386

Winstanley, Nicole, Penguin Random House Canada, 320 Front St W, Suite 1400, Toronto, ON M5V 3B6, Canada Tel: 416-364-4449 Toll Free Tel: 888-523-9292 (cust serv) Fax: 416-598-7764 Web Site: www.penguinrandomhouse.ca, pg 1295

Winterhalter, Ken, Twin Rivers Paper Co, 82 Bridge Ave, Madawaska, ME 04756 Tel: 207-728-3321 Toll Free Tel: 800-920-9988 Fax: 207-728-8701 E-mail: info@twinriverspaper.com Web Site: www.twinriverspaper.com, pg 1269

Wise, LaDonna, O'Neil Digital Solutions LLC, 12655 Beatrice St, Los Angeles, CA 90066 Tel: 310-448-6400 E-mail: sales@oneildata.com Web Site: www.oneildata.com, pg 1224, 1252, 1266, 1278

Wise, Nancy, Sandhill Book Marketing Ltd, Millcreek Industrial Park, Unit 4, 3308 Appaloosa Rd, Kelowna, BC V1V 2W5, Canada Tel: 250-491-1446 Toll Free Tel: 800-667-3848 (CN only) Fax: 250-491-4066 E-mail: info@sandhillbooks.com Web Site: www.sandhillbooks.com, pg 1320

Wisniewski, Cassie, Chicago Distribution Center (CDC), 11030 S Langley Ave, Chicago, IL 60628 Tel: 773-702-7010 Toll Free Fax: 800-621-8476 Web Site: press.uchicago.edu/cdc, pg 1285

Wisotzkey, James S, Maple Logistics Solutions, 60 Grumbacher Rd, York, PA 17406 Tel: 717-764-4596 Fax: 717-764-4494 E-mail: info@maplesoln.com Web Site: www.maplelogisticssolutions.com, pg 1291, 1332

Wisotzkey, James S, Maple Press, 480 Willow Springs Lane, York, PA 17406 Tel: 717-764-5911 Toll Free Tel: 800-999-5911 Fax: 717-764-4702 E-mail: sales@maplepress.com Web Site: www.maplepress.com, pg 1207, 1250, 1277

Wiswell, Bill, Ryukyu Books & Periodicals Inc, PO Box 535, Olathe, KS 66051 Tel: 913-782-3920 Toll Free Tel: 800-383-4017 Fax: 913-780-1750 E-mail: info@ryukyubooks.com Web Site: www.ryukyu.com, pg 1319

Wiswell, Bill, Ryukyu Books & Periodicals Inc, 5005 Merriam Dr, Merriam, KS 66203 Tel: 913-782-3920 Toll Free Tel: 800-383-4017 Fax: 913-780-1750 Web Site: www.ryukyu.com, pg 1327

Wittman, Allan, Wittman Associates, 43 Valley Lane N, Valley Stream, NY 11581 Tel: 516-791-3779, pg 1353

Wittman, Ruth, Wittman Associates, 43 Valley Lane N, Valley Stream, NY 11581 Tel: 516-791-3779, pg 1353

Wodtke, Larissa, Jeunesse: Young People, Texts, Cultures, University of Winnipeg, Centre for Research in Young People's Texts & Cultures, 515 Portage Ave, Winnipeg, MB R3B 2E9, Canada Tel: 204-786-9351 Fax: 204-774-4134 E-mail: jeunesse@uwinnipeg.ca Web Site: www.jeunessejournal.ca, pg 1127

Wolf, Larry, CyberWolf® Inc, 1596 Pacheco, Suite 203, Santa Fe, NM 87505 Tel: 505-983-6463 E-mail: sales@cyberwolf.com Web Site: www.cyberwolf.com; www.accumenbook.com; www.ebookdownloadservice.com, pg 1375

Wolf, Tom, Ascend Public Relations, 2629 Second Ave N, Seattle, WA 98109, pg 1095

Wolff, Harvey, Haynes North America Inc, 859 Lawrence Dr, Newbury Park, CA 91320-1514 Tel: 805-498-6703 Toll Free Tel: 800-4-HAYNES (442-9637) Fax: 805-498-2867 E-mail: cstn@haynes.com Web Site: www.haynes.com, pg 1326

Wolff, Richard J, Kreab, House of Sweden, Suite 504, 2900 "K" St NW, Washington, DC 20007 Tel: 202-536-1590 E-mail: washingtondc@kreab.com Web Site: www.kreab.com/washington-dc, pg 1099

Wolfson, Milt, FIM, 18 Central Blvd, South Hackensack, NJ 07606 Tel: 201-549-1037 Web Site: www.fimheadbands.com, pg 1263

Wolin, Gary, McManus & Morgan, 2506 W Seventh St, Los Angeles, CA 90057 Tel: 213-387-4433 Web Site: www.mcmanusandmorgan.com, pg 1265

Wong, Ms Chi-Li, AEI (Atchity Entertainment International Inc), 9601 Wilshire Blvd, Unit 1202, Beverly Hills, CA 90210 Tel: 323-932-1685 Web Site: www.aeionline.com, pg 1341

Wong, Kit, C & C Offset Printing Co USA Inc, 70 W 36 St, Unit 10C, New York, NY 10018 Tel: 212-431-4210 Toll Free Fax: 866-540-4134 Web Site: www.ccoffset.com, pg 1202, 1217, 1243

Wood, Glenn, Fujitsu Computer Products of America Inc, 1250 E Arques Ave, Sunnyvale, CA 94085-4701 Tel: 408-746-6000 Toll Free Tel: 800-626-4686 E-mail: scanner-sales@us.fujitsu.com Web Site: www.fujitsu.com, pg 1378

Wood, Jeff, Data Conversion Laboratory Inc (DCL), 61-18 190 St, Suite 205, Fresh Meadows, NY 11365 Tel: 718-357-8700 Toll Free Tel: 800-321-2816 (provider problems) E-mail: info@dclab.com Web Site: www.dataconversionlaboratory.com, pg 1218, 1375

Wood, Leighann, Reference & User Services Quarterly (RUSQ), 225 N Michigan Ave, Suite 1300, Chicago, IL 60601 Tel: 312-280-4395 Toll Free Tel: 800-545-2433 Fax: 312-280-5273 E-mail: rusa@ala.org Web Site: www.ala.org/rusa, pg 1131

Wood, Linda, Signature Book Printing Inc, 8041 Cessna Ave, Gaithersburg, MD 20879 Tel: 301-258-8353 Fax: 301-670-4147 E-mail: book@sbpbooks.com Web Site: sbpbooks.com, pg 1209, 1226, 1254

Wood, Mark PhD, School of World Studies, 312 N Shafer St, Richmond, VA 23284-2021 Tel: 804-827-1111 Fax: 804-828-0127 Web Site: www.has.vcu.edu/wld, pg 1413

Wood, Naomi J, The Lion and the Unicorn, 2715 N Charles St, Baltimore, MD 21218-4363 Toll Free Tel: 800-548-1784 (journal orders) Fax: 410-516-6968 E-mail: jrnlcirc@press.jhu.edu (journal orders) Web Site: www.press.jhu.edu/journals/lion_and_the_unicorn/index.html, pg 1128

Wood, Richard, Richard Wood Photography, 50 Boylston St, Brookline, MA 02445 Tel: 617-872-0654 Web Site: www.rwoodphotography.com, pg 1444

Woodhouse, Sharon, Conspire Creative, PO Box 1524, Milwaukee, WI 53201 Tel: 312-226-8400 Fax: 312-226-8420 Web Site: www.conspirecreative.com, pg 1344

Woolf, Fred, Fred Woolf List Co Inc, 60 Newtown Rd, PMB 132, Danbury, CT 06810 Tel: 203-456-6239 Toll Free Tel: 800-431-1557 Fax: 914-694-1710 E-mail: info@woolflist.com Web Site: www.woolflist.com, pg 1113

Woolf, Sheila, Fred Woolf List Co Inc, 60 Newtown Rd, PMB 132, Danbury, CT 06810 Tel: 203-456-6239 Toll Free Tel: 800-431-1557 Fax: 914-694-1710 E-mail: info@woolflist.com Web Site: www.woolflist.com, pg 1113

Woolforde, Marlon, Printronix Inc, 6440 Oak Canyon, Suite 200, Irvine, CA 92618 Tel: 714-368-2300 Toll Free Tel: 800-665-6210 Web Site: www.printronix.com, pg 1384

Worden, Trip, Universal Bookbindery Inc, 1200 N Colorado, San Antonio, TX 78207 Tel: 210-734-9502 Toll Free Tel: 800-594-2015 Fax: 210-736-0867 E-mail: service@universalbookbindery.com Web Site: www.universalbookbindery.com, pg 1256

Worman, Megan, Melcher Media Inc, 124 W 13 St, New York, NY 10011 Tel: 212-727-2322 Fax: 212-627-1973 E-mail: info@melcher.com Web Site: www.melcher.com, pg 1360

Worthen, Janice, Small Press Distribution Inc, 1341 Seventh St, Berkeley, CA 94710-1409 Tel: 510-524-1668 Toll Free Tel: 800-869-7553 (within the US) Fax: 510-524-0852 E-mail: spd@spdbooks.org Web Site: www.spdbooks.org, pg 1298

Wortman, Shawn, La Crosse Graphics Inc, 3025 East Ave S, La Crosse, WI 54601 Tel: 608-788-2500 Toll Free Tel: 800-832-2503 Fax: 608-788-2660 Web Site: www.lacrossegraphics.com, pg 1250

Wren, Mark, Texas Bookman, 2700 Lone Star Dr, Dallas, TX 75212 Tel: 214-678-6680 Toll Free Tel: 800-566-2665 Fax: 214-678-6699 E-mail: orders@texasbookman.com Web Site: www.texasbookman.com, pg 1321

Wrenn, Kevin, PTC, 121 Seaport Blvd, Boston, MA 02210 Tel: 781-370-5000 Fax: 781-370-6000 Web Site: www.ptc.com, pg 1384

Wright, George IV, Publication Identification & Processing Systems, 10 Midland Ave, Suite M-02, Port Chester, NY 10573 Tel: 212-996-6000 Toll Free Tel: 888-783-7439 Fax: 212-410-7477 Toll Free Fax: 800-241-7477 E-mail: info@pips.com Web Site: www.pips.com, pg 1224

Wright, Randy, Product Identification & Processing Systems Inc, 10 Midland Ave, Suite M-02, Port Chester, NY 10573-5911 Tel: 212-996-6000 Toll Free Tel: 888-783-7439 Fax: 212-410-7477 Toll Free Fax: 800-241-PIPS (241-7477) E-mail: info@pips.com Web Site: www.pips.com, pg 1224

Wyatt, Neal, Library Journal, 123 William St, Suite 802, New York, NY 10038 Tel: 646-380-0700 Toll Free Tel: 800-588-1030 Fax: 646-380-0756 E-mail: ljinfo@mediasourceinc.com Web Site: www.libraryjournal.com, pg 1128

Wyatt, Neal, Reference & User Services Quarterly (RUSQ), 225 N Michigan Ave, Suite 1300, Chicago, IL 60601 Tel: 312-280-4395 Toll Free Tel: 800-545-2433 Fax: 312-280-5273 E-mail: rusa@ala.org Web Site: www.ala.org/rusa, pg 1131

Wybel, Sheryl L, Wybel Marketing Group Inc, 213 W Main St, Barrington, IL 60010 Tel: 847-382-0384; 847-382-0382 Toll Free Tel: 800-323-5297 Fax: 847-382-0385 Toll Free Fax: 800-595-5252 E-mail: bookreps@wybel.com, pg 1301

Wyrostok, Chuck, AppaLight, 230 Griffith Run, Spencer, WV 25276 Tel: 304-927-2978 Web Site: www.appalight.com, pg 1445

Xu, Meifang, Signature Print Services, 3565 Sierra Rd, San Jose, CA 95132 Tel: 408-213-3393 Fax: 408-213-3399 Web Site: www.signatureprint.com, pg 1254

Yambao, Mariluz, FIM, 18 Central Blvd, South Hackensack, NJ 07606 Tel: 201-549-1037 Web Site: www.fimheadbands.com, pg 1263

Zuznicki, Matt, Datalogics Inc, 101 N Wacker, Suite 1800, Chicago, IL 60606 *Tel:* 312-853-8200 *Fax:* 312-853-8282 *E-mail:* sales@datalogics.com; marketing@datalogics.com *Web Site:* www.datalogics.com, pg 1375

Zwergel, Gerrit, Koenig & Bauer (US) Inc, 2555 Regent Blvd, Dallas, TX 75229 *Tel:* 469-532-8000 *Fax:* 469-532-8190 *Web Site:* us.koenig-bauer.com, pg 1277

Zychowicz, James, A-R Editions Inc, 1600 Aspen Commons, Suite 100, Middleton, WI 53562 *Tel:* 608-836-9000 *Fax:* 608-831-8200 *E-mail:* info@areditions.com *Web Site:* www.areditions.com, pg 1201, 1215, 1273, 1341, 1423

Index to Sections

Index to Advertisers